# 2020–2021
## FORTY-THIRD EDITION

# Texas
# School Directory

A State Guide to K-12 Districts, Dioceses, and Schools...

## Powered by MDR's ConnectED Cloud

### Key Features In This Edition

- Charter Management Organization Index
- Facebook and Twitter Indicators
- Email Address Availability Highlighted
- Detailed School and District Listings
- Names and Job Titles of Key Personnel
- New Schools and Personnel Index

A Dun & Bradstreet Division

Copyright 2020 Market Data Retrieval | 6 Armstrong Road, Shelton, CT 06484

**51-Volume National Set**     ISBN# 978-1-57953-640-4

## Individual Bound State Editions

| | ISSN# | ISBN# | | ISSN# | ISBN# |
|---|---|---|---|---|---|
| Alabama | 1077-7393 | 978-1-951295-52-3 | Montana | 1077-7652 | 978-1-57953-608-4 |
| Alaska | 1077-7407 | 978-1-57953-332-8 | Nebraska | 1077-7660 | 978-1-57953-609-1 |
| Arizona | 1077-7415 | 978-1-57953-343-4 | Nevada | 1077-7679 | 978-1-57953-610-7 |
| Arkansas | 1077-7423 | 978-1-57953-353-3 | New Hampshire | 1077-7687 | 978-1-57953-612-1 |
| California | 1077-7431 | 978-1-57953-355-7 | New Jersey | 1077-7695 | 978-1-57953-613-8 |
| Colorado | 1077-744X | 978-1-57953-374-8 | New Mexico | 1077-7709 | 978-1-57953-614-5 |
| Connecticut | 1077-7458 | 978-1-57953-376-2 | New York | 1077-7717 | 978-1-57953-615-2 |
| Delaware | 1077-7466 | 978-1-57953-430-1 | North Carolina | 1077-7725 | 978-1-57953-616-9 |
| District of Columbia | 1077-7474 | 978-1-57953-484-4 | North Dakota | 1077-7733 | 978-1-57953-617-6 |
| Florida | 1077-7482 | 978-1-57953-538-4 | Ohio | 1077-7741 | 978-1-57953-618-3 |
| Georgia | 1077-7490 | 978-1-57953-592-6 | Oklahoma | 1077-775X | 978-1-57953-619-0 |
| Hawaii | 1077-7504 | 978-1-57953-593-3 | Oregon | 1077-7768 | 978-1-57953-620-6 |
| Idaho | 1077-7512 | 978-1-57953-594-0 | Pennsylvania | 1077-7776 | 978-1-57953-621-3 |
| Illinois | 1077-7520 | 978-1-57953-595-7 | Rhode Island | 1077-7784 | 978-1-57953-622-0 |
| Indiana | 1077-7539 | 978-1-57953-596-4 | South Carolina | 1077-7792 | 978-1-57953-624-4 |
| Iowa | 1077-7547 | 978-1-57953-597-1 | South Dakota | 1077-7806 | 978-1-57953-626-8 |
| Kansas | 1077-7555 | 978-1-57953-598-8 | Tennessee | 1077-7814 | 978-1-57953-627-5 |
| Kentucky | 1077-7563 | 978-1-57953-599-5 | Texas | 1077-7822 | 978-1-57953-629-9 |
| Louisiana | 1077-7571 | 978-1-57953-600-8 | Utah | 1077-7830 | 978-1-57953-630-5 |
| Maine | 1077-758X | 978-1-57953-601-5 | Vermont | 1077-7849 | 978-1-57953-632-9 |
| Maryland | 1077-7598 | 978-1-57953-602-2 | Virginia | 1077-7857 | 978-1-57953-633-6 |
| Massachusetts | 1077-7601 | 978-1-57953-603-9 | Washington | 1077-7865 | 978-1-57953-634-3 |
| Michigan | 1077-761X | 978-1-57953-604-6 | West Virginia | 1077-7873 | 978-1-57953-635-0 |
| Minnesota | 1077-7628 | 978-1-57953-605-3 | Wisconsin | 1077-7881 | 978-1-57953-637-4 |
| Mississippi | 1077-7636 | 978-1-57953-606-0 | Wyoming | 1077-789X | 978-1-57953-638-1 |
| Missouri | 1077-7644 | 978-1-57953-607-7 | Sales Manager's Guide | 2150-2021 | 978-1-57953-639-8 |

If you have any questions or comments concerning this directory, please write to MDR, 6 Armstrong Road, Shelton, CT 06484, or call us toll-free at 800-333-8802 or collect at 203-926-4800.

# MDR's School Directory

## TABLE OF CONTENTS

# Sample Directory Listings

MDR's School Directories are your complete reference source, providing comprehensive data on public school districts and schools, Catholic and other independent schools, and regional and county centers in all 50 states and the District of Columbia. Every public school district and school entry in MDR's School Directories is updated each year through telephone interviews conducted with school district personnel. These interviews take place from July to September, capturing the most current school year data available. In addition, information obtained from state, district and school directories is used to verify information contained in MDR's School Directories.

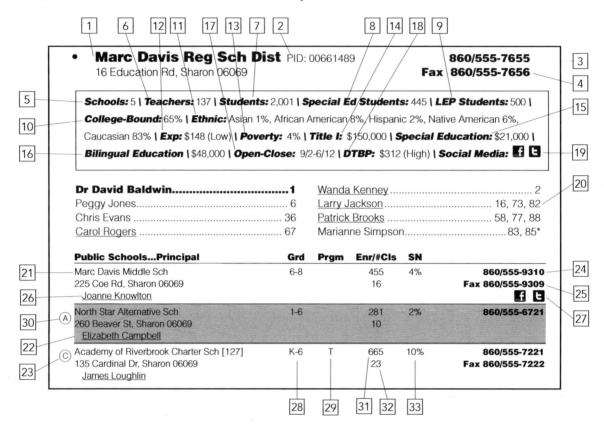

Each directory listing is uniformly organized to reflect the following data as applicable.

## Definitions of Codes and Data:

### DISTRICT DATA

**1 District Name and Address**
The physical location address for the superintendent's office is listed. MDR also maintains the mailing address, if different, for each district office. For this alternative mailing address, contact MDR directly at 800-333-8802.

**2 District PID Number**
Personal Identification Number of the district. Helps identify specific institutions when speaking to an MDR Representative or searching in Education MarketView.

**3 Telephone Number**
The telephone number of the district's central administration office.

**4 Fax Number**
The fax number of the district's central administration office. Please use the fax numbers in the directory appropriately.

The FCC prohibits the use of a telephone facsimile machine to send unsolicited advertisements. If you need further clarification of the laws that exist, you can contact the FCC directly at 888-225-5322, or you can visit their website at http://www.fcc.gov.

**5 Number of Schools**
The number of schools reporting directly to the district. In the case of decentralized large districts (such as Chicago Public Schools), the number of schools reflects those reporting directly to the central school district in addition to those administered directly by each of the subdistrict offices.

**6 Number of Teachers**
The number of full-time equivalent teachers throughout the district as reported by the U.S. Department of Education.

**7** District Enrollment
The projected number of students enrolled in the district for fall 2020.

**8** Special Ed Students
The number of students having a written Individualized Education Plan (IEP) indicating their participation in a Special Education Program.

**9** LEP Students
The number of Limited-English Proficient students being served in appropriate programs of language assistance (i.e., English as a second language, high-intensity language training, bilingual education).

**10** College-Bound Students
The percentage of the district's 12th grade enrollment planning to attend two- or four-year colleges.

**11** Student Ethnic Percentages
The student enrollment percentage by ethnic group: Asian, African American, Hispanic, Native American and Caucasian. This information is reported annually by the U.S. Department of Education. Due to rounding, the percentages may not add up to 100%.

**12** District Expenditure
The district's expenditure per student for instructional materials. In addition to the actual dollar amount, a level of expenditure is provided as follows:
    High = $300+
    Med = $200-299
    Low = Under $200

**13** Poverty Level
This census data reflects the percentage of school-age children in the district from families below the poverty line. Poverty levels are as follows:
    Low = 0-5%
    Med-Low = 6-15%
    Med-High = 16-29%
    High = 30%+

**14** Title I
The district's Title I dollar allocation is for the 2019 fiscal year. Funding levels are as follows:
    Highest = $2.5 Million+
    High = $500,000-2.49 Million
    Medium = $150,000-499,999
    Low = Under $150,000

**15** Special Education
The sum of federal and state dollars earmarked for special education programs in the district.

**16** Bilingual Education
The sum of federal and state dollars earmarked for English Language Acquisition programs in the district.

**17** District Opening/Closing Dates
The month and day of the official opening and closing dates of the school district.

**18** District Tech Budget Per Pupil
The district's total IT technology budget dollars per pupil. DTBP levels are as follows:
    High = $100+
    Med = $80-99
    Low = $1-79

**19** Social Media
The use of Facebook ⨍ and/or Twitter ⨮ for information communication, messaging and other content.

**20** District-Level Administrators and Job Title Codes
The names of administrative staff with district-wide responsibilities are listed, followed by numeric codes representing their specific areas of responsibility. A full list of job title codes and their descriptions can be found on the bottom of the directory pages.

The names are listed, from left to right, in numeric job title sequence to facilitate identification of individuals responsible for specific administrative areas. In cases where an individual has multiple responsibilities, the job title with the lowest code number is used for sequencing.

An asterisk (*) denotes district administrators who maintain offices at one of the schools in the district rather than at the district office.

Superintendents who are new to the district are printed in **bold** type. Also see our index of new personnel on page NEW1.

An underscore of a district-level administrator indicates an email address at that institution in our database and in Education MarketView.

## SCHOOL DATA

**21** School Name and Address
The physical location address of the school is listed. MDR also maintains the mailing address, if different, for every school. For this alternative address, contact MDR directly at 800-333-8802.

**22** New Schools
The listings of public schools opening for the first time during this school year are shaded for easy identification. Also see our index of new public schools on page NEW1.

**23** Charter Management Organization (CMO)
Indicates the CMO number from the CMO Index to which this school reports.

**24** Telephone Number
The telephone number of the school's central administration office. Note that in some cases a school district may require that all calls to schools must first go through a central switchboard to be routed to individual schools. In these cases, the central switchboard number is given for all schools affected.

**25** Fax Number
The fax number of the school's administration office. Please use the fax numbers in the directory appropriately.

> The FCC prohibits the use of a telephone facsimile machine to send unsolicited advertisements. If you need further clarification of the laws that exist, you can contact the FCC directly at 888-225-5322, or you can visit their website at http://www.fcc.gov.

## 26 Principal Name

The name of the school principal. When a school has both an elementary and secondary principal, both names are given. The elementary principal is listed first, with the secondary principal listed below.

Principals who are new to their public school are printed in **bold** type. Also see our index of new personnel on page NEW1.

All principals printed with an underscore have an email address at that institution in our database and in Education MarketView.

## 27 Social Media

The use of Facebook and/or Twitter for information communication, messaging and other content.

## 28 School Grade Span/Voc, Special, Adult Schools

The lowest and highest grades taught in the school. Schools with dedicated programs in the areas of vocational, special and adult education are designated as Voc, Spec and Adult, respectively.

## 29 School Program Codes

In addition to the grades taught within the school, schools that have special curriculum programs are indicated with these codes following the school grade span.

A = Alternative Program: Identifies traditional schools that also provide a special setting/curriculum for students who do not function well in traditional classroom settings.

G = Adult Classes: Identifies schools that offer adult education classes.

M = Magnet Program: Identifies traditional schools that also offer an enriched curricula in a special subject area to qualified students.

T = Title I Schoolwide: Identifies public schools that have a Title I Schoolwide program, allowing greater spending flexibility.

V = Career & Technical Education Programs: Identifies schools that offer Career & Technical Education programs.

## 30 Other School Types

Schools that are unique in the curriculum they offer or in the way they operate are indicated to the left of the school name.

(A) = Alternative School: Identifies schools that provide instruction exclusively for students who do not function well in traditional classroom settings.

(C) = Charter School: Public schools that have certain freedoms from state and local regulations and policies, having more administrative independence.

(M) = Magnet School: Identifies schools where all students are offered enriched curricula. Students qualify for admission by competitive exams.

(Y) = Year-Round School: Schools that operate 12 months a year.

## 31 Student Enrollment

The projected number of students enrolled for fall 2020.

## 32 Number of Classrooms

The number of classrooms within a school. The number of classrooms prints below student enrollment when known.

## 33 Student Need

Percentage of students eligible for the free and reduced-price lunch program at the school.

# Texas

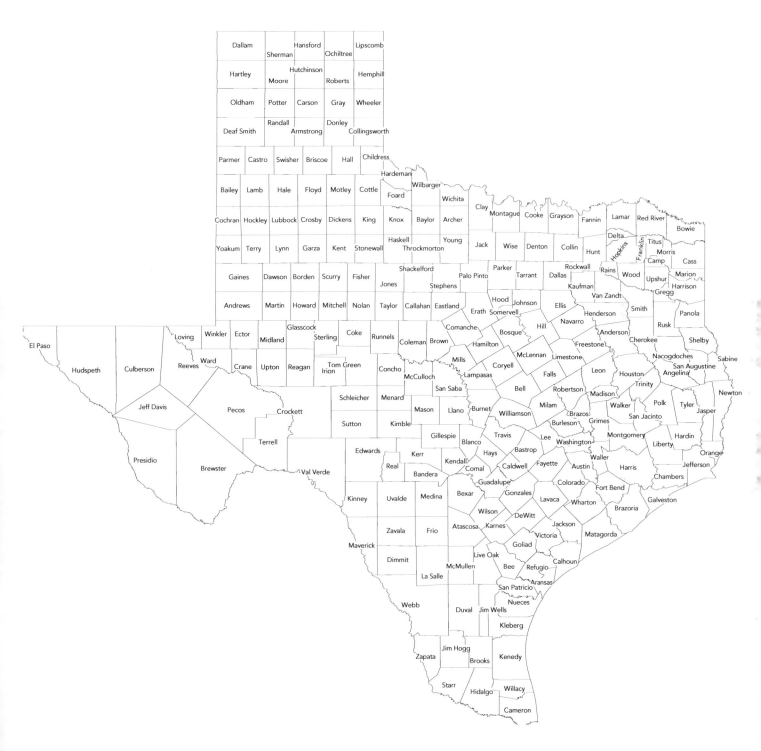

## STATE STATISTICS

### DISTRICT PERSONNEL BY JOB FUNCTION

| Job Code | Job Description | Total | Enrollment Under 2,500 | 2,500-9,000 | 10,000+ |
|---|---|---|---|---|---|
| 1 | SUPERINTENDENT | 1,064 | 735 | 175 | 114 |
| 2 | BUS/FINANCE/PURCHASING | 1,206 | 714 | 231 | 221 |
| 3 | BUILDINGS AND GROUNDS | 868 | 496 | 198 | 165 |
| 4 | FOOD SERVICE | 834 | 532 | 173 | 123 |
| 5 | TRANSPORTATION | 745 | 454 | 177 | 113 |
| 6 | ATHLETIC | 815 | 540 | 164 | 109 |
| 7 | HEALTH SERVICES | 452 | 252 | 99 | 95 |
| 8 | CURRIC/INSTRUCT K-12 | 809 | 457 | 187 | 143 |
| 9 | CURRIC/INSTRUCT ELEM | 194 | 87 | 45 | 62 |
| 10 | CURRIC/INSTRUCT SEC | 145 | 52 | 42 | 51 |
| 11 | FEDERAL PROGRAM | 955 | 672 | 156 | 106 |
| 12 | TITLE I | 137 | 100 | 17 | 19 |
| 13 | TITLE V | 40 | 21 | 12 | 7 |
| 15 | ASST SUPERINTENDENT | 845 | 142 | 259 | 403 |
| 16 | INSTRUCTIONAL MEDIA SERVICES | 542 | 358 | 96 | 77 |
| 17 | CHIEF OPERATIONS OFFICER | 65 | 23 | 14 | 28 |
| 18 | CHIEF ACADEMIC OFFICER | 67 | 11 | 17 | 39 |
| 19 | CHIEF FINANCIAL OFFICER | 245 | 83 | 75 | 75 |
| 20 | ART K-12 | 99 | 3 | 17 | 78 |
| 21 | ART ELEM | 0 | 0 | 0 | 0 |
| 22 | ART SEC | 3 | 1 | 2 | 0 |
| 23 | MUSIC K-12 | 106 | 10 | 24 | 71 |
| 24 | MUSIC ELEM | 1 | 0 | 0 | 1 |
| 25 | MUSIC SEC | 0 | 0 | 0 | 0 |
| 26 | BUSINESS EDUCATION | 8 | 4 | 2 | 2 |
| 27 | CAREER & TECH ED | 276 | 94 | 68 | 107 |
| 28 | TECHNOLOGY EDUCATION | 35 | 12 | 14 | 9 |
| 29 | FAMILY/CONSUMER SCIENCE | 9 | 6 | 2 | 1 |
| 30 | ADULT EDUCATION | 52 | 8 | 19 | 20 |
| 31 | CAREER/SCH-TO-WORK K-12 | 253 | 129 | 41 | 78 |
| 32 | CAREER/SCH-TO-WORK ELEM | 2 | 2 | 0 | 0 |
| 33 | CAREER/SCH-TO-WORK SEC | 8 | 6 | 1 | 1 |
| 34 | EARLY CHILDHOOD ED | 174 | 60 | 44 | 63 |
| 35 | HEALTH/PHYS EDUCATION | 125 | 42 | 40 | 42 |
| 36 | GUIDANCE SERVICES K-12 | 323 | 182 | 50 | 87 |
| 37 | GUIDANCE SERVICES ELEM | 70 | 60 | 7 | 3 |
| 38 | GUIDANCE SERVICES SEC | 90 | 79 | 10 | 1 |
| 39 | SOCIAL STUDIES K-12 | 61 | 2 | 16 | 42 |
| 40 | SOCIAL STUDIES ELEM | 12 | 0 | 4 | 8 |
| 41 | SOCIAL STUDIES SEC | 14 | 1 | 3 | 10 |
| 42 | SCIENCE K-12 | 59 | 4 | 18 | 36 |
| 43 | SCIENCE ELEM | 18 | 0 | 6 | 12 |
| 44 | SCIENCE SEC | 22 | 0 | 6 | 16 |
| 45 | MATH K-12 | 51 | 4 | 19 | 27 |
| 46 | MATH ELEM | 32 | 0 | 11 | 21 |
| 47 | MATH SEC | 35 | 0 | 15 | 20 |
| 48 | ENGLISH/LANG ARTS K-12 | 42 | 4 | 16 | 20 |
| 49 | ENGLISH/LANG ARTS ELEM | 25 | 0 | 10 | 15 |
| 50 | ENGLISH/LANG ARTS SEC | 22 | 1 | 5 | 16 |
| 51 | READING K-12 | 31 | 11 | 8 | 10 |
| 52 | READING ELEM | 19 | 8 | 6 | 5 |
| 53 | READING SEC | 7 | 0 | 2 | 5 |
| 54 | REMEDIAL READING K-12 | 38 | 20 | 11 | 7 |
| 55 | REMEDIAL READING ELEM | 6 | 4 | 1 | 1 |
| 56 | REMEDIAL READING SEC | 0 | 0 | 0 | 0 |

### DISTRICT PERSONNEL BY JOB FUNCTION

| Job Code | Job Description | Total | Enrollment Under 2,500 | 2,500-9,000 | 10,000+ |
|---|---|---|---|---|---|
| 57 | BILINGUAL/ELL | 668 | 404 | 141 | 114 |
| 58 | SPECIAL EDUCATION K-12 | 827 | 486 | 184 | 136 |
| 59 | SPECIAL EDUCATION ELEM | 45 | 39 | 2 | 4 |
| 60 | SPECIAL EDUCATION SEC | 20 | 16 | 1 | 3 |
| 61 | FOREIGN/WORLD LANG K-12 | 33 | 4 | 4 | 25 |
| 62 | FOREIGN/WORLD LANG ELEM | 0 | 0 | 0 | 0 |
| 63 | FOREIGN/WORLD LANG SEC | 4 | 2 | 0 | 2 |
| 64 | RELIGIOUS EDUCATION K-12 | 1 | 0 | 0 | 0 |
| 65 | RELIGIOUS EDUCATION ELEM | 0 | 0 | 0 | 0 |
| 66 | RELIGIOUS EDUCATION SEC | 0 | 0 | 0 | 0 |
| 67 | SCHOOL BOARD PRESIDENT | 1,027 | 734 | 175 | 111 |
| 68 | TEACHER PERSONNEL | 446 | 114 | 156 | 161 |
| 69 | ACADEMIC ASSESSMENT | 613 | 363 | 128 | 117 |
| 70 | RESEARCH/DEVELOPMENT | 63 | 2 | 14 | 43 |
| 71 | PUBLIC INFORMATION | 260 | 30 | 99 | 123 |
| 72 | SUMMER SCHOOL | 20 | 3 | 10 | 7 |
| 73 | INSTRUCTIONAL TECH | 1,075 | 704 | 195 | 148 |
| 74 | INSERVICE TRAINING | 172 | 53 | 39 | 72 |
| 75 | MARKETING/DISTRIBUTIVE | 18 | 4 | 8 | 6 |
| 76 | INFO SYSTEMS | 419 | 181 | 109 | 115 |
| 77 | PSYCHOLOGICAL ASSESSMENT | 104 | 35 | 28 | 35 |
| 78 | AFFIRMATIVE ACTION | 47 | 3 | 25 | 17 |
| 79 | STUDENT PERSONNEL | 265 | 71 | 75 | 116 |
| 80 | DRIVER ED/SAFETY | 8 | 3 | 5 | 0 |
| 81 | GIFTED/TALENTED | 150 | 23 | 48 | 78 |
| 82 | VIDEO SERVICES | 95 | 72 | 15 | 8 |
| 83 | SUBSTANCE ABUSE PREVENTION | 496 | 390 | 69 | 36 |
| 84 | ERATE | 200 | 151 | 35 | 14 |
| 85 | AIDS EDUCATION | 190 | 138 | 30 | 20 |
| 88 | ALTERNATIVE/AT RISK | 432 | 294 | 91 | 45 |
| 89 | MULTI-CULTURAL CURRICULUM | 11 | 1 | 3 | 7 |
| 90 | SOCIAL WORK | 37 | 9 | 13 | 15 |
| 91 | SAFETY/SECURITY | 336 | 121 | 113 | 100 |
| 92 | MAGNET SCHOOL | 21 | 9 | 2 | 10 |
| 93 | PARENTAL INVOLVEMENT | 87 | 25 | 24 | 38 |
| 95 | TECH PREP PROGRAM | 36 | 7 | 15 | 14 |
| 97 | CHIEF INFORMATION OFFICER | 34 | 13 | 4 | 17 |
| 98 | CHIEF TECHNOLOGY OFFICER | 107 | 35 | 29 | 41 |
| 270 | CHARACTER EDUCATION | 149 | 120 | 15 | 14 |
| 271 | MIGRANT EDUCATION | 330 | 202 | 75 | 51 |
| 273 | TEACHER MENTOR | 161 | 92 | 41 | 28 |
| 274 | BEFORE/AFTER SCH | 100 | 46 | 29 | 25 |
| 275 | RESPONSE TO INTERVENTION | 154 | 73 | 36 | 43 |
| 277 | REMEDIAL MATH K-12 | 13 | 2 | 7 | 4 |
| 280 | LITERACY COACH | 63 | 28 | 13 | 22 |
| 285 | STEM | 150 | 78 | 46 | 26 |
| 286 | DIGITAL LEARNING | 347 | 210 | 72 | 59 |
| 288 | COMMON CORE STANDARDS | 245 | 183 | 50 | 12 |
| 294 | ACCOUNTABILITY | 266 | 94 | 83 | 85 |
| 295 | NETWORK SYSTEM | 581 | 336 | 157 | 84 |
| 296 | TITLE II PROGRAMS | 293 | 196 | 72 | 25 |
| 297 | WEBMASTER | 130 | 53 | 38 | 38 |
| 298 | GRANT WRITER/PTNRSHIPS | 290 | 170 | 67 | 49 |
| 750 | CHIEF INNOVATION OFFICER | 11 | 1 | 1 | 9 |
| 751 | CHIEF OF STAFF | 31 | 3 | 3 | 25 |
| 752 | SOCIAL EMOTIONAL LEARNING | 83 | 54 | 11 | 18 |

### DISTRICTS BY EXPENDITURE AND ENROLLMENT

| Expenditure | Total | Under 2500 | 2500-9999 | 10,000+ |
|---|---|---|---|---|
| Low (Under $200) | 18 | 3 | 6 | 9 |
| Medium ($200 - 299) | 97 | 39 | 24 | 34 |
| High ($300+) | 906 | 693 | 146 | 67 |
| TOTAL DISTRICTS | 1,021 | 735 | 176 | 110 |

### SCHOOLS BY LEVEL AND TYPE

| School Level | Total | Public | Private | Catholic |
|---|---|---|---|---|
| Elementary | 5,458 | 4,956 | 316 | 186 |
| Middle/Junior | 1,512 | 1,505 | 4 | 3 |
| Senior | 1,691 | 1,611 | 45 | 35 |
| K-12 (Combined) | 984 | 631 | 335 | 18 |
| Adult/Special/Voc Ed | 115 | 82 | 32 | 1 |
| TOTAL SCHOOLS | 9,760 | 8,785 | 732 | 243 |

## COUNTY STATISTICS

| COUNTY | | DISTRICTS | SCHOOLS | ELEM ENROLL[1] | MIDDLE/JHS ENROLL[2] | SENIOR ENROLL[3] | TOTAL ENROLL[4] | % OF STATE | K-5[5] | K-6 | K-8 | 5-8[6] | 7-9[7] | 7-12[8] | K-12[9] | OTHER[10] |
|---|---|---|---|---|---|---|---|---|---|---|---|---|---|---|---|---|
| ANDERSON | PUBLIC | 7 | 21 | 4,613 | 1,118 | 2,280 | 8,110 | | 7 | 2 | 1 | 2 | 2 | 5 | 2 | 0 |
| | NONPUBLIC | 0 | 1 | 128 | 0 | 0 | 128 | | 0 | 0 | 1 | 0 | 0 | 0 | 0 | 0 |
| | **TOTAL** | **7** | **22** | **4,741** | **1,118** | **2,280** | **8,238** | **0.2** | **7** | **2** | **2** | **2** | **2** | **5** | **2** | **0** |
| ANDREWS | PUBLIC | 1 | 6 | 2,109 | 1,026 | 1,087 | 4,200 | | 3 | 0 | 0 | 1 | 0 | 2 | 0 | 0 |
| | NONPUBLIC | 0 | 0 | 0 | 0 | 0 | 0 | | 0 | 0 | 0 | 0 | 0 | 0 | 0 | 0 |
| | **TOTAL** | **1** | **6** | **2,109** | **1,026** | **1,087** | **4,200** | **0.1** | **3** | **0** | **0** | **1** | **0** | **2** | **0** | **0** |
| ANGELINA | PUBLIC | 6 | 35 | 7,428 | 2,975 | 3,333 | 16,200 | | 20 | 1 | 0 | 4 | 1 | 7 | 2 | 0 |
| | NONPUBLIC | 0 | 2 | 250 | 0 | 0 | 250 | | 1 | 0 | 1 | 0 | 0 | 0 | 0 | 0 |
| | **TOTAL** | **6** | **37** | **7,678** | **2,975** | **3,333** | **16,450** | **0.3** | **21** | **1** | **1** | **4** | **1** | **7** | **2** | **0** |
| ARANSAS | PUBLIC | 1 | 4 | 933 | 648 | 858 | 2,975 | | 2 | 0 | 0 | 1 | 0 | 1 | 0 | 0 |
| | NONPUBLIC | 0 | 2 | 182 | 0 | 0 | 182 | | 2 | 0 | 0 | 0 | 0 | 0 | 0 | 0 |
| | **TOTAL** | **1** | **6** | **1,115** | **648** | **858** | **3,157** | **0.1** | **4** | **0** | **0** | **1** | **0** | **1** | **0** | **0** |
| ARCHER | PUBLIC | 3 | 8 | 907 | 341 | 685 | 1,946 | | 2 | 1 | 0 | 2 | 0 | 3 | 0 | 0 |
| | NONPUBLIC | 0 | 0 | 0 | 0 | 0 | 0 | | 0 | 0 | 0 | 0 | 0 | 0 | 0 | 0 |
| | **TOTAL** | **3** | **8** | **907** | **341** | **685** | **1,946** | | **2** | **1** | **0** | **2** | **0** | **3** | **0** | **0** |
| ARMSTRONG | PUBLIC | 1 | 1 | 220 | 0 | 88 | 308 | | 0 | 0 | 0 | 0 | 0 | 0 | 1 | 0 |
| | NONPUBLIC | 0 | 0 | 0 | 0 | 0 | 0 | | 0 | 0 | 0 | 0 | 0 | 0 | 0 | 0 |
| | **TOTAL** | **1** | **1** | **220** | **0** | **88** | **308** | | **0** | **0** | **0** | **0** | **0** | **0** | **1** | **0** |
| ATASCOSA | PUBLIC | 5 | 19 | 4,235 | 1,397 | 1,317 | 7,838 | | 8 | 0 | 0 | 5 | 0 | 5 | 1 | 0 |
| | NONPUBLIC | 0 | 1 | 65 | 0 | 0 | 65 | | 1 | 0 | 0 | 0 | 0 | 0 | 0 | 0 |
| | **TOTAL** | **5** | **20** | **4,300** | **1,397** | **1,317** | **7,903** | **0.2** | **9** | **0** | **0** | **5** | **0** | **5** | **1** | **0** |
| AUSTIN | PUBLIC | 3 | 14 | 2,457 | 1,345 | 1,653 | 5,569 | | 6 | 0 | 0 | 3 | 0 | 3 | 2 | 0 |
| | NONPUBLIC | 0 | 1 | 150 | 0 | 60 | 210 | | 0 | 0 | 0 | 0 | 0 | 0 | 1 | 0 |
| | **TOTAL** | **3** | **15** | **2,607** | **1,345** | **1,713** | **5,779** | **0.1** | **6** | **0** | **0** | **3** | **0** | **3** | **3** | **0** |
| BAILEY | PUBLIC | 1 | 4 | 712 | 340 | 362 | 1,450 | | 2 | 0 | 0 | 1 | 0 | 1 | 0 | 0 |
| | NONPUBLIC | 0 | 0 | 0 | 0 | 0 | 0 | | 0 | 0 | 0 | 0 | 0 | 0 | 0 | 0 |
| | **TOTAL** | **1** | **4** | **712** | **340** | **362** | **1,450** | | **2** | **0** | **0** | **1** | **0** | **1** | **0** | **0** |
| BANDERA | PUBLIC | 2 | 6 | 1,108 | 599 | 732 | 2,420 | | 3 | 0 | 0 | 1 | 0 | 1 | 1 | 0 |
| | NONPUBLIC | 0 | 0 | 0 | 0 | 0 | 0 | | 0 | 0 | 0 | 0 | 0 | 0 | 0 | 0 |
| | **TOTAL** | **2** | **6** | **1,108** | **599** | **732** | **2,420** | **0.1** | **3** | **0** | **0** | **1** | **0** | **1** | **1** | **0** |
| BASTROP | PUBLIC | 4 | 28 | 9,055 | 2,805 | 4,577 | 17,670 | | 11 | 3 | 0 | 1 | 3 | 8 | 2 | 0 |
| | NONPUBLIC | 0 | 1 | 59 | 0 | 24 | 83 | | 0 | 0 | 0 | 0 | 0 | 0 | 1 | 0 |
| | **TOTAL** | **4** | **29** | **9,114** | **2,805** | **4,601** | **17,753** | **0.3** | **11** | **3** | **0** | **1** | **3** | **8** | **3** | **0** |

[1] **Elem Enroll** is the school by school total of enrollments in K-4, K-5, K-6, K-8 schools, elementary and middle/JHS students in K-12 schools and students in special ed schools. Public enrollments include public and county-operated schools.

[2] **Middle/JHS Enroll** is the school by school total of enrollments in 5-8 and 7-9 public schools. Public enrollments include public and county-operated schools. Private middle/JHS enrollments in 5-8 and 7-9 schools are included in Senior Enroll.

[3] **Senior Enroll** is the school by school total of enrollments in 7-12 and 9-12 schools, the secondary students in K-12 schools and students in vocational ed schools. Public enrollments include public and county-operated schools. For private schools, Senior Enroll includes middle/JHS enrollment plus senior enrollment.

[4] **Public Total Enroll** columns are not the sum of school building enrollments. They are projected district-wide Fall enrollments provided to MDR by each school district office, plus county-operated school enrollments.

[5] **K-5** includes pre-kindergarten, kindergarten, K-3, K-4, K-5 schools.

[6] **5-8** includes schools with low grades of 4, 5, 6 and high grades of 7, 8, 9 (e.g. 4-8, 5-8, 6-8, 6-9).

[7] **7-9** includes schools with low grades of 7, 8 and high grades of 7, 8, 9 (e.g. 7-7, 7-8, 7-9, 8-9).

[8] **7-12** includes 7-12, 8-12, 9-12, 10-12, etc.

[9] **K-12** includes schools with both elementary and secondary grades.

[10] **Other** includes special ed, vocational and adult schools.

**\*Public State Totals** for all columns can exceed the sum of the counties because state totals include state-operated schools and their enrollments

| COUNTY | | DISTRICTS | SCHOOLS | ELEM ENROLL[1] | MIDDLE/JHS ENROLL[2] | SENIOR ENROLL[3] | TOTAL ENROLL[4] | % OF STATE | SCHOOLS BY GRADE SPAN K-5[5] | K-6 | K-8 | 5-8[6] | 7-9[7] | 7-12[8] | K-12[9] | OTHER[10] |
|---|---|---|---|---|---|---|---|---|---|---|---|---|---|---|---|---|
| BAYLOR | PUBLIC | 1 | 3 | 254 | 176 | 152 | 582 | | 1 | 0 | 0 | 1 | 0 | 1 | 0 | 0 |
| | NONPUBLIC | 0 | 0 | 0 | 0 | 0 | 0 | | 0 | 0 | 0 | 0 | 0 | 0 | 0 | 0 |
| | **TOTAL** | **1** | **3** | **254** | **176** | **152** | **582** | | **1** | **0** | **0** | **1** | **0** | **1** | **0** | **0** |
| BEE | PUBLIC | 4 | 12 | 2,512 | 1,072 | 1,395 | 5,200 | | 5 | 0 | 1 | 2 | 1 | 2 | 1 | 0 |
| | NONPUBLIC | 0 | 2 | 171 | 0 | 0 | 171 | | 0 | 2 | 0 | 0 | 0 | 0 | 0 | 0 |
| | **TOTAL** | **4** | **14** | **2,683** | **1,072** | **1,395** | **5,371** | **0.1** | **5** | **2** | **1** | **2** | **1** | **2** | **1** | **0** |
| BELL | PUBLIC | 9 | 106 | 35,865 | 15,486 | 19,985 | 73,293 | | 60 | 0 | 0 | 24 | 0 | 17 | 4 | 1 |
| | NONPUBLIC | 0 | 8 | 1,026 | 0 | 377 | 1,403 | | 1 | 1 | 2 | 0 | 0 | 2 | 2 | 0 |
| | **TOTAL** | **9** | **114** | **36,891** | **15,486** | **20,362** | **74,696** | **1.4** | **61** | **1** | **2** | **24** | **0** | **19** | **6** | **1** |
| BEXAR | PUBLIC | 17 | 457 | 152,147 | 65,452 | 94,288 | 323,114 | | 258 | 6 | 21 | 70 | 4 | 68 | 21 | 9 |
| | NONPUBLIC | 0 | 66 | 14,267 | 0 | 5,513 | 19,780 | | 6 | 2 | 29 | 0 | 0 | 7 | 20 | 2 |
| | **TOTAL** | **17** | **523** | **166,414** | **65,452** | **99,801** | **342,894** | **6.4** | **264** | **8** | **50** | **70** | **4** | **75** | **41** | **11** |
| BLANCO | PUBLIC | 2 | 6 | 598 | 466 | 547 | 1,670 | | 2 | 0 | 0 | 2 | 0 | 2 | 0 | 0 |
| | NONPUBLIC | 0 | 0 | 0 | 0 | 0 | 0 | | 0 | 0 | 0 | 0 | 0 | 0 | 0 | 0 |
| | **TOTAL** | **2** | **6** | **598** | **466** | **547** | **1,670** | | **2** | **0** | **0** | **2** | **0** | **2** | **0** | **0** |
| BORDEN | PUBLIC | 1 | 1 | 148 | 0 | 66 | 214 | | 0 | 0 | 0 | 0 | 0 | 0 | 1 | 0 |
| | NONPUBLIC | 0 | 0 | 0 | 0 | 0 | 0 | | 0 | 0 | 0 | 0 | 0 | 0 | 0 | 0 |
| | **TOTAL** | **1** | **1** | **148** | **0** | **66** | **214** | | **0** | **0** | **0** | **0** | **0** | **0** | **1** | **0** |
| BOSQUE | PUBLIC | 8 | 14 | 1,543 | 418 | 779 | 2,850 | | 3 | 0 | 0 | 0 | 0 | 0 | 9 | 0 |
| | NONPUBLIC | 0 | 0 | 0 | 0 | 0 | 0 | | 0 | 0 | 0 | 0 | 0 | 0 | 0 | 0 |
| | **TOTAL** | **8** | **14** | **1,543** | **418** | **779** | **2,850** | **0.1** | **3** | **0** | **0** | **0** | **0** | **0** | **9** | **0** |
| BOWIE | PUBLIC | 13 | 43 | 8,693 | 4,378 | 4,328 | 17,593 | | 19 | 2 | 3 | 7 | 1 | 9 | 2 | 0 |
| | NONPUBLIC | 0 | 2 | 178 | 0 | 0 | 178 | | 0 | 1 | 1 | 0 | 0 | 0 | 0 | 0 |
| | **TOTAL** | **13** | **45** | **8,871** | **4,378** | **4,328** | **17,771** | **0.3** | **19** | **3** | **4** | **7** | **1** | **9** | **2** | **0** |
| BRAZORIA | PUBLIC | 8 | 94 | 36,277 | 13,156 | 20,922 | 72,221 | | 45 | 12 | 1 | 10 | 8 | 15 | 2 | 1 |
| | NONPUBLIC | 0 | 11 | 2,043 | 0 | 355 | 2,398 | | 3 | 0 | 2 | 0 | 0 | 0 | 6 | 0 |
| | **TOTAL** | **8** | **105** | **38,320** | **13,156** | **21,277** | **74,619** | **1.4** | **48** | **12** | **3** | **10** | **8** | **15** | **8** | **1** |
| BRAZOS | PUBLIC | 3 | 44 | 16,614 | 3,928 | 8,706 | 30,746 | | 24 | 5 | 0 | 0 | 5 | 7 | 2 | 1 |
| | NONPUBLIC | 0 | 7 | 1,263 | 0 | 492 | 1,755 | | 0 | 1 | 0 | 0 | 0 | 0 | 6 | 0 |
| | **TOTAL** | **3** | **51** | **17,877** | **3,928** | **9,198** | **32,501** | **0.6** | **24** | **6** | **0** | **0** | **5** | **7** | **8** | **1** |
| BREWSTER | PUBLIC | 4 | 7 | 473 | 311 | 372 | 1,138 | | 1 | 0 | 2 | 1 | 0 | 2 | 1 | 0 |
| | NONPUBLIC | 0 | 1 | 32 | 0 | 13 | 45 | | 0 | 0 | 0 | 0 | 0 | 0 | 1 | 0 |
| | **TOTAL** | **4** | **8** | **505** | **311** | **385** | **1,183** | | **1** | **0** | **2** | **1** | **0** | **2** | **2** | **0** |
| BRISCOE | PUBLIC | 1 | 1 | 124 | 0 | 50 | 174 | | 0 | 0 | 0 | 0 | 0 | 0 | 1 | 0 |
| | NONPUBLIC | 0 | 0 | 0 | 0 | 0 | 0 | | 0 | 0 | 0 | 0 | 0 | 0 | 0 | 0 |
| | **TOTAL** | **1** | **1** | **124** | **0** | **50** | **174** | | **0** | **0** | **0** | **0** | **0** | **0** | **1** | **0** |

[1] **Elem Enroll** is the school by school total of enrollments in K-4, K-5, K-6, K-8 schools, elementary and middle/JHS students in K-12 schools and students in special ed schools. Public enrollments include public and county-operated schools.

[2] **Middle/JHS Enroll** is the school by school total of enrollments in 5-8 and 7-9 public schools. Public enrollments include public and county-operated schools. Private middle/JHS enrollments are included in Senior Enroll.

[3] **Senior Enroll** is the school by school total of enrollments in 7-12 and 9-12 schools, the secondary students in K-12 schools and students in vocational ed schools. Public enrollments include public and county-operated schools. For private schools, Senior Enroll includes middle/JHS enrollment plus senior enrollment.

[4] **Public Total Enroll** columns are not the sum of school building enrollments. They are projected district-wide Fall enrollments provided to MDR by each school district office, plus county-operated school enrollments.

[5] **K-5** includes pre-kindergarten, kindergarten, K-3, K-4, K-5 schools.

[6] **5-8** includes schools with low grades of 4, 5, 6 and high grades of 7, 8, 9 (e.g., 4-8, 5-8, 6-8, 6-9).

[7] **7-9** includes schools with low grades of 7, 8 and high grades of 7, 8, 9 (e.g., 7-7, 7-8, 7-9, 8-9).

[8] **7-12** includes 7-12, 8-12, 9-12, 10-12, etc.

[9] **K-12** includes schools with both elementary and secondary grades.

[10] **Other** includes special ed, vocational ed and adult schools.

***Public State Totals** for all columns can exceed the sum of the counties because state totals include state-operated schools and their enrollments

| COUNTY | | DISTRICTS | SCHOOLS | ELEM ENROLL[1] | MIDDLE/JHS ENROLL[2] | SENIOR ENROLL[3] | TOTAL ENROLL[4] | % OF STATE | K-5[5] | K-6 | K-8 | 5-8[6] | 7-9[7] | 7-12[8] | K-12[9] | OTHER[10] |
|---|---|---|---|---|---|---|---|---|---|---|---|---|---|---|---|---|
| BROOKS | PUBLIC | 1 | 4 | 724 | 349 | 397 | 1,470 | | 2 | 0 | 0 | 1 | 0 | 1 | 0 | 0 |
| | NONPUBLIC | 0 | 0 | 0 | 0 | 0 | 0 | | 0 | 0 | 0 | 0 | 0 | 0 | 0 | 0 |
| | **TOTAL** | **1** | **4** | **724** | **349** | **397** | **1,470** | | **2** | **0** | **0** | **1** | **0** | **1** | **0** | **0** |
| BROWN | PUBLIC | 7 | 21 | 3,497 | 1,094 | 1,901 | 6,351 | | 7 | 2 | 0 | 3 | 1 | 6 | 2 | 0 |
| | NONPUBLIC | 0 | 1 | 82 | 0 | 33 | 115 | | 0 | 0 | 0 | 0 | 0 | 0 | 1 | 0 |
| | **TOTAL** | **7** | **22** | **3,579** | **1,094** | **1,934** | **6,466** | **0.1** | **7** | **2** | **0** | **3** | **1** | **6** | **3** | **0** |
| BURLESON | PUBLIC | 3 | 9 | 1,404 | 605 | 819 | 2,800 | | 3 | 0 | 0 | 2 | 0 | 2 | 2 | 0 |
| | NONPUBLIC | 0 | 0 | 0 | 0 | 0 | 0 | | 0 | 0 | 0 | 0 | 0 | 0 | 0 | 0 |
| | **TOTAL** | **3** | **9** | **1,404** | **605** | **819** | **2,800** | **0.1** | **3** | **0** | **0** | **2** | **0** | **2** | **2** | **0** |
| BURNET | PUBLIC | 2 | 13 | 3,116 | 1,739 | 813 | 7,000 | | 7 | 0 | 0 | 2 | 0 | 4 | 0 | 0 |
| | NONPUBLIC | 0 | 2 | 340 | 0 | 85 | 425 | | 0 | 0 | 0 | 0 | 0 | 0 | 1 | 0 |
| | **TOTAL** | **2** | **15** | **3,456** | **1,739** | **898** | **7,425** | **0.1** | **7** | **0** | **0** | **2** | **0** | **4** | **1** | **0** |
| CALDWELL | PUBLIC | 3 | 14 | 3,606 | 1,797 | 1,288 | 7,966 | | 8 | 0 | 0 | 2 | 0 | 3 | 1 | 0 |
| | NONPUBLIC | 0 | 0 | 0 | 0 | 0 | 0 | | 0 | 0 | 0 | 0 | 0 | 0 | 0 | 0 |
| | **TOTAL** | **3** | **14** | **3,606** | **1,797** | **1,288** | **7,966** | **0.2** | **8** | **0** | **0** | **2** | **0** | **3** | **1** | **0** |
| CALHOUN | PUBLIC | 1 | 7 | 1,951 | 744 | 548 | 3,738 | | 3 | 0 | 1 | 1 | 0 | 2 | 0 | 0 |
| | NONPUBLIC | 0 | 1 | 90 | 0 | 0 | 90 | | 0 | 0 | 1 | 0 | 0 | 0 | 0 | 0 |
| | **TOTAL** | **1** | **8** | **2,041** | **744** | **548** | **3,828** | **0.1** | **3** | **0** | **2** | **1** | **0** | **2** | **0** | **0** |
| CALLAHAN | PUBLIC | 4 | 12 | 1,240 | 476 | 755 | 2,510 | | 3 | 2 | 0 | 2 | 1 | 4 | 0 | 0 |
| | NONPUBLIC | 0 | 0 | 0 | 0 | 0 | 0 | | 0 | 0 | 0 | 0 | 0 | 0 | 0 | 0 |
| | **TOTAL** | **4** | **12** | **1,240** | **476** | **755** | **2,510** | **0.1** | **3** | **2** | **0** | **2** | **1** | **4** | **0** | **0** |
| CAMERON | PUBLIC | 10 | 146 | 40,554 | 20,634 | 30,252 | 96,378 | | 79 | 3 | 0 | 25 | 4 | 30 | 5 | 0 |
| | NONPUBLIC | 0 | 15 | 2,771 | 0 | 1,272 | 4,043 | | 0 | 4 | 5 | 1 | 0 | 3 | 2 | 0 |
| | **TOTAL** | **10** | **161** | **43,325** | **20,634** | **31,524** | **100,421** | **1.9** | **79** | **7** | **5** | **26** | **4** | **33** | **7** | **0** |
| CAMP | PUBLIC | 1 | 5 | 1,324 | 368 | 664 | 2,356 | | 2 | 1 | 0 | 0 | 1 | 1 | 0 | 0 |
| | NONPUBLIC | 0 | 0 | 0 | 0 | 0 | 0 | | 0 | 0 | 0 | 0 | 0 | 0 | 0 | 0 |
| | **TOTAL** | **1** | **5** | **1,324** | **368** | **664** | **2,356** | | **2** | **1** | **0** | **0** | **1** | **1** | **0** | **0** |
| CARSON | PUBLIC | 3 | 6 | 603 | 157 | 400 | 1,175 | | 1 | 1 | 0 | 1 | 0 | 2 | 1 | 0 |
| | NONPUBLIC | 0 | 0 | 0 | 0 | 0 | 0 | | 0 | 0 | 0 | 0 | 0 | 0 | 0 | 0 |
| | **TOTAL** | **3** | **6** | **603** | **157** | **400** | **1,175** | | **1** | **1** | **0** | **1** | **0** | **2** | **1** | **0** |
| CASS | PUBLIC | 7 | 18 | 2,470 | 1,226 | 1,589 | 5,357 | | 5 | 0 | 0 | 4 | 0 | 4 | 5 | 0 |
| | NONPUBLIC | 0 | 0 | 0 | 0 | 0 | 0 | | 0 | 0 | 0 | 0 | 0 | 0 | 0 | 0 |
| | **TOTAL** | **7** | **18** | **2,470** | **1,226** | **1,589** | **5,357** | **0.1** | **5** | **0** | **0** | **4** | **0** | **4** | **5** | **0** |
| CASTRO | PUBLIC | 3 | 7 | 864 | 455 | 542 | 1,689 | | 2 | 0 | 0 | 1 | 0 | 2 | 2 | 0 |
| | NONPUBLIC | 0 | 0 | 0 | 0 | 0 | 0 | | 0 | 0 | 0 | 0 | 0 | 0 | 0 | 0 |
| | **TOTAL** | **3** | **7** | **864** | **455** | **542** | **1,689** | | **2** | **0** | **0** | **1** | **0** | **2** | **2** | **0** |

[1] **Elem Enroll** is the school by school total of enrollments in K-4, K-5, K-6, K-8 schools, elementary and middle/JHS students in K-12 schools and students in special ed schools. Public enrollments include public and county-operated schools.

[2] **Middle/JHS Enroll** is the school by school total of enrollments in 5-8 and 7-9 public schools. Public enrollments include public and county-operated schools. Private middle/JHS enrollments are included in Senior Enroll.

[3] **Senior Enroll** is the school by school total of enrollments in 7-12 and 9-12 schools, the secondary students in K-12 schools and students in vocational ed schools. Public enrollments include public and county-operated schools. For private schools, Senior Enroll includes middle/JHS enrollment plus senior enrollment.

[4] **Public Total Enroll** columns are not the sum of school building enrollments. They are projected district-wide Fall enrollments provided to MDR by each school district office, plus county-operated school enrollments.

[5] **K-5** includes pre-kindergarten, kindergarten, K-3, K-4, K-5 schools.

[6] **5-8** includes schools with low grades of 4, 5, 6 and high grades of 7, 8, 9 (e.g., 4-8, 5-8, 6-8, 6-9).

[7] **7-9** includes schools with low grades of 7, 8 and high grades of 7, 8, 9 (e.g., 7-7, 7-8, 7-9, 8-9).

[8] **7-12** includes 7-12, 8-12, 9-12, 10-12, etc.

[9] **K-12** includes schools with both elementary and secondary grades.

[10] **Other** includes special ed, vocational and adult schools.

**Public State Totals** for all columns can exceed the sum of the counties because state totals include state-operated schools and their enrollments

| COUNTY | | DISTRICTS | SCHOOLS | ELEM ENROLL[1] | MIDDLE/JHS ENROLL[2] | SENIOR ENROLL[3] | TOTAL ENROLL[4] | % OF STATE | SCHOOLS BY GRADE SPAN K-5[5] | K-6 | K-8 | 5-8[6] | 7-9[7] | 7-12[8] | K-12[9] | OTHER[10] |
|---|---|---|---|---|---|---|---|---|---|---|---|---|---|---|---|---|
| CHAMBERS | PUBLIC | 3 | 15 | 4,005 | 1,359 | 1,892 | 7,698 | | 7 | 0 | 0 | 4 | 0 | 3 | 1 | 0 |
| | NONPUBLIC | 0 | 0 | 0 | 0 | 0 | 0 | | 0 | 0 | 0 | 0 | 0 | 0 | 0 | 0 |
| | **TOTAL** | **3** | **15** | **4,005** | **1,359** | **1,892** | **7,698** | **0.1** | **7** | **0** | **0** | **4** | **0** | **3** | **1** | **0** |
| CHEROKEE | PUBLIC | 5 | 19 | 4,403 | 1,358 | 2,392 | 8,558 | | 8 | 2 | 0 | 2 | 1 | 4 | 2 | 0 |
| | NONPUBLIC | 0 | 1 | 69 | 0 | 31 | 100 | | 0 | 0 | 0 | 0 | 0 | 0 | 1 | 0 |
| | **TOTAL** | **5** | **20** | **4,472** | **1,358** | **2,423** | **8,658** | **0.2** | **8** | **2** | **0** | **2** | **1** | **4** | **3** | **0** |
| CHILDRESS | PUBLIC | 1 | 4 | 477 | 249 | 326 | 1,052 | | 1 | 0 | 0 | 1 | 0 | 1 | 1 | 0 |
| | NONPUBLIC | 0 | 0 | 0 | 0 | 0 | 0 | | 0 | 0 | 0 | 0 | 0 | 0 | 0 | 0 |
| | **TOTAL** | **1** | **4** | **477** | **249** | **326** | **1,052** | | **1** | **0** | **0** | **1** | **0** | **1** | **1** | **0** |
| CLAY | PUBLIC | 4 | 7 | 863 | 191 | 555 | 1,661 | | 1 | 1 | 0 | 1 | 0 | 2 | 2 | 0 |
| | NONPUBLIC | 0 | 0 | 0 | 0 | 0 | 0 | | 0 | 0 | 0 | 0 | 0 | 0 | 0 | 0 |
| | **TOTAL** | **4** | **7** | **863** | **191** | **555** | **1,661** | | **1** | **1** | **0** | **1** | **0** | **2** | **2** | **0** |
| COCHRAN | PUBLIC | 2 | 5 | 360 | 158 | 193 | 745 | | 2 | 0 | 0 | 1 | 0 | 1 | 1 | 0 |
| | NONPUBLIC | 0 | 0 | 0 | 0 | 0 | 0 | | 0 | 0 | 0 | 0 | 0 | 0 | 0 | 0 |
| | **TOTAL** | **2** | **5** | **360** | **158** | **193** | **745** | | **2** | **0** | **0** | **1** | **0** | **1** | **1** | **0** |
| COKE | PUBLIC | 2 | 3 | 317 | 0 | 205 | 485 | | 0 | 0 | 0 | 0 | 0 | 1 | 1 | 0 |
| | NONPUBLIC | 0 | 0 | 0 | 0 | 0 | 0 | | 0 | 0 | 0 | 0 | 0 | 0 | 0 | 0 |
| | **TOTAL** | **2** | **3** | **317** | **0** | **205** | **485** | | **0** | **0** | **0** | **0** | **0** | **1** | **1** | **0** |
| COLEMAN | PUBLIC | 3 | 6 | 629 | 240 | 414 | 1,269 | | 1 | 1 | 0 | 1 | 0 | 2 | 1 | 0 |
| | NONPUBLIC | 0 | 0 | 0 | 0 | 0 | 0 | | 0 | 0 | 0 | 0 | 0 | 0 | 0 | 0 |
| | **TOTAL** | **3** | **6** | **629** | **240** | **414** | **1,269** | | **1** | **1** | **0** | **1** | **0** | **2** | **1** | **0** |
| COLLIN | PUBLIC | 14 | 280 | 100,741 | 47,102 | 64,109 | 222,608 | | 157 | 24 | 0 | 45 | 9 | 40 | 2 | 3 |
| | NONPUBLIC | 0 | 33 | 7,994 | 0 | 2,658 | 10,652 | | 7 | 3 | 6 | 0 | 0 | 1 | 16 | 0 |
| | **TOTAL** | **14** | **313** | **108,735** | **47,102** | **66,767** | **233,260** | **4.3** | **164** | **27** | **6** | **45** | **9** | **41** | **18** | **3** |
| COLLINGSWORTH | PUBLIC | 1 | 3 | 270 | 124 | 155 | 530 | | 1 | 0 | 0 | 1 | 0 | 1 | 0 | 0 |
| | NONPUBLIC | 0 | 0 | 0 | 0 | 0 | 0 | | 0 | 0 | 0 | 0 | 0 | 0 | 0 | 0 |
| | **TOTAL** | **1** | **3** | **270** | **124** | **155** | **530** | | **1** | **0** | **0** | **1** | **0** | **1** | **0** | **0** |
| COLORADO | PUBLIC | 3 | 14 | 1,206 | 574 | 870 | 3,448 | | 6 | 0 | 0 | 3 | 0 | 5 | 0 | 0 |
| | NONPUBLIC | 0 | 2 | 265 | 0 | 0 | 265 | | 0 | 0 | 2 | 0 | 0 | 0 | 0 | 0 |
| | **TOTAL** | **3** | **16** | **1,471** | **574** | **870** | **3,713** | **0.1** | **6** | **0** | **2** | **3** | **0** | **5** | **0** | **0** |
| COMAL | PUBLIC | 2 | 48 | 14,767 | 7,298 | 9,197 | 33,020 | | 28 | 0 | 0 | 9 | 0 | 10 | 1 | 0 |
| | NONPUBLIC | 0 | 7 | 1,082 | 0 | 318 | 1,400 | | 1 | 0 | 2 | 0 | 0 | 1 | 3 | 0 |
| | **TOTAL** | **2** | **55** | **15,849** | **7,298** | **9,515** | **34,420** | **0.6** | **29** | **0** | **2** | **9** | **0** | **11** | **4** | **0** |
| COMANCHE | PUBLIC | 4 | 9 | 1,200 | 475 | 601 | 2,318 | | 3 | 0 | 0 | 2 | 0 | 2 | 2 | 0 |
| | NONPUBLIC | 0 | 0 | 0 | 0 | 0 | 0 | | 0 | 0 | 0 | 0 | 0 | 0 | 0 | 0 |
| | **TOTAL** | **4** | **9** | **1,200** | **475** | **601** | **2,318** | | **3** | **0** | **0** | **2** | **0** | **2** | **2** | **0** |

[1] **Elem Enroll** is the school by school total of enrollments in K-4, K-5, K-6, K-8 schools, elementary and middle/JHS students in K-12 schools and students in special ed schools. Public enrollments include public and county-operated schools. Public enrollments include public and county-operated schools.

[2] **Middle/JHS Enroll** is the school by school total of enrollments in 5-8 and 7-9 public schools. Public enrollments include public and county-operated schools. Private middle/JHS enrollments are included in Senior Enroll.

[3] **Senior Enroll** is the school by school total of enrollments in 7-12 and 9-12 schools, the secondary students in K-12 schools and students in vocational ed schools. Public enrollments include public and county-operated schools. For private schools, Senior Enroll includes middle/JHS enrollment plus senior enrollment.

[4] **Public Total Enroll** columns are not the sum of school building enrollments. They are projected district-wide Fall enrollments provided to MDR by each school district office, plus county-operated school enrollments.

[5] **K-5** includes pre-kindergarten, kindergarten, K-3, K-4, K-5 schools.

[6] **5-8** includes schools with low grades of 4, 5, 6 and high grades of 7, 8, 9 (e.g., 4-8, 5-8, 6-8, 6-9).

[7] **7-9** includes schools with low grades of 7, 8 and high grades of 7, 8, 9 (e.g., 7-7, 7-8, 7-9, 8-9).

[8] **7-12** includes 7-12, 8-12, 9-12, 10-12, etc.

[9] **K-12** includes schools with both elementary and secondary grades.

[10] **Other** includes special ed, vocational and adult schools.

**\*Public State Totals** for all columns can exceed the sum of the counties because state totals include state-operated schools and their enrollments

| COUNTY | | DISTRICTS | SCHOOLS | ELEM ENROLL[1] | MIDDLE/JHS ENROLL[2] | SENIOR ENROLL[3] | TOTAL ENROLL[4] | % OF STATE | K-5[5] | K-6[6] | K-8 | 5-8[6] | 7-9[7] | 7-12[8] | K-12[9] | OTHER[10] |
|---|---|---|---|---|---|---|---|---|---|---|---|---|---|---|---|---|
| CONCHO | PUBLIC | 2 | 3 | 376 | 58 | 141 | 455 | | 1 | 0 | 0 | 0 | 0 | 0 | 2 | 0 |
| | NONPUBLIC | 0 | 0 | 0 | 0 | 0 | 0 | | 0 | 0 | 0 | 0 | 0 | 0 | 0 | 0 |
| | **TOTAL** | **2** | **3** | **376** | **58** | **141** | **455** | | **1** | **0** | **0** | **0** | **0** | **0** | **2** | **0** |
| COOKE | PUBLIC | 8 | 16 | 3,929 | 697 | 2,117 | 6,639 | | 3 | 3 | 2 | 0 | 1 | 4 | 3 | 0 |
| | NONPUBLIC | 0 | 2 | 368 | 0 | 81 | 449 | | 0 | 0 | 1 | 0 | 0 | 0 | 1 | 0 |
| | **TOTAL** | **8** | **18** | **4,297** | **697** | **2,198** | **7,088** | **0.1** | **3** | **3** | **3** | **0** | **1** | **4** | **4** | **0** |
| CORYELL | PUBLIC | 5 | 19 | 6,253 | 2,153 | 2,128 | 11,703 | | 9 | 1 | 0 | 2 | 1 | 3 | 3 | 0 |
| | NONPUBLIC | 0 | 0 | 0 | 0 | 0 | 0 | | 0 | 0 | 0 | 0 | 0 | 0 | 0 | 0 |
| | **TOTAL** | **5** | **19** | **6,253** | **2,153** | **2,128** | **11,703** | **0.2** | **9** | **1** | **0** | **2** | **1** | **3** | **3** | **0** |
| COTTLE | PUBLIC | 1 | 1 | 143 | 0 | 57 | 200 | | 0 | 0 | 0 | 0 | 0 | 0 | 1 | 0 |
| | NONPUBLIC | 0 | 0 | 0 | 0 | 0 | 0 | | 0 | 0 | 0 | 0 | 0 | 0 | 0 | 0 |
| | **TOTAL** | **1** | **1** | **143** | **0** | **57** | **200** | | **0** | **0** | **0** | **0** | **0** | **0** | **1** | **0** |
| CRANE | PUBLIC | 1 | 3 | 499 | 253 | 329 | 1,172 | | 1 | 0 | 0 | 1 | 0 | 1 | 0 | 0 |
| | NONPUBLIC | 0 | 0 | 0 | 0 | 0 | 0 | | 0 | 0 | 0 | 0 | 0 | 0 | 0 | 0 |
| | **TOTAL** | **1** | **3** | **499** | **253** | **329** | **1,172** | | **1** | **0** | **0** | **1** | **0** | **1** | **0** | **0** |
| CROCKETT | PUBLIC | 1 | 3 | 347 | 180 | 200 | 720 | | 1 | 0 | 0 | 1 | 0 | 1 | 0 | 0 |
| | NONPUBLIC | 0 | 0 | 0 | 0 | 0 | 0 | | 0 | 0 | 0 | 0 | 0 | 0 | 0 | 0 |
| | **TOTAL** | **1** | **3** | **347** | **180** | **200** | **720** | | **1** | **0** | **0** | **1** | **0** | **1** | **0** | **0** |
| CROSBY | PUBLIC | 3 | 8 | 506 | 173 | 269 | 1,065 | | 2 | 1 | 0 | 1 | 0 | 3 | 1 | 0 |
| | NONPUBLIC | 0 | 0 | 0 | 0 | 0 | 0 | | 0 | 0 | 0 | 0 | 0 | 0 | 0 | 0 |
| | **TOTAL** | **3** | **8** | **506** | **173** | **269** | **1,065** | | **2** | **1** | **0** | **1** | **0** | **3** | **1** | **0** |
| CULBERSON | PUBLIC | 1 | 1 | 270 | 0 | 108 | 378 | | 0 | 0 | 0 | 0 | 0 | 0 | 1 | 0 |
| | NONPUBLIC | 0 | 0 | 0 | 0 | 0 | 0 | | 0 | 0 | 0 | 0 | 0 | 0 | 0 | 0 |
| | **TOTAL** | **1** | **1** | **270** | **0** | **108** | **378** | | **0** | **0** | **0** | **0** | **0** | **0** | **1** | **0** |
| DALLAM | PUBLIC | 2 | 5 | 978 | 406 | 557 | 1,880 | | 2 | 0 | 0 | 1 | 0 | 1 | 1 | 0 |
| | NONPUBLIC | 3 | 3 | 252 | 0 | 0 | 252 | | 0 | 2 | 1 | 0 | 0 | 0 | 0 | 0 |
| | **TOTAL** | **2** | **8** | **1,230** | **406** | **557** | **2,132** | | **2** | **2** | **1** | **1** | **0** | **1** | **1** | **0** |
| DALLAS | PUBLIC | 16 | 642 | 232,631 | 86,922 | 126,939 | 456,055 | | 322 | 72 | 23 | 84 | 17 | 95 | 25 | 4 |
| | NONPUBLIC | 0 | 120 | 26,281 | 0 | 9,729 | 36,010 | | 13 | 14 | 36 | 0 | 0 | 9 | 40 | 8 |
| | **TOTAL** | **16** | **762** | **258,912** | **86,922** | **136,668** | **492,065** | **9.2** | **335** | **86** | **59** | **84** | **17** | **104** | **65** | **12** |
| DAWSON | PUBLIC | 4 | 8 | 1,361 | 334 | 342 | 2,436 | | 2 | 0 | 0 | 1 | 0 | 2 | 3 | 0 |
| | NONPUBLIC | 0 | 0 | 0 | 0 | 0 | 0 | | 0 | 0 | 0 | 0 | 0 | 0 | 0 | 0 |
| | **TOTAL** | **4** | **8** | **1,361** | **334** | **342** | **2,436** | **0.1** | **2** | **0** | **0** | **1** | **0** | **2** | **3** | **0** |
| DE WITT | PUBLIC | 6 | 15 | 2,239 | 942 | 1,345 | 4,369 | | 6 | 0 | 2 | 3 | 0 | 3 | 1 | 0 |
| | NONPUBLIC | 0 | 1 | 73 | 0 | 0 | 73 | | 0 | 1 | 0 | 0 | 0 | 0 | 0 | 0 |
| | **TOTAL** | **6** | **16** | **2,312** | **942** | **1,345** | **4,442** | **0.1** | **6** | **1** | **2** | **3** | **0** | **3** | **1** | **0** |

[1] **Elem Enroll** is the school by school total of enrollments in K-4, K-5, K-6, K-8 schools, elementary and middle/JHS students in K-12 schools and students in special ed schools. Public enrollments include public and county-operated schools.

[2] **Middle/JHS Enroll** is the school by school total of enrollments in 5-8 and 7-9 public schools. Public enrollments include public and county-operated schools. Private middle/JHS enrollments are included in Senior Enroll.

[3] **Senior Enroll** is the school by school total of enrollments in 7-12 and 9-12 schools, the secondary students in K-12 schools and students in vocational ed schools. Public enrollments include public and county-operated schools. For private schools, Senior Enroll includes middle/JHS enrollment plus senior enrollment.

[4] **Public Total Enroll** columns are not the sum of school building enrollments. They are projected district-wide Fall enrollments provided to MDR by each school district office, plus county-operated school enrollments.

[5] **K-5** includes pre-kindergarten, kindergarten, K-3, K-4, K-5 schools.

[6] **5-8** includes schools with low grades of 4, 5, 6 and high grades of 7, 8, 9 (e.g., 4-8, 5-8, 6-8, 6-9).

[7] **7-9** includes schools with low grades of 7, 8 and high grades of 7, 8, 9 (e.g., 7-7, 7-8, 7-9, 8-9).

[8] **7-12** includes 7-12, 8-12, 9-12, 10-12, etc.

[9] **K-12** includes schools with both elementary and secondary grades.

[10] **Other** includes special ed, vocational and adult schools.

***Public State Totals** for all columns can exceed the sum of the counties because state totals include state-operated schools and their enrollments

| COUNTY | | DISTRICTS | SCHOOLS | ELEM ENROLL[1] | MIDDLE/JHS ENROLL[2] | SENIOR ENROLL[3] | TOTAL ENROLL[4] | % OF STATE | SCHOOLS BY GRADE SPAN K-5[5] | K-6 | K-8 | 5-8[6] | 7-9[7] | 7-12[8] | K-12[9] | OTHER[10] |
|---|---|---|---|---|---|---|---|---|---|---|---|---|---|---|---|---|
| DEAF SMITH | PUBLIC | 2 | 10 | 2,216 | 894 | 1,181 | 4,246 | | 5 | 1 | 0 | 1 | 1 | 2 | 0 | 0 |
| | NONPUBLIC | 0 | 2 | 179 | 0 | 0 | 179 | | 0 | 2 | 0 | 0 | 0 | 0 | 0 | 0 |
| | **TOTAL** | **2** | **12** | **2,395** | **894** | **1,181** | **4,425** | **0.1** | **5** | **3** | **0** | **1** | **1** | **2** | **0** | **0** |
| DELTA | PUBLIC | 2 | 4 | 441 | 208 | 277 | 1,000 | | 2 | 0 | 0 | 0 | 0 | 0 | 2 | 0 |
| | NONPUBLIC | 0 | 0 | 0 | 0 | 0 | 0 | | 0 | 0 | 0 | 0 | 0 | 0 | 0 | 0 |
| | **TOTAL** | **2** | **4** | **441** | **208** | **277** | **1,000** | | **2** | **0** | **0** | **0** | **0** | **0** | **2** | **0** |
| DENTON | PUBLIC | 11 | 187 | 59,349 | 29,996 | 37,648 | 136,245 | | 107 | 3 | 1 | 34 | 3 | 31 | 4 | 4 |
| | NONPUBLIC | 0 | 17 | 4,437 | 0 | 1,489 | 5,926 | | 3 | 0 | 4 | 0 | 0 | 0 | 10 | 0 |
| | **TOTAL** | **11** | **204** | **63,786** | **29,996** | **39,137** | **142,171** | **2.7** | **110** | **3** | **5** | **34** | **3** | **31** | **14** | **4** |
| DICKENS | PUBLIC | 2 | 2 | 237 | 0 | 95 | 332 | | 0 | 0 | 0 | 0 | 0 | 0 | 2 | 0 |
| | NONPUBLIC | 0 | 0 | 0 | 0 | 0 | 0 | | 0 | 0 | 0 | 0 | 0 | 0 | 0 | 0 |
| | **TOTAL** | **2** | **2** | **237** | **0** | **95** | **332** | | **0** | **0** | **0** | **0** | **0** | **0** | **2** | **0** |
| DIMMIT | PUBLIC | 1 | 4 | 1,259 | 333 | 623 | 2,200 | | 1 | 1 | 0 | 1 | 0 | 1 | 0 | 0 |
| | NONPUBLIC | 0 | 0 | 0 | 0 | 0 | 0 | | 0 | 0 | 0 | 0 | 0 | 0 | 0 | 0 |
| | **TOTAL** | **1** | **4** | **1,259** | **333** | **623** | **2,200** | | **1** | **1** | **0** | **1** | **0** | **1** | **0** | **0** |
| DONLEY | PUBLIC | 2 | 4 | 271 | 114 | 155 | 562 | | 1 | 0 | 0 | 1 | 0 | 1 | 1 | 0 |
| | NONPUBLIC | 0 | 0 | 0 | 0 | 0 | 0 | | 0 | 0 | 0 | 0 | 0 | 0 | 0 | 0 |
| | **TOTAL** | **2** | **4** | **271** | **114** | **155** | **562** | | **1** | **0** | **0** | **1** | **0** | **1** | **1** | **0** |
| DUVAL | PUBLIC | 4 | 9 | 1,257 | 516 | 790 | 2,443 | | 2 | 2 | 0 | 2 | 0 | 3 | 0 | 0 |
| | NONPUBLIC | 0 | 0 | 0 | 0 | 0 | 0 | | 0 | 0 | 0 | 0 | 0 | 0 | 0 | 0 |
| | **TOTAL** | **4** | **9** | **1,257** | **516** | **790** | **2,443** | **0.1** | **2** | **2** | **0** | **2** | **0** | **3** | **0** | **0** |
| EASTLAND | PUBLIC | 5 | 13 | 1,310 | 534 | 864 | 2,617 | | 3 | 1 | 0 | 3 | 0 | 5 | 1 | 0 |
| | NONPUBLIC | 0 | 0 | 0 | 0 | 0 | 0 | | 0 | 0 | 0 | 0 | 0 | 0 | 0 | 0 |
| | **TOTAL** | **5** | **13** | **1,310** | **534** | **864** | **2,617** | **0.1** | **3** | **1** | **0** | **3** | **0** | **5** | **1** | **0** |
| ECTOR | PUBLIC | 1 | 42 | 16,997 | 6,993 | 8,401 | 32,391 | | 30 | 0 | 0 | 6 | 0 | 5 | 1 | 0 |
| | NONPUBLIC | 0 | 5 | 670 | 0 | 71 | 741 | | 0 | 0 | 3 | 0 | 0 | 2 | 0 | 0 |
| | **TOTAL** | **1** | **47** | **17,667** | **6,993** | **8,472** | **33,132** | **0.6** | **30** | **0** | **3** | **6** | **0** | **7** | **1** | **0** |
| EDWARDS | PUBLIC | 2 | 3 | 364 | 0 | 189 | 553 | | 0 | 1 | 0 | 0 | 0 | 1 | 1 | 0 |
| | NONPUBLIC | 0 | 0 | 0 | 0 | 0 | 0 | | 0 | 0 | 0 | 0 | 0 | 0 | 0 | 0 |
| | **TOTAL** | **2** | **3** | **364** | **0** | **189** | **553** | | **0** | **1** | **0** | **0** | **0** | **1** | **1** | **0** |
| EL PASO | PUBLIC | 9 | 235 | 77,776 | 32,035 | 54,681 | 167,638 | | 107 | 25 | 8 | 39 | 5 | 44 | 4 | 3 |
| | NONPUBLIC | 0 | 33 | 5,461 | 0 | 1,994 | 7,455 | | 5 | 3 | 12 | 0 | 0 | 3 | 9 | 1 |
| | **TOTAL** | **9** | **268** | **83,237** | **32,035** | **56,675** | **175,093** | **3.3** | **112** | **28** | **20** | **39** | **5** | **47** | **13** | **4** |
| ELLIS | PUBLIC | 10 | 62 | 16,850 | 8,239 | 10,979 | 36,711 | | 32 | 4 | 1 | 8 | 2 | 11 | 4 | 0 |
| | NONPUBLIC | 0 | 4 | 627 | 0 | 163 | 790 | | 0 | 0 | 2 | 0 | 0 | 0 | 2 | 0 |
| | **TOTAL** | **10** | **66** | **17,477** | **8,239** | **11,142** | **37,501** | **0.7** | **32** | **4** | **3** | **8** | **2** | **11** | **6** | **0** |

[1] **Elem Enroll** is the school by school total of enrollments in K-4, K-5, K-6, K-8 schools, elementary and middle/JHS students in K-12 schools and students in special ed schools. Public enrollments include public and county-operated schools.

[2] **Middle/JHS Enroll** is the school by school total of enrollments in 5-8 and 7-9 public schools. Public enrollments include public and county-operated schools. Private middle/JHS enrollments are included in Senior Enroll.

[3] **Senior Enroll** is the school by school total of enrollments in 7-12 and 9-12 schools, the secondary students in K-12 schools and students in vocational ed schools. Public enrollments include public and county-operated schools. For private schools, Senior Enroll includes middle/JHS enrollment plus senior enrollment.

[4] **Public Total Enroll** columns are not the sum of school building enrollments. They are projected district-wide Fall enrollments provided to MDR by each school district office, plus county-operated school enrollments.

[5] **K-5** includes pre-kindergarten, kindergarten, K-3, K-4, K-5 schools.

[6] **5-8** includes schools with low grades of 4, 5, 6 and high grades of 7, 8, 9 (e.g., 4-8, 5-8, 6-8, 6-9).

[7] **7-9** includes schools with low grades of 7, 8 and high grades of 7, 8, 9 (e.g., 7-7, 7-8, 7-9, 8-9).

[8] **7-12** includes 7-12, 8-12, 9-12, 10-12, etc.

[9] **K-12** includes schools with both elementary and secondary grades.

[10] **Other** includes special ed, vocational ed and adult schools.

***Public State Totals** for all columns can exceed the sum of the counties because state totals include state-operated schools and their enrollments

| COUNTY | | DISTRICTS | SCHOOLS | ELEM ENROLL[1] | MIDDLE/JHS ENROLL[2] | SENIOR ENROLL[3] | TOTAL ENROLL[4] | % OF STATE | K-5[5] | K-6 | K-8 | 5-8[6] | 7-9[7] | 7-12[8] | K-12[9] | OTHER[10] |
|---|---|---|---|---|---|---|---|---|---|---|---|---|---|---|---|---|
| ERATH | PUBLIC | 7 | 15 | 3,508 | 590 | 1,814 | 5,840 | | 4 | 2 | 2 | 0 | 1 | 3 | 3 | 0 |
| | NONPUBLIC | 0 | 1 | 57 | 0 | 0 | 57 | | 0 | 1 | 0 | 0 | 0 | 0 | 0 | 0 |
| | **TOTAL** | **7** | **16** | **3,565** | **590** | **1,814** | **5,897** | **0.1** | **4** | **3** | **2** | **0** | **1** | **3** | **3** | **0** |
| FALLS | PUBLIC | 4 | 8 | 1,276 | 278 | 599 | 2,153 | | 1 | 1 | 1 | 1 | 1 | 2 | 1 | 0 |
| | NONPUBLIC | 0 | 0 | 0 | 0 | 0 | 0 | | 0 | 0 | 0 | 0 | 0 | 0 | 0 | 0 |
| | **TOTAL** | **4** | **8** | **1,276** | **278** | **599** | **2,153** | **0.1** | **1** | **1** | **1** | **1** | **1** | **2** | **1** | **0** |
| FANNIN | PUBLIC | 8 | 20 | 2,995 | 797 | 1,634 | 5,384 | | 6 | 2 | 0 | 3 | 1 | 5 | 3 | 0 |
| | NONPUBLIC | 0 | 0 | 0 | 0 | 0 | 0 | | 0 | 0 | 0 | 0 | 0 | 0 | 0 | 0 |
| | **TOTAL** | **8** | **20** | **2,995** | **797** | **1,634** | **5,384** | **0.1** | **6** | **2** | **0** | **3** | **1** | **5** | **3** | **0** |
| FAYETTE | PUBLIC | 5 | 11 | 2,292 | 525 | 1,095 | 4,157 | | 2 | 2 | 0 | 0 | 1 | 2 | 3 | 1 |
| | NONPUBLIC | 0 | 2 | 305 | 0 | 0 | 305 | | 0 | 1 | 1 | 0 | 0 | 0 | 0 | 0 |
| | **TOTAL** | **5** | **13** | **2,597** | **525** | **1,095** | **4,462** | **0.1** | **2** | **3** | **1** | **0** | **1** | **2** | **3** | **1** |
| FISHER | PUBLIC | 2 | 4 | 331 | 52 | 134 | 517 | | 1 | 0 | 1 | 0 | 0 | 1 | 1 | 0 |
| | NONPUBLIC | 0 | 0 | 0 | 0 | 0 | 0 | | 0 | 0 | 0 | 0 | 0 | 0 | 0 | 0 |
| | **TOTAL** | **2** | **4** | **331** | **52** | **134** | **517** | | **1** | **0** | **1** | **0** | **0** | **1** | **1** | **0** |
| FLOYD | PUBLIC | 2 | 5 | 591 | 116 | 278 | 1,150 | | 1 | 1 | 0 | 1 | 0 | 2 | 0 | 0 |
| | NONPUBLIC | 0 | 0 | 0 | 0 | 0 | 0 | | 0 | 0 | 0 | 0 | 0 | 0 | 0 | 0 |
| | **TOTAL** | **2** | **5** | **591** | **116** | **278** | **1,150** | | **1** | **1** | **0** | **1** | **0** | **2** | **0** | **0** |
| FOARD | PUBLIC | 1 | 2 | 119 | 0 | 98 | 230 | | 0 | 0 | 1 | 0 | 0 | 1 | 0 | 0 |
| | NONPUBLIC | 0 | 0 | 0 | 0 | 0 | 0 | | 0 | 0 | 0 | 0 | 0 | 0 | 0 | 0 |
| | **TOTAL** | **1** | **2** | **119** | **0** | **98** | **230** | | **0** | **0** | **1** | **0** | **0** | **1** | **0** | **0** |
| FORT BEND | PUBLIC | 5 | 211 | 91,278 | 41,231 | 59,657 | 205,009 | | 124 | 8 | 0 | 33 | 5 | 32 | 6 | 3 |
| | NONPUBLIC | 0 | 21 | 4,124 | 0 | 963 | 5,087 | | 5 | 1 | 7 | 1 | 0 | 1 | 6 | 0 |
| | **TOTAL** | **5** | **232** | **95,402** | **41,231** | **60,620** | **210,096** | **3.9** | **129** | **9** | **7** | **34** | **5** | **33** | **12** | **3** |
| FRANKLIN | PUBLIC | 1 | 3 | 553 | 518 | 499 | 1,570 | | 1 | 0 | 0 | 1 | 0 | 1 | 0 | 0 |
| | NONPUBLIC | 0 | 0 | 0 | 0 | 0 | 0 | | 0 | 0 | 0 | 0 | 0 | 0 | 0 | 0 |
| | **TOTAL** | **1** | **3** | **553** | **518** | **499** | **1,570** | | **1** | **0** | **0** | **1** | **0** | **1** | **0** | **0** |
| FREESTONE | PUBLIC | 4 | 13 | 1,716 | 821 | 1,084 | 3,615 | | 5 | 0 | 1 | 3 | 0 | 4 | 0 | 0 |
| | NONPUBLIC | 0 | 0 | 0 | 0 | 0 | 0 | | 0 | 0 | 0 | 0 | 0 | 0 | 0 | 0 |
| | **TOTAL** | **4** | **13** | **1,716** | **821** | **1,084** | **3,615** | **0.1** | **5** | **0** | **1** | **3** | **0** | **4** | **0** | **0** |
| FRIO | PUBLIC | 2 | 8 | 1,402 | 696 | 993 | 3,050 | | 3 | 0 | 0 | 2 | 0 | 3 | 0 | 0 |
| | NONPUBLIC | 0 | 1 | 25 | 0 | 10 | 35 | | 0 | 0 | 0 | 0 | 0 | 0 | 1 | 0 |
| | **TOTAL** | **2** | **9** | **1,427** | **696** | **1,003** | **3,085** | **0.1** | **3** | **0** | **0** | **2** | **0** | **3** | **1** | **0** |
| GAINES | PUBLIC | 3 | 10 | 1,730 | 853 | 391 | 3,290 | | 4 | 0 | 0 | 2 | 0 | 2 | 2 | 0 |
| | NONPUBLIC | 0 | 0 | 0 | 0 | 0 | 0 | | 0 | 0 | 0 | 0 | 0 | 0 | 0 | 0 |
| | **TOTAL** | **3** | **10** | **1,730** | **853** | **391** | **3,290** | **0.1** | **4** | **0** | **0** | **2** | **0** | **2** | **2** | **0** |

[1] **Elem Enroll** is the school by school total of enrollments in K-4, K-5, K-6, K-8 schools, elementary and middle/JHS students in K-12 schools and students in special ed schools. Public enrollments include public and county-operated schools.

[2] **Middle/JHS Enroll** is the school by school total of enrollments in 5-8 and 7-9 public schools. Public enrollments include public and county-operated schools. Private middle/JHS enrollments are included in Senior Enroll.

[3] **Senior Enroll** is the school by school total of enrollments in 7-12 and 9-12 schools, the secondary students in K-12 schools and students in vocational ed schools. Public enrollments include public and county-operated schools. For private schools, Senior Enroll includes middle/JHS enrollment plus senior enrollment.

[4] **Public Total Enroll** columns are not the sum of school building enrollments. They are projected district-wide Fall enrollments provided to MDR by each school district office, plus county-operated school enrollments.

[5] **K-5** includes pre-kindergarten, kindergarten, K-3, K-4, K-5 schools.

[6] **5-8** includes schools with low grades of 4, 5, 6 and high grades of 7, 8, 9 (e.g., 4-8, 5-8, 6-8, 6-9).

[7] **7-9** includes schools with low grades of 7, 8 and high grades of 7, 8, 9 (e.g., 7-7, 7-8, 7-9, 8-9).

[8] **7-12** includes schools in 7-12, 8-12, 9-12, 10-12, etc.

[9] **K-12** includes schools with both elementary and secondary grades.

[10] **Other** includes special ed, vocational and adult schools.

**\*Public State Totals** for all columns can exceed the sum of the counties because state totals include state-operated schools and their enrollments

| COUNTY | | DISTRICTS | SCHOOLS | ELEM ENROLL[1] | MIDDLE/JHS ENROLL[2] | SENIOR ENROLL[3] | TOTAL ENROLL[4] | % OF STATE | K-5[5] | K-6 | K-8 | 5-8[6] | 7-9[7] | 7-12[8] | K-12[9] | OTHER[10] |
|---|---|---|---|---|---|---|---|---|---|---|---|---|---|---|---|---|
| GALVESTON | PUBLIC | 8 | 101 | 37,120 | 17,088 | 23,029 | 80,971 | | 55 | 4 | 1 | 17 | 3 | 15 | 5 | 1 |
| | NONPUBLIC | 0 | 12 | 1,725 | 0 | 387 | 2,112 | | 1 | 2 | 6 | 0 | 0 | 1 | 2 | 0 |
| | **TOTAL** | **8** | **113** | **38,845** | **17,088** | **23,416** | **83,083** | **1.6** | **56** | **6** | **7** | **17** | **3** | **16** | **7** | **1** |
| GARZA | PUBLIC | 2 | 4 | 455 | 70 | 164 | 689 | | 1 | 0 | 0 | 1 | 0 | 1 | 1 | 0 |
| | NONPUBLIC | 0 | 0 | 0 | 0 | 0 | 0 | | 0 | 0 | 0 | 0 | 0 | 0 | 0 | 0 |
| | **TOTAL** | **2** | **4** | **455** | **70** | **164** | **689** | | **1** | **0** | **0** | **1** | **0** | **1** | **1** | **0** |
| GILLESPIE | PUBLIC | 3 | 10 | 1,712 | 873 | 1,171 | 3,782 | | 4 | 0 | 1 | 2 | 0 | 3 | 0 | 0 |
| | NONPUBLIC | 0 | 3 | 514 | 0 | 96 | 610 | | 0 | 0 | 1 | 0 | 0 | 0 | 2 | 0 |
| | **TOTAL** | **3** | **13** | **2,226** | **873** | **1,267** | **4,392** | **0.1** | **4** | **0** | **2** | **2** | **0** | **3** | **2** | **0** |
| GLASSCOCK | PUBLIC | 1 | 1 | 209 | 0 | 83 | 292 | | 0 | 0 | 0 | 0 | 0 | 0 | 1 | 0 |
| | NONPUBLIC | 0 | 0 | 0 | 0 | 0 | 0 | | 0 | 0 | 0 | 0 | 0 | 0 | 0 | 0 |
| | **TOTAL** | **1** | **1** | **209** | **0** | **83** | **292** | | **0** | **0** | **0** | **0** | **0** | **0** | **1** | **0** |
| GOLIAD | PUBLIC | 1 | 3 | 731 | 194 | 405 | 1,325 | | 0 | 1 | 0 | 0 | 1 | 1 | 0 | 0 |
| | NONPUBLIC | 0 | 0 | 0 | 0 | 0 | 0 | | 0 | 0 | 0 | 0 | 0 | 0 | 0 | 0 |
| | **TOTAL** | **1** | **3** | **731** | **194** | **405** | **1,325** | | **0** | **1** | **0** | **0** | **1** | **1** | **0** | **0** |
| GONZALES | PUBLIC | 3 | 10 | 2,249 | 747 | 1,003 | 4,268 | | 4 | 1 | 0 | 1 | 1 | 2 | 1 | 0 |
| | NONPUBLIC | 0 | 1 | 16 | 0 | 7 | 23 | | 0 | 0 | 0 | 0 | 0 | 0 | 1 | 0 |
| | **TOTAL** | **3** | **11** | **2,265** | **747** | **1,010** | **4,291** | **0.1** | **4** | **1** | **0** | **1** | **1** | **2** | **2** | **0** |
| GRAY | PUBLIC | 4 | 10 | 2,003 | 772 | 609 | 3,954 | | 4 | 1 | 0 | 1 | 0 | 2 | 2 | 0 |
| | NONPUBLIC | 0 | 1 | 71 | 0 | 0 | 71 | | 0 | 0 | 1 | 0 | 0 | 0 | 0 | 0 |
| | **TOTAL** | **4** | **11** | **2,074** | **772** | **609** | **4,025** | **0.1** | **4** | **1** | **1** | **1** | **0** | **2** | **2** | **0** |
| GRAYSON | PUBLIC | 13 | 54 | 11,462 | 3,917 | 5,719 | 22,353 | | 25 | 3 | 0 | 9 | 2 | 14 | 1 | 0 |
| | NONPUBLIC | 0 | 7 | 713 | 0 | 147 | 860 | | 1 | 1 | 1 | 0 | 0 | 0 | 4 | 0 |
| | **TOTAL** | **13** | **61** | **12,175** | **3,917** | **5,866** | **23,213** | **0.4** | **26** | **4** | **1** | **9** | **2** | **14** | **5** | **0** |
| GREGG | PUBLIC | 7 | 41 | 12,244 | 4,720 | 5,985 | 24,277 | | 21 | 1 | 0 | 8 | 1 | 9 | 1 | 0 |
| | NONPUBLIC | 0 | 7 | 927 | 0 | 375 | 1,302 | | 0 | 0 | 0 | 0 | 0 | 0 | 6 | 1 |
| | **TOTAL** | **7** | **48** | **13,171** | **4,720** | **6,360** | **25,579** | **0.5** | **21** | **1** | **0** | **8** | **1** | **9** | **7** | **1** |
| GRIMES | PUBLIC | 4 | 11 | 2,396 | 856 | 1,338 | 4,586 | | 4 | 1 | 0 | 1 | 0 | 3 | 2 | 0 |
| | NONPUBLIC | 0 | 1 | 1,200 | 0 | 0 | 1,200 | | 1 | 0 | 1 | 0 | 0 | 0 | 0 | 0 |
| | **TOTAL** | **4** | **12** | **3,596** | **856** | **1,338** | **5,786** | **0.1** | **5** | **1** | **1** | **1** | **0** | **3** | **2** | **0** |
| GUADALUPE | PUBLIC | 4 | 38 | 13,056 | 4,737 | 6,801 | 26,382 | | 19 | 4 | 0 | 3 | 3 | 7 | 2 | 0 |
| | NONPUBLIC | 0 | 5 | 949 | 0 | 103 | 1,052 | | 0 | 0 | 2 | 0 | 0 | 0 | 3 | 0 |
| | **TOTAL** | **4** | **43** | **14,005** | **4,737** | **6,904** | **27,434** | **0.5** | **19** | **4** | **2** | **3** | **3** | **7** | **5** | **0** |
| HALE | PUBLIC | 5 | 18 | 3,474 | 1,651 | 917 | 6,600 | | 8 | 0 | 0 | 4 | 0 | 4 | 2 | 0 |
| | NONPUBLIC | 0 | 1 | 152 | 0 | 61 | 213 | | 0 | 0 | 0 | 0 | 0 | 0 | 1 | 0 |
| | **TOTAL** | **5** | **19** | **3,626** | **1,651** | **978** | **6,813** | **0.1** | **8** | **0** | **0** | **4** | **0** | **4** | **3** | **0** |

[1] **Elem Enroll** is the school by school total of enrollments in K-4, K-5, K-6, K-8 schools, elementary and middle/JHS students in K-12 schools and students in special ed schools. Public enrollments include public and county-operated schools.

[2] **Middle/JHS Enroll** is the school by school total of enrollments in 5-8 and 7-9 public schools. Public enrollments include public and county-operated schools. Private middle/JHS enrollments are included in Senior Enroll.

[3] **Senior Enroll** is the school by school total of enrollments in 7-12 and 9-12 schools, the secondary students in K-12 schools and students in vocational ed schools. Public enrollments include public and county-operated schools. For private schools, Senior Enroll includes middle/JHS enrollment plus senior enrollment.

[4] **Public Total Enroll** columns are not the sum of school building enrollments. They are projected district-wide Fall enrollments provided to MDR by each school district office, plus county-operated school enrollments.

[5] **K-5** includes pre-kindergarten, kindergarten, K-3, K-4, K-5 schools.

[6] **5-8** includes schools with low grades of 4, 5, 6 and high grades of 7, 8, 9 (e.g., 4-8, 5-8, 6-8, 6-9).

[7] **7-9** includes schools with low grades of 7, 8 and high grades of 7, 8, 9 (e.g., 7-7, 7-8, 7-9, 8-9).

[8] **7-12** includes 7-12, 8-12, 9-12, 10-12, etc.

[9] **K-12** includes schools with both elementary and secondary grades.

[10] **Other** includes special ed, vocational ed and adult schools.

\***Public State Totals** for all columns can exceed the sum of the counties because state totals include state-operated schools and their enrollments

| COUNTY | | DISTRICTS | SCHOOLS | ELEM ENROLL[1] | MIDDLE/JHS ENROLL[2] | SENIOR ENROLL[3] | TOTAL ENROLL[4] | % OF STATE | K-5[5] | K-6 | K-8 | 5-8[6] | 7-9[7] | 7-12[8] | K-12[9] | OTHER[10] |
|---|---|---|---|---|---|---|---|---|---|---|---|---|---|---|---|---|
| HALL | PUBLIC | 2 | 5 | 364 | 104 | 205 | 585 | | 2 | 0 | 0 | 1 | 0 | 1 | 1 | 0 |
| | NONPUBLIC | 0 | 0 | 0 | 0 | 0 | 0 | | 0 | 0 | 0 | 0 | 0 | 0 | 0 | 0 |
| | **TOTAL** | **2** | **5** | **364** | **104** | **205** | **585** | | **2** | **0** | **0** | **1** | **0** | **1** | **1** | **0** |
| HAMILTON | PUBLIC | 2 | 5 | 657 | 295 | 400 | 1,352 | | 2 | 0 | 0 | 1 | 0 | 1 | 1 | 0 |
| | NONPUBLIC | 0 | 0 | 0 | 0 | 0 | 0 | | 0 | 0 | 0 | 0 | 0 | 0 | 0 | 0 |
| | **TOTAL** | **2** | **5** | **657** | **295** | **400** | **1,352** | | **2** | **0** | **0** | **1** | **0** | **1** | **1** | **0** |
| HANSFORD | PUBLIC | 3 | 7 | 641 | 337 | 452 | 1,409 | | 2 | 0 | 0 | 2 | 0 | 2 | 1 | 0 |
| | NONPUBLIC | 0 | 0 | 0 | 0 | 0 | 0 | | 0 | 0 | 0 | 0 | 0 | 0 | 0 | 0 |
| | **TOTAL** | **3** | **7** | **641** | **337** | **452** | **1,409** | | **2** | **0** | **0** | **2** | **0** | **2** | **1** | **0** |
| HARDEMAN | PUBLIC | 2 | 5 | 339 | 125 | 236 | 725 | | 1 | 1 | 0 | 1 | 0 | 2 | 0 | 0 |
| | NONPUBLIC | 0 | 0 | 0 | 0 | 0 | 0 | | 0 | 0 | 0 | 0 | 0 | 0 | 0 | 0 |
| | **TOTAL** | **2** | **5** | **339** | **125** | **236** | **725** | | **1** | **1** | **0** | **1** | **0** | **2** | **0** | **0** |
| HARDIN | PUBLIC | 5 | 19 | 5,772 | 1,519 | 2,504 | 9,829 | | 8 | 2 | 0 | 2 | 2 | 5 | 0 | 0 |
| | NONPUBLIC | 0 | 0 | 0 | 0 | 0 | 0 | | 0 | 0 | 0 | 0 | 0 | 0 | 0 | 0 |
| | **TOTAL** | **5** | **19** | **5,772** | **1,519** | **2,504** | **9,829** | **0.2** | **8** | **2** | **0** | **2** | **2** | **5** | **0** | **0** |
| HARRIS | PUBLIC | 18 | 894 | 394,359 | 152,528 | 212,389 | 765,574 | | 532 | 25 | 11 | 132 | 19 | 133 | 31 | 11 |
| | NONPUBLIC | 0 | 174 | 37,578 | 0 | 13,391 | 50,969 | | 20 | 9 | 62 | 1 | 0 | 19 | 56 | 7 |
| | **TOTAL** | **18** | **1,068** | **431,937** | **152,528** | **225,780** | **816,543** | **15.2** | **552** | **34** | **73** | **133** | **19** | **152** | **87** | **18** |
| HARRISON | PUBLIC | 6 | 22 | 6,130 | 3,089 | 3,689 | 12,945 | | 11 | 0 | 1 | 5 | 0 | 5 | 0 | 0 |
| | NONPUBLIC | 0 | 2 | 155 | 0 | 56 | 211 | | 0 | 0 | 1 | 0 | 0 | 1 | 0 | 0 |
| | **TOTAL** | **6** | **24** | **6,285** | **3,089** | **3,745** | **13,156** | **0.2** | **11** | **0** | **2** | **5** | **0** | **6** | **0** | **0** |
| HARTLEY | PUBLIC | 2 | 2 | 270 | 0 | 108 | 378 | | 0 | 0 | 0 | 0 | 0 | 0 | 2 | 0 |
| | NONPUBLIC | 0 | 0 | 0 | 0 | 0 | 0 | | 0 | 0 | 0 | 0 | 0 | 0 | 0 | 0 |
| | **TOTAL** | **2** | **2** | **270** | **0** | **108** | **378** | | **0** | **0** | **0** | **0** | **0** | **0** | **2** | **0** |
| HASKELL | PUBLIC | 3 | 5 | 416 | 108 | 229 | 772 | | 1 | 0 | 0 | 1 | 0 | 1 | 2 | 0 |
| | NONPUBLIC | 0 | 0 | 0 | 0 | 0 | 0 | | 0 | 0 | 0 | 0 | 0 | 0 | 0 | 0 |
| | **TOTAL** | **3** | **5** | **416** | **108** | **229** | **772** | | **1** | **0** | **0** | **1** | **0** | **1** | **2** | **0** |
| HAYS | PUBLIC | 4 | 48 | 17,077 | 8,772 | 12,091 | 37,163 | | 27 | 1 | 0 | 11 | 0 | 8 | 1 | 0 |
| | NONPUBLIC | 0 | 12 | 1,122 | 0 | 523 | 1,645 | | 0 | 3 | 3 | 0 | 0 | 1 | 5 | 0 |
| | **TOTAL** | **4** | **60** | **18,199** | **8,772** | **12,614** | **38,808** | **0.7** | **27** | **4** | **3** | **11** | **0** | **9** | **6** | **0** |
| HEMPHILL | PUBLIC | 1 | 4 | 378 | 221 | 267 | 860 | | 2 | 0 | 0 | 1 | 0 | 1 | 0 | 0 |
| | NONPUBLIC | 0 | 0 | 0 | 0 | 0 | 0 | | 0 | 0 | 0 | 0 | 0 | 0 | 0 | 0 |
| | **TOTAL** | **1** | **4** | **378** | **221** | **267** | **860** | | **2** | **0** | **0** | **1** | **0** | **1** | **0** | **0** |
| HENDERSON | PUBLIC | 8 | 27 | 5,040 | 1,891 | 2,541 | 10,026 | | 10 | 2 | 1 | 4 | 1 | 6 | 3 | 0 |
| | NONPUBLIC | 0 | 2 | 93 | 0 | 13 | 106 | | 0 | 1 | 0 | 0 | 0 | 0 | 1 | 0 |
| | **TOTAL** | **8** | **29** | **5,133** | **1,891** | **2,554** | **10,132** | **0.2** | **10** | **3** | **1** | **4** | **1** | **6** | **4** | **0** |

[1] **Elem Enroll** is the school by school total of enrollments in K-4, K-5, K-6, K-8 schools, elementary and middle/JHS students in K-12 schools and students in special ed schools. Public enrollments include public and county-operated schools.

[2] **Middle/JHS Enroll** is the school by school total of enrollments in 5-8 and 7-9 public schools. Public enrollments include public and county-operated schools. Private middle/JHS enrollments are included in Senior Enroll.

[3] **Senior Enroll** is the school by school total of enrollments in 7-12 and 9-12 schools, the secondary students in K-12 schools and students in vocational ed schools. Public enrollments include public and county-operated schools. For private schools, Senior Enroll includes middle/JHS enrollment plus senior enrollment.

[4] **Public Total Enroll** columns are not the sum of school building enrollments. They are projected district-wide Fall enrollments provided to MDR by each school district office, plus county-operated school enrollments.

[5] K-5 includes pre-kindergarten, kindergarten, K-3, K-4, K-5 schools.

[6] 5-8 includes schools with low grades of 4, 5, 6 and high grades of 7, 8, 9 (e.g., 4-8, 5-8, 6-8, 6-9).

[7] 7-9 includes schools with low grades of 7, 8 and high grades of 7, 8, 9 (e.g., 7-7, 7-8, 7-9, 8-9).

[8] 7-12 includes 7-12, 8-12, 9-12, 10-12, etc.

[9] K-12 includes schools with both elementary and secondary grades.

[10] **Other** includes special ed, vocational and adult schools.

*Public **State Totals** for all columns can exceed the sum of the counties because state totals include state-operated schools and their enrollments

| COUNTY | | DISTRICTS | SCHOOLS | ELEM ENROLL[1] | MIDDLE/JHS ENROLL[2] | SENIOR ENROLL[3] | TOTAL ENROLL[4] | % OF STATE | K-5[5] | K-6 | K-8 | 5-8[6] | 7-9[7] | 7-12[8] | K-12[9] | OTHER[10] |
|---|---|---|---|---|---|---|---|---|---|---|---|---|---|---|---|---|
| HIDALGO | PUBLIC | 15 | 278 | 86,156 | 40,557 | 56,315 | 196,740 | | 157 | 8 | 1 | 48 | 3 | 53 | 8 | 0 |
| | NONPUBLIC | 0 | 19 | 3,088 | 0 | 500 | 3,588 | | 3 | 2 | 6 | 0 | 0 | 1 | 7 | 0 |
| | **TOTAL** | **15** | **297** | **89,244** | **40,557** | **56,815** | **200,328** | **3.7** | **160** | **10** | **7** | **48** | **3** | **54** | **15** | **0** |
| HILL | PUBLIC | 12 | 23 | 3,810 | 980 | 1,432 | 6,535 | | 6 | 1 | 2 | 2 | 1 | 4 | 7 | 0 |
| | NONPUBLIC | 0 | 0 | 0 | 0 | 0 | 0 | | 0 | 0 | 0 | 0 | 0 | 0 | 0 | 0 |
| | **TOTAL** | **12** | **23** | **3,810** | **980** | **1,432** | **6,535** | **0.1** | **6** | **1** | **2** | **2** | **1** | **4** | **7** | **0** |
| HOCKLEY | PUBLIC | 6 | 14 | 2,707 | 723 | 1,299 | 4,785 | | 5 | 1 | 0 | 2 | 0 | 3 | 3 | 0 |
| | NONPUBLIC | 0 | 1 | 48 | 0 | 0 | 48 | | 0 | 0 | 1 | 0 | 0 | 0 | 0 | 0 |
| | **TOTAL** | **6** | **15** | **2,755** | **723** | **1,299** | **4,833** | **0.1** | **5** | **1** | **1** | **2** | **0** | **3** | **3** | **0** |
| HOOD | PUBLIC | 3 | 15 | 4,049 | 1,903 | 787 | 8,184 | | 7 | 0 | 0 | 3 | 0 | 3 | 2 | 0 |
| | NONPUBLIC | 0 | 3 | 306 | 0 | 97 | 403 | | 0 | 0 | 1 | 0 | 0 | 0 | 2 | 0 |
| | **TOTAL** | **3** | **18** | **4,355** | **1,903** | **884** | **8,587** | **0.2** | **7** | **0** | **1** | **3** | **0** | **3** | **4** | **0** |
| HOPKINS | PUBLIC | 7 | 16 | 4,138 | 1,047 | 1,985 | 6,901 | | 7 | 0 | 0 | 1 | 0 | 1 | 7 | 0 |
| | NONPUBLIC | 0 | 1 | 60 | 0 | 0 | 60 | | 1 | 0 | 0 | 0 | 0 | 0 | 0 | 0 |
| | **TOTAL** | **7** | **17** | **4,198** | **1,047** | **1,985** | **6,961** | **0.1** | **8** | **0** | **0** | **1** | **0** | **1** | **7** | **0** |
| HOUSTON | PUBLIC | 5 | 13 | 1,554 | 425 | 1,078 | 3,172 | | 3 | 2 | 0 | 2 | 0 | 5 | 1 | 0 |
| | NONPUBLIC | 0 | 0 | 0 | 0 | 0 | 0 | | 0 | 0 | 0 | 0 | 0 | 0 | 0 | 0 |
| | **TOTAL** | **5** | **13** | **1,554** | **425** | **1,078** | **3,172** | **0.1** | **3** | **2** | **0** | **2** | **0** | **5** | **1** | **0** |
| HOWARD | PUBLIC | 3 | 14 | 3,174 | 1,032 | 1,031 | 5,832 | | 7 | 1 | 0 | 0 | 1 | 3 | 1 | 0 |
| | NONPUBLIC | 0 | 0 | 0 | 0 | 0 | 0 | | 0 | 0 | 0 | 0 | 0 | 0 | 0 | 0 |
| | **TOTAL** | **3** | **14** | **3,174** | **1,032** | **1,031** | **5,832** | **0.1** | **7** | **1** | **0** | **1** | **1** | **3** | **1** | **0** |
| HUDSPETH | PUBLIC | 3 | 5 | 300 | 87 | 154 | 541 | | 1 | 0 | 0 | 1 | 0 | 1 | 2 | 0 |
| | NONPUBLIC | 0 | 0 | 0 | 0 | 0 | 0 | | 0 | 0 | 0 | 0 | 0 | 0 | 0 | 0 |
| | **TOTAL** | **3** | **5** | **300** | **87** | **154** | **541** | **0.1** | **1** | **0** | **0** | **1** | **0** | **1** | **2** | **0** |
| HUNT | PUBLIC | 10 | 43 | 7,941 | 2,937 | 4,394 | 15,029 | | 17 | 2 | 0 | 8 | 1 | 10 | 5 | 0 |
| | NONPUBLIC | 0 | 1 | 143 | 0 | 57 | 200 | | 0 | 0 | 0 | 0 | 0 | 0 | 1 | 0 |
| | **TOTAL** | **10** | **44** | **8,084** | **2,937** | **4,451** | **15,229** | **0.3** | **17** | **2** | **0** | **8** | **1** | **10** | **6** | **0** |
| HUTCHINSON | PUBLIC | 4 | 13 | 2,038 | 748 | 1,184 | 4,228 | | 5 | 1 | 0 | 2 | 1 | 3 | 1 | 0 |
| | NONPUBLIC | 0 | 0 | 0 | 0 | 0 | 0 | | 0 | 0 | 0 | 0 | 0 | 0 | 0 | 0 |
| | **TOTAL** | **4** | **13** | **2,038** | **748** | **1,184** | **4,228** | **0.1** | **5** | **1** | **0** | **2** | **1** | **3** | **1** | **0** |
| IRION | PUBLIC | 1 | 2 | 122 | 0 | 126 | 300 | | 0 | 1 | 0 | 0 | 0 | 1 | 0 | 0 |
| | NONPUBLIC | 0 | 0 | 0 | 0 | 0 | 0 | | 0 | 0 | 0 | 0 | 0 | 0 | 0 | 0 |
| | **TOTAL** | **1** | **2** | **122** | **0** | **126** | **300** | | **0** | **1** | **0** | **0** | **0** | **1** | **0** | **0** |
| JACK | PUBLIC | 3 | 6 | 825 | 249 | 524 | 1,604 | | 1 | 1 | 0 | 1 | 0 | 2 | 0 | 0 |
| | NONPUBLIC | 0 | 1 | 286 | 0 | 115 | 401 | | 0 | 0 | 0 | 0 | 0 | 0 | 1 | 0 |
| | **TOTAL** | **3** | **7** | **1,111** | **249** | **639** | **2,005** | | **1** | **1** | **0** | **1** | **0** | **2** | **2** | **0** |

SCHOOLS BY GRADE SPAN

[1] **Elem Enroll** is the school by school total of enrollments in K-4, K-5, K-6, K-8 schools, elementary and middle/JHS students in K-12 schools and students in special ed schools. Public enrollments include public and county-operated schools.

[2] **Middle/JHS Enroll** is the school by school total of enrollments in 5-8 and 7-9 public schools. Public enrollments include public and county-operated schools. Private middle/JHS enrollments are included in Senior Enroll.

[3] **Senior Enroll** is the school by school total of enrollments in 7-12 and 9-12 schools, the secondary students in K-12 schools and students in vocational ed schools. Public enrollments include public and county-operated schools. For private schools, Senior Enroll includes middle/JHS enrollment plus senior enrollment.

[4] **Public Total Enroll** columns are not the sum of school building enrollments. They are projected district-wide Fall enrollments provided to MDR by each school district office, plus county-operated school enrollments.

[5] **K-5** includes pre-kindergarten, kindergarten, K-3, K-4, K-5 schools.

[6] **5-8** includes schools with low grades of 4, 5, 6 and high grades of 7, 8, 9 (e.g., 4-8, 5-8, 6-8, 6-9).

[7] **7-9** includes schools with low grades of 7, 8 and high grades of 7, 8, 9 (e.g., 7-7, 7-8, 7-9, 8-9).

[8] **7-12** includes 7-12, 8-12, 9-12, 10-12, etc.

[9] **K-12** includes schools with both elementary and secondary grades.

[10] **Other** includes special ed, vocational ed and adult schools.

***Public State Totals** for all counties can exceed the sum of the counties because state totals include state-operated schools and their enrollments.

| COUNTY | | DISTRICTS | SCHOOLS | ELEM ENROLL[1] | MIDDLE/JHS ENROLL[2] | SENIOR ENROLL[3] | TOTAL ENROLL[4] | % OF STATE | K-5[5] | K-6 | K-8 | 5-8[6] | 7-9[7] | 7-12[8] | K-12[9] | OTHER[10] |
|---|---|---|---|---|---|---|---|---|---|---|---|---|---|---|---|---|
| JACKSON | PUBLIC | 3 | 11 | 1,546 | 815 | 771 | 3,128 | | 4 | 0 | 0 | 3 | 0 | 3 | 1 | 0 |
| | NONPUBLIC | 0 | 0 | 0 | 0 | 0 | 0 | | 0 | 0 | 0 | 0 | 0 | 0 | 0 | 0 |
| | **TOTAL** | **3** | **11** | **1,546** | **815** | **771** | **3,128** | **0.1** | **4** | **0** | **0** | **3** | **0** | **3** | **1** | **0** |
| JASPER | PUBLIC | 5 | 13 | 3,017 | 1,265 | 1,787 | 6,171 | | 4 | 0 | 1 | 3 | 0 | 4 | 1 | 0 |
| | NONPUBLIC | 0 | 0 | 0 | 0 | 0 | 0 | | 0 | 0 | 0 | 0 | 0 | 0 | 0 | 0 |
| | **TOTAL** | **5** | **13** | **3,017** | **1,265** | **1,787** | **6,171** | **0.1** | **4** | **0** | **1** | **3** | **0** | **4** | **1** | **0** |
| JEFF DAVIS | PUBLIC | 2 | 3 | 130 | 54 | 81 | 259 | | 1 | 0 | 0 | 0 | 0 | 0 | 2 | 0 |
| | NONPUBLIC | 0 | 0 | 0 | 0 | 0 | 0 | | 0 | 0 | 0 | 0 | 0 | 0 | 0 | 0 |
| | **TOTAL** | **2** | **3** | **130** | **54** | **81** | **259** | | **1** | **0** | **0** | **0** | **0** | **0** | **2** | **0** |
| JEFFERSON | PUBLIC | 6 | 67 | 19,360 | 7,882 | 10,071 | 39,544 | | 36 | 1 | 0 | 11 | 1 | 10 | 6 | 2 |
| | NONPUBLIC | 0 | 9 | 1,602 | 0 | 561 | 2,163 | | 0 | 0 | 0 | 0 | 0 | 1 | 3 | 0 |
| | **TOTAL** | **6** | **76** | **20,962** | **7,882** | **10,632** | **41,707** | **0.8** | **36** | **1** | **0** | **11** | **1** | **11** | **9** | **2** |
| JIM HOGG | PUBLIC | 1 | 3 | 510 | 275 | 314 | 1,100 | | 1 | 0 | 0 | 1 | 0 | 1 | 0 | 0 |
| | NONPUBLIC | 0 | 0 | 0 | 0 | 0 | 0 | | 0 | 0 | 0 | 0 | 0 | 0 | 0 | 0 |
| | **TOTAL** | **1** | **3** | **510** | **275** | **314** | **1,100** | | **1** | **0** | **0** | **1** | **0** | **1** | **0** | **0** |
| JIM WELLS | PUBLIC | 5 | 18 | 4,114 | 1,335 | 2,243 | 7,967 | | 8 | 4 | 0 | 1 | 1 | 3 | 1 | 0 |
| | NONPUBLIC | 0 | 3 | 311 | 0 | 8 | 319 | | 0 | 1 | 1 | 0 | 0 | 0 | 1 | 0 |
| | **TOTAL** | **5** | **21** | **4,425** | **1,335** | **2,251** | **8,286** | **0.2** | **8** | **5** | **1** | **1** | **1** | **3** | **2** | **0** |
| JOHNSON | PUBLIC | 9 | 65 | 16,358 | 7,738 | 9,412 | 36,396 | | 31 | 2 | 0 | 10 | 3 | 18 | 1 | 0 |
| | NONPUBLIC | 0 | 9 | 1,079 | 0 | 224 | 1,303 | | 0 | 0 | 5 | 0 | 0 | 1 | 3 | 0 |
| | **TOTAL** | **9** | **74** | **17,437** | **7,738** | **9,636** | **37,699** | **0.7** | **31** | **2** | **5** | **10** | **3** | **19** | **4** | **0** |
| JONES | PUBLIC | 5 | 13 | 1,333 | 526 | 800 | 2,644 | | 3 | 1 | 1 | 3 | 0 | 5 | 0 | 0 |
| | NONPUBLIC | 0 | 0 | 0 | 0 | 0 | 0 | | 0 | 0 | 0 | 0 | 0 | 0 | 0 | 0 |
| | **TOTAL** | **5** | **13** | **1,333** | **526** | **800** | **2,644** | **0.1** | **3** | **1** | **1** | **3** | **0** | **5** | **0** | **0** |
| KARNES | PUBLIC | 4 | 11 | 1,215 | 285 | 524 | 2,140 | | 3 | 1 | 0 | 2 | 0 | 4 | 1 | 0 |
| | NONPUBLIC | 0 | 0 | 0 | 0 | 0 | 0 | | 0 | 0 | 0 | 0 | 0 | 0 | 0 | 0 |
| | **TOTAL** | **4** | **11** | **1,215** | **285** | **524** | **2,140** | | **3** | **1** | **0** | **2** | **0** | **4** | **1** | **0** |
| KAUFMAN | PUBLIC | 7 | 54 | 15,598 | 5,996 | 7,165 | 28,529 | | 18 | 12 | 0 | 5 | 3 | 10 | 6 | 0 |
| | NONPUBLIC | 0 | 2 | 253 | 0 | 77 | 330 | | 0 | 1 | 0 | 0 | 0 | 0 | 1 | 0 |
| | **TOTAL** | **7** | **56** | **15,851** | **5,996** | **7,242** | **28,859** | **0.5** | **18** | **13** | **0** | **5** | **3** | **10** | **7** | **0** |
| KENDALL | PUBLIC | 2 | 15 | 4,487 | 3,216 | 3,218 | 10,052 | | 7 | 0 | 0 | 4 | 0 | 3 | 1 | 0 |
| | NONPUBLIC | 0 | 4 | 612 | 0 | 216 | 828 | | 0 | 0 | 1 | 0 | 0 | 0 | 3 | 0 |
| | **TOTAL** | **2** | **19** | **5,099** | **3,216** | **3,434** | **10,880** | **0.2** | **7** | **0** | **1** | **4** | **0** | **3** | **4** | **0** |
| KENEDY | PUBLIC | 1 | 1 | 80 | 0 | 0 | 80 | | 0 | 1 | 0 | 0 | 0 | 0 | 0 | 0 |
| | NONPUBLIC | 0 | 0 | 0 | 0 | 0 | 0 | | 0 | 0 | 0 | 0 | 0 | 0 | 0 | 0 |
| | **TOTAL** | **1** | **1** | **80** | **0** | **0** | **80** | | **0** | **1** | **0** | **0** | **0** | **0** | **0** | **0** |

[1] **Elem Enroll** is the school by school total of enrollments in K-4, K-5, K-6, K-8 schools, elementary and middle/JHS students in K-12 schools and students in special ed schools. Public enrollments include public and county-operated schools.

[2] **Middle/JHS Enroll** is the school by school total of enrollments in 5-8 and 7-9 public schools. Public enrollments include public and county-operated schools. Private middle/JHS enrollments are included in Senior Enroll.

[3] **Senior Enroll** is the school by school total of enrollments in 7-12 and 9-12 schools, the secondary students in K-12 schools and students in vocational ed schools. Public enrollments include public and county-operated schools. For private schools, Senior Enroll includes middle/JHS enrollment plus senior enrollment.

[4] **Public Total Enroll** columns are not the sum of school building enrollments. They are projected district-wide Fall enrollments provided to MDR by each school district office, plus county-operated school enrollments.

[5] **K-5** includes pre-kindergarten, kindergarten, K-3, K-4, K-5 schools.

[6] **5-8** includes schools with low grades of 4, 5, 6 and high grades of 7, 8, 9 (e.g., 4-8, 5-8, 6-8, 6-9).

[7] **7-9** includes schools with low grades of 7, 8, 9 and high grades of 7, 8, 9 (e.g., 7-7, 7-8, 7-9, 8-9).

[8] **7-12** includes 7-12, 8-12, 9-12, 10-12, etc.

[9] **K-12** includes schools with both elementary and secondary grades.

[10] **Other** includes special ed, vocational ed and adult schools.

**\*Public State Totals** for all columns can exceed the sum of the counties because state totals include state-operated schools and their enrollments

# COUNTY STATISTICS

| COUNTY | | DISTRICTS | SCHOOLS | ELEM ENROLL[1] | MIDDLE/JHS ENROLL[2] | SENIOR ENROLL[3] | TOTAL ENROLL[4] | % OF STATE | K-5[5] | K-6 | K-8 | 5-8[6] | 7-9[7] | 7-12[8] | K-12[9] | OTHER[10] |
|---|---|---|---|---|---|---|---|---|---|---|---|---|---|---|---|---|
| KENT | PUBLIC | 1 | 1 | 102 | 0 | 41 | 143 | | 0 | 0 | 0 | 0 | 0 | 0 | 1 | 0 |
| | NONPUBLIC | 0 | 0 | 0 | 0 | 0 | 0 | | 0 | 0 | 0 | 0 | 0 | 0 | 0 | 0 |
| | **TOTAL** | **1** | **1** | **102** | **0** | **41** | **143** | | **0** | **0** | **0** | **0** | **0** | **0** | **1** | **0** |
| KERR | PUBLIC | 5 | 18 | 3,822 | 1,146 | 878 | 6,696 | | 7 | 2 | 1 | 2 | 1 | 5 | 0 | 0 |
| | NONPUBLIC | 0 | 3 | 147 | 0 | 109 | 256 | | 0 | 0 | 1 | 0 | 0 | 1 | 1 | 0 |
| | **TOTAL** | **5** | **21** | **3,969** | **1,146** | **987** | **6,952** | **0.1** | **7** | **2** | **2** | **2** | **1** | **6** | **1** | **0** |
| KIMBLE | PUBLIC | 1 | 3 | 296 | 136 | 173 | 605 | | 1 | 0 | 0 | 1 | 0 | 1 | 0 | 0 |
| | NONPUBLIC | 0 | 0 | 0 | 0 | 0 | 0 | | 0 | 0 | 0 | 0 | 0 | 0 | 0 | 0 |
| | **TOTAL** | **1** | **3** | **296** | **136** | **173** | **605** | | **1** | **0** | **0** | **1** | **0** | **1** | **0** | **0** |
| KING | PUBLIC | 1 | 1 | 68 | 0 | 27 | 95 | | 0 | 0 | 0 | 0 | 0 | 0 | 1 | 0 |
| | NONPUBLIC | 0 | 0 | 0 | 0 | 0 | 0 | | 0 | 0 | 0 | 0 | 0 | 0 | 0 | 0 |
| | **TOTAL** | **1** | **1** | **68** | **0** | **27** | **95** | | **0** | **0** | **0** | **0** | **0** | **0** | **1** | **0** |
| KINNEY | PUBLIC | 1 | 3 | 233 | 133 | 169 | 570 | | 1 | 0 | 0 | 1 | 0 | 1 | 0 | 0 |
| | NONPUBLIC | 0 | 0 | 0 | 0 | 0 | 0 | | 0 | 0 | 0 | 0 | 0 | 0 | 0 | 0 |
| | **TOTAL** | **1** | **3** | **233** | **133** | **169** | **570** | | **1** | **0** | **0** | **1** | **0** | **1** | **0** | **0** |
| KLEBERG | PUBLIC | 4 | 13 | 3,167 | 404 | 1,580 | 4,960 | | 4 | 2 | 2 | 0 | 1 | 4 | 0 | 0 |
| | NONPUBLIC | 0 | 2 | 25 | 0 | 140 | 165 | | 1 | 0 | 0 | 0 | 0 | 1 | 0 | 0 |
| | **TOTAL** | **4** | **15** | **3,192** | **404** | **1,720** | **5,125** | **0.1** | **5** | **2** | **2** | **0** | **1** | **5** | **0** | **0** |
| KNOX | PUBLIC | 3 | 6 | 442 | 72 | 239 | 780 | | 1 | 1 | 0 | 1 | 0 | 2 | 1 | 0 |
| | NONPUBLIC | 0 | 0 | 0 | 0 | 0 | 0 | | 0 | 0 | 0 | 0 | 0 | 0 | 0 | 0 |
| | **TOTAL** | **3** | **6** | **442** | **72** | **239** | **780** | | **1** | **1** | **0** | **1** | **0** | **2** | **1** | **0** |
| LA SALLE | PUBLIC | 1 | 4 | 511 | 302 | 375 | 1,180 | | 2 | 0 | 0 | 1 | 0 | 1 | 0 | 0 |
| | NONPUBLIC | 0 | 0 | 0 | 0 | 0 | 0 | | 0 | 0 | 0 | 0 | 0 | 0 | 0 | 0 |
| | **TOTAL** | **1** | **4** | **511** | **302** | **375** | **1,180** | | **2** | **0** | **0** | **1** | **0** | **1** | **0** | **0** |
| LAMAR | PUBLIC | 3 | 15 | 3,310 | 1,026 | 1,017 | 6,008 | | 7 | 1 | 0 | 2 | 1 | 3 | 1 | 0 |
| | NONPUBLIC | 0 | 0 | 0 | 0 | 0 | 0 | | 0 | 0 | 0 | 0 | 0 | 0 | 0 | 0 |
| | **TOTAL** | **3** | **15** | **3,310** | **1,026** | **1,017** | **6,008** | **0.1** | **7** | **1** | **0** | **2** | **1** | **3** | **1** | **0** |
| LAMB | PUBLIC | 5 | 12 | 1,647 | 430 | 809 | 2,824 | | 3 | 0 | 2 | 2 | 0 | 4 | 1 | 0 |
| | NONPUBLIC | 0 | 0 | 0 | 0 | 0 | 0 | | 0 | 0 | 0 | 0 | 0 | 0 | 0 | 0 |
| | **TOTAL** | **5** | **12** | **1,647** | **430** | **809** | **2,824** | **0.1** | **3** | **0** | **2** | **2** | **0** | **4** | **1** | **0** |
| LAMPASAS | PUBLIC | 2 | 6 | 1,581 | 762 | 1,081 | 3,700 | | 3 | 0 | 0 | 1 | 0 | 1 | 1 | 0 |
| | NONPUBLIC | 0 | 0 | 0 | 0 | 0 | 0 | | 0 | 0 | 0 | 0 | 0 | 0 | 0 | 0 |
| | **TOTAL** | **2** | **6** | **1,581** | **762** | **1,081** | **3,700** | **0.1** | **3** | **0** | **0** | **1** | **0** | **1** | **1** | **0** |
| LAVACA | PUBLIC | 6 | 10 | 1,159 | 286 | 791 | 2,390 | | 1 | 2 | 3 | 1 | 0 | 3 | 0 | 0 |
| | NONPUBLIC | 0 | 3 | 544 | 0 | 168 | 712 | | 0 | 0 | 1 | 0 | 0 | 0 | 2 | 0 |
| | **TOTAL** | **6** | **13** | **1,703** | **286** | **959** | **3,102** | **0.1** | **1** | **2** | **4** | **1** | **0** | **3** | **2** | **0** |

SCHOOLS BY GRADE SPAN

1 **Elem Enroll** is the school by school total of enrollments in K-4, K-5, K-6, K-8 schools, elementary and middle/JHS students in K-12 schools and students in special ed schools. Public enrollments include public and county-operated schools.

2 **Middle/JHS Enroll** is the school by school total of enrollments in 5-8 and 7-9 public schools. Public enrollments include public and county-operated schools. Private middle/JHS enrollments are included in Senior Enroll.

3 **Senior Enroll** is the school by school total of enrollments in 7-12 and 9-12 schools, the secondary students in K-12 schools and students in vocational ed schools. Public enrollments include public and county-operated schools. For private schools, Senior Enroll includes middle/JHS enrollment plus senior enrollment.

4 **Public Total Enroll** columns are not the sum of school building enrollments. They are projected district-wide Fall enrollments provided to MDR by each school district office, plus county-operated school enrollments.

5 **K-5** includes pre-kindergarten, kindergarten, K-3, K-4, K-5 schools.

6 **5-8** includes schools with low grades of 4, 5, 6 and high grades of 7, 8, 9 (e.g., 4-8, 5-8, 6-8, 6-9).

7 **7-9** includes schools with low grades of 7, 8 and high grades of 7, 8, 9 (e.g., 7-7, 7-8, 7-9, 8-9).

8 **7-12** includes 7-12, 8-12, 9-12, 10-12, etc.

9 **K-12** includes schools with both elementary and secondary grades.

10 **Other** includes special ed, vocational ed and adult schools.

**Public State Totals** for all columns can exceed the sum of the counties because state totals include state-operated schools and their enrollments.

| COUNTY | | DISTRICTS | SCHOOLS | ELEM ENROLL[1] | MIDDLE/JHS ENROLL[2] | SENIOR ENROLL[3] | TOTAL ENROLL[4] | % OF STATE | K-5[5] | K-6 | K-8 | 5-8[6] | 7-9[7] | 7-12[8] | K-12[9] | OTHER[10] |
|---|---|---|---|---|---|---|---|---|---|---|---|---|---|---|---|---|
| **LEE** | PUBLIC | 3 | 8 | 1,332 | 675 | 942 | 3,126 | | 3 | 0 | 0 | 2 | 0 | 2 | 1 | 0 |
| | NONPUBLIC | 0 | 2 | 233 | 0 | 0 | 233 | | 0 | 0 | 2 | 0 | 0 | 0 | 0 | 0 |
| | **TOTAL** | **3** | **10** | **1,565** | **675** | **942** | **3,359** | **0.1** | **3** | **0** | **2** | **2** | **0** | **2** | **1** | **0** |
| **LEON** | PUBLIC | 5 | 13 | 1,558 | 338 | 1,142 | 3,104 | | 3 | 3 | 0 | 2 | 0 | 5 | 0 | 0 |
| | NONPUBLIC | 0 | 0 | 0 | 0 | 0 | 0 | | 0 | 0 | 0 | 0 | 0 | 0 | 0 | 0 |
| | **TOTAL** | **5** | **13** | **1,558** | **338** | **1,142** | **3,104** | **0.1** | **3** | **3** | **0** | **2** | **0** | **5** | **0** | **0** |
| **LIBERTY** | PUBLIC | 7 | 29 | 8,866 | 3,299 | 4,831 | 18,104 | | 13 | 1 | 1 | 5 | 1 | 8 | 0 | 0 |
| | NONPUBLIC | 0 | 0 | 0 | 0 | 0 | 0 | | 0 | 0 | 0 | 0 | 0 | 0 | 0 | 0 |
| | **TOTAL** | **7** | **29** | **8,866** | **3,299** | **4,831** | **18,104** | **0.3** | **13** | **1** | **1** | **5** | **1** | **8** | **0** | **0** |
| **LIMESTONE** | PUBLIC | 3 | 11 | 2,310 | 588 | 922 | 3,595 | | 4 | 1 | 0 | 1 | 1 | 2 | 1 | 1 |
| | NONPUBLIC | 0 | 0 | 0 | 0 | 0 | 0 | | 0 | 0 | 0 | 0 | 0 | 0 | 0 | 0 |
| | **TOTAL** | **3** | **11** | **2,310** | **588** | **922** | **3,595** | **0.1** | **4** | **1** | **0** | **1** | **1** | **2** | **1** | **1** |
| **LIPSCOMB** | PUBLIC | 4 | 5 | 447 | 80 | 210 | 737 | | 1 | 0 | 0 | 0 | 0 | 0 | 4 | 0 |
| | NONPUBLIC | 0 | 0 | 0 | 0 | 0 | 0 | | 0 | 0 | 0 | 0 | 0 | 0 | 0 | 0 |
| | **TOTAL** | **4** | **5** | **447** | **80** | **210** | **737** | | **1** | **0** | **0** | **0** | **0** | **0** | **4** | **0** |
| **LIVE OAK** | PUBLIC | 2 | 6 | 918 | 159 | 618 | 1,728 | | 1 | 2 | 0 | 0 | 1 | 2 | 0 | 0 |
| | NONPUBLIC | 0 | 0 | 0 | 0 | 0 | 0 | | 0 | 0 | 0 | 0 | 0 | 0 | 0 | 0 |
| | **TOTAL** | **2** | **6** | **918** | **159** | **618** | **1,728** | | **1** | **2** | **0** | **0** | **1** | **2** | **0** | **0** |
| **LLANO** | PUBLIC | 1 | 4 | 789 | 407 | 505 | 1,701 | | 2 | 0 | 0 | 1 | 0 | 1 | 0 | 0 |
| | NONPUBLIC | 0 | 1 | 54 | 0 | 22 | 76 | | 0 | 0 | 0 | 0 | 0 | 0 | 1 | 0 |
| | **TOTAL** | **1** | **5** | **843** | **407** | **527** | **1,777** | | **2** | **0** | **0** | **1** | **0** | **1** | **1** | **0** |
| **LUBBOCK** | PUBLIC | 8 | 87 | 23,163 | 10,650 | 12,250 | 46,947 | | 51 | 0 | 0 | 19 | 0 | 12 | 4 | 1 |
| | NONPUBLIC | 0 | 9 | 1,476 | 0 | 722 | 2,198 | | 1 | 0 | 1 | 0 | 0 | 0 | 7 | 0 |
| | **TOTAL** | **8** | **96** | **24,639** | **10,650** | **12,972** | **49,145** | **0.9** | **52** | **0** | **1** | **19** | **0** | **12** | **11** | **1** |
| **LYNN** | PUBLIC | 4 | 7 | 895 | 219 | 432 | 1,574 | | 2 | 0 | 0 | 1 | 0 | 1 | 3 | 0 |
| | NONPUBLIC | 0 | 0 | 0 | 0 | 0 | 0 | | 0 | 0 | 0 | 0 | 0 | 0 | 0 | 0 |
| | **TOTAL** | **4** | **7** | **895** | **219** | **432** | **1,574** | | **2** | **0** | **0** | **1** | **0** | **1** | **3** | **0** |
| **MADISON** | PUBLIC | 2 | 5 | 1,261 | 529 | 753 | 2,543 | | 2 | 0 | 0 | 1 | 0 | 1 | 1 | 0 |
| | NONPUBLIC | 0 | 0 | 0 | 0 | 0 | 0 | | 0 | 0 | 0 | 0 | 0 | 0 | 0 | 0 |
| | **TOTAL** | **2** | **5** | **1,261** | **529** | **753** | **2,543** | **0.1** | **2** | **0** | **0** | **1** | **0** | **1** | **1** | **0** |
| **MARION** | PUBLIC | 1 | 4 | 557 | 393 | 374 | 1,324 | | 2 | 0 | 0 | 1 | 0 | 1 | 0 | 0 |
| | NONPUBLIC | 0 | 2 | 29 | 0 | 40 | 69 | | 0 | 0 | 1 | 0 | 0 | 1 | 0 | 0 |
| | **TOTAL** | **1** | **6** | **586** | **393** | **414** | **1,393** | | **2** | **0** | **1** | **1** | **0** | **2** | **0** | **0** |
| **MARTIN** | PUBLIC | 2 | 4 | 696 | 243 | 347 | 1,286 | | 1 | 0 | 0 | 1 | 0 | 1 | 1 | 0 |
| | NONPUBLIC | 0 | 0 | 0 | 0 | 0 | 0 | | 0 | 0 | 0 | 0 | 0 | 0 | 0 | 0 |
| | **TOTAL** | **2** | **4** | **696** | **243** | **347** | **1,286** | | **1** | **0** | **0** | **1** | **0** | **1** | **1** | **0** |

[1] **Elem Enroll** is the school by school total of enrollments in K-4, K-5, K-6, K-8 schools, elementary and middle/JHS students in K-12 schools and students in special ed schools. Public enrollments include public and county-operated schools.

[2] **Middle/JHS Enroll** is the school by school total of enrollments in 5-8 and 7-9 public schools. Public enrollments include public and county-operated schools. Private middle/JHS enrollments are included in Senior Enroll.

[3] **Senior Enroll** is the school by school total of enrollments in 7-12 and 9-12 schools, the secondary students in K-12 schools and students in vocational schools. Public enrollments include public and county-operated schools. For private schools, Senior Enroll includes middle/JHS enrollment plus senior enrollment.

[4] **Public Total Enroll** columns are not the sum of school building enrollments. They are projected district-wide Fall enrollments provided to MDR by each school district office, plus county-operated school enrollments.

[5] K-5 includes pre-kindergarten, kindergarten, K-3, K-4, K-5 schools.

[6] 5-8 includes schools with low grades of 4, 5, 6 and high grades of 7, 8, 9 (e.g., 4-8, 5-8, 6-8, 6-9).

[7] 7-9 includes schools with low grades of 7, 8 and high grades of 7, 8, 9 (e.g., 7-7, 7-8, 7-9, 8-9).

[8] 7-12 includes 7-12, 8-12, 9-12, 10-12, etc.

[9] K-12 includes schools with both elementary and secondary grades.

[10] **Other** includes special ed, vocational and adult schools.

*Public State Totals for all columns can exceed the sum of the counties because state totals include state-operated schools and their enrollments

| COUNTY | | DISTRICTS | SCHOOLS | ELEM ENROLL[1] | MIDDLE/JHS ENROLL[2] | SENIOR ENROLL[3] | TOTAL ENROLL[4] | % OF STATE | SCHOOLS BY GRADE SPAN | | | | | | | |
| --- | --- | --- | --- | --- | --- | --- | --- | --- | --- | --- | --- | --- | --- | --- | --- | --- |
| | | | | | | | | | K-5[5] | K-6 | K-8 | 5-8[6] | 7-9[7] | 7-12[8] | K-12[9] | OTHER[10] |
| MASON | PUBLIC | 1 | 3 | 280 | 219 | 216 | 674 | | 1 | 0 | 0 | 1 | 0 | 1 | 0 | 0 |
| | NONPUBLIC | 0 | 0 | 0 | 0 | 0 | 0 | | 0 | 0 | 0 | 0 | 0 | 0 | 0 | 0 |
| | TOTAL | 1 | 3 | 280 | 219 | 216 | 674 | | 1 | 0 | 0 | 1 | 0 | 1 | 0 | 0 |
| MATAGORDA | PUBLIC | 5 | 18 | 3,647 | 1,479 | 1,979 | 7,303 | | 8 | 1 | 1 | 3 | 1 | 4 | 0 | 0 |
| | NONPUBLIC | 0 | 1 | 110 | 0 | 0 | 110 | | 0 | 1 | 0 | 0 | 0 | 0 | 0 | 0 |
| | TOTAL | 5 | 19 | 3,757 | 1,479 | 1,979 | 7,413 | 0.1 | 8 | 2 | 1 | 3 | 1 | 4 | 0 | 0 |
| MAVERICK | PUBLIC | 1 | 23 | 7,962 | 2,174 | 3,455 | 15,000 | | 4 | 15 | 0 | 0 | 2 | 2 | 0 | 0 |
| | NONPUBLIC | 0 | 2 | 280 | 0 | 0 | 280 | | 0 | 1 | 1 | 0 | 0 | 0 | 0 | 0 |
| | TOTAL | 1 | 25 | 8,242 | 2,174 | 3,455 | 15,280 | 0.3 | 4 | 16 | 1 | 0 | 2 | 2 | 0 | 0 |
| MCCULLOCH | PUBLIC | 3 | 6 | 695 | 260 | 406 | 1,329 | | 1 | 0 | 0 | 1 | 0 | 1 | 3 | 0 |
| | NONPUBLIC | 0 | 0 | 0 | 0 | 0 | 0 | | 0 | 0 | 0 | 0 | 0 | 0 | 0 | 0 |
| | TOTAL | 3 | 6 | 695 | 260 | 406 | 1,329 | | 1 | 0 | 0 | 1 | 0 | 1 | 3 | 0 |
| MCLENNAN | PUBLIC | 18 | 87 | 22,051 | 7,300 | 10,082 | 42,010 | | 38 | 9 | 1 | 11 | 4 | 18 | 6 | 0 |
| | NONPUBLIC | 0 | 10 | 1,208 | 0 | 659 | 1,867 | | 0 | 2 | 1 | 0 | 0 | 2 | 5 | 0 |
| | TOTAL | 18 | 97 | 23,259 | 7,300 | 10,741 | 43,877 | 0.8 | 38 | 11 | 2 | 11 | 4 | 20 | 11 | 0 |
| MCMULLEN | PUBLIC | 1 | 1 | 206 | 0 | 83 | 289 | | 0 | 0 | 0 | 0 | 0 | 0 | 1 | 0 |
| | NONPUBLIC | 0 | 0 | 0 | 0 | 0 | 0 | | 0 | 0 | 0 | 0 | 0 | 0 | 0 | 0 |
| | TOTAL | 1 | 1 | 206 | 0 | 83 | 289 | | 0 | 0 | 0 | 0 | 0 | 0 | 1 | 0 |
| MEDINA | PUBLIC | 5 | 20 | 4,891 | 2,101 | 2,424 | 10,193 | | 10 | 0 | 0 | 5 | 0 | 4 | 1 | 0 |
| | NONPUBLIC | 0 | 2 | 145 | 0 | 0 | 145 | | 2 | 0 | 0 | 0 | 0 | 0 | 0 | 0 |
| | TOTAL | 5 | 22 | 5,036 | 2,101 | 2,424 | 10,338 | 0.2 | 12 | 0 | 0 | 5 | 0 | 4 | 1 | 0 |
| MENARD | PUBLIC | 1 | 2 | 223 | 0 | 82 | 305 | | 0 | 0 | 1 | 0 | 0 | 1 | 0 | 0 |
| | NONPUBLIC | 0 | 0 | 0 | 0 | 0 | 0 | | 0 | 0 | 0 | 0 | 0 | 0 | 0 | 0 |
| | TOTAL | 1 | 2 | 223 | 0 | 82 | 305 | | 0 | 0 | 1 | 0 | 0 | 1 | 0 | 0 |
| MIDLAND | PUBLIC | 2 | 44 | 16,342 | 4,438 | 7,498 | 28,831 | | 3 | 26 | 0 | 3 | 3 | 8 | 0 | 1 |
| | NONPUBLIC | 0 | 7 | 2,475 | 0 | 715 | 3,190 | | 0 | 1 | 1 | 0 | 0 | 0 | 4 | 1 |
| | TOTAL | 2 | 51 | 18,817 | 4,438 | 8,213 | 32,021 | 0.6 | 3 | 27 | 1 | 3 | 3 | 8 | 4 | 2 |
| MILAM | PUBLIC | 6 | 16 | 2,077 | 955 | 1,365 | 4,487 | | 6 | 0 | 1 | 4 | 0 | 4 | 1 | 0 |
| | NONPUBLIC | 0 | 1 | 97 | 0 | 0 | 97 | | 0 | 0 | 1 | 0 | 0 | 0 | 0 | 0 |
| | TOTAL | 6 | 17 | 2,174 | 955 | 1,365 | 4,584 | 0.1 | 6 | 0 | 2 | 4 | 0 | 4 | 1 | 0 |
| MILLS | PUBLIC | 3 | 10 | 368 | 140 | 442 | 964 | | 1 | 1 | 0 | 1 | 0 | 4 | 3 | 0 |
| | NONPUBLIC | 0 | 0 | 0 | 0 | 0 | 0 | | 0 | 0 | 0 | 0 | 0 | 0 | 0 | 0 |
| | TOTAL | 3 | 10 | 368 | 140 | 442 | 964 | | 1 | 1 | 0 | 1 | 0 | 4 | 3 | 0 |
| MITCHELL | PUBLIC | 3 | 6 | 1,005 | 0 | 261 | 1,314 | | 1 | 0 | 1 | 0 | 0 | 2 | 2 | 0 |
| | NONPUBLIC | 0 | 0 | 0 | 0 | 0 | 0 | | 0 | 0 | 0 | 0 | 0 | 0 | 0 | 0 |
| | TOTAL | 3 | 6 | 1,005 | 0 | 261 | 1,314 | | 1 | 0 | 1 | 0 | 0 | 2 | 2 | 0 |

[1] **Elem Enroll** is the school by school total of enrollments in K-4, K-5, K-6, K-8 schools, elementary and middle/JHS students in K-12 schools and students in special ed schools. Public enrollments include public and county-operated schools.

[2] **Middle/JHS Enroll** is the school by school total of enrollments in 5-8 and 7-9 public schools. Public enrollments include public and county-operated schools. Private middle/JHS enrollments are included in Senior Enroll.

[3] **Senior Enroll** is the school by school total of enrollments in 7-12 and 9-12 schools, the secondary students in K-12 schools and students in vocational ed schools. Public enrollments include public and county-operated schools. For private schools, Senior Enroll includes middle/JHS enrollment plus senior enrollment.

[4] **Public Total Enroll** columns are not the sum of the school building enrollments. They are projected district-wide Fall enrollments provided to MDR by each school district office, plus county-operated school enrollments.

[5] **K-5** includes pre-kindergarten, kindergarten, K-3, K-4, K-5 schools.

[6] **5-8** includes schools with low grades of 4, 5, 6 and high grades of 7, 8, 9 (e.g., 4-8, 5-8, 6-8, 6-9).

[7] **7-9** includes schools with low grades of 7, 8 and high grades of 7, 8, 9 (e.g., 7-7, 7-8, 7-9, 8-9).

[8] **7-12** includes 7-12, 8-12, 9-12, 10-12, etc.

[9] **K-12** includes schools with both elementary and secondary grades.

[10] **Other** includes special ed, vocational ed and adult schools.

**\*Public State Totals** for all columns can exceed the sum of the counties because state totals include state-operated schools and their enrollments

| COUNTY | | DISTRICTS | SCHOOLS | ELEM ENROLL[1] | MIDDLE/JHS ENROLL[2] | SENIOR ENROLL[3] | TOTAL ENROLL[4] | % OF STATE | K-5[5] | K-6 | K-8 | 5-8[6] | 7-9[7] | 7-12[8] | K-12[9] | OTHER[10] |
|---|---|---|---|---|---|---|---|---|---|---|---|---|---|---|---|---|
| MONTAGUE | PUBLIC | 7 | 13 | 1,786 | 558 | 1,032 | 3,408 | | 3 | 1 | 1 | 2 | 0 | 3 | 3 | 0 |
| | NONPUBLIC | 0 | 0 | 0 | 0 | 0 | 0 | | 0 | 0 | 0 | 0 | 0 | 0 | 0 | 0 |
| | TOTAL | 7 | 13 | 1,786 | 558 | 1,032 | 3,408 | 0.1 | 3 | 1 | 1 | 2 | 0 | 3 | 3 | 0 |
| MONTGOMERY | PUBLIC | 6 | 125 | 57,631 | 19,375 | 32,155 | 112,557 | | 63 | 17 | 0 | 9 | 10 | 24 | 2 | 0 |
| | NONPUBLIC | 0 | 19 | 3,514 | 0 | 879 | 4,393 | | 1 | 2 | 4 | 0 | 0 | 0 | 12 | 0 |
| | TOTAL | 6 | 144 | 61,145 | 19,375 | 33,034 | 116,950 | 2.2 | 64 | 19 | 4 | 9 | 10 | 24 | 14 | 0 |
| MOORE | PUBLIC | 2 | 12 | 2,435 | 821 | 678 | 4,856 | | 6 | 1 | 0 | 1 | 1 | 3 | 0 | 0 |
| | NONPUBLIC | 0 | 0 | 0 | 0 | 0 | 0 | | 0 | 0 | 0 | 0 | 0 | 0 | 0 | 0 |
| | TOTAL | 2 | 12 | 2,435 | 821 | 678 | 4,856 | 0.1 | 6 | 1 | 0 | 1 | 1 | 3 | 0 | 0 |
| MORRIS | PUBLIC | 2 | 7 | 853 | 396 | 534 | 1,840 | | 3 | 0 | 0 | 2 | 0 | 2 | 0 | 0 |
| | NONPUBLIC | 0 | 0 | 0 | 0 | 0 | 0 | | 0 | 0 | 0 | 0 | 0 | 0 | 0 | 0 |
| | TOTAL | 2 | 7 | 853 | 396 | 534 | 1,840 | | 3 | 0 | 0 | 2 | 0 | 2 | 0 | 0 |
| MOTLEY | PUBLIC | 1 | 1 | 116 | 0 | 46 | 162 | | 0 | 0 | 0 | 0 | 0 | 0 | 1 | 0 |
| | NONPUBLIC | 0 | 0 | 0 | 0 | 0 | 0 | | 0 | 0 | 0 | 0 | 0 | 0 | 0 | 0 |
| | TOTAL | 1 | 1 | 116 | 0 | 46 | 162 | | 0 | 0 | 0 | 0 | 0 | 0 | 1 | 0 |
| NACOGDOCHES | PUBLIC | 9 | 25 | 5,516 | 2,086 | 1,996 | 10,826 | | 10 | 0 | 1 | 5 | 0 | 5 | 4 | 0 |
| | NONPUBLIC | 0 | 4 | 407 | 0 | 49 | 456 | | 1 | 2 | 0 | 0 | 0 | 0 | 1 | 0 |
| | TOTAL | 9 | 29 | 5,923 | 2,086 | 2,045 | 11,282 | 0.2 | 11 | 2 | 1 | 5 | 0 | 5 | 5 | 0 |
| NAVARRO | PUBLIC | 7 | 23 | 5,743 | 1,318 | 2,913 | 10,135 | | 10 | 1 | 1 | 2 | 1 | 4 | 4 | 0 |
| | NONPUBLIC | 0 | 3 | 289 | 0 | 51 | 340 | | 0 | 0 | 1 | 0 | 0 | 0 | 2 | 0 |
| | TOTAL | 7 | 26 | 6,032 | 1,318 | 2,964 | 10,475 | 0.2 | 10 | 1 | 2 | 2 | 1 | 4 | 6 | 0 |
| NEWTON | PUBLIC | 2 | 5 | 681 | 221 | 382 | 1,291 | | 1 | 1 | 0 | 1 | 0 | 2 | 0 | 0 |
| | NONPUBLIC | 0 | 1 | 14 | 0 | 6 | 20 | | 0 | 0 | 0 | 0 | 0 | 0 | 1 | 0 |
| | TOTAL | 2 | 6 | 695 | 221 | 388 | 1,311 | | 1 | 1 | 0 | 1 | 0 | 2 | 1 | 0 |
| NOLAN | PUBLIC | 4 | 12 | 1,629 | 659 | 582 | 2,870 | | 6 | 0 | 0 | 1 | 0 | 1 | 4 | 0 |
| | NONPUBLIC | 0 | 0 | 0 | 0 | 0 | 0 | | 0 | 0 | 0 | 0 | 0 | 0 | 0 | 0 |
| | TOTAL | 4 | 12 | 1,629 | 659 | 582 | 2,870 | 0.1 | 6 | 0 | 0 | 1 | 0 | 1 | 4 | 0 |
| NUECES | PUBLIC | 12 | 101 | 28,103 | 11,941 | 16,531 | 57,968 | | 54 | 3 | 1 | 18 | 1 | 19 | 3 | 2 |
| | NONPUBLIC | 0 | 19 | 2,271 | 0 | 1,022 | 3,293 | | 6 | 2 | 4 | 2 | 0 | 2 | 3 | 0 |
| | TOTAL | 12 | 120 | 30,374 | 11,941 | 17,553 | 61,261 | 1.1 | 60 | 5 | 5 | 20 | 1 | 21 | 6 | 2 |
| OCHILTREE | PUBLIC | 1 | 6 | 970 | 512 | 314 | 2,217 | | 3 | 0 | 0 | 1 | 0 | 2 | 0 | 0 |
| | NONPUBLIC | 0 | 1 | 42 | 0 | 0 | 42 | | 0 | 1 | 0 | 0 | 0 | 0 | 0 | 0 |
| | TOTAL | 1 | 7 | 1,012 | 512 | 314 | 2,259 | | 3 | 1 | 0 | 1 | 0 | 2 | 0 | 0 |
| OLDHAM | PUBLIC | 4 | 7 | 435 | 198 | 380 | 940 | | 2 | 0 | 0 | 1 | 0 | 1 | 3 | 0 |
| | NONPUBLIC | 0 | 0 | 0 | 0 | 0 | 0 | | 0 | 0 | 0 | 0 | 0 | 0 | 0 | 0 |
| | TOTAL | 4 | 7 | 435 | 198 | 380 | 940 | | 2 | 0 | 0 | 1 | 0 | 1 | 3 | 0 |

[1] **Elem Enroll** is the school by school total of enrollments in K-4, K-5, K-6, K-8 schools, elementary and middle/JHS students in K-12 schools and students in special ed schools. Public enrollments include public and county-operated schools.

[2] **Middle/JHS Enroll** is the school by school total of enrollments in 5-8 and 7-9 public schools. Public enrollments include public and county-operated schools. Private middle/JHS enrollments are included in Senior Enroll.

[3] **Senior Enroll** is the school by school total of enrollments in 7-12 and 9-12 schools, the secondary students in K-12 schools and students in vocational ed schools. Public enrollments include public and county-operated schools. For private schools, Senior Enroll includes middle/JHS enrollment plus senior enrollment.

[4] **Public Total Enroll** columns are not the sum of school building enrollments. They are projected district-wide Fall enrollments provided to MDR by each school district office, plus county-operated school enrollments.

[5] **K-5** includes pre-kindergarten, kindergarten, K-3, K-4, K-5 schools.

[6] **5-8** includes schools with low grades of 4, 5, 6 and high grades of 7, 8, 9 (e.g., 4-8, 5-8, 6-8, 6-9).

[7] **7-9** includes schools with low grades of 7, 8 and high grades of 7, 8, 9 (e.g., 7-7, 7-8, 7-9, 8-9).

[8] **7-12** includes 7-12, 8-12, 9-12, 10-12, etc.

[9] **K-12** includes schools with both elementary and secondary grades.

[10] **Other** includes special ed, vocational and adult schools.

*Public State Totals for all columns can exceed the sum of the counties because state totals include state-operated schools and their enrollments

| COUNTY | | DISTRICTS | SCHOOLS | ELEM ENROLL[1] | MIDDLE/JHS ENROLL[2] | SENIOR ENROLL[3] | TOTAL ENROLL[4] | % OF STATE | K-5[5] | K-6 | K-8 | 5-8[6] | 7-9[7] | 7-12[8] | K-12[9] | OTHER[10] |
|---|---|---|---|---|---|---|---|---|---|---|---|---|---|---|---|---|
| ORANGE | PUBLIC | 6 | 26 | 7,730 | 3,163 | 3,806 | 15,402 | | 12 | 1 | 0 | 5 | 1 | 6 | 1 | 0 |
| | NONPUBLIC | 0 | 2 | 432 | | 93 | 525 | | 0 | 0 | 1 | 5 | 0 | 0 | 1 | 0 |
| | TOTAL | 6 | 28 | 8,162 | 3,163 | 3,899 | 15,927 | 0.3 | 12 | 1 | 1 | 5 | 1 | 6 | 2 | 0 |
| PALO PINTO | PUBLIC | 6 | 13 | 2,670 | 678 | 631 | 4,461 | | 4 | 2 | 0 | 0 | 1 | 2 | 4 | 0 |
| | NONPUBLIC | 0 | 1 | 51 | 0 | 21 | 72 | | 0 | 0 | 0 | 0 | 0 | 0 | 1 | 0 |
| | TOTAL | 6 | 14 | 2,721 | 678 | 652 | 4,533 | 0.1 | 4 | 2 | 0 | 0 | 1 | 2 | 5 | 0 |
| PANOLA | PUBLIC | 3 | 9 | 2,113 | 565 | 1,133 | 3,743 | | 3 | 1 | 0 | 0 | 1 | 1 | 3 | 0 |
| | NONPUBLIC | 0 | 1 | 64 | 0 | 26 | 90 | | 0 | 0 | 0 | 0 | 0 | 0 | 1 | 0 |
| | TOTAL | 3 | 10 | 2,177 | 565 | 1,159 | 3,833 | 0.1 | 3 | 1 | 0 | 0 | 1 | 1 | 4 | 0 |
| PARKER | PUBLIC | 8 | 42 | 11,807 | 3,430 | 6,350 | 21,907 | | 11 | 11 | 1 | 3 | 5 | 11 | 0 | 0 |
| | NONPUBLIC | 0 | 5 | 1,529 | 0 | 252 | 1,781 | | 0 | 0 | 1 | 0 | 0 | 0 | 4 | 0 |
| | TOTAL | 8 | 47 | 13,336 | 3,430 | 6,602 | 23,688 | 0.4 | 11 | 11 | 2 | 3 | 5 | 11 | 4 | 0 |
| PARMER | PUBLIC | 4 | 11 | 1,120 | 460 | 643 | 2,212 | | 4 | 0 | 0 | 3 | 0 | 3 | 1 | 0 |
| | NONPUBLIC | 0 | 0 | 0 | 0 | 0 | 0 | | 0 | 0 | 0 | 0 | 0 | 0 | 0 | 0 |
| | TOTAL | 4 | 11 | 1,120 | 460 | 643 | 2,212 | 0.1 | 4 | 0 | 0 | 3 | 0 | 3 | 1 | 0 |
| PECOS | PUBLIC | 3 | 9 | 1,555 | 663 | 876 | 3,094 | | 4 | 0 | 0 | 2 | 0 | 2 | 1 | 0 |
| | NONPUBLIC | 0 | 0 | 0 | 0 | 0 | 0 | | 0 | 0 | 0 | 0 | 0 | 0 | 0 | 0 |
| | TOTAL | 3 | 9 | 1,555 | 663 | 876 | 3,094 | 0.1 | 4 | 0 | 0 | 2 | 0 | 2 | 1 | 0 |
| POLK | PUBLIC | 6 | 16 | 3,425 | 1,197 | 1,172 | 6,718 | | 6 | 1 | 0 | 2 | 0 | 4 | 3 | 0 |
| | NONPUBLIC | 0 | 0 | 0 | 0 | 0 | 0 | | 0 | 0 | 0 | 0 | 0 | 0 | 0 | 0 |
| | TOTAL | 6 | 16 | 3,425 | 1,197 | 1,172 | 6,718 | 0.1 | 6 | 1 | 0 | 2 | 0 | 4 | 3 | 0 |
| POTTER | PUBLIC | 4 | 65 | 18,482 | 7,090 | 10,008 | 36,853 | | 40 | 4 | 0 | 8 | 4 | 9 | 0 | 0 |
| | NONPUBLIC | 0 | 5 | 960 | 0 | 165 | 1,125 | | 1 | 1 | 1 | 0 | 0 | 0 | 2 | 0 |
| | TOTAL | 4 | 70 | 19,442 | 7,090 | 10,173 | 37,978 | 0.7 | 41 | 5 | 1 | 8 | 4 | 9 | 2 | 0 |
| PRESIDIO | PUBLIC | 2 | 5 | 767 | 397 | 526 | 1,504 | | 1 | 1 | 0 | 0 | 1 | 1 | 1 | 0 |
| | NONPUBLIC | 0 | 0 | 0 | 0 | 0 | 0 | | 0 | 0 | 0 | 0 | 0 | 0 | 0 | 0 |
| | TOTAL | 2 | 5 | 767 | 397 | 526 | 1,504 | | 1 | 1 | 0 | 0 | 1 | 1 | 1 | 0 |
| RAINS | PUBLIC | 1 | 4 | 807 | 371 | 461 | 1,500 | | 2 | 0 | 0 | 1 | 0 | 1 | 0 | 0 |
| | NONPUBLIC | 0 | 0 | 0 | 0 | 0 | 0 | | 0 | 0 | 0 | 0 | 0 | 0 | 0 | 0 |
| | TOTAL | 1 | 4 | 807 | 371 | 461 | 1,500 | | 2 | 0 | 0 | 1 | 0 | 1 | 0 | 0 |
| RANDALL | PUBLIC | 1 | 16 | 4,968 | 1,563 | 2,856 | 11,000 | | 8 | 3 | 0 | 0 | 2 | 0 | 0 | 0 |
| | NONPUBLIC | 0 | 3 | 124 | 0 | 302 | 426 | | 1 | 0 | 0 | 1 | 0 | 3 | 2 | 0 |
| | TOTAL | 1 | 19 | 5,092 | 1,563 | 3,158 | 11,426 | 0.2 | 9 | 3 | 0 | 1 | 2 | 3 | 2 | 0 |
| REAGAN | PUBLIC | 1 | 3 | 386 | 197 | 238 | 850 | | 1 | 0 | 0 | 0 | 0 | 1 | 0 | 0 |
| | NONPUBLIC | 0 | 0 | 0 | 0 | 0 | 0 | | 0 | 0 | 0 | 1 | 0 | 0 | 0 | 0 |
| | TOTAL | 1 | 3 | 386 | 197 | 238 | 850 | | 1 | 0 | 0 | 1 | 0 | 1 | 0 | 0 |

[1] **Elem Enroll** is the school by school total of enrollments in K-4, K-5, K-6, K-8 schools, elementary and middle/JHS students in K-12 schools and students in special ed schools. Public enrollments include public and county-operated schools. Private middle/JHS enrollments are included in Senior Enroll.

[2] **Middle/JHS Enroll** is the school by school total of enrollments in 5-8 and 7-9 public schools. Public enrollments include public and county-operated schools. Private middle/JHS enrollments are included in Senior Enroll.

[3] **Senior Enroll** is the school by school total of enrollments in 7-12 and 9-12 schools, the secondary students in K-12 schools and students in vocational ed schools. Public enrollments include public and county-operated schools. For private schools, Senior Enroll includes middle/JHS enrollment plus senior enrollment.

[4] **Public Total Enroll** columns are not the sum of school building enrollments. They are projected district-wide Fall enrollments provided to MDR by each school district office, plus county-operated school enrollments.

[5] **K-5** includes pre-kindergarten, kindergarten, K-3, K-4, K-5 schools.

[6] **5-8** includes schools with low grades of 4, 5, 6 and high grades of 7, 8, 9 (e.g., 4-8, 5-8, 6-8, 6-9).

[7] **7-9** includes schools with low grades of 7, 8 and high grades of 7, 8, 9 (e.g., 7-7, 7-8, 7-9, 8-9).

[8] **7-12** includes 7-12, 8-12, 9-12, 10-12, etc.

[9] **K-12** includes schools with both elementary and secondary grades.

[10] **Other** includes special ed, vocational ed and adult schools.

**\*Public State Totals** for all columns can exceed the sum of the counties because state totals include state-operated schools and their enrollments

## SCHOOLS BY GRADE SPAN

| COUNTY | | DISTRICTS | SCHOOLS | ELEM ENROLL[1] | MIDDLE/JHS ENROLL[2] | SENIOR ENROLL[3] | TOTAL ENROLL[4] | % OF STATE | K-5[5] | K-6 | K-8 | 5-8[6] | 7-97[7] | 7-12[8] | K-12[9] | OTHER[10] |
|---|---|---|---|---|---|---|---|---|---|---|---|---|---|---|---|---|
| **REAL** | PUBLIC | 1 | 1 | 199 | 0 | 80 | 279 | | 0 | 0 | 0 | 0 | 0 | 0 | 1 | 0 |
| | NONPUBLIC | 0 | 0 | 0 | 0 | 0 | 0 | | 0 | 0 | 0 | 0 | 0 | 0 | 0 | 0 |
| | **TOTAL** | **1** | **1** | **199** | **0** | **80** | **279** | | **0** | **0** | **0** | **0** | **0** | **0** | **1** | **0** |
| **RED RIVER** | PUBLIC | 4 | 10 | 971 | 443 | 627 | 2,087 | | 4 | 0 | 0 | 2 | 0 | 2 | 2 | 0 |
| | NONPUBLIC | 0 | 0 | 0 | 0 | 0 | 0 | | 0 | 0 | 0 | 0 | 0 | 0 | 0 | 0 |
| | **TOTAL** | **4** | **10** | **971** | **443** | **627** | **2,087** | | **4** | **0** | **0** | **2** | **0** | **2** | **2** | **0** |
| **REEVES** | PUBLIC | 6 | 6 | 1,509 | 594 | 743 | 2,865 | | 3 | 0 | 0 | 1 | 0 | 1 | 1 | 0 |
| | NONPUBLIC | 0 | 0 | 0 | 0 | 0 | 0 | | 0 | 0 | 0 | 0 | 0 | 0 | 0 | 0 |
| | **TOTAL** | **6** | **6** | **1,509** | **594** | **743** | **2,865** | **0.1** | **3** | **0** | **0** | **1** | **0** | **1** | **1** | **0** |
| **REFUGIO** | PUBLIC | 3 | 7 | 678 | 119 | 438 | 1,235 | | 1 | 2 | 0 | 1 | 1 | 2 | 1 | 0 |
| | NONPUBLIC | 0 | 0 | 0 | 0 | 0 | 0 | | 0 | 0 | 0 | 0 | 0 | 0 | 0 | 0 |
| | **TOTAL** | **3** | **7** | **678** | **119** | **438** | **1,235** | | **1** | **2** | **0** | **1** | **1** | **2** | **1** | **0** |
| **ROBERTS** | PUBLIC | 1 | 1 | 136 | 0 | 54 | 190 | | 0 | 0 | 0 | 0 | 0 | 0 | 1 | 0 |
| | NONPUBLIC | 0 | 0 | 0 | 0 | 0 | 0 | | 0 | 0 | 0 | 0 | 0 | 0 | 0 | 0 |
| | **TOTAL** | **1** | **1** | **136** | **0** | **54** | **190** | | **0** | **0** | **0** | **0** | **0** | **0** | **1** | **0** |
| **ROBERTSON** | PUBLIC | 4 | 10 | 1,210 | 627 | 751 | 2,532 | | 2 | 1 | 0 | 2 | 1 | 3 | 1 | 0 |
| | NONPUBLIC | 0 | 0 | 0 | 0 | 0 | 0 | | 0 | 0 | 0 | 0 | 0 | 0 | 0 | 0 |
| | **TOTAL** | **4** | **10** | **1,210** | **627** | **751** | **2,532** | **0.1** | **2** | **1** | **0** | **2** | **1** | **3** | **1** | **0** |
| **ROCKWALL** | PUBLIC | 2 | 31 | 12,263 | 3,648 | 5,719 | 23,378 | | 4 | 17 | 0 | 0 | 4 | 5 | 0 | 1 |
| | NONPUBLIC | 0 | 2 | 294 | 0 | 108 | 402 | | 1 | 0 | 0 | 0 | 0 | 0 | 1 | 0 |
| | **TOTAL** | **2** | **33** | **12,557** | **3,648** | **5,827** | **23,780** | **0.4** | **5** | **17** | **0** | **0** | **4** | **5** | **1** | **1** |
| **RUNNELS** | PUBLIC | 4 | 8 | 1,084 | 346 | 578 | 2,008 | | 2 | 0 | 0 | 2 | 0 | 2 | 2 | 0 |
| | NONPUBLIC | 0 | 0 | 0 | 0 | 0 | 0 | | 0 | 0 | 0 | 0 | 0 | 0 | 0 | 0 |
| | **TOTAL** | **4** | **8** | **1,084** | **346** | **578** | **2,008** | | **2** | **0** | **0** | **2** | **0** | **2** | **2** | **0** |
| **RUSK** | PUBLIC | 8 | 20 | 3,802 | 1,484 | 2,287 | 7,723 | | 8 | 0 | 0 | 3 | 0 | 4 | 5 | 0 |
| | NONPUBLIC | 0 | 1 | 93 | 0 | 42 | 135 | | 0 | 0 | 0 | 0 | 0 | 0 | 1 | 0 |
| | **TOTAL** | **8** | **21** | **3,895** | **1,484** | **2,329** | **7,858** | **0.2** | **8** | **0** | **0** | **3** | **0** | **4** | **6** | **0** |
| **SABINE** | PUBLIC | 2 | 5 | 579 | 412 | 431 | 1,484 | | 2 | 0 | 0 | 1 | 0 | 1 | 1 | 0 |
| | NONPUBLIC | 0 | 0 | 0 | 0 | 0 | 0 | | 0 | 0 | 0 | 0 | 0 | 0 | 0 | 0 |
| | **TOTAL** | **2** | **5** | **579** | **412** | **431** | **1,484** | | **2** | **0** | **0** | **1** | **0** | **1** | **1** | **0** |
| **SAN AUGUSTINE** | PUBLIC | 2 | 4 | 528 | 252 | 334 | 1,120 | | 2 | 0 | 0 | 0 | 0 | 0 | 2 | 0 |
| | NONPUBLIC | 0 | 0 | 0 | 0 | 0 | 0 | | 0 | 0 | 0 | 0 | 0 | 0 | 0 | 0 |
| | **TOTAL** | **2** | **4** | **528** | **252** | **334** | **1,120** | | **2** | **0** | **0** | **0** | **0** | **0** | **2** | **0** |
| **SAN JACINTO** | PUBLIC | 2 | 8 | 1,686 | 818 | 1,002 | 3,506 | | 4 | 0 | 0 | 2 | 0 | 2 | 0 | 0 |
| | NONPUBLIC | 0 | 0 | 0 | 0 | 0 | 0 | | 0 | 0 | 0 | 0 | 0 | 0 | 0 | 0 |
| | **TOTAL** | **2** | **8** | **1,686** | **818** | **1,002** | **3,506** | **0.1** | **4** | **0** | **0** | **2** | **0** | **2** | **0** | **0** |

[1] **Elem Enroll** is the school by school total of enrollments in K-4, K-5, K-6, K-8 schools, elementary and middle/JHS students in K-12 schools and students in special ed schools. Public enrollments include public and county-operated schools.

[2] **Middle/JHS Enroll** is the school by school total of enrollments in 5-8 and 7-9 public schools. Public enrollments include public and county-operated schools. Private middle/JHS enrollments are included in Senior Enroll.

[3] **Senior Enroll** is the school by school total of enrollments in 7-12 and 9-12 schools, the secondary students in K-12 schools and students in vocational ed schools. Public enrollments include public and county-operated schools. For private schools, Senior Enroll includes middle/JHS enrollment plus senior enrollment.

[4] **Public Total Enroll** columns are not the sum of school building enrollments. They are projected district-wide Fall enrollments provided to MDR by each school district office, plus county-operated school enrollments.

[5] **K-5** includes pre-kindergarten, kindergarten, K-3, K-4, K-5 schools.

[6] **5-8** includes schools with low grades of 4, 5, 6 and high grades of 7, 8, 9 (e.g., 4-8, 5-8, 6-8, 6-9).

[7] **7-9** includes schools with low grades of 7, 8 and high grades of 7, 8, 9 (e.g., 7-7, 7-8, 7-9, 8-9).

[8] **7-12** includes 7-12, 8-12, 9-12, 10-12, etc.

[9] **K-12** includes schools with both elementary and secondary grades.

[10] **Other** includes special ed, vocational ed and adult schools.

**\*Public State Totals** for all columns can exceed the sum of the counties because state totals include state-operated schools and their enrollments

| COUNTY | | DISTRICTS | SCHOOLS | ELEM ENROLL[1] | MIDDLE/JHS ENROLL[2] | SENIOR ENROLL[3] | TOTAL ENROLL[4] | % OF STATE[4] | K-5[5] | K-6 | K-8 | 5-8[6] | 7-9[7] | 7-12[8] | K-12[9] | OTHER[10] |
|---|---|---|---|---|---|---|---|---|---|---|---|---|---|---|---|---|
| SAN PATRICIO | PUBLIC | 7 | 32 | 6,160 | 2,907 | 3,622 | 13,123 | | 16 | 1 | 0 | 6 | 1 | 8 | 0 | 0 |
| | NONPUBLIC | 0 | 0 | 0 | 0 | 0 | 0 | | 0 | 0 | 0 | 0 | 0 | 0 | 0 | 0 |
| | **TOTAL** | **7** | **32** | **6,160** | **2,907** | **3,622** | **13,123** | **0.2** | **16** | **1** | **0** | **6** | **1** | **8** | **0** | **0** |
| SAN SABA | PUBLIC | 3 | 5 | 463 | 213 | 276 | 952 | | 1 | 0 | 0 | 1 | 0 | 1 | 2 | 0 |
| | NONPUBLIC | 0 | 0 | 0 | 0 | 0 | 0 | | 0 | 0 | 0 | 0 | 0 | 0 | 0 | 0 |
| | **TOTAL** | **3** | **5** | **463** | **213** | **276** | **952** | | **1** | **0** | **0** | **1** | **0** | **1** | **2** | **0** |
| SCHLEICHER | PUBLIC | 1 | 3 | 197 | 164 | 154 | 540 | | 1 | 0 | 0 | 1 | 0 | 1 | 0 | 0 |
| | NONPUBLIC | 0 | 0 | 0 | 0 | 0 | 0 | | 0 | 0 | 0 | 0 | 0 | 0 | 0 | 0 |
| | **TOTAL** | **1** | **3** | **197** | **164** | **154** | **540** | | **1** | **0** | **0** | **1** | **0** | **1** | **0** | **0** |
| SCURRY | PUBLIC | 3 | 6 | 1,850 | 588 | 873 | 3,250 | | 2 | 0 | 0 | 1 | 0 | 1 | 2 | 0 |
| | NONPUBLIC | 0 | 0 | 0 | 0 | 0 | 0 | | 0 | 0 | 0 | 0 | 0 | 0 | 0 | 0 |
| | **TOTAL** | **3** | **6** | **1,850** | **588** | **873** | **3,250** | **0.1** | **2** | **0** | **0** | **1** | **0** | **1** | **2** | **0** |
| SHACKELFORD | PUBLIC | 2 | 3 | 323 | 0 | 251 | 617 | | 0 | 1 | 0 | 0 | 0 | 1 | 1 | 0 |
| | NONPUBLIC | 0 | 0 | 0 | 0 | 0 | 0 | | 0 | 0 | 0 | 0 | 0 | 0 | 0 | 0 |
| | **TOTAL** | **2** | **3** | **323** | **0** | **251** | **617** | | **0** | **1** | **0** | **0** | **0** | **1** | **1** | **0** |
| SHELBY | PUBLIC | 6 | 17 | 2,600 | 1,100 | 1,433 | 5,320 | | 6 | 0 | 1 | 4 | 0 | 4 | 2 | 0 |
| | NONPUBLIC | 0 | 1 | 30 | 0 | 12 | 42 | | 0 | 0 | 0 | 0 | 0 | 0 | 1 | 0 |
| | **TOTAL** | **6** | **18** | **2,630** | **1,100** | **1,445** | **5,362** | **0.1** | **6** | **0** | **1** | **4** | **0** | **4** | **3** | **0** |
| SHERMAN | PUBLIC | 2 | 4 | 334 | 185 | 154 | 690 | | 2 | 0 | 0 | 1 | 0 | 1 | 0 | 0 |
| | NONPUBLIC | 0 | 0 | 0 | 0 | 0 | 0 | | 0 | 0 | 0 | 0 | 0 | 0 | 0 | 0 |
| | **TOTAL** | **2** | **4** | **334** | **185** | **154** | **690** | | **2** | **0** | **0** | **1** | **0** | **1** | **0** | **0** |
| SMITH | PUBLIC | 9 | 67 | 19,040 | 7,365 | 10,225 | 36,633 | | 35 | 3 | 0 | 9 | 3 | 11 | 4 | 2 |
| | NONPUBLIC | 0 | 15 | 2,314 | 0 | 1,894 | 4,208 | | 4 | 0 | 1 | 0 | 0 | 1 | 8 | 1 |
| | **TOTAL** | **9** | **82** | **21,354** | **7,365** | **12,119** | **40,841** | **0.8** | **39** | **3** | **1** | **9** | **3** | **12** | **12** | **3** |
| SOMERVELL | PUBLIC | 1 | 4 | 812 | 435 | 536 | 1,970 | | 2 | 0 | 0 | 1 | 0 | 1 | 0 | 0 |
| | NONPUBLIC | 0 | 0 | 0 | 0 | 0 | 0 | | 0 | 0 | 0 | 0 | 0 | 0 | 0 | 0 |
| | **TOTAL** | **1** | **4** | **812** | **435** | **536** | **1,970** | | **2** | **0** | **0** | **1** | **0** | **1** | **0** | **0** |
| STARR | PUBLIC | 3 | 29 | 7,294 | 3,960 | 3,692 | 16,375 | | 16 | 0 | 0 | 6 | 0 | 4 | 3 | 0 |
| | NONPUBLIC | 0 | 1 | 94 | 0 | 0 | 94 | | 0 | 0 | 1 | 0 | 0 | 0 | 0 | 0 |
| | **TOTAL** | **3** | **30** | **7,388** | **3,960** | **3,692** | **16,469** | **0.3** | **16** | **0** | **1** | **6** | **0** | **4** | **3** | **0** |
| STEPHENS | PUBLIC | 1 | 5 | 757 | 230 | 426 | 1,413 | | 2 | 1 | 0 | 0 | 1 | 1 | 0 | 0 |
| | NONPUBLIC | 0 | 0 | 0 | 0 | 0 | 0 | | 0 | 0 | 0 | 0 | 0 | 0 | 0 | 0 |
| | **TOTAL** | **1** | **5** | **757** | **230** | **426** | **1,413** | | **2** | **1** | **0** | **0** | **1** | **1** | **0** | **0** |
| STERLING | PUBLIC | 1 | 2 | 141 | 64 | 86 | 320 | | 1 | 0 | 0 | 0 | 0 | 0 | 1 | 0 |
| | NONPUBLIC | 0 | 0 | 0 | 0 | 0 | 0 | | 0 | 0 | 0 | 0 | 0 | 0 | 0 | 0 |
| | **TOTAL** | **1** | **2** | **141** | **64** | **86** | **320** | | **1** | **0** | **0** | **0** | **0** | **0** | **1** | **0** |

[1] **Elem Enroll** is the school by school total of enrollments in K-4, K-5, K-6, K-8 schools, elementary and middle/JHS students in K-12 schools and students in special ed schools. Public enrollments include public and county-operated schools.

[2] **Middle/JHS Enroll** is the school by school total of enrollments in 5-8 and 7-9 public schools. Public enrollments include public and county-operated schools. Private middle/JHS enrollments are included in Senior Enroll.

[3] **Senior Enroll** is the school by school total of enrollments in 7-12 and 9-12 schools, the secondary students in K-12 schools and students in vocational ed schools. Public enrollments include public and county-operated schools. For private schools, Senior Enroll includes middle/JHS enrollment plus senior enrollment.

[4] **Public Total Enroll** columns are not the sum of school building enrollments. They are projected district-wide Fall enrollments provided to MDR by each school district office, plus county-operated school enrollments.

[5] **K-5** includes pre-kindergarten, kindergarten, K-3, K-4, K-5 schools.

[6] **5-8** includes schools with low grades of 4, 5, 6 and high grades of 7, 8, 9 (e.g., 4-8, 5-8, 6-8, 6-9).

[7] **7-9** includes schools with low grades of 7, 8 and high grades of 7, 8, 9 (e.g., 7-7, 7-8, 7-9, 8-9).

[8] **7-12** includes 7-12, 8-12, 9-12, 10-12, etc.

[9] **K-12** includes schools with both elementary and secondary grades.

[10] **Other** includes special ed, vocational ed and adult schools.

*Public State Totals for all columns can exceed the sum of the counties because state totals include state-operated schools and their enrollments

| COUNTY | | DISTRICTS | SCHOOLS | ELEM ENROLL[1] | MIDDLE/JHS ENROLL[2] | SENIOR ENROLL[3] | TOTAL ENROLL[4] | % OF STATE | SCHOOLS BY GRADE SPAN | | | | | | | |
|---|---|---|---|---|---|---|---|---|---|---|---|---|---|---|---|---|
| | | | | | | | | | K-5[5] | K-6 | K-8 | 5-8[6] | 7-9[7] | 7-12[8] | K-12[9] | OTHER[10] |
| STONEWALL | PUBLIC | 1 | 2 | 93 | 51 | 69 | 214 | | 1 | 0 | 0 | 0 | 0 | 0 | 1 | 0 |
| | NONPUBLIC | 0 | 0 | 0 | 0 | 0 | 0 | | 0 | 0 | 0 | 0 | 0 | 0 | 0 | 0 |
| | TOTAL | 1 | 2 | 93 | 51 | 69 | 214 | | 1 | 0 | 0 | 0 | 0 | 0 | 1 | 0 |
| SUTTON | PUBLIC | 1 | 3 | 387 | 181 | 257 | 767 | | 0 | 1 | 0 | 0 | 1 | 1 | 0 | 0 |
| | NONPUBLIC | 0 | 0 | 0 | 0 | 0 | 0 | | 0 | 0 | 0 | 0 | 0 | 0 | 0 | 0 |
| | TOTAL | 1 | 3 | 387 | 181 | 257 | 767 | | 0 | 1 | 0 | 0 | 1 | 1 | 0 | 0 |
| SWISHER | PUBLIC | 3 | 7 | 746 | 246 | 521 | 1,530 | | 1 | 2 | 0 | 1 | 0 | 3 | 0 | 0 |
| | NONPUBLIC | 0 | 0 | 0 | 0 | 0 | 0 | | 0 | 0 | 0 | 0 | 0 | 0 | 0 | 0 |
| | TOTAL | 3 | 7 | 746 | 246 | 521 | 1,530 | | 1 | 2 | 0 | 1 | 0 | 3 | 0 | 0 |
| TARRANT | PUBLIC | 16 | 499 | 173,133 | 63,657 | 101,470 | 352,934 | | 217 | 101 | 2 | 42 | 38 | 76 | 10 | 13 |
| | NONPUBLIC | 79 | 79 | 16,244 | 0 | 5,413 | 21,657 | | 8 | 9 | 18 | 0 | 0 | 7 | 30 | 7 |
| | TOTAL | 16 | 578 | 189,377 | 63,657 | 106,883 | 374,591 | 7.0 | 225 | 110 | 20 | 42 | 38 | 83 | 40 | 20 |
| TAYLOR | PUBLIC | 5 | 41 | 11,128 | 5,316 | 6,319 | 24,583 | | 22 | 0 | 0 | 8 | 0 | 7 | 1 | 3 |
| | NONPUBLIC | 0 | 5 | 628 | 0 | 86 | 714 | | 3 | 0 | 1 | 0 | 0 | 0 | 1 | 0 |
| | TOTAL | 5 | 46 | 11,756 | 5,316 | 6,405 | 25,297 | 0.5 | 25 | 0 | 1 | 8 | 0 | 7 | 2 | 3 |
| TERRELL | PUBLIC | 1 | 1 | 77 | 0 | 31 | 108 | | 0 | 0 | 0 | 0 | 0 | 0 | 0 | 0 |
| | NONPUBLIC | 0 | 0 | 0 | 0 | 0 | 0 | | 0 | 0 | 0 | 0 | 0 | 0 | 1 | 0 |
| | TOTAL | 1 | 1 | 77 | 0 | 31 | 108 | | 0 | 0 | 0 | 0 | 0 | 0 | 1 | 0 |
| TERRY | PUBLIC | 3 | 6 | 1,342 | 361 | 281 | 2,243 | | 2 | 0 | 0 | 1 | 0 | 1 | 2 | 0 |
| | NONPUBLIC | 0 | 0 | 0 | 0 | 0 | 0 | | 0 | 0 | 0 | 0 | 0 | 0 | 0 | 0 |
| | TOTAL | 3 | 6 | 1,342 | 361 | 281 | 2,243 | | 2 | 0 | 0 | 1 | 0 | 1 | 2 | 0 |
| THROCKMORTON | PUBLIC | 2 | 2 | 216 | 0 | 86 | 302 | | 0 | 0 | 0 | 0 | 0 | 0 | 2 | 0 |
| | NONPUBLIC | 0 | 0 | 0 | 0 | 0 | 0 | | 0 | 0 | 0 | 0 | 0 | 0 | 0 | 0 |
| | TOTAL | 2 | 2 | 216 | 0 | 86 | 302 | | 0 | 0 | 0 | 0 | 0 | 0 | 2 | 0 |
| TITUS | PUBLIC | 3 | 12 | 3,809 | 951 | 728 | 6,825 | | 6 | 1 | 0 | 1 | 1 | 2 | 0 | 0 |
| | NONPUBLIC | 0 | 1 | 7 | 0 | 3 | 10 | | 0 | 0 | 1 | 0 | 0 | 0 | 1 | 0 |
| | TOTAL | 3 | 13 | 3,816 | 951 | 731 | 6,835 | 0.1 | 6 | 1 | 1 | 1 | 1 | 2 | 1 | 0 |
| TOM GREEN | PUBLIC | 6 | 37 | 8,366 | 3,886 | 4,741 | 17,860 | | 20 | 1 | 0 | 5 | 0 | 7 | 4 | 0 |
| | NONPUBLIC | 0 | 4 | 402 | 0 | 84 | 486 | | 0 | 0 | 2 | 0 | 0 | 0 | 2 | 0 |
| | TOTAL | 6 | 41 | 8,768 | 3,886 | 4,825 | 18,346 | 0.3 | 20 | 1 | 2 | 5 | 0 | 7 | 6 | 0 |
| TRAVIS | PUBLIC | 7 | 204 | 68,572 | 32,130 | 38,812 | 148,585 | | 126 | 6 | 0 | 36 | 1 | 29 | 4 | 3 |
| | NONPUBLIC | 0 | 47 | 7,951 | 0 | 3,863 | 11,814 | | 4 | 1 | 17 | 2 | 0 | 7 | 12 | 4 |
| | TOTAL | 7 | 251 | 76,523 | 32,130 | 42,675 | 160,399 | 3.0 | 130 | 7 | 17 | 38 | 1 | 36 | 16 | 7 |
| TRINITY | PUBLIC | 4 | 9 | 1,076 | 464 | 710 | 2,265 | | 2 | 2 | 0 | 1 | 0 | 0 | 0 | 0 |
| | NONPUBLIC | 0 | 0 | 0 | 0 | 0 | 0 | | 0 | 0 | 0 | 0 | 0 | 0 | 1 | 0 |
| | TOTAL | 4 | 9 | 1,076 | 464 | 710 | 2,265 | | 2 | 2 | 0 | 1 | 0 | 0 | 1 | 0 |

[1] **Elem Enroll** is the school by school total of enrollments in K-4, K-5, K-6, K-8 schools, elementary and middle/JHS students in K-12 schools and students in special ed schools. Public enrollments include public and county-operated schools.

[2] **Middle/JHS Enroll** is the school by school total of enrollments in 5-8 and 7-9 public schools. Public enrollments include public and county-operated schools. Private middle/JHS enrollments are included in Senior Enroll.

[3] **Senior Enroll** is the school by school total of enrollments in 7-12 and 9-12 schools, the secondary students in K-12 schools and students in vocational ed schools. Public enrollments include public and county-operated schools. For private schools, Senior Enroll includes middle/JHS enrollment plus senior enrollment.

[4] **Public Total Enroll** columns are not the sum of school building enrollments. They are projected district-wide Fall enrollments provided to MDR by each school district office, plus county-operated school enrollments.

[5] **K-5** includes pre-kindergarten, kindergarten, K-3, K-4, K-5 schools.
[6] **5-8** includes schools with low grades of 4, 5, 6 and high grades of 7, 8, 9 (e.g., 4-8, 5-8, 6-8, 6-9).
[7] **7-9** includes schools with low grades of 7, 8 and high grades of 7, 8, 9 (e.g., 7-7, 7-8, 7-9, 8-9).
[8] **7-12** includes schools 7-12, 8-12, 9-12, 10-12, etc.
[9] **K-12** includes schools with both elementary and secondary grades.
[10] **Other** includes special ed, vocational and adult schools.
**\*Public State Totals** for all columns can exceed the sum of the counties because state totals include state-operated schools and their enrollments

| COUNTY | | DISTRICTS | SCHOOLS | ELEM ENROLL[1] | MIDDLE/JHS ENROLL[2] | SENIOR ENROLL[3] | TOTAL ENROLL[4] | % OF STATE | K-5[5] | K-6 | K-8 | 5-8[6] | 7-9[7] | 7-12[8] | K-12[9] | OTHER[10] |
|---|---|---|---|---|---|---|---|---|---|---|---|---|---|---|---|---|
| TYLER | PUBLIC | 5 | 14 | 1,698 | 729 | 938 | 3,534 | | 6 | 1 | 0 | 2 | 0 | 3 | 2 | 0 |
| | NONPUBLIC | 0 | 1 | 28 | 0 | 0 | 28 | | 1 | 0 | 0 | 0 | 0 | 0 | 0 | 0 |
| | **TOTAL** | **5** | **15** | **1,726** | **729** | **938** | **3,562** | **0.1** | **7** | **1** | **0** | **2** | **0** | **3** | **2** | **0** |
| UPSHUR | PUBLIC | 7 | 20 | 3,680 | 1,262 | 2,261 | 7,156 | | 6 | 2 | 0 | 4 | 1 | 6 | 1 | 0 |
| | NONPUBLIC | 0 | 0 | 0 | 0 | 0 | 0 | | 0 | 0 | 0 | 0 | 0 | 0 | 0 | 0 |
| | **TOTAL** | **7** | **20** | **3,680** | **1,262** | **2,261** | **7,156** | **0.1** | **6** | **2** | **0** | **4** | **1** | **6** | **1** | **0** |
| UPTON | PUBLIC | 2 | 5 | 377 | 151 | 253 | 854 | | 2 | 0 | 0 | 1 | 0 | 2 | 0 | 0 |
| | NONPUBLIC | 0 | 0 | 0 | 0 | 0 | 0 | | 0 | 0 | 0 | 0 | 0 | 0 | 0 | 0 |
| | **TOTAL** | **2** | **5** | **377** | **151** | **253** | **854** | | **2** | **0** | **0** | **1** | **0** | **2** | **0** | **0** |
| UVALDE | PUBLIC | 4 | 12 | 2,925 | 780 | 1,627 | 5,320 | | 4 | 2 | 0 | 0 | 1 | 2 | 3 | 0 |
| | NONPUBLIC | 0 | 2 | 116 | 0 | 0 | 116 | | 1 | 1 | 0 | 0 | 0 | 0 | 0 | 0 |
| | **TOTAL** | **4** | **14** | **3,041** | **780** | **1,627** | **5,436** | **0.1** | **5** | **3** | **0** | **0** | **1** | **2** | **3** | **0** |
| VAL VERDE | PUBLIC | 2 | 13 | 5,527 | 1,537 | 3,014 | 10,671 | | 8 | 1 | 0 | 0 | 1 | 2 | 0 | 0 |
| | NONPUBLIC | 0 | 3 | 613 | 0 | 0 | 613 | | 1 | 0 | 2 | 0 | 0 | 0 | 1 | 0 |
| | **TOTAL** | **2** | **16** | **6,140** | **1,537** | **3,014** | **11,284** | **0.2** | **9** | **1** | **2** | **0** | **1** | **2** | **1** | **0** |
| VAN ZANDT | PUBLIC | 7 | 26 | 4,783 | 1,851 | 2,639 | 9,905 | | 11 | 2 | 0 | 4 | 2 | 6 | 1 | 1 |
| | NONPUBLIC | 0 | 1 | 26 | 0 | 11 | 37 | | 0 | 0 | 0 | 0 | 0 | 0 | 1 | 1 |
| | **TOTAL** | **7** | **27** | **4,809** | **1,851** | **2,650** | **9,942** | **0.2** | **11** | **2** | **0** | **4** | **2** | **6** | **2** | **2** |
| VICTORIA | PUBLIC | 3 | 29 | 6,625 | 2,950 | 4,142 | 14,905 | | 17 | 0 | 0 | 5 | 0 | 5 | 1 | 1 |
| | NONPUBLIC | 0 | 8 | 1,556 | 0 | 431 | 1,987 | | 1 | 0 | 4 | 0 | 0 | 1 | 1 | 1 |
| | **TOTAL** | **3** | **37** | **8,181** | **2,950** | **4,573** | **16,892** | **0.3** | **18** | **0** | **4** | **5** | **0** | **6** | **2** | **2** |
| WALKER | PUBLIC | 2 | 13 | 3,994 | 1,104 | 2,015 | 7,500 | | 7 | 1 | 0 | 0 | 1 | 2 | 1 | 0 |
| | NONPUBLIC | 0 | 2 | 366 | 0 | 154 | 520 | | 0 | 0 | 0 | 1 | 0 | 0 | 2 | 0 |
| | **TOTAL** | **2** | **15** | **4,360** | **1,104** | **2,169** | **8,020** | **0.2** | **7** | **1** | **0** | **1** | **1** | **2** | **3** | **0** |
| WALLER | PUBLIC | 3 | 15 | 5,549 | 2,632 | 2,906 | 11,700 | | 8 | 0 | 0 | 4 | 0 | 3 | 0 | 0 |
| | NONPUBLIC | 0 | 0 | 0 | 0 | 0 | 0 | | 0 | 0 | 0 | 0 | 0 | 0 | 0 | 0 |
| | **TOTAL** | **3** | **15** | **5,549** | **2,632** | **2,906** | **11,700** | **0.2** | **8** | **0** | **0** | **4** | **0** | **3** | **0** | **0** |
| WARD | PUBLIC | 2 | 7 | 1,534 | 349 | 288 | 2,484 | | 2 | 1 | 0 | 0 | 1 | 2 | 1 | 0 |
| | NONPUBLIC | 0 | 0 | 0 | 0 | 0 | 0 | | 0 | 0 | 0 | 0 | 0 | 0 | 0 | 0 |
| | **TOTAL** | **2** | **7** | **1,534** | **349** | **288** | **2,484** | **0.1** | **2** | **1** | **0** | **0** | **1** | **2** | **1** | **0** |
| WASHINGTON | PUBLIC | 2 | 9 | 2,518 | 785 | 1,688 | 5,440 | | 3 | 2 | 0 | 0 | 1 | 3 | 0 | 0 |
| | NONPUBLIC | 0 | 4 | 384 | 0 | 0 | 384 | | 1 | 1 | 2 | 0 | 0 | 0 | 0 | 0 |
| | **TOTAL** | **2** | **13** | **2,902** | **785** | **1,688** | **5,824** | **0.1** | **4** | **3** | **2** | **0** | **1** | **3** | **0** | **0** |
| WEBB | PUBLIC | 3 | 84 | 30,113 | 14,529 | 19,611 | 72,149 | | 50 | 0 | 0 | 16 | 0 | 16 | 2 | 0 |
| | NONPUBLIC | 0 | 5 | 1,554 | 0 | 627 | 2,181 | | 0 | 0 | 4 | 0 | 0 | 1 | 0 | 0 |
| | **TOTAL** | **3** | **89** | **31,667** | **14,529** | **20,238** | **74,330** | **1.4** | **50** | **0** | **4** | **16** | **0** | **17** | **2** | **0** |

[1] **Elem Enroll** is the school by school total of enrollments in K-4, K-5, K-6, K-8 schools, elementary and middle/JHS students in K-12 schools and students in special ed schools. Public enrollments include public and county-operated schools.

[2] **Middle/JHS Enroll** is the school by school total of enrollments in 5-8 and 7-9 public schools. Public enrollments include public and county-operated schools. Private middle/JHS enrollments are included in Senior Enroll.

[3] **Senior Enroll** is the school by school total of enrollments in 7-12 and 9-12 schools, the secondary students in K-12 schools and students in vocational ed schools. Public enrollments include public and county-operated schools. For private schools, Senior Enroll includes middle/JHS enrollment plus senior enrollment.

[4] **Public Total Enroll** columns are not the sum of school building enrollments. They are projected district-wide Fall enrollments provided to MDR by each school district office, plus county-operated school enrollments.

[5] **K-5** includes pre-kindergarten, kindergarten, K-3, K-4, K-5 schools.

[6] **5-8** includes schools with low grades of 4, 5, 6 and high grades of 7, 8, 9 (e.g., 4-8, 5-8, 6-8, 6-9).

[7] **7-9** includes schools with low grades of 7, 8 and high grades of 7, 8 and 9 (e.g., 7-7, 7-8, 7-9, 8-9).

[8] **7-12** includes 7-12, 8-12, 9-12, 10-12, etc.

[9] **K-12** includes schools with both elementary and secondary grades.

[10] **Other** includes special ed, vocational and adult schools.

**\*Public State Totals** for all columns can exceed the sum of the counties because state totals include state-operated schools and their enrollments

| COUNTY | | DISTRICTS | SCHOOLS | ELEM ENROLL[1] | MIDDLE/JHS ENROLL[2] | SENIOR ENROLL[3] | TOTAL ENROLL[4] | % OF STATE | K-5[5] | K-6 | K-8 | 5-8[6] | 7-9[7] | 7-12[8] | K-12[9] | OTHER[10] |
|---|---|---|---|---|---|---|---|---|---|---|---|---|---|---|---|---|
| **WHARTON** | PUBLIC | 5 | 19 | 3,942 | 1,822 | 2,566 | 9,112 | | 7 | 1 | 0 | 4 | 1 | 6 | 0 | 0 |
| | NONPUBLIC | 0 | 2 | 401 | 0 | 29 | 430 | | 0 | 0 | 1 | 0 | 0 | 0 | 1 | 0 |
| | **TOTAL** | **5** | **21** | **4,343** | **1,822** | **2,595** | **9,542** | **0.2** | **7** | **1** | **1** | **4** | **1** | **6** | **1** | **0** |
| **WHEELER** | PUBLIC | 4 | 6 | 638 | 79 | 296 | 1,013 | | 1 | 0 | 0 | 1 | 0 | 1 | 3 | 0 |
| | NONPUBLIC | 0 | 0 | 0 | 0 | 0 | 0 | | 0 | 0 | 0 | 0 | 0 | 0 | 0 | 0 |
| | **TOTAL** | **4** | **6** | **638** | **79** | **296** | **1,013** | | **1** | **0** | **0** | **1** | **0** | **1** | **3** | **0** |
| **WICHITA** | PUBLIC | 5 | 43 | 10,011 | 3,782 | 4,534 | 20,583 | | 24 | 3 | 0 | 5 | 0 | 7 | 3 | 1 |
| | NONPUBLIC | 0 | 4 | 511 | 0 | 211 | 722 | | 0 | 0 | 0 | 0 | 0 | 0 | 4 | 0 |
| | **TOTAL** | **5** | **47** | **10,522** | **3,782** | **4,745** | **21,305** | **0.4** | **24** | **3** | **0** | **5** | **0** | **7** | **7** | **1** |
| **WILBARGER** | PUBLIC | 3 | 8 | 1,156 | 299 | 250 | 2,028 | | 3 | 0 | 0 | 1 | 0 | 1 | 3 | 0 |
| | NONPUBLIC | 0 | 0 | 0 | 0 | 0 | 0 | | 0 | 0 | 0 | 0 | 0 | 0 | 0 | 0 |
| | **TOTAL** | **3** | **8** | **1,156** | **299** | **250** | **2,028** | | **3** | **0** | **0** | **1** | **0** | **1** | **3** | **0** |
| **WILLACY** | PUBLIC | 4 | 11 | 1,916 | 502 | 1,258 | 4,059 | | 3 | 0 | 1 | 2 | 0 | 4 | 1 | 0 |
| | NONPUBLIC | 0 | 0 | 0 | 0 | 0 | 0 | | 0 | 0 | 0 | 0 | 0 | 0 | 0 | 0 |
| | **TOTAL** | **4** | **11** | **1,916** | **502** | **1,258** | **4,059** | **0.1** | **3** | **0** | **1** | **2** | **0** | **4** | **1** | **0** |
| **WILLIAMSON** | PUBLIC | 11 | 152 | 57,036 | 27,288 | 35,933 | 125,838 | | 89 | 1 | 1 | 30 | 1 | 24 | 5 | 1 |
| | NONPUBLIC | 0 | 14 | 2,526 | 0 | 761 | 3,287 | | 1 | 2 | 6 | 0 | 0 | 2 | 3 | 0 |
| | **TOTAL** | **11** | **166** | **59,562** | **27,288** | **36,694** | **129,125** | **2.4** | **90** | **3** | **7** | **30** | **1** | **26** | **8** | **1** |
| **WILSON** | PUBLIC | 4 | 15 | 3,552 | 1,524 | 1,872 | 7,078 | | 6 | 0 | 0 | 4 | 0 | 4 | 1 | 0 |
| | NONPUBLIC | 0 | 2 | 135 | 0 | 5 | 140 | | 0 | 1 | 0 | 0 | 0 | 0 | 1 | 0 |
| | **TOTAL** | **4** | **17** | **3,687** | **1,524** | **1,877** | **7,218** | **0.1** | **6** | **1** | **0** | **4** | **0** | **4** | **2** | **0** |
| **WINKLER** | PUBLIC | 2 | 5 | 820 | 453 | 567 | 1,817 | | 1 | 1 | 0 | 1 | 0 | 2 | 0 | 0 |
| | NONPUBLIC | 0 | 0 | 0 | 0 | 0 | 0 | | 0 | 0 | 0 | 0 | 0 | 0 | 0 | 0 |
| | **TOTAL** | **2** | **5** | **820** | **453** | **567** | **1,817** | **0.1** | **1** | **1** | **0** | **1** | **0** | **2** | **0** | **0** |
| **WISE** | PUBLIC | 8 | 33 | 5,419 | 2,469 | 3,650 | 11,941 | | 15 | 1 | 0 | 6 | 1 | 7 | 3 | 0 |
| | NONPUBLIC | 0 | 1 | 286 | 0 | 115 | 401 | | 0 | 0 | 0 | 0 | 0 | 0 | 1 | 0 |
| | **TOTAL** | **8** | **34** | **5,705** | **2,469** | **3,765** | **12,342** | **0.2** | **15** | **1** | **0** | **6** | **1** | **7** | **4** | **0** |
| **WOOD** | PUBLIC | 6 | 17 | 2,769 | 1,298 | 1,623 | 5,749 | | 7 | 0 | 0 | 4 | 0 | 4 | 2 | 0 |
| | NONPUBLIC | 0 | 0 | 0 | 0 | 0 | 0 | | 0 | 0 | 0 | 0 | 0 | 0 | 0 | 0 |
| | **TOTAL** | **6** | **17** | **2,769** | **1,298** | **1,623** | **5,749** | **0.1** | **7** | **0** | **0** | **4** | **0** | **4** | **2** | **0** |
| **YOAKUM** | PUBLIC | 2 | 8 | 1,029 | 528 | 614 | 2,216 | | 3 | 0 | 0 | 2 | 0 | 3 | 0 | 0 |
| | NONPUBLIC | 0 | 0 | 0 | 0 | 0 | 0 | | 0 | 0 | 0 | 0 | 0 | 0 | 0 | 0 |
| | **TOTAL** | **2** | **8** | **1,029** | **528** | **614** | **2,216** | | **3** | **0** | **0** | **2** | **0** | **3** | **0** | **0** |
| **YOUNG** | PUBLIC | 3 | 9 | 1,604 | 703 | 584 | 3,198 | | 4 | 0 | 0 | 2 | 0 | 2 | 0 | 0 |
| | NONPUBLIC | 0 | 1 | 120 | 0 | 0 | 120 | | 0 | 1 | 0 | 0 | 0 | 0 | 1 | 0 |
| | **TOTAL** | **3** | **10** | **1,724** | **703** | **584** | **3,318** | **0.1** | **4** | **1** | **0** | **2** | **0** | **2** | **1** | **0** |

[1] **Elem Enroll** is the school by school total of enrollments in K-4, K-5, K-6, K-8 schools, elementary and middle/JHS students in K-12 schools and students in special ed schools. Public enrollments include public and county-operated schools.

[2] **Middle/JHS Enroll** is the school by school total of enrollments in 5-8 and 7-9 public schools. Public enrollments include public and county-operated schools. Private middle/JHS enrollments are included in Senior Enroll.

[3] **Senior Enroll** is the school by school total of enrollments in 7-12 and 9-12 schools, the secondary students in K-12 schools and students in vocational ed schools. Public enrollments include public and county-operated schools. For private schools, Senior Enroll includes middle/JHS enrollment plus senior enrollment.

[4] **Public Total Enroll** columns are not the sum of school building enrollments. They are projected district-wide Fall enrollments provided to MDR by each school district office, plus county-operated school enrollments.

[5] **K-5** includes pre-kindergarten, kindergarten, K-3, K-4, K-5 schools.

[6] **5-8** includes schools with low grades of 4, 5, 6 and high grades of 7, 8, 9 (e.g., 4-8, 5-8, 6-8, 6-9).

[7] **7-9** includes schools with low grades of 7, 8 and high grades of 7, 8, 9 (e.g., 7-7, 7-8, 7-9, 8-9).

[8] **7-12** includes 7-12, 8-12, 9-12, 10-12, etc.

[9] **K-12** includes schools with both elementary and secondary grades.

[10] **Other** includes special ed, vocational and adult schools.

***Public State Totals** for all columns can exceed the sum of the counties because state totals include state-operated schools and their enrollments

| COUNTY | | DISTRICTS | SCHOOLS | ELEM ENROLL[1] | MIDDLE/JHS ENROLL[2] | SENIOR ENROLL[3] | TOTAL ENROLL[4] | % OF STATE | SCHOOLS BY GRADE SPAN | | | | | | | |
|---|---|---|---|---|---|---|---|---|---|---|---|---|---|---|---|---|
| | | | | | | | | | K-5[5] | K-6 | K-8 | 5-8[6] | 7-9[7] | 7-12[8] | K-12[9] | OTHER[10] |
| ZAPATA | PUBLIC | 1 | 6 | 1,482 | 771 | 947 | 3,500 | | 4 | 0 | 0 | 1 | 0 | 1 | 0 | 0 |
| | NONPUBLIC | 0 | 0 | 0 | 0 | 0 | 0 | | 0 | 0 | 0 | 1 | 0 | 0 | 0 | 0 |
| | TOTAL | 1 | 6 | 1,482 | 771 | 947 | 3,500 | 0.1 | 4 | 0 | 0 | 1 | 0 | 1 | 0 | 0 |
| ZAVALA | PUBLIC | 2 | 7 | 1,398 | 301 | 741 | 2,450 | | 2 | 2 | 0 | 0 | 1 | 2 | 0 | 0 |
| | NONPUBLIC | 0 | 0 | 0 | 0 | 0 | 0 | | 0 | 0 | 0 | 0 | 0 | 0 | 0 | 0 |
| | TOTAL | 2 | 7 | 1,398 | 301 | 741 | 2,450 | 0.1 | 2 | 2 | 0 | 0 | 1 | 2 | 0 | 0 |
| STATE TOTAL | PUBLIC* | 1,026 | 8,785 | 2,494,643 | 1,012,232 | 1,427,816 | 5,438,946 | | 3,936 | 564 | 118 | 1,191 | 236 | 1,469 | 454 | 74 |
| | NONPUBLIC | 0 | 975 | 181,568 | | 62,035 | 243,603 | | 115 | 88 | 299 | 7 | 0 | 80 | 353 | 33 |
| | TOTAL | 1,026 | 9,760 | 2,676,211 | 1,012,232 | 1,489,851 | 5,682,549 | | 4,051 | 652 | 417 | 1,198 | 236 | 1,549 | 807 | 107 |

[1] **Elem Enroll** is the school by school total of enrollments in K-4, K-5, K-6, K-8 schools, elementary and middle/JHS students in K-12 schools and students in special ed schools. Public enrollments include public and county-operated schools.

[2] **Middle/JHS Enroll** is the school by school total of enrollments in 5-8 and 7-9 public schools. Public enrollments include public and county-operated schools. Private middle/JHS enrollments are included in Senior Enroll.

[3] **Senior Enroll** is the school by school total of enrollments in 7-12 and 9-12 schools, the secondary students in K-12 schools and students in vocational ed schools. Public enrollments include public and county-operated schools. For private schools, Senior Enroll includes middle/JHS enrollment plus senior enrollment.

[4] **Public Total Enroll** columns are not the sum of school building enrollments. They are projected district-wide Fall enrollments provided to MDR by each school district office, plus county-operated school enrollments.

[5] **K-5** includes pre-kindergarten, kindergarten, K-3, K-4, K-5 schools

[6] **5-8** includes schools with low grades of 4, 5, 6 and high grades of 7, 8, 9 (e.g., 4-8, 5-8, 6-8, 6-9).

[7] **7-9** includes schools with low grades of 7, 8 and high grades of 7, 8, 9 (e.g., 7-7, 7-8, 7-9, 8-9).

[8] **7-12** includes 7-12, 8-12, 9-12, 10-12, etc.

[9] **K-12** includes schools with both elementary and secondary grades.

[10] **Other** includes special ed, vocational and adult schools.

**\*Public State Totals** for all columns can exceed the sum of the counties because state totals include state-operated schools and their enrollments.

## DISTRICT BUYING POWER INDEX
### COUNTIES RANKED BY PERCENTAGE OF STATE SPENDING

| COUNTY<br>DISTRICT | PID | COUNTY %<br>OF STATE | DISTRICT %<br>OF COUNTY | DISTRICT %<br>OF STATE | NUMBER OF<br>SCHOOLS | ENROLL | EXP | POV |
|---|---|---|---|---|---|---|---|---|
| **HARRIS** | | 10.21 | | | | | | |
| Houston Ind School Dist | 01023770 | | 27.68 | 2.83 | 276 | 207,809 | MED | HIGH |
| Alief Ind School Dist | 01022972 | | 12.76 | 1.30 | 46 | 46,000 | HIGH | HIGH |
| Cypress-Fairbanks Ind Sch Dist | 01023184 | | 10.33 | 1.05 | 92 | 113,256 | LOW | MED-LOW |
| Pasadena Ind School Dist | 01026631 | | 9.23 | 0.94 | 68 | 53,157 | HIGH | MED-HIGH |
| Humble Ind School Dist | 01026150 | | 6.96 | 0.71 | 47 | 43,189 | MED | MED-LOW |
| Aldine Ind School Dist | 01022697 | | 5.14 | 0.52 | 82 | 67,331 | LOW | HIGH |
| Goose Creek Cons Ind Sch Dist | 01023562 | | 4.31 | 0.44 | 28 | 24,000 | HIGH | MED-HIGH |
| Klein Ind School Dist | 01026289 | | 3.93 | 0.40 | 49 | 53,292 | LOW | MED-LOW |
| Spring Branch Ind School Dist | 01027087 | | 3.90 | 0.40 | 47 | 35,300 | MED | MED-HIGH |
| Galena Park Ind School Dist | 01023419 | | 3.73 | 0.38 | 27 | 21,045 | MED | MED-HIGH |
| Spring Ind School Dist | 01027465 | | 3.61 | 0.37 | 41 | 35,600 | LOW | MED-HIGH |
| Channelview Ind School Dist | 01023079 | | 1.80 | 0.18 | 13 | 9,700 | HIGH | MED-HIGH |
| Tomball Ind School Dist | 01027568 | | 1.59 | 0.16 | 20 | 16,289 | LOW | MED-LOW |
| Sheldon Ind School Dist | 01027013 | | 1.55 | 0.16 | 12 | 8,500 | HIGH | MED-HIGH |
| Deer Park Ind School Dist | 01023316 | | 1.16 | 0.12 | 16 | 13,000 | LOW | MED-LOW |
| La Porte Ind School Dist | 01026370 | | 1.11 | 0.11 | 13 | 7,679 | MED | MED-LOW |
| Huffman Ind School Dist | 01026112 | | 0.99 | 0.10 | 4 | 3,600 | HIGH | MED-LOW |
| Crosby Ind School Dist | 01023134 | | 0.21 | 0.02 | 7 | 6,350 | LOW | MED-HIGH |
| **DALLAS** | | 8.62 | | | | | | |
| Dallas Ind School Dist | 01008354 | | 30.72 | 2.65 | 233 | 153,861 | HIGH | MED-HIGH |
| Garland Ind School Dist | 01010395 | | 18.86 | 1.63 | 72 | 55,848 | HIGH | MED-HIGH |
| Mesquite Ind School Dist | 01011399 | | 10.90 | 0.94 | 48 | 38,266 | HIGH | MED-HIGH |
| Irving Ind School Dist | 01011105 | | 9.80 | 0.84 | 38 | 33,901 | HIGH | MED-HIGH |
| Grand Prairie Ind School Dist | 01010814 | | 7.82 | 0.67 | 42 | 29,334 | HIGH | MED-HIGH |
| Carrollton-Farmers Branch ISD | 01008134 | | 4.68 | 0.40 | 37 | 24,500 | MED | MED-LOW |
| Richardson Ind School Dist | 01011624 | | 4.01 | 0.35 | 56 | 38,700 | LOW | MED-HIGH |
| Duncanville Ind School Dist | 01010292 | | 3.92 | 0.34 | 19 | 12,250 | HIGH | MED-HIGH |
| Coppell Ind School Dist | 01008328 | | 2.45 | 0.21 | 18 | 13,500 | HIGH | LOW |
| DeSoto Ind School Dist | 01010242 | | 2.10 | 0.18 | 14 | 9,872 | HIGH | MED-HIGH |
| Cedar Hill Ind School Dist | 01008275 | | 1.87 | 0.16 | 14 | 7,866 | HIGH | MED-LOW |
| Lancaster Ind School Dist | 01011337 | | 1.29 | 0.11 | 11 | 7,600 | MED | MED-HIGH |
| Highland Park Ind Sch Dist | 01011038 | | 1.12 | 0.10 | 8 | 7,000 | MED | LOW |
| Sunnyvale Ind School Dist | 01012018 | | 0.47 | 0.04 | 3 | 2,200 | HIGH | LOW |
| **TARRANT** | | 6.15 | | | | | | |
| Ft Worth Ind School Dist | 01052525 | | 26.72 | 1.64 | 134 | 89,000 | HIGH | MED-HIGH |
| Keller Ind School Dist | 01053983 | | 11.68 | 0.72 | 42 | 35,352 | HIGH | LOW |
| Arlington Ind School Dist | 01051624 | | 11.15 | 0.69 | 78 | 59,500 | MED | MED-HIGH |
| Mansfield Ind School Dist | 01054119 | | 8.88 | 0.55 | 46 | 35,626 | MED | MED-LOW |
| Hurst-Euless-Bedford ISD | 01053737 | | 7.73 | 0.48 | 31 | 23,000 | HIGH | MED-LOW |
| Birdville Ind School Dist | 01052032 | | 5.97 | 0.37 | 33 | 23,513 | MED | MED-HIGH |
| Eagle Mtn-Saginaw Ind Sch Dist | 01052408 | | 5.26 | 0.32 | 27 | 21,000 | HIGH | MED-LOW |
| Crowley Ind School Dist | 01052355 | | 4.48 | 0.28 | 25 | 15,215 | HIGH | MED-LOW |
| Everman Ind School Dist | 01052460 | | 3.50 | 0.22 | 11 | 6,345 | HIGH | MED-HIGH |
| Azle Ind School Dist | 01051973 | | 2.94 | 0.18 | 12 | 5,900 | HIGH | MED-LOW |
| White Settlement Ind Sch Dist | 01054183 | | 2.81 | 0.17 | 9 | 6,909 | HIGH | MED-LOW |
| Grapevine-Colleyville Ind SD | 01053672 | | 2.74 | 0.17 | 21 | 14,000 | MED | LOW |
| Castleberry Ind School Dist | 01052290 | | 1.79 | 0.11 | 7 | 3,574 | HIGH | MED-HIGH |
| Carroll Independent Sch Dist | 01052252 | | 1.71 | 0.11 | 11 | 8,000 | MED | LOW |
| Lake Worth Ind School Dist | 01054078 | | 1.64 | 0.10 | 6 | 3,000 | HIGH | MED-HIGH |
| Kennedale Ind School Dist | 01054030 | | 0.99 | 0.06 | 6 | 3,000 | HIGH | MED-LOW |
| **BEXAR** | | 5.98 | | | | | | |
| Northside Ind School Dist | 00998017 | | 31.32 | 1.87 | 124 | 106,863 | HIGH | MED-LOW |
| San Antonio Ind School Dist | 00998366 | | 17.93 | 1.07 | 94 | 48,178 | HIGH | HIGH |
| North East Ind School Dist | 00997661 | | 16.27 | 0.97 | 74 | 66,759 | MED | MED-LOW |
| Harlandale Ind School Dist | 00997350 | | 6.45 | 0.39 | 24 | 14,500 | HIGH | HIGH |
| Judson Ind School Dist | 00997582 | | 5.10 | 0.30 | 33 | 23,000 | MED | MED-HIGH |
| South San Antonio Ind Sch Dist | 00999384 | | 4.51 | 0.27 | 16 | 8,800 | HIGH | HIGH |
| Southwest Ind School Dist | 00999578 | | 4.47 | 0.27 | 19 | 13,928 | HIGH | MED-HIGH |
| Edgewood Ind School Dist | 00997075 | | 3.92 | 0.23 | 21 | 10,881 | HIGH | HIGH |
| East Central Ind School Dist | 00996992 | | 3.37 | 0.20 | 12 | 10,146 | HIGH | MED-HIGH |
| Southside Ind School Dist | 00999516 | | 1.83 | 0.11 | 9 | 5,800 | HIGH | MED-HIGH |
| Somerset Ind School Dist | 00999346 | | 1.69 | 0.10 | 7 | 3,990 | HIGH | MED-HIGH |
| Ft Sam Houston Ind School Dist | 01534949 | | 1.15 | 0.07 | 2 | 1,560 | HIGH | MED-LOW |
| Randolph Field Ind School Dist | 01601786 | | 0.77 | 0.05 | 3 | 1,442 | HIGH | MED-LOW |
| Alamo Heights Ind School Dist | 00996928 | | 0.63 | 0.04 | 5 | 4,800 | LOW | MED-LOW |
| Lackland Ind School Dist | 01808829 | | 0.60 | 0.04 | 2 | 1,000 | HIGH | MED-LOW |
| **HIDALGO** | | 5.15 | | | | | | |
| Pharr-San Juan-Alamo Ind SD | 01030333 | | 19.19 | 0.99 | 42 | 32,000 | HIGH | HIGH |
| La Joya Ind School Dist | 01029841 | | 18.72 | 0.96 | 41 | 27,000 | HIGH | HIGH |
| Edinburg Cons Ind School Dist | 01029671 | | 16.40 | 0.84 | 43 | 34,500 | HIGH | HIGH |

## DISTRICT BUYING POWER INDEX
### COUNTIES RANKED BY PERCENTAGE OF STATE SPENDING

| COUNTY<br>DISTRICT | PID | COUNTY %<br>OF STATE | DISTRICT %<br>OF COUNTY | DISTRICT %<br>OF STATES | NUMBER OF<br>SCHOOLS | ENROLL | EXP | POV |
|---|---|---|---|---|---|---|---|---|
| McAllen Ind School Dist | 01029918 | | 10.84 | 0.56 | 31 | 24,000 | HIGH | HIGH |
| Mission Cons Ind School Dist | 01030228 | | 9.03 | 0.47 | 23 | 16,000 | HIGH | HIGH |
| Donna Ind School Dist | 01029554 | | 5.25 | 0.27 | 22 | 14,459 | HIGH | HIGH |
| Weslaco Ind School Dist | 01030589 | | 5.18 | 0.27 | 19 | 18,000 | MED | HIGH |
| Sharyland Ind School Dist | 01030527 | | 4.53 | 0.23 | 14 | 10,295 | HIGH | MED-HIGH |
| Edcouch Elsa Ind School Dist | 01029621 | | 3.04 | 0.16 | 8 | 5,450 | HIGH | HIGH |
| Mercedes Ind School Dist | 01030149 | | 2.62 | 0.14 | 9 | 4,781 | HIGH | HIGH |
| Valley View Ind School Dist | 01030565 | | 1.60 | 0.08 | 8 | 4,300 | HIGH | HIGH |
| Hidalgo Ind School Dist | 01029827 | | 1.26 | 0.06 | 7 | 2,600 | HIGH | HIGH |
| Monte Alto Ind School Dist | 01030319 | | 1.23 | 0.06 | 3 | 900 | HIGH | HIGH |
| Progreso Ind School Dist | 01030503 | | 0.75 | 0.04 | 5 | 1,900 | HIGH | HIGH |
| La Villa Ind School Dist | 01029891 | | 0.35 | 0.02 | 3 | 555 | HIGH | HIGH |
| **EL PASO** | | 4.36 | | | | | | |
| El Paso Ind School Dist | 01015450 | | 36.83 | 1.61 | 86 | 57,315 | HIGH | MED-HIGH |
| Socorro Ind School Dist | 01016208 | | 22.26 | 0.97 | 50 | 44,992 | HIGH | MED-HIGH |
| Ysleta Ind School Dist | 01016296 | | 21.77 | 0.95 | 57 | 40,304 | HIGH | HIGH |
| Clint Ind School Dist | 01015424 | | 7.46 | 0.32 | 14 | 11,522 | HIGH | HIGH |
| Canutillo Ind School Dist | 01015383 | | 4.69 | 0.20 | 10 | 6,200 | HIGH | MED-HIGH |
| San Elizario Ind School Dist | 01016179 | | 3.21 | 0.14 | 6 | 3,560 | HIGH | HIGH |
| Anthony Ind School Dist | 01015357 | | 1.37 | 0.06 | 3 | 795 | HIGH | MED-HIGH |
| Fabens Ind School Dist | 01016129 | | 1.23 | 0.05 | 5 | 2,000 | HIGH | HIGH |
| Tornillo Ind School Dist | 01016260 | | 1.18 | 0.05 | 4 | 950 | HIGH | HIGH |
| **COLLIN** | | 3.17 | | | | | | |
| Plano Ind School Dist | 01006344 | | 25.44 | 0.81 | 73 | 52,692 | MED | MED-LOW |
| Frisco Ind School Dist | 01006186 | | 23.72 | 0.75 | 72 | 63,015 | MED | LOW |
| Wylie Ind School Dist | 01006605 | | 13.78 | 0.44 | 20 | 17,500 | HIGH | MED-LOW |
| McKinney Ind School Dist | 01006241 | | 8.81 | 0.28 | 31 | 24,335 | MED | MED-LOW |
| Prosper Ind School Dist | 01006552 | | 6.46 | 0.20 | 18 | 19,000 | HIGH | LOW |
| Allen Ind School Dist | 01005986 | | 5.58 | 0.18 | 24 | 21,404 | LOW | LOW |
| Princeton Ind School Dist | 01006502 | | 4.16 | 0.13 | 9 | 5,567 | HIGH | MED-LOW |
| Anna Ind School Dist | 01006021 | | 3.38 | 0.11 | 6 | 3,800 | HIGH | MED-LOW |
| Community Ind School Dist | 01006124 | | 2.03 | 0.06 | 4 | 2,600 | HIGH | MED-LOW |
| Lovejoy Ind School Dist | 01006227 | | 1.78 | 0.06 | 6 | 4,424 | MED | LOW |
| Melissa Ind School Dist | 01006320 | | 1.68 | 0.05 | 4 | 3,102 | HIGH | LOW |
| Farmersville Ind School Dist | 01006148 | | 1.63 | 0.05 | 4 | 1,594 | HIGH | MED-LOW |
| Celina Ind School Dist | 01006083 | | 1.15 | 0.04 | 6 | 2,600 | MED | LOW |
| Blue Ridge Ind School Dist | 01006057 | | 0.39 | 0.01 | 3 | 975 | MED | MED-LOW |
| **FORT BEND** | | 3.11 | | | | | | |
| Katy Ind School Dist | 01026227 | | 46.55 | 1.45 | 72 | 84,299 | HIGH | MED-LOW |
| Ft Bend Ind School Dist | 01018115 | | 32.09 | 1.00 | 82 | 79,076 | MED | MED-LOW |
| Lamar Cons Ind School Dist | 01018232 | | 16.36 | 0.51 | 46 | 34,806 | MED | MED-LOW |
| Needville Ind School Dist | 01018347 | | 3.06 | 0.10 | 4 | 3,228 | HIGH | MED-LOW |
| Stafford Municipal Sch Dist | 02228624 | | 1.95 | 0.06 | 7 | 3,600 | HIGH | MED-LOW |
| **TRAVIS** | | 2.62 | | | | | | |
| Austin Ind School Dist | 01055993 | | 46.50 | 1.22 | 117 | 80,950 | MED | MED-HIGH |
| Pflugerville Ind School Dist | 01056935 | | 21.44 | 0.56 | 33 | 26,269 | HIGH | MED-LOW |
| Del Valle Ind School Dist | 01056789 | | 11.79 | 0.31 | 15 | 12,100 | HIGH | MED-HIGH |
| Manor Ind School Dist | 01056894 | | 8.61 | 0.23 | 16 | 9,200 | HIGH | MED-HIGH |
| Lake Travis Ind School Dist | 02178653 | | 7.58 | 0.20 | 10 | 10,410 | HIGH | LOW |
| Eanes Ind School Dist | 01056844 | | 3.06 | 0.08 | 9 | 8,156 | LOW | LOW |
| Lago Vista Ind School Dist | 01056870 | | 1.02 | 0.03 | 4 | 1,500 | HIGH | MED-LOW |
| **CAMERON** | | 2.28 | | | | | | |
| Brownsville Ind School Dist | 01003445 | | 41.24 | 0.94 | 54 | 44,356 | HIGH | HIGH |
| San Benito Cons Ind Sch Dist | 01004140 | | 15.22 | 0.35 | 18 | 10,600 | HIGH | HIGH |
| Harlingen Cons Ind School Dist | 01003756 | | 13.36 | 0.31 | 31 | 18,600 | HIGH | HIGH |
| Los Fresnos Cons Ind Sch Dist | 01004009 | | 9.90 | 0.23 | 16 | 10,379 | HIGH | MED-HIGH |
| South Texas Ind School Dist | 01808984 | | 9.51 | 0.22 | 6 | 4,245 | HIGH | |
| La Feria Ind School Dist | 01003940 | | 4.60 | 0.11 | 7 | 2,880 | HIGH | MED-HIGH |
| Rio Hondo Ind School Dist | 01004102 | | 2.02 | 0.05 | 3 | 1,650 | HIGH | MED-HIGH |
| Santa Rosa Ind School Dist | 01004322 | | 1.63 | 0.04 | 3 | 960 | HIGH | HIGH |
| Point Isabel Ind Sch Dist | 01004061 | | 1.55 | 0.04 | 4 | 2,017 | MED | HIGH |
| Santa Maria Ind School Dist | 01004308 | | 0.97 | 0.02 | 4 | 691 | HIGH | HIGH |
| **DENTON** | | 2.28 | | | | | | |
| Lewisville Ind School Dist | 01013402 | | 36.04 | 0.82 | 71 | 52,300 | MED | MED-LOW |
| Denton Ind School Dist | 01013220 | | 19.99 | 0.46 | 42 | 33,485 | MED | MED-LOW |
| Northwest Ind School Dist | 01013517 | | 18.55 | 0.42 | 31 | 25,000 | HIGH | LOW |
| Little Elm Ind School Dist | 01013490 | | 8.30 | 0.19 | 9 | 8,100 | HIGH | MED-LOW |
| Lake Dallas Ind School Dist | 01013373 | | 3.28 | 0.07 | 5 | 4,000 | HIGH | MED-LOW |
| Sanger Ind School Dist | 01013646 | | 3.11 | 0.07 | 7 | 2,660 | HIGH | MED-LOW |
| Aubrey Ind School Dist | 01013191 | | 2.95 | 0.07 | 5 | 2,500 | HIGH | MED-LOW |
| Ponder Ind School Dist | 01013610 | | 2.67 | 0.06 | 3 | 1,600 | HIGH | MED-HIGH |

## DISTRICT BUYING POWER INDEX
### COUNTIES RANKED BY PERCENTAGE OF STATE SPENDING

| COUNTY<br>DISTRICT | PID | COUNTY %<br>OF STATE | DISTRICT %<br>OF COUNTY | DISTRICT %<br>OF STATES | NUMBER OF<br>SCHOOLS | ENROLL | EXP | POV |
|---|---|---|---|---|---|---|---|---|
| Argyle Ind School Dist | 01013177 | | 2.24 | 0.05 | 5 | 3,100 | HIGH | LOW |
| Krum Ind School Dist | 01013347 | | 1.79 | 0.04 | 5 | 2,100 | HIGH | MED-LOW |
| Pilot Point Ind School Dist | 01013581 | | 1.08 | 0.02 | 4 | 1,400 | HIGH | MED-LOW |
| **WILLIAMSON** | | 1.92 | | | | | | |
| Leander Ind School Dist | 01061007 | | 34.24 | 0.66 | 44 | 43,000 | HIGH | LOW |
| Round Rock Ind School Dist | 01061083 | | 31.30 | 0.60 | 54 | 51,008 | MED | MED-LOW |
| Hutto Ind School Dist | 01060948 | | 10.82 | 0.21 | 10 | 8,129 | HIGH | MED-LOW |
| Georgetown Ind School Dist | 01060869 | | 8.47 | 0.16 | 18 | 12,403 | MED | MED-LOW |
| Liberty Hill Ind School Dist | 01061069 | | 4.30 | 0.08 | 6 | 4,000 | HIGH | LOW |
| Taylor Ind School Dist | 01061162 | | 4.22 | 0.08 | 7 | 3,200 | HIGH | MED-LOW |
| Jarrell Ind School Dist | 01060974 | | 2.90 | 0.06 | 5 | 1,800 | HIGH | MED-LOW |
| Florence Ind School Dist | 01060833 | | 1.66 | 0.03 | 3 | 957 | HIGH | MED-LOW |
| Thrall Ind School Dist | 01061227 | | 0.96 | 0.02 | 3 | 750 | HIGH | MED-LOW |
| Granger Ind School Dist | 01060912 | | 0.90 | 0.02 | 1 | 426 | HIGH | MED-LOW |
| Coupland Ind School Dist | 01060819 | | 0.24 | 0.00 | 1 | 165 | HIGH | MED-HIGH |
| **MONTGOMERY** | | 1.74 | | | | | | |
| Conroe Ind School Dist | 01042439 | | 54.32 | 0.94 | 65 | 64,500 | MED | MED-LOW |
| Magnolia Ind School Dist | 01042582 | | 15.51 | 0.27 | 16 | 13,100 | HIGH | MED-HIGH |
| New Caney Ind School Dist | 01042661 | | 13.68 | 0.24 | 19 | 15,000 | MED | MED-HIGH |
| Splendora Ind School Dist | 01042726 | | 6.18 | 0.11 | 6 | 4,200 | HIGH | MED-LOW |
| Montgomery Ind School Dist | 01042623 | | 5.92 | 0.10 | 10 | 9,048 | MED | MED-LOW |
| Willis Ind School Dist | 01042764 | | 4.38 | 0.08 | 9 | 6,709 | LOW | MED-LOW |
| **BELL** | | 1.49 | | | | | | |
| Killeen Ind School Dist | 00996423 | | 64.65 | 0.96 | 53 | 45,500 | HIGH | MED-HIGH |
| Belton Ind School Dist | 00996318 | | 13.47 | 0.20 | 17 | 11,950 | HIGH | MED-LOW |
| Temple Ind School Dist | 00996708 | | 12.16 | 0.18 | 15 | 8,700 | HIGH | MED-HIGH |
| Salado Ind School Dist | 00996679 | | 3.59 | 0.05 | 3 | 2,056 | HIGH | MED-LOW |
| Troy Ind School Dist | 00996899 | | 2.55 | 0.04 | 4 | 1,600 | HIGH | MED-LOW |
| Academy Ind School Dist | 00996253 | | 1.22 | 0.02 | 5 | 1,602 | MED | MED-LOW |
| Rogers Ind School Dist | 00996643 | | 1.11 | 0.02 | 3 | 869 | HIGH | MED-LOW |
| Holland Ind School Dist | 00996394 | | 0.84 | 0.01 | 3 | 636 | HIGH | MED-HIGH |
| Bartlett Ind School Dist | 00996289 | | 0.40 | 0.01 | 3 | 380 | HIGH | MED-HIGH |
| **WEBB** | | 1.46 | | | | | | |
| United Ind School Dist | 01059470 | | 60.01 | 0.87 | 48 | 48,174 | HIGH | MED-HIGH |
| Laredo Ind School Dist | 01059183 | | 38.69 | 0.56 | 33 | 23,737 | HIGH | HIGH |
| Webb Cons Ind School Dist | 01059145 | | 1.30 | 0.02 | 3 | 238 | HIGH | HIGH |
| **NUECES** | | 1.37 | | | | | | |
| Corpus Christi Ind Sch Dist | 01044176 | | 58.80 | 0.81 | 58 | 37,000 | HIGH | MED-HIGH |
| Tuloso-Midway Ind School Dist | 01045015 | | 8.56 | 0.12 | 5 | 3,043 | HIGH | MED-HIGH |
| Flour Bluff Ind School Dist | 01044815 | | 8.20 | 0.11 | 7 | 5,750 | HIGH | MED-LOW |
| Calallen Ind School Dist | 01044114 | | 6.74 | 0.09 | 5 | 3,914 | HIGH | MED-LOW |
| Robstown Ind School Dist | 01044906 | | 5.71 | 0.08 | 7 | 2,000 | HIGH | HIGH |
| West Oso Ind School Dist | 01045065 | | 3.70 | 0.05 | 4 | 1,946 | HIGH | MED-HIGH |
| Bishop Cons Ind School Dist | 01044059 | | 2.57 | 0.04 | 5 | 1,380 | HIGH | MED-HIGH |
| Banquete Ind School Dist | 01044011 | | 2.26 | 0.03 | 3 | 900 | HIGH | MED-HIGH |
| London Ind School Dist | 01044865 | | 1.38 | 0.02 | 1 | 900 | HIGH | MED-LOW |
| Agua Dulce Ind School Dist | 01043988 | | 0.74 | 0.01 | 2 | 374 | HIGH | MED-HIGH |
| Driscoll Ind School Dist | 01044798 | | 0.68 | 0.01 | 1 | 281 | HIGH | MED-HIGH |
| Port Aransas Ind School Dist | 01044889 | | 0.67 | 0.01 | 3 | 480 | HIGH | MED-LOW |
| **LUBBOCK** | | 1.34 | | | | | | |
| Lubbock Ind School Dist | 01038490 | | 60.94 | 0.82 | 48 | 26,000 | HIGH | MED-HIGH |
| Frenship Ind School Dist | 01038402 | | 17.44 | 0.23 | 13 | 9,900 | HIGH | MED-LOW |
| Lubbock-Cooper Ind Sch Dist | 01039030 | | 8.15 | 0.11 | 9 | 6,000 | HIGH | MED-LOW |
| Slaton Ind School Dist | 01039195 | | 3.62 | 0.05 | 4 | 950 | HIGH | MED-HIGH |
| Roosevelt Ind School Dist | 01039119 | | 2.96 | 0.04 | 3 | 1,012 | HIGH | MED-HIGH |
| Shallowater Ind School Dist | 01039157 | | 2.79 | 0.04 | 4 | 1,351 | HIGH | MED-LOW |
| Idalou Ind School Dist | 01038452 | | 2.60 | 0.03 | 3 | 984 | HIGH | MED-LOW |
| New Deal Ind School Dist | 01039080 | | 1.50 | 0.02 | 3 | 750 | HIGH | MED-HIGH |
| **BRAZORIA** | | 1.29 | | | | | | |
| Alvin Ind School Dist | 01001382 | | 43.95 | 0.57 | 31 | 25,926 | HIGH | MED-LOW |
| Pearland Ind School Dist | 01001849 | | 19.18 | 0.25 | 23 | 21,917 | MED | MED-LOW |
| Brazosport Ind School Dist | 01001540 | | 17.82 | 0.23 | 19 | 12,000 | HIGH | MED-HIGH |
| Angleton Ind School Dist | 01001473 | | 7.38 | 0.10 | 9 | 6,787 | MED | MED-LOW |
| Columbia Brazoria ISD | 01001710 | | 5.38 | 0.07 | 5 | 2,681 | HIGH | MED-LOW |
| Sweeny Ind School Dist | 01001904 | | 3.40 | 0.04 | 3 | 1,926 | HIGH | MED-HIGH |
| Danbury Ind School Dist | 01001813 | | 2.02 | 0.03 | 3 | 840 | HIGH | MED-LOW |
| Damon Ind School Dist | 01001796 | | 0.86 | 0.01 | 1 | 144 | HIGH | MED-HIGH |
| **GALVESTON** | | 1.29 | | | | | | |
| Clear Creek Ind School Dist | 01018816 | | 41.40 | 0.53 | 46 | 42,042 | MED | MED-LOW |

## DISTRICT BUYING POWER INDEX
### COUNTIES RANKED BY PERCENTAGE OF STATE SPENDING

| COUNTY<br>DISTRICT | PID | COUNTY %<br>OF STATE | DISTRICT %<br>OF COUNTY | DISTRICT %<br>OF STATES | NUMBER OF<br>SCHOOLS | ENROLL | EXP | POV |
|---|---|---|---|---|---|---|---|---|
| Texas City Ind School Dist | 01019470 | | 17.59 | 0.23 | 14 | 9,000 | HIGH | MED-HIGH |
| Dickinson Ind School Dist | 01018969 | | 17.31 | 0.22 | 14 | 10,400 | HIGH | MED-HIGH |
| Galveston Ind School Dist | 01019078 | | 11.61 | 0.15 | 11 | 7,000 | HIGH | MED-HIGH |
| Friendswood Ind Sch Dist | 01019028 | | 5.44 | 0.07 | 6 | 6,000 | MED | MED-LOW |
| Santa Fe Ind School Dist | 01019432 | | 4.05 | 0.05 | 5 | 4,794 | LOW | MED-LOW |
| Hitchcock Ind School Dist | 01019274 | | 2.17 | 0.03 | 4 | 1,600 | HIGH | MED-HIGH |
| High Island Ind Sch Dist | 01019250 | | 0.42 | 0.01 | 1 | 135 | HIGH | MED-LOW |
| **MCLENNAN** | | 1.01 | | | | | | |
| Waco Ind School Dist | 01040132 | | 39.32 | 0.40 | 24 | 15,050 | HIGH | HIGH |
| Midway Ind School Dist | 01039937 | | 14.41 | 0.15 | 10 | 8,100 | HIGH | MED-LOW |
| La Vega Ind School Dist | 01039779 | | 8.76 | 0.09 | 5 | 3,140 | HIGH | MED-HIGH |
| China Spring Ind School Dist | 01039614 | | 6.92 | 0.07 | 5 | 2,748 | HIGH | MED-HIGH |
| Connally Ind School Dist | 01039640 | | 5.30 | 0.05 | 6 | 2,300 | HIGH | MED-HIGH |
| Lorena Ind School Dist | 01039822 | | 3.57 | 0.04 | 4 | 1,673 | HIGH | MED-LOW |
| Robinson Ind School Dist | 01040039 | | 2.94 | 0.03 | 5 | 2,200 | MED | MED-LOW |
| Moody Ind School Dist | 01039975 | | 2.71 | 0.03 | 3 | 660 | HIGH | MED-HIGH |
| Bosqueville Ind School Dist | 01039561 | | 2.62 | 0.03 | 3 | 699 | HIGH | MED-LOW |
| McGregor Ind School Dist | 01039896 | | 2.53 | 0.03 | 4 | 1,342 | HIGH | MED-HIGH |
| Axtell Ind School Dist | 01039535 | | 2.31 | 0.02 | 2 | 580 | HIGH | MED-HIGH |
| West Ind School Dist | 01040481 | | 2.08 | 0.02 | 4 | 826 | HIGH | MED-LOW |
| Crawford Ind School Dist | 01039705 | | 1.68 | 0.02 | 2 | 560 | HIGH | MED-LOW |
| Bruceville-Eddy Ind Sch Dist | 01039585 | | 1.41 | 0.01 | 4 | 630 | HIGH | MED-HIGH |
| Mart Ind School Dist | 01039858 | | 1.38 | 0.01 | 2 | 426 | HIGH | MED-HIGH |
| Riesel Ind School Dist | 01040003 | | 0.97 | 0.01 | 2 | 660 | MED | MED-LOW |
| Gholson Ind School Dist | 01039731 | | 0.56 | 0.01 | 1 | 246 | HIGH | MED-HIGH |
| Hallsburg Ind School Dist | 01039755 | | 0.52 | 0.01 | 1 | 170 | HIGH | MED-LOW |
| **JEFFERSON** | | 1.00 | | | | | | |
| Beaumont Ind School Dist | 01034092 | | 49.37 | 0.49 | 27 | 18,000 | HIGH | MED-HIGH |
| Port Arthur Ind School Dist | 01033749 | | 24.37 | 0.24 | 16 | 9,000 | HIGH | HIGH |
| Nederland Ind School Dist | 01033660 | | 11.58 | 0.12 | 8 | 5,214 | HIGH | MED-LOW |
| Port Neches-Groves Ind SD | 01033957 | | 10.44 | 0.10 | 10 | 5,000 | HIGH | MED-LOW |
| Hamshire Fannett Ind Sch Dist | 01033610 | | 2.92 | 0.03 | 4 | 1,934 | MED | MED-LOW |
| Sabine Pass Ind School Dist | 01034066 | | 1.33 | 0.01 | 1 | 354 | HIGH | HIGH |
| **SMITH** | | 0.86 | | | | | | |
| Tyler Ind School Dist | 01050747 | | 48.68 | 0.42 | 29 | 18,000 | HIGH | MED-HIGH |
| Chapel Hill Ind School Dist | 01050606 | | 14.12 | 0.12 | 5 | 3,513 | HIGH | MED-HIGH |
| Lindale Ind School Dist | 01050656 | | 11.41 | 0.10 | 6 | 4,200 | HIGH | MED-HIGH |
| Whitehouse Ind School Dist | 01050993 | | 8.82 | 0.08 | 8 | 4,800 | MED | MED-LOW |
| Bullard Ind School Dist | 01050577 | | 6.97 | 0.06 | 6 | 2,700 | HIGH | MED-LOW |
| Troup Ind School Dist | 01050709 | | 4.32 | 0.04 | 3 | 1,100 | HIGH | MED-HIGH |
| Arp Ind School Dist | 01050541 | | 2.97 | 0.03 | 3 | 870 | HIGH | MED-LOW |
| Winona Ind School Dist | 01051038 | | 2.72 | 0.02 | 4 | 1,050 | HIGH | HIGH |
| **ELLIS** | | 0.81 | | | | | | |
| Waxahachie Ind School Dist | 01015292 | | 26.22 | 0.21 | 16 | 9,481 | HIGH | MED-LOW |
| Ennis Ind School Dist | 01014963 | | 20.51 | 0.17 | 11 | 5,800 | HIGH | MED-HIGH |
| Midlothian Ind School Dist | 01015137 | | 20.24 | 0.16 | 11 | 9,500 | HIGH | MED-LOW |
| Red Oak Ind School Dist | 01015242 | | 12.52 | 0.10 | 8 | 6,000 | HIGH | MED-LOW |
| Ferris Ind School Dist | 01015034 | | 8.77 | 0.07 | 5 | 2,400 | HIGH | MED-HIGH |
| Palmer Ind School Dist | 01015216 | | 3.64 | 0.03 | 3 | 1,300 | HIGH | MED-LOW |
| Maypearl Ind School Dist | 01015101 | | 2.83 | 0.02 | 4 | 1,040 | HIGH | MED-LOW |
| Italy Ind School Dist | 01015072 | | 2.41 | 0.02 | 2 | 600 | HIGH | MED-LOW |
| Avalon Ind School Dist | 01014937 | | 1.75 | 0.01 | 1 | 350 | HIGH | MED-LOW |
| Milford Ind School Dist | 01015187 | | 1.12 | 0.01 | 1 | 240 | HIGH | MED-HIGH |
| **BRAZOS** | | 0.80 | | | | | | |
| Bryan Ind School Dist | 01002013 | | 58.39 | 0.47 | 24 | 16,134 | HIGH | MED-HIGH |
| College Station Ind Sch Dist | 01001954 | | 40.10 | 0.32 | 19 | 14,000 | HIGH | MED-LOW |
| Mumford Ind School Dist | 01048691 | | 1.52 | 0.01 | 1 | 612 | HIGH | MED-HIGH |
| **ECTOR** | | 0.79 | | | | | | |
| Ector Co Ind School Dist | 01014547 | | 100.00 | 0.79 | 42 | 32,391 | HIGH | MED-HIGH |
| **JOHNSON** | | 0.77 | | | | | | |
| Burleson Ind School Dist | 01034810 | | 19.60 | 0.15 | 18 | 13,268 | MED | MED-LOW |
| Cleburne Ind School Dist | 01034872 | | 18.57 | 0.14 | 12 | 6,749 | HIGH | MED-HIGH |
| Joshua Ind School Dist | 01035022 | | 17.39 | 0.13 | 10 | 5,626 | HIGH | MED-LOW |
| Alvarado Ind School Dist | 01034767 | | 11.61 | 0.09 | 6 | 3,500 | HIGH | MED-HIGH |
| Godley Ind School Dist | 01034963 | | 10.45 | 0.08 | 5 | 2,027 | HIGH | MED-LOW |
| Venus Ind School Dist | 01035163 | | 10.22 | 0.08 | 4 | 2,095 | HIGH | MED-HIGH |
| Grandview Ind School Dist | 01034999 | | 5.28 | 0.04 | 3 | 1,365 | HIGH | MED-LOW |
| Keene Ind School Dist | 01035060 | | 3.96 | 0.03 | 4 | 1,011 | HIGH | MED-HIGH |
| Rio Vista Ind School Dist | 01035137 | | 2.91 | 0.02 | 3 | 755 | HIGH | MED-HIGH |

## DISTRICT BUYING POWER INDEX
### COUNTIES RANKED BY PERCENTAGE OF STATE SPENDING

| COUNTY<br>DISTRICT | PID | COUNTY %<br>OF STATE | DISTRICT %<br>OF COUNTY | DISTRICT %<br>OF STATES | NUMBER OF<br>SCHOOLS | ENROLL | EXP | POV |
|---|---|---|---|---|---|---|---|---|
| **HAYS** | | 0.73 | | | | | | |
| Hays Cons Ind School Dist | 01029059 | | 43.73 | 0.32 | 25 | 20,063 | MED | MED-LOW |
| San Marcos Cons Ind Sch Dist | 01029114 | | 27.20 | 0.20 | 12 | 8,200 | HIGH | MED-HIGH |
| Dripping Springs Ind Sch Dist | 01029011 | | 20.87 | 0.15 | 7 | 6,400 | HIGH | LOW |
| Wimberley Ind School Dist | 02903408 | | 8.19 | 0.06 | 4 | 2,500 | HIGH | MED-LOW |
| **KAUFMAN** | | 0.73 | | | | | | |
| Forney Ind School Dist | 01035565 | | 33.83 | 0.25 | 14 | 9,681 | HIGH | MED-LOW |
| Crandall Ind School Dist | 01035539 | | 17.78 | 0.13 | 8 | 4,700 | HIGH | MED-LOW |
| Terrell Ind School Dist | 01035759 | | 15.09 | 0.11 | 10 | 4,711 | HIGH | MED-HIGH |
| Kaufman Ind School Dist | 01035606 | | 12.98 | 0.09 | 7 | 3,500 | HIGH | MED-HIGH |
| Mabank Ind School Dist | 01035682 | | 11.73 | 0.09 | 8 | 3,664 | HIGH | MED-HIGH |
| Kemp Ind School Dist | 01035656 | | 5.79 | 0.04 | 4 | 1,236 | HIGH | MED-HIGH |
| Scurry Rosser Ind School Dist | 01035723 | | 2.80 | 0.02 | 3 | 1,037 | HIGH | MED-HIGH |
| **POTTER** | | 0.70 | | | | | | |
| Amarillo Ind School Dist | 01047128 | | 88.35 | 0.62 | 55 | 33,311 | HIGH | MED-HIGH |
| Bushland Ind School Dist | 01047568 | | 4.47 | 0.03 | 3 | 1,400 | HIGH | MED-LOW |
| River Road Ind School Dist | 01047609 | | 3.72 | 0.03 | 4 | 1,278 | HIGH | MED-HIGH |
| Highland Park Ind School Dist | 01047582 | | 3.46 | 0.02 | 3 | 864 | HIGH | MED-HIGH |
| **GREGG** | | 0.67 | | | | | | |
| Longview Ind School Dist | 01020986 | | 46.70 | 0.31 | 13 | 8,700 | HIGH | MED-HIGH |
| Kilgore Ind School Dist | 01020900 | | 17.09 | 0.11 | 5 | 4,086 | HIGH | MED-HIGH |
| Pine Tree Ind School Dist | 01021148 | | 14.15 | 0.09 | 8 | 4,700 | HIGH | MED-HIGH |
| Spring Hill Ind School Dist | 01021253 | | 7.68 | 0.05 | 4 | 2,100 | HIGH | MED-LOW |
| White Oak Ind School Dist | 01021306 | | 5.64 | 0.04 | 4 | 1,496 | HIGH | MED-HIGH |
| Sabine Ind School Dist | 01021215 | | 5.36 | 0.04 | 3 | 1,495 | HIGH | MED-LOW |
| Gladewater Ind School Dist | 01020857 | | 3.39 | 0.02 | 4 | 1,700 | MED | MED-HIGH |
| **GRAYSON** | | 0.60 | | | | | | |
| Denison Ind School Dist | 01020297 | | 29.33 | 0.18 | 9 | 3,885 | HIGH | MED-HIGH |
| Sherman Ind School Dist | 01020596 | | 22.91 | 0.14 | 12 | 7,500 | HIGH | MED-HIGH |
| Van Alstyne Ind School Dist | 01020742 | | 7.74 | 0.05 | 4 | 1,576 | HIGH | MED-LOW |
| Pottsboro Ind School Dist | 01020510 | | 7.05 | 0.04 | 3 | 1,384 | HIGH | MED-LOW |
| Whitesboro Ind School Dist | 01020780 | | 5.29 | 0.03 | 4 | 1,540 | HIGH | MED-LOW |
| Whitewright Ind School Dist | 01020821 | | 5.15 | 0.03 | 3 | 823 | HIGH | MED-LOW |
| Gunter Ind School Dist | 01020443 | | 4.08 | 0.02 | 3 | 1,000 | HIGH | MED-LOW |
| Howe Ind School Dist | 01020479 | | 3.99 | 0.02 | 4 | 1,100 | HIGH | MED-HIGH |
| S & S Cons Ind School Dist | 01020560 | | 3.91 | 0.02 | 3 | 896 | HIGH | MED-LOW |
| Bells Ind School Dist | 01020235 | | 3.46 | 0.02 | 3 | 850 | HIGH | MED-LOW |
| Tioga Ind School Dist | 01020699 | | 3.34 | 0.02 | 1 | 639 | HIGH | MED-LOW |
| Collinsville Ind School Dist | 01020261 | | 2.14 | 0.01 | 2 | 540 | HIGH | MED-LOW |
| Tom Bean Ind School Dist | 01020716 | | 1.62 | 0.01 | 3 | 620 | MED | MED-LOW |
| **PARKER** | | 0.58 | | | | | | |
| Weatherford Ind School Dist | 01046564 | | 43.92 | 0.26 | 12 | 8,000 | HIGH | MED-LOW |
| Aledo Ind School Dist | 01046306 | | 20.73 | 0.12 | 10 | 6,000 | HIGH | LOW |
| Springtown Ind School Dist | 01046514 | | 13.75 | 0.08 | 6 | 3,470 | HIGH | MED-LOW |
| Millsap Ind School Dist | 01046394 | | 6.87 | 0.04 | 3 | 989 | HIGH | MED-LOW |
| Peaster Ind School Dist | 01046423 | | 5.96 | 0.03 | 3 | 1,210 | HIGH | MED-LOW |
| Brock Ind School Dist | 01046344 | | 5.44 | 0.03 | 4 | 1,476 | HIGH | LOW |
| Poolville Ind School Dist | 01046459 | | 2.59 | 0.02 | 3 | 550 | HIGH | MED-LOW |
| Garner Ind School Dist | 01046370 | | 0.74 | 0.00 | 1 | 212 | HIGH | MED-LOW |
| **GUADALUPE** | | 0.51 | | | | | | |
| Schertz-Cibolo-Univ City ISD | 01021552 | | 56.96 | 0.29 | 17 | 15,925 | HIGH | MED-LOW |
| Seguin Ind School Dist | 01021631 | | 21.57 | 0.11 | 13 | 7,048 | MED | MED-HIGH |
| Navarro Ind School Dist | 01021526 | | 14.08 | 0.07 | 4 | 1,909 | HIGH | MED-LOW |
| Marion Ind School Dist | 01021485 | | 7.38 | 0.04 | 4 | 1,500 | HIGH | MED-LOW |
| **BOWIE** | | 0.49 | | | | | | |
| Texarkana Ind School Dist | 01001215 | | 35.81 | 0.18 | 13 | 7,174 | HIGH | HIGH |
| Liberty-Eylau Ind School Dist | 01000948 | | 14.56 | 0.07 | 4 | 2,465 | HIGH | MED-HIGH |
| Pleasant Grove Ind School Dist | 01001112 | | 11.36 | 0.06 | 4 | 2,200 | HIGH | MED-LOW |
| Redwater Ind School Dist | 01001150 | | 8.41 | 0.04 | 4 | 1,076 | HIGH | MED-LOW |
| New Boston Ind School Dist | 01001069 | | 8.00 | 0.04 | 4 | 1,198 | HIGH | MED-HIGH |
| Hooks Ind School Dist | 01000857 | | 6.92 | 0.03 | 3 | 884 | HIGH | MED-HIGH |
| Maud Ind School Dist | 01001033 | | 4.21 | 0.02 | 1 | 475 | HIGH | MED-LOW |
| De Kalb Ind School Dist | 01000819 | | 3.83 | 0.02 | 3 | 650 | HIGH | HIGH |
| Simms Ind School Dist | 01001186 | | 2.74 | 0.01 | 3 | 500 | HIGH | MED-HIGH |
| Red Lick Ind School Dist | 01001136 | | 2.59 | 0.01 | 1 | 520 | HIGH | MED-HIGH |
| Malta Ind School Dist | 01001019 | | 1.17 | 0.01 | 1 | 225 | HIGH | MED-HIGH |
| Hubbard Ind School Dist | 01000900 | | 0.22 | 0.00 | 1 | 107 | MED | MED-LOW |
| Leary Ind School Dist | 01000924 | | 0.17 | 0.00 | 1 | 119 | LOW | MED-HIGH |

## DISTRICT BUYING POWER INDEX
### COUNTIES RANKED BY PERCENTAGE OF STATE SPENDING

| COUNTY<br>DISTRICT | PID | COUNTY %<br>OF STATE | DISTRICT %<br>OF COUNTY | DISTRICT %<br>OF STATES | NUMBER OF<br>SCHOOLS | ENROLL | EXP | POV |
|---|---|---|---|---|---|---|---|---|
| **BASTROP** | | 0.48 | | | | | | |
| Bastrop Ind School Dist | 00995833 | | 65.42 | 0.32 | 15 | 11,000 | HIGH | MED-HIGH |
| Elgin Ind School Dist | 00995883 | | 22.98 | 0.11 | 7 | 4,500 | HIGH | MED-HIGH |
| Smithville Ind School Dist | 00995974 | | 10.18 | 0.05 | 5 | 1,800 | HIGH | MED-LOW |
| McDade Ind School Dist | 00995936 | | 1.42 | 0.01 | 1 | 370 | HIGH | HIGH |
| **TOM GREEN** | | 0.43 | | | | | | |
| San Angelo Ind School Dist | 01055539 | | 76.78 | 0.33 | 25 | 14,520 | HIGH | MED-HIGH |
| Grape Creek Ind School Dist | 01055515 | | 7.88 | 0.03 | 3 | 1,160 | HIGH | MED-HIGH |
| Wall Ind School Dist | 01055840 | | 5.58 | 0.02 | 4 | 1,100 | HIGH | MED-LOW |
| Christoval Ind School Dist | 01055486 | | 4.73 | 0.02 | 2 | 505 | HIGH | MED-LOW |
| Water Valley Ind School Dist | 01055888 | | 2.59 | 0.01 | 2 | 300 | HIGH | MED-HIGH |
| Veribest Ind School Dist | 01055826 | | 2.44 | 0.01 | 1 | 275 | HIGH | MED-HIGH |
| **COMAL** | | 0.42 | | | | | | |
| Comal Ind School Dist | 01006887 | | 74.00 | 0.31 | 33 | 23,800 | MED | MED-LOW |
| New Braunfels Ind School Dist | 01006966 | | 26.00 | 0.11 | 15 | 9,220 | MED | MED-LOW |
| **LIBERTY** | | 0.42 | | | | | | |
| Cleveland Ind School Dist | 01037719 | | 47.69 | 0.20 | 7 | 6,338 | HIGH | MED-HIGH |
| Dayton Ind School Dist | 01037771 | | 20.46 | 0.09 | 7 | 5,400 | MED | MED-HIGH |
| Liberty Ind School Dist | 01037927 | | 12.42 | 0.05 | 4 | 2,227 | HIGH | MED-HIGH |
| Hardin Ind School Dist | 01037848 | | 9.29 | 0.04 | 3 | 1,700 | HIGH | MED-HIGH |
| Tarkington Ind School Dist | 01037977 | | 5.40 | 0.02 | 4 | 1,810 | MED | MED-HIGH |
| Hull Daisetta Ind School Dist | 01037886 | | 3.56 | 0.01 | 3 | 453 | HIGH | MED-LOW |
| Devers Ind School Dist | 01037824 | | 1.17 | 0.00 | 1 | 176 | HIGH | MED-LOW |
| **ROCKWALL** | | 0.42 | | | | | | |
| Rockwall Ind School Dist | 01048718 | | 53.53 | 0.23 | 22 | 17,078 | MED | MED-LOW |
| Royse City Ind School Dist | 01048770 | | 46.47 | 0.20 | 9 | 6,300 | HIGH | MED-LOW |
| **ANGELINA** | | 0.41 | | | | | | |
| Lufkin Ind School Dist | 00994932 | | 44.66 | 0.19 | 15 | 8,000 | HIGH | MED-HIGH |
| Hudson Ind School Dist | 00994853 | | 16.00 | 0.07 | 5 | 2,950 | HIGH | MED-HIGH |
| Diboll Ind School Dist | 00994815 | | 13.46 | 0.06 | 5 | 1,800 | HIGH | MED-HIGH |
| Huntington Ind School Dist | 00994891 | | 12.93 | 0.05 | 5 | 1,750 | HIGH | MED-HIGH |
| Central Ind School Dist | 00994774 | | 8.19 | 0.03 | 3 | 1,400 | HIGH | MED-HIGH |
| Zavalla Ind School Dist | 00995089 | | 4.76 | 0.02 | 2 | 300 | HIGH | HIGH |
| **ORANGE** | | 0.41 | | | | | | |
| Little Cypress Mauriceville SD | 01045651 | | 26.48 | 0.11 | 6 | 3,100 | HIGH | MED-LOW |
| Vidor Ind School Dist | 01045754 | | 23.12 | 0.09 | 7 | 4,400 | HIGH | MED-HIGH |
| West Orange-Cove Cons ISD | 01045819 | | 16.53 | 0.07 | 4 | 2,485 | HIGH | HIGH |
| Orangefield Ind School Dist | 01045704 | | 16.02 | 0.07 | 3 | 1,785 | HIGH | MED-LOW |
| Bridge City Ind School Dist | 01045601 | | 14.85 | 0.06 | 4 | 3,057 | HIGH | MED-LOW |
| Deweyville Ind School Dist | 01043718 | | 3.00 | 0.01 | 2 | 575 | HIGH | MED-HIGH |
| **MIDLAND** | | 0.36 | | | | | | |
| Midland Ind School Dist | 01041423 | | 81.38 | 0.29 | 40 | 26,000 | MED | MED-LOW |
| Greenwood Ind School Dist | 01041394 | | 18.62 | 0.07 | 4 | 2,831 | HIGH | MED-HIGH |
| **VICTORIA** | | 0.36 | | | | | | |
| Victoria Ind School Dist | 01058440 | | 88.86 | 0.32 | 23 | 13,900 | HIGH | MED-HIGH |
| Bloomington Ind School Dist | 01058311 | | 10.44 | 0.04 | 5 | 850 | HIGH | MED-HIGH |
| Nursery ISD School Dist | 01058414 | | 0.70 | 0.00 | 1 | 155 | HIGH | MED-LOW |
| **SAN PATRICIO** | | 0.35 | | | | | | |
| Gregory-Portland Ind Sch Dist | 01049530 | | 26.02 | 0.09 | 7 | 4,600 | HIGH | MED-LOW |
| Sinton Ind School Dist | 01049762 | | 16.20 | 0.06 | 4 | 1,339 | HIGH | HIGH |
| Ingleside Ind School Dist | 01049592 | | 15.07 | 0.05 | 5 | 2,046 | HIGH | MED-HIGH |
| Mathis Ind School Dist | 01049645 | | 14.92 | 0.05 | 4 | 1,600 | HIGH | HIGH |
| Aransas Pass Ind School Dist | 01049487 | | 14.09 | 0.05 | 5 | 1,484 | HIGH | MED-HIGH |
| Taft Ind School Dist | 01049827 | | 6.98 | 0.02 | 3 | 1,154 | HIGH | MED-HIGH |
| Odem-Edroy Ind School Dist | 01049700 | | 6.71 | 0.02 | 4 | 900 | HIGH | HIGH |
| **WICHITA** | | 0.34 | | | | | | |
| Wichita Falls Ind School Dist | 01060132 | | 42.76 | 0.14 | 28 | 14,500 | LOW | MED-HIGH |
| Burkburnett Ind Sch Dist | 01059925 | | 25.10 | 0.08 | 6 | 3,350 | HIGH | MED-LOW |
| City View Ind School Dist | 01059999 | | 14.84 | 0.05 | 2 | 921 | HIGH | MED-HIGH |
| Iowa Park Consolidated Ind SD | 01060065 | | 14.08 | 0.05 | 4 | 1,421 | HIGH | MED-LOW |
| Electra Ind School Dist | 01060015 | | 3.22 | 0.01 | 3 | 391 | HIGH | MED-HIGH |
| **TAYLOR** | | 0.33 | | | | | | |
| Abilene Ind School Dist | 01054523 | | 69.64 | 0.23 | 26 | 17,000 | MED | MED-HIGH |
| Wylie Ind School Dist | 01055008 | | 14.79 | 0.05 | 7 | 5,000 | MED | MED-LOW |
| Jim Ned Cons Ind School Dist | 01054896 | | 8.80 | 0.03 | 4 | 1,360 | HIGH | MED-LOW |
| Merkel Ind School Dist | 01054925 | | 5.28 | 0.02 | 3 | 1,073 | MED | MED-HIGH |
| Trent Isn School Dist | 01054987 | | 1.50 | 0.01 | 1 | 150 | HIGH | MED-HIGH |

## DISTRICT BUYING POWER INDEX
### COUNTIES RANKED BY PERCENTAGE OF STATE SPENDING

| COUNTY DISTRICT | PID | COUNTY % OF STATE | DISTRICT % OF COUNTY | DISTRICT % OF STATES | NUMBER OF SCHOOLS | ENROLL | EXP | POV |
|---|---|---|---|---|---|---|---|---|
| **HUNT** | | 0.32 | | | | | | |
| Greenville Ind School Dist | 01032446 | | 31.38 | 0.10 | 12 | 5,400 | HIGH | MED-HIGH |
| Quinlan Ind School Dist | 01032575 | | 18.55 | 0.06 | 5 | 2,516 | HIGH | MED-HIGH |
| Caddo Mills Ind Sch Dist | 01032290 | | 12.11 | 0.04 | 5 | 2,000 | HIGH | MED-LOW |
| Commerce Independent Sch Dist | 01032381 | | 7.49 | 0.02 | 4 | 1,442 | MED | MED-HIGH |
| Wolfe City Ind School Dist | 01032616 | | 6.99 | 0.02 | 3 | 646 | HIGH | MED-HIGH |
| Lone Oak Ind School Dist | 01032549 | | 6.49 | 0.02 | 4 | 1,000 | HIGH | MED-LOW |
| Celeste Ind School Dist | 01032355 | | 5.41 | 0.02 | 3 | 480 | HIGH | MED-LOW |
| Bland Ind School Dist | 01032238 | | 4.72 | 0.02 | 3 | 700 | HIGH | MED-HIGH |
| Boles Ind School Dist | 01032264 | | 4.51 | 0.01 | 3 | 545 | HIGH | MED-HIGH |
| Campbell Ind School Dist | 01032329 | | 2.35 | 0.01 | 1 | 300 | HIGH | MED-HIGH |
| **HARRISON** | | 0.31 | | | | | | |
| Marshall Ind School Dist | 01028603 | | 41.87 | 0.13 | 7 | 5,345 | HIGH | MED-HIGH |
| Hallsville Ind School Dist | 01028483 | | 33.10 | 0.10 | 5 | 5,000 | HIGH | MED-HIGH |
| Waskom Ind School Dist | 01028744 | | 12.00 | 0.04 | 3 | 850 | HIGH | MED-HIGH |
| Elysian Fields Ind School Dist | 01028433 | | 6.73 | 0.02 | 3 | 889 | HIGH | MED-HIGH |
| Harleton Ind School Dist | 01028536 | | 5.13 | 0.02 | 3 | 716 | HIGH | MED-HIGH |
| Karnack Ind School Dist | 01028574 | | 1.16 | 0.00 | 1 | 145 | HIGH | MED-HIGH |
| **CORYELL** | | 0.30 | | | | | | |
| Copperas Cove Ind School Dist | 01007556 | | 70.40 | 0.21 | 11 | 8,200 | HIGH | MED-HIGH |
| Gatesville Ind School Dist | 01007661 | | 19.01 | 0.06 | 5 | 2,744 | HIGH | MED-HIGH |
| Evant Ind School Dist | 01007635 | | 5.72 | 0.02 | 1 | 249 | HIGH | MED-HIGH |
| Jonesboro Ind School Dist | 01007714 | | 3.16 | 0.01 | 1 | 330 | HIGH | MED-HIGH |
| Oglesby Ind School Dist | 01007740 | | 1.72 | 0.01 | 1 | 180 | HIGH | HIGH |
| **NACOGDOCHES** | | 0.29 | | | | | | |
| Nacogdoches Ind School Dist | 01043275 | | 53.67 | 0.16 | 10 | 6,400 | HIGH | MED-HIGH |
| Central Heights Ind Sch Dist | 01043079 | | 10.73 | 0.03 | 3 | 1,100 | HIGH | MED-HIGH |
| Chireno ISD School Dist | 01043108 | | 7.62 | 0.02 | 1 | 400 | HIGH | MED-HIGH |
| Woden Ind School Dist | 01043354 | | 6.54 | 0.02 | 3 | 780 | HIGH | MED-HIGH |
| Martinsville Ind School Dist | 01043249 | | 5.37 | 0.02 | 1 | 400 | HIGH | MED-HIGH |
| Cushing Ind School Dist | 01043134 | | 5.23 | 0.02 | 2 | 524 | HIGH | MED-HIGH |
| Douglass Ind School Dist | 01043160 | | 4.72 | 0.01 | 1 | 440 | HIGH | MED-HIGH |
| Garrison Ind School Dist | 01043213 | | 4.29 | 0.01 | 3 | 682 | HIGH | MED-HIGH |
| Etoile Ind School Dist | 01043196 | | 1.86 | 0.01 | 1 | 100 | HIGH | MED-HIGH |
| **STARR** | | 0.29 | | | | | | |
| Rio Grande City Ind Sch Dist | 01051117 | | 58.33 | 0.17 | 18 | 10,175 | MED | HIGH |
| Roma Ind School Dist | 01051222 | | 39.20 | 0.12 | 10 | 6,000 | HIGH | HIGH |
| San Isidro Ind School Dist | 01051296 | | 2.47 | 0.01 | 1 | 200 | HIGH | HIGH |
| **VAN ZANDT** | | 0.27 | | | | | | |
| Van Ind School Dist | 01058232 | | 30.87 | 0.08 | 5 | 2,400 | HIGH | MED-HIGH |
| Canton Ind School Dist | 01058086 | | 19.28 | 0.05 | 4 | 2,300 | HIGH | MED-LOW |
| Wills Point Ind School Dist | 01058270 | | 15.94 | 0.04 | 5 | 2,500 | HIGH | MED-HIGH |
| Grand Saline Ind School Dist | 01058165 | | 13.23 | 0.04 | 4 | 1,100 | HIGH | MED-HIGH |
| Edgewood Ind School Dist | 01058115 | | 10.60 | 0.03 | 4 | 950 | HIGH | MED-HIGH |
| Fruitvale Ind School Dist | 01058141 | | 6.40 | 0.02 | 3 | 425 | HIGH | MED-HIGH |
| Martin's Mill Ind Sch Dist | 01058191 | | 3.67 | 0.01 | 1 | 230 | HIGH | MED-HIGH |
| **COOKE** | | 0.26 | | | | | | |
| Gainesville Ind School Dist | 01007348 | | 41.64 | 0.11 | 6 | 3,100 | HIGH | HIGH |
| Muenster Ind School Dist | 01007453 | | 22.41 | 0.06 | 2 | 481 | HIGH | MED-LOW |
| Callisburg Ind School Dist | 01007271 | | 15.45 | 0.04 | 2 | 1,100 | HIGH | MED-HIGH |
| Valley View ISD-Cooke Co | 01007506 | | 10.37 | 0.03 | 1 | 875 | HIGH | MED-HIGH |
| Lindsay Ind School Dist | 01007427 | | 4.51 | 0.01 | 2 | 500 | HIGH | MED-LOW |
| Era Ind School Dist | 01007312 | | 4.00 | 0.01 | 1 | 454 | HIGH | MED-LOW |
| Walnut Bend Ind School Dist | 01007532 | | 0.89 | 0.00 | 1 | 72 | HIGH | MED-HIGH |
| Sivells Bend Ind School Dist | 01007489 | | 0.72 | 0.00 | 1 | 57 | HIGH | MED-HIGH |
| **HARDIN** | | 0.26 | | | | | | |
| Lumberton Ind School Dist | 01022544 | | 33.15 | 0.09 | 5 | 3,437 | HIGH | MED-LOW |
| Silsbee Ind School Dist | 01022582 | | 25.90 | 0.07 | 4 | 2,800 | HIGH | MED-HIGH |
| Hardin Jefferson Ind Sch Dist | 01022439 | | 19.12 | 0.05 | 4 | 2,300 | HIGH | MED-LOW |
| Kountze Ind School Dist | 01022491 | | 12.09 | 0.03 | 4 | 767 | HIGH | MED-HIGH |
| West Hardin Co Cons Sch Dist | 01022659 | | 9.74 | 0.03 | 2 | 525 | HIGH | MED-LOW |
| **HENDERSON** | | 0.26 | | | | | | |
| Athens Ind School Dist | 01029231 | | 30.20 | 0.08 | 5 | 3,000 | HIGH | MED-HIGH |
| Brownsboro Ind School Dist | 01029322 | | 25.75 | 0.07 | 7 | 2,800 | HIGH | MED-HIGH |
| Malakoff Ind School Dist | 01029449 | | 16.50 | 0.04 | 5 | 1,300 | HIGH | MED-HIGH |
| Eustace Ind School Dist | 01029384 | | 12.96 | 0.03 | 4 | 1,566 | HIGH | MED-HIGH |
| Cross Roads Ind School Dist | 01029360 | | 9.62 | 0.03 | 3 | 545 | HIGH | MED-HIGH |
| La Poynor Ind School Dist | 01029413 | | 3.04 | 0.01 | 1 | 470 | HIGH | MED-HIGH |
| Trinidad Ind School Dist | 01029504 | | 1.17 | 0.00 | 1 | 145 | HIGH | HIGH |

## DISTRICT BUYING POWER INDEX
### COUNTIES RANKED BY PERCENTAGE OF STATE SPENDING

| COUNTY<br>DISTRICT | PID | COUNTY %<br>OF STATE | DISTRICT %<br>OF COUNTY | DISTRICT %<br>OF STATES | NUMBER OF<br>SCHOOLS | ENROLL | EXP | POV |
|---|---|---|---|---|---|---|---|---|
| Murchison Ind Sch Dist | 01029487 | | 0.76 | 0.00 | 1 | 200 | MED | HIGH |
| **MAVERICK** | | 0.25 | | | | | | |
| Eagle Pass Ind School Dist | 01041057 | | 100.00 | 0.25 | 23 | 15,000 | MED | HIGH |
| **MEDINA** | | 0.25 | | | | | | |
| Medina Valley Ind School Dist | 01041277 | | 55.52 | 0.14 | 7 | 5,087 | HIGH | MED-HIGH |
| Devine Ind School Dist | 01041198 | | 14.40 | 0.04 | 4 | 1,900 | HIGH | MED-HIGH |
| Hondo Ind School Dist | 01041239 | | 12.58 | 0.03 | 4 | 1,838 | MED | MED-HIGH |
| Natalia Ind School Dist | 01041320 | | 12.05 | 0.03 | 4 | 1,000 | HIGH | MED-LOW |
| D'Hanis Ind School Dist | 01041162 | | 5.45 | 0.01 | 1 | 368 | HIGH | MED-HIGH |
| **WALLER** | | 0.25 | | | | | | |
| Waller Ind School Dist | 01058866 | | 63.06 | 0.16 | 8 | 7,700 | HIGH | MED-HIGH |
| Royal Ind School Dist | 01058816 | | 25.02 | 0.06 | 4 | 2,400 | HIGH | MED-HIGH |
| Hempstead Ind School Dist | 01058775 | | 11.92 | 0.03 | 3 | 1,600 | HIGH | MED-HIGH |
| **VAL VERDE** | | 0.24 | | | | | | |
| San Felipe-Del Rio Cons Ind SD | 01057941 | | 97.52 | 0.24 | 12 | 10,472 | HIGH | MED-HIGH |
| Comstock Ind School Dist | 01057898 | | 2.48 | 0.01 | 1 | 199 | HIGH | MED-HIGH |
| **WHARTON** | | 0.23 | | | | | | |
| El Campo Ind School Dist | 01059602 | | 48.18 | 0.11 | 5 | 4,500 | HIGH | MED-HIGH |
| Wharton Ind School Dist | 01059690 | | 20.92 | 0.05 | 5 | 2,015 | HIGH | MED-HIGH |
| East Bernard Ind Sch Dist | 01059573 | | 13.34 | 0.03 | 3 | 950 | HIGH | MED-HIGH |
| Boling Ind School Dist | 01059535 | | 11.98 | 0.03 | 3 | 1,137 | HIGH | MED-LOW |
| Louise Ind School Dist | 01059664 | | 5.57 | 0.01 | 3 | 510 | HIGH | MED-HIGH |
| **WISE** | | 0.23 | | | | | | |
| Decatur Ind School Dist | 01061655 | | 26.63 | 0.06 | 5 | 3,390 | HIGH | MED-LOW |
| North Lamar Ind School Dist | 01036636 | | 23.08 | 0.05 | 7 | 2,417 | HIGH | MED-LOW |
| Bridgeport Ind School Dist | 01061588 | | 19.23 | 0.04 | 5 | 1,994 | HIGH | MED-LOW |
| Alvord Ind School Dist | 01061526 | | 9.06 | 0.02 | 3 | 700 | HIGH | MED-LOW |
| Boyd Ind School Dist | 01061552 | | 6.75 | 0.02 | 4 | 1,281 | MED | MED-LOW |
| Chico Ind School Dist | 01061629 | | 6.22 | 0.01 | 3 | 600 | HIGH | MED-HIGH |
| Paradise Ind School Dist | 01061722 | | 6.16 | 0.01 | 4 | 1,209 | MED | MED-LOW |
| Slidell Ind School Dist | 01061758 | | 2.88 | 0.01 | 2 | 350 | HIGH | MED-LOW |
| **JIM WELLS** | | 0.22 | | | | | | |
| Alice Ind School Dist | 01034511 | | 68.26 | 0.15 | 9 | 4,784 | HIGH | HIGH |
| Orange Grove Ind School Dist | 01034688 | | 18.05 | 0.04 | 4 | 1,850 | HIGH | HIGH |
| Premont Ind School Dist | 01034717 | | 6.96 | 0.01 | 2 | 705 | HIGH | HIGH |
| Ben Bolt-Palito Blanco ISD | 01034638 | | 4.65 | 0.01 | 2 | 520 | HIGH | MED-HIGH |
| La Gloria Ind School Dist | 01034664 | | 2.08 | 0.00 | 1 | 108 | HIGH | HIGH |
| **CHEROKEE** | | 0.21 | | | | | | |
| Jacksonville Ind School Dist | 01005235 | | 52.95 | 0.11 | 8 | 5,091 | HIGH | MED-HIGH |
| Rusk Ind School Dist | 01005364 | | 24.43 | 0.05 | 5 | 1,979 | HIGH | MED-HIGH |
| Alto Ind School Dist | 01005209 | | 9.43 | 0.02 | 3 | 664 | HIGH | MED-HIGH |
| New Summerfield Ind Sch Dist | 01005340 | | 7.41 | 0.02 | 1 | 544 | HIGH | MED-HIGH |
| Wells Ind School Dist | 01005405 | | 5.78 | 0.01 | 2 | 280 | HIGH | MED-HIGH |
| **HOOD** | | 0.21 | | | | | | |
| Granbury Ind School Dist | 01031375 | | 84.21 | 0.18 | 11 | 6,971 | HIGH | MED-LOW |
| Tolar Ind School Dist | 01031430 | | 10.54 | 0.02 | 3 | 800 | HIGH | MED-LOW |
| Lipan Ind School Dist | 01031416 | | 5.25 | 0.01 | 1 | 413 | HIGH | MED-HIGH |
| **RANDALL** | | 0.21 | | | | | | |
| Canyon Ind School Dist | 01047934 | | 100.00 | 0.21 | 16 | 11,000 | HIGH | MED-LOW |
| **RUSK** | | 0.21 | | | | | | |
| Henderson Ind School Dist | 01048976 | | 42.47 | 0.09 | 6 | 3,400 | HIGH | MED-HIGH |
| Tatum Ind School Dist | 01049188 | | 14.50 | 0.03 | 4 | 1,461 | HIGH | MED-HIGH |
| Carlisle Ind School Dist | 01048940 | | 10.87 | 0.02 | 1 | 587 | HIGH | MED-HIGH |
| West Rusk Co Cons Ind Sch Dist | 01049217 | | 10.84 | 0.02 | 4 | 980 | HIGH | MED-HIGH |
| Overton Ind School Dist | 01049152 | | 8.68 | 0.02 | 2 | 500 | HIGH | MED-HIGH |
| Mt Enterprise Ind School Dist | 01049126 | | 5.68 | 0.01 | 1 | 398 | HIGH | MED-LOW |
| Leveretts Chapel Ind Sch Dist | 01049097 | | 4.32 | 0.01 | 1 | 240 | HIGH | MED-HIGH |
| Laneville Ind School Dist | 01049061 | | 2.66 | 0.01 | 1 | 157 | HIGH | MED-HIGH |
| **ANDERSON** | | 0.20 | | | | | | |
| Palestine Ind School Dist | 00994528 | | 48.35 | 0.10 | 6 | 3,300 | HIGH | MED-HIGH |
| Westwood Ind School Dist | 00994669 | | 21.75 | 0.04 | 4 | 1,500 | HIGH | MED-LOW |
| Elkhart Ind School Dist | 00994437 | | 9.74 | 0.02 | 4 | 1,250 | MED | MED-HIGH |
| Frankston Ind School Dist | 00994463 | | 6.80 | 0.01 | 3 | 766 | HIGH | MED-HIGH |
| Cayuga Ind School Dist | 00994401 | | 5.93 | 0.01 | 1 | 564 | HIGH | MED-HIGH |
| Neches Ind School Dist | 00994499 | | 3.85 | 0.01 | 2 | 330 | HIGH | MED-HIGH |
| Slocum ISD School Dist | 00994633 | | 3.58 | 0.01 | 1 | 400 | HIGH | MED-HIGH |

## DISTRICT BUYING POWER INDEX
### COUNTIES RANKED BY PERCENTAGE OF STATE SPENDING

| COUNTY<br>DISTRICT | PID | COUNTY %<br>OF STATE | DISTRICT %<br>OF COUNTY | DISTRICT %<br>OF STATES | NUMBER OF<br>SCHOOLS | ENROLL | EXP | POV |
|---|---|---|---|---|---|---|---|---|
| **MATAGORDA** | | 0.20 | | | | | | |
| Bay City Ind School Dist | 01040819 | | 54.88 | 0.11 | 5 | 3,670 | HIGH | HIGH |
| Van Vleck Ind School Dist | 01041019 | | 15.79 | 0.03 | 4 | 1,027 | HIGH | MED-LOW |
| Tidehaven Ind School Dist | 01040962 | | 15.36 | 0.03 | 4 | 980 | HIGH | MED-HIGH |
| Palacios Ind School Dist | 01040912 | | 11.14 | 0.02 | 4 | 1,506 | MED | MED-HIGH |
| Matagorda Ind School Dist | 01040895 | | 2.83 | 0.01 | 1 | 120 | HIGH | MED-HIGH |
| **CHAMBERS** | | 0.19 | | | | | | |
| Barbers Hill Ind School Dist | 01005118 | | 46.16 | 0.09 | 8 | 5,214 | HIGH | LOW |
| East Chambers Ind School Dist | 01005156 | | 38.56 | 0.07 | 4 | 1,534 | HIGH | MED-LOW |
| Anahuac Ind School Dist | 01005077 | | 15.28 | 0.03 | 3 | 950 | HIGH | MED-LOW |
| **WILSON** | | 0.19 | | | | | | |
| Floresville Ind School Dist | 01061265 | | 47.96 | 0.09 | 5 | 3,000 | HIGH | MED-HIGH |
| La Vernia Ind School Dist | 01061318 | | 28.43 | 0.05 | 4 | 2,400 | MED | MED-LOW |
| Stockdale Ind School Dist | 01061382 | | 13.61 | 0.03 | 3 | 820 | HIGH | MED-HIGH |
| Poth Ind School Dist | 01061344 | | 10.00 | 0.02 | 3 | 858 | HIGH | MED-LOW |
| **BROWN** | | 0.18 | | | | | | |
| Brownwood Ind School Dist | 01002489 | | 58.45 | 0.11 | 7 | 3,500 | HIGH | MED-HIGH |
| Early Ind School Dist | 01002556 | | 16.00 | 0.03 | 4 | 1,200 | HIGH | MED-HIGH |
| Bangs Ind School Dist | 01002398 | | 10.96 | 0.02 | 3 | 868 | HIGH | MED-LOW |
| Zephyr Ind School Dist | 01002611 | | 5.03 | 0.01 | 1 | 208 | HIGH | MED-LOW |
| May Ind School Dist | 01002582 | | 5.00 | 0.01 | 2 | 230 | HIGH | MED-HIGH |
| Blanket Ind School Dist | 01002427 | | 2.72 | 0.00 | 1 | 145 | HIGH | MED-LOW |
| Brookesmith Ind School Dist | 01002453 | | 1.84 | 0.00 | 3 | 200 | HIGH | MED-LOW |
| **CASS** | | 0.18 | | | | | | |
| Atlanta Ind School Dist | 01004671 | | 30.91 | 0.06 | 5 | 1,760 | HIGH | HIGH |
| Hughes Springs Ind Sch Dist | 01004786 | | 30.53 | 0.06 | 3 | 1,145 | HIGH | MED-HIGH |
| Queen City Ind School Dist | 01004920 | | 14.92 | 0.03 | 4 | 1,005 | HIGH | HIGH |
| Linden Kildare Cons Ind SD | 01004827 | | 10.74 | 0.02 | 3 | 647 | HIGH | MED-HIGH |
| McLeod Ind School Dist | 01004891 | | 6.80 | 0.01 | 1 | 388 | HIGH | HIGH |
| Avinger Ind School Dist | 01004724 | | 3.51 | 0.01 | 1 | 140 | HIGH | HIGH |
| Bloomburg Ind School Dist | 01004750 | | 2.59 | 0.00 | 1 | 272 | HIGH | HIGH |
| **HILL** | | 0.18 | | | | | | |
| Hillsboro Ind School Dist | 01030852 | | 23.14 | 0.04 | 5 | 2,000 | HIGH | MED-HIGH |
| Itasca Ind School Dist | 01030955 | | 16.22 | 0.03 | 3 | 670 | HIGH | MED-HIGH |
| Whitney Ind School Dist | 01031052 | | 15.58 | 0.03 | 4 | 1,311 | HIGH | MED-HIGH |
| Covington ISD School Dist | 01030826 | | 7.94 | 0.01 | 1 | 390 | HIGH | MED-LOW |
| Aquilla Ind School Dist | 01030735 | | 7.28 | 0.01 | 1 | 330 | HIGH | MED-LOW |
| Hubbard Ind School Dist | 01030917 | | 6.95 | 0.01 | 2 | 422 | HIGH | MED-HIGH |
| Abbott Ind School Dist | 01030709 | | 6.65 | 0.01 | 1 | 280 | HIGH | MED-LOW |
| Mt Calm Ind School Dist | 01031002 | | 5.05 | 0.01 | 2 | 200 | HIGH | HIGH |
| Blum Ind School Dist | 01030761 | | 4.69 | 0.01 | 1 | 344 | HIGH | MED-LOW |
| Penelope ISD School Dist | 01031026 | | 2.89 | 0.01 | 1 | 215 | HIGH | MED-LOW |
| Malone Independent School Dist | 01030981 | | 1.82 | 0.00 | 1 | 178 | HIGH | MED-LOW |
| Bynum Ind School Dist | 01030797 | | 1.79 | 0.00 | 1 | 195 | HIGH | MED-LOW |
| **NAVARRO** | | 0.18 | | | | | | |
| Corsicana Ind School Dist | 01043421 | | 45.77 | 0.08 | 9 | 6,000 | MED | MED-HIGH |
| Blooming Grove Ind School Dist | 01043392 | | 13.64 | 0.03 | 3 | 950 | HIGH | MED-LOW |
| Dawson Ind School Dist | 01043524 | | 10.63 | 0.02 | 1 | 512 | HIGH | MED-HIGH |
| Rice Ind School Dist | 01043641 | | 10.22 | 0.02 | 4 | 975 | HIGH | MED-HIGH |
| Kerens Ind School Dist | 01043586 | | 8.84 | 0.02 | 3 | 600 | HIGH | HIGH |
| Mildred Ind School Dist | 01043615 | | 6.49 | 0.01 | 1 | 730 | HIGH | MED-LOW |
| Frost Ind School Dist | 01043550 | | 4.40 | 0.01 | 2 | 368 | HIGH | MED-HIGH |
| **POLK** | | 0.18 | | | | | | |
| Livingston Ind School Dist | 01047075 | | 51.88 | 0.09 | 7 | 3,963 | HIGH | MED-HIGH |
| Onalaska Ind School Dist | 01809809 | | 17.77 | 0.03 | 2 | 1,056 | HIGH | MED-HIGH |
| Corrigan-Camden Ind Sch Dist | 01046980 | | 15.62 | 0.03 | 3 | 830 | HIGH | MED-HIGH |
| Goodrich Ind School Dist | 01047025 | | 6.74 | 0.01 | 2 | 218 | HIGH | MED-HIGH |
| Big Sandy Ind School Dist | 01046954 | | 5.72 | 0.01 | 1 | 484 | HIGH | MED-HIGH |
| Leggett Ind School Dist | 01047051 | | 2.27 | 0.00 | 1 | 167 | HIGH | MED-HIGH |
| **UPSHUR** | | 0.18 | | | | | | |
| Gilmer Ind School Dist | 01057408 | | 25.43 | 0.05 | 4 | 2,437 | HIGH | MED-HIGH |
| Ore City Ind School Dist | 01057525 | | 14.84 | 0.03 | 3 | 850 | HIGH | HIGH |
| Harmony Ind School Dist | 01057458 | | 14.56 | 0.03 | 4 | 1,050 | HIGH | MED-HIGH |
| Union Grove Ind School Dist | 01057551 | | 14.50 | 0.03 | 2 | 754 | HIGH | MED-LOW |
| Big Sandy Ind School Dist | 01057379 | | 13.09 | 0.02 | 3 | 667 | HIGH | MED-HIGH |
| New Diana Ind School Dist | 01057484 | | 11.42 | 0.02 | 3 | 1,073 | HIGH | MED-LOW |
| Union Hill Ind School Dist | 01057587 | | 6.16 | 0.01 | 1 | 325 | HIGH | MED-HIGH |
| **WALKER** | | 0.18 | | | | | | |
| Huntsville Ind School Dist | 01058672 | | 92.79 | 0.16 | 9 | 6,500 | HIGH | MED-HIGH |

## DISTRICT BUYING POWER INDEX

### COUNTIES RANKED BY PERCENTAGE OF STATE SPENDING

| COUNTY<br>DISTRICT | PID | COUNTY %<br>OF STATE | DISTRICT %<br>OF COUNTY | DISTRICT %<br>OF STATES | NUMBER OF<br>SCHOOLS | ENROLL | EXP | POV |
|---|---|---|---|---|---|---|---|---|
| New Waverly Ind School Dist | 01058737 | | 7.21 | 0.01 | 4 | 1,000 | MED | MED-HIGH |
| **WOOD** | | 0.18 | | | | | | |
| Winnsboro Ind School Dist | 01061942 | | 30.06 | 0.05 | 3 | 1,422 | HIGH | MED-HIGH |
| Mineola Ind School Dist | 01061851 | | 21.08 | 0.04 | 4 | 1,556 | HIGH | MED-HIGH |
| Quitman Ind School Dist | 01061904 | | 17.96 | 0.03 | 3 | 1,083 | HIGH | MED-HIGH |
| Alba-Golden Ind School Dist | 01061784 | | 16.73 | 0.03 | 2 | 588 | HIGH | MED-HIGH |
| Hawkins Ind School Dist | 01061813 | | 10.53 | 0.02 | 3 | 750 | HIGH | MED-HIGH |
| Yantis Ind School Dist | 01061980 | | 3.64 | 0.01 | 2 | 350 | HIGH | HIGH |
| **ATASCOSA** | | 0.17 | | | | | | |
| Poteet Ind School Dist | 00995493 | | 31.67 | 0.05 | 4 | 1,339 | HIGH | MED-HIGH |
| Pleasanton Ind School Dist | 00995431 | | 27.91 | 0.05 | 4 | 3,540 | MED | MED-HIGH |
| Jourdanton Ind School Dist | 00995376 | | 14.67 | 0.02 | 4 | 1,200 | MED | MED-HIGH |
| Lytle Ind School Dist | 00995405 | | 13.80 | 0.02 | 4 | 1,309 | MED | MED-HIGH |
| Charlotte Ind School Dist | 00995338 | | 11.96 | 0.02 | 3 | 450 | HIGH | MED-HIGH |
| **HOWARD** | | 0.17 | | | | | | |
| Big Spring Ind School Dist | 01031870 | | 71.61 | 0.12 | 9 | 4,000 | HIGH | MED-HIGH |
| Forsan Ind School Dist | 01032094 | | 16.43 | 0.03 | 2 | 771 | HIGH | MED-LOW |
| Coahoma Ind School Dist | 01032056 | | 11.97 | 0.02 | 3 | 1,061 | HIGH | MED-HIGH |
| **JACKSON** | | 0.17 | | | | | | |
| Ganado Ind School Dist | 01033050 | | 48.24 | 0.08 | 3 | 700 | HIGH | MED-HIGH |
| Edna Ind School Dist | 01032991 | | 30.24 | 0.05 | 4 | 1,328 | HIGH | MED-HIGH |
| Industrial Ind School Dist | 01033086 | | 21.52 | 0.04 | 4 | 1,100 | HIGH | MED-LOW |
| **TITUS** | | 0.17 | | | | | | |
| Mt Pleasant Ind School Dist | 01055369 | | 66.37 | 0.11 | 8 | 5,100 | HIGH | MED-HIGH |
| Chapel Hill Ind School Dist | 01055307 | | 24.68 | 0.04 | 3 | 1,050 | HIGH | MED-HIGH |
| Harts Bluff Ind School Dist | 01055345 | | 8.95 | 0.01 | 1 | 675 | HIGH | MED-HIGH |
| **ERATH** | | 0.16 | | | | | | |
| Stephenville Ind School Dist | 01017135 | | 63.76 | 0.11 | 6 | 3,650 | HIGH | MED-HIGH |
| Dublin Ind School Dist | 01017018 | | 16.90 | 0.03 | 3 | 1,121 | HIGH | MED-HIGH |
| Lingleville Ind School Dist | 01017082 | | 5.14 | 0.01 | 1 | 282 | HIGH | MED-HIGH |
| Morgan Mill Ind School Dist | 01017111 | | 4.74 | 0.01 | 1 | 125 | HIGH | MED-LOW |
| Huckabay Ind School Dist | 01017056 | | 3.28 | 0.01 | 1 | 250 | HIGH | MED-LOW |
| Three Way Ind School Dist | 01017185 | | 3.10 | 0.01 | 2 | 190 | HIGH | MED-LOW |
| Bluff Dale Ind Sch Dist | 01016997 | | 3.09 | 0.01 | 1 | 222 | HIGH | MED-LOW |
| **FANNIN** | | 0.16 | | | | | | |
| Bonham Ind School Dist | 01017367 | | 31.48 | 0.05 | 5 | 1,850 | HIGH | MED-HIGH |
| Leonard Ind School Dist | 01017501 | | 21.06 | 0.03 | 4 | 878 | HIGH | MED-HIGH |
| Sam Rayburn Ind School Dist | 01017549 | | 11.95 | 0.02 | 1 | 525 | HIGH | MED-HIGH |
| Honey Grove Ind School Dist | 01017472 | | 10.97 | 0.02 | 3 | 614 | HIGH | MED-HIGH |
| Dodd City Ind School Dist | 01017422 | | 7.91 | 0.01 | 1 | 364 | HIGH | MED-LOW |
| Trenton Ind School Dist | 01017604 | | 6.35 | 0.01 | 3 | 573 | HIGH | MED-LOW |
| Savoy Ind School Dist | 01017575 | | 6.07 | 0.01 | 2 | 320 | HIGH | MED-LOW |
| Ector Ind School Dist | 01017458 | | 4.20 | 0.01 | 1 | 260 | HIGH | MED-HIGH |
| **HALE** | | 0.16 | | | | | | |
| Plainview Ind School Dist | 01021904 | | 58.76 | 0.09 | 10 | 4,717 | HIGH | MED-HIGH |
| Abernathy Ind School Dist | 01021746 | | 18.06 | 0.03 | 3 | 850 | HIGH | MED-HIGH |
| Hale Center Ind School Dist | 01021813 | | 15.45 | 0.02 | 3 | 628 | HIGH | MED-HIGH |
| Petersburg Ind School Dist | 01021863 | | 5.06 | 0.01 | 1 | 280 | HIGH | MED-HIGH |
| Cotton Center Ind School Dist | 01021784 | | 2.66 | 0.00 | 1 | 125 | HIGH | MED-HIGH |
| **JASPER** | | 0.16 | | | | | | |
| Jasper Ind School Dist | 01033244 | | 51.87 | 0.08 | 4 | 2,400 | HIGH | HIGH |
| Kirbyville Cons Ind Sch Dist | 01033282 | | 18.92 | 0.03 | 3 | 1,500 | HIGH | HIGH |
| Buna Ind School Dist | 01033177 | | 17.23 | 0.03 | 3 | 1,497 | HIGH | MED-HIGH |
| Brookeland Ind School Dist | 01033141 | | 7.47 | 0.01 | 1 | 380 | HIGH | MED-HIGH |
| Evadale Ind School Dist | 01033218 | | 4.51 | 0.01 | 2 | 394 | MED | MED-HIGH |
| **KERR** | | 0.16 | | | | | | |
| Kerrville Ind School Dist | 01036076 | | 67.64 | 0.11 | 10 | 4,800 | HIGH | MED-HIGH |
| Ingram Ind School Dist | 01036052 | | 17.37 | 0.03 | 3 | 1,100 | HIGH | MED-HIGH |
| Center Point Ind School Dist | 01035979 | | 10.85 | 0.02 | 3 | 569 | HIGH | MED-HIGH |
| Hunt Ind School Dist | 01036038 | | 3.94 | 0.01 | 1 | 204 | HIGH | MED-LOW |
| Divide ISD School Dist | 01036014 | | 0.20 | 0.00 | 1 | 23 | MED | MED-HIGH |
| **HOPKINS** | | 0.15 | | | | | | |
| Sulphur Springs Ind Sch Dist | 01031624 | | 45.52 | 0.07 | 9 | 4,400 | MED | MED-HIGH |
| North Hopkins Ind School Dist | 01031545 | | 18.17 | 0.03 | 1 | 550 | HIGH | MED-HIGH |
| Como Pickton Cons Ind SD | 01031466 | | 15.17 | 0.02 | 1 | 700 | HIGH | MED-HIGH |
| Cumby Ind School Dist | 01031492 | | 7.32 | 0.01 | 2 | 400 | HIGH | MED-LOW |
| Miller Grove Ind School Dist | 01031521 | | 6.67 | 0.01 | 1 | 345 | HIGH | MED-LOW |
| Saltillo Ind School Dist | 01031571 | | 4.27 | 0.01 | 1 | 276 | HIGH | MED-HIGH |

## DISTRICT BUYING POWER INDEX
### COUNTIES RANKED BY PERCENTAGE OF STATE SPENDING

| COUNTY<br>DISTRICT | PID | COUNTY %<br>OF STATE | DISTRICT %<br>OF COUNTY | DISTRICT %<br>OF STATES | NUMBER OF<br>SCHOOLS | ENROLL | EXP | POV |
|---|---|---|---|---|---|---|---|---|
| Sulphur Bluff Ind School Dist | 01031595 | | 2.88 | 0.00 | 1 | 230 | HIGH | MED-LOW |
| **LAMAR** | | 0.15 | | | | | | |
| Paris Ind School Dist | 01036698 | | 68.80 | 0.10 | 8 | 3,900 | HIGH | MED-HIGH |
| Prairiland Ind School Dist | 01036789 | | 16.01 | 0.02 | 4 | 1,088 | HIGH | MED-LOW |
| Chisum Ind School Dist | 01036600 | | 15.19 | 0.02 | 3 | 1,020 | HIGH | MED-HIGH |
| **CALDWELL** | | 0.14 | | | | | | |
| Lockhart Ind School Dist | 01003031 | | 65.37 | 0.09 | 9 | 6,350 | MED | MED-HIGH |
| Luling Ind School Dist | 01003093 | | 31.17 | 0.04 | 4 | 1,400 | HIGH | MED-HIGH |
| Prairie Lea Ind School Dist | 01003122 | | 3.46 | 0.00 | 1 | 216 | HIGH | MED-HIGH |
| **MILAM** | | 0.14 | | | | | | |
| Cameron Ind School Dist | 01041758 | | 49.44 | 0.07 | 4 | 1,684 | HIGH | MED-HIGH |
| Rockdale Ind School Dist | 01041851 | | 22.01 | 0.03 | 4 | 1,432 | HIGH | MED-HIGH |
| Milano Ind School Dist | 01041825 | | 11.41 | 0.02 | 3 | 419 | HIGH | MED-HIGH |
| Thorndale Ind School Dist | 01041904 | | 8.60 | 0.01 | 3 | 650 | HIGH | MED-LOW |
| Gause Ind School Dist | 01041801 | | 5.46 | 0.01 | 1 | 170 | HIGH | MED-HIGH |
| Buckholts Ind School Dist | 01041722 | | 3.09 | 0.00 | 1 | 132 | HIGH | MED-HIGH |
| **SHELBY** | | 0.14 | | | | | | |
| Center Ind School Dist | 01050278 | | 43.06 | 0.06 | 6 | 2,600 | HIGH | HIGH |
| Timpson Ind School Dist | 01050450 | | 16.26 | 0.02 | 3 | 628 | HIGH | MED-HIGH |
| Tenaha Ind School Dist | 01050424 | | 14.50 | 0.02 | 1 | 542 | HIGH | HIGH |
| Shelbyville Ind School Dist | 01050395 | | 12.70 | 0.02 | 3 | 790 | HIGH | HIGH |
| Joaquin Ind School Dist | 01050357 | | 11.46 | 0.02 | 3 | 680 | HIGH | HIGH |
| Excelsior Ind School Dist | 01050321 | | 2.02 | 0.00 | 1 | 80 | HIGH | MED-HIGH |
| **UVALDE** | | 0.14 | | | | | | |
| Uvalde Cons Ind School Dist | 01057795 | | 76.61 | 0.10 | 8 | 4,221 | HIGH | HIGH |
| Sabinal Ind School Dist | 01057733 | | 10.51 | 0.01 | 2 | 429 | HIGH | MED-HIGH |
| Knippa Ind School Dist | 01057692 | | 7.72 | 0.01 | 1 | 460 | HIGH | HIGH |
| Utopia Ind School Dist | 01057769 | | 5.16 | 0.01 | 1 | 210 | HIGH | MED-HIGH |
| **HOCKLEY** | | 0.13 | | | | | | |
| Levelland Ind School Dist | 01031129 | | 49.96 | 0.06 | 6 | 2,936 | HIGH | MED-HIGH |
| Ropes Ind School Dist | 01031234 | | 14.59 | 0.02 | 1 | 479 | HIGH | MED-HIGH |
| Sundown Ind School Dist | 01031301 | | 14.41 | 0.02 | 3 | 595 | HIGH | MED-HIGH |
| Smyer Ind School Dist | 01031272 | | 12.88 | 0.02 | 2 | 415 | HIGH | MED-HIGH |
| Whitharral Ind School Dist | 01031349 | | 4.46 | 0.01 | 1 | 175 | HIGH | MED-HIGH |
| Anton Ind School Dist | 01031090 | | 3.70 | 0.00 | 1 | 185 | HIGH | HIGH |
| **KLEBERG** | | 0.13 | | | | | | |
| Kingsville Ind School Dist | 01036258 | | 73.52 | 0.10 | 8 | 3,050 | HIGH | HIGH |
| Santa Gertrudis Ind Sch Dist | 01809536 | | 14.08 | 0.02 | 2 | 800 | HIGH | HIGH |
| Riviera Ind School Dist | 01036399 | | 6.81 | 0.01 | 2 | 440 | HIGH | MED-HIGH |
| Ricardo Ind School Dist | 01036375 | | 5.59 | 0.01 | 1 | 670 | LOW | MED-HIGH |
| **NOLAN** | | 0.13 | | | | | | |
| Sweetwater ISD School Dist | 01043914 | | 63.36 | 0.09 | 7 | 1,888 | HIGH | MED-HIGH |
| Roscoe Collegiate Ind Sch Dist | 01043885 | | 21.47 | 0.03 | 3 | 593 | HIGH | MED-HIGH |
| Blackwell Cons Ind Sch Dist | 01043794 | | 7.65 | 0.01 | 1 | 150 | HIGH | MED-HIGH |
| Highland Ind School Dist | 01043859 | | 7.52 | 0.01 | 1 | 239 | HIGH | MED-HIGH |
| **WILLACY** | | 0.13 | | | | | | |
| Lyford Cons Ind School Dist | 01060651 | | 43.46 | 0.06 | 3 | 1,422 | HIGH | HIGH |
| Raymondville Ind Sch Dist | 01060716 | | 35.58 | 0.05 | 5 | 2,000 | HIGH | HIGH |
| Lasara Ind School Dist | 01060637 | | 12.75 | 0.02 | 2 | 368 | HIGH | HIGH |
| San Perlita Ind School Dist | 01060780 | | 8.22 | 0.01 | 1 | 269 | HIGH | HIGH |
| **DE WITT** | | 0.12 | | | | | | |
| Cuero Ind School Dist | 01013684 | | 40.66 | 0.05 | 4 | 1,990 | HIGH | MED-HIGH |
| Yoakum Ind School Dist | 01013804 | | 37.05 | 0.05 | 5 | 1,500 | HIGH | MED-HIGH |
| Yorktown Ind School Dist | 01013866 | | 12.43 | 0.02 | 3 | 513 | HIGH | MED-HIGH |
| Meyersville Ind School Dist | 01013737 | | 3.60 | 0.00 | 1 | 137 | HIGH | MED-LOW |
| Nordheim Ind School Dist | 01013751 | | 3.43 | 0.00 | 1 | 149 | HIGH | MED-HIGH |
| Westhoff Ind School Dist | 01013787 | | 2.83 | 0.00 | 1 | 80 | HIGH | HIGH |
| **GAINES** | | 0.12 | | | | | | |
| Seminole Ind School Dist | 01018751 | | 68.22 | 0.08 | 6 | 2,619 | HIGH | MED-HIGH |
| Seagraves Ind School Dist | 01018713 | | 24.82 | 0.03 | 3 | 547 | HIGH | MED-HIGH |
| Loop Ind School Dist | 01018684 | | 6.96 | 0.01 | 1 | 124 | HIGH | MED-LOW |
| **GRIMES** | | 0.12 | | | | | | |
| Navasota Ind School Dist | 01021409 | | 75.42 | 0.09 | 6 | 3,000 | HIGH | MED-HIGH |
| Anderson-Shiro Cons Ind SD | 01021344 | | 11.83 | 0.01 | 2 | 879 | HIGH | MED-LOW |
| Iola Ind School Dist | 01021370 | | 7.84 | 0.01 | 2 | 527 | HIGH | MED-HIGH |
| Richards Ind School Dist | 01021459 | | 4.91 | 0.01 | 1 | 180 | HIGH | MED-HIGH |

## DISTRICT BUYING POWER INDEX
### COUNTIES RANKED BY PERCENTAGE OF STATE SPENDING

| COUNTY / DISTRICT | PID | COUNTY % OF STATE | DISTRICT % OF COUNTY | DISTRICT % OF STATES | NUMBER OF SCHOOLS | ENROLL | EXP | POV |
|---|---|---|---|---|---|---|---|---|
| **KENDALL** | | 0.12 | | | | | | |
| Boerne Ind School Dist | 01035814 | | 81.57 | 0.09 | 12 | 9,000 | MED | MED-LOW |
| Comfort Ind School Dist | 01035864 | | 18.43 | 0.02 | 3 | 1,052 | HIGH | MED-HIGH |
| **PALO PINTO** | | 0.12 | | | | | | |
| Mineral Wells Ind School Dist | 01046019 | | 68.38 | 0.08 | 6 | 3,200 | HIGH | MED-HIGH |
| Santo Ind School Dist | 01046124 | | 11.98 | 0.01 | 2 | 451 | HIGH | MED-HIGH |
| Gordon Ind School Dist | 01045950 | | 6.70 | 0.01 | 1 | 210 | HIGH | MED-HIGH |
| Graford Ind School Dist | 01045986 | | 6.08 | 0.01 | 2 | 340 | HIGH | MED-HIGH |
| Strawn Ind School Dist | 01046150 | | 5.77 | 0.01 | 1 | 160 | HIGH | MED-HIGH |
| Palo Pinto Ind Sch Dist 906 | 01046100 | | 1.09 | 0.00 | 1 | 100 | MED | MED-LOW |
| **AUSTIN** | | 0.11 | | | | | | |
| Bellville Ind School Dist | 00995534 | | 38.08 | 0.04 | 6 | 2,200 | HIGH | MED-HIGH |
| Sealy Ind School Dist | 00995584 | | 36.21 | 0.04 | 4 | 2,669 | MED | MED-LOW |
| Brazos Ind School Dist | 00995625 | | 25.71 | 0.03 | 4 | 700 | HIGH | MED-LOW |
| **BURNET** | | 0.11 | | | | | | |
| Burnet Cons Ind Sch Dist | 01002752 | | 58.26 | 0.06 | 6 | 3,000 | HIGH | MED-HIGH |
| Marble Falls Ind School Dist | 01002817 | | 41.74 | 0.05 | 7 | 4,000 | MED | MED-HIGH |
| **BEE** | | 0.10 | | | | | | |
| Beeville Ind School Dist | 00996069 | | 67.40 | 0.06 | 6 | 3,400 | MED | HIGH |
| Skidmore Tynan Ind SD | 00996215 | | 16.15 | 0.02 | 3 | 850 | HIGH | MED-HIGH |
| Pettus Ind School Dist | 00996174 | | 10.66 | 0.01 | 2 | 400 | HIGH | MED-HIGH |
| Pawnee Ind School Dist | 00996148 | | 5.79 | 0.01 | 1 | 550 | MED | MED-HIGH |
| **COLORADO** | | 0.10 | | | | | | |
| Columbus Ind School Dist | 01006746 | | 41.63 | 0.04 | 4 | 1,494 | HIGH | MED-HIGH |
| Rice Cons Ind School Dist | 01006784 | | 38.52 | 0.04 | 7 | 1,325 | HIGH | MED-HIGH |
| Weimar Ind School Dist | 01006849 | | 19.85 | 0.02 | 3 | 629 | HIGH | MED-HIGH |
| **DAWSON** | | 0.10 | | | | | | |
| Lamesa Ind School Dist | 01012862 | | 76.60 | 0.08 | 5 | 1,800 | HIGH | MED-HIGH |
| Sands Consolidated ISD | 01012941 | | 9.83 | 0.01 | 1 | 247 | HIGH | MED-HIGH |
| Klondike Ind School Dist | 01012824 | | 9.41 | 0.01 | 1 | 249 | HIGH | MED-HIGH |
| Dawson Ind School Dist | 01012795 | | 4.17 | 0.00 | 1 | 140 | HIGH | MED-HIGH |
| **DUVAL** | | 0.10 | | | | | | |
| San Diego Ind School Dist | 01014274 | | 42.17 | 0.04 | 3 | 1,385 | HIGH | HIGH |
| Freer Ind School Dist | 01809196 | | 38.15 | 0.04 | 3 | 701 | HIGH | HIGH |
| Benavides Ind School Dist | 01014171 | | 18.69 | 0.02 | 2 | 320 | HIGH | HIGH |
| Ramirez Common School Dist | 01014250 | | 0.99 | 0.00 | 1 | 37 | HIGH | MED-HIGH |
| **FAYETTE** | | 0.10 | | | | | | |
| La Grange Ind School Dist | 01017721 | | 47.62 | 0.05 | 3 | 2,350 | HIGH | MED-HIGH |
| Flatonia Ind School Dist | 01017692 | | 18.47 | 0.02 | 3 | 580 | HIGH | MED-HIGH |
| Schulenburg Ind School Dist | 01017800 | | 15.57 | 0.02 | 2 | 700 | HIGH | MED-HIGH |
| Fayetteville Ind School Dist | 01017666 | | 13.20 | 0.01 | 1 | 260 | HIGH | MED-LOW |
| Round Top-Carmine Ind Sch Dist | 01017771 | | 5.14 | 0.01 | 2 | 267 | HIGH | MED-LOW |
| **JONES** | | 0.10 | | | | | | |
| Anson Ind School Dist | 01035199 | | 33.75 | 0.03 | 3 | 700 | HIGH | MED-HIGH |
| Stamford Ind School Dist | 01035321 | | 26.86 | 0.03 | 3 | 630 | HIGH | MED-HIGH |
| Hawley Ind School Dist | 01035266 | | 21.18 | 0.02 | 3 | 784 | HIGH | MED-HIGH |
| Hamlin Collegiate Ind Sch Dist | 01035228 | | 14.36 | 0.01 | 2 | 430 | HIGH | MED-HIGH |
| Lueders-Avoca Ind School Dist | 01035292 | | 3.85 | 0.00 | 2 | 100 | HIGH | MED-HIGH |
| **LEON** | | 0.10 | | | | | | |
| Buffalo Ind School Dist | 01037551 | | 33.61 | 0.03 | 4 | 900 | HIGH | MED-HIGH |
| Centerville Ind School Dist | 01037587 | | 24.71 | 0.02 | 2 | 700 | HIGH | HIGH |
| Leon Ind School Dist | 01037628 | | 23.51 | 0.02 | 2 | 700 | HIGH | MED-LOW |
| Normangee Ind School Dist | 01037654 | | 12.04 | 0.01 | 3 | 605 | HIGH | MED-LOW |
| Oakwood Ind School Dist | 01037680 | | 6.12 | 0.01 | 2 | 199 | HIGH | HIGH |
| **MOORE** | | 0.10 | | | | | | |
| Dumas Ind School Dist | 01042817 | | 83.07 | 0.08 | 9 | 4,300 | HIGH | MED-HIGH |
| Sunray Ind School Dist | 01042910 | | 16.93 | 0.02 | 3 | 556 | HIGH | MED-LOW |
| **REEVES** | | 0.10 | | | | | | |
| Pecos-Barstow-Toyah Ind SD | 01048304 | | 92.53 | 0.09 | 5 | 2,700 | HIGH | MED-HIGH |
| Balmorhea Ind School Dist | 01048251 | | 7.47 | 0.01 | 1 | 165 | HIGH | MED-LOW |
| **SAN JACINTO** | | 0.10 | | | | | | |
| Shepherd Ind School Dist | 01049449 | | 60.61 | 0.06 | 4 | 2,041 | HIGH | MED-HIGH |
| Coldspring-Oakhurst Cons ISD | 01049401 | | 39.39 | 0.04 | 4 | 1,465 | HIGH | MED-HIGH |
| **SCURRY** | | 0.10 | | | | | | |
| Snyder Ind School Dist | 01050101 | | 84.68 | 0.09 | 4 | 2,700 | HIGH | MED-HIGH |
| Hermleigh Ind School Dist | 01050046 | | 8.21 | 0.01 | 1 | 275 | HIGH | MED-LOW |

## DISTRICT BUYING POWER INDEX
### COUNTIES RANKED BY PERCENTAGE OF STATE SPENDING

| COUNTY<br>DISTRICT | PID | COUNTY %<br>OF STATE | DISTRICT %<br>OF COUNTY | DISTRICT %<br>OF STATES | NUMBER OF<br>SCHOOLS | ENROLL | EXP | POV |
|---|---|---|---|---|---|---|---|---|
| Ira Ind School Dist | 01050072 | | 7.11 | 0.01 | 1 | 275 | HIGH | MED-LOW |
| **CALHOUN** | | 0.09 | | | | | | |
| Calhoun Co Ind School Dist | 01003158 | | 100.00 | 0.09 | 7 | 3,738 | HIGH | MED-HIGH |
| **DEAF SMITH** | | 0.09 | | | | | | |
| Hereford Ind School Dist | 01012989 | | 89.22 | 0.08 | 9 | 4,100 | HIGH | MED-HIGH |
| Walcott Ind School Dist | 01013086 | | 10.78 | 0.01 | 1 | 146 | HIGH | MED-HIGH |
| **EASTLAND** | | 0.09 | | | | | | |
| Eastland Ind School Dist | 01014406 | | 38.92 | 0.04 | 3 | 1,000 | HIGH | MED-HIGH |
| Cisco Independent Sch Dist | 01014353 | | 26.71 | 0.02 | 4 | 830 | HIGH | MED-HIGH |
| Gorman Ind School Dist | 01014444 | | 13.68 | 0.01 | 3 | 287 | HIGH | MED-HIGH |
| Ranger Ind School Dist | 01014470 | | 13.05 | 0.01 | 1 | 350 | HIGH | MED-HIGH |
| Rising Star Ind Sch Dist | 01014511 | | 7.65 | 0.01 | 2 | 150 | HIGH | MED-HIGH |
| **FREESTONE** | | 0.09 | | | | | | |
| Fairfield Ind School Dist | 01018452 | | 47.14 | 0.04 | 4 | 1,800 | HIGH | MED-LOW |
| Teague Ind School Dist | 01018505 | | 30.28 | 0.03 | 5 | 1,160 | HIGH | MED-HIGH |
| Wortham Ind School Dist | 01018543 | | 17.63 | 0.02 | 3 | 500 | HIGH | MED-HIGH |
| Dew Ind School Dist | 01018438 | | 4.95 | 0.00 | 1 | 155 | HIGH | MED-LOW |
| **GONZALES** | | 0.09 | | | | | | |
| Gonzales Ind School Dist | 01019860 | | 59.66 | 0.05 | 6 | 2,875 | HIGH | MED-HIGH |
| Nixon-Smiley Cons Ind Sch Dist | 01019937 | | 32.13 | 0.03 | 3 | 1,076 | HIGH | MED-HIGH |
| Waelder Ind School Dist | 01020003 | | 8.22 | 0.01 | 1 | 317 | HIGH | MED-HIGH |
| **MONTAGUE** | | 0.09 | | | | | | |
| Bowie Ind School Dist | 01042180 | | 43.73 | 0.04 | 4 | 1,720 | HIGH | MED-HIGH |
| Nocona Ind School Dist | 01042336 | | 26.46 | 0.02 | 3 | 725 | HIGH | MED-HIGH |
| St Jo Ind School Dist | 01042403 | | 8.14 | 0.01 | 2 | 330 | HIGH | MED-LOW |
| Forestburg Ind School Dist | 01042257 | | 7.49 | 0.01 | 1 | 173 | HIGH | MED-HIGH |
| Gold-Burg Ind School Dist | 01042283 | | 6.39 | 0.01 | 1 | 127 | HIGH | MED-HIGH |
| Montague Ind School Dist | 01042312 | | 4.78 | 0.00 | 1 | 166 | HIGH | HIGH |
| Prairie Valley Ind School Dist | 01042374 | | 3.02 | 0.00 | 1 | 167 | MED | MED-HIGH |
| **PANOLA** | | 0.09 | | | | | | |
| Carthage Ind School Dist | 01046215 | | 75.52 | 0.07 | 6 | 2,600 | HIGH | MED-HIGH |
| Gary Ind School Dist | 01046277 | | 12.33 | 0.01 | 1 | 443 | HIGH | HIGH |
| Beckville Ind School Dist | 01046186 | | 12.15 | 0.01 | 2 | 700 | MED | MED-HIGH |
| **WASHINGTON** | | 0.09 | | | | | | |
| Brenham Ind School Dist | 01059042 | | 84.84 | 0.07 | 7 | 5,000 | MED | MED-HIGH |
| Burton Ind School Dist | 01059107 | | 15.16 | 0.01 | 2 | 440 | HIGH | MED-LOW |
| **BOSQUE** | | 0.08 | | | | | | |
| Valley Mills Ind School Dist | 01000754 | | 25.93 | 0.02 | 2 | 600 | HIGH | MED-HIGH |
| Clifton Ind School Dist | 01808893 | | 23.86 | 0.02 | 3 | 1,000 | HIGH | MED-HIGH |
| Meridian Ind School Dist | 01000699 | | 16.22 | 0.01 | 4 | 475 | HIGH | MED-HIGH |
| Kopperl Ind School Dist | 01000663 | | 7.47 | 0.01 | 1 | 200 | HIGH | MED-HIGH |
| Cranfills Gap ISD School Dist | 01000601 | | 7.31 | 0.01 | 1 | 120 | HIGH | MED-HIGH |
| Morgan Ind School Dist | 01000728 | | 6.64 | 0.01 | 1 | 130 | HIGH | MED-HIGH |
| Iredell Ind School Dist | 01000637 | | 6.61 | 0.01 | 1 | 138 | HIGH | MED-HIGH |
| Walnut Springs Ind Sch Dist | 01000780 | | 5.96 | 0.00 | 1 | 187 | HIGH | HIGH |
| **BURLESON** | | 0.08 | | | | | | |
| Caldwell Ind School Dist | 01002647 | | 64.34 | 0.05 | 5 | 1,750 | HIGH | MED-HIGH |
| Snook Ind School Dist | 01002685 | | 25.76 | 0.02 | 1 | 500 | HIGH | MED-HIGH |
| Somerville Ind School Dist | 01002714 | | 9.90 | 0.01 | 3 | 550 | MED | MED-HIGH |
| **CALLAHAN** | | 0.08 | | | | | | |
| Clyde Consolidated Ind SD | 01003316 | | 51.46 | 0.04 | 4 | 1,440 | HIGH | MED-HIGH |
| Cross Plains Ind Sch Dist | 01003354 | | 20.49 | 0.02 | 2 | 340 | HIGH | MED-HIGH |
| Eula Ind School Dist | 01003380 | | 14.59 | 0.01 | 3 | 441 | HIGH | MED-LOW |
| Baird Ind School Dist | 01003287 | | 13.46 | 0.01 | 3 | 289 | HIGH | MED-HIGH |
| **DIMMIT** | | 0.08 | | | | | | |
| Carrizo Spgs Cons Ind SD | 01014030 | | 100.00 | 0.08 | 4 | 2,200 | HIGH | HIGH |
| **GRAY** | | 0.08 | | | | | | |
| Pampa Ind School Dist | 01020132 | | 81.68 | 0.07 | 7 | 3,500 | HIGH | MED-HIGH |
| Lefors Ind School Dist | 01020077 | | 8.35 | 0.01 | 1 | 168 | HIGH | HIGH |
| McLean Ind School Dist | 01020106 | | 7.63 | 0.01 | 1 | 236 | HIGH | MED-HIGH |
| Grandview-Hopkins Ind Sch Dist | 01020053 | | 2.34 | 0.00 | 1 | 50 | HIGH | MED-HIGH |
| **HOUSTON** | | 0.08 | | | | | | |
| Crockett Ind School Dist | 01031715 | | 44.97 | 0.03 | 5 | 1,331 | HIGH | HIGH |
| Grapeland Ind School Dist | 01031753 | | 16.58 | 0.01 | 3 | 600 | HIGH | HIGH |
| Latexo Ind School Dist | 01031820 | | 16.06 | 0.01 | 2 | 475 | HIGH | HIGH |
| Lovelady Ind School Dist | 01031844 | | 12.99 | 0.01 | 2 | 510 | HIGH | MED-HIGH |

## DISTRICT BUYING POWER INDEX
### COUNTIES RANKED BY PERCENTAGE OF STATE SPENDING

| COUNTY<br>DISTRICT | PID | COUNTY %<br>OF STATE | DISTRICT %<br>OF COUNTY | DISTRICT %<br>OF STATES | NUMBER OF<br>SCHOOLS | ENROLL | EXP | POV |
|---|---|---|---|---|---|---|---|---|
| Kennard Ind Sch Dist | 01031791 | | 9.40 | 0.01 | 1 | 256 | HIGH | HIGH |
| **HUTCHINSON** | | 0.08 | | | | | | |
| Borger Ind School Dist | 01032642 | | 62.96 | 0.05 | 6 | 2,700 | HIGH | MED-HIGH |
| Plemons-Stinnett-Phillips CISD | 01032836 | | 16.88 | 0.01 | 3 | 731 | HIGH | MED-HIGH |
| Sanford-Fritch Ind School Dist | 01032771 | | 15.06 | 0.01 | 3 | 687 | HIGH | MED-LOW |
| Spring Creek Ind School Dist | 01032812 | | 5.11 | 0.00 | 1 | 110 | HIGH | MED-LOW |
| **KARNES** | | 0.08 | | | | | | |
| Karnes City Ind School Dist | 01035395 | | 43.85 | 0.04 | 5 | 1,062 | HIGH | MED-HIGH |
| Kenedy Ind School Dist | 01035450 | | 22.69 | 0.02 | 3 | 500 | HIGH | MED-HIGH |
| Runge Ind School Dist | 01035503 | | 20.20 | 0.02 | 1 | 238 | HIGH | MED-HIGH |
| Falls City Ind School Dist | 01035369 | | 13.26 | 0.01 | 2 | 340 | HIGH | MED-LOW |
| **LAMB** | | 0.08 | | | | | | |
| Littlefield Ind School Dist | 01036911 | | 36.51 | 0.03 | 4 | 1,300 | HIGH | HIGH |
| Springlake-Earth Ind Sch Dist | 01037044 | | 25.37 | 0.02 | 2 | 370 | HIGH | MED-LOW |
| Olton Ind School Dist | 01036973 | | 15.71 | 0.01 | 3 | 600 | HIGH | MED-HIGH |
| Sudan Ind School Dist | 01037082 | | 15.38 | 0.01 | 2 | 424 | HIGH | MED-HIGH |
| Amherst Ind School Dist | 01036882 | | 7.03 | 0.01 | 1 | 130 | HIGH | MED-HIGH |
| **LAVACA** | | 0.08 | | | | | | |
| Hallettsville Ind Sch Dist | 01037288 | | 55.13 | 0.04 | 3 | 1,100 | HIGH | MED-HIGH |
| Shiner Ind School Dist | 01037355 | | 20.48 | 0.02 | 2 | 650 | HIGH | MED-LOW |
| Moulton Ind School Dist | 01037329 | | 12.71 | 0.01 | 2 | 300 | HIGH | MED-HIGH |
| Sweet Home Ind School Dist | 01037381 | | 5.23 | 0.00 | 1 | 140 | HIGH | MED-HIGH |
| Ezzell Ind School Dist | 01037264 | | 3.95 | 0.00 | 1 | 85 | HIGH | MED-LOW |
| Vysehrad Ind School Dist | 01037408 | | 2.51 | 0.00 | 1 | 115 | MED | MED-LOW |
| **LIMESTONE** | | 0.08 | | | | | | |
| Mexia Ind School Dist | 01038086 | | 58.67 | 0.05 | 5 | 1,800 | HIGH | HIGH |
| Groesbeck Ind School Dist | 01038048 | | 28.03 | 0.02 | 4 | 1,500 | MED | MED-HIGH |
| Coolidge Ind School Dist | 01038012 | | 13.29 | 0.01 | 2 | 295 | HIGH | HIGH |
| **PECOS** | | 0.08 | | | | | | |
| Ft Stockton Ind School Dist | 01046837 | | 75.91 | 0.06 | 5 | 2,469 | HIGH | MED-HIGH |
| Iraan-Sheffield Ind Sch Dist | 01046904 | | 14.79 | 0.01 | 3 | 375 | HIGH | MED-HIGH |
| Buena Vista Ind School Dist | 01046801 | | 9.30 | 0.01 | 1 | 250 | HIGH | MED-HIGH |
| **RUNNELS** | | 0.08 | | | | | | |
| Winters Ind School Dist | 01048914 | | 34.70 | 0.03 | 3 | 525 | HIGH | MED-HIGH |
| Ballinger Ind School Dist | 01048809 | | 33.27 | 0.03 | 3 | 798 | HIGH | MED-HIGH |
| Miles Ind School Dist | 01048847 | | 20.22 | 0.02 | 1 | 480 | HIGH | MED-HIGH |
| Olfen Ind School Dist | 01048873 | | 11.80 | 0.01 | 1 | 205 | HIGH | MED-LOW |
| **TERRY** | | 0.08 | | | | | | |
| Brownfield Ind Sch Dist | 01055084 | | 72.80 | 0.06 | 4 | 1,623 | HIGH | HIGH |
| Meadow Ind School Dist | 01055149 | | 13.91 | 0.01 | 1 | 285 | HIGH | HIGH |
| Wellman Union Ind School Dist | 01055199 | | 13.29 | 0.01 | 1 | 335 | HIGH | HIGH |
| **TYLER** | | 0.08 | | | | | | |
| Woodville Ind School Dist | 01057331 | | 48.50 | 0.04 | 4 | 1,300 | HIGH | MED-HIGH |
| Warren Ind School Dist | 01057288 | | 24.03 | 0.02 | 4 | 1,200 | MED | MED-HIGH |
| Colmesneil Ind School Dist | 01057226 | | 15.18 | 0.01 | 2 | 450 | HIGH | MED-HIGH |
| Spurger Ind School Dist | 01057252 | | 7.97 | 0.01 | 2 | 400 | MED | MED-HIGH |
| Chester Ind School Dist | 01057197 | | 4.31 | 0.00 | 2 | 184 | HIGH | MED-HIGH |
| **WARD** | | 0.08 | | | | | | |
| Monahans-Wickett-Pyote ISD | 01058957 | | 95.32 | 0.08 | 6 | 2,300 | HIGH | MED-HIGH |
| Grandfalls-Royalty Ind SD | 01058919 | | 4.68 | 0.00 | 1 | 184 | HIGH | MED-LOW |
| **WINKLER** | | 0.08 | | | | | | |
| Kermit Ind School Dist | 01061423 | | 69.56 | 0.06 | 3 | 1,397 | HIGH | MED-HIGH |
| Wink Loving Ind School Dist | 01061485 | | 30.44 | 0.03 | 2 | 420 | HIGH | MED-LOW |
| **YOUNG** | | 0.08 | | | | | | |
| Graham Ind School Dist | 01062104 | | 60.82 | 0.05 | 5 | 2,354 | HIGH | MED-HIGH |
| Olney Ind School Dist | 01062192 | | 28.08 | 0.02 | 3 | 639 | HIGH | MED-HIGH |
| Newcastle Ind School Dist | 01062166 | | 11.10 | 0.01 | 1 | 205 | HIGH | MED-HIGH |
| **BAILEY** | | 0.07 | | | | | | |
| Muleshoe Ind School Dist | 00995699 | | 100.00 | 0.07 | 4 | 1,450 | HIGH | MED-HIGH |
| **CLAY** | | 0.07 | | | | | | |
| Henrietta Ind School Dist | 01005546 | | 61.23 | 0.04 | 3 | 937 | HIGH | MED-LOW |
| Petrolia Cons Ind School Dist | 01005601 | | 27.61 | 0.02 | 2 | 450 | HIGH | MED-LOW |
| Midway Ind School Dist | 01005584 | | 7.02 | 0.00 | 1 | 134 | HIGH | MED-HIGH |
| Bellevue Ind School Dist | 01005481 | | 4.14 | 0.00 | 1 | 140 | HIGH | MED-LOW |

## DISTRICT BUYING POWER INDEX
### COUNTIES RANKED BY PERCENTAGE OF STATE SPENDING

| COUNTY<br>DISTRICT | PID | COUNTY %<br>OF STATE | DISTRICT %<br>OF COUNTY | DISTRICT %<br>OF STATES | NUMBER OF<br>SCHOOLS | ENROLL | EXP | POV |
|---|---|---|---|---|---|---|---|---|
| **JACK** | | 0.07 | | | | | | |
| Jacksboro Ind Sch Dist | 01032927 | | 73.40 | 0.05 | 3 | 1,023 | HIGH | MED-HIGH |
| Perrin-Whitt Cons Ind Sch Dist | 01032965 | | 13.90 | 0.01 | 2 | 340 | HIGH | MED-LOW |
| Bryson Ind School Dist | 01032898 | | 12.70 | 0.01 | 1 | 241 | HIGH | MED-HIGH |
| **LAMPASAS** | | 0.07 | | | | | | |
| Lampasas Ind School Dist | 01037111 | | 87.64 | 0.06 | 5 | 3,400 | HIGH | MED-HIGH |
| Lometa Ind School Dist | 01037161 | | 12.36 | 0.01 | 1 | 300 | HIGH | MED-HIGH |
| **MADISON** | | 0.07 | | | | | | |
| Madisonville Cons ISD | 01040596 | | 88.77 | 0.06 | 4 | 2,233 | HIGH | MED-HIGH |
| North Zulch Ind School Dist | 01040637 | | 11.23 | 0.01 | 1 | 310 | HIGH | MED-HIGH |
| **PRESIDIO** | | 0.07 | | | | | | |
| Presidio Ind School Dist | 01047867 | | 74.65 | 0.05 | 3 | 1,162 | HIGH | HIGH |
| Marfa Ind School Dist | 01047829 | | 25.35 | 0.02 | 2 | 342 | HIGH | HIGH |
| **WILBARGER** | | 0.07 | | | | | | |
| Vernon Ind School Dist | 01060560 | | 74.64 | 0.05 | 6 | 1,700 | HIGH | MED-HIGH |
| Northside Ind School Dist | 01060534 | | 16.99 | 0.01 | 1 | 222 | HIGH | MED-HIGH |
| Harrold Ind School Dist | 01060508 | | 8.37 | 0.01 | 1 | 106 | HIGH | MED-HIGH |
| **ZAPATA** | | 0.07 | | | | | | |
| Zapata Co Ind School Dist | 01062245 | | 100.00 | 0.07 | 6 | 3,500 | HIGH | HIGH |
| **ARCHER** | | 0.06 | | | | | | |
| Holliday Ind School Dist | 00995211 | | 50.20 | 0.03 | 3 | 1,051 | HIGH | MED-LOW |
| Archer City Ind School Dist | 00995182 | | 28.68 | 0.02 | 2 | 505 | HIGH | MED-HIGH |
| Windthorst Ind School Dist | 00995273 | | 21.12 | 0.01 | 3 | 390 | HIGH | MED-LOW |
| **CAMP** | | 0.06 | | | | | | |
| Pittsburg Ind School Dist | 01004504 | | 100.00 | 0.06 | 5 | 2,356 | HIGH | MED-HIGH |
| **CASTRO** | | 0.06 | | | | | | |
| Dimmitt Ind School Dist | 01004968 | | 72.14 | 0.05 | 4 | 1,230 | HIGH | MED-HIGH |
| Nazareth Ind School Dist | 01005041 | | 20.72 | 0.01 | 1 | 253 | HIGH | MED-LOW |
| Hart Ind School Dist | 01005015 | | 7.13 | 0.00 | 2 | 206 | HIGH | HIGH |
| **COMANCHE** | | 0.06 | | | | | | |
| Comanche Ind School Dist | 01007051 | | 41.81 | 0.03 | 4 | 1,325 | HIGH | MED-HIGH |
| De Leon Ind School Dist | 01007099 | | 35.77 | 0.02 | 3 | 720 | HIGH | MED-HIGH |
| Sidney Ind School Dist | 01007154 | | 11.84 | 0.01 | 1 | 139 | HIGH | MED-HIGH |
| Gustine Ind School Dist | 01007128 | | 10.58 | 0.01 | 1 | 134 | HIGH | MED-HIGH |
| **DALLAM** | | 0.06 | | | | | | |
| Dalhart Ind School Dist | 01008067 | | 81.65 | 0.05 | 4 | 1,700 | HIGH | MED-LOW |
| Texline Ind School Dist | 01008108 | | 18.35 | 0.01 | 1 | 180 | HIGH | MED-HIGH |
| **FALLS** | | 0.06 | | | | | | |
| Marlin Ind School Dist | 01017238 | | 34.73 | 0.02 | 3 | 821 | HIGH | HIGH |
| Rosebud-Lott Ind School Dist | 01017276 | | 29.36 | 0.02 | 3 | 637 | HIGH | MED-HIGH |
| Chilton Ind School Dist | 01017202 | | 27.35 | 0.02 | 1 | 540 | HIGH | MED-HIGH |
| Westphalia Ind School Dist | 01017329 | | 8.56 | 0.00 | 1 | 155 | HIGH | MED-LOW |
| **FLOYD** | | 0.06 | | | | | | |
| Floydada Ind School Dist | 01017977 | | 78.59 | 0.05 | 2 | 700 | HIGH | HIGH |
| Lockney Independent Sch Dist | 01018024 | | 21.41 | 0.01 | 3 | 450 | HIGH | HIGH |
| **FRIO** | | 0.06 | | | | | | |
| Pearsall Ind School Dist | 01018610 | | 52.19 | 0.03 | 4 | 2,100 | MED | HIGH |
| Dilley Ind School Dist | 01018579 | | 47.81 | 0.03 | 4 | 950 | HIGH | HIGH |
| **GILLESPIE** | | 0.06 | | | | | | |
| Fredericksburg Ind School Dist | 01019688 | | 71.72 | 0.05 | 6 | 3,200 | MED | MED-LOW |
| Harper Ind School Dist | 01019731 | | 22.25 | 0.01 | 3 | 557 | HIGH | MED-LOW |
| Doss Consolidated Common SD | 01019664 | | 6.03 | 0.00 | 1 | 25 | HIGH | MED-LOW |
| **LEE** | | 0.06 | | | | | | |
| Giddings Ind School Dist | 01037458 | | 46.71 | 0.03 | 4 | 1,900 | MED | MED-HIGH |
| Lexington Ind School Dist | 01037496 | | 40.43 | 0.03 | 3 | 1,066 | HIGH | MED-LOW |
| Dime Box Ind School Dist | 01037422 | | 12.86 | 0.01 | 1 | 160 | HIGH | MED-LOW |
| **MITCHELL** | | 0.06 | | | | | | |
| Colorado Ind School Dist | 01042063 | | 60.11 | 0.04 | 4 | 900 | HIGH | MED-HIGH |
| Westbrook Ind School Dist | 01042154 | | 32.26 | 0.02 | 1 | 272 | HIGH | HIGH |
| Loraine Ind School Dist | 01042128 | | 7.63 | 0.00 | 1 | 142 | HIGH | MED-HIGH |
| **OCHILTREE** | | 0.06 | | | | | | |
| Perryton Ind School Dist | 01045455 | | 100.00 | 0.06 | 6 | 2,217 | HIGH | MED-LOW |

## DISTRICT BUYING POWER INDEX
### COUNTIES RANKED BY PERCENTAGE OF STATE SPENDING

| COUNTY<br>DISTRICT | PID | COUNTY %<br>OF STATE | DISTRICT %<br>OF COUNTY | DISTRICT %<br>OF STATES | NUMBER OF<br>SCHOOLS | ENROLL | EXP | POV |
|---|---|---|---|---|---|---|---|---|
| **RED RIVER** | | 0.06 | | | | | | |
| Rivercrest Ind School Dist | 01048213 | | 31.56 | 0.02 | 3 | 700 | HIGH | MED-HIGH |
| Clarksville Ind School Dist | 01048110 | | 26.89 | 0.02 | 2 | 534 | HIGH | HIGH |
| Detroit Ind School Dist | 01048172 | | 24.00 | 0.02 | 3 | 530 | HIGH | MED-HIGH |
| Avery Ind School Dist | 01048081 | | 17.54 | 0.01 | 2 | 323 | HIGH | MED-HIGH |
| **REFUGIO** | | 0.06 | | | | | | |
| Woodsboro Ind School Dist | 01048495 | | 61.89 | 0.04 | 2 | 441 | HIGH | MED-HIGH |
| Refugio Ind School Dist | 01048457 | | 31.64 | 0.02 | 3 | 654 | HIGH | MED-HIGH |
| Austwell Tivoli Ind SD | 01048419 | | 6.47 | 0.00 | 2 | 140 | HIGH | HIGH |
| **ROBERTSON** | | 0.06 | | | | | | |
| Hearne Ind School Dist | 01048641 | | 46.87 | 0.03 | 3 | 766 | HIGH | MED-HIGH |
| Franklin Ind School Dist | 01048615 | | 34.07 | 0.02 | 3 | 1,100 | HIGH | MED-LOW |
| Bremond Ind School Dist | 01048550 | | 12.54 | 0.01 | 3 | 500 | MED | MED-HIGH |
| Calvert Ind School Dist | 01048586 | | 6.51 | 0.00 | 1 | 166 | HIGH | HIGH |
| **SWISHER** | | 0.06 | | | | | | |
| Tulia Ind School Dist | 01051571 | | 66.87 | 0.04 | 3 | 1,040 | HIGH | MED-HIGH |
| Happy Ind School Dist | 01051519 | | 20.55 | 0.01 | 2 | 248 | HIGH | MED-HIGH |
| Kress Ind School Dist | 01051545 | | 12.58 | 0.01 | 2 | 242 | HIGH | MED-HIGH |
| **ARANSAS** | | 0.05 | | | | | | |
| Aransas Co Ind School Dist | 00995120 | | 100.00 | 0.05 | 4 | 2,975 | HIGH | HIGH |
| **BANDERA** | | 0.05 | | | | | | |
| Bandera Ind School Dist | 00995778 | | 79.88 | 0.04 | 4 | 2,120 | HIGH | MED-HIGH |
| Medina Ind School Dist | 00995807 | | 20.12 | 0.01 | 2 | 300 | HIGH | MED-LOW |
| **BREWSTER** | | 0.05 | | | | | | |
| Alpine Ind School Dist | 01002192 | | 80.10 | 0.04 | 3 | 965 | HIGH | MED-HIGH |
| Marathon Ind School Dist | 01002233 | | 9.17 | 0.00 | 1 | 55 | HIGH | MED-LOW |
| Terlingua Common School Dist | 01002283 | | 6.48 | 0.00 | 2 | 105 | HIGH | MED-HIGH |
| San Vicente Ind School Dist | 01002269 | | 4.25 | 0.00 | 1 | 13 | HIGH | MED-LOW |
| **BROOKS** | | 0.05 | | | | | | |
| Brooks Co Ind School Dist | 01002336 | | 100.00 | 0.05 | 4 | 1,470 | HIGH | HIGH |
| **FRANKLIN** | | 0.05 | | | | | | |
| Mount Vernon Ind School Dist | 01018385 | | 100.00 | 0.05 | 3 | 1,570 | HIGH | MED-HIGH |
| **LLANO** | | 0.05 | | | | | | |
| Llano Ind School Dist | 01038347 | | 100.00 | 0.05 | 4 | 1,701 | HIGH | MED-HIGH |
| **LYNN** | | 0.05 | | | | | | |
| Tahoka Ind School Dist | 01039341 | | 47.86 | 0.03 | 3 | 600 | HIGH | MED-HIGH |
| New Home Ind School Dist | 01039274 | | 23.42 | 0.01 | 1 | 580 | HIGH | MED-HIGH |
| O'Donnell Ind School Dist | 01039315 | | 20.81 | 0.01 | 2 | 300 | HIGH | MED-HIGH |
| Wilson Ind School Dist | 01039391 | | 7.91 | 0.00 | 1 | 94 | HIGH | HIGH |
| **MARION** | | 0.05 | | | | | | |
| Jefferson Ind School Dist | 01040687 | | 100.00 | 0.05 | 4 | 1,324 | HIGH | HIGH |
| **MARTIN** | | 0.05 | | | | | | |
| Stanton Ind School Dist | 01040754 | | 86.17 | 0.04 | 3 | 1,053 | HIGH | MED-HIGH |
| Grady Ind School Dist | 01040730 | | 13.83 | 0.01 | 1 | 233 | HIGH | HIGH |
| **MORRIS** | | 0.05 | | | | | | |
| Pewitt Cons Ind School Dist | 01043005 | | 60.45 | 0.03 | 3 | 870 | HIGH | MED-HIGH |
| Daingerfield-Lone Star Ind SD | 01042946 | | 39.55 | 0.02 | 4 | 970 | HIGH | HIGH |
| **OLDHAM** | | 0.05 | | | | | | |
| Boys Ranch Ind School Dist | 01484461 | | 45.31 | 0.02 | 3 | 240 | HIGH | MED-LOW |
| Vega Ind School Dist | 01045558 | | 30.50 | 0.01 | 2 | 370 | HIGH | MED-LOW |
| Adrian Ind School Dist | 01045522 | | 12.56 | 0.01 | 1 | 120 | HIGH | MED-LOW |
| Wildorado Ind Sch Dist | 01045584 | | 11.63 | 0.01 | 1 | 210 | HIGH | MED-HIGH |
| **PARMER** | | 0.05 | | | | | | |
| Friona Ind School Dist | 01046734 | | 36.05 | 0.02 | 4 | 1,045 | HIGH | MED-HIGH |
| Farwell Ind School Dist | 01046693 | | 30.10 | 0.02 | 3 | 539 | HIGH | MED-LOW |
| Bovina Ind School Dist | 01046655 | | 22.04 | 0.01 | 3 | 460 | HIGH | MED-HIGH |
| Lazbuddie Ind School Dist | 01046772 | | 11.81 | 0.01 | 1 | 168 | HIGH | MED-HIGH |
| **REAGAN** | | 0.05 | | | | | | |
| Reagan Co Ind School Dist | 01048017 | | 100.00 | 0.05 | 3 | 850 | HIGH | MED-LOW |
| **SOMERVELL** | | 0.05 | | | | | | |
| Glen Rose Ind School Dist | 01051088 | | 100.00 | 0.05 | 4 | 1,970 | HIGH | MED-LOW |
| **TRINITY** | | 0.05 | | | | | | |
| Groveton Ind School Dist | 01057109 | | 47.87 | 0.03 | 2 | 750 | HIGH | MED-HIGH |

## DISTRICT BUYING POWER INDEX
### COUNTIES RANKED BY PERCENTAGE OF STATE SPENDING

| COUNTY<br>DISTRICT | PID | COUNTY %<br>OF STATE | DISTRICT %<br>OF COUNTY | DISTRICT %<br>OF STATES | NUMBER OF<br>SCHOOLS | ENROLL | EXP | POV |
|---|---|---|---|---|---|---|---|---|
| Trinity Ind School Dist | 01057147 | | 35.36 | 0.02 | 3 | 1,188 | MED | MED-HIGH |
| Apple Springs Ind School Dist | 01057044 | | 9.06 | 0.00 | 2 | 200 | HIGH | HIGH |
| Centerville Ind School Dist | 01057070 | | 7.71 | 0.00 | 2 | 127 | HIGH | MED-HIGH |
| **YOAKUM** | | 0.05 | | | | | | |
| Denver City Ind School Dist | 01062013 | | 70.42 | 0.03 | 5 | 1,741 | HIGH | MED-LOW |
| Plains Ind School Dist | 01062063 | | 29.58 | 0.01 | 3 | 475 | HIGH | MED-HIGH |
| **ANDREWS** | | 0.04 | | | | | | |
| Andrews Ind School Dist | 00994700 | | 100.00 | 0.04 | 6 | 4,200 | LOW | MED-LOW |
| **CARSON** | | 0.04 | | | | | | |
| Panhandle Ind School Dist | 01004592 | | 58.24 | 0.02 | 3 | 670 | HIGH | MED-LOW |
| Groom Ind School Dist | 01004554 | | 23.00 | 0.01 | 1 | 145 | HIGH | MED-HIGH |
| White Deer Ind School Dist | 01004633 | | 18.76 | 0.01 | 2 | 360 | HIGH | LOW |
| **COLEMAN** | | 0.04 | | | | | | |
| Coleman Ind School Dist | 01005819 | | 55.84 | 0.03 | 3 | 869 | HIGH | MED-HIGH |
| Santa Anna Ind School Dist | 01005924 | | 31.07 | 0.01 | 2 | 250 | HIGH | MED-HIGH |
| Panther Creek Cons Ind SD | 01005950 | | 13.09 | 0.01 | 1 | 150 | HIGH | HIGH |
| **CROSBY** | | 0.04 | | | | | | |
| Ralls Ind School Dist | 01007984 | | 39.94 | 0.02 | 4 | 485 | HIGH | MED-HIGH |
| Crosbyton Cons Ind Sch Dist | 01007908 | | 37.17 | 0.01 | 2 | 330 | HIGH | HIGH |
| Lorenzo Ind School Dist | 01007958 | | 22.89 | 0.01 | 2 | 250 | HIGH | HIGH |
| **GOLIAD** | | 0.04 | | | | | | |
| Goliad Ind School Dist | 01019810 | | 100.00 | 0.04 | 3 | 1,325 | HIGH | MED-HIGH |
| **HAMILTON** | | 0.04 | | | | | | |
| Hamilton Ind School Dist | 01022166 | | 57.92 | 0.03 | 3 | 789 | HIGH | MED-HIGH |
| Hico Ind School Dist | 01022192 | | 42.08 | 0.02 | 2 | 563 | HIGH | MED-HIGH |
| **HANSFORD** | | 0.04 | | | | | | |
| Spearman Ind School Dist | 01022312 | | 54.69 | 0.02 | 3 | 834 | HIGH | MED-HIGH |
| Gruver Ind School Dist | 01022257 | | 34.41 | 0.01 | 3 | 450 | HIGH | MED-LOW |
| Pringle-Morse Cons ISD | 01022295 | | 10.90 | 0.00 | 1 | 125 | HIGH | MED-LOW |
| **HUDSPETH** | | 0.04 | | | | | | |
| Ft Hancock Ind School Dist | 01032173 | | 65.37 | 0.03 | 3 | 377 | HIGH | MED-HIGH |
| Dell City Ind School Dist | 01032147 | | 24.10 | 0.01 | 1 | 61 | HIGH | MED-LOW |
| Sierra Blanca Ind School Dist | 01032202 | | 10.53 | 0.00 | 1 | 103 | HIGH | MED-HIGH |
| **KNOX** | | 0.04 | | | | | | |
| Munday Consolidated Ind SD | 01036533 | | 38.60 | 0.02 | 2 | 392 | HIGH | HIGH |
| Knox City-O'Brien Cons Ind SD | 01036507 | | 36.73 | 0.02 | 3 | 280 | HIGH | MED-HIGH |
| Benjamin Ind School Dist | 01036442 | | 24.66 | 0.01 | 1 | 108 | HIGH | MED-HIGH |
| **LA SALLE** | | 0.04 | | | | | | |
| Cotulla Ind School Dist | 01037197 | | 100.00 | 0.04 | 4 | 1,180 | HIGH | HIGH |
| **LIVE OAK** | | 0.04 | | | | | | |
| George West Ind School Dist | 01038256 | | 52.73 | 0.02 | 4 | 1,100 | HIGH | MED-HIGH |
| Three Rivers Ind School Dist | 01038309 | | 47.27 | 0.02 | 2 | 628 | HIGH | MED-HIGH |
| **MCCULLOCH** | | 0.04 | | | | | | |
| Brady Ind School Dist | 01039420 | | 70.58 | 0.03 | 4 | 1,050 | HIGH | MED-HIGH |
| Rochelle Ind School Dist | 01039509 | | 14.72 | 0.01 | 1 | 179 | HIGH | MED-HIGH |
| Lohn Ind School Dist | 01039482 | | 14.70 | 0.01 | 1 | 100 | HIGH | MED-HIGH |
| **MILLS** | | 0.04 | | | | | | |
| Goldthwaite Consolidated ISD | 01041942 | | 72.26 | 0.03 | 3 | 555 | HIGH | MED-HIGH |
| Mullin Ind School Dist | 01041978 | | 19.09 | 0.01 | 6 | 294 | HIGH | HIGH |
| Priddy Ind School Dist | 01042001 | | 8.65 | 0.00 | 1 | 115 | HIGH | MED-HIGH |
| **NEWTON** | | 0.04 | | | | | | |
| Newton Ind School Dist | 01043744 | | 78.37 | 0.03 | 3 | 1,041 | HIGH | MED-HIGH |
| Burkeville Ind School Dist | 01043677 | | 21.63 | 0.01 | 2 | 250 | HIGH | MED-HIGH |
| **RAINS** | | 0.04 | | | | | | |
| Rains Ind School Dist | 01047893 | | 100.00 | 0.04 | 4 | 1,500 | HIGH | MED-HIGH |
| **SABINE** | | 0.04 | | | | | | |
| Hemphill Ind School Dist | 01049267 | | 70.74 | 0.03 | 3 | 906 | HIGH | MED-HIGH |
| West Sabine Ind Sch Dist | 01049293 | | 29.26 | 0.01 | 2 | 578 | HIGH | MED-HIGH |
| **SAN AUGUSTINE** | | 0.04 | | | | | | |
| San Augustine Ind School Dist | 01049360 | | 73.34 | 0.03 | 2 | 720 | HIGH | HIGH |
| Broaddus Ind School Dist | 01049334 | | 26.66 | 0.01 | 2 | 400 | HIGH | HIGH |
| **STEPHENS** | | 0.04 | | | | | | |
| Breckenridge Ind School Dist | 01051325 | | 100.00 | 0.04 | 5 | 1,413 | HIGH | MED-HIGH |

## DISTRICT BUYING POWER INDEX
### COUNTIES RANKED BY PERCENTAGE OF STATE SPENDING

| COUNTY<br>DISTRICT | PID | COUNTY %<br>OF STATE | DISTRICT %<br>OF COUNTY | DISTRICT %<br>OF STATES | NUMBER OF<br>SCHOOLS | ENROLL | EXP | POV |
|---|---|---|---|---|---|---|---|---|
| **UPTON** | | 0.04 | | | | | | |
| Rankin Ind School Dist | 01057654 | | 61.65 | 0.03 | 2 | 294 | HIGH | MED-LOW |
| McCamey Ind School Dist | 01057616 | | 38.35 | 0.02 | 3 | 560 | HIGH | MED-HIGH |
| **WHEELER** | | 0.04 | | | | | | |
| Shamrock Ind School Dist | 01059858 | | 41.83 | 0.02 | 3 | 342 | HIGH | MED-HIGH |
| Wheeler Ind School Dist | 01059896 | | 30.42 | 0.01 | 1 | 441 | HIGH | MED-HIGH |
| Kelton Ind School Dist | 01059808 | | 18.32 | 0.01 | 1 | 84 | HIGH | MED-LOW |
| Ft Elliott Cons Ind Sch Dist | 01059779 | | 9.43 | 0.00 | 1 | 146 | HIGH | MED-LOW |
| **ZAVALA** | | 0.04 | | | | | | |
| Crystal City Ind School Dist | 01062295 | | 64.33 | 0.03 | 5 | 1,950 | MED | HIGH |
| La Pryor Ind School Dist | 01062374 | | 35.67 | 0.01 | 2 | 500 | HIGH | HIGH |
| **BAYLOR** | | 0.03 | | | | | | |
| Seymour Ind School Dist | 00996021 | | 100.00 | 0.03 | 3 | 582 | HIGH | MED-HIGH |
| **BLANCO** | | 0.03 | | | | | | |
| Blanco Ind School Dist | 01000481 | | 51.73 | 0.02 | 3 | 1,020 | HIGH | MED-HIGH |
| Johnson City Ind School Dist | 01000510 | | 48.27 | 0.02 | 3 | 650 | HIGH | MED-LOW |
| **CHILDRESS** | | 0.03 | | | | | | |
| Childress Ind School Dist | 01005431 | | 100.00 | 0.03 | 4 | 1,052 | HIGH | MED-HIGH |
| **COCHRAN** | | 0.03 | | | | | | |
| Whiteface Con Ind School Dist | 01005728 | | 50.79 | 0.01 | 2 | 345 | HIGH | MED-HIGH |
| Morton Ind School Dist | 01005675 | | 49.21 | 0.01 | 3 | 400 | HIGH | MED-HIGH |
| **COKE** | | 0.03 | | | | | | |
| Robert Lee Ind School Dist | 01005780 | | 67.38 | 0.02 | 1 | 260 | HIGH | MED-HIGH |
| Bronte Ind School Dist | 01005754 | | 32.62 | 0.01 | 2 | 225 | HIGH | MED-HIGH |
| **CRANE** | | 0.03 | | | | | | |
| Crane Ind School Dist | 01007817 | | 100.00 | 0.03 | 3 | 1,172 | HIGH | MED-LOW |
| **CROCKETT** | | 0.03 | | | | | | |
| Crockett Co Cons Common SD | 01007855 | | 100.00 | 0.03 | 3 | 720 | HIGH | MED-HIGH |
| **CULBERSON** | | 0.03 | | | | | | |
| Culberson Co Allamoore Ind SD | 01008029 | | 100.00 | 0.03 | 1 | 378 | HIGH | HIGH |
| **DELTA** | | 0.03 | | | | | | |
| Cooper Ind School Dist | 01013103 | | 86.33 | 0.02 | 2 | 800 | HIGH | MED-HIGH |
| Fannindel Ind School Dist | 01013141 | | 13.67 | 0.00 | 2 | 200 | HIGH | MED-HIGH |
| **GARZA** | | 0.03 | | | | | | |
| Post Ind School Dist | 01019597 | | 74.75 | 0.02 | 3 | 566 | HIGH | MED-HIGH |
| Southland Ind School Dist | 01019638 | | 25.25 | 0.01 | 1 | 123 | HIGH | MED-HIGH |
| **IRION** | | 0.03 | | | | | | |
| Irion Co Ind School Dist | 01032862 | | 100.00 | 0.03 | 2 | 300 | HIGH | MED-LOW |
| **JIM HOGG** | | 0.03 | | | | | | |
| Jim Hogg Co Ind School Dist | 01034470 | | 100.00 | 0.03 | 3 | 1,100 | HIGH | HIGH |
| **LIPSCOMB** | | 0.03 | | | | | | |
| Booker Ind School Dist | 01038139 | | 47.35 | 0.01 | 2 | 371 | HIGH | MED-LOW |
| Higgins Ind School Dist | 01038220 | | 24.22 | 0.01 | 1 | 96 | HIGH | MED-HIGH |
| Follett Ind School Dist | 01038191 | | 17.42 | 0.01 | 1 | 165 | HIGH | MED-HIGH |
| Darrouzett Ind School Dist | 01038165 | | 11.01 | 0.00 | 1 | 105 | HIGH | MED-HIGH |
| **MASON** | | 0.03 | | | | | | |
| Mason Ind School Dist | 01040780 | | 100.00 | 0.03 | 3 | 674 | HIGH | MED-HIGH |
| **SAN SABA** | | 0.03 | | | | | | |
| San Saba Ind School Dist | 01049944 | | 59.20 | 0.02 | 3 | 717 | HIGH | MED-HIGH |
| Richland Springs Ind Sch Dist | 01049918 | | 20.46 | 0.01 | 1 | 123 | HIGH | MED-LOW |
| Cherokee Ind School Dist | 01049889 | | 20.34 | 0.01 | 1 | 112 | HIGH | MED-HIGH |
| **SUTTON** | | 0.03 | | | | | | |
| Sonora Ind School Dist | 01051478 | | 100.00 | 0.03 | 3 | 767 | HIGH | MED-HIGH |
| **BORDEN** | | 0.02 | | | | | | |
| Borden Co Ind School Dist | 01000546 | | 100.00 | 0.02 | 1 | 214 | HIGH | MED-LOW |
| **CONCHO** | | 0.02 | | | | | | |
| Paint Rock Ind School Dist | 01007245 | | 52.95 | 0.01 | 1 | 225 | HIGH | HIGH |
| Eden Cons Ind School Dist | 01007180 | | 47.05 | 0.01 | 2 | 230 | HIGH | MED-HIGH |
| **DONLEY** | | 0.02 | | | | | | |
| Clarendon Cons Ind Sch Dist | 01014119 | | 63.03 | 0.01 | 3 | 450 | HIGH | MED-HIGH |
| Hedley Ind School Dist | 01014145 | | 36.97 | 0.01 | 1 | 112 | HIGH | MED-HIGH |

## DISTRICT BUYING POWER INDEX
### COUNTIES RANKED BY PERCENTAGE OF STATE SPENDING

| COUNTY DISTRICT | PID | COUNTY % OF STATE | DISTRICT % OF COUNTY | DISTRICT % OF STATES | NUMBER OF SCHOOLS | ENROLL | EXP | POV |
|---|---|---|---|---|---|---|---|---|
| **EDWARDS** | | 0.02 | | | | | | |
| Rocksprings Ind School Dist | 01014901 | | 70.03 | 0.02 | 1 | 289 | HIGH | HIGH |
| Nueces Canyon Cons Ind SD | 01014872 | | 29.97 | 0.01 | 2 | 264 | HIGH | HIGH |
| **FISHER** | | 0.02 | | | | | | |
| Roby Cons Ind School Dist | 01017886 | | 50.02 | 0.01 | 2 | 277 | HIGH | MED-HIGH |
| Rotan Ind School Dist | 01017915 | | 49.98 | 0.01 | 2 | 240 | HIGH | MED-HIGH |
| **GLASSCOCK** | | 0.02 | | | | | | |
| Glasscock Co Ind School Dist | 01019781 | | 100.00 | 0.02 | 1 | 292 | HIGH | MED-LOW |
| **HALL** | | 0.02 | | | | | | |
| Memphis Ind School Dist | 01022087 | | 76.86 | 0.01 | 4 | 400 | HIGH | HIGH |
| Turkey-Quitaque Cons Ind SD | 01022130 | | 23.14 | 0.00 | 1 | 185 | HIGH | MED-HIGH |
| **HARDEMAN** | | 0.02 | | | | | | |
| Quanah Ind School Dist | 01022398 | | 73.98 | 0.02 | 3 | 525 | HIGH | MED-HIGH |
| Chillicothe ISD School Dist | 01022350 | | 26.02 | 0.01 | 2 | 200 | HIGH | MED-HIGH |
| **HASKELL** | | 0.02 | | | | | | |
| Haskell Cons Ind School Dist | 01028873 | | 66.56 | 0.01 | 3 | 550 | HIGH | MED-HIGH |
| Rule Ind School Dist | 01028964 | | 22.00 | 0.00 | 1 | 114 | HIGH | HIGH |
| Paint Creek Ind School Dist | 01028914 | | 11.44 | 0.00 | 1 | 108 | HIGH | MED-HIGH |
| **KIMBLE** | | 0.02 | | | | | | |
| Junction Ind School Dist | 01036155 | | 100.00 | 0.02 | 3 | 605 | HIGH | HIGH |
| **KINNEY** | | 0.02 | | | | | | |
| Brackett Ind School Dist | 01036222 | | 100.00 | 0.02 | 3 | 570 | HIGH | MED-HIGH |
| **MCMULLEN** | | 0.02 | | | | | | |
| McMullen Co Ind Sch Dist | 01040560 | | 100.00 | 0.02 | 1 | 289 | HIGH | MED-LOW |
| **SCHLEICHER** | | 0.02 | | | | | | |
| Schleicher Co Ind Sch Dist | 01049982 | | 100.00 | 0.02 | 3 | 540 | HIGH | MED-HIGH |
| **SHACKELFORD** | | 0.02 | | | | | | |
| Albany Ind School Dist | 01050216 | | 88.94 | 0.02 | 2 | 512 | HIGH | MED-LOW |
| Moran Ind School Dist | 01050242 | | 11.06 | 0.00 | 1 | 105 | HIGH | HIGH |
| **SHERMAN** | | 0.02 | | | | | | |
| Stratford Ind School Dist | 01050486 | | 91.33 | 0.02 | 3 | 560 | HIGH | MED-LOW |
| Texhoma Ind School Dist | 01050527 | | 8.67 | 0.00 | 1 | 130 | MED | MED-LOW |
| **THROCKMORTON** | | 0.02 | | | | | | |
| Throckmorton Ind School Dist | 01055228 | | 53.42 | 0.01 | 1 | 158 | HIGH | MED-HIGH |
| Woodson Ind School Dist | 01055254 | | 46.58 | 0.01 | 1 | 144 | HIGH | MED-HIGH |
| **ARMSTRONG** | | 0.01 | | | | | | |
| Claude Ind School Dist | 00995302 | | 100.00 | 0.01 | 1 | 308 | HIGH | MED-LOW |
| **BRISCOE** | | 0.01 | | | | | | |
| Silverton Ind School Dist | 01002300 | | 100.00 | 0.01 | 1 | 174 | HIGH | MED-HIGH |
| **COLLINGSWORTH** | | 0.01 | | | | | | |
| Wellington Ind School Dist | 01006708 | | 100.00 | 0.01 | 3 | 530 | HIGH | MED-HIGH |
| **COTTLE** | | 0.01 | | | | | | |
| Paducah Ind School Dist | 01007776 | | 100.00 | 0.01 | 1 | 200 | HIGH | HIGH |
| **DICKENS** | | 0.01 | | | | | | |
| Spur Ind School Dist | 01013969 | | 74.06 | 0.01 | 1 | 235 | HIGH | MED-HIGH |
| Patton Springs Ind School Dist | 01013933 | | 25.94 | 0.00 | 1 | 97 | HIGH | HIGH |
| **FOARD** | | 0.01 | | | | | | |
| Crowell Ind School Dist | 01018086 | | 100.00 | 0.01 | 2 | 230 | HIGH | MED-HIGH |
| **HARTLEY** | | 0.01 | | | | | | |
| Hartley Ind School Dist | 01028823 | | 54.73 | 0.01 | 1 | 205 | HIGH | MED-LOW |
| Channing Ind School Dist | 01028794 | | 45.27 | 0.01 | 1 | 173 | HIGH | MED-HIGH |
| **HEMPHILL** | | 0.01 | | | | | | |
| Canadian Ind School Dist | 01029205 | | 100.00 | 0.01 | 4 | 860 | LOW | MED-LOW |
| **JEFF DAVIS** | | 0.01 | | | | | | |
| Fort Davis Ind School Dist | 01033323 | | 73.56 | 0.01 | 2 | 225 | HIGH | MED-HIGH |
| Valentine Ind School Dist | 01033359 | | 26.44 | 0.00 | 1 | 34 | HIGH | MED-HIGH |
| **KENEDY** | | 0.01 | | | | | | |
| Kenedy Co Wide Common Sch Dist | 01035905 | | 100.00 | 0.01 | 1 | 80 | HIGH | MED-LOW |
| **KENT** | | 0.01 | | | | | | |
| Jayton-Girard Ind School Dist | 01035931 | | 100.00 | 0.01 | 1 | 143 | HIGH | MED-HIGH |

## DISTRICT BUYING POWER INDEX
### COUNTIES RANKED BY PERCENTAGE OF STATE SPENDING

| COUNTY<br>DISTRICT | PID | COUNTY %<br>OF STATE | DISTRICT %<br>OF COUNTY | DISTRICT %<br>OF STATES | NUMBER OF<br>SCHOOLS | ENROLL | EXP | POV |
|---|---|---|---|---|---|---|---|---|
| **KING** | | 0.01 | | | | | | |
| Guthrie Common School Dist | 01036193 | | 100.00 | 0.01 | 1 | 95 | HIGH | MED-LOW |
| **MENARD** | | 0.01 | | | | | | |
| Menard Ind School Dist | 01041368 | | 100.00 | 0.01 | 2 | 305 | HIGH | HIGH |
| **MOTLEY** | | 0.01 | | | | | | |
| Motley Co Ind School Dist | 01043043 | | 100.00 | 0.01 | 1 | 162 | HIGH | MED-HIGH |
| **REAL** | | 0.01 | | | | | | |
| Leakey Ind School Dist | 01048055 | | 100.00 | 0.01 | 1 | 279 | HIGH | HIGH |
| **ROBERTS** | | 0.01 | | | | | | |
| Miami Ind School Dist | 01048536 | | 100.00 | 0.01 | 1 | 190 | HIGH | MED-LOW |
| **STERLING** | | 0.01 | | | | | | |
| Sterling City Ind School Dist | 01051387 | | 100.00 | 0.01 | 2 | 320 | HIGH | MED-HIGH |
| **STONEWALL** | | 0.00 | | | | | | |
| Aspermont Ind School Dist | 01051416 | | 100.00 | 0.00 | 2 | 214 | HIGH | MED-LOW |
| **TERRELL** | | 0.00 | | | | | | |
| Terrell Co Ind School Dist | 01055046 | | 100.00 | 0.00 | 1 | 108 | HIGH | MED-HIGH |

## NEW SCHOOLS/NEW PRINCIPALS

| SCHOOL | PRINCIPAL | GRADES | ENROLLMENT | COUNTY | PAGE |
|---|---|---|---|---|---|
| Elgin Intermediate Sch | Truhill, Robert | 5-6 | 401 | Bastrop | 27 |
| Jones Magnet Middle Sch | Wheat, Michella | 6-6 | 140 | Bexar | 40 |
| Rodriguez Montessori Elem Sch | Craig, Alicia | PK-K | 100 | Bexar | 44 |
| Wernli Elem Sch | Shaw, Lori | PK-5 | 490 | Bexar | 42 |
| Johnson Elem Sch | Andrews, Alissa | K-5 | 401 | Collin | 88 |
| Rushing Middle Sch | Wallace, Danielle | 6-8 | 401 | Collin | 88 |
| Davenport High Sch | DeLoach, Matthew | 9-11 | 401 | Comal | 91 |
| Hill Country Clg Prep High Sch | Wiley, Julie | 9-9 | 75 | Comal | 92 |
| Downtown Montessori Sch | Korobovskaya, Olga, Dr | PK-2 | 250 | Dallas | 103 |
| Michael M Boone Elem Sch | Reyes, Amanda | K-4 | 401 | Dallas | 112 |
| Jackie Fuller Elem Sch | Abrams, Kari | PK-5 | 300 | Denton | 124 |
| Jordan High Sch | Crowell, Ethan, Dr | 9-12 | 1,000 | Fort Bend | 156 |
| Tammaron Elem Sch | Melendez, Mark | PK-5 | 538 | Fort Bend | 158 |
| Centennial Elem Sch | Pierce, Alison | PK-5 | 575 | Harris | 200 |
| Rowe Middle Sch | Carew, Stacia | 6-8 | 450 | Harris | 190 |
| Cottonwood Elem Sch | Pena, Richard | PK-5 | 200 | Liberty | 268 |
| Stockton Junior High Sch | Gorka, Bryan | 7-8 | 1,000 | Montgomery | 295 |
| Timber Lakes Elem Sch | Garza, Carrie | PK-6 | 500 | Montgomery | 297 |
| J P Cowan Achievement Center | Stanaland, Betsy | 4-12 | 36 | Nolan | 305 |
| Southeast Early Childhood Ctr | Hargrove, David | PK-PK | 157 | Nolan | 305 |
| Sherry & Paul Hamm Elem Sch | Smith, Megan | K-6 | 500 | Rockwall | 328 |
| Jerry Knight STEM Academy | Webster, Victoria | 6-8 | 285 | Tarrant | 359 |
| Bear Creek Elem Sch | Crissey, David | PK-5 | 522 | Travis | 369 |
| Crossroads Connect Academy | Hernandez, Sylvia | 9-12 | 40 | Victoria | 384 |
| Elias Herrera Middle Sch | Martinez, Carlos | 6-8 | 401 | Webb | 390 |
| Williams Elem Sch | Sniffin, Jeanna | PK-5 | 850 | Williamson | 399 |

## NEW PRINCIPALS

| SCHOOL | PRINCIPAL | GRADES | ENROLLMENT | COUNTY | PAGE |
|---|---|---|---|---|---|
| Elkhart Elem Sch | Steely, Kristin | PK-2 | 339 | Anderson | 18 |
| Frankston Middle Sch | Owens, Cindy | 6-8 | 194 | Anderson | 18 |
| Northside Primary Sch | Pridgen, Traci | K-1 | 494 | Anderson | 19 |
| Anderson Elem Sch | Nerren, Cindy | 3-5 | 258 | Angelina | 21 |
| Brookhollow Elem Sch | Fain, Amy | 3-5 | 300 | Angelina | 21 |
| Central High Sch | Garza, Miguel | 9-12 | 310 | Angelina | 20 |
| Diboll High Sch | Emmons, Andre | 9-12 | 256 | Angelina | 20 |
| Kurth Primary Sch | Bickley, Dana | PK-2 | 207 | Angelina | 21 |
| Trout Primary Sch | Stewart, Cindy | PK-2 | 192 | Angelina | 21 |
| Zavalla Elem Sch | Vaughan, Glen | PK-5 | 170 | Angelina | 21 |
| Brazos Elem Sch | Boss, Tracy | PK-5 | 197 | Austin | 25 |
| O'Bryant Intermediate Sch | McLemore, Marcus | 4-5 | 296 | Austin | 25 |
| O'Bryant Primary Sch | Krueger, Kandis | PK-3 | 560 | Austin | 25 |
| Sealy Elem Sch | Johnson, Sarah | PK-5 | 634 | Austin | 25 |
| Audie Murphy Middle Sch | Warren, Jennifer | 6-8 | 822 | Bell | 30 |
| Eastern Hills Middle Sch | Brown, Gina | 6-8 | 743 | Bell | 31 |
| Fowler Elem Sch | Hardy, Donna | PK-5 | 1,146 | Bell | 31 |
| Fred W Edwards Academy | Mitchell, Tricia | 9-12 | 37 | Bell | 32 |
| Lamar Middle Sch | Bradford, Yvette | 6-8 | 202 | Bell | 32 |
| Maude Moore Wood Elem Sch | Disher, Pamela | PK-5 | 600 | Bell | 31 |
| Meadows Elem Sch | Smith, Nickolas | PK-5 | 842 | Bell | 31 |
| Oveta Culp Hobby Elem Sch | Thomas, Alena | PK-5 | 553 | Bell | 31 |
| Pershing Park Elem Sch | Taylor, Jessica | PK-5 | 621 | Bell | 31 |
| Rogers High Sch | Vi Moses, Lee | 9-12 | 187 | Bell | 32 |
| Trimmier Elem Sch | Avery, Beckie | PK-5 | 839 | Bell | 31 |
| Alamo Heights High Sch | Smith, Cory | 9-12 | 1,606 | Bexar | 33 |
| Artemisia Bowden Academy | Sparks, Brian | PK-8 | 512 | Bexar | 43 |
| Brackenridge High Sch | Cordova, Yesenia | 9-12 | 1,685 | Bexar | 43 |
| Cambridge Elem Sch | Hawkins, Jana | 1-5 | 836 | Bexar | 33 |
| Camelot Elem Sch | Payne, Wilma | PK-5 | 534 | Bexar | 37 |
| Carroll Early Chldhd Center | Barraza, Alejandra, Dr | PK-PK | 306 | Bexar | 43 |
| Coronado Village Elem Sch | Garza, Erika | PK-5 | 351 | Bexar | 36 |
| De Zavala Elem Sch | Finch, Donna | PK-5 | 600 | Bexar | 43 |
| E H Gilbert Elem Sch | Wing, Geralynn | PK-5 | 559 | Bexar | 35 |
| Escondido Elem Sch | Keeler, Cynthia | PK-5 | 425 | Bexar | 36 |
| Franklin Elem Sch | Adan, Jennifer | PK-5 | 458 | Bexar | 43 |
| Hawthorne Academy | Walker, Valerie | K-8 | 731 | Bexar | 43 |
| Helotes Elem Sch | Crick, Kasey | PK-5 | 359 | Bexar | 40 |
| Hidden Forest Elem Sch | Powell, Renette | PK-5 | 478 | Bexar | 38 |
| Highland Forest Elem Sch | Ervin, Brittany | PK-3 | 387 | Bexar | 34 |
| Hirsch Elem Sch | Persaud, Erika | PK-5 | 727 | Bexar | 43 |

| | | | | | |
|---|---|---|---|---|---|
| Huebner Elem Sch | Halliburton, Kelli | PK-5 | 680 | Bexar | 38 |
| Ira C Ogden Academy | Martinez, Nikki | PK-8 | 679 | Bexar | 43 |
| Ira C Ogden Academy | Calejo, Gisella | PK-8 | 679 | Bexar | 43 |
| Kirby Middle Sch | Arredondo, Sue | 6-8 | 468 | Bexar | 36 |
| Kirby Middle Sch | Johnson, Jerome | 6-8 | 468 | Bexar | 36 |
| Knox Early Chldhd Center | Macias, Raymond | PK-PK | 256 | Bexar | 44 |
| Larkspur Elem Sch | Miller, Cody | PK-5 | 698 | Bexar | 38 |
| Loma Park Elem Sch | Gavin, Courtney, Dr | PK-5 | 642 | Bexar | 35 |
| Mary Hartman Elem Sch | Pena, Sara | PK-5 | 701 | Bexar | 36 |
| Northwood Elem Sch | Harper, Catherine | PK-5 | 375 | Bexar | 38 |
| Oak Meadow Elem Sch | Campos, Lisa | PK-5 | 463 | Bexar | 38 |
| Ollie Perry Storm Elem Sch | Cartwright, Vanessa | PK-5 | 305 | Bexar | 44 |
| Olympia Elem Sch | George, S | PK-5 | 381 | Bexar | 36 |
| PK Academy at West Avenue | Kienlen, Paul | PK-PK | 100 | Bexar | 38 |
| Redland Oaks Elem Sch | Barr, Randy | PK-5 | 396 | Bexar | 38 |
| Stafford Elem Sch | Cruz, Stephanie | K-5 | 453 | Bexar | 35 |
| Vineyard Ranch Elem Sch | Pierce, Carol | PK-5 | 790 | Bexar | 39 |
| Walzem Elem Sch | Washington, Liz | PK-5 | 576 | Bexar | 39 |
| Blanco High Sch | Hinson, Patrick | 9-12 | 331 | Blanco | 49 |
| Kopperl Sch | Janek, Brad | PK-12 | 200 | Bosque | 50 |
| Valley Millsjr Sr High Sch | Halfmann, Eric | 6-12 | 200 | Bosque | 50 |
| De Kalb High Sch | Hodgson, Melinda | 9-12 | 220 | Bowie | 51 |
| De Kalb High Sch | Burgin, Cody | 9-12 | 220 | Bowie | 51 |
| Hooks Elem Sch | Deanda, Jennifer | PK-4 | 282 | Bowie | 51 |
| James Bowie High Sch | May, Eddy | 9-12 | 174 | Bowie | 53 |
| James Bowie High Sch | McClure, Chris | 9-12 | 174 | Bowie | 53 |
| Redwater High Sch | Haugh, Brett | 9-12 | 345 | Bowie | 53 |
| Westlawn Elem Sch | Witterstaetter, Elodia | 3-5 | 334 | Bowie | 54 |
| Barbara Cockrell Elem Sch | Mathis, Rusty | PK-4 | 665 | Brazoria | 56 |
| Bill Hasse Elem Sch | Froberg, Kristi | PK-5 | 708 | Brazoria | 54 |
| Brazosport High Sch | White, Ian | 9-12 | 965 | Brazoria | 55 |
| Clute Intermediate Sch | Fulton, Tara | 5-8 | 694 | Brazoria | 55 |
| Danbury High Sch | Ziehl, Kimberly | 9-12 | 194 | Brazoria | 56 |
| Dr James Red Duke Elem Sch | Hall, Emily | PK-5 | 552 | Brazoria | 54 |
| Freeport Intermediate Sch | Johnson, Jarrett, Dr | 7-8 | 515 | Brazoria | 55 |
| Pearland Jr High School West | Miller, Kathleen | 7-8 | 858 | Brazoria | 57 |
| Rodeo Palms Junior High Sch | Patterson, Tonya | 6-8 | 815 | Brazoria | 54 |
| Stephen F Austin STEM Academy | Hoppock, Harland | PK-6 | 151 | Brazoria | 56 |
| West Brazos Junior High Sch | Kinney, Jeffrey | 7-8 | 481 | Brazoria | 56 |
| Marathon Sch | Saldana, Juan | PK-12 | 55 | Brewster | 60 |
| Falfurrias Elem Sch | Castillo, Sandra | 2-5 | 445 | Brooks | 61 |
| Early Elem Sch | Schafer, Julie | 3-5 | 289 | Brown | 62 |
| Early High Sch | Ozuna, Judy | 9-12 | 359 | Brown | 62 |
| Northwest Elem Sch | Northcutt, Allison | PK-3 | 650 | Brown | 62 |
| Snook Sch | Hafley, Lee | PK-12 | 500 | Burleson | 63 |
| Somerville Elem Sch | Little, James | PK-4 | 182 | Burleson | 63 |
| Falls Career High Sch | Rowland, Shelli | 9-12 | 32 | Burnet | 64 |
| Alma Brewer Strawn Elem Sch | Grijalva, Benjamin | K-5 | 497 | Caldwell | 64 |
| Leonard Shanklin Elem Sch | Schwarzlose, Michelle | 2-5 | 425 | Caldwell | 65 |
| Lockhart High Sch | Bacom, Barry | 9-12 | 780 | Caldwell | 64 |
| Navarro Elem Sch | Canales, Anna | K-5 | 517 | Caldwell | 64 |
| Navarro Elem Sch | Holmes, Analeasa | K-5 | 517 | Caldwell | 64 |
| Baird Elem Sch | Bessent, Cynthia | PK-5 | 139 | Callahan | 66 |
| Clyde High Sch | Acevedo, David | 9-12 | 410 | Callahan | 66 |
| El Jardin Elem Sch | Flores, Marina | PK-5 | 453 | Cameron | 67 |
| James Pace Early Clg HS | Wood, Joel | 9-12 | 2,085 | Cameron | 67 |
| Josephine Castaneda Elem Sch | Camargo, Nora | PK-5 | 518 | Cameron | 67 |
| Laureles Elem Sch | Escareno, Ramon | PK-5 | 619 | Cameron | 69 |
| Lee H Means Elem Sch | Almaraz, Melissa | PK-5 | 647 | Cameron | 68 |
| Lopez-Riggins Elem Sch | Elizondo, Jennifer | PK-5 | 490 | Cameron | 69 |
| Oliveira Middle Sch | Medina, Martha | 6-8 | 996 | Cameron | 67 |
| Rising Scholars Acad of S TX | Rodriguez, Criselda | 7-8 | 545 | Cameron | 71 |
| Riverside Middle Sch | Lopez, Manuela | 6-8 | 603 | Cameron | 70 |
| San Benito High Sch | Ramirez, Rudy | 10-12 | 2,132 | Cameron | 71 |
| Stell Middle Sch | Segura, Luis | 6-8 | 982 | Cameron | 68 |
| White Deer Elem Sch | Bolding, Kandy | PK-6 | 210 | Carson | 73 |
| Linden Elem Sch | Hemby, Missy | PK-5 | 300 | Cass | 74 |
| Nazareth Sch | O'Connor, Robert | PK-12 | 253 | Castro | 75 |
| Anahuac Elem Sch | Powell, Tish | PK-5 | 582 | Chambers | 75 |
| New Summerfield Sch | Jeffus, Donna | PK-12 | 544 | Cherokee | 76 |
| Wells High Sch | Hise, Kristel | 7-12 | 129 | Cherokee | 77 |
| Henrietta Elem Sch | McClure, Debra | PK-5 | 419 | Clay | 78 |
| Petrolia Elem Sch | Perkins, Clint | PK-6 | 251 | Clay | 78 |
| Bronte High Sch | Kuhlmann, Doug | 7-12 | 131 | Coke | 79 |
| Santa Anna High Sch | Morales, Edward | 7-12 | 117 | Coleman | 80 |
| Allen High Sch | Russell, Matt | 9-12 | 5,098 | Collin | 80 |

| | | | | | |
|---|---|---|---|---|---|
| Boyer Elem Sch | David, Bill | PK-5 | 705 | Collin | 88 |
| Brinker Elem Sch | Cockrell, Andrea | K-5 | 639 | Collin | 86 |
| Canup Early Childhood Center | Dillard, Vickey | PK-PK | 420 | Collin | 87 |
| Celina Junior High Sch | Briscoe, Jamey | 7-8 | 426 | Collin | 81 |
| Chandler Elem Sch | Allen, Bobbie | PK-6 | 587 | Collin | 80 |
| Community High Sch | Ryan, Charles | 9-12 | 650 | Collin | 81 |
| Gibson Caldwell Elem Sch | Massey, Karla | K-5 | 533 | Collin | 84 |
| Harper Elem Sch | Estep, Heidi | K-5 | 448 | Collin | 87 |
| Izetta Sparks Elem Sch | Dellinger, Carrie | PK-5 | 640 | Collin | 83 |
| J W Webb Elem Sch | Hafner, Maria | K-5 | 404 | Collin | 85 |
| Jackson Elem Sch | Roach, Crystal | PK-5 | 520 | Collin | 86 |
| John A Baker Elem Sch | Gannon, Ashley | PK-5 | 695 | Collin | 88 |
| Pete Ford Middle Sch | Wilhelm, Doug | 7-8 | 925 | Collin | 80 |
| Raymond Cooper Junior High Sch | Chavoya, Jesse | 7-8 | 929 | Collin | 89 |
| Rock Hill High Sch | Toth, Dustin | 9-12 | 401 | Collin | 88 |
| Shawnee Trail Elem Sch | Koyle, Suzanne | K-5 | 512 | Collin | 83 |
| Thomas Elem Sch | Pruett, Zack | PK-5 | 656 | Collin | 87 |
| Weatherford Elem Sch | Cedillo, Nidia | PK-5 | 446 | Collin | 87 |
| Willow Springs Middle Sch | Parker, Kevin | 7-8 | 725 | Collin | 84 |
| Wylie High Sch | Alexander, Brian | 9-12 | 2,428 | Collin | 89 |
| Columbus High Sch | Hall, Pennee | 9-12 | 358 | Colorado | 90 |
| Columbus Junior High Sch | Russell, Amy | 6-8 | 126 | Colorado | 90 |
| Weimar Elem Sch | Kristy, Janecka | PK-4 | 254 | Colorado | 91 |
| Arlon Seay Elem Sch | Engel, Theressa | K-5 | 391 | Comal | 91 |
| Canyon High Sch | Davisson, Dustin | 9-12 | 2,700 | Comal | 91 |
| Hoffmann Lane Elem Sch | Schumann, Amanda | PK-5 | 685 | Comal | 92 |
| Mountain Valley Middle Sch | Looney, Angela | 6-8 | 758 | Comal | 92 |
| Paint Rock Sch | Gonzales, Joellen | PK-12 | 225 | Concho | 94 |
| Muenster Elem Sch | Sicking, Debra | PK-6 | 260 | Cooke | 95 |
| Evant Sch | Cox, Howard | PK-12 | 249 | Coryell | 96 |
| J L Williams-Lovett Ledger ES | Hensley, Lori | K-5 | 780 | Coryell | 96 |
| Jonesboro Sch | Gustin, Kendra | PK-12 | 330 | Coryell | 97 |
| Ozona Middle Sch | Sesson, Kristin | 6-8 | 180 | Crockett | 98 |
| Crosbyton Elem Sch | Villegas, Rene | PK-5 | 97 | Crosby | 98 |
| Acton Elem Sch | Linwood, Jessica | PK-4 | 543 | Dallas | 108 |
| Adelfa Botello Callejo ES | Samuel, Christie | PK-5 | 606 | Dallas | 102 |
| Adelle Turner Elem Sch | Thomas, Derek | PK-5 | 255 | Dallas | 102 |
| Ascher Silberstein Elem Sch | Pasieczny, Erika, Dr | PK-5 | 704 | Dallas | 103 |
| Back Elem Sch | Ramos, Amanda | PK-5 | 380 | Dallas | 109 |
| Barack Obama Male Ldrshp Acad | Jackson, Rashad | 6-12 | 461 | Dallas | 103 |
| Barbara S Austin Elem Sch | Perryman, Kristan | PK-5 | 680 | Dallas | 102 |
| Barton Elem Sch | Ruiz, Christine | K-5 | 733 | Dallas | 113 |
| Beaver Tech Ctr-Math & Science | Devantier, Vicki | K-5 | 580 | Dallas | 109 |
| Big Springs Elem Sch | Dawes, Vince | PK-6 | 295 | Dallas | 116 |
| Birdie Alexander Elem Sch | Welch, David | PK-5 | 343 | Dallas | 103 |
| Bradfield Elem Sch | Bados, Cecilia | PK-5 | 488 | Dallas | 109 |
| Cedar Crest Elem Sch | Berry, Tara | PK-5 | 354 | Dallas | 103 |
| Cisneros Pre-K Sch | Kiser, Andy | PK-PK | 607 | Dallas | 109 |
| Coppell Middle School North | Squalls, Lorie | 6-8 | 983 | Dallas | 102 |
| Country Place Elem Sch | Miller, Amy | PK-5 | 356 | Dallas | 100 |
| Coyle Middle Sch | Washington, Kenneth | 6-8 | 1,007 | Dallas | 109 |
| Daniel Intermediate Sch | Chase, Terrence | 5-6 | 628 | Dallas | 108 |
| Dr Linda Henrie Elem Sch | Felton, Elizabeth | PK-6 | 961 | Dallas | 115 |
| Dr Ralph H Poteet High Sch | Long, Kelly | 9-12 | 1,791 | Dallas | 115 |
| Duncanville High Sch | Leiva, Napoleon | 9-12 | 4,346 | Dallas | 109 |
| E B Comstock Middle Sch | Sellers, Wesley | 6-8 | 798 | Dallas | 103 |
| E D Walker Middle Sch | Toole, Mrs | 6-8 | 738 | Dallas | 103 |
| E S McKenzie Elem Sch | Langston, Emmalee | K-6 | 538 | Dallas | 115 |
| Ethridge Elem Sch | Vincent, Jill | K-5 | 727 | Dallas | 109 |
| Frank B Agnew Middle Sch | Reed, Thomas | 7-8 | 831 | Dallas | 115 |
| G W Kennemer Middle Sch | Wesco, Tambia | 7-8 | 723 | Dallas | 109 |
| GW Carver 6th GR STEM Lrng Ctr | Wesson, Rickyl | 6-6 | 515 | Dallas | 114 |
| Herbert Marcus Elem Sch | Romero, Jonatan | PK-5 | 744 | Dallas | 104 |
| Hickman Elem Sch | Beltran, Karla | PK-5 | 450 | Dallas | 110 |
| Highland Park High Sch | Gilbert, Jeremy | 9-12 | 2,148 | Dallas | 112 |
| Highlands Elem Sch | Griffin, Candice | PK-5 | 604 | Dallas | 101 |
| Hobbs Williams Elem Sch | Trejo, Mesias | K-5 | 641 | Dallas | 111 |
| Houston Middle Sch | Espino, Manny | 6-8 | 935 | Dallas | 113 |
| Hudson Middle Sch | Hope, Amber | 6-8 | 1,298 | Dallas | 110 |
| Int'l Ldrshp TX-Arlington ES | McKoy, Angel | K-8 | 935 | Dallas | 112 |
| Int'l Ldrshp TX-East Ft Worth | Porter, Michelle | K-8 | 1,166 | Dallas | 112 |
| Int'l Ldrshp TX-Katy Westpark | Villaflor, Laura, Dr | 9-12 | 221 | Dallas | 113 |
| Int'l Ldrshp TX-N Richlnd Hill | Dubhghaill, Gearoid | K-8 | 1,357 | Dallas | 113 |
| Int'l Ldrshp TX-Westpark | Hilaire, Arelis | K-8 | 1,300 | Dallas | 113 |
| Irving High Sch | Dorman, Jeffrey | 9-12 | 2,646 | Dallas | 113 |
| J O Schulze Elem Sch | Torres-Rangel, Linda | K-5 | 607 | Dallas | 113 |

| School | Personnel | Grades | Enrollment | County | |
|---|---|---|---|---|---|
| J P Starks Mst Vanguard | Howard, Lynette | PK-5 | 312 | Dallas | 104 |
| Joe Lawrence Elem Sch | Jenkins, Roshanda | PK-6 | 440 | Dallas | 115 |
| Jose May Elem Sch | Nava, Rossee | PK-5 | 675 | Dallas | 105 |
| Las Colinas Elem Sch | Ahmad, Shahnaj | K-5 | 579 | Dallas | 101 |
| Lee Elem Sch | Carattini, Carla | K-5 | 492 | Dallas | 111 |
| Liberty Grove Elem Sch | Bottoms, Debra | PK-5 | 518 | Dallas | 110 |
| Martha Turner Reilly Elem Sch | O'Neal, Nichole | PK-5 | 553 | Dallas | 105 |
| McLaughlin Strickland ES | Cisneros, Victoria | K-5 | 535 | Dallas | 101 |
| Merrifield Elem Sch | Jones, Tanya, Dr | PK-4 | 440 | Dallas | 109 |
| Montclair Elem Sch | Massey, Karla | PK-5 | 523 | Dallas | 110 |
| Nita Pearson Elem Sch | Wilson, Cherelle | PK-5 | 658 | Dallas | 110 |
| North Lake Early Clg High Sch | Lysowski, Tristan | 9-9 | 85 | Dallas | 106 |
| North Mesquite High Sch | Washington, Kenneth | 9-12 | 2,591 | Dallas | 115 |
| Northlake Elem Sch | Kathy, Metzinger, Dr | PK-5 | 508 | Dallas | 110 |
| Northrich Elem Sch | Gammaro, Lindsey | PK-6 | 388 | Dallas | 117 |
| O'Banion Middle Sch | Gilmore, Earl | 6-8 | 1,210 | Dallas | 110 |
| Pathfinder Achievement Center | Guillory, Danny | Spec | 46 | Dallas | 110 |
| Pleasant Run Elem Sch | Waites, Marlon | PK-5 | 730 | Dallas | 114 |
| R E Good Elem Sch | Paredes, Agueda | PK-5 | 536 | Dallas | 101 |
| R L Turner High Sch | Grinage, Adam | 9-12 | 2,127 | Dallas | 101 |
| Raul Quintanilla Middle Sch | Ward, Tameca | 6-8 | 691 | Dallas | 106 |
| Richland Elem Sch | Hogan, Pharah | PK-6 | 600 | Dallas | 117 |
| Ronald E McNair Elem Sch | Bell-Ellis, Demetria | PK-5 | 600 | Dallas | 106 |
| Ronald Reagan Middle Sch | Potts, Ami | 6-8 | 855 | Dallas | 112 |
| Rowlett High Sch | Blakey, Carmen | 9-12 | 2,587 | Dallas | 110 |
| Sam Rayburn Steam Acad | Schmitter, Amanda | PK-5 | 490 | Dallas | 112 |
| Sarah Zumwalt Middle Sch | Nevels, Bobby | 6-8 | 396 | Dallas | 106 |
| Sellers Middle Sch | Howard, Janice | 6-8 | 867 | Dallas | 110 |
| Sheffield Primary Elem Sch | Jones, Ahveance | K-5 | 654 | Dallas | 101 |
| Smith Elem Sch | Stephens, Kellee | PK-4 | 319 | Dallas | 109 |
| Spring Creek Elem Sch | McCutcheon, Teresa | PK-5 | 570 | Dallas | 110 |
| Stults Road Elem Sch | Barnett, Jason | PK-6 | 726 | Dallas | 117 |
| Stults Road Elem Sch | Balch, Jennifer | PK-6 | 726 | Dallas | 117 |
| T H McDonald Middle Sch | Simmons, Jordan | 7-8 | 1,002 | Dallas | 116 |
| Thomas J Rusk Middle Sch | Scott, Jennifer | 6-8 | 648 | Dallas | 107 |
| Thomas J Rusk Middle Sch | Hernandez, Gabriel | 6-8 | 648 | Dallas | 107 |
| Thomas J Rusk Middle Sch | Guerra, Marina | 6-8 | 648 | Dallas | 107 |
| Vernal Lister Elem Sch | Riddick, Danielle | PK-5 | 367 | Dallas | 111 |
| Wallace Elem Sch | Anderson, Tonya | PK-6 | 738 | Dallas | 117 |
| Walter Wilkinson Middle Sch | Johnson, Tomika | 6-8 | 523 | Dallas | 116 |
| Watson Tech Center Math & Sci | Leday, Adrian | PK-5 | 512 | Dallas | 111 |
| Webb Middle Sch | Wilson, Nikketta | 6-8 | 1,193 | Dallas | 111 |
| West Mesquite High Sch | Faulkner, Shelly, Dr | 9-12 | 2,095 | Dallas | 116 |
| William B Miller Elem Sch | Varner-Busby, Chinqua | PK-5 | 292 | Dallas | 107 |
| Williams Elem Sch | Pizana, Lucas | PK-5 | 228 | Dallas | 111 |
| Wilmer-Hutchins Elem Sch | White, Samantha | PK-5 | 954 | Dallas | 108 |
| South Elem Sch | Ritchey, David | PK-2 | 513 | Dawson | 121 |
| Cuero High Sch | Fleener, Kimberly | 9-12 | 640 | De Witt | 122 |
| Cuero Junior High Sch | Dracos, Jennifer | 6-8 | 473 | De Witt | 122 |
| Yorktown Elem Sch | Patek, Laura | PK-5 | 243 | De Witt | 122 |
| Cooper Elem Sch | Gibson, Cody | PK-5 | 346 | Delta | 124 |
| Argyle Intermediate Sch | Jordan, Dawn | 4-5 | 442 | Denton | 124 |
| Braswell High Sch | Hailey, Decorian | 9-12 | 2,007 | Denton | 125 |
| Briarhill Middle Sch | Davenport, Leslie | 6-8 | 870 | Denton | 126 |
| Collegiate Academy | Kirkland, Kelly | 9-12 | 401 | Denton | 126 |
| Delay Middle Sch | Dockery, Charde | 6-8 | 1,016 | Denton | 127 |
| Forestwood Middle Sch | Hawes, Jennifer | 6-8 | 911 | Denton | 127 |
| Hebron Valley Elem Sch | Zamora, Laura | PK-5 | 567 | Denton | 127 |
| Hilltop Elem Sch | Lumsden, Dona | PK-3 | 930 | Denton | 124 |
| Krum Early Education Center | Stupka, Lyndi | PK-1 | 249 | Denton | 126 |
| Lake Dallas Elem Sch | Dominguez, Larry | PK-5 | 571 | Denton | 126 |
| Lewisville High Sch | Baker, Jim | 11-12 | 1,921 | Denton | 127 |
| Lewisville HS-B Harmon Campus | Cartmill, Joi | 9-10 | 1,256 | Denton | 127 |
| Linda Tutt High Sch | Love, Anthony | 9-12 | 30 | Denton | 130 |
| Michael G Killian Middle Sch | Krol, Tina, Dr | 6-8 | 996 | Denton | 127 |
| Mill St Elem Sch | Bailey, Deborah | PK-5 | 246 | Denton | 127 |
| Ponder Elem Sch | Manning, Emily | PK-5 | 742 | Denton | 130 |
| Thomas O Hicks Elem Sch | Webb, Misty | PK-5 | 499 | Denton | 128 |
| V R Eaton High Sch | Miles, Stacy | 9-10 | 1,603 | Denton | 129 |
| Clarendon Elem Sch | Bessent, Cynthia | PK-5 | 191 | Donley | 131 |
| Gorman High Sch | Robinson, Karen | 9-12 | 77 | Eastland | 133 |
| Gorman Middle Sch | Robinson, Karen | 6-8 | 73 | Eastland | 133 |
| Blanton Elem Sch | Ybarra, Stacey | PK-5 | 555 | Ector | 134 |
| Bonham Middle Sch | Austin, Mareka | 6-8 | 690 | Ector | 134 |
| Burnet Elem Sch | Serrano, Maria | K-5 | 559 | Ector | 134 |
| Permian High Sch | Styles, Delesa, Dr | 9-12 | 3,817 | Ector | 135 |

| School | Principal | Grades | Enrollment | County | Page |
|--------|-----------|--------|-----------|--------|------|
| Reagan Magnet Elem Sch | Bizzell, Jennifer | K-5 | 576 | Ector | 135 |
| Aoy Elem Sch | Arnold, Mary | PK-5 | 397 | El Paso | 137 |
| Capistrano Elem Sch | Myers, Norma | K-5 | 410 | El Paso | 142 |
| Cesar Chavez Academy | Gurany, Daniel | 7-12 | 42 | El Paso | 142 |
| Clardy Elem Sch | Corral, Michelle | PK-5 | 498 | El Paso | 137 |
| Del Norte Heights Elem Sch | Merfa, Roxanne | K-6 | 322 | El Paso | 142 |
| Del Valle Elem Sch | Balderrama, Maritza | PK-5 | 383 | El Paso | 142 |
| Douglass Elem Sch | Barraza, Alonzo | PK-5 | 198 | El Paso | 137 |
| Dr Joseph E Torres | Ese, Kathleen | PK-5 | 850 | El Paso | 137 |
| East Point Elem Sch | Poblano, Claudia | PK-6 | 787 | El Paso | 142 |
| Edgemere Elem Sch | Maldonado, Graciela | PK-6 | 721 | El Paso | 142 |
| Hacienda Heights Elem Sch | Perez, Sandra | PK-6 | 393 | El Paso | 142 |
| Johnson Elem Sch | Perez, Luz | PK-5 | 447 | El Paso | 138 |
| North Loop Elem Sch | Puga, Christopher | K-6 | 344 | El Paso | 142 |
| Parkland Elem Sch | Boyd, Dana | K-5 | 575 | El Paso | 142 |
| Pasodale Elem Sch | Alvarez, Natalie | PK-5 | 679 | El Paso | 142 |
| Ramona Elem Sch | Solis, Darlene | K-6 | 274 | El Paso | 142 |
| Sgt Jose Carrasco Elem Sch | Sepulveda, Jesus | PK-5 | 672 | El Paso | 141 |
| Sun Ridge Middle Sch | Herrera, David | 6-8 | 883 | El Paso | 141 |
| Donald T Shields Elem Sch | Bell, Allyson | K-4 | 545 | Ellis | 146 |
| H A Wooden Elem Sch | Weis, Amy | PK-4 | 540 | Ellis | 146 |
| Margaret L Felty Elem Sch | East, Rusty | K-5 | 529 | Ellis | 146 |
| Milford Sch | Johnson, David | PK-12 | 240 | Ellis | 146 |
| Oliver E Clift Elem Sch | Malone, Tanisha | K-5 | 504 | Ellis | 147 |
| Palmer Elem Sch | Cunningham, Melissa | PK-4 | 525 | Ellis | 146 |
| Red Oak High Sch | Gatewood, Howard | 9-12 | 1,885 | Ellis | 146 |
| Red Oak Middle Sch | Garcia, Fabian | 6-8 | 1,433 | Ellis | 146 |
| Shackelford Elem Sch | Schaeffer, Veronica | K-5 | 524 | Ellis | 147 |
| Stafford Elem Sch | Bray, Stafford | PK-5 | 304 | Ellis | 145 |
| Walnut Grove Middle Sch | Woolery, Carly | 6-8 | 1,120 | Ellis | 145 |
| Bluff Dale Elem Sch | Berngen, Frank | PK-12 | 222 | Erath | 147 |
| Dublin Intermediate Sch | Schneider, Chesta | 4-6 | 272 | Erath | 147 |
| Ector Sch | Bankston, Justin | K-12 | 260 | Fannin | 150 |
| Leonard High Sch | Hutchings, Tammy | 9-12 | 277 | Fannin | 150 |
| Leonard Junior High Sch | Gregory, Jacob | 6-8 | 217 | Fannin | 150 |
| Trenton High Sch | Foster, Stephen | 9-12 | 185 | Fannin | 151 |
| Round Top Carmine High Sch | Kuecker, Rachelle | 7-12 | 116 | Fayette | 152 |
| Schulenburg Elem Sch | McBride, Kristi | PK-5 | 302 | Fayette | 152 |
| A B Duncan Elem Sch | Smith, Monica | PK-6 | 381 | Floyd | 153 |
| Lockney High Sch | Southard, Michelle | 9-12 | 124 | Floyd | 153 |
| Alternative Learning Center | Smith, Melissia, Dr | K-12 | 80 | Fort Bend | 158 |
| Anne Sullivan Elem Sch | Whisonant, Donna | PK-5 | 1,310 | Fort Bend | 154 |
| Barbara Jordan Elem Sch | Charles, Kimberly | PK-5 | 438 | Fort Bend | 154 |
| Bear Creek Elem Sch | McElroy, Stephanie | PK-5 | 599 | Fort Bend | 156 |
| Beckendorff Junior High Sch | Moussavi, Paul | 6-8 | 1,699 | Fort Bend | 156 |
| Billy Baines Middle Sch | Williams, Elizabeth | 6-8 | 1,212 | Fort Bend | 154 |
| Blue Ridge Elem Sch | Evans-Williams, Sonya | PK-5 | 219 | Fort Bend | 154 |
| Cinco Ranch Junior High Sch | Salinas, Mona | 6-8 | 1,272 | Fort Bend | 156 |
| Colony Bend Elem Sch | Brown, Stacy | PK-5 | 538 | Fort Bend | 154 |
| Diane Winborn Elem Sch | Lowry, Leah | PK-5 | 695 | Fort Bend | 156 |
| Edna Mae Fielder Elem Sch | Kampwerth, Mark | PK-5 | 950 | Fort Bend | 156 |
| Elkins High Sch | Ward, Cynthia | 9-12 | 2,389 | Fort Bend | 154 |
| Fred and Patti Shafer ES | Smith, Shannon | PK-5 | 985 | Fort Bend | 156 |
| Hunters Glen Elem Sch | Williams, Lavanta | PK-5 | 431 | Fort Bend | 154 |
| James E Taylor High Sch | Stone, Melinda, Dr | 9-12 | 2,884 | Fort Bend | 156 |
| James Patterson Elem Sch | Wallace, Angela | PK-5 | 719 | Fort Bend | 154 |
| Lantern Lane Elem Sch | Kowrach, Justin | PK-5 | 409 | Fort Bend | 154 |
| Loraine T Golbow Elem Sch | Hale, Jessica | PK-5 | 790 | Fort Bend | 156 |
| Mission Glen Elem Sch | Nichols, Jacob | PK-5 | 475 | Fort Bend | 155 |
| Missouri City Middle Sch | Miles-Essone, Jeannie | 6-8 | 1,041 | Fort Bend | 155 |
| Navarro Middle Sch | Darjean, Toshila | 6-6 | 513 | Fort Bend | 158 |
| Stockdick Jr High Sch | Lalime, Ann, Dr | 6-8 | 903 | Fort Bend | 157 |
| Woodcreek Junior High Sch | Lowry, Andrew, Dr | 6-8 | 1,587 | Fort Bend | 157 |
| Zelma Hutsell Elem Sch | Blount, Margie | PK-5 | 727 | Fort Bend | 157 |
| Mount Vernon Elem Sch | Orren, Rhonda | PK-4 | 553 | Franklin | 160 |
| Fairfield Junior High Sch | Johnson, Daniel | 6-8 | 436 | Freestone | 160 |
| Dilley Elem Sch | Martinez, Adam | PK-5 | 424 | Frio | 161 |
| Pearsall Intermediate Sch | Hicks, Brian | 3-5 | 517 | Frio | 161 |
| Seagraves Elem Sch | Fleenor, Jeff | PK-5 | 320 | Gaines | 162 |
| Clear Connections Online Acad | Washburn, Adrian | K-12 | 100 | Galveston | 163 |
| Dan J Kubacak Elem Sch | Payne, Harold | 5-5 | 1,065 | Galveston | 165 |
| Dickinson Alt Lrng Center | Martinez, Valerie | 9-12 | 64 | Galveston | 164 |
| Hughes Road Elem Sch | Colburn, Kelly | PK-4 | 664 | Galveston | 164 |
| Santa Fe Junior High Sch | Adkins, Florence, Dr | 6-8 | 1,082 | Galveston | 165 |
| Windsong Intermediate Sch | McAshlan, Wendy | 3-5 | 450 | Galveston | 164 |
| Fredericksburg Elem Sch | Flack, Laura | 1-5 | 1,061 | Gillespie | 167 |

| School | Contact | Grades | Enrollment | County | |
|---|---|---|---|---|---|
| Gonzales Primary Academy | Bell, Brandi | PK-K | 350 | Gonzales | 169 |
| Waelder Sch | Kesselus, Darren | PK-12 | 317 | Gonzales | 169 |
| McLean Sch | Rainer, Bradley | PK-12 | 236 | Gray | 170 |
| McLean Sch | Villegas, Robert | PK-12 | 236 | Gray | 170 |
| Collinsville High Sch | Patterson, Kim | 7-12 | 237 | Grayson | 171 |
| Fairview Elem Sch | Matejko, Daniel | K-4 | 425 | Grayson | 172 |
| Gunter High Sch | Woods, Kensie | 9-12 | 305 | Grayson | 171 |
| Gunter Middle Sch | Dodd, Chris | 5-8 | 280 | Grayson | 171 |
| Pottsboro High Sch | Curry, Danielle | 9-12 | 402 | Grayson | 172 |
| S & S Cons High Sch | Johnston, Scott | 9-12 | 275 | Grayson | 172 |
| Sherman High Sch | Chancellor, Jeffrey | 9-12 | 1,884 | Grayson | 172 |
| Washington Elem Sch | Wood, Heather | PK-4 | 406 | Grayson | 172 |
| Whitesboro Intermediate Sch | Kupper, Kacy | 3-5 | 370 | Grayson | 173 |
| Whitesboro Middle Sch | Dodson, Aaron | 6-8 | 367 | Grayson | 173 |
| Whitewright Elem Sch | Price, Allyson | PK-5 | 353 | Grayson | 173 |
| Whitewright High Sch | Long, Chad | 9-12 | 285 | Grayson | 173 |
| Whitewright High Sch | Morrow, Steve | 9-12 | 285 | Grayson | 173 |
| Birch Elem Sch | Smith, Sharon | 1-4 | 648 | Gregg | 175 |
| Johnston-McQueen Elem Sch | Bailey, Jennifer, Dr | PK-5 | 709 | Gregg | 175 |
| Kilgore Middle Sch | Gholson, Jennifer | 6-8 | 924 | Gregg | 174 |
| Pine Tree Primary Sch | Walker, Ruthie | PK-K | 518 | Gregg | 175 |
| Ware Elem Sch | Worsham, Josh | 1-5 | 514 | Gregg | 175 |
| W B Bizzell Academy | Bates, Jamie | 9-12 | 34 | Grimes | 177 |
| Jim Barnes Middle Sch | Schmidt, Jason | 6-8 | 876 | Guadalupe | 179 |
| Marion Middle Sch | Stevens, Jeff | 6-8 | 356 | Guadalupe | 177 |
| Navarro High Sch | Scarborough, Clay | 9-12 | 638 | Guadalupe | 178 |
| Navarro Intermediate Sch | McMullen, Wendy | 4-6 | 433 | Guadalupe | 178 |
| Rose Garden Elem Sch | Reed, Sarah | PK-4 | 586 | Guadalupe | 178 |
| Samuel Clemens High Sch | Sirizzotti, Amy | 9-12 | 2,631 | Guadalupe | 178 |
| Cotton Center Sch | Bobo, Ryan | PK-12 | 125 | Hale | 180 |
| Petersburg Sch | Fortune, Cash | PK-12 | 280 | Hale | 180 |
| Petersburg Sch | Newberry, Todd | PK-12 | 280 | Hale | 180 |
| Thunderbird Elem Sch | Garcia, Edna | PK-5 | 447 | Hale | 180 |
| Hico Elem Sch | Hunt, Brian | PK-5 | 273 | Hamilton | 181 |
| Spearman High Sch | Wheeler, Sandi | 9-12 | 265 | Hansford | 182 |
| Reagan Elem Sch | Miller, Connie | PK-5 | 226 | Hardeman | 182 |
| Edwards-Johnson Memorial MS | Jenkins, Amanda | 6-8 | 628 | Hardin | 183 |
| Kountze Middle Sch | Hatton, Michael | 7-8 | 78 | Hardin | 183 |
| A A Milne Elem Sch | Johnson, Bronchell | PK-5 | 559 | Harris | 198 |
| Alamo Elem Sch | Abbate, Leah | PK-5 | 769 | Harris | 192 |
| Alief Taylor High Sch | Price, William | 9-12 | 3,112 | Harris | 187 |
| Ashford Elem Sch | Vasquez, Kylene | PK-5 | 584 | Harris | 198 |
| Bane Elem Sch | Diaz, Cesar | PK-5 | 877 | Harris | 189 |
| Barbara Jordan Career Center | McAlpine, John | 11-12 | 150 | Harris | 196 |
| Bastian Elem Sch | Holloway, Alana | PK-5 | 708 | Harris | 197 |
| Benfer Elem Sch | Johnson, Ashley | PK-5 | 801 | Harris | 202 |
| Biotech Academy-Rusk | Herrera, Jesse | 6-8 | 484 | Harris | 197 |
| Briargrove Elem Sch | McDonald, Kelli | PK-5 | 881 | Harris | 198 |
| Browning Elem Sch | Garcia, Annie | PK-5 | 489 | Harris | 196 |
| Buffalo Creek Elem Sch | Young, Carrmilla | K-5 | 507 | Harris | 206 |
| Burbank Elem Sch | Luebbers, Heather | PK-5 | 912 | Harris | 195 |
| C E King High Sch | Saeed, Raff, Dr | 9-12 | 1,849 | Harris | 205 |
| C E King Middle Sch | Sampson, Ashley | 6-8 | 1,047 | Harris | 205 |
| Carl Wunsche Sr High Sch | Jones, Alfred | 9-12 | 1,473 | Harris | 207 |
| Charles R Drew Academy | Walker, Christopher | 6-8 | 583 | Harris | 186 |
| Clifford Dunn Elem Sch | Pollard, Terese | 1-5 | 501 | Harris | 185 |
| Cook Jr Elem Sch | Harris-Mosley, Shundra | PK-5 | 625 | Harris | 195 |
| Creekview Elem Sch | Shaughnessy, Bianca | PK-5 | 614 | Harris | 208 |
| Daep Sch | Stewart, Deborah | 6-12 | 20 | Harris | 203 |
| Davila Elem Sch | Cerda, Avisay | PK-5 | 403 | Harris | 194 |
| Davis Senior High Sch | Watkins, Anthony | 10-12 | 2,621 | Harris | 185 |
| Dean Middle Sch | Pham, Hoang | 6-8 | 1,384 | Harris | 189 |
| Deer Park High Sch-N Campus | Taylor, Kirk | 9-9 | 1,073 | Harris | 191 |
| Doerre Intermediate Sch | Land, Katherine | 6-8 | 1,361 | Harris | 202 |
| Dwight D Eisenhower High Sch | Davis, Mandele | 10-12 | 1,750 | Harris | 185 |
| Eliot Elem Sch | Schwer, Matthew | PK-5 | 605 | Harris | 195 |
| Eliot Elem Sch | Aguilar, Zandra | PK-5 | 605 | Harris | 195 |
| Elm Grove Elem Sch | Pfeifer, Cassie | K-5 | 533 | Harris | 201 |
| Elrod Elem Sch | Hutchins, Michael | PK-5 | 763 | Harris | 198 |
| Energized for STEM Acad Ctrl | Clark, Shavon | 9-12 | 315 | Harris | 199 |
| Energized for STEM Academy MS | Kho, Arlene | 6-8 | 218 | Harris | 199 |
| Fleming Middle Sch | Bruce, Yolanda | 6-8 | 486 | Harris | 196 |
| Fondren Elem Sch | Contreras, Edgar | PK-5 | 314 | Harris | 194 |
| Forest Brook Middle Sch | Jenkins, Ashley | 6-8 | 828 | Harris | 194 |
| Frost Elem Sch | Starks, Cedric | PK-5 | 615 | Harris | 197 |
| Gallegos Elem Sch | Gonzalez, Norma | PK-5 | 357 | Harris | 195 |

| School | Key Personnel | Grades | Enrollment | County | Page |
|---|---|---|---|---|---|
| Gloria B Sammons Elem Sch | Foroi, Georgina | 1-5 | 524 | Harris | 184 |
| Golfcrest Elem Sch | Blanco, Miguel | PK-5 | 656 | Harris | 197 |
| Griggs EC-PK-K Sch | Porter Brisker, Tonya | PK-K | 865 | Harris | 186 |
| Helms Elem Sch | Perejon, Lola | PK-5 | 473 | Harris | 197 |
| Herod Elem Sch | Collon-Hernand, Gina | PK-5 | 818 | Harris | 199 |
| Hill Elem Sch | White, Constance | 1-5 | 641 | Harris | 185 |
| Holbrook Elem Sch | Mendez, Becky | PK-5 | 983 | Harris | 190 |
| J R Harris Elem Sch | Rivero, Jessica | PK-5 | 411 | Harris | 195 |
| James R Reynolds Elem Sch | Marshall, Renesiaha | PK-5 | 467 | Harris | 198 |
| Jewel S Houston Academy | Stewart, Cedric, Dr | 6-8 | 604 | Harris | 186 |
| Joan Link Elm Sch | Stith, Tangy | PK-5 | 547 | Harris | 207 |
| Keeble EC-PK-K Sch | Marshall, Andrenetta, Dr | PK-K | 785 | Harris | 186 |
| Ketelsen Elem Sch | Aguirre, Christina | PK-5 | 579 | Harris | 197 |
| Kleb Intermediate Sch | Hodge, Ellen | 6-8 | 1,412 | Harris | 202 |
| La Porte Elem Sch | Hyde, Linda | PK-5 | 518 | Harris | 203 |
| Labay Middle Sch | Bellamy, Lanette | 6-8 | 1,334 | Harris | 190 |
| Landrum Middle Sch | Moore, Roy | 6-8 | 670 | Harris | 206 |
| Langham Creek High Sch | Martinez, Jose | 9-12 | 2,980 | Harris | 190 |
| Laurenzo ECC | Benavides, Janet | PK-K | 344 | Harris | 195 |
| Lawson Middle Sch | Dunn, Keoshya | 6-8 | 1,210 | Harris | 194 |
| Lemm Elem Sch | Tietze, Adam | PK-5 | 708 | Harris | 202 |
| Lockhart Elem Sch | Emerson, Cameshia | PK-5 | 589 | Harris | 198 |
| Lomax Elem Sch | Greenwood, Tracy | PK-5 | 393 | Harris | 203 |
| Long Academy | Soto, Benigno | 6-12 | 896 | Harris | 199 |
| Lorenzo De Zavala Elem Sch | Cobb, Bart | PK-5 | 752 | Harris | 193 |
| Love Elem Sch | Bass, Eden | PK-5 | 377 | Harris | 197 |
| MacArthur 9th Grade Sch | Everline, Yul, Dr | 9-9 | 918 | Harris | 185 |
| Mading Elem Sch | Gaddis, Angela | PK-5 | 433 | Harris | 194 |
| Mading Elem Sch | Dudley, Tabitha | PK-5 | 433 | Harris | 194 |
| Mahaffey Elem Sch | Davenport, Sherri | PK-5 | 851 | Harris | 202 |
| Mattie A Teague Middle Sch | Dussette, Kimberly | 6-8 | 1,268 | Harris | 186 |
| McGowen Elem Sch | Woods, Jessie | PK-5 | 452 | Harris | 196 |
| McReynolds Middle Sch | Giron, Jasmine | 6-8 | 595 | Harris | 196 |
| McReynolds Middle Sch | Steuernagel, Philip | 6-8 | 595 | Harris | 196 |
| Memorial Drive Elem Sch | Hutcheson, Thayer | PK-5 | 426 | Harris | 206 |
| Michael R Null Middle Sch | White, Katrina | 6-8 | 779 | Harris | 205 |
| Mitchell Elem Sch | Guajardo, Elizabeth | PK-5 | 384 | Harris | 198 |
| Navarro Mid Sch | Cruz, Emeterio | 6-8 | 682 | Harris | 195 |
| North Houston Early College HS | Brooks, Samantha | 9-12 | 484 | Harris | 197 |
| Orange Grove Elem Sch | Flores-Bolivar, Fernanda | 1-5 | 804 | Harris | 185 |
| Osborne Elem Sch | Barnes, Mikia | PK-5 | 407 | Harris | 196 |
| Park Place Elem Sch | Thomas, Nimmi | PK-5 | 951 | Harris | 195 |
| Patterson Elem Sch | Saenz, Luis | PK-5 | 931 | Harris | 195 |
| Pleasantville Elem Sch | Rogers, Samyra | PK-5 | 266 | Harris | 195 |
| Project Chrysalis Middle Sch | Rodriguez, Lisa | 6-8 | 279 | Harris | 195 |
| Ralph G Goodman Elem Sch | Ward, Ladon | 1-5 | 404 | Harris | 186 |
| Reed Elem Sch | Richardson, Karen | PK-5 | 924 | Harris | 190 |
| Rick Ogden Elem Sch | Johnson, Ashley | 1-5 | 665 | Harris | 185 |
| River Pines Elem Sch | Pearce, Alicia | PK-5 | 835 | Harris | 201 |
| Royalwood Elem Sch | Altamirano, Jesus | 1-5 | 647 | Harris | 205 |
| Rummel Creek Elem Sch | Sloan, Laura, Dr | PK-5 | 689 | Harris | 206 |
| Salyers Elem Sch | Presswood, Asia | PK-5 | 723 | Harris | 208 |
| Sanchez Elem Sch | Mena, Ricardo | PK-5 | 581 | Harris | 195 |
| Shadydale Elem Sch | Hampton, Teri | PK-5 | 897 | Harris | 196 |
| Sheldon Early Childhood Acad | Leal, Joel | PK-K | 574 | Harris | 205 |
| Sherman Elem Sch | Rosenbaum, Racquel | PK-5 | 570 | Harris | 196 |
| Spring Shadows Elem Sch | Stubblefield, Raymond | K-5 | 614 | Harris | 206 |
| Stovall EC-PK-K Sch | Ames, Jeremy | PK-K | 561 | Harris | 186 |
| Texas Connections Academy [190] | Chaplin, Benjamin | 3-12 | 5,680 | Harris | 194 |
| Thomas Middle Sch | Haskins, Nicole | 6-8 | 594 | Harris | 198 |
| Thomas S Grantham Academy | Hepworth, Ivan | 6-8 | 1,140 | Harris | 186 |
| Tijerina Elem Sch | Olaizola, Alesander | PK-5 | 342 | Harris | 195 |
| Valley West Elem Sch | VanNest, Brian | PK-5 | 861 | Harris | 200 |
| Vernon & Kathy Lewis Mid Sch | Clark-Antwine, Tonya | 6-8 | 1,141 | Harris | 186 |
| Vistas High Sch | Anderson, Bob | 9-12 | 75 | Harris | 203 |
| Voyde Caraway Elem Sch | Marshall, Andrenetta, Dr | 1-5 | 548 | Harris | 184 |
| W A Carpenter Elem Sch | Galvan, Blanca | K-5 | 824 | Harris | 191 |
| Wainwright Elem Sch | Hutchings, Ryan | PK-5 | 519 | Harris | 197 |
| Westbury High Sch | Nixon, Jerri | 9-12 | 2,341 | Harris | 198 |
| Westside High Sch | Stewart, Peggi | 9-12 | 2,897 | Harris | 200 |
| Wildwood Elem Sch | Shaughnessy, Beatriz | PK-4 | 1,041 | Harris | 208 |
| Willie J Hargrave High Sch | Skinner, Adam | 9-12 | 787 | Harris | 200 |
| Woodson PK-5 Sch | Wilkins, Gina | PK-5 | 643 | Harris | 194 |
| Worthing High Sch | Hare, Everett | 9-12 | 781 | Harris | 194 |
| Wunderlich Intermediate Sch | Huggins, Clay | 6-8 | 1,525 | Harris | 203 |
| Youens Elem Sch | Rose, Sancionett | PK-5 | 900 | Harris | 188 |

| School | Personnel | Grades | Enrollment | County | Code |
|---|---|---|---|---|---|
| Youens Elem Sch | Brixey, Tessia | PK-5 | 900 | Harris | 188 |
| Marshall High Sch | Gregory, Matt | 9-12 | 1,413 | Harrison | 214 |
| Waskom Elem Sch | Jones, Andrew | PK-5 | 373 | Harrison | 214 |
| Chapa Middle Sch | Chapa, Mr | 6-8 | 753 | Hays | 216 |
| Doris Miller Middle Sch | Gipprich, Jessie | 6-8 | 791 | Hays | 217 |
| Hernandez Elem Sch | Gonzalez, Jennifer | K-5 | 623 | Hays | 217 |
| Jacobs Well Elem Sch | Thomas, Sueanna | 3-5 | 703 | Hays | 217 |
| Mendez Elem Sch | Woody, Kristina | K-5 | 587 | Hays | 217 |
| Red Simon Middle Sch | Watson, Michael, Dr | 6-8 | 757 | Hays | 216 |
| Canadian Middle Sch | Daniel, Drew | 6-8 | 221 | Hemphill | 218 |
| Athens High Sch | Cornish, Nicole | 9-12 | 899 | Henderson | 218 |
| Brownsboro Junior High Sch | Roach, Jake | 7-8 | 412 | Henderson | 218 |
| Malakoff Elem Sch | Robinson, Chris | PK-5 | 423 | Henderson | 219 |
| Tool Elem Sch | Sutton, Brandi | PK-5 | 200 | Henderson | 219 |
| Alamo Middle Sch | Ortega, Francisco | 6-8 | 625 | Hidalgo | 226 |
| Augusto Guerra Elem Sch | Villarreal, L | PK-5 | 622 | Hidalgo | 226 |
| Brewster Sch | Garcia, Zulema | PK-8 | 171 | Hidalgo | 221 |
| Carmen Avila Elem Sch | Leal, Ramiro | PK-5 | 605 | Hidalgo | 221 |
| Crawford Elem Sch | Vega, Denise | PK-5 | 521 | Hidalgo | 221 |
| Disciplinary Alt Ed Program | Perez, Roger | 6-12 | 60 | Hidalgo | 228 |
| Dora M Sauceda Middle Sch | Robledo, Karina | 6-8 | 828 | Hidalgo | 220 |
| Drs Reed & Mock Elem Sch | Montemayor, Karla, Dr | PK-5 | 618 | Hidalgo | 226 |
| Henry B Gonzalez Elem Sch | Sandoval, Sylvia | PK-5 | 496 | Hidalgo | 223 |
| Henry Ford Elem Sch | Alaniz, Elizabeth | PK-5 | 679 | Hidalgo | 226 |
| La Villa Middle Sch | Elizondo, Paz | 6-8 | 121 | Hidalgo | 224 |
| Lorenzo De Zavala Elem Sch | Garza, Marisa | PK-5 | 438 | Hidalgo | 222 |
| M D Betts Elem Sch | Cano, Ernestina | PK-5 | 468 | Hidalgo | 222 |
| Marcia R Garza Elem Sch | Santoy, Marisa | PK-5 | 625 | Hidalgo | 227 |
| Narciso Cavazos Elem Sch | Longoria, Liz | PK-5 | 443 | Hidalgo | 223 |
| Psja T Jefferson Echs | Maldonado, Virna | 9-12 | 805 | Hidalgo | 227 |
| Robert Vela High Sch | Pena, Michele | 9-12 | 1,194 | Hidalgo | 222 |
| Salinas STEM Early College Sch | Rodriguez, Victor | 9-12 | 408 | Hidalgo | 223 |
| Valley View Early College Sch | Vidal, Isaias | 8-9 | 623 | Hidalgo | 228 |
| Blum Sch | Brandenberger, Charles | PK-12 | 344 | Hill | 230 |
| Hubbard Elem Sch | Beseda, Sunny | PK-5 | 208 | Hill | 231 |
| Hubbard High Sch | Dennie, Danny | 6-12 | 214 | Hill | 231 |
| Itasca High Sch | Webb, Robert | 9-12 | 199 | Hill | 231 |
| Penelope Sch | Hueske, Sherry | PK-12 | 215 | Hill | 231 |
| Anton Sch | Bentancourt, Deeanne | PK-12 | 185 | Hockley | 232 |
| Levelland ABC | Howad, Mrs | PK-1 | 428 | Hockley | 232 |
| Tolar Elem Sch | Hollinger, Christal | PK-5 | 344 | Hood | 233 |
| Tolar Junior High Sch | Tidwell, Jerrod | 6-8 | 186 | Hood | 234 |
| Lamar Primary Sch | Crawford, Chandra | K-3 | 319 | Hopkins | 235 |
| Crockett Elem Sch | Montgomery, Crystal | 1-5 | 488 | Houston | 235 |
| Crockett Junior High Sch | Gomez, Johnny | 6-8 | 306 | Houston | 235 |
| Latexo Elem Sch | Gallaway, Rachel | PK-6 | 214 | Houston | 236 |
| Latexo High Sch | Watson, Kimberly | 7-12 | 207 | Houston | 236 |
| Bland Elem Sch | Owen, Cinda | PK-5 | 338 | Hunt | 238 |
| Celeste Elem Sch | Walker, Lindsay | PK-5 | 188 | Hunt | 239 |
| Katherine G Johnson STEM Acad | Bozas, Sebastian | K-5 | 204 | Hunt | 239 |
| Borger Intermediate Sch | Bodey, Teresa | 5-6 | 392 | Hutchinson | 240 |
| Gateway Elem Sch | Russell, James | 1-2 | 349 | Hutchinson | 240 |
| Spring Creek Sch | Finch, Danny | K-12 | 110 | Hutchinson | 241 |
| Jacksboro Elem Sch | Qualls, Michael | PK-5 | 474 | Jack | 242 |
| Edna Junior High Sch | Koop, Melissa | 6-8 | 336 | Jackson | 242 |
| Industrial Elem Sch West | Bain, Stacey | PK-5 | 191 | Jackson | 243 |
| Brookeland Sch | Odam, Charlotte | PK-12 | 380 | Jasper | 243 |
| Jean C Few Primary Sch | Stanley, Wendi | PK-3 | 677 | Jasper | 244 |
| Kirbyville Junior High Sch | Odom, Chad | 6-8 | 330 | Jasper | 244 |
| Kirbyville Junior High Sch | Powell, Ashley | 6-8 | 330 | Jasper | 244 |
| Dirks-Anderson Sch | Wimberly, Cyndi | PK-5 | 106 | Jeff Davis | 244 |
| Amelia Elem Sch | Haynes, Dimitrise | PK-5 | 710 | Jefferson | 244 |
| Bingham Head Start Ctr | Bolton, Lisa | PK-PK | 510 | Jefferson | 245 |
| Lucas Pre-K Center | Langley, L Parker | PK-PK | 332 | Jefferson | 245 |
| M L King Middle Sch | Corona, Julie | 6-8 | 627 | Jefferson | 245 |
| Marshall Middle Sch | Paul, Breaux | 6-8 | 910 | Jefferson | 245 |
| Marshall Middle Sch | Colvin, Charles | 6-8 | 910 | Jefferson | 245 |
| Paul A Brown Learning Center | Rice, Calvin, Dr | 9-12 | 115 | Jefferson | 245 |
| Smith Magnet Middle Sch | Lee, Andrea Renee | 6-8 | 574 | Jefferson | 245 |
| Alice High Sch | Morales, Gianna | 9-12 | 1,290 | Jim Wells | 248 |
| Salazar Elem Sch | Snyder, Vanessa | PK-4 | 259 | Jim Wells | 248 |
| Alvarado Elem North Sch | Payne, Kristi | PK-3 | 328 | Johnson | 249 |
| Alvarado Elem South Sch | Burnes, Jalynn | PK-3 | 323 | Johnson | 249 |
| Burleson Collegiate High Sch | Byrd, Lindsey | 9-12 | 76 | Johnson | 249 |
| Caddo Grove Elem Sch | Chernow, Tanya | PK-5 | 541 | Johnson | 251 |
| H D Staples Elem Sch | Howell, Kate | PK-5 | 445 | Johnson | 251 |

| School | Personnel | Grades | Enrollment | County | Page |
|---|---|---|---|---|---|
| Joshua 9th Grade Campus | Cox, Toby | 9-9 | 408 | Johnson | 251 |
| Lillian Elem Sch | Kelley, Tonya | PK-3 | 335 | Johnson | 249 |
| New Horizons High Sch | Cox, Toby | 9-12 | 19 | Johnson | 251 |
| Rio Vista Elem Sch | Zook, Michael | PK-5 | 355 | Johnson | 251 |
| Steam Middle Sch | Greenwood, Noel | 6-8 | 592 | Johnson | 250 |
| Hawley Elem Sch | Cox, Jacob | PK-5 | 378 | Jones | 253 |
| Lueders-Avoca Elem Jr High Sch | Gaspar, Chris | PK-8 | 70 | Jones | 253 |
| Lueders-Avoca Elem Jr High Sch | Cummings, Robert | PK-8 | 70 | Jones | 253 |
| Stamford Middle Sch | Price, Torrey | 6-8 | 164 | Jones | 253 |
| Falls City Elem Sch | Ruple, Jessica | PK-6 | 173 | Karnes | 253 |
| Kenedy Elem Sch | Wiatrek, Katy | PK-5 | 323 | Karnes | 254 |
| Crandall High Sch | Miller, Jared | 9-12 | 522 | Kaufman | 254 |
| Gary W Campbell High Sch | Fowler, Cindy | 6-12 | 40 | Kaufman | 255 |
| Hollis T Dietz Elem Sch | Baker, Jennifer | PK-6 | 563 | Kaufman | 254 |
| Kemp Intermediate Sch | Adams, Shelby | 3-5 | 391 | Kaufman | 255 |
| Mabank High Sch | Groom, Charity | 9-12 | 1,018 | Kaufman | 256 |
| O P Norman Junior High Sch | McNeely, Meagan | 6-8 | 935 | Kaufman | 255 |
| Scurry Rosser High Sch | Casas, Adan | 9-12 | 316 | Kaufman | 256 |
| Junction Elem Sch | Murff, Janel | PK-5 | 296 | Kimble | 260 |
| Jones Elem Sch | Diaz, Eliza | PK-5 | 233 | Kinney | 260 |
| Academy High Sch | Odom, Charles | 9-12 | 355 | Kleberg | 261 |
| Gillett Intermediate Sch | Gutierrez, Adriana | 5-6 | 453 | Kleberg | 260 |
| Perez Elem Sch | Tennyson, Analese | PK-4 | 445 | Kleberg | 260 |
| Santa Gertrudis Elem MS | Garcia, Fatima | PK-8 | 449 | Kleberg | 261 |
| Knox City High Sch | Tucker, Mark | 9-12 | 82 | Knox | 261 |
| O'Brien Middle Sch | Carter, Jordan | 5-8 | 72 | Knox | 261 |
| Littlefield High Sch | Read, Mike | 9-12 | 373 | Lamb | 263 |
| Olton Junior High Sch | Huseman, Colby | 6-8 | 128 | Lamb | 263 |
| Hallettsville Elem Sch | Grahmann, Stephanie | PK-4 | 354 | Lavaca | 265 |
| Hallettsville Elem Sch | Patek, Trina | PK-4 | 354 | Lavaca | 265 |
| Moulton Elem Sch | Simper, April | PK-6 | 140 | Lavaca | 265 |
| Giddings Intermediate Sch | Mahoney, Michael | 4-5 | 283 | Lee | 266 |
| Leon Elem Sch | Grisham, Nan | PK-6 | 425 | Leon | 267 |
| Hardin Elem Sch | Scott, Ronald | PK-5 | 701 | Liberty | 268 |
| Hardin High Sch | Tucker, Stacy | 9-12 | 353 | Liberty | 268 |
| Tarkington High Sch | Fierro, Jennifer | 9-12 | 520 | Liberty | 269 |
| Tarkington Middle Sch | McCabe, Sean | 6-8 | 445 | Liberty | 269 |
| Tarkington Primary Sch | House, Calesta | PK-3 | 568 | Liberty | 269 |
| Tarkington Primary Sch | McCabe, Sean | PK-3 | 568 | Liberty | 269 |
| Llano High Sch | Patrick, Scott | 9-12 | 505 | Llano | 271 |
| Cathelene Thomas Elem Sch | Francis, Margaret | 1-5 | 461 | Lubbock | 275 |
| Idalou High Sch | Estrada, Jerry | 9-12 | 294 | Lubbock | 272 |
| North Ridge Elem Sch | Stroope, Aimee | PK-5 | 605 | Lubbock | 272 |
| Roosevelt High Sch | Crane, Tim | 9-12 | 300 | Lubbock | 274 |
| Roosevelt Junior High Sch | Franklin, Stacy | 6-8 | 270 | Lubbock | 274 |
| Shallowater High Sch | Nell, Craig | 9-12 | 323 | Lubbock | 275 |
| Stephen F Austin Primary | Johnson, Sammi | PK-K | 193 | Lubbock | 275 |
| Waters Elem Sch | Portwood, Melissa | PK-5 | 541 | Lubbock | 273 |
| New Home Sch | Webb, Brady | PK-12 | 580 | Lynn | 276 |
| Cherry Elem Sch | White, Jana | PK-5 | 705 | Matagorda | 278 |
| Roberts Elem Sch | Wendel, Marissa | K-5 | 487 | Matagorda | 278 |
| Tenie Holmes Elem Sch | Hagg, Ashley | K-5 | 708 | Matagorda | 278 |
| China Spring Elem Sch | Dutschmann, Kristen | PK-3 | 900 | McLennan | 281 |
| China Spring Elem Sch | Coe, Kim | PK-3 | 900 | McLennan | 281 |
| China Spring Middle Sch | Boykin, Lath | 7-8 | 427 | McLennan | 282 |
| G W Carver Middle Sch | Carrier, Isaac, Dr | 6-8 | 488 | McLennan | 285 |
| J H Hines Elem Sch | Taylor, Everette | PK-5 | 452 | McLennan | 285 |
| Mart High Sch | Sanchez, Beau | 7-12 | 146 | McLennan | 283 |
| Mart High Sch | Burnett, Betsy | 7-12 | 146 | McLennan | 283 |
| Moody Elem Sch | Stansel, Tina | K-4 | 237 | McLennan | 284 |
| Parkdale Elem Sch | Ortiz, Lena | PK-5 | 669 | McLennan | 285 |
| Menard High Sch | Hand, Jacob | 9-12 | 82 | Menard | 288 |
| Burnet Elem Sch | Hernandez, Maribel | PK-6 | 471 | Midland | 288 |
| Fannin Elem Sch | Cisneros, Lisa | PK-6 | 525 | Midland | 289 |
| Jones Elem Sch | Harmon, Amber | PK-6 | 298 | Midland | 289 |
| Robert E Lee Freshman High Sch | Tarlton, Judi | 9-9 | 853 | Midland | 289 |
| San Jacinto Junior High Sch | Gore, Jessica | 6-8 | 528 | Midland | 289 |
| Mullin Oaks Sch | Feist, Chayden | 9-12 | 91 | Mills | 291 |
| Gold-Burg Sch | Tallon, Chad | PK-12 | 127 | Montague | 293 |
| Anderson Elem Sch | Quinonesaceved, Laura | PK-4 | 543 | Montgomery | 294 |
| Armstrong Elem Sch | Waller, Theresa | PK-4 | 444 | Montgomery | 294 |
| Bear Branch Junior High Sch | Venghaus, Julia | 7-8 | 984 | Montgomery | 296 |
| C C Hardy Elem Sch | Bond, Jason | K-5 | 518 | Montgomery | 297 |
| Colin Powell Elem Sch | Mathe, Erin | PK-4 | 871 | Montgomery | 294 |
| Conroe 9th Grade High Sch | Gorka, Bryan | 9-9 | 1,000 | Montgomery | 294 |
| Coulson Tough Elem Sch | Julien, Christina | PK-6 | 791 | Montgomery | 294 |

| School | Personnel | Grades | Enrollment | County | Code |
|--------|-----------|--------|-----------:|--------|-----:|
| Creighton Elem Sch | Thacker, Patricia | PK-4 | 745 | Montgomery | 294 |
| Dogwood Elem Sch | Lowe, Sheri | PK-5 | 696 | Montgomery | 296 |
| Edward B Cannan Elem Sch | Copley, Kent | K-5 | 660 | Montgomery | 297 |
| Irons Junior High Sch | MacFarlane, Robert | 7-8 | 1,152 | Montgomery | 295 |
| Jean E Stewart Elem Sch | English, Julie | PK-6 | 711 | Montgomery | 295 |
| Keefer Crossing Middle Sch | Powell, Jonathan | 6-8 | 867 | Montgomery | 296 |
| Lynn Lucas Middle Sch | Burns, Eric | 6-8 | 271 | Montgomery | 297 |
| Magnolia Elem Sch | Covarrubias, Donna | PK-5 | 844 | Montgomery | 296 |
| McCullough Junior High Sch | Hooser, Jill | 7-8 | 1,800 | Montgomery | 295 |
| Meador Elem Sch | Good, Tamara | K-5 | 733 | Montgomery | 297 |
| Montgomery High Sch | Schur, Andria, Dr | 9-12 | 1,775 | Montgomery | 296 |
| Porter Elem Sch | Land, Nicole | PK-5 | 640 | Montgomery | 297 |
| Porter High Sch | Condarco, Cesar | 9-12 | 2,017 | Montgomery | 297 |
| Rice Elem Sch | Sciba, Melissa | PK-4 | 441 | Montgomery | 295 |
| San Jacinto Elem Sch | Almond, Jamie | PK-4 | 591 | Montgomery | 295 |
| Tavola Elem Sch | Felts, Kimberly | PK-5 | 594 | Montgomery | 297 |
| Valley Ranch Elem Sch | Coronado, Stephanie | PK-5 | 728 | Montgomery | 297 |
| Wilkinson Elem Sch | Stewart, Malinda | PK-4 | 676 | Montgomery | 295 |
| Dumas Senior High Sch | Clements, Carl | 9-12 | 535 | Moore | 298 |
| North Plains Opportunity Ctr | Williams, Stan | 9-12 | 35 | Moore | 298 |
| Pewitt Junior High Sch | Cartwright, James | 6-8 | 185 | Morris | 299 |
| Brooks-Quinn Jones Elem Sch | Fonzie, Gerald | PK-5 | 778 | Nacogdoches | 301 |
| Central Heights Elem Sch | Engle, Kathryn | PK-5 | 497 | Nacogdoches | 300 |
| Garrison Middle Sch | Prince, Larry | 6-8 | 110 | Nacogdoches | 301 |
| Blooming Grove Elem Sch | King, Allyson | PK-5 | 378 | Navarro | 302 |
| Kerens Elem Sch | Satterwhite, Cindy | PK-4 | 229 | Navarro | 303 |
| Burkeville Elem Sch | Day, Kevin | PK-6 | 144 | Newton | 304 |
| Berlanga Elem Sch | Winchester, Cynthia | PK-5 | 521 | Nueces | 306 |
| Bishop Elem Sch | Trevino, Rosalinda | 3-5 | 190 | Nueces | 305 |
| Claude Cunningham Middle Sch | Salinas-DeLeon, Sandy | 6-8 | 557 | Nueces | 306 |
| Evans Elem Sch | Martinez, Molli | PK-5 | 305 | Nueces | 306 |
| J A Garcia Elem Sch | Noyola, Daniel | PK-5 | 595 | Nueces | 306 |
| Lotspeich Elem Sch | Perez-Peterson, Vanessa | PK-3 | 301 | Nueces | 308 |
| Miller HS-Metro Sch of Design | Wilson, Bruce | 7-12 | 1,225 | Nueces | 307 |
| Montclair Elem Sch | Barrera, Steve | PK-5 | 275 | Nueces | 307 |
| Tuloso-Midway High Sch | Portillo, Benito | 9-12 | 578 | Nueces | 309 |
| University Preparatory HS | Kellar, Kathy | 9-12 | 302 | Nueces | 308 |
| Vidor Elem Sch | Antill, Brandy | PK-4 | 643 | Orange | 312 |
| Graford Elem Sch | Alverado, Tina | PK-5 | 174 | Palo Pinto | 313 |
| Mineral Wells Jr High Sch | Spillers, Shanna | 7-8 | 493 | Palo Pinto | 313 |
| Beckville Jr Sr High Sch | Kruebbe, Brandon | 6-12 | 364 | Panola | 314 |
| Carthage High Sch | Smith, Justin | 9-12 | 798 | Panola | 314 |
| Gary Sch | Price, Chris | PK-12 | 443 | Panola | 314 |
| Brock Intermediate Sch | Lane, Ranae | 3-6 | 467 | Parker | 315 |
| Joe Tison Middle Sch | Treat, Renee | 7-8 | 597 | Parker | 317 |
| McAnally Intermediate Sch | Jenkins, Joshua | 5-6 | 834 | Parker | 315 |
| Peaster Middle Sch | Steen, Jimmy | 6-8 | 201 | Parker | 316 |
| Friona Junior High Sch | Rosales, Daniel | 6-8 | 217 | Parmer | 318 |
| Lazbuddie Sch | Chambers, Gina | PK-12 | 168 | Parmer | 318 |
| Corrigan-Camden High Sch | Locke, Diana | 9-12 | 239 | Polk | 319 |
| Amarillo High Sch | Pfeifer, Andrea | 9-12 | 2,090 | Potter | 320 |
| Bivins Elem Sch | Soleyjacks, R | PK-5 | 501 | Potter | 320 |
| Coronado Elem Sch | Garcia, Ramon | PK-5 | 509 | Potter | 320 |
| Highland Park Elem Sch | Woodward, Shannon | PK-5 | 424 | Potter | 322 |
| Margaret Wills Elem Sch | Elliott, Lindsay | PK-5 | 562 | Potter | 321 |
| Mesa Verde Elem Sch | Cobb, Charla | PK-5 | 468 | Potter | 321 |
| North Heights Alt Sch | Leach, Mark | 7-12 | 429 | Potter | 321 |
| Pleasant Valley Elem Sch | Cardenas, Nick | PK-5 | 238 | Potter | 321 |
| Stephen F Austin Middle Sch | Self, Brandy | 6-8 | 793 | Potter | 321 |
| Presidio Elem Sch | Tibayan, Edgar, Dr | PK-6 | 565 | Presidio | 323 |
| Presidio High Sch | Ramos, Hevila | 10-12 | 440 | Presidio | 323 |
| Hillside Elem Sch | Kerns, Adam | PK-4 | 563 | Randall | 323 |
| Reagan Co Elem Sch | Soto, Trish | PK-5 | 386 | Reagan | 324 |
| Reagan Co High Sch | Brown, Kyle | 9-12 | 238 | Reagan | 324 |
| Reagan Co Middle Sch | McKay, Kalum | 6-8 | 197 | Reagan | 324 |
| Balmorhea Sch | Laramore, Gary | PK-12 | 165 | Reeves | 326 |
| Bessie Haynes Elem Sch | Henson, Chris | 4-5 | 513 | Reeves | 326 |
| Pecos Kindergarten | Abundez, Paul | PK-K | 207 | Reeves | 326 |
| Woodsboro Jr Sr High Sch | Segers, David, Dr | 7-12 | 190 | Refugio | 326 |
| Miami Sch | Tritz, Tommy | PK-12 | 190 | Roberts | 327 |
| Amy Parks-Heath Elem Sch | Lewis, Lindy | PK-6 | 445 | Rockwall | 328 |
| Dr Gene Burton C & C Academy | Belliveau, Alison | Voc | 800 | Rockwall | 328 |
| Howard Dobbs Elem Sch | Mejia, Laura | PK-6 | 569 | Rockwall | 328 |
| Rockwall Quest Academy | Bradford, Christina | 7-12 | 59 | Rockwall | 328 |
| Royse City High Sch | Craighead, Jere | 9-12 | 1,752 | Rockwall | 329 |
| Miles Sch | Taubert, Lela | PK-12 | 480 | Runnels | 329 |

| School | Principal | Grades | Enrollment | County | Page |
|---|---|---|---|---|---|
| Overton Secondary Sch | Hogg, Jeff | 6-12 | 234 | Rusk | 331 |
| Tatum Elem Sch | Malone, Jennifer | 3-5 | 314 | Rusk | 331 |
| Hemphill Elem Sch | Butler, Monica | PK-4 | 313 | Sabine | 332 |
| West Sabine Jr Sr High Sch | Conn, Colleen | 6-12 | 312 | Sabine | 332 |
| Broaddus Elem Sch | Grant, Karianna | PK-5 | 180 | San Augustine | 332 |
| Broaddus High Sch | Crawford, Zach | 6-12 | 216 | San Augustine | 332 |
| Shepherd Intermediate Sch | Stein, Jennifer | 3-5 | 456 | San Jacinto | 333 |
| Shepherd Middle Sch | Gore, Heather | 6-8 | 452 | San Jacinto | 333 |
| Shepherd Primary Sch | Lott, Alisa | PK-2 | 570 | San Jacinto | 333 |
| Gilbert Mircovich Elem Sch | Ponton, Suzy | 2-4 | 478 | San Patricio | 334 |
| Ingleside High Sch | Edlin, Steven | 9-12 | 609 | San Patricio | 334 |
| Wildcat Learning Alt Center | Eddleman, Kyde | 9-12 | 50 | San Patricio | 333 |
| Cherokee Sch | Panter, Rick | PK-12 | 112 | San Saba | 335 |
| Snyder High Sch | Murphy, Shaye | 9-12 | 715 | Scurry | 336 |
| Mary Allen Elem Sch | Rawlins, Doug | PK-4 | 204 | Sherman | 338 |
| Austin Elem Sch | Currie, Joshua | K-5 | 420 | Smith | 340 |
| Boulter Middle Sch | Holmes, Vanessa | 6-8 | 957 | Smith | 340 |
| Bullard Middle Sch | McDonald, Mark | 7-8 | 385 | Smith | 339 |
| Chapel Hill High Sch | Caldwell, Jason | 9-12 | 1,013 | Smith | 339 |
| Dixie Elem Sch | Simmons, Kimberly | PK-5 | 567 | Smith | 340 |
| E J Moss Intermediate Sch | Widemon, Candace | 4-6 | 970 | Smith | 340 |
| Higgins Elem Sch | Saul, Joanne | PK-5 | 523 | Smith | 341 |
| James S Hogg Middle Sch | Walls, Kristen | 6-8 | 366 | Smith | 340 |
| Moore Mst Magnet Sch | Ballard, Aubrey | 6-8 | 1,131 | Smith | 340 |
| Tyler High Sch | Lane, Claude | 9-12 | 2,097 | Smith | 341 |
| Winona High Sch | Sparkman, Keith | 9-12 | 318 | Smith | 341 |
| Academy Academic Enhancemnt-MS | Jones, Lillian | 6-8 | 267 | Starr | 343 |
| John & Olive Hinojosa Elem Sch | Olivarez, Mark | PK-5 | 406 | Starr | 343 |
| Rafaela T Barrera Elem Sch | Garcia, Marissa | PK-5 | 244 | Starr | 343 |
| San Isidro Sch | Rodriquez, Jesse | PK-12 | 200 | Starr | 344 |
| Aspermont Elem Sch | Van Meter, Trent | PK-5 | 93 | Stonewall | 344 |
| Aspermont High Sch | Garcia, Ronnie | 6-12 | 120 | Stonewall | 344 |
| Sonora High Sch | Valeriano, Rene | 9-12 | 257 | Sutton | 345 |
| Sonora Middle Sch | Valeriano, Rene | 7-8 | 181 | Sutton | 345 |
| Happy Middle High Sch | Sperry, Jennifer | 7-12 | 115 | Swisher | 345 |
| Tulia High Sch | Johnson, Dixie | 9-12 | 302 | Swisher | 345 |
| Alliene Mullendore Elem Sch | Dobecka, Merritt | PK-5 | 327 | Tarrant | 348 |
| Bailey Junior High Sch | Davis, Jason | 7-8 | 827 | Tarrant | 346 |
| Baxter Junior High Sch | Boone, Tanisha | 7-8 | 1,027 | Tarrant | 351 |
| Beckham Elem Sch | Hicks, Karen | PK-6 | 552 | Tarrant | 346 |
| Bedford Heights Elem Sch | Harrell, Kathleen | PK-6 | 670 | Tarrant | 356 |
| Berry Elem Sch | Lopez, Carlos | PK-6 | 611 | Tarrant | 346 |
| Bransford Elem Sch | Gerdes, Erin | PK-5 | 461 | Tarrant | 355 |
| Bridges Accel Lrng Ctr | Ramos, Jessica | 9-12 | 21 | Tarrant | 355 |
| Carter Park Elem Sch | McCalister, Cassandra | PK-5 | 631 | Tarrant | 352 |
| Castleberry High Sch | Ridley, Catherine | 9-12 | 768 | Tarrant | 350 |
| Chisholm Trail High Sch | McCowan, Winston | 9-12 | 2,019 | Tarrant | 351 |
| Colleyville Elem Sch | Lafara, Tracey | PK-5 | 475 | Tarrant | 355 |
| Como Montessori Sch | McAlister, Daniel | K-8 | 313 | Tarrant | 352 |
| Cora Spencer Elem Sch | Hobdy, Jocelyn | PK-4 | 558 | Tarrant | 359 |
| Cross Timbers Middle Sch | Halliburton, Jamie, Dr | 6-8 | 853 | Tarrant | 355 |
| Danny Jones Middle Sch | Kennedy, Sharlonda | 7-8 | 1,106 | Tarrant | 359 |
| Edward J Briscoe Elem Sch | Burgess, Devona | PK-5 | 430 | Tarrant | 353 |
| Glen Park Elem Sch | Herrera, Hilda | PK-5 | 496 | Tarrant | 353 |
| Green Valley Elem Sch | Calvin, Jim, Dr | PK-5 | 484 | Tarrant | 348 |
| Greenbriar Elem Sch | Guajardo, Staros | PK-5 | 513 | Tarrant | 353 |
| Harlean Beal Elem Sch | Adair, Jodie | PK-5 | 359 | Tarrant | 353 |
| Harrison Lane Elem Sch | Huber, Shannon | PK-6 | 686 | Tarrant | 356 |
| J Martin Jacquet Middle Sch | Foreman, Kristin | 6-8 | 729 | Tarrant | 353 |
| Jack C Binion Elem Sch | Bartlett, Donald | PK-5 | 712 | Tarrant | 348 |
| James L Coble Middle Sch | Moore, Travis | 7-8 | 906 | Tarrant | 359 |
| Jean McClung Middle Sch | Thomas, Tremayna | 6-8 | 716 | Tarrant | 353 |
| Jo Kelly Sch | McMillen, Amelia | Spec | 43 | Tarrant | 353 |
| Kenneth Davis Elem Sch | Bender, Adam | PK-4 | 419 | Tarrant | 359 |
| Lake Ridge High Sch | Alloway, Ashley | 9-12 | 2,632 | Tarrant | 359 |
| Leadership Acad Mitchell Blvd | Fracassi, Danny | PK-5 | 370 | Tarrant | 353 |
| Leonard Middle Sch | Ridley, Cathy | 6-8 | 831 | Tarrant | 353 |
| Leonard Middle Sch | Murphy, Mandi | 6-8 | 831 | Tarrant | 353 |
| Luella Merrett Elem Sch | Sandifer, Delain | PK-5 | 564 | Tarrant | 353 |
| Major Cheney ES-S Birdville | Conklin, Shane | PK-5 | 394 | Tarrant | 349 |
| Marine Creek Middle Sch | Gatlin, Ron | 6-8 | 1,000 | Tarrant | 351 |
| Meadow Creek Elem Sch | Rodriguez, Ann | PK-6 | 738 | Tarrant | 356 |
| Meadowbrook Middle Sch | Culton, Crystal | 6-8 | 776 | Tarrant | 354 |
| Morton Elem Sch | Adams, Leigh | PK-6 | 544 | Tarrant | 347 |
| North Crowley High Sch | Stapinski, Camcea | 10-12 | 1,759 | Tarrant | 350 |
| Roark Elem Sch | Eaton, Angela, Dr | PK-6 | 407 | Tarrant | 347 |

| School | Contact | Grades | Enrollment | County | Code |
|---|---|---|---|---|---|
| Rosemont Middle Sch | Sanchez, Xavier | 7-8 | 950 | Tarrant | 354 |
| Saginaw Elem Sch | Curtis, Melissa | PK-5 | 238 | Tarrant | 351 |
| Shackelford Junior High Sch | Smith, Kelli | 7-8 | 649 | Tarrant | 347 |
| Souder Elem Sch | Little, Kimberly | PK-4 | 467 | Tarrant | 352 |
| Speer Elem Sch | McDonald, Tashalon | PK-6 | 655 | Tarrant | 347 |
| Wedgwood 6th Grade Middle Sch | Johnson, Cheryl, Dr | 6-6 | 443 | Tarrant | 355 |
| William James Middle Sch | Rincon, Melissa | 6-8 | 895 | Tarrant | 355 |
| Willow Creek Elem Sch | Witt, Stacie | PK-5 | 520 | Tarrant | 351 |
| Bassetti Elem Sch | Zertuche, Cecelia | PK-5 | 454 | Taylor | 362 |
| Buffalo Gap Elem Sch | McClure, Alana | PK-5 | 303 | Taylor | 363 |
| Byron Craig Middle Sch | Stewart, Debra | 6-8 | 960 | Taylor | 363 |
| Dyess Elem Sch | Drake, Chad | PK-5 | 456 | Taylor | 363 |
| Meadow Sch | Coffman, Tabitha | PK-12 | 285 | Terry | 365 |
| Wellman-Union Sch | Conatser, Kyle | PK-12 | 335 | Terry | 365 |
| Harts Bluff Elem Sch | Ponce De Leon, Erika | PK-8 | 675 | Titus | 366 |
| Central Freshman Campus | Waters, Mr | 9-9 | 765 | Tom Green | 367 |
| Lake View High Sch | Ramirez, Zachary | 9-12 | 971 | Tom Green | 367 |
| Veribest Sch | Palmer, Amber | PK-12 | 275 | Tom Green | 368 |
| Allison Elem Sch | Molina, Lupe | PK-5 | 446 | Travis | 369 |
| Becker Elem Sch | Barrett, Travis | PK-5 | 445 | Travis | 369 |
| Cedar Creek Elem Sch | Wirht, Brad | K-5 | 523 | Travis | 372 |
| Decker Elem Sch | Cauman, Samuel | K-5 | 431 | Travis | 373 |
| Garcia Young Men's Leadership | Mejia, Jose | 6-8 | 411 | Travis | 371 |
| Lake Travis Elem Sch | Frankhouser, Angela | PK-5 | 793 | Travis | 373 |
| Lake Travis Elem Sch | Schaeffer, Pam | PK-5 | 793 | Travis | 373 |
| Lyndon B Johnson High Sch | Bailey, Jon | 9-12 | 842 | Travis | 371 |
| Manor New Tech Middle Sch | Ramirez, Francisco | 6-8 | 696 | Travis | 374 |
| Manor Senior High Sch | Powell, Brandon | 11-12 | 900 | Travis | 374 |
| Oak Springs Elem Sch | Jackson, Cynthia | PK-5 | 225 | Travis | 370 |
| Pickle Elem Sch | Waters, Rosa | PK-5 | 459 | Travis | 370 |
| St Elmo Elem Sch | McCormack, Ben | PK-5 | 299 | Travis | 370 |
| Westview Middle Sch | Ramirez, Alma | 6-8 | 763 | Travis | 375 |
| Trinity High Sch | Cassidy, Brittaney | 9-12 | 349 | Trinity | 377 |
| Chester High Sch | Loughner, Katy | 6-12 | 98 | Tyler | 377 |
| Spurger High Sch | Hatton, Amanda | 6-12 | 191 | Tyler | 378 |
| Woodville High Sch | Minyard, Rusty | 9-12 | 344 | Tyler | 378 |
| Woodville Intermediate Sch | Trammell, Bonnie | 3-5 | 289 | Tyler | 378 |
| Woodville Middle Sch | Frauenberger, Kevin | 6-8 | 305 | Tyler | 378 |
| Big Sandy Elem Sch | Blavier, Andrea | PK-5 | 314 | Upshur | 378 |
| Gilmer High Sch | Bowman, Brian | 9-12 | 708 | Upshur | 379 |
| Harmony Irons-Smith Interm Sch | Whitaker, Lynn | 4-5 | 158 | Upshur | 379 |
| James E Poole Elem Sch | Chevalier, Diane | PK-3 | 345 | Upshur | 379 |
| New Diana High Sch | Gross, John | 9-12 | 324 | Upshur | 379 |
| Robert F Hunt Elem Sch | Zucosky, Ashley | PK-5 | 487 | Upshur | 379 |
| Anthon Elem Sch | Martinez, Beatrice | 1-2 | 678 | Uvalde | 381 |
| Robb Elem Sch | Contreras, Abraham | 3-4 | 597 | Uvalde | 381 |
| Canton Junior High Sch | Boyd, Dawn | 6-8 | 519 | Van Zandt | 382 |
| Martin's Mill Sch | Latimer, Audra | PK-12 | 230 | Van Zandt | 383 |
| Wills Point Middle Sch | Harle, Kelly | 5-6 | 405 | Van Zandt | 384 |
| Estella Stewart Elem Sch | Fox, Kimberly | K-4 | 513 | Walker | 386 |
| Huntsville High Sch | Trevino, Paul | 9-12 | 1,708 | Walker | 386 |
| Huntsville Intermediate Sch | Branch, Racheal | 5-6 | 955 | Walker | 386 |
| Samuel Houston Elem Sch | Simmons, Natasha | K-4 | 445 | Walker | 386 |
| Grandfalls Royalty Sch | Chesser, Charles | PK-12 | 184 | Ward | 388 |
| Sudderth Elem Sch | Thomas, Kim | 4-6 | 578 | Ward | 388 |
| C G Sivells Elem Sch | Foyt, Dana | PK-2 | 494 | Wharton | 393 |
| East Bernard Jr High Sch | Janecek, David | 5-8 | 268 | Wharton | 392 |
| El Campo Middle Sch | Stary, Alicia | 6-8 | 863 | Wharton | 392 |
| Wheeler Sch | Hardcastle, Heather | PK-12 | 441 | Wheeler | 394 |
| City View Elem Sch | Moffett, Ronda | PK-6 | 461 | Wichita | 394 |
| City View Jr Sr High Sch | McDaniel, Christina | 7-12 | 460 | Wichita | 394 |
| Electra Elem Sch | Russell, Jim, Dr | PK-6 | 255 | Wichita | 394 |
| Electra Jr Senior High Sch | Hasley, Don | 7-12 | 136 | Wichita | 394 |
| Central Elem Sch | Merrell, Stefanie | 2-3 | 278 | Wilbarger | 396 |
| L C Smith Elem Sch | Ramos, Sylvia | PK-5 | 389 | Willacy | 397 |
| Blackland Prairie Elem Sch | Hildebrand, Sue | PK-5 | 833 | Williamson | 401 |
| Canyon Ridge Middle Sch | Sturdevant, Wendy | 6-8 | 1,265 | Williamson | 400 |
| Danielson Middle Sch | Koller, Mark | 6-8 | 970 | Williamson | 400 |
| Early Clg High Sch | Wilson, Elizabeth, Dr | 9-10 | 250 | Williamson | 401 |
| Fern Bluff Elem Sch | Hultman, Tyler | K-5 | 609 | Williamson | 402 |
| Granger Sch | Shirocky, Tawnya | PK-12 | 426 | Williamson | 399 |
| Jack Frost Elem Sch | Marbibi, Tamara | PK-5 | 260 | Williamson | 398 |
| Laura Welch Bush Elem Sch | Bailon-Valdez, Jon | PK-5 | 596 | Williamson | 400 |
| Live Oak Elem Sch | Braudrick, Brian | PK-5 | 598 | Williamson | 402 |
| Nadine Johnson Elem Sch | Reichel, Bridgit | PK-5 | 423 | Williamson | 399 |
| Noel Grisham Middle Sch | Serna, Amanda | 6-8 | 442 | Williamson | 402 |

| | | | | | |
|---|---|---|---|---|---|
| Round Rock Opportunity Center | Bosier, Donald | 6-12 | 250 | Williamson | 402 |
| Wiley Middle Sch | Hodges, Angela | 6-8 | 1,072 | Williamson | 401 |
| Boyd High Sch | Reeves, Chelsea | 9-12 | 410 | Wise | 405 |
| Boyd High Sch | Magryta, Christine | 9-12 | 410 | Wise | 405 |
| Boyd Intermediate Sch | Harrison, Morgan | 4-6 | 278 | Wise | 405 |
| Decatur High Sch | Matthew, Jadie, Dr | 9-12 | 1,053 | Wise | 406 |
| McCarroll Middle Sch | Nunn, Roby | 6-8 | 495 | Wise | 406 |
| North Lamar High Sch | Keith, Mark | 9-12 | 762 | Wise | 407 |
| Paradise Elem Sch | Cota, Melissa | PK-3 | 373 | Wise | 407 |
| Paradise Junior High Sch | Carter, Nicki | 6-8 | 309 | Wise | 407 |
| Rann Elem Sch | Vargas, Galindo | PK-5 | 563 | Wise | 406 |
| Quitman Elem Sch | Eldred, Brittany | PK-5 | 475 | Wood | 408 |
| Zapata High Sch | Garcia, Jerry | 9-12 | 947 | Zapata | 410 |

## NEW SUPERINTENDENTS

| DISTRICT | SUPERINTENDENT | GRADES | ENROLLMENT | COUNTY | PAGE |
|---|---|---|---|---|---|
| Frankston Ind School Dist | Cook, Nicci | PK-12 | 766 | Anderson | 18 |
| Central Ind School Dist | Risner, Justin | PK-12 | 1,400 | Angelina | 20 |
| Holliday Ind School Dist | Carroll, Cody | PK-12 | 1,051 | Archer | 22 |
| Bellville Ind School Dist | Poenitzsch, Nicole, Dr | PK-12 | 2,200 | Austin | 24 |
| Sealy Ind School Dist | Hallmark, Bryan, Dr | PK-12 | 2,669 | Austin | 25 |
| Beeville Ind School Dist | Fanning, Travis | PK-12 | 3,400 | Bee | 28 |
| Skidmore Tynan Ind SD | Waterhouse, Richard | K-12 | 850 | Bee | 29 |
| Belton Ind School Dist | Smith, Matt, Dr | PK-12 | 11,950 | Bell | 29 |
| Braination Schools | Whitt, Ken | K-12 | 818 | Bexar | 33 |
| Harlandale Ind School Dist | Soto, Gerardo | PK-12 | 14,500 | Bexar | 35 |
| Randolph Field Ind School Dist | Holt, Brian, Dr | PK-12 | 1,442 | Bexar | 42 |
| South San Antonio Ind Sch Dist | Puig, Marc, Dr | PK-12 | 8,800 | Bexar | 45 |
| Southside Ind School Dist | Ramirez, Rolando | PK-12 | 5,800 | Bexar | 46 |
| Iredell Ind School Dist | Eubanks, Ben | PK-12 | 138 | Bosque | 50 |
| Morgan Ind School Dist | Ramerez, Juan | PK-12 | 130 | Bosque | 50 |
| Hooks Ind School Dist | Minter, Keith | PK-12 | 884 | Bowie | 51 |
| Texarkana Ind School Dist | Thomas, Autumn | PK-12 | 7,174 | Bowie | 53 |
| Danbury Ind School Dist | Sandlin, Nancy | PK-12 | 840 | Brazoria | 56 |
| College Station Ind Sch Dist | Martindale, Mike | PK-12 | 14,000 | Brazos | 59 |
| Mumford Ind School Dist | Reese, Allen | PK-12 | 612 | Brazos | 59 |
| San Vicente Ind School Dist | Milam, Jessica | K-8 | 13 | Brewster | 60 |
| Bangs Ind School Dist | Martin, Josh, Dr | PK-12 | 868 | Brown | 61 |
| Early Ind School Dist | Wilkins, DeWayne, Dr | PK-12 | 1,200 | Brown | 62 |
| Baird Ind School Dist | Little, Tim | PK-12 | 289 | Callahan | 65 |
| Rio Hondo Ind School Dist | Ellis, Roger | PK-12 | 1,650 | Cameron | 70 |
| White Deer Ind School Dist | Lucas, Scott | PK-12 | 360 | Carson | 73 |
| Dimmitt Ind School Dist | Millican, Jill | PK-12 | 1,230 | Castro | 74 |
| Hart Ind School Dist | Lara, Christa | PK-12 | 206 | Castro | 75 |
| New Summerfield Ind Sch Dist | Brannen, Joe | PK-12 | 544 | Cherokee | 76 |
| Wells Ind School Dist | Gaston, Jill | PK-12 | 280 | Cherokee | 77 |
| Bellevue Ind School Dist | Wesley, Wade | PK-12 | 140 | Clay | 77 |
| Henrietta Ind School Dist | Clayton, Scot | PK-12 | 937 | Clay | 78 |
| Santa Anna Ind School Dist | White, Todd | PK-12 | 250 | Coleman | 79 |
| Celina Ind School Dist | Maglisceau, Thopmas, Dr | PK-12 | 2,600 | Collin | 81 |
| Farmersville Ind School Dist | French, Micheal | PK-12 | 1,594 | Collin | 82 |
| Princeton Ind School Dist | McIntyre, Donald | PK-12 | 5,567 | Collin | 87 |
| Prosper Ind School Dist | Fergerson, Holly, Dr | PK-12 | 19,000 | Collin | 88 |
| Comanche Ind School Dist | Worrell, Daron | PK-12 | 1,325 | Comanche | 93 |
| Ralls Ind School Dist | Maxwell, Nathan, Dr | PK-12 | 485 | Crosby | 98 |
| Krum Ind School Dist | Davis, Mike | PK-12 | 2,100 | Denton | 126 |
| Carrizo Spgs Cons Ind SD | Cervantes, Osae, Dr | PK-12 | 2,200 | Dimmit | 131 |
| Clarendon Cons Ind Sch Dist | Bellar, Jarod | PK-12 | 450 | Donley | 131 |
| Rising Star Ind Sch Dist | Atkins, Mary Jane | PK-12 | 150 | Eastland | 133 |
| Rocksprings Ind School Dist | Taylor, Larry | PK-12 | 289 | Edwards | 135 |
| El Paso ISD-Elementary | Cabrera, Juan | PK-5 | | El Paso | 137 |
| El Paso ISD-High Schools | Cabrera, Juan | 6-12 | | El Paso | 138 |
| El Paso ISD-Middle Schools | Cabrera, Juan | 6-8 | | El Paso | 139 |
| Red Oak Ind School Dist | Sanford, Brenda | PK-12 | 6,000 | Ellis | 146 |
| Bonham Ind School Dist | Trompler, Kelly | PK-12 | 1,850 | Fannin | 149 |
| Dodd City Ind School Dist | Reed, Craig | PK-12 | 364 | Fannin | 150 |
| Ector Ind School Dist | Morris, Jennifer | PK-12 | 260 | Fannin | 150 |
| Sam Rayburn Ind School Dist | Arthur, Steve | PK-12 | 525 | Fannin | 150 |
| Trenton Ind School Dist | Strickland, Jeremy | PK-12 | 573 | Fannin | 151 |
| Crowell Ind School Dist | Rhodes, Donald, Dr | PK-12 | 230 | Foard | 153 |
| Wortham Ind School Dist | Bosley, Melissa | PK-12 | 500 | Freestone | 161 |
| Dilley Ind School Dist | Leo, Maria, Dr | PK-12 | 950 | Frio | 161 |
| Texas City Ind School Dist | Duarte, Melissa, Dr | PK-12 | 9,000 | Galveston | 166 |
| Harper Ind School Dist | Stewart, Bonnie | PK-12 | 557 | Gillespie | 168 |

| | | | | | |
|---|---|---|---|---|---|
| Goliad Ind School Dist | Acklery, Stacy | PK-12 | 1,325 | Goliad | 168 |
| White Oak Ind School Dist | Gray, Brian | PK-12 | 1,496 | Gregg | 176 |
| Navarro Ind School Dist | Russell, Wendi | PK-12 | 1,909 | Guadalupe | 178 |
| Schertz-Cibolo-Univ City ISD | Ealy, Clark, Dr | PK-12 | 15,925 | Guadalupe | 178 |
| Quanah Ind School Dist | Johnson, Tom | PK-12 | 525 | Hardeman | 182 |
| Kountze Ind School Dist | Reyenga, Shane | PK-12 | 767 | Hardin | 183 |
| Lumberton Ind School Dist | Tipton, Tony, Dr | PK-12 | 3,437 | Hardin | 183 |
| Galena Park Ind School Dist | Moore, John, Dr | PK-12 | 21,045 | Harris | 191 |
| La Porte Ind School Dist | Jackson, Walter, Dr | PK-12 | 7,679 | Harris | 203 |
| Harleton Ind School Dist | Ratcliff, Jay | PK-12 | 716 | Harrison | 213 |
| Waskom Ind School Dist | Patty, Rae Ann | PK-12 | 850 | Harrison | 214 |
| Canadian Ind School Dist | Pulliam, Lynn | PK-12 | 860 | Hemphill | 218 |
| Athens Ind School Dist | Sims, Janie, Dr | PK-12 | 3,000 | Henderson | 218 |
| La Villa Ind School Dist | Elizondo, Paz | PK-12 | 555 | Hidalgo | 223 |
| Pharr-San Juan-Alamo Ind SD | Arrendondo, Jorge | PK-12 | 32,000 | Hidalgo | 226 |
| Valley View Ind School Dist | Luna, Monica | PK-12 | 4,300 | Hidalgo | 228 |
| Smyer Ind School Dist | Wade, Chris | PK-12 | 415 | Hockley | 232 |
| Lipan Ind School Dist | Carter, Ralph | PK-12 | 413 | Hood | 233 |
| Crockett Ind School Dist | Emrich, John | PK-12 | 1,331 | Houston | 235 |
| Boles Ind School Dist | Goss, Micheal | PK-12 | 545 | Hunt | 238 |
| Irion Co Ind School Dist | Despain, Ray, Dr | PK-12 | 300 | Irion | 241 |
| Ganado Ind School Dist | Fasel, Erin | PK-12 | 700 | Jackson | 242 |
| Industrial Ind School Dist | Klimitchek, Missy, Dr | PK-12 | 1,100 | Jackson | 243 |
| Jasper Ind School Dist | Seybold, John | PK-12 | 2,400 | Jasper | 243 |
| Beaumont Ind School Dist | Allen, Shannon, Dr | PK-12 | 18,000 | Jefferson | 244 |
| Karnes City Ind School Dist | Madrigal, Hector | PK-12 | 1,062 | Karnes | 253 |
| Runge Ind School Dist | Bettin, Linda | PK-12 | 238 | Karnes | 254 |
| Mabank Ind School Dist | Koskelin, Brad | PK-12 | 3,664 | Kaufman | 256 |
| Kenedy Co Wide Common Sch Dist | Tinsley, Kristen | PK-6 | 80 | Kenedy | 258 |
| Kingsville Ind School Dist | Reynolds-Perez, Cecilia, Dr | PK-12 | 3,050 | Kleberg | 260 |
| Ricardo Ind School Dist | Bueno, Sam, Dr | PK-8 | 670 | Kleberg | 261 |
| Moulton Ind School Dist | Ulcak, Chris | PK-12 | 300 | Lavaca | 265 |
| Follett Ind School Dist | Copley, Jamie | PK-12 | 165 | Lipscomb | 270 |
| George West Ind School Dist | Quesada, Roland, Dr | PK-12 | 1,100 | Live Oak | 271 |
| Idalou Ind School Dist | Gibson, Robert | PK-12 | 984 | Lubbock | 272 |
| Shallowater Ind School Dist | Hebert, Anita | PK-12 | 1,351 | Lubbock | 274 |
| Brady Ind School Dist | Martinez, Hector | PK-12 | 1,050 | McCulloch | 280 |
| Devine Ind School Dist | Grandjean, Todd | PK-12 | 1,900 | Medina | 286 |
| Natalia Ind School Dist | Collavo, Lana | PK-12 | 1,000 | Medina | 287 |
| Buckholts Ind School Dist | Oliver, Joe | PK-12 | 132 | Milam | 290 |
| Montgomery Ind School Dist | Morrison, Heath, Dr | PK-12 | 9,048 | Montgomery | 296 |
| Pewitt Cons Ind School Dist | Reid, Melissa | PK-12 | 870 | Morris | 299 |
| Chireno ISD School Dist | Skinner, Michael | PK-12 | 400 | Nacogdoches | 300 |
| Nacogdoches Ind School Dist | Trujillo, Gabriel, Dr | PK-12 | 6,400 | Nacogdoches | 301 |
| Blooming Grove Ind School Dist | Hartley, Rick | PK-12 | 950 | Navarro | 302 |
| Rice Ind School Dist | Harvell, Amy | PK-12 | 975 | Navarro | 303 |
| Sweetwater ISD School Dist | Howard, Drew, Dr | PK-12 | 1,888 | Nolan | 304 |
| Agua Dulce Ind School Dist | Wright, Richard | PK-12 | 374 | Nueces | 305 |
| Perryton Ind School Dist | Mireles, James | PK-12 | 2,217 | Ochiltree | 310 |
| Gordon Ind School Dist | Campbell, Holly | PK-12 | 210 | Palo Pinto | 313 |
| Friona Ind School Dist | Burns, Jimmy | PK-12 | 1,045 | Parmer | 318 |
| Iraan-Sheffield Ind Sch Dist | Canter, Tracy, Dr | PK-12 | 375 | Pecos | 318 |
| Balmorhea Ind School Dist | Massey, John | PK-12 | 165 | Reeves | 325 |
| Pecos-Barstow-Toyah Ind SD | Jaco, Brent | PK-12 | 2,700 | Reeves | 326 |
| Winters Ind School Dist | Leamon, Sean | PK-12 | 525 | Runnels | 329 |
| Leveretts Chapel Ind Sch Dist | Johnson, Josh | PK-12 | 240 | Rusk | 330 |
| West Sabine Ind Sch Dist | Joslin, Cristal | PK-12 | 578 | Sabine | 332 |
| Shepherd Ind School Dist | Hewitt, Jason | PK-12 | 2,041 | San Jacinto | 333 |
| Gregory-Portland Ind Sch Dist | Cazazos, Michelle | PK-12 | 4,600 | San Patricio | 333 |
| Taft Ind School Dist | Trevino, Ricardo | PK-12 | 1,154 | San Patricio | 334 |
| Cherokee Ind School Dist | Bordner, Jennifer | K-12 | 112 | San Saba | 335 |
| Center Ind School Dist | Morris, Brian, Dr | PK-12 | 2,600 | Shelby | 337 |
| Texhoma Ind School Dist | Yates, Kayla | PK-4 | 130 | Sherman | 338 |
| Bullard Ind School Dist | Lee, Jack, Dr | PK-12 | 2,700 | Smith | 339 |
| Winona Ind School Dist | Miller, Damenion | PK-12 | 1,050 | Smith | 341 |
| Breckenridge Ind School Dist | Allen, Bryan | PK-12 | 1,413 | Stephens | 344 |
| White Settlement Ind Sch Dist | Molinar, Frank | PK-12 | 6,909 | Tarrant | 360 |
| Merkel Ind School Dist | O'Malley, Joseph | PK-12 | 1,073 | Taylor | 363 |
| Trent Isn School Dist | Carter, Charles | PK-12 | 150 | Taylor | 363 |
| Wellman Union Ind School Dist | Prowell, Ben | PK-12 | 335 | Terry | 365 |
| Austin Ind School Dist | Elizalde, Stephanie, Dr | PK-12 | 80,950 | Travis | 369 |
| Lake Travis Ind School Dist | Norton, Paul | PK-12 | 10,410 | Travis | 373 |
| Manor Ind School Dist | Spencer, Andre, Dr | PK-12 | 9,200 | Travis | 373 |
| Colmesneil Ind School Dist | Franco, Eldon | K-12 | 450 | Tyler | 377 |
| Big Sandy Ind School Dist | Burns, Mike | PK-12 | 667 | Upshur | 378 |
| McCamey Ind School Dist | Valencia, Michael | PK-12 | 560 | Upton | 380 |

| | | | | | |
|---|---|---|---|---|---|
| Utopia Ind School Dist | Derry, Michael | PK-12 | 210 | Uvalde | 381 |
| Canton Ind School Dist | Nicoles, Brain, Dr | PK-12 | 2,300 | Van Zandt | 382 |
| Edgewood Ind School Dist | Prater, Kristin | PK-12 | 950 | Van Zandt | 382 |
| Nursery ISD School Dist | Gieski, Larry | PK-5 | 155 | Victoria | 384 |
| Grandfalls-Royalty Ind SD | Starkweather, Brett | PK-12 | 184 | Ward | 388 |
| Brenham Ind School Dist | Chaplin, Tylor, Dr | PK-12 | 5,000 | Washington | 388 |
| El Campo Ind School Dist | Calligan, Bob | PK-12 | 4,500 | Wharton | 392 |
| Wharton Ind School Dist | O'Guin, Michael, Dr | PK-12 | 2,015 | Wharton | 393 |
| Kelton Ind School Dist | Berry, Leslie | PK-12 | 84 | Wheeler | 393 |
| Jarrell Ind School Dist | Boles, Keith | PK-12 | 1,800 | Williamson | 399 |
| La Vernia Ind School Dist | Cone, Hensley | PK-12 | 2,400 | Wilson | 404 |
| Boyd Ind School Dist | Bardy, Tamara, Dr | PK-12 | 1,281 | Wise | 405 |
| Decatur Ind School Dist | Coburn, Dr | PK-12 | 3,390 | Wise | 406 |
| Alba-Golden Ind School Dist | McClendon, Cole | PK-12 | 588 | Wood | 407 |
| Hawkins Ind School Dist | McConnell, Stephanie | PK-12 | 750 | Wood | 407 |
| Mineola Ind School Dist | Mize, Cody | PK-12 | 1,556 | Wood | 408 |
| Denver City Ind School Dist | Azam, Mr | PK-12 | 1,741 | Yoakum | 409 |

# Texas School Directory

## TEXAS

- **Texas Dept of Education** PID: 00994396     512/463-9734
  1701 N Congress Ave, Austin 78701     Fax 512/463-9838

**Schools:** 743

## STATE-OPERATED SCHOOLS

| State Schs..Principal | Grd | Prgm | Enr/#Cls | SN | |
|---|---|---|---|---|---|
| © A Plus Academy Elementary [287]<br>10327 Rylie Rd, Dallas 75217<br>Michelle Thrash | PK-6 | T | 823 | 91% | 972/557-5578<br>Fax 972/557-4128 |
| © A Plus Academy Secondary [287]<br>445 S Masters Dr, Dallas 75217<br>Norman Lee | 7-12 | T | 586 | 89% | 469/677-1000 |
| © A Plus Up-Museum Campus<br>5555 Hermann Dr, Houston 77004<br>Thomas McWhorter | 6-8 | T | 106 | 57% | 713/955-7543 |
| © A Plus Up-University Campus<br>3353 Elgin St, Houston 77004<br>Rachel Clarke | 6-8 | T | 74 | 91% | 713/955-7583 |
| © A W Brown Leadership Academy<br>5701 Red Bird Center Dr, Dallas 75237<br>Chastity Armstead \ Shenikwa Cager | PK-8 | T | 1,800<br>32 | 53% | 972/709-4700<br>Fax 214/339-2273 |
| © Abundant Life Christian Sch<br>5130 Casey St, La Marque 77568<br>Cynthia Hallam | PK-12 | | 422 | | 409/935-8773 |
| © Aca Primary Campus<br>2800 W Arkansas Ln, Arlington 76016<br>Melissa Fambrough | K-2 | | 532<br>25 | 20% | 817/274-2008<br>Fax 817/394-6010 |
| © Academy of Accelerated Lrng<br>6025 Chimney Rock Rd, Houston 77081<br>Janelle Glover | PK-6 | T | 419<br>30 | 96% | 713/773-4766<br>Fax 713/666-2532 |
| © Academy of Dallas-Oak Park [196]<br>1030 Oak Park Dr, Dallas 75232<br>Ross Williams | PK-1 | T | 476<br>11 | 99% | 214/371-9600<br>Fax 214/371-1053 |
| © Accel Inter Academy-Lancaster<br>901 E Belt Line Rd, Lancaster 75146<br>Lashawn Hoskins | PK-5 | T | 250 | | 972/227-2105 |
| © Accelerated Intermediate Acad<br>12825 Summit Ridge Dr, Houston 77085<br>Lashawn Hoskins | PK-6 | T | 248<br>15 | 97% | 713/728-9330<br>Fax 713/283-6190 |
| © Alief Montessori Cmty Sch<br>12013 6th St, Houston 77072<br>Delia Presillas | PK-6 | T | 272<br>9 | 70% | 281/530-9406<br>Fax 281/530-2233 |
| © Amarillo Collegiate Academy<br>6000 S Georgia St, Amarillo 79118<br>Michael Griffin | K-12 | | 481 | | 806/352-0171<br>Fax 866/397-5456 |
| © Amarillo Collegiate Academy [318]<br>6000 S Georgia St, Amarillo 79118<br>Michael Griffin | K-12 | | 437 | 29% | 806/352-0171<br>Fax 806/367-5449 |
| © Ambassadors Preparatory Acad<br>5001 Avenue U, Galveston 77551<br>Dr Pat Williams | PK-8 | T | 323<br>18 | 85% | 409/762-1115<br>Fax 409/762-1114 |
| Ⓐ American Youthworks<br>© 1901 E Ben White Blvd, Austin 78741<br>Cynthia Jones | 9-12 | | 73<br>7 | | 512/744-1954<br>Fax 866/368-9413 |
| © Amigos Por Vida Charter Sch<br>5503 El Camino Del Rey St, Houston 77081<br>Freddy DelGado | PK-8 | T | 494<br>15 | 98% | 713/349-9945<br>Fax 713/349-0671 |
| © Aristoi Classical Academy<br>5618 11th St, Katy 77493<br>Terrence Boling \ Jermon Malone \ Kathryn Locheed | K-12 | AT | 593 | 27% | 281/391-5003<br>Fax 281/391-5010 |
| © Arlington Classics Acad-Bowen<br>5200 S Bowen Rd, Arlington 76017<br>Teri Rodgers | 3-5 | | 526 | 19% | 817/303-1553<br>Fax 817/549-0246 |
| © Arrow-Champions Academy [288]<br>2700 Cypress Creek Pkwy, Houston 77068<br>Sonja Williams | K-6 | T | 123 | 73% | 832/446-6762<br>Fax 832/446-6790 |
| © Arrow-Harvest Preparatory Acad [288]<br>17770 Imperial Valley Dr, Houston 77060<br>Michael Blackshire | K-6 | T | 240 | 98% | 281/872-5201 |
| © Arrow-Las Americas Lrng Ctr<br>5901 Glenmont Dr Apt 17, Houston 77081<br>Lillian Martinez | K-7 | | 125 | | 832/582-7327<br>Fax 832/582-7325 |
| © Arrow-Liberation Academy [288]<br>11600 W Airport Blvd, Meadows Place 77477<br>Ranston Chandler | K-5 | T | 166 | 68% | 281/969-7766<br>Fax 281/969-7762 |
| © Arrow-Save Our Streets Ctr [288]<br>1700 Groesbeck St, Bryan 77803<br>Becky Tucker | K-5 | T | 99 | 95% | 979/703-1810<br>Fax 979/703-1834 |
| © Austin Achieve PS High Sch<br>7424 E Highway 290 Bldg 2, Austin 78723<br>MacKee Mason | 9-12 | | 401 | | 512/522-4190 |
| © Austin Achieve PS Manor<br>5908 Manor Rd, Austin 78723<br>Reece Hartle \ MacKee Mason | 5-12 | T | 527 | 97% | 512/522-4190<br>Fax 512/727-0376 |
| © Austin Achieve PS NE Campus<br>7424 E Highway 290, Austin 78723<br>Daniela Rubio | PK-4 | | 401 | 94% | 512/522-4190 |
| © Austin Classical Academy [318]<br>1504 E 51st St, Austin 78723<br>Miriam Trollo | K-8 | | 163 | | 512/371-8933<br>Fax 866/433-9225 |
| © Austin Discovery Academy<br>8509 FM 969 Ste 200, Austin 78724<br>Leigh Moss | K-8 | | 508 | 20% | 512/674-0700<br>Fax 512/674-3133 |
| Aw Brown-Fla Early Childhood<br>6901 S Westmoreland Rd, Dallas 75237<br>Chavala Arnold | PK-5 | T | 1,240 | 71% | 214/330-8686 |
| © Baker-Ripley Promise Cmty CS<br>6500 Rookin St Bldg A, Houston 77074<br>Roel Saldivar | K-6 | T | 400 | 100% | 713/273-3731<br>Fax 713/273-3797 |
| © Basis San Antonio Prim-Med Ctr [013]<br>8519 Floyd Curl Dr, San Antonio 78240<br>April Hallfrisch | K-5 | | 764 | 5% | 210/319-5525<br>Fax 210/877-9214 |
| © Basis San Antonio Primary N [013]<br>318 E Ramsey Rd, San Antonio 78216<br>America Palmer | K-5 | | 775 | 5% | 210/775-4125<br>Fax 210/855-4888 |
| © Basis San Antonio Shavano [013]<br>4114 Lockhill Selma Rd, San Antonio 78230<br>David King | 6-12 | | 1,058 | 6% | 210/874-9250<br>Fax 210/579-6030 |
| © Beatrice Mayes Institute CS<br>5807 Calhoun Rd, Houston 77021<br>Beatrice Mayes | K-8 | T | 462<br>32 | 63% | 713/747-5629<br>Fax 281/809-7842 |
| © Beaumont Classical Academy [318]<br>10255 Eastex Fwy Ste 100, Beaumont 77708<br>Myrna Ramirez | K-5 | | 168 | | 409/434-4549 |
| © Beta Academy<br>9701 Almeda Genoa Rd, Houston 77075<br>Kendra Hampton | K-10 | T | 585 | 68% | 832/331-2460 |
| © Bexar County Academy [196]<br>1485 Hillcrest Dr, San Antonio 78228<br>Edison Marcos | PK-8 | T | 349<br>27 | 94% | 210/432-8600<br>Fax 210/432-8667 |
| Ⓐ Big Springs-Brune Charter Sch<br>© 10664 N US Highway 83, Leakey 78873<br>Dr Carmen Boatright | K-12 | T | 55<br>7 | 79% | 830/232-7101<br>Fax 830/232-4279 |

| School | Grades | | Enroll | % | Phone |
|---|---|---|---|---|---|
| © Big Springs-Cailloux CS<br>3522 Junction Hwy 27, Ingram 78025<br>Dr Maria De'LaCruz | 1-12 | A | 71 | | 830/367-6100<br>Fax 830/367-6108 |
| © Bloom Academy Charter Sch<br>3129 Southmore Blvd, Houston 77004<br>Courtney Sales | K-1 | | 401 | | 346/333-1320 |
| © Bob Hope Elem Sch<br>4301 32nd St, Port Arthur 77642<br>Virginia Roberts | PK-2 | T | 310 | 86% | 409/983-3244 |
| Ⓐ Bob Hope Middle High Sch<br>© 2849 9th Ave, Port Arthur 77642<br>Bobby Lopez | 6-12 | T | 767 | 72% | 409/983-3244<br>Fax 409/983-6408 |
| Ⓐ Brazos River Charter Sch<br>© 1964 FM 199, Nemo 76070<br>Bengie Laning | 9-12 | T | 125<br>13 | 63% | 254/898-9226<br>Fax 254/898-2297 |
| © Brazos Sch Inquiry-Bryan [291]<br>410 Bethel Ln, Bryan 77802<br>Chris Osgood | PK-8 | T | 165<br>6 | 93% | 979/774-5032<br>Fax 979/774-5037 |
| © Brazos Sch Inquiry-Tidwell [291]<br>1055 W Tidwell Rd, Houston 77091<br>John Bean | PK-6 | T | 190 | 99% | 713/681-1960<br>Fax 713/681-1979 |
| © Bridgeway Preparatory Academy<br>2405 E Belt Line Rd, Carrollton 75006<br>Dr Natalie Davenport | PK-5 | | 97 | 30% | 214/257-8883 |
| © Brooks Acad-Science Engineerng [138]<br>3803 Lyster Rd, San Antonio 78235<br>Bonnie Salas | PK-12 | T | 1,698<br>28 | 79% | 210/633-9006<br>Fax 210/633-9990 |
| © Brooks Collegiate Academy<br>4802 Vance Jackson Rd, San Antonio 78230<br>Lisa Schutz | K-12 | T | 928 | 62% | |
| © Brooks Estrella Academy<br>3803 Lyster Rd, San Antonio 78235<br>Bonnie Salas | K-6 | | 275 | | 210/257-5175<br>Fax 210/257-8147 |
| © Brooks Int'l Studies Academy<br>134 E Lambert St, San Antonio 78204<br>Patricia Lazono-Landry | K-7 | | 162 | | 210/998-4452<br>Fax 210/998-4454 |
| © Brooks Lonestar Academy<br>4802 Vance Jackson Rd, San Antonio 78230<br>Barry Lemaitre | K-6 | T | 95 | 80% | 210/998-4452<br>Fax 210/998-4454 |
| © Brooks Oaks Academy<br>6070 Babcock Rd, San Antonio 78240<br>Talisa Wilson | PK-5 | T | 230 | 60% | 210/627-6013<br>Fax 210/627-6016 |
| © Buckner Preparatory Sch<br>8510 Military Pkwy, Dallas 75227<br>Clarencia Wade | PK-3 | | 250 | | 214/545-6552 |
| © Calvin Nelms Charter Sch [290]<br>20625 Clay Rd, Katy 77449<br>Mike Dean | 6-12 | AV | 311 | 42% | 281/398-8031 |
| © Carrollton Classical Academy [318]<br>2400 N Josey Ln, Carrollton 75006<br>Stephanie Scott | K-8 | | 364<br>13 | 31% | 972/245-2900<br>Fax 972/245-2999 |
| © Cedar Park Charter Academy [316]<br>201 Buttercup Creek Blvd, Cedar Park 78613<br>Sylvia Sharp | PK-12 | T | 165 | 34% | 512/331-2980<br>Fax 512/628-6700 |
| © Cedars International Academy<br>8416 N Interstate 35, Austin 78753<br>Heather Rauls | PK-7 | T | 400<br>8 | 95% | 512/419-1551<br>Fax 512/419-1581 |
| © Cedars Intl Next Generation HS<br>6700 Middle Fiskville Rd, Austin 78752<br>Steven Zipkes | 8-12 | T | 148 | 66% | 512/956-4406 |
| © Cesar E Chavez Academy [315]<br>4613 S Padre Island Dr, Corp Christi 78411<br>Sandra Valencia | 9-12 | T | 39 | 78% | 361/561-5651<br>Fax 361/561-5654 |
| © Chaparral Star Academy<br>14046 Summit Dr, Austin 78728<br>Marsha Hagin | K-12 | | 388<br>19 | | 512/989-2672<br>Fax 512/251-9799 |
| © Chapel Hill Academy CS<br>4640 Sycamore School Rd, Fort Worth 76133<br>Audrey Alloway | PK-8 | T | 800 | 65% | 817/289-0242<br>Fax 817/289-3657 |
| © Clay Classical Academy [318]<br>3303 Potters House Way, Dallas 75236<br>Jacqueline Mercury-Owens | K-8 | T | 278 | 85% | 214/467-4143<br>Fax 214/467-4066 |
| Ⓐ Coastal Horizons Academy<br>© 1220 Gregory St, Taft 78390<br>Elizabeth Phillips | 9-12 | G | 51<br>4 | | 361/528-3959 |
| © Compass Academy Charter Sch<br>5530 Billy Hext Rd, Odessa 79765<br>Valerie Minyen \ Jason Inman | K-10 | | 1,126 | 13% | 432/272-1836<br>Fax 432/272-1835 |
| © Compass Rose Academy<br>8005 Outer Circle Rd, San Antonio 78235<br>Paul Morrissey | 6-12 | T | 90 | 86% | 210/540-9265 |
| © Comquest Academy<br>207 Peach St, Tomball 77375<br>Tanis Stanfield | 7-12 | AT | 50<br>7 | 61% | 281/516-0611<br>Fax 281/516-9807 |
| © Condra Sch for Educ Innovation<br>1921 Broadway, Lubbock 79401<br>Leisa Buckner | K-3 | | 150 | | 806/407-0878 |
| © Coppell Classical Academy [318]<br>140 S Heartz Rd, Coppell 75019<br>Christopher Sisk | K-8 | | 465 | 24% | 972/393-3077 |
| © Corinth Classical Acad Upper [318]<br>3600 Meadowview Dr, Corinth 76210<br>John Heitzenrater | 7-12 | | 723 | | 940/497-0059<br>Fax 866/231-9437 |
| © Corinth Classical Acad-Grammar [318]<br>800 Point Vista Dr Ste 518, Hickory Creek 75065<br>Amie Giacumakis | K-6 | | 71 | | 940/321-1144 |
| © Corpus Christi College Prep HS [315]<br>4613 S Padre Island Dr, Corp Christi 78411<br>Ashley Trevino | 9-12 | | 24<br>10 | | 361/225-4240<br>Fax 361/541-5967 |
| © Corpus Christi Montessori Sch<br>822 Ayers St, Corp Christi 78404<br>Cerise Weeks | 1-8 | | 135 | 14% | 361/852-0707 |
| © Cove Charter Academy [316]<br>2205 FM 3046, Copperas Cove 76522<br>Michael Anderson | PK-12 | T | 219 | 62% | 254/238-8231<br>Fax 254/247-3931 |
| © Crockett Classical Academy [318]<br>1303 E Houston Ave, Crockett 75835<br>Frances Spivey | K-6 | | 151 | | 936/546-0487<br>Fax 936/546-0034 |
| © Crosstimbers Academy<br>242 Harmony Rd, Weatherford 76087<br>Dr Kendra Nelson | 9-12 | T | 151 | 46% | 817/594-6220<br>Fax 817/594-6227 |
| © Cumberland Academy<br>1340 Shiloh Rd, Tyler 75703<br>Michelle Dean \ Jenny Gibbs \ Tim Schodowski | K-12 | T | 1,000<br>28 | 54% | 903/581-2890<br>Fax 903/581-1476 |
| © Da Vinci School Science & Arts<br>785 Southwestern Dr, El Paso 79912<br>Alexandro Medina | 6-12 | | 431 | 55% | 915/584-4024<br>Fax 915/581-9840 |
| © Denton Classical Academy [318]<br>4420 Country Club Rd, Denton 76210<br>Susan Thomas | K-5 | | 162 | 25% | 940/565-8333 |
| Ⓐ Depelchin-Richmond Charter Sch<br>© 710 S 7th St, Richmond 77469<br>Dorothy Goodman | K-8 | T | 20 | 79% | 713/558-3980<br>Fax 713/558-3985 |
| © Dr M L Garza-Gonzalez Chtr Sch [298]<br>4129 Greenwood Dr, Corp Christi 78416<br>Ricardo Godoy | PK-12 | AGT | 189 | 93% | 361/881-9988<br>Fax 361/881-9994 |
| © Draw Acad Early Learning Ctr<br>7914 Westglen Dr, Houston 77063<br>Fernando Donatti | PK-PK | | 138 | | 713/706-3729<br>Fax 713/706-3711 |
| © Draw Academy<br>3920 Stoney Brook Dr, Houston 77063<br>Patricia Beistegui | PK-8 | T | 649<br>12 | 98% | 713/706-3729<br>Fax 713/706-3711 |

| | | | |
|---|---|---|---|
| 1 Superintendent | 19 Chief Financial Officer | 39 Social Studies K-12 | 59 Special Education Elem | 69 Academic Assessment |
| 2 Bus/Finance/Purchasing | 8 Curric/Instruct K-12 | 20 Art K-12 | 40 Social Studies Elem | 49 English/Lang Arts Elem |
| 3 Buildings And Grounds | 9 Curric/Instruct Elem | 21 Art Elem | 30 Adult Education | 41 Social Studies Sec |
| 4 Food Service | 10 Curric/Instruct Sec | 22 Art Sec | 31 Career/Sch-to-Work K-12 | 42 Science K-12 |
| 5 Transportation | 11 Federal Program | 23 Music K-12 | 32 Career/Sch-to-Work Elem | 43 Science Elem |
| 6 Athletic | 12 Title I | 24 Music Elem | 33 Career/Sch-to-Work Sec | 44 Science Sec |
| 7 Health Services | 13 Title V | 25 Music Sec | 34 Early Childhood Ed | 45 Math K-12 |

Legend (full):

1 Superintendent
2 Bus/Finance/Purchasing
3 Buildings And Grounds
4 Food Service
5 Transportation
6 Athletic
7 Health Services
8 Curric/Instruct K-12
9 Curric/Instruct Elem
10 Curric/Instruct Sec
11 Federal Program
12 Title I
13 Title V
15 Asst Superintendent
16 Instructional Media Svcs
17 Chief Operations Officer
18 Chief Academic Officer
19 Chief Financial Officer
20 Art K-12
21 Art Elem
22 Art Sec
23 Music K-12
24 Music Elem
25 Music Sec
26 Business Education
27 Career & Tech Ed
28 Technology Education
29 Family/Consumer Science
30 Adult Education
31 Career/Sch-to-Work K-12
32 Career/Sch-to-Work Elem
33 Career/Sch-to-Work Sec
34 Early Childhood Ed
35 Health/Phys Education
36 Guidance Services K-12
37 Guidance Services Elem
38 Guidance Services Sec
39 Social Studies K-12
40 Social Studies Elem
41 Social Studies Sec
42 Science K-12
43 Science Elem
44 Science Sec
45 Math K-12
46 Math Elem
47 Math Sec
48 English/Lang Arts K-12
49 English/Lang Arts Elem
50 English/Lang Arts Sec
51 Reading K-12
52 Reading Elem
53 Reading Sec
54 Remedial Reading K-12
55 Remedial Reading Elem
56 Remedial Reading Sec
57 Bilingual/ELL
58 Special Education K-12
59 Special Education Elem
60 Special Education Sec
61 Foreign/World Lang K-12
62 Foreign/World Lang Elem
63 Foreign/World Lang Sec
64 Religious Education K-12
65 Religious Education Elem
66 Religious Education Sec
67 School Board President
68 Teacher Personnel
69 Academic Assessment
70 Research/Development
71 Public Information
72 Summer School
73 Instructional Tech
74 Inservice Training
75 Marketing/Distributive
76 Info Systems
77 Psychological Assess
78 Affirmative Action

| School | Grades | Prog | Enroll | % | Phone |
|---|---|---|---|---|---|
| © E Kolitz Hebrew Language Acad<br>11327 Dreamland Dr, San Antonio 78230<br>Kathryn Davis | K-8 | | 337 | | 210/302-6900<br>Fax 210/302-6913 |
| © East Ft Worth Montessori Acad<br>501 Oakland Blvd, Fort Worth 76103<br>Shello Tabb | PK-5 | T | 302<br>8 | 75% | 817/496-3003<br>Fax 817/496-3004 |
| © East Grand Preparatory Academy<br>6211 E Grand Ave, Dallas 75223<br>Aaliyah Miranda | PK-8 | T | 800<br>16 | 92% | 214/824-4747<br>Fax 214/824-4447 |
| © East TX Charter Sch-Chadwick<br>2402 Alpine Rd, Longview 75601<br>Terry Lapic | 9-12 | A | 140<br>13 | 30% | 903/753-9400<br>Fax 903/753-0285 |
| © Ecia-Rowlett 2<br>8200 Schrade Rd, Rowlett 75088<br>Lisa Hiatt | PK-8 | | 200 | | 972/412-8080<br>Fax 214/628-9124 |
| © Ecia-Royse City 3<br>201 N Erby Campbell Blvd, Royse City 75189<br>Angelia Carpenter | K-6 | | 117 | | 972/636-2600<br>Fax 214/628-9124 |
| © Ecia-Sunnyvale 1<br>302 N Town East Blvd, Sunnyvale 75182<br>Dr Randy Lamb | PK-8 | | 295 | | 214/628-9152<br>Fax 214/628-9124 |
| © Edinburg Classical Academy [318]<br>2110 S McColl Rd, Edinburg 78539<br>Elizabeth Alaniz | K-8 | T | 165 | 100% | 956/720-4361 |
| © Ehrhart Sch<br>3380 Fannin St Ste A, Beaumont 77701<br>Corina Long | PK-8 | T | 430 | 88% | 409/839-8200<br>Fax 409/839-8242 |
| © El Paso Academy East<br>11000 Argal Ct, El Paso 79935 | 9-12 | T | 199<br>15 | 63% | 915/590-8589<br>Fax 915/590-8618 |
| © El Paso Academy West<br>201 W Redd Rd, El Paso 79932<br>Sarahi Gross | 9-12 | V | 165<br>13 | | 915/845-7997<br>Fax 915/845-7522 |
| © El Paso Leadership Academy<br>1918 Texas Ave, El Paso 79901<br>Dianne Jones | 6-8 | T | 207 | 92% | 915/298-3900<br>Fax 915/400-7971 |
| © Elite College Prep Acad-Bowie<br>7310 Bowie St, Houston 77012<br>Yuridia Garcia \ Tiffany Wright | PK-12 | | 1,600 | | 832/649-2700<br>Fax 713/649-8268 |
| © Enhanced Horizons<br>149 Camp Scenic Rd, Ingram 78025<br>Kelly Bluemel | K-12 | A | 90 | | 830/367-4330<br>Fax 830/367-2814 |
| © Etoile Acad Charter Sch<br>6648 Hornwood Dr, Houston 77074<br>Kayleigh Colombero | 5-5 | T | 65 | 95% | 713/201-5714 |
| Evins Regional Juvenile Ctr<br>3801 E Monte Cristo Rd, Edinburg 78542<br>Steve Van Nest | 9-12 | GV | 140<br>15 | | 956/289-5500<br>Fax 956/381-1425 |
| © Evolution Academy-Beaumont [294]<br>3920 W Cardinal Dr, Beaumont 77705<br>Dr Veronica Durden | 9-12 | | 148 | | 409/239-5553<br>Fax 409/347-7135 |
| © Evolution Academy-Houston [294]<br>2414 Spring Cypress Rd, Spring 77388<br>Julia Askew | 9-12 | | 327 | | 281/907-6440<br>Fax 281/907-6442 |
| Ⓐ Evolution Academy-Richardson [294]<br>© 1101 S Sherman St, Richardson 75081<br>Tina Shaw | 9-12 | TV | 357<br>20 | 73% | 972/907-3755<br>Fax 972/907-3765 |
| Ⓐ Excel Academy Charter Sch<br>© 6500 Chimney Rock Rd, Houston 77081<br>Henry Gonzales | 9-12 | T | 32 | 91% | 713/222-4577<br>Fax 713/437-4121 |
| Ⓐ Excel Center-Fort Worth<br>© 1220 W Presidio St, Fort Worth 76102<br>Carolynn Epperson | K-12 | | 40 | | 817/335-6429<br>Fax 817/335-7927 |
| © Excellence In Leadership Acad<br>915 W Interstate Highway 2, Mission 78572<br>Ana Mendoza | PK-8 | T | 300 | 81% | 956/424-9504<br>Fax 956/585-4673 |
| © Faith Family Acad-Waxahachie [295]<br>701 Ovilla Rd, Waxahachie 75167<br>Monica Kramer | PK-8 | | 258<br>25 | | 972/937-3704<br>Fax 469/383-3075 |
| © Faith Family Academy-Oak Cliff [295]<br>300 W Kiest Blvd, Dallas 75224<br>Tien Nguyen \ Tara Carter | PK-12 | V | 1,968<br>95 | | 214/375-7682<br>Fax 214/375-7681 |
| © Fallbrook Academy [318]<br>12512 Walters Rd Ste 100, Houston 77014<br>Dr Dawn Doucet | K-8 | T | 225 | 77% | 281/880-1360 |
| © Foundation School for Autism [318]<br>2235 Thousand Oaks Dr Ste 130, San Antonio 78232<br>Rheatha Miller | Spec | | 39 | | 210/402-0253 |
| © Founders Classical Acad Flower [318]<br>4901 Cross Timbers Rd, Flower Mound 75028<br>Briton Smith | K-8 | | 518 | | 972/899-2521 |
| © Founders Classical Acad Frisco [318]<br>10710 Frisco St, Frisco 75033<br>Melanie Sharpless | K-8 | | 604 | 8% | 972/532-0952 |
| © Founders Classical Acad Leandr [318]<br>1303 Leander Dr, Leander 78641<br>Dr Kathleen O'Toole | K-12 | | 637 | 9% | 512/259-0103<br>Fax 512/532-6503 |
| © Founders Classical Acad Lwsvll [318]<br>1010 Bellaire Blvd, Lewisville 75067<br>Jason Caros | K-12 | | 930 | 17% | 469/464-3415<br>Fax 866/390-8034 |
| © Founders Classical Acad Mesq [318]<br>790 Windbell Cir, Mesquite 75149<br>Linea Dowler \ Daniel Carter | K-11 | T | 652 | 83% | 469/453-0977 |
| © Founders Classical Acad Schrtz [318]<br>8453 E 1518 N, Schertz 78154<br>James Farmer | K-9 | | 549 | 26% | 210/510-2618<br>Fax 866/422-4225 |
| © Frank L Madla Accel Coll Acad [312]<br>4018 S Presa St, San Antonio 78223<br>Dr Monica Villarreal | PK-8 | T | 471<br>30 | 92% | 210/533-3655<br>Fax 210/533-5077 |
| © Frank L Madla Early College HS [312]<br>1400 W Villaret Blvd, San Antonio 78224<br>Jeff Flores | 9-12 | T | 192 | 80% | 210/486-3686 |
| © Ft Worth Academy of Fine Arts [326]<br>3901 S Hulen St, Fort Worth 76109<br>Jennifer Jackson | 3-12 | | 577<br>40 | 10% | 817/924-1482<br>Fax 817/926-9932 |
| Ⓐ Gainesville State Sch<br>1379 FM 678, Gainesville 76240<br>Andre Jenerson | 8-12 | GV | 197<br>25 | | 940/665-0701<br>Fax 940/665-9416 |
| © Garland Classical Academy [318]<br>3024 Anita Dr, Garland 75041<br>Matthew Haid | K-8 | | 248 | | 972/840-1100<br>Fax 972/840-1105 |
| © Gateway Charter Academy<br>1015 E Wheatland Rd, Dallas 75241<br>Raymond Edwards | 6-12 | T | 288 | 89% | 214/375-1921<br>Fax 214/375-2730 |
| © Gateway Charter Elem Academy<br>6103 University Hills Blvd, Dallas 75241<br>Raymond Edwards | PK-5 | T | 312<br>18 | 92% | 214/375-2039<br>Fax 214/375-1842 |
| © Gateway College Prep Sch [313]<br>3360 Westinghouse Rd, Georgetown 78626<br>Kristin Hunt \ Jackie Hanke \ Shawn Lance | K-12 | | 1,300 | 6% | 512/868-4947<br>Fax 512/868-4946 |
| © Gateway Tech High Sch [313]<br>2951 Williams Dr Bldg 2, Georgetown 78628<br>Jolene Bruce | 9-12 | | 40<br>15 | 17% | 512/868-5299<br>Fax 512/869-3030 |
| © George Gervin Academy<br>6944 S Sunbelt Dr, San Antonio 78218<br>Daniel Martinez \ Tyrone Darden \ Julio Sanchez | PK-12 | ATV | 861<br>27 | 100% | 210/568-8800<br>Fax 210/568-8897 |
| © George I Sanchez Charter HS<br>6001 Gulf Fwy, Houston 77023<br>Araceli Altamirano | 7-12 | GT | 500<br>45 | 93% | 713/926-1112<br>Fax 713/926-8129 |
| © Georgetown Behavioral Hlth CS<br>3101 S Austin Ave, Georgetown 78626<br>C Cunningham | 6-12 | | 15 | 33% | 254/644-9111 |

© Georgetown Charter Academy [316] | PK-8 | T | 68 | 51% 512/863-9236
302 Serenada Dr, Georgetown 78628 | | | | Fax 512/863-9290
Josiah Perkins

Giddings State Sch | 9-12 | V | 220 | 979/542-4500
2261 James Turman Rd, Giddings 78942 | | | 24 | Fax 979/542-0177
Dennis Smith

© Golden Rule CS-DeSoto [296] | PK-6 | T | 218 | 96% 469/248-4463
135 W Wintergreen Rd, Desoto 75115 | | | | Fax 469/248-4471
Diana Lara

© Golden Rule CS-Grand Prairie [296] | PK-3 | | 85 | 214/988-3257
1729 Avenue B, Grand Prairie 75051 | | | | Fax 214/988-3261
Norma Brisno

© Golden Rule CS-Illinois [296] | PK-8 | T | 720 | 97% 214/333-9330
2602 W Illinois Ave, Dallas 75233 | | | 20 | Fax 214/333-9325
Dania Gomez \ Leslie Sharp | | | | 🇹

© Golden Rule CS-Pleasant Grove [296] | PK-4 | T | 272 | 99% 469/341-5780
10747 Bruton Rd, Dallas 75217 | | | | Fax 469/341-5779
Cesar Hernandez

© Golden Rule CS-Sunnyside [296] | PK-4 | | 187 | 214/393-6911
622 Sunnyside Ave, Dallas 75211 | | | |
Jimmy Wright

© Golden Rule CS-Wilmer [296] | PK-K | T | 20 | 81% 972/525-6204
520 N I-45, Wilmer 75172 | | | |
Cesar Hernandez

© Goodwater Mont Charter Sch | PK-8 | | 350 | 29% 512/966-5484
710 Stadium Dr, Georgetown 78626

© Great Hearts Forest Heights [297] | K-5 | | 401 | 210/892-3665
5538 Research Drive, San Antonio 78240
Jason Doughty

© Great Hearts Irving [297] | K-10 | | 885 | 13% 469/759-3030
3350 Story Rd W, Irving 75038
Tami Perkins \ Philip Althage

© Great Hearts Monte Vista-North [297] | 6-12 | | 476 | 18% 210/888-9485
319 E Mulberry Ave, San Antonio 78212
William Rutherford

© Great Hearts Monte Vista-South [297] | K-5 | | 446 | 17% 210/888-9485
211 Belknap Pl, San Antonio 78212
Mandi Cannon

© Great Hearts Northern Oaks [297] | K-10 | | 1,216 | 15% 210/888-9483
17223 Jones Maltsberger Rd, San Antonio 78247 | | | | Fax 210/888-9484
Trinette Keffer \ Samuel Heisman

© Great Hearts Western Hills [297] | K-6 | | 592 | 31% 210/888-9488
8702 Ingram Rd, San Antonio 78245
Robby Kuhlman

© Harbach-Ripley Charter Sch | PK-5 | | 114 | 713/669-5202
6225 Northdale St, Houston 77087 | | | | Fax 713/640-7152
Dawnyell Brown

© Harmony Sch Achievement-Houstn [299] | K-5 | T | 630 | 55% 281/855-2500
16205 Kieth Harrow Blvd, Houston 77084 | | | | Fax 281/858-2505
Melissa Knight

© Harmony Sch Adv-Houston [299] | 9-12 | T | 633 | 63% 281/741-8899
3171 N Sam Houston Pkwy W, Houston 77038 | | | | Fax 281/741-8006
Fatih Oner

© Harmony Sch DSC-Houston [299] | 6-12 | T | 756 | 64% 281/861-5105
6270 Barker Cypress Rd, Houston 77084 | | | | Fax 281/656-8525
Ednan Karanci

© Harmony Sch Endeavor-Austin [299] | PK-12 | T | 532 | 46% 512/284-9880
13415 Ranch Road 620 N, Austin 78717 | | | | Fax 512/284-9632
Waylon Stengler

© Harmony Sch Endeavor-Houston [299] | K-8 | T | 533 | 91% 281/999-8400
5668 W Little York Rd, Houston 77091 | | | | Fax 281/999-8404
Kamil Yilmaz

© Harmony Sch Enrichment-Houston [299] | K-5 | T | 642 | 79% 281/999-0606
3207 N Sam Houston Pkwy W, Houston 77038
Brent Bardo

© Harmony Sch Exc-Austin [299] | 6-12 | T | 551 | 79% 512/693-0000
2100 E Saint Elmo Rd, Austin 78744 | | | | Fax 512/693-0008
Agil Sharifov

© Harmony Sch Exc-El Paso [299] | K-6 | T | 705 | 72% 915/307-4772
9435 Betel Dr, El Paso 79907 | | | | Fax 915/307-3689
Michelle Melendez

© Harmony Sch Exc-Houston [299] | K-8 | T | 834 | 45% 713/983-8668
7340 Gessner Rd, Houston 77040 | | | | Fax 713/983-8667
Mugire Ayci

© Harmony Sch Exc-Laredo [299] | 9-12 | | 424 | 956/791-0007
4401 San Francisco Ave Bldg B, Laredo 78041
Mustafa Ayik

© Harmony Sch Exc-San Antonio [299] | PK-5 | T | 521 | 74% 210/645-7166
2015 SW Loop 410, San Antonio 78227 | | | | Fax 210/645-7178
Bambi Teaff

© Harmony Sch Exc-Sugar Land [299] | 6-8 | T | 579 | 55% 832/532-0728
1428 Eldridge Rd, Sugar Land 77478 | | | | Fax 832/532-0738
Sefik Fkmen

© Harmony Sch Excellence-Dallas [299] | 6-12 | | 564 | 972/296-1000
8120 W Camp Wisdom Rd, Dallas 75249 | | | | Fax 972/296-2125
Ilker Fidan

© Harmony Sch Exploration-Houstn [299] | K-5 | T | 589 | 88% 832/831-7406
9305 W Sam Houston Pkwy S, Houston 77099 | | | | Fax 832/831-7408
Nora Morales

© Harmony Sch Fine Arts & Tech [299] | K-8 | T | 672 | 80% 832/433-7001
9115 Kirby Dr, Houston 77054 | | | | Fax 832/433-7083
Atila Akyurek

© Harmony Sch Ingenuity-Houston [299] | 6-12 | T | 630 | 82% 713/664-1020
10555 Stella Link Rd, Houston 77025 | | | | Fax 713/664-1025
Jasmeen Kohli

© Harmony Sch Innov-Austin [299] | PK-5 | T | 438 | 84% 512/300-0895
2124 E Saint Elmo Rd A, Austin 78744 | | | | Fax 512/330-4225
Tiffany Molina

© Harmony Sch Innov-Brownsville [299] | 6-12 | T | 482 | 87% 956/544-1348
3451 Dana Ave, Brownsville 78526 | | | | Fax 956/544-1349
Mustafa Altindag

© Harmony Sch Innov-Carrolltn [299] | K-5 | T | 538 | 45% 469/892-5556
1024 W Rosemeade Pkwy Bldg 1, Carrollton 75007 | | | | Fax 469/892-5667
Sara Sponsel

© Harmony Sch Innov-Dallas [299] | 6-12 | | 397 | 214/321-0100
8080 W Pres G Bush Hwy, Dallas 75252 | | | | Fax 214/919-4352
Husegin Sari

© Harmony Sch Innov-El Paso [299] | K-12 | T | 1,086 | 69% 915/757-2929
5210 Fairbanks Dr, El Paso 79924 | | | 22 | Fax 915/757-2202
Riza Gurlek

© Harmony Sch Innov-Euless [299] | K-6 | T | 743 | 56% 817/554-2800
701 S Industrial Blvd Ste 105, Euless 76040
Crystal McAnalley

© Harmony Sch Innov-Ft Worth [299] | 6-12 | T | 893 | 44% 817/386-5505
8100 S Hulen St, Fort Worth 76123 | | | | Fax 817/977-1727
Mehmet Basoglu

© Harmony Sch Innov-Garland [299] | 7-12 | | 553 | 469/814-0059
2250 Firewheel Pkwy, Garland 75040 | | | | Fax 469/814-0579
Dan Bell

© Harmony Sch Innov-Gran Prairie | K-5 | T | 401 | 64% 972/269-6182
1441 E Fishcreek Rd, Grand Prairie 75052
Erin Wolfe

© Harmony Sch Innov-Houston [299] | 6-8 | T | 468 | 89% 713/541-3030
9421 W Sam Houston Pkwy S, Houston 77099 | | | | Fax 713/541-3032
Paul Ryan

© Harmony Sch Innov-Laredo [299] | K-5 | T | 651 | 78% 956/568-9495
4608 Daugherty Ave, Laredo 78041
Geraldine Salas

© Harmony Sch Innov-San Antonio [299] | PK-8 | T | 494 | 87% 210/265-1715
8125 Glen Mont, San Antonio 78239 | | | | Fax 210/265-5364
Mert Aykanat

# Texas School Directory

| School | Grades | Prog | Enroll | Title I % | Phone |
|---|---|---|---|---|---|
| © Harmony Sch Innov-Sugar Land [299]<br>13522 W Airport Blvd, Sugar Land 77498<br>Hakan Simsek | 9-12 | T | 689 | 55% | 281/302-6445<br>Fax 281/302-6745 |
| © Harmony Sch Innov-Waco [299]<br>1110 S Valley Mills Dr, Waco 76711<br>Orhan Avci | 6-12 | | 480 | | 254/235-0321<br>Fax 254/235-1373 |
| © Harmony Sch Sci-Austin [299]<br>11800 Stonehollow Dr Ste 100, Austin 78758<br>Waylon Stengler | K-5 | T | 476 | 54% | 512/821-1700<br>Fax 512/821-1702 |
| © Harmony Sch Sci-Houston [299]<br>5435 S Braeswood Blvd, Houston 77096<br>Oguzkaan Torun | K-8 | T | 328 | 88% | 713/729-4400<br>Fax 713/729-6600 |
| © Harmony Sch Tech-Houston [299]<br>3203 N Sam Houston Pkwy W, Houston 77038<br>Celil Kucukbasol | 6-8 | T | 660 | 71% | 281/444-1555<br>Fax 281/444-1015 |
| © Harmony Sci Acad-Austin [299]<br>930 E Rundberg Ln, Austin 78753<br>Kyle Borel | PK-8<br>11 | T | 713 | 87% | 512/835-7900<br>Fax 512/835-7901 |
| © Harmony Sci Acad-Beaumont [299]<br>4055 Calder Ave, Beaumont 77706<br>Klediol Murati | K-12 | T | 572 | 58% | 409/838-4000<br>Fax 409/838-4009 |
| © Harmony Sci Acad-Brownsville [299]<br>1124 Central Blvd, Brownsville 78520<br>Joel Alaffa | PK-8 | T | 512 | 91% | 956/574-9555<br>Fax 956/574-9558 |
| © Harmony Sci Acad-Bryan [299]<br>2031 S Texas Ave, Bryan 77802<br>Laura Mattingly | PK-8<br>32 | T | 376 | 82% | 979/779-2100<br>Fax 979/779-2110 |
| © Harmony Sci Acad-Carrollton [299]<br>1024 W Rosemeade Pkwy Bldg 2, Carrollton 75007<br>Huseyin Sari | 6-12 | T | 499 | 47% | 972/394-9560<br>Fax 469/892-5667 |
| © Harmony Sci Acad-Cedar Park [299]<br>12200 Anderson Mill Rd, Austin 78726<br>Ilker Yilmaz | PK-5 | | 429 | 45% | 512/494-5151<br>Fax 512/494-5177 |
| © Harmony Sci Acad-Cypress [299]<br>7047 Greenhouse Rd, Cypress 77433 | K-5 | | 401 | | 281/444-1555 |
| © Harmony Sci Acad-El Paso [299]<br>9405 Betel Dr, El Paso 79907<br>Mucahit Turel | K-12 | T | 800 | 72% | 915/859-4620<br>Fax 915/859-4630 |
| © Harmony Sci Acad-Euless [299]<br>701 S Industrial Blvd Ste 115, Euless 76040<br>Sevde Aslan | 7-12 | T | 556 | 54% | 817/354-3000 |
| © Harmony Sci Acad-Ft Worth [299]<br>5651 Westcreek Dr, Fort Worth 76133<br>Serena Jackson | K-5 | T | 627 | 55% | 817/263-0700<br>Fax 817/263-0705 |
| © Harmony Sci Acad-Garland [299]<br>2302 Firewheel Pkwy, Garland 75040<br>Sofieh Hopovac | PK-6 | T | 676 | 62% | 972/212-4777<br>Fax 972/212-4778 |
| © Harmony Sci Acad-Grand Prairie [299]<br>1102 NW 7th St, Grand Prairie 75050<br>Angela Knapp | PK-8 | T | 481 | 74% | 972/642-9911<br>Fax 972/642-9922 |
| © Harmony Sci Acad-Houston [299]<br>9431 W Sam Houston Pkwy S, Houston 77099<br>Serdar Haytiyev | 9-12 | T | 625 | 80% | 713/492-0214<br>Fax 713/383-2839 |
| © Harmony Sci Acad-Katy [299]<br>22400 Grand Corner Dr, Katy 77494<br>Meredith Marchante | K-5 | T | 652 | 51% | 832/437-3926<br>Fax 832/437-3927 |
| © Harmony Sci Acad-Laredo [299]<br>4401 San Francisco Ave Bldg E, Laredo 78041<br>Abdullah Tatir | 6-8 | T | 643 | 88% | 956/712-1177<br>Fax 956/712-1188 |
| © Harmony Sci Acad-Lubbock [299]<br>1516 53rd St, Lubbock 79412<br>Selcuk Bakir | PK-8 | T | 413 | 85% | 806/747-1000<br>Fax 806/747-1005 |
| © Harmony Sci Acad-Odessa [299]<br>2755 N Grandview Ave, Odessa 79762<br>Cetin Demir | K-8 | T | 498 | 62% | 432/363-6000<br>Fax 432/363-6001 |
| © Harmony Sci Acad-Pflugerville [299]<br>1421 W Wells Branch Pkwy #200, Pflugerville 78660<br>Agil Sharifov | 6-12 | T | 886 | 70% | 512/251-5000<br>Fax 512/251-5001 |
| © Harmony Sci Acad-Plano [299]<br>550 Talbert Dr, Plano 75093<br>Gregory Coleman | PK-5 | T | 304 | 65% | 972/596-0041 |
| © Harmony Sci Acad-San Antonio [299]<br>8505 Lakeside Pkwy, San Antonio 78245<br>Klediol Murati | 6-12 | T | 785<br>40 | 70% | 210/674-7788<br>Fax 210/674-7766 |
| © Harmony Sci Acad-Sugar Land [299]<br>13415 W Bellfort Ave, Sugar Land 77478<br>Afreen Merchant | K-5 | T | 698 | 66% | 281/265-2525<br>Fax 281/265-2565 |
| © Harmony Sci Acad-Waco [299]<br>1900 N Valley Mills Dr, Waco 76710<br>Lindy Ermoian | PK-6 | T | 662 | 83% | 254/751-7878<br>Fax 254/751-7877 |
| © Harmony Science Acad-Dallas [299]<br>11945 Forestgate Dr, Dallas 75243<br>Omer Toycu | K-12 | | 1,147 | | 469/730-2477<br>Fax 469/341-9138 |
| Ⓐ Harris Co Juvenile Justice CS<br>© 1200 Congress St, Houston 77002<br>Oliver Burbridge | 5-12 | GV | 602 | | 713/222-4100<br>Fax 713/222-4388 |
| Ⓐ Harris Cty Leadership Academy<br>9120 Katy Hockley Rd, Katy 77493<br>Kaoenya Warren | 6-12 | T | 96<br>8 | 96% | 713/222-4629<br>Fax 713/222-4630 |
| Ⓐ Helping Hand Charter Sch<br>© 3804 Avenue B, Austin 78751<br>Holly Engleman | K-6 | T | 25 | 88% | 512/751-4534 |
| © Heritage Academy<br>8750 Fourwinds Dr, Windcrest 78239 | 7-8 | T | 100 | 75% | 210/354-7753 |
| © Heritage Academy Del Rio [300]<br>709B Kings Way, Del Rio 78840<br>Judy Galindo | 4-12 | T | 346 | 53% | 830/774-6230 |
| © Heritage Academy San Antonio [300]<br>8750 Fourwinds Dr, Windcrest 78239<br>Eric Davis | 6-6 | T | 100 | 82% | 210/354-7753<br>Fax 210/547-9459 |
| © Heritage Academy Windcrest<br>8750 Fourwinds Dr, Windcrest 78239<br>Eric Davis | PK-5 | T | 100 | 88% | 210/354-7753 |
| © Hfa-Alameda Sch-Art & Design<br>318 W Houston St, San Antonio 78205<br>Jeremiah Montez | 9-12 | T | 127 | 53% | 210/226-4031<br>Fax 210/802-3025 |
| © High Point Academy<br>1256 N Jim Wright Fwy, Fort Worth 76108<br>Heather Houpt \ Craig Shreckengast | K-12 | T | 1,041 | 21% | 817/600-6401 |
| © Hill Country Yth Rch-Najim Sch<br>3522 Junction Hwy 27, Ingram 78025<br>Kelly Bluemel | K-12 | | 47 | | 830/367-6100<br>Fax 830/367-2611 |
| © Horizon Montessori I McAllen [322]<br>320 N Main St, McAllen 78501<br>Patricia Masso | PK-8 | T | 598<br>19 | 59% | 956/631-0234<br>Fax 956/668-1404 |
| © Horizon Montessori II Weslaco [322]<br>1222 W Sugarcane Dr, Weslaco 78599<br>Gabriela Rodriguez | PK-8 | T | 343 | 64% | 956/969-0044<br>Fax 956/969-0065 |
| © Horizon Montessori III Hrlgtn [322]<br>2802 S 77 Sunshine Strip, Harlingen 78550<br>Gabriela Rodriguez | PK-8 | T | 383 | 77% | 956/423-8200<br>Fax 956/423-8207 |
| © Horizon Montessori Pearland<br>2319 N Grand Blvd, Pearland 77581<br>Michael Gollihugh | PK-8 | | 120 | | 281/485-2500 |
| © Houston Gateway Acad-Evergreen<br>3400 Evergreen Dr, Houston 77087<br>Sheila Marsh \ Lucio Rodriguez | PK-8 | T | 712 | 21% | 713/649-2706<br>Fax 713/649-8165 |
| © Houston Gateway Academy-Coral<br>1020 Coral St, Houston 77012<br>John Smith | PK-12 | T | 890<br>29 | 23% | 713/923-5060<br>Fax 713/923-9070 |

This is the legend/key at the bottom.

79   Student Personnel
80   Driver Ed/Safety
81   Gifted/Talented
82   Video Services
83   Substance Abuse Prev
84   Erate
85   AIDS Education
88   Alternative/At Risk
89   Multi-Cultural Curriculum
90   Social Work

91   Safety/Security
92   Magnet School
93   Parental Involvement
95   Tech Prep Program
97   Chief Information Officer
98   Chief Technology Officer
270  Character Education
271  Migrant Education
273  Teacher Mentor
274  Before/After Sch

275  Response To Intervention
277  Remedial Math K-12
280  Literacy Coach
285  STEM
286  Digital Learning
288  Common Core Standards
294  Accountability
295  Network System
296  Title II Programs
297  Webmaster

298  Grant Writer/Ptnrships
750  Chief Innovation Officer
751  Chief of Staff
752  Social Emotional Learning

**Other School Types**
Ⓐ = Alternative School
© = Charter School
Ⓜ = Magnet School
Ⓨ = Year-Round School

**School Programs**
A = Alternative Program
G = Adult Classes
M = Magnet Program
T = Title I Schoolwide
V = Career & Tech Ed Programs

New Schools are shaded
New Superintendents and Principals are bold
Personnel with email addresses are underscored

**Social Media**
🅕 = Facebook
🅣 = Twitter

| | | | | | |
|---|---|---|---|---|---|
| © Houston Gateway Elite Clg Prep<br>7310 Bowie St, Houston 77012<br>Tiffany Wright | PK-5 | T | 745 | 19% | 832/649-2700<br>Fax 713/649-8268 |
| © Houston Heights High Sch<br>1125 Lawrence St, Houston 77008<br>Erica McCready | 9-12 | T | 193<br>15 | 81% | 713/868-9797<br>Fax 713/868-9750 |
| © Howard Burnham Elem Sch<br>7310 Bishop Flores Dr, El Paso 79912<br>Martha Franco | K-5 | GT | 419 | 59% | 915/584-9499<br>Fax 915/585-8814 |
| © Humble Classical Academy [318]<br>901 Wilson Rd Bldg B, Humble 77338<br>Alyson Kelly | K-7 | T | 313 | 70% | 281/913-5107<br>Fax 866/655-1476 |
| © Hunstville Classical Academy [318]<br>2407 Sam Houston Ave Ste B, Huntsville 77340<br>Sherry Sheppard | K-8 | | 300 | | 936/291-0203<br>Fax 936/293-8096 |
| Ⓐ Huston Academy<br>© 680 Peach Orchard Rd, Stephenville 76401<br>Carol Taylor | 9-12 | TV | 34<br>7 | 100% | 254/965-8883<br>Fax 254/965-8654 |
| © Idea Academy-Achieve [304]<br>1900 Thomas Rd, Haltom City 76117<br>Shandra Johnson | PK-3 | | 250 | | 817/885-4700 |
| © Idea Academy-Alamo [301]<br>325 State Highway 495, Alamo 78516<br>Anna Garza | PK-5 | T | 862 | 93% | 956/588-4005<br>Fax 956/588-4006 |
| © Idea Academy-Bluff Springs [302]<br>1700 E Slaughter Ln, Austin 78747<br>Jayne Pocquette | K-4 | T | 599 | 79% | 512/822-4200 |
| © Idea Academy-Brackenridge [305]<br>5555 Old Pearsall Rd, San Antonio 78242<br>Elisha McCardell | PK-2 | T | 548 | 88% | 210/239-4300 |
| © Idea Academy-Brownsville [301]<br>4395 Paredes Line Rd, Brownsville 78526<br>Erica Matamoros | K-5 | T | 699 | 80% | 956/832-5150<br>Fax 956/832-5716 |
| © Idea Academy-Burke [305]<br>10434 Marbach Rd, San Antonio 78245<br>Tiffany Langbien | PK-2 | | 263 | | 210/239-4650 |
| © Idea Academy-Carver [305]<br>217 Robinson Pl, San Antonio 78202<br>Guadalupe Diaz | K-5 | T | 679 | 82% | 210/223-8885<br>Fax 210/223-8970 |
| © Idea Academy-Converse [305]<br>5160 Martinez Converse Rd, Converse 78109<br>Hely Hillman | K-2 | | 200 | | 210/529-3800 |
| © Idea Academy-Donna [301]<br>401 S 1st St, Donna 78537<br>Sylvia Verdooran | PK-5 | T | 889 | 96% | 956/464-0203<br>Fax 956/464-8532 |
| © Idea Academy-Eastside [305]<br>2519 Martin Luther King Dr, San Antonio 78203<br>Myrla Feria | K-5 | T | 728 | 93% | 210/239-4800 |
| © Idea Academy-Edgecliff [304]<br>1640 Altamesa Blvd, Fort Worth 76134<br>Jason Fitzgerald | K-2 | | 300 | | 817/885-4800 |
| © Idea Academy-Edgemere [303]<br>15101 Edgemere Blvd, El Paso 79938<br>Rebecca Cobian | PK-2 | | 300 | 83% | 915/444-0200 |
| © Idea Academy-Edinburg [301]<br>2553 N Roegiers Rd, Edinburg 78541<br>Nora Perez | PK-5 | T | 747 | 82% | 956/287-6100<br>Fax 956/287-6101 |
| © Idea Academy-Elsa [301]<br>411 S Fanin St, Elsa 78543<br>Saron Mata | PK-2 | | 300 | 99% | 956/567-4700 |
| © Idea Academy-Ewing Halsell [305]<br>2523 W Ansley Blvd, San Antonio 78224<br>Pam Ray | PK-2 | T | 526 | 84% | 210/239-4850 |
| © Idea Academy-Frontier [301]<br>2800 S Dakota Ave, Brownsville 78521<br>Dora Villegas | PK-5 | T | 856 | 94% | 956/541-2002<br>Fax 956/544-2004 |

| | | | | | |
|---|---|---|---|---|---|
| © Idea Academy-Hardy [301]<br>1930 Little York Rd, Houston 77093<br>Gerald Boyd | K-3 | | 200 | | 832/844-4100 |
| © Idea Academy-Harlingen [301]<br>24240 Chester Park Rd, Harlingen 78552<br>Patricia Rodriguez | K-3 | | 200 | | 956/564-7200 |
| © Idea Academy-Harvey Najim [305]<br>926 S WW White Rd, San Antonio 78220<br>Hope Walker | PK-10 | T | 994 | 91% | 210/239-4900 |
| © Idea Academy-Hidden Meadow [305]<br>10138 Culebra Rd, San Antonio 78250<br>Gabriel Demiero | K-2 | | 200 | | 210/529-3900 |
| © Idea Academy-Hlth Professions [302]<br>5816 Wilcab Rd, Austin 78721<br>Jarod Hawk | K-3 | | 234 | | 512/822-4350 |
| © Idea Academy-Horizon Vista [303]<br>201 Horizon Crossing St, El Paso 79928<br>Heather Click-Cuellar | K-3 | | 200 | | |
| © Idea Academy-Ingram Hills [305]<br>3115 Majestic Dr, San Antonio 78228<br>Nancy Bethencourt | PK-2 | | 300 | 90% | 210/529-3700 |
| © Idea Academy-Judson [305]<br>13427 Judson Rd, San Antonio 78233<br>Hope Williams | K-4 | T | 593 | 70% | 210/529-3600 |
| © Idea Academy-Kyle [302]<br>640 Philomena Dr, Kyle 78640<br>Ester Polanco | K-3 | | 372 | 70% | 512/822-4300 |
| © Idea Academy-Los Encinos [301]<br>5400 S Ware Rd, McAllen 78503<br>Esmeralda Ortiz | PK-2 | | 263 | | 956/429-4150 |
| © Idea Academy-Mays [305]<br>1210 Horal Dr, San Antonio 78245<br>Maria Sepulveda | K-5 | T | 349 | 74% | 210/529-3200 |
| © Idea Academy-McAllen [301]<br>201 N Bentsen Rd, McAllen 78501<br>Darlene Cavazos | PK-5 | T | 887 | 79% | 956/429-4100<br>Fax 956/429-4126 |
| © Idea Academy-Mesa Hills [303]<br>405 Wallenberg Dr, El Paso 79912<br>Patricia Landavazo | PK-2 | | 263 | | 915/888-4050 |
| © Idea Academy-Mission [301]<br>1600 S Schuerbach Rd, Mission 78572<br>Christina Escamilla | PK-5 | T | 909 | 93% | 956/583-8315<br>Fax 956/424-3248 |
| © Idea Academy-Monterrey Park [305]<br>222 SW 39th St, San Antonio 78237<br>Martha Short | K-5 | T | 724 | 91% | 210/239-4200 |
| © Idea Academy-Montopolis [302]<br>1701 Vargas Rd, Austin 78741<br>Disha Jain | K-5 | T | 717 | 90% | 512/646-2800<br>Fax 512/385-2512 |
| © Idea Academy-North Mission [301]<br>2706 N Holland Ave, Mission 78574<br>Adrianna Villarreal | PK-5 | T | 733 | 91% | 956/424-4300 |
| © Idea Academy-Owassa [301]<br>1000 E Owassa Rd, Pharr 78577<br>Cyndi Delafuente | PK-2 | | 300 | 93% | 956/588-4300 |
| © Idea Academy-Palmview [301]<br>4100 N Schuerbach Rd, Mission 78574<br>Marisol Flores | K-3 | | 200 | | 956/272-5394 |
| © Idea Academy-Parmer Park [302]<br>1438 E Yager Ln, Austin 78753<br>Katie Mackey | K-3 | | 234 | | 512/822-4850 |
| © Idea Academy-Pflugerville [302]<br>1901 E Wells Branch Pkwy, Pflugerville 78660<br>Mera Dougherty | K-3 | | 300 | 82% | 512/822-4700 |
| © Idea Academy-Pharr [301]<br>600 E Las Milpas Rd, Pharr 78577<br>Sonia Aguilar | PK-5 | T | 867 | 94% | 956/283-1515<br>Fax 956/783-1557 |

1 Superintendent
2 Bus/Finance/Purchasing
3 Buildings And Grounds
4 Food Service
5 Transportation
6 Athletic
7 Health Services
8 Curric/Instruct K-12
9 Curric/Instruct Elem
10 Curric/Instruct Sec
11 Federal Program
12 Title I
13 Title V
15 Asst Superintendent
16 Instructional Media Svcs
17 Chief Operations Officer
18 Chief Academic Officer
19 Chief Financial Officer
20 Art K-12
21 Art Elem
22 Art Sec
23 Music K-12
24 Music Elem
25 Music Sec
26 Business Education
27 Career & Tech Ed
28 Technology Education
29 Family/Consumer Science
30 Adult Education
31 Career/Sch-to-Work K-12
32 Career/Sch-to-Work Elem
33 Career/Sch-to-Work Sec
34 Early Childhood Ed
35 Health/Phys Education
36 Guidance Services K-12
37 Guidance Services Elem
38 Guidance Services Sec
39 Social Studies K-12
40 Social Studies Elem
41 Social Studies Sec
42 Science K-12
43 Science Elem
44 Science Sec
45 Math K-12
46 Math Elem
47 Math Sec
48 English/Lang Arts K-12
49 English/Lang Arts Elem
50 English/Lang Arts Sec
51 Reading K-12
52 Reading Elem
53 Reading Sec
54 Remedial Reading K-12
55 Remedial Reading Elem
56 Remedial Reading Sec
57 Bilingual/ELL
58 Special Education K-12
59 Special Education Elem
60 Special Education Sec
61 Foreign/World Lang K-12
62 Foreign/World Lang Elem
63 Foreign/World Lang Sec
64 Religious Education K-12
65 Religious Education Elem
66 Religious Education Sec
67 School Board President
68 Teacher Personnel
69 Academic Assessment
70 Research/Development
71 Public Information
72 Summer School
73 Instructional Tech
74 Inservice Training
75 Marketing/Distributive
76 Info Systems
77 Psychological Assess
78 Affirmative Action

| School | Grades | Title | Enrollment | % | Phone |
|---|---|---|---|---|---|
| © Idea Academy-Quest [301]<br>14001 N Rooth Rd, Edinburg 78541<br><u>Rosa Chapa</u> | PK-5 | T | 860 | 95% | 956/287-1003<br>Fax 956/287-2737<br>🅕 |
| © Idea Academy-Rio Grande City [301]<br>2803 W Monarch Ln, Rio Grande Cy 78582<br><u>Fernando Salinas</u> | K-5 | T | 551 | 89% | 956/263-4900 |
| © Idea Academy-Rio Vista [303]<br>210 N Rio Vista Rd, Socorro 79927<br>Yanira Aguilar | PK-3 | | 300 | 92% | 915/444-0188 |
| © Idea Academy-Rise [304]<br>3000 Cherry Ln, Fort Worth 76116<br>Kristin Olson | K-3 | | 234 | | 817/885-4150 |
| © Idea Academy-Riverview [301]<br>30 Palm Blvd, Brownsville 78520<br>Radha Guajardo | PK-5 | T | 392 | 95% | 956/832-5900 |
| © Idea Academy-Robindale [301]<br>3802 E Ruben Torres Sr Blvd, Brownsville 78521<br>Monica Araiza | K-3 | | 263 | | 956/832-5300 |
| © Idea Academy-Round Rock Tech [302]<br>3301 Greenlawn Blvd, Round Rock 78664<br>Betty Torgerson | K-3 | | 284 | | 512/822-4750 |
| © Idea Academy-Rundberg [302]<br>9504 N Interstate 35, Austin 78753<br>Maya Martin | K-10 | T | 338 | 93% | 512/822-4800 |
| © Idea Academy-San Benito [301]<br>2151 Russell Ln, San Benito 78586<br>Christina Villarreal | PK-5 | T | 874<br>24 | 85% | 956/399-5252<br>Fax 956/361-9478 |
| © Idea Academy-San Juan [301]<br>200 N Nebraska Ave, San Juan 78589<br><u>Melissa Finch</u> | PK-5 | T | 847 | 89% | 956/702-5150<br>Fax 956/702-4554<br>🅕🅣 |
| © Idea Academy-South Flores [305]<br>6919 S Flores St, San Antonio 78221<br>Hailey McCarthy | PK-5 | T | 855 | 77% | 210/239-4150 |
| © Idea Academy-Spears [301]<br>2010 Spears Rd, Houston 77067<br>Reynaldo Flores | K-3 | | 200 | | 832/844-4200 |
| © Idea Academy-Sports Park [301]<br>1000 Sports Park Blvd, Olmito 78575<br>Richard Bell | K-3 | | 100 | | 956/377-8000 |
| © Idea Academy-Tres Lagos [301]<br>5200 Tres Lagos Blvd, McAllen 78504<br><u>Benigna Carcano</u> | PK-3 | | 500 | 84% | 956/375-8550 |
| © Idea Academy-Walzem [305]<br>6445 Walzem Rd, San Antonio 78239<br>Ryane Burke | PK-5 | T | 618 | 75% | 210/239-4600 |
| © Idea Academy-Weslaco [301]<br>2931 E Sugarcane Dr, Weslaco 78599<br>Sylvia Mejia | K-5 | T | 697 | 91% | 956/351-4100<br>Fax 956/351-4101 |
| © Idea Academy-Weslaco Pike [301]<br>1000 E Pike Blvd, Weslaco 78596<br>Silvia Martinez | PK-5 | T | 931 | 85% | 956/351-4850<br>Fax 956/351-4851 |
| © Idea Clg Prep-Achieve [304]<br>1900 Thomas Rd, Haltom City 76117<br><u>Jaeil Kim</u> | 5-7 | | 250 | | 817/885-4700 |
| © Idea Clg Prep-Alamo [301]<br>325 State Highway 495, Alamo 78516<br><u>Mayra Martinez</u> | 6-12 | T | 735 | 94% | 956/588-4005<br>Fax 956/588-4006 |
| © Idea Clg Prep-Bluff Sprgs [302]<br>1700 E Slaughter Ln, Austin 78747<br>Deanna Bruce | 6-8 | T | 361 | 80% | 512/822-4200 |
| © Idea Clg Prep-Brackenridge [305]<br>5555 Old Pearsall Rd, San Antonio 78242<br><u>Zachary Sting</u> | 6-8 | T | 118 | 86% | 210/239-4300 |
| © Idea Clg Prep-Brownsville [301]<br>4395 Paredes Line Rd, Brownsville 78526<br>Marco Lopez | 6-12 | T | 755 | 80% | 956/832-5150<br>Fax 956/832-5716 |
| © Idea Clg Prep-Burke [305]<br>10434 Marbach Rd, San Antonio 78245<br>Ramon Gutierrez | 6-7 | | 263 | | 210/239-4650 |
| © Idea Clg Prep-Carver [305]<br>217 Robinson Pl, San Antonio 78202<br>Byong Chang Yu | 6-12 | T | 604 | 83% | 210/223-8885 |
| © Idea Clg Prep-Converse [305]<br>5160 Martinez Converse Rd, Converse 78109<br>Joseph Lowe | 6-7 | | 250 | | 210/529-3800 |
| © Idea Clg Prep-Donna [301]<br>401 S 1st St, Donna 78537<br>Amanda Canales | 6-12 | T | 755 | 94% | 956/464-0203<br>Fax 956/464-8532 |
| © Idea Clg Prep-Eastside [305]<br>2519 Martin Luther King Dr, San Antonio 78203<br>Deion Brown | 6-10 | T | 117 | 96% | 210/239-4800 |
| © Idea Clg Prep-Edgecliff [304]<br>1640 Altamesa Blvd, Fort Worth 76134<br>Kenieka Francis | 5-6 | | 190 | | 817/885-4800 |
| © Idea Clg Prep-Edgemere [303]<br>15101 Edgemere Blvd, El Paso 79938<br>Rodrigo Wong | 6-7 | | 300 | 71% | 915/444-0200 |
| © Idea Clg Prep-Edinburg [301]<br>2553 N Roegiers Rd, Edinburg 78541<br>Ramiro Gomez | 6-12 | T | 722 | 81% | 956/287-6100 |
| © Idea Clg Prep-Elsa [301]<br>411 S Fanin Ave, Elsa 78543<br>Antonio Garza | 6-7 | | 300 | 97% | 956/567-4700 |
| © Idea Clg Prep-Ewing Halsell [305]<br>2523 W Ansley Blvd, San Antonio 78224<br><u>William Chermak</u> | 6-7 | T | 253 | 79% | 210/239-4850 |
| © Idea Clg Prep-Frontier [301]<br>2800 S Dakota Ave, Brownsville 78521<br>Virginia Callaway | 6-12 | T | 787 | 90% | 956/541-2002<br>Fax 956/544-2004 |
| © Idea Clg Prep-Hardy [301]<br>1930 Little York Rd, Houston 77093<br>Gerald Boyd | 6-7 | | 250 | | 832/844-4100 |
| © Idea Clg Prep-Harlingen [301]<br>24240 Chester Park Rd, Harlingen 78552 | 6-7 | | 250 | | 956/564-7200 |
| © Idea Clg Prep-Harvey Najim [305]<br>926 S WW White Rd, San Antonio 78220<br>Theresa Hall | 6-7 | T | 500 | 86% | 210/239-4900 |
| © Idea Clg Prep-Hidden Meadow [305]<br>10138 Culebra Rd, San Antonio 78250<br>Mark Ruth | 6-7 | | 250 | | 210/529-3900 |
| © Idea Clg Prep-Hlth Professions [302]<br>5816 Wilcab Rd, Austin 78721<br>Cameron Cook | 5-7 | | 234 | | 512/822-4350 |
| © Idea Clg Prep-Horizon Vista [303]<br>201 Horizon Crossing St, El Paso 79928<br>Stephen Lopez | 6-7 | | 250 | | |
| © Idea Clg Prep-Ingram Hills [305]<br>3115 Majestic Dr, San Antonio 78228<br>Jeffrey Rothschild | 6-7 | | 300 | 87% | 210/529-3700 |
| © Idea Clg Prep-Judson [305]<br>13427 Judson Rd, San Antonio 78233<br>Joaquin Hernandez | 6-8 | T | 352 | 70% | 210/529-3600 |
| © Idea Clg Prep-Kyle [302]<br>640 Philomena Dr, Kyle 78640<br><u>Jorge Chipres</u> | 6-7 | | 133 | 64% | 512/822-4300 |
| © Idea Clg Prep-Los Encinos [301]<br>5400 S Ware Rd, McAllen 78503<br>Raj Desai | 6-7 | | 263 | | 956/429-4150 |
| © Idea Clg Prep-Mays [305]<br>1210 Horal Dr, San Antonio 78245<br><u>Gerald Boyd</u> | 6-8 | T | 373 | 80% | 210/529-3200 |

© Idea Clg Prep-McAllen [301]   6-12   T   772   75%   956/429-4100
201 N Bentsen Rd, McAllen 78501   Fax 956/429-4126
Joan Alvarez

© Idea Clg Prep-Mesa Hills [303]   6-7   263   915/888-4050
405 Wallenberg Dr, El Paso 79912
Nayeli Velasquez

© Idea Clg Prep-Monterrey Park [305]   6-10   T   567   91%   210/239-4200
222 SW 39th St, San Antonio 78237
Jonathan Tyrrell

© Idea Clg Prep-Montopolis [302]   6-12   T   739   91%   512/646-2800
1701 Vargas Rd, Austin 78741
Cristopher Rubio

© Idea Clg Prep-N Mission [301]   6-10   255   956/424-4300
2706 N Holland Ave, McAllen 78502
Dave Wagner

© Idea Clg Prep-Owassa [301]   6-7   300   92%   956/588-4300
1000 E Owassa Rd, Pharr 78577
Stevie Luera

© Idea Clg Prep-Palmview [301]   6-7   250   956/272-5394
4100 N Schuerbach Rd, Mission 78574
Dierdre Medina

© Idea Clg Prep-Parmer Park [302]   5-7   234   512/822-4850
1438 E Yager Ln, Austin 78753
Katherine Christon

© Idea Clg Prep-Pflugerville [302]   6-7   300   78%   512/822-4700
1901 E Wells Branch Pkwy, Pflugerville 78660
Mera Dougherty

© Idea Clg Prep-Pharr [301]   6-12   T   764   94%   956/283-1515
600 E Las Milpas Rd, Pharr 78577   Fax 956/783-1557
Claudia Ash

© Idea Clg Prep-Quest [301]   6-12   T   735   94%   956/287-1003
14001 N Rooth Rd, Edinburg 78541   Fax 956/287-2737
Jose De Leon

© Idea Clg Prep-Rio Grande City   6-8   T   191   87%   956/263-4900
2803 W Monarch Ln, Rio Grande Cy 78582
Fernando Salinas

© Idea Clg Prep-Rio Vista [303]   6-7   300   915/444-0188
210 N Rio Vista Rd, Socorro 79927
Adrian Hernandez

© Idea Clg Prep-Rise [304]   6-7   234   817/885-4150
3000 Cherry Ln, Fort Worth 76116
Nicholas Ditto

© Idea Clg Prep-Riverview [301]   6-9   T   489   94%   956/832-5900
30 Palm Blvd, Brownsville 78520
Adriana Alvarado

© Idea Clg Prep-Robindale [301]   6-7   263   956/832-5300
3802 E Ruben Torres Sr Blvd, Brownsville 78521
Juana Ibarra

© Idea Clg Prep-Round Rock Tech [302]   5-7   300   512/822-4750
3301 Greenlawn Blvd, Round Rock 78664
Stacia Comer

© Idea Clg Prep-Rundberg [302]   6-10   T   253   95%   512/822-4800
9504 N Interstate 35, Austin 78753
Pike Nichols

© Idea Clg Prep-San Juan [301]   6-12   T   742   96%   956/588-4021
600 E Sioux Rd, San Juan 78589   Fax 956/702-4554
Lindsey Campbell

© Idea Clg Prep-South Flores [305]   6-12   T   233   75%   210/239-4150
6919 S Flores St, San Antonio 78221
Constantine Polites

© Idea Clg Prep-Spears [301]   6-7   250   832/844-4200
2010 Spears Rd, Houston 77067
Anna Farias

© Idea Clg Prep-Sports Park [301]   9-11   100   956/377-8000
1000 Sports Park Blvd, Olmito 78575
Rebecca Jeffries

© Idea Clg Prep-Toros [301]   6-12   141   956/287-6350
3300 E Texas Rd, Edinburg 78542
Vivianne Manzano

© Idea Clg Prep-Tres Lagos [301]   6-8   T   123   81%   956/252-9227
5200 Tres Lagos Blvd, McAllen 78504
Megan Arenas-Goossen

© Idea Clg Prep-Walzem [305]   6-10   T   540   81%   210/239-4600
6445 Walzem Rd, San Antonio 78239
Andrea Lopez

© Idea Clg Prep-Weslaco [301]   K-12   T   1,550   94%   956/351-4100
2931 E Sugarcane Dr, Weslaco 78599   Fax 956/351-4101
Leanna Sarinana \ Sylvia Mejia

© Idea Clg Prep-Weslaco Pike [301]   6-11   T   119   84%   956/351-4850
1000 E Pike Blvd, Weslaco 78596
Nate Lowry

© Idea Mission [301]   PK-12   T   1,624   93%   956/583-8315
1600 S Schuerbach Rd, Mission 78572   Fax 956/424-3248
Christina Escamilla

© Idea San Benito [301]   PK-12   T   1,624   81%   956/583-8315
2151 Russell Ln, San Benito 78586   Fax 956/361-9478
Casey Sawceda

© Imagine Intl Academy-N Texas [032]   K-12   1,406   10%   214/491-1500
2860 Virginia Pkwy, McKinney 75071   Fax 214/491-1504
Holly Baker \ Elisha Upton

© Inspired Vision Elem Sch [287]   PK-6   T   778   94%   214/391-7964
8421 Bohannon Dr, Dallas 75217   12   Fax 214/391-7954
Joy-Lena Waites

© Inspired Vision Secondary Sch [287]   7-12   T   575   94%   972/285-5758
8501 Bruton Rd, Dallas 75217   25   Fax 972/285-0061
Tara Addison

© Ischool High Lewisville [318]   9-12   70   29%   972/317-2470
1800 Lakeway Dr Ste 100, Lewisville 75057
Gary Wilhelmi

© Ischool High the Woodlands [318]   9-12   301   24%   936/231-8594
3232 College Park Dr Ste 212, The Woodlands 77384
Guamma Goff

© Ischool High University Park [318]   9-12   338   35%   281/251-5770
20515 State Highway 249, Houston 77070
Stacy Bare

© Ischool Lewisville STEM Acad [318]   6-12   384   972/829-4492
650 Bennett Ln, Lewisville 75057
Alan Wimberley

© Ischool Virtual Acad of TX [318]   3-12   1,501   888/729-0622
1301 Waters Ridge Dr, Lewisville 75057
Tammany Olson

© Jasper Classical Academy [318]   K-7   98   409/489-9222
1501B S Wheeler St, Jasper 75951   Fax 409/489-9272
Patricia Oliver

© Jean Massieu Acad for the Deaf   Spec   T   196   96%   817/460-0396
823 N Center St, Arlington 76011   13   Fax 817/460-9867
Monica Fox

© Jubilee Academic Center   PK-8   TV   620   77%   210/333-6227
4434 Roland Rd, San Antonio 78222   30   Fax 210/337-2357
Cheryl Stewart

© Jubilee Brownsville [306]   PK-12   T   1,001   62%   956/509-2690
4955 Pablo Kisel Blvd, Brownsville 78526   Fax 956/509-2326
Carlos Moreno

© Jubilee Harlingen [306]   PK-8   125   956/708-2030
123 S Palm Court Dr, Harlingen 78552   Fax 956/364-2453
Tanya Perez

© Jubilee Highland Hills [306]   PK-8   T   1,019   82%   210/634-7590
1515 Goliad Rd, San Antonio 78223
Trina Cardenas

© Jubilee Highland Park [306]   PK-8   T   312   81%   210/801-8030
901 E Drexel Ave, San Antonio 78210   Fax 210/532-3810
James Montano

---

| 1 | Superintendent | 8 | Curric/Instruct K-12 | 19 | Chief Financial Officer | 29 | Family/Consumer Science | 39 | Social Studies K-12 | 49 | English/Lang Arts Elem | 59 | Special Education Elem | 69 | Academic Assessment |
| 2 | Bus/Finance/Purchasing | 9 | Curric/Instruct Elem | 20 | Art K-12 | 30 | Adult Education | 40 | Social Studies Elem | 50 | English/Lang Arts Sec | 60 | Special Education Sec | 70 | Research/Development |
| 3 | Buildings And Grounds | 10 | Curric/Instruct Sec | 21 | Art Elem | 31 | Career/Sch-to-Work K-12 | 41 | Social Studies Sec | 51 | Reading K-12 | 61 | Foreign/World Lang K-12 | 71 | Public Information |
| 4 | Food Service | 11 | Federal Program | 22 | Art Sec | 32 | Career/Sch-to-Work Elem | 42 | Science K-12 | 52 | Reading Elem | 62 | Foreign/World Lang Elem | 72 | Summer School |
| 5 | Transportation | 12 | Title I | 23 | Music K-12 | 33 | Career/Sch-to-Work Sec | 43 | Science Elem | 53 | Reading Sec | 63 | Foreign/World Lang Sec | 73 | Instructional Tech |
| 6 | Athletic | 13 | Title V | 24 | Music Elem | 34 | Early Childhood Ed | 44 | Science Sec | 54 | Remedial Reading K-12 | 64 | Religious Education K-12 | 74 | Inservice Training |
| 7 | Health Services | 15 | Asst Superintendent | 25 | Music Sec | 35 | Health/Phys Education | 45 | Math K-12 | 55 | Remedial Reading Elem | 65 | Religious Education Elem | 75 | Marketing/Distributive |
| | | 16 | Instructional Media Svcs | 26 | Business Education | 36 | Guidance Services K-12 | 46 | Math Elem | 56 | Remedial Reading Sec | 66 | Religious Education Sec | 76 | Info Systems |
| | | 17 | Chief Operations Officer | 27 | Career & Tech Ed | 37 | Guidance Services Elem | 47 | Math Sec | 57 | Bilingual/ELL | 67 | School Board President | 77 | Psychological Assess |
| | | 18 | Chief Academic Officer | 28 | Technology Education | 38 | Guidance Services Sec | 48 | English/Lang Arts K-12 | 58 | Special Education K-12 | 68 | Teacher Personnel | 78 | Affirmative Action |

# Texas School Directory

| School | Grades | Prog | Enroll | % | Phone/Fax |
|---|---|---|---|---|---|
| © Jubilee Kingsville [306]<br>201 N 19th St, Kingsville 78363 | PK-8 | T | 262 | 74% | 361/516-0840<br>Fax 361/516-0874 |
| © Jubilee Lake View Univ Prep [306]<br>325 Castroville Rd, San Antonio 78207<br>Nadine Pabst | PK-12 | T | 545 | 83% | 210/963-3900 |
| © Jubilee Leadership Academy [306]<br>4150 Jaime J Zapata Ave, Brownsville 78521<br>Yolanda Cantu | PK-5 | | 218 | | 956/641-4250<br>Fax 956/641-4255 |
| © Jubilee Livingway [306]<br>350 Ruben Torres Sr Blvd, Brownsville 78520<br>Cecilia Septimo | PK-5 | | 345 | | 956/708-2020<br>Fax 956/554-9701 |
| © Jubilee San Antonio [306]<br>4427 Chandler, San Antonio 78222<br>Hector Gomez | K-12 | T | 1,061 | 81% | 210/278-3880<br>Fax 210/278-3929 |
| © Jubilee Sendero [306]<br>5408 Daughtry Dr, San Antonio 78238<br>Kimberly Minyard | PK-3 | | 36 | | 210/380-9538 |
| © Jubilee Wells Branch [306]<br>3711 Shoreline Dr, Austin 78728<br>Shrlene Andrews | PK-10 | | 700 | | 512/872-8440<br>Fax 512/341-0816 |
| © Jubilee Westwood [306]<br>8038 W Military Dr, San Antonio 78227<br>Michael Wagner | PK-8 | | 180 | | 210/963-3930 |
| © Jubilee-Wells Academies<br>3711 Shoreline Dr, Austin 78728<br>Cynthia Sneed | PK-9 | | 500 | | 512/872-8440 |
| © Katherine Anne Porter Sch<br>515 FM 2325, Wimberley 78676<br>Dr Leslie Bonds | 9-12 | ATV | 168<br>15 | 40% | 512/847-6867<br>Fax 512/847-0737 |
| © Kauffman Leadership Academy<br>1108 N Anglin St, Cleburne 76031<br>Dr Theresa Kauffman | 5-12 | T | 89 | 49% | 682/459-2800<br>Fax 817/740-7521 |
| © Ki Charter Academy<br>120 Bert Brown St, San Marcos 78666<br>Javier Garcia \ Adrienne Durham | 1-12 | T | 164 | 90% | 512/618-0787 |
| © Kingsland Sch [313]<br>2112 W Ranch Road 1431, Kingsland 78639<br>Meloni Puishes | K-8 | T | 152 | 52% | 325/388-0020 |
| © KIPP 3D Academy [309]<br>500 Tidwell Rd, Houston 77022<br>Kelsey Lyman | 5-8 | T | 447 | 92% | 832/230-0566<br>Fax 713/692-1631 |
| © KIPP Acad West MS [309]<br>8500 Highway 6 S, Houston 77083<br>Steven Khadam-Hir | 5-8 | T | 423 | 88% | 832/230-0573 |
| © KIPP Academy MS [309]<br>10711 Kipp Way Dr, Houston 77099<br>Andrew Rubin | 5-8 | T | 431<br>20 | 92% | 832/328-1051<br>Fax 281/498-4201 |
| © KIPP Aspire Academy [310]<br>239 Stark, San Antonio 78204<br>Jaime Jaen | 5-8 | T | 502 | 91% | 210/735-7300<br>Fax 210/735-7305 [f] |
| © KIPP Austin Acad Arts Letters [307]<br>8509 FM 969 Ste 676, Austin 78724<br>Jamie Holley | 5-6 | T | 455 | 86% | 512/501-3640<br>Fax 512/501-3641 [f] |
| © KIPP Austin Beacon Prep [307]<br>5107 S Interstate 35 Ste 8, Austin 78744<br>Kristi Michaels | 5-8 | | 457 | | 512/651-1918<br>Fax 866/924-2872 |
| © KIPP Austin Brave HS [307]<br>5107 S Interstate 35 Ste A, Austin 78744<br>Stephanie Burns | 9-11 | | 532 | | 512/651-2225<br>Fax 866/857-6541 |
| © KIPP Austin College Prep [307]<br>8004 Cameron Rd, Austin 78754<br>Katie Carpenter | 5-8 | T | 435 | 88% | 512/501-4969<br>Fax 512/637-6899 |
| © KIPP Austin Collegiate [307]<br>8004 Cameron Rd, Austin 78754<br>James Pasto | 9-12 | T | 718 | 87% | 512/501-3586<br>Fax 512/501-3587 [f] |
| © KIPP Austin Comunidad [307]<br>8004 Cameron Rd, Austin 78754<br>Kelly Doyle | K-4 | T | 581 | 88% | 512/501-3911<br>Fax 512/870-9224 |
| © KIPP Austin Connections ES [307]<br>8509 FM 969 Ste 629, Austin 78724<br>Elizabeth Reiter | K-4 | T | 580 | 87% | 512/651-5537<br>Fax 512/870-9537 |
| © KIPP Austin Leadership ES [307]<br>8509 FM 969 Ste 628, Austin 78724<br>Nicole Seltman | K-4 | T | 473 | | 512/651-2168<br>Fax 866/461-8086 |
| © KIPP Austin Obras [307]<br>5107 S Interstate 35 Ste A, Austin 78744<br>Briana Anderson | K-4 | T | 585 | 86% | 512/651-2069<br>Fax 866/700-5197 |
| © KIPP Austin Vista Middle Sch [307]<br>8509 FM 969 Ste 627, Austin 78724<br>Breanne Diaz | 5-8 | T | 414 | 88% | 512/651-1921<br>Fax 512/501-3641 |
| © KIPP Camino Academy [310]<br>4343 W Commerce St, San Antonio 78237<br>Delisa Morales | 5-8 | T | 486 | 92% | 210/829-4200<br>Fax 210/829-4207 |
| © KIPP Climb Academy [309]<br>8805 Ferndale, Houston 77017<br>Autumn Figueroa | PK-3 | T | 789 | 92% | 832/230-0578<br>Fax 713/944-4316 |
| © KIPP Connect Houston High Sch [309]<br>6700 Bellaire Blvd, Houston 77074<br>Geoffrey Roy | 9-9 | | 160 | 86% | 281/879-3023 |
| © KIPP Connect Houston MS [309]<br>6700 Bellaire Blvd, Houston 77074<br>Pegah Taylor | 5-8 | T | 442 | 90% | 281/879-3023<br>Fax 713/774-0387 |
| © KIPP Connect Houston Primary [309]<br>6700 Bellaire Blvd, Houston 77074<br>Adam Kutac | PK-4 | T | 869 | 94% | 281/879-3023 |
| © KIPP Courage College Prep [309]<br>2200 Ridgecrest Dr, Houston 77055<br>Eric Schmidt | 5-8 | | 400 | | 713/251-3800 |
| © KIPP Destiny Elem Sch [308]<br>3663 W Camp Wisdom Rd, Dallas 75237<br>Dexter Chaney | K-4 | T | 552 | 93% | 972/323-4220<br>Fax 972/708-8598 |
| © KIPP Destiny Middle Sch [308]<br>3663 W Camp Wisdom Rd, Dallas 75237<br>Cynite Cooke | 5-8 | T | 407 | 92% | 972/323-4225 |
| © KIPP Dream Prep [309]<br>500 Tidwell Rd, Houston 77022<br>Haley Simonton | PK-4 | T | 898 | 94% | 832/230-0566 |
| © KIPP Esperanza Dual Lang Acad [310]<br>239 Stark, San Antonio 78204<br>Dorene Benavidez | K-4 | T | 654 | 86% | 210/888-6601<br>Fax 210/888-6602 |
| © KIPP Explore Academy [309]<br>5402 Lawndale St, Houston 77023<br>Amy Stabile | PK-4 | T | 851 | 94% | 832/230-0547<br>Fax 832/230-0178 |
| © KIPP Generations Collegiate HS [309]<br>500 Tidwell Rd, Houston 77022<br>Amanda Ybarsabal | 9-12 | T | 597 | 83% | 832/230-0566<br>Fax 832/201-9988 |
| © KIPP Houston High Sch [309]<br>10711 Kipp Way Dr, Houston 77099<br>Latronica Madison | 9-12 | T | 676 | 80% | 832/328-1082<br>Fax 832/838-4293 |
| © KIPP Intrepid Prep Sch [309]<br>5402 Lawndale St, Houston 77023<br>Joy Taluyo | 5-8 | T | 418 | 89% | 281/879-3100<br>Fax 713/924-5046 |
| © KIPP Legacy Prep Sch [309]<br>9606 Mesa Dr, Houston 77078<br>Monique Payton | PK-4 | T | 946 | 95% | 832/230-0567<br>Fax 713/491-7311 |
| © KIPP Liberation College Prep [309]<br>5400 Martin Luther King Blvd, Houston 77021<br>Tai Ingram | 5-8 | T | 427 | 88% | 832/230-0564<br>Fax 713/748-0471 |
| © KIPP Nexus MS [309]<br>4211 Watonga Blvd, Houston 77092<br>Lisa McClinton | 5-5 | T | 107 | 91% | 832/230-0553 |

© KIPP Nexus Primary-Houston [309]   PK-2   T   90   90%  832/230-0553
4211 Watonga Blvd, Houston 77092
Lindsay Hatcher

© KIPP Northeast College Prep [309]   9-12   T   547   77%  832/230-0567
9680 Mesa Dr, Houston 77078

© KIPP Oak Cliff Academy [308]   9-10    125   96%  972/323-4240
3200 S Lancaster Rd Ste 230A, Dallas 75216
Aaron Castillo

© KIPP Peace Elem Sch [309]   PK-4   T   655   93%  832/230-0564
5400 Martin Luther King Blvd, Houston 77021   Fax 713/440-0667
Precious Parks

© KIPP Pleasant Grove Mid Sch [308]   5-5   T   355   96%  972/323-4235
2200 N Saint Augustine Dr, Dallas 75227
Delshon Henry

© KIPP Pleasant Grove Primary [308]   K-4   T   600   95%  972/323-4230
2200 N Saint Augustine Dr, Dallas 75227
Dexter Chaney

© KIPP Poder Academy [310]   5-8   T   450   92%  210/888-6513
128 S Audubon Dr, San Antonio 78212   Fax 210/888-6515
Nicole Winsett

© KIPP Polaris Academy for Boys [309]   5-8   T   339   85%  832/230-0567
9636 Mesa Dr, Houston 77078   Fax 713/633-4783
Jamaal Henry

© KIPP Prime College Prep [309]   5-8   T   319   87%  832/230-0578
8805 Ferndale, Houston 77017
Rob Gill

© KIPP Sharp Prep [309]   PK-4   T   898   95%  281/879-3000
8430 Westglen Dr, Houston 77063   Fax 281/879-3001
Michelle Bennett

© KIPP Sharpstown College Prep [309]   5-8   T   430   92%  281/879-3005
8440 Westpark Dr, Houston 77063   Fax 281/915-0074
Catherine Presley

© KIPP Shine Prep [309]   PK-4   T   863   96%  832/328-1051
10711 Kipp Way Dr, Houston 77099   Fax 832/230-0579
Deborah Shifrine

© KIPP Somos Collegiate High Sch [310]   9-9    160
735 Fredericksburg Rd, San Antonio 78201
Jeremy Gray

© KIPP Spirit College Prep [309]   5-8   T   449   84%  832/230-0562
11000 Scott St, Houston 77047   Fax 713/731-1644
Tiffany Prados

© KIPP Sunnyside High Sch [309]   9-12   T   565   76%  832/230-0562
11000 Scott St, Houston 77047   Fax 832/201-8695
Dr Rian Wright

© KIPP Truth Academy [308]   5-8   T   468   95%  972/323-4215
1545 S Ewing Ave, Dallas 75216   Fax 214/375-2990
Ellen Prueitt

© KIPP Truth Elem Sch [308]   K-3   T   120   96%  972/323-4240
1545 S Ewing Ave, Dallas 75216
Katie Jubert

© KIPP UN Mundo Dual Lang Acad [310]   K-4   T   654   91%  210/824-1905
4343 W Commerce St, San Antonio 78237   Fax 210/485-1393
Lorraine Bernal   f

© KIPP Unity Primary [309]   PK-4   T   501   94%  832/230-0572
8500 Highway 6 S, Houston 77083   Fax 281/933-8169
Kaleena Rosenbauer

© KIPP University Prep High Sch [310]   9-12   T   827   90%  210/290-8720
239 Stark, San Antonio 78204   Fax 210/290-9427
Abigail Morton-Garland   f

© KIPP Voyage Academy for Girls [309]   5-8   T   336   88%  832/230-0567
9616 Mesa Dr, Houston 77078   Fax 713/491-7311
Kristen Pappas

© KIPP Zenith Academy [309]   PK-4   T   842   91%  832/230-0562
11000 Scott St, Houston 77047   Fax 713/731-0386
Cassandra Cotman

---

© La Academia De Estrellas CS   PK-8   T   1,096   86%  214/946-8908
4680 W Kiest Blvd, Dallas 75236   18
Ivelisse Centeno \ Kemlyn Stephens

© La Fe Preparatory Sch   PK-7   T   243   97%  915/533-4690
616 E Father Rahm Ave, El Paso 79901   Fax 915/533-4175
Marina Lopez

© Lawson Academy   6-8   T   226   90%  713/225-1551
5052 Scott St, Houston 77004   Fax 713/225-1561
Dr Marthea Raney

© Leadership Academy   K-7    194    903/561-1002
6720 Oak Hill Blvd, Tyler 75703   Fax 903/303-2069
Louise Dyer \ Javier Garcia

© Leadership Prep Sch Secondary   5-12    560   4%  972/370-3650
8100 Teel Pkwy, Frisco 75034   Fax 972/370-3651
Dr Audra Flloyd

© Leadership Prep School Elem   K-4    500   2%  972/294-6921
8500 Teel Pkwy, Frisco 75034   Fax 972/370-3651
Michelle Creamer

© Legacy Prep Charter Acad-Plano   K-12   T   353   60%  469/998-0213
601 Accent Dr, Plano 75075   Fax 469/287-8579
Nicole May

© Legacy Prep Chtr Acad-Mesquite   K-12   T   1,037   83%  469/287-8610
2727 Military Pkwy, Mesquite 75149   Fax 469/461-0793
Vivian Rivera \ Javier Chaparro

© Legacy Sch of Sport Sciences   6-11    393   29%  713/396-0837
2727 Spring Creek Dr, Spring 77373
Ralph Butler

© Life High School-Waxahachie [311]   9-12   T   970   47%  469/708-4444
170 Butcher Rd, Waxahachie 75165   Fax 469/708-4445
Candace Johnson

© Life Middle School Waxahachie [311]   7-8   T   487   54%  972/937-0715
3295 N Highway 77, Waxahachie 75165   Fax 972/937-0503
Fred Stanmore

© Life School Carrollton [311]   K-5    200    469/701-1355
2660 E Trinity Mills Rd, Carrollton 75006
Jennifer Villavaso

© Life School Cedar Hill [311]   K-6   T   632   62%  972/293-2825
129 W Wintergreen Rd, Cedar Hill 75104   Fax 972/291-2877
Christopher Carter

© Life School Lancaster [311]   K-6   T   519   68%  972/274-7950
950 S Interstate 35 E, Lancaster 75146   Fax 972/274-7991
Deborah Garton

© Life School Mountain Creek [311]   K-5   T   444   69%  214/623-0012
5525 W Illinois Ave, Dallas 75211   Fax 214/613-3166
Eva Mease

© Life School Oak Cliff [311]   K-12   T   1,539   83%  214/376-8200
4400 S R L Thornton Fwy, Dallas 75224   Fax 214/371-0297
Anita Sanders \ Anne Beckman

© Life School Red Oak [311]   K-6   T   1,064   49%  469/552-9200
777 S I-35 E, Red Oak 75154   Fax 972/617-5765
Danielle Dillard

© Lighthouse Charter Sch   PK-1   T   106   89%  210/674-4100
2718 Frontier Dr, San Antonio 78227   15   Fax 210/674-4108
Dr Donald Mills

© Lighthouse Chtr Sch-B Campus   PK-8   T   220   88%  210/257-6746
8138 Westshire Dr, San Antonio 78227   Fax 210/254-9284
Blanca Gonzalez

© Lone Star Language Academy   K-5    171    972/244-7220
5301 Democracy Dr, Plano 75024
Jamie Vella

Lubbock Adult Learning Center   Adult   V   24    806/281-5750
1601 24th St, Lubbock 79411   6   Fax 806/281-5758
Larry Morgan

© Lumin E Dallas Community Sch   PK-3    102    214/824-8950
924 Wayne St, Dallas 75223   4   Fax 214/827-7683
Sylvie Fitzgerald

---

| | | | | | |
|---|---|---|---|---|---|
| **1** Superintendent | **8** Curric/Instruct K-12 | **19** Chief Financial Officer | **29** Family/Consumer Science | **39** Social Studies K-12 | **49** English/Lang Arts Elem | **59** Special Education Elem | **69** Academic Assessment |
| **2** Bus/Finance/Purchasing | **9** Curric/Instruct Elem | **20** Art K-12 | **30** Adult Education | **40** Social Studies Elem | **50** English/Lang Arts Sec | **60** Special Education Sec | **70** Research/Development |
| **3** Buildings And Grounds | **10** Curric/Instruct Sec | **21** Art Elem | **31** Career/Sch-to-Work K-12 | **41** Social Studies Sec | **51** Reading K-12 | **61** Foreign/World Lang K-12 | **71** Public Information |
| **4** Food Service | **11** Federal Program | **22** Art Sec | **32** Career/Sch-to-Work Elem | **42** Science K-12 | **52** Reading Elem | **62** Foreign/World Lang Elem | **72** Summer School |
| **5** Transportation | **12** Title I | **23** Music K-12 | **33** Career/Sch-to-Work Sec | **43** Science Elem | **53** Reading Sec | **63** Foreign/World Lang Sec | **73** Instructional Tech |
| **6** Athletic | **13** Title V | **24** Music Elem | **34** Early Childhood Ed | **44** Science Sec | **54** Remedial Reading K-12 | **64** Religious Education K-12 | **74** Inservice Training |
| **7** Health Services | **15** Asst Superintendent | **25** Music Sec | **35** Health/Phys Education | **45** Math K-12 | **55** Remedial Reading Elem | **65** Religious Education Elem | **75** Marketing/Distributive |
| | **16** Instructional Media Svcs | **26** Business Education | **36** Guidance Services K-12 | **46** Math Elem | **56** Remedial Reading Sec | **66** Religious Education Sec | **76** Info Systems |
| | **17** Chief Operations Officer | **27** Career & Tech Ed | **37** Guidance Services Elem | **47** Math Sec | **57** Bilingual/ELL | **67** School Board President | **77** Psychological Assess |
| | **18** Chief Academic Officer | **28** Technology Education | **38** Guidance Services Sec | **48** English/Lang Arts K-12 | **58** Special Education K-12 | **68** Teacher Personnel | **78** Affirmative Action |

# Texas School Directory

| School / Address / Personnel | Grades | Prog | Enroll | % | Phone / Fax |
|---|---|---|---|---|---|
| © Lumin Lindsley Park Cmty Sch<br>722 Tenison Memorial Dr, Dallas 75223<br>Rebekah Hardie | PK-3 | T | 296 | 65% | 214/321-9155<br>Fax 214/321-0702 |
| © Magnolia Montessori for All<br>5100 Pecan Brook Dr, Austin 78724<br>Madison Schmakel | PK-6 | T | 457 | 44% | 512/522-2429 |
| ©Ⓜ Mainland Prep Classical Acad [318]<br>319 Newman Rd, La Marque 77568<br>Diane Merchant | PK-8 | T | 449<br>40 | 87% | 409/934-9100<br>Fax 409/934-9130 |
| © Manara Acad Leadership Acad<br>8001 Jetstar Dr Ste 100, Irving 75063<br>Denise Woodward | 7-11 | T | 149 | 56% | 972/304-1155<br>Fax 972/304-1150 |
| © Manara Acad-Arlington STEM<br>6101 S Collins St, Arlington 76018<br>Luis Valdez | PK-8 | T | 297 | 53% | 972/304-1155<br>Fax 972/304-1150 |
| © Manara Acad-Irving Elem Sch<br>8201 Tristar Dr, Irving 75063<br>Rick Dix | PK-6 | T | 433 | 40% | 972/304-1155<br>Fax 972/304-1150 [fb][tw] |
| Ⓐ McLennan Co State Juvenile Sch<br>116 W Burleson Rd, Mart 76664<br>Carol Jo Mize | 9-12 | | 200<br>19 | | 254/297-8200<br>Fax 254/297-8392 |
| Ⓐ Meadowland CS Stepping Stones<br>© 3103 West Ave, San Antonio 78213<br>James Chavis | 1-5 | | 4 | | 830/331-4094 |
| © Meadowland CS-Oaks Acad<br>121 Old San Antonio Rd, Boerne 78006<br>Jerry Zapata | Spec | T | 85 | 89% | 830/331-4094<br>Fax 830/331-4096 |
| © Meridian World Charter Sch<br>2555 N Interstate 35, Round Rock 78664<br>Melissa Reese \ Melina Berduo \ Charles Ryder | K-12 | | 1,648 | 12% | 512/660-5230<br>Fax 512/660-5231 |
| © Meyer High Sch [292]<br>1020 Elm St Bldg 500, Waco 76704<br>Tyler Ellis | 9-12 | | 172 | 58% | 254/754-2288<br>Fax 254/754-8002 |
| © Meyerpark Charter Sch<br>13663 Main St, Houston 77035<br>Julia Wright | PK-6 | T | 278 | 96% | 713/729-9712<br>Fax 713/729-9720 |
| © Midland Academy Charter Sch<br>500 N Baird St, Midland 79701<br>Janet Wallace | PK-9 | T | 500<br>36 | 49% | 432/686-0003<br>Fax 432/686-0845 [tw] |
| © Munday Charter Sch<br>4800 Manor Rd, Austin 78723<br>N Whetstone | 6-12 | AT | 27 | 89% | 512/791-2270<br>Fax 512/232-9177 |
| © Nci CS Without Walls<br>6565 Rookin St, Houston 77074<br>Cimberli Darrough | PK-PK | T | 1,107 | 100% | 713/779-4856<br>Fax 713/779-2984 |
| © New Horizons Ranch Sch [313]<br>850 FM Road Hwy 574W, Goldthwaite 76844<br>Shelley Williams | K-12 | T | 70<br>12 | 96% | 325/938-5518<br>Fax 325/938-5665 |
| © Newman Int'l Acad-Cedar Hill<br>1114 W FM 1382, Cedar Hill 75104<br>Carinia Hornbuckle | PK-12 | T | 1,126 | 48% | 972/293-5460 |
| © Newman Int'l Acad-Ft Worth<br>6801 Meadowbrook Dr, Fort Worth 76112<br>Dale Duncan | K-4 | T | 166 | 74% | 817/655-2255 |
| © Newman Int'l Acad-Grace<br>308 W Park Row Dr, Arlington 76010<br>Donna Hart | K-6 | | 218 | | 682/220-9210 |
| © Newman Int'l Acad-Mansfield<br>1201 N State Highway 360, Mansfield 76063<br>Keith Shull | K-8 | | 273 | 27% | 682/400-4010 |
| © Newman Int'l Acad-Pioneer<br>1619 W Pioneer Pkwy, Arlington 76013<br>Dr Angelette Lindsey | 7-8 | T | 401 | 42% | 682/331-7095 |
| © Newman Int'l Academy-Arlington<br>1111 Gibbins Rd, Arlington 76011<br>Kristen Stock \ Jay Tinklenberg | PK-12 | | 896 | | 682/207-5175 |
| © Nolan Creek Sch [313]<br>505 E Avenue C, Belton 76513<br>Ken Wiseman | K-6 | | 71 | 24% | 254/939-4491 |
| © North Texas Collegiate Acad-E [321]<br>1851 Oak Grove Pkwy, Little Elm 75068<br>Susan Taraba | PK-8 | T | 165 | 70% | 972/292-3562<br>Fax 972/292-3563 |
| © North Texas Collegiate Acad-N [321]<br>4601 N Interstate 35, Denton 76207<br>Amanda Jordan | PK-8 | T | 181 | 88% | 940/383-1972<br>Fax 940/383-7655 |
| © North Texas Collegiate Acad-S [321]<br>968 Raldon St, Lewisville 75067<br>Donica Hill | PK-8 | T | 210<br>10 | 95% | 972/221-3564<br>Fax 972/221-3576 |
| © Nova Academy Cedar Hill<br>820 E Wintergreen Rd Bldg B, Cedar Hill 75104<br>Janice Foster | PK-6 | | 68 | | 972/291-1900<br>Fax 972/293-8049 |
| © Nova Academy Prichard<br>2800 Prichard Ln, Dallas 75227<br>Lashun Jasper | PK-8 | T | 548 | 88% | 972/808-7470<br>Fax 972/808-7471 |
| © Nova Academy Scyene<br>6459 Scyene Rd, Dallas 75227<br>Nichole Ward | PK-3 | T | 192 | 92% | 214/381-3088<br>Fax 214/381-3499 |
| © Nova Academy-Prichard<br>2800 Prichard Ln, Dallas 75227<br>Lashun Jasper | PK-8 | T | 530<br>19 | 94% | 972/808-7470<br>Fax 972/808-7471 |
| © Nyos Charter Sch-Lamar Campus<br>12301 N Lamar Blvd, Austin 78753<br>Will Jaramillo | 4-12 | T | 655 | 28% | 512/583-6967<br>Fax 512/583-6973 |
| © Nyos Charter School-M M Campus<br>1605 Kramer Ln, Austin 78758<br>Terry Berkenhoff \ Curtis Wilson | K-12 | T | 355<br>5 | 39% | 512/275-1593<br>Fax 512/287-5258 |
| © Odyssey Academy Bay Area ES<br>2600 Stanley Ln, El Lago 77586<br>Aimee Felchak | PK-8 | T | 249 | 44% | 281/326-4555 |
| © Odyssey Academy Galveston<br>2412 61st St, Galveston 77551<br>Jennifer Goodman | PK-12 | T | 948<br>29 | 79% | 409/750-9289<br>Fax 409/740-3735 [fb][tw] |
| © Olive Tree Montessori Academy<br>8601 Randol Mill Rd, Fort Worth 76120<br>Sadia Haq | PK-5 | | 79 | | 817/460-5000 |
| Ⓐ Panola Charter HS [314]<br>© 1110 FM 10, Carthage 75633<br>Keith Koonce | 8-12 | V | 10<br>2 | 59% | 903/693-6355<br>Fax 903/693-6391 |
| © Panola Early College High Sch [314]<br>1109 W Panola St, Carthage 75633<br>Robert Bruce | 8-12 | | 35 | 48% | 903/693-6355<br>Fax 903/693-6391 |
| © Pasadena Classical Academy [318]<br>6109 Fairmont Pkwy, Pasadena 77505<br>Lillian Pope | K-6 | | 166 | | 281/372-8999 |
| Ⓐ Pathways 3H Campus<br>© 110 Youth Ranch Rd, Mountain Home 78058<br>Sally Arnold | 4-12 | T | 27 | 89% | 512/560-8132 |
| © PCA Dr Sarah Strinden Elem Sch<br>602 S Raguet St, Lufkin 75904<br>Dr Jennifer Shaw | PK-5 | T | 514 | 57% | 936/634-5515 |
| © PCA Dr Terry Robbins Mid Sch<br>602 S Raguet St, Lufkin 75904<br>Jason Perry | 6-8 | T | 257 | 53% | 936/634-5515 |
| © Pegasus Sch Liberal Arts & Sci<br>601 N Akard St Ste 203, Dallas 75201<br>Kristen Clements | K-12 | T | 676<br>20 | 84% | 214/740-9991<br>Fax 214/740-9799 |
| © Permian Basin Classical Acad [318]<br>4320 W Illinois Ave Ste A, Midland 79703<br>Sharla Butler | K-8 | | 274 | 28% | 432/217-6122 |
| © Pineywoods Community Academy<br>602 S Raguet St, Lufkin 75904<br>Lacey Coleman \ Jennifer Shaw | PK-12 | T | 1,005<br>30 | 37% | 936/634-5515<br>Fax 936/634-5518 |

| | School / Address / Contact | Grades | Codes | Enroll | % | Phone / Fax |
|---|---|---|---|---|---|---|
| © | Por Vida Academy Charter HS [315]<br>1135 Mission Rd, San Antonio 78210<br>Loren Franckowiak | 9-12 | AGTV | 123<br>11 | 96% | 210/775-1132<br>Fax 210/390-1744 [t] |
| © | Positive Solutions Charter Sch<br>1325 N Flores St Ste 100, San Antonio 78212<br>Ruby Torres | 9-12 | AGT | 131<br>11 | 83% | 210/299-1025<br>Fax 210/299-1052 |
| Ⓐ | Premier HS-Abilene [318]<br>© 3161 S 23rd St Ste 4, Abilene 79605<br>Sue Pond | 9-12 | | 151<br>6 | | 325/698-8111<br>Fax 325/695-5620 |
| Ⓐ | Premier HS-Amarillo [318]<br>© 3242 Hobbs Rd Ste F, Amarillo 79109<br>Rebekah Pinson | 9-12 | | 229 | | 806/367-5447 |
| Ⓐ | Premier HS-Arlington [318]<br>© 551 Ryan Plaza Dr, Arlington 76011<br>Devon Turner | 9-12 | | 159 | | 682/350-8865 |
| © | Premier HS-Brenham Miracle Frm [318]<br>10632 FM 2621, Brenham 77833<br>Caty Paben | 7-12 | | 40 | | 979/836-0901<br>Fax 979/277-0939 |
| © | Premier HS-Brownsville [318]<br>© 955 Paredes Line Rd, Brownsville 78521<br>Maria Alvarado | 9-12 | | 149<br>10 | | 956/550-0084<br>Fax 866/677-8626 |
| © | Premier HS-Brownwood Early [318]<br>819 Early Blvd, Early 76802<br>Tim Garcia | 7-12 | | 40 | | 325/643-3735<br>Fax 866/363-4987 |
| © | Premier HS-Career Tech Ed Ctr [318]<br>4701 S Sugar Rd, Edinburg 78539<br>Julianna Lopez | 9-12 | | 147 | | 956/386-1793<br>Fax 877/622-9224 |
| © | Premier HS-Comanche [318]<br>1008 S Austin St, Comanche 76442<br>Eutimio Garcia | 7-12 | | 40 | | 325/356-9673<br>Fax 866/892-8875 |
| Ⓐ | Premier HS-Dayton [318]<br>© 1709 County Road 611, Dayton 77535<br>Suzanne Thomas | 9-12 | | 89 | | 936/257-8017 |
| Ⓐ | Premier HS-Del Rio [318]<br>© 1701 Kings Way, Del Rio 78840<br>Myra Jaramillo | 9-12 | V | 100<br>3 | | 830/703-1631<br>Fax 830/298-2122 |
| © | Premier HS-El Paso East [318]<br>8720 Gateway Blvd E Ste E, El Paso 79907<br>Osvaldo Morales | 9-12 | | 114 | | 915/633-1598<br>Fax 877/693-5206 |
| © | Premier HS-El Paso West [318]<br>1035 Belvidere St Ste 116, El Paso 79912<br>Laura Dominguez | 9-12 | A | 127 | | 915/581-4300<br>Fax 866/399-0201 |
| Ⓐ | Premier HS-Fort Worth [318]<br>© 6411 Camp Bowie Blvd Ste B, Fort Worth 76116<br>Danny Perez | 9-12 | | 134<br>8 | | 817/731-2028<br>Fax 866/728-0824 |
| Ⓐ | Premier HS-Granbury [318]<br>© 919 E US Highway 377 Ste 1, Granbury 76048<br>Marsha Grissom | 9-12 | | 147 | | 817/573-0435<br>Fax 866/895-9616 |
| Ⓐ | Premier HS-Huntsville [318]<br>© 2407 Sam Houston Ave Ste C, Huntsville 77340<br>Kevin Nichols | 9-12 | | 67 | | 936/439-5204 |
| Ⓐ | Premier HS-Irving South [318]<br>© 1081 W Shady Grove Rd, Irving 75060<br>Dennis Bingham | 9-12 | | 118 | | 972/254-1016 |
| Ⓐ | Premier HS-Laredo [318]<br>© 2201 Chihuahua St, Laredo 78043<br>Veronica Khan | 9-12 | | 107<br>5 | | 956/723-7788<br>Fax 956/284-0175 |
| Ⓐ | Premier HS-Lewisville [318]<br>1800 Lakeway Dr Ste 100, Lewisville 75057<br>Gary Wilhelmi | 9-12 | | 19 | | 972/521-1592<br>Fax 866/262-8996 |
| Ⓐ | Premier HS-Lubbock [318]<br>© 2002 W Loop 289 Ste 121, Lubbock 79407<br>Rodrick Saldana | 9-12 | | 137<br>5 | | 806/763-1518<br>Fax 806/763-9310 |
| Ⓐ | Premier HS-Midland [318]<br>© 4320 W Illinois Ave Ste A, Midland 79703<br>Jarret Hostas | 9-12 | | 151<br>8 | | 432/682-0384<br>Fax 432/682-0897 |
| © | Premier HS-Mission [318]<br>1203 St Claire Blvd, Mission 78572<br>Laura Thatcher | 9-12 | | 120 | | 956/424-9290<br>Fax 866/859-0140 |
| Ⓐ | Premier HS-N Austin [318]<br>© 13801 Burnet Rd Ste 300, Austin 78727<br>Wayne Williams | 9-12 | | 76 | | 512/614-4537 |
| Ⓐ | Premier HS-New Braunfels [318]<br>© 1928 S Seguin Ave Ste 100A, New Braunfels 78130<br>Richard Ramirez | 9-12 | | 104 | | 830/609-6606 |
| Ⓐ | Premier HS-North Houston [318]<br>© 12512 Walters Rd, Houston 77014<br>Kevin Nichols | 9-12 | | 86 | | 281/537-7272 |
| Ⓐ | Premier HS-Palmview [318]<br>406 W Veterans Blvd, Palmview 78572<br>Selma Femat | 9-12 | | 132<br>7 | | 956/584-8458 |
| © | Premier HS-Pflugerville [318]<br>616 FM 685 Ste 204B, Pflugerville 78660<br>Paulita Zuniga | 9-12 | | 110 | | 512/969-5100 |
| Ⓐ | Premier HS-Pharr [318]<br>© 200 E Interstate 2 Ste E, Pharr 78577<br>Rosario Zamora | 9-12 | | 125<br>7 | | 956/781-8800<br>Fax 877/512-1175 |
| © | Premier HS-S Austin [318]<br>© 1701 W Ben White Blvd Ste 100A, Austin 78704<br>Elizabeth Camarena | 9-12 | | 210<br>5 | | 512/444-8442<br>Fax 866/673-0058 |
| Ⓐ | Premier HS-San Angelo [318]<br>© 4102 Sunset Dr, San Angelo 76904<br>Bree Sherwood | 9-12 | | 79 | | 325/823-7758 |
| © | Premier HS-San Antonio East [318]<br>8220 Windsor Cross, San Antonio 78239<br>Dr Luis Gonzalez | 9-12 | | 146 | | 210/650-0944<br>Fax 866/836-6493 |
| © | Premier HS-San Antonio West [318]<br>6218 NW Loop 410, San Antonio 78238<br>Manuela Allen | 9-12 | | 107 | | 830/587-4730<br>Fax 866/864-2743 |
| Ⓐ | Premier HS-San Juan [318]<br>© 1202 E Business Highway 83, San Juan 78589<br>Alma Prado | 9-12 | | 130 | | 956/961-4721 |
| Ⓐ | Premier HS-Texarkana [318]<br>© 3448 Summerhill Rd, Texarkana 75503<br>Heather McNeill | 9-12 | | 72 | | 430/200-4385 |
| © | Premier HS-Tyler [318]<br>© 1106 N Glenwood Blvd, Tyler 75702<br>Joshua Groth | 9-12 | | 112<br>8 | | 903/592-5222<br>Fax 866/365-0336 |
| Ⓐ | Premier HS-Waco [318]<br>© 4720 N 19th St, Waco 76708<br>Lisa Linton | 9-12 | | 169<br>4 | | 254/752-0441<br>Fax 254/752-0445 |
| Ⓐ | Pro-Vision Academy<br>© 4590 Wilmington St, Houston 77051<br>Dr Phillis Tyler | 3-12 | | 500<br>6 | | 713/748-0030<br>Fax 713/748-0037 |
| © | Promesa Clg Prep-Brownsville<br>1944 E Alton Gloor Blvd, Brownsville 78526<br>Julie Trevino | PK-4 | | 401 | 86% | 956/295-7778 |
| © | Promesa Clg Prep-E Austin Key<br>6002 Jain Ln, Austin 78721<br>Ricardo Garza | PK-5 | T | 190<br>13 | 87% | 512/287-5000 |
| © | Promesa Clg Prep-E Austin MLK<br>5800 E Mlk Blvd, Austin 78721<br>Erica Gonzalez | 6-12 | T | 556 | 91% | 512/287-5050 |
| © | Promesa Clg Prep-W Corp Cristi<br>3102 Baldwin Blvd, Corp Christi 78405<br>Lucy Munoz | PK-5 | | 401 | 95% | 361/400-8293 |
| © | Promise Cmty Sch-New Nghbr [289]<br>6500 Rookin St, Houston 77074<br>Roel Saldivar | PK-6 | | 36 | | 713/273-3731<br>Fax 713/273-3797 |
| © | Promise Community Sch Ripley [289]<br>4410 Navigation Blvd, Houston 77011<br>Jennifer Galvan | PK-8 | | 470<br>11 | | 713/315-6429<br>Fax 713/547-8201 |

| # | | # | | # | | # | |
|---|---|---|---|---|---|---|---|
| 1 | Superintendent | 19 | Chief Financial Officer | 39 | Social Studies K-12 | 59 | Special Education Elem |
| 2 | Bus/Finance/Purchasing | 20 | Art K-12 | 40 | Social Studies Elem | 60 | Special Education Sec |
| 3 | Buildings And Grounds | 21 | Art Elem | 41 | Social Studies Sec | 61 | Foreign/World Lang K-12 |
| 4 | Food Service | 22 | Art Sec | 42 | Science K-12 | 62 | Foreign/World Lang Elem |
| 5 | Transportation | 23 | Music K-12 | 43 | Science Elem | 63 | Foreign/World Lang Sec |
| 6 | Athletic | 24 | Music Elem | 44 | Science Sec | 64 | Religious Education K-12 |
| 7 | Health Services | 25 | Music Sec | 45 | Math K-12 | 65 | Religious Education Elem |
| 8 | Curric/Instruct K-12 | 26 | Business Education | 46 | Math Elem | 66 | Religious Education Sec |
| 9 | Curric/Instruct Elem | 27 | Career & Tech Ed | 47 | Math Sec | 67 | School Board President |
| 10 | Curric/Instruct Sec | 28 | Technology Education | 48 | English/Lang Arts K-12 | 68 | Teacher Personnel |
| 11 | Federal Program | 29 | Family/Consumer Science | 49 | English/Lang Arts Elem | 69 | Academic Assessment |
| 12 | Title I | 30 | Adult Education | 50 | English/Lang Arts Sec | 70 | Research/Development |
| 13 | Title V | 31 | Career/Sch-to-Work K-12 | 51 | Reading K-12 | 71 | Public Information |
| 15 | Asst Superintendent | 32 | Career/Sch-to-Work Elem | 52 | Reading Elem | 72 | Summer School |
| 16 | Instructional Media Svcs | 33 | Career/Sch-to-Work Sec | 53 | Reading Sec | 73 | Instructional Tech |
| 17 | Chief Operations Officer | 34 | Early Childhood Ed | 54 | Remedial Reading K-12 | 74 | Inservice Training |
| 18 | Chief Academic Officer | 35 | Health/Phys Education | 55 | Remedial Reading Elem | 75 | Marketing/Distributive |
| | | 36 | Guidance Services K-12 | 56 | Remedial Reading Sec | 76 | Info Systems |
| | | 37 | Guidance Services Elem | 57 | Bilingual/ELL | 77 | Psychological Assess |
| | | 38 | Guidance Services Sec | 58 | Special Education K-12 | 78 | Affirmative Action |

# Texas School Directory

| School / Address / Personnel | Grades | Prog | Enroll | % | Phone / Fax |
|---|---|---|---|---|---|
| © Ptaa Greenville Elem Sch<br>8501 Jack Finney Blvd, Greenville 75402<br>Heather Sumroe | K-5 | | 190 | | 903/257-3920 |
| © Ptaa Mesquite Elem Sch<br>1412 S Belt Line Rd, Mesquite 75149<br>Nicole Dabney | K-5 | | 200 | | 972/285-6895 |
| © Ptaa Royse City Elem Sch<br>3200 S FM 548, Royse City 75189<br>Betty Hastings | K-5 | | 153 | | 469/707-3505 |
| © Ptaa-Greenville Mid High Sch<br>300 Aerobic Ln, Greenville 75402<br>Jennifer Cayce | 6-12 | T | 83 | 47% | 903/454-7153 |
| © Ptaa-Mesquite Mid High Sch<br>3200 Oates Dr, Mesquite 75150<br>Jennifer Cayce | 6-11 | T | 320 | 73% | 972/375-9672<br>Fax 469/301-2135 |
| © Quinn Middle Sch [292]<br>1020 Elm St Bldg 100, Waco 76704<br>Tyler Ellis | 5-8 | T | 246<br>10 | 66% | 254/754-8000<br>Fax 254/754-8009 |
| © Ranch Academy<br>3120 Vzcr 2318, Canton 75103<br>Bruce Blair | 6-12 | AT | 102<br>6 | 51% | 903/479-3601<br>Fax 903/479-1161 |
| © Ranch Academy-Tyler<br>3120 Von Van Dt Cr 2318, Canton 75103<br>Melissa Parduce | K-12 | | 50 | | 903/479-3601<br>Fax 903/939-8045 |
| © Rapoport Acad-E Campus ES [292]<br>2000 J J Flewellen Rd, Waco 76704<br>Jennifer Whitlark | PK-1 | T | 399<br>15 | 79% | 254/799-4191 |
| © Rapoport Acad-N Campus ES [292]<br>2200 MacArthur Dr, Waco 76708<br>Michelene Bess | 2-4 | | 205 | | 254/313-1313 |
| © Raul Yzaguirre Sch for Success<br>2255 N Coria St, Brownsville 78520<br>Maria Knosel | K-8 | T | 379 | 96% | 956/574-7100<br>Fax 956/542-2667 |
| © Raul Yzaguirre Sch for Success [317]<br>2950 Broadway St, Houston 77017<br>Mario Sandoval | K-12 | | 916<br>14 | | 713/640-3700<br>Fax 713/641-1853 |
| © Reve Preparatory Charter Sch<br>4315 W Fuqua St, Houston 77045<br>Traci Thibodeaux | K-5 | | 401 | | 832/982-2083 |
| © Rhodes School-Lee<br>11821 East Fwy Ste 400, Houston 77029<br>William Davis | PK-8 | | 130 | | 281/458-4334<br>Fax 281/458-7595 |
| Ⓐ Richard Milburn Acad-Amarillo [319]<br>4106 SW 51st Ave, Amarillo 79109<br>Rebecca Gerhardt | 9-12 | T | 159<br>15 | 78% | 806/463-2284<br>Fax 806/463-2331 |
| Ⓐ Richard Milburn Acad-CC [319]<br>© 5333 Everhart Rd Bldg C, Corp Christi 78411<br>Elizabeth Hanna | 9-12 | TV | 277<br>18 | 76% | 361/225-4424<br>Fax 361/225-4945 |
| Ⓐ Richard Milburn Acad-Ft Worth [319]<br>© 6785 Camp Bowie Blvd Ste 200, Fort Worth 76116<br>Rachel King-Sanders | 9-12 | T | 173<br>12 | 84% | 817/731-7627<br>Fax 817/731-7628 |
| Ⓐ Richard Milburn Acad-Houston [319]<br>© 713 E Airtex Dr Bldg B, Houston 77073<br>Nato James | 9-12 | T | 211<br>16 | 63% | 281/209-3505<br>Fax 281/209-9475 |
| Ⓐ Richard Milburn Acad-Killeen [319]<br>© 802 N 8th St, Killeen 76541<br>Lucette Bredt | 9-12 | T | 232<br>12 | 71% | 254/634-4444<br>Fax 254/526-0461 |
| Ⓐ Richard Milburn Acad-Lubbock [319]<br>© 2333 50th St, Lubbock 79412<br>Brenda Ewerz | 9-12 | T | 130<br>9 | 88% | 806/740-0811<br>Fax 806/740-0804 |
| Ⓐ Richard Milburn Acad-Midland [319]<br>© 503 E I20 Frontage #110, Midland 79703<br>Debra Theesfield | 9-12 | | 135<br>10 | | 432/203-9829<br>Fax 432/803-5393 |
| Ⓐ Richard Milburn Acad-Odessa [319]<br>© 2419 N County Rd W Ste 100, Odessa 79763<br>Mary Jansen | 9-12 | T | 477<br>6 | 43% | 432/614-1859<br>Fax 432/614-1913 |
| © Richard Milburn Acad-Pasadena [319]<br>320 Southmore Ave Ste 306, Pasadena 77502<br>Keith Garcia | 9-12 | T | 158 | 91% | 832/730-4570 |
| © Richardson Classical Academy [318]<br>2101 E Renner Rd, Richardson 75082<br>Ashley Cooper | K-7 | T | 96 | 46% | 972/479-9584 |
| © Richland Collegiate High Sch<br>12800 Abrams Rd, Dallas 75243<br>Craig Hinkle | 11-12 | | 592 | 22% | 972/761-6888<br>Fax 972/761-6890 |
| © Ripley House Middle Sch<br>4410 Navigation Blvd, Houston 77011<br>Rachael Purdom | 6-8 | T | 174 | 95% | 713/315-6429<br>Fax 713/315-6404 |
| © Rise Academy<br>207 N Martin Luther King Blvd, Lubbock 79403<br>Richard Baumgartner | PK-8 | T | 289<br>20 | 83% | 806/744-0438<br>Fax 832/201-7088 |
| © Rspa Northeast-Humble<br>600 Charles St, Humble 77338<br>William Davis | K-8 | T | 100 | 83% | 281/319-9300 |
| © Rspa Northshore<br>13334 Wallisville Rd, Houston 77049<br>Tonya McBride | PK-6 | T | 100 | | 281/459-9797 |
| © Rspa Northwest-Living Word<br>6601 Antoine Dr, Houston 77091<br>Charles Russell | K-5 | T | 127 | 44% | 832/562-2822 |
| © Rspa-Channelview<br>1215 Pecan St, Channelview 77530<br>Ashley Miller | PK-5 | | 115 | | 281/864-7015 |
| © Rspa-E Northshore<br>12818 Tidwell Rd, Houston 77044<br>Joesette Simeon | PK-5 | | 534 | | 281/459-9797 |
| © Rspa-NE Humble<br>600 Charles St, Humble 77338<br>William Davis | PK-8 | | 743 | | 281/319-9300 |
| © Ruth Jones McClendon Mid Sch<br>3460 Northeast Pkwy, San Antonio 78218<br>Keith Thomas | 6-8 | T | 110 | 100% | 210/568-8800 |
| © Sch of Sci & Tech Advancement [320]<br>10550 Westoffice Dr, Houston 77042<br>Haci Dilli | K-8 | T | 316 | 73% | 713/266-2522<br>Fax 713/266-2494 |
| © Sch of Sci & Tech Excellence [320]<br>330 N Sam Houston Pkwy E, Houston 77060<br>Hasan Kendirci | PK-7 | T | 370 | 43% | 832/672-6671<br>Fax 832/202-0700 |
| © Sch of Sci & Tech Main [320]<br>1450 NE Loop 410, San Antonio 78209<br>Ahmed Mamedov | 6-12 | T | 484 | 52% | 210/804-0222<br>Fax 210/822-3422 |
| © Sch of Sci & Tech Northwest [320]<br>12042 Culebra Rd, San Antonio 78253 | K-5 | | 104 | 32% | 210/530-8366 |
| © Sch of Sci & Tech-Alamo [320]<br>12200 Crownpoint, San Antonio 78233<br>Elizabeth James | K-8 | T | 342 | 47% | 210/657-6400 |
| © Sch of Sci & Tech-Corpus Crsti [320]<br>6633 Evans Rd, Corp Christi 78413<br>Ekrem Demirci | PK-12 | | 1,188 | | 361/851-2450<br>Fax 361/851-2475 |
| © Sch of Sci & Tech-Discovery [320]<br>5707 Bandera Rd, Leon Valley 78238<br>Jessica Romero | PK-8 | T | 571 | 65% | 210/543-1111<br>Fax 210/543-1112 |
| © Sch of Sci & Tech-Hill Country [320]<br>12042 Culebra Rd, San Antonio 78253<br>Musa Bocky | PK-4 | | 104 | | 210/688-9758 |
| © Sch of Sci & Tech-Houston [320]<br>16200 Tx 249, Houston 77086<br>Alpaslan Uzgoren | PK-8 | T | 474 | 62% | 346/270-2101<br>Fax 346/270-2187 |
| © Sch of Sci & Tech-Spring [320]<br>2105 Louetta Rd, Spring 77388<br>Murat Atakov | PK-6 | | 118 | | 832/698-2179 |
| © Sch of Sci & Tech-Sugarland [320]<br>10007 Clodine Rd, Richmond 77407 | K-5 | | 118 | 80% | 281/277-7923 |

© Seashore Learning Center | K-4 | | 280 | 1% | 361/949-1222
15801 S Padre Island Dr Ste A, Corp Christi 78418 | | | 14 | | Fax 361/949-6762
Cherryl Carroll

© Seashore Middle Academy | 5-8 | | 207 | 3% | 361/654-1134
15437 S Padre Island Dr, Corp Christi 78418 | | | 11 | | Fax 361/654-1139
Barbara Beeler

© Ser-Ninos Charter Middle Sch | 6-8 | T | 262 | 96% | 713/592-6055
5610 Gulfton St, Houston 77081
Charmaine Constantine

© Ser-Ninos Charter School II | PK-5 | T | 308 | 99% | 713/432-9400
5919 Dashwood Dr, Houston 77081 | | | | | Fax 713/432-0624
Sheronda Oliphant

© Ser-Ninos Elementary | PK-5 | GT | 589 | 96% | 713/667-6145
5815 Alder Dr, Houston 77081 | | | 35 | | Fax 713/667-0645
Charmaine Constantine

Ⓐ Seton Home Charter Education | 9-12 | | 25 | 88% | 512/560-8132
© 1115 Mission Rd, San Antonio 78210
S Arnold

© Shekinah Radiance Acad-Garland | K-7 | | 91 | | 214/320-2500
10715 Garland Rd Ste 100, Dallas 75218
Trina Garnes

© Shsu CS-Brighton Academy | K-6 | | 110 | | 281/465-4111
10801 Falconwing Dr, The Woodlands 77381
Renee O'Neal

© Shsu CS-Cypress Trails | K-2 | | 260 | | 936/294-3229
22801 Aldine Westfield Rd, Spring 77373
Renee Oneal

© Shsu CS-Greengate Academy | K-4 | | 109 | | 281/288-0880
18490 Kuykendahl Rd, Spring 77379
Katie Statlander

© Shsu CS-Little Geniuses Acad | K-1 | | 99 | | 832/995-5916
150 Isaacks Rd, Humble 77338 | | | | | Fax 832/218-3758
Tanassa Joseph

Ⓐ Southwest Prep New Directions [323] | 6-12 | T | 116 | 90% | 210/829-8017
© 1258 Austin Hwy Bldg 1, San Antonio 78209 | | | | | Fax 210/829-8514
Carolyn Martinez

© Southwest Prep Sch NE [323] | PK-12 | TV | 225 | 89% | 210/829-8017
1258 Austin Hwy, San Antonio 78209 | | | 8 | | Fax 210/829-8514
Laura Rangel

© Southwest Prep Sch NW [323] | 6-12 | T | 339 | 81% | 210/432-2634
6535 Culebra Rd, San Antonio 78238 | | | | | Fax 210/432-5482
Sheryl Wills-Pacheco

© Southwest Prep Sch SE [323] | PK-12 | T | 204 | 89% | 210/333-1403
735 S WW White Rd, San Antonio 78220 | | | | | Fax 210/333-3024
Dr Geneva Ricowatson

© Southwest Prep-Seguin [323] | PK-8 | T | 210 | 65% | 830/549-5930
2400 E Walnut St, Seguin 78155 | | | | | Fax 830/433-4534
Sherry Head

© Southwest Preparatory-NW ES | PK-5 | T | 86 | 95% | 210/819-7860
4151 Culebra Rd, San Antonio 78228 | | | | | Fax 210/438-8523
Cheryl Wills-Pacheco

© Southwest Sch-Bissonnet [293] | PK-5 | T | 377 | 96% | 713/988-5839
8440 Bissonnet St, Houston 77074 | | | | | Fax 713/270-0076
Pamela Sailors

Ⓐ Southwest Sch-Discovery MS [293] | 6-8 | T | 104 | 88% | 713/954-9528
© 6400 Westpark Dr Ste 200, Houston 77057 | | | 25 | | Fax 713/785-1014
Deborah Silber

© Southwest Sch-Empowerment HS [293] | 9-12 | T | 361 | 86% | 713/954-9528
6400 Westpark Dr Ste 200, Houston 77057
Bianca Clark

© Southwest Sch-Mangum [293] | K-5 | T | 132 | 92% | 713/688-0505
4515 Mangum Rd, Houston 77092 | | | | | Fax 713/688-3386
Ruben Gomez

© Southwest Schools-Phoenix [293] | K-12 | T | 132 | 63% | 346/571-6060
6400 Westpark Dr, Houston 77057 | | | | | Fax 346/571-6061
Tonya Woods

© St Anthony Academy | K-8 | T | 204 | 77% | 214/421-3645
3732 Myrtle St, Dallas 75215 | | | 13
Onjaleke Brown

© St Mary's Academy Charter Sch | K-6 | T | 430 | 83% | 361/358-5601
410 N Tyler St, Beeville 78102 | | | 15 | | Fax 361/358-5704
Hirma Elizondo

Staggs Acad Intl STEM Studies | 11-12 | | 100 | | 956/326-2861
5201 University Blvd, Laredo 78041 | | | | | Fax 956/326-2429
Dr Patricia Uribe

© STEM Acadmy-Lewisville | 6-12 | | 376 | 18% | 972/316-6700
650 Bennett Ln, Lewisville 75057 | | | | | Fax 972/316-6705
Carolyn Anderson

© Step Charter School II | K-6 | T | 300 | 93% | 281/988-7797
11250 S Wilcrest Dr, Houston 77099 | | | | | Fax 281/988-7736
William Clark

© Stephen F Austin Univ CS | K-5 | | 256 | 6% | 936/468-5899
2428 Raguet St, Nacogdoches 75965 | | | 6 | | Fax 936/468-7015
Lysa Hagan

© Tekoa Academy-Orange [324] | PK-8 | | 146 | | 409/886-9864
1408 W Park Ave, Orange 77630 | | | | | Fax 409/886-0961
Princess Chretien

© Tekoa Academy-Port Arthur [324] | PK-12 | T | 420 | 90% | 409/982-5400
327 Thomas Blvd, Port Arthur 77640 | | | 14 | | Fax 409/982-9711
Paula Richardson

© Temple Charter Academy [316] | PK-12 | T | 280 | 71% | 254/206-2013
7177 Airport Rd, Temple 76502 | | | 8 | | Fax 254/853-4144
Devera Shipp

© Texans Can Acad Carrltn-Farmrs [325] | 9-12 | T | 333 | 98% | 972/243-2178
2720 Hollandale Ln, Dallas 75234 | | | 20 | | Fax 972/243-2669
Alba Marrerro

Ⓐ Texans Can Acad Dallas North [325] | 9-12 | G | 273 | | 214/824-4226
© 9704 Skillman St, Dallas 75243 | | | 30 | | Fax 214/234-8617
Rufus Johnson

© Texans Can Acad Dallas Pl Grv [325] | 9-12 | T | 540 | 71% | 972/225-1194
1227 N Masters Dr, Dallas 75217 | | | | | Fax 972/225-1164
Mene Khepera

© Texans Can Acad Fw Lancaster [325] | 9-12 | | 413 | | 817/735-1515
1316 E Lancaster Ave, Fort Worth 76102 | | | 15 | | Fax 817/735-1465
Philip Tucker

© Texans Can Acad Fw Westcreek [325] | 9-12 | AGT | 347 | 80% | 817/531-3223
6620 Westcreek Dr, Fort Worth 76133 | | | 14 | | Fax 817/292-3432
Ku-Masi Lewis

Ⓐ Texans Can Acad Garland [325] | 9-12 | | 224 | | 972/441-7202
© 2256 Arapaho Rd, Garland 75044
Daniel Johnson

© Texans Can Acad Houston Hobby [325] | 9-12 | | 347 | | 832/379-4226
9020 Gulf Fwy, Houston 77017 | | | | | Fax 713/944-6736
Yardley Williams

© Texans Can Acad Houston North [325] | 9-12 | AG | 443 | | 713/659-4226
3401 Hardy St, Houston 77009 | | | 28 | | Fax 713/651-1493
Leon Gilmore

© Texans Can Acad Houston SW [325] | 9-12 | | 309 | | 281/918-4316
9745 Bissonnet St, Houston 77036 | | | | | Fax 713/271-0257
Justin Reyes

© Texans Can Acad San Antonio [325] | 9-12 | | 359 | | 210/923-1226
1807 Centennial Blvd, San Antonio 78211 | | | 16 | | Fax 210/928-3366
Debra Cruz

Ⓐ Texans Can Acad-Oak Cliff [325] | 9-12 | GT | 585 | 91% | 214/943-2244
© 325 W 12th St, Dallas 75208 | | | 31 | | Fax 214/943-8899
Cynthia Miles

Ⓐ Texans Can Academy Austin [325] | 9-12 | | 405 | | 512/477-4226
© 2406 Rosewood Ave, Austin 78702 | | | 13 | | Fax 512/477-4223
William Arevalo

© Texans Can Academy-Grant East [325] | 9-12 | | 336 | | 972/228-4226
2901 Morgan Dr, Dallas 75241
Rodney Milliner

| 1 | Superintendent | 8 | Curric/Instruct K-12 | 19 | Chief Financial Officer | 29 | Family/Consumer Science | 39 | Social Studies K-12 | 49 | English/Lang Arts Elem | 59 | Special Education Elem | 69 | Academic Assessment |
| 2 | Bus/Finance/Purchasing | 9 | Curric/Instruct Elem | 20 | Art K-12 | 30 | Adult Education | 40 | Social Studies Elem | 50 | English/Lang Arts Sec | 60 | Special Education Sec | 70 | Research/Development |
| 3 | Buildings And Grounds | 10 | Curric/Instruct Sec | 21 | Art Elem | 31 | Career/Sch-to-Work K-12 | 41 | Social Studies Sec | 51 | Reading K-12 | 61 | Foreign/World Lang K-12 | 71 | Public Information |
| 4 | Food Service | 11 | Federal Program | 22 | Art Sec | 32 | Career/Sch-to-Work Elem | 42 | Science K-12 | 52 | Reading Elem | 62 | Foreign/World Lang Elem | 72 | Summer School |
| 5 | Transportation | 12 | Title I | 23 | Music K-12 | 33 | Career/Sch-to-Work Sec | 43 | Science Elem | 53 | Reading Sec | 63 | Instructional Tech | 73 | Instructional Tech |
| 6 | Athletic | 13 | Title V | 24 | Music Elem | 34 | Early Childhood Ed | 44 | Science Sec | 54 | Remedial Reading K-12 | 64 | Religious Education K-12 | 74 | Inservice Training |
| 7 | Health Services | 15 | Asst Superintendent | 25 | Music Sec | 35 | Health/Phys Education | 45 | Math K-12 | 55 | Remedial Reading Elem | 65 | Religious Education Elem | 75 | Marketing/Distributive |
| | | 16 | Instructional Media Svcs | 26 | Business Education | 36 | Guidance Services K-12 | 46 | Math Elem | 56 | Remedial Reading Sec | 66 | Religious Education Sec | 76 | Info Systems |
| | | 17 | Chief Operations Officer | 27 | Career & Tech Ed | 37 | Guidance Services Elem | 47 | Math Sec | 57 | Bilingual/ELL | 67 | School Board President | 77 | Psychological Assess |
| | | 18 | Chief Academic Officer | 28 | Technology Education | 38 | Guidance Services Sec | 48 | English/Lang Arts K-12 | 58 | Special Education K-12 | 68 | Teacher Personnel | 78 | Affirmative Action |

## TX—14

# Texas School Directory

| School / Address / Personnel | Grades | Prog | Enroll | % | Phone / Fax |
|---|---|---|---|---|---|
| Texas Academy Math & Science<br>1167 Union Circle Rm 320, Denton 76201<br>Glenisson DeOliveira | 11-12 | | 350 | | 940/565-3606<br>Fax 940/369-8696 |
| © Texas Early College High Sch [314]<br>3714 E End Blvd S, Marshall 75672<br>Bob Garcia | 8-12 | | 48 | 37% | 903/935-4109<br>Fax 903/935-4067 |
| Texas Empowerment Academy<br>6414 N Hampton Dr, Austin 78723<br>David Nowlin | 3-11 | T | 214 | 88% | 512/928-0118<br>Fax 512/928-0128 |
| © Texas Empowerment Academy<br>3613 Bluestein Dr, Austin 78721<br>Neisha Nunn | K-2 | T | 100<br>10 | 85% | 512/494-1076<br>Fax 512/494-1009 |
| © Texas Leadership Charter Acad<br>5687 Melrose Ave, San Angelo 76901<br>Eric Haire \ Crystella Morales \ Johnny Burleson | K-12 | | 1,301 | | 325/653-3200<br>Fax 325/942-6795  [f] |
| © Texas Leadership CS-Abilene<br>1840 N 8th St, Abilene 79603<br>Carmen Crane | PK-12 | T | 429 | 62% | 325/480-3500<br>Fax 325/672-2631 |
| © Texas Leadership CS-Arlington<br>2001 Brown Blvd, Arlington 76006<br>Brooke Morrison \ Ron Carroll | K-10 | T | 468 | 73% | 817/385-9338<br>Fax 817/861-1242 |
| © Texas Leadership CS-Midland<br>3300 Thomas Ave, Midland 79703<br>Maggie Speed | K-10 | T | 549 | 36% | 432/242-7117<br>Fax 432/262-0994 |
| © Texas Prep School-San Marcos<br>400 Uhland Rd, San Marcos 78666<br>Brandy Strait | K-6 | T | 120<br>4 | 63% | 512/805-3000<br>Fax 512/805-7739  [f][t] |
| © Texas Preparatory Sch-Austin<br>7540 Ed Bluestein Blvd, Austin 78723<br>Daphne McDole | K-6 | T | 108 | 81% | 512/928-3000 |
| Texas Sch Blind & Visually Imp<br>1100 W 45th St, Austin 78756<br>Miles Fain | Spec | T | 150 | 81% | 512/454-8631<br>Fax 512/206-9450 |
| Texas School for the Deaf<br>1102 S Congress Ave, Austin 78704<br>Barbara Hussey \ Brian Sipek \ Karlin Hummel | Spec | TV | 524 | 56% | 512/462-5353<br>Fax 512/462-5313 |
| © Texas School of the Arts [326]<br>6025 Village Pkwy, Edgecliff Vlg 76134<br>Betsy Compton | K-6 | | 332<br>14 | 2% | 817/732-8372<br>Fax 817/732-8373 |
| Ⓐ Texas Serenity Academy<br>© 8500 Sweetwater Ln, Houston 77037<br>Michelle Foreman | K-8 | | 315 | | 281/820-9540<br>Fax 281/820-6204 |
| © Texas Serenity Academy-Gano<br>4637 Gano St, Houston 77009<br>Michelle Foreman | K-5 | T | 93 | 97% | 713/699-3443<br>Fax 713/699-3929 |
| © Texas Virtual Acad Hallsville<br>1955 Lakeway Dr Ste 250B, Lewisville 75057<br>Daphne Troxell \ Shelby Newman | K-12 | | 6,477 | | 866/360-0161 |
| © The Excel Center Austin [169]<br>1015 Norwood Park Blvd, Austin 78753<br>Charles Moody | Adult | | 300 | | 512/531-5500<br>Fax 512/339-5299 |
| © The Lawson Academy<br>5052 Scott St, Houston 77004<br>Dr Marthea Raney | 6-8 | | 200<br>6 | | 713/225-1551<br>Fax 713/225-1561 |
| © The Varnett School-SW [332]<br>5025 S Willow Dr, Houston 77035<br>Toni Fisher | PK-6 | T | 600 | 81% | 713/723-4699<br>Fax 713/723-5853 |
| © The Woodlands Classical Acad [318]<br>6565 Research Forest Dr, The Woodlands 77381<br>Roxana Butler | K-8 | | 387 | | 936/242-1541<br>Fax 866/688-8037 |
| Ⓐ Thomas Buzbee Vocational Sch<br>© 143 Forest Service Road 233, New Waverly 77358<br>Will Gollihar | 9-12 | TV | 81<br>15 | 97% | 936/344-7238<br>Fax 936/344-6396 |
| © Treetops International Sch<br>12500 S Pipeline Rd, Euless 76040<br>Lou Blancher | K-12 | V | 391<br>23 | 19% | 817/283-1771<br>Fax 817/684-0892  [t] |
| © Trinity Basin Prep-10th Street [327]<br>831 W 10th St Ste B, Dallas 75208<br>Candee Martinez | PK-4 | | 590 | | 214/296-9302<br>Fax 214/296-9306 |
| © Trinity Basin Prep-Ewing [327]<br>808 N Ewing Ave, Dallas 75203<br>Jose Carrillo | PK-4 | T | 511 | 91% | 214/942-8846 |
| © Trinity Basin Prep-Ft Worth [327]<br>101 E Pafford St, Fort Worth 76110<br>Jodi Rebarchek | PK-8 | T | 950 | 88% | 817/840-7501<br>Fax 817/840-7502 |
| © Trinity Basin Prep-Jefferson [327]<br>855 E 8th St, Dallas 75203<br>Jennifer Masten | 5-8 | | 750 | | 214/941-4881<br>Fax 214/941-4866 |
| © Trinity Charter Sch-Amarillo [328]<br>4655 S FM 1258, Amarillo 79118<br>Jennifer Chappell | 7-12 | | 10 | | 512/706-7566 |
| © Trinity Charter Sch-Big Sandy [328]<br>1085 Private Road 34814, Big Sandy 75755<br>Nicki Cornejo | 1-12 | | 30 | | 903/565-6801<br>Fax 903/636-9010 |
| © Trinity Charter Sch-Bokenkamp [328]<br>5517 S Alameda St, Corp Christi 78412<br>Hilda Vega | K-8 | | 150 | | 361/994-1214 |
| © Trinity Charter Sch-Brenham [328]<br>4150 Highway 36 S, Brenham 77833<br>Sandra Blasser | 6-12 | | 40 | | 281/392-7505 |
| © Trinity Charter Sch-Ft Worth [328]<br>3001 Grayson St, Fort Worth 76119<br>Nicki Cornejo | 6-12 | | 40 | | 903/565-6801 |
| © Trinity Charter Sch-Landing [328]<br>2058 FM 665 Rd, Corp Christi 78415<br>Kellie Ragland | 6-12 | | 18 | | 361/217-3185 |
| © Trinity Charter Sch-New Hope [328]<br>1000 N McColl Rd, McAllen 78501<br>Hilga Vega | 3-10 | | 58 | | 361/563-7979 |
| © Trinity Charter Sch-New Life [328]<br>650 Scarbourough, Canyon Lake 78133<br>Joshua Machicek | 4-12 | T | 58<br>10 | 95% | 830/964-4390<br>Fax 830/964-4376 |
| Ⓐ Trinity Charter Sch-Parke [328]<br>© 262 N Houston Pkwy, Houston 77060<br>Sandra Blasser | K-12 | | 40 | | 361/994-1214 |
| © Trinity Charter Sch-Willow Bnd [328]<br>2902 State Highway 31 E, Tyler 75702<br>Nicki Cornejo | K-12 | T | 36 | 95% | 512/459-1000 |
| © Trinity Charter School-Krause [328]<br>25752 Kingsland Blvd, Katy 77494<br>Sandra Blasser | 6-12 | T | 57 | 94% | 281/392-7505<br>Fax 281/392-7560 |
| © Trinity Charter School-Pegasus [328]<br>896 Robin Ranch Rd, Lockhart 78644<br>Keely Reynolds | 3-12 | T | 146 | 98% | 512/432-1655<br>Fax 512/432-1653 |
| © Trinity Charter School-Spring [328]<br>2929 FM 2920 Rd, Spring 77388<br>Sandra Flores | 8-11 | | 20 | | 512/706-7566 |
| © Triumph Public HS-Brownsville [329]<br>944 E Los Ebanos Blvd, Brownsville 78520<br>Yolanda Chamberlain | 9-12 | T | 130 | 83% | 956/372-1433<br>Fax 956/801-2052 |
| © Triumph Public HS-El Paso East [329]<br>1599 George Dieter Dr, El Paso 79936<br>Luis Liano | 9-12 | T | 130 | 89% | 915/298-3637<br>Fax 915/298-3644 |
| © Triumph Public HS-El Paso West [329]<br>711 N Mesa St, El Paso 79902<br>Patricia Ramos | 9-12 | T | 105<br>15 | 97% | 915/532-7216<br>Fax 915/356-2205 |
| Ⓐ Triumph Public HS-Laredo South [329]<br>© 4620 S Lucy Ave, Laredo 78046<br>Gerardo Arambula | 9-12 | T | 130 | 92% | 956/723-0345<br>Fax 956/712-1112 |
| Ⓐ Triumph Public HS-Loredo North [329]<br>© 1230 Townlake Dr, Laredo 78041<br>Olga Trevino | 9-12 | GT | 150<br>15 | 84% | 956/722-0747<br>Fax 956/722-0767 |

| School | Grades | | Enroll | % | Phone |
|---|---|---|---|---|---|
| © Triumph Public HS-Lubbock [329]<br>4008 Avenue R, Lubbock 79412<br>Trent Cook | 9-12 | T | 216<br>16 | 92% | 806/744-0330<br>Fax 806/744-1341 |
| Ⓐ Triumph Public HS-McAllen [329]<br>© 200 N 17th St, McAllen 78501<br>Serena Mari Garcia | 9-12 | T | 63<br>8 | 96% | 956/618-2303<br>Fax 956/618-2323 |
| © Triumph Public HS-Mercedes [329]<br>103 E 2nd St, Mercedes 78570<br>Miscellene Pemelton | 9-12 | T | 81 | 98% | 956/565-5417<br>Fax 956/514-2586 |
| Ⓐ Triumph Public HS-San Benito [329]<br>© 1785 W Business Hwy 77, San Benito 78586<br>Dr Hans Schuller | 9-12 | | 123 | | 956/276-9930<br>Fax 956/276-9943 |
| © Trivium Academy<br>2205 E Hebron Pkwy, Carrollton 75010<br>Marsha Cawthon | K-8 | | 593 | 3% | 469/855-5531 |
| © Two Dimensions Prep Academy [330]<br>12121 Veterans Memorial Dr, Houston 77067<br>Deateria Akan | PK-5 | T | 209<br>14 | 94% | 281/227-4700<br>Fax 832/232-0032 |
| © Two Dimensions Prep-Vickery [330]<br>12330 Vickery St, Houston 77039<br>Shirley Harris | PK-5 | | 223 | | 281/227-4700<br>Fax 281/987-7306 |
| © Two Dimensions-Corsicana [330]<br>901 E 10th Ave, Corsicana 75110<br>Shirley Harris | PK-1 | | 50 | | 281/227-4700 |
| © Tyler Classical Academy [318]<br>3405 E Grande Blvd, Tyler 75707<br>Paula Biddle | K-10 | T | 451 | 46% | 903/504-5690 |
| © Ume Prep Acad-Dallas<br>3838 Spur 408, Dallas 75236<br>Valentin Celis | K-12 | T | 625 | 30% | 214/445-6243<br>Fax 972/709-7951 |
| © Ume Prep Acad-Duncanville<br>415 N Cedar Ridge Dr, Duncanville 75116<br>Shannon Horton | K-6 | T | 219 | 51% | 972/296-0084 |
| © Univ of Houston Charter Sch<br>3855 Holman St, Houston 77204<br>Patricia Paquin | K-5 | T | 135<br>6 | 49% | 713/743-9111<br>Fax 713/743-3912 |
| © Univ TX Charter High Sch<br>1616 Guadalupe St Ste 134, Austin 78701<br>Aidan Callahan | 9-12 | | 100 | | 512/232-5000 |
| © Universal Academy-Coppell<br>1001 E Sandy Lake Rd, Coppell 75019<br>Dr Dana Job | K-12 | | 1,339 | 3% | 972/393-5834<br>Fax 972/393-5657 |
| © Universal Academy-Irving<br>2616 N MacArthur Blvd, Irving 75062<br>Sheraton Duffey | PK-12 | T | 719 | 84% | 972/255-1800<br>Fax 972/255-6122 |
| Ⓐ University High Sch<br>© 2007 University Ave, Austin 78705<br>Holly Engleman | 9-12 | | 22 | 18% | 512/382-0072 |
| © University of Texas Elem CS<br>2200 E 6th St, Austin 78702<br>Dr Nicole Whetstone | PK-5 | T | 298 | 57% | 512/495-3300<br>Fax 512/495-9631 |
| © Uplift Ascend Preparatory [331]<br>3301 Turf Paradise Pkwy, Fort Worth 76140<br>Kaitlin McDermott | PK-8 | | 300 | | 817/768-4300 |
| © Uplift Elevate Preparatory [331]<br>10800 Chapin Rd, Fort Worth 76108<br>Karen Salerno \ William Stubbs | K-6 | | 198 | | 817/764-3600 |
| © Uplift Gradus Preparatory [331]<br>121 Seahawk Dr, Desoto 75115<br>Sharon Duplantier | PK-5 | T | 599 | 84% | 214/451-5551 |
| © Uplift Grand Preparatory [331]<br>300 E Church St, Grand Prairie 75050<br>Sarah Chambers \ Allen Anderson | PK-10 | T | 288 | 81% | 972/854-0600 |
| © Uplift Hampton Prep Chtr Sch [331]<br>8915 S Hampton Rd, Dallas 75232<br>Kecia Clark \ Andrea Anderson \ Brady Cooper | K-12 | T | 435 | 83% | 972/421-1982<br>Fax 972/421-1986 |
| © Uplift Heights Prep Prim Sch [331]<br>2202 Calypso St, Dallas 75212<br>Kristin Algier | PK-5 | T | 997 | 92% | 214/873-9700 |
| © Uplift Heights Prep Sch Sec [331]<br>2650 Canada Dr, Dallas 75212<br>Elizabeth Kastiel | 6-12 | T | 1,500 | 89% | 214/442-7094 |
| © Uplift Infinity Prep Sch [331]<br>1401 S MacArthur Blvd, Irving 75060<br>Sarah Hobson \ Arlene Barochin \ Mark Forman | PK-12 | T | 387 | 78% | 469/621-9200<br>Fax 469/621-9191 |
| © Uplift Luna Prep Primary [331]<br>2020 N Lamar St, Dallas 75202<br>Karen Aldridge | PK-5 | T | 507 | 87% | 214/442-7882<br>Fax 214/442-7887 |
| © Uplift Luna Prep Secondary [331]<br>2625 Elm St, Dallas 75226<br>Jeffery Kirby \ Katie Woodiel | 6-12 | T | 250 | 81% | 214/445-3300 |
| © Uplift Meridian Preparatory [331]<br>1801 S Beach St, Fort Worth 76105<br>Shalon Campbell | PK-5 | T | 600 | 90% | 817/288-1700<br>Fax 817/288-1692 |
| © Uplift Mighty Preparatory Acad [331]<br>3700 Mighty Mite Dr, Fort Worth 76105<br>Christian Woods \ Sharla Williams \ Tracy Odom | K-12 | T | 566 | 87% | 817/288-3800 |
| © Uplift North Hills Prep Sch [331]<br>606 E Royal Ln, Irving 75039<br>Nicole Wallin \ George Rutzen \ Heather Pereira | K-12 | T | 1,583<br>12 | 22% | 972/501-0645<br>Fax 972/501-9439 |
| © Uplift Peak Prep Sch [331]<br>4600 Bryan St, Dallas 75204<br>Leetha Harper \ Jamila Thomas \ Samina Noorani | PK-12 | T | 423 | 88% | 214/276-0879<br>Fax 214/276-5207 |
| © Uplift Pinnacle Prep Primary [331]<br>2510 S Vernon Ave, Dallas 75224<br>Katie Leinenkugel | K-5 | T | 577 | 89% | 214/442-6100<br>Fax 214/442-6181 |
| © Uplift Summit Int'l Prep CS [331]<br>1305 N Center St, Arlington 76011<br>Amanda Dudley \ Aleia Mims \ Tracy Odom | K-12 | | 1,000 | | 817/287-5121<br>Fax 817/287-0532 |
| © Uplift Triumph Preparatory [331]<br>9411 Hargrove Dr, Dallas 75220<br>Christine Denison | PK-5 | T | 581 | 94% | 972/590-5100<br>Fax 972/590-5199 |
| © Uplift White Rock Hills Prep [331]<br>7370 Valley Glen Dr, Dallas 75228<br>Christine Lipschitz | PK-4 | T | 400 | 87% | 469/914-7500<br>Fax 469/914-7561 |
| © Uplift Williams Prep Chtr Sch [331]<br>1750 Viceroy Dr, Dallas 75235<br>Kevin Valdez | K-12 | T | 445 | 93% | 214/276-0352<br>Fax 214/637-6393 |
| © Uplift Wisdom Prep Primary Sch [331]<br>301 W Camp Wisdom Rd, Dallas 75232<br>Karen Salerno | K-3 | | 401 | | 972/330-7291 |
| © Uplift Wisdom Prep Sec Sch [331]<br>301 W Camp Wisdom Rd, Dallas 75232<br>Jacob Stainbrook | 6-10 | T | 401 | 92% | 972/330-7291 |
| Ⓐ UT Univ CS-Annunciation<br>© 3610 Shell Rd, Georgetown 78628<br>Cristy Cunningham | 8-12 | | 29 | | 512/654-7755 |
| © UT Univ CS-Laurel Ridge<br>17720 Corporate Woods Dr, San Antonio 78259<br>Sally Arnold | K-12 | A | 40 | 25% | 210/491-9400<br>Fax 210/491-3550 |
| Ⓐ UT Univ CS-Memorial Hermann<br>© 3043 Gessner Rd, Houston 77080<br>Dorothy Goodman | 7-12 | | 25 | | 713/939-7272<br>Fax 713/329-7485 |
| © UT Univ CS-Methodist Children<br>1111 Herring Ave, Waco 76708<br>Michelle Arocha | 6-12 | AT | 97 | 97% | 512/471-4864 |
| © UT Univ CS-Settlement Home<br>1600 Payton Gin Rd, Austin 78758<br>Holly Engleman | 6-12 | AT | 39 | 91% | 512/836-2150<br>Fax 512/836-2159 |
| © Utpb STEM Academy<br>4901 E University Blvd, Odessa 79762<br>Monica Elizondo \ Cody Griffen | K-10 | | 721 | 19% | 432/552-2580 |

| | | | |
|---|---|---|---|
| 1 Superintendent | 8 Curric/Instruct K-12 | 19 Chief Financial Officer | 29 Family/Consumer Science |
| 2 Bus/Finance/Purchasing | 9 Curric/Instruct Elem | 20 Art K-12 | 30 Adult Education |
| 3 Buildings And Grounds | 10 Curric/Instruct Sec | 21 Art Elem | 31 Career/Sch-to-Work K-12 |
| 4 Food Service | 11 Federal Program | 22 Art Sec | 32 Career/Sch-to-Work Elem |
| 5 Transportation | 12 Title I | 23 Music K-12 | 33 Career/Sch-to-Work Sec |
| 6 Athletic | 13 Title V | 24 Music Elem | 34 Early Childhood Ed |
| 7 Health Services | 15 Asst Superintendent | 25 Music Sec | 35 Health/Phys Education |
| | 16 Instructional Media Svcs | 26 Business Education | 36 Guidance Services K-12 |
| | 17 Chief Operations Officer | 27 Career & Tech Ed | 37 Guidance Services Elem |
| | 18 Chief Academic Officer | 28 Technology Education | 38 Guidance Services Sec |

| | | |
|---|---|---|
| 39 Social Studies K-12 | 49 English/Lang Arts Elem | 59 Special Education Elem |
| 40 Social Studies Elem | 50 English/Lang Arts Sec | 60 Special Education Sec |
| 41 Social Studies Sec | 51 Reading K-12 | 61 Foreign/World Lang K-12 |
| 42 Science K-12 | 52 Reading Elem | 62 Foreign/World Lang Elem |
| 43 Science Elem | 53 Reading Sec | 63 Foreign/World Lang Sec |
| 44 Science Sec | 54 Remedial Reading K-12 | 64 Religious Education K-12 |
| 45 Math K-12 | 55 Remedial Reading Elem | 65 Religious Education Elem |
| 46 Math Elem | 56 Remedial Reading Sec | 66 Religious Education Sec |
| 47 Math Sec | 57 Bilingual/ELL | 67 School Board President |
| 48 English/Lang Arts K-12 | 58 Special Education K-12 | 68 Teacher Personnel |

| |
|---|
| 69 Academic Assessment |
| 70 Research/Development |
| 71 Public Information |
| 72 Summer School |
| 73 Instructional Tech |
| 74 Inservice Training |
| 75 Marketing/Distributive |
| 76 Info Systems |
| 77 Psychological Assess |
| 78 Affirmative Action |

| School | Grades | Title | Enrollment | % | Phone |
|---|---|---|---|---|---|
| © Valor South Austin<br>220 Foremost Dr, Austin 78745<br>Steve Gordon | K-9 | | 450 | 25% | 512/646-4170 |
| © Vanguard Academy-Beethoven<br>2215 S Veterans Blvd, Edinburg 78539<br>R Salinas \ Angelica Martinez | PK-8 | T | 978 | 80% | 956/318-0211<br>Fax 956/318-0220 |
| © Vanguard Academy-Mozart<br>155 E Business 83, Alamo 78516<br>Federico Gonzalez | PK-5 | | 400 | | 956/702-2548<br>Fax 956/702-2731 |
| © Vanguard Academy-Picasso<br>901 S Athol St, Pharr 78577<br>Zacarias Martinez | PK-5 | T | 585 | 82% | 956/702-0134<br>Fax 956/702-0166 |
| © Vanguard Academy-Rembrandt<br>1200 E Kelly Ave, Pharr 78577<br>Maria Farias | PK-12 | | 1,693 | | 956/781-1701<br>Fax 956/781-8055 |
| © Varnett School Southeast [332]<br>12707 Cullen Blvd, Houston 77047<br>Jessika Hearne | PK-8 | T | 209 | 45% | 713/726-7654 |
| © Varnett School-East [332]<br>804A Maxey Rd, Houston 77013<br>Gayle Voltz | PK-6 | T | 361 | 75% | 713/637-6574<br>Fax 713/637-8319 |
| © Varnett School-NE [332]<br>8305 Mesa Dr, Houston 77028<br>Dr T Wooldridge | PK-8 | T | 501 | 74% | 713/631-4396 |
| © Village Technical Sch<br>402 W Danieldale Rd, Duncanville 75137<br>Brandi Olmstead \ Schretta Mays | PK-12 | T | 1,115 | 41% | 469/454-4441<br>Fax 409/454-4442 |
| © Vista Del Futuro Charter Sch<br>1671 Bob Hope Dr, El Paso 79936<br>Ana Candelaria | PK-7 | T | 368 | 61% | 915/855-8143<br>Fax 915/855-8179 🅃 |
| Waco Center for Youth-Spec Ed<br>3501 N 19th St, Waco 76708<br>Charles Freeto | Spec | | 65<br>11 | | 254/756-2171<br>Fax 254/745-5398 |
| © Waco Charter Sch<br>615 N 25th St, Waco 76707<br>Nancy Cross | PK-5 | T | 240<br>15 | 98% | 254/754-8169<br>Fax 254/754-7389 |
| © Walipp Tsu Prep Academy<br>5052 Scott St, Houston 77004<br>Marthea Raney | 6-8 | | 190 | | 713/741-3600<br>Fax 713/741-3603 |
| © Wayside Altamira Academy<br>10704 Bradshaw Rd, Austin 78747 | PK-5 | T | 485 | 58% | 512/220-9105 |
| © Wayside Eden Park Academy<br>6215 Manchaca Rd, Austin 78745<br>Hope Astor | PK-5 | T | 346<br>14 | 45% | 512/358-1800 |
| © Wayside Real Learning Academy<br>6405 S Interstate 35, Austin 78744<br>Kierstin Howard | PK-5 | T | 665 | 66% | 512/438-7325 |
| © Wayside Sci-Tech Middle & HS<br>6405 S Interstate 35, Austin 78744<br>Brian Clason \ Tammy Underwood | 6-12 | T | 599 | 47% | 512/220-9120 |
| © Westlake Academy<br>2600 J T Ottinger Rd, Westlake 76262<br>Stacy Stoyanoff \ Rod Harding | K-12 | | 879<br>30 | 2% | 817/490-5757<br>Fax 817/490-5758 |
| © Willis Classical Academy [318]<br>202 S Thomason St, Willis 77378<br>Russell Shafer | K-8 | | 152 | | 936/890-0100 |
| © Winfree Academy-Dallas [333]<br>2550 Beckleymeade Ave Ste 170, Dallas 75237<br>Brad Landis | 9-12 | | 135 | | 469/930-5199<br>Fax 469/930-5206 |
| © Winfree Academy-Grand Prairie [333]<br>2985 S State Hwy 360 Ste 160, Grand Prairie 75052<br>Corrine Johnson | 9-12 | | 307 | | 214/204-2030<br>Fax 214/204-2034 |
| Ⓐ Winfree Academy-Irving [333]<br>© 3110 Skyway Cir S, Irving 75038<br>Ridwan Williams | 9-12 | | 168<br>6 | | 972/251-2010<br>Fax 972/251-4301 |
| Ⓐ Winfree Academy-Lewisville [333]<br>© 341 Bennett Ln, Lewisville 75057<br>David Stubblefield | 9-12 | | 161<br>4 | | 214/222-2200<br>Fax 214/222-0201 |
| © Winfree Academy-N Rchlnd Hills [333]<br>6311 Boulevard 26, Richland Hls 76180<br>Tiranus Edwards | 9-12 | T | 259 | 68% | 817/590-2240<br>Fax 817/590-8724 |
| Ⓐ Winfree Academy-Richardson [333]<br>© 1661 Gateway Blvd, Richardson 75080<br>Madge Ennis | 9-12 | | 287 | | 972/234-9855<br>Fax 972/234-9975 |
| © Yellowstone Clg Prep CS<br>3000 Trulley St Ste 200, Houston 77004<br>Diedra Lawson | 5-9 | T | 255 | 92% | 713/655-0596 |
| © YES Prep Brays Oaks [334]<br>9000 W Bellfort St, Houston 77031<br>Stephanie Gounder | 6-12 | T | 964 | 83% | 713/967-8400<br>Fax 713/778-0917 |
| © YES Prep East End [334]<br>8329 Lawndale St, Houston 77012<br>Aaron Simmons | 6-12 | T | 945<br>8 | 87% | 713/967-7800<br>Fax 713/589-2502 |
| © YES Prep Fifth Ward [334]<br>1305 Benson St, Houston 77020<br>Antonio Castillo | 6-12 | T | 930 | 85% | 713/924-0600<br>Fax 713/670-0032 |
| © YES Prep Gulfton [334]<br>6565 De Moss Dr, Houston 77074<br>Oscar Romano \ Cintia Arenas | 6-12 | T | 1,078 | 97% | 713/967-9800<br>Fax 713/744-1808 |
| © YES Prep Hobby [334]<br>8787 Tallyho Rd, Houston 77061<br>Chase Sander | 6-12 | | 160 | | 713/842-5600 |
| © YES Prep Hoffman [334]<br>6101 W Little York Rd, Houston 77091<br>Chase Sander | 6-8 | | 402 | | 713/924-5400<br>Fax 866/618-3781 |
| © YES Prep North Centrl [334]<br>13703 Aldine Westfield Rd, Houston 77039<br>Jeffrey Osborne | 6-12 | T | 968 | 83% | 281/227-2044<br>Fax 281/227-2090 |
| © YES Prep North Forest [334]<br>6602 Winfield Rd, Houston 77050<br>James Mosley \ Bryce Moore | 6-12 | T | 941 | 87% | 713/967-8600<br>Fax 281/442-4466 |
| © YES Prep Northbrook MS [334]<br>3030 Rosefield Dr, Houston 77080<br>Eric Newcomer | 6-8 | | 435 | | 713/251-4200<br>Fax 713/251-4209 |
| © YES Prep Northline [334]<br>5815 Airline Dr, Houston 77076<br>Brittany McGruder | 6-7 | T | 298 | 86% | 713/842-5400 |
| © YES Prep Northside [334]<br>5215 Jensen Dr, Houston 77026<br>Maureen Israel | 6-12 | T | 945 | 85% | 713/924-0400 |
| © YES Prep NW [334]<br>14741 Yorktown Plaza Dr, Houston 77040<br>Laura Dugan | 6-12 | T | 280 | 82% | 713/842-5510 |
| © YES Prep Southeast [334]<br>353 Crenshaw Rd, Houston 77034<br>Eileen Galligan | 6-12 | T | 999<br>25 | 78% | 713/910-2510<br>Fax 713/910-2350 |
| © YES Prep Southside [334]<br>5515 South Loop E, Houston 77033<br>Jamie Downs | 6-9 | T | 636 | 92% | 713/924-5500 |
| © YES Prep Southwest [334]<br>4411 Anderson Rd, Houston 77053<br>Eric Espinoza | 6-12 | T | 977 | 88% | 713/413-0001<br>Fax 713/413-0003 🅵 |
| © YES Prep West [334]<br>10535 Harwin Dr, Houston 77036<br>Sara Kaveeshwar | 6-12 | T | 793 | 91% | 713/967-8200<br>Fax 713/541-8518 |
| © YES Prep White Oak [334]<br>5620 W Tidwell Rd, Houston 77091<br>Jennifer Greene | 6-11 | T | 787 | 92% | 713/924-5300<br>Fax 713/956-4874 |

## ANDERSON COUNTY

## ANDERSON PUBLIC SCHOOLS

• **Cayuga Ind School Dist** PID: 00994401     903/928-2102
17750 N US Highway 287, Tenn Colony 75861     Fax 903/928-2646

**Schools:** 1 \ **Teachers:** 50 \ **Students:** 564 \ **Special Ed Students:** 84 \ **LEP Students:** 3 \ **College-Bound:** 43% \ **Ethnic:** African American 3%, Hispanic 6%, Caucasian 91% \ **Exp:** $379 (High) \ **Poverty:** 16% \ **Title I:** $139,561 \ **Special Education:** $73,000 \ **Open-Close:** 08/19 - 05/21 \ **DTBP:** $350 (High)

| | | | |
|---|---|---|---|
| Dr Rick Webb | 1,11,288 | Kellie Gatewood | 2 |
| Leslie Glad | 4 | Roy Feagins | 5 |
| Cody Mohan | 6* | Tim West | 67 |
| Jackie Willingham | 73,295* | Nancy Griffey | 83,85* |

| Public Schs..Principal | Grd | Prgm | Enr/#Cls | SN | |
|---|---|---|---|---|---|
| Cayuga Sch<br>17750 N US Highway 287, Tenn Colony 75861<br>Tracie Campbell \ Sherrie McInnis \ Jes Satterwhite | PK-12 | V | 564<br>58 | 39% | 903/928-2102 |

• **Elkhart Ind School Dist** PID: 00994437     903/764-2952
301 E Parker St, Elkhart 75839     Fax 903/764-2466

**Schools:** 4 \ **Teachers:** 106 \ **Students:** 1,250 \ **Special Ed Students:** 135 \ **LEP Students:** 22 \ **Ethnic:** African American 6%, Hispanic 12%, Native American: 1%, Caucasian 82% \ **Exp:** $287 (Med) \ **Poverty:** 18% \ **Title I:** $265,353 \ **Special Education:** $154,000 \ **Open-Close:** 08/13 - 05/28 \ **DTBP:** $350 (High)

| | | | |
|---|---|---|---|
| Dr Lamont Smith | 1 | Alana Bacon | 2 |
| Ricky Parker | 3 | Marcus Wilkins | 4 |
| Shawn Mattern | 5 | Luke Goode | 6 |
| Stephanie Link | 7* | Tana Herring | 12,298 |
| Michelle Clark | 16,82 | Melody Holloway | 38* |
| David Dominguez | 57* | Harold Holloway | 67 |
| Yancy Bell | 73,76,295 | | |

| Public Schs..Principal | Grd | Prgm | Enr/#Cls | SN | |
|---|---|---|---|---|---|
| Elkhart Elem Sch<br>301 E Parker St, Elkhart 75839<br>**Kristin Steely** | PK-2 | T | 339<br>30 | 70% | 903/764-2979<br>Fax 903/764-8286 |
| Elkhart High Sch<br>301 E Parker St, Elkhart 75839<br>Jason Ives | 9-12 | TV | 268<br>30 | 50% | 903/764-5161<br>Fax 903/764-2414 |
| Elkhart Intermediate Sch<br>301 E Parker St, Elkhart 75839<br>Greg Herring | 3-5 | T | 277 | 56% | 903/764-8535<br>Fax 903/764-8287 |
| Elkhart Middle Sch<br>301 E Parker St, Elkhart 75839<br>Rebecca Huff | 6-8 | T | 168<br>25 | 57% | 903/764-2459<br>Fax 903/764-8288 |

• **Frankston Ind School Dist** PID: 00994463     903/876-2556
100 W Perry St, Frankston 75763     Fax 903/876-4558

**Schools:** 3 \ **Teachers:** 64 \ **Students:** 766 \ **Special Ed Students:** 93 \ **LEP Students:** 20 \ **College-Bound:** 62% \ **Ethnic:** Asian 1%, African American 9%, Hispanic 9%, Native American: 1%, Caucasian 81% \ **Exp:** $303 (High) \ **Poverty:** 25% \ **Title I:** $256,805 \ **Special Education:** $57,000 \ **Open-Close:** 08/12 - 05/21 \ **DTBP:** $333 (High) \ 📘 🅃

| | | | |
|---|---|---|---|
| Nicci Cook | 1,11,57 | Randi Westbrook | 2,19 |
| Kurt Norfleet | 3,5 | Tina Owen | 4 |
| Paul Gould | 6* | Amy Porter | 7* |
| Bob Whitehurst | 67 | Edgar Rodriguez | 69,88,285* |
| Ed Prater | 73,286,295,298* | Becky Hancock | 297 |

| Public Schs..Principal | Grd | Prgm | Enr/#Cls | SN | |
|---|---|---|---|---|---|
| Frankston Elem Sch<br>100 W Perry St, Frankston 75763<br>Melanie Blackwell | PK-5 | T | 344<br>30 | 62% | 903/876-2214 |
| Frankston High Sch<br>100 W Perry St, Frankston 75763<br>Edgar Rodriguez | 9-12 | TV | 228<br>23 | 43% | 903/876-3219<br>📘🅃 |
| Frankston Middle Sch<br>100 W Perry St, Frankston 75763<br>**Cindy Owens** | 6-8 | TV | 194<br>18 | 51% | 903/876-2215<br>📘🅃 |

• **Neches Ind School Dist** PID: 00994499     903/584-3311
Highway 79 County Rd 346, Neches 75779     Fax 903/584-3686

**Schools:** 2 \ **Teachers:** 33 \ **Students:** 330 \ **Special Ed Students:** 32 \ **LEP Students:** 7 \ **College-Bound:** 20% \ **Ethnic:** African American 9%, Hispanic 15%, Caucasian 76% \ **Exp:** $355 (High) \ **Poverty:** 21% \ **Title I:** $70,391 \ **Special Education:** $68,000 \ **Open-Close:** 08/17 - 05/20 \ **DTBP:** $359 (High)

| | | | |
|---|---|---|---|
| Randy Snider | 1 | Tina Bolton | 2 |
| Lynwood Cook | 3,85,91 | Kristi Braaton | 7 |
| Sha-Ree Hudson | 8,12,69,83,88,285,752* | Kimberlyn Snider | 11 |
| Carol Harris | 57* | Kay Campbell | 58 |
| Van Brown | 67 | Rick Seymour | 73,76,286 |
| Lee Blackman | 288 | Tammy Burnett | 288* |

| Public Schs..Principal | Grd | Prgm | Enr/#Cls | SN | |
|---|---|---|---|---|---|
| Neches Elem Jr High Sch<br>3055 FM 2574, Neches 75779<br>Kimberlyn Snider | PK-8 | T | 259<br>18 | 52% | 903/584-3401<br>Fax 903/584-3278 |
| Neches High Sch<br>1509 Acr 346, Neches 75779<br>Trent Cook | 9-12 | TV | 107<br>14 | 37% | 903/584-3311 |

• **Palestine Ind School Dist** PID: 00994528     210/731-8000
1007 E Park Ave, Palestine 75801     Fax 210/766-4983

**Schools:** 6 \ **Teachers:** 254 \ **Students:** 3,300 \ **Special Ed Students:** 366 \ **LEP Students:** 566 \ **College-Bound:** 52% \ **Ethnic:** Asian 1%, African American 28%, Hispanic 43%, Caucasian 29% \ **Exp:** $522 (High) \ **Poverty:** 21% \ **Title I:** $1,119,512 \ **Special Education:** $501,000 \ **Open-Close:** 08/10 - 05/21 \ 📘

| | | | |
|---|---|---|---|
| Jason Marshall | 1 | David Atkeisson | 2,19 |
| Jacob Wheeler | 3,5 | Mimi Spreen | 4 |
| Breck Quarles | 5 | Lance Angel | 6 |
| Tobin Mac | 7,83,85 | Sharon Reed | 8,69 |
| Chris Kiser | 15,31,48,51,54,57,88,271* | Suzanne Eiben | 15,68 |
| Diane Harding | 16* | Rhonda Perrington | 22 |
| Sarah Johnson | 36* | Dee Dietz | 58 |

| | | | | | | | |
|---|---|---|---|---|---|---|---|
| 1 Superintendent | 8 Curric/Instruct K-12 | 19 Chief Financial Officer | 29 Family/Consumer Science | 39 Social Studies K-12 | 49 English/Lang Arts Elem | 59 Special Education Elem | 69 Academic Assessment |
| 2 Bus/Finance/Purchasing | 9 Curric/Instruct Elem | 20 Art K-12 | 30 Adult Education | 40 Social Studies Elem | 50 English/Lang Arts Sec | 60 Special Education Sec | 70 Research/Development |
| 3 Buildings And Grounds | 10 Curric/Instruct Sec | 21 Art Elem | 31 Career/Sch-to-Work K-12 | 41 Social Studies Sec | 51 Reading K-12 | 61 Foreign/World Lang K-12 | 71 Public Information |
| 4 Food Service | 11 Federal Program | 22 Art Sec | 32 Career/Sch-to-Work Elem | 42 Science K-12 | 52 Reading Elem | 62 Foreign/World Lang Elem | 72 Summer School |
| 5 Transportation | 12 Title I | 23 Music K-12 | 33 Career/Sch-to-Work Sec | 43 Science Elem | 53 Reading Sec | 63 Foreign/World Lang Sec | 73 Instructional Tech |
| 6 Athletic | 13 Title V | 24 Music Elem | 34 Early Childhood Ed | 44 Science Sec | 54 Remedial Reading K-12 | 64 Religious Education K-12 | 74 Inservice Training |
| 7 Health Services | 14 Asst Superintendent | 25 Music Sec | 35 Health/Phys Education | 45 Math K-12 | 55 Remedial Reading Elem | 65 Religious Education Elem | 75 Marketing/Distributive |
| | 15 Instructional Media Svcs | 26 Business Education | 36 Guidance Services K-12 | 46 Math Elem | 56 Remedial Reading Sec | 66 Religious Education Sec | 76 Info Systems |
| | 16 Chief Operations Officer | 27 Career & Tech Ed | 37 Guidance Services Elem | 47 Math Sec | 57 Bilingual/ELL | 67 School Board President | 77 Psychological Assess |
| | 17 Chief Academic Officer | 28 Technology Education | 38 Guidance Services Sec | 48 English/Lang Arts K-12 | 58 Special Education K-12 | 68 Teacher Personnel | 78 Affirmative Action |

Kurt Harrington .............................. 67　Mark Schrader ............................73,76,286*
Bruce Bradley ................................. 91

| Public Schs..Principal | Grd | Prgm | Enr/#Cls | SN | |
|---|---|---|---|---|---|
| Northside Primary Sch<br>2509 N State Highway 155, Palestine 75803<br>**Traci Pridgen** | K-1 | T | 494<br>18 | 80% | 903/731-8020<br>Fax 877/655-0742 |
| Palestine High Sch<br>1600 S Loop 256, Palestine 75801<br>William Stewart | 9-12 | ATV | 984<br>60 | 64% | 903/731-8005<br>Fax 877/839-6489 |
| Palestine Jr High Sch<br>233 Ben Milam Dr, Palestine 75801<br>Joseph Mason | 7-8 | T | 519<br>60 | 74% | 903/731-8008<br>Fax 877/655-0731 |
| Southside Elem Sch<br>201 E Gillespie St, Palestine 75801<br>Grace Mancilla | 2-3 | T | 462<br>31 | 77% | 903/731-8023<br>Fax 877/655-0734 |
| Story Intermediate Sch<br>5300 N Loop 256, Palestine 75801<br>David Richardson | 4-6 | T | 756<br>65 | 79% | 903/731-8015<br>Fax 877/655-0732 |
| Washington Early Childhood Ctr<br>1020 W Hamlett St, Palestine 75803<br>Sheila Bradley | PK-PK | T | 192 | 100% | 903/731-8030<br>Fax 877/645-9497 |

● **Slocum ISD School Dist** PID: 00994633　　　903/478-3624
　5765 E State Highway 294, Elkhart 75839　　　Fax 903/478-3030

**Schools:** 1 \ **Teachers:** 40 \ **Students:** 400 \ **Special Ed Students:** 50 \ **LEP Students:** 4 \ **College-Bound:** 75% \ **Ethnic:** Asian 2%, African American 1%, Hispanic 6%, Native American: 1%, Caucasian 90% \ **Exp:** $317 (High) \ **Poverty:** 22% \ **Title I:** $92,182 \ **Special Education:** $79,000 \ **Open-Close:** 08/12 - 05/26 \ **DTBP:** $346 (High) \ 📘

Cliff Lasiter .....................................1　Dana Morgan ...........................2,12
Todd Flecter .....................................3　Joel Parker .........................16,73,286,298*
Lacey Sloane ..................................37　Kim Tutt .....................38,83,85,88,270,275
Julie Neel ........................................58　Daniel Bailey ................................. 67

| Public Schs..Principal | Grd | Prgm | Enr/#Cls | SN | |
|---|---|---|---|---|---|
| Slocum Sch<br>5765 E State Highway 294, Elkhart 75839<br>Gina Kellum \ Errin Deer | PK-12 | TV | 400<br>38 | 43% | 903/478-3624<br><br>📘 |

● **Westwood Ind School Dist** PID: 00994669　　　903/729-1776
　4524 W Oak St, Palestine 75801　　　Fax 903/729-3696

**Schools:** 4 \ **Teachers:** 123 \ **Students:** 1,500 \ **Special Ed Students:** 186 \ **LEP Students:** 83 \ **College-Bound:** 60% \ **Ethnic:** Asian 1%, African American 18%, Hispanic 26%, Native American: 1%, Caucasian 55% \ **Exp:** $445 (High) \ **Poverty:** 15% \ **Title I:** $344,516 \ **Special Education:** $140,000 \ **Open-Close:** 08/19 - 05/21 \ **DTBP:** $350 (High) \ 📘

Wade Stanford ................................1　Kyle Johnson ..............................2
Josh Shultz ...................................3,91　Juan Torez ..................................4,19
Phil Nedbalek ..................................5　Richard Bishop .............................6*
Kim Gilbreath ..............................7,85*　Christine Bedre ..........................8,280
Tiffany Carwell .......11,57,69,83,285,294,298　Kenneth Lively ............................27*
Rosa Perez ....................................34*　Amy Little ...................................54*
Jennifer Sturm ...............................58　Dr Don Rice ................................67
Edwin Schuessler ...........73,98,286,295*　Mindy Talce ................................76

| Public Schs..Principal | Grd | Prgm | Enr/#Cls | SN | |
|---|---|---|---|---|---|
| Westwood Elem Sch<br>2305 Salt Works Rd, Palestine 75803<br>Shinnitta Foreman | 3-6 | T | 460<br>35 | 68% | 903/729-1771<br>Fax 903/723-0169<br>📘 |

| Public Schs..Principal | Grd | Prgm | Enr/#Cls | SN | |
|---|---|---|---|---|---|
| Westwood High Sch<br>1820 Panther Blvd, Palestine 75803<br>Steven Nettles | 9-12 | ATV | 418<br>39 | 45% | 903/729-1773<br>Fax 903/723-8695<br>📘 |
| Westwood Junior High Sch<br>1801 Panther Blvd, Palestine 75803<br>Sonya Brown | 7-8 | ATV | 237<br>25 | 57% | 903/723-0423<br>Fax 903/723-6765<br>📘 |
| Westwood Primary Sch<br>1701 W Point Tap Rd, Palestine 75803<br>Rosa Perez | PK-2 | T | 341<br>23 | 74% | 903/729-1774<br>Fax 903/729-8839 |

## ANDERSON PRIVATE SCHOOLS

| Private Schs..Principal | Grd | Prgm | Enr/#Cls | SN | |
|---|---|---|---|---|---|
| Christian Heritage Academy<br>1500 Crockett Rd, Palestine 75801<br>Tammy Patton | K-8 | | 128 | | 903/723-4685 |

## ANDREWS COUNTY

## ANDREWS PUBLIC SCHOOLS

● **Andrews Ind School Dist** PID: 00994700　　　432/523-3640
　405 NW 3rd St, Andrews 79714　　　Fax 432/523-3343

**Schools:** 6 \ **Teachers:** 264 \ **Students:** 4,200 \ **Special Ed Students:** 351 \ **LEP Students:** 485 \ **College-Bound:** 51% \ **Ethnic:** African American 1%, Hispanic 69%, Caucasian 30% \ **Exp:** $194 (Low) \ **Poverty:** 13% \ **Title I:** $618,677 \ **Special Education:** $891,000 \ **Open-Close:** 08/13 - 05/21 \ **DTBP:** $147 (High)

Dr Bobby Azam .................................1　Bill Butler ...................................2
Daniel Webb ...........................3,15,91　Pam Yocham ...............................4
Donnie Lloyd ..................................5　Ralph Mason ...............................6
Becky Nelson ..................................7　Kevin Vaughan ...............8,30,58,88,273
Belma Avena ..............................11,69　Dennis Haynie ...................16,73,95*
Kari Walinder .................................67　Diana Villa ..................................68
Frank Lopez ................................297*

| Public Schs..Principal | Grd | Prgm | Enr/#Cls | SN | |
|---|---|---|---|---|---|
| Ⓐ Andrews Alternative Sch<br>600 Blk NW 3rd St, Andrews 79714<br>Carlton Johnson | 9-12 | G | 31<br>3 | 56% | 432/524-1946 |
| Andrews High Sch<br>1400 NW Avenue K, Andrews 79714<br>John Carranco | 9-12 | GTV | 1,056<br>70 | 36% | 432/524-1910<br>Fax 432/523-6807 |
| Andrews Middle Sch<br>600 NW 3rd St, Andrews 79714<br>David Lowder | 6-8 | TV | 1,026<br>45 | 40% | 432/524-1940<br>Fax 432/524-1904 |
| Clearfork Elem Sch<br>300 NE Avenue K, Andrews 79714<br>Suzanne Mata | PK-1 | T | 826<br>22 | 47% | 432/524-1930<br>Fax 432/524-1903 |
| Devonian Elem Sch<br>1214 NW 11th Avenue, Andrews 79714<br>Arturo Roman | 2-3 | T | 609<br>15 | 42% | 432/524-1950<br>Fax 432/524-1905 |
| Underwood Elem Sch<br>308 SW 5th St, Andrews 79714<br>Terry Justice | 4-5 | T | 674<br>15 | 41% | 432/524-1960<br>Fax 432/524-1906 |

## ANGELINA COUNTY

### ANGELINA PUBLIC SCHOOLS

● **Central Ind School Dist** PID: 00994774    936/853-2216
7622 N US Highway 69, Pollok 75969    Fax 936/853-2215

**Schools:** 3 \ **Teachers:** 116 \ **Students:** 1,400 \ **Special Ed Students:** 201 \ **LEP Students:** 47 \ **College-Bound:** 75% \ **Ethnic:** African American 5%, Hispanic 22%, Caucasian 74% \ **Exp:** $400 (High) \ **Poverty:** 20% \ **Title I:** $396,949 \ **Special Education:** $320,000 \ **Open-Close:** 08/19 - 05/20 \ **DTBP:** $39 (Low) \ 🞄 🞄

| | | | |
|---|---|---|---|
| Justin Risner | 1 | Joe Collmorgen | 2,3 |
| Kasey Gargg | 2 | Heather Brink | 4 |
| Mark Caldwell | 5 | Anita Byrd | 8,88 |
| Justin Risner | 11,31,57,69,296,298* | Donna Cook | 16,82 |
| Christi Rowe | 37* | Rochelle Metts | 58 |
| Brant Lee | 67 | Kyle Ivey | 73,286 |
| Robbie Thompson | 73 | April Cimmings | 76 |
| Cliff Trevathan | 83,91 | | |

| Public Schs..Principal | Grd | Prgm | Enr/#Cls | SN | |
|---|---|---|---|---|---|
| Central Elem Sch<br>7622 N US Highway 69, Pollok 75969<br>Amanda Wright | PK-4 | T | 578<br>27 | 67% | 936/853-9390<br>Fax 936/853-9319 |
| Central High Sch<br>7622 N US Highway 69, Pollok 75969<br>**Miguel Garza** | 9-12 | T | 310<br>29 | 49% | 936/853-2167<br>Fax 936/853-2208 |
| Central Junior High Sch<br>7622 N US Highway 69, Pollok 75969<br>Ronnie Musgrove | 5-8 | T | 421<br>25 | 57% | 936/853-2115<br>Fax 936/853-2348 |

● **Diboll Ind School Dist** PID: 00994815    936/829-4718
215 N Temple Dr, Diboll 75941    Fax 936/829-5558

**Schools:** 5 \ **Teachers:** 139 \ **Students:** 1,800 \ **Special Ed Students:** 194 \ **LEP Students:** 275 \ **College-Bound:** 64% \ **Ethnic:** African American 13%, Hispanic 53%, Caucasian 34% \ **Exp:** $539 (High) \ **Poverty:** 26% \ **Title I:** $631,215 \ **Special Education:** $396,000 \ **Open-Close:** 08/20 - 06/25 \ **DTBP:** $200 (High)

| | | | |
|---|---|---|---|
| Vicky Thomas | 1 | Katherina Crager | 2 |
| Eric Crager | 3 | Kerri Sanford | 4 |
| Brandon Sanford | 5 | Blake Morrison | 6* |
| Julie Smith | 16* | Laura Hobbs | 16 |
| Carol Mettlen | 38* | Shana Powers | 58 |
| Jay Wyatt | 67 | Mary Hendry | 69 |
| Gerald Craig | 73,286 | Mavis Trout | 294 |

| Public Schs..Principal | Grd | Prgm | Enr/#Cls | SN | |
|---|---|---|---|---|---|
| Diboll High Sch<br>1000 Lumberjack Dr, Diboll 75941<br>**Andre Emmons** | 9-12 | TV | 256<br>40 | 71% | 936/829-5626<br>Fax 936/829-5708 |
| Diboll Junior High Sch<br>403 Dennis St, Diboll 75941<br>Mark Kettering | 7-8 | AT | 268<br>38 | 75% | 936/829-5225<br>Fax 936/829-6915 |
| Diboll Primary Sch<br>113 N Hendrix Ave, Diboll 75941<br>Diana Moore | PK-PK | T | 195<br>30 | 98% | 936/829-4671<br>Fax 936/829-4977 |

| Public Schs..Principal | Grd | Prgm | Enr/#Cls | SN | |
|---|---|---|---|---|---|
| H G Temple Elem Sch<br>1303 Lumberjack Dr, Diboll 75941<br>Nikki Miller | K-3 | T | 509<br>38 | 84% | 936/829-6950<br>Fax 936/829-6960 |
| H G Temple Intermediate Sch<br>1301 Lumberjack Dr, Diboll 75941<br>Nikki Miller | 4-6 | T | 430 | 81% | 936/829-6900<br>Fax 936/829-6910 |

● **Hudson Ind School Dist** PID: 00994853    936/875-3351
6735 Ted Trout Dr, Lufkin 75904    Fax 936/875-9209

**Schools:** 5 \ **Teachers:** 200 \ **Students:** 2,950 \ **Special Ed Students:** 255 \ **LEP Students:** 169 \ **College-Bound:** 65% \ **Ethnic:** Asian 1%, African American 8%, Hispanic 26%, Native American: 1%, Caucasian 64% \ **Exp:** $418 (High) \ **Poverty:** 20% \ **Title I:** $596,151 \ **Special Education:** $575,000 \ **Open-Close:** 08/17 - 05/20 \ **DTBP:** $328 (High)

| | | | |
|---|---|---|---|
| Donny Webb | 1,11,57,83 | Barrett Lankford | 2,19 |
| Billy Russell | 3 | Karen Hutto | 4 |
| Keith Jennings | 5 | Glen Kimble | 6 |
| Shalana Hyde | 7* | Lisa Jeffrey | 8 |
| Emily Meisel | 16* | Laura Mikeal | 34* |
| Leslie March | 58 | Matt Lowe | 67 |
| Joan Ragland | 73* | Josh Smith | 76,295 |
| Teresa Matthews | 90* | Michael Paul Daniel | 91 |
| Robert Inman | 295 | Mark Condron | 297 |

| Public Schs..Principal | Grd | Prgm | Enr/#Cls | SN | |
|---|---|---|---|---|---|
| Hudson High Sch<br>Highway 94 W, Lufkin 75904<br>John Courtney | 9-12 | TV | 230<br>50 | 47% | 936/875-9232<br>Fax 936/875-9307 |
| Hudson Middle Sch<br>Highway 94 W, Lufkin 75904<br>Richard Crenshaw | 6-8 | T | 706<br>35 | 54% | 936/875-9295<br>Fax 936/875-9317 |
| Ⓐ Stubblefield Learning Center<br>Ⓨ 502 College Dr, Lufkin 75904<br>Sally Darmstadter | 9-12 | GMT | 12<br>6 | 82% | 936/634-1100<br>Fax 936/634-1102 |
| W F Peavy Primary Sch<br>6920 State Highway 94, Lufkin 75904<br>Laura Mikeal | PK-2 | T | 648<br>24 | 61% | 936/875-9344<br>Fax 936/875-9378 |
| W H Bonner Elem Sch<br>536 FM 3258, Lufkin 75904<br>Scott Mackey | 3-5 | T | 641<br>28 | 56% | 936/875-9212<br>Fax 936/875-9314 |

● **Huntington Ind School Dist** PID: 00994891    936/876-4287
908 N Main St, Huntington 75949    Fax 936/876-3212

**Schools:** 5 \ **Teachers:** 130 \ **Students:** 1,750 \ **Special Ed Students:** 184 \ **LEP Students:** 18 \ **Ethnic:** African American 3%, Hispanic 7%, Caucasian 89% \ **Exp:** $560 (High) \ **Poverty:** 22% \ **Title I:** $442,929 \ **Special Education:** $402,000 \ **Open-Close:** 08/13 - 05/20 \ **DTBP:** $356 (High) \ 🞄

| | | | |
|---|---|---|---|
| David Flowers | 1 | Glenn Frank | 2 |
| Jon Crane | 3 | Shawn Ricks | 3 |
| Samantha McElroy | 4 | Todd Ricks | 5 |
| Shawn Jones | 6* | Dr Dianne Holbrook | 8,11,57,69,88,280,285,298 |
| Shane Stover | 10* | Robert Williams | 27* |
| Sherri Flynt | 38,69* | Molly Stringer | 58 |
| Tracy Neal | 67 | Jeffery Baird | 73,295 |
| Mike Jinkins | 91 | | |

| Public Schs..Principal | Grd | Prgm | Enr/#Cls | SN | |
|---|---|---|---|---|---|
| Huntington Elem Sch<br>408 E Linn St, Huntington 75949<br>Lauren Hooper | PK-3 | T | 457<br>25 | 62% | 936/876-5194<br>Fax 936/422-4450 |

| | | | | | | | | | |
|---|---|---|---|---|---|---|---|---|---|
| **1** | Superintendent | **8** | Curric/Instruct K-12 | **19** | Chief Financial Officer | **29** | Family/Consumer Science | **39** | Social Studies K-12 |
| **2** | Bus/Finance/Purchasing | **9** | Curric/Instruct Elem | **20** | Art K-12 | **30** | Adult Education | **40** | Social Studies Elem |
| **3** | Buildings And Grounds | **10** | Curric/Instruct Sec | **21** | Art Elem | **31** | Career/Sch-to-Work K-12 | **41** | Social Studies Sec |
| **4** | Food Service | **11** | Federal Program | **22** | Art Sec | **32** | Career/Sch-to-Work Elem | **42** | Science K-12 |
| **5** | Transportation | **12** | Title I | **23** | Music K-12 | **33** | Career/Sch-to-Work Sec | **43** | Science Elem |
| **6** | Athletic | **13** | Title V | **24** | Music Elem | **34** | Early Childhood Ed | **44** | Science Sec |
| **7** | Health Services | **15** | Asst Superintendent | **25** | Music Sec | **35** | Health/Phys Education | **45** | Math K-12 |
| | | **16** | Instructional Media Svcs | **26** | Business Education | **36** | Guidance Services K-12 | **46** | Math Elem |
| | | **17** | Chief Operations Officer | **27** | Career & Tech Ed | **37** | Guidance Services Elem | **47** | Math Sec |
| | | **18** | Chief Academic Officer | **28** | Technology Education | **38** | Guidance Services Sec | **48** | English/Lang Arts K-12 |

| | | | | | |
|---|---|---|---|---|---|
| **49** | English/Lang Arts Elem | **59** | Special Education Elem | **69** | Academic Assessment |
| **50** | English/Lang Arts Sec | **60** | Special Education Sec | **70** | Research/Development |
| **51** | Reading K-12 | **61** | Foreign/World Lang K-12 | **71** | Public Information |
| **52** | Reading Elem | **62** | Foreign/World Lang Elem | **72** | Summer School |
| **53** | Reading Sec | **63** | Foreign/World Lang Sec | **73** | Instructional Tech |
| **54** | Remedial Reading K-12 | **64** | Religious Education K-12 | **74** | Inservice Training |
| **55** | Remedial Reading Elem | **65** | Religious Education Elem | **75** | Marketing/Distributive |
| **56** | Remedial Reading Sec | **66** | Religious Education Sec | **76** | Info Systems |
| **57** | Bilingual/ELL | **67** | School Board President | **77** | Psychological Assess |
| **58** | Special Education K-12 | **68** | Teacher Personnel | **78** | Affirmative Action |

| | | | | | |
|---|---|---|---|---|---|
| Huntington High Sch | 9-12 | TV | 269 | 46% | 936/876-4150 |
| 908 Gibson St, Huntington 75949 | | | 30 | | Fax 936/876-3057 |
| Shane Stover | | | | | |
| Huntington Intermediate Sch | 4-5 | T | 244 | 61% | 936/876-3432 |
| 950 Gibson St, Huntington 75949 | | | 15 | | Fax 936/422-4419 |
| Sandy Flowers | | | | | |
| Huntington Middle Sch | 6-8 | T | 397 | 57% | 936/876-4722 |
| 906 N Main St, Huntington 75949 | | | 30 | | Fax 936/876-4009 |
| Mrs Bosley | | | | | |
| Ⓐ Pride Sch | 9-12 | TV | 21 | 67% | 936/876-4287 |
| 906 N Main St, Huntington 75949 | | | 3 | | Fax 936/876-4352 |
| Lawton Trekell | | | | | |

● **Lufkin Ind School Dist** PID: 00994932      936/634-6696
101 N Cotton Sq, Lufkin 75904      Fax 936/634-8864

> **Schools:** 15 \ **Teachers:** 582 \ **Students:** 8,000 \ **Special Ed Students:** 852
> \ **LEP Students:** 1,289 \ **College-Bound:** 57% \ **Ethnic:** Asian 1%,
> African American 30%, Hispanic 43%, Caucasian 26% \ **Exp:** $423 (High)
> \ **Poverty:** 25% \ **Title I:** $2,778,460 \ **Special Education:** $1,397,000 \
> **Open-Close:** 08/14 - 05/21 \ **DTBP:** $139 (High)

| | | | |
|---|---|---|---|
| Lynn Torres | 1 | Charlotte Bynum | 2 |
| Tim Hobbs | 2 | Johnnie Ross | 3,91 |
| Amanda Calk | 4 | Wayne Grissom | 5 |
| Todd Quick | 6 | Barbara Lazarine | 9,15,74 |
| Dr Anthony Sorola | 13,15,78 | Stephen Rhoades | 27,31,75* |
| Vada Hughes | 42 | Gabe Keese | 45 |
| Sylvia Eubanks | 57,271 | Kim Kassaw | 58 |
| Scott Skelton | 67 | Sheila Adams | 71 |
| Brad Stewart | 73,295,297* | Kelly Foley | 76 |
| Dierdre Harrison | 77 | Allison Hillis | 81 |
| Kurt Stephens | 88,294* | Tonja Akridge | 90,93 |
| Suzi Jungman | 285 | Stacey McCarty | 286 |
| Jason Carr | 295 | Josh Williams | 295 |

| Public Schs..Principal | Grd | Prgm | Enr/#Cls | SN | |
|---|---|---|---|---|---|
| Ⓐ Ace Alternative Sch | K-12 | | 100 | | 936/630-4152 |
| 1121 Winston 8 Ranch Rd, Lufkin 75904 | | | 12 | | Fax 936/632-7209 |
| Scott Walters | | | | | |
| Anderson Elem Sch | 3-5 | T | 258 | 85% | 936/632-5527 |
| 381 Champions Dr, Lufkin 75901 | | | 24 | | Fax 936/632-5487 |
| **Cindy Nerren** | | | | | |
| Brandon Elem Sch | 3-5 | T | 407 | 69% | 936/632-5513 |
| 1612 Sayers St, Lufkin 75904 | | | 30 | | Fax 936/632-5617 |
| **Mark Keith** | | | | | |
| Brookhollow Elem Sch | 3-5 | T | 300 | 86% | 936/639-3100 |
| 1009 Live Oak Ln, Lufkin 75904 | | | 35 | | Fax 936/634-8543 |
| **Amy Fain** | | | | | |
| Burley Primary Sch | K-2 | T | 400 | 82% | 936/639-3100 |
| 502 Joyce Ln, Lufkin 75901 | | | | | Fax 936/633-6222 |
| **Betsy Mijares** | | | | | |
| Coston Elem Sch | 3-5 | T | 77 | 92% | 936/639-3118 |
| 707 Trenton St, Lufkin 75901 | | | 22 | | Fax 936/639-3289 |
| Kathy Jost | | | | | |
| Dunbar Primary Sch | K-2 | T | 298 | 61% | 936/630-4500 |
| 1807 Martin Luther King, Lufkin 75904 | | | 17 | | Fax 936/630-4511 |
| Dorinda Wade | | | | | |
| Garrett Primary Sch | PK-K | T | 400 | 97% | 936/634-8418 |
| 229 Leach St, Lufkin 75904 | | | 18 | | Fax 936/634-8406 |
| Cherree Hall | | | | | |
| Hackney Primary Sch | PK-PK | T | 227 | 99% | 936/634-3324 |
| 708 Lubbock St, Lufkin 75901 | | | 13 | | Fax 936/634-0463 |
| Kelly Ford-Prout | | | | | |
| Herty Primary Sch | PK-2 | T | 269 | 89% | 936/639-2241 |
| 2804 Paul Ave, Lufkin 75901 | | | 24 | | Fax 936/633-6516 |
| Jill Riggs | | | | | |

| | | | | | |
|---|---|---|---|---|---|
| Kurth Primary Sch | PK-2 | T | 207 | 81% | 936/639-3279 |
| 521 York Dr, Lufkin 75901 | | | 21 | | Fax 936/639-3415 |
| **Dana Bickley** | | | | | |
| Lufkin High Sch | 9-12 | TV | 2,126 | 67% | 936/632-7721 |
| 309 S Medford Dr, Lufkin 75901 | | | 100 | | Fax 936/632-8132 |
| Brandon Boyd | | | | | |
| Lufkin Middle Sch | 6-8 | T | 1,102 | 74% | 936/630-4444 |
| 900 E Denman Ave, Lufkin 75901 | | | | | Fax 936/632-6664 |
| Danny Whisenant | | | | | |
| Slack Elem Sch | 3-5 | T | 521 | 84% | 936/639-2279 |
| 1305 Fuller Springs Dr, Lufkin 75901 | | | 26 | | Fax 936/699-2297 |
| Yaneth Clifton | | | | | |
| Trout Primary Sch | PK-2 | T | 192 | 90% | 936/639-3274 |
| 1014 Allendale Dr, Lufkin 75904 | | | 22 | | Fax 936/639-3873 |
| **Cindy Stewart** | | | | | |

● **Zavalla Ind School Dist** PID: 00995089      936/897-2271
431 E Main St, Zavalla 75980      Fax 936/897-2674

> **Schools:** 2 \ **Teachers:** 34 \ **Students:** 300 \ **Special Ed Students:** 47 \
> **Ethnic:** African American 1%, Hispanic 4%, Caucasian 96% \ **Exp:** $976
> (High) \ **Poverty:** 30% \ **Title I:** $206,616 \ **Special Education:** $99,000 \
> **Open-Close:** 08/13 - 05/21 \ **DTBP:** $335 (High)

| | | | |
|---|---|---|---|
| Ricky Oliver | 1 | Alice Boulware | 2 |
| Sue Fletcher | 4 | Greg Fletcher | 5 |
| Kathy Caton | 8 | Sharla Oliver | 11,58,69 |
| Kelli Collins | 36* | James Barge | 67 |
| James Maglothin | 73 | | |

| Public Schs..Principal | Grd | Prgm | Enr/#Cls | SN | |
|---|---|---|---|---|---|
| Zavalla Elem Sch | PK-5 | T | 170 | 72% | 936/897-2611 |
| Highway 63 E, Zavalla 75980 | | | 12 | | Fax 936/897-3586 |
| **Glen Vaughan** | | | | | |
| Zavalla High Sch | 6-12 | TV | 190 | 63% | 936/897-2301 |
| Highway 63 E, Zavalla 75980 | | | 24 | | Fax 936/897-3101 |
| Patricia Cross | | | | | |

## ANGELINA CATHOLIC SCHOOLS

● **Diocese of Tyler Ed Office** PID: 03014660
Listing includes only schools located in this county. See District Index for
location of Diocesan Offices.

| Catholic Schs..Principal | Grd | Prgm | Enr/#Cls | SN | |
|---|---|---|---|---|---|
| St Patrick Catholic Sch | PK-8 | | 50 | | 936/634-6719 |
| 2116 Lowery St, Lufkin 75901 | | | 12 | | Fax 936/639-2776 |
| G Maisonet | | | | | |

## ANGELINA PRIVATE SCHOOLS

| Private Schs..Principal | Grd | Prgm | Enr/#Cls | SN | |
|---|---|---|---|---|---|
| St Cyprian's Episcopal Sch | PK-5 | | 200 | | 936/632-1720 |
| 1115 S John Redditt Dr, Lufkin 75904 | | | 21 | | Fax 936/632-3852 |
| Dr Sherry Durham | | | | | |

| | | | |
|---|---|---|---|
| **79** Student Personnel | **91** Safety/Security | **275** Response To Intervention | **298** Grant Writer/Ptnrships |
| **80** Driver Ed/Safety | **92** Magnet School | **277** Remedial Math K-12 | **750** Chief Innovation Officer |
| **81** Gifted/Talented | **93** Parental Involvement | **280** Literacy Coach | **751** Chief of Staff |
| **82** Video Services | **95** Tech Prep Program | **285** STEM | **752** Social Emotional Learning |
| **83** Substance Abuse Prev | **97** Chief Infomation Officer | **286** Digital Learning | |
| **84** Erate | **98** Chief Technology Officer | **288** Common Core Standards | **Other School Types** |
| **85** AIDS Education | **270** Character Education | **294** Accountability | Ⓐ = Alternative School |
| **88** Alternative/At Risk | **271** Migrant Education | **295** Network System | Ⓒ = Charter School |
| **89** Multi-Cultural Curriculum | **273** Teacher Mentor | **296** Title II Programs | Ⓜ = Magnet School |
| **90** Social Work | **274** Before/After Sch | **297** Webmaster | Ⓨ = Year-Round School |

**School Programs**
A = Alternative Program
G = Adult Classes
M = Magnet Program
T = Title I Schoolwide
V = Career & Tech Ed Programs

**Social Media**
🅕 = Facebook
🅣 = Twitter

New Schools are shaded
New Superintendents and Principals are bold
Personnel with email addresses are underscored

**TX—21**

## ARANSAS COUNTY

### ARANSAS PUBLIC SCHOOLS

- **Aransas Co Ind School Dist** PID: 00995120    361/790-2212
  619 N Live Oak St, Rockport 78382    Fax 361/790-2291

**Schools:** 4 \ **Teachers:** 215 \ **Students:** 2,975 \ **Special Ed Students:** 288 \ **LEP Students:** 136 \ **College-Bound:** 45% \ **Ethnic:** Asian 2%, African American 1%, Hispanic 44%, Caucasian 53% \ **Exp:** $340 (High) \ **Poverty:** 32% \ **Title I:** $1,276,402 \ **Special Education:** $683,000 \ **Open-Close:** 08/13 - 05/27 \ **DTBP:** $183 (High)

| | | | |
|---|---|---|---|
| Joseph Patek | 1 | Gerald Goodwin | 2 |
| Kathy Henderson | 2,19 | Norman Spears | 3,16,73 |
| Ross Schonhoeft | 4 | Robert Douglas | 5 |
| Jay Seibert | 6 | Tonia Ramaker | 7* |
| Rose Tran | 8,11,30,68,74,78,79* | Denise Poland | 9 |
| Tom Jaggard | 10 | Molly Adams | 12* |
| John Owen | 31* | Jessica Robbins | 57,69 |
| Alicia Luttman | 58,270 | Ray Garza | 67 |
| Bridget Johnson | 68 | Kimberly Lawing | 73 |
| Sammy Zapata | 91 | Chris Garis | 295 |

| Public Schs..Principal | Grd | Prgm | Enr/#Cls | SN | |
|---|---|---|---|---|---|
| Fulton 4-5 Learning Center<br>314 N 6th St, Fulton 78358<br>Rose Tran | 4-5 | T | 374<br>22 | 71% | 361/790-2240<br>Fax 361/790-2274 |
| Live Oak Learning Center<br>31 Griffith Dr, Rockport 78382<br>Denise Poland | 1-3 | AT | 559<br>60 | 72% | 361/790-2260<br>Fax 361/790-2207 |
| Rockport-Fulton High Sch<br>1801 Omohundro St, Rockport 78382<br>Rhonda Mieth | 9-12 | AGTV | 858<br>80 | 56% | 361/790-2220<br>Fax 361/790-2206 |
| Rockport-Fulton Middle Sch<br>1701 Colorado St, Rockport 78382<br>Christina Spears | 6-8 | ATV | 648<br>60 | 71% | 361/790-2230<br>Fax 361/790-2030 |

### ARANSAS CATHOLIC SCHOOLS

- **Diocese Corpus Christi Ed Off** PID: 01045170
  Listing includes only schools located in this county. See District Index for location of Diocesan Offices.

| Catholic Schs..Principal | Grd | Prgm | Enr/#Cls | SN | |
|---|---|---|---|---|---|
| Sacred Heart Sch<br>213 S Church St, Rockport 78382<br>Katherine Barnes | 1-5 | | 162<br>8 | | 361/729-2672<br>🄵 🅃 |

### ARANSAS PRIVATE SCHOOLS

| Private Schs..Principal | Grd | Prgm | Enr/#Cls | SN | |
|---|---|---|---|---|---|
| Coastal Oaks Christian Sch<br>2002 FM 3036, Rockport 78382<br>Mary Barlow | K-5 | | 20<br>3 | | 361/790-9597<br>Fax 361/729-4481 |

## ARCHER COUNTY

### ARCHER PUBLIC SCHOOLS

- **Archer City Ind School Dist** PID: 00995182    940/574-4536
  600 S Ash Street, Archer City 76351    Fax 940/574-4051

**Schools:** 2 \ **Teachers:** 45 \ **Students:** 505 \ **Special Ed Students:** 68 \ **LEP Students:** 8 \ **College-Bound:** 82% \ **Ethnic:** Asian 1%, African American 1%, Hispanic 14%, Native American: 1%, Caucasian 84% \ **Exp:** $659 (High) \ **Poverty:** 20% \ **Title I:** $117,781 \ **Open-Close:** 08/17 - 05/20 \ 🄵 🅃

| | | | |
|---|---|---|---|
| Cd Knobloch | 1,11 | Bridget Wylie | 2 |
| Shad Hanna | 6 | Tiarra Truette | 12,34* |
| Amanda Awakuni | 16,82 | Jeanie Hilbers | 67 |
| Leslie Graham | 69,83,88* | Bethann Oswald | 73,286,298* |
| Beth Anne Oswald | 84 | Vicki Lopez | 285 |

| Public Schs..Principal | Grd | Prgm | Enr/#Cls | SN | |
|---|---|---|---|---|---|
| Archer City Elem Sch<br>600 S Ash, Archer City 76351<br>Amy Huseman | PK-6 | T | 274<br>18 | 61% | 940/574-4506<br>Fax 940/574-2675 |
| Archer City High Sch<br>600 S Ash St, Archer City 76351<br>Amanda Stafford | 7-12 | | 231<br>35 | 44% | 940/574-4713<br>Fax 940/574-2636 |

- **Holliday Ind School Dist** PID: 00995211    940/586-1281
  751 College St, Holliday 76366    Fax 940/586-1492

**Schools:** 3 \ **Teachers:** 76 \ **Students:** 1,051 \ **Special Ed Students:** 96 \ **LEP Students:** 3 \ **College-Bound:** 4% \ **Ethnic:** Hispanic 9%, Native American: 1%, Caucasian 90% \ **Exp:** $536 (High) \ **Poverty:** 11% \ **Title I:** $79,556 \ **Open-Close:** 08/17 - 05/28 \ **DTBP:** $383 (High) \ 🅃

| | | | |
|---|---|---|---|
| **Cody Carroll** | 1 | Dustin Scobee | 2 |
| Cindy Mayfield | 3 | Laura Wheatherread | 4 |
| Frank Johnson | 6* | Amber Morrison | 7* |
| Aniece Anderson | 36,83,88,93,271* | Krystal Southard | 59 |
| Krystal Southard | 59* | Barry Hardin | 67 |
| Kim Booher | 69,79* | Karie Miller | 73,84,286 |
| Denise Lawson | 76* | | |

| Public Schs..Principal | Grd | Prgm | Enr/#Cls | SN | |
|---|---|---|---|---|---|
| Holliday Elem Sch<br>751 College St, Holliday 76366<br>Tara Kirkland | PK-5 | AT | 457<br>23 | 27% | 940/586-1986<br>Fax 940/586-0538<br>🄵 🅃 |
| Holliday High Sch<br>751 College St, Holliday 76366<br>Bruce Patterson | 9-12 | AV | 319<br>26 | 13% | 940/586-1624<br>Fax 940/586-9501 |
| Holliday Middle Sch<br>751 College St, Holliday 76366<br>Kelly Carver | 6-8 | ATV | 249<br>14 | 19% | 940/586-1314<br>Fax 940/583-4480 |

| | | | | | | | | |
|---|---|---|---|---|---|---|---|---|
| **1** Superintendent | **8** Curric/Instruct K-12 | **19** Chief Financial Officer | **29** Family/Consumer Science | **39** Social Studies K-12 | **49** English/Lang Arts Elem | **59** Special Education Elem | **69** Academic Assessment |
| **2** Bus/Finance/Purchasing | **9** Curric/Instruct Elem | **20** Art K-12 | **30** Adult Education | **40** Social Studies Elem | **50** English/Lang Arts Sec | **60** Special Education Sec | **70** Research/Development |
| **3** Buildings And Grounds | **10** Curric/Instruct Sec | **21** Art Elem | **31** Career/Sch-to-Work K-12 | **41** Social Studies Sec | **51** Reading K-12 | **61** Foreign/World Lang K-12 | **71** Public Information |
| **4** Food Service | **11** Federal Program | **22** Art Sec | **32** Career/Sch-to-Work Elem | **42** Science K-12 | **52** Reading Elem | **62** Foreign/World Lang Elem | **72** Summer School |
| **5** Transportation | **12** Title I | **23** Music K-12 | **33** Career/Sch-to-Work Sec | **43** Science Elem | **53** Reading Sec | **63** Foreign/World Lang Sec | **73** Instructional Tech |
| **6** Athletic | **13** Title V | **24** Music Elem | **34** Early Childhood Ed | **44** Science Sec | **54** Remedial Reading K-12 | **64** Religious Education K-12 | **74** Inservice Training |
| **7** Health Services | **15** Asst Superintendent | **25** Music Sec | **35** Health/Phys Education | **45** Math K-12 | **55** Remedial Reading Elem | **65** Religious Education Elem | **75** Marketing/Distributive |
| | **16** Instructional Media Svcs | **26** Business Education | **36** Guidance Services K-12 | **46** Math Elem | **56** Remedial Reading Sec | **66** Religious Education Sec | **76** Info Systems |
| | **17** Chief Operations Officer | **27** Career & Tech Ed | **37** Guidance Services Elem | **47** Math Sec | **57** Bilingual/ELL | **67** School Board President | **77** Psychological Assess |
| | **18** Chief Academic Officer | **28** Technology Education | **38** Guidance Services Sec | **48** English/Lang Arts K-12 | **58** Special Education K-12 | **68** Teacher Personnel | **78** Affirmative Action |

● **Windthorst Ind School Dist** PID: 00995273     940/423-6688
100 St Marys Street, Windthorst 76389     Fax 940/423-6505

**Schools:** 3 \ **Teachers:** 35 \ **Students:** 390 \ **Special Ed Students:** 34
\ **LEP Students:** 23 \ **College-Bound:** 35% \ **Ethnic:** Hispanic 28%,
Native American: 1%, Caucasian 72% \ **Exp:** $568 (High) \ **Poverty:** 11% \
**Title I:** $36,340 \ **Open-Close:** 08/17 - 05/20 \ **DTBP:** $355 (High)

Lonnie Hise .......................................1,11   Juhree Vaughn ...........................................2
Chris Tackett ........................................6   Lonnie Hise ..........................................8,31*
Ann Armendarez ......................12,57,275   Shelby Wolf ..............................................58
Chad Steinberger ...............................67   Darla Tackett ..........................69,270,271*
Rob Leopold ..............................73,84,295

| Public Schs..Principal | Grd | Prgm | Enr/#Cls | SN | |
|---|---|---|---|---|---|
| Windthorst Elem Sch<br>100 St Marys Street, Windthorst 76389<br>Ann Armendarez | PK-5 | T | 176<br>30 | 43% | 940/423-6679 |
| Windthorst High Sch<br>100 St Marys Street, Windthorst 76389<br>Roy Longcrier | 9-12 | V | 135<br>15 | 36% | 940/423-6680 |
| Windthorst Junior High Sch<br>100 St Marys, Windthorst 76389<br>Roy Longcrier | 6-8 | | 92 | 40% | 940/423-6605 |

## ARMSTRONG COUNTY

## ARMSTRONG PUBLIC SCHOOLS

● **Claude Ind School Dist** PID: 00995302     806/226-7331
500 5th St, Claude 79019     Fax 806/226-2244

**Schools:** 1 \ **Teachers:** 35 \ **Students:** 308 \ **Special Ed Students:** 39
\ **LEP Students:** 4 \ **Ethnic:** African American 1%, Hispanic 12%, Native
American: 1%, Caucasian 85% \ **Exp:** $401 (High) \ **Poverty:** 14% \
**Title I:** $48,483 \ **Open-Close:** 08/20 - 05/27 \ **DTBP:** $341 (High) \ 🔲

Brock Cartwright ................................1,11   Mike Hook ...........................................3,5
Annett Stanghellini ..............................4   John Moffett .................6,83,88,273,275,294
Jessica Bevill ...............57,77,81,280,296,752   Tony Holland .........................................58*
Lendon Ray ........................................67   M-Lynn Miller ...............................73,76,286
Amy Taylor ......................................752

| Public Schs..Principal | Grd | Prgm | Enr/#Cls | SN | |
|---|---|---|---|---|---|
| Claude Sch<br>500 5th St, Claude 79019<br>Kendra Sherrill \ John Moffett | PK-12 | TV | 308<br>40 | 32% | 806/226-7331<br>Fax 806/226-3822<br>🔲 |

## ATASCOSA PUBLIC SCHOOLS

● **Charlotte Ind School Dist** PID: 00995338     830-277-1431
102 E Hindes Ave, Charlotte 78011     Fax 830/277-1551

**Schools:** 3 \ **Teachers:** 46 \ **Students:** 450 \ **Special Ed Students:** 64
\ **LEP Students:** 23 \ **College-Bound:** 49% \ **Ethnic:** Hispanic 88%,
Caucasian 12% \ **Exp:** $845 (High) \ **Poverty:** 27% \ **Title I:** $215,929 \
**Open-Close:** 08/24 - 05/28 \ **DTBP:** $325 (High) \ 🔲 🔲

Mario Sotelo ......................................1,83   Nora Gaitan ..........................................2,11
Martin Chavarria ..................................3,5   Natasha Pesqueda .........................16,82*
Becky Ramos .......................................67   Jennifer Swan ................................73,76,84
Denise Yanashita .................................288

| Public Schs..Principal | Grd | Prgm | Enr/#Cls | SN | |
|---|---|---|---|---|---|
| Charlotte Elem Sch<br>168 Watson Avenue, Charlotte 78011<br>Laura Mikolajczyk | PK-4 | T | 170<br>18 | 77% | 830/277-1710<br>Fax 830/277-1675 |
| Charlotte High Sch<br>70 Trojan Drive, Charlotte 78011<br>Brianne Brock | 9-12 | TV | 146<br>26 | 74% | 830/277-1432<br>Fax 830/277-1605<br>🔲🔲 |
| Charlotte Middle Sch<br>95 Rose Boulevard, Charlotte 78011<br>Brianne Brock | 5-8 | T | 98<br>8 | 70% | 830/277-1646<br>Fax 830/277-1534 |

● **Jourdanton Ind School Dist** PID: 00995376     830-769-3548
200 Zanderson Ave, Jourdanton 78026     Fax 830/376-5052

**Schools:** 4 \ **Teachers:** 117 \ **Students:** 1,200 \ **Special Ed Students:** 163
\ **LEP Students:** 34 \ **Ethnic:** African American 1%, Hispanic 61%,
Caucasian 37% \ **Exp:** $262 (Med) \ **Poverty:** 17% \ **Title I:** $270,754 \
**Open-Close:** 08/11 - 05/27 \ **DTBP:** $553 (High) \ 🔲

Teresa McCallister ........................1,73,83   Angie Balaszi .........................................2
Jacob Reyna .........................................3   Effron Trevino .......................................4
Braden Boehme ....................................5   Darrel Andrus .........................................6*
Sarah Guiturrez .....................................7   Pepperjo Barley ....................................11
Christie Kinsler ....................................29   Marie Fanno ...............................36,69,88*
Bertha Curara ......................................57   Barbra Peeler .......................................67
Anna Llamas ......................................271   Anna Kindrich ......................................274*

| Public Schs..Principal | Grd | Prgm | Enr/#Cls | SN | |
|---|---|---|---|---|---|
| Jourdanton Elem Sch<br>200 Zanderson Ave, Jourdanton 78026<br>Laurie Daughtrey | PK-5 | T | 636<br>40 | 59% | 830/769-2121<br>Fax 830/376-5058 |
| Jourdanton High Sch<br>200 Zanderson Ave, Jourdanton 78026<br>Virginia Parsons | 9-12 | TV | 329<br>26 | 48% | 830/769-2350<br>Fax 830/376-5076 |
| Jourdanton Junior High Sch<br>200 Zanderson Ave, Jourdanton 78026<br>Casandra McGill | 6-8 | TV | 122<br>23 | 49% | 830/769-2234<br>Fax 830/376-5065 |
| Ⓐ Larry Brown Sch<br>1508 Campbell Ave, Jourdanton 78026<br>Jeff Thornton | 6-12 | | 8<br>2 | | 830/769-2925<br>Fax 830/769-2617 |

● **Lytle Ind School Dist** PID: 00995405
15437 Cottage St, Lytle 78052

830/709-5100
Fax 830/709-5104

---

**Schools:** 4 \ **Teachers:** 114 \ **Students:** 1,309 \ **Special Ed Students:** 138
\ **LEP Students:** 195 \ **College-Bound:** 45% \ **Ethnic:** African American
1%, Hispanic 81%, Caucasian 18% \ **Exp:** $247 (Med) \ **Poverty:** 21% \
**Title I:** $431,025 \ **Special Education:** $343,000 \ **Open-Close:** 08/13 -
05/25 \ **DTBP:** $311 (High)

---

| | | | |
|---|---|---|---|
| Michelle Smith | 1 | Kathy Duran | 2 |
| William Cross | 3,5 | Armando Esquibel | 5 |
| Laurie Wilson | 6 | Harry Piles | 8,15,275,286,288 |
| Laura Uribe-Center | 11,68,296,298 | Richard Tollett | 16,73,76,82,84 |
| Robbie Pierce | 58 | Leanne Mask | 67 |
| Lorianne Magura | 71 | Sandra Jopling | 83 |

| Public Schs..Principal | Grd | Prgm | Enr/#Cls | SN |
|---|---|---|---|---|
| ⓨ Lytle Elem Sch<br>11550 Laredo St, Lytle 78052<br>Wendy Conover | 2-5 | MI | 491<br>24 | 72% 830/709-5130<br>Fax 830/709-5119 |
| Lytle High Sch<br>18975 W FM 2790 S, Lytle 78052<br>Jose Garza | 9-12 | ATV | 325<br>35 | 70% 830/709-5105<br>Fax 830/709-5139 🔒 |
| ⓨ Lytle Junior High Sch<br>18975 W FM 2790 S, Lytle 78052<br>Elizabeth Stewart | 6-8 | AMTV | 125<br>20 | 74% 830/709-5115<br>Fax 830/709-3106 |
| ⓨ Lytle Primary Sch<br>19126 Prairie St, Lytle 78052<br>Jammie Fewell | PK-1 | MT | 368<br>24 | 81% 830/709-5140<br>Fax 830/709-5142 |

● **Pleasanton Ind School Dist** PID: 00995431
831 Stadium Dr, Pleasanton 78064

830/569-1200
Fax 830/569-2171

---

**Schools:** 4 \ **Teachers:** 230 \ **Students:** 3,540 \ **Special Ed Students:** 364
\ **LEP Students:** 116 \ **College-Bound:** 60% \ **Ethnic:** Hispanic 70%,
Caucasian 29% \ **Exp:** $243 (Med) \ **Poverty:** 22% \ **Title I:** $1,089,715 \
**Open-Close:** 09/08 - 06/09 \ **DTBP:** $181 (High)

---

| | | | |
|---|---|---|---|
| Dr Matthew Mann | 1 | Jennifer Donato | 2,19 |
| Dan Striakos | 3,91,295 | Joey Moczygemba | 4 |
| David Zertuche | 5 | Tab Dumont | 6 |
| Jennifer Tracy | 7 | Lindsy Pawelk | 11,58 |
| Cheryl Barron | 15,68,79 | Beth Moos | 16,82* |
| Jennifer Scherrer | 27,35,36,83 | Keri Cooper | 57,288,296 |
| Frank Tudyk | 67 | Jody Lemere | 73,95,297 |
| Mary Zinda | 81* | Dr Venus Velenta | 286,752 |
| Sarah Callihan-Lewis | 294 | Mike Maxwell | 295 |

| Public Schs..Principal | Grd | Prgm | Enr/#Cls | SN |
|---|---|---|---|---|
| Pleasanton Elem Sch<br>616 N Main St, Pleasanton 78064<br>Erica Bernal | 2-5 | T | 1,083<br>30 | 64% 830/569-1340<br>Fax 830/569-3096 🔒 |
| Pleasanton High Sch<br>831 Stadium Dr, Pleasanton 78064<br>Twila Guajardo | 9-12 | TV | 265<br>70 | 56% 830/569-1250<br>Fax 830/569-4747 |
| Pleasanton Junior High Sch<br>1140 Jolly St, Pleasanton 78064<br>Jennifer Garcia | 6-8 | TV | 794<br>40 | 62% 830/569-1280<br>Fax 830/569-1290 |
| Pleasanton Primary Sch<br>1209 Downey, Pleasanton 78064<br>Kari Vickers | PK-1 | T | 650<br>43 | 69% 830/569-1325<br>Fax 830/569-5208 |

● **Poteet Ind School Dist** PID: 00995493
1100 School Dr, Poteet 78065

830/742-3567
Fax 830/742-3332

---

**Schools:** 4 \ **Teachers:** 119 \ **Students:** 1,339 \ **Special Ed Students:** 156
\ **LEP Students:** 94 \ **College-Bound:** 47% \ **Ethnic:** Hispanic 87%,
Caucasian 13% \ **Exp:** $554 (High) \ **Poverty:** 21% \ **Title I:** $510,655 \
**Open-Close:** 08/24 - 05/28 \ **DTBP:** $553 (High)

---

| | | | |
|---|---|---|---|
| Cheryl Mills | 1,57 | Amanda Garcia | 2,3* |
| Fernando Mendez | 4 | Paula Lopez | 5 |
| Ruth Martinez | 7,83,85* | Greta Warner | 11 |
| Tonya Abbott | 16,82 | Carol Wharton | 37* |
| Bernie Bato | 58 | Jo Marie Cervantez | 67 |
| Julie Post | 69 | Adam Gonzalez | 73,295* |
| Mary Ortiz | 90,93 | Adam Gonzales | 295 |
| Craig Smith | 297 | | |

| Public Schs..Principal | Grd | Prgm | Enr/#Cls | SN |
|---|---|---|---|---|
| Poteet Elem Sch<br>1100 School Dr, Poteet 78065<br>Donisha Miller | PK-3 | T | 584<br>45 | 87% 830/742-3503<br>Fax 830/742-8487 |
| Poteet High Sch<br>1020 Farm Rd 1470, Poteet 78065<br>Tony Dominguez | 9-12 | AGTV | 247 | 69% 830/742-3521<br>Fax 830/742-8497 |
| Poteet Intermediate Campus<br>838 School Dr, Poteet 78065<br>Christina Gillespie | 4-5 | T | 253<br>27 | 83% 830/742-3697<br>Fax 830/742-3194 |
| Poteet Junior High Sch<br>1020 Sn 1470, Poteet 78065<br>Julie Poth | 6-8 | TV | 255<br>33 | 79% 830/742-3571<br>Fax 830/742-8495 🔒 |

## ATASCOSA CATHOLIC SCHOOLS

● **Archdiocese San Antonio Ed Off** PID: 00999724
Listing includes only schools located in this county. See District Index for
location of Diocesan Offices.

| Catholic Schs..Principal | Grd | Prgm | Enr/#Cls | SN |
|---|---|---|---|---|
| Our Lady of Grace Academy<br>626 Market St, Pleasanton 78064<br>Jeanette Geyer | PK-5 | | 65 | 830/569-8073 |

## AUSTIN COUNTY

## AUSTIN PUBLIC SCHOOLS

● **Bellville Ind School Dist** PID: 00995534
518 S Mathews St, Bellville 77418

979/865-3133
Fax 979/865-8591

---

**Schools:** 6 \ **Teachers:** 164 \ **Students:** 2,200 \ **Special Ed Students:** 231
\ **LEP Students:** 176 \ **Ethnic:** Asian 1%, African American 9%, Hispanic
31%, Caucasian 59% \ **Exp:** $345 (High) \ **Poverty:** 16% \ **Title I:** $505,305
\ **Special Education:** $469,000 \ **Open-Close:** 08/18 - 05/26 \ **DTBP:** $573
(High) \ 🇹

---

| | | | |
|---|---|---|---|
| Dr Nicole Poenitzsch | 1 | Dennis Jurek | 2,19 |
| JD Higginbotham | 3 | Alyssa Werner | 4 |

| | | | | | | | |
|---|---|---|---|---|---|---|---|
| 1 | Superintendent | 8 | Curric/Instruct K-12 | 19 | Chief Financial Officer | 29 | Family/Consumer Science |
| 2 | Bus/Finance/Purchasing | 9 | Curric/Instruct Elem | 20 | Art K-12 | 30 | Adult Education |
| 3 | Buildings And Grounds | 10 | Curric/Instruct Sec | 21 | Art Elem | 31 | Career/Sch-to-Work K-12 |
| 4 | Food Service | 11 | Federal Program | 22 | Art Sec | 32 | Career/Sch-to-Work Elem |
| 5 | Transportation | 12 | Title I | 23 | Music K-12 | 33 | Career/Sch-to-Work Sec |
| 6 | Athletic | 13 | Title V | 24 | Music Elem | 34 | Early Childhood Ed |
| 7 | Health Services | 15 | Asst Superintendent | 25 | Music Sec | 35 | Health/Phys Education |
| | | 16 | Instructional Media Svcs | 26 | Business Education | 36 | Guidance Services K-12 |
| | | 17 | Chief Operations Officer | 27 | Career & Tech Ed | 37 | Guidance Services Elem |
| | | 18 | Chief Academic Officer | 28 | Technology Education | 38 | Guidance Services Sec |

| | | | | | |
|---|---|---|---|---|---|
| 39 | Social Studies K-12 | 49 | English/Lang Arts Elem | 59 | Special Education Elem |
| 40 | Social Studies Elem | 50 | English/Lang Arts Sec | 60 | Special Education Sec |
| 41 | Social Studies Sec | 51 | Reading K-12 | 61 | Foreign/World Lang K-12 |
| 42 | Science K-12 | 52 | Reading Elem | 62 | Foreign/World Lang Elem |
| 43 | Science Elem | 53 | Reading Sec | 63 | Foreign/World Lang Sec |
| 44 | Science Sec | 54 | Remedial Reading K-12 | 64 | Religious Education K-12 |
| 45 | Math K-12 | 55 | Remedial Reading Elem | 65 | Religious Education Elem |
| 46 | Math Elem | 56 | Remedial Reading Sec | 66 | Religious Education Sec |
| 47 | Math Sec | 57 | Bilingual/ELL | 67 | School Board President |
| 48 | English/Lang Arts K-12 | 58 | Special Education K-12 | 68 | Teacher Personnel |

| | |
|---|---|
| 69 | Academic Assessment |
| 70 | Research/Development |
| 71 | Public Information |
| 72 | Summer School |
| 73 | Instructional Tech |
| 74 | Inservice Training |
| 75 | Marketing/Distributive |
| 76 | Info Systems |
| 77 | Psychological Assess |
| 78 | Affirmative Action |

| | | | | | |
|---|---|---|---|---|---|
| Tiffany Sootoo | ...5 | Grady Rowe | ...6* |
| Suzanne Grawunder | ...7* | Casey Holloman | ...8,11,36,57,69,83,88 |
| Audrau Winkelmann | ...16* | Dr Meggan Poppy | ...34,37,58 |
| Grant Lischka | ...67 | Brian Reid | ...73,286,295* |

| Public Schs..Principal | Grd | Prgm | Enr/#Cls | SN | |
|---|---|---|---|---|---|
| Bellville High Sch<br>850 Schumann Rd, Bellville 77418<br>Casey Hollomon | 9-12 | T | 716<br>40 | 44% | 979/865-3681<br>Fax 979/865-7080 |
| Bellville Junior High Sch<br>1305 S Tesch St, Bellville 77418<br>Daniel Symm | 6-8 | T | 518<br>47 | 49% | 979/865-5966<br>Fax 979/865-7060 |
| O'Bryant Intermediate Sch<br>414 S Tesch St, Bellville 77418<br>**Marcus McLemore** | 4-5 | T | 296<br>24 | 55% | 979/865-3671<br>Fax 979/865-7049 |
| O'Bryant Primary Sch<br>413 S Tesch St, Bellville 77418<br>**Kandis Krueger** | PK-3 | T | 560<br>26 | 57% | 979/865-5907<br>Fax 979/865-7039 |
| Ⓐ Spicer Alternative Ed Center<br>518 S Mathews St, Bellville 77418<br>Sean McEnerney | 6-12 | | 44<br>8 | | 979/865-7095<br>Fax 979/865-7094 |
| West End Elem Sch<br>7453 Ernst Pkwy, Industry 78944<br>Tony Hancock | K-5 | T | 148<br>16 | 35% | 979/357-2595<br>Fax 979/357-4799 |

● **Brazos Ind School Dist** PID: 00995625     979/478-6551
227 Educator Ln, Wallis 77485     Fax 979/478-2300

**Schools:** 4 \ **Teachers:** 62 \ **Students:** 700 \ **Special Ed Students:** 93 \ **LEP Students:** 122 \ **College-Bound:** 52% \ **Ethnic:** African American 9%, Hispanic 54%, Caucasian 36% \ **Exp:** $752 (High) \ **Poverty:** 10% \ **Title I:** $117,969 \ **Special Education:** $230,000 \ **Open-Close:** 08/19 - 05/27 \ **DTBP:** $345 (High)

| | | | | |
|---|---|---|---|---|
| Brian Thompson | ...1 | Courtney Marek | ...2 |
| Pete Robles | ...3,5 | Linda Pustejovsky | ...4 |
| Ryan Roecker | ...6 | Amy Sodolak | ...7 |
| Teresa Ressler | ...8,11,57,74,271,294* | Becca Naseman | ...31,69,83,85* |
| Lana Johnston | ...58 | Christopher Nanez | ...67 |
| Jessie Nanus | ...73,295 | | |

| Public Schs..Principal | Grd | Prgm | Enr/#Cls | SN | |
|---|---|---|---|---|---|
| Brazos Elem Sch<br>9814 Kibler St, Orchard 77464<br>**Tracy Boss** | PK-5 | T | 197<br>24 | 70% | 979/478-6610<br>Fax 979/478-2146 |
| Brazos High Sch<br>16621 Hwy 36 S, Wallis 77485<br>Eric Cormier | 9-12 | TV | 106<br>35 | 49% | 979/478-6832<br>Fax 979/478-6022 |
| Brazos Middle Sch<br>702 Educators Ln, Wallis 77485<br>Clay Hudgins | 6-8 | T | 195<br>16 | 59% | 979/478-6814<br>Fax 979/478-2574 |
| Ⓐ Prairie Harbor Alternative Sch<br>7146 Highway 60, Wallis 77485<br>Michael Glover | 5-12 | T | 50<br>5 | 95% | 979/478-6024 |

● **Sealy Ind School Dist** PID: 00995584     979/885-3516
939 Tiger Ln, Sealy 77474     Fax 979/885-6457

**Schools:** 4 \ **Teachers:** 209 \ **Students:** 2,669 \ **Special Ed Students:** 292 \ **LEP Students:** 374 \ **College-Bound:** 50% \ **Ethnic:** Asian 1%, African American 8%, Hispanic 52%, Caucasian 39% \ **Exp:** $255 (Med) \ **Poverty:** 14% \ **Title I:** $509,034 \ **Special Education:** $1,131,000 \ **Open-Close:** 08/19 - 05/27 \ **DTBP:** $181 (High)

| | | | | |
|---|---|---|---|---|
| **Dr Bryan Hallmark** | ...1 | Lisa Svoboda | ...2,11,19 |
| Mike Zapaliac | ...3 | John Anderson | ...4 |

| | | | | |
|---|---|---|---|---|
| Randall Krichnak | ...5 | Shane Mobley | ...6* |
| Emily Eschenburg | ...10,57,271 | Mary Gajewski | ...11,88,296 |
| Christopher Summers | ...15,294 | Sarah MaGee | ...34 |
| Shay Whatley | ...58 | Ryan Reichardt | ...67 |
| Shawn Hiatt | ...68* | Amy Dyer | ...73,76,295 |
| Shannon Culpepper | ...91 | | |

| Public Schs..Principal | Grd | Prgm | Enr/#Cls | SN | |
|---|---|---|---|---|---|
| Maggie B Selman Elem Sch<br>1741 Highway 90 W, Sealy 77474<br>Mary Gajewski | PK-5 | T | 622<br>43 | 64% | 979/885-6659 |
| Sealy Elem Sch<br>723 FM 2187 Rd, Sealy 77474<br>**Sarah Johnson** | PK-5 | T | 634<br>25 | 65% | 979/885-3852<br>Fax 979/885-0162 |
| Sealy High Sch<br>2372 Championship Dr, Sealy 77474<br>Megan Oliver | 9-12 | AGTV | 806 | 54% | 979/885-3515<br>Fax 979/987-3398 |
| Sealy Junior High Sch<br>939 Tiger Ln, Sealy 77474<br>Laura Villaflor | 6-8 | T | 607<br>40 | 56% | 979/885-3292<br>Fax 979/877-0743 |

## AUSTIN PRIVATE SCHOOLS

| Private Schs..Principal | Grd | Prgm | Enr/#Cls | SN | |
|---|---|---|---|---|---|
| Faith Academy<br>12177 Highway 36, Bellville 77418<br>Zena Lyth | PK-12 | | 210 | | 979/865-1811<br>Fax 979/865-2454 |

## BAILEY COUNTY

## BAILEY PUBLIC SCHOOLS

● **Muleshoe Ind School Dist** PID: 00995699     806/272-7400
514 W Avenue G, Muleshoe 79347     Fax 806/272-4120

**Schools:** 4 \ **Teachers:** 116 \ **Students:** 1,450 \ **Special Ed Students:** 192 \ **LEP Students:** 315 \ **College-Bound:** 52% \ **Ethnic:** African American 1%, Hispanic 85%, Caucasian 14% \ **Exp:** $910 (High) \ **Poverty:** 23% \ **Title I:** $477,506 \ **Special Education:** $312,000 \ **Open-Close:** 08/20 - 05/21 \ **DTBP:** $342 (High) \ 🅕

| | | | | |
|---|---|---|---|---|
| Dr R Richards | ...1,57,83,288 | Lisa Whalin | ...2 |
| Sam Whalin | ...3 | Fiosncio Cortez | ...5 |
| Lee Walker | ...6* | Jennifer Burrus | ...9* |
| Christi Richards | ...11 | Dani Heathington | ...15 |
| Darla Myatt | ...34,58 | Curtis Preston | ...67 |
| Susan Hinojsa | ...73,286 | Susan Hinojosa | ...84 |

| Public Schs..Principal | Grd | Prgm | Enr/#Cls | SN | |
|---|---|---|---|---|---|
| Mary DeShazo Elem Sch<br>514 W Avenue G, Muleshoe 79347<br>Jennifer Burrus | 3-5 | T | 319<br>21 | 88% | 806/272-7364<br>Fax 806/272-7370 |
| Muleshoe High Sch<br>800 W 3rd St, Muleshoe 79347<br>Cindy Bessire | 9-12 | ATV | 362<br>38 | 83% | 806/272-7302<br>Fax 806/272-7574 |
| Neal Dillman Elem Sch<br>510 W 18th St, Muleshoe 79347<br>Letti Tovar | PK-2 | T | 393<br>27 | 87% | 806/272-7383<br>Fax 806/272-7388 |

| | | | | | |
|---|---|---|---|---|---|
| 79 | Student Personnel | 91 | Safety/Security | 275 | Response To Intervention |
| 80 | Driver Ed/Safety | 92 | Magnet School | 277 | Remedial Math K-12 |
| 81 | Gifted/Talented | 93 | Parental Involvement | 280 | Literacy Coach |
| 82 | Video Services | 95 | Tech Prep Program | 285 | STEM |
| 83 | Substance Abuse Prev | 97 | Chief Information Officer | 286 | Digital Learning |
| 84 | Erate | 98 | Chief Technology Officer | 288 | Common Core Standards |
| 85 | AIDS Education | 270 | Character Education | 294 | Accountability |
| 88 | Alternative/At Risk | 271 | Migrant Education | 295 | Network System |
| 89 | Multi-Cultural Curriculum | 273 | Teacher Mentor | 296 | Title II Programs |
| 90 | Social Work | 274 | Before/After Sch | 297 | Webmaster |

| | | | |
|---|---|---|---|
| 298 | Grant Writer/Ptnrships | | |
| 750 | Chief Innovation Officer | | |
| 751 | Chief of Staff | | |
| 752 | Social Emotional Learning | | |

**School Programs**
A = Alternative Program
G = Adult Classes
M = Magnet Program
T = Title I Schoolwide
V = Career & Tech Ed Programs

**Other School Types**
Ⓐ = Alternative School
Ⓒ = Charter School
Ⓜ = Magnet School
Ⓨ = Year-Round School

**Social Media**
🅕 = Facebook
🅣 = Twitter

New Schools are shaded
New Superintendents and Principals are bold
Personnel with email addresses are underscored

| | | | | | |
|---|---|---|---|---|---|
| Watson Junior High Sch<br>500 W Ave F, Muleshoe 79347<br>Melvin Nusser | 6-8 | T | 340<br>33 | 86% | 806/272-7349<br>Fax 806/272-4983 |

| | | | | | |
|---|---|---|---|---|---|
| Medina Secondary Sch<br>One Bobcat Ln, Medina 78055<br>Sarah McCrae | 6-12 | TV | 161<br>20 | 62% | 830/589-2851 |

## BANDERA COUNTY

## BASTROP COUNTY

## BANDERA PUBLIC SCHOOLS

## BASTROP PUBLIC SCHOOLS

• **Bandera Ind School Dist** PID: 00995778     830/796-3313
815 Pecan St, Bandera 78003     Fax 830/796-6282

**Schools:** 4 \ **Teachers:** 148 \ **Students:** 2,120 \ **Special Ed Students:** 283
\ **LEP Students:** 93 \ **College-Bound:** 92% \ **Ethnic:** Hispanic 35%,
Caucasian 64% \ **Exp:** $338 (High) \ **Poverty:** 21% \ **Title I:** $658,367 \
**Special Education:** $469,000 \ **Open-Close:** 08/17 - 05/20 \ **DTBP:** $237
(High) \ ■

| | | |
|---|---|---|
| Jerry Hollingsworth ...................................1 | Scott Tipton ...............................................2 | |
| Ed Barnes ...................................................3 | Kyle Martin ................................................3 | |
| Brian Cleary ...............................................4 | Bryan Crelia ...............................................4 | |
| Billy Biedermann ........................................5 | Kay Miller ...................................................5 | |
| Jeff Hamilton ..............................................6* | Gary Bitzi ...........8,36,48,51,68,74,285 | |
| Tracy Thayer ...............11,31,91,296,298 | David Brown .................16,82,84,295,297 | |
| Michael Derry .............................................27 | Bonnie Hale ..........................................36,83,88 | |
| Patricia Galm .............................................58 | Dr Barbara Skipper ....................................67 | |
| Donald Tosh ...........................................69,294 | Suzy Groff .................................................71 | |
| Charlie Halsell ...........................................73 | Deneise Barta ............................................76 | |

| Public Schs..Principal | Grd | Prgm | Enr/#Cls | SN | |
|---|---|---|---|---|---|
| Alkek Elem Sch<br>1798 State Highway 173 S, Bandera 78003<br>Dixie Moseley | PK-5 | T | 509<br>33 | 59% | 830/460-3900<br>Fax 830/796-6232 |
| Bandera High Sch<br>474 Old San Antonio Hwy, Bandera 78003<br>Sergio Menchaca | 9-12 | TV | 640<br>50 | 45% | 830/460-3898<br>Fax 830/796-6251 |
| Bandera Middle Sch<br>1005 Cherry St, Bandera 78003<br>Patrick Sizemore | 6-8 | T | 530<br>48 | 49% | 830/460-3899<br>Fax 830/460-6945 ■ |
| Hill Country Elem Sch<br>6346 FM 1283, Pipe Creek 78063<br>Laura Klein | PK-5 | T | 441<br>47 | 62% | 830/460-3901<br>Fax 830/535-5111 ■■ |

• **Medina Ind School Dist** PID: 00995807     830/589-2855
1 Bobcat Lane, Medina 78055     Fax 830/589-7150

**Schools:** 2 \ **Teachers:** 30 \ **Students:** 300 \ **Special Ed Students:** 37
\ **LEP Students:** 5 \ **College-Bound:** 95% \ **Ethnic:** African American
1%, Hispanic 29%, Caucasian 69% \ **Exp:** $628 (High) \ **Poverty:** 12% \
**Title I:** $202,226 \ **Special Education:** $80,000 \ **Open-Close:** 08/24 - 05/21
\ **DTBP:** $379 (High)

| | |
|---|---|
| Kevin Newsom .....................................1,73 | Teresa Blair ...........................2,11,76,298 |
| Lindsay Kuntz ....................8,16,57,83,288 | Melissa Dunbar ...................................11,58 |
| Melinda Wheat ....................................16* | Dana Staump ..........................................36 |
| Andy Lautzenheifer ...............................67 | |

| Public Schs..Principal | Grd | Prgm | Enr/#Cls | SN | |
|---|---|---|---|---|---|
| Medina Elem Sch<br>1 Bobcat Lane, Medina 78055<br>Janel Murff | PK-5 | | 158<br>12 | | 830/589-2731 |

• **Bastrop Ind School Dist** PID: 00995833     512/321-2292
906 Farm St, Bastrop 78602     Fax 512/321-1371

**Schools:** 15 \ **Teachers:** 698 \ **Students:** 11,000 \
**Special Ed Students:** 1,232 \ **LEP Students:** 2,889 \ **College-Bound:** 41%
\ **Ethnic:** African American 4%, Hispanic 69%, Caucasian 26% \ **Exp:** $539
(High) \ **Poverty:** 18% \ **Title I:** $2,389,196 \ **Special Education:** $1,733,000 \
**Open-Close:** 08/18 - 05/27 \ **DTBP:** $148 (High) \ ■ ■

| | | |
|---|---|---|
| Barry Edwards ............................................1 | Sandra Callahan ...................................2,19 | |
| Scot Bunch ...........................................3,91 | Andy Sexton ...........................................6,13 | |
| Luis Portillo ...........................................20,23 | Kerri Walker ...............................................39* | |
| Augustina Lozano ......................................57 | Jackie Rodgers .........................................58 | |
| Shelly Pietsch ...........................................59 | James Allen ................................................67 | |
| Pene Liefer ................................................68 | Dr Kristi Lee ...........................................71,298 | |
| Randy Sharp .........................................73,84 | Les Hudson ................................................79 | |
| Noemi Guerra ............................................271 | Kayla Russell .............................................274 | |
| Emily Bain .................................................286 | Heather Christie .........................................294 | |

| Public Schs..Principal | Grd | Prgm | Enr/#Cls | SN | |
|---|---|---|---|---|---|
| Bastrop High Sch<br>1614 Chambers St, Bastrop 78602<br>John Gosselink | 9-12 | T | 1,468 | 56% | 512/772-7200<br>Fax 512/772-7920 ■ ■ |
| Bastrop Intermediate Sch<br>509 Old Austin Hwy, Bastrop 78602<br>Daniel Brown | 5-6 | T | 825<br>40 | 68% | 512/772-7450<br>Fax 512/321-4348 |
| Bastrop Middle Sch<br>725 Old Austin Hwy, Bastrop 78602<br>Krystal Gabriel | 7-8 | T | 821<br>55 | 62% | 512/772-7400<br>Fax 512/321-1557 |
| Bluebonnet Elem Sch<br>416 FM 1209, Bastrop 78602<br>David MacRoberts | PK-4 | T | 706<br>34 | 77% | 512/772-7680<br>Fax 512/308-1306 ■ ■ |
| Cedar Creek Elem Sch<br>5582 FM 535, Cedar Creek 78612<br>Dr Delores Godinez | PK-4 | T | 690<br>30 | 86% | 512/772-7600<br>Fax 512/321-6905 ■ ■ |
| Cedar Creek High Sch<br>793 Union Chapel Rd, Cedar Creek 78612<br>Bridgette Cornelius | 9-12 | T | 1,583 | 67% | 512/772-7300<br>Fax 512/772-7930 |
| Cedar Creek Intermediate Sch<br>151 Voss Pkwy, Cedar Creek 78612<br>Alison Hall | 5-6 | T | 930 | 78% | 512/772-7475<br>Fax 512/321-3484 |
| Cedar Creek Middle Sch<br>125 Voss Pkwy, Cedar Creek 78612<br>Jim Hallamek | 7-8 | T | 920<br>60 | 77% | 512/772-7425<br>Fax 512/332-2631 |
| Colorado River Collegiate Acad<br>1602 Hill St, Bastrop 78602<br>Martin Conrardy | 9-10 | T | 161 | 60% | 512/772-7230<br>Fax 512/321-3212 |
| Emile Elem Sch<br>601 Martin Luther King Dr, Bastrop 78602<br>Windy Burnett | PK-4 | T | 718<br>49 | 64% | 512/772-7620<br>Fax 512/321-3564 |
| Ⓐ Gateway Daep Sch<br>1155 Lovers Ln, Bastrop 78602<br>Patricia Alford | 6-12 | | 60<br>9 | | 512/772-7820<br>Fax 512/332-0498 |

| | | | | | | | |
|---|---|---|---|---|---|---|---|
| 1 Superintendent | 8 Curric/Instruct K-12 | 19 Chief Financial Officer | 29 Family/Consumer Science | 39 Social Studies K-12 | 49 English/Lang Arts Elem | 59 Special Education Elem | 69 Academic Assessment |
| 2 Bus/Finance/Purchasing | 9 Curric/Instruct Elem | 20 Art K-12 | 30 Adult Education | 40 Social Studies Elem | 50 English/Lang Arts Sec | 60 Special Education Sec | 70 Research/Development |
| 3 Buildings And Grounds | 10 Curric/Instruct Sec | 21 Art Elem | 31 Career/Sch-to-Work K-12 | 41 Social Studies Sec | 51 Reading K-12 | 61 Foreign/World Lang K-12 | 71 Public Information |
| 4 Food Service | 11 Federal Program | 22 Art Sec | 32 Career/Sch-to-Work Elem | 42 Science K-12 | 52 Reading Elem | 62 Foreign/World Lang Elem | 72 Summer School |
| 5 Transportation | 12 Title I | 23 Music K-12 | 33 Career/Sch-to-Work Sec | 43 Science Elem | 53 Reading Sec | 63 Foreign/World Lang Sec | 73 Instructional Tech |
| 6 Athletic | 13 Title V | 24 Music Elem | 34 Early Childhood Ed | 44 Science Sec | 54 Remedial Reading K-12 | 64 Religious Education K-12 | 74 Inservice Training |
| 7 Health Services | 15 Asst Superintendent | 25 Music Sec | 35 Health/Phys Education | 45 Math K-12 | 55 Remedial Reading Elem | 65 Religious Education Elem | 75 Marketing/Distributive |
| | 16 Instructional Media Svcs | 26 Business Education | 36 Guidance Services K-12 | 46 Math Elem | 56 Remedial Reading Sec | 66 Religious Education Sec | 76 Info Systems |
| | 17 Chief Operations Officer | 27 Career & Tech Ed | 37 Guidance Services Elem | 47 Math Sec | 57 Bilingual/ELL | 67 School Board President | 77 Psychological Assess |
| | 18 Chief Academic Officer | 28 Technology Education | 38 Guidance Services Sec | 48 English/Lang Arts K-12 | 58 Special Education K-12 | 68 Teacher Personnel | 78 Affirmative Action |

**TX — 26**

| | Grd | Prgm | Enr/#Cls | SN | |
|---|---|---|---|---|---|
| Geneisis High Sch | 9-12 | T | 85 | 88% | 512/772-7230 |
| 1602 Hill St, Bastrop 78602 | | | | | Fax 512/321-3212 |
| Martin Conrardy | | | | | 🄵 🄴 |
| Lost Pines Elem Sch | PK-4 | T | 577 | 87% | 512/772-7700 |
| 151 Tiger Woods Dr, Bastrop 78602 | | | | | Fax 512/321-2385 |
| Stacy Trost | | | | | 🄵 🄴 |
| Mina Elem Sch | PK-4 | T | 656 | 56% | 512/772-7640 |
| 1203 Hill St, Bastrop 78602 | | | 45 | | Fax 512/321-4354 |
| Reba King | | | | | 🄵 🄴 |
| Red Rock Elem Sch | PK-4 | T | 573 | 85% | 512/772-7660 |
| 2401 FM 20, Red Rock 78662 | | | 30 | | Fax 512/332-0126 |
| Kelly Hubley | | | | | |

---

● **Elgin Ind School Dist**   PID: 00995883     512/281-3434
   1002 N Avenue C, Elgin 78621     Fax 512/281-9836

**Schools:** 7 \ **Teachers:** 287 \ **Students:** 4,500 \ **Special Ed Students:** 468 \ **LEP Students:** 1,267 \ **Ethnic:** African American 11%, Hispanic 70%, Caucasian 18% \ **Exp:** $471 (High) \ **Poverty:** 18% \ **Title I:** $1,005,852 \ **Special Education:** $720,000 \ **Open-Close:** 08/24 - 06/03 \ **DTBP:** $189 (High) \ 🄴

| | | |
|---|---|---|
| Dr Jodi Duron ......1 | Debra George ......2,19 |
| Rainey Lann ......3 | Elizabeth Guajardo ......4 |
| Alejandro Guerra ......5 | Jens Anderson ......6 |
| Matthew West ......7,91 | Leshell Reeves ......8 |
| Shannon Luis ......8,15,54,57,61,280 | Natalie Webber ......11 |
| Dr Peter Perez ......11,15,83 | Al Rodriguez ......15,68,71,78 |
| Armando Martinez ......23* | Brian Page ......28,73,84,98 |
| Bruce Peckover ......31 | Teresa Hill ......36 |
| Norma Saavedra ......57 | Bonita Homer ......58 |
| Byron Mitchell ......67 | Lashun Gaines ......275 |
| Cynthia Pawelek ......294 | Debra Mahone ......298 |

| Public Schs..Principal | Grd | Prgm | Enr/#Cls | SN | |
|---|---|---|---|---|---|
| Booker T Washington Elem Sch | PK-4 | T | 553 | 83% | 512/281-3411 |
| 510 M L K Dr, Elgin 78621 | | | 32 | | Fax 512/281-9749 |
| Amanda Phillips | | | | | 🄵 🄴 |
| Elgin Elem Sch | PK-5 | T | 809 | 84% | 512/281-3457 |
| 1005 W 2nd St, Elgin 78621 | | | | | Fax 512/281-9772 |
| Sarah Juarez-Farias | | | | | 🄴 |
| Elgin High Sch | 9-12 | ATV | 623 | 69% | 512/281-3438 |
| 14000 County Line Rd, Elgin 78621 | | | 80 | | Fax 512/281-9804 |
| Rick Reyes | | | | | |
| Elgin Intermediate Sch | 5-6 | | 401 | | 512/281-9701 |
| 902 W 2nd St, Elgin 78621 | | | | | Fax 512/281-9874 |
| **Robert Truhill** | | | | | |
| Elgin Middle Sch | 7-8 | T | 640 | 78% | 512/281-3382 |
| 1351 N Avenue C, Elgin 78621 | | | 46 | | Fax 512/281-9781 |
| Riza Cooper | | | | | 🄵 🄴 |
| Neidig Elem Sch | PK-4 | T | 545 | 75% | 512/281-9702 |
| 13700 County Line Rd, Elgin 78621 | | | 35 | | Fax 512/281-9703 |
| Sarah Borowicz | | | | | 🄴 |
| Phoenix High Sch | 9-12 | T | 18 | 78% | 512/281-9774 |
| 902 W 2nd St, Elgin 78621 | | | 2 | | Fax 512/281-9862 |
| Cheryl Williams | | | | | |

---

● **McDade Ind School Dist**   PID: 00995936     512/273-2522
   156 Marlin St, Mc Dade 78650     Fax 512/273-2101

**Schools:** 1 \ **Teachers:** 37 \ **Students:** 370 \ **Special Ed Students:** 36 \ **LEP Students:** 52 \ **College-Bound:** 71% \ **Ethnic:** African American 1%, Hispanic 53%, Caucasian 45% \ **Exp:** $342 (High) \ **Poverty:** 44% \ **Title I:** $224,439 \ **Special Education:** $44,000 \ **Open-Close:** 08/17 - 05/26 \ **DTBP:** $356 (High)

---

| | | |
|---|---|---|
| Barbara Marchbanks ......1,11,288 | Jana Muery ......2 |
| Terry Johnson ......2,3,5,91* | Annette King ......4 |
| Heather Stidham ......8,69,79,88,294 | Cliff Spurlin ......16,73,295,297* |
| Mark Dube ......67 | |

| Public Schs..Principal | Grd | Prgm | Enr/#Cls | SN | |
|---|---|---|---|---|---|
| McDade Sch | PK-10 | T | 370 | 59% | 512/273-2522 |
| 156 Marlin St, Mc Dade 78650 | | | 10 | | |
| Frances Williams | | | | | |

---

● **Smithville Ind School Dist**   PID: 00995974     512/237-2487
   901 NE 6th St, Smithville 78957     Fax 512/237-2775

**Schools:** 5 \ **Teachers:** 137 \ **Students:** 1,800 \ **Special Ed Students:** 194 \ **LEP Students:** 122 \ **College-Bound:** 60% \ **Ethnic:** Asian 1%, African American 7%, Hispanic 33%, Caucasian 58% \ **Exp:** $504 (High) \ **Poverty:** 14% \ **Title I:** $338,572 \ **Special Education:** $233,000 \ **Open-Close:** 08/24 - 05/27 \ **DTBP:** $550 (High)

| | | |
|---|---|---|
| Cheryl Burns ......1 | Jeanann McCarthy ......2,19 |
| Zachary Harris ......3,5 | Candance Biehle ......4 |
| Cyril Adkins ......6* | Weinheimer Sophie ......7 |
| David Edwards ......11* | Michael Caudill ......15,73 |
| Kim Hemphill ......16* | Shari Bang ......58 |
| Grant Gutierrez ......67 | Ana Murray ......71,97 |

| Public Schs..Principal | Grd | Prgm | Enr/#Cls | SN | |
|---|---|---|---|---|---|
| Brown Primary Sch | PK-2 | T | 377 | 67% | 512/237-2519 |
| 403 4th Ave, Smithville 78957 | | | 38 | | Fax 512/237-5635 |
| Stephanie Foster | | | | | |
| Smithville Elem Sch | 3-5 | T | 387 | 61% | 512/237-2406 |
| 800 Bishop St, Smithville 78957 | | | 23 | | Fax 512/237-5614 |
| Tammie Hewitt | | | | | |
| Smithville High Sch | 9-12 | TV | 547 | 51% | 512/237-2451 |
| 285 Highway 95, Smithville 78957 | | | 48 | | Fax 866/289-8681 |
| Paul Smith | | | | | |
| Smithville Junior High Sch | 6-8 | T | 424 | 58% | 512/237-2407 |
| 801 Wilkes St, Smithville 78957 | | | 22 | | Fax 512/237-5624 |
| Chris Kelly | | | | | |
| Ⓐ Tiger Academy | 9-12 | | 30 | | 512/237-5142 |
| 301 Royston St, Smithville 78957 | | | | | |
| David Edwards | | | | | |

---

## BASTROP PRIVATE SCHOOLS

| Private Schs..Principal | Grd | Prgm | Enr/#Cls | SN | |
|---|---|---|---|---|---|
| Rosanky Christian Academy | PK-12 | | 83 | | 512/360-3109 |
| 2160 FM 535, Rosanky 78953 | | | | | Fax 512/360-4088 |
| Sarah Voigt | | | | | |

---

# BAYLOR COUNTY

## BAYLOR PUBLIC SCHOOLS

- **Seymour Ind School Dist** PID: 00996021　　940/889-3525
  409 W Idaho St, Seymour 76380　　　　　　　Fax 940/889-5340

**Schools:** 3 \ **Teachers:** 50 \ **Students:** 582 \ **Special Ed Students:** 74
\ **LEP Students:** 3 \ **College-Bound:** 47% \ **Ethnic:** African American
1%, Hispanic 20%, Caucasian 78% \ **Exp:** $847 (High) \ **Poverty:** 26% \
**Title I:** $214,932 \ **Open-Close:** 08/20 - 05/21 \ **DTBP:** $373 (High) \ 📘 🇹

| | | | |
|---|---|---|---|
| John Anderson | 1 | Cindy Davis | 2,8,11,83,88,296,298 |
| Phil Holub | 3,5 | Connie Shaw | 4 |
| Hugh Farmer | 6* | Sunday McAdams | 16,82* |
| Jimmie Carter | 27* | Shawn Stout | 29* |
| Edward Wolsch | 31,36,69,77* | Carra Carter | 34* |
| Donna Carver | 57,271* | Mona Wardlaw | 58* |
| Whitney Martischnig | 60* | Bryan Baldwin | 67 |
| Courtney Woodward | 73,76,84 | Brian Bibb | 286,288* |

| Public Schs..Principal | Grd | Prgm | Enr/#Cls | SN | |
|---|---|---|---|---|---|
| Seymour Elem Sch | PK-4 | T | 254 | 65% | 940/889-2533 |
| 300 E Idaho St, Seymour 76380 | | | 40 | | Fax 940/889-8890 |
| Kenda Gilbreath | | | | | |
| Seymour High Sch | 9-12 | ATV | 152 | 51% | 940/889-2947 |
| 500 Stadium Dr, Seymour 76380 | | | 24 | | Fax 940/889-1045 |
| Adam Arredondo | | | | | |
| Seymour Middle Sch | 5-8 | AT | 176 | 55% | 940/889-4548 |
| 500 Stadium Dr, Seymour 76380 | | | 17 | | Fax 940/889-4962 |
| Donny Hearn | | | | | |

# BEE COUNTY

## BEE PUBLIC SCHOOLS

- **Beeville Ind School Dist** PID: 00996069　　361/358-7111
  201 N Saint Marys St, Beeville 78102　　　　Fax 361/362-6046

**Schools:** 6 \ **Teachers:** 202 \ **Students:** 3,400 \ **Special Ed Students:** 358
\ **LEP Students:** 75 \ **College-Bound:** 41% \ **Ethnic:** African American
3%, Hispanic 84%, Caucasian 13% \ **Exp:** $293 (Med) \ **Poverty:** 30% \
**Title I:** $1,739,918 \ **Special Education:** $834,000 \ **Open-Close:** 08/17 -
05/27 \ **DTBP:** $137 (High)

| | | | |
|---|---|---|---|
| **Travis Fanning** | 1 | Eve Cisneros | 2 |
| Victor Ramos | 3,27 | Art Provencio | 4 |
| Ernest Delbosque | 5 | Chris Soza | 6 |
| Erasmo Rodriguez | 15,91 | Jay Viertel | 27,36* |
| Rosario Zambrano | 57,58 | Leticia Munoz | 67 |
| Martina Villarreal | 70,294 | Lawrence Garcia | 84 |
| Art Gomez | 91 | | |

| Public Schs..Principal | Grd | Prgm | Enr/#Cls | SN | |
|---|---|---|---|---|---|
| A C Jones High Sch | 9-12 | TV | 989 | 80% | 361/362-6000 |
| 1902 N Adams St, Beeville 78102 | | | | | Fax 361/358-7837 |
| Ann Ewing | | | | | |
| Fadden-McKeown-Chambliss ES | 1-5 | T | 583 | 89% | 361/362-6050 |
| 100 T J Pfeil Ln, Beeville 78102 | | | 27 | | Fax 361/362-6054 |
| Anita Taylor | | | | | |
| Hampton-Moreno-Dugat ECC | PK-K | T | 388 | 90% | 361/362-6040 |
| 2000 S Mussett, Beeville 78102 | | | 17 | | Fax 361/358-7837 |
| Annette Sanchez | | | | | |
| Ⓜ Joe Barnhart Magnet Academy | 7-8 | | 78 | 59% | 361/358-6262 |
| 301 N Minnesota St, Beeville 78102 | | | | | Fax 361/358-7837 |
| Jaime Rodriguez | | | | | |
| Moreno Junior High Sch | 6-8 | T | 701 | 86% | 361/358-6262 |
| 301 N Minnesota St, Beeville 78102 | | | 56 | | Fax 361/362-6094 |
| Jaime Rodriguez | | | | | |
| R A Hall Elem Sch | 1-5 | T | 516 | 85% | 361/362-6060 |
| 1100 W Huntington St, Beeville 78102 | | | 19 | | Fax 361/358-7837 |
| Belinda Aguirre | | | | | |

- **Pawnee Ind School Dist** PID: 00996148　　361/456-7256
  6229 FM 798, Pawnee 78145　　　　　　　　Fax 361/456-7388

**Schools:** 1 \ **Teachers:** 20 \ **Students:** 550 \ **Special Ed Students:** 15 \
**LEP Students:** 3 \ **Ethnic:** Asian 1%, African American 1%, Hispanic 79%,
Caucasian 19% \ **Exp:** $283 (Med) \ **Poverty:** 18% \ **Title I:** $16,379 \
**Open-Close:** 08/03 - 05/27 \ 📘 🇹

| | | | |
|---|---|---|---|
| Michelle Hartmann | 1,11,84 | Josh West | 3 |
| Monica Flores | 4 | Brooke Mills | 7 |
| Kendra Wuest | 8,12,83,88,294* | Pete Dobson | 67 |
| Billy Polasek | 73* | | |

| Public Schs..Principal | Grd | Prgm | Enr/#Cls | SN | |
|---|---|---|---|---|---|
| Pawnee Sch | PK-8 | T | 550 | 85% | 361/456-7256 |
| 6229 FM 798, Pawnee 78145 | | | 17 | | |
| Kendra Wuest | | | | | |

- **Pettus Ind School Dist** PID: 00996174　　361/375-2296
  500 N May St, Pettus 78146　　　　　　　　Fax 361/375-2830

**Schools:** 2 \ **Teachers:** 40 \ **Students:** 400 \ **Special Ed Students:** 45
\ **LEP Students:** 3 \ **College-Bound:** 60% \ **Ethnic:** African American
1%, Hispanic 68%, Caucasian 31% \ **Exp:** $441 (High) \ **Poverty:** 20% \
**Title I:** $205,479 \ **Open-Close:** 08/14 - 05/27 \ **DTBP:** $48 (Low)

| | | | |
|---|---|---|---|
| Mike Homann | 1,11 | Clark Mansker | 2 |
| Larry Bailey | 3 | Mario Monjaras | 4* |
| Micheal Enriquez | 6 | Steve Sugerek | 16,73* |
| Charla Burns | 38,69,83* | Karla Cypert | 57* |
| Jaime Rodriguez | 67 | | |

| Public Schs..Principal | Grd | Prgm | Enr/#Cls | SN | |
|---|---|---|---|---|---|
| Pettus Elem Sch | PK-5 | T | 168 | 79% | 361/375-2296 |
| 500 N B Street, Pettus 78146 | | | 14 | | Fax 361/375-2930 |
| Karla Cypert | | | | | |
| Pettus Secondary Sch | 6-12 | GTV | 232 | 72% | 361/375-2296 |
| 500 N May St, Pettus 78146 | | | 22 | | Fax 361/375-2565 |
| Ricardo DeLeon | | | | | |

| | | | | | | | |
|---|---|---|---|---|---|---|---|
| 1 | Superintendent | 8 | Curric/Instruct K-12 | 19 | Chief Financial Officer | 29 | Family/Consumer Science |
| 2 | Bus/Finance/Purchasing | 9 | Curric/Instruct Elem | 20 | Art K-12 | 30 | Adult Education |
| 3 | Buildings And Grounds | 10 | Curric/Instruct Sec | 21 | Art Elem | 31 | Career/Sch-to-Work K-12 |
| 4 | Food Service | 11 | Federal Program | 22 | Art Sec | 32 | Career/Sch-to-Work Elem |
| 5 | Transportation | 12 | Title I | 23 | Music K-12 | 33 | Career/Sch-to-Work Sec |
| 6 | Athletic | 13 | Title V | 24 | Music Elem | 34 | Early Childhood Ed |
| 7 | Health Services | 14 | Title V | 25 | Music Sec | 35 | Health/Phys Education |
| | | 15 | Asst Superintendent | 26 | Business Education | 36 | Guidance Services K-12 |
| | | 16 | Instructional Media Svcs | 27 | Career & Tech Ed | 37 | Guidance Services Elem |
| | | 17 | Chief Operations Officer | 28 | Technology Education | 38 | Guidance Services Sec |
| | | 18 | Chief Academic Officer | | | | |

| | | | | | |
|---|---|---|---|---|---|
| 39 | Social Studies K-12 | 49 | English/Lang Arts Elem | 59 | Special Education Elem |
| 40 | Social Studies Elem | 50 | English/Lang Arts Sec | 60 | Special Education Sec |
| 41 | Social Studies Sec | 51 | Reading K-12 | 61 | Foreign/World Lang K-12 |
| 42 | Science K-12 | 52 | Reading Elem | 62 | Foreign/World Lang Elem |
| 43 | Science Elem | 53 | Reading Sec | 63 | Foreign/World Lang Sec |
| 44 | Science Sec | 54 | Remedial Reading K-12 | 64 | Religious Education K-12 |
| 45 | Math K-12 | 55 | Remedial Reading Elem | 65 | Religious Education Elem |
| 46 | Math Elem | 56 | Remedial Reading Sec | 66 | Religious Education Sec |
| 47 | Math Sec | 57 | Bilingual/ELL | 67 | School Board President |
| 48 | English/Lang Arts K-12 | 58 | Special Education K-12 | 68 | Teacher Personnel |

| | |
|---|---|
| 69 | Academic Assessment |
| 70 | Research/Development |
| 71 | Public Information |
| 72 | Summer School |
| 73 | Instructional Tech |
| 74 | Inservice Training |
| 75 | Marketing/Distributive |
| 76 | Info Systems |
| 77 | Psychological Assess |
| 78 | Affirmative Action |

● **Skidmore Tynan Ind SD** PID: 00996215    361/287-3426
224 W Main St, Skidmore 78389    Fax 361/287-3442

**Schools:** 3 \ **Teachers:** 64 \ **Students:** 850 \ **Special Ed Students:** 95 \
**LEP Students:** 15 \ **Ethnic:** Asian 1%, African American 1%, Hispanic 70%,
Caucasian 28% \ **Exp:** $331 (High) \ **Poverty:** 21% \ **Title I:** $151,451 \
**Open-Close:** 08/13 - 05/26 \ **DTBP:** $318 (High) \ [f]

| | | |
|---|---|---|
| Richard Waterhouse ...............1 | Robin Moore .......................2 | |
| Steve Batchelor ...............2,5 | Isidor Reyna .......................3 | |
| Jennifer Franklin ...............4 | Stephan Silva .......................6 | |
| Amanda Michael ...............7 | Dr Stephanie Ashworth 8,11,15,69,83,88,288,296 | |
| Debbie Lopez ...............16* | Tracey Young .......................36,88 | |
| Carissa Calderon ...............58 | Will Carriger .......................67 | |
| Keith Knisely ...............73,84 | Judy Garza .......................270* | |

| Public Schs..Principal | Grd | Prgm | Enr/#Cls | SN |
|---|---|---|---|---|
| Skidmore Tynan Elem Sch<br>325 Bodcat Trail, Skidmore 78389<br>Corina Garcia | PK-5 | T | 307<br>20 | 68% 361/287-3425<br>Fax 361/287-3319 |
| Skidmore Tynan High Sch<br>213 N Walton, Skidmore 78389<br>Dana Scott | 9-12 | TV | 273<br>18 | 60% 361/287-3426<br>Fax 361/287-0146 |
| Skidmore Tynan Jr High Sch<br>201 N 8th St, Skidmore 78389<br>Stella Resio | 6-8 | AT | 194<br>13 | 63% 361/287-3426<br>Fax 361/287-0714 |

## BEE PRIVATE SCHOOLS

| Private Schs..Principal | Grd | Prgm | Enr/#Cls | SN |
|---|---|---|---|---|
| First Baptist Church Sch<br>600 N Saint Marys St, Beeville 78102<br>Dr Susan Warner | PK-6 | | 71<br>10 | 361/358-4161<br>Fax 361/358-4163 |
| St Philip's Episcopal Sch<br>105 N Adams St, Beeville 78102<br>Alan Lenz | PK-6 | | 100<br>18 | 361/358-6242<br>Fax 361/358-8232 |

# BELL COUNTY

## BELL PUBLIC SCHOOLS

● **Academy Ind School Dist** PID: 00996253    254/982-4304
704 E Main St, LTL RVR Acad 76554    Fax 254/982-0023

**Schools:** 5 \ **Teachers:** 114 \ **Students:** 1,602 \ **Special Ed Students:** 159
\ **LEP Students:** 76 \ **College-Bound:** 95% \ **Ethnic:** Asian 1%, African
American 6%, Hispanic 22%, Native American: 1%, Caucasian 70% \
**Exp:** $212 (Med) \ **Poverty:** 9% \ **Title I:** $117,861 \ **Open-Close:** 08/12 -
05/21 \ **DTBP:** $350 (High) \ [f]

| | | |
|---|---|---|
| Billy Harlan ...............1 | Sherry Moore .......................2 | |
| Alex Remchel ...............3,11,15,83,88,271,274* | Oscar Martinez .......................3 | |
| Heather Thies ...............4* | Mike Nichols .......................6* | |
| Carlinda Rex ...............9 | Callie Poncik .......................10,74,273* | |
| Jana Warren ...............37* | Nancy Riley .......................58 | |
| Calvin Eshbaugh ...............67 | Amanda Liebman .......................69 | |
| Jarrod Newman ...............73,295 | Connie Bleer .......................76 | |
| Stephen Ash ...............85* | Terry Timberlake .......................295 | |

| Public Schs..Principal | Grd | Prgm | Enr/#Cls | SN |
|---|---|---|---|---|
| Academy Elem Sch<br>311 N Bumblebee Dr, LTL RVR Acad 76554<br>Andrea Chaney | PK-2 | T | 374<br>20 | 50% 254/982-4621<br>Fax 254/982-4584 |
| Academy High Sch<br>602 E Main St, LTL RVR Acad 76554<br>Logan Chaney | 9-12 | TV | 450<br>21 | 35% 254/982-4201<br>Fax 254/982-4420 |
| Academy Intermediate Sch<br>107 S Pondalily, LTL RVR Acad 76554<br>Dana Coleman | 3-5 | T | 397 | 47% 254/982-0150<br>Fax 254/982-0223 |
| Academy Middle Sch<br>501 N Main St, LTL RVR Acad 76554<br>Glenell Bankhead | 6-8 | T | 381<br>25 | 46% 254/982-4620<br>Fax 254/982-4776<br>[f][t] |
| Ⓐ Bell County Alternative Sch<br>706 E Rio Poco, LTL RVR Acad 76554<br>Terry Day | 6-12 | | 30<br>3 | 254/982-3505<br>Fax 254/982-3506 |

● **Bartlett Ind School Dist** PID: 00996289    254/527-4247
404 N Robinson Street, Bartlett 76511    Fax 254/527-3340

**Schools:** 3 \ **Teachers:** 25 \ **Students:** 380 \ **Special Ed Students:** 31
\ **LEP Students:** 44 \ **Ethnic:** African American 12%, Hispanic 67%,
Caucasian 20% \ **Exp:** $312 (High) \ **Poverty:** 19% \ **Title I:** $119,837 \
**Open-Close:** 08/12 - 05/28 \ **DTBP:** $360 (High) \ [f][t]

| | | |
|---|---|---|
| Theodore Clevenger ...............1 | Monica Crouch .......................2 | |
| Elizabeth Maddox ...............4 | Brian Kozma .......................6 | |
| Angie Peace ...............8,36,69,88* | Rachel Fahrig .......................8,11,36,88 | |
| Monica Hauk ...............16,73,295 | Jessica Belcher .......................67 | |
| Shirley Hall ...............68 | | |

| Public Schs..Principal | Grd | Prgm | Enr/#Cls | SN |
|---|---|---|---|---|
| Bartlett Elem Sch<br>404 N Robinson Street, Bartlett 76511<br>Angie Peace | PK-5 | | 203<br>14 | 254/527-3353<br>Fax 254/527-3441 |
| Bartlett High Sch<br>404 N Robinson Street, Bartlett 76511<br>Angie Peace | 9-12 | V | 103<br>20 | 254/527-3351<br>Fax 254/527-3515 |
| Bartlett Middle Sch<br>404 N Robinson St, Bartlett 76511<br>Angie Peace | 6-8 | T | 75 | 84% 254/527-4247 |

● **Belton Ind School Dist** PID: 00996318    254/215-2000
400 N Wall St, Belton 76513    Fax 254/215-2001

**Schools:** 17 \ **Teachers:** 750 \ **Students:** 11,950 \
**Special Ed Students:** 1,519 \ **LEP Students:** 694 \ **College-Bound:** 65%
\ **Ethnic:** Asian 2%, African American 7%, Hispanic 35%, Caucasian
55% \ **Exp:** $306 (High) \ **Poverty:** 12% \ **Title I:** $1,579,924 \
**Special Education:** $1,833,000 \ **Open-Close:** 08/19 - 05/26 \ **DTBP:** $181
(High) \ [f][t]

| | | |
|---|---|---|
| Dr Matt Smith ...............1 | Jennifer Land .......................2,19 | |
| Kerri Pridemore ...............2 | Tammy Shannon .......................2 | |
| Rick Martinez ...............3 | Rob Pasichnyk .......................4 | |
| Andrew Forrester ...............5 | Sanvel Skidmore .......................6 | |
| Charlotte Smith ...............7*<br>8,15,88,270,275,286,296,298 | Dr Deanna Lovesmith | |
| Celia Ray ...............11 | Mike Morgan .......................15,79 | |
| Dr Robert Muller ...............15 | Todd Shiller .......................15,68,78,273 | |
| Stephanie Ferguson ...............26,31,75* | Sue Banfield .......................34* | |
| Beverly Stephens ...............36* | Lauren Brisbin .......................57,280 | |
| Jennifer Ramirez ...............58 | Sue Jordan .......................67 | |
| Dawn Schiller ...............69,70 | Dr Charlotte Trejo .......................74,273 | |
| Rachel Starnes ...............76 | Barbara Epperson .......................81 | |
| Doug Taylor ...............91 | Vickie Dean .......................294 | |
| Dr Rachelle Warren ...............752 | | |

| | | | | | | |
|---|---|---|---|---|---|---|
| 79 | Student Personnel | 91 | Safety/Security | 275 | Response To Intervention | |
| 80 | Driver Ed/Safety | 92 | Magnet School | 277 | Remedial Math K-12 | |
| 81 | Gifted/Talented | 93 | Parental Involvement | 280 | Literacy Coach | |
| 82 | Video Services | 95 | Tech Prep Program | 285 | STEM | |
| 83 | Substance Abuse Prev | 97 | Chief Infomation Officer | 286 | Digital Learning | |
| 84 | Erate | 98 | Chief Technology Officer | 288 | Common Core Standards | |
| 85 | AIDS Education | 270 | Character Education | 294 | Accountability | |
| 88 | Alternative/At Risk | 271 | Migrant Education | 295 | Network System | |
| 89 | Multi-Cultural Curriculum | 273 | Teacher Mentor | 296 | Title II Programs | |
| 90 | Social Work | 274 | Before/After Sch | 297 | Webmaster | |

| | |
|---|---|
| 298 Grant Writer/Ptnrships | **School Programs** |
| 750 Chief Innovation Officer | A = Alternative Program |
| 751 Chief of Staff | G = Adult Classes |
| 752 Social Emotional Learning | M = Magnet Program |
| | T = Title I Schoolwide |
| **Other School Types** | V = Career & Tech Ed Programs |
| Ⓐ = Alternative Program | |
| Ⓒ = Charter School | **New Schools are shaded** |
| Ⓜ = Magnet School | **New Superintendents and Principals are bold** |
| Ⓨ = Year-Round School | Personnel with email addresses are underscored |

**Social Media**
[f] = Facebook
[t] = Twitter

| Public Schs..Principal | Grd | Prgm | Enr/#Cls | SN |
|---|---|---|---|---|
| Ⓐ Aep Center<br>302 N Blair St, Belton 76513<br>Ted Smith | 6-12 | V | 50<br>2 | 254/215-2571<br>Fax 254/215-2551 |
| Belton Early Childhood Sch<br>501 E 4th Ave, Belton 76513<br>Sue Banfield | PK-PK | T | 441 | 73% 254/215-3700<br>Fax 254/215-3701 |
| Belton High Sch<br>600 Lake Rd, Belton 76513<br>Ben Smith | 9-12 | TV | 2,924 | 44% 254/215-2200<br>Fax 254/215-2201<br>f t |
| Charter Oak Elem Sch<br>8402 Poison Oak Rd, Temple 76502<br>Jennifer Conner | K-5 | | 400 | 254/215-4000<br>Fax 254/215-4001 |
| Chisholm Trail Elem Sch<br>1082 S Wheat Rd, Belton 76513<br>Elizabeth McMurtry | K-5 | T | 794 | 62% 254/316-5100<br>Fax 254/316-5101<br>f t |
| High Point Elem Sch<br>1635 Starlight Dr, Temple 76502<br>Amy Armstrong | K-5 | T | 668 | 42% 254/316-5000<br>Fax 254/316-5001 |
| Joe M Pirtle Elem Sch<br>714 S Pea Ridge Rd, Temple 76502<br>Rebecca Vaughn | K-5 | T | 787<br>39 | 34% 254/215-3400<br>Fax 254/215-3401 |
| Lake Belton Middle Sch<br>8818 Tarver Dr, Temple 76502<br>Kris Hobson | 6-8 | T | 917<br>65 | 49% 254/215-2900<br>Fax 254/780-3493<br>f t |
| Lakewood Elem Sch<br>11200 FM 2305, Belton 76513<br>Judy Schiller | K-5 | | 706<br>35 | 24% 254/215-3100<br>Fax 254/215-3101 |
| Leon Heights Elem Sch<br>1501 N Main St, Belton 76513<br>Marcie Beck | K-5 | T | 260<br>14 | 50% 254/215-3200<br>Fax 254/215-3201<br>f t |
| Miller Heights Elem Sch<br>1110 Fairway Dr, Belton 76513<br>Jennifer Conner | K-5 | T | 319<br>22 | 82% 254/215-3300<br>Fax 254/215-3301 |
| New Tech High Sch at Waskow<br>320 N Blair St, Belton 76513<br>Benjamin Smith | 9-12 | | 521<br>5 | 25% 254/215-2500<br>Fax 254/215-2501 |
| North Belton Middle Sch<br>7907 Prairie View Rd, Temple 76502<br>Joe Brown | 6-8 | | 1,031<br>30 | 35% 254/316-5200<br>Fax 254/316-5201 |
| South Belton Middle Sch<br>805 Sage Brush, Belton 76513<br>Kevin Taylor | 6-8 | T | 879 | 53% 254/215-3000<br>Fax 254/215-3001 |
| Southwest Elem Sch<br>611 Saunders St, Belton 76513<br>Dawn Schiller | K-5 | T | 402<br>26 | 88% 254/215-3500<br>Fax 254/215-3501 |
| Sparta Elem Sch<br>1800 Sparta Rd, Belton 76513<br>Julee Manley | K-5 | | 568<br>22 | 33% 254/215-3600<br>Fax 254/215-3601 |
| Tarver Elem Sch<br>7949 Stonehollow Dr, Temple 76502<br>Aubrey Itz | K-5 | | 668<br>37 | 39% 254/215-3800<br>Fax 254/215-3801<br>f t |

● **Holland Ind School Dist** PID: 00996394    254/657-0175
105 S Rose Ln, Holland 76534    Fax 254/657-0172

**Schools:** 3 \ **Teachers:** 58 \ **Students:** 636 \ **Special Ed Students:** 55 \ **LEP Students:** 18 \ **College-Bound:** 55% \ **Ethnic:** African American 3%, Hispanic 29%, Caucasian 68% \ **Exp:** $370 (High) \ **Poverty:** 16% \ **Title I:** $112,548 \ **Open-Close:** 08/12 - 05/21 \ **DTBP:** $347 (High)

| | | | |
|---|---|---|---|
| Shane Downing .................1,57 | Tracy Wolf ............................2,84 |
| Larry Coufal ..........................3 | Connie Knaus ........................4 |
| Brad Talbert ..........................6 | Cynthia Phaestka ..................7 |
| Melany Cearley ........8,36,79,88,270* | Robbie Edwards .......10,11,57,83,275,285 |
| Terri Crum ...........................16* | Nancy Riley .........................58 |

Jill Marwitz ....................67    Sherry Kallus .................274*
Keith Cabaniss .............295*

| Public Schs..Principal | Grd | Prgm | Enr/#Cls | SN |
|---|---|---|---|---|
| Holland Elem Sch<br>503 Crockett St, Holland 76534<br>Lori Kinard | PK-5 | T | 273<br>20 | 53% 254/657-2525<br>Fax 254/657-2845 |
| Holland High Sch<br>502 Crockett St, Holland 76534<br>Robby Edwards | 9-12 | AV | 210<br>19 | 43% 254/657-2523<br>Fax 254/657-2250 |
| Holland Middle Sch<br>302 Hackberry Rd, Holland 76534<br>Leah Smith | 6-8 | ATV | 147<br>11 | 48% 254/657-2224<br>Fax 254/657-2872 |

● **Killeen Ind School Dist** PID: 00996423    254/336-0000
200 N W S Young Dr, Killeen 76543    Fax 254/336-0010

**Schools:** 53 \ **Teachers:** 2,943 \ **Students:** 45,500 \ **Special Ed Students:** 5,659 \ **LEP Students:** 4,311 \ **College-Bound:** 75% \ **Ethnic:** Asian 3%, African American 39%, Hispanic 34%, Native American: 1%, Caucasian 24% \ **Exp:** $399 (High) \ **Poverty:** 19% \ **Title I:** $13,217,454 \ **Special Education:** $6,078,000 \ **Bilingual Education:** $106,000 \ **Open-Close:** 08/17 - 05/27 \ **DTBP:** $199 (High) \ f

| | | | |
|---|---|---|---|
| Dr John Craft .........................1 | Evan Leach .........................2 |
| Megan Bradley ....................2,19 | Lori Alejandro ......................4 |
| Steven Smith ..........................4 | Edward Thomas ....................5 |
| Randall Hugg .........................6 | Vhonda Gilmore ....................7 |
| David Manley .......................9,15 | Dagmar Harris .....................10 |
| Dr Eric Penrod ......................15 | Dr Karen Herrera ...............20,23 |
| Nancy Duran .........................31 | Deborah Holloway ................34 |
| Shannon Lumar .....................36 | Liodolee Garcia .................57,271 |
| Dr Jacqueline Pilkey ..............58 | Dr Janice Peronto .................58 |
| Corbett Lawler ......................67 | Jessica Neyman ...................68 |
| Jo-Lynette Crayton ........68,74,273 | Teresa Daugherty ..............69,294 |
| Taina Maya ...........................71 | Cyndi Carlton ......................76 |
| Sandra Forsythe ....................79 | Charles Kelley .....................91 |
| Cynthia Hodges ....................285 | Holly Landez .......................286 |
| Joyce Hodson ......................298 | |

| Public Schs..Principal | Grd | Prgm | Enr/#Cls | SN |
|---|---|---|---|---|
| Alice W Douse Elem Sch<br>700 Rebecca Lynn Ln, Killeen 76542<br>Stephanie Ford | PK-5 | T | 897 | 51% 254/336-7480<br>Fax 254/336-7490 |
| Audie Murphy Middle Sch<br>53393 Sun Dance Dr, Fort Hood 76544<br>**Jennifer Warren** | 6-8 | T | 822 | 48% 254/336-6530<br>Fax 254/336-6579 |
| Bellaire Elem Sch<br>108 W Jasper Dr, Killeen 76542<br>Lavonda Loney | PK-5 | T | 598<br>37 | 83% 254/336-1410<br>Fax 254/336-1437 |
| Brookhaven Elem Sch<br>3221 Hilliard Ave, Killeen 76543<br>Iris Felder | PK-5 | T | 638<br>38 | 84% 254/336-1440<br>Fax 254/336-1463 |
| Cedar Valley Elem Sch<br>4801 Chantz Dr, Killeen 76542<br>Connie Morris | PK-5 | T | 670<br>43 | 69% 254/336-1480<br>Fax 254/336-1496<br>f |
| Clarke Elem Sch<br>51612 Comanche Ave, Fort Hood 76544<br>Laura Dart | PK-3 | T | 576<br>50 | 72% 254/336-1510<br>Fax 254/336-1528 |
| Clear Creek Elem Sch<br>4800 Washington St, Fort Hood 76544<br>Maryann Ramos | PK-5 | T | 698<br>40 | 80% 254/336-1550<br>Fax 254/336-1567 |
| Clifton Park Elem Sch<br>2200 Trimmier Rd, Killeen 76541<br>Jennifer Carranza | PK-5 | T | 559<br>29 | 80% 254/336-1580<br>Fax 254/336-1598 |
| Early College High Sch<br>51000 Tank Destroyer Blvd, Fort Hood 76544<br>Kathleen Burke | 9-12 | | 1,023 | 42% 254/336-0260<br>Fax 254/336-0271 |

| | | | | | | |
|---|---|---|---|---|---|---|
| **1** Superintendent | **8** Curric/Instruct K-12 | **19** Chief Financial Officer | **29** Family/Consumer Science | **39** Social Studies K-12 | **49** English/Lang Arts Elem | **59** Special Education Elem | **69** Academic Assessment |
| **2** Bus/Finance/Purchasing | **9** Curric/Instruct Elem | **20** Art K-12 | **30** Adult Education | **40** Social Studies Elem | **50** English/Lang Arts Sec | **60** Special Education Sec | **70** Research/Development |
| **3** Buildings And Grounds | **10** Curric/Instruct Sec | **21** Art Elem | **31** Career/Sch-to-Work K-12 | **41** Social Studies Sec | **51** Reading K-12 | **61** Foreign/World Lang K-12 | **71** Public Information |
| **4** Food Service | **11** Federal Program | **22** Art Sec | **32** Career/Sch-to-Work Elem | **42** Science K-12 | **52** Reading Elem | **62** Foreign/World Lang Elem | **72** Summer School |
| **5** Transportation | **12** Title I | **23** Music K-12 | **33** Career/Sch-to-Work Sec | **43** Science Elem | **53** Reading Sec | **63** Foreign/World Lang Sec | **73** Instructional Tech |
| **6** Athletic | **13** Title V | **24** Music Elem | **34** Early Childhood Ed | **44** Science Sec | **54** Remedial Reading K-12 | **64** Religious Education K-12 | **74** Inservice Training |
| **7** Health Services | **15** Asst Superintendent | **25** Music Sec | **35** Health/Phys Education | **45** Math K-12 | **55** Remedial Reading Elem | **65** Religious Education Elem | **75** Marketing/Distributive |
| | **16** Instructional Media Svcs | **26** Business Education | **36** Guidance Services K-12 | **46** Math Elem | **56** Remedial Reading Sec | **66** Religious Education Sec | **76** Info Systems |
| | **17** Chief Operations Officer | **27** Career & Tech Ed | **37** Guidance Services Elem | **47** Math Sec | **57** Bilingual/ELL | **67** School Board President | **77** Psychological Assess |
| | **18** Chief Academic Officer | **28** Technology Education | **38** Guidance Services Sec | **48** English/Lang Arts K-12 | **58** Special Education K-12 | **68** Teacher Personnel | **78** Affirmative Action |

| School | Grades | Prog | Enroll/Staff | % | Phone/Fax |
|---|---|---|---|---|---|
| Eastern Hills Middle Sch<br>300 Indian Trl, Harker HTS 76548<br>**Gina Brown** | 6-8 | T | 743<br>50 | 70% | 254/336-1100<br>Fax 254/336-1115 |
| Ellison High Sch<br>909 E Elms Rd, Killeen 76542<br>David Dominguez | 9-12 | V | 2,639<br>98 | 45% | 254/336-0600<br>Fax 254/336-0606 |
| Fowler Elem Sch<br>4910 Katy Creek Ln, Killeen 76549<br>**Donna Hardy** | PK-5 | T | 1,146<br>40 | 62% | 254/336-1760<br>Fax 254/336-1789 |
| Ⓐ Gateway High Sch<br>4100 Zephyr Rd, Killeen 76543<br>Nino Etienne | 9-12 | V | 59<br>12 | 66% | 254/336-1700<br>Fax 254/501-1711 |
| Ⓐ Gateway Middle Sch<br>1307 Gowen Dr, Killeen 76543<br>Dr Nino Etienne | 6-8 | | 40<br>9 | 68% | 254/336-1690<br>Fax 254/336-1698 |
| Harker Heights Elem Sch<br>726 S Ann Blvd, Harker HTS 76548<br>Carolyn Dugger | PK-5 | T | 724<br>38 | 87% | 254/336-2050<br>Fax 254/336-2073 |
| Harker Heights High Sch<br>1001 E FM 2410 Rd, Harker HTS 76548<br>Jorge Soldevila | 9-12 | V | 2,520 | 32% | 254/336-0800<br>Fax 254/336-0829 |
| Hay Branch Elem Sch<br>6101 Westcliff Rd, Killeen 76543<br>Cassandra Spearman | PK-5 | T | 589<br>45 | 89% | 254/336-2080<br>Fax 254/336-2097 |
| Haynes Elem Sch<br>3309 Canadian River Loop, Killeen 76549<br>Angela Donovan | PK-5 | T | 943 | 64% | 254/336-6750<br>Fax 254/336-2798 |
| Iduma Elem Sch<br>4400 Foster Ln, Killeen 76549<br>Katy Bohannon | PK-5 | T | 772 | 71% | 254/336-2590<br>Fax 254/336-2598 |
| Ira Cross Jr Elem Sch<br>1910 Herndon Dr, Killeen 76543<br>Tomas Sias | PK-5 | T | 740 | 86% | 254/336-2550<br>Fax 254/336-2560 |
| Killeen High Sch<br>500 N 38th St, Killeen 76543<br>Kara Trevino | 9-12 | TV | 2,296 | 57% | 254/336-7208<br>Fax 254/336-0413 |
| Killeen ISD Career Center<br>1320 Stagecoach Rd, Killeen 76542<br>Russell Porterfield | Voc | | 1,434<br>12 | | 254/336-3800<br>Fax 254/519-7737 |
| Liberty Hill Middle Sch<br>4500 Kit Carson Trl, Killeen 76542<br>Latricia Brown | 6-8 | T | 923<br>45 | 47% | 254/336-1370<br>Fax 254/336-1403 |
| Live Oak Ridge Middle Sch<br>2600 Robinett Rd, Killeen 76549<br>Wanda Stidom | 6-8 | T | 673 | 66% | 254/336-2490<br>Fax 254/336-2498 |
| Manor Middle Sch<br>1700 S W S Young Dr, Killeen 76543<br>Rhea Bell | 6-8 | TV | 729 | 78% | 254/336-1310<br>Fax 254/336-1317 |
| Maude Moore Wood Elem Sch<br>6410 Morganite Ln, Killeen 76542<br>**Pamela Disher** | PK-5 | | 600<br>31 | | 254/336-1650<br>Fax 254/336-1669 |
| Maxdale Elem Sch<br>2600 Westwood Dr, Killeen 76549<br>Bobbie Evans | PK-5 | T | 689<br>44 | 75% | 254/336-2460<br>Fax 254/336-2469 |
| Meadows Elem Sch<br>423 27th St, Fort Hood 76544<br>**Nickolas Smith** | PK-5 | | 842<br>40 | 46% | 254/336-1870<br>Fax 254/336-1893 |
| Montague Village Elem Sch<br>84001 Clements Dr, Fort Hood 76544<br>Natalie Cue | PK-5 | T | 633<br>36 | 59% | 254/336-2230<br>Fax 254/336-2238 |
| Mountain View Elem Sch<br>500 Mountain Lion Rd, Harker HTS 76548<br>Randy Podhaski | PK-5 | | 947<br>53 | 42% | 254/336-1900<br>Fax 254/336-1919 |
| Nolan Middle Sch<br>1600 Warriors Path, Harker HTS 76548<br>Ashley York | 6-8 | TV | 758<br>45 | 84% | 254/336-1150<br>Fax 254/336-1162 |
| Nolanville Elem Sch<br>901 Old Nolanville Rd, Nolanville 76559<br>Wendy Haider | PK-5 | T | 557<br>40 | 55% | 254/336-2180<br>Fax 254/336-2202 |
| Oveta Culp Hobby Elem Sch<br>53210 Lost Moccasin, Fort Hood 76544<br>**Alena Thomas** | PK-5 | AT | 553<br>42 | 65% | 254/336-6500<br>Fax 254/336-6505 |
| Palo Alto Middle Sch<br>2301 W Elms Rd, Killeen 76549<br>Kernisha Hill | 6-8 | T | 705<br>46 | 71% | 254/336-1200<br>Fax 254/336-1217 |
| Ⓐ Pathways Academic Campus<br>1322 Stagecoach Rd, Killeen 76542<br>Dr Bobbie Reeders | 9-12 | | 283<br>12 | 62% | 254/336-7250<br>Fax 254/336-7298 |
| Patterson Middle Sch<br>8383 Trimmier Rd, Killeen 76542<br>Latisha Williams | 6-8 | T | 1,056<br>51 | 49% | 254/336-7100<br>Fax 254/336-7136 |
| Peebles Elem Sch<br>1800 N W S Young Dr, Killeen 76543<br>Carol Correa | PK-5 | T | 695<br>34 | 88% | 254/336-2120<br>Fax 254/336-2131 |
| Pershing Park Elem Sch<br>1500 W Central Texas Expy, Killeen 76549<br>**Jessica Taylor** | PK-5 | T | 621<br>50 | 86% | 254/336-1790<br>Fax 254/336-1804 |
| Rancier Middle Sch<br>3301 Hilliard Ave, Killeen 76543<br>Alan Gawryszewski | 6-8 | TV | 706<br>51 | 76% | 254/336-1250<br>Fax 254/336-1254 |
| Reeces Creek Elem Sch<br>400 W Stan Schlueter Loop, Killeen 76542<br>Sara Watson | PK-5 | T | 801<br>44 | 79% | 254/336-2150<br>Fax 254/336-2165 |
| Richard E Cavazos Elem Sch<br>1200 N 10th St, Nolanville 76559<br>Joe Gullekson | PK-5 | T | 579 | 66% | 254/336-7000<br>Fax 254/336-7030 |
| Robert M Shoemaker High Sch<br>3302 S Clear Creek Rd, Killeen 76549<br>Micah Wells | 9-12 | T | 2,169<br>60 | 56% | 254/336-0900<br>Fax 254/336-2416 |
| Roy J Smith Middle Sch<br>6000 Brushy Creek Dr, Killeen 76549<br>Chad Wolf | 6-8 | T | 1,322 | 54% | 254/336-1050<br>Fax 254/336-1056 |
| Saegert Elem Sch<br>5600 Schorn Dr, Killeen 76542<br>Eli Lopez | PK-5 | AT | 802 | 63% | 254/336-6660<br>Fax 254/336-6684 |
| Skipcha Elem Sch<br>515 Prospector Trl, Harker HTS 76548<br>Jane Apodaca | PK-5 | | 1,056 | 39% | 254/336-6690<br>Fax 254/336-6711 |
| STEM Academy-Killeen<br>6000 Brushy Creek Dr, Killeen 76549<br>Chad Wolf | 6-12 | | 14 | | 254/336-7836 |
| Sugar Loaf Elem Sch<br>1517 Barbara Ln, Killeen 76549<br>Violet Simmons | PK-5 | T | 253<br>34 | 85% | 254/336-1940<br>Fax 254/336-1945 |
| Timber Ridge Elem Sch<br>5402 White Rock Dr, Killeen 76542<br>Tanya Dockery | PK-5 | T | 976 | 48% | 254/336-6630<br>Fax 254/336-6653 |
| Trimmier Elem Sch<br>4400 Success Dr, Killeen 76542<br>**Beckie Avery** | PK-5 | T | 839<br>35 | 78% | 254/336-2270<br>Fax 254/336-2284 |
| Union Grove Middle Sch<br>101 E Iowa Dr, Harker HTS 76548<br>Paula Lawrason | 6-8 | | 932 | 26% | 254/336-6580<br>Fax 254/336-6593 |
| Venable Village Elem Sch<br>60160 Venable Dr, Fort Hood 76544<br>Vickie Wasson | PK-5 | T | 514<br>50 | 71% | 254/336-1980<br>Fax 254/336-2015 |
| West Ward Elem Sch<br>709 W Dean Ave, Killeen 76541<br>Tammy Thornhill | PK-5 | T | 461<br>32 | 96% | 254/336-1830<br>Fax 254/336-1861 |
| Willow Springs Elem Sch<br>2501 W Stan Schlueter Loop, Killeen 76549<br>Connie Locke | PK-5 | T | 880<br>52 | 80% | 254/336-2020<br>Fax 254/336-2047 |

---

| | | | | |
|---|---|---|---|---|
| 79 Student Personnel | 91 Safety/Security | 275 Response To Intervention | 298 Grant Writer/Ptnrships | **School Programs** | **Social Media** |
| 80 Driver Ed/Safety | 92 Magnet School | 277 Remedial Math K-12 | 750 Chief Innovation Officer | A = Alternative Program | |
| 81 Gifted/Talented | 93 Parental Involvement | 280 Literacy Coach | 751 Chief of Staff | G = Adult Classes | 🅕 = Facebook |
| 82 Video Services | 95 Tech Prep Program | 285 STEM | 752 Social Emotional Learning | M = Magnet Program | |
| 83 Substance Abuse Prev | 97 Chief Infomation Officer | 286 Digital Learning | | T = Title I Schoolwide | 🅣 = Twitter |
| 84 Erate | 98 Chief Technology Officer | 288 Common Core Standards | **Other School Types** | V = Career & Tech Ed Programs | |
| 85 AIDS Education | 270 Character Education | 294 Accountability | Ⓐ = Alternative School | | |
| 88 Alternative/At Risk | 271 Migrant Education | 295 Network System | Ⓒ = Charter School | New Schools are shaded | |
| 89 Multi-Cultural Curriculum | 273 Teacher Mentor | 296 Title II Programs | Ⓜ = Magnet School | New Superintendents and Principals are bold | |
| 90 Social Work | 274 Before/After Sch | 297 Webmaster | Ⓨ = Year-Round School | Personnel with email addresses are underscored | |

## • Rogers Ind School Dist  PID: 00996643

1 Eagle Dr, Rogers 76569

254/642-3802
Fax 254/642-3851

**Schools:** 3 \ **Teachers:** 65 \ **Students:** 869 \ **Special Ed Students:** 73
\ **LEP Students:** 37 \ **College-Bound:** 50% \ **Ethnic:** Asian 1%,
African American 1%, Hispanic 32%, Caucasian 66% \ **Exp:** $345 (High)
\ **Poverty:** 10% \ **Title I:** $95,271 \ **Special Education:** $174,000 \
**Open-Close:** 08/10 - 05/27 \ **DTBP:** $341 (High)

| | |
|---|---|
| Joe Criag ...........................1,83 | Tracie Malovets ......................2 |
| Jason Beard ...........................3,5 | Christy Stone ..........................4 |
| Charles Roten ...........................6 | Carol Morris ..........................7 |
| Becky Ralston ...............8,69,294 | Tammy Tucker ...............11,296,298 |
| Garrett Layne ...........12,34,277* | Nicolette Wiesman ......36,85,88,275,288 |
| Kimberly Marek ...........................57 | Keith Caldwell ........................67 |
| Carol Whitley .................68,91* | Cheyenne Doskocil ...........68,297 |
| Glen Kinard ...........................73,295 | |

| Public Schs..Principal | Grd | Prgm | Enr/#Cls | SN |
|---|---|---|---|---|
| Rogers Elem Sch<br>802 Cemetery Rd, Rogers 76569<br>Garrett Layne | PK-5 | T | 363<br>22 | 58% 254/642-3250<br>Fax 254/642-3145 |
| Rogers High Sch<br>1 Eagle Dr, Rogers 76569<br>**Lee Vi Moses** | 9-12 | V | 187<br>22 | 45% 254/642-3224<br>Fax 254/642-3037 |
| Rogers Middle Sch<br>1 Eagle Dr, Rogers 76569<br>Lucinda Smith | 6-8 | TV | 206<br>12 | 48% 254/642-3011<br>Fax 254/642-0033 |

## • Salado Ind School Dist  PID: 00996679

601 N Main St, Salado 76571

254/947-6900
Fax 254/947-5605

**Schools:** 3 \ **Teachers:** 126 \ **Students:** 2,056 \ **Special Ed Students:** 128
\ **LEP Students:** 91 \ **College-Bound:** 64% \ **Ethnic:** Asian 1%, African
American 1%, Hispanic 21%, Caucasian 76% \ **Exp:** $513 (High) \
**Poverty:** 11% \ **Title I:** $172,863 \ **Open-Close:** 08/24 - 05/26 \ **DTBP:** $342
(High)

| | |
|---|---|
| Michael Novotny ...........................1 | Brandy Stanford ......................2,11 |
| Danny Agee ...........................3,5 | Jenni Netherland ...........3,4,5,17 |
| Brenda Hodges ...........................4* | Paul Baird ..........................6 |
| Ashley Faglie ...........................7* | Burt Smith ...............8,15,36,68,69,91,298 |
| Bobette Bell ...........................16 | Kendra Copeland ......................57* |
| Melanie Kasper ...........................58 | Kim Bird ..........................67 |
| Earl Bragg ...........................73 | |

| Public Schs..Principal | Grd | Prgm | Enr/#Cls | SN |
|---|---|---|---|---|
| Salado High Sch<br>1880 Williams Rd, Salado 76571<br>Beth Aycock | 9-12 | AV | 435<br>45 | 18% 254/947-6985<br>Fax 254/947-6984 |
| Salado Junior High Sch<br>620 Thomas Arnold Rd, Salado 76571<br>Smith Ted | 6-8 | | 479 | 28% 254/947-6935<br>Fax 254/947-6934 |
| Thomas Arnold Elem Sch<br>510 Thomas Arnold Rd, Salado 76571<br>Julie Mullins | PK-5 | | 826<br>14 | 254/947-6925<br>Fax 254/947-6924 |

## • Temple Ind School Dist  PID: 00996708

401 Santa Fe Way, Temple 76501

254/215-8473
Fax 254/215-6783

**Schools:** 15 \ **Teachers:** 609 \ **Students:** 8,700 \ **Special Ed Students:** 1,037
\ **LEP Students:** 955 \ **Ethnic:** Asian 2%, African American 28%, Hispanic
47%, Caucasian 24% \ **Exp:** $387 (High) \ **Poverty:** 23% \ **Title I:** $3,561,842
\ **Special Education:** $1,781,000 \ **Open-Close:** 08/19 - 05/27 \ **DTBP:** $160
(High) \ 

| | |
|---|---|
| Dr Bobby Ott ...........................1 | Kallen Vaden ......................2,19 |
| Kent Boyd ...........................2,15 | Kenneth Wolf ..........................3 |
| Ian Vestal ...........................4 | Patrick Cain ..........................5 |
| Scott Stewart ...........................6* | Kim Glawe ..........................7 |
| Renota Rogers ...........................8 | Beth Giniewicz ..........................9 |
| Lisa Adams ...........................10,15 | Dr Karen Morgan ...............11,294,296 |
| Eric Haugeberg ...............13,15,79 | Joe Palmer ...............15,68 |
| Catrina Lotspeich ...............20,23* | Denise Ayres ..........................31* |
| Dr Nichole Riley ...............36,83,275 | Consuelo Sisneros ..........................57 |
| Jennie Mathesen ...........................58 | Dan Posey ..........................67 |
| Amy Hayes ...........................68 | David McCauley ..........................68 |
| Dawn Sills ...........................69,294 | Christian Hernanadez ..........................71 |
| Marc Sivak ...............73,84,286 | Carl Pleasant ..........................88* |
| Gil Hollie ...........................274 | Craig Wilson ..........................286 |

| Public Schs..Principal | Grd | Prgm | Enr/#Cls | SN |
|---|---|---|---|---|
| Bonham Middle Sch<br>4600 Midway Dr, Temple 76502<br>Sandra Atmar | 6-8 | TV | 666<br>40 | 69% 254/215-6600<br>Fax 254/215-6634 |
| Cater Elem Sch<br>4111 Lark Trl, Temple 76502<br>Adrian Lopez | PK-5 | T | 184<br>17 | 75% 254/215-7444<br>Fax 254/215-7479 |
| Ⓐ Fred W Edwards Academy<br>1414 W Barton Ave, Temple 76504<br>**Tricia Mitchell** | 9-12 | GT | 37 | 58% 254/215-6944<br>Fax 254/215-6946<br> |
| Hector P Garcia Elem Sch<br>2525 Lavendusky Dr, Temple 76501<br>Sandra Reyes | K-5 | T | 422<br>35 | 88% 254/215-6100<br>Fax 254/215-6122 |
| Jefferson Elem Sch<br>2616 N 3rd St, Temple 76501<br>Pamela Demny | K-5 | T | 568<br>26 | 76% 254/215-5500<br>Fax 254/215-5545 |
| Kennedy-Powell Elem Sch<br>3707 W Nugent Ave, Temple 76504<br>Kelly Madden | K-5 | T | 484<br>25 | 64% 254/215-6000<br>Fax 254/215-6032 |
| Lamar Middle Sch<br>2120 N 1st St, Temple 76501<br>**Yvette Bradford** | 6-8 | TV | 202<br>42 | 77% 254/215-6444<br>Fax 254/215-6483 |
| Meridith-Dunbar EC Academy<br>1717 E Avenue J, Temple 76501<br>Nikki Murphy | PK-PK | T | 560<br>16 | 98% 254/215-6700<br>Fax 254/215-6728 |
| Raye-Allen Elem Sch<br>5015 S 5th St, Temple 76502<br>Frances Smetana | PK-5 | T | 382<br>27 | 79% 254/215-5800<br>Fax 254/215-5843 |
| Scott Elem Sch<br>2301 W Avenue P, Temple 76504<br>Chrystal Thomas | PK-5 | T | 411<br>18 | 73% 254/215-6222<br>Fax 254/215-6251 |
| Temple High Sch<br>415 N 31st St, Temple 76504<br>Dr Jason Mayo | 9-12 | TV | 2,197 | 58% 254/215-7000<br>Fax 254/899-6926 |
| Thornton Elem Sch<br>2825 Cottonwood Ln, Temple 76502<br>Michelle Moore | PK-5 | T | 625<br>20 | 75% 254/215-5700<br>Fax 254/215-5746 |
| Travis Science Academy<br>1551 S 25th St, Temple 76504<br>Tiffany Weiss | 6-8 | TV | 715<br>41 | 74% 254/215-6300<br>Fax 254/215-6352 |
| Western Hills Elem Sch<br>600 Arapaho Dr, Temple 76504<br>Tiffany Vestal | PK-5 | T | 224<br>29 | 74% 254/215-5600<br>Fax 254/215-5624 |
| Ⓐ Wheatley Alt Ed Center<br>515 E Avenue D, Temple 76501<br>Carl Pleasant | 1-12 | GT | 39<br>6 | 77% 254/215-5655<br>Fax 254/215-5673 |

| | | | | | | | | |
|---|---|---|---|---|---|---|---|---|
| 1 | Superintendent | 8 | Curric/Instruct K-12 | 19 | Chief Financial Officer | 29 | Family/Consumer Science | |
| 2 | Bus/Finance/Purchasing | 9 | Curric/Instruct Elem | 20 | Art K-12 | 30 | Adult Education | |
| 3 | Buildings And Grounds | 10 | Curric/Instruct Sec | 21 | Art Elem | 31 | Career/Sch-to-Work K-12 | |
| 4 | Food Service | 11 | Federal Program | 22 | Art Sec | 32 | Career/Sch-to-Work Elem | |
| 5 | Transportation | 12 | Title I | 23 | Music K-12 | 33 | Career/Sch-to-Work Sec | |
| 6 | Athletic | 13 | Title V | 24 | Music Elem | 34 | Early Childhood Ed | |
| 7 | Health Services | 15 | Asst Superintendent | 25 | Music Sec | 35 | Health/Phys Education | |
| | | 16 | Instructional Media Svcs | 26 | Business Education | 36 | Guidance Services K-12 | |
| | | 17 | Chief Operations Officer | 27 | Career & Tech Ed | 37 | Guidance Services Elem | |
| | | 18 | Chief Academic Officer | 28 | Technology Education | 38 | Guidance Services Sec | |

| | | | | | | | |
|---|---|---|---|---|---|---|---|
| 39 | Social Studies K-12 | 49 | English/Lang Arts Elem | 59 | Special Education Elem | 69 | Academic Assessment |
| 40 | Social Studies Elem | 50 | English/Lang Arts Sec | 60 | Special Education Sec | 70 | Research/Development |
| 41 | Social Studies Sec | 51 | Reading K-12 | 61 | Foreign/World Lang K-12 | 71 | Public Information |
| 42 | Science K-12 | 52 | Reading Elem | 62 | Foreign/World Lang Elem | 72 | Summer School |
| 43 | Science Elem | 53 | Reading Sec | 63 | Foreign/World Lang Sec | 73 | Instructional Tech |
| 44 | Science Sec | 54 | Remedial Reading K-12 | 64 | Religious Education K-12 | 74 | Inservice Training |
| 45 | Math K-12 | 55 | Remedial Reading Elem | 65 | Religious Education Elem | 75 | Marketing/Distributive |
| 46 | Math Elem | 56 | Remedial Reading Sec | 66 | Religious Education Sec | 76 | Info Systems |
| 47 | Math Sec | 57 | Bilingual/ELL | 67 | School Board President | 77 | Psychological Assess |
| 48 | English/Lang Arts K-12 | 58 | Special Education K-12 | 68 | Teacher Personnel | 78 | Affirmative Action |

## Troy Ind School Dist PID: 00996899
1 Trojan Rd, Troy 76579

254/938-2595
Fax 254/938-7323

**Schools:** 4 \ **Teachers:** 104 \ **Students:** 1,600 \ **Special Ed Students:** 204 \ **LEP Students:** 52 \ **Ethnic:** African American 2%, Hispanic 28%, Caucasian 69% \ **Exp:** $452 (High) \ **Poverty:** 12% \ **Title I:** $187,840 \ **Special Education:** $12,000 \ **Open-Close:** 08/24 - 05/26 \ **DTBP:** $350 (High) \ 🇹

| | | |
|---|---|---|
| Neil Jeter | ...... 1 | Cindy Holloway ...... 2 |
| Brad McMurtry | ...... 3,68,79,288 | Lisa Mays ...... 4 |
| Leah Glenn | ...... 5 | Ronnie Porter ...... 6* |
| Penny Braeuer | ...... 7,85 | Dr Darrell Becker ...... 8,11,32,58,69,273 |
| Trista Falcon | ...... 16,82* | Mindy Howard ...... 27,33,273* |
| Dawn Robinson | ...... 34,37* | Mollie Huber ...... 38 |
| Gary McMurtry | ...... 67 | Clay Osburn ...... 73,295 |
| Dwayne Frei | ...... 83,88* | |

| Public Schs..Principal | Grd | Prgm | Enr/#Cls | SN | |
|---|---|---|---|---|---|
| Edna Bigham Mays Elem Sch<br>725 W Main St, Troy 76579<br>Kelli Frisch | PK-1 | T | 222<br>15 | 60% | 254/938-0304<br>Fax 254/938-0233 |
| Raymond Mays Middle Sch<br>915 W Main St, Troy 76579<br>Michelle Jolliff | 6-8 | TV | 352<br>40 | 47% | 254/938-2543<br>Fax 254/938-2880 |
| Troy Elem Sch<br>808 E Austin St, Troy 76579<br>Andrea Durbin | 2-5 | T | 460<br>47 | 55% | 254/938-2503<br>Fax 254/938-2080 |
| Troy High Sch<br>205 N Waco Rd, Troy 76579<br>Randy Hicks | 9-12 | TV | 448<br>32 | 45% | 254/938-2561<br>Fax 254/938-2328 |

## BELL CATHOLIC SCHOOLS

## Diocese of Austin Ed Office PID: 01420568
Listing includes only schools located in this county. See District Index for location of Diocesan Offices.

| Catholic Schs..Principal | Grd | Prgm | Enr/#Cls | SN | |
|---|---|---|---|---|---|
| Holy Trinity Catholic High Sch<br>6608 W Adams Ave, Temple 76502<br>Isabelle Brogan | 9-12 | | 94<br>13 | | 254/771-0787<br>Fax 254/771-2285 |
| St Joseph Catholic Sch<br>2901 E Rancier Ave, Killeen 76543<br>Dirk Steffens | PK-6 | | 85<br>8 | | 254/634-7272<br>Fax 254/634-1224 |
| St Mary's Catholic Sch<br>1019 S 7th St, Temple 76504<br>Theresa Wyles | PK-8 | | 242<br>22 | | 254/778-8141<br>Fax 254/778-1396 |

## BELL PRIVATE SCHOOLS

| Private Schs..Principal | Grd | Prgm | Enr/#Cls | SN | |
|---|---|---|---|---|---|
| American Preparatory Institute<br>6200 W Central Expy, Killeen 76549<br>Colvin Davis | 9-12 | | 100 | | 254/526-1321<br>Fax 254/526-1481 |
| Central Texas Christian Sch<br>4141 W FM 93, Temple 76502<br>Janet Blacklock | PK-12 | | 416<br>20 | | 254/939-5700<br>Fax 254/939-5733 |
| Education Connection<br>1020 Trimmier Rd, Killeen 76541<br>Nikki Luther | K-5 | | 190 | | 254/526-9299<br>Fax 254/526-0631 |

| Killeen Adventist Jr Academy<br>3412 Lake Rd, Killeen 76543<br>Lizzette Garcia | PK-8 | 52<br>7 | 254/699-9466<br>Fax 254/699-0519 |
|---|---|---|---|
| Memorial Christian Academy<br>4001 Trimmier Rd, Killeen 76542<br>Barbra Carpenter | PK-12 | 224<br>25 | 254/526-5403<br>Fax 254/634-2030 |

## BEXAR COUNTY

## BEXAR PUBLIC SCHOOLS

## Alamo Heights Ind School Dist PID: 00996928
7101 Broadway, San Antonio 78209

210/824-2483
Fax 210/822-2221

**Schools:** 5 \ **Teachers:** 345 \ **Students:** 4,800 \ **Special Ed Students:** 410 \ **LEP Students:** 289 \ **College-Bound:** 98% \ **Ethnic:** Asian 3%, African American 2%, Hispanic 40%, Caucasian 53% \ **Exp:** $144 (Low) \ **Poverty:** 7% \ **Title I:** $444,925 \ **Special Education:** $1,100,000 \ **Open-Close:** 08/17 - 05/27 \ **DTBP:** $156 (High) \ 🇫 🇹

| | | |
|---|---|---|
| Dr Dana Bashara | ...... 1 | Mike Hagar ...... 2,15 |
| Louis Cardenas | ...... 3 | Sean Sheets ...... 4 |
| Leah Roudebush | ...... 5 | Ron Rittimann ...... 6* |
| Catherine Widder | ...... 7* | Dr Jimmie Walker ...... 8,11,81,296 |
| Frank Alfaro | ...... 15,57,88 | Susan Peery ...... 34* |
| Melissa Benavidez | ...... 58,77,78,90 | David Hornberger ...... 67 |
| Frank Stange | ...... 68,71 | Kristen Ascencao ...... 69 |
| Jamie Locklin | ...... 73,295 | Lisa Lucas ...... 83* |
| Kevin Lam | ...... 295 | Patti Pawlik-Perales ...... 297 |

| Public Schs..Principal | Grd | Prgm | Enr/#Cls | SN | |
|---|---|---|---|---|---|
| Alamo Heights High Sch<br>6900 Broadway, San Antonio 78209<br>**Cory Smith** | 9-12 | AV | 1,606<br>80 | 17% | 210/820-8850<br>Fax 210/832-5777 |
| Alamo Heights Jr High Sch<br>7607 N New Braunfels Ave, San Antonio 78209<br>Laura Ancira | 6-8 | | 1,121<br>100 | 20% | 210/824-3231<br>Fax 210/832-5825<br>🇫🇹 |
| Cambridge Elem Sch<br>1001 Townsend Ave, San Antonio 78209<br>**Jana Hawkins** | 1-5 | | 836<br>75 | 23% | 210/822-3611<br>Fax 210/832-5840<br>🇫🇹 |
| Howard Early Childhood Center<br>7800 Broadway, San Antonio 78209<br>Susan Peery | PK-K | | 415<br>32 | 23% | 210/832-5900<br>Fax 210/832-5898<br>🇫🇹 |
| Woodridge Elem Sch<br>100 Woodridge Dr, San Antonio 78209<br>Gerrie Spellmann | 1-5 | | 886<br>45 | 20% | 210/826-8021<br>Fax 210/832-5871<br>🇫🇹 |

## Braination Schools PID: 11701354
10325 Bandera Rd, San Antonio 78250

210/638-5000
Fax 210/638-5075

**Schools:** 8 \ **Students:** 818 \ **Ethnic:** African American 11%, Hispanic 54%, Caucasian 34% \ **Open-Close:** 08/20 - 06/04

| | | |
|---|---|---|
| **Ken Whitt** | ...... 1 | Ymelda Y'Herrera ...... 2,19 |
| Jennifer Rower | ...... 3,5,17,68 | Mandy Alandzes ...... 4 |
| Brenda Murphy | ...... 8,18 | Orlando De Los Santos ...... 11,298 |
| Charles Winkler | ...... 36,76,84,295 | Alethia Phillips ...... 58 |
| Laura Dominguez | ...... 58 | Olin Tunnell ...... 67 |
| Carol Taly | ...... 68 | Phil Castillo ...... 73 |
| Renee Mancias | ...... 76* | Ronny Almanza ...... 295 |

| | | | | | |
|---|---|---|---|---|---|
| **79** Student Personnel | **91** Safety/Security | **275** Response To Intervention | **298** Grant Writer/Ptnrships | **School Programs** | **Social Media** |
| **80** Driver Ed/Safety | **92** Magnet School | **277** Remedial Math K-12 | **750** Chief Innovation Officer | A = Alternative Program | |
| **81** Gifted/Talented | **93** Parental Involvement | **280** Literacy Coach | **751** Chief of Staff | G = Adult Classes | 🇫 = Facebook |
| **82** Video Services | **95** Tech Prep Program | **285** STEM | **752** Social Emotional Learning | M = Magnet Program | |
| **83** Substance Abuse Prev | **97** Chief Information Officer | **286** Digital Learning | | T = Title I Schoolwide | 🇹 = Twitter |
| **84** Erate | **98** Chief Technology Officer | **288** Common Core Standards | **Other School Types** | V = Career & Tech Ed Programs | |
| **85** AIDS Education | **270** Character Education | **294** Accountability | Ⓐ = Alternative School | | |
| **88** Alternative/At Risk | **271** Migrant Education | **295** Network System | Ⓒ = Charter School | **New Schools are shaded** | |
| **89** Multi-Cultural Curriculum | **273** Teacher Mentor | **296** Title II Programs | Ⓜ = Magnet School | **New Superintendents and Principals are bold** | |
| **90** Social Work | **274** Before/After Day | **297** Webmaster | Ⓨ = Year-Round School | **Personnel with email addresses are underscored** | **TX—33** |

| Public Schs..Principal | Grd | Prgm | Enr/#Cls | SN |
|---|---|---|---|---|
| © Anne Frank Inspire Academy<br>11216 Bandera Rd, San Antonio 78250<br>R Payne | K-12 | V | 382 | 17% 210/638-5900<br>Fax 210/638-5975 |
| © Jhw Inspire Acad-Afton Oaks<br>620 E Afton Oaks Blvd, San Antonio 78232<br>Asa Cuellar | 5-12 | T | 138 | 98% 210/638-5500<br>Fax 210/638-5575 |
| Ⓐ Jhw Inspire Acad-Legacy Ranch<br>© 13326 N US Highway 183, Gonzales 78629<br>Patricia Smith | K-6 | | 40 | 210/638-5300 |
| © Jhw Inspire Acad-Meridell<br>12550 W State Highway 29, Liberty Hill 78642<br>Gwyn Rollins | K-12 | T | 101 | 97% 512/528-2100<br>Fax 512/528-2193 |
| © Jhw Inspire Acad-Rockdale<br>696 N FM 487, Rockdale 76567<br>Tamra Vance | 6-12 | T | 61 | 94% 210/638-5700<br>Fax 210/638-5775 |
| © Jhw Inspire Acad-Williams Hse<br>107 W Railway, Lometa 76853<br>Lois Knox | 3-12 | A | 34 | 210/638-5800<br>Fax 512/515-5875 |
| Ⓐ Jhw Inspire Academy-Bell Co<br>© 4800 E Rancier Ave, Killeen 76543<br>Stephanie House | 4-12 | | 37 | 254/618-4280 |
| © Jhw Inspire Academy-Hays Co<br>2250 Clovis R Barker Rd, San Marcos 78666<br>Kayla Heyward | 6-12 | T | 25<br>7 | 94% 210/638-5400<br>Fax 210/638-5475 |

## • East Central Ind School Dist PID: 00996992

6634 New Sulphur Springs Rd, San Antonio 78263

210/648-7861
Fax 210/648-0931

**Schools:** 12 \ **Teachers:** 602 \ **Students:** 10,146 \
**Special Ed Students:** 1,110 \ **LEP Students:** 1,095 \ **College-Bound:** 41%
\ **Ethnic:** Asian 1%, African American 9%, Hispanic 75%, Caucasian
16% \ **Exp:** $363 (High) \ **Poverty:** 19% \ **Title I:** $2,619,424 \
**Special Education:** $1,789,000 \ **Open-Close:** 08/17 - 05/26 \ **DTBP:** $148
(High)

| | | | |
|---|---|---|---|
| Roland Toscano | 1 | Judy Burns | 2,19 |
| Matt Morgan | 2 | Stephen Priour | 3 |
| Nancy Britton | 4 | Donald Jurek | 5 |
| Suzette Arriola | 6* | Jaelynn Hart | 7* |
| Jennifer Kasper | 8* | Shannon Fuller | 8 |
| Taffi Hertz | 8,15 | Meredith Rokas | 11,31,296 |
| Dr Alma Rosa Martinez | 57 | Nina Puth | 58 |
| John Massengale | 67 | Yvette Sanders | 68 |
| Jonathan Hulbert | 69 | Ashley Chohlis | 71,79 |
| Dirk Dykstra | 73 | John Hernandez | 79 |
| George Dranowsky | 91 | | |

| Public Schs..Principal | Grd | Prgm | Enr/#Cls | SN |
|---|---|---|---|---|
| Ⓐ Bexar Co Learning Center<br>3621 Farm Rd, San Antonio 78223<br>Patricia White | 6-12 | | 90<br>15 | 60% 210/335-1745<br>Fax 210/335-1746 |
| East Central Development Ctr<br>12271 Donop Rd, San Antonio 78223<br>Damon Trainer | PK-PK | T | 114<br>19 | 94% 210/633-3020<br>Fax 210/633-0323 |
| East Central High Sch<br>7173 FM 1628, San Antonio 78263<br>Shane McKay | 9-12 | TV | 1,667 | 60% 210/634-7100<br>Fax 210/634-7446 |
| Harmony Elem Sch<br>10625 Green Lake Dr, San Antonio 78223<br>Stephanie Orsak | K-3 | T | 458<br>26 | 78% 210/633-0231<br>Fax 210/633-2176 |
| Heritage Middle Sch<br>8004 New Sulphur Springs Rd, San Antonio 78263<br>Mary Gomez | 6-8 | TV | 1,230<br>70 | 66% 210/648-6500<br>Fax 210/648-3501 |
| Highland Forest Elem Sch<br>3736 SE Military Dr, San Antonio 78223<br>**Brittany Ervin** | PK-3 | T | 387<br>32 | 74% 210/333-7385<br>Fax 210/333-4069 |

| Public Schs..Principal | Grd | Prgm | Enr/#Cls | SN |
|---|---|---|---|---|
| Legacy Middle Sch<br>5903 SE Loop 410, San Antonio 78222<br>Nicole Lewis | 6-8 | T | 1,192 | 74% 210/648-3118<br>Fax 210/648-1068 |
| Oak Crest Elem Sch<br>7806 New Sulphur Springs Rd, San Antonio 78263<br>Joette Barnes | PK-5 | T | 669<br>45 | 67% 210/648-9484<br>Fax 210/648-6967 |
| Pecan Valley Elem Sch<br>3966 E Southcross Blvd, San Antonio 78222<br>Kristin Wurzbach | PK-3 | T | 549<br>27 | 84% 210/333-1230<br>Fax 210/359-1352 |
| Salado Elem Sch<br>3602 S WW White Rd, San Antonio 78222<br>Teresa Triana | PK-5 | T | 761<br>56 | 75% 210/648-3310<br>Fax 210/359-1245 |
| Sinclair Elem Sch<br>6126 Sinclair Rd, San Antonio 78222<br>Stacey Johnston | K-3 | T | 505<br>32 | 70% 210/648-4620<br>Fax 210/648-0422 |
| Tradition Elem Sch<br>12885 FM 1346, Saint Hedwig 78152<br>Karen Kopeck | PK-5 | T | 698<br>37 | 60% 210/649-2021<br>Fax 210/649-1226 |

## • Edgewood Ind School Dist PID: 00997075

5358 W Commerce St, San Antonio 78237

210/444-4500
Fax 210/444-4525

**Schools:** 21 \ **Teachers:** 636 \ **Students:** 10,881 \
**Special Ed Students:** 1,043 \ **LEP Students:** 1,835 \ **College-Bound:** 70%
\ **Ethnic:** Asian 1%, African American 1%, Hispanic 97%, Caucasian
1% \ **Exp:** $387 (High) \ **Poverty:** 39% \ **Title I:** $8,492,854 \
**Special Education:** $1,916,000 \ **Open-Close:** 08/19 - 05/26 \ **DTBP:** $201
(High)

| | | | |
|---|---|---|---|
| Dr Eduardo Hernandez | 1 | Betty Galindo | 2 |
| Myrna Martinez | 2,15,19 | Elsa Rosas | 3 |
| Ernesto Cantu | 3 | Roxanne Ruiz | 4 |
| Will Thornton | 5 | Robert Gomez | 6,35 |
| Jennifer Milla | 7 | Stefanie Chatelain | 7 |
| Phillip Chavez | 8,15,18 | Theresa Salinas | 8 |
| Becky Goodwin | 11 | Olga Moucoulis | 15,751 |
| Dr Emma Dromgoole | 20,23 | Chriselda Bazaldua | 27,31,285 |
| Dr Mary Miller-Baker | 34* | Rosemary Hernandez | 34 |
| Linda Vargas-Lew | 36,78,90 | Doris Perez | 57,61 |
| Emily Sauceda | 58 | Martha Castilla | 67 |
| Travis McKelvain | 68 | Robert Miller | 69,70 |
| Keyhla Calderon-Lugo | 71 | Juan Vazquez-Cruz | 73 |
| Kimberly Gonzalez | 73 | Judith Torres | 74 |
| Angelica Garza | 76 | Angelica Lozano | 79 |
| Dr Bertha Ortiz | 81 | Valerie Galan | 88 |
| Jesse Quiroga | 91 | Ron Foster | 286 |
| Sylvia Morales | 294* | | |

| Public Schs..Principal | Grd | Prgm | Enr/#Cls | SN |
|---|---|---|---|---|
| Alonso S Perales Elem Sch<br>1507 Ceralvo St, San Antonio 78237<br>Teresa Silva | PK-5 | T | 423<br>28 | 96% 210/444-8350<br>Fax 210/444-8373 |
| Brentwood Middle Sch<br>1626 Thompson Pl, San Antonio 78226<br>Eva Reyna | 6-8 | TV | 206<br>40 | 95% 210/444-7675<br>Fax 210/444-7698 |
| Burleson Early Chldhd Center<br>4415 Monterey St, San Antonio 78237<br>Sheila Ballagh | PK-PK | | 242 | 210/444-7725<br>Fax 210/444-7748 |
| Cardenas Center<br>3300 Ruiz St, San Antonio 78228<br>Claudia Barrios | PK-PK | T | 365 | 99% 210/444-7900 |
| E T Wrenn Middle Sch<br>627 S Acme Rd, San Antonio 78237<br>Timothy Vaughn | 6-8 | TV | 429<br>35 | 95% 210/444-8475<br>Fax 210/444-8498 |
| Edgewood Fine Arts Academy<br>607 SW 34th St, San Antonio 78237<br>Daniel Pina | 9-12 | T | 200 | 90% 210/444-7925<br>Fax 210/444-7973 |

| | | | | | |
|---|---|---|---|---|---|
| 1 | Superintendent | 8 | Curric/Instruct K-12 | 19 | Chief Financial Officer |
| 2 | Bus/Finance/Purchasing | 9 | Curric/Instruct K-12 | 20 | Art K-12 |
| 3 | Buildings And Grounds | 10 | Curric/Instruct Sec | 21 | Art Elem |
| 4 | Food Service | 11 | Federal Program | 22 | Art Sec |
| 5 | Transportation | 12 | Title I | 23 | Music K-12 |
| 6 | Athletic | 13 | Title V | 24 | Music Elem |
| 7 | Health Services | 15 | Asst Superintendent | 25 | Music Sec |
| | | 16 | Instructional Media Svcs | 26 | Business Education |
| | | 17 | Chief Operations Officer | 27 | Career & Tech Ed |
| | | 18 | Chief Academic Officer | 28 | Technology Education |

| | | | | | |
|---|---|---|---|---|---|
| 29 | Family/Consumer Science | 39 | Social Studies K-12 | 49 | English/Lang Arts Elem |
| 30 | Adult Education | 40 | Social Studies Elem | 50 | English/Lang Arts Sec |
| 31 | Career/Sch-to-Work K-12 | 41 | Social Studies Sec | 51 | Reading K-12 |
| 32 | Career/Sch-to-Work Elem | 42 | Science K-12 | 52 | Reading Elem |
| 33 | Career/Sch-to-Work Sec | 43 | Science Elem | 53 | Reading Sec |
| 34 | Early Childhood Ed | 44 | Science Sec | 54 | Remedial Reading K-12 |
| 35 | Health/Phys Education | 45 | Math K-12 | 55 | Remedial Reading Elem |
| 36 | Business Education | 46 | Math Elem | 56 | Remedial Reading Sec |
| 37 | Guidance Services Elem | 47 | Math Sec | 57 | Bilingual/ELL |
| 38 | Guidance Services Sec | 48 | English/Lang Arts K-12 | 58 | Special Education K-12 |

| | | | | | |
|---|---|---|---|---|---|
| 59 | Special Education Elem | 69 | Academic Assessment |
| 60 | Special Education Sec | 70 | Research/Development |
| 61 | Foreign/World Lang K-12 | 71 | Public Information |
| 62 | Foreign/World Lang Elem | 72 | Summer School |
| 63 | Foreign/World Lang Sec | 73 | Instructional Tech |
| 64 | Religious Education K-12 | 74 | Inservice Training |
| 65 | Religious Education Elem | 75 | Marketing/Distributive |
| 66 | Religious Education Sec | 76 | Info Systems |
| 67 | School Board President | 77 | Psychological Assess |
| 68 | Teacher Personnel | 78 | Affirmative Action |

| | Grd | Prgm | Enr/#Cls | SN | |
|---|---|---|---|---|---|
| Ⓐ Emma Frey Discip Alt Ed Pgrm<br>900 S San Eduardo Ave, San Antonio 78237<br>Daniel Pina | 6-12 | V | 25<br>10 | | 210/444-8230<br>Fax 210/444-8233 |
| Gardendale Elem Sch<br>1731 Dahlgreen Ave, San Antonio 78237<br>Kristin Willmann | PK-5 | T | 452<br>45 | 92% | 210/444-8150<br>Fax 210/444-8173 |
| Gus Garcia Middle Sch<br>3306 Ruiz St, San Antonio 78228<br>Christopher Bland | 6-8 | TV | 735<br>50 | 94% | 210/444-8075<br>Fax 210/444-8098 |
| H B Gonzalez Elem Sch<br>2803 Castroville Rd, San Antonio 78237<br>Tania Moran | PK-5 | T | 471<br>29 | 94% | 210/444-7800<br>Fax 210/444-7823 |
| John F Kennedy High Sch<br>1922 S General McMullen Dr, San Antonio 78226<br>Graciela Martinez | 9-12 | GTV | 628 | 92% | 210/444-8040<br>Fax 210/444-8020 |
| L B Johnson Elem Sch<br>6515 W Commerce St, San Antonio 78227<br>Ellie Gearhart | PK-5 | T | 486<br>29 | 95% | 210/444-8175<br>Fax 210/444-8198 |
| Las Palmas Elem Sch<br>115 Las Palmas Dr, San Antonio 78237<br>Monica Munoz | PK-5 | T | 417 | 96% | 210/444-8050<br>Fax 210/444-8073 |
| Loma Park Elem Sch<br>400 Aurora Ave, San Antonio 78228<br>Dr Courtney Gavin | PK-5 | T | 642<br>39 | 100% | 210/444-8250<br>Fax 210/444-8273 |
| Memorial High Sch<br>1227 Memorial St, San Antonio 78228<br>Pamela Reece | 9-12 | GTV | 1,294<br>70 | 94% | 210/444-8300<br>Fax 210/444-8336 |
| Roosevelt Elem Sch<br>3823 Fortuna Ct, San Antonio 78237<br>Dr Patricia Ortiz | K-5 | T | 450 | 89% | 210/444-8375<br>Fax 210/444-7798 |
| Roy Cisneros Elem Sch<br>3011 Ruiz St, San Antonio 78228<br>Dr Jennifer Herrera | PK-5 | T | 538<br>26 | 93% | 210/444-7850<br>Fax 210/444-7873 |
| Stafford Early Childhd Ctr<br>611 SW 36th St, San Antonio 78237<br>Lilly Benavidez | PK-PK | T | 406 | 100% | 210/444-7900<br>Fax 210/444-7923 |
| Stafford Elem Sch<br>415 SW 36th St, San Antonio 78237<br>Stephanie Cruz | K-5 | T | 453<br>29 | 93% | 210/444-8400<br>Fax 210/444-8423 |
| Toltech T-STEM Academy<br>1018 NW 34th St, San Antonio 78228<br>Dr Rose Narvaez | 9-12 | | 320 | | 210/444-8425<br>Fax 210/444-8448 |
| Winston Elem Sch<br>2525 S General McMullen Dr, San Antonio 78226<br>Claudia Sanchez | PK-5 | T | 455<br>26 | 95% | 210/444-8450<br>Fax 210/444-8473 |

● **Ft Sam Houston Ind School Dist** PID: 01534949    210/368-8701
4005 Winans Rd, San Antonio 78234    Fax 210/368-8741

**Schools:** 2 \ **Teachers:** 132 \ **Students:** 1,560 \ **Special Ed Students:** 192 \
**LEP Students:** 30 \ **Ethnic:** Asian 2%, African American 18%, Hispanic 34%,
Native American: 1%, Caucasian 45% \ **Exp:** $809 (High) \ **Poverty:** 10% \
**Title I:** $141,155 \ **Open-Close:** 08/17 - 05/21 \ **DTBP:** $206 (High) \ 🅵 🅣

| | | | |
|---|---|---|---|
| Dr Gary Bates ...................................1 | Julie Novak .................................2,11 |
| Richard Allen ...................................3 | Brenda Rodriguez .........................4 |
| Jesse Sandoval ...............................5 | Christina Guerreo .........................6* |
| Dr Mina Schintta .....8,11,16,57,83,88,285,296 | Roland Rios .......................16,73,295* |
| Hans Palmer ...........................34,58 | Willie White ....................................67 |
| Debbie Kramme ...........................68 | |

| Public Schs..Principal | Grd | Prgm | Enr/#Cls | SN | |
|---|---|---|---|---|---|
| Ft Sam Houston Elem Sch<br>4351 Nursery Rd, San Antonio 78234<br>Dr Joseph Cerna | PK-5 | | 766<br>40 | 31% | 210/368-8800<br>Fax 210/368-8801 |

| | Grd | | Enr/#Cls | SN | |
|---|---|---|---|---|---|
| Robert G Cole Jr/Sr High Sch<br>4001 Winans Rd, San Antonio 78234<br>Isabell Clayton | 6-12 | | 718 | 22% | 210/368-8730<br>Fax 210/368-8731<br>🅣 |

● **Harlandale Ind School Dist** PID: 00997350    210/989-4300
102 Genevieve Dr, San Antonio 78214    Fax 210/989-4481

**Schools:** 24 \ **Teachers:** 965 \ **Students:** 14,500 \
**Special Ed Students:** 1,390 \ **LEP Students:** 2,184 \ **College-Bound:** 51%
\ **Ethnic:** Hispanic 98%, Caucasian 2% \ **Exp:** $469 (High) \ **Poverty:** 31% \
**Title I:** $6,187,632 \ **Special Education:** $3,187,000 \ **Open-Close:** 08/24 -
06/04 \ **DTBP:** $201 (High)

| | | | |
|---|---|---|---|
| Gerardo Soto .........................................1 | Ben Mora ........................................2 |
| Richard Hernandez ...........................2,15 | Christopher Ramirez ....................3* |
| Kyle Blakeney ......................................3 | Marcos Rodriguez .........................4 |
| Jacob Garcia .......................................5 | Isaac Martinez .........................6,35* |
| Deborah Hernandez ...........................7 | Ronnie Cantu ..................................9 |
| Melissa Casey ...........................10,15 | Michael Littlefield .......................10 |
| Nadine Wolfe ..............11,30,85,271,296,298 | Lisa Kukla .....................................16 |
| Tracy Anderson ..............................27,31 | Rubina Pantoja .............................39 |
| Matthew Simonds ............................42 | Nora Lugo ......................................45 |
| Kari Espinoza .............48,51,54,61,280 | Rosa Torres ..................................57 |
| Della Taylor ......................................58 | Norma Cavazos .............................67 |
| Dr Melinda Salinas ..........................68 | Albert Rosales ..............................71 |
| Myrna Martinez ....................73,76,295 | James Klein ...................................79 |
| Anthony Khosravi ...........................81* | Mike Ramirez .................................91 |
| Ruth Zambrano ................................93 | Mariano Verava ............................97 |
| Megan Guerrero .............................285 | |

| Public Schs..Principal | Grd | Prgm | Enr/#Cls | SN | |
|---|---|---|---|---|---|
| Armando Leal Jr Middle Sch<br>743 W Southcross Blvd, San Antonio 78211<br>Ricardo Salmon | 6-8 | T | 771<br>60 | 92% | 210/989-2400<br>Fax 210/989-2440 |
| Bellaire Elem Sch<br>142 E Amber St, San Antonio 78221<br>Elizabeth Lozano | PK-5 | T | 538<br>36 | 86% | 210/989-2850<br>Fax 210/989-2887 |
| Carroll Bell Elem Sch<br>519 W Harding Blvd, San Antonio 78221<br>Dr Gina Christenson | PK-5 | T | 430<br>47 | 83% | 210/989-2900<br>Fax 210/989-2396 |
| Collier Elem Sch<br>834 W Southcross Blvd, San Antonio 78211<br>Patricia Garcia | PK-5 | T | 434<br>26 | 92% | 210/989-2950<br>Fax 210/989-2986 |
| Columbia Heights Elem Sch<br>1610 Fitch St, San Antonio 78211<br>Santos Flores | PK-5 | T | 380<br>25 | 92% | 210/989-3000<br>Fax 210/989-3029 |
| E H Gilbert Elem Sch<br>931 E Southcross Blvd, San Antonio 78214<br>Herlinda Longoria \ Geralynn Wing | PK-5 | T | 559<br>31 | 91% | 210/989-3050<br>Fax 210/989-3297 |
| Fenley PK Center<br>934 Flanders Ave, San Antonio 78211<br>Elaine Jimenez | PK-PK | | 164 | | 210/921-7000<br>Fax 210/977-1481 |
| Ⓐ Frank M Tejeda Academy<br>12121 SE Loop 410, San Antonio 78221<br>Geri Belleza | 6-12 | GT | 185<br>22 | 97% | 210/989-4900<br>Fax 210/989-4937 |
| Gillette Elem Sch<br>625 Gillette Blvd, San Antonio 78221<br>Lorena Jasso | PK-5 | T | 588<br>34 | 91% | 210/989-3100<br>Fax 210/989-3136 |
| H W Schulze Elem Sch<br>9131 Yett Ave Bldg 1, San Antonio 78221<br>Victoria Trevino | PK-5 | GT | 734<br>31 | 88% | 210/989-3250<br>Fax 210/989-3271 |
| Ⓐ Harlandale Alternative Center<br>4050 Apollo, San Antonio 78214<br>Andrew Dominguez | 6-12 | GV | 88<br>16 | 100% | 210/989-5200<br>Fax 210/989-5236 |
| Harlandale High Sch<br>114 E Gerald Ave, San Antonio 78214<br>Fred Anthony | 9-12 | TV | 1,817<br>100 | 85% | 210/989-1000<br>Fax 210/989-1082 |

| | Grd | Prgm | Enr/#Cls | SN | |
|---|---|---|---|---|---|
| Harlandale Middle Sch<br>300 W Huff Ave, San Antonio 78214<br><u>Ricardo Marroquin</u> | 6-8 | T | 837 | 89% | 210/989-2000<br>Fax 210/989-2062 |
| Jewel C Wietzel Center<br>9131 Yett Ave Bldg B, San Antonio 78221<br><u>Jennifer Bernal-Tamaren</u> | Spec | T | 15<br>5 | 26% | 210/989-3280<br>Fax 210/989-3296 |
| Kingsborough Middle Sch<br>422 E Ashley Rd, San Antonio 78221<br>Sylvia Tovar | 6-8 | T | 436<br>55 | 88% | 210/989-2200<br>Fax 210/989-2240 |
| McCollum High Sch<br>500 W Formosa Blvd, San Antonio 78221<br><u>Jacob Garcia</u> | 9-12 | TV | 1,525 | 80% | 210/989-1500<br>Fax 210/989-1580 |
| Morrill Elem Sch<br>5200 S Flores St, San Antonio 78214<br><u>Tina Mireles</u> | PK-5 | T | 328<br>39 | 89% | 210/989-3150<br>Fax 210/989-3186 |
| Rayburn Elem Sch<br>635 Rayburn Dr, San Antonio 78221<br><u>Juanita Santos</u> | PK-5 | T | 329<br>25 | 87% | 210/989-3200<br>Fax 210/989-3245 |
| STEM Early College High Sch<br>4040 Apollo, San Antonio 78214<br>Michael Littlefield | 9-12 | T | 359 | 69% | 210/989-3500<br>Fax 210/989-3528 |
| Stonewall Flanders Elem Sch<br>804 Stonewall St, San Antonio 78211<br>Dr Traci Smith | PK-5 | T | 715<br>36 | 97% | 210/989-3300<br>Fax 210/989-3336 |
| Terrell Wells Middle Sch<br>422 W Hutchins Pl, San Antonio 78221<br>Jessie Gipprich | 6-8 | T | 708<br>53 | 89% | 210/989-2600<br>Fax 210/989-2640 |
| Verda Mae Adams Elem Sch<br>135 E Southcross Blvd, San Antonio 78214<br>Leticia Rodriguez | PK-5 | T | 650<br>60 | 96% | 210/989-2800<br>Fax 210/989-2828 |
| Vestal Elem Sch<br>1102 Cantrell Dr, San Antonio 78221<br>Marianela Sanchez | PK-5 | T | 381<br>44 | 93% | 210/989-3350<br>Fax 210/989-3386 |
| Wright Elem Sch<br>115 E Huff Ave, San Antonio 78214<br>Griselda Raley | PK-5 | T | 497<br>25 | 92% | 210/989-3400<br>Fax 210/989-3444 |

● **Judson Ind School Dist**  PID: 00997582           210/945-5100
8012 Shin Oak Dr, Live Oak 78233                       Fax 210/945-6922

---

**Schools:** 33 \ **Teachers:** 1,613 \ **Students:** 23,000 \
**Special Ed Students:** 2,666 \ **LEP Students:** 2,128 \ **Ethnic:** Asian 2%,
African American 22%, Hispanic 60%, Caucasian 15% \ **Exp:** $243 (Med)
\ **Poverty:** 19% \ **Title I:** $7,621,472 \ **Special Education:** $4,335,000 \
**Bilingual Education:** $7,000 \ **Open-Close:** 08/24 - 06/03 \ **DTBP:** $199
(High) \ 🅵 🆃

---

| | | | |
|---|---|---|---|
| <u>Dr Janette Ball</u> ........................1 | William Adkin .........................2,19,73 |
| <u>Milton Fields</u> ...................3,15,91 | Ruben Moreno ........................3 |
| <u>Terry Yaklin</u> ........................3 | <u>Beveylon Concha</u> ................4 |
| Kenneth Johnson ...................5 | <u>Mike Miller</u> ...........................6 |
| Jodi Burton ..................11,296,298 | <u>Becky Robinson</u> .................15 |
| Cecilia Davis ........................15 | Marsha Bellinger ...................16 |
| <u>Ann Lachner</u> ...................27,31 | <u>Yvonne Schuler</u> .............30,274 |
| Monica Garcia .......................36 | <u>Maria Richardson</u> ...........57,271 |
| Dr Teresa Arocha-Gill .......58,275 | Rene Pafchall ........................67 |
| Janlen Waclawczyk .............76 | Michael Davis ......................295 |

| **Public Schs..Principal** | **Grd** | **Prgm** | **Enr/#Cls** | **SN** |
|---|---|---|---|---|
| Candlewood Elem Sch<br>3635 Candleglenn, San Antonio 78244<br><u>Andrea Johnson</u> | PK-5 | GT | 582<br>50 | 84% | 210/662-1060<br>Fax 210/662-9327 |
| Converse Elem Sch<br>6720 FM 1516 N, Converse 78109<br><u>Cynthia Davis</u> | PK-5 | T | 493<br>29 | 76% | 210/945-1210<br>Fax 210/945-6944<br>🅵🆃 |
| Copperfield Elem Sch<br>7595 E Loop 1604 N, Converse 78109<br><u>Sherri Wrather</u> | PK-5 | T | 659 | 60% | 210/619-0460<br>Fax 210/619-0469 |
| Coronado Village Elem Sch<br>213 Amistad Blvd, Universal Cty 78148<br>**Erika Garza** | PK-5 | T | 351<br>29 | 61% | 210/945-5110<br>Fax 210/945-6948 |
| Crestview Elem Sch<br>7710 Narrow Pass St, Live Oak 78233<br><u>Linda Cruz</u> | PK-5 | T | 536<br>44 | 64% | 210/945-5111<br>Fax 210/945-6953<br>🅵🆃 |
| Ed Franz Elem Sch<br>12301 Welcome Dr, Live Oak 78233<br><u>Kelle Lofton</u> | PK-5 | GT | 363<br>24 | 69% | 210/945-5640<br>Fax 210/945-6946<br>🅵🆃 |
| Elolf Elem Sch<br>6335 Beech Trail Dr, Converse 78109<br>Scott Wilson | PK-5 | T | 477<br>39 | 75% | 210/661-1130<br>Fax 210/945-6959 |
| Escondido Elem Sch<br>5000 Texas Palm Dr, Converse 78109<br>**Cynthia Keeler** | PK-5 | | 425 | 68% | 210/662-2250<br>Fax 210/945-6991 |
| Henry Metzger Middle Sch<br>7475 Binz Engleman Rd, San Antonio 78244<br>L Davidson | 6-8 | T | 983 | 76% | 210/662-2210<br>Fax 210/945-6967 |
| James Masters Elem Sch<br>2650 Woodlake Pkwy, Converse 78109<br><u>Latanya Baker</u> | PK-5 | T | 345 | 61% | 210/945-1150<br>Fax 210/945-6963 |
| Joseph Hopkins Elem Sch<br>2440 Ackerman Rd, San Antonio 78219<br><u>Terry Combs</u> | PK-5 | T | 665<br>44 | 85% | 210/661-1120<br>Fax 210/945-6945<br>🅵🆃 |
| Jstem Academy<br>9695 Schaefer Rd, Converse 78109<br>Dawn Worley | 6-8 | | 375 | | 210/945-1159<br>Fax 210/619-0421 |
| Judson Early College Academy<br>8230 Palisades Dr, Universal Cty 78148<br>Josephine Juarez | 9-12 | | 481 | | 210/619-0200<br>Fax 210/945-6981 |
| Judson High Sch<br>9142 FM 78, Converse 78109<br><u>Jesus Hernandez</u> | 9-12 | TV | 2,712<br>100 | 62% | 210/945-1100<br>Fax 210/945-6976 |
| Ⓐ Judson Learning Academy<br>6909 N Loop 1604 E Ste 2010, San Antonio 78247<br><u>Liza Guerrero</u> | 9-12 | TV | 91<br>1 | 62% | 210/651-4080<br>Fax 210/945-6980<br>🅵🆃 |
| Judson Middle Sch<br>9695 Schaefer Rd, Converse 78109<br>D Worley | 6-8 | T | 1,245 | 63% | 210/357-0801<br>Fax 210/945-6969 |
| Ⓐ Judson Secondary Alt Sch<br>102 School St, Converse 78109<br><u>Ricci Bethely-Day</u> | 6-12 | T | 76<br>11 | 91% | 210/619-0330<br>Fax 210/619-0359 |
| Karen Wagner High Sch<br>3000 N Foster Rd, San Antonio 78244<br><u>Mary Duhart-Toppen</u> | 9-12 | TV | 2,137 | 76% | 210/662-5000<br>Fax 210/945-6979 |
| Kirby Middle Sch<br>5441 Seguin Rd, San Antonio 78219<br>**Sue Arredondo** \ **Jerome Johnson** | 6-8 | TV | 468<br>80 | 85% | 210/661-1140<br>Fax 210/945-6964 |
| Kitty Hawk Middle Sch<br>840 Old Cimarron Trl, Universal Cty 78148<br><u>Beverly Broom</u> | 6-8 | TV | 1,353<br>96 | 54% | 210/945-1220<br>Fax 210/945-6965 |
| Mary Hartman Elem Sch<br>7203 Woodlake Pkwy, San Antonio 78218<br><u>Monica Rodriguez</u> \ **Sara Pena** | PK-5 | T | 701<br>47 | 74% | 210/564-1520<br>Fax 210/619-0320 |
| Miller's Point Elem Sch<br>7027 Misty Ridge Dr, Converse 78109<br><u>Barbara Smejkal</u> | PK-5 | T | 525<br>48 | 75% | 210/945-5114<br>Fax 210/945-6957 |
| Olympia Elem Sch<br>8439 Athenian, Universal Cty 78148<br>**S George** | PK-5 | T | 381<br>31 | 53% | 210/945-5113<br>Fax 210/945-6955 |
| Park Village Elem Sch<br>5855 Midcrown Dr, San Antonio 78218<br>Sharon Balderas | PK-5 | T | 429<br>44 | 99% | 210/637-4890<br>Fax 210/945-6952 |

| | | | | | |
|---|---|---|---|---|---|
| **1** Superintendent | **8** Curric/Instruct K-12 | **19** Chief Financial Officer | **29** Family/Consumer Science | **39** Social Studies K-12 | **49** English/Lang Arts Elem | **59** Special Education Elem | **69** Academic Assessment |
| **2** Bus/Finance/Purchasing | **9** Curric/Instruct Elem | **20** Art K-12 | **30** Adult Education | **40** Social Studies Elem | **50** English/Lang Arts Sec | **60** Special Education Sec | **70** Research/Development |
| **3** Buildings And Grounds | **10** Curric/Instruct Sec | **21** Art Elem | **31** Career/Sch-to-Work K-12 | **41** Social Studies Sec | **51** Reading K-12 | **61** Foreign/World Lang K-12 | **71** Public Information |
| **4** Food Service | **11** Federal Program | **22** Art Sec | **32** Career/Sch-to-Work Elem | **42** Science K-12 | **52** Reading Elem | **62** Foreign/World Lang Elem | **72** Summer School |
| **5** Transportation | **12** Title I | **23** Music K-12 | **33** Career/Sch-to-Work Sec | **43** Science Elem | **53** Reading Sec | **63** Foreign/World Lang Sec | **73** Instructional Tech |
| **6** Athletic | **13** Title V | **24** Music Elem | **34** Early Childhood Ed | **44** Science Sec | **54** Remedial Reading K-12 | **64** Religious Education K-12 | **74** Inservice Training |
| **7** Health Services | **15** Asst Superintendent | **25** Music Sec | **35** Health/Phys Education | **45** Math K-12 | **55** Remedial Reading Elem | **65** Religious Education Elem | **75** Marketing/Distributive |
| | **16** Instructional Media Svcs | **26** Business Education | **36** Guidance Services K-12 | **46** Math Elem | **56** Remedial Reading Sec | **66** Religious Education Sec | **76** Info Systems |
| | **17** Chief Operations Officer | **27** Career & Tech Ed | **37** Guidance Services Elem | **47** Math Sec | **57** Bilingual/ELL | **67** School Board President | **77** Psychological Assess |
| | **18** Chief Academic Officer | **28** Technology Education | **38** Guidance Services Sec | **48** English/Lang Arts K-12 | **58** Special Education K-12 | **68** Teacher Personnel | **78** Affirmative Action |

| | | | | | |
|---|---|---|---|---|---|
| Ricardo Salinas Elem Sch<br>10560 Old Cimarron Trl, Universal Cty 78148<br>Martin Silverman | PK-5 | T | 642<br>36 | 59% | 210/659-5045<br>Fax 210/945-6962 |
| Rolling Meadows Elem Sch<br>17222 FM 2252, San Antonio 78266<br>Michelle La Rue | PK-5 | | 697 | 40% | 210/945-5700<br>Fax 210/945-6989 |
| Spring Meadows Elem Sch<br>7135 Elm Trail Dr, San Antonio 78244<br>Destiny Barrera | PK-5 | T | 583<br>37 | 83% | 210/662-1050<br>Fax 210/945-6956 |
| Ⓐ Thompson Learning Center<br>8555 E Loop 1604 N, Converse 78109<br>Joe Gonzalez | 9-12 | | 10 | | 210/945-5053<br>Fax 210/945-7525 |
| Veterans Memorial High Sch<br>7618 E Evans Rd, San Antonio 78266<br>Gregory Brauer | 9-12 | T | 1,333 | 47% | 210/619-0220<br>Fax 210/945-6990 |
| William Paschall Elem Sch<br>6351 Lakeview Dr, San Antonio 78244<br>Tricia Davila | PK-5 | T | 583 | 85% | 210/662-2240<br>Fax 210/945-6961 |
| Woodlake Elem Sch<br>5501 Lakebend East Dr, San Antonio 78244<br>Kristin Saunders | PK-5 | T | 574<br>34 | 75% | 210/662-2220<br>Fax 210/945-6954 |
| Woodlake Hills Middle Sch<br>6625 Woodlake Pkwy, San Antonio 78244<br>Daniel Brooks | 6-8 | TV | 823<br>85 | 77% | 210/661-1110<br>Fax 210/945-6966 |
| Wortham Oaks Elem Sch<br>5710 Carriage Cpe, San Antonio 78261<br>Yvonne Munoz | PK-5 | | 216 | | 210/945-5750 |

● **Lackland Ind School Dist** PID: 01808829    210/357-5000
2460 Kenly Ave Bldg 8265, San Antonio 78236    Fax 210/357-5050

**Schools:** 2 \ **Teachers:** 82 \ **Students:** 1,000 \ **Special Ed Students:** 139 \ **LEP Students:** 15 \ **College-Bound:** 45% \ **Ethnic:** Asian 2%, African American 16%, Hispanic 29%, Caucasian 53% \ **Exp:** $620 (High) \ **Poverty:** 14% \ **Title I:** $101,253 \ **Open-Close:** 08/17 - 05/27 \ **DTBP:** $333 (High)

| | | | | |
|---|---|---|---|---|
| Dr Bernie Roper ........................1 | | Rebecca Estrada .................. 2,13,19 | | |
| Alfredo Concha ......... 3,4,5,73,76,91,295 | | Steven Rodriguez ..........................3 | | |
| Edward Rodriguez ......................4 | | Maricella Reyna ............................4 | | |
| Jarvis Sims ............................5 | | Dr Tonya Hyde .......... 8,11,57,83,88,288 | | |
| Gentry Haussie ......................58,77 | | Brian Miller ................................ 67 | | |
| Christina Larkin ........................69 | | Ben Pease ................................. 76 | | |

| Public Schs..Principal | Grd | Prgm | Enr/#Cls | SN | |
|---|---|---|---|---|---|
| Lackland Elem Sch<br>2460 Kenly Ave Bldg 8265, San Antonio 78236<br>Teresa Leija | PK-5 | | 586<br>55 | 19% | 210/357-5053<br>Fax 210/357-5060 |
| Stacey Jr Sr High Sch<br>2460 Kenly Ave Bldg 8265, San Antonio 78236<br>Hunter Shelby | 6-12 | | 353<br>31 | 16% | 210/357-5100<br>Fax 210/357-5109 |

● **North East Ind School Dist** PID: 00997661    210/407-0000
8961 Tesoro Dr, San Antonio 78217    Fax 210/804-7017

**Schools:** 74 \ **Teachers:** 4,174 \ **Students:** 66,759 \ **Special Ed Students:** 6,663 \ **LEP Students:** 8,081 \ **College-Bound:** 83% \ **Ethnic:** Asian 4%, African American 8%, Hispanic 62%, Caucasian 26% \ **Exp:** $261 (Med) \ **Poverty:** 15% \ **Title I:** $20,334,098 \ **Special Education:** $9,273,000 \ **Open-Close:** 08/17 - 05/28 \ **DTBP:** $191 (High) \ ⓔ

| | | |
|---|---|---|
| Dr Sean Maika ............................1 | | Brian Moy .......................................2 |
| Dan Villarreal ..............2,7,15,19,91 | | David Bohannon ..............................2 |
| Barry Lanford ............................3 | | Dan Lugo ........................................3 |
| Larry Fowler ............................3 | | Sharon Glosson ..............................4 |

| | | | | |
|---|---|---|---|---|
| Jack Deforrest ................5 | | Kelly Parker ..........................6 | | |
| Maria Perez .....................7 | | Anthony Jarrett ...................8,15 | | |
| Dr Donna Newman ....8,15,58,68,79 | | Jennifer Gutierrez ...................9 | | |
| Susan Diaz ......................10 | | Celeste LaFuente-Garza ....... 11,27,34,36,69 | | |
| Dr Esmerelda Munoz ....... 11,27,34,36,69 | | Kellye Pear ...........................11 | | |
| Rudy Jimenez ...................15 | | Theresa Sanchez ...................16 | | |
| Tom Johnson .................16,73 | | Julie Shore ........................20,23 | | |
| Ben Peterson ...................27 | | Dr Caprica Wells ...................30 | | |
| Cori McGhee ....................31 | | Natalie Hierholzer ...................36 | | |
| Alicia Calderon .................57 | | Alicia Calperon ......................57 | | |
| Brenda Oates ...................58 | | Dr Debbie Dingle ...................61 | | |
| Shannon Grona .................67 | | Gina Elliott ...........................68 | | |
| Joel Trevino .....................68 | | Alex Verdell .....................69,70,294 | | |
| Beverly Lebherz ................69 | | Brande Merriman ...............69,294 | | |
| Dr Dorian Galindo ....... 69,70,294 | | Aubrey Chancellor ...................71 | | |
| Paige Felter .....................72 | | Christi Ramsey ......................73 | | |
| Cathy Hinojosa .................74 | | Christi Wilbur .......................76 | | |
| Roxanne Brown .................81 | | Tyler Shoesmith ...............83,275,752 | | |
| Wallace McCampbell ...........91 | | Jennifer Jensen ....................285 | | |
| Doretta Walker .................295 | | Peter Ruiz ...........................295 | | |
| Deborah Caldwell ...............298 | | | | |

| Public Schs..Principal | Grd | Prgm | Enr/#Cls | SN | |
|---|---|---|---|---|---|
| Ⓐ Academy of Creative Education<br>3736 Perrin Ctl Bldg 2, San Antonio 78217<br>Patrick Valdez | 11-12 | TV | 150<br>10 | 39% | 210/407-0740<br>Fax 210/657-8976 |
| Ⓐ Behavior Support Services<br>8438 Ahern Dr, San Antonio 78216<br>Christine Condren | 9-12 | GV | 100 | | 210/356-7520 |
| Bradley Middle Sch<br>14819 Heimer Rd, San Antonio 78232<br>Brenda Cerroni | 6-8 | V | 1,265<br>65 | 36% | 210/356-2600<br>Fax 210/491-8314 |
| Bulverde Creek Elem Sch<br>3839 Canyon Pkwy, San Antonio 78259<br>Michelle McCoy | PK-5 | | 1,055 | 31% | 210/407-1000<br>Fax 210/491-8333 |
| Bush Middle Sch<br>1500 Evans Rd, San Antonio 78258<br>Stuart Guthrie | 6-8 | | 1,135<br>100 | 18% | 210/356-2900<br>Fax 210/491-8471 |
| Camelot Elem Sch<br>5311 Merlin Dr, San Antonio 78218<br>**Wilma Payne** | PK-5 | T | 534<br>30 | 88% | 210/407-1400<br>Fax 210/564-1782<br>ⓔ |
| Canyon Ridge Elem Sch<br>20522 Stone Oak Pkwy, San Antonio 78258<br>Laura Huggins | PK-5 | | 621 | 23% | 210/407-1600<br>Fax 210/482-2293<br>ⓕⓔ |
| Career & Tech Education Center<br>3736 Perrin Central Bldg 4, San Antonio 78217<br>Justin Missildine | Voc | | 150 | | 210/407-0743<br>Fax 210/637-4992 |
| Ⓜ Castle Hills Elem Sch<br>Ⓨ 200 Lemonwood Dr, San Antonio 78213<br>Betsy Asheim | PK-5 | M | 404<br>30 | 38% | 210/407-1800<br>Fax 210/407-1809 |
| Cibolo Green Elem Sch<br>24315 Bulverde Grn, San Antonio 78261<br>Adam Schwab | PK-5 | | 786 | 18% | 210/407-1200<br>Fax 830/438-3540 |
| Clear Spring Elem Sch<br>4311 Clear Spring Dr, San Antonio 78217<br>Carlos Hoffman | K-5 | T | 363<br>25 | 83% | 210/407-2000<br>Fax 210/407-2009 |
| Coker Elem Sch<br>302 Heimer Rd, San Antonio 78232<br>Elizabeth Fischer | PK-5 | T | 819<br>40 | 51% | 210/407-2200<br>Fax 210/407-2209<br>ⓔ |
| Colonial Hills Elem Sch<br>2627 Kerrybrook Ct, San Antonio 78230<br>Jenae Mai | PK-5 | T | 627<br>40 | 85% | 210/407-2400<br>Fax 210/442-0730 |
| Ⓨ David Tex Hill Middle Sch<br>21314 Bowerde Rd, San Antonio 78259<br>Charles Reininger | 6-8 | MV | 1,115 | 21% | 210/356-8000<br>Fax 210/494-2380 |
| Dellview Elem Sch<br>7235 Dewhurst Rd, San Antonio 78213<br>Kelli Nungesser | PK-5 | T | 338<br>40 | 83% | 210/407-2600<br>Fax 210/407-2609<br>ⓔ |

| | | | | |
|---|---|---|---|---|
| 79 Student Personnel | 91 Safety/Security | 275 Response To Intervention | 298 Grant Writer/Ptnrships | **School Programs** |
| 80 Driver Ed/Safety | 92 Magnet School | 277 Remedial Math K-12 | 750 Chief Innovation Officer | A = Alternative Program |
| 81 Gifted/Talented | 93 Parental Involvement | 280 Literacy Coach | 751 Chief of Staff | G = Adult Classes |
| 82 Video Services | 95 Tech Prep Program | 285 STEM | 752 Social Emotional Learning | M = Magnet Program |
| 83 Substance Abuse Prev | 97 Chief Infomation Officer | 286 Digital Learning | | T = Title I Schoolwide |
| 84 Erate | 98 Chief Technology Officer | 288 Common Core Standards | **Other School Types** | V = Career & Tech Ed Programs |
| 85 AIDS Education | 270 Character Education | 294 Accountability | Ⓐ = Alternative School | |
| 88 Alternative/At Risk | 271 Migrant Education | 295 Network System | Ⓒ = Charter School | **New Schools are shaded** |
| 89 Multi-Cultural Curriculum | 273 Teacher Mentor | 296 Title II Programs | Ⓜ = Magnet School | **New Superintendents and Principals are bold** |
| 90 Social Work | 274 Before/After Sch | 297 Webmaster | Ⓨ = Year-Round School | **Personnel with email addresses are underscored** |

**Social Media**

ⓕ = Facebook

ⓔ = Twitter

**Ⓜ Design & Technology Academy** — 9-12, 100, 210/356-2237, Fax 210/650-1285
5110 Walzem Rd, San Antonio 78218
Christina Mank-Allen

**Dr Bernard Harris Middle Sch** — 6-8, T, 1,069, 49%, 210/356-4100, Fax 210/657-8892
5300 Knollcreek, San Antonio 78247
Jeremi Niehoff

**Driscoll Middle Sch** — 6-8, TV, 755, 91, 46%, 210/356-3200, Fax 210/491-6467
17150 Jones Maltsberger Rd, San Antonio 78247
John Hill

**East Terrell Hills Elem Sch** — PK-5, T, 627, 33, 87%, 210/407-2800, Fax 210/564-1604
4415 Bloomdale, San Antonio 78218
Ross McGlothlin

**Edward H White Middle Sch** — 6-8, TV, 1,072, 65, 69%, 210/356-5900, Fax 210/650-1443
7800 Midcrown Dr, San Antonio 78218
Bethany Lorge

**Eisenhower Middle Sch** — 6-8, TV, 983, 57%, 210/356-3500, Fax 210/442-0537
8231 Blanco Rd, San Antonio 78216
John Smith

**El Dorado Elem Sch** — PK-5, T, 592, 30, 82%, 210/407-3000, Fax 210/407-3009
12634 El Sendero St, San Antonio 78233
Glenn Forde

**Encino Park Elem Sch** — PK-5, G, 658, 54, 25%, 210/407-3200, Fax 210/497-6238
2550 Encino Rio, San Antonio 78259
James Miller

**Fox Run Elem Sch** — PK-5, T, 703, 65%, 210/407-3400, Fax 210/564-1732
6111 Fox Creek St, San Antonio 78247
Kimberly Orihuela

**Frank Tejeda Middle Sch** — 6-8, 1,185, 65, 22%, 210/356-5600, Fax 210/482-2277
2909 E Evans Rd, San Antonio 78259
Martha Reyes

**Garner Middle Sch** — 6-8, TV, 931, 40, 76%, 210/356-3800, Fax 210/805-5138
4302 Harry Wurzbach Rd, San Antonio 78209
John Bojescul

**Hardy Oak Elem Sch** — PK-5, 605, 60, 9%, 210/407-3600, Fax 210/481-4004
22900 Hardy Oak Blvd, San Antonio 78258
Lola Folkes

**Harmony Hills Elem Sch** — PK-5, T, 584, 40, 72%, 210/407-3800, Fax 210/407-3809
10727 Memory Ln, San Antonio 78216
Alan Rochkus

**Hidden Forest Elem Sch** — PK-5, 478, 29, 19%, 210/407-4000, Fax 210/407-4009
802 Silver Spruce St, San Antonio 78232
Renette Powell

**Huebner Elem Sch** — PK-5, 680, 48, 27%, 210/407-4200, Fax 210/408-5529
16311 Huebner Rd, San Antonio 78248
Kelli Halliburton

**Ⓜ International Sch of Americas** — 9-12, 494, 18, 23%, 210/356-0900, Fax 210/442-0409
1400 Jackson Keller Rd, San Antonio 78213
Steven Magadance

**Jackson Middle Sch** — 6-8, TV, 723, 70, 72%, 210/356-4400, Fax 210/442-0580
4538 Vance Jackson Rd, San Antonio 78230
Erin Deason

**Jackson-Keller Elem Sch** — PK-5, T, 666, 32, 86%, 210/407-4400, Fax 210/442-0706
1601 Jackson Keller Rd, San Antonio 78213
Anna Nicolai

**Johnson High Sch** — 9-12, 3,164, 17%, 210/356-0400, Fax 210/356-0430
23203 Bulverde Rd, San Antonio 78259
Gary Comalander

**Jose M Lopez Middle Sch** — 6-8, V, 1,274, 11%, 210/356-5000, Fax 210/481-4072
23103 Hardy Oak Blvd, San Antonio 78258
Eric Wernli

**Krueger Middle Sch** — 6-8, TV, 968, 76%, 210/356-4700, Fax 210/650-1124
438 Lanark Dr, San Antonio 78218
Cynthia Rubio

**Larkspur Elem Sch** — PK-5, T, 698, 80%, 210/407-4600, Fax 210/407-4609
1802 Larkspur, San Antonio 78213
Cody Miller

**Las Lomas Elem Sch** — PK-5, 508, 31%, 210/356-7000, Fax 210/481-4012
20303 Hardy Oak Blvd, San Antonio 78258
Harold Massey

**Legacy of Educl Excellence HS** — 9-12, AGTV, 2,601, 64%, 210/356-0800, Fax 210/442-0325
1400 Jackson Keller Rd, San Antonio 78213
David Crowe

**Longs Creek Elem Sch** — PK-5, 595, 46, 40%, 210/407-4800, Fax 210/657-8754
15806 Oconnor Rd, San Antonio 78247
Amy Copes

**MacArthur High Sch** — 9-12, GTV, 2,374, 100, 49%, 210/356-7600, Fax 210/650-1195
2923 MacArthur Vw, San Antonio 78217
Peter Martinez

**Madison High Sch** — 9-12, TV, 3,285, 100, 46%, 210/356-1400, Fax 210/637-4435
5005 Stahl Rd, San Antonio 78247
Steven Zimmerman

**Montgomery Elem Sch** — PK-5, T, 490, 90%, 210/407-5000, Fax 210/564-1758
7047 Montgomery, San Antonio 78239
John Merrill

**Ⓐ NE Transition Sch** — 9-12, G, 100, 210/356-7520, Fax 210/637-4956
8438 Ahern Dr, San Antonio 78216
Christine Condren

**Nimitz Middle Sch** — 6-8, TV, 1,305, 48, 74%, 210/356-5300, Fax 210/442-0489
5426 Blanco Rd, San Antonio 78216
Jennifer Cooper

**Ⓐ North East Alternative Center** — 6-12, G, 93, 27, 210/356-7400, Fax 210/442-0623
103 W Rampart Dr, San Antonio 78216
Brian Kennedy

**Northern Hills Elem Sch** — PK-5, T, 617, 57, 69%, 210/407-5200, Fax 210/650-1482
13901 Higgins Rd, San Antonio 78217
Marisa Wulfsberg

**Northwood Elem Sch** — PK-5, T, 375, 26, 51%, 210/407-5400, Fax 210/805-5157
519 Pike Rd, San Antonio 78209
Catherine Harper

**Oak Grove Elem Sch** — PK-5, T, 313, 34, 81%, 210/407-5600, Fax 210/407-5609
3250 Nacogdoches Rd, San Antonio 78217
Taleen Bloom

**Oak Meadow Elem Sch** — PK-5, 463, 36, 39%, 210/407-5800, Fax 210/407-5809
2800 Hunters Green St, San Antonio 78231
Lisa Campos

**Olmos Elem Sch** — PK-5, T, 609, 46, 95%, 210/407-6000, Fax 210/442-0654
1103 Allena Dr, San Antonio 78213
Gaila Booth

**PK Academy at West Avenue** — PK-PK, T, 100, 26, 92%, 210/407-8600, Fax 210/442-0756
3915 West Ave, San Antonio 78213
Paul Kienlen

**Redland Oaks Elem Sch** — PK-5, 396, 29, 39%, 210/407-6200, Fax 210/491-8383
16650 Redland Rd, San Antonio 78247
Randy Barr

**Regency Place Elem Sch** — PK-5, T, 426, 28, 77%, 210/407-6400, Fax 210/650-1532
10222 Broadway, San Antonio 78217
Estelia Wallace

**Ridgeview Elem Sch** — PK-5, T, 603, 40, 88%, 210/407-6600, Fax 210/407-6609
8223 McCullough Ave, San Antonio 78216
Veronica Garza

**Roan Forest Elem Sch** — PK-5, 809, 34%, 210/407-6800, Fax 210/481-4053
22710 Roan Park, San Antonio 78259
Christopher Specia

**Ronald Reagan High Sch** — 9-12, 3,491, 13%, 210/356-1800, Fax 210/482-2222
19000 Ronald Reagan, San Antonio 78258
Brenda Shelton

**Roosevelt High Sch** — 9-12, GTV, 2,790, 66%, 210/356-2200, Fax 210/650-1291
5110 Walzem Rd, Windcrest 78218
Bryan Norwood

**Royal Ridge Elem Sch** — PK-5, T, 577, 61%, 210/407-7000, Fax 210/564-1620
5933 Royal Rdg, San Antonio 78239
Jana Carter

---

| | | | |
|---|---|---|---|
| 1 Superintendent | 8 Curric/Instruct K-12 | 19 Chief Financial Officer | 29 Family/Consumer Science |
| 2 Bus/Finance/Purchasing | 9 Curric/Instruct Elem | 20 Art K-12 | 30 Adult Education |
| 3 Buildings And Grounds | 10 Curric/Instruct Sec | 21 Art Elem | 31 Career/Sch-to-Work K-12 |
| 4 Food Service | 11 Federal Program | 22 Art Sec | 32 Career/Sch-to-Work Elem |
| 5 Transportation | 12 Title I | 23 Music K-12 | 33 Career/Sch-to-Work Sec |
| 6 Athletic | 13 Title V | 24 Music Elem | 34 Early Childhood Ed |
| 7 Health Services | 15 Asst Superintendent | 25 Music Sec | 35 Health/Phys Education |
| | 16 Instructional Media Svcs | 26 Business Education | 36 Guidance Services K-12 |
| | 17 Chief Operations Officer | 27 Career & Tech Ed | 37 Guidance Services Elem |
| | 18 Chief Academic Officer | 28 Technology Education | 38 Guidance Services Sec |

| | | | |
|---|---|---|---|
| 39 Social Studies K-12 | 49 English/Lang Arts Elem | 59 Special Education Elem | 69 Academic Assessment |
| 40 Social Studies Elem | 50 English/Lang Arts Sec | 60 Special Education Sec | 70 Research/Development |
| 41 Social Studies Sec | 51 Reading K-12 | 61 Foreign/World Lang K-12 | 71 Public Information |
| 42 Science K-12 | 52 Reading Elem | 62 Foreign/World Lang Elem | 72 Summer School |
| 43 Science Elem | 53 Reading Sec | 63 Foreign/World Lang Sec | 73 Instructional Tech |
| 44 Science Sec | 54 Remedial Reading K-12 | 64 Religious Education K-12 | 74 Inservice Training |
| 45 Math K-12 | 55 Remedial Reading Elem | 65 Religious Education Elem | 75 Marketing/Distributive |
| 46 Math Elem | 56 Remedial Reading Sec | 66 Religious Education Sec | 76 Info Systems |
| 47 Math Sec | 57 Bilingual/ELL | 67 School Board President | 77 Psychological Assess |
| 48 English/Lang Arts K-12 | 58 Special Education K-12 | 68 Teacher Personnel | 78 Affirmative Action |

| School | Grd | Prgm | Enr/#Cls | SN | Phone |
|---|---|---|---|---|---|
| Serna Elem Sch<br>2569 NE Loop 410, San Antonio 78217<br>Jennifer Lomas | PK-5 | T | 493<br>25 | 89% | 210/407-7200<br>Fax 210/407-7209 |
| Stahl Elem Sch<br>5222 Stahl Rd, San Antonio 78247<br>Emma Yates | PK-5 | T | 711<br>44 | 71% | 210/407-7400<br>Fax 210/564-1682 |
| Steubing Ranch Elem Sch<br>5100 Knollcreek, San Antonio 78247<br>Mario Guillen | PK-5 | T | 829 | 50% | 210/407-7600<br>Fax 210/650-1248 |
| Stone Oak Elem Sch<br>21045 Crescent Oaks, San Antonio 78258<br>Ann Karrer | PK-5 | | 714<br>40 | 29% | 210/407-7800<br>Fax 210/497-6204 |
| Thousand Oaks Elem Sch<br>16080 Henderson Pass, San Antonio 78232<br>Holly Salazar | PK-5 | | 590<br>45 | 47% | 210/407-8000<br>Fax 210/491-8358 |
| Tuscany Heights Elem Sch<br>25001 Wilderness Oak, San Antonio 78260<br>Tara Bailey | PK-5 | | 603 | 15% | 210/407-8200<br>Fax 830/438-6330 |
| Vineyard Ranch Elem Sch<br>16818 Huebner Rd, San Antonio 78258<br>**Carol Pierce** | PK-5 | | 790 | 16% | 210/356-7200<br>Fax 210/408-5515 |
| Walzem Elem Sch<br>4618 Walzem Rd, San Antonio 78218<br>**Liz Washington** | PK-5 | T | 576<br>40 | 90% | 210/407-8400<br>Fax 210/564-1730 |
| Wetmore Elem Sch<br>3250 Thousand Oaks Dr, San Antonio 78247<br>Catherine Leach | PK-5 | T | 662<br>41 | 47% | 210/407-8800<br>Fax 210/481-4037 |
| Wilderness Oak Elem Sch<br>21019 Wilderness Oak, San Antonio 78258<br>Elias Harrington | PK-5 | | 518 | 12% | 210/407-9200<br>Fax 210/491-8371 |
| Wilshire Elem Sch<br>6523 Cascade Pl, San Antonio 78218<br>Stacy Deming-Garcia | PK-5 | T | 238<br>24 | 88% | 210/407-9400<br>Fax 210/805-5181 |
| Windcrest Elem Sch<br>465 Faircrest Dr, San Antonio 78239<br>Todd Voges | PK-5 | T | 619<br>25 | 77% | 210/407-9600<br>Fax 210/407-9701 |
| Winston Churchill High Sch<br>12049 Blanco Rd, San Antonio 78216<br>Todd Bloomer | 9-12 | GV | 2,825<br>100 | 38% | 210/356-0000<br>Fax 210/442-0879 |
| Wood Middle Sch<br>14800 Judson Rd, San Antonio 78233<br>Marcus Alvarez | 6-8 | TV | 830<br>60 | 67% | 210/356-6200<br>Fax 210/650-1309 |
| Woodstone Elem Sch<br>5602 Fountainwood Dr, San Antonio 78233 | PK-5 | T | 584<br>49 | 69% | 210/407-9800<br>Fax 210/564-1708 |

● **Northside Ind School Dist** PID: 00998017    210/397-8500
5900 Evers Rd, San Antonio 78238    Fax 210/706-8772

**Schools:** 124 \ **Teachers:** 6,962 \ **Students:** 106,863 \
**Special Ed Students:** 13,153 \ **LEP Students:** 9,056 \ **College-Bound:** 85%
\ **Ethnic:** Asian 3%, African American 7%, Hispanic 70%, Caucasian
20% \ **Exp:** $322 (High) \ **Poverty:** 15% \ **Title I:** $28,073,537 \
**Special Education:** $19,876,000 \ **Bilingual Education:** $210,000 \
**Open-Close:** 08/24 - 06/03 \ **DTBP:** $181 (High)

| | | | |
|---|---|---|---|
| Dr Brian Woods | 1 | Rene Barajas | 2,15 |
| Wesley Scott | 2,15 | Leroy San Miguel | 3,15 |
| Thomas Wherry | 4 | Rafael Salazar | 5 |
| Stan Laing | 6 | Jennifer Krueger | 7 |
| Shirley Schreiber | 7* | Dr Janis Jordan | 8,15 |
| Deonna Dean | 9 | Levina Lara | 9,15 |
| Patti Sanchez | 9 | Stephen Daniel | 10,15 |
| Lisa DelGado | 11 | Carolyn Rozelle | 12 |
| Don Schmidt | 15,79 | Henry Acosta | 15 |
| Lori Jones | 15,73 | Patricia Denham-Hill | 15,68 |
| Ray Galindo | 15 | Doug Shudde | 16,73 |
| James Miculka | 20,23 | Lydia Martinez | 30,93 |

| | |
|---|---|
| Deborah Ruel Schafer | 31,34 |
| Victor Raga | 57 |
| Dr Carol Harle | 67 |
| Carin Adermann | 69 |
| Kris Trejo | 73,286 |
| Melissa Oshman | 76 |
| Tracy Wernli | 79 |
| Kim Stewart | 81 |
| Sharon Sanchez | 298* |
| Dr Kimberly Ridgley | 36,752 |
| Krista Garcia | 58 |
| Dr Brenda Ward | 69,294 |
| Barry Perez | 71 |
| Diana Ely | 74 |
| Dr Coleman Heckman | 77 |
| Courtney Mayer | 81 |
| Charlie Carnes | 91 |

| Public Schs..Principal | Grd | Prgm | Enr/#Cls | SN | Phone |
|---|---|---|---|---|---|
| Adams Hill Elem Sch<br>9627 Adams Hill Dr, San Antonio 78245<br>Annette Robinson | PK-5 | T | 443<br>32 | 82% | 210/397-1400<br>Fax 210/678-2937 |
| Allen Elem Sch<br>101 Dumont Dr, San Antonio 78227<br>Erika Zagala | PK-5 | T | 576<br>30 | 93% | 210/397-0800<br>Fax 210/678-2946 |
| Anson Jones Middle Sch<br>1256 Pinn Rd, San Antonio 78227<br>Michella Wheat | 6-8 | TV | 998<br>62 | 90% | 210/397-2100<br>Fax 210/678-2113 |
| Aue Elem Sch<br>24750 Baywater Stage, San Antonio 78255<br>Ursula Silberschlag | PK-5 | | 698<br>52 | 11% | 210/397-6750<br>Fax 210/698-4422 |
| Bennie Cole Elem Sch<br>13185 Tillman Rdg, San Antonio 78253<br>Tod Kuenning | PK-5 | | 892 | 26% | 210/398-2100<br>Fax 210/678-2127 |
| Bob Beard Elem Sch<br>8725 Sonoma Pkwy, Helotes 78023<br>Blanca Hemann | PK-5 | | 681<br>31 | 10% | 210/397-6600<br>Fax 210/695-3849 |
| Bob Lewis Elem Sch<br>1000 Seascape, San Antonio 78251<br>Kendra Merrell | PK-5 | T | 686<br>44 | 42% | 210/397-2650<br>Fax 210/257-3004 |
| Bobbye Behlau Elem Sch<br>2355 Camp Light Way, San Antonio 78245<br>Jody Fries | PK-5 | T | 773 | 45% | 210/398-1000<br>Fax 210/678-2107 |
| Bonnie Ellison Elem Sch<br>7132 Oak Dr, San Antonio 78256<br>Julie Meneses | PK-5 | | 588 | 25% | 210/398-1850<br>Fax 210/687-1093 |
| Brandeis High Sch<br>13011 Kyle Seale Pkwy, San Antonio 78249<br>Dr Geri Berger | 9-12 | GV | 2,773 | 23% | 210/397-8200<br>Fax 210/561-2000 |
| Braun Station Elem Sch<br>8631 Tezel Rd, San Antonio 78254<br>Jack Funkhouser | PK-5 | | 526<br>38 | 36% | 210/397-1550<br>Fax 210/706-7463 |
| Cable Elem Sch<br>1706 Pinn Rd, San Antonio 78227<br>Debra Pinon | PK-5 | T | 536<br>30 | 96% | 210/397-2850<br>Fax 210/678-2878 |
| Carl Wanke Elem Sch<br>10419 Old Prue Rd, San Antonio 78249<br>Claudia Sanchez | PK-5 | T | 732 | 40% | 210/397-6700<br>Fax 210/257-4340 |
| Carlos Coon Elem Sch<br>3110 Timber View Dr, San Antonio 78251<br>Mark Garcia | PK-5 | T | 735<br>35 | 77% | 210/397-7250<br>Fax 210/706-7288 |
| Carnahan Elem Sch<br>6839 Babcock Rd, San Antonio 78249<br>Andi Sosa | PK-5 | T | 534 | 64% | 210/397-5850<br>Fax 210/516-2050 |
| Christian Evers Elem Sch<br>1715 Richland Hills Dr, San Antonio 78251<br>Talia Hernandez | PK-5 | T | 773<br>47 | 49% | 210/397-2550<br>Fax 210/706-7564 |
| Clarence Galm Elem Sch<br>1454 Saxonhill Dr, San Antonio 78253<br>Michelle Alongi | PK-5 | T | 541<br>47 | 47% | 210/397-1150<br>Fax 210/678-2863 |
| Colby Glass Elem Sch<br>519 Clearview Dr, San Antonio 78228<br>Jennifer Bock | PK-5 | T | 566<br>27 | 77% | 210/397-1950<br>Fax 210/431-5817 |
| Colonies North Elem Sch<br>9915 Northampton Dr, San Antonio 78230<br>Norma Farrell | PK-5 | T | 584<br>32 | 75% | 210/397-1700<br>Fax 210/561-5240 |

| | | | | | |
|---|---|---|---|---|---|
| 79 Student Personnel | 91 Safety/Security | 275 Response To Intervention | 298 Grant Writer/Ptnrships | **School Programs** | **Social Media** |
| 80 Driver Ed/Safety | 92 Magnet School | 277 Remedial Math K-12 | 750 Chief Innovation Officer | **A** = Alternative Program | |
| 81 Gifted/Talented | 93 Parental Involvement | 280 Literacy Coach | 751 Chief of Staff | **G** = Adult Classes | **f** = Facebook |
| 82 Video Services | 95 Tech Prep Program | 285 STEM | 752 Social Emotional Learning | **M** = Magnet Program | |
| 83 Substance Abuse Prev | 97 Chief Information Officer | 286 Digital Learning | | **T** = Title I Schoolwide | **t** = Twitter |
| 84 Erate | 98 Chief Technology Officer | 288 Common Core Standards | **Other School Types** | **V** = Career & Tech Ed Programs | |
| 85 AIDS Education | 270 Character Education | 294 Accountability | Ⓐ = Alternative School | | |
| 88 Alternative/At Risk | 271 Migrant Education | 295 Network System | Ⓒ = Charter School | **New Schools are shaded** | |
| 89 Multi-Cultural Curriculum | 273 Teacher Mentor | 296 Title II Programs | Ⓜ = Magnet School | **New Superintendents and Principals are bold** | **TX—39** |
| 90 Social Work | 274 Before/After Sch | 297 Webmaster | Ⓨ = Year-Round School | **Personnel with email addresses are underscored** | |

| School | Grades | | Enroll | % | Phone |
|---|---|---|---|---|---|
| ⓜ Communications Arts High Sch<br>11600 Culebra Rd, San Antonio 78253<br>Lisa Baker | 9-12 | | 525<br>15 | | 210/397-6043<br>Fax 210/688-6092 |
| Construction Careers Academy<br>9411 W Military Dr, San Antonio 78251<br>Phillip Edge | Voc | | 520 | | 210/397-4294 |
| Dean H Krueger Elem Sch<br>9900 Wildhorse Pkwy, San Antonio 78254<br>Laneil Belko | PK-5 | | 720<br>48 | 27% | 210/397-3850<br>Fax 210/257-1130 |
| Dolores Linton Elem Sch<br>2103 Oakhill Rd, San Antonio 78238<br>Marty Ortega | PK-5 | T | 455<br>28 | 85% | 210/397-0750<br>Fax 210/706-7186 |
| Dolph Briscoe Middle Sch<br>4265 Lone Star Pkwy, San Antonio 78253<br>Christina Rather | 6-8 | | 1,399 | 22% | 210/398-1100<br>Fax 210/674-0220 |
| Dr Joe Bernal Middle Sch<br>14045 Bella Vista Pl, San Antonio 78253<br>Glenda Munson | 6-8 | | 1,018 | 30% | 210/398-1900<br>Fax 210/679-8216 |
| Dr Joe Ward Elem Sch<br>8400 Cavern Hl, San Antonio 78254<br>Sunday Nelson | PK-5 | T | 850<br>48 | 52% | 210/397-6800<br>Fax 210/257-1195 |
| Dr Martha Mead Elem Sch<br>3803 Midhorizon Dr, San Antonio 78229<br>Annette Lopez | PK-5 | T | 653 | 90% | 210/397-1750<br>Fax 210/366-0770 |
| Dr Pat Henderson Elem Sch<br>14605 Kallison Bnd, San Antonio 78254<br>Thomas Mackey | PK-5 | | 536 | 31% | 210/398-1050<br>Fax 210/256-0985 |
| Dr Winn Murnin Elem Sch<br>9019 Dugas Dr, San Antonio 78251<br>Amber Freeman | PK-5 | T | 893<br>40 | 61% | 210/397-4550<br>Fax 210/257-4335 |
| E M Pease Middle Sch<br>201 Hunt Ln, San Antonio 78245<br>Katherine Lyssy | 6-8 | TV | 1,119<br>75 | 76% | 210/397-2950<br>Fax 210/678-2974 |
| Earl Rudder Middle Sch<br>6558 Horn Blvd, San Antonio 78240<br>Dr Mary Jewell | 6-8 | AT | 979<br>65 | 69% | 210/397-5000<br>Fax 210/561-5022 |
| Ed Rawlinson Middle Sch<br>14100 Vance Jackson Rd, San Antonio 78249<br>Sherry Mireles | 6-8 | V | 1,342<br>75 | 30% | 210/397-4900<br>Fax 210/697-4055 |
| Edmund Cody Elem Sch<br>10403 Dugas Dr, San Antonio 78245<br>Kittiya Johnson | PK-5 | T | 640<br>45 | 78% | 210/397-1650<br>Fax 210/678-2797 |
| F R Scobee Elem Sch<br>11223 Cedar Park, San Antonio 78249<br>Jocelyn Dudney | PK-5 | T | 539<br>32 | 42% | 210/397-0700<br>Fax 210/561-5076 |
| Fields Elem Sch<br>9570 FM 1560 N, San Antonio 78254<br>P Jennifer Hammond | PK-5 | T | 859 | 44% | 210/398-2150<br>Fax 210/688-0347 |
| Folks Middle Sch<br>9855 Swayback Rnch, San Antonio 78254<br>Shawn McKenzie | 6-8 | | 1,517 | 28% | 210/398-1600<br>Fax 210/257-3060 |
| Forester Elem Sch<br>10726 Rousseau St, San Antonio 78245<br>Kelly Mantle | PK-5 | T | 862 | 52% | 210/397-0200<br>Fax 210/257-1030 |
| Frances M Rhodes Elem Sch<br>5714 N Knoll, San Antonio 78240<br>Vicki Kilpatrick | PK-5 | T | 508<br>35 | 65% | 210/397-4000<br>Fax 210/697-4020 |
| Glenoaks Elem Sch<br>5103 Newcome Dr, San Antonio 78229<br>Maria Meza | PK-5 | T | 705<br>42 | 77% | 210/397-2300<br>Fax 210/617-5452 |
| Gregorio Esparza Elem Sch<br>5700 Hemphill Dr, San Antonio 78228<br>Gabriela Garcia | PK-5 | T | 542<br>35 | 74% | 210/397-1850<br>Fax 210/431-5843 |
| Gregory Luna Middle Sch<br>200 Grosenbacher Rd N, San Antonio 78253<br>Lisa Richard | 6-8 | T | 1,444 | 41% | 210/397-5300<br>Fax 210/645-5246 |
| Harlan High Sch<br>14350 Culebra Rd, San Antonio 78253<br>Robert Harris | 9-12 | V | 2,291 | 29% | 210/398-2200<br>Fax 210/688-0494 |
| Health Careers High Sch<br>4646 Hamilton Wolfe Rd, San Antonio 78229<br>Linda Burk | Voc | A | 862<br>40 | 22% | 210/397-5400<br>Fax 210/617-5423 |
| Hector Garcia Middle Sch<br>14900 Kyle Seale Pkwy, San Antonio 78255<br>Tracy Wernli | 6-8 | | 1,483 | 11% | 210/397-8400<br>Fax 210/695-3830 |
| Helotes Elem Sch<br>13878 Riggs Rd, Helotes 78023<br>**Kasey Crick** | PK-5 | | 359<br>26 | 22% | 210/397-3800<br>Fax 210/695-3827 |
| Henry Brauchle Elem Sch<br>8555 Bowens Crossing St, San Antonio 78250<br>Adriana Mata-Tausch | PK-5 | T | 620<br>40 | 65% | 210/397-1500<br>Fax 210/706-7448 |
| Henry Steubing Elem Sch<br>11655 Braefield, San Antonio 78249<br>McGdalia Powers | PK-5 | | 446<br>50 | 30% | 210/397-4350<br>Fax 210/706-4374 |
| Herbert Boldt Elem Sch<br>310 Hollimon Pkwy, San Antonio 78253<br>Ms Siller | PK-5 | | 879 | 22% | 210/398-2000<br>Fax 210/398-2048 |
| Hoffmann Elem Sch<br>12118 Volunteer Pkwy, San Antonio 78253<br>Carrie Squyres | PK-5 | | 1,004 | 24% | 210/397-8350<br>Fax 210/645-3305 |
| ⓐ Irene L Chavez Excel Academy<br>11937 W Interstate 10, San Antonio 78230<br>Darren Calvert | 11-12 | | 93<br>8 | 36% | 210/397-8120<br>Fax 210/706-8953 |
| J B Passmore Elem Sch<br>570 Pinn Rd, San Antonio 78227<br>Veronica Arteaga | PK-5 | T | 534<br>30 | 91% | 210/397-0500<br>Fax 210/678-2808 |
| Jack C Jordan Middle Sch<br>1725 Richland Hills Dr, San Antonio 78251<br>Anabel Romero | 6-8 | TV | 1,266<br>80 | 53% | 210/397-6150<br>Fax 210/523-4876 |
| James Carson Elem Sch<br>8151 Old Tezel Rd, San Antonio 78250<br>Lori Shaw | PK-5 | | 579<br>32 | 34% | 210/397-1100<br>Fax 210/257-1103 |
| Jim G Martin Elem Sch<br>730 Canterbury, San Antonio 78228<br>Juan Perez | PK-5 | T | 615 | 90% | 210/398-1400<br>Fax 210/431-5810 |
| Jimmy Elrod Elem Sch<br>8885 Heath Circle Dr, San Antonio 78250<br>Mrs Flores | PK-5 | T | 421<br>32 | 52% | 210/397-1800<br>Fax 210/706-7493 |
| John B Connally Middle Sch<br>8661 Silent Sunrise, San Antonio 78250<br>Jaime Liendo | 6-8 | TV | 952<br>40 | 48% | 210/397-1000<br>Fax 210/257-1004 |
| John C Holmgreen Center<br>8580 Ewing Halsell Dr, San Antonio 78229<br>Melissa Benavidez | Spec | AV | 130<br>20 | 20% | 210/397-6100<br>Fax 210/617-5476 |
| John Glenn Elem Sch<br>2385 Horal St, San Antonio 78227<br>Michelle Fine | PK-5 | T | 486<br>55 | 93% | 210/397-2250<br>Fax 210/678-2891 |
| John Jay High Sch<br>7611 Marbach Rd, San Antonio 78227<br>Jay Sumpter | 9-12 | ATV | 2,896 | 75% | 210/397-2700<br>Fax 210/645-3310 |
| ⓜ John Jay Sci & Engineer Acad<br>7611 Marbach Rd, San Antonio 78227<br>Teresa Hernandez | 9-12 | | 732<br>5 | | 210/397-2773<br>Fax 210/678-2145 |
| John Marshall High Sch<br>8000 Lobo Ln, San Antonio 78240<br>Susan Cleveland | 9-12 | ATV | 2,519 | 47% | 210/397-7100<br>Fax 210/706-7175 |
| John Paul Stevens High Sch<br>600 N Ellison Dr, San Antonio 78251<br>Ryan Purtell | 9-12 | TV | 2,840 | 50% | 210/397-6450<br>Fax 210/257-4304 ⓔ |
| ⓦ Jones Magnet Middle Sch<br>1256 Pinn Rd, San Antonio 78227<br>**Michella Wheat** | 6-6 | | 140 | | 210/397-2230 |

| | | | | | | | | | | | |
|---|---|---|---|---|---|---|---|---|---|---|---|
| 1 | Superintendent | 8 | Curric/Instruct K-12 | 19 | Chief Financial Officer | 29 | Family/Consumer Science | 39 | Social Studies K-12 | 49 | English/Lang Arts Elem | 59 | Special Education Elem | 69 | Academic Assessment |

1 Superintendent
2 Bus/Finance/Purchasing
3 Buildings And Grounds
4 Food Service
5 Transportation
6 Athletic
7 Health Services
8 Curric/Instruct K-12
9 Curric/Instruct Elem
10 Curric/Instruct Sec
11 Federal Program
12 Title I
13 Title V
14 Instructional Media Svcs
15 Asst Superintendent
16 Instructional Media Svcs
17 Chief Operations Officer
18 Chief Academic Officer
19 Chief Financial Officer
20 Art K-12
21 Art Elem
22 Art Sec
23 Music K-12
24 Music Elem
25 Music Sec
26 Business Education
27 Career & Tech Ed
28 Technology Education
29 Family/Consumer Science
30 Adult Education
31 Career/Sch-to-Work K-12
32 Career/Sch-to-Work Elem
33 Career/Sch-to-Work Sec
34 Early Childhood Ed
35 Health/Phys Education
36 Guidance Services K-12
37 Guidance Services Elem
38 Guidance Services Sec
39 Social Studies K-12
40 Social Studies Elem
41 Social Studies Sec
42 Science K-12
43 Science Elem
44 Science Sec
45 Math K-12
46 Math Elem
47 Math Sec
48 English/Lang Arts K-12
49 English/Lang Arts Elem
50 English/Lang Arts Sec
51 Reading K-12
52 Reading Elem
53 Reading Sec
54 Remedial Reading K-12
55 Remedial Reading Elem
56 Remedial Reading Sec
57 Bilingual/ELL
58 Special Education K-12
59 Special Education Elem
60 Special Education Sec
61 Foreign/World Lang K-12
62 Foreign/World Lang Elem
63 Foreign/World Lang Sec
64 Religious Education K-12
65 Religious Education Elem
66 Religious Education Sec
67 School Board President
68 Teacher Personnel
69 Academic Assessment
70 Research/Development
71 Public Information
72 Summer School
73 Instructional Tech
74 Inservice Training
75 Marketing/Distributive
76 Info Systems
77 Psychological Assess
78 Affirmative Action

| School | Grades | Prog | Enroll | % | Phone |
|---|---|---|---|---|---|
| Judge Andy Mireles Elem Sch<br>12260 Rockwall Ml, San Antonio 78253<br>Laura Hernandez | PK-5 | | 980 | 21% | 210/398-1500<br>Fax 210/257-3044 |
| Kallison Elem Sch<br>8610 Ranch Vw E, San Antonio 78254<br>Billy Navin | PK-5 | | 840 | 25% | 210/398-2350<br>Fax 210/688-9034 |
| Kay Franklin Elem Sch<br>9180 Silver Spot, San Antonio 78254<br>Brenda Gallardo | PK-5 | | 797 | 32% | 210/398-1700<br>Fax 210/257-3013 |
| Kuentz Elem Sch<br>12303 Leslie Rd, Helotes 78023<br>Lori Gallegos | PK-5 | | 679 | 21% | 210/397-8050<br>Fax 210/695-4810 |
| Leon Springs Elem Sch<br>23881 W Interstate 10, San Antonio 78257<br>Gracie Espinoza | PK-5 | | 538<br>27 | 15% | 210/397-4400<br>Fax 210/698-4407 |
| Leon Valley Elem Sch<br>7111 Huebner Rd, San Antonio 78240<br>Rebecca Barron-Flores | PK-5 | T | 585<br>45 | 76% | 210/397-4650<br>Fax 210/706-7391 |
| Lieck Elem Sch<br>12600 Reid Ranch Rd, San Antonio 78245<br>Rachel DelGado | PK-5 | | 696 | 38% | 210/398-1450<br>Fax 210/678-2108 |
| Lloyd M Knowlton Elem Sch<br>9500 Timber Path, San Antonio 78250<br>Dr Maricela Alarcon | PK-5 | T | 621<br>40 | 78% | 210/397-2600<br>Fax 210/706-7534 |
| Locke Hill Elem Sch<br>5050 De Zavala Rd, San Antonio 78249<br>Danielle Frei | PK-5 | T | 644<br>45 | 56% | 210/397-1600<br>Fax 210/561-5062 |
| Los Reyes Elem Sch<br>10785 Triana Pkwy, Helotes 78023<br>Erika Pruneda | PK-5 | | 548 | 20% | 210/398-1200<br>Fax 210/695-5394 |
| Marshall Law & Med Svc Mag HS<br>8000 Lobo Ln, San Antonio 78240<br>Margaret Bray | 9-12 | | 175 | | 210/397-7100<br>Fax 210/706-7175 |
| Mary Hull Elem Sch<br>7320 Remuda Dr, San Antonio 78227<br>Patricia Noriega | PK-5 | T | 442<br>27 | 93% | 210/397-0950<br>Fax 210/678-2917 |
| Mary Lou Fisher Elem Sch<br>3430 Barrel Pass, San Antonio 78245<br>Rhapsody Quintero | PK-5 | T | 702 | 68% | 210/397-4450<br>Fax 210/645-3911 |
| McAndrew Elem Sch<br>26615 Toutant Beauregard Rd, Boerne 78006<br>De'Ann Upright | PK-5 | | 284 | 8% | 210/398-1750<br>Fax 210/398-1799 |
| McDermott Elem Sch<br>5111 Usaa Blvd, San Antonio 78240<br>Belinda Trevino | PK-5 | T | 670<br>47 | 74% | 210/397-5100<br>Fax 210/561-5118 |
| Meadow Village Elem Sch<br>1406 Meadow Way Dr, San Antonio 78227<br>Jennifer Escamilla | PK-5 | T | 472<br>30 | 88% | 210/397-0650<br>Fax 210/678-2846 |
| Michael Elem Sch<br>3155 Quiet Plain Dr, San Antonio 78245<br>Melissa Lopez-Brouse | PK-5 | T | 674<br>50 | 73% | 210/397-3900<br>Fax 210/645-3905 |
| Monroe S May Jr Elem Sch<br>15707 Chase Hill Blvd, San Antonio 78256<br>Geri Benitez | PK-5 | | 528<br>70 | 37% | 210/397-2000<br>Fax 210/561-2024 |
| Mora Elem Sch<br>1520 American Lotus, San Antonio 78245<br>Jill Holmes | PK-5 | T | 477 | 43% | 210/398-2400<br>Fax 210/678-2739 |
| Murray E Boone Elem Sch<br>6614 Spring Time St, San Antonio 78249<br>Manuela Haberer | PK-5 | T | 570<br>31 | 70% | 210/397-1450<br>Fax 210/561-5143 |
| Nellie M Reddix Center<br>4711 Sid Katz Dr, San Antonio 78229<br>Robin Fields | Spec | | 211<br>4 | 37% | 210/397-2401<br>Fax 210/615-2411 |
| Nichols Elem Sch<br>9560 Braun Rd, San Antonio 78254<br>Jeff Davenport | PK-5 | | 465<br>32 | 42% | 210/397-4050<br>Fax 210/767-5951 |
| Ⓐ Northside Alt Middle Sch-North<br>11937 W Interstate 10, San Antonio 78230<br>Anthony Persyn | 6-8 | | 120<br>6 | 82% | 210/397-2070<br>Fax 210/561-2074 |
| Ⓐ Northside Alt Middle Sch<br>11937 W Interstate 10, San Antonio 78230<br>Anthony Persyn | 6-8 | | 125<br>10 | | 210/397-2070<br>Fax 210/561-2074 |
| Ⓐ Northside Alternative High Sch<br>144 Hunt Ln, San Antonio 78245<br>Dr Darrell Rice | 9-12 | V | 180<br>24 | 73% | 210/397-7080<br>Fax 210/706-7086<br>🇫 🇹 |
| Ⓜ Northside Sch Innovation Tech<br>6500 Ingram Rd, San Antonio 78238<br>Randolph Neuenfeldt | 9-12 | V | 700<br>15 | | 210/397-7070<br>Fax 210/706-7076 |
| Northwest Crossing Elem Sch<br>10255 Dover Rdg, San Antonio 78250<br>Priscilla Siano | PK-5 | T | 494<br>30 | 60% | 210/397-0600<br>Fax 210/706-7546 |
| Oak Hills Terrace Elem Sch<br>5710 Cary Grant Dr, San Antonio 78240<br>Angela Robinson | PK-5 | T | 627<br>28 | 74% | 210/397-0550<br>Fax 210/706-7348 |
| Oliver Wendell Holmes High Sch<br>6500 Ingram Rd, San Antonio 78238<br>Ada Bohlken | 9-12 | TV | 2,813 | 76% | 210/397-7000<br>Fax 210/706-7030 |
| Pat Neff Middle Sch<br>5227 Evers Rd, San Antonio 78238<br>Yvonne Correa | 6-8 | TV | 1,061<br>45 | 78% | 210/397-4100<br>Fax 210/523-4566 |
| Patricia J Blattman Elem Sch<br>3300 N Loop 1604 W, San Antonio 78231<br>Raymond Macias | PK-5 | | 545<br>35 | 10% | 210/397-4600<br>Fax 210/408-6219 |
| Paul W Ott Elem Sch<br>100 Grosenbacher Rd N, San Antonio 78253<br>Madeline Bueno | PK-5 | T | 719 | 42% | 210/397-5550<br>Fax 210/645-5235 |
| Powell Elem Sch<br>6003 Thunder Dr, San Antonio 78238<br>Priscilla Paul | PK-5 | T | 484<br>30 | 75% | 210/397-0450<br>Fax 210/706-7361 |
| R K Driggers Elem Sch<br>6901 Shadow Mist, San Antonio 78238<br>Paul Brusewitz | PK-5 | T | 581<br>31 | 77% | 210/397-5900<br>Fax 210/257-4993 |
| Raba Elem Sch<br>9740 Raba Dr, San Antonio 78251<br>Francesca Neal | PK-5 | T | 764<br>50 | 43% | 210/397-1350<br>Fax 210/257-1335 |
| Ralph Langley Elem Sch<br>14185 Bella Vista Pl, San Antonio 78253<br>Aydee Ruiz-Ufland | PK-5 | | 452 | 31% | 210/397-0150<br>Fax 210/645-3325 |
| Raul B Fernandez Elem Sch<br>6845 Ridgebrook St, San Antonio 78250<br>Chaisleigh Southworth | PK-5 | T | 609<br>57 | 55% | 210/397-1900<br>Fax 210/706-7376 |
| Sam Rayburn Middle Sch<br>1400 Cedarhurst Dr, San Antonio 78227<br>Dr Scott McKenzie | 6-8 | TV | 980<br>60 | 81% | 210/397-2150<br>Fax 210/678-2181<br>🇫 🇹 |
| Sandra Day O'Connor High Sch<br>12221 Leslie Rd, Helotes 78023<br>Jackie Horras | 9-12 | GV | 3,256 | 23% | 210/397-4800<br>Fax 210/695-4804 |
| Scarborough Elem Sch<br>12280 Silver Pointe, San Antonio 78254<br>Mrs Cotton | PK-5 | | 1,007 | 34% | 210/397-8000<br>Fax 210/257-1019 |
| Shirley J Howsman Elem Sch<br>11431 Vance Jackson Rd, San Antonio 78230<br>Thomas Buente | PK-5 | T | 699<br>36 | 67% | 210/397-2350<br>Fax 210/561-5047 |
| Stevenson Middle Sch<br>8403 Tezel Rd, San Antonio 78254<br>Julie Schweers | 6-8 | V | 1,233<br>75 | 39% | 210/397-7300<br>Fax 210/706-7336 |
| Stinson Middle Sch<br>13200 Skyhawk Dr, San Antonio 78249<br>Lou Medina | 6-8 | ATV | 1,144<br>60 | 40% | 210/397-3600<br>Fax 210/561-3609 |
| Sul Ross Middle Sch<br>3630 Callaghan Rd, San Antonio 78228<br>Faustino Ortega | 6-8 | TV | 1,154<br>83 | 84% | 210/397-6350<br>Fax 210/431-6383 |

| | | | | | |
|---|---|---|---|---|---|
| Thomas Hatchett Elem Sch<br>10700 Ingram Rd, San Antonio 78245<br>Adam Bock | PK-5 | T | 759<br>40 | 67% | 210/397-6850<br>Fax 210/645-5222 |
| Timberwilde Elem Sch<br>8838 Timberwilde St, San Antonio 78250<br>Wendy Tiemann | PK-5 | T | 602<br>42 | 65% | 210/397-0400<br>Fax 210/706-7478 |
| Tom C Clark High Sch<br>5150 De Zavala Rd, San Antonio 78249<br>Dr Jerry Woods | 9-12 | AV | 2,849 | 33% | 210/397-5150<br>Fax 210/561-5250 |
| Vale Middle Sch<br>2120 N Ellison Dr, San Antonio 78251<br>Dana Gilbert-Perry | 6-8 | T | 1,354 | 49% | 210/397-5700<br>Fax 210/257-1000 |
| Valley Hi Elem Sch<br>8503 Ray Ellison Blvd, San Antonio 78227<br>Andrew Morris | PK-5 | T | 385<br>20 | 76% | 210/397-0350<br>Fax 210/678-2928 |
| Villarreal Elem Sch<br>2902 White Tail Dr, San Antonio 78228<br>Roxanne Gutierrez | PK-5 | T | 625<br>35 | 82% | 210/397-5800<br>Fax 210/431-5809 |
| Virginia Myers Elem Sch<br>3031 Village Pkwy, San Antonio 78251<br>Tesilia Garza | PK-5 | T | 598<br>36 | 71% | 210/397-6650<br>Fax 210/706-6674 |
| W Z Burke Elem Sch<br>10111 Terra Oak, San Antonio 78250<br>Misty Knapp | PK-5 | T | 463<br>45 | 72% | 210/397-1300<br>Fax 210/257-1305 |
| Wallace Jefferson Middle Sch<br>10900 Shaenfield Rd, San Antonio 78254<br>Monica Cabico | 6-8 | | 1,475 | 34% | 210/397-3700<br>Fax 210/257-4988 |
| Warren High Sch<br>9411 W Military Dr, San Antonio 78251<br>Valerie Sisk | 9-12 | TV | 3,077 | 42% | 210/397-4200<br>Fax 210/257-4246 |
| Wernli Elem Sch<br>1881 Arcadia Path, San Antonio 78245<br>Lori Shaw | PK-5 | | 490 | | 210/398-2450 |
| Westwood Terrace Elem Sch<br>2315 Hackamore Ln, San Antonio 78227<br>Tom Knapp | PK-5 | T | 461<br>25 | 91% | 210/397-0300<br>Fax 210/678-2786 |
| William Hobby Middle Sch<br>11843 Vance Jackson Rd, San Antonio 78230<br>Lawrence Carranco | 6-8 | TV | 926<br>60 | 63% | 210/397-6300<br>Fax 210/690-6332 |
| William Howard Taft High Sch<br>11600 Culebra Rd, San Antonio 78253<br>Martha Fernandez | 9-12 | ATV | 2,477 | 38% | 210/397-6000<br>Fax 210/688-6072 |
| William J Brennan High Sch<br>2400 Cottonwood Way, San Antonio 78253<br>John Trimble | 9-12 | | 2,588 | 35% | 210/398-1250<br>Fax 210/645-3311 |
| William J Thornton Elem Sch<br>6450 Pembroke Rd, San Antonio 78240<br>Justin Bledsoe | PK-5 | T | 571<br>50 | 47% | 210/397-3950<br>Fax 210/561-5128 |
| Zachry Middle Sch<br>9410 Timber Path, San Antonio 78250<br>Susan Allain | 6-8 | ATV | 926<br>80 | 71% | 210/397-7400<br>Fax 210/706-7432 |

- **Randolph Field Ind School Dist**  PID: 01601786　210/357-2300
  Bldg 1225 Randolph AFB, Universal Cty 78148　　Fax 210/357-2469

**Schools:** 3 \ **Teachers:** 102 \ **Students:** 1,442 \ **Special Ed Students:** 127 \ **LEP Students:** 3 \ **College-Bound:** 69% \ **Ethnic:** Asian 3%, African American 23%, Hispanic 26%, Caucasian 48% \ **Exp:** $648 (High) \ **Poverty:** 10% \ **Title I:** $44,198 \ **Open-Close:** 08/21 - 05/21 \ **DTBP:** $563 (High) \ 🇹

| | | |
|---|---|---|
| Dr Brian Holt ...........1 | Lorrie Remick ...............2,19,71 | |
| Hossiny Moharam ...........3 | Cynthia Moczygemba ...........4 | |
| Brandon Casey ...........5 | Pete Wesp ...........6* | |
| Susie Wacker ...........7 | Susan Bendele ........8,11,69,273,275,277,298 | |
| Linda Heier ...........11 | Jennifer Martin ...........16* | |

| | | |
|---|---|---|
| Christina Petofi-Casal ...........58* | Patrick Luna ...........67 | |
| Linda Mills ...........68 | Brian Grenier ...........73,98,295 | |
| Sarah Sanders ...........81 | | |

| Public Schs..Principal | Grd | Prgm | Enr/#Cls | SN | |
|---|---|---|---|---|---|
| Randolph Elem Sch<br>Bldg 146 Harmon -Randolph AFB, Universal Cty 78148<br>Allana Hemenway | PK-5 | | 599<br>30 | 9% | 210/357-2345<br>Fax 210/357-2346 |
| Randolph High Sch<br>Bldg 1225 Randolph AFB, Universal Cty 78148<br>Mark Malone | 9-12 | | 476<br>40 | 5% | 210/357-2400<br>Fax 210/357-2475 |
| Randolph Middle Sch<br>Bldg 1225 Randolph AFB, Universal Cty 78148<br>Merrie Fox | 6-8 | | 367<br>40 | 8% | 210/357-2430<br>Fax 210/357-2431<br>🇹 |

- **San Antonio Ind School Dist**  PID: 00998366　210/554-2200
  141 Lavaca St, San Antonio 78210　　Fax 210/299-5580

**Schools:** 94 \ **Teachers:** 3,156 \ **Students:** 48,178 \ **Special Ed Students:** 5,369 \ **LEP Students:** 8,500 \ **College-Bound:** 54% \ **Ethnic:** African American 6%, Hispanic 91%, Caucasian 2% \ **Exp:** $391 (High) \ **Poverty:** 34% \ **Title I:** $36,540,734 \ **Special Education:** $10,905,000 \ **Bilingual Education:** $208,000 \ **Open-Close:** 08/17 - 06/17 \ **DTBP:** $197 (High)

| | |
|---|---|
| Pedro Martinez ...........1 | Larry Garza ...........2,19 |
| Chris Salley ...........3 | Kamal Elhabr ...........3,15 |
| Willie Burroughs ...........3,17 | Jenny Arredondo ...........4 |
| Nathan Graf ...........5 | Brian Clancy ...........6 |
| Todd Howey ...........6 | Gloria Davis ...........7 |
| Kendra Doyle ...........8 | Barbara Rodriguez ...........11 |
| Angelica Romero ...........15 | Dr Courtney Gober ...........15 |
| Daniel Girard ...........15 | Gerard Cortez ...........15 |
| Dr Joanelda DeLeon ...........15 | Dr Judith Solis ...........15 |
| Olivia Hernandez ...........15,57,271 | Patti Salzmann ...........15,18 |
| Tiffany Grant ...........15,751 | Toni Thompson ...........15,68,79 |
| Becky Landa ...........16,74 | James Orozco ...........20 |
| Isabel Romero ...........23 | Christina Monk-Allen ...........27 |
| Johnny Vahalik ...........27,31 | Darlene Volz ...........30 |
| Aleida Perez ...........34 | Raul Salazar ...........35 |
| Victoria Bustos ...........36 | Patrick Pyle ...........39 |
| Angela Paskell ...........42 | Stacey Knudson ...........46 |
| Jeff Merithew ...........47 | Laura Gamez ...........48 |
| Esmeralda Alday ...........57 | Galadriel Friese ...........57 |
| Monica Valderrama ...........57 | Myrna Rasmussen ...........57 |
| Beth Jones ...........58,77 | Martha Vasquez ...........61 |
| Patti Radle ...........67 | Jamie Brown ...........69 |
| Liza Rosenthal ...........69,294 | Theresa Urrabazo ...........69,70,294 |
| Mohammed Choundhury ...........70,750 | Leslie Price ...........71 |
| Dr Kenneth Thompson ...........73,76,97,98 | Lus Zoch ...........74 |
| Christine Williamson ...........81 | Michael Jordan ...........88 |
| Estella Garza ...........90 | Joe Curiel ...........91 |
| Elsa Pennell ...........93 | Dawn Kulpa ...........275 |
| Carol Bielke ...........286 | John Strelchun ...........298 |

| Public Schs..Principal | Grd | Prgm | Enr/#Cls | SN | |
|---|---|---|---|---|---|
| Advanced Lrng Acad-Euclid<br>621 W Euclid Ave, San Antonio 78212<br>Emily Bieser | PK-3 | T | 100 | 51% | 210/738-9760<br>Fax 210/228-3003 |
| Advanced Lrng Acad-Fox Tech<br>637 N Main Ave, San Antonio 78205<br>Kathy Bieser | 4-12 | | 200 | | 210/738-9763<br>Fax 210/228-3003 |
| Agnes Cotton Academy<br>1616 Blanco Rd, San Antonio 78212<br>Rawan Hammoudeh | PK-8 | T | 437<br>29 | 94% | 210/738-9780<br>Fax 210/228-3033 |
| Antonio Margil Academy<br>1000 Perez St, San Antonio 78207<br>Sandra Galinzoga | PK-7 | T | 557<br>23 | 99% | 210/738-9805<br>Fax 210/228-3054 |

| | | | | | | | |
|---|---|---|---|---|---|---|---|
| 1 | Superintendent | 8 | Curric/Instruct K-12 | 19 | Chief Financial Officer | 29 | Family/Consumer Science |
| 2 | Bus/Finance/Purchasing | 9 | Curric/Instruct Elem | 20 | Art K-12 | 30 | Adult Education |
| 3 | Buildings And Grounds | 10 | Curric/Instruct Sec | 21 | Art Elem | 31 | Career/Sch-to-Work K-12 |
| 4 | Food Service | 11 | Federal Program | 22 | Art Sec | 32 | Career/Sch-to-Work Elem |
| 5 | Transportation | 12 | Title I | 23 | Music K-12 | 33 | Career/Sch-to-Work Sec |
| 6 | Athletic | 13 | Title V | 24 | Music Elem | 34 | Early Childhood Ed |
| 7 | Health Services | 15 | Asst Superintendent | 25 | Music Sec | 35 | Health/Phys Education |
| | | 16 | Instructional Media Svcs | 26 | Business Education | 36 | Guidance Services K-12 |
| | | 17 | Chief Operations Officer | 27 | Career & Tech Ed | 37 | Guidance Services Elem |
| | | 18 | Chief Academic Officer | 28 | Technology Education | 38 | Guidance Services Sec |

| | | | | | | | |
|---|---|---|---|---|---|---|---|
| 39 | Social Studies K-12 | 49 | English/Lang Arts Elem | 59 | Special Education Elem | 69 | Academic Assessment |
| 40 | Social Studies Elem | 50 | English/Lang Arts Sec | 60 | Special Education Sec | 70 | Research/Development |
| 41 | Social Studies Sec | 51 | Reading K-12 | 61 | Foreign/World Lang K-12 | 71 | Public Information |
| 42 | Science K-12 | 52 | Reading Elem | 62 | Foreign/World Lang Elem | 72 | Summer School |
| 43 | Science Elem | 53 | Reading Sec | 63 | Foreign/World Lang Sec | 73 | Instructional Tech |
| 44 | Science Sec | 54 | Remedial Reading K-12 | 64 | Religious Education K-12 | 74 | Inservice Training |
| 45 | Math K-12 | 55 | Remedial Reading Elem | 65 | Religious Education Elem | 75 | Marketing/Distributive |
| 46 | Math Elem | 56 | Remedial Reading Sec | 66 | Religious Education Sec | 76 | Info Systems |
| 47 | Math Sec | 57 | Bilingual/ELL | 67 | School Board President | 77 | Psychological Assess |
| 48 | English/Lang Arts K-12 | 58 | Special Education K-12 | 68 | Teacher Personnel | 78 | Affirmative Action |

| School | Grades | Programs | Enrollment | % | Phone |
|---|---|---|---|---|---|
| Arnold Elem Sch<br>467 Freiling, San Antonio 78213<br>Belinda Hernandez | PK-5 | T | 590<br>22 | 93% | 210/438-6530<br>Fax 210/228-3023 |
| Artemisia Bowden Academy<br>515 Willow, San Antonio 78202<br>**Brian Sparks** | PK-8 | T | 512<br>25 | 94% | 210/738-9770<br>Fax 210/228-3028 |
| © Barkley-Ruiz Academy<br>1111 S Navidad St, San Antonio 78207<br>Jacqueline Lanford | PK-5 | T | 491<br>28 | 96% | 210/978-7940<br>Fax 210/228-3025 |
| Baskin Elem Sch<br>630 Crestview Dr, San Antonio 78201<br>Valarie Garcia | PK-5 | T | 455<br>28 | 87% | 210/438-6535<br>Fax 210/228-3075 |
| Beacon Hill Academy<br>1411 W Ashby Pl, San Antonio 78201<br>Laryn Nelson | PK-8 | T | 500 | 92% | 210/738-9765<br>Fax 210/228-3026 |
| Bella Cameron Elem Sch<br>3635 Belgium Ln, San Antonio 78219<br>Brandy Lewis | PK-5 | T | 332<br>22 | 96% | 210/978-7960<br>Fax 210/228-3078 |
| © Bonham Academy<br>925 S Saint Marys St, San Antonio 78205<br>David Nungaray | K-8 | T | 578<br>25 | 62% | 210/228-3300<br>Fax 210/228-3027 |
| Brackenridge High Sch<br>400 Eagleland Dr, San Antonio 78210<br>**Yesenia Cordova** | 9-12 | TV | 1,685<br>110 | 87% | 210/228-1200<br>Fax 210/228-3000 |
| Ⓐ Brewer Academy<br>© 906 Merida St, San Antonio 78207<br>Angie Griffin | 6-12 | TV | 31<br>12 | 96% | 210/438-6825 |
| © Briscoe Academy<br>2015 S Flores St, San Antonio 78204<br>Jennifer Emerson | PK-5 | T | 404<br>50 | 91% | 210/228-3305<br>Fax 210/228-3077 |
| Burbank High Sch<br>1002 Edwards, San Antonio 78204<br>Miguel Elizondo | 9-12 | TV | 1,243<br>85 | 90% | 210/228-1210<br>Fax 210/228-3001 |
| Carroll Early Chldhd Center<br>463 Holmgreen Rd, San Antonio 78220<br>**Dr Alejandra Barraza** | PK-PK | T | 306 | 100% | 210/978-7965<br>Fax 210/228-3079 |
| Carvajal Early Chldhd Center<br>225 Arizona, San Antonio 78207<br>Sonya Cardenas | PK-PK | T | 394<br>25 | 100% | 210/978-7970<br>Fax 210/228-3031 |
| © Cast Med<br>2601 Louis Bauer Dr, San Antonio 78235<br>Dr Eddie Rodriguez | Voc | | 118 | | 210/228-3380 |
| © Cast Tech High Sch<br>637 N Main Ave, San Antonio 78205<br>Melissa Alcala | 9-11 | T | 147 | 56% | 210/554-2700<br>Fax 210/228-4601 |
| Charles Clyde Ball Academy<br>343 Koehler Ct, San Antonio 78223<br>Gregory Rivers | PK-8 | T | 531<br>22 | 97% | 210/438-6845<br>Fax 210/228-3008 |
| Collins Garden Elem Sch<br>167 Harriman Pl, San Antonio 78204<br>Cynthia Delagarza | PK-5 | T | 510<br>30 | 94% | 210/228-3310<br>Fax 210/228-3032 |
| David Crockett Academy<br>2215 Morales St, San Antonio 78207<br>Anna Garcia | PK-8 | T | 658<br>44 | 98% | 210/738-9785<br>Fax 210/228-3034 |
| Davis Middle Sch<br>4702 E Houston St, San Antonio 78220<br>Sharene Dixon | 6-8 | TV | 602<br>65 | 95% | 210/978-7920<br>Fax 210/228-3010 |
| De Zavala Elem Sch<br>2311 San Luis St, San Antonio 78207<br>**Donna Finch** | PK-5 | T | 600<br>40 | 98% | 210/978-7975<br>Fax 210/228-3035 |
| © Democracy Prep Stewart [235]<br>1950 Rigsby Ave, San Antonio 78210<br>Vivian Silva | PK-5 | T | 350<br>35 | 95% | 210/438-6875<br>Fax 210/228-3065 |
| Dorie Miller Elem Sch<br>207 Lincolnshire Dr, San Antonio 78220<br>Christine Weiland | PK-5 | T | 266<br>20 | 95% | 210/978-7995<br>Fax 210/228-3085 |
| Edison High Sch<br>701 Santa Monica St, San Antonio 78212<br>Cynthia Carielo | 9-12 | TV | 1,546<br>75 | 91% | 210/738-9720<br>Fax 210/228-3002 |
| Eloise Japhet Academy<br>314 Astor St, San Antonio 78210<br>Natasha Gould | PK-8 | T | 508<br>25 | 91% | 210/228-3345<br>Fax 210/228-3048 |
| Estrada Achievement Center<br>1112 S Zarzamora St, San Antonio 78207<br>Gary Pollock | 7-12 | T | 107<br>16 | 91% | 210/438-6820<br>Fax 210/228-3088 |
| Ferdinand Herff Academy<br>996 S Hackberry, San Antonio 78210<br>Kelly Allen | PK-8 | T | 477<br>26 | 97% | 210/228-3330<br>Fax 210/228-3042 |
| Fox Technical High Sch<br>637 N Main Ave, San Antonio 78205<br>Jennifer Benavides | 9-12 | GTV | 371 | 79% | 210/738-9730<br>Fax 210/228-3003 |
| Franklin Elem Sch<br>1915 W Olmos Dr, San Antonio 78201<br>**Jennifer Adan** | PK-5 | T | 458<br>28 | 93% | 210/738-9790<br>Fax 210/228-3039 |
| Frederick Douglass Academy<br>318 Martin Luther King Dr, San Antonio 78203<br>Dr Stephanie Ratliff | PK-8 | T | 347<br>20 | 97% | 210/228-3315<br>Fax 210/228-3080 |
| © Gates Elem Sch<br>510 Morningview Dr, San Antonio 78220<br>Sonya Mora | PK-5 | T | 230<br>100 | 97% | 210/978-7980<br>Fax 210/228-3081 |
| George E Kelly Elem Sch<br>1026 Thompson Pl, San Antonio 78226<br>Claudia Ramos-Coto | PK-5 | T | 249<br>15 | 95% | 210/228-3350<br>Fax 210/228-3049 |
| Gonzales Early Childhood Ctr<br>518 E Magnolia Ave, San Antonio 78212<br>Lisa Frost | PK-PK | | 113 | 87% | 210/438-6830 |
| Graebner Elem Sch<br>530 Hoover Ave, San Antonio 78225<br>Noemi Saldivar | PK-5 | T | 745<br>41 | 95% | 210/228-3320<br>Fax 210/228-3040 |
| © Harris Academy<br>325 Pruitt Ave, San Antonio 78204<br>Dr Carol Velazquez | 6-8 | TV | 746<br>48 | 91% | 210/228-1220<br>Fax 210/228-3011 |
| © Hawthorne Academy<br>115 W Josephine St, San Antonio 78212<br>**Valerie Walker** | K-8 | T | 731<br>45 | 77% | 210/738-9795<br>Fax 210/228-3082 |
| Highland Hills Elem Sch<br>734 Glamis Ave, San Antonio 78223<br>Deborah Esparza | PK-5 | T | 643<br>42 | 92% | 210/438-6860<br>Fax 210/228-3043 |
| © Highland Park Elem Sch<br>635 Rigsby Ave, San Antonio 78210<br>Rose Engelbrecht | PK-5 | T | 458<br>36 | 93% | 210/228-3335<br>Fax 210/228-3044 |
| Highlands High Sch<br>3118 Elgin Ave, San Antonio 78210<br>Julio Garcia | 9-12 | TV | 1,440<br>80 | 91% | 210/438-6800<br>Fax 210/228-3004 |
| Hillcrest Elem Sch<br>211 W Malone Ave, San Antonio 78214<br>Santa Lopez | PK-5 | T | 455<br>27 | 97% | 210/228-3340<br>Fax 210/228-3045 |
| Hirsch Elem Sch<br>4826 Seabreeze Dr, San Antonio 78220<br>**Erika Persaud** | PK-5 | T | 727<br>21 | 95% | 210/978-7985<br>Fax 210/228-3046 |
| Huppertz Elem Sch<br>247 Bangor Dr, San Antonio 78228<br>Linda Rios-Garcia | PK-5 | T | 368<br>26 | 96% | 210/438-6580<br>Fax 210/228-3047 |
| Inez Foster Academy<br>6718 Pecan Valley Dr, San Antonio 78223<br>Johnny Diaz | PK-8 | T | 604<br>35 | 95% | 210/438-6855<br>Fax 210/228-3038 |
| Ira C Ogden Academy<br>2215 Leal St, San Antonio 78207<br>**Nikki Martinez \ Gisella Calejo** | PK-8 | T | 679<br>30 | 97% | 210/738-9815<br>Fax 210/228-3058 |
| © Irving Dual Language Academy<br>1300 Delgado St, San Antonio 78207<br>Olivia Almanza-Pena | PK-3 | T | 137 | 93% | 210/738-9740<br>Fax 210/228-3012 |

| School | Grades | | Enroll | | Phone |
|---|---|---|---|---|---|
| Irving Middle Sch<br>1300 Delgado St, San Antonio 78207<br>Olivia Almanza | 8-8 | TV | 212<br>46 | 97% | 210/738-9740<br>Fax 210/228-3012 |
| J T Brackenridge Elem Sch<br>1214 Guadalupe St, San Antonio 78207<br>Marco Morales | PK-5 | T | 652<br>44 | 99% | 210/978-7950<br>Fax 210/228-3030 |
| Ⓐ James F Cooper Acad at Navarro<br>623 S Pecos La Trinidad, San Antonio 78207<br>Robert Loveland | 9-12 | GT | 347<br>43 | 93% | 210/438-6810<br>Fax 210/228-3009 |
| James Russell Lowell Mid Sch<br>919 Thompson Pl, San Antonio 78226<br>Yvonne Hernandez | 6-8 | TV | 371<br>33 | 98% | 210/228-1225<br>Fax 210/228-3014 |
| Knox Early Chldhd Center<br>302 Tipton Ave, San Antonio 78204<br>**Raymond Macias** | PK-PK | | 256<br>17 | | 210/228-3365<br>Fax 210/228-3051 |
| Lamar Elem Sch<br>201 Parland Pl, San Antonio 78209<br>Brian Sparks | PK-5 | T | 226<br>20 | 69% | 210/738-9800<br>Fax 210/228-3052 |
| Laura Steele Montessori Acad<br>722 Haggin St, San Antonio 78210<br>Laura Christenberry | PK-3 | T | 123 | 62% | 210/438-6870<br>Fax 210/228-3076 |
| Longfellow Middle Sch<br>1130 E Sunshine Dr, San Antonio 78228<br>Nancy Rodriguez | 6-8 | TV | 923<br>30 | 91% | 210/438-6520<br>Fax 210/228-3013 |
| Madison Elem Sch<br>2900 W Woodlawn Ave, San Antonio 78228<br>Lianna Cano | PK-5 | T | 518<br>34 | 95% | 210/438-6545<br>Fax 210/228-3053 |
| Marin B Fenwick Academy<br>1930 Waverly Ave, San Antonio 78228<br>Dr Tambrey Ozuna | PK-7 | T | 443<br>31 | 96% | 210/438-6540<br>Fax 210/228-3036 |
| Mark Twain Dual Language Acad<br>2411 San Pedro Ave, San Antonio 78212<br>David Garcia | PK-5 | TV | 560<br>60 | 69% | 210/738-9745<br>Fax 210/228-3020 |
| Ⓒ Martin Luther King Academy<br>3501 Martin Luther King Dr, San Antonio 78220<br>Natasha Pinnix | K-8 | TV | 329<br>31 | 98% | 210/978-7935<br>Fax 210/228-3083 |
| Maverick Elem Sch<br>107 Raleigh Pl, San Antonio 78201<br>Leila Garza | PK-5 | T | 492<br>31 | 90% | 210/438-6550<br>Fax 210/228-3055 |
| Mission Academy<br>9210 S Presa St, San Antonio 78223<br>Noemi Davila | PK-8 | T | 560 | 88% | 210/438-6880<br>Fax 210/228-3195 |
| Muriel Vance Forbes Academy<br>2630 Sally Gay Dr, San Antonio 78223<br>Erica Lopez | PK-8 | T | 386<br>22 | 93% | 210/438-6850<br>Fax 210/228-3037 |
| Neal Elem Sch<br>3407 Capitol Ave, San Antonio 78201<br>Valerie Henry | PK-5 | T | 521<br>40 | 96% | 210/738-9810<br>Fax 210/228-3056 |
| Nelson Early Chldhd Ed Ctr<br>1014 Waverly Ave, San Antonio 78201<br>Marisa Mendez | PK-PK | T | 206 | 100% | 210/438-6555<br>Fax 210/228-3057 |
| Ollie Perry Storm Elem Sch<br>435 Brady Blvd, San Antonio 78207<br>Jacquelyn Navar \ **Vanessa Cartwright** | PK-5 | T | 305<br>45 | 99% | 210/978-8005<br>Fax 210/228-3066 |
| Page Middle Sch<br>401 Berkshire, San Antonio 78210<br>Stephanie Mihleder | 6-8 | TV | 396<br>35 | 97% | 210/228-1230<br>Fax 210/228-3015 |
| Pershing Elem Sch<br>600 Sandmeyer St, San Antonio 78208<br>Thamesia Handford | PK-5 | T | 424<br>25 | 98% | 210/738-9820<br>Fax 210/228-3059 |
| Poe Middle Sch<br>814 Aransas Ave, San Antonio 78210<br>Christine Perez | 6-8 | TV | 425<br>36 | 96% | 210/228-1235<br>Fax 210/228-3016 |
| Ⓒ Rhodes Middle Sch<br>3000 Tampico St, San Antonio 78207<br>Rick Flores | 6-8 | TV | 647<br>40 | 96% | 210/978-7925<br>Fax 210/228-3017 |
| Riverside Park Academy<br>202 School St, San Antonio 78210<br>Cassie McClung | PK-8 | T | 420<br>25 | 97% | 210/228-3355<br>Fax 210/228-3087 |
| Robert B Green Academy<br>122 W Whittier St, San Antonio 78210<br>Jeanette Vasquez | K-8 | T | 188<br>17 | 91% | 210/228-3325<br>Fax 210/228-3041 |
| Rodriguez Montessori Elem Sch<br>3626 W Cesar E Chavez Blvd, San Antonio 78207<br>**Alicia Craig** | PK-K | | 100 | | 210/438-6873<br>Fax 210/228-3060 |
| Rogers Middle Sch<br>314 Galway St, San Antonio 78223<br>Julie May | 6-8 | T | 426<br>35 | 92% | 210/438-6840<br>Fax 210/228-3018 |
| Sam Houston High Sch<br>4635 E Houston St, San Antonio 78220<br>Dr Mateen Diop | 9-12 | TV | 1,007<br>100 | 91% | 210/978-7900<br>Fax 210/228-3005 |
| Sarah King Elem Sch<br>1001 Ceralvo St, San Antonio 78207<br>Gloria Martinez | PK-5 | T | 615<br>27 | 98% | 210/978-7990<br>Fax 210/228-3050 |
| Schenck Elem Sch<br>101 Kate Schenck Ave, San Antonio 78223<br>Mary Del Toro | PK-5 | T | 514<br>48 | 90% | 210/438-6865<br>Fax 210/228-3062 |
| Sidney Lanier High Sch<br>1514 W Cesar E Chavez Blvd, San Antonio 78207<br>Moises Ortiz | 9-12 | TV | 1,605 | 96% | 210/978-7910<br>Fax 210/228-3007 |
| Smith Elem Sch<br>823 S Gevers St, San Antonio 78203<br>Mayra Ibarra | PK-5 | T | 278<br>38 | 95% | 210/228-3360<br>Fax 210/228-3063 |
| St Philip's Early Clg HS<br>1801 Martin Luther King Dr, San Antonio 78203<br>Dr Derrick Thomas | 9-9 | T | 146 | 90% | 210/486-2406<br>Fax 210/228-3094 |
| Tafolla Middle Sch<br>1303 W Cesar E Chavez Blvd, San Antonio 78207<br>Jeffrey Price | 6-8 | TV | 694<br>56 | 95% | 210/978-7930<br>Fax 210/228-3019 |
| Ⓐ Texans Can Acad-Highlands HS [325]<br>Ⓒ 3118 Elgin Ave, San Antonio 78210<br>Mario Hernandez | 9-12 | T | 140 | 95% | 210/354-9340<br>Fax 210/278-9643 |
| Thomas Jefferson High Sch<br>723 Donaldson Ave, San Antonio 78201<br>Ralf Halderman | 9-12 | ATV | 1,622 | 83% | 210/438-6570<br>Fax 210/228-3006 |
| Ⓒ Travis Early College High Sch<br>1915 N Main Ave, San Antonio 78212<br>Adrianna Arredondo | 9-12 | T | 381 | 73% | 210/738-9830<br>Fax 210/228-3067 |
| Tynan Early Childhood Ctr<br>925 Gulf, San Antonio 78202<br>Gregorio Velazquez | PK-PK | T | 241<br>14 | 100% | 210/738-9835<br>Fax 210/228-3068 |
| Washington Elem Sch<br>1823 Nolan, San Antonio 78202<br>Phyllis Foley-Davis | PK-5 | T | 459<br>25 | 99% | 210/738-9840<br>Fax 210/228-3069 |
| Ⓒ Whittier Middle Sch<br>2101 Edison Dr, San Antonio 78201<br>Irene Talamantes | 6-8 | TV | 776 | 93% | 210/738-9755<br>Fax 210/228-3022 |
| Will Rogers Academy<br>620 McIlvaine, San Antonio 78212<br>Robby Wilson | PK-8 | T | 689<br>35 | 91% | 210/738-9825<br>Fax 210/228-3061 |
| Wilson Elem Sch<br>1421 Clower, San Antonio 78201<br>Jennifer Zavala | PK-5 | T | 443<br>27 | 93% | 210/738-9845<br>Fax 210/228-3071 |
| Woodlawn Academy<br>1717 W Magnolia Ave, San Antonio 78201<br>Karen Rose | PK-8 | T | 615<br>34 | 85% | 210/438-6560<br>Fax 210/228-3072 |
| Woodlawn Hills Elem Sch<br>110 W Quill Dr, San Antonio 78228<br>Martha Silva | PK-5 | T | 483<br>28 | 95% | 210/438-6565<br>Fax 210/228-3073 |
| Ⓒ Young Men's Leadership Academy<br>415 Gabriel, San Antonio 78202<br>Derrick Brown | 4-10 | T | 162 | 60% | 210/354-9652<br>Fax 210/228-3070 |

| | | | | | | | |
|---|---|---|---|---|---|---|---|
| 1 Superintendent | 8 Curric/Instruct K-12 | 19 Chief Financial Officer | 29 Family/Consumer Science | 39 Social Studies K-12 | 49 English/Lang Arts Elem | 59 Special Education Elem | 69 Academic Assessment |
| 2 Bus/Finance/Purchasing | 9 Curric/Instruct Elem | 20 Art K-12 | 30 Adult Education | 40 Social Studies Elem | 50 English/Lang Arts Sec | 60 Special Education Sec | 70 Research/Development |
| 3 Buildings And Grounds | 10 Curric/Instruct Sec | 21 Art Elem | 31 Career/Sch-to-Work K-12 | 41 Social Studies Sec | 51 Reading K-12 | 61 Foreign/World Lang K-12 | 71 Public Information |
| 4 Food Service | 11 Federal Program | 22 Art Sec | 32 Career/Sch-to-Work Elem | 42 Science K-12 | 52 Reading Elem | 62 Foreign/World Lang Elem | 72 Summer School |
| 5 Transportation | 12 Title I | 23 Music K-12 | 33 Career/Sch-to-Work Sec | 43 Science Elem | 53 Reading Sec | 63 Foreign/World Lang Sec | 73 Instructional Tech |
| 6 Athletic | 13 Title V | 24 Music Elem | 34 Early Childhood Ed | 44 Science Sec | 54 Remedial Reading K-12 | 64 Religious Education K-12 | 74 Inservice Training |
| 7 Health Services | 14 Asst Superintendent | 25 Music Sec | 35 Health/Phys Education | 45 Math K-12 | 55 Remedial Reading Elem | 65 Religious Education Elem | 75 Marketing/Distributive |
| | 15 Asst Superintendent | 26 Business Education | 36 Guidance Services K-12 | 46 Math Elem | 56 Remedial Reading Sec | 66 Religious Education Sec | 76 Info Systems |
| | 16 Instructional Media Svcs | 27 Career & Tech Ed | 37 Guidance Services Elem | 47 Math Sec | 57 Bilingual/ELL | 67 School Board President | 77 Psychological Assess |
| | 17 Chief Operations Officer | 28 Technology Education | 38 Guidance Services Sec | 48 English/Lang Arts K-12 | 58 Special Education K-12 | 68 Teacher Personnel | 78 Affirmative Action |
| | 18 Chief Academic Officer | | | | | | |

**TX—44**

© Young Women's Leadership Acad    6-12   T   495   54%   210/438-6525
2123 W Huisache Ave, San Antonio 78201      Fax 210/228-3194
Delia McLerran

Ywla Primary Sch    PK-1     159     210/554-2710
401 Berkshire, San Antonio 78210
Andre'A Pitts

- **School of Excellence In Ed**   PID: 11828823    210/431-9881
  1826 Basse Rd, San Antonio 78213      Fax 210/432-8467

---

**Schools:** 4 \ **Teachers:** 47 \ **Students:** 649 \ **Special Ed Students:** 52 \
**LEP Students:** 111 \ **College-Bound:** 75% \ **Ethnic:** Asian 1%, African
American 28%, Hispanic 69%, Caucasian 2% \ **Open-Close:** 08/19 - 05/28

---

| | | | |
|---|---|---|---|
| Sheilda Madkins | 1 | Karl Knox | 2,11 |
| Sam Reyes | 4 | Teresa Johnson | 11,298 |
| Penelope Borkert | 58 | Patrick Britton | 67 |
| Stephen Trevino | 73 | Dr Lois Butler | 84 |
| Valerie Walker | 285 | | |

| Public Schs..Principal | Grd | Prgm | Enr/#Cls | SN |
|---|---|---|---|---|
| © Dr David C Walker Elem Sch<br>6500 N Interstate 35, San Antonio 78218<br>Andrea Hall | PK-6 | T | 174 | 97% 210/654-4411<br>Fax 210/590-0376 |
| © Dr Harmon W Kelley Elem Sch<br>802 Oblate Dr, San Antonio 78216<br>Tiffany Peterson | PK-6 | T | 289 | 94% 210/431-9881<br>Fax 210/253-2198<br>�facebook twitter |
| © Dr Paul Saenz Junior High Sch<br>1826 Basse Rd, San Antonio 78213<br>Valarie Walker | 7-8 | T | 69 | 88% 210/431-9881<br>Fax 210/582-2587 |
| © Milton B Lee Acad of Sci & Eng<br>1826 Basse Rd, San Antonio 78213<br>Valarie Walker | 9-12 | T | 117 | 85% 210/431-9881<br>Fax 210/582-2587 |

- **Somerset Ind School Dist**   PID: 00999346    866/852-9858
  7791 6th St, Somerset 78069      Fax 210/750-8470

---

**Schools:** 7 \ **Teachers:** 253 \ **Students:** 3,990 \ **Special Ed Students:** 392
\ **LEP Students:** 617 \ **College-Bound:** 40% \ **Ethnic:** Hispanic 89%,
Caucasian 10% \ **Exp:** $410 (High) \ **Poverty:** 28% \ **Title I:** $1,513,336 \
**Special Education:** $870,000 \ **Open-Close:** 08/26 - 05/28 \ **DTBP:** $146
(High) \ twitter

---

| | | | |
|---|---|---|---|
| Saul Hinojosa | 1,11 | Michael Caralez | 2,19 |
| Robert Villafranca | 3,15,79 | Janet Welch | 4* |
| Laura Vasquez | 5 | Johan Dinkelmann | 6* |
| Yvette Trevino | 7 | Kriesti Bunch | 8,18,74 |
| Sheila Collazo | 8,15,57,271 | Diana Barrera | 9,88 |
| Shannon Boyd | 10 | Liliaana Perez | 28,95* |
| Dr Alicia Villarreal | 48,51 | Dr Ramiro Nava | 58 |
| Don Green | 67 | Gloria Wynkoop | 68 |
| Beverley Lee | 69,294 | Maury Vasquez | 71* |
| Rick Valdez | 91 | John Kennedy | 295 |

| Public Schs..Principal | Grd | Prgm | Enr/#Cls | SN |
|---|---|---|---|---|
| Barrera Veterans Elem Sch<br>4135 Smith Rd, Von Ormy 78073<br>Geneva Salinas | PK-4 | T | 503 | 87% 210/750-8963<br>Fax 866/667-2602 |
| Savannah Heights Interm Sch<br>5040 Smith Rd, Von Ormy 78073<br>Maru Falletich | 5-6 | T | 609 | 85% 210/750-8964<br>Fax 888/488-4341 |
| Somerset Early Chldhd Ctr<br>19930 Touchstone Rd, Somerset 78069<br>Sara Gonzales | PK-K | T | 218<br>22 | 93% 866/852-9865<br>Fax 866/667-2599 |
| Somerset Elem Sch<br>7840 6th St, Somerset 78069<br>Tracy Padilla | 1-4 | T | 673<br>50 | 84% 866/852-9864<br>Fax 866/667-2602 |

Somerset High Sch    9-12   ATV   1,078   78%   210/750-8958
7650 S Loop 1604 W, Somerset 78069    35     Fax 866/667-2608
Justin Saunders

Somerset Junior High Sch    7-8   ATV   668   85%   210/750-8967
4370 W Loop 1604, Von Ormy 78073    50     Fax 866/448-2738
Elida Guerra

Zacharias Ecla    9-10   T   76   71%   210/750-8959
7790 E 3rd St, Somerset 78069
Melissa Holguin

- **South San Antonio Ind Sch Dist**   PID: 00999384    210/977-7000
  5622 Ray Ellison Blvd, San Antonio 78242      Fax 210/977-7022

---

**Schools:** 16 \ **Teachers:** 530 \ **Students:** 8,800 \ **Special Ed Students:** 929
\ **LEP Students:** 1,454 \ **Ethnic:** African American 1%, Hispanic 97%,
Caucasian 1% \ **Exp:** $542 (High) \ **Poverty:** 32% \ **Title I:** $5,127,651 \
**Special Education:** $2,336,000 \ **Open-Close:** 08/17 - 05/27 \ **DTBP:** $196
(High) \ facebook twitter

---

| | | | |
|---|---|---|---|
| Dr Marc Puig | 1 | Bettinae Kaiser | 2,19 |
| Chad Doucet | 2 | Ruperto Becerra | 3 |
| Scott Stephens | 4 | Jesse Berlanga | 5 |
| Robert Zamora | 6 | Diane Olivo | 7 |
| Delores Sendejo | 8,18 | Lorraine DeLeon | 8,288 |
| David Abundis | 11,296 | David Cloud | 16,73 |
| Bobbie Shannon | 27 | Rosanna Mercado | 34 |
| Arla Chapa | 57,271 | Julie Silva | 58 |
| Connie Prado | 67 | Sheri Seaman | 68 |
| Denise Orosco | 70,76 | Jennifer Sunga-Collier | 71* |
| Cynthia Bills | 73,81,285 | Scott Laleman | 73,98,295,297 |
| Eugene Tovar | 91 | | |

| Public Schs..Principal | Grd | Prgm | Enr/#Cls | SN |
|---|---|---|---|---|
| Alan B Shepard Middle Sch<br>5558 Ray Ellison Blvd, San Antonio 78242<br>Frank Zavala | 6-8 | TV | 566<br>60 | 92% 210/623-1875<br>Fax 210/623-1880 |
| Dwight Middle Sch<br>2454 W Southcross Blvd, San Antonio 78211<br>Elizabeth Sandoval | 6-8 | T | 627<br>40 | 88% 210/977-7300<br>Fax 210/977-7316 |
| Five Palms Elem Sch<br>7138 Five Palms Dr, San Antonio 78242<br>Greg Martinez | PK-5 | T | 436<br>23 | 93% 210/645-3850<br>Fax 210/645-3858<br>facebook twitter |
| Frank Madla Elem Sch<br>6100 Royalgate Dr, San Antonio 78242<br>Joann Buchanan | PK-5 | T | 489<br>34 | 98% 210/645-3800<br>Fax 210/645-3807 |
| Health Science Academy<br>8638 Larkia St, San Antonio 78224<br>Dyanne Martinez-Munoz | Voc | | 50 | 210/977-7278<br>Fax 210/977-7285 |
| Hutchins Elem Sch<br>1919 W Hutchins Pl, San Antonio 78224<br>Elizabeth Martinez | PK-5 | T | 526<br>30 | 90% 210/977-7200<br>Fax 210/977-7211 |
| Kindred Elem Sch<br>7811 Kindred St, San Antonio 78224<br>Eric Boysen | PK-5 | T | 364<br>27 | 96% 210/977-7575<br>Fax 210/977-7586 |
| Miguel Carrillo Jr Elem Sch<br>500 Price Ave, San Antonio 78211<br>Sandra Sandoval | PK-5 | T | 407<br>26 | 96% 210/977-7550<br>Fax 210/977-7558<br>facebook twitter |
| Neil Armstrong Elem Sch<br>7111 Apple Valley Dr, San Antonio 78242<br>Phillip De La Pena | PK-5 | T | 359<br>32 | 93% 210/623-8787<br>Fax 210/623-8792 |
| Palo Alto Elem Sch<br>1725 Palo Alto Rd, San Antonio 78211<br>Judith Benavidez | PK-5 | T | 453<br>32 | 94% 210/977-7125<br>Fax 210/977-7132 |
| Price Elem Sch<br>245 Price Ave, San Antonio 78211<br>Florinda Castillo | PK-5 | T | 475<br>24 | 98% 210/977-7225<br>Fax 210/977-7236 |

---

| | | | | | |
|---|---|---|---|---|---|
| 79 Student Personnel | 91 Safety/Security | 275 Response To Intervention | 298 Grant Writer/Ptnrships | **School Programs** | **Social Media** |
| 80 Driver Ed/Safety | 92 Magnet School | 277 Remedial Math K-12 | 750 Chief Innovation Officer | A = Alternative Program | |
| 81 Gifted/Talented | 93 Parental Involvement | 280 Literacy Coach | 751 Chief of Staff | G = Adult Classes | 🅵 = Facebook |
| 82 Video Services | 95 Tech Prep Program | 285 STEM | 752 Social Emotional Learning | M = Magnet Program | |
| 83 Substance Abuse Prev | 97 Information Officer | 286 Digital Learning | | T = Title I Schoolwide | 🆃 = Twitter |
| 84 Erate | 98 Chief Technology Officer | 288 Common Core Standards | **Other School Types** | V = Career & Tech Ed Programs | |
| 85 AIDS Education | 270 Character Education | 294 Accountability | Ⓐ = Alternative School | | |
| 88 Alternative/At Risk | 271 Migrant Education | 295 Network System | © = Charter School | New Schools are shaded | |
| 89 Multi-Cultural Curriculum | 273 Teacher Mentor | 296 Title II Programs | Ⓜ = Magnet School | New Superintendents and Principals are bold | |
| 90 Social Work | 274 Before/After Sch | 297 Webmaster | Ⓨ = Year-Round School | Personnel with email addresses are underscored | |

| | | | | | |
|---|---|---|---|---|---|
| Roy P Benavidez Elem Sch<br>8340 Interstate 35 S, San Antonio 78224<br>Evelia Montemayor | PK-5 | T | 646<br>32 | 89% | 210/977-7175<br>Fax 210/977-7184 |
| South San Antonio Career Ctr<br>2615 Navajo St, San Antonio 78224<br>Charles Ervin | Voc | G | 300<br>17 | | 210/977-7350<br>Fax 210/977-7356 |
| South San Antonio High Sch<br>7535 Barlite Blvd, San Antonio 78224<br>Lee Hernandez | 9-12 | GTV | 2,102<br>90 | 87% | 210/977-7400<br>Fax 210/977-7430 |
| West Campus High Sch<br>5622 Ray Ellison Blvd, San Antonio 78242<br>Dr Lee Hernandez | 9-9 | | 401 | | 210/977-7015 |
| Zamora Middle Sch<br>8638 Larkia St, San Antonio 78224<br>Daniel Mauldin | 6-8 | TV | 725<br>45 | 90% | 210/977-7278<br>Fax 210/977-7285 |

## • Southside Ind School Dist PID: 00999516

1460 Martinez Losoya Rd, San Antonio 78221

210/882-1600
Fax 210/626-0101

**Schools:** 9 \ **Teachers:** 359 \ **Students:** 5,800 \ **Special Ed Students:** 617 \ **LEP Students:** 895 \ **Ethnic:** African American 1%, Hispanic 92%, Caucasian 6% \ **Exp:** $364 (High) \ **Poverty:** 29% \ **Title I:** $2,464,648 \ **Special Education:** $651,000 \ **Open-Close:** 08/17 - 05/27 \ **DTBP:** $158 (High) \ **t**

| | | | |
|---|---|---|---|
| Rolando Ramirez | 1 | Julian Monreal | 3* |
| Juana Ramirez | 4 | Jesse Berlanga | 5 |
| Richard Lock | 6* | Melonie Hammons | 8 |
| Dr Genese Bell | 12,15 | Sherri Ferrey | 13 |
| Adriana Bermea | 57 | Christopher Douglas | 58 |
| Delores Sendejo | 67 | Cliff Herring | 73 |
| David Zaragoza | 91 | Christine Rodriguez | 297 |

| Public Schs..Principal | Grd | Prgm | Enr/#Cls | SN | |
|---|---|---|---|---|---|
| Col Menchaca ECC<br>16180 S US Highway 281, San Antonio 78221<br>Rebecca Herrera | PK-K | T | 687 | 92% | 210/822-1610 |
| Freedom Elem Sch<br>3845 S Loop 1604 E, San Antonio 78264<br>Thomasina Montana | 1-5 | T | 581 | 85% | 210/882-1603<br>Fax 210/626-9866 |
| Heritage Elem Sch<br>3223 S Loop 1604 E, San Antonio 78264<br>Elise Puente | 1-5 | T | 472<br>32 | 91% | 210/882-1607<br>Fax 210/626-9788 |
| Julien C Gallardo Elem Sch<br>1300 Del Lago Pkwy, San Antonio 78221<br>Karen Feldman | 1-5 | T | 566<br>35 | 87% | 210/882-1609<br>Fax 210/626-2161 |
| Julius L Matthey Middle Sch<br>20350 Red Forest Ln, San Antonio 78264<br>Miguel Martell | 7-8 | T | 424<br>80 | 84% | 210/882-1601<br>Fax 210/626-0113<br>t |
| Losoya Intermediate Sch<br>1610 Martinez Losoya Rd, San Antonio 78221<br>Joel Gaines | 6-6 | T | 878<br>34 | 88% | 210/882-1602<br>Fax 210/626-0116 |
| Southside Alternative Sch<br>3223 S Loop 1604 E Ste 4, San Antonio 78264<br>Carveth Hall | 1-12 | | 6<br>9 | 76% | 210/882-1604<br>Fax 210/626-0473 |
| Southside High Sch<br>19190 US Highway 281 S No 2, San Antonio 78221<br>Henry Yzaguirre | 9-12 | T | 802<br>80 | 70% | 210/882-1606<br>Fax 210/626-0119 |
| William Pearce Elem Sch<br>19190 US Highway 281 S, San Antonio 78221<br>Brenda Gonzales | 1-5 | T | 463<br>29 | 84% | 210/882-1605<br>Fax 210/626-0117 |

## • Southwest Ind School Dist PID: 00999578

11914 Dragon Ln, San Antonio 78252

210/622-4300
Fax 210/622-4301

**Schools:** 19 \ **Teachers:** 915 \ **Students:** 13,928 \ **Special Ed Students:** 1,724 \ **LEP Students:** 2,180 \ **College-Bound:** 45% \ **Ethnic:** African American 3%, Hispanic 91%, Caucasian 5% \ **Exp:** $359 (High) \ **Poverty:** 27% \ **Title I:** $5,215,825 \ **Special Education:** $2,541,000 \ **Open-Close:** 08/21 - 06/04 \ **DTBP:** $186 (High) \ **f t**

| | | | |
|---|---|---|---|
| Dr Lloyd Verstuyft | 1 | Brandon Crisp | 2,3,4,5,6,15,73 |
| Rafael Barajas | 3 | Thomas Krueger | 3 |
| Winston Gatlin | 4 | Emanuel Tarnyo | 5 |
| Peter Wagner | 6 | Valarie Maldonado | 7 |
| Dalia Garcia | 8,15,58,73,74 | Velia Terrazas | 9 |
| Jennifer Ellison | 10 | Frances Barcenez | 11 |
| Homero Rodriguez | 15,91 | Dr Joann Fey | 15,68,76,79 |
| Marisela Rodriguez | 16 | Richard Flores | 20,23 |
| Crissy Franco | 27,31,285 | Victoria Gaeta | 30,274 |
| Luis Gonzalez | 36 | Marie Phelps | 36,78,79,271 |
| Israel Gonzalez | 57 | Robert Robinson | 58,275 |
| Michael Frazier | 67 | Will Baker | 68 |
| Lisa Boltie | 69,294 | Janice Hernandez | 71 |
| Dale Lockett | 73,286 | Dodie Maddox | 73 |
| Richard Palomo | 91 | Jeff Powell | 295 |
| Albrey Hogan | 752 | | |

| Public Schs..Principal | Grd | Prgm | Enr/#Cls | SN | |
|---|---|---|---|---|---|
| Big Country Elem Sch<br>2250 Pue Rd, San Antonio 78245<br>Wendy Quillin | PK-5 | T | 655<br>45 | 76% | 210/645-7560<br>Fax 210/645-7561 |
| Bob Hope Elem Sch<br>3022 Reforma Dr, San Antonio 78211<br>Brian Pennartz | PK-5 | T | 435<br>23 | 89% | 210/927-8180<br>Fax 210/927-8181 |
| Cast STEM High Sch<br>4495 SW Verano Pkwy Bldg 100, Von Ormy 78073<br>Dr Aja Gardner | 9-12 | T | 401 | 79% | 210/622-4810 |
| Christa McAuliffe Middle Sch<br>9390 SW Loop 410, San Antonio 78242<br>Roxie Freeman | 6-8 | GT | 745 | 95% | 210/623-6260<br>Fax 210/623-6261 |
| Ⓐ Crossroads Alternative Center<br>11914 Dragon Ln Bldg 203, San Antonio 78252<br>Odilia Martinez | 6-12 | V | 20 | | 210/622-4670<br>Fax 210/622-4671 |
| Elm Creek Elem Sch<br>11535 Pearsall Rd, Atascosa 78002<br>Melissa Garza | PK-5 | T | 696<br>40 | 82% | 210/622-4430<br>Fax 210/622-4431 |
| Francis R Scobee Middle Sch<br>10675 Marbach Rd, San Antonio 78245<br>Jorge Cruz | 6-8 | T | 904<br>55 | 73% | 210/645-7500<br>Fax 210/645-7501 |
| Hidden Cove Elem Sch<br>5102 Trading Post Dr, San Antonio 78242<br>Tracy Myers | PK-5 | T | 469<br>40 | 98% | 210/623-6220<br>Fax 210/623-6219 |
| Indian Creek Elem Sch<br>5830 Old Pearsall Rd, San Antonio 78242<br>Aracelie Bunsen | PK-5 | T | 535<br>53 | 96% | 210/623-6520<br>Fax 210/623-6521 |
| Kriewald Road Elem Sch<br>10355 Kriewald Rd, San Antonio 78245<br>Rosie Hidalgo | PK-5 | T | 531<br>33 | 82% | 210/645-7550<br>Fax 210/645-7551 |
| Medio Creek Elem Sch<br>8911 Excellence Dr, San Antonio 78252<br>Amy Garza | PK-5 | T | 529 | 89% | 210/622-4950<br>Fax 210/622-4951 |
| Resnik Middle Sch<br>4495 SW Verano Pkwy Bldg 100, Von Ormy 78073<br>Odilia Martinez | 6-8 | T | 870 | 90% | 210/623-6589<br>Fax 210/623-2700 |
| Ronald E McNair Middle Sch<br>11553 Pearsall Rd, Atascosa 78002<br>Anitra Crisp | 6-8 | T | 738<br>50 | 80% | 210/622-4480<br>Fax 210/622-4481 |

| | | | | | | | | | |
|---|---|---|---|---|---|---|---|---|---|
| 1 | Superintendent | 8 | Curric/Instruct K-12 | 19 | Chief Financial Officer | 29 | Family/Consumer Science | 39 | Social Studies K-12 |
| 2 | Bus/Finance/Purchasing | 9 | Curric/Instruct Elem | 20 | Art K-12 | 30 | Adult Education | 40 | Social Studies Elem |
| 3 | Buildings And Grounds | 10 | Curric/Instruct Sec | 21 | Art Elem | 31 | Career/Sch-to-Work K-12 | 41 | Social Studies Sec |
| 4 | Food Service | 11 | Federal Program | 22 | Art Sec | 32 | Career/Sch-to-Work Elem | 42 | Science K-12 |
| 5 | Transportation | 12 | Title I | 23 | Music K-12 | 33 | Career/Sch-to-Work Sec | 43 | Science Elem |
| 6 | Athletic | 13 | Title V | 24 | Music Elem | 34 | Early Childhood Ed | 44 | Science Sec |
| 7 | Health Services | 15 | Asst Superintendent | 25 | Music Sec | 35 | Health/Phys Education | 45 | Math K-12 |
| | | 16 | Instructional Media Svcs | 26 | Business Education | 36 | Guidance Services K-12 | 46 | Math Elem |
| | | 17 | Chief Operations Officer | 27 | Career & Tech Ed | 37 | Guidance Services Elem | 47 | Math Sec |
| | | 18 | Chief Academic Officer | 28 | Technology Education | 38 | Guidance Services Sec | 48 | English/Lang Arts K-12 |

| | | | | | |
|---|---|---|---|---|---|
| 49 | English/Lang Arts Elem | 59 | Special Education Elem | 69 | Academic Assessment |
| 50 | English/Lang Arts Sec | 60 | Special Education Sec | 70 | Research/Development |
| 51 | Reading K-12 | 61 | Foreign/World Lang K-12 | 71 | Public Information |
| 52 | Reading Elem | 62 | Foreign/World Lang Elem | 72 | Summer School |
| 53 | Reading Sec | 63 | Foreign/World Lang Sec | 73 | Instructional Tech |
| 54 | Remedial Reading K-12 | 64 | Religious Education K-12 | 74 | Inservice Training |
| 55 | Remedial Reading Elem | 65 | Religious Education Elem | 75 | Marketing/Distributive |
| 56 | Remedial Reading Sec | 66 | Religious Education Sec | 76 | Info Systems |
| 57 | Bilingual/ELL | 67 | School Board President | 77 | Psychological Assess |
| 58 | Special Education K-12 | 68 | Teacher Personnel | 78 | Affirmative Action |

| | Grd | Prgm | Enr | /#Cls | SN | |
|---|---|---|---|---|---|---|
| Sky Harbor Elem Sch<br>5902 Fishers Bend St, San Antonio 78242<br>Sylvia Acuna | PK-5 | T | 528<br>45 | | | 96% 210/623-6580<br>Fax 210/623-6584 |
| Southwest Elem Sch<br>11914 Dragon Ln Bldg 100, San Antonio 78252<br>Judy Foster | PK-5 | T | 565<br>30 | | | 78% 210/622-4420<br>Fax 210/622-4421 |
| Southwest High Sch<br>11960 Dragon Ln, San Antonio 78252<br>Paul Black | 9-12 | GTV | 2,018<br>125 | | | 75% 210/622-4500<br>Fax 210/622-4501 |
| Southwest Legacy High Sch<br>4495 SW Verano Pkwy Bldg 100, Von Ormy 78073<br>Anita Chavarria | 9-12 | GTV | 1,869 | | | 92% 210/623-6539<br>Fax 210/623-2716 |
| Spicewood Park Elem Sch<br>11303 Tilson Dr, San Antonio 78224<br>Krista Nail | PK-5 | T | 436 | | | 97% 210/622-4999<br>Fax 210/622-4131 |
| Sun Valley Elem Sch<br>6803 SW Loop 410, San Antonio 78227<br>Veronica Cuenca-Wilson | PK-5 | T | 556<br>42 | | | 80% 210/645-7570<br>Fax 210/645-7571 |

## BEXAR CATHOLIC SCHOOLS

- **Archdiocese San Antonio Ed Off** PID: 00999724    210/734-2620
  2718 W Woodlawn Ave, San Antonio 78228    Fax 210/734-9112

**Schools: 39 \ Students:** 13,050

Listing includes only schools located in this county. See District Index for location of Diocesan Offices.

| Catholic Schs..Principal | Grd | Prgm | Enr/#Cls | SN | |
|---|---|---|---|---|---|
| Antonian College Prep High Sch<br>6425 West Ave, San Antonio 78213<br>Tim Petersen | 9-12 | | 702<br>25 | | 210/344-9265<br>Fax 210/344-9267<br>🔲🔲 |
| Blessed Sacrament Catholic Sch<br>600 Oblate Dr, San Antonio 78216<br>Michael Fierro | PK-8 | | 200<br>17 | | 210/824-3381<br>Fax 210/826-6146 |
| Central Catholic High Sch<br>1403 N Saint Marys St, San Antonio 78215<br>Stephen Walswick | 9-12 | G | 530<br>54 | | 210/225-6794<br>Fax 210/227-9353 |
| Holy Cross of San Antonio Sch<br>426 N San Felipe Ave, San Antonio 78228<br>Dr Rene Escobedo | 6-12 | | 482<br>35 | | 210/433-9395<br>Fax 210/433-1666<br>🔲🔲 |
| Holy Name Catholic Sch<br>3814 Nash Blvd, San Antonio 78223<br>Susie Garcia | PK-8 | | 200<br>14 | | 210/333-7356<br>Fax 210/333-7642 |
| Holy Spirit Catholic Sch<br>770 W Ramsey Rd, San Antonio 78216<br>Margaret Webb | PK-8 | | 500<br>30 | | 210/349-1169<br>Fax 210/349-1247 |
| Incarnate Word High Sch<br>727 E Hildebrand Ave, San Antonio 78212<br>Anna Downey | 9-12 | | 620<br>40 | | 210/829-3100<br>Fax 210/829-3120 |
| Little Flower Sch<br>905 Kentucky Ave, San Antonio 78201<br>Jackie Castro | PK-8 | | 300<br>14 | | 210/732-9207<br>Fax 210/732-3214 |
| Mt Sacred Heart Sch<br>619 Mount Sacred Heart Rd, San Antonio 78216<br>Sharon Longoria | PK-8 | | 380<br>28 | | 210/342-6711<br>Fax 210/342-4032 |
| Providence Catholic Sch<br>1215 N Saint Marys St, San Antonio 78215<br>Alicia Garcia | 6-12 | | 350 | | 210/224-6651<br>Fax 210/224-6214<br>🔲🔲 |

| | Grd | Prgm | Enr/#Cls | SN | |
|---|---|---|---|---|---|
| St Anthony Catholic Elem Sch<br>205 W Huisache Ave, San Antonio 78212<br>Patricia Ramirez | PK-8 | | 428<br>26 | | 210/732-8801<br>Fax 210/732-5968 |
| St Anthony Catholic High Sch<br>3200 McCullough Ave, San Antonio 78212<br>Dr Kristina Vidaurri | 9-12 | | 400<br>29 | | 210/832-5600<br>Fax 210/832-5615 |
| St Gerard Catholic High Sch<br>521 S New Braunfels Ave, San Antonio 78203<br>Oscar Garza | 9-12 | | 110<br>14 | | 210/533-8061<br>Fax 210/761-8548<br>🔲🔲 |
| St Gregory the Great Cath Sch<br>700 Dewhurst Rd, San Antonio 78213<br>Daniel Martinez | PK-8 | G | 480<br>28 | | 210/342-0281<br>Fax 210/308-7177 |
| St James the Apostle Sch<br>907 W Theo Ave, San Antonio 78225<br>Dr Jennifer Grenardo | PK-8 | | 300<br>25 | | 210/924-1201<br>Fax 210/924-0201 |
| St John Berchman's Sch<br>1147 Cupples Rd, San Antonio 78226<br>Nora Garcia | PK-8 | | 270<br>18 | | 210/433-0411<br>Fax 210/433-2335<br>🔲 |
| St John Bosco Sch<br>5630 W Commerce St, San Antonio 78237<br>Roxanne LeBlanc | PK-8 | | 400<br>20 | | 210/432-8011<br>Fax 866/214-8083<br>🔲 |
| St Jose Sanchez Del Rio Sch<br>21140 Gathering Oak, San Antonio 78260<br>Dr Mary Longloy | PK-8 | | 245<br>16 | | 210/497-0323<br>Fax 210/497-5192 |
| St Luke Catholic Sch<br>4603 Manitou, San Antonio 78228<br>Nadine Buhrman | PK-8 | | 500<br>30 | | 210/434-2011<br>Fax 210/432-2419 |
| St Margaret Mary Sch<br>1202 Fair Ave, San Antonio 78223<br>Jackie Castro | PK-8 | | 198<br>11 | | 210/534-6137<br>Fax 210/534-2225 |
| St Mary Magdalen Sch<br>1700 Clower, San Antonio 78201<br>William Daily | PK-8 | | 310<br>11 | | 210/735-1381<br>Fax 210/735-2406<br>🔲 |
| St Matthew Catholic Sch<br>10703 Wurzbach Rd, San Antonio 78230<br>Geneva Salinas | PK-8 | | 715<br>29 | | 210/478-5099<br>Fax 210/696-7624 |
| St Monica Sch<br>515 North St, Converse 78109<br>Abigail Salazar | PK-8 | | 235<br>22 | | 210/658-6701 |
| St Paul Catholic Sch<br>307 John Adams Dr, San Antonio 78228<br>Lisa Barrera | PK-8 | | 305<br>24 | | 210/732-2741<br>Fax 210/732-7702 |
| St Peter Prince of Apostles<br>112 Marcia Pl, San Antonio 78209<br>Gabriel Duarte | PK-8 | | 156<br>23 | | 210/824-3171<br>Fax 210/822-4504<br>🔲 |
| St Pius X Catholic Sch<br>7734 Robin Rest Dr, San Antonio 78209<br>Jenny Kerr | PK-8 | | 240<br>9 | | 210/824-6431<br>Fax 210/824-7454 |
| St Thomas More Catholic Sch<br>4427 Moana Dr, San Antonio 78218<br>Kimberly Gutierrez | PK-8 | | 150<br>10 | | 210/655-2882<br>Fax 210/655-9603 |

## BEXAR PRIVATE SCHOOLS

| Private Schs..Principal | Grd | Prgm | Enr/#Cls | SN | |
|---|---|---|---|---|---|
| Atonement Academy<br>15415 Red Robin Rd, San Antonio 78255<br>James Growdon | PK-12 | | 500 | | 210/695-2240<br>Fax 210/695-9679 |
| Buckner Fanning Christian Sch<br>975 Mission Spgs, San Antonio 78258<br>Sharon Newman | PK-8 | | 220<br>16 | | 210/402-6905<br>Fax 210/495-0688 |
| Calvary Chapel Christian Acad<br>2935 Pat Booker Rd Unit 118, Universal Cty 78148<br>Will Shank | K-12 | | 135 | | 210/658-8337<br>Fax 210/658-1708 |

| School | Grades | | Enrollment | Phone |
|---|---|---|---|---|
| Cedar Creek Sch<br>3427 Northeast Pkwy, San Antonio 78218<br>Julie Brandt | 3-12 | | 36 | 210/822-3792 |
| Child Montessori Sch<br>2829 Hunters Green St, San Antonio 78231<br>Jean Carol Stein | PK-5 | | 85<br>4 | 210/493-6550 |
| Christian School-Castle Hills<br>2216 NW Military Hwy, San Antonio 78213<br>Lisa Jacobs \ Dr Jim Bazar | PK-12 | | 600<br>75 | 210/878-1000<br>**f t** |
| Concordia Lutheran Sch<br>16801 Huebner Rd, San Antonio 78258<br>Sally McBee | PK-8 | | 435<br>25 | 210/479-1477<br>Fax 210/479-9416 |
| Cornerstone Christian Sch<br>17702 NW Military Hwy, San Antonio 78257<br>Peter Barnes \ Robin Davenport | PK-12 | | 1,000 | 210/979-6161 |
| Eisenhauer Rd Baptist DC PS<br>3950 Eisenhauer Rd, San Antonio 78218<br>Lydia Canales | PK-K | | 60<br>11 | 210/655-6831<br>Fax 210/655-0980 |
| First Baptist Acad-Univ City<br>1401 Pat Booker Rd, Universal Cty 78148<br>Bob Payton | PK-12 | | 380<br>26 | 210/658-5331<br>Fax 210/658-7024 |
| Gateway Christian Sch<br>6623 Five Palms Dr, San Antonio 78242<br>Roger Gaines | K-12 | | 78<br>5 | 210/674-5703<br>Fax 210/674-6811 |
| Healy-Murphy Center<br>618 Live Oak St, San Antonio 78202<br>Janie Whitely | 9-12 | V | 174<br>13 | 210/223-2944<br>Fax 210/224-1033 |
| Keystone Sch<br>119 E Craig Pl, San Antonio 78212<br>Jeanette Vilagi \ Bill Spedding | PK-12 | | 405 | 210/735-4022<br>Fax 210/732-4905<br>**f** |
| Leafspring School-Sonterra<br>322 E Sonterra Blvd, San Antonio 78258<br>Erin Cuny | PK-K | | 120 | 210/495-5222<br>Fax 210/495-5851 |
| Legacy Christian Academy<br>2255 Horal St, San Antonio 78227<br>Pedro Garza \ Angie Stewart | PK-12 | | 207<br>20 | 210/674-0490 |
| Leon Valley Christian Academy<br>7990 Grissom Rd, San Antonio 78251<br>John DuPree | PK-5 | | 73<br>6 | 210/684-5662<br>Fax 210/520-9898 |
| Lutheran High Sch<br>18104 Babcock Rd, San Antonio 78255<br>Patrick Maynard | 9-12 | | 100 | 210/694-4962<br>Fax 210/694-9150 |
| Montessori Sch International<br>8222 Wurzbach Rd Ste B, San Antonio 78229<br>Marie Paul | PK-K | | 50<br>4 | 210/614-1665<br>Fax 210/692-1994 |
| Montessori Sch of San Antonio<br>17722 Rogers Ranch Pkwy, San Antonio 78258 | PK-8 | | 277<br>12 | 210/492-3553<br>Fax 210/492-3484 |
| New Life Christian Academy<br>6622 W US Highway 90, San Antonio 78227<br>Anthony Jackson | PK-12 | | 70 | 210/679-6001<br>Fax 210/679-6080 |
| Palm Heights Baptist Sch<br>1106 W Malone Ave, San Antonio 78225<br>Bertha Rodriguez | PK-8 | | 30<br>7 | 210/923-8600<br>Fax 210/921-2173 |
| River City Christian Sch<br>5810 Blanco Rd, San Antonio 78216<br>Erica McCormick \ Larry Romine | K-12 | | 97 | 210/384-0297<br>Fax 210/384-0446<br>**f t** |
| Royal Point Academy<br>9965 Kriewald Rd, San Antonio 78245<br>Veronica Pena | PK-6 | | 58<br>5 | 210/674-5310 |
| Saint Mary's Hall<br>9401 Starcrest Dr, San Antonio 78217<br>Khristi Bates \ Sarah Visagie \ Brent Spicer | PK-12 | | 993<br>30 | 210/483-9100<br>Fax 210/483-9299<br>**f t** |
| Salem Sayers Baptist Academy<br>5212 FM 1628, Adkins 78101<br>Jason Taylor | PK-12 | | 127 | 210/649-1178<br>Fax 210/649-2920 |
| San Antonio Academy-Texas<br>117 E French Pl, San Antonio 78212<br>Clint Dubose | PK-8 | | 344<br>40 | 210/733-7331<br>Fax 210/734-0711 |
| San Antonio Christian Sch<br>19202 Redland Rd, San Antonio 78259<br>Matt Erbaugh \ Catherine Sheats \ Jared Roan | PK-12 | | 800 | 210/340-1864<br>Fax 210/342-0146 |
| Scenic Hills Christian Academy<br>11223 Bandera Rd, San Antonio 78250<br>Jon Dickerson | PK-12 | | 66<br>4 | 210/523-2312<br>Fax 210/684-8155 |
| Shepherd of the Hills Luth Sch<br>6914 Wurzbach Rd, San Antonio 78240<br>Sue Gary | PK-8 | | 372<br>22 | 210/614-3741<br>**f t** |
| St George Episcopal Sch<br>6900 West Ave, San Antonio 78213<br>Rob Devlin | PK-8 | | 500<br>27 | 210/342-4263<br>Fax 210/342-4681 |
| St Luke's Episcopal Sch<br>15 Saint Lukes Ln, San Antonio 78209 | PK-8 | | 341<br>23 | 210/826-0664<br>Fax 210/826-8520<br>**f** |
| St Thomas Episcopal Sch<br>1416 N Loop 1604 E, San Antonio 78232<br>Allison Newman | PK-5 | | 225<br>22 | 210/494-3509<br>Fax 210/494-0678 |
| Sunnybrook Christian Academy<br>1620 Pinn Rd, San Antonio 78227<br>James Hatch | PK-12 | | 111<br>14 | 210/674-8000<br>Fax 210/673-4603 |
| Sunshine Cottage Sch-Deaf Chld<br>603 E Hildebrand Ave, San Antonio 78212<br>Jeff Bryan | Spec | | 120<br>14 | 210/824-0579<br>Fax 210/826-0436 |
| Texas Military Institute<br>20955 W Tejas Trl, San Antonio 78257<br>Victoria Banks \ Dr Matthew Blake | 6-12 | | 400<br>45 | 210/698-7171<br>Fax 210/698-0903 |
| Town East Christian Sch<br>5866 US Highway 87 E, San Antonio 78222<br>J D King | K-12 | | 100<br>12 | 210/648-2601<br>Fax 210/648-1460 |
| Trinity Christian Academy<br>5401 N Loop 1604 E, San Antonio 78247<br>Christopher Belyeu | K-8 | | 95<br>25 | 210/653-2800<br>Fax 210/653-0303<br>**f** |
| Village Parkway Chrn Sch<br>3002 Village Pkwy, San Antonio 78251<br>John Turner | PK-6 | | 90<br>7 | 210/680-8187<br>Fax 210/509-3502 |
| Winston School San Antonio<br>8565 Ewing Halsell Dr, San Antonio 78229<br>Steven Yocham \ Louise Pastorino | Spec | | 200<br>28 | 210/615-6544<br>Fax 210/615-6627 |

## BEXAR REGIONAL CENTERS

● **Region 20 Ed Service Center** PID: 00999645        210/370-5200
1314 Hines, San Antonio 78208                          Fax 210/370-5750

Dr Jeff Goldhorn ...................................1     Jeff Stone .........................2,15,73,76
Paul Neuhoff .....................................2     Michael Peterson ...........................3
Dr Carolyn Castillo ..................8,15,57     Kim Vinton .........................................30
Sherry Marsh .................................58     Paul Patillo ...........................73,76,98

| | | | | | | | |
|---|---|---|---|---|---|---|---|
| **1** Superintendent | **8** Curric/Instruct K-12 | **19** Chief Financial Officer | **29** Family/Consumer Science | **39** Social Studies K-12 | **49** English/Lang Arts Elem | **59** Special Education Elem | **69** Academic Assessment |
| **2** Bus/Finance/Purchasing | **9** Curric/Instruct Elem | **20** Art K-12 | **30** Adult Education | **40** Social Studies Elem | **50** English/Lang Arts Sec | **60** Special Education Sec | **70** Research/Development |
| **3** Buildings And Grounds | **10** Curric/Instruct Sec | **21** Art Elem | **31** Career/Sch-to-Work K-12 | **41** Social Studies Sec | **51** Reading K-12 | **61** Foreign/World Lang K-12 | **71** Public Information |
| **4** Food Service | **11** Federal Program | **22** Art Sec | **32** Career/Sch-to-Work Elem | **42** Science K-12 | **52** Reading Elem | **62** Foreign/World Lang Elem | **72** Summer School |
| **5** Transportation | **12** Title I | **23** Music K-12 | **33** Career/Sch-to-Work Sec | **43** Science Elem | **53** Reading Sec | **63** Foreign/World Lang Sec | **73** Instructional Tech |
| **6** Athletic | **13** Title V | **24** Music Elem | **34** Early Childhood Ed | **44** Science Sec | **54** Remedial Reading K-12 | **64** Religious Education K-12 | **74** Inservice Training |
| **7** Health Services | **14** Asst Superintendent | **25** Music Sec | **35** Health/Phys Education | **45** Math K-12 | **55** Remedial Reading Elem | **65** Religious Education Elem | **75** Marketing/Distributive |
| | **15** Instructional Media Svcs | **26** Business Education | **36** Guidance Services K-12 | **46** Math Elem | **56** Remedial Reading Sec | **66** Religious Education Sec | **76** Info Systems |
| | **16** Instructional Media Sec | **27** Career & Tech Ed | **37** Guidance Services Elem | **47** Math Sec | **57** Bilingual/ELL | **67** School Board President | **77** Psychological Assess |
| | **17** Chief Operations Officer | **28** Technology Education | **38** Guidance Services Sec | **48** English/Lang Arts K-12 | **58** Special Education K-12 | **68** Teacher Personnel | **78** Affirmative Action |
| | **18** Chief Academic Officer | | | | | | |

| **BLANCO COUNTY** | **BORDEN COUNTY** |
|---|---|

## BLANCO PUBLIC SCHOOLS

## BORDEN PUBLIC SCHOOLS

● **Blanco Ind School Dist** PID: 01000481          830/833-4414
814 11th St, Blanco 78606                          Fax 830/833-2019

**Schools:** 3 \ **Teachers:** 78 \ **Students:** 1,020 \ **Special Ed Students:** 115 \ **LEP Students:** 78 \ **Ethnic:** African American 1%, Hispanic 42%, Caucasian 57% \ **Exp:** $318 (High) \ **Poverty:** 17% \ **Title I:** $233,167 \ **Special Education:** $220,000 \ **Open-Close:** 08/24 - 05/27 \ **DTBP:** $341 (High)

| | |
|---|---|
| Clay Rosenbaum ......................1 | Mathew Streger ......................2,4 |
| Tony Petri ...............................3 | William Tesch .............................6* |
| Robin Johnson ........................7* | Deeanna McLendon ...........8,31,36,69,83* |
| Dina Johnson .......8,11,57,88,271,288,294* | Elizabeth Hoff ........................16,82* |
| Kate Patterson .........................58 | Kirt Felps ..................................67 |
| Collin Gaskamp .........................73* | James Caudell ...........................295 |

| Public Schs..Principal | Grd | Prgm | Enr/#Cls | SN |
|---|---|---|---|---|
| Blanco Elem Sch<br>814 11th St, Blanco 78606<br>Jowie Walker | PK-5 | T | 387<br>24 | 52% 830/833-4338<br>Fax 830/833-4389 |
| Blanco High Sch<br>1215 4th St, Blanco 78606<br>**Patrick Hinson** | 9-12 | TV | 331<br>35 | 37% 830/833-4337<br>Fax 830/833-5028 |
| Blanco Middle Sch<br>1500 Rocky Rd, Blanco 78606<br>Brad Kinney | 6-8 | T | 258<br>15 | 45% 830/833-5570<br>Fax 830/833-2507 |

● **Johnson City Ind School Dist** PID: 01000510        830/868-7410
303 N Lbj Dr, Johnson City 78636                     Fax 830/868-7375

**Schools:** 3 \ **Teachers:** 54 \ **Students:** 650 \ **Special Ed Students:** 64 \ **LEP Students:** 43 \ **College-Bound:** 68% \ **Ethnic:** Asian 1%, Hispanic 27%, Caucasian 72% \ **Exp:** $465 (High) \ **Poverty:** 10% \ **Title I:** $97,248 \ **Special Education:** $188,000 \ **Open-Close:** 08/17 - 05/27 \ **DTBP:** $346 (High)

| | |
|---|---|
| Richard Kolek .........................1 | Scott Berry ......................2,11,15 |
| Vance Marks ...........................3,91 | Chelsey Kerr ...........................4 |
| David Sine ..............................6 | Amanda Haley ...........8,57,270,273,288,296* |
| Penny Pulate ........................11,58,69 | Regina Allen ...........................16* |
| Shelly Wenmohs .......................67 | Kevin Jacks ...........................73* |

| Public Schs..Principal | Grd | Prgm | Enr/#Cls | SN |
|---|---|---|---|---|
| Lyndon B Johnson Elem Sch<br>401 E Pecan Dr, Johnson City 78636<br>Amanda Haley | PK-4 | T | 211<br>14 | 52% 830/868-4028<br>Fax 830/215-0586 |
| Lyndon B Johnson High Sch<br>505 N Nugent, Johnson City 78636<br>Russell Maedgen | 9-12 | V | 216<br>25 | 30% 830/868-4025<br>Fax 830/868-9244 |
| Lyndon B Johnson Middle Sch<br>303 N Lbj Dr, Johnson City 78636<br>Michael Norton | 5-8 | | 208<br>16 | 31% 830/868-9025<br>Fax 830/215-0581 |

● **Borden Co Ind School Dist** PID: 01000546        806/756-4313
240 W Kincaid Ave, Gail 79738                       Fax 806/756-4310

**Schools:** 1 \ **Teachers:** 20 \ **Students:** 214 \ **Special Ed Students:** 18 \ **LEP Students:** 3 \ **College-Bound:** 100% \ **Ethnic:** Hispanic 16%, Caucasian 83% \ **Exp:** $1,256 (High) \ **Poverty:** 15% \ **Title I:** $18,971 \ **Open-Close:** 08/27 - 05/25

| | |
|---|---|
| Johnny Tubb ...........................1 | Amy Rinehart ...........................2 |
| Bart McMeans ..........8,11,57,69,88,294,296* | Becky Nix ...........................58,275* |
| Todd Holbrooks .......................67 | Kyle Kuehler ...........................73,84 |
| Ricardo Martinez .......................295* | |

| Public Schs..Principal | Grd | Prgm | Enr/#Cls | SN |
|---|---|---|---|---|
| Borden County Sch<br>240 W Kincaid Ave, Gail 79738<br>Britt Gordon | K-12 | TV | 214<br>14 | 24% 806/756-4313 |

| **BOSQUE COUNTY** |
|---|

## BOSQUE PUBLIC SCHOOLS

● **Clifton Ind School Dist** PID: 01808893          254/675-2827
1102 Key Ave, Clifton 76634                         Fax 254/675-4351

**Schools:** 3 \ **Teachers:** 80 \ **Students:** 1,000 \ **Special Ed Students:** 123 \ **LEP Students:** 70 \ **Ethnic:** Asian 1%, African American 2%, Hispanic 37%, Native American: 1%, Caucasian 59% \ **Exp:** $331 (High) \ **Poverty:** 24% \ **Title I:** $334,544 \ **Special Education:** $214,000 \ **Open-Close:** 08/17 - 05/20 \ **DTBP:** $343 (High) \ 🅵 🆃

| | |
|---|---|
| Andy Ball ...............................1 | Lisa Prescher ...........................2 |
| Tommy Compton .......................3,5 | Jennifer Green ...........................4 |
| Chuck Caniford .........................6* | Tiffany Jones ...........................8,11 |
| Viki Villarreal .........................57* | Karen Schasteen ...........................58 |
| Alex Montes ...........................67 | Mary Maddux ...........................68* |
| Barbi Ernst ...........................73* | |

| Public Schs..Principal | Grd | Prgm | Enr/#Cls | SN |
|---|---|---|---|---|
| Clifton Elem School PK-5<br>1000 Key Ave, Clifton 76634<br>Ronda Kroll | PK-5 | T | 451<br>12 | 70% 254/675-1875<br>Fax 254/675-8725 🆃 |
| Clifton High Sch<br>1101 N Avenue Q, Clifton 76634<br>Jimmy Jackson | 9-12 | ATV | 282<br>28 | 44% 254/675-1845<br>Fax 254/675-8002 🅵 |
| Clifton Middle Sch<br>1102 Key Ave, Clifton 76634<br>Michael Kusler | 6-8 | AT | 230<br>25 | 52% 254/675-1855<br>Fax 254/675-2005 |

| | | | | | | |
|---|---|---|---|---|---|---|
| **79** Student Personnel | **91** Safety/Security | **275** Response To Intervention | **298** Grant Writer/Ptnrships | **School Programs** | **Social Media** | |
| **80** Driver Ed/Safety | **92** Magnet School | **277** Remedial Math K-12 | **750** Chief Innovation Officer | **A** = Alternative Program | | |
| **81** Gifted/Talented | **93** Parental Involvement | **280** Literacy Coach | **751** Chief of Staff | **G** = Adult Classes | 🅵 = Facebook | |
| **82** Video Services | **95** Tech Prep Program | **285** STEM | **752** Social Emotional Learning | **M** = Magnet Program | | |
| **83** Substance Abuse Prev | **97** Chief Infomation Officer | **286** Digital Learning | | **T** = Title I Schoolwide | 🆃 = Twitter | |
| **84** Erate | **98** Chief Technology Officer | **288** Common Core Standards | **Other School Types** | **V** = Career & Tech Ed Programs | | |
| **85** AIDS Education | **270** Character Education | **294** Accountability | Ⓐ = Alternative School | | | |
| **88** Alternative/At Risk | **271** Migrant Education | **295** Network System | Ⓒ = Charter School | **New Schools are shaded** | | |
| **89** Multi-Cultural Curriculum | **273** Teacher Mentor | **296** Title II Programs | Ⓜ = Magnet School | **New Superintendents and Principals are bold** | | |
| **90** Social Work | **274** Before/After Sch | **297** Webmaster | Ⓨ = Year-Round School | Personnel with email addresses are underscored | | |

## Cranfills Gap ISD School Dist  PID: 01000601
505 S 2nd St, Cranfills Gap 76637
254/597-2505
Fax 254/597-0001

**Schools:** 1 \ **Teachers:** 15 \ **Students:** 120 \ **Special Ed Students:** 17 \ **LEP Students:** 10 \ **College-Bound:** 100% \ **Ethnic:** African American 2%, Hispanic 31%, Caucasian 67% \ **Exp:** $751 (High) \ **Poverty:** 25% \ **Title I:** $44,215 \ **Open-Close:** 08/26 - 05/21 \ **DTBP:** $336 (High) \ 🅵 🆃

| | | | |
|---|---|---|---|
| Monti Parchman | 1,11,73,83 | Sara Doyle | 2 |
| Adam Carroll | 6* | Shana Campbell | 8,69* |
| Kenney Wiese | 67 | | |

| Public Schs..Principal | Grd | Prgm | Enr/#Cls | SN | |
|---|---|---|---|---|---|
| Cranfills Gap Sch | PK-12 | ATV | 120 | 69% | 254/597-2505 |
| 505 S 2nd St, Cranfills Gap 76637 | | | 11 | | |
| Shana Campbell | | | | | 🅵 🆃 |

## Iredell Ind School Dist  PID: 01000637
501 E McClain St, Iredell 76649
254/364-2411
Fax 254/364-2206

**Schools:** 1 \ **Teachers:** 15 \ **Students:** 138 \ **Special Ed Students:** 20 \ **College-Bound:** 100% \ **Ethnic:** Hispanic 26%, Caucasian 74% \ **Exp:** $656 (High) \ **Poverty:** 20% \ **Title I:** $41,300 \ **Open-Close:** 08/26 - 05/28 \ **DTBP:** $363 (High)

| | | | |
|---|---|---|---|
| Ben Eubanks | 1 | Deborah Burns | 2* |
| Luis Guereca | 6* | Patrick Murphy | 11,73,83,288 |
| Jeanne Wallace | 58* | Patrick Proffitt | 67 |
| Connie White | 69,275* | William Kammerer | 273* |

| Public Schs..Principal | Grd | Prgm | Enr/#Cls | SN | |
|---|---|---|---|---|---|
| Iredell Sch | PK-12 | T | 138 | 59% | 254/364-2411 |
| 501 E McClain St, Iredell 76649 | | | 10 | | |
| Patrick Murphy | | | | | |

## Kopperl Ind School Dist  PID: 01000663
175 County Road 1240, Kopperl 76652
254/889-3502
Fax 254/889-3545

**Schools:** 1 \ **Teachers:** 18 \ **Students:** 200 \ **Special Ed Students:** 26 \ **LEP Students:** 3 \ **College-Bound:** 75% \ **Ethnic:** African American 1%, Hispanic 10%, Caucasian 89% \ **Exp:** $451 (High) \ **Poverty:** 25% \ **Title I:** $84,602 \ **Open-Close:** 08/25 - 05/21 \ **DTBP:** $329 (High)

| | | | |
|---|---|---|---|
| Katrina Adcock | 1,73 | Yuvonne Wood | 2* |
| John Wood | 6 | Brad Janek | 8,11 |
| Roy Henry | 31,36,83* | Paula Allen | 58* |
| Harold Wellborn | 67 | Robin Flores | 76 |

| Public Schs..Principal | Grd | Prgm | Enr/#Cls | SN | |
|---|---|---|---|---|---|
| Kopperl Sch | PK-12 | T | 200 | 75% | 254/889-3502 |
| 175 County Road 1240, Kopperl 76652 | | | 50 | | |
| Brad Janek | | | | | |

## Meridian Ind School Dist  PID: 01000699
204 2nd St, Meridian 76665
254/435-2081
Fax 254/435-2025

**Schools:** 4 \ **Teachers:** 50 \ **Students:** 475 \ **Special Ed Students:** 75 \ **LEP Students:** 26 \ **College-Bound:** 75% \ **Ethnic:** Asian 1%, African American 4%, Hispanic 36%, Caucasian 60% \ **Exp:** $469 (High) \ **Poverty:** 18% \ **Title I:** $136,246 \ **Open-Close:** 08/13 - 05/27 \ **DTBP:** $231 (High) \ 🅵 🆃

| | | | |
|---|---|---|---|
| Kim Edwards | 1,11,84 | Jami Edwards | 2 |
| Russell Crawford | 3,5 | Debbie Sanchez | 4* |

| | | | |
|---|---|---|---|
| Wade Morton | 6* | Amy Dirkse | 7 |
| Colby Blackwell | 8,79,285,288 | Donna Jarman | 32,37* |
| Michelle Roberson | 58* | Payton Wallace | 67 |
| Karen Robinson | 69,83,85,88,273,274* | B J McDowell | 73,76,295 |
| Alicia Reed | 286 | Kristy Kinney | 298 |

| Public Schs..Principal | Grd | Prgm | Enr/#Cls | SN | |
|---|---|---|---|---|---|
| ⓨ Bosque Co Educational Center | K-12 | AGMV | 88 | | 254/435-6098 |
| 201 Second St, Meridian 76665 | | | 5 | | Fax 254/435-6438 |
| John Bullion | | | | | |
| Ⓐ Meridian Alternative Sch | K-12 | | 12 | | 254/435-6047 |
| 607 F St, Meridian 76665 | | | 2 | | |
| Paul Booth | | | | | |
| Meridian Elem Sch | PK-5 | T | 219 | 67% | 254/435-2731 |
| 550 Yellow Jacket Dr, Meridian 76665 | | | 20 | | Fax 254/435-6099 |
| Jaime Leinhauser | | | | | |
| Meridian Middle High Sch | 6-12 | TV | 238 | 60% | 254/435-2723 |
| 500 Yellow Jacket Dr, Meridian 76665 | | | 18 | | Fax 254/435-2199 |
| Kristi Kinney | | | | | |

## Morgan Ind School Dist  PID: 01000728
1306 Charles St, Morgan 76671
254/635-2311
Fax 254/635-2129

**Schools:** 1 \ **Teachers:** 14 \ **Students:** 130 \ **Special Ed Students:** 26 \ **LEP Students:** 12 \ **College-Bound:** 100% \ **Ethnic:** African American 1%, Hispanic 66%, Native American: 1%, Caucasian 32% \ **Exp:** $709 (High) \ **Poverty:** 27% \ **Title I:** $62,656 \ **Open-Close:** 08/19 - 05/28 \ **DTBP:** $414 (High)

| | | | |
|---|---|---|---|
| Juan Ramerez | 1,11,73,83 | Joyce Riney | 2,19,76 |
| Edward Avieles | 6* | Theresa Stacey | 67 |

| Public Schs..Principal | Grd | Prgm | Enr/#Cls | SN | |
|---|---|---|---|---|---|
| Morgan Sch | PK-12 | TV | 130 | 76% | 254/635-2311 |
| 1306 Charles St, Morgan 76671 | | | 18 | | |
| Juan Ramirez | | | | | |

## Valley Mills Ind School Dist  PID: 01000754
1 Eagle Way, Valley Mills 76689
254/932-5210
Fax 254/932-6601

**Schools:** 2 \ **Teachers:** 50 \ **Students:** 600 \ **Special Ed Students:** 85 \ **LEP Students:** 37 \ **College-Bound:** 40% \ **Ethnic:** Asian 1%, African American 3%, Hispanic 24%, Caucasian 73% \ **Exp:** $554 (High) \ **Poverty:** 19% \ **Title I:** $148,565 \ **Open-Close:** 09/08 - 05/28 \ **DTBP:** $347 (High)

| | | | |
|---|---|---|---|
| Mike Kelly | 1,11 | Brenda Byrom | 2,68 |
| Lisa Danke | 4* | Shelley Sonntag | 5* |
| Sam Moody | 6* | Sherri Fisk | 7* |
| Dianna Richardson | 16,73,295* | Wanda Riggs | 57,83,88* |
| Mike Jones | 67 | | |

| Public Schs..Principal | Grd | Prgm | Enr/#Cls | SN | |
|---|---|---|---|---|---|
| ⓨ Valley Mills Elem Sch | PK-5 | AGMTV | 257 | 67% | |
| 254/932-5526 | | | | | |
| 102 West Ave C, Valley Mills 76689 | | | 20 | | Fax 254/932-5861 |
| Chris Dowdy | | | | | |
| ⓨ Valley Millsjr Sr High Sch | 6-12 | AGMTV | 200 | 50% | |
| 254/932-5251 | | | | | |
| 1 Eagle Way, Valley Mills 76689 | | | 25 | | |
| Eric Halfmann | | | | | |

| | | | | | |
|---|---|---|---|---|---|
| 1 Superintendent | 8 Curric/Instruct K-12 | 19 Chief Financial Officer | 29 Family/Consumer Science | 39 Social Studies K-12 | 49 English/Lang Arts Elem | 59 Special Education Elem | 69 Academic Assessment |
| 2 Bus/Finance/Purchasing | 9 Curric/Instruct Elem | 20 Art K-12 | 30 Adult Education | 40 Social Studies Elem | 50 English/Lang Arts Sec | 60 Special Education Sec | 70 Research/Development |
| 3 Buildings And Grounds | 10 Curric/Instruct Sec | 21 Art Elem | 31 Career/Sch-to-Work K-12 | 41 Social Studies Sec | 51 Reading K-12 | 61 Foreign/World Lang K-12 | 71 Public Information |
| 4 Food Service | 11 Federal Program | 22 Art Sec | 32 Career/Sch-to-Work Elem | 42 Science K-12 | 52 Reading Elem | 62 Foreign/World Lang Elem | 72 Summer School |
| 5 Transportation | 12 Title I | 23 Music K-12 | 33 Career/Sch-to-Work Sec | 43 Science Elem | 53 Reading Sec | 63 Foreign/World Lang Sec | 73 Instructional Tech |
| 6 Athletic | 13 Title V | 24 Music Elem | 34 Early Childhood Ed | 44 Science Sec | 54 Remedial Reading K-12 | 64 Religious Education K-12 | 74 Inservice Training |
| 7 Health Services | 15 Asst Superintendent | 25 Music Sec | 35 Health/Phys Education | 45 Math K-12 | 55 Remedial Reading Elem | 65 Religious Education Elem | 75 Marketing/Distributive |
| | 16 Instructional Media Svcs | 26 Business Education | 36 Guidance Services K-12 | 46 Math Elem | 56 Remedial Reading Sec | 66 Religious Education Sec | 76 Info Systems |
| | 17 Chief Operations Officer | 27 Career & Tech Ed | 37 Guidance Services Elem | 47 Math Sec | 57 Bilingual/ELL | 67 School Board President | 77 Psychological Assess |
| | 18 Chief Academic Officer | 28 Technology Education | 38 Guidance Services Sec | 48 English/Lang Arts K-12 | 58 Special Education K-12 | 68 Teacher Personnel | 78 Affirmative Action |

- **Walnut Springs Ind Sch Dist** PID: 01000780
  184 Avenue A, Walnut Spgs 76690
  254/797-2133
  Fax 254/797-2191

Schools: 1 \ Teachers: 18 \ Students: 187 \ Special Ed Students: 28 \ LEP Students: 36 \ College-Bound: 75% \ Ethnic: African American 1%, Hispanic 57%, Caucasian 42% \ Exp: $447 (High) \ Poverty: 39% \ Title I: $137,260 \ Open-Close: 08/26 - 05/21 \ DTBP: $392 (High)

| | | |
|---|---|---|
| Pat Garrett | 1,11,84 | |
| Tim Trotter | 6* | |
| Sandra Uloth | 16* | |
| Clint Pullin | 67 | |
| Karen Prescher | 2 | |
| Christy Halbert | 8,12,57,88,288* | |
| Jonathan Harbour | 58* | |

| Public Schs..Principal | Grd | Prgm | Enr/#Cls | SN |
|---|---|---|---|---|
| Walnut Springs Sch 184 Avenue A, Walnut Spgs 76690 Christy Halbert | PK-12 | ATV | 187 23 | 86% 254/797-2133 |

## BOWIE COUNTY

## BOWIE PUBLIC SCHOOLS

- **De Kalb Ind School Dist** PID: 01000819
  101 Maple St, De Kalb 75559
  903/667-2566
  Fax 903/667-3791

Schools: 3 \ Teachers: 69 \ Students: 650 \ Special Ed Students: 77 \ LEP Students: 44 \ College-Bound: 51% \ Ethnic: African American 20%, Hispanic 14%, Native American: 1%, Caucasian 64% \ Exp: $412 (High) \ Poverty: 30% \ Title I: $324,499 \ Open-Close: 08/13 - 05/25 \ DTBP: $329 (High)

| | | |
|---|---|---|
| John Booth | 1 | |
| Cortney White | 3,5 | |
| Emily Lee | 11,69 | |
| Michael White | 23 | |
| Blake Hodges | 67 | |
| Nielan Hensley | 91* | |
| Matteson Jennifer | 2 | |
| Eddy May | 6 | |
| Randall Brown | 16,73,295* | |
| Michele Fannin | 52,55,57,59* | |
| Melissa Motes | 73 | |

| Public Schs..Principal | Grd | Prgm | Enr/#Cls | SN |
|---|---|---|---|---|
| De Kalb Elem Sch 101 Maple St, De Kalb 75559 Melinda Hodgson | PK-4 | T | 267 28 | 75% 903/667-2328 Fax 903/667-5151 |
| De Kalb High Sch 101 Maple St, De Kalb 75559 Clayton Little \ Melinda Hodgson \ Cody Burgin | 9-12 | TV | 220 35 | 51% 903/667-2422 Fax 903/667-4086 |
| De Kalb Middle Sch 101 Maple St, De Kalb 75559 Cody Burgin | 5-8 | T | 266 30 | 68% 903/667-2834 Fax 903/667-5509 |

- **Hooks Ind School Dist** PID: 01000857
  100 E 5th St, Hooks 75561
  903/547-6077
  Fax 903/547-2943

Schools: 3 \ Teachers: 74 \ Students: 884 \ Special Ed Students: 99 \ LEP Students: 28 \ Ethnic: African American 13%, Hispanic 11%, Caucasian 76% \ Exp: $657 (High) \ Poverty: 26% \ Title I: $287,339 \ Open-Close: 08/13 - 05/27 \ DTBP: $574 (High) \ 🟦 🇹

| | | |
|---|---|---|
| Keith Minter | 1,73 | |
| Chris Crawford | 3,5 | |
| Tracy Cook | 8,11,30,34,36,57,288,296 | |
| Judy Cochrane | 2 | |
| Chris Birdwell | 6* | |
| Scot Duncan | 67 | |

Beverly Shannon ........................88*

| Public Schs..Principal | Grd | Prgm | Enr/#Cls | SN |
|---|---|---|---|---|
| Hooks Elem Sch 401 Precinct Rd, Hooks 75561 Jennifer Deanda | PK-4 | T | 282 30 | 69% 903/547-2291 Fax 903/547-3172 🇹 |
| Hooks High Sch 401 E Avenue A, Hooks 75561 Danny Garrett | 9-12 | TV | 350 40 | 56% 903/547-2215 Fax 903/547-6514 |
| Hooks Junior High Sch 3921 FM 560, Hooks 75561 Craig Mahar | 5-8 | T | 252 22 | 58% 903/547-2568 Fax 903/547-2595 |

- **Hubbard Ind School Dist** PID: 01000900
  3347 US Highway 259 S, De Kalb 75559
  903/667-2645
  Fax 903/667-5835

Schools: 1 \ Teachers: 9 \ Students: 107 \ Special Ed Students: 18 \ LEP Students: 11 \ Ethnic: Hispanic 24%, Native American: 2%, Caucasian 74% \ Exp: $213 (Med) \ Poverty: 14% \ Title I: $20,675 \ Open-Close: 08/14 - 05/21 \ DTBP: $350 (High)

| | | |
|---|---|---|
| Traci Drake | 1,11,83 | |
| Traci Drake | 12* | |
| Johnny Pate | 57* | |
| Mechelle McMichael | 73,76,270 | |
| Cayla Brown | 752 | |
| Auttumn Owens | 2 | |
| Becky Buttrum | 16* | |
| Brian Tripplett | 67 | |
| Shellye McDaniel | 271* | |

| Public Schs..Principal | Grd | Prgm | Enr/#Cls | SN |
|---|---|---|---|---|
| Hubbard Elem Sch 3347 US Highway 259 S, De Kalb 75559 Traci Drake | PK-8 | T | 107 12 | 66% 903/667-2645 |

- **Leary Ind School Dist** PID: 01000924
  9500 W New Boston Rd, Texarkana 75501
  903/838-8960
  Fax 903/838-6036

Schools: 1 \ Teachers: 12 \ Students: 119 \ Special Ed Students: 16 \ Ethnic: African American 4%, Hispanic 8%, Caucasian 88% \ Exp: $125 (Low) \ Poverty: 20% \ Title I: $46,737 \ Open-Close: 08/14 - 05/27 \ DTBP: $510 (High)

| | | |
|---|---|---|
| Jennifer Dear | 1,11,57 | |
| Kim Fernandez | 59* | |
| Ken Autrey | 67 | |
| Auttum Owens | 2,288 | |
| Tamera Jones | 59* | |
| Heath Shelton | 73,286* | |

| Public Schs..Principal | Grd | Prgm | Enr/#Cls | SN |
|---|---|---|---|---|
| Leary Elem Sch 9500 W New Boston Rd, Texarkana 75501 | PK-8 | AT | 119 15 | 78% 903/838-8960 |

- **Liberty-Eylau Ind School Dist** PID: 01000948
  2901 Leopard Dr, Texarkana 75501
  903/832-1535
  Fax 903/838-9444

Schools: 4 \ Teachers: 187 \ Students: 2,465 \ Special Ed Students: 330 \ LEP Students: 45 \ Ethnic: African American 57%, Hispanic 7%, Native American: 1%, Caucasian 36% \ Exp: $521 (High) \ Poverty: 27% \ Title I: $868,272 \ Open-Close: 08/12 - 05/21 \ DTBP: $158 (High) \ 🟦 🇹

| | | |
|---|---|---|
| Ronnie Thompson | 1 | |
| Jeff Wright | 3,15 | |
| Malisa Mathews | 4* | |
| Ronda Jameson | 8 | |
| Brandy Burnett | 12,68 | |
| Madeline Cooper | 26* | |
| Jean Ford | 57,271* | |
| Trevelyan Hodge | 67 | |
| Diane Niemyer | 88 | |
| Frank Routheau | 2 | |
| Wayne Harmon | 3 | |
| Dewaski Davis | 6 | |
| Dr Ceretha Levingston | 11,15,80,298 | |
| Jason Brown | 16,73 | |
| Linda Block | 27 | |
| Angela Featherson | 58 | |
| Matthew Fry | 71 | |
| Bart Zeal | 91 | |

Joseph Lavender .................................. 295

| Public Schs..Principal | Grd | Prgm | Enr/#Cls | SN | |
|---|---|---|---|---|---|
| Liberty-Eylau Early Chldhd Ctr<br>3105 Norris Cooley Dr, Texarkana 75501<br>Amy Norwood | PK-K | T | 425<br>14 | 92% | 903/831-5352<br>Fax 903/831-5354 |
| Liberty-Eylau Elem Sch<br>5492 US Highway 59 S, Texarkana 75501<br>Kristi Brown | 1-4 | T | 662<br>42 | 87% | 903/831-5390<br>Fax 903/831-5393 |
| Liberty-Eylau High Sch<br>2905 Leopard Dr, Texarkana 75501<br>Kendrick Smith | 9-12 | GTV | 705<br>68 | 69% | 903/832-1530<br>Fax 903/831-6113 |
| Liberty-Eylau Middle Sch<br>5555 Leopard Dr, Texarkana 75501<br>Jakeb Goff | 5-8 | TV | 673<br>45 | 79% | 903/838-5555<br>Fax 903/832-6700 |

- **Malta Ind School Dist** PID: 01001019     903/667-2950
  6178 W US Highway 82, New Boston 75570    Fax 903/667-0546

> **Schools:** 1 \ **Teachers:** 16 \ **Students:** 225 \ **Special Ed Students:** 14 \
> **Ethnic:** Hispanic 6%, Native American: 2%, Caucasian 91% \ **Exp:** $458 (High)
> \ **Poverty:** 17% \ **Title I:** $20,898 \ **Open-Close:** 08/12 - 05/21 \ **DTBP:** $303
> (High)

Stacy Starrett .......................1,11   David Lee .........................6,9,57,69,74,270*
Doug Russell .......................... 67

| Public Schs..Principal | Grd | Prgm | Enr/#Cls | SN | |
|---|---|---|---|---|---|
| Malta Elem Sch<br>6178 W US Highway 82, New Boston 75570<br>David Lee | PK-6 | T | 225<br>13 | 45% | 903/667-2950<br>Fax 903/667-2984 |

- **Maud Ind School Dist** PID: 01001033     903/585-2219
  389 Houston St, Maud 75567    Fax 903/585-5451

> **Schools:** 1 \ **Teachers:** 38 \ **Students:** 475 \ **Special Ed Students:** 52
> \ **LEP Students:** 3 \ **College-Bound:** 29% \ **Ethnic:** African American
> 5%, Hispanic 6%, Caucasian 88% \ **Exp:** $793 (High) \ **Poverty:** 13% \
> **Title I:** $95,107 \ **Special Education:** $14,000 \ **Open-Close:** 08/10 - 05/20 \
> **DTBP:** $365 (High)

Chris Bradshaw ......................................1   Tommy Van Deaver ...................................2
Debbie Johnson ...................................... 4*   Josh Turner ...........................................6*
Amanda Sanders ... 8,11,57,271,288,296,298*   Mark Forsyth ....................16,73,84,286,295*
Angela Featherson ................................. 58   Aaron Brower ....................................... 67
Ella Duren .............................................. 69   Chequita Gant ....................................... 76
Kayla Harrell ................... 83,85,88,270,752*

| Public Schs..Principal | Grd | Prgm | Enr/#Cls | SN | |
|---|---|---|---|---|---|
| Maud Sch<br>389 Houston St, Maud 75567<br>Erica Fouche \ Joel Windham | PK-12 | TV | 475<br>50 | 63% | 903/585-2219 |

- **New Boston Ind School Dist** PID: 01001069    903/628-2521
  201 Rice St, New Boston 75570    Fax 903/628-8990

> **Schools:** 4 \ **Teachers:** 119 \ **Students:** 1,198 \ **Special Ed Students:** 200
> \ **LEP Students:** 26 \ **College-Bound:** 39% \ **Ethnic:** African American
> 27%, Hispanic 8%, Caucasian 65% \ **Exp:** $534 (High) \ **Poverty:** 21% \
> **Title I:** $352,683 \ **Open-Close:** 08/17 - 05/28 \ **DTBP:** $363 (High) \ [f]

Brian Bobbitt ..........................................1   Jackie Barnwell ...................................2,12
Rick Forugs ............................................3   Jimmie Thomas ......................................5*
Justin Waltz ...........................................6   Patty Greene ................. 8,11,57,69,273,298
Justin Dragoescu ........................16,73,295   Tonya Briggs .........................................27*

Kimberly Fernandez ..........................58,83   Paula Turner ........................... 67
Melissa Farris .................................75*   Tim Williams ................................ 84

| Public Schs..Principal | Grd | Prgm | Enr/#Cls | SN | |
|---|---|---|---|---|---|
| Crestview Elem Sch<br>604 N McCoy Blvd, New Boston 75570<br>Lindsey Skinner | 3-5 | T | 272<br>28 | 81% | 903/628-6521<br>Fax 903/628-4205 |
| New Boston High Sch<br>1 W Lion Dr, New Boston 75570<br>Neil Koenig | 9-12 | ATV | 380<br>45 | 54% | 903/628-6551<br>Fax 903/628-3695 |
| New Boston Middle Sch<br>1215 N State Highway 8, New Boston 75570<br>Lindsay Skinner | 6-8 | T | 280<br>40 | 75% | 903/628-6588<br>Fax 903/628-5132 |
| Oakview Primary Sch<br>530 Hospital Dr, New Boston 75570<br>Lindseyy Skinner | PK-2 | T | 266 | 85% | 903/628-8900<br>Fax 903/628-8910 |

- **Pleasant Grove Ind School Dist** PID: 01001112    903/831-4086
  8500 N Kings Hwy, Texarkana 75503    Fax 903/831-4435

> **Schools:** 4 \ **Teachers:** 165 \ **Students:** 2,200 \ **Special Ed Students:** 228
> \ **LEP Students:** 61 \ **Ethnic:** Asian 3%, African American 17%, Hispanic
> 8%, Caucasian 71% \ **Exp:** $467 (High) \ **Poverty:** 10% \ **Title I:** $227,864
> \ **Special Education:** $377,000 \ **Open-Close:** 08/10 - 05/28 \ **DTBP:** $213
> (High)

Chad Pirtele .........................................1   Derick Sibley .....................................2,11
Steve Shatto .........................................3   Bill Harp ....................................4,68,83
Gary Stauty ..........................................4   Terry Spivey ....................................5,91
Josh Gibson ........................................ 6*   Lakeisha Girley ......................................7*
Julie McClurg ............8,11,58,85,285,296*   Patricia Long ....................................... 26
Regan Summers ...................................37*   Louanne Smith .......................................38*
Dr Tina Antley ...........................57,63,271   Amy Damron ....................................... 67
Jim McClurg ............................... 73,297   Shelby Akin .......................................75,298*
Wanda Wortham ................................. 294

| Public Schs..Principal | Grd | Prgm | Enr/#Cls | SN | |
|---|---|---|---|---|---|
| Pleasant Grove Elem Sch<br>6500 Pleasant Grove Rd, Texarkana 75503<br>Chad Blain | PK-2 | T | 408<br>37 | 51% | 903/838-0528<br>Fax 903/831-3799 |
| Pleasant Grove High Sch<br>5406 McKnight Rd, Texarkana 75503<br>Todd Marshall | 9-12 | V | 682<br>45 | 22% | 903/832-8005<br>Fax 903/832-5381 |
| Pleasant Grove Interm Sch<br>8480 N Kings Hwy, Texarkana 75503<br>Pam Bradford | 3-5 | T | 464<br>30 | 41% | 903/832-0001<br>Fax 903/832-0147 |
| Pleasant Grove Middle Sch<br>5605 Cooks Ln, Texarkana 75503<br>Linda Erie | 6-8 | | 527<br>40 | 30% | 903/831-4295<br>Fax 903/831-5501 |

- **Red Lick Ind School Dist** PID: 01001136    903/838-8230
  3511 N FM 2148, Texarkana 75503    Fax 903/831-6134

> **Schools:** 1 \ **Teachers:** 40 \ **Students:** 520 \ **Special Ed Students:** 32 \
> **Ethnic:** African American 1%, Hispanic 4%, Caucasian 94% \ **Exp:** $463 (High)
> \ **Poverty:** 16% \ **Title I:** $92,058 \ **Open-Close:** 08/12 - 05/25

Brandon Bynard ......................................1   Lacey McMillon .....................................2*
Neil Kiser .......................................... 6*   Debbie Cooper .................9,11,57,69,74,88*
Matt Windham ...............................16,73*   Crystal Roach ....................................... 37
Melissa Whitecotton ............................59*   Monica Harrison ....................................... 67
Theresa Write ...............................83,85

| | | | |
|---|---|---|---|
| **1** Superintendent | **8** Curric/Instruct K-12 | **19** Chief Financial Officer | **29** Family/Consumer Science |
| **2** Bus/Finance/Purchasing | **9** Curric/Instruct Elem | **20** Art K-12 | **30** Adult Education |
| **3** Buildings And Grounds | **10** Curric/Instruct Sec | **21** Art Elem | **31** Career/Sch-to-Work K-12 |
| **4** Food Service | **11** Federal Program | **22** Art Sec | **32** Career/Sch-to-Work Elem |
| **5** Transportation | **12** Title I | **23** Music K-12 | **33** Career/Sch-to-Work Sec |
| **6** Athletic | **13** Title V | **24** Music Elem | **34** Early Childhood Ed |
| **7** Health Services | **14** Asst Superintendent | **25** Music Sec | **35** Health/Phys Education |
| | **15** Asst Superintendent | **26** Business Education | **36** Guidance Services K-12 |
| | **16** Instructional Media Svcs | **27** Career & Tech Ed | **37** Guidance Services Elem |
| | **17** Chief Operations Officer | **28** Technology Education | **38** Guidance Services Sec |
| | **18** Chief Academic Officer | | |

| | | |
|---|---|---|
| **39** Social Studies K-12 | **49** English/Lang Arts Elem | **59** Special Education Elem | **69** Academic Assessment |
| **40** Social Studies Elem | **50** English/Lang Arts Sec | **60** Special Education Sec | **70** Research/Development |
| **41** Social Studies Sec | **51** Reading K-12 | **61** Foreign/World Lang K-12 | **71** Public Information |
| **42** Science K-12 | **52** Reading Elem | **62** Foreign/World Lang Elem | **72** Summer School |
| **43** Science Elem | **53** Reading Sec | **63** Foreign/World Lang Sec | **73** Instructional Tech |
| **44** Science Sec | **54** Remedial Reading K-12 | **64** Religious Education K-12 | **74** Inservice Training |
| **45** Math K-12 | **55** Remedial Reading Elem | **65** Religious Education Elem | **75** Marketing/Distributive |
| **46** Math Elem | **56** Remedial Reading Sec | **66** Religious Education Sec | **76** Info Systems |
| **47** Math Sec | **57** Bilingual/ELL | **67** School Board President | **77** Psychological Assess |
| **48** English/Lang Arts K-12 | **58** Special Education K-12 | **68** Teacher Personnel | **78** Affirmative Action |

| Public Schs..Principal | Grd | Prgm | Enr/#Cls | SN | |
|---|---|---|---|---|---|
| Red Lick Sch<br>3511 N FM 2148, Texarkana 75503<br>Debbie Cooper \ Jason Dempsey | K-8 | | 520<br>20 | 11% | 903/838-8230 |

● **Redwater Ind School Dist** PID: 01001150 — 903/671-3481
202 Red River Rd N, Redwater 75573 — Fax 903/671-2019

**Schools:** 4 \ **Teachers:** 100 \ **Students:** 1,076 \ **Special Ed Students:** 106 \ **LEP Students:** 11 \ **College-Bound:** 65% \ **Ethnic:** Asian 1%, African American 4%, Hispanic 4%, Caucasian 91% \ **Exp:** $654 (High) \ **Poverty:** 10% \ **Title I:** $123,161 \ **Special Education:** $155,000 \ **Open-Close:** 08/13 - 05/27 \ **DTBP:** $333 (High) \ t

| | | | |
|---|---|---|---|
| Kelly Burns ..............1 | | Tess Baker ..............2 |
| Connie Mears ..............5 | | Thomas Graf ..............6 |
| Laura Magnum ..............7 | | Leeann Corbin ......8,11,57,69,83,273,288,296 |
| Lori Baffern ..............16,286 | | Wendy May ..............31,36,93,270,271,274 |
| Wendy May ..............31,36,93,270,271,274* | | Anne White ..............58* |
| Stephanie Brooks ..............67 | | Karen Zink ..............73* |
| Karen Arnett ..............79* | | Kaye Derrick ..............88* |

| Public Schs..Principal | Grd | Prgm | Enr/#Cls | SN | |
|---|---|---|---|---|---|
| Redwater Elem Sch<br>206 Red River Rd N, Redwater 75573<br>Kasey Coggin | PK-3 | T | 289<br>21 | 59% | 903/671-3425<br>Fax 903/671-3196 |
| Redwater High Sch<br>120 Red River Rd N, Redwater 75573<br>**Brett Haugh** | 9-12 | TV | 345<br>23 | 34% | 903/671-3421<br>Fax 903/671-3259 |
| Redwater Junior High Sch<br>204 Red River Rd N, Redwater 75573<br>Kim Cody | 7-8 | T | 174<br>19 | 42% | 903/671-3227 |
| Redwater Middle Sch<br>108 Ware St, Redwater 75573<br>Audrey Shumate | 4-6 | T | 268<br>16 | 44% | 903/671-3412<br>Fax 903/671-2444 |

● **Simms Ind School Dist** PID: 01001186 — 903/543-2219
47 James Bowie Ln, Simms 75574 — Fax 903/543-2512

**Schools:** 3 \ **Teachers:** 46 \ **Students:** 500 \ **Special Ed Students:** 77 \ **LEP Students:** 3 \ **College-Bound:** 60% \ **Ethnic:** Asian 1%, Hispanic 4%, Native American: 1%, Caucasian 94% \ **Exp:** $491 (High) \ **Poverty:** 18% \ **Title I:** $218,171 \ **Open-Close:** 08/12 - 05/27 \ **DTBP:** $396 (High)

| | | | |
|---|---|---|---|
| Jana Brown ..............2,296 | | Andy Johnson ..............8,11,298 |
| Wendy May ..............57,69,83,85,88,270 | | Russell Meadows ..............67 |
| Torie Ceynowa ..............752 | | |

| Public Schs..Principal | Grd | Prgm | Enr/#Cls | SN | |
|---|---|---|---|---|---|
| James Bowie Elem Sch<br>47 James Bowie Ln, Simms 75574<br>Justin Tyndell | PK-5 | T | 209<br>26 | 60% | 903/543-2245 |
| James Bowie High Sch<br>47 James Bowie Ln, Simms 75574<br>**Chris McClure \ Eddy May** | 9-12 | TV | 174<br>25 | 53% | 903/543-2275 |
| James Bowie Middle Sch<br>47 James Bowie Ln, Simms 75574<br>Christopher McClure | 6-8 | T | 115 | 56% | 903/543-2275 |

● **Texarkana Ind School Dist** PID: 01001215 — 903/794-3651
4241 Summerhill Rd, Texarkana 75503 — Fax 903/792-2632

**Schools:** 13 \ **Teachers:** 529 \ **Students:** 7,174 \ **Special Ed Students:** 642 \ **LEP Students:** 497 \ **Ethnic:** Asian 1%, African American 47%, Hispanic 16%, Caucasian 35% \ **Exp:** $439 (High) \ **Poverty:** 30% \ **Title I:** $2,642,647 \ **Special Education:** $1,225,000 \ **Open-Close:** 08/19 - 05/26 \ **DTBP:** $158 (High) \ f t

| | | | |
|---|---|---|---|
| Autumn Thomas ..............1 | | Anita Clay ..............2 |
| David Defoy ..............2 | | Myron Stringer ..............3 |
| Christie Lammers ..............4 | | Kaye Oliver ..............5 |
| Barry Norton ..............6 | | Suzie Inman ..............7* |
| Suzie Inman ..............7 | | Christy Tidwell ..............8,74 |
| Holly Tucker ..............8,18 | | Jamie Friday ..............8 |
| Shawn Davis ..............11,58,85,274,275 | | George Moore ..............15,88 |
| Joann Rice ..............15,79,93 | | Dr Sandra Austin ..............16,286* |
| Rusty Ogburn ..............27,76,92,295 | | Dean Ransdell ..............30 |
| Kim Lee ..............40,49 | | Lori Bailey ..............40,49 |
| Amy Frierson ..............43,46 | | Jennifer Sells ..............44,47 |
| April Davis ..............58 | | Becky Graham ..............58 |
| Amy Nix ..............68 | | Tina Veal-Gooch ..............71 |
| Jennifer Beck ..............73 | | Kim Icenhower ..............73 |
| Debra Shelby ..............74 | | Amanda Manca ..............76 |
| Monica Harrison ..............81 | | Tony Dollarhide ..............83,91 |
| Stacy Courson ..............90* | | Jennell Ingram ..............273 |
| Georgette Duke ..............274* | | Cathy Klopper ..............285 |
| Felita Gilmore ..............286 | | |

| Public Schs..Principal | Grd | Prgm | Enr/#Cls | SN | |
|---|---|---|---|---|---|
| Dunbar Early Education Center<br>2315 W 10th St, Texarkana 75501<br>Lakesha Taylor | PK-PK | AT | 290<br>20 | 100% | 903/794-8112<br>Fax 903/794-5841 |
| Eschool Prep Virtual Sch<br>4241 Summerhill Rd, Texarkana 75503<br>Nanette Power | 5-11 | | 1,000 | | 903/794-3651 |
| Highland Park Elem Sch<br>401 W 25th St, Texarkana 75503<br>Jennifer Cross | PK-5 | T | 277<br>17 | 98% | 903/794-8001<br>Fax 903/793-1702 |
| Jones Early Literacy Center<br>2600 W 15th St, Texarkana 75501<br>Melodie White | K-2 | T | 404<br>30 | 97% | 903/793-4871<br>Fax 903/793-7596<br>f t |
| Morriss Elem Sch<br>4826 University Park, Texarkana 75503<br>Brandy Debenport | K-5 | | 402 | 21% | 903/791-2262<br>Fax 903/798-6875 |
| Nash Elem Sch<br>100 E Burton St, Nash 75569<br>Patti O'Bannon | PK-5 | AT | 685<br>27 | 81% | 903/838-4321<br>Fax 903/831-7158 |
| Ⓐ Options Academic High Sch<br>3201 Lincoln Ave, Texarkana 75503<br>Amy Doss | 9-12 | T | 49<br>3 | 83% | 903/793-5632<br>Fax 903/798-2131 |
| Spring Lake Park Elem Sch<br>4324 Ghio Fish Blvd, Texarkana 75503<br>Anne Slade | PK-5 | T | 348<br>14 | 90% | 903/794-7525<br>Fax 903/255-3270 |
| Texas High Sch<br>4001 Summerhill Rd, Texarkana 75503<br>Carla DuPree | 9-12 | TV | 858<br>100 | 50% | 903/794-3891<br>Fax 903/792-8971<br>f t |
| Texas Middle Sch<br>2100 College Dr, Texarkana 75503<br>Tim Lambert | 6-8 | T | 1,520<br>90 | 69% | 903/793-5631<br>Fax 903/792-2935 |
| Waggoner Creek Elem Sch<br>6335 Gibson Ln, Texarkana 75503<br>Angie Griffin | PK-5 | T | 280 | 44% | 903/255-3301<br>Fax 903/223-7945 |
| Wake Village Elem Sch<br>400 Wildcat Dr, Wake Village 75501<br>Mindy Gennings | PK-5 | AT | 551<br>38 | 83% | 903/838-4261<br>Fax 903/255-3272<br>t |

| | | | | | |
|---|---|---|---|---|---|
| Westlawn Elem Sch | 3-5 | T | 334 | 92% | 903/223-4252 |
| 410 Westlawn Dr, Texarkana 75501 | | | 27 | | Fax 903/223-4262 |
| **Elodia Witterstaetter** | | | | | 🄵🅣 |

## BOWIE PRIVATE SCHOOLS

| Private Schs..Principal | Grd | Prgm | Enr/#Cls | SN | |
|---|---|---|---|---|---|
| Bethel SDA Sch | K-8 | | 13 | | 903/838-4215 |
| 489 S Kings Hwy, Texarkana 75501 | | | 2 | | Fax 903/832-6216 |
| Galsmine Ellis | | | | | |
| St James Day Sch | PK-6 | | 165 | | 903/793-5554 |
| 5501 N State Line Ave, Texarkana 75503 | | | 10 | | Fax 903/793-1775 |
| | | | | | 🄵 |

## BRAZORIA COUNTY

## BRAZORIA PUBLIC SCHOOLS

● **Alvin Ind School Dist** PID: 01001382                 281/388-1130
301 E House St, Alvin 77511                                Fax 281/388-2719

**Schools:** 31 \ **Teachers:** 1,700 \ **Students:** 25,926 \
**Special Ed Students:** 2,728 \ **LEP Students:** 3,946 \ **Ethnic:** Asian 10%,
African American 22%, Hispanic 41%, Caucasian 27% \ **Exp:** $398 (High)
\ **Poverty:** 13% \ **Title I:** $3,196,277 \ **Special Education:** $3,450,000 \
**Open-Close:** 08/20 - 05/28 \ **DTBP:** $181 (High) \ 🄵 🅣

| | | | |
|---|---|---|---|
| Carol Nelson | 1 | Cheryl Ryan | 2 |
| Dr Daniel Combs | 2,15,19,71 | Mickie Dietrich | 2 |
| David Bolton | 3 | Jennifer Basich | 4 |
| Jeff Dungen | 5 | Mike Bass | 6 |
| Dr Loree Bruton | 7,11,15,36,58 | Jennifer Valdez | 8,15,37,270 |
| Dr Kathy Windsor | 8,68,79* | Kathy Windsor | 11 |
| Allen Roberts | 15 | Don Rabalais | 16,73,76,98 |
| Lisa Savage | 20,23 | Christina Rice-Wiltz | 27,31,95 |
| Charlotte Liptack | 39,48 | Virginia Lively | 39* |
| Erica Price | 42 | Diane Peltier | 45* |
| Paula Camacho | 57,89,271 | Carl Hauberd | 67 |
| Kim Alvarez | 68 | Melba Morales | 68 |
| Brent Shaw | 69,294 | John Wilds | 84,295 |
| Mike Putnal | 91 | | |

| Public Schs..Principal | Grd | Prgm | Enr/#Cls | SN | |
|---|---|---|---|---|---|
| Alvin Elem Sch | 3-5 | T | 497 | 67% | 281/585-2511 |
| 2200 Westpark Dr, Alvin 77511 | | | 36 | | Fax 281/331-9888 |
| Tracy Olvera | | | | | 🄵🅣 |
| Alvin High Sch | 9-12 | ATV | 2,766 | 56% | 281/245-3000 |
| 802 S Johnson St, Alvin 77511 | | | | | Fax 281/331-3053 |
| Karen Taylor | | | | | 🄵🅣 |
| Alvin ISD Career & Tech Ed Ctr | Voc | | 250 | | 281/245-2160 |
| 7381 Lewis Ln, Manvel 77578 | | | | | |
| Dr Kathy Windsor | | | | | |
| Alvin Junior High Sch | 6-8 | AT | 907 | 63% | 281/245-2770 |
| 2300 W South St, Alvin 77511 | | | 60 | | Fax 281/331-5926 |
| Leroy Castro | | | | | 🄵🅣 |
| Ⓐ Assets Academy | 9-12 | T | 59 | 65% | 281/331-1690 |
| 605 W House St, Alvin 77511 | | | 4 | | Fax 281/331-1667 |
| Brandy Johanson | | | | | 🄵🅣 |

| | | | | | |
|---|---|---|---|---|---|
| Bel Nafegar Sanchez Elem Sch | K-6 | | 800 | | 713/814-7000 |
| 1721 Sterling Lakes W Dr, Rosharon 77583 | | | | | Fax 281/245-3445 |
| Rosemary Reed | | | | | |
| Bill Hasse Elem Sch | PK-5 | T | 708 | 74% | 281/585-3397 |
| 1200 House St, Alvin 77511 | | | 26 | | Fax 281/331-1190 |
| Diana Baker \ **Kristi Froberg** | | | | | 🄵🅣 |
| Bob and Betty Nelson Elem Sch | PK-6 | | 800 | | 713/814-7300 |
| 14400 County Road 185, Alvin 77511 | | | | | Fax 281/326-9059 |
| Tracy Olvera | | | | | |
| Don Jeter Elem Sch | PK-5 | T | 884 | 67% | 281/245-3055 |
| 2455 County Road 58, Manvel 77578 | | | | | Fax 281/489-4630 |
| Tina McCorkle | | | | | |
| Ⓨ Dr James Red Duke Elem Sch | PK-5 | M | 552 | 32% | 281/245-3400 |
| 11330 Magnolia Pkwy, Manvel 77578 | | | | | Fax 281/489-1760 |
| **Emily Hall** | | | | | 🅣 |
| Dr Ronald E McNair Junior HS | 7-9 | | 1,020 | 31% | 713/814-7200 |
| 2950 Kingsley Dr, Pearland 77584 | | | | | Fax 281/245-2155 |
| Craig Rhodes | | | | | |
| E C Mason Elem Sch | PK-5 | T | 628 | 60% | 281/245-2832 |
| 7400 Lewis Ln, Manvel 77578 | | | 35 | | Fax 281/245-3777 |
| Dixie Jones | | | | | 🄵🅣 |
| Fairview Junior High Sch | 6-8 | T | 732 | 68% | 281/245-3100 |
| 2600 County Road 190, Alvin 77511 | | | | | Fax 281/245-3213 |
| Gregory Bingham | | | | | 🄵🅣 |
| G W Harby Junior High Sch | 6-8 | T | 769 | 72% | 281/585-6626 |
| 1500 Heights Rd, Alvin 77511 | | | | | Fax 281/388-2247 |
| Elizabeth Lawson | | | | | |
| Glenn York Elem Sch | PK-5 | | 864 | 21% | 281/245-2100 |
| 2720 Kingsley Dr, Pearland 77584 | | | | | Fax 713/340-1797 |
| Lisa Hicks | | | | | |
| Hood-Case Elem Sch | PK-5 | T | 643 | 68% | 281/585-5786 |
| 1450 Heights Rd, Alvin 77511 | | | 40 | | Fax 281/388-0692 |
| Donna Reynolds | | | | | 🄵🅣 |
| Laura Ingalls Wilder Elem Sch | PK-5 | | 830 | 28% | 281/245-3090 |
| 2225 Kingsley Dr, Pearland 77584 | | | 42 | | Fax 713/340-0694 |
| Stacie Vanloenen | | | | | |
| Manvel High Sch | 9-12 | TV | 1,826 | 54% | 281/245-2232 |
| 19601 Highway 6, Manvel 77578 | | | | | Fax 281/245-2268 |
| Aneiqua Flowers | | | | | |
| Manvel Junior High Sch | 6-8 | | 910 | | 281/245-3700 |
| 7302 McCoy Rd, Manvel 77578 | | | | | Fax 281/692-9078 |
| Robert Ford | | | | | |
| Mark Twain Elem Sch | PK-5 | T | 836 | 78% | 281/585-5318 |
| 345 Kendall Crest Dr, Alvin 77511 | | | 43 | | Fax 281/331-2584 |
| Brenda Vincent | | | | | |
| Mary Burks Marek Elem Sch | PK-5 | | 714 | 34% | 281/245-3232 |
| 1947 Kirby Dr, Pearland 77584 | | | | | Fax 281/436-3796 |
| Roman Nieto | | | | | 🄵🅣 |
| Melba Passmore Elem Sch | PK-5 | T | 656 | 69% | 281/585-6696 |
| 600 Kost Rd, Alvin 77511 | | | 55 | | Fax 281/331-6697 |
| Natalie Hoskins | | | | | |
| Meridiana Elem Sch | PK-5 | T | 804 | 47% | 281/245-3636 |
| 9815 Meridiana Pkwy, Iowa Colony 77583 | | | | | Fax 281/245-3665 |
| Julie Weiss | | | | | |
| Nolan Ryan Junior High Sch | 6-8 | | 781 | 30% | 281/245-3210 |
| 11500 Shadow Creek Pkwy, Pearland 77584 | | | | | Fax 281/245-3221 |
| Ashley Marquez | | | | | |
| Pomona Elem Sch | PK-5 | | 554 | 33% | 281/245-3670 |
| 4480 Kirby Dr, Manvel 77578 | | | | | Fax 281/245-2412 |
| Victoria Kwan | | | | | |
| Robert L Stevenson Primary Sch | PK-2 | T | 549 | 75% | 281/585-3349 |
| 4715 Mustang Rd, Alvin 77511 | | | 33 | | Fax 281/245-2904 |
| Kim Graham | | | | | |
| Rodeo Palms Junior High Sch | 6-8 | T | 815 | 54% | 281/245-2078 |
| 101 Palm Desert Dr, Manvel 77578 | | | 30 | | Fax 281/489-8169 |
| **Tonya Patterson** | | | | | 🄵🅣 |

| | | | | | | | | | | |
|---|---|---|---|---|---|---|---|---|---|---|
| 1 | Superintendent | 8 | Curric/Instruct K-12 | 19 | Chief Financial Officer | 29 | Family/Consumer Science | 39 | Social Studies K-12 |
| 2 | Bus/Finance/Purchasing | 9 | Curric/Instruct Elem | 20 | Art K-12 | 30 | Adult Education | 40 | Social Studies Elem |
| 3 | Buildings And Grounds | 10 | Curric/Instruct Sec | 21 | Art Elem | 31 | Career/Sch-to-Work K-12 | 41 | Social Studies Sec |
| 4 | Food Service | 11 | Federal Program | 22 | Art Sec | 32 | Career/Sch-to-Work Elem | 42 | Science K-12 |
| 5 | Transportation | 12 | Title I | 23 | Music K-12 | 33 | Career/Sch-to-Work Sec | 43 | Science Elem |
| 6 | Athletic | 13 | Title V | 24 | Music Elem | 34 | Early Childhood Ed | 44 | Science Sec |
| 7 | Health Services | 15 | Asst Superintendent | 25 | Music Sec | 35 | Health/Phys Education | 45 | Math K-12 |
| | | 16 | Instructional Media Svcs | 26 | Business Education | 36 | Guidance Services K-12 | 46 | Math Elem |
| | | 17 | Chief Operations Officer | 27 | Career & Tech Ed | 37 | Guidance Services Elem | 47 | Math Sec |
| | | 18 | Chief Academic Officer | 28 | Technology Education | 38 | Guidance Services Sec | 48 | English/Lang Arts K-12 |

| | | | | | | |
|---|---|---|---|---|---|---|
| 49 | English/Lang Arts Elem | 59 | Special Education Elem | 69 | Academic Assessment |
| 50 | English/Lang Arts Sec | 60 | Special Education Sec | 70 | Research/Development |
| 51 | Reading K-12 | 61 | Foreign/World Lang K-12 | 71 | Public Information |
| 52 | Reading Elem | 62 | Foreign/World Lang Elem | 72 | Summer School |
| 53 | Reading Sec | 63 | Foreign/World Lang Sec | 73 | Instructional Tech |
| 54 | Remedial Reading K-12 | 64 | Religious Education K-12 | 74 | Inservice Training |
| 55 | Remedial Reading Elem | 65 | Religious Education Elem | 75 | Marketing/Distributive |
| 56 | Remedial Reading Sec | 66 | Religious Education Sec | 76 | Info Systems |
| 57 | Bilingual/ELL | 67 | School Board President | 77 | Psychological Assess |
| 58 | Special Education K-12 | 68 | Teacher Personnel | 78 | Affirmative Action |

| | | | | | |
|---|---|---|---|---|---|
| Savannah Lakes Elem Sch<br>5151 Savannah Pkwy, Rosharon 77583<br>Charles Bagley | PK-5 | T | 770 | 57% | 281/245-3214<br>Fax 281/245-3161 |
| Shadow Creek High Sch<br>11850 Broadway St, Pearland 77584<br>Kelly Hestand | 9-12 | | 2,586 | 38% | 281/245-3800<br>Fax 281/245-3901 |
| Shirley Dill Brothers Elem Sch<br>2910 Half Moon Bay Dr, Pearland 77584<br>Krystal Hawks | PK-5 | | 883 | 17% | 281/245-3660<br>Fax 281/245-2411 |
| Walt Disney Elem Sch<br>5000 Mustang Rd, Alvin 77511<br>Dale Tribble | 3-5 | T | 508<br>30 | 68% | 281/585-6234<br>Fax 281/585-6503 |

● **Angleton Ind School Dist**　PID: 01001473　　　979/864-8000
1900 N Downing Rd, Angleton 77515　　　　　　Fax 979/864-8070

**Schools:** 9 \ **Teachers:** 400 \ **Students:** 6,787 \ **Special Ed Students:** 738 \ **LEP Students:** 821 \ **College-Bound:** 56% \ **Ethnic:** African American 11%, Hispanic 50%, Native American: 1%, Caucasian 38% \ **Exp:** $255 (Med) \ **Poverty:** 15% \ **Title I:** $1,405,739 \ **Special Education:** $1,329,000 \ **Open-Close:** 08/19 - 05/28 \ **DTBP:** $176 (High) \ 

| | | | |
|---|---|---|---|
| Phil Edwards | 1 | Connie Cox | 2 |
| Kirk Crim | 3 | Amy Anderson | 4 |
| Tracy Turner | 4 | Angel Kersten | 5 |
| Jason Brittain | 6* | Mark Comneck | 8,15 |
| Vicki Harmon | 9 | Lisa Davis | 10 |
| Roy Gardner | 16,27,31,88* | Marbella Hooper | 57,81* |
| Michelle Lebleu | 58,77 | Regina Bieri | 67 |
| Cindy Pullen | 68 | Hanna Chalmers | 71 |
| Jeff Stout | 73 | Kalean Bowie | 79 |
| James Gayle | 91* | Brian Heironimus | 295 |
| Allison Hemphill | 298 | | |

| Public Schs..Principal | Grd | Prgm | Enr/#Cls | SN | |
|---|---|---|---|---|---|
| Angleton High Sch<br>1 Campus Dr, Angleton 77515<br>Anthony Smedley | 9-12 | TV | 1,951<br>200 | 49% | 979/864-8001<br>Fax 979/848-9865 |
| Angleton Junior High Sch<br>1201 E Henderson Rd, Angleton 77515<br>Alice Clayton | 6-8 | TV | 966<br>50 | 61% | 979/864-8002<br>Fax 979/864-8675 |
| Ⓐ Cats Academy-Student Alt Ctr<br>300 S Walker St, Angleton 77515<br>Colleen Tribble | 5-12 | V | 6<br>3 | 66% | 979/864-8003<br>Fax 979/864-8736 |
| Central Elem Sch<br>429 E Locust St, Angleton 77515<br>Maria MacEdo | PK-5 | T | 529<br>34 | 81% | 979/864-8004<br>Fax 979/864-8704 |
| Frontier Elem Sch<br>5200 Airline Rd, Angleton 77515<br>Stephanie Ramirez | PK-5 | T | 397<br>18 | 49% | 979/864-8005<br>Fax 979/864-8715 |
| Northside Elem Sch<br>1000 Ridgecrest St, Angleton 77515<br>Laurie Gonzalez | PK-5 | T | 372<br>30 | 63% | 979/864-8006<br>Fax 979/864-8696 |
| Rancho Isabella Elem Sch<br>100 Corral Loop, Angleton 77515<br>Christopher Kocurek | PK-5 | T | 306<br>20 | 61% | 979/864-8007<br>Fax 979/864-8725 |
| Southside Elem Sch<br>1200 Park Ln, Angleton 77515<br>Jerri McNeill | PK-5 | T | 253<br>27 | 80% | 979/864-8008<br>Fax 979/864-8730 |
| Westside Elem Sch<br>1001 W Mulberry St, Angleton 77515<br>Robin Braun | K-5 | T | 1,060<br>30 | 76% | 979/864-8009<br>Fax 979/864-8686 |

● **Brazosport Ind School Dist**　PID: 01001540　　979/730-7000
301 W Brazoswood Dr, Clute 77531　　　　　Fax 979/266-2409

**Schools:** 19 \ **Teachers:** 844 \ **Students:** 12,000 \
**Special Ed Students:** 1,112 \ **LEP Students:** 1,472 \ **College-Bound:** 87% \
**Ethnic:** Asian 2%, African American 7%, Hispanic 58%, Native American: 1%,
Caucasian 33% \ **Exp:** $341 (High) \ **Poverty:** 16% \ **Title I:** $3,259,888 \
**Special Education:** $2,534,000 \ **Open-Close:** 08/17 - 05/27 \ **DTBP:** $188
(High) \ 

| | | | |
|---|---|---|---|
| Danny Massey | 1 | Kaley Crisp | 2 |
| Rebecca Kelley | 2,19 | Ken Schulte | 3 |
| Monty Burger | 3,17,73,98 | John Craig | 5 |
| Alan Weddell | 6,35 | Molly James | 7,85 |
| Clara Sale-Davis | 8,18,288 | John Murtell | 9,15 |
| Brian Cole | 11,16,34,69,73,271,285,286 | Jay Whitehead | 15,68,74,79,273 |
| Richard Yose | 15,45,751 | David Mendoza | 28,73,76,295 |
| Jessie Jennings | 31 | Allison Jasso | 36 |
| Angela McCabe | 39 | Kristen Piper | 48,51,54 |
| Rita Angel-Cundieff | 57,89,93 | Lorin Furlow | 58,77,90,296 |
| Mason Howard | 67 | Kristi Kirschner | 68,71,97 |
| Ron Redden | 69,294 | Robin Pelton | 79,83,270,275 |
| Dedee Wilson | 81,92 | Lindsey Blackstock | 286 |
| Amber Casey | 297 | | |

| Public Schs..Principal | Grd | Prgm | Enr/#Cls | SN | |
|---|---|---|---|---|---|
| A P Beutel Elem Sch<br>300 Ligustrum St, Lake Jackson 77566<br>Laura Morris | PK-4 | T | 659<br>50 | 50% | 979/730-7165<br>Fax 979/730-7235 |
| Bess Brannen Elem Sch<br>802 That Way St, Lake Jackson 77566<br>Julie Evans | PK-4 | T | 588<br>28 | 40% | 979/730-7170<br>Fax 979/292-2834 |
| Ⓐ Brazos Success Academy<br>500 Circle Way St, Lake Jackson 77566<br>Brooke Merritt | 9-12 | | 150 | | 979/730-7090 |
| Brazosport High Sch<br>1800 W 2nd St, Freeport 77541<br>**Ian White** | 9-12 | GTV | 965<br>70 | 73% | 979/730-7260<br>Fax 979/730-7366 |
| Brazoswood High Sch<br>302 W Brazoswood Dr, Clute 77531<br>**Rita Pintavalle** | 9-12 | TV | 2,438<br>70 | 41% | 979/730-7300<br>Fax 979/266-2447 |
| Clute Intermediate Sch<br>421 E Main St, Clute 77531<br>**Tara Fulton** | 5-8 | T | 694<br>120 | 78% | 979/730-7230<br>Fax 979/730-7363 |
| Elisabeth Ney Elem Sch<br>308 Winding Way St, Lake Jackson 77566<br>Vicky Parr | PK-4 | T | 420<br>50 | 61% | 979/730-7190<br>Fax 979/292-2829 |
| Freeport Elem Sch<br>1200 W 11th St, Freeport 77541<br>Maria Espinoza | PK-1 | T | 368<br>20 | 89% | 979/730-7175<br>Fax 979/233-9671 |
| Freeport Intermediate Sch<br>1815 W 4th St, Freeport 77541<br>**Dr Jarrett Johnson** | 7-8 | T | 515<br>40 | 81% | 979/730-7240<br>Fax 979/237-6329 |
| Gladys Polk Elem Sch<br>600 Audubon, Richwood 77531<br>Tara Fulton | PK-4 | T | 480<br>25 | 63% | 979/730-7200<br>Fax 979/730-7350 |
| Grady B Rasco Middle Sch<br>92 Lake Rd, Lake Jackson 77566<br>Jennifer Gonzalez | 5-6 | T | 831<br>40 | 48% | 979/730-7225<br>Fax 979/292-2817 |
| Lake Jackson Intermediate Sch<br>100 Oyster Creek Dr, Lake Jackson 77566<br>Susan Wood | 7-8 | T | 884<br>50 | 43% | 979/730-7250<br>Fax 979/292-2804 |
| Ⓐ Lighthouse Learning Center<br>1035 Dixie Dr, Clute 77531<br>Dr A'Lesia Land | 1-12 | T | 58<br>20 | 82% | 979/730-7340<br>Fax 979/730-7369 |
| Madge Griffith Elem Sch<br>101 Lexington Ave, Clute 77531<br>Karen Matt | PK-4 | T | 538<br>28 | 75% | 979/730-7180<br>Fax 979/266-2469 |

| | | | | | |
|---|---|---|---|---|---|
| O M Roberts Elem Sch<br>110 Cedar St, Lake Jackson 77566<br>Jennifer Nabors | PK-4 | T | 451<br>25 | 64% | 979/730-7205<br>Fax 979/292-2825 |
| R O'Hara Lanier Middle Sch<br>522 N Avenue B, Freeport 77541<br>**Bridgette Percle** | 5-6 | T | 424<br>32 | 81% | 979/730-7220<br>Fax 979/237-6348<br>🛂🅣 |
| Stephen F Austin STEM Academy<br>7351 Stephen F Austin Rd, Freeport 77541<br>**Harland Hoppock** | PK-6 | T | 151<br>19 | 67% | 979/730-7160<br>Fax 979/237-6341<br>🛂🅣 |
| T W Ogg Elem Sch<br>208 N Lazy Ln, Clute 77531<br>Kristine Traylor | PK-4 | T | 516<br>32 | 86% | 979/730-7195<br>Fax 979/730-7198<br>🛂🅣 |
| Velasco Elem Sch<br>401 N Gulf Blvd, Freeport 77541<br>Margaret Meadows | 2-4 | T | 616<br>40 | 86% | 979/730-7210<br>Fax 979/237-6318 |

---

● **Columbia Brazoria ISD** PID: 01001710     979/345-5147
520 S 16th St, West Columbia 77486     Fax 979/345-4890

**Schools:** 5 \ **Teachers:** 200 \ **Students:** 2,681 \ **Special Ed Students:** 296 \ **LEP Students:** 190 \ **College-Bound:** 53% \ **Ethnic:** African American 9%, Hispanic 31%, Caucasian 59% \ **Exp:** $404 (High) \ **Poverty:** 12% \ **Title I:** $556,210 \ **Special Education:** $644,000 \ **Open-Close:** 08/20 - 05/21 \ **DTBP:** $177 (High)

| | | | |
|---|---|---|---|
| Steven Galloway | 1 | Jason Tracy | 2 |
| Henry Schuble | 3 | Justen Williams | 3 |
| Cynthia King | 4 | Debbie Jones | 5 |
| Herman Ornelas | 5 | Brent Mascheck | 6 |
| Patti Heidel | 8,54,275,280 | Lynn Grell-Boethel | 11,36,57,77,79,83,88,296 |
| Chris Miller | 15 | Greg Fields | 16,73,295 |
| Jennifer Kelly | 58,69* | Jonathan Champagne | 67 |
| Brenda Matthews | 68 | Lynne Eubanks | 76 |
| Cyndy Pullen | 273 | Aaron Murphy | 295 |

| Public Schs..Principal | Grd | Prgm | Enr/#Cls | SN | |
|---|---|---|---|---|---|
| Barrow Elem Sch<br>112 Gaines St, Brazoria 77422<br>Tara Belote | PK-6 | T | 505<br>35 | 65% | 979/991-1740<br>Fax 979/798-6784 |
| Columbia High Sch<br>521 S 16th St, West Columbia 77486<br>Scott Moody | 9-12 | ATV | 611<br>55 | 39% | 979/799-1720<br>Fax 979/345-6785 |
| West Brazos Junior High Sch<br>111 Roustabout Dr, Brazoria 77422<br>**Jeffrey Kinney** | 7-8 | AT | 481<br>30 | 51% | 979/991-1730<br>Fax 979/798-8000 |
| West Columbia Elem Sch<br>711 S Gray Ave, West Columbia 77486<br>Roxana Bolton | PK-6 | T | 787<br>30 | 45% | 979/799-1760<br>Fax 979/345-3170 |
| Wild Peach Elem Sch<br>3311 County Road 353, Brazoria 77422<br>Mary McCarthy | PK-6 | T | 297<br>18 | 71% | 979/991-1750<br>Fax 979/798-9198 |

---

● **Damon Ind School Dist** PID: 01001796     979/742-3457
1211 Mulcahy St, Damon 77430     Fax 979/742-3275

**Schools:** 1 \ **Teachers:** 15 \ **Students:** 144 \ **Special Ed Students:** 29 \ **LEP Students:** 27 \ **Ethnic:** African American 1%, Hispanic 59%, Caucasian 40% \ **Exp:** $971 (High) \ **Poverty:** 24% \ **Title I:** $93,960 \ **Open-Close:** 08/26 - 05/28 \ **DTBP:** $340 (High)

| | | | |
|---|---|---|---|
| David Hayward | 1,73 | Bubba Schneider | 67 |
| Shelly Schneider | 83 | Shelly Schneider | 286* |

| Public Schs..Principal | Grd | Prgm | Enr/#Cls | SN | |
|---|---|---|---|---|---|
| Damon Sch<br>1211 Mulcahy Street, Damon 77430<br>David Hayward | PK-8 | T | 144<br>12 | 90% | 979/742-3457 |

---

● **Danbury Ind School Dist** PID: 01001813     979/922-1218
5611 Panther Dr, Danbury 77534     Fax 979/922-8246

**Schools:** 3 \ **Teachers:** 54 \ **Students:** 840 \ **Special Ed Students:** 52 \ **LEP Students:** 29 \ **College-Bound:** 67% \ **Ethnic:** Asian 1%, African American 1%, Hispanic 20%, Caucasian 79% \ **Exp:** $635 (High) \ **Poverty:** 7% \ **Title I:** $66,788 \ **DTBP:** $73 (Low)

| | | | |
|---|---|---|---|
| **Nancy Sandlin** | 1 | Disa Schulze | 3,4,5,91 |
| Crystal Pounds | 8 | Stacey Matheson | 11,73,76,295* |
| Sherry Phillips | 15 | Ace Filipp | 16,82* |
| Debra Murphey | 37 | Diane Thompson | 38 |
| Daryl Peltier | 67 | Sherry Phillips | 273* |

| Public Schs..Principal | Grd | Prgm | Enr/#Cls | SN | |
|---|---|---|---|---|---|
| Danbury Elem Sch<br>2222 Ave F, Danbury 77534<br>Jennifer Williams | PK-5 | AT | 334<br>20 | 42% | 979/922-8787<br>Fax 979/922-1589 |
| Danbury High Sch<br>5611 Panther Dr, Danbury 77534<br>**Kimberly Ziehl** | 9-12 | AV | 194<br>15 | 29% | 979/922-1226<br>Fax 979/922-1051 |
| Danbury Middle Sch<br>5611 Panther Dr, Danbury 77534<br>Crystal Pounds | 6-8 | A | 186<br>11 | 43% | 979/922-1226<br>Fax 979/922-1051 |

---

● **Pearland Ind School Dist** PID: 01001849     281/485-3203
1928 N Main St, Pearland 77581     Fax 281/412-1560

**Schools:** 23 \ **Teachers:** 1,307 \ **Students:** 21,917 \ **Special Ed Students:** 2,137 \ **LEP Students:** 1,782 \ **Ethnic:** Asian 11%, African American 15%, Hispanic 36%, Caucasian 37% \ **Exp:** $206 (Med) \ **Poverty:** 7% \ **Title I:** $2,038,168 \ **Special Education:** $2,646,000 \ **Open-Close:** 08/19 - 05/27 \ **DTBP:** $182 (High) \ 🛂 🅣

| | | | |
|---|---|---|---|
| Dr John Kelly | 1 | Jorgannie Carter | 2,19,76 |
| Don Tellis | 3,91 | Dorothy Simpson | 4 |
| Ben Pardo | 6 | Dr Nyla Watson | 8,15,77,273 |
| Thomas Bell | 8,20 | Dr Brenda Waters | 9,15 |
| Sonia Serrano | 10,15 | David Moody | 15,68,79 |
| Nanette Weimer | 15 | Kim Hocott | 16,71 |
| Dr Toby Nix | 27,31,95 | Greg Bartay | 28,295 |
| Chenda Moore | 36,83,88,275 | Dr Susana Fuenmayor | 57 |
| Lisa Nixon | 58 | Charles Gooden | 67 |
| Ellen Akers | 69 | Victor Bushfield | 297 |
| Donna Tate | 298 | | |

| Public Schs..Principal | Grd | Prgm | Enr/#Cls | SN | |
|---|---|---|---|---|---|
| Alexander Middle Sch<br>3001 Old Alvin Rd, Pearland 77581<br>Brad Hayes | 5-6 | | 829 | 29% | 832/736-6700<br>Fax 281/485-1115<br>🛂🅣 |
| Barbara Cockrell Elem Sch<br>3500 McHard Rd, Pearland 77581<br>**Rusty Mathis** | PK-4 | T | 665 | 33% | 832/736-6600<br>Fax 281/412-7763<br>🛂🅣 |
| Berry Miller Junior High Sch<br>3301 Manvel Rd, Pearland 77584<br>Tony Barcelona | 7-8 | | 897 | 17% | 281/997-3900<br>Fax 281/997-7893 |
| C J Harris Elem Sch<br>2314 Schleider Dr, Pearland 77581<br>Brenda Keimig | PK-4 | T | 660<br>33 | 43% | 281/485-4024<br>Fax 281/412-1559 |

| | | | | | |
|---|---|---|---|---|---|
| **1** Superintendent | **8** Curric/Instruct K-12 | **19** Chief Financial Officer | **29** Family/Consumer Science | **39** Social Studies K-12 | **49** English/Lang Arts Elem |
| **2** Bus/Finance/Purchasing | **9** Curric/Instruct Elem | **20** Art K-12 | **30** Adult Education | **40** Social Studies Elem | **50** English/Lang Arts Sec |
| **3** Buildings And Grounds | **10** Curric/Instruct Sec | **21** Art Elem | **31** Career/Sch-to-Work K-12 | **41** Social Studies Sec | **51** Reading K-12 |
| **4** Food Service | **11** Federal Program | **22** Art Sec | **32** Career/Sch-to-Work Elem | **42** Science K-12 | **52** Reading Elem |
| **5** Transportation | **12** Title I | **23** Music K-12 | **33** Career/Sch-to-Work Sec | **43** Science Elem | **53** Reading Sec |
| **6** Athletic | **13** Title V | **24** Music Elem | **34** Early Childhood Ed | **44** Science Sec | **54** Remedial Reading K-12 |
| **7** Health Services | **15** Asst Superintendent | **25** Music Sec | **35** Health/Phys Education | **45** Math K-12 | **55** Remedial Reading Elem |
| | **16** Instructional Media Svcs | **26** Business Education | **36** Guidance Services K-12 | **46** Math Elem | **56** Remedial Reading Sec |
| | **17** Chief Operations Officer | **27** Career & Tech Ed | **37** Guidance Services Elem | **47** Math Sec | **57** Bilingual/ELL |
| | **18** Chief Academic Officer | **28** Technology Education | **38** Guidance Services Sec | **48** English/Lang Arts K-12 | **58** Special Education K-12 |

| | |
|---|---|
| **59** Special Education Elem | **69** Academic Assessment |
| **60** Special Education Sec | **70** Research/Development |
| **61** Foreign/World Lang K-12 | **71** Public Information |
| **62** Foreign/World Lang Elem | **72** Summer School |
| **63** Foreign/World Lang Sec | **73** Instructional Tech |
| **64** Religious Education K-12 | **74** Inservice Training |
| **65** Religious Education Elem | **75** Marketing/Distributive |
| **66** Religious Education Sec | **76** Info Systems |
| **67** School Board President | **77** Psychological Assess |
| **68** Teacher Personnel | **78** Affirmative Action |

| School | Grd | Prgm | Enr | #Cls | | | |
|---|---|---|---|---|---|---|---|
| Challenger Elem Sch<br>9434 Hughes Ranch Rd, Pearland 77584<br>Becky Morris | PK-4 | | 626<br>35 | 27% | 281/485-7912<br>Fax 281/412-1105 |
| E A Lawhon Elem Sch<br>5810 Brookside Rd, Pearland 77581<br>Jennifer Walker | PK-4 | T | 752<br>40 | 54% | 281/412-1445<br>Fax 281/412-1448 |
| Glenda Dawson High Sch<br>2050 Cullen Pkwy, Pearland 77581<br>Kelly Holt | 9-12 | V | 2,579 | 21% | 281/412-8800<br>Fax 281/727-1660 |
| H C Carleston Elem Sch<br>3010 Harkey Rd, Pearland 77584<br>Amy Beverly | PK-4 | T | 737<br>48 | 56% | 281/412-1412<br>Fax 281/412-1415 |
| Leon Sablatura Middle Sch<br>2201 N Galveston Ave, Pearland 77581<br>Verna Tipton | 5-6 | T | 858<br>65 | 34% | 281/412-1500<br>Fax 281/412-1504 |
| Magnolia Elem Sch<br>5350 Magnolia Pkwy, Pearland 77584<br>Sharon Gifford | PK-4 | T | 881<br>22 | 41% | 281/727-1750<br>Fax 281/692-1437 |
| Massey Ranch Elem Sch<br>3900 Manvel Rd, Pearland 77584<br>Melanie Grote | PK-4 | | 683 | 34% | 281/727-1700<br>Fax 281/692-0300 |
| Ⓐ Pace Center<br>2314 Old Alvin Rd, Pearland 77581<br>Kimberly Darden | 9-12 | T | 82<br>14 | 58% | 281/412-1599<br>Fax 281/412-1580 |
| Pearland High Sch<br>3775 S Main St, Pearland 77581<br>John Palombo | 9-12 | AGV | 3,068<br>189 | 31% | 281/997-7445<br>Fax 281/412-1113 |
| Pearland Jr High School East<br>2315 Old Alvin Rd, Pearland 77581<br>Charles Allen | 7-8 | A | 422<br>60 | 29% | 281/485-2481<br>Fax 281/412-1203 |
| Pearland Jr High School South<br>4719 Bailey Rd, Pearland 77584<br>Jason Frerking | 7-8 | T | 852<br>50 | 44% | 281/727-1500<br>Fax 281/727-1580 |
| Pearland Jr High School West<br>2337 N Galveston Ave, Pearland 77581<br>Dana Miles \ **Kathleen Miller** | 7-8 | AT | 858<br>60 | 37% | 281/412-1222<br>Fax 281/412-1228 |
| Rogers Middle Sch<br>3121 Manvel Rd, Pearland 77584<br>Ajunta Thomas | 5-6 | | 800<br>35 | 19% | 832/736-6400<br>Fax 281/736-6444 |
| Rustic Oak Elem Sch<br>1302 Rustic Ln, Pearland 77581<br>Beth West | PK-4 | | 670<br>38 | 24% | 281/482-5400<br>Fax 281/996-3658 |
| Sam Jamison Middle Sch<br>2506 Woody Rd, Pearland 77581<br>Sharon Bradley | 5-6 | T | 888<br>60 | 47% | 281/412-1440<br>Fax 281/412-1461 |
| Shadycrest Elem Sch<br>2405 Shadybend Dr, Pearland 77581<br>Michelle Kiefer | PK-4 | | 546<br>42 | 18% | 281/412-1404<br>Fax 281/412-1401 |
| Silvercrest Elem Sch<br>3003 Southwyck Pkwy, Pearland 77584<br>Lori Campbell | PK-4 | | 716<br>40 | 9% | 832/736-6000<br>Fax 713/436-2209 |
| Silverlake Elem Sch<br>2550 County Road 90, Pearland 77584<br>Shayla McGrew | PK-4 | | 559<br>45 | 18% | 713/436-8000<br>Fax 713/436-8008 |
| Turner College-Career High Sch<br>4717 Bailey Rd, Pearland 77584<br>Kai Bouchard | 9-12 | V | 1,175 | 32% | 281/727-1600<br>Fax 281/727-1616 |

## • Sweeny Ind School Dist  PID: 01001904

1310 N Elm St, Sweeny 77480

979/491-8000
Fax 979/491-8030

**Schools:** 3 \ **Teachers:** 133 \ **Students:** 1,926 \ **Special Ed Students:** 148 \ **LEP Students:** 56 \ **College-Bound:** 57% \ **Ethnic:** African American 11%, Hispanic 25%, Caucasian 63% \ **Exp:** $406 (High) \ **Poverty:** 20% \ **Title I:** $573,180 \ **Special Education:** $444,000 \ **Open-Close:** 08/17 - 05/26 \ **DTBP:** $553 (High) \ 🇫 🇪

| | | | |
|---|---|---|---|
| Dr Tory Hill ................1 | Amy Carter ................2,19 |
| Jackie Hornback ................2 | Stewart Crouc ................3 |
| Kathy Wolford ................4 | Diane McNeill ................5 |
| Brett Miksch ................6* | Darin Presto ................8,294 |
| Amy Pope ...... 11,15,69,83,88,275,294,296 | Kelly Bertsch ................16,73,295 |
| Mark Manley ................27 | Renee Mitchell ................36* |
| Michael Heinroth ................37* | Laura Genella ................52* |
| Betty Bartness ................58 | Rhonda Alexander ................58 |
| Sandra Vandaveer ................58 | Earl Mathis ................67 |
| Gerald Nixon ................68 | Dedra Phillips ................76 |
| Les Kluttz ................79 | Michael Saul ................79 |
| LaBonne Casey ................81,298 | Jesse Cisneros ................91 |
| John Ideus ................91* | Stacey Branch ................295 |

| Public Schs..Principal | Grd | Prgm | Enr/#Cls | SN | | |
|---|---|---|---|---|---|---|
| Sweeny Elem Sch<br>709 Sycamore St, Sweeny 77480<br>Denise Papillion | PK-5 | T | 862<br>71 | 60% | 979/491-8300<br>Fax 979/491-8373 |
| Sweeny High Sch<br>600 Ashley Wilson Road, Sweeny 77480<br>William Mader | 9-12 | ATV | 600<br>50 | 41% | 979/491-8100<br>Fax 979/491-8171 |
| Sweeny Junior High Sch<br>800 N Elm St, Sweeny 77480<br>David Smothers | 6-8 | T | 464<br>40 | 48% | 979/491-8200<br>Fax 979/491-8274 |

## BRAZORIA CATHOLIC SCHOOLS

## • Archdiocese Galveston-Houston  PID: 01027855

Listing includes only schools located in this county. See District Index for location of Diocesan Offices.

| Catholic Schs..Principal | Grd | Prgm | Enr/#Cls | SN |
|---|---|---|---|---|
| Our Lady Queen of Peace Sch<br>1600 Highway 2004, Richwood 77531<br>Nirmala Thomas | PK-8 | | 285<br>17 | 979/265-3909<br>Fax 979/265-9780 |
| St Helen Sch<br>2213 Old Alvin Rd, Pearland 77581<br>Dr Phyliss Coleman | K-8 | | 237<br>10 | 281/485-2845<br>Fax 281/485-7607 |

## BRAZORIA PRIVATE SCHOOLS

| Private Schs..Principal | Grd | Prgm | Enr/#Cls | SN |
|---|---|---|---|---|
| Angleton Christian Sch<br>976 Anchor Road, Angleton 77515<br>Terri Jones \ Steve Davis | PK-12 | | 330<br>13 | 979/864-3842 |
| Brazosport Christian Sch<br>200B Willow Dr, Lake Jackson 77566<br>Todd Landers | PK-12 | | 220<br>25 | 979/297-0722<br>Fax 979/297-8455 |
| Eagle Heights Christian Acad<br>3005 Pearland Pkwy, Pearland 77581<br>Lana Stahl | PK-12 | | 330 | 281/485-6330<br>Fax 281/485-8682 |

| | | | | |
|---|---|---|---|---|
| First Christian Academy<br>2411 S Grand Blvd, Pearland 77581<br>Diane DuVall | PK-12 | 125 | | 281/760-4201 |
| Heritage Christian Academy<br>12006 Shadow Creek Pkwy, Pearland 77584<br>Kara Marsh | PK-5 | 290 | | 713/436-8422<br>Fax 713/436-5350 |
| Living Stones Christian Sch<br>1407 Victory Ln, Alvin 77511<br>Jessica Sanders | PK-12 | 150<br>16 | | 281/331-0086<br>Fax 281/331-6747 |
| Shiloh Sch<br>3926 Bahler Ave, Manvel 77578<br>Brenda Gardner-Valdes | 1-12 | 75 | | 281/489-1290<br>Fax 281/489-0167 |
| Silverline Montessori Sch<br>2080 Reflection Bay Dr, Pearland 77584<br>Teresa Conn | PK-5 | 300 | | 713/436-5070<br>Fax 713/436-5076 |
| Sweeny Christian Sch<br>904 Texas Ave, Sweeny 77480<br>Lynette McKinney | PK-5 | 56<br>7 | | 979/548-6001<br>Fax 979/548-0210 |

## BRAZOS COUNTY

## BRAZOS PUBLIC SCHOOLS

• **Bryan Ind School Dist**  PID: 01002013
801 S Ennis St, Bryan 77803

979/209-1000
Fax 979/209-1004

**Schools:** 24 \ **Teachers:** 1,142 \ **Students:** 16,134 \
**Special Ed Students:** 1,659 \ **LEP Students:** 3,890 \ **College-Bound:** 52%
\ **Ethnic:** African American 19%, Hispanic 60%, Caucasian 21% \ **Exp:** $532
(High) \ **Poverty:** 23% \ **Title I:** $6,621,943 \ **Special Education:** $3,619,000 \
**Open-Close:** 08/19 - 05/26 \ **DTBP:** $195 (High) \

| | | | |
|---|---|---|---|
| Dr Christie Whitbeck ...................1 | James Brau ..........................2 |
| Kevin Beesaw ..................2,15,275 | Ronnie O'Neal ................2,275 |
| Stefanie Brumfield ......................2 | Norris McDaniel ...................3 |
| Paul Buckner .............................3 | Steve Peterson ....................3 |
| Sundy Fryrear ...........................4 | Claudell Lipscomb ................5 |
| Simeon Gates ............................5 | Warren Lanphier ..................5 |
| Lance Angel ..............................6 | Barbara Ybarra .........8,15,294 |
| Christina Richardson ...............8,81 | Dr Leslie Holtkamp ...............8 |
| Jolyn Bricker .............................9 | Debbie Richards ..............10,42 |
| Ginger Carrabine ..............15,751 | Denise Kersten ...................16 |
| Lamanda Jatzlau ......................16 | Rachel Whitely ....................16 |
| Robin Cox ................................16 | Patrick Corbett ...............20,23 |
| David Reynolds .....................27,31 | Kevin Ross .........................27 |
| Larry White .............................27 | Rachel Curlin .................34,298 |
| Schronda McKnight ...................34 | Janice Williamson ...............35 |
| Donna Willett .......................36,77 | Dr Wanda Baker ............57,271 |
| Dr Catherine George ................58 | Kate Patterson ....................58 |
| Lora Ouren .............................58 | Mark McCall .......................67 |
| Carol Cune ..............................68 | Crystal Goodman .................68 |
| Dr Jill Morris ....................69,70,76 | Hugo Ibarra .......................71 |
| Matthew LeBlanc ......................71 | Jana Wenzel .......................73 |
| Julea Johnson .........................73 | Kelli Norgaard ....................74 |
| Jennifer Lemons ...................76,79 | Robert Hayes .....................76 |
| Dr Shantina Dixon ...................77 | Juana Garcia .....................271 |
| Charlie Zapalac ......................295 | Chris Cannon ....................295 |

| Public Schs..Principal | Grd | Prgm | Enr/#Cls | SN | |
|---|---|---|---|---|---|
| Alton O Bowen Elem Sch<br>3870 Copperfield Dr, Bryan 77802<br>Bridget Cooper | PK-4 | T | 279<br>26 | 57% | 979/209-1300<br>Fax 979/209-1306 |
| Arthur L Davila Middle Sch<br>2751 N Earl Rudder Fwy, Bryan 77803<br>Shannon McGehee | 7-8 | T | 1,075 | 78% | 979/209-7150<br>Fax 979/209-7151 |
| Bonham Elem Sch<br>3100 Wilkes St, Bryan 77803<br>Gloria Rhodes | PK-4 | T | 520<br>41 | 89% | 979/209-1200<br>Fax 979/209-1218 |
| Bryan Adult Learning Center<br>1700 Palasota Dr, Bryan 77803<br>Becky Collet | Adult | | 210<br>6 | | 979/703-7740<br>Fax 979/209-7041 |
| Bryan Collegiate High Sch<br>1901 E Villa Maria Rd, Bryan 77802<br>Tommy Roberts | 9-12 | T | 476 | 71% | 979/209-2790<br>Fax 979/209-2704 |
| Crockett Elem Sch<br>401 Elm Ave, Bryan 77801<br>Debi Ehrhardt | PK-4 | T | 378<br>32 | 93% | 979/209-2960<br>Fax 979/209-2965 |
| ⓐ Disciplinary Alt Ed Program<br>1901 E Villa Maria Rd, Bryan 77802<br>Michael Watts | 6-12 | | 150 | 89% | 979/209-2752<br>Fax 979/209-2754 |
| Fannin Elem Sch<br>1200 Baker Ave, Bryan 77803<br>Dr Desiree Caperton | PK-4 | T | 417<br>27 | 95% | 979/209-3800<br>Fax 979/209-3826 |
| Henderson Elem Sch<br>801 Matous Dr, Bryan 77802<br>Danielle Legg | K-4 | T | 542<br>23 | 90% | 979/209-1560<br>Fax 979/209-1566 |
| James E Rudder High Sch<br>3251 Austins Colony Pkwy, Bryan 77808<br>Mario Bye | 9-12 | TV | 1,611 | 75% | 979/209-7900<br>Fax 979/209-7901 |
| Johnson Elem Sch<br>3800 Oak Hill Dr, Bryan 77802<br>Amy Thomman | PK-4 | T | 366<br>30 | 50% | 979/209-1460<br>Fax 979/209-1462 |
| Jones Elem Sch<br>1400 Pecan St, Bryan 77803<br>Linda Montoya | PK-4 | T | 474<br>21 | 98% | 979/209-3900<br>Fax 979/209-3912 |
| Kemp-Carver Elem Sch<br>750 Bruin Trce, Bryan 77803<br>Alison Boggan | PK-4 | T | 623<br>26 | 97% | 979/209-3700<br>Fax 979/209-3764 |
| Long Intermediate Sch<br>1106 N Harvey Mitchell Pkwy, Bryan 77803<br>Cody Satterfield | 5-6 | TV | 1,292<br>65 | 88% | 979/209-6500<br>Fax 979/209-6566 |
| Mary Branch Elem Sch<br>2040 W Villa Maria Rd, Bryan 77807<br>Amy Bruner | PK-4 | T | 374<br>29 | 83% | 979/209-2900<br>Fax 979/209-2910 |
| ⓐ Mary Catherine Harris Sch<br>1307 Memorial Dr, Bryan 77802<br>Karen Kaspar | 9-12 | T | 228<br>6 | 81% | 979/209-2812<br>Fax 979/209-2813 |
| Mitchell Elem Sch<br>2500 Austins Colony Pkwy, Bryan 77808<br>Shari Hedstrom | PK-4 | T | 301<br>26 | 63% | 979/209-1400<br>Fax 979/209-1420 |
| Navarro Elem Sch<br>4619 Northwood Dr, Bryan 77803<br>Sara Rueda | PK-4 | T | 325<br>40 | 88% | 979/209-1260<br>Fax 979/209-1270 |
| Neal Elem Sch<br>801 W Martin Luther King Jr St, Bryan 77803<br>Juanita Collins | PK-4 | T | 306<br>30 | 96% | 979/209-3860<br>Fax 979/209-3863 |
| Rayburn Intermediate Sch<br>1048 N Earl Rudder Fwy, Bryan 77802<br>Justin Smith | 5-6 | TV | 1,186<br>78 | 70% | 979/209-6600<br>Fax 979/209-6611 |
| Sam Houston Elem Sch<br>4501 Canterbury Dr, Bryan 77802<br>Mandy Wells | PK-4 | | 308<br>21 | 29% | 979/209-1360<br>Fax 979/209-1364 |
| Stephen F Austin Middle Sch<br>8000 S Coulter Dr, Bryan 77803<br>Rachel Layton | 7-8 | TV | 1,195<br>85 | 74% | 979/209-6700<br>Fax 979/209-6741 |
| Sul Ross Elem Sch<br>3300 Parkway Ter, Bryan 77802<br>Amy Bay | PK-4 | T | 418<br>18 | 76% | 979/209-1500<br>Fax 979/209-1513 |

| | | | |
|---|---|---|---|
| **1** Superintendent | **8** Curric/Instruct K-12 | **19** Chief Financial Officer | **29** Family/Consumer Science |
| **2** Bus/Finance/Purchasing | **9** Curric/Instruct Elem | **20** Art K-12 | **30** Adult Education |
| **3** Buildings And Grounds | **10** Curric/Instruct Sec | **21** Art Elem | **31** Career/Sch-to-Work K-12 |
| **4** Food Service | **11** Federal Program | **22** Art Sec | **32** Career/Sch-to-Work Elem |
| **5** Transportation | **12** Title I | **23** Music K-12 | **33** Career/Sch-to-Work Sec |
| **6** Athletic | **13** Title V | **24** Music Elem | **34** Early Childhood Ed |
| **7** Health Services | **14** | **25** Music Sec | **35** Health/Phys Education |
| | **15** Asst Superintendent | **26** Business Education | **36** Guidance Services K-12 |
| | **16** Instructional Media Svcs | **27** Career & Tech Ed | **37** Guidance Services Elem |
| | **17** Chief Operations Officer | **28** Technology Education | **38** Guidance Services Sec |
| | **18** Chief Academic Officer | | |

| | | |
|---|---|---|
| **39** Social Studies K-12 | **49** English/Lang Arts Elem | **59** Special Education Elem |
| **40** Social Studies Elem | **50** English/Lang Arts Sec | **60** Special Education Sec |
| **41** Social Studies Sec | **51** Reading K-12 | **61** Foreign/World Lang K-12 |
| **42** Science K-12 | **52** Reading Elem | **62** Foreign/World Lang Elem |
| **43** Science Elem | **53** Reading Sec | **63** Foreign/World Lang Sec |
| **44** Science Sec | **54** Remedial Reading K-12 | **64** Religious Education K-12 |
| **45** Math K-12 | **55** Remedial Reading Elem | **65** Religious Education Elem |
| **46** Math Elem | **56** Remedial Reading Sec | **66** Religious Education Sec |
| **47** Math Sec | **57** Bilingual/ELL | **67** School Board President |
| **48** English/Lang Arts K-12 | **58** Special Education K-12 | **68** Teacher Personnel |

| |
|---|
| **69** Academic Assessment |
| **70** Research/Development |
| **71** Public Information |
| **72** Summer School |
| **73** Instructional Tech |
| **74** Inservice Training |
| **75** Marketing/Distributive |
| **76** Info Systems |
| **77** Psychological Assess |
| **78** Affirmative Action |

| | Grd | Prgm | Enr/#Cls | SN | |
|---|---|---|---|---|---|
| Travis Bryan High Sch | 9-12 | TV | 2,374 | 65% | 979/209-2400 |
| 3450 Campus Dr, Bryan 77802 | | | 250 | | Fax 979/209-2402 |
| Lane Buban | | | | | 🆕 🇹 |

● **College Station Ind Sch Dist** PID: 01001954     979/764-5400
1812 Welsh Ave, College Sta 77840     Fax 979/764-5492

---

**Schools:** 19 \ **Teachers:** 965 \ **Students:** 14,000 \
**Special Ed Students:** 1,487 \ **LEP Students:** 1,009 \ **College-Bound:** 64%
\ **Ethnic:** Asian 8%, African American 14%, Hispanic 24%, Caucasian
54% \ **Exp:** $433 (High) \ **Poverty:** 11% \ **Title I:** $1,808,159 \
**Special Education:** $1,732,000 \ **Open-Close:** 08/18 - 05/27 \ **DTBP:** $188
(High) \ 🆕 🇹

---

| | | | | |
|---|---|---|---|---|
| Mike Martindale | .....1 | Thad Lasater | .....2 |
| Jon Hall | .....3 | Bridget Goodlett | .....4 |
| Sarah Dluhos | .....4 | Shelby Cryer | .....4 |
| Hector Silva | .....5 | Jeff Mann | .....9,74* |
| Chrissy Hester | .....16,36,79 | Dr Penny Tramel | .....18 |
| Karen Ferguson | .....27,31 | Chad Gardner | .....30,274 |
| Susan Heath | .....34 | Amanda Gibson | .....42 |
| Jennifer Smith | .....45 | Aaron Hogan | .....48 |
| Marla Ramirez | .....57* | Lindsey Fuentes | .....58,77 |
| Kayce Jones | .....59 | Eric Roberts | .....60 |
| Jeff Harris | .....67 | Nkrumah Dixon | .....68 |
| Stormy Hickman | .....68 | Becky Burghardt | .....69 |
| Atakan Berkmen | .....71 | Chuck Glenewinkel | .....71 |
| David Hutchison | .....73* | Shannon Long | .....73 |
| Jackie Janacek | .....76 | Molley Perry | .....77,751 |
| Justin Grimes | .....83,88* | Stephanie Ryon | .....286 |
| Brad Recek | .....295 | Keith Slaughter | .....295 |
| Trey Sparks | .....295 | | |

| Public Schs..Principal | Grd | Prgm | Enr/#Cls | SN | |
|---|---|---|---|---|---|
| A & M Consolidated High Sch | 9-12 | V | 1,763 | 35% | 979/764-5500 |
| 1801 Harvey Mitchell Pkwy S, College Sta 77840 | | | | | Fax 979/693-0212 |
| Gwendolyn Elder | | | | | |
| A & M Consolidated Middle Sch | 7-8 | T | 706 | 39% | 979/764-5575 |
| 105 Holik St, College Sta 77840 | | | 50 | | Fax 979/764-5577 |
| Omar Espitia | | | | | 🆕 |
| College Hills Elem Sch | PK-4 | T | 668 | 60% | 979/764-5565 |
| 1101 Williams St, College Sta 77840 | | | 30 | | Fax 979/764-5497 |
| Josh Hatfield | | | | | |
| College Station High Sch | 9-12 | V | 2,009 | | 979/694-5800 |
| 4002 Victoria Ave, College Sta 77845 | | | | | Fax 979/694-5865 |
| Tiffany Parkerson | | | | | 🆕 🇹 |
| College Station Middle Sch | 7-8 | | 332 | 35% | 979/764-5545 |
| 900 Rock Prairie Rd, College Sta 77845 | | | 48 | | Fax 979/764-5557 |
| Oliver Hadnot | | | | | |
| College View High Sch | 9-12 | ATV | 70 | 36% | 979/764-5540 |
| 1300 George Bush Dr, College Sta 77840 | | | 4 | | Fax 979/764-5564 |
| Justin Grimes | | | | | 🆕 🇹 |
| Creek View Elem Sch | PK-4 | | 549 | 40% | 979/694-5890 |
| 1001 Eagle Ave, College Sta 77845 | | | | | Fax 979/694-5893 |
| Annette Roraback | | | | | 🆕 🇹 |
| Cypress Grove Intermediate Sch | 5-6 | | 666 | 36% | 979/694-5600 |
| 900 Graham Rd, College Sta 77845 | | | 40 | | Fax 979/694-5604 |
| Holly Scott | | | | | 🆕 🇹 |
| Forest Ridge Elem Sch | PK-4 | | 680 | 29% | 979/694-5801 |
| 1950 Greens Prairie Rd W, College Sta 77845 | | | | | Fax 979/694-5805 |
| Teresa Katt | | | | | 🆕 🇹 |
| Greens Prairie Elem Sch | PK-4 | | 743 | 24% | 979/694-5870 |
| 4315 Greens Prairie Trl, College Sta 77845 | | | | | Fax 979/694-3871 |
| Donna Bairrington | | | | | 🆕 🇹 |
| Oakwood Intermediate Sch | 5-6 | T | 704 | 47% | 979/764-5530 |
| 106 Holik St, College Sta 77840 | | | 33 | | Fax 979/764-5533 |
| Josh Symank | | | | | 🆕 🇹 |

| | Grd | Prgm | Enr/#Cls | SN | |
|---|---|---|---|---|---|
| Pebble Creek Elem Sch | PK-4 | | 397 | 17% | 979/764-5595 |
| 200 Parkview Dr, College Sta 77845 | | | 31 | | Fax 979/764-5478 |
| Blaire Grande | | | | | 🆕 🇹 |
| Pecan Trail Interm Sch | 5-6 | | 759 | 25% | 979/694-5874 |
| 4319 Greens Prairie Trl, College Sta 77845 | | | | | Fax 979/694-5869 |
| Kelli Deegear | | | | | |
| River Bend Elem Sch | PK-4 | | 450 | | 979/694-5841 |
| 4070 Holleman Dr S, College Sta 77845 | | | | | Fax 979/694-5842 |
| Robyn Jones | | | | | |
| Rock Prairie Elem Sch | PK-4 | | 592 | 44% | 979/764-5570 |
| 3400 Welsh Ave, College Sta 77845 | | | 36 | | Fax 979/764-5486 |
| Jeff Durand | | | | | 🆕 🇹 |
| South Knoll Elem Sch | PK-4 | T | 656 | 60% | 979/764-5580 |
| 1220 Boswell St, College Sta 77840 | | | 31 | | Fax 979/764-5485 |
| Laura Richter | | | | | |
| Southwood Valley Elem Sch | PK-4 | T | 572 | 53% | 979/764-5590 |
| 2700 Brothers Blvd, College Sta 77845 | | | 35 | | Fax 979/764-5488 |
| Alison DeLuna | | | | | 🆕 🇹 |
| Spring Creek Elem Sch | PK-4 | | 632 | 21% | 979/694-5838 |
| 2450 Brewster Dr, College Sta 77845 | | | | | |
| Laura Casper-Teague | | | | | |
| Wellborn Middle Sch | 7-8 | | 620 | 27% | 979/694-5880 |
| 15510 Royder Rd, College Sta 77845 | | | | | Fax 979/694-5881 |
| Julia Mishler | | | | | |

● **Mumford Ind School Dist** PID: 01048691     979/279-3678
9755 FM 50, Mumford 77807     Fax 979/279-5044

---

**Schools:** 1 \ **Teachers:** 38 \ **Students:** 612 \ **Special Ed Students:** 57 \
**LEP Students:** 72 \ **College-Bound:** 75% \ **Exp:** $356 (High) \ **Poverty:** 20%
\ **Open-Close:** 08/19 - 05/21 \ **DTBP:** $334 (High)

---

| | | | | |
|---|---|---|---|---|
| Allen Reese | .....1 | Luanne Lockhart | .....2 |
| Barbara Brannon | .....3,4,5,69,71,74,271* | Michael Scarborough | .....6* |
| Melissa McDonough | .....8,31,36,58,85* | Blayne Davis | .....11 |
| Ann Swaner | .....16* | Anthony Scamardo | .....67 |
| Flavio Saucedo | .....73* | | |

| Public Schs..Principal | Grd | Prgm | Enr/#Cls | SN | |
|---|---|---|---|---|---|
| Mumford Sch | PK-12 | V | 612 | | 979/279-3678 |
| 9755 FM 50, Mumford 77867 | | | 50 | | |
| Blayne Davis | | | | | |

## BRAZOS CATHOLIC SCHOOLS

● **Diocese of Austin Ed Office** PID: 01420568
Listing includes only schools located in this county. See District Index for
location of Diocesan Offices.

| Catholic Schs..Principal | Grd | Prgm | Enr/#Cls | SN | |
|---|---|---|---|---|---|
| St Joseph Catholic Sch | PK-12 | | 381 | | 979/822-6641 |
| 600 S Coulter Dr, Bryan 77803 | | | 31 | | Fax 979/779-2810 |
| Jim Rike | | | | | |

## BRAZOS PRIVATE SCHOOLS

| Private Schs..Principal | Grd | Prgm | Enr/#Cls | SN | |
|---|---|---|---|---|---|
| Aggieland Country Mont Sch | PK-6 | | 75 | | 979/696-1674 |
| 1500 Quail Run, College Sta 77845 | | | 3 | | |
| Lynn Adams | | | | | |

| | | | | |
|---|---|---|---|---|
| 79 Student Personnel | 91 Safety/Security | 275 Response To Intervention | 298 Grant Writer/Ptnrships | **School Programs** |
| 80 Driver Ed/Safety | 92 Magnet School | 277 Remedial Math K-12 | 750 Chief Innovation Officer | A = Alternative Program |
| 81 Gifted/Talented | 93 Parental Involvement | 280 Literacy Coach | 751 Chief of Staff | G = Adult Classes |
| 82 Video Services | 95 Tech Prep Program | 285 STEM | 752 Social Emotional Learning | M = Magnet Program |
| 83 Substance Abuse Prev | 97 Chief Information Officer | 286 Digital Learning | | T = Title I Schoolwide |
| 84 Erate | 98 Chief Technology Officer | 288 Common Core Standards | **Other School Types** | V = Career & Tech Ed Programs |
| 85 AIDS Education | 270 Character Education | 294 Accountability | Ⓐ = Alternative School | |
| 88 Alternative/At Risk | 271 Migrant Education | 295 Network System | Ⓒ = Charter School | **Social Media** |
| 89 Multi-Cultural Curriculum | 273 Teacher Mentor | 296 Title II Programs | Ⓜ = Magnet School | 🆕 = Facebook |
| 90 Social Work | 274 Before/After Sch | 297 Webmaster | Ⓨ = Year-Round School | 🇹 = Twitter |

New Schools are shaded
New Superintendents and Principals are bold
Personnel with email addresses are underscored

| | | | | |
|---|---|---|---|---|
| Allen Academy | PK-12 | 310 | 979/776-0731 | |
| 3201 Boonville Rd, Bryan 77802 | | 30 | Fax 979/774-7769 | |
| Mike Notaro | | | 🇫🇹 | |
| Brazos Christian Sch | PK-12 | 430 | 979/823-1000 | |
| 3000 W Villa Maria Rd, Bryan 77807 | | 32 | Fax 979/823-1774 | |
| Jeff McMaster | | | | |
| Cornerstone Christian Academy | K-12 | 93 | 979/694-8200 | |
| 3200 Cavitt Ave, Bryan 77801 | | 6 | Fax 979/703-6263 | |
| Rebecca Curry | | | 🇫🇹 | |
| Kor Education Sch | K-12 | 401 | 979/777-1213 | |
| 6110 Elmo Weedon Rd, College Sta 77845 | | | | |
| Gena Richter | | | | |
| St Michaels Episcopal Sch | PK-12 | 65 | 979/822-2715 | |
| 2500 S College Ave, Bryan 77801 | | 23 | Fax 979/823-4971 | |
| Jenny Morris | | | | |

# BREWSTER COUNTY

## BREWSTER PUBLIC SCHOOLS

● **Alpine Ind School Dist** PID: 01002192　　　432/837-7700
704 W Sul Ross Ave, Alpine 79830　　　　　　　Fax 432/837-7740

**Schools:** 3 \ **Teachers:** 87 \ **Students:** 965 \ **Special Ed Students:** 87 \
**LEP Students:** 85 \ **Ethnic:** Asian 2%, African American 1%, Hispanic 64%,
Caucasian 33% \ **Exp:** $685 (High) \ **Poverty:** 20% \ **Title I:** $256,264 \
**Special Education:** $131,000 \ **Open-Close:** 08/19 - 05/20 \ **DTBP:** $351
(High)

| | | |
|---|---|---|
| Rebecca McCutchen ...............................1 | Tucker Durham ...............................2,19 | |
| Chayo Gonzales ...............................3,5 | Courtney Cobb .............................................4 | |
| Jonathan Fellows ...............................6* | Caroline Fox .........8,11,18,286,296,298 | |
| Mesinda Llanez ...................................58 | Eddie Netera ...............................................67 | |
| Nancy Roll ..................................69,294 | Darin Nance ...............................73,98,295 | |
| Stephanie Panya ...............................76 | Lauraley Portillo ................................. 280 | |
| Carla Cheetum ....................................752 | | |

| Public Schs..Principal | Grd | Prgm | Enr/#Cls | SN | |
|---|---|---|---|---|---|
| Alpine Elem Sch | PK-4 | T | 342 | 60% | 432/837-7730 |
| 200 W Avenue A, Alpine 79830 | | | 38 | | Fax 432/837-7744 |
| Verl Obryant | | | | | |
| Alpine High Sch | 9-12 | ATV | 312 | 39% | 432/837-7710 |
| 300 E Hendryx Ave, Alpine 79830 | | | 32 | | Fax 432/837-9813 |
| Justin Gonzales | | | | | |
| Alpine Middle Sch | 5-8 | T | 311 | 45% | 432/837-7720 |
| 801 Middle School Dr, Alpine 79830 | | | 30 | | Fax 432/837-9814 |
| Justin Gonzales | | | | | |

● **Marathon Ind School Dist** PID: 01002233　　　432/386-4431
109 N 5th St, Marathon 79842　　　　　　　　　Fax 432/386-4395

**Schools:** 1 \ **Teachers:** 10 \ **Students:** 55 \ **Special Ed Students:** 3 \
**College-Bound:** 50% \ **Ethnic:** Hispanic 60%, Native American: 2%,
Caucasian 38% \ **Exp:** $1,297 (High) \ **Poverty:** 11% \ **Open-Close:** 08/24 -
05/28 \ **DTBP:** $331 (High)

| | | |
|---|---|---|
| Victoria Sanchez .........................................2 | Monica Pinedo ...........................57,83,271* | |
| Travis Jarrell ...........................................58* | Judy Briones ...........................................67 | |
| Juan Saldana ...........................................69 | | |

| Public Schs..Principal | Grd | Prgm | Enr/#Cls | SN | |
|---|---|---|---|---|---|
| Marathon Sch | PK-12 | TV | 55 | 76% | 432/386-4431 |
| 109 N 5th St, Marathon 79842 | | | 20 | | |
| Juan Saldana | | | | | |

● **San Vicente Ind School Dist** PID: 01002269　　　432/477-2220
195 Escuela Vista Dr, Bg BND NTL Pk 79834　　　Fax 432/477-2221

**Schools:** 1 \ **Teachers:** 4 \ **Students:** 13 \ **Special Ed Students:** 3 \
**Ethnic:** Hispanic 45%, Caucasian 55% \ **Exp:** $2,867 (High) \ **Poverty:** 12% \
**Open-Close:** 09/03 - 06/03 \ **DTBP:** $389 (High)

| | | |
|---|---|---|
| Jessica Milam ...........................................1 | Rocky Northrip ...........................................2 | |
| Eric Stoddard ...........................................11 | Pamela Priddy ...........................................57* | |
| Toni Sammons ...........................................67 | Rocky Noahrip ...........................................73 | |
| Jennifer Pena ...........................83,85,270* | Jeani Stoddard ...........................................285* | |

| Public Schs..Principal | Grd | Prgm | Enr/#Cls | SN | |
|---|---|---|---|---|---|
| San Vicente Elem Sch | K-8 | | 13 | 23% | 432/477-2220 |
| 195 Escuela Vista Dr, Bg BND NTL Pk 79834 | | | 5 | | |
| Eric Stoddard | | | | | |

● **Terlingua Common School Dist** PID: 01002283　　　432/371-2281
550 Roadrunner Cir, Terlingua 79852　　　　　　Fax 432/371-2245

**Schools:** 2 \ **Teachers:** 12 \ **Students:** 105 \ **Special Ed Students:** 11
\ **LEP Students:** 49 \ **College-Bound:** 95% \ **Ethnic:** Hispanic 83%,
Native American: 1%, Caucasian 16% \ **Exp:** $541 (High) \ **Poverty:** 25% \
**Title I:** $92,633 \ **Open-Close:** 08/20 - 06/01 \ **DTBP:** $396 (High)

| | | |
|---|---|---|
| Reagan Reed ...........................................1 | Jeanette Hall ...........................................2,12 | |
| Reagan Reed ...........................................6* | Bobbie Jones ...........................................11,83 | |
| Jennifer Pena ...........................................36* | Christin Orren ...........................................57* | |
| Scott Watkins ...........................................67 | Ted Arbogast ...........................73,285,295 | |

| Public Schs..Principal | Grd | Prgm | Enr/#Cls | SN | |
|---|---|---|---|---|---|
| Big Bend High Sch | 9-12 | T | 44 | 73% | 432/371-2281 |
| 550 Roadrunner Cir, Terlingua 79852 | | | 7 | | |
| Reagan Reed | | | | | |
| Terlingua Elem Sch | K-8 | | 79 | | 432/371-2281 |
| 550 Roadrunner Cir, Terlingua 79852 | | | 15 | | |
| Reagan Reed | | | | | |

## BREWSTER PRIVATE SCHOOLS

| Private Schs..Principal | Grd | Prgm | Enr/#Cls | SN | |
|---|---|---|---|---|---|
| Alpine Christian Sch | PK-12 | | 45 | | 432/837-5757 |
| 203 N 4th St, Alpine 79830 | | | | | Fax 432/837-9057 |
| Caroline Luna | | | | | |

| | | | | | | | | | |
|---|---|---|---|---|---|---|---|---|---|
| 1 Superintendent | 8 Curric/Instruct K-12 | 19 Chief Financial Officer | 29 Family/Consumer Science | 39 Social Studies K-12 | 49 English/Lang Arts Elem | 59 Special Education Elem | 69 Academic Assessment |
| 2 Bus/Finance/Purchasing | 9 Curric/Instruct Elem | 20 Art K-12 | 30 Adult Education | 40 Social Studies Elem | 50 English/Lang Arts Sec | 60 Special Education Sec | 70 Research/Development |
| 3 Buildings And Grounds | 10 Curric/Instruct Sec | 21 Art Elem | 31 Career/Sch-to-Work K-12 | 41 Social Studies Sec | 51 Reading K-12 | 61 Foreign/World Lang K-12 | 71 Public Information |
| 4 Food Service | 11 Federal Program | 22 Art Sec | 32 Career/Sch-to-Work Elem | 42 Science K-12 | 52 Reading Elem | 62 Foreign/World Lang Elem | 72 Summer School |
| 5 Transportation | 12 Title I | 23 Music K-12 | 33 Career/Sch-to-Work Sec | 43 Science Elem | 53 Reading Sec | 63 Foreign/World Lang Sec | 73 Instructional Tech |
| 6 Athletic | 13 Title V | 24 Music Elem | 34 Early Childhood Ed | 44 Science Sec | 54 Remedial Reading K-12 | 64 Religious Education K-12 | 74 Inservice Training |
| 7 Health Services | 14 Asst Superintendent | 25 Music Sec | 35 Health/Phys Education | 45 Math K-12 | 55 Remedial Reading Elem | 65 Religious Education Elem | 75 Marketing/Distributive |
| | 16 Instructional Media Svcs | 26 Business Education | 36 Guidance Services K-12 | 46 Math Elem | 56 Remedial Reading Sec | 66 Religious Education Sec | 76 Info Systems |
| | 17 Chief Operations Officer | 27 Career & Tech Ed | 37 Guidance Services Elem | 47 Math Sec | 57 Bilingual/ELL | 67 School Board President | 77 Psychological Assess |
| | 18 Chief Academic Officer | 28 Technology Education | 38 Guidance Services Sec | 48 English/Lang Arts K-12 | 58 Special Education K-12 | 68 Teacher Personnel | 78 Affirmative Action |

## BRISCOE COUNTY

### BRISCOE PUBLIC SCHOOLS

● **Silverton Ind School Dist** PID: 01002300  806/823-2476
700 S Loretta St, Silverton 79257  Fax 806/823-2276

**Schools:** 1 \ **Teachers:** 19 \ **Students:** 174 \ **Special Ed Students:** 15
\ **LEP Students:** 5 \ **College-Bound:** 100% \ **Ethnic:** African American
2%, Hispanic 46%, Caucasian 52% \ **Exp:** $723 (High) \ **Poverty:** 22% \
**Title I:** $38,941 \ **Open-Close:** 08/14 - 05/21 \ **DTBP:** $350 (High)

| | | | |
|---|---|---|---|
| Michelle Francis | 1,11 | Michael Hayes | 2 |
| Mike Juarez | 3,5* | Delysa Maciel | 4 |
| Clyde Parham | 6* | Michelle Francis | 8,11,31,68,69,74,88* |
| Colleen Reed | 27,73,286,295* | Molly Forman | 67 |
| Vicki Perry | 271 | | |

| Public Schs..Principal | Grd | Prgm | Enr/#Cls | SN | |
|---|---|---|---|---|---|
| Silverton Sch | PK-12 | TV | 174 | 59% | 806/823-2476 |
| 700 S Loretta St, Silverton 79257 | | | 35 | | Fax 806/832-2276 |
| Michael Hayes | | | | | |

## BROOKS COUNTY

### BROOKS PUBLIC SCHOOLS

● **Brooks Co Ind School Dist** PID: 01002336  361/325-5681
200 E Allen St, Falfurrias 78355  Fax 361/325-1913

**Schools:** 4 \ **Teachers:** 103 \ **Students:** 1,470 \ **Special Ed Students:** 178
\ **LEP Students:** 43 \ **College-Bound:** 45% \ **Ethnic:** Hispanic 98%,
Caucasian 1% \ **Exp:** $630 (High) \ **Poverty:** 49% \ **Title I:** $1,264,941 \
**Open-Close:** 08/03 - 05/26 \ **DTBP:** $356 (High)

| | | | |
|---|---|---|---|
| Dr Maria Casas | 1 | Alissa Sanchez | 2 |
| Romeo Ozuna | 3,5 | Guadalupe De Luna | 7* |
| Enrique Ruiz | 8 | Diana Sheeran | 11,88 |
| Jose Salinas | 27,73,295 | Patricia Mendez | 34,58 |
| Servando Guerra | 67 | Maria Anzualda | 271 |

| Public Schs..Principal | Grd | Prgm | Enr/#Cls | SN | |
|---|---|---|---|---|---|
| Falfurrias Elem Sch | 2-5 | T | 445 | 89% | 361/325-8040 |
| 100 E Allen St, Falfurrias 78355 | | | 25 | | Fax 361/325-1010 |
| Enrique Ruiz \ **Sandra Castillo** | | | | | |
| Falfurrias High Sch | 9-12 | ATV | 397 | 69% | 361/325-8091 |
| 100 Jersey Blvd, Falfurrias 78355 | | | 28 | | Fax 361/325-9284 |
| Richard Wright | | | | | |
| Falfurrias Junior High Sch | 6-8 | ATV | 349 | 76% | 361/325-8071 |
| 600 S Center St, Falfurrias 78355 | | | 33 | | Fax 361/325-8156 |
| Dr Cynthia Perez | | | | | |
| Lasater Elem Sch | PK-1 | T | 279 | 89% | 361/325-8060 |
| 200 W Bennett, Falfurrias 78355 | | | 17 | | Fax 361/325-2673 |
| Louella Garcia | | | | | |

## BROWN COUNTY

### BROWN PUBLIC SCHOOLS

● **Bangs Ind School Dist** PID: 01002398  325/752-6612
200 E Hall St, Bangs 76823  Fax 325/752-6253

**Schools:** 3 \ **Teachers:** 76 \ **Students:** 868 \ **Special Ed Students:** 90
\ **LEP Students:** 17 \ **College-Bound:** 60% \ **Ethnic:** African American
2%, Hispanic 27%, Caucasian 71% \ **Exp:** $403 (High) \ **Poverty:** 14% \
**Title I:** $190,671 \ **Open-Close:** 08/19 - 05/28 \ **DTBP:** $367 (High) \ 

| | | | |
|---|---|---|---|
| **Dr Josh Martin** | 1 | Teresa Roberts | 2 |
| Randy Sharp | 3 | Milla McCown | 4 |
| Mandy Johnson | 5 | Kyle Maxfield | 6 |
| Trumon Westfall | 11,84 | Linda Ratliff | 12,57* |
| Shalee Moore | 58 | Eric Lykins | 67 |
| Bridgette Bowen | 73,76 | Kristi Davis | 83* |
| Bridgette Bowen | 295* | | |

| Public Schs..Principal | Grd | Prgm | Enr/#Cls | SN | |
|---|---|---|---|---|---|
| Bangs High Sch | 9-12 | ATV | 311 | 46% | 325/752-6822 |
| 305 N Third St, Bangs 76823 | | | 27 | | Fax 325/752-7028 |
| Scott Patrick | | | | | |
| Bangs Middle Sch | 5-8 | T | 269 | 55% | 325/752-6088 |
| 400 N 3rd St, Bangs 76823 | | | 11 | | Fax 325/752-6367 |
| Damon Wilson | | | | | |
| J B Stephens Elem Sch | PK-4 | T | 288 | 72% | 325/752-7236 |
| 2001 N 6th St, Bangs 76823 | | | 30 | | Fax 325/752-6974 |
| Candace Wilson | | | | | |

● **Blanket Ind School Dist** PID: 01002427  325/748-5311
901 Avenue H, Blanket 76432  Fax 325/748-3391

**Schools:** 1 \ **Teachers:** 21 \ **Students:** 145 \ **Special Ed Students:** 21
\ **LEP Students:** 4 \ **College-Bound:** 58% \ **Ethnic:** African American
1%, Hispanic 32%, Caucasian 67% \ **Exp:** $480 (High) \ **Poverty:** 14% \
**Title I:** $44,557 \ **Open-Close:** 08/17 - 06/01 \ **DTBP:** $358 (High)

| | | | |
|---|---|---|---|
| David Whisenhunt | 1,11 | Trisha Amos | 2 |
| Tyler Tabor | 6 | Larry Smith | 16,73 |
| Belinda Bailey | 58 | Beth Bowyer | 67 |
| Deb Jones | 69,83,85,88 | | |

| Public Schs..Principal | Grd | Prgm | Enr/#Cls | SN | |
|---|---|---|---|---|---|
| Blanket Sch | PK-12 | T | 145 | 57% | 325/748-3341 |
| 901 Avenue H, Blanket 76432 | | | 26 | | Fax 325/748-2110 |
| Chris Morrow | | | | | |

● **Brookesmith Ind School Dist** PID: 01002453  325/643-3023
13400 FM 586 S, Brookesmith 76827  Fax 325/643-8137

**Schools:** 3 \ **Teachers:** 16 \ **Students:** 200 \ **Special Ed Students:** 17
\ **College-Bound:** 50% \ **Ethnic:** African American 3%, Hispanic 21%,
Caucasian 76% \ **Exp:** $419 (High) \ **Poverty:** 9% \ **Title I:** $17,343 \
**Open-Close:** 09/01 - 05/28 \ **DTBP:** $64 (Low)

| | | | |
|---|---|---|---|
| Steve Mickelson | 1 | Rena Allgood | 2,11* |
| Scott Edmonson | 6,35 | Jennifer Barrow | 16,286 |
| Terry Been | 67 | | |

| Public Schs..Principal | Grd | Prgm | Enr/#Cls | SN |
|---|---|---|---|---|
| Brookesmith Elem Sch<br>13400 FM 586 S, Brookesmith 76827<br>Sandra Lehman | PK-5 | | 70<br>21 | 325/643-3023 |
| Brookesmith High Sch<br>13400 FM 586 S, Brookesmith 76827<br>Danny Copeland | 9-12 | T | 43<br>25 | 57% 325/643-3023<br>Fax 325/645-3378 |
| Genesis Academy<br>13400 FM 568 S, Brookesmith 76827<br>Mercathia Hughes | 6-8 | | 35 | 83% 713/955-4414 |

● **Brownwood Ind School Dist** PID: 01002489    325/643-5644
2707 4th St, Brownwood 76801    Fax 325/643-5640

**Schools:** 7 \ **Teachers:** 262 \ **Students:** 3,500 \ **Special Ed Students:** 377 \ **LEP Students:** 89 \ **College-Bound:** 47% \ **Ethnic:** Asian 1%, African American 5%, Hispanic 42%, Caucasian 52% \ **Exp:** $569 (High) \ **Poverty:** 21% \ **Title I:** $1,061,762 \ **Special Education:** $751,000 \ **Open-Close:** 08/19 - 05/27 \ **DTBP:** $157 (High) \ 🅣

| | | | |
|---|---|---|---|
| Joe Young ..........1 | Mitch Moore ..........2,15 | | |
| Bobby August ..........3 | Samuel Burnett ..........6 | | |
| Helen Lacy ..........7* | Liesa Land ..........8,83,275,298 | | |
| Heidi Gardner ..........11,31,57,88,285,296 | Emily Wilson ..........16* | | |
| Darla Peters ..........58 | Michael Cloy ..........67 | | |
| Mark Stanley ..........73,286,295 | Jimmy Fisher ..........295 | | |

| Public Schs..Principal | Grd | Prgm | Enr/#Cls | SN |
|---|---|---|---|---|
| Ⓐ Brownwood Accelerated High Sch<br>2707 4th St, Brownwood 76801<br>David McUllough | 9-12 | T | 10<br>6 | 67% 325/646-1652<br>Fax 325/646-2477 |
| Brownwood High Sch<br>2100 Slayden St, Brownwood 76801<br>Mitchell Moore | 9-12 | T | 945<br>100 | 52% 325/646-9549<br>Fax 325/643-1965 |
| Brownwood Middle Sch<br>1600 Calvert Rd, Brownwood 76801<br>Richard Sweaney | 7-8 | TV | 522<br>35 | 60% 325/646-9545<br>Fax 325/646-3785 |
| Coggin Intermediate Sch<br>800 Rogan St, Brownwood 76801<br>Stacy Loftin | 4-6 | T | 818<br>35 | 66% 325/646-0462<br>Fax 325/646-9317 |
| East Elem Sch<br>2700 Vincent St, Brownwood 76801<br>Dee Wright | PK-3 | T | 336<br>14 | 70% 325/646-2937<br>Fax 325/646-5900 |
| Northwest Elem Sch<br>311 Bluffview Dr, Brownwood 76801<br>**Allison Northcutt** | PK-3 | T | 650<br>39 | 87% 325/646-0707<br>Fax 325/646-2449 |
| Woodland Heights Elem Sch<br>3900 4th St, Brownwood 76801<br>Jeanette Lancaster | PK-3 | T | 402<br>25 | 54% 325/646-8633<br>Fax 325/641-0109 |

● **Early Ind School Dist** PID: 01002556    325/646-7934
101 Turtle Creek, Early 76802    Fax 325/646-9238

**Schools:** 4 \ **Teachers:** 102 \ **Students:** 1,200 \ **Special Ed Students:** 106 \ **LEP Students:** 9 \ **College-Bound:** 99% \ **Ethnic:** Asian 1%, African American 2%, Hispanic 24%, Caucasian 73% \ **Exp:** $441 (High) \ **Poverty:** 18% \ **Title I:** $243,814 \ **Open-Close:** 08/24 - 05/27 \ **DTBP:** $424 (High)

| | |
|---|---|
| **Dr DeWayne Wilkins** ..........1,11,57,83 | Becky Seale ..........2,19 |
| Stewart Dickerson ..........3,5 | Carol Wakefield ..........4 |
| Kimberly Leigh ..........4 | Blake Sandford ..........6* |
| Chalet Moore ..........58 | Shawn Russell ..........67 |
| Rick Lancaster ..........73 | Terri Brinson ..........79 |

| Public Schs..Principal | Grd | Prgm | Enr/#Cls | SN |
|---|---|---|---|---|
| Early Elem Sch<br>201 Sudderth Dr, Early 76802<br>**Julie Schafer** | 3-5 | T | 289<br>15 | 63% 325/646-5511<br>Fax 325/646-5469 🅕 |
| Early High Sch<br>115 Sudderth Dr, Early 76802<br>**Judy Ozuna** | 9-12 | TV | 359<br>35 | 50% 325/643-4593<br>Fax 325/646-4061 |
| Early Middle Sch<br>700 Sunrise St, Early 76802<br>Robert Weyman | 6-8 | T | 268<br>30 | 56% 325/643-5665<br>Fax 325/646-9972 |
| Early Primary Sch<br>965 Early Blvd, Early 76802<br>Teresa Cooley | PK-2 | AT | 258<br>18 | 58% 325/643-9622<br>Fax 325/646-5336 🅕 |

● **May Ind School Dist** PID: 01002582    254/259-2091
3400 E County Road 411, May 76857    Fax 254/259-3514

**Schools:** 2 \ **Teachers:** 25 \ **Students:** 230 \ **Special Ed Students:** 25 \ **LEP Students:** 6 \ **Ethnic:** African American 2%, Hispanic 21%, Caucasian 77% \ **Exp:** $570 (High) \ **Poverty:** 22% \ **Title I:** $90,602 \ **Open-Close:** 08/17 - 05/27 \ **DTBP:** $350 (High)

| | |
|---|---|
| Steve Howard ..........1 | Michele Owings ..........2 |
| Tony Norvil ..........3,5 | Jenny Martin ..........4 |
| Craig Steele ..........6 | Natalie Steele ..........11,58,296,298,752 |
| Cynthia Wade ..........16 | Christy Smith ..........58 |
| Jeff Phillips ..........67 | Larry Owings ..........73,76,286 |
| Mike Martin ..........286 | |

| Public Schs..Principal | Grd | Prgm | Enr/#Cls | SN |
|---|---|---|---|---|
| May Elem Sch<br>3400 E County Road 411, May 76857<br>Nick Heupel | PK-6 | T | 133<br>16 | 75% 254/259-3711<br>Fax 254/259-2135 |
| May High Sch<br>3400 E County Road 411, May 76857<br>Nicholas Heupel | 7-12 | TV | 133<br>15 | 64% 254/259-2131<br>Fax 254/259-2706 |

● **Zephyr Ind School Dist** PID: 01002611    325/739-5331
11625 County Road 281, Zephyr 76890    Fax 325/739-2126

**Schools:** 1 \ **Teachers:** 19 \ **Students:** 208 \ **Special Ed Students:** 20 \ **Ethnic:** Hispanic 14%, Caucasian 85% \ **Exp:** $767 (High) \ **Poverty:** 11% \ **Title I:** $40,903 \ **Open-Close:** 08/17 - 05/27 \ **DTBP:** $386 (High)

| | |
|---|---|
| Stanton Marwitz ..........1,83,84 | Shana King ..........2 |
| Ronda King ..........4 | Kelsa Blair ..........11* |
| Sutton Spieckerman ..........58* | John Rockefeller ..........67 |
| Wade Lowry ..........73 | |

| Public Schs..Principal | Grd | Prgm | Enr/#Cls | SN |
|---|---|---|---|---|
| Zephyr Sch<br>11625 County Road 281, Zephyr 76890<br>Kelsa Blair | PK-12 | T | 208<br>7 | 61% 325/739-5331 |

## BROWN PRIVATE SCHOOLS

| Private Schs..Principal | Grd | Prgm | Enr/#Cls | SN |
|---|---|---|---|---|
| Victory Life Academy<br>901 C C Woodson Rd, Brownwood 76802<br>Yesy Sandoval | PK-12 | | 115<br>14 | 325/641-2223 🅕 |

| | | | | | | |
|---|---|---|---|---|---|---|
| 1 Superintendent | 8 Curric/Instruct K-12 | 19 Chief Financial Officer | 29 Family/Consumer Science | 39 Social Studies K-12 | 49 English/Lang Arts Elem | 59 Special Education Elem | 69 Academic Assessment |
| 2 Bus/Finance/Purchasing | 9 Curric/Instruct Elem | 20 Art K-12 | 30 Adult Education | 40 Social Studies Elem | 50 English/Lang Arts Sec | 60 Special Education Sec | 70 Research/Development |
| 3 Buildings And Grounds | 10 Curric/Instruct Sec | 21 Art Elem | 31 Career/Sch-to-Work K-12 | 41 Social Studies Sec | 51 Reading K-12 | 61 Foreign/World Lang K-12 | 71 Public Information |
| 4 Food Service | 11 Federal Program | 22 Art Sec | 32 Career/Sch-to-Work Elem | 42 Science K-12 | 52 Reading Elem | 62 Foreign/World Lang Elem | 72 Summer School |
| 5 Transportation | 12 Title I | 23 Music K-12 | 33 Career/Sch-to-Work Sec | 43 Science Elem | 53 Reading Sec | 63 Foreign/World Lang Sec | 73 Instructional Tech |
| 6 Athletic | 13 Title V | 24 Music Elem | 34 Early Childhood Ed | 44 Science Sec | 54 Remedial Reading K-12 | 64 Religious Education K-12 | 74 Inservice Training |
| 7 Health Services | 15 Asst Superintendent | 25 Music Sec | 35 Health/Phys Education | 45 Math K-12 | 55 Remedial Reading Elem | 65 Religious Education Elem | 75 Marketing/Distributive |
| | 16 Instructional Media Svcs | 26 Business Education | 36 Guidance Services K-12 | 46 Math Elem | 56 Remedial Reading Sec | 66 Religious Education Sec | 76 Info Systems |
| | 17 Chief Operations Officer | 27 Career & Tech Ed | 37 Guidance Services Elem | 47 Math Sec | 57 Bilingual/ELL | 67 School Board President | 77 Psychological Assess |
| | 18 Chief Academic Officer | 28 Technology Education | 38 Guidance Services Sec | 48 English/Lang Arts K-12 | 58 Special Education K-12 | 68 Teacher Personnel | 78 Affirmative Action |

---

## BURLESON COUNTY

### BURLESON PUBLIC SCHOOLS

• **Caldwell Ind School Dist** PID: 01002647
203 N Gray St, Caldwell 77836
979/567-2400
Fax 979/567-9876

**Schools:** 5 \ **Teachers:** 128 \ **Students:** 1,750 \ **Special Ed Students:** 159 \ **LEP Students:** 172 \ **College-Bound:** 55% \ **Ethnic:** Asian 1%, African American 10%, Hispanic 39%, Native American: 1%, Caucasian 50% \ **Exp:** $527 (High) \ **Poverty:** 21% \ **Title I:** $497,746 \ **Open-Close:** 08/13 - 05/27 \ **DTBP:** $541 (High)

Andrew Peters ...................1,11
Brady Beavers ...................3
Tony Stone ...................5
Susan Groce ...................8
Trip Warren ...................67
Keith Johnson ...................73,76
Heather Escalante ...................2,19
Ashley Charanza ...................4
Matt Langley ...................6*
Dr Alex Salazar ...................15,18,57,88
Kim McManus ...................69
Deanie Gold ...................83,85*

| Public Schs..Principal | Grd | Prgm | Enr/#Cls | SN | |
|---|---|---|---|---|---|
| Ⓐ Burleson Co Alt Sch 203 N Gray St, Caldwell 77836 John Meckel | 6-12 | | 27 1 | | 979/567-2670 Fax 979/567-7476 |
| Caldwell Elem Sch 675 Country Rd 300, Caldwell 77836 Erin Supak | PK-2 | T | 448 27 | 66% | 979/567-2404 Fax 979/567-9422 |
| Caldwell High Sch 550 County Road 307, Caldwell 77836 Vicki Ochs | 9-12 | T | 530 60 | 47% | 979/567-2401 Fax 979/567-6735 |
| Caldwell Intermediate Sch 765 County Road 300, Caldwell 77836 Kimberly Pagach | 3-5 | T | 417 24 | 55% | 979/567-2403 Fax 979/567-7131 |
| Caldwell Middle Sch 200 N Gray St, Caldwell 77836 Shaunna Savage | 6-8 | T | 413 37 | 58% | 979/567-2402 Fax 979/567-7433 |

• **Snook Ind School Dist** PID: 01002685
10110 FM2155, Snook 77878
979/272-8307
Fax 979/272-5041

**Schools:** 1 \ **Teachers:** 48 \ **Students:** 500 \ **Special Ed Students:** 68 \ **LEP Students:** 33 \ **College-Bound:** 50% \ **Ethnic:** African American 29%, Hispanic 28%, Caucasian 44% \ **Exp:** $717 (High) \ **Poverty:** 16% \ **Title I:** $103,732 \ **Open-Close:** 08/12 - 05/21 \ **DTBP:** $330 (High)

Brenda Krchnak ...................1
John Cooper ...................3
Emily Vacha ...................7,35
Christie Everette ...................9,11,88
Kristine Brisco ...................67
Brandon McCord ...................73,76,286
Darrell Saint Clair ...................2,13,296,298
Laura Sebesta ...................5,288*
Jeff Meff ...................8
Megan Brock ...................36
Theresa Schoppe ...................68
Teresa Allen ...................83,90*

| Public Schs..Principal | Grd | Prgm | Enr/#Cls | SN | |
|---|---|---|---|---|---|
| Snook Sch 10110 FM 2155, Snook 77878 Christi Everett \ **Lee Hafley** | PK-12 | T | 500 38 | 66% | 979/272-8307 |

• **Somerville Ind School Dist** PID: 01002714
625 8th St, Somerville 77879
979/596-2153
Fax 979/596-1778

**Schools:** 3 \ **Teachers:** 47 \ **Students:** 550 \ **Special Ed Students:** 56 \ **LEP Students:** 37 \ **College-Bound:** 20% \ **Ethnic:** Asian 1%, African American 24%, Hispanic 35%, Caucasian 41% \ **Exp:** $255 (Med) \ **Poverty:** 28% \ **Title I:** $221,957 \ **Open-Close:** 08/13 - 06/01 \ **DTBP:** $343 (High)

Karla Sparks ...................1,11,83
Bryan Crook ...................67
Amanda Flencher ...................2

| Public Schs..Principal | Grd | Prgm | Enr/#Cls | SN | |
|---|---|---|---|---|---|
| Somerville Elem Sch 700 8th St, Somerville 77879 **James Little** | PK-4 | T | 182 14 | 78% | 979/596-1502 |
| Somerville High Sch 570 8th St, Somerville 77879 Jennifer Wood | 8-12 | ATV | 146 30 | 68% | 979/596-1534 Fax 979/596-3649 |
| Somerville Intermediate Sch 700 8th St, Somerville 77879 Joshua Pinkerton | 5-7 | | 192 | | 979/596-1502 |

---

## BURNET COUNTY

### BURNET PUBLIC SCHOOLS

• **Burnet Cons Ind Sch Dist** PID: 01002752
208 E Brier Ln, Burnet 78611
512/756-2124
Fax 512/756-7498

**Schools:** 6 \ **Teachers:** 214 \ **Students:** 3,000 \ **Special Ed Students:** 459 \ **LEP Students:** 232 \ **College-Bound:** 50% \ **Ethnic:** Asian 1%, African American 1%, Hispanic 32%, Caucasian 66% \ **Exp:** $368 (High) \ **Poverty:** 17% \ **Title I:** $769,146 \ **Special Education:** $570,000 \ **Open-Close:** 08/17 - 05/28 \ **DTBP:** $155 (High)

Keith McBurnett ...................1
Charlie Goble ...................3
Josh Albro ...................5
Amy Murray ...................7*
Dr Kelly McCord ...................10
Jennifer Simpson ...................58
Michele Gilmore ...................68
Rchard Torrez ...................295
Clay Goehring ...................2
Pamela Holcomb ...................4*
Kurt Jones ...................6*
B J Gates ...................9
Racheal Jones ...................11,16,27,57,83,296,298
Andy Field ...................67
Adam Hermes ...................73*

| Public Schs..Principal | Grd | Prgm | Enr/#Cls | SN | |
|---|---|---|---|---|---|
| Bertram Elem Sch 315 Main St, Bertram 78605 Alicia Harris | PK-5 | T | 341 21 | 63% | 512/355-2111 Fax 512/355-2261 |
| Burnet High Sch 1000 the Green Mile Rd, Burnet 78611 Casey Burkhart | 9-12 | TV | 201 | 55% | 512/756-6193 Fax 512/756-4553 |
| Burnet Middle Sch 1401 N Main St, Burnet 78611 Jeremy LeJeune | 6-8 | T | 787 25 | 56% | 512/756-6182 Fax 512/756-7955 |
| Ⓐ Quest High Sch 702 N Wood St, Burnet 78611 Douglas Marvin | 9-12 | T | 11 9 | 83% | 512/756-6747 Fax 512/756-6289 |
| R J Richey Elem Sch 500 E Graves St, Burnet 78611 Bobbie Steiner | 3-5 | T | 522 18 | 61% | 512/756-2609 Fax 512/756-2624 |

---

| | | | |
|---|---|---|---|
| 79 Student Personnel | 91 Safety/Security | 275 Response To Intervention | 298 Grant Writer/Ptnrships |
| 80 Driver Ed/Safety | 92 Magnet School | 277 Remedial Math K-12 | 750 Chief Innovation Officer |
| 81 Gifted/Talented | 93 Parental Involvement | 280 Literacy Coach | 751 Chief of Staff |
| 82 Video Services | 95 Tech Prep Program | 285 STEM | 752 Social Emotional Learning |
| 83 Substance Abuse Prev | 97 Chief Information Officer | 286 Digital Learning | |
| 84 Erate | 98 Chief Technology Officer | 288 Common Core Standards | |
| 85 AIDS Education | 270 Character Education | 294 Accountability | |
| 88 Alternative/At Risk | 271 Migrant Education | 295 Network System | |
| 89 Multi-Cultural Curriculum | 273 Teacher Mentor | 296 Title II Programs | |
| 90 Social Work | 274 Before/After Sch | 297 Webmaster | |

**School Programs**
A = Alternative Program
G = Adult Classes
M = Magnet Program
T = Title I Schoolwide
V = Career & Tech Ed Programs

**Other School Types**
Ⓐ = Alternative School
Ⓒ = Charter School
Ⓜ = Magnet School
Ⓨ = Year-Round School

**Social Media**
 = Facebook
 = Twitter

New Schools are shaded
New Superintendents and Principals are bold
Personnel with email addresses are underscored

**TX—63**

| Shady Grove Elem Sch | PK-2 | T | 481 | 68% 512/756-2126 |
| 111 Shady Grove Rd, Burnet 78611 | | | 24 | Fax 512/756-6993 |
| Tasha Briseno | | | | |

● **Marble Falls Ind School Dist** PID: 01002817    830/693-4357
1800 Colt Cir, Marble Falls 78654    Fax 830/693-5685

**Schools:** 7 \ **Teachers:** 316 \ **Students:** 4,000 \ **Special Ed Students:** 552 \ **LEP Students:** 683 \ **College-Bound:** 48% \ **Ethnic:** Asian 1%, African American 2%, Hispanic 49%, Caucasian 48% \ **Exp:** $202 (Med) \ **Poverty:** 16% \ **Title I:** $794,355 \ **Special Education:** $747,000 \ **Open-Close:** 08/19 - 05/27 \ t

| | | | |
|---|---|---|---|
| Dr Chris Allen | 1 | Jeff Gasaway | 2,15 |
| Melissa Lafferty | 2 | Jeff Rowland | 3 |
| Mike Phillips | 3 | Mary Davidson | 4 |
| Gina Solorzano | 5 | Leslie Baty | 8 |
| Heather Metzgar | 10 | Yarda Leflet | 11,88 |
| Soor-El Puga | 57 | Dr Shanna Fancher | 58 |
| Kevin Naumann | 67 | Betsy Russell | 68 |
| Melissa Fields | 69,294 | Nathan Fink | 73,295 |
| Ashley Bernard | 285 | Ashley Bernard | 285* |
| Jeanna Jette | 298 | | |

| Public Schs..Principal | Grd | Prgm | Enr/#Cls | SN |
|---|---|---|---|---|
| Colt Elem Sch<br>2200 Manzano Mile, Marble Falls 78654<br>Erika O'Connor | PK-5 | T | 570<br>29 | 66% 830/693-3474<br>Fax 830/693-7092 |
| Ⓐ Falls Career High Sch<br>1800 Colt Cir, Marble Falls 78654<br>**Shelli Rowland** | 9-12 | T | 32<br>5 | 73% 830/798-3621<br>Fax 830/798-3636 |
| Highland Lakes Elem Sch<br>8200 W FM 1431, Granite SHLS 78654<br>Leslie Talamantes | PK-5 | T | 532<br>31 | 89% 830/798-3650<br>Fax 830/598-9349 |
| Marble Falls Elem Sch<br>901 Avenue U, Marble Falls 78654<br>Michael Haley | PK-5 | T | 527<br>27 | 69% 830/693-2385<br>Fax 830/693-5421 |
| Marble Falls High Sch<br>2101 Mustang Dr, Marble Falls 78654<br>Damon Adams | 9-12 | ATV | 569<br>75 | 55% 830/693-4375<br>Fax 830/693-6079 |
| Marble Falls Middle Sch<br>1511 Pony Dr, Marble Falls 78654<br>Roger Barr | 6-8 | TV | 952<br>63 | 63% 830/693-4439<br>Fax 830/693-7788 |
| Spicewood Elem Sch<br>1005 Spur 191, Spicewood 78669<br>Susan Cox | PK-5 | T | 143<br>19 | 48% 830/798-3675<br>Fax 830/798-3676<br>t |

## BURNET PRIVATE SCHOOLS

| Private Schs..Principal | Grd | Prgm | Enr/#Cls | SN |
|---|---|---|---|---|
| Faith Academy of Marble Falls<br>3151 E FM 1431, Marble Falls 78654<br>Joe Rispoli | K-12 | | 275<br>11 | 830/798-1333<br>Fax 830/798-1332 |
| First Baptist Christian Sch<br>901 La Ventana, Marble Falls 78654<br>Dr Sandra Phelps | PK-8 | | 150 | 830/693-3930<br>Fax 830/693-1105 |

# CALDWELL COUNTY

## CALDWELL PUBLIC SCHOOLS

● **Lockhart Ind School Dist** PID: 01003031    512/398-0000
419 Bois Darc St, Lockhart 78644    Fax 512/398-0031

**Schools:** 9 \ **Teachers:** 372 \ **Students:** 6,350 \ **Special Ed Students:** 692 \ **LEP Students:** 1,520 \ **College-Bound:** 80% \ **Ethnic:** African American 3%, Hispanic 77%, Caucasian 19% \ **Exp:** $272 (Med) \ **Poverty:** 18% \ **Title I:** $1,154,715 \ **Special Education:** $1,599,000 \ **Open-Close:** 08/19 - 05/27 \ **DTBP:** $169 (High)

| | | | |
|---|---|---|---|
| Mark Estrades | 1 | Tanya Homann | 2 |
| Tina Knudsen | 2,19 | Lee Raspberry | 3* |
| James Akuna | 4 | Salanon Torres | 5 |
| Todd Moebes | 6 | Shelly Webber | 7 |
| Stephanie Camarillo | 8,15 | Faith Pope | 9 |
| Barry Bacom | 10,83 | Kim Brents | 11,91,270 |
| Adam Galvan | 15,73,76,271 | Christina Vazques | 57,271 |
| Melissa Corona | 58,81 | Steve Johnson | 67 |
| Karla Tate | 274 | Paul Hodge | 295* |

| Public Schs..Principal | Grd | Prgm | Enr/#Cls | SN |
|---|---|---|---|---|
| Alma Brewer Strawn Elem Sch<br>9000 FM 1854, Dale 78616<br>Analeasa Holmes \ **Benjamin Grijalva** | K-5 | T | 497 | 85% 512/398-0630<br>Fax 512/398-0631 |
| Bluebonnet Elem Sch<br>211 Mockingbird Ln, Lockhart 78644<br>Belinda Vasquez | K-5 | T | 572 | 74% 512/398-0900<br>Fax 512/398-0901 |
| Clear Fork Elem Sch<br>1102 Clearfork St, Lockhart 78644<br>Rebecca Leonard | 1-5 | T | 489<br>38 | 66% 512/398-0450<br>Fax 512/398-0536 |
| George W Carver Early Ed Ctr<br>371 Carver St, Lockhart 78644<br>Karen Nixon | PK-K | T | 228<br>24 | 79% 512/398-0060<br>Fax 512/398-0110 |
| Lockhart High Sch<br>906 Center St, Lockhart 78644<br>**Barry Bacom** | 9-12 | ATV | 780<br>59 | 63% 512/398-0300<br>Fax 512/398-0302 |
| Lockhart Junior High Sch<br>500 City Line Rd, Lockhart 78644<br>Edgar Torres | 6-8 | ATV | 1,491<br>40 | 70% 512/398-0770<br>Fax 512/398-0772 |
| Ⓐ Lockhart Pride High Sch<br>500 Pecos St, Lockhart 78644<br>Ethan Peters | 9-12 | T | 31<br>4 | 76% 512/398-0130<br>Fax 512/398-0132 |
| Navarro Elem Sch<br>715 S Medina St, Lockhart 78644<br>Deanna Juarez \ Anna Canales \ Analeasa Holmes | K-5 | T | 517<br>20 | 74% 512/398-0690<br>Fax 512/398-0692 |
| Plum Creek Elem Sch<br>710 Flores St, Lockhart 78644<br>Janey Griebel | 1-5 | T | 550<br>59 | 84% 512/398-0570<br>Fax 512/398-0572 |

● **Luling Ind School Dist** PID: 01003093    830/875-3191
212 E Bowie St, Luling 78648    Fax 830/875-3193

**Schools:** 4 \ **Teachers:** 96 \ **Students:** 1,400 \ **Special Ed Students:** 145 \ **LEP Students:** 183 \ **College-Bound:** 40% \ **Ethnic:** African American 6%, Hispanic 71%, Caucasian 22% \ **Exp:** $556 (High) \ **Poverty:** 27% \ **Title I:** $554,449 \ **Open-Close:** 08/10 - 05/20 \ **DTBP:** $604 (High)

| | | | | | | | |
|---|---|---|---|---|---|---|---|
| 1 | Superintendent | 19 | Chief Financial Officer | 39 | Social Studies K-12 | 59 | Special Education Elem | 69 | Academic Assessment |
| 2 | Bus/Finance/Purchasing | 20 | Art K-12 | 40 | Social Studies Elem | 60 | Special Education Sec | 70 | Research/Development |
| 3 | Buildings And Grounds | 21 | Art Elem | 41 | Social Studies Sec | 61 | Foreign/World Lang K-12 | 71 | Public Information |
| 4 | Food Service | 22 | Art Sec | 42 | Science K-12 | 62 | Foreign/World Lang Elem | 72 | Summer School |
| 5 | Transportation | 23 | Music K-12 | 43 | Science Elem | 63 | Foreign/World Lang Sec | 73 | Instructional Tech |
| 6 | Athletic | 24 | Music Elem | 44 | Science Sec | 64 | Religious Education K-12 | 74 | Inservice Training |
| 7 | Health Services | 25 | Music Sec | 45 | Math K-12 | 65 | Religious Education Elem | 75 | Marketing/Distributive |
| 8 | Curric/Instruct K-12 | 26 | Business Education | 46 | Math Elem | 66 | Religious Education Sec | 76 | Info Systems |
| 9 | Curric/Instruct Elem | 27 | Career & Tech Ed | 47 | Math Sec | 67 | School Board President | 77 | Psychological Assess |
| 10 | Curric/Instruct Sec | 28 | Technology Education | 48 | English/Lang Arts K-12 | 68 | Teacher Personnel | 78 | Affirmative Action |
| 11 | Federal Program | 29 | Family/Consumer Science | 49 | English/Lang Arts Elem | 58 | Special Education K-12 | | |
| 12 | Title I | 30 | Adult Education | 50 | English/Lang Arts Sec | | | | |
| 13 | Title V | 31 | Career/Sch-to-Work K-12 | 51 | Reading K-12 | | | | |
| 14 | | 32 | Career/Sch-to-Work Elem | 52 | Reading Elem | | | | |
| 15 | Asst Superintendent | 33 | Career/Sch-to-Work Sec | 53 | Reading Sec | | | | |
| 16 | Instructional Media Svcs | 34 | Early Childhood Ed | 54 | Remedial Reading K-12 | | | | |
| 17 | Chief Operations Officer | 35 | Health/Phys Education | 55 | Remedial Reading Elem | | | | |
| 18 | Chief Academic Officer | 36 | Guidance Services K-12 | 56 | Remedial Reading Sec | | | | |
| | | 37 | Guidance Services Elem | 57 | Bilingual/ELL | | | | |
| | | 38 | Guidance Services Sec | | | | | | |

| | |
|---|---|
| Erin Warren .................................1,11 | Menell Martin ..............................2,19 |
| Bryan Tucker ....................................3 | Bill Hathaway ...................................4 |
| Diana Dietz ......................................5 | Stacey Martin ..................................6* |
| Haley Almaguer .................................7 | Errin Jennings ..................................8 |
| Kimberley Hardy ..........................16,82* | Leanna Coulter ...............................37 |
| Laurinda Webb ...........................57,58* | Jeff Ferry ........................................67 |
| Susan Guzman .................................68 | Steven Goodall ............................73,76 |
| Lauri Webb ......................83,85,271 | Perla Castro .................................271 |
| David Smith ...................................285 | |

| Public Schs..Principal | Grd | Prgm | Enr/#Cls | SN |
|---|---|---|---|---|
| Gilbert Gerdes Jr High Sch<br>214 E Bowie St, Luling 78648<br>Kelly Meshell | 6-8 | T | 306<br>20 | 71% 830/875-2121<br>Fax 830/875-5482 |
| Leonard Shanklin Elem Sch<br>122 E Houston St, Luling 78648<br>**Michelle Schwarzlose** | 2-5 | T | 425<br>18 | 75% 830/875-2515<br>Fax 830/875-6708 |
| Luling High Sch<br>218 E Travis St, Luling 78648<br>Joseph Alvarez | 9-12 | AGTV | 415<br>35 | 71% 830/875-2458<br>Fax 830/875-2751 |
| Luling Primary Sch<br>118 W Bowie St, Luling 78648<br>Hank Weikert | PK-1 | T | 174<br>12 | 79% 830/875-2223<br>Fax 830/875-6712 |

● **Prairie Lea Ind School Dist** PID: 01003122     512/488-2328
6910 San Marcus Hwy, Prairie Lea 78661     Fax 512/488-9006

---

**Schools:** 1 \ **Teachers:** 17 \ **Students:** 216 \ **Special Ed Students:** 19 \ **LEP Students:** 17 \ **College-Bound:** 75% \ **Ethnic:** African American 9%, Hispanic 60%, Caucasian 30% \ **Exp:** $447 (High) \ **Poverty:** 19% \ **Title I:** $63,410 \ **Open-Close:** 08/26 - 05/28 \ **DTBP:** $373 (High)

---

| | |
|---|---|
| Larry Markert .................................1,11 | Charlie Simpson ................................3 |
| Debbie Hardaway ..............................4* | Teresa Acklin ..................................6* |
| Shelley Hardaway ............................27* | Kay Markert ....................................57* |
| Kimberly Durick ..............................58 | Margarito Zapata ............................67 |
| John Ray ........................................73* | |

| Public Schs..Principal | Grd | Prgm | Enr/#Cls | SN |
|---|---|---|---|---|
| Prairie Lea Sch<br>6910 San Marcus Hwy 80, Prairie Lea 78661<br>Monica Guillory | PK-12 | TV | 216<br>16 | 78% 512/488-2328<br>Fax 512/488-2425 |

## CALHOUN COUNTY

## CALHOUN PUBLIC SCHOOLS

● **Calhoun Co Ind School Dist** PID: 01003158     361/552-9728
525 N Commerce St, Port Lavaca 77979     Fax 361/551-2648

---

**Schools:** 7 \ **Teachers:** 264 \ **Students:** 3,738 \ **Special Ed Students:** 338 \ **LEP Students:** 416 \ **Ethnic:** Asian 6%, African American 2%, Hispanic 64%, Caucasian 28% \ **Exp:** $420 (High) \ **Poverty:** 22% \ **Title I:** $1,054,143 \ **Special Education:** $715,000 \ **Open-Close:** 08/11 - 05/27 \ **DTBP:** $183 (High)

---

| | |
|---|---|
| Larry Nichols .....................................1 | Robin Martinez ..................................2 |
| Joe Hernandez ...........................3,5,91 | Nicole Nguyen ...................................4 |
| Richard Whitaker ..............................6* | Shari Dierlam ....................................7* |
| Maggie Hernadez ...........8,15,57,69,74,271 | Kelly Taylor .........13,57,69,74,83,271 |
| Dana Dworaczyk ..............................27 | Gina Bethany .........................58,275 |

| | |
|---|---|
| Dr Bill Harvey ................................67 | Lela Tyson .....................................69 |
| Marcus Martinez ...............73,286,295 | Dwana Finster ................................88* |

| Public Schs..Principal | Grd | Prgm | Enr/#Cls | SN |
|---|---|---|---|---|
| Calhoun High Sch<br>201 Sandcrab Blvd, Port Lavaca 77979<br>Nicole Amason | 9-12 | TV | 521 | 60% 361/552-3775<br>Fax 361/551-2620 |
| Harrison-Jefferson-Madison ES<br>605 N Commerce St, Port Lavaca 77979<br>Tiffany O'Donnell | PK-5 | T | 701<br>40 | 75% 361/552-5253<br>Fax 361/551-2628 |
| Ⓐ Hope High Sch<br>900 N Virginia St, Port Lavaca 77979<br>Dwana Finster | 9-12 | TV | 27<br>6 | 90% 361/552-7084<br>Fax 361/551-2677 |
| Jackson-Roosevelt Elem Sch<br>1512 Jackson St, Port Lavaca 77979<br>Sherry Phillips | PK-5 | T | 873<br>50 | 74% 361/552-3317<br>Fax 361/551-2699 |
| Port O'Connor Elem Sch<br>508 W Monroe Ave, Port O Connor 77982<br>Kelly Wehmeyer | PK-5 | T | 87<br>10 | 67% 361/983-2341<br>Fax 361/551-2605 |
| Seadrift Sch<br>1801 W Broadway, Seadrift 77983<br>Lynda Bermea | PK-8 | T | 290<br>28 | 60% 361/785-3511<br>Fax 361/785-5720 |
| Travis Middle Sch<br>705 N Nueces St, Port Lavaca 77979<br>Jimmy Sides | 6-8 | TV | 744<br>50 | 65% 361/552-3784<br>Fax 361/551-2692 |

## CALHOUN CATHOLIC SCHOOLS

● **Diocese of Victoria Ed Office** PID: 02181727
Listing includes only schools located in this county. See District Index for location of Diocesan Offices.

| Catholic Schs..Principal | Grd | Prgm | Enr/#Cls | SN |
|---|---|---|---|---|
| Our Lady of the Gulf Cath Sch<br>301 S San Antonio St, Port Lavaca 77979<br>Theresa Dent | PK-8 | | 90<br>9 | 361/552-6140<br>Fax 361/552-4300<br>🇫 |

## CALLAHAN COUNTY

## CALLAHAN PUBLIC SCHOOLS

● **Baird Ind School Dist** PID: 01003287     325/854-1400
600 W 7th St, Baird 79504     Fax 325/854-2058

---

**Schools:** 3 \ **Teachers:** 34 \ **Students:** 289 \ **Special Ed Students:** 38 \ **LEP Students:** 3 \ **Ethnic:** Hispanic 23%, Caucasian 77% \ **Exp:** $617 (High) \ **Poverty:** 22% \ **Title I:** $105,878 \ **Open-Close:** 08/25 - 05/20 \ **DTBP:** $343 (High)

---

| | |
|---|---|
| Tim Little ...........................................1 | Cindy Clark .......................................2 |
| Kevin Davis ...................................3,5 | Tiffany Voights-Pettit ........................4 |
| Marilu Hall .......................................7 | Kenneth Brock .................................67 |
| Glendell Barr .............................73,295* | |

| | |
|---|---|
| 79 Student Personnel | 91 Safety/Security |
| 80 Driver Ed/Safety | 92 Magnet School |
| 81 Gifted/Talented | 93 Parental Involvement |
| 82 Video Services | 95 Tech Prep Program |
| 83 Substance Abuse Prev | 97 Chief Information Officer |
| 84 Erate | 98 Chief Technology Officer |
| 85 AIDS Education | 270 Character Education |
| 88 Alternative/At Risk | 271 Migrant Education |
| 89 Multi-Cultural Curriculum | 273 Teacher Mentor |
| 90 Social Work | 274 Before/After Sch |

| | |
|---|---|
| 275 Response To Intervention | 298 Grant Writer/Ptnrships |
| 277 Remedial Math K-12 | 750 Chief Innovation Officer |
| 280 Literacy Coach | 751 Chief of Staff |
| 285 STEM | 752 Social Emotional Learning |
| 286 Digital Learning | |
| 288 Common Core Standards | **Other School Types** |
| 294 Accountability | Ⓐ = Alternative School |
| 295 Network System | Ⓒ = Charter School |
| 296 Title II Programs | Ⓜ = Magnet School |
| 297 Webmaster | Ⓨ = Year-Round School |

**School Programs**
A = Alternative Program
G = Adult Classes
M = Magnet Program
T = Title I Schoolwide
V = Career & Tech Ed Programs

New Schools are shaded
New Superintendents and Principals are bold
Personnel with email addresses are underscored

**Social Media**
🇫 = Facebook
🇹 = Twitter

**TX—65**

| Public Schs..Principal | Grd | Prgm | Enr/#Cls | SN | |
|---|---|---|---|---|---|
| Baird Elem Sch<br>400 W 7th St, Baird 79504<br>**Cynthia Bessent** | PK-5 | T | 139<br>14 | 70% | 325/854-1400<br>Fax 325/854-2808 |
| Baird High Sch<br>600 W 7th St, Baird 79504<br>Torrey Price | 9-12 | TV | 84<br>20 | 58% | 325/854-1400<br>Fax 325/854-2808 |
| Baird Middle Sch<br>400 W 7th St, Baird 79504<br>Cynthia Bessent | 6-8 | T | 60 | 65% | 325/854-1400<br>Fax 325/854-2808 |

● **Clyde Consolidated Ind SD** PID: 01003316          325/893-4222
526 Shalimar Dr, Clyde 79510          Fax 325/893-4024

**Schools:** 4 \ **Teachers:** 111 \ **Students:** 1,440 \ **Special Ed Students:** 191
\ **LEP Students:** 8 \ **Ethnic:** African American 2%, Hispanic 15%,
Caucasian 83% \ **Exp:** $505 (High) \ **Poverty:** 18% \ **Title I:** $346,744 \
**Open-Close:** 08/20 - 05/20 \ **DTBP:** $340 (High) \ 🅣

| | | | |
|---|---|---|---|
| Kenny Berry | .............................1 | Terry Phillips | ..............................................2 |
| Melanie Brown | ...........................4 | Scott Campbell | ...........................................6 |
| Lois Burleson | ...........................7* | Paula Kinslow | ..... 8,11,58,69,271,273,285,298 |
| Teresa Howard | .........................16* | Carrie Atchinson | ......................36,83,85,88* |
| Greg Welch | ..............................67 | Mike Neal | .......................................73,286 |
| Paul McGuire | .........................295 | | |

| Public Schs..Principal | Grd | Prgm | Enr/#Cls | SN | |
|---|---|---|---|---|---|
| Clyde Elem Sch<br>318 Forrest Rd, Clyde 79510<br>Kim Jones | PK-2 | T | 300<br>26 | 52% | 325/893-4788<br>Fax 325/893-5642 |
| Clyde High Sch<br>500 N Hays Rd, Clyde 79510<br>**David Acevedo** | 9-12 | AV | 410<br>42 | 46% | 325/893-2161<br>Fax 325/893-2993 |
| Clyde Intermediate Sch<br>505 N Hays Rd, Clyde 79510<br>Jill Morphis | 3-5 | T | 339<br>25 | 56% | 325/893-2815<br>Fax 325/893-3067 |
| Clyde Junior High Sch<br>211 S 3rd St W, Clyde 79510<br>Jared Duncum | 6-8 | T | 358<br>17 | 54% | 325/893-5788<br>Fax 325/893-2134<br>🅕🅣 |

● **Cross Plains Ind Sch Dist** PID: 01003354          254/725-6121
700 N Main St, Cross Plains 76443          Fax 254/725-6559

**Schools:** 2 \ **Teachers:** 37 \ **Students:** 340 \ **Special Ed Students:** 34
\ **LEP Students:** 7 \ **College-Bound:** 80% \ **Ethnic:** Hispanic 12%,
Caucasian 88% \ **Exp:** $765 (High) \ **Poverty:** 21% \ **Title I:** $101,354 \
**Open-Close:** 08/27 - 05/21 \ **DTBP:** $342 (High)

| | | | |
|---|---|---|---|
| Dade Cosby | ...............................1 | Linda Birdwell | .....................................2,298 |
| Clarence Tennison | ...................3,5 | Barbara Barnette | ......................................4 |
| Leslie Lawrence | ...................4,11* | Stephanie Thompson | ...........................4 |
| Daniel Purvis | ...........................6* | Stacy Jones | ...................8,69,83,88,275,294* |
| Roy Richey | ..............................67 | Gary Moses | ...........................................73 |
| Dave Crosby | .....................286,295 | | |

| Public Schs..Principal | Grd | Prgm | Enr/#Cls | SN | |
|---|---|---|---|---|---|
| Cross Plains Elem Sch<br>800 N Main St, Cross Plains 76443<br>Jeanette Barron | PK-6 | T | 194<br>18 | 71% | 254/725-6123 |
| Cross Plains High Sch<br>700 N Main St, Cross Plains 76443<br>Wesley Jones | 7-12 | TV | 146<br>15 | 50% | 254/725-6121 |

● **Eula Ind School Dist** PID: 01003380          325/529-3186
6040 FM 603, Clyde 79510          Fax 325/529-4461

**Schools:** 3 \ **Teachers:** 40 \ **Students:** 441 \ **Special Ed Students:** 63
\ **LEP Students:** 3 \ **College-Bound:** 70% \ **Ethnic:** Asian 1%, African
American 1%, Hispanic 15%, Caucasian 83% \ **Exp:** $501 (High) \
**Poverty:** 14% \ **Title I:** $120,648 \ **Open-Close:** 08/26 - 05/21 \ **DTBP:** $180
(High)

| | | | |
|---|---|---|---|
| Tim Kelley | ...............................1 | Joshua Fostel | ..............................2,6,296* |
| Susan Faircloth | ...........................2 | Glen Smith | ........................................3,91 |
| Sue Pounds | .............................4* | Debra Frazier | ..........................................5 |
| Joye Fuller | ..............................7* | Danette Price | ..........................................8 |
| Katie Fostel | ............9,11,69,93,273* | David Turner | ....................16,73,82,83,286* |
| Lori Oglesby | ............................31* | Bill Dean | .............................................67 |
| Kortni Collins | .........................270* | | |

| Public Schs..Principal | Grd | Prgm | Enr/#Cls | SN | |
|---|---|---|---|---|---|
| Eula Elem Sch<br>6040 FM 603, Clyde 79510<br>Cody Williams | PK-6 | T | 268 | 53% | 325/529-3212<br>Fax 325/529-2001 |
| Eula High Sch<br>6040 FM 603, Clyde 79510<br>Wayland Damron | 9-12 | TV | 115<br>20 | 36% | 325/529-3605<br>Fax 325/529-5534 |
| Eula Middle Sch<br>6040 FM 603, Clyde 79510<br>Wayland Damron | 7-8 | T | 58<br>6 | 50% | 325/529-3605<br>Fax 325/529-5534 |

## CAMERON COUNTY

## CAMERON PUBLIC SCHOOLS

● **Brownsville Ind School Dist** PID: 01003445          956/548-8000
1900 Price Rd, Brownsville 78521          Fax 956/574-6497

**Schools:** 54 \ **Teachers:** 2,912 \
**Students:** 44,356 \ **Special Ed Students:** 5,383 \ **LEP Students:** 13,378 \
**College-Bound:** 95% \ **Ethnic:** Hispanic 98%, Caucasian 1% \ **Exp:** $366
(High) \ **Poverty:** 40% \ **Title I:** $30,666,178 \ **Special Education:** $8,067,000
\ **Bilingual Education:** $92,000 \ **Open-Close:** 08/25 - 06/10 \ **DTBP:** $195
(High)

| | | | |
|---|---|---|---|
| Dr Rene Gutierrez | ......................1 | Mary Garza | ...........................................2 |
| Dr Nereida Cantu | ...................2,3,15 | Cesar Lopez | ...........................................3 |
| Jimmy Haynes | ......................3,15* | Laura Villareal | .........................................4 |
| Eliud Ornelas | ............................5 | Gilbert Leal | ............................................6 |
| Rosa Pones | ..............................7 | Alma Cardenas-Rubio | ............................8,15 |
| Dr Anysia Trevino | ...........8,15,68,88 | Dr Dora Sauceda | ...............................8,15 |
| Rose Longoria | ......................8,15 | Sandra Lopez | .....................................8,15* |
| Dolores Emerson | ........................9 | Dr Norma Ibarra | .....................................10 |
| Mary Tolman | ............................11 | Carmelita Rodriguez | .....................15,68,78 |
| Dr Timothy Cuff | ...................15,79 | Rosie Ara | ............................................16 |
| David Robledo | ..........................19 | Dr Juan Chavez | .................................27,31* |
| Reyes Rivera | ...........................30 | Merrill Hammons | .....................................31 |
| Maria Gonzales | ........................34 | Sara Garza | ......................................36,752 |
| Carlos Olvera | ...........................57 | Adriana Lippa | .........................................58 |
| Minerva Pena | ...........................67 | Maricela Franco | ......................................68 |
| Pam Van Ravensway | ...............69,70 | Jason Moody | .........................................71 |
| Denise Gallegos | ...................73,285 | Cynthia Castro | .......................................74 |
| Devanira Garcia | ........................74 | Dr Lee Garcia | ........................................76 |
| Robert Fisher | ...................76,95,286 | Randy Park | ...........................................79 |
| Oscar Garcia | ...........................91 | Rosalva Larrasquitu | .................................93 |
| Estela Barrientes | .....................271 | Dr Gregorio Garcia | ................................298 |

| | | | | | | | |
|---|---|---|---|---|---|---|---|
| **1** Superintendent | **8** Curric/Instruct K-12 | **19** Chief Financial Officer | **29** Family/Consumer Science | **39** Social Studies K-12 | **49** English/Lang Arts Elem | **59** Special Education Elem | **69** Academic Assessment |
| **2** Bus/Finance/Purchasing | **9** Curric/Instruct Elem | **20** Art K-12 | **30** Adult Education | **40** Social Studies Elem | **50** English/Lang Arts Sec | **60** Special Education Sec | **70** Research/Development |
| **3** Buildings And Grounds | **10** Curric/Instruct Sec | **21** Art Elem | **31** Career/Sch-to-Work K-12 | **41** Social Studies Sec | **51** Reading K-12 | **61** Foreign/World Lang K-12 | **71** Public Information |
| **4** Food Service | **11** Federal Program | **22** Art Sec | **32** Career/Sch-to-Work Elem | **42** Science K-12 | **52** Reading Elem | **62** Foreign/World Lang Elem | **72** Summer School |
| **5** Transportation | **12** Title I | **23** Music K-12 | **33** Career/Sch-to-Work Sec | **43** Science Elem | **53** Reading Sec | **63** Foreign/World Lang Sec | **73** Instructional Tech |
| **6** Athletic | **13** Title V | **24** Music Elem | **34** Early Childhood Ed | **44** Science Sec | **54** Remedial Reading K-12 | **64** Religious Education K-12 | **74** Inservice Training |
| **7** Health Services | **14** Asst Superintendent | **25** Music Sec | **35** Health/Phys Education | **45** Math K-12 | **55** Remedial Reading Elem | **65** Religious Education Elem | **75** Marketing/Distributive |
| | **16** Instructional Media Svcs | **26** Business Education | **36** Guidance Services K-12 | **46** Math Elem | **56** Remedial Reading Sec | **66** Religious Education Sec | **76** Info Systems |
| | **17** Chief Operations Officer | **27** Career & Tech Ed | **37** Guidance Services Elem | **47** Math Sec | **57** Bilingual/ELL | **67** School Board President | **77** Psychological Assess |
| | **18** Chief Academic Officer | **28** Technology Education | **38** Guidance Services Sec | **48** English/Lang Arts K-12 | **58** Special Education K-12 | **68** Teacher Personnel | **78** Affirmative Action |

| Public Schs..Principal | Grd | Prgm | Enr/#Cls | SN |
|---|---|---|---|---|
| Ben L Brite Elem Sch<br>450 S Browne Ave, Brownsville 78521<br>Nicole Clint | PK-5 | T | 600 | 96% 956/698-3000<br>Fax 956/831-5146 |
| Benavides Elem Sch<br>3101 McAllen Rd, Brownsville 78520<br>Sherry Stout | PK-5 | T | 715<br>58 | 89% 956/350-3250<br>Fax 956/350-3273 |
| Besteiro Middle Sch<br>6280 Southmost Rd, Brownsville 78521<br>Teresa Nunez | 6-8 | GTV | 698 | 97% 956/544-3900<br>Fax 956/544-3946 |
| Breeden Elem Sch<br>3955 Dana Ave, Brownsville 78526<br>Mandy DelGado | PK-5 | T | 617 | 73% 956/554-4730<br>Fax 956/547-4305 |
| Ⓐ Brownsville Academic Center<br>3308 Robindale Rd, Brownsville 78526<br>Hector Hernandez | 6-12 | | 152<br>16 | 956/504-6305<br>Fax 956/831-9726 |
| Brownsville Early Clg HS<br>343 Ringgold Rd, Brownsville 78520<br>Aimee Garza | 9-12 | T | 394 | 86% 956/698-1476<br>Fax 956/574-5600 |
| Ⓐ Brownsville Lrng Acad High Sch<br>1800 Cummings Pl, Brownsville 78520<br>Teresita De Saro | 6-12 | | 350 | 96% 956/548-8630<br>Fax 956/831-8267 |
| Bruce Aiken Elem Sch<br>6290 Southmost Rd, Brownsville 78521<br>Dora Fasci-Marquez | PK-5 | T | 610<br>33 | 96% 956/986-5200<br>Fax 956/986-5208 |
| Burns Elem Sch<br>1974 E Alton Gloor Blvd, Brownsville 78526<br>Leticia Rodriguez-Bohn | PK-5 | T | 675<br>66 | 97% 956/548-8490<br>Fax 956/548-8489 |
| Canales Elem Sch<br>1811 International Blvd, Brownsville 78521<br>Myrta Garza | PK-5 | T | 462<br>65 | 99% 956/548-8900<br>Fax 956/548-8912 |
| Champion Elem Sch<br>4750 Bowie Rd, Brownsville 78521<br>Ricardo Torres | PK-5 | T | 683<br>36 | 94% 956/832-6200<br>Fax 956/832-6225 |
| Cromack Elem Sch<br>3200 E 30th St, Brownsville 78521<br>Lucinda Hernandez | PK-5 | T | 518<br>60 | 94% 956/548-8820<br>Fax 956/548-8824 |
| Del Castillo Elem Sch<br>105 Morningside Rd, Brownsville 78521<br>Petra Torres | PK-5 | T | 292<br>45 | 96% 956/982-2600<br>Fax 956/982-2622 |
| Egly Elem Sch<br>445 Land O Lakes Dr, Brownsville 78521<br>Pedro Vidal | PK-5 | T | 729<br>40 | 92% 956/548-8850<br>Fax 956/982-3074 |
| El Jardin Elem Sch<br>6911 Boca Chica Blvd, Brownsville 78521<br>**Marina Flores** | PK-5 | T | 453<br>60 | 96% 956/831-6000<br>Fax 956/831-6002 |
| Faulk Middle Sch<br>2000 Roosevelt St, Brownsville 78521<br>Benita Villarreal | 6-8 | T | 1,102<br>60 | 97% 956/548-8500<br>Fax 956/548-8507 |
| Filemon B Vela Middle Sch<br>4905 Paredes Line Rd, Brownsville 78526<br>Joel Wood | 6-8 | TV | 752<br>60 | 80% 956/548-7770<br>Fax 956/548-7780 |
| Gallegos Elem Sch<br>2700 Avenida Rancho Viejo, Brownsville 78521<br>Theresa Villafuerte | PK-5 | T | 471<br>48 | 93% 956/547-4230<br>Fax 956/547-4232 |
| Garden Park Elem Sch<br>855 Military Rd, Brownsville 78520<br>Victor Caballero | PK-5 | T | 569<br>60 | 95% 956/982-2630<br>Fax 956/982-2644 |
| Garza Elem Sch<br>200 Esperanza Rd, Brownsville 78521<br>Maria Lara | PK-5 | T | 352<br>60 | 99% 956/982-2660<br>Fax 956/982-2682 |
| Ⓜ Gladys Porter Early Clg HS<br>3500 International Blvd, Brownsville 78521<br>Maria Solis | 9-12 | GTV | 1,995 | 96% 956/548-7800<br>Fax 956/548-7988 |
| Gonzalez Elem Sch<br>4350 Jaime J Zapata Ave, Brownsville 78521<br>Billy Cobos | PK-5 | T | 825<br>65 | 89% 956/831-6030<br>Fax 956/831-6035 |
| Ⓜ Homer Hanna Early Clg HS<br>2615 E Price Rd, Brownsville 78521<br>Blanca Lambarri | 9-12 | GTV | 2,603 | 83% 956/548-7600<br>Fax 956/548-7603 |
| Hudson Elem Sch<br>2980 Ruben Torres Sr Blvd, Brownsville 78526<br>Rachel Ayala | PK-5 | T | 689<br>35 | 93% 956/574-6400<br>Fax 956/574-6403 |
| Ⓜ James Pace Early Clg HS<br>314 W Los Ebanos Blvd, Brownsville 78520<br>**Joel Wood** | 9-12 | GTV | 2,085<br>100 | 92% 956/548-7700<br>Fax 956/548-6018 |
| Josephine Castaneda Elem Sch<br>3201 Lima St, Brownsville 78521<br>**Nora Camargo** | PK-5 | T | 518<br>17 | 96% 956/548-8800<br>Fax 956/548-8811 |
| Julia Garcia Middle Sch<br>5701 Ruben Torres Sr Blvd, Brownsville 78526<br>Luis Segura | 6-8 | T | 1,085 | 90% 956/832-6300<br>Fax 956/832-6304 |
| Keller Elem Sch<br>2540 W Alton Gloor Blvd, Brownsville 78520<br>Javier Garza | PK-5 | T | 520 | 85% 956/547-4400<br>Fax 956/554-7150 |
| Ⓐ Lincoln Park Sch<br>7 Orange St, Brownsville 78521<br>Dawn Hall | 6-12 | V | 107<br>17 | 100% 956/548-7880<br>Fax 956/982-3090 |
| Ⓜ Lopez Early College High Sch<br>3205 S Dakota Ave, Brownsville 78521<br>Dahlia Aguilar | 9-12 | GTV | 2,013<br>104 | 94% 956/982-7400<br>Fax 956/986-5099 |
| Lucio Middle Sch<br>300 N Vermillion Ave, Brownsville 78521<br>Chester Arizmendi | 6-8 | T | 849<br>55 | 93% 956/831-4550<br>Fax 956/838-2298 |
| Manzano Middle Sch<br>2580 W Alton Gloor Blvd, Brownsville 78520<br>Marisol Trevino | 6-8 | T | 906 | 82% 956/548-9800<br>Fax 956/548-6772 |
| Mary & Frank Yturria Elem Sch<br>2955 W Tandy Rd, Brownsville 78520<br>Sandra Cortez | PK-5 | T | 529<br>46 | 75% 956/350-3200<br>Fax 956/350-3207 |
| Morningside Elem Sch<br>1025 Morningside Rd, Brownsville 78521<br>Jose Martinez | PK-5 | T | 526<br>60 | 93% 956/982-2760<br>Fax 956/982-2787 |
| Oliveira Middle Sch<br>444 Land O Lakes Dr, Brownsville 78521<br>**Martha Medina** | 6-8 | T | 996<br>120 | 86% 956/548-8530<br>Fax 956/544-3968 |
| Ortiz Elem Sch<br>2500 W Alton Gloor Blvd, Brownsville 78520<br>Patricia Garza | PK-5 | T | 538<br>21 | 92% 956/698-1100<br>Fax 956/546-6611 |
| Palm Grove Elem Sch<br>7942 Southmost Rd, Brownsville 78521<br>Patricia Chacon | PK-6 | T | 408<br>35 | 94% 956/982-3850<br>Fax 956/986-5070 |
| Paredes Elem Sch<br>3700 Heritage Trl, Brownsville 78526<br>Melissa Werbiski | PK-5 | T | 968 | 78% 956/574-5582<br>Fax 956/574-5584 |
| Pena Elem Sch<br>4975 Salida De Luna, Brownsville 78526<br>Yolanda Turbeville | PK-5 | T | 489 | 90% 956/547-7100<br>Fax 956/838-6545 |
| Perez Elem Sch<br>2514 Shidler Dr, Brownsville 78521<br>Michael Moreno | PK-5 | T | 474<br>35 | 95% 956/982-2800<br>Fax 956/982-2806 |
| Perkins Middle Sch<br>4750 Austin Rd, Brownsville 78521<br>Beatriz Hernandez | 6-8 | T | 710<br>75 | 98% 956/831-8770<br>Fax 956/831-8789 |
| Pullam Elem Sch<br>3200 Madrid Ave, Brownsville 78520<br>Celia De Los Santos | PK-5 | T | 707 | 70% 956/547-3700<br>Fax 956/350-2880 |
| Putegnat Elem Sch<br>730 E 8th St, Brownsville 78520<br>Aidee Vasquez | PK-5 | T | 442<br>35 | 100% 956/548-8930<br>Fax 956/548-8947 |
| R L Martin Elem Sch<br>1701 Stanford Ave, Brownsville 78520<br>Gilda Jo Pena | PK-5 | T | 414<br>45 | 92% 956/982-2730<br>Fax 956/982-3032 |

| School | Grd | Prgm | Enr/#Cls | SN | Phone/Fax |
|--------|-----|------|----------|-----|-----------|
| Russell Elem Sch<br>800 Lakeside Blvd, Brownsville 78520<br>Oscar Cantu | PK-5 | T | 664<br>40 | 95% | 956/548-8960<br>Fax 956/548-8889 |
| Sharp Elem Sch<br>1439 Palm Blvd, Brownsville 78520<br>Irma Segura | PK-5 | T | 420<br>36 | 89% | 956/982-2930<br>Fax 956/982-2948 |
| Ⓜ Simon Rivera Early Clg HS<br>6955 Ruben Torres Sr Blvd, Brownsville 78526<br>Norma Canales | 9-12 | TV | 2,348 | 88% | 956/831-8700<br>Fax 956/831-8705 |
| Skinner Elem Sch<br>411 W Saint Charles St, Brownsville 78520<br>Mary Rodriguez | PK-5 | T | 425<br>50 | 98% | 956/982-2830<br>Fax 956/982-2849 |
| Southmost Elem Sch<br>5245 Southmost Rd, Brownsville 78521<br>Anabela Almanza | PK-5 | T | 326<br>40 | 94% | 956/548-8870<br>Fax 956/548-8875 |
| Stell Middle Sch<br>1105 E Los Ebanos Blvd, Brownsville 78520<br>**Luis Segura** | 6-8 | T | 982 | 93% | 956/698-0363<br>Fax 956/548-8666 |
| Stillman Middle Sch<br>2977 W Tandy Rd, Brownsville 78520<br>Eduardo Martinez | 6-8 | T | 1,098<br>85 | 59% | 956/698-1000<br>Fax 956/350-3231 |
| Vermillion Elem Sch<br>6895 Ruben Torres Sr Blvd, Brownsville 78526<br>Socorro Houghtaling | PK-5 | T | 691<br>66 | 93% | 956/831-6060<br>Fax 956/831-1093 |
| Veterans Memorial Early Clg HS<br>4550 US Highway 281, Brownsville 78520<br>Norma Gallegos | 9-12 | | 1,988 | 60% | 956/574-5600<br>Fax 956/542-1341 |
| Villa Nueva Elem Sch<br>7455 Old Military Rd, Brownsville 78520<br>Melissa Gutierrez | PK-5 | T | 416<br>26 | 88% | 956/542-3957<br>Fax 956/544-0720 |

● **Harlingen Cons Ind School Dist** PID: 01003756    956/430-9500
407 N 77 Sunshine Strip, Harlingen 78550    Fax 956/430-9514

**Schools:** 31 \ **Teachers:** 1,250 \ **Students:** 18,600 \
**Special Ed Students:** 1,903 \ **LEP Students:** 2,369 \ **College-Bound:** 59% \
\ **Ethnic:** African American 1%, Hispanic 94%, Caucasian 5% \ **Exp:** $310
(High) \ **Poverty:** 37% \ **Title I:** $9,802,145 \ **Special Education:** $3,616,000 \
**Open-Close:** 08/10 - 05/21 \ **DTBP:** $192 (High) \ **f**

| | | | |
|---|---|---|---|
| Art Cavazos | 1 | Julio Cavazos | 2,15,19 |
| Kimberly Anderson | 2 | Oscar Tapia | 3,4,5,15 |
| Judy Baker | 4,7 | Luciano Rubio | 5 |
| Robert Davies | 6 | Dr Alicia Noyola | 8,18 |
| Loranda Romero | 9,15 | Lori Romero | 9 |
| Joseph Villareal | 10 | Thelma Reynolds | 11 |
| Debbie Scogin | 15,68 | Ronnie Rios | 23* |
| Luis Solorio | 35 | Sandra Tovar | 36 |
| Norma Garcia | 57 | Daniel Garcia | 58* |
| Alejandra Lara | 59* | Dr Nolan Perez | 67 |
| Melissa Nieto | 68 | Cynthia Castillo | 69 |
| Shane Strubhart | 71 | Jessica Hruska | 73 |
| Maria Kortan | 74 | Olga Garcia | 76 |
| Myliss Parker | 81 | Dr Jose Cavazos | 88,93 |
| Jennifer Maldonado | 286 | Dalia Garcia | 294 |
| Jessica Martinez | 297* | | |

| Public Schs..Principal | Grd | Prgm | Enr/#Cls | SN | Phone/Fax |
|------------------------|-----|------|----------|-----|-----------|
| Austin Elem Sch<br>700 E Austin Ave, Harlingen 78550<br>Magda Gonzales | PK-5 | T | 375<br>32 | 92% | 956/427-3060<br>Fax 956/427-3063 |
| Ben Milam Elem Sch<br>1215 S Rangerville Rd, Harlingen 78552<br>Brenda McKinney | PK-5 | T | 417<br>28 | 91% | 956/427-3150<br>Fax 956/427-3153 |
| Bonham Elem Sch<br>2400 E Jefferson Ave, Harlingen 78550<br>Herminia Ramirez | PK-5 | T | 622<br>44 | 88% | 956/427-3070<br>Fax 956/427-3073 |
| Bowie Elem Sch<br>309 W Lincoln Ave, Harlingen 78550<br>Jaymie Galan | PK-5 | T | 367<br>21 | 90% | 956/427-3080<br>Fax 956/427-3083 |
| Coakley Middle Sch<br>1402 S 6th St, Harlingen 78550<br>Pedro Sanchez | 6-8 | TV | 761<br>60 | 79% | 956/427-3000<br>Fax 956/427-3006 |
| Crockett Elem Sch<br>1406 W Jefferson Ave, Harlingen 78550<br>Juan Manuel Garcia | PK-5 | T | 360<br>23 | 94% | 956/427-3090<br>Fax 956/427-3093 |
| Dishman Elem Sch<br>309 Madeley St, Combes 78535<br>Irma Davis | PK-5 | T | 312<br>24 | 97% | 956/427-3100<br>Fax 956/427-3103 |
| Dr Abraham P Cano Fresh Acad<br>1701 W Lozano St, Harlingen 78550<br>Imelda Trevino | 9-9 | T | 1,135 | 76% | 956/430-4900<br>Fax 956/427-3772 |
| © Early College High Sch<br>2510 Pecan St Bldg R, Harlingen 78550<br>Dr Pamela Flores | 9-12 | T | 341<br>13 | 66% | 956/430-9690<br>Fax 956/430-9693 |
| Gutierriez Middle Sch<br>3205 Wilson Rd, Harlingen 78552<br>Mike Reyes | 6-8 | T | 815<br>50 | 81% | 956/430-4400<br>Fax 956/430-4480 |
| Harlingen High Sch<br>1201 Marshall St, Harlingen 78550<br>Vivian Bauer | 9-12 | TV | 1,974 | 80% | 956/427-3600<br>Fax 956/427-3792 |
| Harlingen High School South<br>1701 Dixieland Rd, Harlingen 78552<br>Fernando Reyes | 9-12 | ATV | 1,544<br>60 | 72% | 956/427-3800<br>Fax 956/427-3995<br>f |
| Harlingen Sch of Health Prof<br>2302 N 21st St, Harlingen 78550<br>Tina Garza | 8-12 | T | 421 | 60% | 956/430-4078<br>Fax 956/427-3763 |
| Houston Elem Sch<br>301 E Taft Ave, Harlingen 78550<br>Virginia Armstrong | PK-5 | T | 437 | 90% | 956/427-3110<br>Fax 956/427-3114 |
| Jane Long Elem Sch<br>2601 N 7th St, Harlingen 78550<br>Bobbie Hushen | PK-5 | T | 587<br>42 | 78% | 956/427-3140<br>Fax 956/427-3144 |
| Jefferson Elem Sch<br>601 S J St, Harlingen 78550<br>Alejandra Lara | PK-5 | T | 253<br>26 | 100% | 956/427-3120<br>Fax 956/427-3127 |
| Ⓐ Keys Academy<br>Ⓥ 2809 N 7th St, Harlingen 78550<br>Isidoro Nieto | 8-12 | GMT | 100<br>12 | 91% | 956/427-3220<br>Fax 956/427-3223 |
| Lamar Elem Sch<br>1100 McLarry Rd, Harlingen 78550<br>Alma Atkinson | PK-5 | T | 624<br>30 | 90% | 956/427-3130<br>Fax 956/427-3133 |
| Lee H Means Elem Sch<br>1201 E Loop 499, Harlingen 78550<br>**Melissa Almaraz** | PK-5 | T | 647 | 69% | 956/427-3377<br>Fax 956/427-3376 |
| Memorial Middle Sch<br>1901 Rio Hondo Rd, Harlingen 78550<br>William Snavely | 6-8 | TV | 830<br>35 | 79% | 956/427-3020<br>Fax 956/427-3024 |
| Moises Vela Middle Sch<br>801 S Palm Blvd, Harlingen 78552<br>Graciela Gutierrez | 6-8 | TV | 851<br>35 | 72% | 956/427-3479<br>Fax 956/427-3549 |
| Ⓐ New Pathways Center<br>208 S F St, Harlingen 78550<br>Venee Harrell | 1-5 | | 15<br>2 | | 956/427-3250<br>Fax 956/427-3254 |
| Rodriguez Elem Sch<br>8402 Wilson Rd, Harlingen 78552<br>Adriana Arellano | PK-5 | | 656<br>43 | | 956/430-4060<br>Fax 956/430-4065<br>f |
| Ⓐ Secondary Alternative Center<br>1310 Sam Houston Dr, Harlingen 78550<br>Dan Araiza | 6-12 | | 48<br>6 | 89% | 956/427-3210<br>Fax 956/430-4487 |
| STEM2 Preparatory Academy<br>1920 E Washington Ave, Harlingen 78550<br>Sonya Brandenburg | 6-8 | | 250 | | 956/368-6100<br>Fax 956/430-4447 |

| | | | | | |
|---|---|---|---|---|---|
| 1 | Superintendent | 8 | Curric/Instruct K-12 | 19 | Chief Financial Officer |
| 2 | Bus/Finance/Purchasing | 9 | Curric/Instruct Elem | 20 | Art K-12 |
| 3 | Buildings And Grounds | 10 | Curric/Instruct Sec | 21 | Art Elem |
| 4 | Food Service | 11 | Federal Program | 22 | Art Sec |
| 5 | Transportation | 12 | Title I | 23 | Music K-12 |
| 6 | Athletic | 13 | Title V | 24 | Music Elem |
| 7 | Health Services | 14 | Instructional Media Svcs | 25 | Music Sec |
| | | 15 | Asst Superintendent | 26 | Business Education |
| | | 16 | Instructional Media Svcs | 27 | Career & Tech Ed |
| | | 17 | Chief Operations Officer | 28 | Technology Education |
| | | 18 | Chief Academic Officer | | |

| | | | | | |
|---|---|---|---|---|---|
| 29 | Family/Consumer Science | 39 | Social Studies K-12 | 49 | English/Lang Arts Elem |
| 30 | Adult Education | 40 | Social Studies Elem | 50 | English/Lang Arts Sec |
| 31 | Career/Sch-to-Work K-12 | 41 | Social Studies Sec | 51 | Reading K-12 |
| 32 | Career/Sch-to-Work Elem | 42 | Science K-12 | 52 | Reading Elem |
| 33 | Career/Sch-to-Work Sec | 43 | Science Elem | 53 | Reading Sec |
| 34 | Early Childhood Ed | 44 | Science Sec | 54 | Remedial Reading K-12 |
| 35 | Health/Phys Education | 45 | Math K-12 | 55 | Remedial Reading Elem |
| 36 | Guidance Services K-12 | 46 | Math Elem | 56 | Remedial Reading Sec |
| 37 | Guidance Services Elem | 47 | Math Sec | 57 | Bilingual/ELL |
| 38 | Guidance Services Sec | 48 | English/Lang Arts K-12 | 58 | Special Education K-12 |

| | | | |
|---|---|---|---|
| 59 | Special Education Elem | 69 | Academic Assessment |
| 60 | Special Education Sec | 70 | Research/Development |
| 61 | Foreign/World Lang K-12 | 71 | Public Information |
| 62 | Foreign/World Lang Elem | 72 | Summer School |
| 63 | Foreign/World Lang Sec | 73 | Instructional Tech |
| 64 | Religious Education K-12 | 74 | Inservice Training |
| 65 | Religious Education Elem | 75 | Marketing/Distributive |
| 66 | Religious Education Sec | 76 | Info Systems |
| 67 | School Board President | 77 | Psychological Assess |
| 68 | Teacher Personnel | 78 | Affirmative Action |

| | | | | | | |
|---|---|---|---|---|---|---|
| Stuart Place Elem Sch<br>6701 W Business 83, Harlingen 78552<br>Dawn Burbach | PK-5 | T | 701<br>34 | 55% | 956/427-3160<br>Fax 956/427-3159<br>f |
| Travis Elem Sch<br>600 E Polk St, Harlingen 78550<br>Beulah Rangel | PK-5 | T | 346<br>24 | 92% | 956/427-3170<br>Fax 956/427-3173 |
| Treasure Hills Elem Sch<br>2525 Haine Dr, Harlingen 78550<br>Roland Ingram | PK-5 | T | 811<br>38 | 66% | 956/427-3180<br>Fax 956/427-3187 |
| Vernon Middle Sch<br>125 S 13th St, Harlingen 78550<br>Arely Tamez | 6-8 | TV | 428<br>54 | 90% | 956/427-3040<br>Fax 956/427-3046 |
| Wilson Elem Sch<br>16495 Primera Rd, Harlingen 78552<br>Michele Todd | PK-5 | T | 450<br>40 | 84% | 956/427-3190<br>Fax 956/427-3197 |
| Zavala Elem Sch<br>1111 N B St, Harlingen 78550<br>Tanya Garza | PK-5 | T | 361<br>26 | 100% | 956/427-3200<br>Fax 956/427-3203<br>f |

## ● La Feria Ind School Dist  PID: 01003940      956/797-8300
203 E Oleander Ave, La Feria 78559                Fax 956/797-3737

**Schools:** 7 \ **Teachers:** 221 \ **Students:** 2,880 \ **Special Ed Students:** 356 \ **LEP Students:** 408 \ **Ethnic:** Hispanic 97%, Caucasian 2% \ **Exp:** $640 (High) \ **Poverty:** 29% \ **Title I:** $1,558,713 \ **Special Education:** $1,000 \ **Open-Close:** 08/24 - 05/27 \ **DTBP:** $176 (High)

| | |
|---|---|
| Cathy Hernandez ....................................1 | Antonio Aguilar ........................................2,19 |
| Darrell Guerra .....................................3,5 | Cynthia Casas ..............................................4 |
| Oscar Salinas ...................................6,35* | Sarah Saldivar ..............................................7 |
| Dr Isaac Roderiquez .............................8 | Dr Miriam Guerra ............... 11,27,285 |
| Cynthia Torres .......................................15 | Veronica Torres ...................28,73,84,295 |
| Haydee Rodriguez ..............................36* | Annette Pena .............................................57 |
| Lilian Ramos ..........................................58 | Juan Bronis .................................................67 |
| Jaime Rodriguez ...........................93,271 | |

| Public Schs..Principal | Grd | Prgm | Enr/#Cls | SN | |
|---|---|---|---|---|---|
| C E Vail Elem Sch<br>209 W Jessamine Ave, La Feria 78559<br>Rosie Garza | PK-4 | T | 389<br>42 | 88% | 956/797-8460<br>Fax 956/797-3429 |
| David Sanchez Elem Sch<br>1601 S Main St, La Feria 78559<br>Umberto Flores | PK-4 | T | 345 | 82% | 956/797-8550<br>Fax 956/797-8530 |
| Ⓐ La Feria Academy<br>505 N Villarreal St, La Feria 78559<br>Carlos Verduzco | 9-12 | T | 18 | 92% | 956/797-8360<br>Fax 956/797-1583 |
| La Feria High Sch<br>901 N Canal St, La Feria 78559<br>Chairez Cynthia | 9-12 | AGTV | 207<br>100 | 82% | 956/797-8370<br>Fax 956/797-9374 |
| Noemi Dominguez Elem Sch<br>600 Pancho Maples Dr, La Feria 78559<br>Yvette Cantu | 5-6 | T | 480<br>60 | 84% | 956/797-8430<br>Fax 956/797-2600 |
| Sam Houston Elem Sch<br>500 Beddoes Rd, La Feria 78559<br>Hector Cazares | PK-4 | T | 496<br>21 | 80% | 956/797-8490<br>Fax 956/797-5169 |
| W B Green Junior High Sch<br>501 N Canal St, La Feria 78559<br>Sarah Torres | 7-8 | T | 506<br>45 | 84% | 956/797-8400<br>Fax 956/797-2157 |

## ● Los Fresnos Cons Ind Sch Dist  PID: 01004009      956/254-5000
600 N Mesquite St, Los Fresnos 78566                Fax 956/233-3599

**Schools:** 16 \ **Teachers:** 668 \ **Students:** 10,379 \ **Special Ed Students:** 1,193 \ **LEP Students:** 1,974 \ **Ethnic:** Hispanic 96%, Caucasian 3% \ **Exp:** $386 (High) \ **Poverty:** 29% \ **Title I:** $4,024,858 \ **Special Education:** $1,856,000 \ **Open-Close:** 09/08 - 06/17 \ **DTBP:** $188 (High)

| | |
|---|---|
| Dr Gonzalo Salazar ...................................1 | Belinda Mendez .......................................2 |
| David Young ..................................................2 | Jose Leal .......................................................3 |
| Rey Ovalle ......................................................4 | Suzanne Ramirez .....................................5 |
| Patrick Brown .............................................6* | Ada Amaro-Sibaja .....7,58,74,78,79,88,93 |
| Diana Davis ...................................................7 | Sara Tudon ..................................................8 |
| Valarie Londrie ............................................9 | Jimmy McDonough ............................. 10 |
| Noe Guillen ........................................ 11,271 | Cynthia Garcia ...................................... 16 |
| Pablo Bazaloua ........................................ 19 | Ronnie Rodriguez ............................... 27 |
| Claudia Larrasquitu .............................. 34 | Sandra Ruiz ................................36,81,83 |
| Anna Villareal .......................................... 57 | Dr Griselda Wells .................................. 58 |
| Leonel Garza ............................................ 67 | Marlen Anaya .......................................... 68 |
| Ben Estrada .............................................. 69 | Ronnie Zamora ...................................... 71 |
| Dr Jesse Garza ................................. 73,286 | Jennifer Stumbaugh ........................... 74 |
| Daniel Araujo ............................................ 76 | Billy Simpson ................................84,295 |
| Joe Vasquez .............................................. 91 | Claudia Medina-Garcia ..................... 93 |
| Marco Resendez .................................... 297 | |

| Public Schs..Principal | Grd | Prgm | Enr/#Cls | SN | |
|---|---|---|---|---|---|
| Ⓐ AMI Kids Rio Grande Valley<br>27615 Buena Vista Blvd, Los Fresnos 78566<br>Javier Ibarra | 9-12 | V | 15<br>6 | | 956/233-5795<br>Fax 956/233-3124 |
| Ⓐ College Career & Tech Acad<br>32614 State Highway 100, Los Fresnos 78566<br>Jeri Gomez | 9-12 | | 31 | | 956/254-5296<br>Fax 956/233-6328 |
| Dora Romero Elem Sch<br>9705 Cajaun Blvd, Brownsville 78521<br>Laura Trevino | PK-5 | T | 472 | 82% | 956/254-5210<br>Fax 956/350-2645 |
| Las Yescas Elem Sch<br>24313 FM 803, San Benito 78586<br>Lynn Martinez | PK-5 | T | 235<br>30 | 84% | 956/233-6955<br>Fax 956/748-2540 |
| Laureles Elem Sch<br>31393 FM 2893, Los Fresnos 78566<br>**Ramon Escareno** | PK-5 | T | 619<br>35 | 86% | 956/254-5141<br>Fax 956/233-3690 |
| Liberty Middle Sch<br>31579 FM 2893, San Benito 78586<br>Annice Garza | 6-8 | T | 764 | 88% | 956/233-3900<br>Fax 956/233-1074 |
| Lopez-Riggins Elem Sch<br>613 N Mesquite St, Los Fresnos 78566<br>**Jennifer Elizondo** | PK-5 | T | 490<br>36 | 86% | 956/233-6916<br>Fax 956/233-3696 |
| Los Cuates Middle Sch<br>32477 Highway 100, Los Fresnos 78566<br>Antonio Padilla | 6-8 | T | 557<br>48 | 81% | 956/254-5182<br>Fax 956/233-1487 |
| Los Fresnos Elem Sch<br>32602 State Highway 100, Los Fresnos 78566<br>Veronica Grimaldo | PK-5 | T | 523<br>37 | 77% | 956/233-6900<br>Fax 956/233-6235 |
| Los Fresnos High Sch<br>907 N Arroyo Blvd, Los Fresnos 78566<br>Justin Stumbaugh | 10-12 | ATV | 1,669<br>150 | 80% | 956/254-5300<br>Fax 956/233-3510 |
| Los Fresnos United Sch<br>33790 Farm Rd 803, San Benito 78586<br>Dr William Roach | 9-10 | | 1,657 | | 956/254-5250<br>Fax 956/399-2047 |
| Olmito Elem Sch<br>2500 Arroyo Blvd, Brownsville 78526<br>Rosemary Leal | PK-5 | T | 646 | 71% | 956/233-3950<br>Fax 956/350-8835 |
| Palmer-Laakso Elem Sch<br>30515 FM 1847, San Benito 78586<br>Celia Ontiveros | PK-5 | T | 554 | 78% | 956/254-5121<br>Fax 956/233-3659 |

---

| | | | | | |
|---|---|---|---|---|---|
| Rancho Verde Elem Sch<br>101 Rancho Alegre, Brownsville 78526<br>Mary Chavez | PK-5 | T | 634 | 60% | 956/254-5230<br>Fax 956/350-8843 |
| Resaca Middle Sch<br>22422 FM 1575, Los Fresnos 78566<br>Maria Pineda | 6-8 | T | 823<br>53 | 73% | 956/254-5159<br>Fax 956/233-6210 |
| Villareal Elem Sch<br>7700 E Lakeside Blvd, Olmito 78575<br>Pablo Leal | PK-5 | T | 347<br>34 | 82% | 956/233-3975<br>Fax 956/350-2087 |

## • Point Isabel Ind Sch Dist  PID: 01004061

101 Port Rd, Port Isabel 78578

956/943-0000
Fax 956/943-0014

**Schools:** 4 \ **Teachers:** 146 \ **Students:** 2,017 \ **Special Ed Students:** 223 \ **LEP Students:** 820 \ **Ethnic:** Hispanic 92%, Caucasian 7% \ **Exp:** $258 (Med) \ **Poverty:** 39% \ **Title I:** $1,567,154 \ **Special Education:** $530,000 \ **Open-Close:** 08/27 - 05/25 \ **DTBP:** $553 (High)

| | | |
|---|---|---|
| Theresa Alarcon ........................................ 1 | Henry Levrier ................. 2,3,11,27,30,83,296 |
| Audrey Pena-Rodriguez ............................ 4 | Ernie Mata ............................................... 5 |
| Jason Strunk .............................................. 6 | Ana Holland ............ 8,16,57,69,72,85,273,274 |
| Kirstie Ramirez ...................... 11,270,271 | D J Canales ................................ 16,73,297 |
| Lindsey Zimmerman ......................... 38* | Juan Lopez ............................................ 58 |
| Jimmy Vela ............................................. 67 | Debbie Hernandez ................................ 69 |

| Public Schs..Principal | Grd | Prgm | Enr/#Cls | SN | |
|---|---|---|---|---|---|
| Derry Elem Sch<br>1702 2nd St, Port Isabel 78578<br>Maribel Valdez | PK-5 | T | 549<br>31 | 86% | 956/943-0070<br>Fax 956/943-0074 |
| Garriga Elem Sch<br>400 W Adam St, Port Isabel 78578<br>Reina Salinas | PK-5 | T | 492<br>40 | 90% | 956/943-0080<br>Fax 956/943-0640 |
| Port Isabel High Sch<br>18000 Highway 100, Port Isabel 78578<br>Imelda Munivez | 9-12 | ATV | 493<br>45 | 81% | 956/943-0030<br>Fax 956/943-0648 [f] |
| Port Isabel Junior High Sch<br>17001 Highway 100, Port Isabel 78578<br>Nancy Gonzalez | 6-8 | T | 483<br>35 | 89% | 956/943-0060<br>Fax 956/943-0055 [f] |

## • Rio Hondo Ind School Dist  PID: 01004102

215 W Colorado St, Rio Hondo 78583

956/748-1000
Fax 956/748-1038

**Schools:** 3 \ **Teachers:** 137 \ **Students:** 1,650 \ **Special Ed Students:** 180 \ **LEP Students:** 188 \ **College-Bound:** 80% \ **Ethnic:** Hispanic 97%, Caucasian 2% \ **Exp:** $443 (High) \ **Poverty:** 27% \ **Title I:** $913,874 \ **Open-Close:** 08/24 - 05/28 \ **DTBP:** $158 (High)

| | | |
|---|---|---|
| **Roger Ellis** ............................................ 1 | Noe Alaniz ............................................... 2 |
| Stan Martienez ......................................... 2 | Racao Madrigal ........................................ 4 |
| Rocky James .......................................... 6* | Veronica Puente ....................... 11,57,58,69 |
| Hector Chavira ........................................ 15 | Saul Rodriguez ............. 16,19,73,84,98,295 |
| Claudia Villalobos .................................. 67 | Paul Arce ............................................. 297 |

| Public Schs..Principal | Grd | Prgm | Enr/#Cls | SN | |
|---|---|---|---|---|---|
| Rio Hondo Elem Sch<br>700 N Reynolds St, Rio Hondo 78583<br>Annette Jaramillo | PK-4 | T | 810<br>40 | 87% | 956/748-1050<br>Fax 956/748-1073 |
| Rio Hondo High Sch<br>22547 State Highway 345, Rio Hondo 78583<br>Asael Ruvalcaba | 9-12 | ATV | 583<br>40 | 82% | 956/748-1200<br>Fax 956/748-1204 |
| Rio Hondo Middle Sch<br>501 N Reynolds St, Rio Hondo 78583<br>Ramiro Moreno | 5-8 | T | 408<br>35 | 90% | 956/748-1150<br>Fax 956/748-1168 |

## • San Benito Cons Ind Sch Dist  PID: 01004140

240 N Crockett St, San Benito 78586

956/361-6100
Fax 956/361-6115

**Schools:** 18 \ **Teachers:** 671 \ **Students:** 10,600 \ **Special Ed Students:** 966 \ **LEP Students:** 2,127 \ **College-Bound:** 55% \ **Ethnic:** Hispanic 99%, Caucasian 1% \ **Exp:** $600 (High) \ **Poverty:** 41% \ **Title I:** $7,084,343 \ **Special Education:** $1,781,000 \ **Open-Close:** 09/08 - 06/23 \ **DTBP:** $187 (High)

| | | |
|---|---|---|
| Dr Nate Carman ........................................ 1 | Eddie Bacavazos ..................................... 2 |
| Hilda Rendon ................................... 2,15 | Arceli Soto .............................................. 4 |
| Nancy Martinez ............................... 5,274 | Dan Gomez .............................................. 6 |
| Janette Rodriguez .................................... 7 | Dilia Cornett ............................................ 9 |
| Connie Cruz ...................................... 12,271 | Sara Alavardo ................................... 15,68 |
| Leonila Pena .............................. 16,76,286 | Fernando Rosa ...................................... 27 |
| Dr Patricia Quesada ............................... 57 | Ernesto Manriquez ................................ 58 |
| Orlando Lopez ........................................ 67 | Kristina Sandoval ...................... 69,70,294 |
| Isabelle Gonzalez ................................... 71 | Stephanie Ramirez .............................. 74* |
| Ray Saldana .......................................... 79* | Juan Sosa ............................................. 91 |
| Luis Gonzales ........................................ 93 | |

| Public Schs..Principal | Grd | Prgm | Enr/#Cls | SN | |
|---|---|---|---|---|---|
| Angela Leal Elem Sch<br>33356 FM 732, San Benito 78586<br>Rudy Ramirez | PK-5 | T | 437 | 95% | 956/276-5055 |
| Berta Cabaza Middle Sch<br>2901 Shafer Rd, San Benito 78586<br>Saul Ibarra | 6-8 | T | 856<br>75 | 83% | 956/361-6600<br>Fax 956/361-6608 |
| Dr C M Cash Elem Sch<br>400 Ponciana St, San Benito 78586<br>Marleen Araiza | PK-5 | T | 655<br>40 | 89% | 956/361-6700<br>Fax 956/361-6708 |
| Dr Raul Garza Jr Elem Sch<br>845 8th St, San Benito 78586<br>Elsa Lambert | PK-5 | T | 518<br>35 | 83% | 956/361-6900<br>Fax 956/361-6908 |
| Ed Downs Elem Sch<br>1302 N Dick Dowling St, San Benito 78586<br>Manuela Lopez | PK-5 | T | 332<br>32 | 79% | 956/361-6720<br>Fax 956/361-6728 |
| Frank Roberts Elem Sch<br>451 Biddle St, San Benito 78586<br>Rolando Diaz | PK-5 | T | 344<br>20 | 97% | 956/361-6740<br>Fax 956/361-6748 |
| Fred Booth Elem Sch<br>705 Zaragosa St, San Benito 78586<br>Nedia Espinoza | PK-5 | T | 553<br>39 | 92% | 956/361-6860<br>Fax 956/361-6868 |
| Ⓐ Gateway to Graduation Academy<br>600 N Austin St, San Benito 78586<br>Henry Sanchez | 9-12 | T | 68 | 98% | 956/361-6446<br>Fax 956/361-0000 |
| Judge Oscar De La Fuente ES<br>2700 S Sam Houston St, San Benito 78586<br>Olivia Flores | PK-5 | T | 248<br>30 | 90% | 956/361-6820<br>Fax 956/361-6828 |
| La Encantada Elem Sch<br>35001 FM 1577, San Benito 78586<br>Gracie Martinez | PK-5 | T | 374<br>25 | 96% | 956/361-6760<br>Fax 956/361-6768 |
| La Paloma Elem Sch<br>35076 Padilla St, San Benito 78586<br>Ema Gonzalez | PK-5 | T | 443<br>30 | 93% | 956/361-6780<br>Fax 956/361-6788 |
| Miller Jordan Middle Sch<br>700 N McCullough St, San Benito 78586<br>Jo Fernandez | 6-8 | T | 849<br>60 | 91% | 956/361-6650<br>Fax 956/361-6688 |
| Ⓐ Positive Redirection Center<br>450 S Dick Dowling St, San Benito 78586<br>Scott Hausler | 6-12 | T | 25<br>6 | | 956/361-6275<br>Fax 956/361-6278 |
| Rangerville Elem Sch<br>17558 Landrum Park Rd, San Benito 78586<br>Nora Martinez | PK-5 | T | 369<br>18 | 89% | 956/361-6840<br>Fax 956/361-6848 |
| Riverside Middle Sch<br>35428 Padilla St, San Benito 78586<br>**Manuela Lopez** | 6-8 | AT | 603<br>40 | 92% | 956/361-6940<br>Fax 956/361-6948 |

| | | | | | | | |
|---|---|---|---|---|---|---|---|
| 1 | Superintendent | 8 | Curric/Instruct K-12 | 19 | Chief Financial Officer | 29 | Family/Consumer Science |
| 2 | Bus/Finance/Purchasing | 9 | Curric/Instruct Elem | 20 | Art K-12 | 30 | Adult Education |
| 3 | Buildings And Grounds | 10 | Curric/Instruct Sec | 21 | Art Elem | 31 | Career/Sch-to-Work K-12 |
| 4 | Food Service | 11 | Federal Program | 22 | Art Sec | 32 | Career/Sch-to-Work Elem |
| 5 | Transportation | 12 | Title I | 23 | Music K-12 | 33 | Career/Sch-to-Work Sec |
| 6 | Athletic | 13 | Title V | 24 | Music Elem | 34 | Early Childhood Ed |
| 7 | Health Services | 15 | Asst Superintendent | 25 | Music Sec | 35 | Health/Phys Education |
| | | 16 | Instructional Media Svcs | 26 | Business Education | 36 | Guidance Services K-12 |
| | | 17 | Chief Operations Officer | 27 | Career & Tech Ed | 37 | Guidance Services Elem |
| | | 18 | Chief Academic Officer | 28 | Technology Education | 38 | Guidance Services Sec |

| | | | | | |
|---|---|---|---|---|---|
| 39 | Social Studies K-12 | 49 | English/Lang Arts Elem | 59 | Special Education Elem |
| 40 | Social Studies Elem | 50 | English/Lang Arts Sec | 60 | Special Education Sec |
| 41 | Social Studies Sec | 51 | Reading K-12 | 61 | Foreign/World Lang K-12 |
| 42 | Science K-12 | 52 | Reading Elem | 62 | Foreign/World Lang Elem |
| 43 | Science Elem | 53 | Reading Sec | 63 | Foreign/World Lang Sec |
| 44 | Science Sec | 54 | Remedial Reading K-12 | 64 | Religious Education K-12 |
| 45 | Math K-12 | 55 | Remedial Reading Elem | 65 | Religious Education Elem |
| 46 | Math Elem | 56 | Remedial Reading Sec | 66 | Religious Education Sec |
| 47 | Math Sec | 57 | Bilingual/ELL | 67 | School Board President |
| 48 | English/Lang Arts K-12 | 58 | Special Education K-12 | 68 | Teacher Personnel |

| | |
|---|---|
| 69 | Academic Assessment |
| 70 | Research/Development |
| 71 | Public Information |
| 72 | Summer School |
| 73 | Instructional Tech |
| 74 | Inservice Training |
| 75 | Marketing/Distributive |
| 76 | Info Systems |
| 77 | Psychological Assess |
| 78 | Affirmative Action |

| | Grd | Prgm | Enr/#Cls | SN | |
|---|---|---|---|---|---|
| San Benito High Sch<br>450 S Williams Rd, San Benito 78586<br>**Rudy Ramirez** | 10-12 | ATV | 2,132<br>50 | 85% | 956/361-6500<br>Fax 956/361-6473 |
| Sullivan Elem Sch<br>900 Elizabeth St, San Benito 78586<br>Diana Atkinson | PK-5 | T | 308<br>24 | 90% | 956/361-6880<br>Fax 956/361-6888 |
| Veterans Memorial Academy<br>2115 N Williams Rd, San Benito 78586<br>Gilbert Galvan | 9-9 | T | 783 | 86% | 956/276-6000<br>Fax 956/276-6008 |

## ● Santa Maria Ind School Dist PID: 01004308

11119 Military Road, Santa Maria 78592

956/565-6308
Fax 956/565-0598

**Schools:** 4 \ **Teachers:** 55 \ **Students:** 691 \ **Special Ed Students:** 41 \ **LEP Students:** 227 \ **College-Bound:** 55% \ **Ethnic:** Hispanic 99%, Caucasian 1% \ **Exp:** $585 (High) \ **Poverty:** 36% \ **Title I:** $372,479 \ **Open-Close:** 09/08 - 06/17

| | | |
|---|---|---|
| Martin Cuellar ........1 | Enrique Cuellar ........2 | |
| Adolfo Hinojosa ........67 | Simon Martinez ........73 | |
| Daniel Kaffka ........91 | | |

| Public Schs..Principal | Grd | Prgm | Enr/#Cls | SN | |
|---|---|---|---|---|---|
| Santa Maria High Sch<br>11224 Military Rd, Santa Maria 78592<br>Jose Vela | 9-12 | AGTV | 201 | 98% | 956/565-9144<br>Fax 956/514-1968 |
| Santa Maria Junior High Sch<br>11142 Military Rd, Santa Maria 78592<br>Jose Vela | 7-8 | T | 105 | 97% | 956/565-5348 |
| Santa Maria Middle Sch<br>11100 Military Rd, Santa Maria 78592<br>Rogelio Campa | 5-6 | AT | 75<br>17 | 100% | 956/565-6309<br>Fax 956/565-6720 |
| Tony Gonzalez Elem Sch<br>11100 Military Rd, Santa Maria 78592<br>Mark Aguero | PK-4 | T | 272<br>15 | 98% | 956/565-6309<br>Fax 956/565-2698 |

## ● Santa Rosa Ind School Dist PID: 01004322

232 E Jesus T Avila, Santa Rosa 78593

956/636-9800
Fax 956/636-1439

**Schools:** 3 \ **Teachers:** 87 \ **Students:** 960 \ **Special Ed Students:** 131 \ **LEP Students:** 172 \ **College-Bound:** 48% \ **Ethnic:** Hispanic 99%, Caucasian 1% \ **Exp:** $615 (High) \ **Poverty:** 31% \ **Title I:** $665,820 \ **Open-Close:** 08/17 - 05/28 \ **DTBP:** $484 (High)

| | | |
|---|---|---|
| Dr Angela Gonzalez ........1 | David Robledo ........2,4,19 | |
| Ren Rergel ........3,5 | Catherine Diaz ........4 | |
| Juan Cipriano ........6* | Malesa Salera ........8,58 | |
| Heriberto Villarreal ........11,73 | Santos Castareda ........67 | |
| Nephalit Gonzalez ........76 | Alberto Trevino ........274 | |

| Public Schs..Principal | Grd | Prgm | Enr/#Cls | SN | |
|---|---|---|---|---|---|
| Elma Barrera Elem Sch<br>Hwy 107, Santa Rosa 78593<br>Gregorio Camarillo | PK-5 | T | 484<br>33 | 90% | 956/636-9870<br>Fax 956/636-2746 |
| Jo Nelson Middle Sch<br>102 S Main, Santa Rosa 78593<br>Jacinto Sauceda | 6-8 | ATV | 167<br>17 | 91% | 956/636-9850<br>Fax 956/636-1519 |
| Santa Rosa High Sch<br>102 Jesus R Cruz St, Santa Rosa 78593<br>Jaime Garcia | 9-12 | ATV | 74<br>40 | 83% | 956/636-9830<br>Fax 956/636-1496 |

## ● South Texas Ind School Dist PID: 01808984

100 Med High Dr, Mercedes 78570

956/565-2454
Fax 956/565-9129

**Schools:** 6 \ **Teachers:** 300 \ **Students:** 4,245 \ **Special Ed Students:** 113 \ **LEP Students:** 166 \ **Ethnic:** Asian 8%, African American 1%, Hispanic 85%, Caucasian 6% \ **Exp:** $936 (High) \ **Special Education:** $498,000 \ **Open-Close:** 08/17 - 05/26 \ **DTBP:** $181 (High)

| | | |
|---|---|---|
| Marco Antonio Lara ........1 | Marla Knaub ........2,15 | |
| Juan Villarreal ........3,5,91 | Jeff Hembree ........11,57,73,76,285,286,295,296 | |
| Ann Vickman ........16* | Josie Garcia ........58* | |
| Doug Buchanan ........67 | Amanda Odom ........71 | |
| Maricela Hinojosa ........83,88* | Candace Guillen ........93* | |

| Public Schs..Principal | Grd | Prgm | Enr/#Cls | SN | |
|---|---|---|---|---|---|
| Rising Scholars Acad of S TX<br>151 Helen Moore Rd, San Benito 78586<br>**Criselda Rodriguez** | 7-8 | T | 545 | 52% | 956/399-4358<br>Fax 956/399-3570 |
| ⓜ Science Acad of South Texas<br>900 Med High Dr, Mercedes 78570<br>Irma Castillo | 9-12 | ATV | 774<br>48 | 41% | 956/565-4620<br>Fax 956/565-9112 |
| ⓜ South Texas HS for Health Prof<br>700 Med High Dr, Mercedes 78570<br>Barbara Heater | 9-12 | TV | 791<br>54 | 54% | 956/565-2237<br>Fax 956/574-3017 |
| South Texas ISD Med Professns<br>10650 N Expressway 77 77/83, Olmito 78575<br>Harry Goette | 9-12 | TV | 817<br>25 | 71% | 956/214-6100<br>Fax 956/399-3570 |
| ⓜ South Texas Prep Academy<br>724 S Sugar Rd, Edinburg 78539<br>Ana Castro | 7-8 | TV | 573 | 42% | 956/381-5522<br>Fax 956/381-1177 |
| ⓜ South TX ISD World Scholars<br>510 S Sugar Rd, Edinburg 78539<br>Efrain Garza | 9-12 | TV | 623<br>50 | 60% | 956/383-1684<br>Fax 956/383-8544 |

## CAMERON CATHOLIC SCHOOLS

## ● Diocese of Brownsville Ed Off PID: 01004372

Listing includes only schools located in this county. See District Index for location of Diocesan Offices.

| Catholic Schs..Principal | Grd | Prgm | Enr/#Cls | SN | |
|---|---|---|---|---|---|
| Guadalupe Regional Middle Sch<br>1214 Lincoln St, Brownsville 78521<br>Dr Virginia Miller | 6-8 | | 90<br>7 | | 956/504-5568<br>Fax 956/504-9393<br>ⓣ |
| Incarnate Word Academy<br>244 Resaca Blvd, Brownsville 78520<br>Michael Camarillo | PK-8 | | 150<br>19 | | 956/546-4486<br>Fax 956/504-3960 |
| St Anthony Sch<br>1015 E Harrison Ave, Harlingen 78550<br>Kathy Stapleton | PK-6 | | 270<br>12 | | 956/423-2486<br>Fax 956/412-0084 |
| St Joseph Academy<br>101 Saint Joseph Dr, Brownsville 78520<br>Melissa Valadez | 7-12 | | 784<br>43 | | 956/542-3581<br>Fax 956/542-4748 |
| St Luke Catholic Sch<br>2850 E Price Rd, Brownsville 78521<br>Anne Marie Serrato | PK-8 | | 120<br>18 | | 956/544-7982<br>Fax 956/544-4874 |
| St Mary's Sch<br>1300 E Los Ebanos Blvd, Brownsville 78520<br>Ana Gomez | PK-6 | | 500<br>25 | | 956/546-1805<br>Fax 956/546-0787 |

| | | | | | |
|---|---|---|---|---|---|
| 79 Student Personnel | 91 Safety/Security | 275 Response To Intervention | 298 Grant Writer/Ptnrships | **School Programs** | **Social Media** |
| 80 Driver Ed/Safety | 92 Magnet School | 277 Remedial Math K-12 | 750 Chief Innovation Officer | **A** = Alternative Program | |
| 81 Gifted/Talented | 93 Parental Involvement | 280 Literacy Coach | 751 Chief of Staff | **G** = Adult Classes | 🅕 = Facebook |
| 82 Video Services | 95 Tech Prep Program | 285 STEM | 752 Social Emotional Learning | **M** = Magnet Program | |
| 83 Substance Abuse Prev | 97 Chief Information Officer | 286 Digital Learning | | **T** = Title I Schoolwide | 🅣 = Twitter |
| 84 Erate | 98 Chief Technology Officer | 288 Common Core Standards | **Other School Types** | **V** = Career & Tech Ed Programs | |
| 85 AIDS Education | 270 Character Education | 294 Accountability | Ⓐ = Alternative School | | |
| 88 Alternative/At Risk | 271 Migrant Education | 295 Network System | Ⓒ = Charter School | New Schools are shaded | |
| 89 Multi-Cultural Curriculum | 273 Teacher Mentor | 296 Title II Programs | Ⓜ = Magnet School | New Superintendents and Principals are bold | |
| 90 Social Work | 274 Before/After Sch | 297 Webmaster | Ⓨ = Year-Round School | Personnel with email addresses are underscored | |

**TX—71**

## CAMERON PRIVATE SCHOOLS

| Private Schs..Principal | Grd | Prgm | Enr/#Cls | SN |
|---|---|---|---|---|
| Calvary Christian Sch<br>1815 N 7th St, Harlingen 78550<br>Karen Zeissel | PK-8 | | 450<br>25 | 956/425-1882<br>Fax 956/412-0324 |
| Episcopal Day Sch<br>34 N Coria St, Brownsville 78520<br>Brian Clyne | PK-6 | | 305<br>20 | 956/542-5231<br>Fax 956/504-9486 |
| Faith Christian Academy<br>1944 E Alton Gloor Blvd, Brownsville 78526<br>Desi Najera | PK-8 | | 140 | 956/546-7726 |
| First Baptist Sch<br>1600 Boca Chica Blvd, Brownsville 78520<br>Deborah Batsell | PK-12 | | 300<br>20 | 956/542-4854<br>Fax 956/542-6188 |
| Kenmont Montessori Sch<br>2734 N Coria St, Brownsville 78520<br>Dr Sonia Saenz | PK-8 | | 350<br>10 | 956/542-0500<br>Fax 956/542-0591 |
| Laguna Madre Christian Academy<br>30640 Holly Bch, Laguna Vista 78578<br>Robin Stepan | PK-10 | | 32<br>4 | 956/943-4446 |
| Marine Military Academy<br>320 Iwo Jima Blvd, Harlingen 78550<br>Dr John Butler | 8-12 | | 250<br>35 | 956/423-6006<br>Fax 956/421-9273 |
| St Alban's Episcopal Day Sch<br>1417 E Austin Ave, Harlingen 78550<br>Mary Kathryn Duffy | PK-6 | | 245<br>21 | 956/428-2326<br>Fax 956/428-8457 |
| Valley Christian High Sch<br>1190 MacKintosh Dr, Brownsville 78521<br>Elizabeth Rivera | 9-12 | | 57<br>5 | 956/542-5222<br>Fax 956/544-0038 |

# CAMP COUNTY

## CAMP PUBLIC SCHOOLS

● **Pittsburg Ind School Dist** PID: 01004504　　903/856-3628
402 Broach St, Pittsburg 75686　　Fax 903/856-0269

**Schools:** 5 \ **Teachers:** 198 \ **Students:** 2,356 \ **Special Ed Students:** 231 \ **LEP Students:** 361 \ **Ethnic:** Asian 1%, African American 19%, Hispanic 42%, Caucasian 38% \ **Exp:** $483 (High) \ **Poverty:** 29% \ **Title I:** $1,024,661 \ **Special Education:** $555,000 \ **Open-Close:** 08/13 - 05/20 \ **DTBP:** $345 (High)

| | | | |
|---|---|---|---|
| Terry Waldrep .........................1 | Julie Wetzel ...........................2 |
| Joe Marsh ............................3,5 | Chris Hackett .........................4 |
| Kenneth Shelton .......................5 | Brad Baca ............................6 |
| Laura Smith ...........................7*<br>8,11,88,285,288,294,296,298 | Beth Anne Dunavant ................... |
| Neil Morrison ...........16,73,76,295,297 | Kelly Hobbs ........................34,58 |
| Jean Carrell ......................57,271* | Alan Brison ...........................67 |
| Sherri Seale ..........................68 | |

| Public Schs..Principal | Grd | Prgm | Enr/#Cls | SN |
|---|---|---|---|---|
| Pittsburg Elem Sch<br>110 Fulton St, Pittsburg 75686<br>Terri Brown | 2-4 | AT | 498<br>32 | 82% 903/856-6472<br>Fax 903/855-3370 |

| Public Schs..Principal (cont.) | Grd | Prgm | Enr/#Cls | SN |
|---|---|---|---|---|
| Pittsburg High Sch<br>300 N Texas St, Pittsburg 75686<br>Jonathan Hill | 9-12 | ATV | 664<br>60 | 74% 903/856-3646<br>Fax 903/855-3325 |
| Pittsburg Intermediate Sch<br>209 Lafayette St, Pittsburg 75686<br>Sarah Richmond | 5-6 | AT | 383<br>28 | 81% 903/855-3395<br>Fax 903/855-3398 |
| Pittsburg Junior High Sch<br>313 Broach St, Pittsburg 75686<br>Kristane Moore | 7-8 | AT | 368<br>34 | 75% 903/856-6432<br>Fax 903/855-3357 |
| Pittsburg Primary Sch<br>405 Broach St, Pittsburg 75686<br>Jyl Wood | PK-1 | AT | 443<br>30 | 80% 903/856-6482<br>Fax 903/855-3385 |

## CAMP REGIONAL CENTERS

● **Region 8 Ed Service Center** PID: 01055450　　903/575-2600
4845 US Highway 271 N, Pittsburg 75686　　Fax 903/575-2611

| | |
|---|---|
| Dr David Fitts .........................1 | Michele Leach ....................2,3,19 |
| Niki Jones ...........................7,271 | Debra Crooms ........................8 |
| Richele Langley ...................8,11,15 | Leonard Beles ...................11,57,88 |
| Brent Baker .........................16,73 | Dr Jason McCullough ................31 |
| Janis McClure .........................58 | Heather McGregor .................74,294 |
| Wayne Snyder .........................76 | |

# CARSON COUNTY

## CARSON PUBLIC SCHOOLS

● **Groom Ind School Dist** PID: 01004554　　806/248-7474
304 W 3rd Street, Groom 79039　　Fax 806/248-7949

**Schools:** 1 \ **Teachers:** 18 \ **Students:** 145 \ **Special Ed Students:** 20 \ **LEP Students:** 3 \ **College-Bound:** 11% \ **Ethnic:** African American 1%, Hispanic 12%, Native American: 1%, Caucasian 86% \ **Exp:** $1,066 (High) \ **Poverty:** 25% \ **Title I:** $33,770 \ **Open-Close:** 08/17 - 05/26 \ **DTBP:** $69 (Low)

| | |
|---|---|
| Jay Lamb ........................1,11,84 | Jennifer Peet ...........................2 |
| Kenneth Payton .......................3 | Irma Thias .............................4 |
| Stephen Vanderpool ........8,57,69,275* | Tony Dodson ......................16,295* |
| Aimee Fields ........................58* | Ron Kuehler ...........................67 |

| Public Schs..Principal | Grd | Prgm | Enr/#Cls | SN |
|---|---|---|---|---|
| Groom Sch<br>304 W 3rd Street, Groom 79039<br>Stephen Vanderpool | PK-12 | | 145<br>23 | 33% 806/248-7474 |

● **Panhandle Ind School Dist** PID: 01004592　　806/537-3568
1001 Elsie St, Panhandle 79068　　Fax 806/537-4055

**Schools:** 3 \ **Teachers:** 58 \ **Students:** 670 \ **Special Ed Students:** 88 \ **LEP Students:** 4 \ **Ethnic:** African American 1%, Hispanic 11%, Native American: 1%, Caucasian 87% \ **Exp:** $578 (High) \ **Poverty:** 10% \ **Title I:** $73,663 \ **Open-Close:** 08/17 - 06/15 \ **DTBP:** $350 (High) \

| | |
|---|---|
| Blair Brown .........................1,11 | Jamie Moore ...........................2 |
| Joe Bonner ...........................3 | Candy Greening .......................4 |

| | | | | | | |
|---|---|---|---|---|---|---|
| 1 | Superintendent | 8 | Curric/Instruct K-12 | 19 | Chief Financial Officer | 29 Family/Consumer Science |
| 2 | Bus/Finance/Purchasing | 9 | Curric/Instruct Elem | 20 | Art K-12 | 30 Adult Education |
| 3 | Buildings And Grounds | 10 | Curric/Instruct Sec | 21 | Art Elem | 31 Career/Sch-to-Work K-12 |
| 4 | Food Service | 11 | Federal Program | 22 | Art Sec | 32 Career/Sch-to-Work Elem |
| 5 | Transportation | 12 | Title I | 23 | Music K-12 | 33 Career/Sch-to-Work Sec |
| 6 | Athletic | 13 | Title V | 24 | Music Elem | 34 Early Childhood Ed |
| 7 | Health Services | 14 | Instructional Media Svcs | 25 | Music Sec | 35 Health/Phys Education |
| | | 15 | Asst Superintendent | 26 | Business Education | 36 Guidance Services K-12 |
| | | 16 | Instructional Media Svcs | 27 | Career & Tech Ed | 37 Guidance Services Elem |
| | | 17 | Chief Operations Officer | 28 | Technology Education | 38 Guidance Services Sec |
| | | 18 | Chief Academic Officer | | | |

| | | | |
|---|---|---|---|
| 39 Social Studies K-12 | 49 English/Lang Arts Elem | 59 Special Education Elem | 69 Academic Assessment |
| 40 Social Studies Elem | 50 English/Lang Arts Sec | 60 Special Education Sec | 70 Research/Development |
| 41 Social Studies Sec | 51 Reading K-12 | 61 Foreign/World Lang K-12 | 71 Public Information |
| 42 Science K-12 | 52 Reading Elem | 62 Foreign/World Lang Elem | 72 Summer School |
| 43 Science Elem | 53 Reading Sec | 63 Foreign/World Lang Sec | 73 Instructional Tech |
| 44 Science Sec | 54 Remedial Reading K-12 | 64 Religious Education K-12 | 74 Inservice Training |
| 45 Math K-12 | 55 Remedial Reading Elem | 65 Religious Education Elem | 75 Marketing/Distributive |
| 46 Math Elem | 56 Remedial Reading Sec | 66 Religious Education Sec | 76 Info Systems |
| 47 Math Sec | 57 Bilingual/ELL | 67 School Board President | 77 Psychological Assess |
| 48 English/Lang Arts K-12 | 58 Special Education K-12 | 68 Teacher Personnel | 78 Affirmative Action |

| | | |
|---|---|---|
| Dane Ashley ............6 | Allison Mitchell ............9,74 | |
| Lina Morale ............57 | Patricia Heck ............58* | |
| Patti Brown ............58 | Bubba Smith ............67 | |
| John Strother ............69,83,88,270* | Rusty Howes ............73,295 | |

| Public Schs..Principal | Grd | Prgm | Enr/#Cls | SN |
|---|---|---|---|---|
| Panhandle Elem Sch<br>106 W 9th St, Panhandle 79068<br>**Allison Mitchell** | PK-5 | T | 289<br>27 | 32% 806/537-3579<br>Fax 806/537-4230 ⓕⓣ |
| Panhandle High Sch<br>106 W 11th St, Panhandle 79068<br>**Brent Kirkland** | 9-12 | AV | 217<br>23 | 19% 806/537-3851<br>Fax 806/537-3476 ⓕⓣ |
| Panhandle Junior High Sch<br>1001 Elsie Ave, Panhandle 79068<br>**Gary Cates** | 6-8 | | 157<br>20 | 24% 806/537-3541<br>Fax 806/537-5725 ⓕⓣ |

● **White Deer Ind School Dist** PID: 01004633    806/883-2311
601 Omohundro Street, White Deer 79097    Fax 806/883-2321

---

**Schools:** 2 \ **Teachers:** 33 \ **Students:** 360 \ **Special Ed Students:** 37 \ **LEP Students:** 5 \ **College-Bound:** 59% \ **Ethnic:** Asian 1%, African American 1%, Hispanic 14%, Native American: 1%, Caucasian 84% \ **Exp:** $362 (High) \ **Poverty:** 5% \ **Title I:** $17,139 \ **Open-Close:** 08/20 - 05/25 \ **DTBP:** $374 (High) \ ⓕ ⓣ

---

| | | |
|---|---|---|
| Scott Lucas ............1,11,83 | Yvette Bryan ............58 | |
| Shane Grange ............67 | Julie Brown ............69,88 | |
| Rosalea McAnally ............73* | | |

| Public Schs..Principal | Grd | Prgm | Enr/#Cls | SN |
|---|---|---|---|---|
| White Deer Elem Sch<br>604 Main Street, White Deer 79097<br>**Kandy Bolding** | PK-6 | T | 210<br>25 | 54% 806/883-2311<br>Fax 806/883-5008 |
| White Deer Jr Sr High Sch<br>604 S Doucette Street, White Deer 79097<br>**Darla Forney** | 7-12 | TV | 142<br>18 | 38% 806/883-2311<br>Fax 806/883-5029 |

# CASS COUNTY

## CASS PUBLIC SCHOOLS

● **Atlanta Ind School Dist** PID: 01004671    903/796-4194
106 W Main St, Atlanta 75551    Fax 903/796-3487

---

**Schools:** 5 \ **Teachers:** 133 \ **Students:** 1,760 \ **Special Ed Students:** 227 \ **LEP Students:** 36 \ **College-Bound:** 50% \ **Ethnic:** Asian 1%, African American 35%, Hispanic 10%, Caucasian 54% \ **Exp:** $608 (High) \ **Poverty:** 37% \ **Title I:** $1,029,186 \ **Special Education:** $19,000 \ **Open-Close:** 08/14 - 05/21 \ **DTBP:** $348 (High) \ ⓕ

---

| | | |
|---|---|---|
| Sidney Harrist ............1 | Marilyn Cobb ............2,15 | |
| Dave Wilcox ............3,4,5,10,11,15 | Donna Wilkins ............4 | |
| Matt McClure ............6,35,85* | Diane Whatley ............9 | |
| Gloria Herring ............16* | Christina Kelley ............34,58 | |
| Charlotte Stanner ............67 | Holly Triamrose ............68 | |
| Brandon Prince ............73,286,297* | | |

| Public Schs..Principal | Grd | Prgm | Enr/#Cls | SN |
|---|---|---|---|---|
| Atlanta Elem Sch<br>902 Abc Ln, Atlanta 75551<br>**Dena McCord** | 2-4 | T | 335<br>35 | 70% 903/796-7164<br>Fax 903/799-1018 |
| Atlanta High Sch<br>705 Rabbit Blvd, Atlanta 75551<br>**Nancy Rinehart** | 9-12 | TV | 480<br>38 | 57% 903/796-4411<br>Fax 903/799-1033 |
| Atlanta Middle Sch<br>600 High School Ln, Atlanta 75551<br>**Colby Boyce** | 5-8 | T | 487<br>35 | 65% 903/796-7928<br>Fax 903/796-7290 |
| Atlanta Primary Sch<br>505 Rabbit Blvd, Atlanta 75551<br>**Donna Rice** | PK-1 | T | 386<br>30 | 78% 903/796-8115<br>Fax 903/799-1014 |
| Ⓐ Daep Center<br>309 N Buckner St, Atlanta 75551<br>**Pamela Boyce** | K-12 | | 20<br>3 | 903/799-1044<br>Fax 903/796-2520 |

● **Avinger Ind School Dist** PID: 01004724    903/562-1355
245 Conner, Avinger 75630    Fax 903/562-1271

---

**Schools:** 1 \ **Teachers:** 17 \ **Students:** 140 \ **Special Ed Students:** 12 \ **LEP Students:** 3 \ **College-Bound:** 50% \ **Ethnic:** Asian 1%, African American 15%, Hispanic 9%, Native American: 1%, Caucasian 74% \ **Exp:** $864 (High) \ **Poverty:** 32% \ **Title I:** $71,428 \ **Open-Close:** 08/17 - 05/21

---

| | | |
|---|---|---|
| Jacquelyn Smith ............1,11 | Pam Miller ............2 | |
| Amanda Bicklham ............58* | Ann Linwood ............67 | |
| April Grogan ............73* | Martha Giddens ............88* | |

| Public Schs..Principal | Grd | Prgm | Enr/#Cls | SN |
|---|---|---|---|---|
| Avinger Sch<br>245 Conner, Avinger 75630<br>**Terry Giddens** | PK-12 | TV | 140<br>22 | 70% 903/562-1355 |

● **Bloomburg Ind School Dist** PID: 01004750    903/728-5216
307 W Cypress St, Bloomburg 75556    Fax 903/728-5399

---

**Schools:** 1 \ **Teachers:** 25 \ **Students:** 272 \ **Special Ed Students:** 20 \ **LEP Students:** 3 \ **College-Bound:** 100% \ **Ethnic:** African American 3%, Hispanic 6%, Native American: 2%, Caucasian 90% \ **Exp:** $311 (High) \ **Poverty:** 35% \ **Title I:** $123,902 \ **Open-Close:** 08/12 - 05/19 \ **DTBP:** $371 (High)

---

| | | |
|---|---|---|
| Brian Stroman ............1,11 | Kim Ratcliff ............2 | |
| Mike Carter ............3* | Chad Sheffield ............6 | |
| Jennifer Camley ............7* | Natalie Imnan ............17,69,273 | |
| Kacie Reneau ............58* | Thresha Jones ............67 | |
| Stephen Belk ............73* | Cindy Shofner ............79 | |
| Shannon Peacock ............83* | | |

| Public Schs..Principal | Grd | Prgm | Enr/#Cls | SN |
|---|---|---|---|---|
| Bloomburg Sch<br>307 W Cypress St, Bloomburg 75556<br>**Amy Barron** \ Silvia Stroman | PK-12 | ATV | 272<br>28 | 67% 903/728-5216 |

● **Hughes Springs Ind Sch Dist** PID: 01004786    903/639-3800
871 Taylor St, Hughes Spgs 75656    Fax 903/639-2624

---

**Schools:** 3 \ **Teachers:** 98 \ **Students:** 1,145 \ **Special Ed Students:** 121 \ **LEP Students:** 40 \ **College-Bound:** 64% \ **Ethnic:** Asian 1%, African American 12%, Hispanic 12%, Caucasian 75% \ **Exp:** $797 (High) \ **Poverty:** 28% \ **Title I:** $327,195 \ **Open-Close:** 08/14 - 05/21 \ **DTBP:** $338 (High) \ ⓕ

---

| | | |
|---|---|---|
| 79 Student Personnel | 91 Safety/Security | 275 Response To Intervention |
| 80 Driver Ed/Safety | 92 Magnet School | 277 Remedial Math K-12 |
| 81 Gifted/Talented | 93 Parental Involvement | 280 Literacy Coach |
| 82 Video Services | 95 Tech Prep Program | 285 STEM |
| 83 Substance Abuse Prev | 97 Chief Information Officer | 286 Digital Learning |
| 84 Erate | 98 Chief Technology Officer | 288 Common Core Standards |
| 85 AIDS Education | 270 Character Education | 294 Accountability |
| 88 Alternative/At Risk | 271 Migrant Education | 295 Network System |
| 89 Multi-Cultural Curriculum | 273 Teacher Mentor | 296 Title II Programs |
| 90 Social Work | 274 Before/After Sch | 297 Webmaster |

| | |
|---|---|
| 296 Grant Writer/Ptnrships | |
| 750 Chief Innovation Officer | |
| 751 Chief of Staff | |
| 752 Social Emotional Learning | |
| **Other School Types** | |
| Ⓐ = Alternative School | |
| Ⓒ = Charter School | |
| Ⓜ = Magnet School | |
| Ⓨ = Year-Round School | |

**School Programs**
A = Alternative Program
G = Adult Classes
M = Magnet Program
T = Title I Schoolwide
V = Career & Tech Ed Programs

New Schools are shaded
New Superintendents and Principals are bold
Personnel with email addresses are underscored

**Social Media**
ⓕ = Facebook
ⓣ = Twitter

Sarah Dildine ...................................1,57
David Hinerman .............................3,5,91
Chris Edwards .......................................6
Thersa Jennings ...8,11,16,58,88,288,296,298
Van Hall ..............................................67
Doug Stewart ............................73,76,286*

Jaylyn Setser .................................2,11
Elizabeth Martinez ...............................4
Brandi Pittman ...................................7*
Vanessa Murphy .................................37*
Mary Trevino .......................................68

| Public Schs..Principal | Grd | Prgm | Enr/#Cls | SN | |
|---|---|---|---|---|---|
| Hughes Springs Elem Sch<br>809 Russell, Hughes Spgs 75656<br>**Scott Hanes** | PK-5 | T | 541<br>24 | 66% | 903/639-3881<br>Fax 903/639-3930 |
| Hughes Springs High Sch<br>701 Russell, Hughes Spgs 75656<br>**Brian Nation** | 9-12 | TV | 325 | 52% | 903/639-3841<br>Fax 903/639-3928 |
| Hughes Springs Jr High Sch<br>609 Russell, Hughes Spgs 75656<br>**Rusty Duke** | 6-8 | T | 279<br>18 | 57% | 903/639-3812<br>Fax 903/639-3929 |

● **Linden Kildare Cons Ind SD** PID: 01004827    903/756-7071
205 Kildare Rd, Linden 75563    Fax 903/756-7242

**Schools:** 3 \ **Teachers:** 63 \ **Students:** 647 \ **Special Ed Students:** 71 \ **LEP Students:** 25 \ **College-Bound:** 57% \ **Ethnic:** Asian 1%, African American 19%, Hispanic 8%, Caucasian 71% \ **Exp:** $509 (High) \ **Poverty:** 27% \ **Title I:** $318,566 \ **Special Education:** $247,000 \ **Open-Close:** 08/14 - 05/21 \ **DTBP:** $31 (Low)

Keri Winters ...................................1,83
Derek Simmons ...................................6*
Ginny Leuba .........................................58
Tyson Knopp ......................................73*
Tony McDuffy .......................................91

Kenneth Hooten ....................................2
Keith Owen ......................11,88,288,298*
Kay Stephens .......................................67
Shannon Crenshaw ..............................76

| Public Schs..Principal | Grd | Prgm | Enr/#Cls | SN | |
|---|---|---|---|---|---|
| Linden Elem Sch<br>205 Kildare Rd, Linden 75563<br>**Missy Hemby** | PK-5 | AT | 300<br>45 | 82% | 903/756-5471<br>Fax 903/756-5022 |
| Linden Kildare High Sch<br>2913 Farm Rd 125 S, Linden 75563<br>Shekita Martin | 9-12 | ATV | 207<br>35 | 62% | 903/756-5314<br>Fax 903/756-8512 |
| Mae Luster Stephens Jr HS<br>Highway 59 S, Linden 75563<br>Rebecca Owen | 6-8 | AT | 140<br>25 | 67% | 903/756-5381<br>Fax 903/756-8832 |

● **McLeod Ind School Dist** PID: 01004891    903/796-7181
19395 Farm Rd 125, Mc Leod 75565    Fax 903/796-8443

**Schools:** 1 \ **Teachers:** 32 \ **Students:** 388 \ **Special Ed Students:** 46 \ **College-Bound:** 35% \ **Ethnic:** African American 2%, Hispanic 1%, Caucasian 97% \ **Exp:** $591 (High) \ **Poverty:** 47% \ **Title I:** $138,318 \ **Open-Close:** 08/17 - 05/21 \ **DTBP:** $334 (High)

Cathy May ...........................................1
Steven Lambeth .....................................6
Shana Whittemore ..............11,57,271,296*
Kathleen O'Kelley ..............................36*
Don Blackwell ......................................67

Brandie Parker ......................................2
Jennifer Lance .....................................8*
Justin Huckabee ..................16,73,286,295*
Twyla Davis .....................................52,55*
Keith Jones ..........................................91

| Public Schs..Principal | Grd | Prgm | Enr/#Cls | SN | |
|---|---|---|---|---|---|
| McLeod Sch<br>19395 FM 125 E, Bivins 75555<br>Erin Lambeth \ Shana Whittemore \ Jennifer Lance | K-12 | TV | 388<br>50 | 45% | 903/796-7181 |

● **Queen City Ind School Dist** PID: 01004920    903/796-8256
1015 Houston St, Queen City 75572    Fax 903/796-0248

**Schools:** 4 \ **Teachers:** 85 \ **Students:** 1,005 \ **Special Ed Students:** 127 \ **LEP Students:** 3 \ **College-Bound:** 27% \ **Ethnic:** African American 16%, Hispanic 3%, Native American: 1%, Caucasian 79% \ **Exp:** $476 (High) \ **Poverty:** 35% \ **Title I:** $443,774 \ **Open-Close:** 08/13 - 05/28 \ **DTBP:** $350 (High) \ **f**

Charlotte Williams .................................1
Pam Upchurch ...................................3,5
Eric Droddy .........................................6*
Kendra Bates ................................38,83*
Jonathan Stanmore ..............................67
Heather Bolt .......................................77

Yolanda Hawkins ....................................2
Shannon Coats .....................................4
Shannon Henderson ...8,11,36,69,72,73,285*
Karen Promza .......................................58
Angie Parker .......................................68

| Public Schs..Principal | Grd | Prgm | Enr/#Cls | SN | |
|---|---|---|---|---|---|
| Ⓐ Dawson-Hillmon Alt Ed Center<br>605 Walker Ln, Queen City 75572<br>Kippie Hartcraft | 5-12 | G | 20<br>3 | | 903/796-0774<br>Fax 903/799-5419 |
| J K Hileman Elem Sch<br>1013 Houston St, Queen City 75572<br>David Estes | PK-4 | T | 345<br>23 | 67% | 903/796-2579<br>Fax 903/799-5275 |
| Morris Upchurch Middle Sch<br>500 5th St, Queen City 75572<br>Steve Holmes | 5-8 | T | 320<br>30 | 53% | 903/796-6412<br>Fax 903/796-0834 |
| Queen City High Sch<br>905 Houston St, Queen City 75572<br>Steve Holmes | 9-12 | GTV | 340<br>25 | 56% | 903/796-8259<br>Fax 903/796-8258 |

## CASTRO COUNTY

## CASTRO PUBLIC SCHOOLS

● **Dimmitt Ind School Dist** PID: 01004968    806/647-3101
608 W Halsell St, Dimmitt 79027    Fax 806/647-5433

**Schools:** 4 \ **Teachers:** 106 \ **Students:** 1,230 \ **Special Ed Students:** 92 \ **LEP Students:** 244 \ **College-Bound:** 45% \ **Ethnic:** Asian 1%, African American 2%, Hispanic 89%, Caucasian 9% \ **Exp:** $679 (High) \ **Poverty:** 22% \ **Title I:** $310,397 \ **Open-Close:** 08/17 - 05/20 \ **DTBP:** $350 (High)

**Jill Millican** .......................................1
Larry Leivas ......................................2,3
Clay Lytle ........................................5,67
Stacy Boozer ...................................11,296
Patrice Hill .....................................34,58
Anthony Montelongo ....................73,295

Becky Standlee .....................................2
Vanessa Escarcega ................................4*
Bret Bethke ..........................................6
Vanesa McClure ...................................16
Sue Summers ......................................69*
Tammy McLain ...................................286

| Public Schs..Principal | Grd | Prgm | Enr/#Cls | SN | |
|---|---|---|---|---|---|
| Ⓐ Dimmitt Alternative Center<br>210 W Jones St, Dimmitt 79027<br>Max Newman | 9-12 | | 10<br>1 | | 806/647-5186<br>Fax 806/647-0701 |
| Dimmitt High Sch<br>1405 Western Cir, Dimmitt 79027<br>Christine Arnold | 9-12 | TV | 337<br>35 | 65% | 806/647-3105<br>Fax 806/647-5795 |
| Dimmitt Middle Sch<br>1505 Western Cir, Dimmitt 79027<br>Tiffany Seaton | 5-8 | TV | 355<br>34 | 77% | 806/647-3108<br>Fax 806/647-2996 |

| | | | | | | | | |
|---|---|---|---|---|---|---|---|---|
| 1 | Superintendent | 8 | Curric/Instruct K-12 | 19 | Chief Financial Officer | 29 | Family/Consumer Science | 39 Social Studies K-12 | 49 English/Lang Arts Elem | 59 Special Education Elem | 69 Academic Assessment |
| 2 | Bus/Finance/Purchasing | 9 | Curric/Instruct Elem | 20 | Art K-12 | 30 | Adult Education | 40 Social Studies Elem | 50 English/Lang Arts Sec | 60 Special Education Sec | 70 Research/Development |
| 3 | Buildings And Grounds | 10 | Curric/Instruct Sec | 21 | Art Elem | 31 | Career/Sch-to-Work K-12 | 41 Social Studies Sec | 51 Reading K-12 | 61 Foreign/World Lang K-12 | 71 Public Information |
| 4 | Food Service | 11 | Federal Program | 22 | Art Sec | 32 | Career/Sch-to-Work Elem | 42 Science K-12 | 52 Reading Elem | 62 Foreign/World Lang Elem | 72 Summer School |
| 5 | Transportation | 12 | Title I | 23 | Music K-12 | 33 | Career/Sch-to-Work Sec | 43 Science Elem | 53 Reading Sec | 63 Foreign/World Lang Sec | 73 Instructional Tech |
| 6 | Athletic | 13 | Title V | 24 | Music Elem | 34 | Early Childhood Ed | 44 Science Sec | 54 Remedial Reading K-12 | 64 Religious Education K-12 | 74 Inservice Training |
| 7 | Health Services | 14 | Asst Superintendent | 25 | Music Sec | 35 | Health/Phys Education | 45 Math K-12 | 55 Remedial Reading Elem | 65 Religious Education Elem | 75 Marketing/Distributive |
| | | 15 | Asst Superintendent | 26 | Business Education | 36 | Guidance Services K-12 | 46 Math Elem | 56 Remedial Reading Sec | 66 Religious Education Sec | 76 Info Systems |
| | | 16 | Instructional Media Svcs | 27 | Career & Tech Ed | 37 | Guidance Services Elem | 47 Math Sec | 57 Bilingual/ELL | 67 School Board President | 77 Psychological Assess |
| | | 17 | Chief Operations Officer | 28 | Technology Education | 38 | Guidance Services Sec | 48 English/Lang Arts K-12 | 58 Special Education K-12 | 68 Teacher Personnel | 78 Affirmative Action |
| | | 18 | Chief Academic Officer | | | | | | | |

| | | | | | |
|---|---|---|---|---|---|
| Richardson Elem Sch | PK-4 | T | 560 | 82% | 806/647-4131 |
| 708 W Stinson St, Dimmitt 79027 | | | 30 | | Fax 806/647-4438 |
| Maritssa Flores | | | | | |

---

● **Hart Ind School Dist** PID: 01005015      806/938-2143
710 2nd Street, Hart 79043      Fax 806/938-2610

**Schools:** 2 \ **Teachers:** 26 \ **Students:** 206 \ **Special Ed Students:** 20 \ **LEP Students:** 29 \ **College-Bound:** 50% \ **Ethnic:** African American 2%, Hispanic 94%, Caucasian 4% \ **Exp:** $397 (High) \ **Poverty:** 31% \ **Title I:** $139,847 \ **Open-Close:** 08/17 - 05/21 \ **DTBP:** $265 (High) \ f t

| | | | |
|---|---|---|---|
| Christa Lara .................1,11 | Tiffany Bradford ................2,298 |
| Eliazar Castillo ..............3,5* | Lupe Lujan ............................4 |
| Christa Chambers .................8 | Retta Knox ...........13,35,83,85,88* |
| Daisy Hernandez ................36 | Mark Castillo ......................57 |
| Senaida De La Fuente ..........58 | Maryann Carrasco ...............67 |
| Ramona Neudorf ................73 | Kelbi Hernandez ..................76 |
| Gloria Godino ..................271 | |

| Public Schs..Principal | Grd | Prgm | Enr/#Cls | SN | |
|---|---|---|---|---|---|
| Hart Elem Sch | PK-5 | T | 123 | 89% | 806/938-2142 |
| 710 2nd Street, Hart 79043 | | | 13 | | Fax 806/938-2188 |
| Krista Lara | | | | | f t |
| Hart Junior Senior High Sch | 6-12 | AGV | 233 | | 806/938-2141 |
| 710 2nd Street, Hart 79043 | | | 26 | | Fax 806/938-2199 |
| Ramona Neudorf | | | | | |

---

● **Nazareth Ind School Dist** PID: 01005041    806/945-2231
101 S 1st Avenue, Nazareth 79063    Fax 806/945-2431

**Schools:** 1 \ **Teachers:** 22 \ **Students:** 253 \ **Special Ed Students:** 11 \ **LEP Students:** 3 \ **College-Bound:** 87% \ **Ethnic:** African American 1%, Hispanic 11%, Native American: 2%, Caucasian 87% \ **Exp:** $955 (High) \ **Poverty:** 11% \ **Title I:** $18,976 \ **Open-Close:** 08/21 - 05/21 \ **DTBP:** $157 (High) \ f

| | |
|---|---|
| Glen Waldo ...............1,11,288 | K'Lynn Gerber .......................2 |
| Ralph Albracht .................3,5 | Robert O'Connor ...............8,57* |
| Nikki Wethington ...............12 | Dana Stanfield ....................26* |
| Austin Heck .....................27* | Marty Gerber .......................67 |
| Cory Hoelting ...............73,295 | |

| Public Schs..Principal | Grd | Prgm | Enr/#Cls | SN | |
|---|---|---|---|---|---|
| Nazareth Sch | PK-12 | TV | 253 | 14% | 806/945-2231 |
| 101 S 1st Avenue, Nazareth 79063 | | | 20 | | |
| **Robert O'Connor** | | | | | |

---

## CHAMBERS COUNTY

---

### CHAMBERS PUBLIC SCHOOLS

---

● **Anahuac Ind School Dist** PID: 01005077    409/267-3600
804 Michael Ricks Dr, Anahuac 77514    Fax 409/267-3855

**Schools:** 3 \ **Teachers:** 96 \ **Students:** 950 \ **Special Ed Students:** 122 \ **LEP Students:** 74 \ **Ethnic:** Asian 2%, African American 11%, Hispanic 33%, Caucasian 52% \ **Exp:** $394 (High) \ **Poverty:** 15% \ **Title I:** $260,775 \ **Open-Close:** 08/13 - 05/20 \ **DTBP:** $1,182 (High)

| | |
|---|---|
| Dennis Wagner .........................1 | Rosie Womack ...................2,5,84 |
| Jim Felice ..............................3 | Stacey Medders ......................3 |
| Marty Murr .............................6* | Patti Nauman .........................8 |
| Deanna Humphrey ......11,36,57,58,69,83,88* | Kenny Dean ................16,73,295* |
| Kristi Henry ........................38,79* | Leslie Todd ........................38* |
| Lane Bertrand .......................67 | |

| Public Schs..Principal | Grd | Prgm | Enr/#Cls | SN | |
|---|---|---|---|---|---|
| Anahuac Elem Sch | PK-5 | T | 582 | 58% | 409/267-3600 |
| 905 S Ross Sterling Rd, Anahuac 77514 | | | 60 | | Fax 409/267-6119 |
| **Tish Powell** | | | | | |
| Anahuac High Sch | 9-12 | TV | 263 | 50% | 409/267-2013 |
| 201 S Kansas St, Anahuac 77514 | | | 40 | | Fax 409/267-5192 |
| Eric Humphrey | | | | | |
| Anahuac Middle Sch | 6-8 | T | 105 | 53% | 409/267-2042 |
| 706 Michael Ricks Dr, Anahuac 77514 | | | 25 | | Fax 409/267-3643 |
| Tammy Duhon | | | | | |

---

● **Barbers Hill Ind School Dist** PID: 01005118    281/576-2221
9600 Eagle Dr, Mont Belvieu 77580    Fax 281/576-5879

**Schools:** 8 \ **Teachers:** 396 \ **Students:** 5,214 \ **Special Ed Students:** 469 \ **LEP Students:** 149 \ **College-Bound:** 80% \ **Ethnic:** Asian 1%, African American 3%, Hispanic 25%, Caucasian 70% \ **Exp:** $305 (High) \ **Poverty:** 5% \ **Title I:** $259,768 \ **Special Education:** $691,000 \ **Open-Close:** 08/19 - 05/27 \ **DTBP:** $164 (High)

| | |
|---|---|
| Dr Greg Poole .........................1 | Becky McManus ...................2,15 |
| Stan Frazier ..................3,5,15,91 | Susan LeBlanc .......................4* |
| Tom Westerberg ..................6,35* | Colleen Goundrey .....................7 |
| Sandra Duree ..........8,15,275,280,286 | Linda Gerhart ..........11,57,271,298* |
| Barbara Ponder ...................15,68 | Kristen Davis ...........16,73,76,82,295 |
| Sue Garcia ......................34,58,77 | Stormy Thibodeaux ..................45 |
| Michelle James .......................48 | Marilyn Ropp ........................58 |
| Kristen Brown ........................59 | George Barrera ......................67 |
| Christine Bruton ..................69,294 | Carla Rabalais ......................71 |
| Stacy Pennington .....................73 | Denise King ........................285* |
| Sebastian Lopez ....................295 | Tim LeBlanc .........................295 |

| Public Schs..Principal | Grd | Prgm | Enr/#Cls | SN | |
|---|---|---|---|---|---|
| Barbers Hill Elem Sch North | 2-5 | T | 840 | 22% | 281/567-2221 |
| PO Box 1108, Mont Belvieu 77580 | | | | | Fax 281/576-3434 |
| **Stephanie Martin** | | | | | |
| Barbers Hill Elem Sch South | 2-5 | T | 920 | 20% | 281/576-3421 |
| 9600 Eagle Dr, Mont Belvieu 77580 | | | | | Fax 281/576-3420 |
| Melissa Barrington | | | | | |
| Barbers Hill High Sch | 9-12 | V | 1,196 | 17% | 281/576-3400 |
| 9696 Eagle Dr, Mont Belvieu 77580 | | | 60 | | Fax 281/576-3356 |
| Rick Kana | | | | | |
| Barbers Hill Kindergarten Ctr | PK-K | T | 597 | 26% | 281/576-3407 |
| 9600 Eagle Dr, Mont Belvieu 77580 | | | | | Fax 281/576-3412 |
| Lisa Watkins | | | | | |
| Barbers Hill Middle Sch North | 6-8 | | 212 | 23% | 281/576-2221 |
| 9600 Eagle Dr, Mont Belvieu 77580 | | | 34 | | Fax 281/576-3352 |
| Lance Murphy | | | | | |
| Barbers Hill Middle Sch South | 6-8 | | 706 | 20% | 281/576-2221 |
| 9600 Eagle Dr, Mont Belvieu 77580 | | | 50 | | Fax 281/576-3350 |
| Chloe Yowell | | | | | |
| Barbers Hill Primary Sch | 1-1 | T | 399 | 20% | 281/576-2221 |
| 9600 Eagle Dr, Mont Belvieu 77580 | | | 27 | | Fax 281/576-3415 |
| Mandy Malone | | | | | |
| Ⓐ Epic Daep Alt Sch | 6-12 | | 35 | | 281/576-2221 |
| 9600 Eagle Dr, Mont Belvieu 77580 | | | | | Fax 281/576-3422 |
| Daniel Andrews | | | | | |

---

**TX—75**

- **East Chambers Ind School Dist** PID: 01005156    409/296-6100
  216 Champions Loop, Winnie 77665    Fax 409/296-3528

> **Schools:** 4 \ **Teachers:** 106 \ **Students:** 1,534 \ **Special Ed Students:** 136 \ **LEP Students:** 319 \ **Ethnic:** Asian 1%, African American 8%, Hispanic 46%, Caucasian 46% \ **Exp:** $886 (High) \ **Poverty:** 6% \ **Title I:** $104,526 \ **Special Education:** $227,000 \ **Open-Close:** 08/17 - 06/01 \ **DTBP:** $575 (High)

| | | | |
|---|---|---|---|
| Scott Campbell | 1 | Gena Huddleston | 2 |
| Darren Smith | 3,5,91 | Dawn Nelson | 4 |
| Russ Sutherland | 6* | Katie Sparks | 7* |
| Renee Brawner | 8,288* | Cindy Bull | 11,57,58,77,83,88,271,296 |
| Mitchell Long | 16,73,288 | Maria Garcia | 57* |
| Gary Hoffpauir | 67 | Nicole Touchet | 68 |
| Tammie Gilsillian | 69,270* | | |

| Public Schs..Principal | Grd | Prgm | Enr/#Cls | SN | |
|---|---|---|---|---|---|
| East Chambers Elem Sch<br>2045 State Highway 124, Winnie 77665<br>Becky Dale | 3-5 | T | 342 | 67% | 409/296-6100<br>Fax 409/296-3259 |
| East Chambers High Sch<br>234 E Buccaneer Dr, Winnie 77665<br>Tom Duoto | 9-12 | GTV | 433<br>32 | 44% | 409/296-4184<br>Fax 409/296-9596 |
| East Chambers Jr High Sch<br>1931 State Highway 124, Winnie 77665<br>Lou Ann Rainey | 6-8 | T | 336<br>20 | 63% | 409/296-4183<br>Fax 409/296-2724 |
| East Chambers Primary Sch<br>316 E Fear Rd, Winnie 77665<br>Andrea Smith | PK-2 | T | 325<br>30 | 61% | 409/296-2980<br>Fax 409/296-3259 |

## CHEROKEE COUNTY

## CHEROKEE PUBLIC SCHOOLS

- **Alto Ind School Dist** PID: 01005209    936/858-7101
  244 County Road 2429, Alto 75925    Fax 936/858-2101

> **Schools:** 3 \ **Teachers:** 58 \ **Students:** 664 \ **Special Ed Students:** 89 \ **LEP Students:** 107 \ **College-Bound:** 58% \ **Ethnic:** African American 24%, Hispanic 34%, Caucasian 42% \ **Exp:** $549 (High) \ **Poverty:** 29% \ **Title I:** $280,715 \ **Special Education:** $20,000 \ **Open-Close:** 08/17 - 05/20 \ **DTBP:** $350 (High)

| | | | |
|---|---|---|---|
| Kelly West | 1 | Kelly Robertson | 2 |
| Kim Bradshaw | 3 | Donnita Lucas | 4 |
| Kerry Birdwell | 11 | Courtney Marshall | 31,83,88* |
| Janette Moore | 57* | Noreen Freeman | 58 |
| Jeff Duplichain | 67 | Adam Knight | 73 |
| Paula Low | 271 | | |

| Public Schs..Principal | Grd | Prgm | Enr/#Cls | SN | |
|---|---|---|---|---|---|
| Alto Elem Sch<br>236 County Road 2429, Alto 75925<br>Candis Mabry | PK-4 | T | 271<br>20 | 71% | 936/587-7174<br>Fax 936/858-4382 |
| Alto High Sch<br>248 County Road 2429, Alto 75925<br>Shanequa Redd-Dorsey | 9-12 | TV | 192<br>30 | 64% | 936/858-7110<br>Fax 936/858-4387 |
| Alto Middle Sch<br>240 County Road 2429, Alto 75925<br>Brandi Tiner | 5-8 | T | 201<br>16 | 68% | 936/858-7140<br>Fax 936/858-4579 |

- **Jacksonville Ind School Dist** PID: 01005235    903/586-6511
  800 College Ave, Jacksonville 75766    Fax 903/586-3133

> **Schools:** 8 \ **Teachers:** 343 \ **Students:** 5,091 \ **Special Ed Students:** 455 \ **LEP Students:** 1,241 \ **College-Bound:** 54% \ **Ethnic:** African American 17%, Hispanic 53%, Native American: 1%, Caucasian 29% \ **Exp:** $406 (High) \ **Poverty:** 25% \ **Title I:** $1,730,320 \ **Special Education:** $1,027,000 \ **Open-Close:** 08/28 - 05/28 \ **DTBP:** $157 (High)

| | | | |
|---|---|---|---|
| Dr Chad Kelly | 1 | Lindy Finley | 2 |
| Troy Parker | 2 | Tommy Wade | 3,91 |
| Clay Carter | 4 | Mark Turney | 5 |
| Wayne Coleman | 6* | Nicole Fontenot | 7* |
| Lisa Cox | 8,72,79,275* | Lisa Dailey | 8,11,16,83,273,294,298 |
| Hedda Alexander | 16,73,76,98,295 | Amber Penn | 57,89,271 |
| Sara Gill | 58 | Randy McCown | 67 |
| Brad Stewart | 68 | Kala Moore | 68 |
| Grace Traylor | 71 | Lynne Bullock | 73,84 |
| Marvin Acker | 91* | Buddy Attaway | 295 |

| Public Schs..Principal | Grd | Prgm | Enr/#Cls | SN | |
|---|---|---|---|---|---|
| Ⓐ Compass Center<br>436 SW Loop 456, Jacksonville 75766<br>Timothy Rucker | PK-12 | T | 3<br>7 | | 903/589-3926<br>Fax 903/586-7158 |
| East Side Elem Sch<br>711 Fort Worth St, Jacksonville 75766<br>Jodi Alderete | PK-4 | T | 517<br>35 | 68% | 903/586-5146<br>Fax 903/589-4977 |
| Fred Douglass Elem Sch<br>1501 E Pine St, Jacksonville 75766<br>Carlos Franz | PK-4 | T | 518<br>40 | 86% | 903/586-6519<br>Fax 903/589-4341 |
| Jacksonville High Sch<br>1210 Corinth Rd, Jacksonville 75766<br>Ben Peacock | 9-12 | TV | 1,311 | 72% | 903/586-3661<br>Fax 903/586-8229 |
| Jacksonville Middle Sch<br>1541 E Pine St, Jacksonville 75766<br>Patsy Whitaker | 7-8 | T | 721<br>51 | 82% | 903/586-3686<br>Fax 903/586-8071 |
| Joe Wright Elem Sch<br>1055 N Pineda St, Jacksonville 75766<br>Cindy Slovacek | PK-4 | T | 405<br>27 | 89% | 903/586-5286<br>Fax 903/589-8108 |
| Nichols Intermediate Sch<br>818 SW Loop 456, Jacksonville 75766<br>Holly Searcy | 5-6 | T | 803<br>45 | 85% | 903/541-0213<br>Fax 903/541-0199 |
| West Side Elem Sch<br>1105 College Ave, Jacksonville 75766<br>Alicia Tennison | PK-4 | T | 427<br>26 | 93% | 903/586-5165<br>Fax 903/586-6196 |

- **New Summerfield Ind Sch Dist** PID: 01005340    903/726-3306
  13307 Hwy 110 S, New Summerfld 75780    Fax 903/726-3405

> **Schools:** 1 \ **Teachers:** 46 \ **Students:** 544 \ **Special Ed Students:** 36 \ **LEP Students:** 214 \ **College-Bound:** 59% \ **Ethnic:** Asian 1%, African American 3%, Hispanic 84%, Caucasian 12% \ **Exp:** $532 (High) \ **Poverty:** 17% \ **Title I:** $120,268 \ **Open-Close:** 08/14 - 05/20 \ **DTBP:** $350 (High) \ 🇹

| | | | |
|---|---|---|---|
| Joe Brannen | 1 | Lanita Parker-Felder | 2 |
| Eric Boyett | 3,5* | Dawn Sutlive | 4 |
| Kent Willis | 6* | Dr Craig Wilcox | 8,11,57* |
| Troy Jenkins | 16,73,297* | Michael Davis | 67 |
| Ashley Faucett | 69,83,270* | Marina Francis | 76 |

| Public Schs..Principal | Grd | Prgm | Enr/#Cls | SN | |
|---|---|---|---|---|---|
| New Summerfield Sch<br>13307 Hwy 110 S, New Summerfld 75780<br>**Donna Jeffus** \ Angela Tucker \ Joshua Faucett | PK-12 | TV | 544<br>38 | 92% | 903/726-3306<br>Fax 903/726-3421 |

| | | | | |
|---|---|---|---|---|
| 1 | Superintendent | 8 | Curric/Instruct K-12 | 19 | Chief Financial Officer |
| 2 | Bus/Finance/Purchasing | 9 | Curric/Instruct Elem | 20 | Art K-12 |
| 3 | Buildings And Grounds | 10 | Curric/Instruct Sec | 21 | Art Elem |
| 4 | Food Service | 11 | Federal Program | 22 | Art Sec |
| 5 | Transportation | 12 | Title I | 23 | Music K-12 |
| 6 | Athletic | 13 | Title V | 24 | Music Elem |
| 7 | Health Services | 14 | Instructional Media Svcs | 25 | Music Sec |
| | | 15 | Asst Superintendent | 26 | Business Education |
| | | 16 | Instructional Media Svcs | 27 | Career & Tech Ed |
| | | 17 | Chief Operations Officer | 28 | Technology Education |
| | | 18 | Chief Academic Officer | | |

29 Family/Consumer Science · 30 Adult Education · 31 Career/Sch-to-Work K-12 · 32 Career/Sch-to-Work Elem · 33 Career/Sch-to-Work Sec · 34 Early Childhood Ed · 35 Health/Phys Education · 36 Guidance Services K-12 · 37 Guidance Services Elem · 38 Guidance Services Sec

39 Social Studies K-12 · 40 Social Studies Elem · 41 Social Studies Sec · 42 Science K-12 · 43 Science Elem · 44 Science Sec · 45 Math K-12 · 46 Math Elem · 47 Math Sec · 48 English/Lang Arts K-12

49 English/Lang Arts Elem · 50 English/Lang Arts Sec · 51 Reading K-12 · 52 Reading Elem · 53 Reading Sec · 54 Remedial Reading K-12 · 55 Remedial Reading Elem · 56 Remedial Reading Sec · 57 Bilingual/ELL · 58 Special Education K-12

59 Special Education Elem · 60 Special Education Sec · 61 Foreign/World Lang K-12 · 62 Foreign/World Lang Elem · 63 Foreign/World Lang Sec · 64 Religious Education K-12 · 65 Religious Education Elem · 66 Religious Education Sec · 67 School Board President · 68 Teacher Personnel

69 Academic Assessment · 70 Research/Development · 71 Public Information · 72 Summer School · 73 Instructional Tech · 74 Inservice Training · 75 Marketing/Distributive · 76 Info Systems · 77 Psychological Assess · 78 Affirmative Action

● **Rusk Ind School Dist** PID: 01005364
203 E 7th St, Rusk 75785

903/683-5592
Fax 903/683-2104

**Schools:** 5 \ **Teachers:** 157 \ **Students:** 1,979 \ **Special Ed Students:** 251 \ **LEP Students:** 115 \ **Ethnic:** African American 14%, Hispanic 18%, Caucasian 67% \ **Exp:** $477 (High) \ **Poverty:** 19% \ **Title I:** $476,136 \ **Open-Close:** 08/12 - 05/20 \ **DTBP:** $343 (High) \ t

| | |
|---|---|
| Grey Barton ..............................1 | Stacie Young ..................2,15,294 |
| Greg Dover ...............................3 | John Hood .....................4,11,288* |
| Joseph Eckel ............................5 | Jowell Hancock ....................6,35 |
| Teara Newman .........................7 | Betty Collins ....... 8,27,57,74,88,271,296,298 |
| Gary Cruseturner .... 16,28,73,76,295,297 | Tammy Hancock ...................34* |
| Theresa Gates ....................38,91 | Donna Tugwell ..................58,77 |
| Britt Patterson ......................67 | Kim Henson .........................68 |
| Scott Blackmon .....................84 | |

| Public Schs..Principal | Grd | Prgm | Enr/#Cls | SN | |
|---|---|---|---|---|---|
| Rusk Elem Sch<br>300 N Henderson St, Rusk 75785<br>Deborah Welch | 2-3 | T | 286<br>30 | 72% | 903/683-2595<br>Fax 903/683-6299 |
| Rusk High Sch<br>495 Eagle Dr, Rusk 75785<br>Ronny Snow | 9-12 | ATV | 604<br>35 | 54% | 903/683-5401<br>Fax 903/683-6090 |
| Rusk Intermediate Sch<br>1143 Loop 343, Rusk 75785<br>Jan Evans | 4-5 | T | 336 | 74% | 903/683-1726<br>Fax 903/683-5167 |
| Rusk Junior High Sch<br>1345 S Main St, Rusk 75785<br>Jon Burkhalter | 6-8 | ATV | 436<br>35 | 67% | 903/683-2502<br>Fax 903/683-4363 |
| Rusk Primary Sch<br>440 Collins St, Rusk 75785<br>Tammy Hancock | PK-1 | T | 280<br>24 | 78% | 903/683-6106<br>Fax 903/683-6299 |

● **Wells Ind School Dist** PID: 01005405
160 Rusk Ave, Wells 75976

936/867-4466
Fax 936/867-4497

**Schools:** 2 \ **Teachers:** 28 \ **Students:** 280 \ **Special Ed Students:** 35 \ **LEP Students:** 9 \ **Ethnic:** African American 9%, Hispanic 11%, Caucasian 80% \ **Exp:** $806 (High) \ **Poverty:** 27% \ **Title I:** $137,209 \ **Open-Close:** 08/10 - 05/27 \ **DTBP:** $138 (High)

| | |
|---|---|
| **Jill Gaston** ...............................1 | Jana Oquinn ...........................2 |
| Brett Redd ............................3,5 | Cindy Totin .............................4 |
| Lisa Cockrum ............8,11,69,294* | Kathy Ford ......... 31,34,36,83,85,88,270 |
| Lisa Cockrum ........................57 | Joy Julian ...........................58* |
| Wayne Montes ......................67 | Slade Johnson .............73,295,296* |

| Public Schs..Principal | Grd | Prgm | Enr/#Cls | SN | |
|---|---|---|---|---|---|
| Wells Elem Sch<br>Highway 69, Wells 75976<br>Bryan Caughlin | PK-6 | T | 169<br>15 | 69% | 936/867-4400<br>Fax 936/867-4466 |
| Wells High Sch<br>Highway 69, Wells 75976<br>Kristel Hise | 7-12 | TV | 129<br>10 | 62% | 936/867-4400 |

## CHEROKEE PRIVATE SCHOOLS

| Private Schs..Principal | Grd | Prgm | Enr/#Cls | SN | |
|---|---|---|---|---|---|
| Christ the Redeemer Sch<br>247 S Barron St, Rusk 75785<br>Debra McCormick | K-12 | | 100 | | 903/683-1404<br>Fax 903/683-1341 |

## CHILDRESS PUBLIC SCHOOLS

● **Childress Ind School Dist** PID: 01005431
308 3rd St NW, Childress 79201

940/937-2501
Fax 940/937-2938

**Schools:** 4 \ **Teachers:** 91 \ **Students:** 1,052 \ **Special Ed Students:** 132 \ **LEP Students:** 31 \ **College-Bound:** 50% \ **Ethnic:** Asian 2%, African American 4%, Hispanic 42%, Caucasian 52% \ **Exp:** $530 (High) \ **Poverty:** 22% \ **Title I:** $311,302 \ **Open-Close:** 08/13 - 05/20 \ **DTBP:** $377 (High) \ f t

| | |
|---|---|
| Rick Teran ...........................1,83 | Karen Leonard .......................2 |
| Joel Camacho .........................3 | Tracee Herbstritt ....................4 |
| Jayson Read ...........................5 | Jason Sims ............................6 |
| Sarah Mills .......................8,11,58 | Janet Word ............................9* |
| Faith Self ..........................16* | Roy Novak ..........................27* |
| Sherry Davis .......................36* | Alicia Jurado .......................57* |
| Mark Keys ............................67 | John Galligan ...............73,295* |

| Public Schs..Principal | Grd | Prgm | Enr/#Cls | SN | |
|---|---|---|---|---|---|
| Childress Elem Sch<br>300 3rd St SE, Childress 79201<br>Janet Word | PK-5 | T | 477<br>34 | 67% | 940/937-6313<br>Fax 940/937-2165 |
| Childress High Sch<br>800 Avenue J NW, Childress 79201<br>Paige Steed | 9-12 | TV | 326 | 50% | 940/937-6131<br>Fax 940/937-2039<br>f t |
| Childress Junior High Sch<br>700 Commerce St, Childress 79201<br>Marsha Meacham | 6-8 | T | 249<br>22 | 55% | 940/937-3641<br>Fax 940/937-8427 |
| Ⓐ Gateway Academy<br>600 Avenue F NW, Childress 79201<br>Janet Word \ Marsha Meacham | 3-12 | | 20<br>2 | | 940/937-3099 |

## CLAY PUBLIC SCHOOLS

● **Bellevue Ind School Dist** PID: 01005481
500 7th Street, Bellevue 76228

940/928-2104
Fax 940/928-2583

**Schools:** 1 \ **Teachers:** 17 \ **Students:** 140 \ **Special Ed Students:** 13 \ **College-Bound:** 75% \ **Ethnic:** Asian 1%, African American 1%, Hispanic 7%, Native American: 1%, Caucasian 91% \ **Exp:** $401 (High) \ **Poverty:** 13% \ **Title I:** $20,667 \ **Open-Close:** 08/13 - 05/14 \ f t

| | |
|---|---|
| Wade Wesley ........................1,11 | Colby Broussard .....................6* |
| Terry Dunlap ....................58,296 | John Grunseich ....................67 |
| Johney Chandler ................69,88* | Sunny Mitchell .............73,295* |
| Marshal Hanson ......................81 | |

| Public Schs..Principal | Grd | Prgm | Enr/#Cls | SN | |
|---|---|---|---|---|---|
| Bellevue Sch<br>500 7th Street, Bellevue 76228<br>Terry Dunlap | K-12 | TV | 140<br>17 | 51% | 940/928-2104 |

- **Henrietta Ind School Dist** PID: 01005546  940/720-7900
  1801 E Crafton St, Henrietta 76365  Fax 940/538-7505

**Schools:** 3 \ **Teachers:** 77 \ **Students:** 937 \ **Special Ed Students:** 118 \
**LEP Students:** 5 \ **College-Bound:** 59% \ **Ethnic:** Asian 1%, Hispanic 10%,
Native American: 1%, Caucasian 88% \ **Exp:** $795 (High) \ **Poverty:** 14% \
**Title I:** $145,792 \ **Open-Close:** 08/20 - 05/27 \ **DTBP:** $533 (High)

| | | | |
|---|---|---|---|
| Scot Clayton | 1 | Joy Campbell | 2 |
| Brittanie Brown | 4 | George Gisler | 5 |
| Michael Johnson | 6 | Jeanette Holding | 7* |
| Kendra Bennett | 8,11,15,288,296 | Mandy Story | 16* |
| Cheryl Holbert | 31,69,83,85* | Dr Terell White | 58 |
| Betty Ellsworth | 67 | Derek Leach | 73,76 |

| Public Schs..Principal | Grd | Prgm | Enr/#Cls | SN | |
|---|---|---|---|---|---|
| Henrietta Elem Sch<br>1600 E Crafton St, Henrietta 76365<br>**Debra McClure** | PK-5 | T | 419<br>24 | 50% | 940/720-7910<br>Fax 940/538-7515 |
| Henrietta High Sch<br>1700 E Crafton St, Henrietta 76365<br>Michael Smiley | 9-12 | V | 275<br>20 | 35% | 940/720-7930<br>Fax 940/538-7535 |
| Henrietta Junior High Sch<br>308 E Gilbert St, Henrietta 76365<br>Terry McCutchen | 6-8 | | 191<br>20 | 45% | 940/720-7920<br>Fax 940/538-7525 |

- **Midway Ind School Dist** PID: 01005584  940/476-2215
  12142 State Highway 148 S, Henrietta 76365  Fax 940/476-2226

**Schools:** 1 \ **Teachers:** 16 \ **Students:** 134 \ **Special Ed Students:** 27 \
**College-Bound:** 75% \ **Ethnic:** Hispanic 10%, Caucasian 90% \ **Exp:** $625
(High) \ **Poverty:** 21% \ **Title I:** $22,871 \ **Open-Close:** 08/13 - 05/26

| | | | |
|---|---|---|---|
| Randel Beaver | 1 | Julie Laude | 2 |
| Cami Franke | 4* | Darla Hutchins | 11,73,84,286 |
| Glenda Terry | 16* | Treva Byrne | 58* |
| Derek Leach | 67 | | |

| Public Schs..Principal | Grd | Prgm | Enr/#Cls | SN | |
|---|---|---|---|---|---|
| Midway Sch<br>12142 State Highway 148 S, Henrietta 76365<br>Daniel Hutchins | PK-12 | TV | 134<br>13 | 60% | 940/476-2215 |

- **Petrolia Cons Ind School Dist** PID: 01005601  940/524-3555
  701 S Prairie Avenue, Petrolia 76377  Fax 940/524-3370

**Schools:** 2 \ **Teachers:** 46 \ **Students:** 450 \ **Special Ed Students:** 52 \
**LEP Students:** 4 \ **College-Bound:** 62% \ **Ethnic:** African American 1%,
Hispanic 12%, Native American: 1%, Caucasian 86% \ **Exp:** $766 (High) \
**Poverty:** 15% \ **Title I:** $79,625 \ **Open-Close:** 08/19 - 05/21 \ **DTBP:** $362
(High)

| | | | |
|---|---|---|---|
| David Hedges | 1 | Theresa Harrison | 2,84 |
| David Sizemore | 3,5,79,91 | Skyla Barger | 4* |
| Mitch McLamore | 6 | Dustin Barger | 67 |
| Clint Perkins | 69,83,88* | | |

| Public Schs..Principal | Grd | Prgm | Enr/#Cls | SN | |
|---|---|---|---|---|---|
| Petrolia Elem Sch<br>701 S Prairie Ave, Petrolia 76377<br>**Clint Perkins** | PK-6 | T | 251<br>15 | 64% | 940/524-3433<br>Fax 940/524-3302 |
| Petrolia Jr Sr High Sch<br>8307 FM810, Petrolia 76377<br>Clint Perkins | 7-12 | V | 199<br>17 | 55% | 940/524-3264<br>Fax 940/524-3215 |

## COCHRAN COUNTY

---

## COCHRAN PUBLIC SCHOOLS

- **Morton Ind School Dist** PID: 01005675  806/266-5505
  500 Champion Dr, Morton 79346  Fax 806/266-5449

**Schools:** 3 \ **Teachers:** 39 \ **Students:** 400 \ **Special Ed Students:** 44
\ **LEP Students:** 63 \ **College-Bound:** 80% \ **Ethnic:** African American
1%, Hispanic 89%, Caucasian 10% \ **Exp:** $623 (High) \ **Poverty:** 27% \
**Title I:** $197,820 \ **Open-Close:** 08/24 - 05/24 \ **DTBP:** $350 (High)

| | | | |
|---|---|---|---|
| Karen Saunders | 1 | Tera Cruz | 2 |
| Gerry McLendon | 5 | Brain Ramsey | 6 |
| Kina Ramas | 8 | Holly Boggs | 9,11,57,88* |
| Rina Ramos | 9* | Rod Cottrell | 16,73,76,295 |
| Russell Hill | 16* | Ann Hill | 58 |
| Glen Lyon | 67 | Regina Ingle | 271* |
| Becky Cottrell | 274* | Natasha Newman | 298 |

| Public Schs..Principal | Grd | Prgm | Enr/#Cls | SN | |
|---|---|---|---|---|---|
| Morton Elem Sch<br>500 Champion Dr, Morton 79346<br>Kellye Kuehler | PK-5 | | 195<br>18 | | 806/266-5505<br>Fax 806/266-5123 |
| Morton High Sch<br>500 Champion Dr, Morton 79346<br>Regina Ingle | 9-12 | TV | 98<br>15 | 79% | 806/266-5505<br>Fax 806/266-5780 |
| Morton Junior High Sch<br>500 Champion Dr, Morton 79346<br>Smith Glen | 6-8 | | 87<br>12 | | 806/266-5505<br>Fax 806/266-5739 |

- **Whiteface Con Ind School Dist** PID: 01005728  806/287-1154
  401 Antelope Blvd, Whiteface 79379  Fax 806/287-1131

**Schools:** 2 \ **Teachers:** 31 \ **Students:** 345 \ **Special Ed Students:** 30 \
**LEP Students:** 21 \ **College-Bound:** 70% \ **Ethnic:** African American 1%,
Hispanic 60%, Native American: 1%, Caucasian 38% \ **Exp:** $801 (High) \
**Poverty:** 29% \ **Title I:** $68,957 \ **Open-Close:** 08/19 - 05/20 \ **DTBP:** $362
(High)

| | | | |
|---|---|---|---|
| Nate Wheeler | 1,11 | Tammie Bentley | 2 |
| Tom Rohmfeld | 3,5 | Linda Stockman | 4 |
| Maranda Tucker | 9,93,274 | Carrie Casarez | 16* |
| Kyna Wheeler | 18 | Bev Byrne | 31* |
| Beverly Byrne | 36,69,83,85,88,270* | Audra Davis | 57,271* |
| Teresa Desautell | 60* | Corey Ayers | 67 |
| Joel Dietz | 73,98 | Christopher Mendez | 280* |

| Public Schs..Principal | Grd | Prgm | Enr/#Cls | SN | |
|---|---|---|---|---|---|
| Whiteface Elem Sch<br>2nd St & Arthur St, Whiteface 79379<br>Scott Lucas | PK-5 | | 165<br>15 | | 806/287-1285 |

| | | | | | | | | | |
|---|---|---|---|---|---|---|---|---|---|
| 1 | Superintendent | 8 | Curric/Instruct K-12 | 19 | Chief Financial Officer | 29 | Family/Consumer Science | 39 | Social Studies K-12 |
| 2 | Bus/Finance/Purchasing | 9 | Curric/Instruct Elem | 20 | Art K-12 | 30 | Adult Education | 40 | Social Studies Elem |
| 3 | Buildings And Grounds | 10 | Curric/Instruct Sec | 21 | Art Elem | 31 | Career/Sch-to-Work K-12 | 41 | Social Studies Sec |
| 4 | Food Service | 11 | Federal Program | 22 | Art Sec | 32 | Career/Sch-to-Work Elem | 42 | Science K-12 |
| 5 | Transportation | 12 | Title I | 23 | Music K-12 | 33 | Career/Sch-to-Work Sec | 43 | Science Elem |
| 6 | Athletic | 13 | Title V | 24 | Music Elem | 34 | Early Childhood Ed | 44 | Science Sec |
| 7 | Health Services | 14 | Asst Superintendent | 25 | Music Sec | 35 | Health/Phys Education | 45 | Math K-12 |
| | | 15 | Instructional Media Svcs | 26 | Business Education | 36 | Guidance Services K-12 | 46 | Math Elem |
| | | 16 | Chief Operations Officer | 27 | Career & Tech Ed | 37 | Guidance Services Elem | 47 | Math Sec |
| | | 17 | Chief Academic Officer | 28 | Technology Education | 38 | Guidance Services Sec | 48 | English/Lang Arts K-12 |

| | | | | | |
|---|---|---|---|---|---|
| 49 | English/Lang Arts Elem | 59 | Special Education Elem | 69 | Academic Assessment |
| 50 | English/Lang Arts Sec | 60 | Special Education Sec | 70 | Research/Development |
| 51 | Reading K-12 | 61 | Foreign/World Lang K-12 | 71 | Public Information |
| 52 | Reading Elem | 62 | Foreign/World Lang Elem | 72 | Summer School |
| 53 | Reading Sec | 63 | Foreign/World Lang Sec | 73 | Instructional Tech |
| 54 | Remedial Reading K-12 | 64 | Religious Education K-12 | 74 | Inservice Training |
| 55 | Remedial Reading Elem | 65 | Religious Education Elem | 75 | Marketing/Distributive |
| 56 | Remedial Reading Sec | 66 | Religious Education Sec | 76 | Info Systems |
| 57 | Bilingual/ELL | 67 | School Board President | 77 | Psychological Assess |
| 58 | Special Education K-12 | 68 | Teacher Personnel | 78 | Affirmative Action |

| Whiteface High Sch<br>3 2nd St, Whiteface 79379<br>Christopher Mendez | 6-12 | T | 166<br>20 | 61% | 806/287-1104 |

## COKE COUNTY

## COLEMAN COUNTY

## COKE PUBLIC SCHOOLS

## COLEMAN PUBLIC SCHOOLS

● **Bronte Ind School Dist** PID: 01005754          325/473-2511
210 S Jefferson St, Bronte 76933          Fax 325/473-2313

Schools: 2 \ Teachers: 26 \ Students: 225 \ Special Ed Students: 24 \
LEP Students: 4 \ Ethnic: Hispanic 32%, Caucasian 67% \ Exp: $666 (High)
\ Poverty: 19% \ Title I: $63,720 \ Open-Close: 08/10 - 05/27 \ DTBP: $372
(High)

| | | | |
|---|---|---|---|
| Tim Siler | 1,11 | Danielle Queen | 4 |
| Natasha Sullivan | 5 | Rocky Rawls | 6* |
| Jennifer Neglert | 8* | John Phillips | 9,11,52,55 |
| Rebecca Siler | 11,73,286,295,296,297* | Mary McMullan | 16,73,82,286,295,297 |
| Sara Baxter | 23* | Daisy Sanchez | 36,57,69,83,88,270,273* |
| Rose Whitehurst | 57 | Paula Connally | 58,280 |
| Blake Braswell | 67 | | |

| Public Schs..Principal | Grd | Prgm | Enr/#Cls | SN | |
|---|---|---|---|---|---|
| Bronte Elem Sch<br>210 S Jefferson St, Bronte 76933<br>Donna Poehls | PK-6 | | 131<br>10 | | 325/473-2251 |
| Bronte High Sch<br>210 S Jefferson St, Bronte 76933<br>**Doug Kuhlmann** | 7-12 | ATV | 131<br>16 | 47% | 325/473-2521<br>Fax 325/473-2022 |

● **Robert Lee Ind School Dist** PID: 01005780          325/453-4555
1323 W Hamilton St, Robert Lee 76945          Fax 325/453-2326

Schools: 1 \ Teachers: 29 \ Students: 260 \ Special Ed Students: 34 \
LEP Students: 6 \ College-Bound: 50% \ Ethnic: African American 1%,
Hispanic 32%, Native American: 3%, Caucasian 64% \ Exp: $1,227 (High) \
Poverty: 20% \ Title I: $58,538 \ Open-Close: 08/17 - 05/21 \ DTBP: $350
(High)

| | | | |
|---|---|---|---|
| Aaron Hood | 1,11 | Robin Allen | 2 |
| Mariann Hill | 12,57* | Sandy Sawyer | 16,73,76,286* |
| Wes Washam | 67 | | |

| Public Schs..Principal | Grd | Prgm | Enr/#Cls | SN | |
|---|---|---|---|---|---|
| Robert Lee Sch<br>1323 W Hamilton St, Robert Lee 76945<br>David Odell \ Lee McCown | PK-12 | ATV | 260<br>36 | 51% | 325/453-4555 |

● **Coleman Ind School Dist** PID: 01005819          325/625-3575
300 W Pecan St, Coleman 76834          Fax 325/625-4751

Schools: 3 \ Teachers: 78 \ Students: 869 \ Special Ed Students: 91
\ LEP Students: 22 \ College-Bound: 59% \ Ethnic: Asian 1%, African
American 2%, Hispanic 27%, Caucasian 70% \ Exp: $518 (High) \
Poverty: 26% \ Title I: $412,807 \ Open-Close: 08/19 - 05/27 \ DTBP: $392
(High)

| | | | |
|---|---|---|---|
| Brandon McDowell | 1 | Karen Huff | 2 |
| Weldon Thompson | 3 | Shirley Bartell | 4 |
| Chris Burton | 5 | John Elder | 6* |
| Joy Thompson | 8,12,34,57,296* | Ed Pryor | 11,69 |
| Anthony Beggs | 27* | Alissa Hohmann | 36* |
| Angelita Stephenson | 58* | Mark Martinez | 67 |
| Gay Martin | 73 | Paul Martin | 73,76,295,297* |
| Amy Flippin | 83,85,270,273* | | |

| Public Schs..Principal | Grd | Prgm | Enr/#Cls | SN | |
|---|---|---|---|---|---|
| Coleman Elem Sch<br>303 15th St, Coleman 76834<br>Joy Thompson | PK-4 | T | 375<br>30 | 65% | 325/625-3546<br>Fax 325/625-4064 |
| Coleman High Sch<br>201 15th St, Coleman 76834<br>Diana Dobbins | 9-12 | TV | 254<br>30 | 43% | 325/625-2156<br>Fax 325/625-4557 |
| Coleman Junior High Sch<br>301 15th St, Coleman 76834<br>Thomas King | 5-8 | T | 240<br>20 | 58% | 325/625-3593<br>Fax 325/625-3358 |

● **Panther Creek Cons Ind SD** PID: 01005950          325/357-4449
Farm Road 503, Voss 76888          Fax 325/357-4470

Schools: 1 \ Teachers: 18 \ Students: 150 \ Special Ed Students: 16 \
College-Bound: 80% \ Ethnic: Asian 1%, African American 3%, Hispanic
19%, Native American: 1%, Caucasian 77% \ Exp: $628 (High) \ Poverty: 34%
\ Title I: $105,883 \ Open-Close: 08/19 - 05/19 \ DTBP: $382 (High) \ 

| | | | |
|---|---|---|---|
| Dwin Nanny | 1,11 | Jan Romina | 2,8,19 |
| Jeanene Pricer | 57 | Brin Ball | 58 |
| Jay Dalton | 67 | Mark Romine | 73* |
| Seth Jackson | 88,285 | | |

| Public Schs..Principal | Grd | Prgm | Enr/#Cls | SN | |
|---|---|---|---|---|---|
| Panther Creek Sch<br>Farm Road 503, Voss 76888<br>Dwin Nanny | PK-12 | TV | 150<br>34 | 77% | 325/357-4449 |

● **Santa Anna Ind School Dist** PID: 01005924          325/348-3136
701 Bowie St, Santa Anna 76878          Fax 325/348-3141

Schools: 2 \ Teachers: 26 \ Students: 250 \ Special Ed Students: 22
\ College-Bound: 75% \ Ethnic: African American 3%, Hispanic 27%,
Native American: 2%, Caucasian 68% \ Exp: $985 (High) \ Poverty: 25% \
Title I: $185,139 \ Open-Close: 08/17 - 05/21 \ DTBP: $344 (High) \ 

| | | | |
|---|---|---|---|
| **Todd White** | 1 | Katrina Tomlinson | 2,11* |

| | | | | |
|---|---|---|---|---|
| 79 Student Personnel | 91 Safety/Security | 275 Response To Intervention | 298 Grant Writer/Ptnrships | School Programs |
| 80 Driver Ed/Safety | 92 Magnet School | 277 Remedial Math K-12 | 750 Chief Innovation Officer | A = Alternative Program |
| 81 Gifted/Talented | 93 Parental Involvement | 280 Literacy Coach | 751 Chief of Staff | G = Adult Classes |
| 82 Video Services | 95 Tech Prep Program | 285 STEM | 752 Social Emotional Learning | M = Magnet Program |
| 83 Substance Abuse Prev | 97 Chief Infomation Officer | 286 Digital Learning | | T = Title I Schoolwide |
| 84 Erate | 98 Chief Technology Officer | 288 Common Core Standards | Other School Types | V = Career & Tech Ed Programs |
| 85 AIDS Education | 270 Character Education | 294 Accountability | Ⓐ = Alternative School | |
| 88 Alternative/At Risk | 271 Migrant Education | 295 Network System | Ⓒ = Charter School | Social Media |
| 89 Multi-Cultural Curriculum | 273 Teacher Mentor | 296 Title II Programs | Ⓜ = Magnet School | 🔵 = Facebook |
| 90 Social Work | 274 Before/After Sch | 297 Webmaster | Ⓨ = Year-Round School | 🔵 = Twitter |

New Schools are shaded
New Superintendents and Principals are bold
Personnel with email addresses are underscored

**TX—79**

| Public Schs..Principal | Grd | Prgm | Enr/#Cls | SN |
|---|---|---|---|---|
| Santa Anna Elem Sch<br>506 Jefferson St, Santa Anna 76878<br>Aletha Patterson | PK-6 | T | 147<br>10 | 98% 325/348-3138<br>Fax 325/348-3142 |
| Santa Anna High Sch<br>701 Bowie St, Santa Anna 76878<br>**Edward Morales** | 7-12 | TV | 117<br>14 | 97% 325/348-3137<br>Fax 325/348-3149 |

# COLLIN COUNTY

## COLLIN PUBLIC SCHOOLS

• **Allen Ind School Dist** PID: 01005986    972/727-0511
612 E Bethany Dr, Allen 75002    Fax 972/727-0500

**Schools:** 24 \ **Teachers:** 1,351 \ **Students:** 21,404 \
**Special Ed Students:** 2,416 \ **LEP Students:** 1,512 \ **College-Bound:** 75%
\ **Ethnic:** Asian 22%, African American 14%, Hispanic 15%, Native American:
1%, Caucasian 49% \ **Exp:** $151 (Low) \ **Poverty:** 4% \ **Title I:** $1,256,553 \
**Special Education:** $2,667,000 \ **Open-Close:** 08/12 - 05/21 \ **DTBP:** $181
(High) \ [f]

| Public Schs..Principal | Grd | Prgm | Enr/#Cls | SN |
|---|---|---|---|---|
| Allen High Sch<br>300 Rivercrest Blvd, Allen 75002<br>**Matt Russell** | 9-12 | V | 5,098<br>175 | 15% 972/727-0400<br>Fax 972/727-0515 |
| Alton Boyd Elem Sch<br>800 S Jupiter Rd, Allen 75002<br>Judith Coffman | PK-6 | T | 561<br>35 | 71% 972/727-0560<br>Fax 972/727-0566 |
| Alvis C Story Elem Sch<br>1550 Edelweiss Dr, Allen 75002<br>Amanda Tabor | PK-6 | | 432<br>45 | 24% 972/727-0570<br>Fax 972/727-0573 |
| Beverly Cheatham Elem Sch<br>1501 Hopewell Dr, Allen 75013<br>Stephanie Logan | PK-6 | | 542 | 7% 972/396-3016<br>Fax 972/396-3035 |
| Boon Elem Sch<br>1050 Comanche Dr, Allen 75013<br>Lauren Cypert | PK-6 | | 627 | 12% 972/747-3331<br>Fax 972/747-3335 |

| Public Schs..Principal | Grd | Prgm | Enr/#Cls | SN |
|---|---|---|---|---|
| Chandler Elem Sch<br>1000 Water Oak Dr, Allen 75002<br>**Bobbie Allen** | PK-6 | | 587 | 19% 469/467-1400<br>Fax 469/467-1410 |
| D L Rountree Elem Sch<br>800 E Main St, Allen 75002<br>Lara Utecht | PK-6 | T | 540<br>35 | 78% 972/727-0550<br>Fax 972/727-0555 |
| Ⓐ Dillard Spec Achievement Ctr<br>610 E Bethany Dr, Allen 75002<br>Eric Pacheco | K-12 | | 100<br>4 | 972/727-7163<br>Fax 972/727-7162 |
| Ereckson Middle Sch<br>450 Tatum Dr, Allen 75013<br>Leslie Norris | 7-8 | V | 1,241 | 15% 972/747-3308<br>Fax 972/747-3311 |
| Flossie Floyd Green Elem Sch<br>1315 Comanche Dr, Allen 75013<br>Stacia Butler | PK-6 | | 546<br>30 | 18% 972/727-0370<br>Fax 972/727-0373 |
| Frances Norton Elem Sch<br>1120 Newport Dr, Allen 75013<br>Julie DeLeon | PK-6 | | 443<br>40 | 12% 972/396-6918<br>Fax 972/396-6923 |
| Gene M Reed Elem Sch<br>1200 Rivercrest Blvd, Allen 75002<br>Ardath Streitmatter | PK-6 | | 516<br>35 | 36% 972/727-0580<br>Fax 972/727-0588 |
| George Anderson Elem Sch<br>305 N Alder Dr, Allen 75002<br>Chris Koder | PK-6 | | 422<br>40 | 19% 972/396-6924<br>Fax 972/396-6929 |
| James & Margie Marion ES<br>1595 Stablerun Dr, Allen 75002<br>Brooke Cherry | PK-6 | | 609<br>38 | 13% 214/495-6784<br>Fax 214/495-6787 |
| James D Kerr Elem Sch<br>1325 Glendover Dr, Allen 75013<br>Aretha Jackson | PK-6 | | 620<br>41 | 6% 214/495-6765<br>Fax 214/495-6771 |
| Lois Lindsey Elem Sch<br>5730 Wilford Dr, McKinney 75070<br>Melissa Pursifull | PK-6 | | 656 | 21% 972/908-4000<br>Fax 469/319-6999 |
| Lowery Freshman Center<br>368 N Greenville Ave, Allen 75002<br>Jill Stafford | 9-9 | V | 1,728 | 18% 972/396-6975<br>Fax 972/396-6981 |
| Luther & Anna Bolin Elem Sch<br>5705 Cheyenne Dr, Parker 75002<br>Reena Varughese | PK-6 | | 486<br>39 | 19% 214/495-6750<br>Fax 214/495-6756 |
| Mary Evans Elem Sch<br>1225 Walnut Springs Dr, Allen 75013<br>Pam Hale | PK-6 | | 611 | 6% 972/747-3373<br>Fax 972/747-3376 |
| Max Vaughan Elem Sch<br>820 Cottonwood Dr, Allen 75002<br>Tonya Jasenof | PK-6 | | 656<br>30 | 20% 972/727-0470<br>Fax 972/727-0579 |
| Olson Elem Sch<br>1751 E Exchange Pkwy, Allen 75002<br>Susanne Miller | PK-6 | | 544 | 14% 972/562-1800<br>Fax 972/562-1835<br>[f] |
| Pete Ford Middle Sch<br>630 Park Place Dr, Allen 75002<br>**Doug Wilhelm** | 7-8 | V | 925<br>70 | 24% 972/727-0590<br>Fax 972/727-0596<br>[f][t] |
| Preston Elem Sch<br>2455 Hilliard Dr, Allen 75013<br>Alana Chisum | PK-6 | | 468 | 3% 972/908-8780<br>Fax 214/383-7640 |
| Walter & Lois Curtis Mid Sch<br>1530 Rivercrest Blvd, Allen 75002<br>Sonya Pitcock | 7-8 | V | 1,345<br>58 | 14% 972/727-0340<br>Fax 972/727-0345 |

## Anna Ind School Dist PID: 01006021

501 S Sherley Ave, Anna 75409

972/924-1000
Fax 972/924-1001

**Schools:** 6 \ **Teachers:** 246 \ **Students:** 3,800 \ **Special Ed Students:** 445 \ **LEP Students:** 418 \ **Ethnic:** Asian 1%, African American 13%, Hispanic 32%, Caucasian 54% \ **Exp:** $559 (High) \ **Poverty:** 8% \ **Title I:** $251,436 \ **Special Education:** $443,000 \ **Open-Close:** 08/19 - 05/27 \ **DTBP:** $350 (High)

| | | | |
|---|---|---|---|
| Michael Comeaux | 1 | Dr Thomas Oneal | 2,15,19 |
| Kenneth Lindsey | 3 | Mitchell Burney | 4 |
| Jason Heath | 6 | Sue Akins | 8,15 |
| Paula McMillion | 11,57 | Brad Duncan | 15 |
| Jay Underwood | 15,68,79 | Greta Adams | 16 |
| Jennifer Kelly | 33 | Dr Wendy Stanley | 58 |
| Shelly Conway | 67 | Denisa Stewart | 68 |
| Mindi Vandagriff | 73,286 | Patti Matthews | 76 |
| Vince Sharp | 77,83 | Cane Sweet | 88 |
| Jeff Jones | 91 | Theodore Mackey | 285 |

| Public Schs..Principal | Grd | Prgm | Enr/#Cls | SN |
|---|---|---|---|---|
| Anna Education Center<br>601 S Sherley Ave, Anna 75409<br>Gabriel Medrano | 6-6 | | 401 | 972/924-1340 |
| Anna High Sch<br>1107 W Rosamond Pkwy, Anna 75409<br>Shelley Anderson | 9-12 | V | 947<br>20 | 39% 972/924-1100<br>Fax 972/924-1101 |
| Anna Middle Sch<br>1201 N Powell Pkwy, Anna 75409<br>Tressi Bridges | 7-8 | T | 783<br>35 | 44% 972/924-1200<br>Fax 972/924-1201 |
| Harlow Elem Sch<br>2412 Leonard Ave, Anna 75409<br>Karen Reddell | K-5 | | 554 | 972/924-1320<br>Fax 972/924-9145 |
| Joe K Bryant Elem Sch<br>2725 Bryant Farm Rd, Anna 75409<br>Robin Latham | PK-5 | T | 686<br>29 | 47% 972/924-1300<br>Fax 972/924-1301 |
| Sue E Rattan Elem Sch<br>1221 S Ferguson Pkwy, Anna 75409<br>Todd Frazier | K-5 | T | 548<br>42 | 46% 972/924-1400<br>Fax 972/924-1401 |

## Blue Ridge Ind School Dist PID: 01006057

318 School St, Blue Ridge 75424

972/752-5554
Fax 972/752-9084

**Schools:** 3 \ **Teachers:** 60 \ **Students:** 975 \ **Special Ed Students:** 104 \ **LEP Students:** 76 \ **College-Bound:** 66% \ **Ethnic:** Hispanic 28%, Caucasian 71% \ **Exp:** $272 (Med) \ **Poverty:** 13% \ **Title I:** $98,217 \ **Open-Close:** 08/13 - 05/28 \ **DTBP:** $350 (High)

| | | | |
|---|---|---|---|
| Matt Kimball | 1 | Amanda Ray | 2 |
| Terri Rodriquez | 4 | Mark Chester | 6 |
| Helen Thompson | 7* | Matthew Todd | 8,11,69,74,88,294,298* |
| Melissaa Stieney | 57,73,286 | Mike McCreary | 67 |

| Public Schs..Principal | Grd | Prgm | Enr/#Cls | SN |
|---|---|---|---|---|
| Blue Ridge Elem Sch<br>425 N Church St, Blue Ridge 75424<br>Shelley Reeves | PK-5 | T | 390<br>15 | 54% 972/752-5554<br>Fax 972/752-9950 ⓕ |
| Blue Ridge High Sch<br>11020 County Road 504, Blue Ridge 75424<br>Chris Miller | 9-12 | TV | 252<br>50 | 44% 972/752-5554<br>Fax 972/752-5361 |
| Blue Ridge Middle Sch<br>710 Tiger Pride Cir, Blue Ridge 75424<br>Phillip Lentz | 6-8 | T | 210<br>10 | 60% 972/752-4243<br>Fax 972/752-5363 ⓕⓣ |

## Celina Ind School Dist PID: 01006083

205 S Colorado St, Celina 75009

469/742-9100
Fax 972/382-3607

**Schools:** 6 \ **Teachers:** 176 \ **Students:** 2,600 \ **Special Ed Students:** 249 \ **LEP Students:** 162 \ **College-Bound:** 50% \ **Ethnic:** Asian 1%, African American 4%, Hispanic 25%, Native American: 1%, Caucasian 69% \ **Exp:** $271 (Med) \ **Poverty:** 5% \ **Title I:** $146,734 \ **Open-Close:** 08/19 - 05/27 \ **DTBP:** $320 (High)

| | | | |
|---|---|---|---|
| Dr Thopmas Maglisceau | 1 | Amber Parnell | 2 |
| William Hemby | 3,15 | Ofelia Almendarez | 4 |
| Kevin Vollweiler | 5 | Bill Elliot | 6 |
| Lori Sitzes | 8,15 | Lisa Bergin | 9,88,294 |
| Russell McDaniel | 11 | Dr John Matthews | 15,68 |
| Rick Demasters | 15,84 | Vanessa Jaramillo | 57 |
| Kelly Juergens | 67 | Marilyn Chamberlin | 73* |
| Bobby Manson | 91 | | |

| Public Schs..Principal | Grd | Prgm | Enr/#Cls | SN |
|---|---|---|---|---|
| Celina 6th Grade Center<br>706 E Pecan St, Celina 75009<br>Kimber Kincaid | 6-6 | V | 200 | 469/742-9105<br>Fax 972/382-8543 |
| Celina Elem Sch<br>550 S Utah St, Celina 75009<br>Starla Martin | 1-5 | T | 565<br>24 | 27% 469/742-9103<br>Fax 972/382-3789 |
| Celina High Sch<br>3455 N Preston Rd, Celina 75009<br>David Wilson | 9-12 | V | 844<br>20 | 19% 469/742-9102<br>Fax 972/382-4830 |
| Celina Junior High Sch<br>710 E Pecan St, Celina 75009<br>**Jamey Briscoe** | 7-8 | | 426<br>17 | 22% 469/742-9101<br>Fax 972/382-4258 |
| Celina Primary Sch<br>507 E Malone St, Celina 75009<br>Nancy Alvarez | PK-K | T | 240 | 35% 469/742-9104<br>Fax 972/382-4792 |
| O'Dell Elem Sch<br>750 Punk Carter Pkwy, Celina 75009<br>Stacy Ceci | 1-5 | | 402 | 19% 469/742-9106<br>Fax 214/851-3667 |

## Community Ind School Dist PID: 01006124

611 N FM 1138, Nevada 75173

972/843-8400
Fax 972/843-8401

**Schools:** 4 \ **Teachers:** 161 \ **Students:** 2,600 \ **Special Ed Students:** 247 \ **LEP Students:** 425 \ **College-Bound:** 44% \ **Ethnic:** Asian 2%, African American 7%, Hispanic 37%, Caucasian 55% \ **Exp:** $519 (High) \ **Poverty:** 8% \ **Title I:** $199,381 \ **Special Education:** $316,000 \ **Open-Close:** 08/26 - 05/28 \ **DTBP:** $354 (High) \ ⓕ

| | | | |
|---|---|---|---|
| Roosevelt Nivins | 1 | Greg Buchanan | 2,19,288 |
| Cody Cox | 3,5 | Cindy Lewis | 4 |
| Karen Collins | 7,85 | Christi Farish | 8,12,18,69,270,271,296 |
| Julie Meek | 11,58 | Brie Kaser | 16,73,76,286,295 |
| Margarita Solis | 57 | Michael Shepard | 67 |
| Alphonso Bates | 68,79 | | |

| Public Schs..Principal | Grd | Prgm | Enr/#Cls | SN |
|---|---|---|---|---|
| Carylene McClendon Elem Sch<br>601 N FM 1138, Nevada 75173<br>Gilberto Salinas | PK-5 | T | 589<br>32 | 62% 972/843-6800<br>Fax 972/843-6801 ⓕ |
| Community High Sch<br>620 N FM 1138, Nevada 75173<br>**Charles Ryan** | 9-12 | TV | 650<br>45 | 45% 972/843-6500<br>Fax 972/843-6501 |
| Edge Middle Sch<br>615 N FM 1138, Nevada 75173<br>Charles Ryan | 6-8 | T | 566<br>40 | 50% 972/843-6670<br>Fax 972/843-6671 ⓕⓣ |
| Nesmith Elem Sch<br>801 President Blvd, Lavon 75166<br>Julie Meek | PK-5 | T | 580<br>17 | 41% 972/843-6100<br>Fax 972/843-6101 |

| | | | | |
|---|---|---|---|---|
| 79 Student Personnel | 91 Safety/Security | 275 Response To Intervention | 298 Grant Writer/Ptnrships | **School Programs** |
| 80 Driver Ed/Safety | 92 Magnet School | 277 Remedial Math K-12 | 750 Chief Innovation Officer | A = Alternative Program |
| 81 Gifted/Talented | 93 Parental Involvement | 280 Literacy Coach | 751 Chief of Staff | G = Adult Classes |
| 82 Video Services | 95 Tech Prep Program | 285 STEM | 752 Social Emotional Learning | M = Magnet Program |
| 83 Substance Abuse Prev | 97 Chief Infomation Officer | 286 Digital Learning | | T = Title I Schoolwide |
| 84 Erate | 98 Chief Technology Officer | 288 Common Core Standards | **Other School Types** | V = Career & Tech Ed Programs |
| 85 AIDS Education | 270 Character Education | 294 Accountability | Ⓐ = Alternative School | |
| 88 Alternative/At Risk | 271 Migrant Education | 295 Network System | Ⓒ = Charter School | |
| 89 Multi-Cultural Curriculum | 273 Teacher Mentor | 296 Title II Programs | Ⓜ = Magnet School | |
| 90 Social Work | 274 Before/After Sch | 297 Webmaster | Ⓨ = Year-Round School | |

**Social Media**

ⓕ = Facebook
ⓣ = Twitter

New Schools are shaded
New Superintendents and Principals are bold
Personnel with email addresses are underscored

# TX—81

## • Farmersville Ind School Dist  PID: 01006148

501A State Highway 78 N, Farmersville 75442

972/782-6601
Fax 972/784-7293

**Schools:** 4 \ **Teachers:** 114 \ **Students:** 1,594 \ **Special Ed Students:** 221 \
**LEP Students:** 201 \ **Ethnic:** Asian 1%, African American 3%, Hispanic 39%,
Native American: 1%, Caucasian 57% \ **Exp:** $573 (High) \ **Poverty:** 11% \
**Title I:** $225,515 \ **Special Education:** $272,000 \ **Open-Close:** 08/12 -
05/27 \ **DTBP:** $559 (High)

| | |
|---|---|
| Micheal French ...................................1 | Amber Pennell ...........................2,19,271 |
| Ernie Phelps ..................................3,5 | Tammy Pyle .....................................4 |
| Brandon Hankins ................................6 | Aimee Howard ...................................7* |
| Garry Jameson ...........8,15,288,294,296,298 | Trish Carnagey .........................11,57,280 |
| Wiley Sullivan .....................27,73,295,297* | Josh Martin ...........................58,69,77,88 |
| Tony Gray ......................................67 | Tina Murray ....................................76 |
| Brian Alford ....................................91 | |

| Public Schs..Principal | Grd | Prgm | Enr/#Cls | SN | |
|---|---|---|---|---|---|
| Farmersville High Sch | 9-12 | ATV | 530 | 45% | 972/782-7757 |
| 499 State Highway 78 N, Farmersville 75442 | | | 40 | | Fax 972/782-7245 |
| Wayne Callaway | | | | | |
| Farmersville Intermediate Sch | 2-5 | T | 500 | 57% | 972/782-8108 |
| 807 N Main St, Farmersville 75442 | | | | | Fax 972/782-7527 |
| Tad Myers | | | | | |
| Farmersville Jr High Sch | 6-8 | AT | 296 | 52% | 972/782-6202 |
| 501 State Highway 78 N, Farmersville 75442 | | | 20 | | Fax 972/782-7029 |
| Dave Warren | | | | | |
| Tatum Elem Sch | PK-1 | T | 268 | 54% | 972/782-7251 |
| 405 N Washington St, Farmersville 75442 | | | 25 | | Fax 972/782-8109 |
| Ginger Ketcher | | | | | |

## • Frisco Ind School Dist  PID: 01006186

5515 Ohio Dr, Frisco 75035

469/633-6000
Fax 469/633-6050

**Schools:** 72 \ **Teachers:** 4,071 \ **Students:** 63,015 \
**Special Ed Students:** 5,842 \ **LEP Students:** 3,449 \ **College-Bound:** 50%
\ **Ethnic:** Asian 30%, African American 12%, Hispanic 14%, Native American:
1%, Caucasian 43% \ **Exp:** $233 (Med) \ **Poverty:** 3% \ **Title I:** $927,034 \
**Special Education:** $5,361,000 \ **Open-Close:** 08/13 - 05/21 \ **DTBP:** $172
(High)

| | |
|---|---|
| Dr Mike Waldrip .................................1 | Kimberly Smith ...............................2,19 |
| Scott Warstler ..................................2 | Todd Fouche .................................2,15 |
| Blake Vaughn ...................................3 | Cecil Cypert ....................................3 |
| Doug Zambiasi ...............................3,17 | Lisa Jenkins ....................................4 |
| Doug Becker ....................................5 | David Kuykendall ...............................6 |
| Kathy Tolbert ....................................7 | Phil Evans ......................................8 |
| Mary Webb ......................................9 | Angela Romney ............................10,81 |
| Gary Nye ........................11,69,273,294 | Kenny Chandler ............................15,79 |
| Stacy Cameron ................................16 | Dr Wes Cunningham ...........................18 |
| Preston Hazzard ...............................20 | Dianna Manuel ..............................27,31* |
| Dr Stephanie Cook ............................36 | Merideth Choate ...............................57 |
| Christine Davis .................................58 | Garrett Jackson ................................58 |
| Tracy Cartas ....................................58 | Chad Rudy ......................................67 |
| Dr Pamela Linton ............................68,78 | Amanda McCune ............................71,97 |
| Jamie Driskill ...................................71 | Melissa Fouche ....................73,76,98,295 |
| Sherri Wakeland ...............................74* | Dana Reid ......................................81 |
| Jennifer Adams .................................81* | Kevin Haller ....................................91 |
| Denise Debaugh ..............................274 | Cheryl McDonald .............................286 |
| John Curran ...................................295 | |

| Public Schs..Principal | Grd | Prgm | Enr/#Cls | SN | |
|---|---|---|---|---|---|
| Adelle R Clark Middle Sch | 6-8 | | 805 | 20% | 469/633-4600 |
| 4600 Colby Dr, Frisco 75035 | | | 45 | | Fax 469/633-4650 |
| Lanina Duffey | | | | | |
| Anderson Elem Sch | K-5 | | 704 | 16% | 469/633-2300 |
| 2800 Oakland Hills Dr, Plano 75025 | | | 40 | | Fax 469/633-2350 |
| Laura Del Hierro | | | | | |

| | Grd | Prgm | Enr/#Cls | SN | |
|---|---|---|---|---|---|
| Bennett & Alma Griffin Mid Sch | 6-8 | | 844 | 3% | 469/633-4900 |
| 3703 Eldorado Pkwy, Frisco 75033 | | | | | Fax 469/633-4950 |
| Tommy Hill | | | | | |
| Benton A Staley Middle Sch | 6-8 | T | 648 | 40% | 469/633-4500 |
| 6927 Stadium Ln, Frisco 75033 | | | | | Fax 469/633-4550 |
| Anita Robinson | | | | | |
| Bessie Gunstream Elem Sch | K-5 | | 628 | 20% | 469/633-3100 |
| 7600 Rockyridge Dr, Frisco 75035 | | | | | Fax 469/633-3150 |
| David Smolka | | | | | |
| Billy Vandeventer Middle Sch | 6-8 | | 854 | 11% | 469/633-4350 |
| 6075 Independence Pkwy, Frisco 75035 | | | | | Fax 469/633-4360 |
| Stephanie Taylor | | | | | |
| Cal & Walt Wester Middle Sch | 6-8 | | 807 | 15% | 469/633-4800 |
| 12293 Shepherds Hill Ln, Frisco 75035 | | | | | Fax 469/633-4850 |
| Richard Manuel | | | | | |
| Calvin Bledsoe Elem Sch | PK-5 | | 586 | 3% | 469/633-3600 |
| 1900 Timber Ridge Dr, Frisco 75036 | | | | | Fax 469/633-3610 |
| Sherry Klingenberg | | | | | |
| Career & Tech Education Center | Voc | | 400 | | 469/633-6780 |
| 9889 Wade Blvd, Frisco 75035 | | | | | Fax 469/633-6790 |
| Monica Manuel | | | | | |
| Centennial High Sch | 9-12 | G | 1,986 | 10% | 469/633-5600 |
| 6901 Coit Rd, Frisco 75035 | | | | | Fax 469/633-5650 |
| Alicia Maphies | | | | | |
| Claude Curtsinger Elem Sch | K-5 | | 519 | 9% | 469/633-2100 |
| 12450 Jereme Trl, Frisco 75035 | | | 37 | | Fax 469/633-2150 |
| Angela Borgarello | | | | | |
| Comstock Elem Sch | K-5 | | 702 | 9% | 469/633-3900 |
| 7152 Silverado Trl, McKinney 75070 | | | | | Fax 469/633-3910 |
| Amanda Dalton | | | | | |
| Dr Erwin & Elizabeth Pink ES | K-5 | | 541 | 3% | 469/633-3500 |
| 3650 Overhill Dr, Frisco 75033 | | | | | Fax 469/633-3510 |
| Danielle Record | | | | | |
| Dr JM Ogle Elem Sch | K-5 | T | 666 | 17% | 469/633-3525 |
| 4200 Big Fork Trl, McKinney 75070 | | | | | Fax 469/633-3535 |
| Phyllis Pope | | | | | |
| Edris Childres Elliot Elem Sch | K-5 | T | 609 | 29% | 469/633-3750 |
| 3721 Hudson Xing, McKinney 75070 | | | | | Fax 469/633-3760 |
| Natalie Miller | | | | | |
| Frisco High Sch | 9-12 | V | 1,567 | 22% | 469/633-5500 |
| 6401 Parkwood Blvd, Frisco 75034 | | | 55 | | Fax 469/633-5550 |
| Daniel Barrentine | | | | | |
| Frisco ISD Early Childhood Sch | PK-PK | | 831 | 27% | 469/633-3825 |
| 10330 Red Cedar Dr, Frisco 75035 | | | | | Fax 469/633-3835 |
| Bethany Birdwell | | | | | |
| George & Deborah Purefoy ES | K-5 | | 521 | 4% | 469/633-3875 |
| 11880 Teel Pkwy, Frisco 75033 | | | | | Fax 469/633-3885 |
| Kena Robertson | | | | | |
| Gerald Sonntag Elem Sch | K-5 | T | 546 | 23% | 469/633-3850 |
| 2001 Reagan Dr, McKinney 75072 | | | | | Fax 469/633-3860 |
| Shannon Acosta | | | | | |
| Heritage High Sch | 9-12 | | 1,994 | 16% | 469/633-5900 |
| 14040 Eldorado Pkwy, Frisco 75035 | | | | | Fax 469/633-5950 |
| Kathryn Gray | | | | | |
| I S Rogers Elem Sch | K-5 | T | 503 | 24% | 469/633-2000 |
| 10500 Rogers Rd, Frisco 75033 | | | 34 | | Fax 469/633-2050 |
| Jenny McGowan | | | | | |
| Ida Lee Bright Elem Sch | K-5 | T | 533 | 47% | 469/633-2700 |
| 7600 Woodstream Dr, Frisco 75034 | | | | | Fax 469/633-2750 |
| Serita Dodson | | | | | |
| Independence High Sch | 9-12 | | 2,071 | 12% | 469/633-5400 |
| 10555 Independence Pkwy, Frisco 75035 | | | | | Fax 469/633-5450 |
| Alan Waligura | | | | | |
| Isabel Pierce Sem Elem Sch | K-5 | | 654 | 8% | 469/633-3575 |
| 12721 Honeygrove Dr, Frisco 75035 | | | | | Fax 469/633-3585 |
| Jose Mira | | | | | |

| | | | | | | |
|---|---|---|---|---|---|---|
| **1** Superintendent | **8** Curric/Instruct K-12 | **19** Chief Financial Officer | **29** Family/Consumer Science | **39** Social Studies K-12 | **49** English/Lang Arts Elem | **59** Special Education Elem | **69** Academic Assessment |
| **2** Bus/Finance/Purchasing | **9** Curric/Instruct Elem | **20** Art K-12 | **30** Adult Education | **40** Social Studies Elem | **50** English/Lang Arts Sec | **60** Special Education Sec | **70** Research/Development |
| **3** Buildings And Grounds | **10** Curric/Instruct Sec | **21** Art Elem | **31** Career/Sch-to-Work K-12 | **41** Social Studies Sec | **51** Reading K-12 | **61** Foreign/World Lang K-12 | **71** Public Information |
| **4** Food Service | **11** Federal Program | **22** Art Sec | **32** Career/Sch-to-Work Elem | **42** Science K-12 | **52** Reading Elem | **62** Foreign/World Lang Elem | **72** Summer School |
| **5** Transportation | **12** Title I | **23** Music K-12 | **33** Career/Sch-to-Work Sec | **43** Science Elem | **53** Reading Sec | **63** Foreign/World Lang Sec | **73** Instructional Tech |
| **6** Athletic | **13** Title V | **24** Music Elem | **34** Early Childhood Ed | **44** Science Sec | **54** Remedial Reading K-12 | **64** Religious Education K-12 | **74** Inservice Training |
| **7** Health Services | **14** Instructional Media Svcs | **25** Music Sec | **35** Health/Phys Education | **45** Math K-12 | **55** Remedial Reading Elem | **65** Religious Education Elem | **75** Marketing/Distributive |
| | **15** Asst Superintendent | **26** Business Education | **36** Guidance Services K-12 | **46** Math Elem | **56** Remedial Reading Sec | **66** Religious Education Sec | **76** Info Systems |
| | **16** Instructional Media Svcs | **27** Career & Tech Ed | **37** Guidance Services Elem | **47** Math Sec | **57** Bilingual/ELL | **67** School Board President | **77** Psychological Assess |
| | **17** Chief Operations Officer | **28** Technology Education | **38** Guidance Services Sec | **48** English/Lang Arts K-12 | **58** Special Education K-12 | **68** Teacher Personnel | **78** Affirmative Action |
| | **18** Chief Academic Officer | | | | | | |

| School | Grades | Prog | Enroll | % | Phone |
|---|---|---|---|---|---|
| Isbell Elem Sch<br>6000 Maltby Dr, Frisco 75035<br>Kandra Wooten | K-5 | | 679<br>40 | 5% | 469/633-3400<br>Fax 469/633-3450 |
| Izetta Sparks Elem Sch<br>8200 Otis Dr, Frisco 75036<br>**Carrie Dellinger** | PK-5 | | 640<br>18 | 4% | 469/633-3000<br>Fax 469/633-3050 |
| James R Newman Elem Sch<br>12333 Briar Ridge Rd, Frisco 75033<br>Rachael Gilbert | K-5 | | 684 | 2% | 469/633-3975<br>Fax 469/633-3985 |
| Janice Stanly Scott Elem Sch<br>10550 Millbend Dr, McKinney 75072<br>T Leanne Crane | K-5 | | 681 | 10% | 469/633-4000<br>Fax 469/633-4010 |
| Justin Wakeland High Sch<br>10700 Legacy Dr, Frisco 75033<br>Donna Edge | 9-12 | AV | 2,064 | 5% | 469/633-5700<br>Fax 469/633-5750 |
| JW & Ruth Christie Elem Sch<br>10300 Huntington Rd, Frisco 75035<br>Cynthia Brewer | K-5 | T | 491<br>35 | 61% | 469/633-2400<br>Fax 469/633-2450 |
| Lamar & Norma Hunt Middle Sch<br>4900 Legendary Dr, Frisco 75034<br>Chris Clark | 6-8 | | 837 | 17% | 469/633-5200<br>Fax 469/633-5210 |
| Lawler Middle Sch<br>12921 Rolater Rd, Frisco 75035<br>Travis Zambiasi | 6-8 | | 709 | 3% | 469/633-4150<br>Fax 469/633-4160 |
| Lebanon Trail High Sch<br>5151 Ohio Dr, Frisco 75035<br>Jacob Duce | 9-12 | | 1,413 | 10% | 469/633-6600<br>Fax 469/633-6657 |
| Libby Cash Maus Middle Sch<br>12175 Coit Rd, Frisco 75035<br>Chakosha Powell | 6-8 | | 972 | 14% | 469/633-5250<br>Fax 469/633-5260 |
| Liberty High Sch<br>15250 Rolater Rd, Frisco 75035<br>Ashley Rainwater | 9-12 | | 1,968 | 11% | 469/633-5800<br>Fax 469/633-5850 � 📘🐦 |
| Liscano Elem Sch<br>11222 Mammoth Cave, Frisco 75035<br>Michele Lott | K-5 | | 753 | 6% | 469/633-2275<br>Fax 469/633-2285 |
| Lone Star High Sch<br>2606 Panther Creek Pkwy, Frisco 75033<br>Karen Kraft | 9-12 | | 2,090 | 17% | 469/633-5300<br>Fax 469/633-5350 |
| Lucile Rogers Ashley Elem Sch<br>15601 Christopher Ln, Frisco 75035<br>Kimberly Frankson | K-5 | | 650<br>44 | 7% | 469/633-3700<br>Fax 469/633-3710 |
| Mary M Boals Elem Sch<br>2035 Jaguar Dr, Frisco 75033<br>Christina Beran | K-5 | | 642 | 9% | 469/633-3300<br>Fax 469/633-3350 |
| McSpedden Elem Sch<br>14140 Countrybrook Dr, Frisco 75035<br>Kranti Singh | K-5 | | 593 | 2% | 469/633-4025<br>Fax 469/633-4035 |
| Memorial High Sch<br>12300 Frisco St, Frisco 75033<br>Jennifer Redden | 9-11 | V | 1,136 | 17% | 469/633-7300<br>Fax 469/633-7350 |
| Miller Elem Sch<br>300 Cypress Hill Dr, Little Elm 75068<br>Ashley Miller | K-5 | | 687 | 17% | 469/633-2075<br>Fax 469/633-2085 |
| Mooneyham Elem Sch<br>2301 Eden Dr, McKinney 75072<br>Ingrid Dodd | K-5 | | 669 | 9% | 469/633-3650<br>Fax 469/633-3660 |
| Nelson Middle Sch<br>10100 Independence Pkwy, Frisco 75035<br>Mitzi Garner | 6-8 | | 788 | 5% | 469/633-4100<br>Fax 469/633-4110 |
| Nichols Elem Sch<br>7411 Nichols Trl, Frisco 75036<br>Zachary Wiley | PK-5 | | 620 | 6% | 469/633-3950<br>Fax 469/633-3960 |
| Noel A Smith Elem Sch<br>9800 Sean Dr, Frisco 75035<br>Catherine Young | K-5 | | 606<br>37 | 14% | 469/633-2200<br>Fax 469/633-2250 |
| Norris Elem Sch<br>10101 Shepton Ln, Frisco 75035<br>Loryn Tobey | K-5 | | 289 | 3% | 469/633-4075<br>Fax 469/633-4085 |
| Otis Spears Elem Sch<br>8500 Wade Blvd, Frisco 75034<br>Becca Bustillo | K-5 | T | 650<br>40 | 18% | 469/633-2900<br>Fax 469/633-2950 |
| Pat & Katherine Fowler Mid Sch<br>3801 McDermott Rd, Plano 75025<br>Donnie Wiseman | 6-8 | V | 1,044 | 9% | 469/633-5050<br>Fax 469/633-5060 |
| Pearson Middle Sch<br>2323 Stonebrook Pkwy, Frisco 75036<br>Jamie Wisneski | 6-8 | | 868 | 6% | 469/633-4450<br>Fax 469/633-4460 |
| Pete & Gracie Hosp Elem Sch<br>5050 Lone Star Ranch Pkwy, Frisco 75036<br>Aaron Else | K-5 | | 701 | 5% | 469/633-4050<br>Fax 469/633-4060 |
| Phillips Elem Sch<br>2285 Little River Rd, Frisco 75033<br>Dana Solomon | K-5 | | 653 | 8% | 469/633-3925<br>Fax 469/633-3935 |
| Pioneer Heritage Middle Sch<br>1649 High Shoals Dr, Frisco 75036<br>Rocky Agan | 6-8 | | 945 | 3% | 469/633-4700<br>Fax 469/633-4750 |
| Polly Tadlock Elem Sch<br>12515 Godfrey Dr, Frisco 75035<br>Kellie Rapp | K-5 | T | 677 | 19% | 469/633-3775<br>Fax 469/633-3785 |
| Portia Ross Taylor Elem Sch<br>9865 Gillespie Dr, Plano 75025<br>Christy Garza | K-5 | T | 708 | 17% | 469/633-3625<br>Fax 469/633-3635 |
| Reba Cobb Carroll Elem Sch<br>4380 Throne Hall Dr, Frisco 75033<br>John Waldrip | K-5 | | 528 | 23% | 469/633-3725<br>Fax 469/633-3735 |
| Rick Reedy High Sch<br>3003 Stonebrook Pkwy, Frisco 75034<br>Jon-Eric Ziaer | 9-10 | | 1,335 | 5% | 469/633-6400<br>Fax 469/633-6450 |
| Riddle Elem Sch<br>8201 Robinson Rd, Plano 75024<br>Heather Cox | K-5 | | 769<br>42 | 7% | 469/633-3200<br>Fax 469/633-3250 |
| Robert Cobb Middle Sch<br>9400 Teel Pkwy, Frisco 75033<br>Jamie Lakey | 6-8 | | 916 | 12% | 469/633-4300<br>Fax 469/633-4310 |
| Robertson Elem Sch<br>2501 Woodlake Pkwy, Little Elm 75068<br>Kyla Prusak | K-5 | | 725 | 11% | 469/633-3675<br>Fax 469/633-3685 |
| Ruth Borchardt Elem Sch<br>4300 Waskom Dr, Plano 75024<br>Jodi Davis | K-5 | | 764 | 5% | 469/633-2800<br>Fax 469/633-2850 |
| Sam & Ann Roach Middle Sch<br>12499 Independence Pkwy, Frisco 75035<br>Natasha McDonald | 6-8 | | 925 | 18% | 469/633-5000<br>Fax 469/633-5010 |
| Scoggins Middle Sch<br>7070 Stacy Rd, McKinney 75070<br>Barbara Warner | 6-8 | | 912 | 19% | 469/633-5150<br>Fax 469/633-5160 |
| Shawnee Trail Elem Sch<br>10701 Preston Vineyard Dr, Frisco 75035<br>**Suzanne Koyle** | K-5 | T | 512<br>33 | 22% | 469/633-2500<br>Fax 469/633-2550 |
| Ⓐ Student Opportunity Center<br>6928 Maple St, Frisco 75033<br>Kecia Theodore | 9-12 | | 150<br>20 | | 469/633-6700<br>Fax 469/633-6710 |
| Sue Wilson Stafford Middle Sch<br>2288 Little River Rd, Frisco 75033<br>Robin Scott | 6-8 | | 897 | 14% | 469/633-5100<br>Fax 469/633-5110 🐦 |
| Talley Elem Sch<br>5900 Colt Rd, Frisco 75035<br>Jamie Peden | K-5 | | 521 | 1% | 469/633-2175<br>Fax 469/633-2185 |
| Trent Middle Sch<br>13131 Coleto Creek Dr, Frisco 75033<br>Shawn Perry | 6-8 | | 920 | 6% | 469/633-4400<br>Fax 469/633-4410 |

| School | Grd | Enr | SN | Phone |
|---|---|---|---|---|
| Vaughn Elem Sch<br>3535 Guinn Gate Dr, Frisco 75034<br>Susie Graham | K-5 | 598 | 4% | 469/633-2575<br>Fax 469/633-2585 |
| Weldon Corbell Elem Sch<br>11095 Monarch Dr, Frisco 75033<br>Brenda Youngblood | K-5 | 719 | 22% | 469/633-3550<br>Fax 469/633-3560 |
| William & Abbie Allen Elem Sch<br>5800 Legacy Dr, Frisco 75034<br>Chastity Johnson | PK-5 | 496 | 8% | 469/633-3800<br>Fax 469/633-3810 |
| Wilma Fisher Elem Sch<br>2500 Old Orchard Rd, Frisco 75033<br>Nancy Fatheree | K-5 | 559 | 4% | 469/633-2600<br>Fax 469/633-2650 |

## ● Lovejoy Ind School Dist PID: 01006227
259 Country Club Rd, Allen 75002 — 469/742-8000 — Fax 469/742-8001

**Schools:** 6 \ **Teachers:** 292 \ **Students:** 4,424 \ **Special Ed Students:** 368 \ **LEP Students:** 40 \ **College-Bound:** 96% \ **Ethnic:** Asian 8%, African American 3%, Hispanic 9%, Native American: 1%, Caucasian 79% \ **Exp:** $267 (Med) \ **Poverty:** 2% \ **Title I:** $83,500 \ **Special Education:** $469,000 \ **Open-Close:** 08/17 - 05/28 \ **DTBP:** $181 (High)

Dr Michael Goddard ...1
Shay Adams ...2,19
David Dillon ...3,5
Juliana Elandary ...4
Sunny Cleveland ...4
Sancy Fuller ...7,57,58
Mary Mullen ...8
Kristin Dawson ...16*
Mary Ruggeri ...37*
Diana Saylack ...46
Megan Frankenberg ...52
Stacey Dillon ...71
Brie Smith ...81
Stephanie Kranz ...273
Taylor Denison ...274
Dee Dee White ...2
Tina Tomson ...2
Dr Dennis Womack ...3,5,15,91
Matt McCarty ...4
Jim Bob Puckett ...6
Dennis Muizers ...8,15,69
Mitci Allen ...11,73
Brice McCasland ...20
Cindy Bronson ...43
Kelly Cowan ...47*
Chad Collins ...67
Michael Voth ...73
Ajck Vestal ...98
Lisa Leirer ...274*
Trevor Davis ...295

| Public Schs..Principal | Grd | Prgm | Enr/#Cls | SN | |
|---|---|---|---|---|---|
| Hart Elem Sch<br>450 Country Club Rd, Lucas 75002<br>Lacey Moser | PK-4 | T | 461<br>35 | 4% | 469/742-8200<br>Fax 469/742-8201 |
| Lovejoy Elem Sch<br>256 Country Club Rd, Allen 75002<br>Wendy Craft | PK-4 | T | 348<br>31 | 5% | 469/742-8100<br>Fax 469/742-8101 |
| Lovejoy High Sch<br>2350 E States Pkwy, Lucas 75002<br>Chris Mayfield | 9-12 | | 1,528 | 4% | 469/742-8700<br>Fax 469/742-8701 |
| Puster Elem Sch<br>856 Stoddard Rd, Fairview 75069<br>Holly Haynes | PK-4 | | 365 | 2% | 469/742-8300<br>Fax 469/742-8301 |
| Sloan Creek Intermediate Sch<br>440 Country Club Rd, Fairview 75069<br>Ray Winkler | 5-6 | | 705 | 4% | 469/742-8400<br>Fax 469/742-8401 |
| Willow Springs Middle Sch<br>1101 W Lucas Rd, Allen 75002<br>**Kevin Parker** | 7-8 | | 725 | 4% | 469/742-8500<br>Fax 469/742-8501 |

## ● McKinney Ind School Dist PID: 01006241
1 Duvall St, McKinney 75069 — 469/302-4000 — Fax 469/302-4071

**Schools:** 31 \ **Teachers:** 1,656 \ **Students:** 24,335 \ **Special Ed Students:** 2,978 \ **LEP Students:** 2,465 \ **College-Bound:** 56% \ **Ethnic:** Asian 5%, African American 15%, Hispanic 30%, Native American: 1%, Caucasian 50% \ **Exp:** $208 (Med) \ **Poverty:** 7% \ **Title I:** $2,599,536 \ **Special Education:** $3,323,000 \ **Open-Close:** 08/13 - 05/21 \ **DTBP:** $198 (High) \ 🅵 🆃

Dr Rick McDaniel ...1
Jason Bird ...2,19
Erica Wright ...3
Justin Price ...3
Robert Montgomery ...5,91
Julie Blankenship ...7
Melinda DeFelice ...10,15
Lara Lindsey ...16,73
Todd Young ...31*
Karin Kelmm ...35
Lisa Witt ...41
Misty Young ...46
Andrea Coachman ...50
Adrienne Morris ...58,69,77
Amy Dankel ...67
Cody Cunningham ...71
Greg Grimes ...76
Luke Hurst ...81
Shun Ying ...295
Beverly Biering ...2
Corey Gililland ...3
Greg Suttle ...3
James Shoemake ...4
Shawn Pratt ...6
Suzanne Woodard ...9,15
Tamira Griffin ...15,68,270,273
Dan White ...20,23
Dr Pamela Parmley ...34,274
Jennifer Akins ...36
Kendra Henke ...44
Judy Vega ...49
Zabi Gonzalez ...57
Sally Riche ...58
Chad Teague ...68
David Spann ...71,73,97
Jeff Gilliam ...76
Geoff Sanderson ...294

| Public Schs..Principal | Grd | Prgm | Enr/#Cls | SN | |
|---|---|---|---|---|---|
| Albert & Iola Davis Malvern ES<br>1100 Eldorado Pkwy, McKinney 75069<br>Rhonda Gilliam | K-5 | T | 511<br>34 | 83% | 469/302-5300<br>Fax 469/302-5301 |
| Arthur McNeil Elem Sch<br>3650 S Hardin Blvd, McKinney 75070<br>Tracy Meador | K-5 | | 396<br>40 | 43% | 469/302-5200<br>Fax 469/302-5201 |
| Bennett Elem Sch<br>7760 Coronado Dr, McKinney 75072<br>Amy Holderman | K-5 | | 559 | 12% | 469/302-5400<br>Fax 469/302-5401 |
| C T Eddins Elem Sch<br>311 Peregrine Dr, McKinney 75072<br>Sharon Havard | K-5 | | 388<br>35 | 12% | 469/302-6600<br>Fax 469/302-6601 |
| Earl & Lottie Wolford Elem Sch<br>6951 Berkshire Rd, McKinney 75072<br>Francine Gratt | K-5 | | 447<br>30 | 15% | 469/302-4700<br>Fax 469/302-4701 |
| Earl Slaughter Elem Sch<br>2706 Wolford St, McKinney 75071<br>Nick DeFelice | K-5 | T | 621<br>27 | 56% | 469/302-6100<br>Fax 469/302-6101 |
| Evans Middle Sch<br>6998 Eldorado Pkwy, McKinney 75070<br>Darla Jackson | 6-8 | V | 1,072 | 27% | 469/302-7100<br>Fax 469/302-7101 |
| Fanny Finch Elem Sch<br>1205 S Tennessee St, McKinney 75069<br>Erika Echegaray | K-5 | GT | 358<br>75 | 83% | 469/302-5600<br>Fax 469/302-5601 |
| Gibson Caldwell Elem Sch<br>601 W Louisiana St, McKinney 75069<br>**Karla Massey** | K-5 | T | 533<br>42 | 64% | 469/302-5500<br>Fax 469/302-5501 🅵🆃 |
| Glen Oaks Elem Sch<br>6100 Glen Oaks Dr, McKinney 75072<br>Molly Hovan | K-5 | | 489<br>35 | 9% | 469/302-6400<br>Fax 469/302-6401 🅵🆃 |
| Herman Lawson Early Chldhd Ctr<br>500 Dowell St, McKinney 75071<br>Susie Towber | PK-PK | T | 598 | 96% | 469/302-2400<br>Fax 469/302-2401 |
| J B Wilmeth Elem Sch<br>901 La Cima Dr, McKinney 75071<br>Kristin Ellis | K-5 | | 647 | 6% | 469/302-7400<br>Fax 469/302-7401 |

1 Superintendent | 8 Curric/Instruct K-12 | 19 Chief Financial Officer | 29 Family/Consumer Science | 39 Social Studies K-12 | 49 English/Lang Arts Elem | 59 Special Education Elem | 69 Academic Assessment
2 Bus/Finance/Purchasing | 9 Curric/Instruct Elem | 20 Art K-12 | 30 Adult Education | 40 Social Studies Elem | 50 English/Lang Arts Sec | 60 Special Education Sec | 70 Research/Development
3 Buildings And Grounds | 10 Curric/Instruct Sec | 21 Art Elem | 31 Career/Sch-to-Work K-12 | 41 Social Studies Sec | 51 Reading K-12 | 61 Foreign/World Lang K-12 | 71 Public Information
4 Food Service | 11 Federal Program | 22 Art Sec | 32 Career/Sch-to-Work Elem | 42 Science K-12 | 52 Reading Elem | 62 Foreign/World Lang Elem | 72 Summer School
5 Transportation | 12 Title I | 23 Music K-12 | 33 Career/Sch-to-Work Sec | 43 Science Elem | 53 Reading Sec | 63 Foreign/World Lang Sec | 73 Instructional Tech
6 Athletic | 13 Title V | 24 Music Elem | 34 Early Childhood Ed | 44 Science Sec | 54 Remedial Reading K-12 | 64 Religious Education K-12 | 74 Inservice Training
7 Health Services | 14 Asst Superintendent | 25 Music Sec | 35 Health/Phys Education | 45 Math K-12 | 55 Remedial Reading Elem | 65 Religious Education Elem | 75 Marketing/Distributive
| 16 Instructional Media Svcs | 26 Business Education | 36 Guidance Services K-12 | 46 Math Elem | 56 Remedial Reading Sec | 66 Religious Education Sec | 76 Info Systems
| 17 Chief Operations Officer | 27 Career & Tech Ed | 37 Guidance Services Elem | 47 Math Sec | 57 Bilingual/ELL | 67 School Board President | 77 Psychological Assess
| 18 Chief Academic Officer | 28 Technology Education | 38 Guidance Services Sec | 48 English/Lang Arts K-12 | 58 Special Education K-12 | 68 Teacher Personnel | 78 Affirmative Action

| School | Grd | Prgm | Enr/#Cls | SN | Phone/Fax |
|---|---|---|---|---|---|
| **J W Webb Elem Sch**<br>810 E Louisiana St, McKinney 75069<br>Maria Hafner | K-5 | GT | 404<br>35 | 74% | 469/302-6000<br>Fax 469/302-6001 🇫🇧 🇹 |
| **Jack Cockrill Middle Sch**<br>1351 N Hardin Blvd, McKinney 75071<br>Dr Amber Epperson | 6-8 | | 1,275 | 20% | 469/302-7900<br>Fax 469/302-7901 |
| **Jack Faubion Middle Sch**<br>2000 Rollins St, McKinney 75069<br>Jimmy Bowser | 6-8 | V | 1,289 | 38% | 469/302-6900<br>Fax 469/302-6901 |
| **Jesse McGowen Elem Sch**<br>4300 Columbus Dr, McKinney 75070<br>Kimberly Luyster | K-5 | | 643 | 29% | 469/302-7500<br>Fax 469/302-7501 |
| **Lizzie Nell C McClure Elem Sch**<br>1753 N Ridge Rd, McKinney 75071<br>Matthew Arend | K-5 | | 638 | 12% | 469/302-9400<br>Fax 469/302-9401 |
| **McKinney Boyd High Sch**<br>600 N Lake Forest Dr, McKinney 75071<br>Jennifer Peirson | 9-12 | AV | 2,834 | 18% | 469/302-3400<br>Fax 469/302-3401 🇫🇧 🇹 |
| Ⓐ **McKinney Daep Learning Center**<br>2100 W White Ave, McKinney 75069<br>Cynthia Morton | K-12 | G | 75<br>6 | | 469/302-7800<br>Fax 469/302-7801 |
| **McKinney High Sch**<br>1400 Wilson Creek Pkwy, McKinney 75069<br>Alan Arbabi | 9-12 | GV | 2,964 | 34% | 469/302-5700<br>Fax 469/302-5701 🇫🇧 |
| **McKinney North High Sch**<br>2550 Wilmeth Rd, McKinney 75071<br>Jae Gaskill | 9-12 | V | 2,137<br>90 | 26% | 469/302-4300<br>Fax 469/302-4301 |
| **Minshew Elem Sch**<br>300 Joplin Dr, McKinney 75071<br>Inetra Nelson | K-5 | | 653 | 24% | 469/302-7300<br>Fax 469/302-7301 |
| **Naomi Press Elem Sch**<br>4101 Shawnee Rd, McKinney 75071<br>Rachel Constantinescu | K-5 | T | 602<br>30 | 33% | 469/302-7600<br>Fax 469/302-7601 |
| **Nell Burks Elem Sch**<br>1801 Hill St, McKinney 75069<br>Alvin Conley | K-5 | T | 404<br>30 | 78% | 469/302-6200<br>Fax 469/302-6203 |
| **Reuben Johnson Elem Sch**<br>3400 Ash Ln, McKinney 75070<br>Michelle Bauman | K-5 | | 508<br>38 | 22% | 469/302-6500<br>Fax 469/302-6501 |
| **Roy Lee Walker Elem Sch**<br>4000 Cockrill Dr, McKinney 75072<br>Melanie Raleeh | K-5 | | 527<br>35 | 9% | 469/302-4600<br>Fax 469/302-4601 |
| **Ruth Dowell Middle Sch**<br>301 S Ridge Rd, McKinney 75072<br>Holly Rogers | 6-8 | GV | 1,182<br>100 | 25% | 469/302-6700<br>Fax 469/302-6701 🇫🇧 🇹 |
| **Scott Johnson Middle Sch**<br>3400 Community Ave, McKinney 75071<br>Mitchell Curry | 6-8 | TV | 309<br>80 | 49% | 469/302-4900<br>Fax 469/302-4901 |
| **Serenity High Sch**<br>2100 W White Ave, McKinney 75069<br>Stephen Issa | 9-12 | | 12<br>4 | | 469/302-7830<br>Fax 469/302-7831 |
| **Valley Creek Elem Sch**<br>2800 Valley Creek Trl, McKinney 75072<br>Megan Richards | K-5 | | 509<br>36 | 15% | 469/302-4800<br>Fax 469/302-4801 |
| **Vega Elem Sch**<br>2511 Cattleman Dr, McKinney 75071<br>Mike Forsyth | K-5 | T | 493<br>34 | 66% | 469/302-5100<br>Fax 469/302-5101 |

---

## • Melissa Ind School Dist  PID: 01006320
1904 Cooper St, Melissa 75454

972/837-2411  
Fax 972/837-4233

**Schools:** 4 \ **Teachers:** 191 \ **Students:** 3,102 \ **Special Ed Students:** 353 \ **LEP Students:** 108 \ **Ethnic:** Asian 2%, African American 11%, Hispanic 19%, Native American: 1%, Caucasian 67% \ **Exp:** $349 (High) \ **Poverty:** 3% \ **Title I:** $38,885 \ **Special Education:** $287,000 \ **Open-Close:** 08/25 - 05/26 \ **DTBP:** $360 (High) \ 🇫🇧 🇹

| | | | |
|---|---|---|---|
| Keith Murphy | 1 | Lance Rainey | 2 |
| Kenny Deel | 3,4,91 | Mike Price | 4* |
| Weston Bartlett | 5 | Sharon Carroll | 8,11,36,69,294 |
| Dr Robert Rich | 11,68,271,296 | Leanne Bush | 57 |
| Adrienne Morris | 58,77 | Jennifer Clark | 58 |
| Rick Restivo | 67 | Kim Boedeker | 69 |

| Public Schs..Principal | Grd | Prgm | Enr/#Cls | SN | Phone/Fax |
|---|---|---|---|---|---|
| **Harry McKillop Elem Sch**<br>3509 Liberty Way, Melissa 75454<br>Krissy Womack | PK-5 | T | 686<br>16 | 18% | 972/837-2632<br>Fax 469/729-7737 🇫🇧 |
| **Melissa High Sch**<br>3030 Milrany Ln, Melissa 75454<br>Kenneth Wooten | 9-12 | | 920<br>28 | | 972/837-4216<br>Fax 469/729-7751 |
| **Melissa Middle Sch**<br>3150 Cardinal Dr, Melissa 75454<br>Marcus Eckert | 6-8 | | 757 | | 972/837-4355<br>Fax 469/729-7750 |
| **North Creek Elem Sch**<br>4401 Cypress Dr, Melissa 75454<br>Michele Austin | PK-5 | T | 739 | 17% | 972/837-4530<br>Fax 469/729-7739 🇫🇧 |

## • Plano Ind School Dist  PID: 01006344
2700 W 15th St, Plano 75075

469/752-8100  
Fax 469/752-8096

**Schools:** 73 \ **Teachers:** 3,907 \ **Students:** 52,692 \ **Special Ed Students:** 6,258 \ **LEP Students:** 7,810 \ **College-Bound:** 65% \ **Ethnic:** Asian 25%, African American 13%, Hispanic 26%, Caucasian 35% \ **Exp:** $273 (Med) \ **Poverty:** 7% \ **Title I:** $6,834,155 \ **Special Education:** $9,273,000 \ **Open-Close:** 09/09 - 05/27 \ **DTBP:** $187 (High) \ 🇫🇧 🇹

| | | | |
|---|---|---|---|
| Sara Bonser | 1 | John Orr | 2 |
| Randy McDowell | 2,19 | Juan Ramos | 3 |
| Dr Theresa Williams | 3,17 | Ashley Hipp | 4 |
| Dr Kary Cooper | 4,5,15,35,68,91 | Mark Skinner | 5 |
| Jeff Smith | 6 | Megan Schuler | 7 |
| Amy Bates | 8 | Dr Katrina Hasley | 8,15,27,34,57 |
| Laurie Taylor | 9 | Ashley Helms | 10 |
| Nardeen Boxell | 11 | Dr Beth Brockman | 15,68 |
| Dr Courtney Gober | 15,79 | Dan Armstrong | 15,16,73,76,295 |
| Karla Oliver | 15,71,298 | Marylynn Skinner | 16 |
| Kathy Kuddes | 20,23 | Karen Buechman | 27 |
| Molly Pipak | 35 | Jana Hancock | 36 |
| Eric Haggard | 41 | Mary Swinton | 42 |
| Ashley Carter | 44 | Ginger Teaff | 45 |
| Susan Dyer | 49 | Deborah Brannon | 50 |
| Roxanne Burchfiel | 53,54 | Talle Gomez | 57* |
| Janna Crow | 58 | Stephany Sipes | 61 |
| Tammy Richards | 67 | Dr Dash Weerasinghe | 69,70,294 |
| Matt Frey | 73 | Rhonda Davis | 81 |
| Gary Carter | 83* | Joseph Parks | 91 |

| Public Schs..Principal | Grd | Prgm | Enr/#Cls | SN | Phone/Fax |
|---|---|---|---|---|---|
| **Academy High Sch**<br>1701 Alma Dr, Plano 75075<br>Lynn Ojeda | 9-12 | | 95 | 11% | 972/905-8100<br>Fax 972/905-8101 |
| **Aldridge Elem Sch**<br>720 Pleasant Valley Ln, Richardson 75080<br>Antreshawn Buhl | K-5 | | 601<br>45 | 22% | 469/752-0000<br>Fax 469/752-0001 |

---

| | | |
|---|---|---|
| 79 Student Personnel | 91 Safety/Security | 275 Response To Intervention |
| 80 Driver Ed/Safety | 92 Magnet School | 277 Remedial Math K-12 |
| 81 Gifted/Talented | 93 Parental Involvement | 280 Literacy Coach |
| 82 Video Services | 95 Tech Prep Program | 285 STEM |
| 83 Substance Abuse Prev | 97 Chief Infomation Officer | 286 Digital Learning |
| 84 Erate | 98 Chief Technology Officer | 288 Common Core Standards |
| 85 AIDS Education | 270 Character Education | 294 Accountability |
| 88 Alternative/At Risk | 271 Migrant Education | 295 Network System |
| 89 Multi-Cultural Curriculum | 273 Teacher Mentor | 296 Title II Programs |
| 90 Social Work | 274 Before/After Sch | 297 Webmaster |

| | |
|---|---|
| 298 Grant Writer/Ptnrships | |
| 750 Chief Innovation Officer | **School Programs** |
| 751 Chief of Staff | A = Alternative Program |
| 752 Social Emotional Learning | G = Adult Classes |
| | M = Magnet Program |
| **Other School Types** | T = Title I Schoolwide |
| Ⓐ = Alternative School | V = Career & Tech Ed Programs |
| Ⓒ = Charter School | |
| Ⓜ = Magnet School | **New Schools are shaded** |
| Ⓨ = Year-Round School | **New Superintendents and Principals are bold** |
| | Personnel with email addresses are underscored |

**Social Media**  
🇫🇧 = Facebook  
🇹 = Twitter

| School | Grades | | Enroll | % | Phone / Fax |
|---|---|---|---|---|---|
| Armstrong Middle Sch<br>3805 Timberline Dr, Plano 75074<br>Melissa Blank | 6-8 | T | 472<br>35 | 72% | 469/752-4600<br>Fax 469/752-4601 |
| Barksdale Elem Sch<br>2424 Midway Rd, Plano 75093<br>Jennifer Caplinger | K-5 | | 641 | 14% | 469/752-0100<br>Fax 469/752-0101 |
| Barron Elem Sch<br>3300 P Ave, Plano 75074<br>Tricia Lancaster | K-5 | T | 353<br>28 | 83% | 469/752-0200<br>Fax 469/752-0201 |
| Beaty Early Childhood Sch<br>1717 Nevada Dr, Plano 75093<br>Kristen Fislar | PK-PK | | 458 | 16% | 469/752-4200<br>Fax 469/752-4201 |
| Bethany Elem Sch<br>2418 Micarta Dr, Plano 75025<br>Bryan Bird | K-5 | | 367 | 17% | 469/752-0300<br>Fax 469/752-0301 |
| Bettye Haun Elem Sch<br>4500 Quincy Ln, Plano 75024<br>Jayne Smith | K-5 | | 651 | 13% | 469/752-1600<br>Fax 469/752-1601 |
| Bowman Middle Sch<br>2501 Jupiter Rd, Plano 75074<br>Brooks Baca | 6-8 | T | 987<br>100 | 65% | 469/752-4800<br>Fax 469/752-4801 |
| Brinker Elem Sch<br>3800 Clark Pkwy, Plano 75093<br>Andrea Cockrell | K-5 | | 639<br>30 | 20% | 469/752-0500<br>Fax 469/752-0501 |
| C M Rice Middle Sch<br>8500 Gifford Dr, Plano 75025<br>Christopher Glasscock | 6-8 | | 1,044 | 6% | 469/752-6000<br>Fax 469/752-6001 |
| Carlisle Elem Sch<br>6525 Old Orchard Dr, Plano 75023<br>Linda Patrick | K-5 | | 540<br>40 | 25% | 469/752-0600<br>Fax 469/752-0601 |
| Carpenter Middle Sch<br>3905 Rainier Rd, Plano 75023<br>Courtney Washington | 6-8 | | 446 | 61% | 469/752-5000<br>Fax 469/752-5001 |
| Centennial Elem Sch<br>2609 Ventura Dr, Plano 75093<br>Sara Stewart | K-5 | | 570 | 9% | 469/752-0700<br>Fax 469/752-0701 |
| Christie Elem Sch<br>3801 Rainier Rd, Plano 75023<br>Sean Flynn | PK-5 | T | 686<br>40 | 59% | 469/752-0800<br>Fax 469/752-0801 |
| Clark High Sch<br>523 W Spring Creek Pkwy, Plano 75023<br>Pamela Clark | 9-10 | GV | 1,377<br>70 | 32% | 469/752-7200<br>Fax 469/752-7201 |
| Daffron Elem Sch<br>3900 Preston Meadow Dr, Plano 75093<br>Stefanie Ramos | K-5 | T | 624 | 42% | 469/752-0900<br>Fax 469/752-0901 |
| David McCall Elem Sch<br>6601 Cloverhaven Way, Plano 75074<br>Stacy Kimbriel | K-5 | | 549 | 35% | 469/752-4500<br>Fax 469/752-4501 |
| Davis Elem Sch<br>2701 Parkhaven Dr, Plano 75075<br>Karma Cunningham | K-5 | T | 405<br>30 | 40% | 469/752-1000<br>Fax 469/752-1001 |
| Dennis Miller Elem Sch<br>5651 Coventry Dr, Richardson 75082<br>Jennifer Bero | K-5 | | 396<br>38 | 17% | 469/752-2700<br>Fax 469/752-2701 |
| Dooley Elem Sch<br>2425 San Gabriel Dr, Plano 75074<br>Tramy Tran | K-5 | T | 358<br>24 | 49% | 469/752-1100<br>Fax 469/752-1101 |
| Dr Allan & Carolyn Bird Ed Ctr<br>1300 19th St, Plano 75074<br>Jana Sandall | Spec | A | 80 | | 469/752-2200<br>Fax 469/752-2201 |
| Forman Elem Sch<br>3600 Timberline Dr, Plano 75074<br>Carmen Casamayor-Ryan | PK-5 | T | 554<br>40 | 82% | 469/752-1200<br>Fax 469/752-1201 |
| Frankford Middle Sch<br>7706 Osage Plaza Pkwy, Dallas 75252<br>Melanie Schulte | 6-8 | T | 1,030<br>50 | 44% | 469/752-5200<br>Fax 469/752-5201 |
| Gulledge Elem Sch<br>6801 Preston Meadow Dr, Plano 75024<br>Deni Bleggi | K-5 | | 728 | 13% | 469/752-1300<br>Fax 469/752-1301 |
| Haggard Middle Sch<br>2832 Parkhaven Dr, Plano 75075<br>Shauna Koehne | 6-8 | | 854 | 25% | 469/752-5400<br>Fax 469/752-5401 |
| Harrington Elem Sch<br>1540 Baffin Bay Dr, Plano 75075<br>Jacye Jamar | K-5 | | 374<br>23 | 27% | 469/752-1500<br>Fax 469/752-1501 |
| Hedgcoxe Elem Sch<br>7701 Prescott Dr, Plano 75025<br>Kristi Graham | K-5 | | 428 | 23% | 469/752-1700<br>Fax 469/752-1701 |
| Hendrick Middle Sch<br>7400 Red River Dr, Plano 75025<br>Lisa Long | 6-8 | | 729<br>70 | 31% | 469/752-5600<br>Fax 469/752-5601 |
| Henry Dye Boggess Elem Sch<br>225 Glen Ridge Dr, Murphy 75094<br>Shurandia Holden | K-5 | | 535 | 13% | 469/752-4000<br>Fax 469/752-4001 |
| Hightower Elem Sch<br>2601 Decator Dr, Plano 75093<br>Mariea Sprott | K-5 | | 532<br>35 | 21% | 469/752-1800<br>Fax 469/752-1801 |
| Huffman Elem Sch<br>5510 Channel Isle Dr, Plano 75093<br>Jamey Allen | PK-5 | T | 452<br>30 | 68% | 469/752-1900<br>Fax 469/752-1901 |
| Hughston Elem Sch<br>2601 Cross Bend Rd, Plano 75023<br>Carrie D'Argo | K-5 | | 351 | 15% | 469/752-2000<br>Fax 469/752-2001 |
| Isaacs Early Childhood Sch<br>3400 E Parker Rd, Plano 75074<br>Jane Oestreich | PK-PK | | 391 | 24% | 469/752-3480<br>Fax 469/752-3481 |
| Jackson Elem Sch<br>1101 Jackson Dr, Plano 75075<br>Crystal Roach | PK-5 | T | 520<br>40 | 63% | 469/752-2100<br>Fax 469/752-2101 |
| Jasper High Sch<br>6800 Archgate Dr, Plano 75024<br>Billie-Jean Lee | 9-10 | GV | 1,418 | 12% | 469/752-7400<br>Fax 469/752-7401 |
| ⓐ Larry D Guinn Spec Pgrms Ctr<br>2221 Legacy Dr, Plano 75023<br>Sonja Pegram | 9-12 | | 194 | | 469/752-6900<br>Fax 469/752-6901 |
| Loreta Hickey Elem Sch<br>4100 Coldwater Creek Ln, Plano 75074<br>Dina Rowe | K-5 | | 537 | 35% | 469/752-4100<br>Fax 469/752-4101 |
| Martha Hunt Elem Sch<br>415 Oriole Dr, Murphy 75094<br>Arron Moeller | K-5 | | 705 | 9% | 469/752-4400<br>Fax 469/752-4401 |
| Mathews Elem Sch<br>7500 Marchman Way, Plano 75025<br>Ryan Steele | K-5 | | 481<br>43 | 11% | 469/752-2300<br>Fax 469/752-2301 |
| McMillen High Sch<br>750 N Murphy Rd, Plano 75094<br>Brian Lyons | 9-10 | | 1,251 | 33% | 469/752-8600<br>Fax 469/752-8601 |
| Meadows Elem Sch<br>2800 18th St, Plano 75074<br>Katherine Foster | K-5 | T | 412<br>34 | 87% | 469/752-2400<br>Fax 469/752-2401 |
| Memorial Elem Sch<br>2200 Laurel Ln, Plano 75074<br>Mary Hardin | PK-5 | T | 493<br>27 | 83% | 469/752-2500<br>Fax 469/752-2501 |
| Mendenhall Elem Sch<br>1330 19th St, Plano 75074<br>Jana Prince | PK-5 | T | 590<br>49 | 88% | 469/752-2600<br>Fax 469/752-2601 |
| Mitchell Elem Sch<br>4223 Briargrove Ln, Dallas 75287<br>Lariza Liner | PK-5 | T | 668<br>50 | 50% | 469/752-2800<br>Fax 469/752-2801 |
| Murphy Middle Sch<br>620 N Murphy Rd, Murphy 75094<br>Matt Conrad | 6-8 | | 1,216 | 10% | 469/752-7000<br>Fax 469/752-7001 |

1 Superintendent
2 Bus/Finance/Purchasing
3 Buildings And Grounds
4 Food Service
5 Transportation
6 Athletic
7 Health Services
8 Curric/Instruct K-12
9 Curric/Instruct Elem
10 Curric/Instruct Sec
11 Federal Program
12 Title I
13 Title V
15 Asst Superintendent
16 Instructional Media Svcs
17 Chief Operations Officer
18 Chief Academic Officer
19 Chief Financial Officer
20 Art K-12
21 Art Elem
22 Art Sec
23 Music K-12
24 Music Elem
25 Music Sec
26 Business Education
27 Career & Tech Ed
28 Technology Education
29 Family/Consumer Science
30 Adult Education
31 Career/Sch-to-Work K-12
32 Career/Sch-to-Work Elem
33 Career/Sch-to-Work Sec
34 Early Childhood Ed
35 Health/Phys Education
36 Guidance Services K-12
37 Guidance Services Elem
38 Guidance Services Sec
39 Social Studies K-12
40 Social Studies Elem
41 Social Studies Sec
42 Science K-12
43 Science Elem
44 Science Sec
45 Math K-12
46 Math Elem
47 Math Sec
48 English/Lang Arts K-12
49 English/Lang Arts Elem
50 English/Lang Arts Sec
51 Reading K-12
52 Reading Elem
53 Reading Sec
54 Remedial Reading K-12
55 Remedial Reading Elem
56 Remedial Reading Sec
57 Bilingual/ELL
58 Special Education K-12
59 Special Education Elem
60 Special Education Sec
61 Foreign/World Lang K-12
62 Foreign/World Lang Elem
63 Foreign/World Lang Sec
64 Religious Education K-12
65 Religious Education Elem
66 Religious Education Sec
67 School Board President
68 Teacher Personnel
69 Academic Assessment
70 Research/Development
71 Public Information
72 Summer School
73 Instructional Tech
74 Inservice Training
75 Marketing/Distributive
76 Info Systems
77 Psychological Assess
78 Affirmative Action

| School | Grd | Prgm | Enr/#Cls | SN | Phone |
|---|---|---|---|---|---|
| Otto Middle Sch<br>504 N Star Rd, Plano 75074<br>Antoine Spencer | 6-8 | V | 1,101 | 34% | 469/752-8500<br>Fax 469/752-8501 |
| Pearson Early Childhood Sch<br>4000 Eagle Pass, Plano 75023<br>Jennifer Haugh | PK-PK | | 338<br>18 | 16% | 469/752-4300<br>Fax 469/752-4301 |
| Plano East Senior High Sch<br>3000 Los Rios Blvd, Plano 75074<br>King George | 11-12 | V | 2,944 | 28% | 469/752-9000<br>Fax 469/752-9001 |
| Plano Head Start Center<br>1600 Rigsbee Dr, Plano 75074<br>Dr Denise Lohmiller | PK-PK | T | 145 | 98% | 469/752-7160<br>Fax 469/752-7161 |
| Plano Senior High Sch<br>2200 Independence Pkwy, Plano 75075<br>Sarah Watkins | 11-12 | GV | 2,741 | 28% | 469/752-9300<br>Fax 469/752-9301 |
| Plano West Senior High Sch<br>5601 W Parker Rd, Plano 75093<br>Janis Williams | 11-12 | | 2,741 | 17% | 469/752-9600<br>Fax 469/752-9601 |
| Rasor Elem Sch<br>945 Hedgcoxe Rd, Plano 75025<br>Leigh Earnhart | K-5 | T | 461<br>30 | 54% | 469/752-2900<br>Fax 469/752-2901 |
| Renner Middle Sch<br>5701 W Parker Rd, Plano 75093<br>Jill Engelking | 6-8 | | 1,230<br>55 | 26% | 469/752-5800<br>Fax 469/752-5801 |
| Robinson Middle Sch<br>6701 Preston Meadow Dr, Plano 75024<br>Kennitra Robertson | 6-8 | | 914 | 19% | 469/752-6200<br>Fax 469/752-6201 |
| Rose Haggar Elem Sch<br>17820 Campbell Rd, Dallas 75252<br>Katie Brittain | PK-5 | T | 579<br>34 | 38% | 469/752-1400<br>Fax 469/752-1401<br>f t |
| Saigling Elem Sch<br>3600 Matterhorn Dr, Plano 75075<br>Chris Dunkle | K-5 | | 396 | 16% | 469/752-3000<br>Fax 469/752-3001 |
| Schell Elem Sch<br>5301 E Renner Rd, Richardson 75082<br>Bob Farris | K-5 | | 682 | 25% | 469/752-6600<br>Fax 469/752-6601<br>f t |
| Schimelpfenig Middle Sch<br>2400 Maumelle Dr, Plano 75023<br>Dr Brant Perry | 6-8 | | 857<br>90 | 17% | 469/752-6400<br>Fax 469/752-6401 |
| Shepard Elem Sch<br>1000 Wilson Dr, Plano 75075<br>Kristin Bishop | K-5 | | 457<br>30 | 17% | 469/752-3100<br>Fax 469/752-3101 |
| Shepton High Sch<br>5505 W Plano Pkwy, Plano 75093<br>Jeffrey Banner | 9-10 | V | 1,456<br>85 | 32% | 469/752-7600<br>Fax 469/752-7601 |
| Sigler Elem Sch<br>1400 Janwood Dr, Plano 75075<br>Carrie Tracy | PK-5 | T | 418<br>31 | 76% | 469/752-3200<br>Fax 469/752-3201 |
| Skaggs Elem Sch<br>3201 Russell Creek Dr, Plano 75025<br>Karen Lee | K-5 | | 387 | 8% | 469/752-3300<br>Fax 469/752-3301 |
| Stinson Elem Sch<br>4201 Greenfield Dr, Richardson 75082<br>Michele Taylor | K-5 | | 637<br>40 | 12% | 469/752-3400<br>Fax 469/752-3401 |
| Thomas Elem Sch<br>1800 Montana Trl, Plano 75023<br>**Zack Pruett** | PK-5 | T | 656 | 71% | 469/752-3500<br>Fax 469/752-3501<br>f t |
| Thomas Wesley Andrews Elem Sch<br>2520 Scenic Dr, Plano 75025<br>Joy Lovell | K-5 | | 574 | 7% | 469/752-3900<br>Fax 469/752-3901 |
| Vines High Sch<br>1401 Highedge Dr, Plano 75075<br>Julie-Anne Dean | 9-10 | V | 1,026<br>70 | 34% | 469/752-7800<br>Fax 469/752-7801 |
| Weatherford Elem Sch<br>2941 Mollimar Dr, Plano 75075<br>**Nidia Cedillo** | PK-5 | T | 446<br>30 | 59% | 469/752-3600<br>Fax 469/752-3601<br>f t |
| Wells Elem Sch<br>3427 Mission Ridge Rd, Plano 75023<br>Sara Meyer | K-5 | | 562<br>27 | 17% | 469/752-3700<br>Fax 469/752-3701 |
| William Beverly Elem Sch<br>715 Duchess Dr, Allen 75013<br>Cindy Savant | K-5 | | 438<br>23 | 17% | 469/752-0400<br>Fax 469/752-0401 |
| Williams High Sch<br>1717 17th St, Plano 75074<br>Matthew Endsley | 9-10 | TV | 1,236<br>50 | 50% | 469/752-8300<br>Fax 469/752-8301 |
| Wilson Middle Sch<br>1001 Custer Rd, Plano 75075<br>Mark Letterer | 6-8 | T | 810 | 41% | 469/752-6700<br>Fax 469/752-6701 |
| Wyatt Elem Sch<br>8900 Coit Rd, Plano 75025<br>Cynthia Hentges | K-5 | | 459<br>34 | 8% | 469/752-3800<br>Fax 469/752-3801 |

● **Princeton Ind School Dist** PID: 01006502    469/952-5400
321 Panther Pkwy, Princeton 75407    Fax 972/736-3505

**Schools:** 9 \ **Teachers:** 307 \ **Students:** 5,567 \ **Special Ed Students:** 563 \ **LEP Students:** 821 \ **Ethnic:** Asian 1%, African American 10%, Hispanic 47%, Native American: 1%, Caucasian 41% \ **Exp:** $560 (High) \ **Poverty:** 11% \ **Title I:** $502,293 \ **Special Education:** $650,000 \ **Open-Close:** 08/13 - 05/26 \ **DTBP:** $176 (High)

Donald McIntyre .................................1
Jim Staley ........................................3
Kelly Alvis ........................................4
Stacey Dillard ...................................6*
Dr Jackie Hendricks ....... 8,15,36,57,271,288
James Lovelady .............................. 10,15
Carol Bodwell ..................................67
Jeanann Collins ................................71
Jona Boitmann .........................2,11,15,298
Philip Anthony ...................................3
Ric Wayman .....................................5
Dacia Jondron ...................................7
Rene Mullins .....................................9
Liz Goen ...............................34,58,88*
Amber McIntrye ................................69
David Vincent ...................................73

| Public Schs..Principal | Grd | Prgm | Enr/#Cls | SN | Phone |
|---|---|---|---|---|---|
| Canup Early Childhood Center<br>301 N 5th St, Princeton 75407<br>**Vickey Dillard** | PK-PK | | 420 | | 469/952-5416 |
| Clark Middle Sch<br>301 Panther Pkwy, Princeton 75407<br>Casey Gunnels | 6-8 | AT | 620<br>40 | 59% | 469/952-5404<br>Fax 972/736-5903 |
| Godwin Elem Sch<br>1019 N 6th St, Princeton 75407<br>Marlena Brown | K-5 | AT | 494 | 70% | 469/952-5402<br>Fax 972/736-3533 |
| Harper Elem Sch<br>8080 County Road 398, Princeton 75407<br>Nichole Powell \ **Heidi Estep** | K-5 | AT | 448 | 70% | 469/952-5409<br>Fax 972/736-2621 |
| Lacy Elem Sch<br>224 E College St, Princeton 75407<br>Thomas Osburn | K-5 | AT | 701<br>37 | 62% | 469/952-5401<br>Fax 972/736-6795 |
| Lowe Elem Sch<br>540 Beauchamp Blvd, Princeton 75407<br>Jeff Coburn | K-5 | | 450 | | 469/952-5419 |
| Princeton High Sch<br>1000 E Princeton Dr, Princeton 75407<br>Clinton Sadler | 9-12 | ATV | 1,322<br>39 | 54% | 469/952-5405<br>Fax 972/736-5902 |
| Smith Elem Sch<br>2101 Forest Meadow Dr, Princeton 75407<br>Rachel Nicks | K-5 | T | 660 | 41% | 469/952-5411<br>Fax 469/952-5421 |
| Southard Middle Sch<br>455 E Monte Carlo Blvd, Princeton 75407<br>Richard Boring | 6-8 | A | 600<br>20 | | 469/952-5419<br>Fax 972/736-6162 |

---

## • Prosper Ind School Dist PID: 01006552
605 E 7th St, Prosper 75078

469/219-2000
Fax 972/346-9247

**Schools:** 18 \ **Teachers:** 905 \
**Students:** 19,000 \ **Special Ed Students:** 1,240 \ **LEP Students:** 638 \
**College-Bound:** 57% \ **Ethnic:** Asian 11%, African American 9%, Hispanic 14%, Caucasian 66% \ **Exp:** $492 (High) \ **Poverty:** 2% \ **Title I:** $66,498 \
**Special Education:** $959,000 \ **Open-Close:** 08/12 - 05/21 \ **DTBP:** $147 (High) \ 🖪 🇹

| | | | |
|---|---|---|---|
| Dr Holly Fergerson | 1 | Annette Folmar | 2,19 |
| McHelle Seese | 2 | Danny Roberts | 3 |
| Cassandra Williams | 4 | Eileen Johnson | 4 |
| Leslie Beach | 4 | Anna Hamrick | 5,91 |
| Valerie Little | 6* | Theresa Biggs | 8,285 |
| Lauri Slicker | 12,296* | Greg Bradley | 15 |
| Todd Shirley | 18 | Melissa Gassman | 57 |
| Blair Hickey | 58 | Jim Bridges | 67 |
| Chrystal Hankey | 71 | Fernando De Velasco | 73,98,286,295 |
| Patrick Oneil | 73 | Scott Cox | 76 |
| Jeff Crownover | 79 | Seth Rutledge | 81 |
| Alexis Webb | 288 | | |

| Public Schs..Principal | Grd | Prgm | Enr/#Cls | SN | |
|---|---|---|---|---|---|
| Boyer Elem Sch<br>1616 Montgomery, Prosper 75078<br>**Bill David** | PK-5 | | 705 | 3% | 469/219-2240<br>Fax 972/346-9625 |
| Cockrell Elem Sch<br>1075 Escalante Trl, Prosper 75078<br>Glenda Dophied | PK-5 | | 672 | 2% | 469/219-2130<br>Fax 972/346-2456 |
| Folsom Elem Sch<br>800 Sommerville Dr, Prosper 75078<br>Stephanie Cockrell | PK-5 | | 673<br>30 | 7% | 469/219-2110<br>Fax 972/346-9245 |
| Furr Elem Sch<br>551 S Bluestem Dr, McKinney 75072<br>Cindy Zukowski | K-5 | | 760 | | 469/219-2280<br>Fax 972/346-3151 |
| Hays Middle Sch<br>14441 Hillcrest Rd, Frisco 75035<br>Nicholas Jones | 6-8 | | 800 | | 469/219-2260<br>Fax 972/346-9650 |
| Hughes Elem Sch<br>1551 Prestwick Holw, McKinney 75071<br>Kimberly Newman | PK-5 | T | 875 | 13% | 469/219-2230<br>Fax 972/346-9620 |
| John A Baker Elem Sch<br>3125 Bluewood Dr, McKinney 75071<br>**Ashley Gannon** | PK-5 | T | 695 | 11% | 469/219-2120<br>Fax 972/529-1142<br>🖪 🇹 |
| Johnson Elem Sch<br>4001 Waterview Trail, Prosper 75078<br>**Alissa Andrews** | K-5 | | 401 | | 469/219-2340<br>Fax 214/491-1925 |
| Judy Rucker Elem Sch<br>402 S Craig Rd, Prosper 75078<br>Shelly Spears | PK-5 | T | 597 | 13% | 469/219-2100<br>Fax 972/346-9249 |
| Light Farms Elem Sch<br>1100 Cypress Creek Way, Celina 75009<br>Haley Stelly | PK-5 | | 838 | 3% | 469/219-2140<br>Fax 972/346-9630 |
| Prosper High Sch<br>301 Eagle Dr, Prosper 75078<br>John Burdett | 9-12 | AV | 3,450 | 8% | 469/219-2180<br>Fax 972/346-9246 |
| Reynolds Middle Sch<br>700 N Coleman St, Prosper 75078<br>Justin Goldsmith | 6-8 | | 1,679 | 6% | 469/219-2165<br>Fax 972/346-2455 |
| Rock Hill High Sch<br>16061 Coit Rd, Frisco 75035<br>**Dustin Toth** | 9-12 | | 401 | | 469/219-2300<br>Fax 972/346-2756 |
| Rogers Middle Sch<br>1001 S Coit Rd, Prosper 75078<br>Jason Jetton | 6-8 | | 1,627 | 11% | 469/219-2150<br>Fax 972/346-9248 |

| Rushing Middle Sch<br>3080 Fishtrap Rd, Prosper 75078<br>**Danielle Wallace** | 6-8 | | 401 | | 469/219-2370<br>Fax 972/433-1360 |
|---|---|---|---|---|---|
| Spradley Elem Sch<br>11411 Leona St, Frisco 75035<br>Machelle Scogin | PK-5 | | 718 | 6% | 469/219-2250<br>Fax 972/346-9635 |
| Stuber Elem Sch<br>721 Village Park Lane, Prosper 75078<br>Dr Jennifer Hinson | K-5 | | 780 | | 469/219-2290<br>Fax 972/346-3120 |
| Windsong Ranch Elem Sch<br>800 Copper Canyon Dr, Prosper 75078<br>Kardel Miller | PK-5 | | 942 | 8% | 469/219-2220<br>Fax 972/346-9615 |

## • Wylie Ind School Dist PID: 01006605
951 S Ballard Ave, Wylie 75098

972/429-3000
Fax 972/442-5368

**Schools:** 20 \ **Teachers:** 1,034 \ **Students:** 17,500 \
**Special Ed Students:** 1,834 \ **LEP Students:** 1,844 \ **College-Bound:** 98% \ **Ethnic:** Asian 11%, African American 15%, Hispanic 23%, Caucasian 50% \ **Exp:** $504 (High) \ **Poverty:** 6% \ **Title I:** $1,020,639 \
**Special Education:** $1,865,000 \ **Bilingual Education:** $15,000 \
**Open-Close:** 08/13 - 05/25 \ **DTBP:** $183 (High) \ 🖪

| | | | |
|---|---|---|---|
| Dr David Vinson | 1 | Gina Smilie | 2 |
| Lynn Lyon | 2 | Scott Roderick | 2,15 |
| Nathan Watson | 3 | Dawn Lin | 4 |
| Kyle Craighead | 6 | Amy Hillin | 7 |
| Joei Shermer | 9,54 | Dr Stephen Davis | 10 |
| Jessica Branch | 11 | Jill Vasquez | 11,57,271 |
| Casey Whittle | 15,68 | Dr Kim Spicer | 15 |
| Scott Winn | 15,79 | D'Anne Mosby | 16* |
| Glenn Lambert | 20 | Jason Hudson | 27 |
| Ian Halperin | 30,71 | Sara Roland | 34,58,77 |
| Amanda Martin | 36 | Matt Atkins | 67 |
| Dr Judy Bolen | 69,294 | Chris Lamb | 71,84,97 |
| Lee Hadaway | 73,74 | James Matthews | 76 |
| Belinda Feverbacher | 275 | Doug Bellamy | 297 |

| Public Schs..Principal | Grd | Prgm | Enr/#Cls | SN | |
|---|---|---|---|---|---|
| A B Harrison Intermediate Sch<br>1001 S Ballard Ave, Wylie 75098<br>Christa Smyder | 5-6 | | 397<br>36 | 29% | 972/429-3300<br>Fax 972/442-3971 |
| Achieve Academy<br>300 Pirate Dr, Wylie 75098<br>Dana Roberts | Spec | AT | 100<br>9 | 40% | 972/429-2390<br>Fax 972/941-9720 |
| Bill F Davis Intermediate Sch<br>950 Park Blvd, Wylie 75098<br>Cody Summers | 5-6 | | 837 | 29% | 972/429-3325<br>Fax 972/429-9729 |
| Cheri L Cox Elem Sch<br>7009 Woodbridge Pkwy, Sachse 75048<br>Krista Wilson | PK-4 | | 538<br>42 | 24% | 972/429-2500<br>Fax 972/429-4435 |
| Dodd Elem Sch<br>1500 Park Blvd, Wylie 75098<br>Magan Porter | PK-4 | | 471<br>31 | 28% | 972/429-3440<br>Fax 972/442-9856 |
| Don Whitt Elem Sch<br>7520 Woodcreek Way, Sachse 75048<br>Amber Teamann | PK-4 | | 542 | 14% | 972/429-2560<br>Fax 972/941-8564<br>🖪 🇹 |
| Dr AL Draper Intermediate Sch<br>103 Hensley Ln, Wylie 75098<br>Beth Craighead | 5-6 | | 982 | 28% | 972/429-3350<br>Fax 972/442-9317 |
| George W Bush Elem Sch<br>2000 Eagle Aerie Ln, Wylie 75098<br>Dr Maricella Helm | PK-4 | T | 594 | 41% | 972/429-2600<br>Fax 469/661-9428 |
| Grady Burnett Jr Senior HS<br>516 Hilltop Ln, Wylie 75098<br>Ryan Bickley | 7-8 | V | 772 | 27% | 972/429-3200<br>Fax 972/442-1447 |

| | | | | | | | |
|---|---|---|---|---|---|---|---|
| 1 | Superintendent | 8 | Curric/Instruct K-12 | 19 | Chief Financial Officer | 29 | Family/Consumer Science |
| 2 | Bus/Finance/Purchasing | 9 | Curric/Instruct Elem | 20 | Art K-12 | 30 | Adult Education |
| 3 | Buildings And Grounds | 10 | Curric/Instruct Sec | 21 | Art Elem | 31 | Career/Sch-to-Work K-12 |
| 4 | Food Service | 11 | Federal Program | 22 | Art Sec | 32 | Career/Sch-to-Work Elem |
| 5 | Transportation | 12 | Title I | 23 | Music K-12 | 33 | Career/Sch-to-Work Sec |
| 6 | Athletic | 13 | Title V | 24 | Music Elem | 34 | Early Childhood Ed |
| 7 | Health Services | 14 | Asst Superintendent | 25 | Music Sec | 35 | Health/Phys Education |
| | | 15 | Asst Superintendent | 26 | Business Education | 36 | Guidance Services K-12 |
| | | 16 | Instructional Media Svcs | 27 | Career & Tech Ed | 37 | Guidance Services Elem |
| | | 17 | Chief Operations Officer | 28 | Technology Education | 38 | Guidance Services Sec |
| | | 18 | Chief Academic Officer | | | | |

| | | | | | | | |
|---|---|---|---|---|---|---|---|
| 39 | Social Studies K-12 | 49 | English/Lang Arts Elem | 59 | Special Education Elem | 69 | Academic Assessment |
| 40 | Social Studies Elem | 50 | English/Lang Arts Sec | 60 | Special Education Sec | 70 | Research/Development |
| 41 | Social Studies Sec | 51 | Reading K-12 | 61 | Foreign/World Lang K-12 | 71 | Public Information |
| 42 | Science K-12 | 52 | Reading Elem | 62 | Foreign/World Lang Elem | 72 | Summer School |
| 43 | Science Elem | 53 | Reading Sec | 63 | Foreign/World Lang Sec | 73 | Instructional Tech |
| 44 | Science Sec | 54 | Remedial Reading K-12 | 64 | Religious Education K-12 | 74 | Inservice Training |
| 45 | Math K-12 | 55 | Remedial Reading Elem | 65 | Religious Education Elem | 75 | Marketing/Distributive |
| 46 | Math Elem | 56 | Remedial Reading Sec | 66 | Religious Education Sec | 76 | Info Systems |
| 47 | Math Sec | 57 | Bilingual/ELL | 67 | School Board President | 77 | Psychological Assess |
| 48 | English/Lang Arts K-12 | 58 | Special Education K-12 | 68 | Teacher Personnel | 78 | Affirmative Action |

| | | | | | |
|---|---|---|---|---|---|
| Hartman Elem Sch<br>510 S Birmingham St, Wylie 75098<br>Shawnell Bradshaw | PK-4 | GT | 490<br>27 | 56% | 972/429-3480<br>Fax 972/442-7072<br>**f** |
| McMillan Junior High Sch<br>1050 Park Blvd, Wylie 75098<br>Jon Peters | 7-8 | V | 892<br>46 | 28% | 972/492-3225<br>Fax 972/941-6372 |
| P M Akin Elem Sch<br>1100 Springwood Ln, Wylie 75098<br>Valerie Mann | PK-4 | | 377<br>31 | 29% | 972/429-3400<br>Fax 972/442-5744 |
| R V Groves Elem Sch<br>1100 McCreary Rd, Wylie 75098<br>Vanessa Hudgins | PK-4 | GT | 477 | 36% | 972/429-3460<br>Fax 972/429-7906<br>**f** |
| Raymond Cooper Junior High Sch<br>101 Hensley Ln, Wylie 75098<br>Shawn Miller \ **Jesse Chavoya** | 7-8 | | 929 | 26% | 972/429-3250<br>Fax 972/941-9175 |
| Rita Smith Elem Sch<br>2221 FM 1378, Wylie 75098<br>Kellye Morton | PK-4 | | 422 | 18% | 972/429-2540<br>Fax 972/442-5493 |
| T F Birmingham Elem Sch<br>700 W Brown St, Wylie 75098<br>Tracy Halligan | PK-4 | T | 428<br>58 | 42% | 972/429-3420<br>Fax 972/442-1215<br>**f t** |
| Tibbals Elem Sch<br>621 Waters Edge Way, Murphy 75094<br>Jamie Fletcher | PK-4 | | 537 | 13% | 972/429-2520<br>Fax 972/429-2260 |
| Wally Watkins Elem Sch<br>1301 Elm Dr, Wylie 75098<br>Jennifer Wiseman | PK-4 | | 536 | 17% | 972/429-2580<br>Fax 972/429-9345 |
| Wylie East High Sch<br>3000 E Stone Rd, Wylie 75098<br>Mike Williams | 9-12 | V | 1,938 | 29% | 972/429-3150<br>Fax 972/442-2874<br>**f** |
| Wylie High Sch<br>2550 W FM 544, Wylie 75098<br>**Brian Alexander** | 9-12 | V | 2,428 | 24% | 972/429-3100<br>Fax 972/442-1879 |

## COLLIN CATHOLIC SCHOOLS

- **Diocese of Dallas Ed Office** PID: 01012367

  Listing includes only schools located in this county. See District Index for location of Diocesan Offices.

| Catholic Schs..Principal | Grd | Prgm | Enr/#Cls | SN |
|---|---|---|---|---|
| All Saints Catholic Sch<br>7777 Osage Plaza Pkwy, Dallas 75252<br>Shana Druffner | PK-8 | | 292<br>24 | 214/217-3300<br>Fax 214/217-3339 |
| John Paul II High Sch<br>900 Coit Rd, Plano 75075<br>Dr Marlene Hammerle | 9-12 | | 785 | 972/867-0005<br>Fax 972/867-7555<br>**f t** |
| Prince of Peace Catholic Sch<br>5100 W Plano Pkwy, Plano 75093<br>Meghan Jones | PK-8 | | 825<br>27 | 972/380-5505<br>Fax 972/380-2570 |
| St Mark Catholic Sch<br>1201 Alma Dr, Plano 75075<br>Patricia Opon | K-8 | | 644 | 972/578-0610<br>Fax 972/423-3299 |
| St Martin De Porres Cath Sch<br>4000 W University Dr, Prosper 75078<br>Susan Flanagan | PK-3 | | 100 | 469/362-2400<br>Fax 972/370-2400 |

- **Diocese of Fort Worth Ed Off** PID: 01054339

  Listing includes only schools located in this county. See District Index for location of Diocesan Offices.

## COLLIN PRIVATE SCHOOLS

| Private Schs..Principal | Grd | Prgm | Enr/#Cls | SN |
|---|---|---|---|---|
| Bethany Christian Sch<br>3300 W Parker Rd, Plano 75075<br>Dr Marvin Effa | PK-12 | | 103<br>10 | 972/596-5811<br>Fax 972/596-5814 |
| Choices Leadership Academy<br>18106 Marsh Ln, Dallas 75287<br>Karen Harkey | K-5 | | 100 | 972/662-0665<br>Fax 972/307-3440 |
| Coram Deo Academy-Collin Cnty<br>9645 Independence Pkwy, Plano 75025<br>Stephanie Garland \ Toby Oaks | PK-12 | | 400 | 469/854-1300<br>Fax 972/692-5140 |
| Cornerstone Christian Academy<br>808 S College St Ste 101, McKinney 75069<br>Sandy Hanson | PK-12 | | 360 | 972/562-8200 |
| Dallas International Sch<br>17811 Waterview Pkwy, Dallas 75252<br>Catherine Lvy | 5-12 | | 180 | 469/250-0001<br>Fax 214/570-4900 |
| Einstein School Plano<br>4011 W Plano Pkwy, Plano 75093<br>Willetta Edinburgh \ Armando Castellanos | K-12 | | 401 | 972/564-8040 |
| Faith Lutheran Sch<br>1701 E Park Blvd, Plano 75074<br>Stephen Kieser | PK-12 | | 130<br>20 | 972/423-7448<br>Fax 972/423-9618 |
| Fusion Academy-Plano<br>2400 Dallas Pkwy Ste 180Q, Plano 75093<br>Troy Byrne | 6-12 | | 50 | 972/403-9018 |
| Good Tree Academy<br>3600 K Ave, Plano 75074<br>Uzma Khan | PK-12 | | 401 | 972/836-6322<br>Fax 972/502-9432 |
| Great Lakes Academy<br>6000 Custer Rd Ste 7, Plano 75023<br>Jason Campbell | K-12 | | 60<br>20 | 972/517-7498<br>Fax 972/517-0133 |
| Guidepost Montessori-Stonebria<br>10247 Warren Pkwy, Frisco 75035<br>Baljeet Jawanda | PK-6 | | 401 | 214/387-8202<br>**f t** |
| Legacy Christian Academy<br>5000 Academy Dr, Frisco 75034<br>Tiffany McCollum \ Glenn Dibley \ Kevin Mosley | PK-12 | | 650 | 469/633-1330<br>Fax 469/633-1348<br>**f t** |
| Levine Academy<br>18011 Hillcrest Rd, Dallas 75252<br>Liz Lawlor | PK-8 | | 520<br>80 | 972/248-3032<br>Fax 972/248-0695<br>**f t** |
| Lucas Christian Academy<br>505 W Lucas Rd, Lucas 75002<br>Ann DeSantis \ Robin Dembicki | K-12 | | 435 | 972/429-4362<br>Fax 972/429-5141 |
| McKinney Christian Academy<br>3601 Bois D Arc Rd, McKinney 75071<br>Chris Hydock \ David Etheredge \ Laura Smith | PK-12 | | 470 | 214/544-2658<br>Fax 972/542-5056<br>**f t** |
| Mona Montessori McKinney<br>513 N Central Expy, McKinney 75070<br>Tina Kasturi | PK-K | | 55<br>4 | 972/542-5825<br>Fax 972/542-7273 |
| Montessori Sch of North Dallas<br>18303 Davenport Rd, Dallas 75252<br>Reena Khandtur | PK-3 | | 200<br>9 | 972/985-8844 |
| Montessori School at Starcreek<br>915 Ridgeview Dr, Allen 75013<br>Monica Cook | PK-6 | | 150 | 972/727-2800 |
| New Hope Christian Academy<br>1501 H Ave, Plano 75074<br>Deedee Mims | PK-4 | | 50 | 972/656-9951 |
| New Star Sch<br>7700 San Jacinto Pl Ste 300, Plano 75024<br>Holly Hao | K-7 | | 200 | 972/897-9217 |

| | | | |
|---|---|---|---|
| Pebblecreek Montessori Sch<br>8104 Coit Rd, Plano 75025<br>Pinky Kohli | PK-6 | 50 | 972/908-3797<br>Fax 972/908-3790 |
| Prestonwood Christian Academy<br>6801 W Park Blvd, Plano 75093<br>Paige DeLeon \ Bill Wendl \ Wendy Morris | PK-12 | 1,500<br>75 | 972/820-5300<br>Fax 972/820-5068<br>f t |
| Spring Creek Academy<br>6000 Custer Rd Ste 5, Plano 75023<br>Walter Ritchie | 1-12 | 150 | 972/517-6730 |
| St Philip's Academy-Frisco<br>6400 Stonebrook Pkwy, Frisco 75034<br>Beverly Woodson | K-3 | 40 | 214/929-7787<br>Fax 214/387-9531<br>f |
| Torah Day School of Dallas<br>6921 Frankford Rd, Dallas 75252<br>Chana Ruderman | PK-8 | 500 | 972/964-0090 |
| West Plano Montessori Sch<br>3425 Ashington Ln, Plano 75023<br>Adhirai Basaaran | PK-3 | 120<br>6 | 972/618-8844<br>Fax 972/398-1798 |
| Willow Bend Academy-Plano<br>2220 Coit Rd Ste 500, Plano 75075<br>Dr Peter Berner | 5-12 | 100 | 972/599-7882<br>Fax 972/672-7858 |
| Wylie Preparatory Academy<br>4110 Skyview Ct, Wylie 75098<br>Sara Killian \ Elizabeth Caperton | K-12 | 230 | 972/442-1388<br>Fax 972/429-3568<br>f t |

## COLLINGSWORTH COUNTY

## COLLINGSWORTH PUBLIC SCHOOLS

- **Wellington Ind School Dist** PID: 01006708          806/447-3102
  609 15th St, Wellington 79095                         Fax 806/447-5124

**Schools:** 3 \ **Teachers:** 56 \ **Students:** 530 \ **Special Ed Students:** 62
\ **LEP Students:** 51 \ **Ethnic:** African American 3%, Hispanic 50%,
Caucasian 46% \ **Exp:** $422 (High) \ **Poverty:** 23% \ **Title I:** $177,535 \
**Open-Close:** 08/17 - 05/18 \ **DTBP:** $402 (High)

| | | |
|---|---|---|
| Kurt Ashmore .................1,11 | Diane Souder ......................2 |
| Toby Silva ...........................3 | Debbie Hungteres ..............4 |
| Reggie Sauder .....................5 | Greg Proffitt .......................6 |
| Asheley Long .......................7 | Diedra Kane ........................8 |
| Vicki Decker ..................16,82 | Jermaine Cantu ........17,58,296 |
| Marnie Kane .......................20 | Linda Castillo ...........57,270,271 |
| Lynn Bartlett .......................67 | Renessa Klink ..........69,83,88* |
| John Scott ....................73,295* | |

| Public Schs..Principal | Grd | Prgm | Enr/#Cls | SN |
|---|---|---|---|---|
| Wellington Elem Sch<br>606 16th St, Wellington 79095<br>Deidre Kane | PK-5 | T | 270<br>25 | 68% 806/447-3112<br>Fax 806/447-5097 |
| Wellington High Sch<br>811 15th St, Wellington 79095<br>Jermaine Cantu | 9-12 | TV | 155<br>20 | 57% 806/447-3172<br>Fax 806/447-9012 |
| Wellington Junior High Sch<br>1504 Amarillo St, Wellington 79095<br>Edward Beck | 6-8 | T | 124<br>20 | 73% 806/447-3152<br>Fax 806/447-5089 |

## COLORADO COUNTY

## COLORADO PUBLIC SCHOOLS

- **Columbus Ind School Dist** PID: 01006746          979/732-5704
  105 Cardinal Ln, Columbus 78934                       Fax 979/732-5960

**Schools:** 4 \ **Teachers:** 119 \ **Students:** 1,494 \ **Special Ed Students:** 215
\ **LEP Students:** 191 \ **Ethnic:** Asian 1%, African American 11%, Hispanic
47%, Caucasian 41% \ **Exp:** $495 (High) \ **Poverty:** 19% \ **Title I:** $380,654
\ **Special Education:** $333,000 \ **Open-Close:** 08/12 - 05/20 \ **DTBP:** $350
(High) \ f

| | | |
|---|---|---|
| Dr Brian Morris .....................1 | Scott Leopold ..................2,19 |
| Kenny Koehl ........................3 | Cheryl Woytek ....................4 |
| Chris Everett ........................5 | Matt Schobel ......................6 |
| Shelly Roman .......................7 | Jim Connor .........................8 |
| Amber Berger ...............11,68,296 | Sarah Wanjura ...................58 |
| Rick Restivo .......................67 | Zachary Venghaus .............73 |
| Lance Portwood ................295 | |

| Public Schs..Principal | Grd | Prgm | Enr/#Cls | SN |
|---|---|---|---|---|
| Ⓐ Columbus Alternative Sch<br>1421 Austin St, Columbus 78934<br>Michael Koehl | 7-12 | | 60 | 979/732-2963 |
| Columbus Elem Sch<br>1324 Bowie St, Columbus 78934<br>Shana Neisner | PK-5 | T | 391 | 65% 979/732-2078<br>Fax 979/732-8627 |
| Columbus High Sch<br>103 Cardinal Ln, Columbus 78934<br>**Pennee Hall** | 9-12 | ATV | 358<br>40 | 49% 979/732-5746<br>Fax 979/732-8862 |
| Columbus Junior High Sch<br>702 Rampart St, Columbus 78934<br>**Amy Russell** | 6-8 | AT | 126<br>30 | 61% 979/732-2891<br>Fax 979/732-9081 |

- **Rice Cons Ind School Dist** PID: 01006784          979/234-3531
  1094 Raider Dr, Altair 77412                          Fax 979/234-3409

**Schools:** 7 \ **Teachers:** 107 \ **Students:** 1,325 \ **Special Ed Students:** 161
\ **LEP Students:** 109 \ **College-Bound:** 62% \ **Ethnic:** Asian 1%, African
American 17%, Hispanic 58%, Caucasian 24% \ **Exp:** $516 (High) \
**Poverty:** 24% \ **Title I:** $385,392 \ **Open-Close:** 08/19 - 05/27 \ **DTBP:** $349
(High)

| | | |
|---|---|---|
| Bill Hefner ........................1,11 | John Post ...........................2 |
| Douglas Behlen ...................3 | Rachel Barten ....................4 |
| Jared Sloan .........................6 | Debbie Ugarte ...................7* |
| Melody Grigar .......8,11,15,83,88,288,296,298 | Connie Gertson ................16* |
| Jacqueline Kovar ...............31* | Vicki Nelson .......................57 |
| Amy Bosse ........................58 | John Carey ........................67 |
| Robyn Machac ................69,79 | Ralph Gertson ..............73,295 |
| Janet Mahalitc ....................76 | Eric Grogan .....................271* |

| Public Schs..Principal | Grd | Prgm | Enr/#Cls | SN |
|---|---|---|---|---|
| Eagle Lake Intermediate Sch<br>701 Tate Ave, Eagle Lake 77434<br>Gene Glover | 3-5 | T | 203<br>17 | 87% 979/234-3531<br>Fax 979/234-5207 |
| Eagle Lake Primary Sch<br>600 J D Hutchins Dr, Eagle Lake 77434<br>Kimberly Etheridge | PK-2 | T | 217 | 91% 979/234-3531<br>Fax 979/234-6337 |

| | | | | | |
|---|---|---|---|---|---|
| 1 Superintendent | 8 Curric/Instruct K-12 | 19 Chief Financial Officer | 29 Family/Consumer Science | 39 Social Studies K-12 | 49 English/Lang Arts Elem | 59 Special Education Elem | 69 Academic Assessment |
| 2 Bus/Finance/Purchasing | 9 Curric/Instruct Elem | 20 Art K-12 | 30 Adult Education | 40 Social Studies Elem | 50 English/Lang Arts Sec | 60 Special Education Sec | 70 Research/Development |
| 3 Buildings And Grounds | 10 Curric/Instruct Sec | 21 Art Elem | 31 Career/Sch-to-Work K-12 | 41 Social Studies Sec | 51 Reading K-12 | 61 Foreign/World Lang K-12 | 71 Public Information |
| 4 Food Service | 11 Federal Program | 22 Art Sec | 32 Career/Sch-to-Work Elem | 42 Science K-12 | 52 Reading Elem | 62 Foreign/World Lang Elem | 72 Summer School |
| 5 Transportation | 12 Title I | 23 Music K-12 | 33 Career/Sch-to-Work Sec | 43 Science Elem | 53 Reading Sec | 63 Foreign/World Lang Sec | 73 Instructional Tech |
| 6 Athletic | 13 Title V | 24 Music Elem | 34 Early Childhood Ed | 44 Science Sec | 54 Remedial Reading K-12 | 64 Religious Education K-12 | 74 Inservice Training |
| 7 Health Services | 15 Asst Superintendent | 25 Music Sec | 35 Health/Phys Education | 45 Math K-12 | 55 Remedial Reading Elem | 65 Religious Education Elem | 75 Marketing/Distributive |
| | 16 Instructional Media Svcs | 26 Business Education | 36 Guidance Services K-12 | 46 Math Elem | 56 Remedial Reading Sec | 66 Religious Education Sec | 76 Info Systems |
| | 17 Chief Operations Officer | 27 Career & Tech Ed | 37 Guidance Services Elem | 47 Math Sec | 57 Bilingual/ELL | 67 School Board President | 77 Psychological Assess |
| | 18 Chief Academic Officer | 28 Technology Education | 38 Guidance Services Sec | 48 English/Lang Arts K-12 | 58 Special Education K-12 | 68 Teacher Personnel | 78 Affirmative Action |

| | | | | | | |
|---|---|---|---|---|---|---|
| Garwood Elem Sch | K-5 | T | 99 | 61% | 979/758-3531 | |
| Highway 71 S, Garwood 77442 | | | 6 | | Fax 979/758-3751 | |
| Leroy Stavinoha | | | | | | |
| Ⓐ Rice Challenge Academy | 9-12 | | 64 | 97% | 979/234-3531 | |
| 600 FM 3013 W, Eagle Lake 77434 | | | | | Fax 979/234-2302 | |
| Dan Garza | | | | | | |
| Rice High Sch | 9-12 | TV | 187 | 74% | 979/234-3531 | |
| 1095 Raider Dr, Altair 77412 | | | 30 | | Fax 979/234-5901 | |
| Eric Grogan | | | | | | |
| Rice Junior High Sch | 6-8 | T | 274 | 78% | 979/234-3531 | |
| 1095 Raider Dr, Altair 77412 | | | 19 | | Fax 979/234-5901 | |
| Brian Leist | | | | | | |
| Sheridan Elem Sch | PK-5 | T | 42 | 80% | 979/234-3531 | |
| Farm Road 2437, Sheridan 77475 | | | 8 | | Fax 979/234-6322 | |
| Virgil Knowlton | | | | | | |

● **Weimar Ind School Dist** PID: 01006849     979/725-9504
506 W Main St, Weimar 78962     Fax 979/725-8737

Schools: 3 \ Teachers: 59 \ Students: 629 \ Special Ed Students: 73 \ LEP Students: 111 \ College-Bound: 50% \ Ethnic: African American 11%, Hispanic 45%, Caucasian 44% \ Exp: $539 (High) \ Poverty: 17% \ Title I: $134,831 \ Special Education: $354,000 \ Open-Close: 08/13 - 05/20 \ DTBP: $367 (High)

| | | | |
|---|---|---|---|
| Jonathan Wunderlich | 1 | Angela Luksovsky | 2 |
| Stephen Jurek | 3 | Theresa Rerich | 4* |
| Ryan McLver | 6* | Codi Guenther | 11* |
| Eleazar Moreno | 16,73,76,295 | Lisa Marak | 57* |
| Amanda Turlington | 58* | Ken Kram | 67 |

| Public Schs..Principal | Grd | Prgm | Enr/#Cls | SN | |
|---|---|---|---|---|---|
| Weimar Elem Sch | PK-4 | T | 254 | 68% | 979/725-6009 |
| 515 W Main St, Weimar 78962 | | | 16 | | Fax 979/725-9527 |
| **Janecka Kristy** | | | | | |
| Weimar High Sch | 9-12 | V | 201 | 46% | 979/725-9504 |
| 506 W Main St, Weimar 78962 | | | 18 | | Fax 979/725-9765 |
| Stacy Heger | | | | | |
| Weimar Junior High Sch | 5-8 | T | 174 | 57% | 979/725-9515 |
| 101 N West St, Weimar 78962 | | | 8 | | Fax 979/725-8383 |
| Stacy Heger | | | | | |

# COLORADO CATHOLIC SCHOOLS

● **Diocese of Victoria Ed Office** PID: 02181727
Listing includes only schools located in this county. See District Index for location of Diocesan Offices.

| Catholic Schs..Principal | Grd | Prgm | Enr/#Cls | SN | |
|---|---|---|---|---|---|
| St Anthony Sch | PK-8 | | 185 | | 979/732-5505 |
| 635 Bonham St, Columbus 78934 | | | 14 | | Fax 979/732-9758 |
| John O'Leary | | | | | |
| St Michael Sch | PK-8 | | 80 | | 979/725-8461 |
| 103 E North St, Weimar 78962 | | | 12 | | Fax 979/725-8344 |
| Judy Roeder | | | | | |

## COMAL COUNTY

# COMAL PUBLIC SCHOOLS

● **Comal Ind School Dist** PID: 01006887     830/221-2000
1404 N Interstate 35, New Braunfels 78130     Fax 830/221-2001

Schools: 33 \ Teachers: 1,499 \ Students: 23,800 \ Special Ed Students: 2,666 \ LEP Students: 1,244 \ College-Bound: 51% \ Ethnic: Asian 1%, African American 2%, Hispanic 41%, Caucasian 55% \ Exp: $228 (Med) \ Poverty: 8% \ Title I: $2,263,359 \ Special Education: $3,493,000 \ Open-Close: 08/25 - 05/27 \ DTBP: $180 (High) \ 🇫 🇹

| | | | |
|---|---|---|---|
| Andrew Kim | 1 | Catherine Janda | 2 |
| David Anderson | 2,19 | Mike McCuller | 3 |
| Jessica Fischer | 5 | Liana Gombert | 6* |
| Michael Smith | 7,35* | Kerry Gain | 8,15 |
| Carla Schumann | 20,23 | Becky Walker | 27,31,95 |
| Taylor Keller | 42 | Michele Martella | 58 |
| David Drastata | 67 | Mandy Epley | 68 |
| Courtney Witherell | 69,294 | Steve Stanford | 71 |
| Jarrett Cochran | 73,76,295,297 | Hannah Schramm | 74 |
| Daniel Mendez | 75 | Jennifer Johnson | 79,275 |
| Tiffany Newkirk | 83,90 | Sarah Permentor | 271 |

| Public Schs..Principal | Grd | Prgm | Enr/#Cls | SN | |
|---|---|---|---|---|---|
| Arlon Seay Elem Sch | K-5 | | 391 | 23% | 830/885-8700 |
| 20911 State Highway 46 W, Spring Branch 78070 | | | 20 | | Fax 830/885-8701 |
| **Theressa Engel** | | | | | |
| Bill Brown Elem Sch | PK-5 | | 666 | 24% | 830/885-1400 |
| 20410 State Highway 46 W, Spring Branch 78070 | | | | | Fax 830/885-1401 |
| Jillian Jurica | | | | | 🇫🇹 |
| Canyon High Sch | 9-12 | AGV | 2,700 | 32% | 830/221-2400 |
| 1510 N Interstate 35 1H, New Braunfels 78130 | | | 75 | | Fax 830/221-2401 |
| **Dustin Davisson** | | | | | |
| Canyon Lake High Sch | 9-12 | A | 1,045 | 38% | 830/885-1700 |
| 8555 Rm 32, Fischer 78623 | | | | | Fax 830/885-1701 |
| Kristy Castilleja | | | | | |
| Canyon Middle Sch | 6-8 | TV | 723 | 50% | 830/221-2300 |
| 2014 FM 1101, New Braunfels 78130 | | | 57 | | Fax 830/221-2301 |
| Ernie Reynolds | | | | | |
| Church Hill Middle Sch | 6-8 | | 923 | 28% | 830/221-2800 |
| 1275 N Business Ih 35, New Braunfels 78130 | | | 38 | | Fax 830/221-2801 |
| Jaime Calderon | | | | | |
| Clear Spring Elem Sch | PK-5 | T | 712 | 50% | 830/837-7300 |
| 550 Avery Pkwy, New Braunfels 78130 | | | | | Fax 830/837-7301 |
| Janelle Hardin | | | | | |
| Ⓐ Comal Academy | 11-12 | T | 51 | 27% | 830/221-2951 |
| 1413 N Business Ih 35, New Braunfels 78130 | | | | | |
| Lori Lehmberg | | | | | |
| Ⓐ Comal Discipline Center | K-12 | T | 60 | 45% | 830/221-2950 |
| 1413 N Business Ih 35, New Braunfels 78130 | | | | | Fax 830/221-2951 |
| Lori Lehmberg | | | | | |
| Danville Middle Sch | 6-8 | | 705 | 36% | 830/837-7400 |
| 370 Hubertus Rd, New Braunfels 78132 | | | | | |
| Julie Cronkhite | | | | | |
| Davenport High Sch | 9-11 | | 401 | | 830/837-7500 |
| 23255 FM 3009, San Antonio 78266 | | | | | |
| **Matthew DeLoach** | | | | | |

| | | | | | | |
|---|---|---|---|---|---|---|
| 79 | Student Personnel | 91 | Safety/Security | 275 | Response To Intervention | 298 Grant Writer/Ptnrships |
| 80 | Driver Ed/Safety | 92 | Magnet School | 277 | Remedial Math K-12 | 750 Chief Innovation Officer |
| 81 | Gifted/Talented | 93 | Parental Involvement | 280 | Literacy Coach | 751 Chief of Staff |
| 82 | Video Services | 95 | Tech Prep Program | 285 | STEM | 752 Social Emotional Learning |
| 83 | Substance Abuse Prev | 97 | Chief Information Officer | 286 | Digital Learning | |
| 84 | Erate | 98 | Chief Technology Officer | 288 | Common Core Standards | **Other School Types** |
| 85 | AIDS Education | 270 | Character Education | 294 | Accountability | Ⓐ = Alternative School |
| 88 | Alternative/At Risk | 271 | Migrant Education | 295 | Network System | Ⓒ = Charter School |
| 89 | Multi-Cultural Curriculum | 273 | Teacher Mentor | 296 | Title II Programs | Ⓜ = Magnet School |
| 90 | Social Work | 274 | Before/After Sch | 297 | Webmaster | Ⓨ = Year-Round School |

**School Programs**
A = Alternative Program
G = Adult Classes
M = Magnet Program
T = Title I Schoolwide
V = Career & Tech Ed Programs

**Social Media**
🇫 = Facebook
🇹 = Twitter

New Schools are shaded
New Superintendents and Principals are bold
Personnel with email addresses are underscored

# TX—91

| | | | | | |
|---|---|---|---|---|---|
| Freiheit Elem Sch<br>2002 FM 1101, New Braunfels 78130<br>Shelly Crofford | PK-5 | T | 696<br>23 | 53% | 830/221-2700<br>Fax 830/221-2701 |
| Garden Ridge Elem Sch<br>9401 Municipal Pkwy, Garden Ridge 78266<br>Jennifer Schultz | PK-5 | | 846<br>22 | 22% | 830/837-7000<br>Fax 830/837-7001 |
| Goodwin Frazier Elem Sch<br>1441 N Business Ih 35, New Braunfels 78130<br>Carolyn Gump | PK-5 | T | 591<br>22 | 61% | 830/221-2200<br>Fax 830/221-2201 |
| Hill Country Clg Prep High Sch<br>21077 State Highway 46 W, Spring Branch 78070<br>**Julie Wiley** | 9-9 | | 75 | | 830/885-9000 |
| Hoffmann Lane Elem Sch<br>4600 FM 306, New Braunfels 78132<br>**Amanda Schumann** | PK-5 | | 685<br>33 | 5% | 830/221-2500<br>Fax 830/221-2501 |
| Indian Springs Elem Sch<br>25751 Wilderness Oak, San Antonio 78261<br>Mary Stults | PK-5 | | 817 | 9% | 830/885-9300<br>Fax 830/885-9301 |
| Johnson Ranch Elem Sch<br>30501 Johnson Way, Bulverde 78163<br>Suzanne Seabolt | PK-5 | | 508 | 14% | 830/885-8600<br>Fax 830/885-8601<br>f |
| Kinder Ranch Elem Sch<br>2035 Kinder Pkwy, San Antonio 78260<br>Nicole DuVall | PK-5 | | 504 | 29% | 830/885-8900<br>Fax 830/885-8901 |
| M H Specht Elem Sch<br>25815 Overlook Pkwy, San Antonio 78260<br>Jackie Sundt | PK-5 | | 772<br>35 | 21% | 830/885-1500<br>Fax 830/885-1501 |
| Ⓐ Memorial Early College HS<br>1419 N Business Ih 35, New Braunfels 78130<br>Meredith Pappas | 9-12 | | 260<br>6 | 20% | 830/221-2900<br>Fax 830/221-2901<br>f t |
| Morningside Elem Sch<br>3855 Morningside Dr, New Braunfels 78132<br>Ashley Fredo | PK-5 | T | 726 | 68% | 830/837-7100<br>Fax 830/837-7101 |
| Mountain Valley Elem Sch<br>310 Cannan Rd, Canyon Lake 78133<br>Jennifer Smith | PK-5 | | 472 | | 830/885-9500<br>Fax 830/885-9501 |
| Mountain Valley Middle Sch<br>1165 Sattler Rd, Canyon Lake 78132<br>**Angela Looney** | 6-8 | T | 758 | 46% | 830/885-1300<br>Fax 830/885-1301 |
| Oak Creek Elem Sch<br>3060 Goodwin Ln, New Braunfels 78130<br>Stacy Wilkie | PK-5 | | 435 | 35% | 830/837-7200<br>Fax 830/837-7201 |
| Pieper Ranch Middle Sch<br>1106 Kinder Pkwy, San Antonio 78260<br>Scott Hammond | 6-8 | | 1,254 | 17% | 830/885-9600<br>Fax 830/885-9601 |
| Rahe Bulverde Elem Sch<br>1715 E Ammann Rd, Bulverde 78163<br>Amy Malone | PK-5 | | 433<br>10 | 21% | 830/885-1600<br>Fax 830/885-1601 |
| Rebecca Creek Elem Sch<br>125 Quest Ave, Spring Branch 78070<br>Wendy Moore | PK-5 | T | 524 | 50% | 830/885-1800<br>Fax 830/885-1801 |
| Smithson Valley High Sch<br>14001 State Highway 46 W, Spring Branch 78070<br>Michael Wahl | 9-12 | AGV | 2,849<br>100 | 13% | 830/885-1000<br>Fax 830/885-1001 |
| Smithson Valley Middle Sch<br>6101 FM 311, Spring Branch 78070<br>Michael Keranen | 6-8 | V | 667<br>30 | 10% | 830/885-1200<br>Fax 830/885-1201 |
| Spring Branch Middle Sch<br>21053 State Highway 46 W, Spring Branch 78070<br>Chris Smith | 6-8 | V | 175<br>30 | 23% | 830/885-8800<br>Fax 830/885-8801 |
| Startzville Elem Sch<br>42111 FM 3159, Canyon Lake 78133<br>Melinda Shinn | PK-5 | T | 331<br>30 | 64% | 830/885-8000<br>Fax 830/885-8001 |
| Timberwood Park Elem Sch<br>26715 S Glenrose Rd, San Antonio 78260<br>Kim Lyssy | PK-5 | | 669<br>38 | 12% | 830/885-8500<br>Fax 830/885-8501<br>f |

● **New Braunfels Ind School Dist** PID: 01006966    830/643-5700
430 W Mill St, New Braunfels 78130    Fax 830/643-5701

> **Schools:** 15 \ **Teachers:** 541 \ **Students:** 9,220 \ **Special Ed Students:** 782 \ **LEP Students:** 724 \ **College-Bound:** 48% \ **Ethnic:** Asian 1%, African American 2%, Hispanic 49%, Caucasian 48% \ **Exp:** $219 (Med) \ **Poverty:** 10% \ **Title I:** $1,312,630 \ **Special Education:** $1,466,000 \ **Bilingual Education:** $34,000 \ **Open-Close:** 08/24 - 05/27 \ **DTBP:** $176 (High)

| | | | |
|---|---|---|---|
| Randy Moczygemba | 1 | Rosanne Stockhorst | 2 |
| Steve Brown | 2 | Daryl Stoker | 3 |
| Catherine Vanderbrook | 4 | Brian Gibson | 5,91 |
| Jim Streety | 6 | Karen Schwind | 7 |
| Victoria Pursch | 8,15,34,69,294 | Ron Rychel | 11 |
| Matthew Jones | 16,73,295 | Rachel Behnke | 27 |
| Kimberly Brann | 57 | Martha Moke | 58 |
| Sherry Harrison | 6/ | Kathy Kenney | 68 |
| Dena Schroeder | 69 | Rebecca Villarreal | 71 |
| Lori Gruwell | 74 | Francie Novander | 76 |
| Clay Gillentine | 79 | Blake Haygood | 81 |

| Public Schs..Principal | Grd | Prgm | Enr/#Cls | SN |
|---|---|---|---|---|
| Carl Schurz Elem Sch<br>633 W Coll St, New Braunfels 78130<br>Duane Trujillo | K-5 | T | 423<br>24 | 50% 830/627-6680<br>Fax 830/627-6681 |
| County Line Elem Sch<br>1200 W County Line Rd, New Braunfels 78130<br>Taylor Danielle | PK-5 | | 318<br>28 | 33% 830/627-6610<br>Fax 830/627-6611 |
| Klein Road Elem Sch<br>2620 Klein Way, New Braunfels 78130<br>Marisela Lopez | K-5 | T | 580 | 46% 830/221-1700<br>Fax 830/221-1701 |
| Lamar Elem Sch<br>240 N Central Ave, New Braunfels 78130<br>Christopher Russell | K-5 | T | 309<br>24 | 47% 830/627-6890<br>Fax 830/629-2660 |
| Lone Star Early Childhood Ctr<br>2343 W San Antonio St, New Braunfels 78130<br>Heather Salas | PK-PK | T | 348 | 82% 830/627-6820<br>Fax 830/627-6821 |
| Memorial Elem Sch<br>1911 S Walnut Ave, New Braunfels 78130<br>Nicole Haecker | PK-5 | T | 314<br>21 | 45% 830/627-6470<br>Fax 830/627-6471 |
| New Braunfels High Sch<br>2551 Loop 337, New Braunfels 78130<br>Kara Bock | 9-12 | GV | 1,161<br>110 | 27% 830/627-6000<br>Fax 830/627-6001 |
| New Braunfels HS 9th GR Ctr<br>659 S Guenther Ave, New Braunfels 78130<br>Jeffrey Lightsey | 9-9 | A | 655 | 36% 830/629-8600<br>Fax 830/629-8601 |
| New Braunfels Middle Sch<br>4150 Klein Mdws, New Braunfels 78130<br>Greg Hughes | 6-9 | V | 1,163<br>65 | 39% 830/627-6270<br>Fax 830/627-6271 |
| Oak Run Middle Sch<br>415 Oak Run Pt, New Braunfels 78132<br>Shana Behling | 6-8 | | 930<br>25 | 35% 830/627-6400<br>Fax 830/627-6401 |
| Ⓐ School of Choice<br>659 S Guenther Ave, New Braunfels 78130<br>Jerry Clark | 9-12 | T | 150<br>5 | 61% 830/629-8650<br>Fax 830/629-8651 |
| Seele Elem Sch<br>540 Howard St, New Braunfels 78130<br>Deanna Callahan | K-5 | T | 255<br>18 | 43% 830/627-6750<br>Fax 830/627-6751 |
| Veramendi Elem Sch<br>2290 Oak Run Pkwy, New Braunfels 78132<br>Leah Droddy | PK-5 | | 674 | 32% 830/608-5900<br>Fax 830/608-5901 |
| Voss Farms Elem Sch<br>2510 Pahmeyer Rd, New Braunfels 78130<br>Deborah Cary | PK-5 | T | 542 | 38% 830/608-5800<br>Fax 830/608-5801 |

| | | | | | | | |
|---|---|---|---|---|---|---|---|
| 1 | Superintendent | 8 | Curric/Instruct K-12 | 19 | Chief Financial Officer | 29 | Family/Consumer Science |
| 2 | Bus/Finance/Purchasing | 9 | Curric/Instruct Elem | 20 | Art K-12 | 30 | Adult Education |
| 3 | Buildings And Grounds | 10 | Curric/Instruct Sec | 21 | Art Elem | 31 | Career/Sch-to-Work K-12 |
| 4 | Food Service | 11 | Federal Program | 22 | Art Sec | 32 | Career/Sch-to-Work Elem |
| 5 | Transportation | 12 | Title I | 23 | Music K-12 | 33 | Career/Sch-to-Work Sec |
| 6 | Athletic | 13 | Title V | 24 | Music Elem | 34 | Early Childhood Ed |
| 7 | Health Services | 15 | Asst Superintendent | 25 | Music Sec | 35 | Health/Phys Education |
| | | 16 | Instructional Media Svcs | 26 | Business Education | 36 | Guidance Services K-12 |
| | | 17 | Chief Operations Officer | 27 | Career & Tech Ed | 37 | Guidance Services Elem |
| | | 18 | Chief Academic Officer | 28 | Technology Education | 38 | Guidance Services Sec |

| | | | | | | | |
|---|---|---|---|---|---|---|---|
| 39 | Social Studies K-12 | 49 | English/Lang Arts Elem | 59 | Special Education Elem | 69 | Academic Assessment |
| 40 | Social Studies Elem | 50 | English/Lang Arts Sec | 60 | Special Education Sec | 70 | Research/Development |
| 41 | Social Studies Sec | 51 | Reading K-12 | 61 | Foreign/World Lang K-12 | 71 | Public Information |
| 42 | Science K-12 | 52 | Reading Elem | 62 | Foreign/World Lang Elem | 72 | Summer School |
| 43 | Science Elem | 53 | Reading Sec | 63 | Foreign/World Lang Sec | 73 | Instructional Tech |
| 44 | Science Sec | 54 | Remedial Reading K-12 | 64 | Religious Education K-12 | 74 | Inservice Training |
| 45 | Math K-12 | 55 | Remedial Reading Elem | 65 | Religious Education Elem | 75 | Marketing/Distributive |
| 46 | Math Elem | 56 | Remedial Reading Sec | 66 | Religious Education Sec | 76 | Info Systems |
| 47 | Math Sec | 57 | Bilingual/ELL | 67 | School Board President | 77 | Psychological Assess |
| 48 | English/Lang Arts K-12 | 58 | Special Education K-12 | 68 | Teacher Personnel | 78 | Affirmative Action |

| | Grd | | Enr/#Cls | SN |
|---|---|---|---|---|
| Walnut Springs Elem Sch | K-5 | | 226 | 35% 830/627-6540 |
| 1900 S Walnut Ave, New Braunfels 78130 | | | 22 | Fax 830/627-6541 |
| Leigh Ann Bailey | | | | |

## COMAL CATHOLIC SCHOOLS

- **Archdiocese San Antonio Ed Off** PID: 00999724
  Listing includes only schools located in this county. See District Index for location of Diocesan Offices.

| Catholic Schs..Principal | Grd | Prgm | Enr/#Cls | SN |
|---|---|---|---|---|
| SS Peter & Paul Sch | PK-8 | | 377 | 830/625-4531 |
| 198 W Bridge St, New Braunfels 78130 | | | 20 | Fax 830/606-6916 |
| Janet Buras | | | | |
| St John Paul II High Sch | 9-12 | | 200 | 830/643-0802 |
| 6720 FM 482, New Braunfels 78132 | | | | Fax 830/643-0806 |
| Andrew Iliff | | | | |

## COMAL PRIVATE SCHOOLS

| Private Schs..Principal | Grd | Prgm | Enr/#Cls | SN |
|---|---|---|---|---|
| Bracken Christian Sch | PK-12 | | 250 | 830/438-3211 |
| 670 Old Boerne Rd, Bulverde 78163 | | | 40 | Fax 830/980-2327 |
| Frank Riley \ Sheila Kerby | | | | 🇫 🇹 |
| Cross Lutheran Sch | PK-8 | | 165 | 830/625-3969 |
| 2171 E Common St, New Braunfels 78130 | | | 13 | Fax 830/625-5019 |
| Corey Brandenburger | | | | |
| Gloria Deo Academy | K-10 | | 120 | 830/708-5463 |
| 1100 Bulverde Rd Ste 2, Bulverde 78163 | | | | |
| Joe Fesler | | | | |
| Living Rock Academy | PK-12 | | 88 | 830/387-2929 |
| 2500 Bulverde Rd, Bulverde 78163 | | | | Fax 210/787-4091 |
| Melanie Raposo \ Linda Swierc | | | | |
| New Braunfels Chrn Acad-Lower | PK-5 | | 200 | 830/629-6222 |
| 995 Mission Hills Dr, New Braunfels 78130 | | | 15 | Fax 830/629-8049 |
| Darren West | | | | |

## COMANCHE COUNTY

## COMANCHE PUBLIC SCHOOLS

- **Comanche Ind School Dist** PID: 01007051       325/356-2727
  200 E Highland Ave, Comanche 76442                Fax 325/356-2312

**Schools:** 4 \ **Teachers:** 113 \ **Students:** 1,325 \ **Special Ed Students:** 152 \ **LEP Students:** 181 \ **College-Bound:** 68% \ **Ethnic:** Hispanic 53%, Native American: 1%, Caucasian 46% \ **Exp:** $349 (High) \ **Poverty:** 24% \ **Title I:** $382,520 \ **Open-Close:** 08/17 - 05/25 \ **DTBP:** $379 (High)

| | | | | |
|---|---|---|---|---|
| Daron Worrell | 1 | Kathy Herring | 2 |
| Howard Gifford | 3 | Amy Brooks | 4 |
| Chad Brown | 5 | Jimmy Eaton | 5 |
| Lupe Moreno | 5 | Stephen Hermesmeyer | 6* |
| Mona Clifton | 7* | Della Hicks | 10,36,69,77,83,85* |
| Gwinn Smith | 37* | Curtis Stahnke | 54* |

| | | | | |
|---|---|---|---|---|
| Becky Jones | 58 | Jason Pate | 67 |
| Linda McGinnis | 73* | Roxann Gray | 76 |
| Scott Carlisle | 91* | | |

| Public Schs..Principal | Grd | Prgm | Enr/#Cls | SN |
|---|---|---|---|---|
| Comanche Early Childhood Ctr | PK-PK | T | 68 | 100% 325/356-2440 |
| 200 E Highland Ave, Comanche 76442 | | | | Fax 325/356-1454 |
| Melinda Megna | | | | |
| Comanche Elem Sch | PK-5 | T | 580 | 70% 325/356-2727 |
| 308 FM 3381, Comanche 76442 | | | 25 | Fax 325/356-3990 |
| Curtis Stahnke | | | | |
| Comanche High Sch | 9-12 | T | 328 | 59% 325/356-2581 |
| Highway 16 N, Comanche 76442 | | | 50 | Fax 325/356-2658 |
| Steven Lewis | | | | |
| H R Jefferies Junior High Sch | 6-8 | T | 286 | 67% 325/356-5220 |
| 1 Valley Forge St, Comanche 76442 | | | 25 | Fax 325/356-1949 |
| Joseph Simmons | | | | |

- **De Leon Ind School Dist** PID: 01007099       254/893-8210
  425 S Texas St, De Leon 76444                      Fax 254/893-8214

**Schools:** 3 \ **Teachers:** 53 \ **Students:** 720 \ **Special Ed Students:** 76 \ **LEP Students:** 33 \ **College-Bound:** 37% \ **Ethnic:** African American 1%, Hispanic 34%, Caucasian 65% \ **Exp:** $528 (High) \ **Poverty:** 21% \ **Title I:** $187,523 \ **Open-Close:** 09/08 - 05/28 \ **DTBP:** $335 (High)

| | | | | |
|---|---|---|---|---|
| Dana Marable | 1 | Eli Reeves | 2 |
| David White | 3,5,73,84 | Samantha Jones | 4,11,271,286,298* |
| Andy Dickson | 6 | Meagan Golden | 7 |
| Kalliier Hare | 8 | Liesa Nowlin | 10,27* |
| Kaye Quinn | 12,31,36,69,85,88,270,296 | Michell Simpson | 16* |
| Roxanna Tibo | 54* | Deanna Downs | 57* |
| Craig Hopper | 58 | Josh Mahan | 67 |
| Chuck Miller | 91 | Michielle McIlcain | 285 |
| Amber Bates | 288,752 | Mike Taylor | 295 |

| Public Schs..Principal | Grd | Prgm | Enr/#Cls | SN |
|---|---|---|---|---|
| De Leon Elem Sch | PK-5 | T | 357 | 68% 254/893-8220 |
| 133 E Pecan Ave, De Leon 76444 | | | 17 | Fax 254/893-8224 |
| Lori Womack | | | | |
| De Leon High Sch | 9-12 | ATV | 195 | 56% 254/893-8240 |
| 200 W Manchaca Ave, De Leon 76444 | | | 20 | Fax 254/893-4985 |
| Liesa Nowlin | | | | |
| Perkins Middle Sch | 6-8 | T | 189 | 65% 254/893-8230 |
| 600 N Johnson St, De Leon 76444 | | | 16 | Fax 254/893-8234 |
| Joshua Sepeda | | | | |

- **Gustine Ind School Dist** PID: 01007128       325/667-7981
  503 W Main St, Gustine 76455                      Fax 325/667-0203

**Schools:** 1 \ **Teachers:** 17 \ **Students:** 134 \ **Special Ed Students:** 21 \ **LEP Students:** 51 \ **College-Bound:** 70% \ **Ethnic:** Hispanic 71%, Caucasian 29% \ **Exp:** $728 (High) \ **Poverty:** 17% \ **Title I:** $70,950 \ **Special Education:** $19,000 \ **Open-Close:** 08/12 - 05/20

| | | | | |
|---|---|---|---|---|
| Patti Blue | 1,11,73 | Brandy Ruedas | 57* |
| Anita McCutchen | 67 | | |

| Public Schs..Principal | Grd | Prgm | Enr/#Cls | SN |
|---|---|---|---|---|
| Gustine Sch | PK-12 | TV | 134 | 76% 325/667-7303 |
| 503 W Main St, Gustine 76455 | | | 20 | |
| Kenny Eudy | | | | |

- **Sidney Ind School Dist** PID: 01007154
  4100 FM 1689, Sidney 76474

  254/842-5500
  Fax 254/842-5139

> **Schools:** 1 \ **Teachers:** 15 \ **Students:** 139 \ **Special Ed Students:** 25 \
> **College-Bound:** 80% \ **Ethnic:** Hispanic 22%, Caucasian 78% \ **Exp:** $937
> (High) \ **Poverty:** 23% \ **Title I:** $29,231 \ **Open-Close:** 08/14 - 05/28 \
> **DTBP:** $408 (High)

| | | | |
|---|---|---|---|
| James Rucker | 1,11,73,83 | Anita Wright | 2 |
| Betty Stanley | 4* | Sigrid Huddleston | 8,58,88* |
| Doug Caffey | 67 | Deanna Drummond | 73,98,298* |

| Public Schs..Principal | Grd | Prgm | Enr/#Cls | SN |
|---|---|---|---|---|
| ⓨ Sidney Sch | PK-12 | MTV | 139 | 57% 254/842-5500 |
| 4100 FM 1689, Sidney 76474 | | | 10 | Fax 254/842-5731 |
| Deanna Drummond | | | | |

## CONCHO COUNTY

## CONCHO PUBLIC SCHOOLS

- **Eden Cons Ind School Dist** PID: 01007180
  113 W Bryan St, Eden 76837

  325/869-4121
  Fax 325/869-5210

> **Schools:** 2 \ **Teachers:** 18 \ **Students:** 230 \ **Special Ed Students:** 30
> \ **LEP Students:** 12 \ **College-Bound:** 70% \ **Ethnic:** Asian 1%, African
> American 1%, Hispanic 65%, Caucasian 32% \ **Exp:** $844 (High) \
> **Poverty:** 18% \ **Title I:** $65,857 \ **Open-Close:** 08/13 - 05/21 \ **DTBP:** $378
> (High)

| | | | |
|---|---|---|---|
| Misty Gandy | 1,11,73 | Margo Rucker | 2 |
| Chris Castillo | 3 | Dawn Torres | 4 |
| Jonie Whiteley | 16* | Tiffany Estrada | 31 |
| Geneva Garza | 36,57,69,83,270* | Amanda Rurup | 58 |
| Shan Click | 67 | Kelli Dillard | 286* |

| Public Schs..Principal | Grd | Prgm | Enr/#Cls | SN |
|---|---|---|---|---|
| Eden Elem Sch | K-5 | | 215 | 325/869-4121 |
| 101 W Bryan, Eden 76837 | | | 13 | Fax 325/869-5672 |
| Deanna Beachum | | | | |
| Eden High Sch | 6-12 | TV | 135 | 64% 325/869-4121 |
| 180 W Bryan, Eden 76837 | | | 15 | Fax 325/869-5023 |
| Matt Odom | | | | |

- **Paint Rock Ind School Dist** PID: 01007245
  698 S Sims St, Paint Rock 76866

  325/732-4314
  Fax 325/732-4384

> **Schools:** 1 \ **Teachers:** 24 \ **Students:** 225 \ **Special Ed Students:** 27
> \ **LEP Students:** 11 \ **College-Bound:** 50% \ **Ethnic:** Asian 1%, African
> American 1%, Hispanic 50%, Caucasian 48% \ **Exp:** $794 (High) \
> **Poverty:** 41% \ **Title I:** $62,236 \ **Open-Close:** 08/19 - 05/28 \ **DTBP:** $328
> (High)

| | | | |
|---|---|---|---|
| Ron Cline | 1,11 | Tracy Grimes | 2* |
| Allison Tonne | 16* | Anthony Brown | 67 |
| Russell Hoelscher | 73* | | |

| Public Schs..Principal | Grd | Prgm | Enr/#Cls | SN |
|---|---|---|---|---|
| Paint Rock Sch | PK-12 | T | 225 | 76% 325/732-4314 |
| 698 Sims St, Paint Rock 76866 | | | 20 | |
| Allison Tonne \ **Joellen Gonzales** | | | | |

## COOKE COUNTY

## COOKE PUBLIC SCHOOLS

- **Callisburg Ind School Dist** PID: 01007271
  148 Dozier St, Gainesville 76240

  940/665-0540
  Fax 940/668-2706

> **Schools:** 2 \ **Teachers:** 85 \ **Students:** 1,100 \ **Special Ed Students:** 119 \
> **LEP Students:** 30 \ **College-Bound:** 38% \ **Ethnic:** African American 1%,
> Hispanic 14%, Native American: 1%, Caucasian 83% \ **Exp:** $662 (High) \
> **Poverty:** 20% \ **Title I:** $271,778 \ **Open-Close:** 08/19 - 05/21 \ **DTBP:** $463
> (High)

| | | | |
|---|---|---|---|
| Donald Metzler | 1,11 | Janie Lewis | 2,12 |
| Gene May | 3,5 | Eddie Gill | 6 |
| Melissa Blatnik | 31,36,83 | Vicki Reasor | 58 |
| Brandon Parker | 67 | Jeff Threadgill | 76,295 |

| Public Schs..Principal | Grd | Prgm | Enr/#Cls | SN |
|---|---|---|---|---|
| Callisburg Elem Sch | PK-5 | T | 511 | 50% 940/612-4196 |
| 648 FM 3164, Gainesville 76240 | | | 45 | Fax 940/612-4804 |
| Lisa Herring | | | | |
| Callisburg Middle High Sch | 6-12 | ATV | 590 | 33% 940/665-0961 |
| 308 Dozier St, Gainesville 76240 | | | 45 | Fax 940/665-2849 |
| Bronwyn Werts \ Jason Hooper | | | | |

- **Era Ind School Dist** PID: 01007312
  108 Hargrove St, Era 76238

  940/665-5961
  Fax 940/665-5311

> **Schools:** 1 \ **Teachers:** 38 \ **Students:** 454 \ **Special Ed Students:** 54
> \ **LEP Students:** 7 \ **College-Bound:** 80% \ **Ethnic:** Hispanic 12%,
> Native American: 1%, Caucasian 86% \ **Exp:** $377 (High) \ **Poverty:** 9% \
> **Title I:** $42,060 \ **Open-Close:** 08/14 - 05/21 \ **DTBP:** $352 (High)

| | | | |
|---|---|---|---|
| Jeremy Thompson | 1 | Suzette Henderson | 2,11 |
| Jeremy Diets | 5* | Donald New | 6 |
| Samantha Gumes | 7* | Todd Jones | 8* |
| Lisa Jones | 12,57* | John Erwin | 31,36,69,83,85* |
| Vickie Beckham | 58* | Jeffrey Stevens | 67 |
| Leann Spears | 81* | | |

| Public Schs..Principal | Grd | Prgm | Enr/#Cls | SN |
|---|---|---|---|---|
| Era Sch | PK-12 | ATV | 454 | 33% 940/665-5961 |
| 108 Hargrove St, Era 76238 | | | 40 | |
| Courtney Stevens \ Michael Parkhill \ Todd Jones | | | | |

| | | | | | | |
|---|---|---|---|---|---|
| 1 | Superintendent | 8 | Curric/Instruct K-12 | 19 | Chief Financial Officer |
| 2 | Bus/Finance/Purchasing | 9 | Curric/Instruct Elem | 20 | Art K-12 |
| 3 | Buildings And Grounds | 10 | Curric/Instruct Sec | 21 | Art Elem |
| 4 | Food Service | 11 | Federal Program | 22 | Art Sec |
| 5 | Transportation | 12 | Title I | 23 | Music K-12 |
| 6 | Athletic | 13 | Title V | 24 | Music Elem |
| 7 | Health Services | 15 | Asst Superintendent | 25 | Music Sec |
| | | 16 | Instructional Media Svcs | 26 | Business Education |
| | | 17 | Chief Operations Officer | 27 | Career & Tech Ed |
| | | 18 | Chief Academic Officer | 28 | Technology Education |

| | | | | | |
|---|---|---|---|---|
| 29 | Family/Consumer Science | 39 | Social Studies K-12 |
| 30 | Adult Education | 40 | Social Studies Elem |
| 31 | Career/Sch-to-Work K-12 | 41 | Social Studies Sec |
| 32 | Career/Sch-to-Work Elem | 42 | Science K-12 |
| 33 | Career/Sch-to-Work Sec | 43 | Science Elem |
| 34 | Early Childhood Ed | 44 | Science Sec |
| 35 | Health/Phys Education | 45 | Math K-12 |
| 36 | Guidance Services K-12 | 46 | Math Elem |
| 37 | Guidance Services Elem | 47 | Math Sec |
| 38 | Guidance Services Sec | 48 | English/Lang Arts K-12 |

| | | | | | |
|---|---|---|---|---|
| 49 | English/Lang Arts Elem | 59 | Special Education Elem |
| 50 | English/Lang Arts Sec | 60 | Special Education Sec |
| 51 | Reading K-12 | 61 | Foreign/World Lang K-12 |
| 52 | Reading Elem | 62 | Foreign/World Lang Elem |
| 53 | Reading Sec | 63 | Foreign/World Lang Sec |
| 54 | Remedial Reading K-12 | 64 | Religious Education K-12 |
| 55 | Remedial Reading Elem | 65 | Religious Education Elem |
| 56 | Remedial Reading Sec | 66 | Religious Education Sec |
| 57 | Bilingual/ELL | 67 | School Board President |
| 58 | Special Education K-12 | 68 | Teacher Personnel |

| | | |
|---|---|
| 69 | Academic Assessment |
| 70 | Research/Development |
| 71 | Public Information |
| 72 | Summer School |
| 73 | Instructional Tech |
| 74 | Inservice Training |
| 75 | Marketing/Distributive |
| 76 | Info Systems |
| 77 | Psychological Assess |
| 78 | Affirmative Action |

## • Gainesville Ind School Dist PID: 01007348
800 S Morris St, Gainesville 76240    940/665-4362    Fax 940/668-0354

Schools: 6 \ Teachers: 207 \ Students: 3,100 \ Special Ed Students: 285 \ LEP Students: 698 \ College-Bound: 61% \ Ethnic: Asian 1%, African American 7%, Hispanic 60%, Caucasian 33% \ Exp: $634 (High) \ Poverty: 32% \ Title I: $1,551,903 \ Special Education: $556,000 \ Open-Close: 08/19 - 05/21 \ DTBP: $203 (High)

| | | | |
|---|---|---|---|
| Dr Desmontes Stewart | 1 | Alyce Greer | 2,19 |
| Joe Warren | 3 | Corey Ray | 4 |
| Shelton Price | 5 | James Polk | 6 |
| Lisa Lawson | 7,85 | Dana Dudenhoeffer | 8 |
| J Spikeston | 8 | Linda Cox | 8 |
| Vonda McFarlin | 8 | David Glancy | 10* |
| Paula Moore | 11,57,68,83,88,271,298 | Reagan Lynch | 11 |
| Lacrsasha Stille | 15 | Russ Rutherford | 20,23 |
| Amber Rains | 57,275 | Brittanie Polk | 58 |
| Corey Hardin | 67 | Leslie Crutsinger | 71 |
| Jennifer Coleman | 73,98 | Tiffany Scott | 76 |

| Public Schs..Principal | Grd | Prgm | Enr/#Cls | SN | |
|---|---|---|---|---|---|
| Gainesville High Sch<br>2201 S Interstate 35, Gainesville 76240<br>David Glancy | 9-12 | T | 919<br>40 | 75% | 940/665-5528<br>Fax 940/612-2795 |
| Gainesville Jr High Sch<br>1201 S Lindsay St, Gainesville 76240<br>Krista Beal | 7-8 | T | 444<br>55 | 81% | 940/665-4062<br>Fax 940/665-1432 |
| Margaret Galubenski Achiev Ctr<br>1000 N Radio Hill Rd, Gainesville 76240<br>Todd Kitchens | 7-12 | | 16<br>3 | | 940/665-0277<br>Fax 940/665-0154 |
| Robert E Lee Intermediate Sch<br>2100 N Grand Ave, Gainesville 76240<br>Nina Coody | 5-6 | T | 465<br>24 | 76% | 940/668-6662<br>Fax 940/668-0353 |
| Thomas A Edison Elem Sch<br>1 Edison Dr, Gainesville 76240<br>Pablo De Santiago | PK-1 | T | 672<br>40 | 77% | 940/665-6091<br>Fax 940/665-5728 |
| W E Chalmers Elem Sch<br>600 S Radio Hill Rd, Gainesville 76240<br>Brandon Whiten | 2-4 | T | 695<br>43 | 80% | 940/665-4147<br>Fax 940/665-9290 |

## • Lindsay Ind School Dist PID: 01007427
495 6th St, Lindsay 76250    940/668-8923    Fax 940/668-2662

Schools: 2 \ Teachers: 40 \ Students: 500 \ Special Ed Students: 41 \ College-Bound: 99% \ Ethnic: Asian 2%, Hispanic 2%, Native American: 1%, Caucasian 94% \ Exp: $430 (High) \ Poverty: 10% \ Title I: $44,198 \ Open-Close: 08/19 - 05/28

| | | | |
|---|---|---|---|
| Trevor Rogers | 1,11 | Diane Zimmerer | 2 |
| Jeff Smiley | 6* | Pat Autry | 8,11,31,58,273* |
| Ben Hawkins | 67 | James Moats | 73,84 |
| Steffani Cornelison | 752* | | |

| Public Schs..Principal | Grd | Prgm | Enr/#Cls | SN | |
|---|---|---|---|---|---|
| Lindsay Elem Sch<br>495 W 6th St, Lindsay 76250<br>Pat Autry | PK-6 | | 248<br>33 | 15% | 940/668-8923 |
| Lindsay High Sch<br>631 Knight Dr, Lindsay 76250<br>Steven Cope | 7-12 | V | 244<br>20 | 9% | 940/668-8474<br>Fax 940/665-1637 |

## • Muenster Ind School Dist PID: 01007453
113 E 7th St, Muenster 76252    940/759-2281    Fax 940/759-5200

Schools: 2 \ Teachers: 40 \ Students: 481 \ Special Ed Students: 77 \ LEP Students: 6 \ College-Bound: 76% \ Ethnic: Asian 1%, Hispanic 5%, Caucasian 94% \ Exp: $2,114 (High) \ Poverty: 7% \ Title I: $44,198 \ Open-Close: 08/05 - 05/21 \ DTBP: $363 (High) \ 

| | | | |
|---|---|---|---|
| Steven Self | 1 | Carol Klement | 2 |
| James Koelzer | 3 | Susie Fleitman | 5 |
| Brady Carney | 6 | Lou Heers | 9,11,271* |
| Vickie Eldridge | 16* | Kristi Schneider | 36,69,83,88,270* |
| Vikki Reasor | 58 | Darren Bindel | 67 |
| Jeffrey Presnall | 73* | | |

| Public Schs..Principal | Grd | Prgm | Enr/#Cls | SN | |
|---|---|---|---|---|---|
| Muenster Elem Sch<br>912 N Walnut St, Muenster 76252<br>Debra Sicking | PK-6 | T | 260<br>20 | 19% | 940/759-2282<br>Fax 940/759-5201 |
| Muenster High Sch<br>135 E 7th Street, Muenster 76252<br>John York | 7-12 | ATV | 221<br>27 | 11% | 940/759-2281<br>Fax 940/759-4614 |

## • Sivells Bend Ind School Dist PID: 01007489
1053 County Road 403, Gainesville 76240    940/665-6411    Fax 940/665-2527

Schools: 1 \ Teachers: 8 \ Students: 57 \ Special Ed Students: 8 \ Ethnic: Hispanic 14%, Native American: 8%, Caucasian 78% \ Exp: $501 (High) \ Poverty: 17% \ Title I: $12,659 \ Open-Close: 08/25 - 05/28 \ DTBP: $401 (High)

| | | | |
|---|---|---|---|
| Lisa Slaughter | 1,11,83,288 | Angela Beaudin | 2* |
| Randy Jenkins | 3,5* | Rod Tipps | 6,16,59,73* |
| Cheryl Downey | 11* | Coleen Gunter | 57* |
| Jamai Freeman | 67 | | |

| Public Schs..Principal | Grd | Prgm | Enr/#Cls | SN | |
|---|---|---|---|---|---|
| Sivells Bend Sch<br>1053 County Road 403, Gainesville 76240<br>Lisa Slaughter | PK-8 | T | 57<br>7 | 65% | 940/665-6411 |

## • Valley View ISD-Cooke Co PID: 01007506
106 Newton St, Valley View 76272    940/726-3659    Fax 940/726-3614

Schools: 1 \ Teachers: 54 \ Students: 875 \ Special Ed Students: 102 \ LEP Students: 112 \ College-Bound: 80% \ Ethnic: African American 1%, Hispanic 31%, Native American: 1%, Caucasian 67% \ Exp: $600 (High) \ Poverty: 19% \ Title I: $130,196 \ Open-Close: 08/18 - 05/28 \ DTBP: $349 (High)

| | | | |
|---|---|---|---|
| Willaim Stokes | 1 | Jennifer Bennett | 2,5 |
| Jennifer Kassen | 4 | Curtis King | 6 |
| Monica Parkhill | 8,11,79,296 | Mike Wilson | 36,73* |
| Vikki Reasor | 58 | Corinne French | 67 |

| Public Schs..Principal | Grd | Prgm | Enr/#Cls | SN | |
|---|---|---|---|---|---|
| Valley View Sch<br>106 Newton St, Valley View 76272<br>Jesse Newton \ Susan Smith | PK-12 | T | 875<br>25 | 53% | 940/726-3659 |

- **Walnut Bend Ind School Dist** PID: 01007532
  47 County Road 198, Gainesville 76240

  940/665-5990
  Fax 940/665-9660

  **Schools:** 1 \ **Teachers:** 6 \ **Students:** 72 \ **Special Ed Students:** 6 \
  **LEP Students:** 3 \ **Ethnic:** Hispanic 28%, Caucasian 72% \ **Exp:** $515 (High) \
  **Poverty:** 23% \ **Open-Close:** 08/19 - 05/20 \ **DTBP:** $360 (High)

  Troy Humphrey .......................... 1,11,73,83    Barbara Smith ....................................... 16*
  Randy Clark ............................................ 67   Gabby Probst ....................................... 273*

  | Public Schs..Principal | Grd | Prgm | Enr/#Cls | SN | |
  |---|---|---|---|---|---|
  | Walnut Bend Elem Sch | PK-8 | T | 72 | 69% | 940/665-5990 |
  | 47 County Road 198, Gainesville 76240 | | | 6 | | |
  | Troy Humphrey | | | | | |

## COOKE CATHOLIC SCHOOLS

- **Diocese of Fort Worth Ed Off** PID: 01054339
  Listing includes only schools located in this county. See District Index for location of Diocesan Offices.

  | Catholic Schs..Principal | Grd | Prgm | Enr/#Cls | SN | |
  |---|---|---|---|---|---|
  | Sacred Heart Sch | PK-12 | | 284 | | 940/759-2511 |
  | 153 E 6th St, Muenster 76252 | | | 22 | | Fax 940/759-4422 |
  | Beth Bartush | | | | | |
  | St Mary's Catholic Sch | PK-8 | | 165 | | 940/665-5395 |
  | 931 N Weaver St, Gainesville 76240 | | | 11 | | Fax 940/665-9538 |
  | Kim Otto | | | | | |

## CORYELL COUNTY

## CORYELL PUBLIC SCHOOLS

- **Copperas Cove Ind School Dist** PID: 01007556
  408 S Main St, Copperas Cove 76522

  254/547-1227
  Fax 254/547-1542

  **Schools:** 11 \ **Teachers:** 540 \ **Students:** 8,200 \ **Special Ed Students:** 896
  \ **LEP Students:** 387 \ **College-Bound:** 55% \ **Ethnic:** Asian 2%,
  African American 20%, Hispanic 31%, Native American: 1%, Caucasian
  46% \ **Exp:** $472 (High) \ **Poverty:** 19% \ **Title I:** $1,429,694 \
  **Special Education:** $1,256,000 \ **Open-Close:** 08/18 - 05/27 \ **DTBP:** $187
  (High) \ 🅵 🅴

  Dr Joseph Burns ............................... 1     Deidra Hall ............................................... 2
  June Crawford ............................. 2,11,19   Gary Elliott ..................................... 3,5,91
  Melissa Bryan ..................................... 4    Lisa Edgar ........................... 8,12,74,275
  Dr Patricia Remissong .............. 8,15,288    Rick Kirkpatrick ............................. 15,91
  Henry Blair .............................. 16,76,295    Leah Miller ...................................... 31,38
  Rhonda Burnell ................................. 58    Joan Manning ..................................... 67
  Kayleen Love ..................................68*    Wendy Sledd .............................. 71,298
  Dr Earl Parcell .......................... 73,286    Kim Alverez ...................................... 294

  | Public Schs..Principal | Grd | Prgm | Enr/#Cls | SN | |
  |---|---|---|---|---|---|
  | Clements-Parsons Elem Sch | K-5 | T | 814 | 63% | 254/547-2235 |
  | 1115 Northern Dancer Dr, Copperas Cove 76522 | | | 60 | | Fax 254/547-0845 |
  | Katherine Baney | | | | | |

| | | | | | |
|---|---|---|---|---|---|
| Copperas Cove High Sch | 9-12 | T | 1,026 | 46% | 254/547-2534 |
| 400 S 25th St, Copperas Cove 76522 | | | | | Fax 254/547-9870 |
| Dr Jimmy Shuck | | | | | |
| Copperas Cove Jr High Sch | 6-8 | T | 827 | 61% | 254/547-6959 |
| 702 Sunny Ave, Copperas Cove 76522 | | | 50 | | Fax 254/518-2620 |
| Robert Turner | | | | | |
| Crossroads High Sch | 9-12 | T | 46 | 72% | 254/547-9164 |
| 306 E Avenue E, Copperas Cove 76522 | | | 13 | | Fax 254/547-4039 |
| Patrick Crawley | | | | | |
| Fairview-Miss Jewel Elem Sch | K-5 | T | 528 | 81% | 254/547-4212 |
| 710 S 5th St, Copperas Cove 76522 | | | 46 | | Fax 254/547-6378 |
| Rebekah Shuck | | | | | |
| Hettie Halstead Elem Sch | K-5 | T | 352 | 76% | 254/547-3440 |
| 910 N Main St, Copperas Cove 76522 | | | 27 | | Fax 254/547-6896 |
| Brian Jost | | | | | |
| House Creek Elementray Sch | K-5 | T | 677 | 49% | 254/518-3000 |
| 351 Lutheran Church Rd, Copperas Cove 76522 | | | | | Fax 254/518-7400 |
| Todd Williams | | | | | |
| J L Williams-Lovett Ledger ES | K-5 | T | 780 | 58% | 254/542-1001 |
| 909 Courtney Ln, Copperas Cove 76522 | | | 25 | | Fax 254/542-2794 |
| **Lori Hensley** | | | | | |
| Mae Stevens Early Learng Acad | PK-PK | T | 592 | 63% | 254/547-8289 |
| 302 Manning Dr, Copperas Cove 76522 | | | 19 | | Fax 254/547-8325 |
| Mary Derrick | | | | | |
| Martin Walker Elem Sch | K-5 | T | 482 | 57% | 254/547-2283 |
| 100 FM 3046, Copperas Cove 76522 | | | 29 | | Fax 254/547-5984 |
| Earl Parcell | | | | | |
| S C Lee Junior High Sch | 6-8 | T | 907 | 55% | 254/542-7877 |
| 1205 Courtney Ln, Copperas Cove 76522 | | | 34 | | Fax 254/542-8103 |
| Brian Jost | | | | | |

- **Evant Ind School Dist** PID: 01007635
  339 Memory Lane, Evant 76525

  254/471-3160
  Fax 254/471-5629

  **Schools:** 1 \ **Teachers:** 22 \ **Students:** 249 \ **Special Ed Students:** 25
  \ **LEP Students:** 18 \ **Ethnic:** African American 1%, Hispanic 20%,
  Caucasian 79% \ **Exp:** $1,269 (High) \ **Poverty:** 23% \ **Title I:** $65,976 \
  **Open-Close:** 08/10 - 05/27 \ **DTBP:** $331 (High) \ 🅵 🅴

  Ken Wimberly ...........................................1     Jennifer Ingram ....................................... 2
  Steve Adcock ....................................3,17    Lupe Hernandez ...................................... 4
  Mike Lancaster .........................................5    Donna Watson .......................................... 7
  Stacey Lowery . 11,57,81,88,271,275,280,296*    Randy Newby ........... 16,73,76,97,98,285,295
  Whitie Decker .....................................27,31*    Lora Slaughter ...........36,69,79,83,270,286*
  Elizabeth Gandy .................................. 42    Heather Wooten .............................58,77
  Sheila Williams .................................... 67    Danny Hemphill ....................................... 84

  | Public Schs..Principal | Grd | Prgm | Enr/#Cls | SN | |
  |---|---|---|---|---|---|
  | Evant Sch | PK-12 | TV | 249 | 51% | 254/471-5536 |
  | 339 Memory Ln, Evant 76525 | | | 25 | | |
  | **Howard Cox** | | | | | |

- **Gatesville Ind School Dist** PID: 01007661
  311 S Lovers Ln, Gatesville 76528

  254/865-7251
  Fax 254/865-2279

  **Schools:** 5 \ **Teachers:** 202 \ **Students:** 2,744 \ **Special Ed Students:** 321
  \ **LEP Students:** 109 \ **College-Bound:** 47% \ **Ethnic:** Asian 1%, African
  American 3%, Hispanic 24%, Native American: 1%, Caucasian 72% \
  **Exp:** $374 (High) \ **Poverty:** 18% \ **Title I:** $534,931 \ **Open-Close:** 08/13 -
  05/20 \ **DTBP:** $178 (High) \ 🅵 🅴

  Dr Barrett Pollard .................................. 1     Darrell Frazier .................................2,19
  Toby Williams ........................................3    Gail Shelton ...........................................4*
  Marty Williams .......................................5    Kyle Cooper ............................................ 6
  Shane Webb ........................................ 10    Marsha Worthington  11,31,36,69,273,275,288
  Mary Leib ............................................ 67    Shelly Harper ........................................ 73

| 1 | Superintendent | 8 | Curric/Instruct K-12 | 19 | Chief Financial Officer | 29 | Family/Consumer Science | 39 | Social Studies K-12 | 49 | English/Lang Arts Elem | 59 | Special Education Elem | 69 | Academic Assessment |
|---|---|---|---|---|---|---|---|---|---|---|---|---|---|---|---|
| 2 | Bus/Finance/Purchasing | 9 | Curric/Instruct Elem | 20 | Art K-12 | 30 | Adult Education | 40 | Social Studies Elem | 50 | English/Lang Arts Sec | 60 | Special Education Sec | 70 | Research/Development |
| 3 | Buildings and Grounds | 10 | Curric/Instruct Sec | 21 | Art Elem | 31 | Career/Sch-to-Work K-12 | 41 | Social Studies Sec | 51 | Reading K-12 | 61 | Foreign/World Lang K-12 | 71 | Public Information |
| 4 | Food Service | 11 | Federal Program | 22 | Art Sec | 32 | Career/Sch-to-Work Elem | 42 | Science K-12 | 52 | Reading Elem | 62 | Foreign/World Lang Elem | 72 | Summer School |
| 5 | Transportation | 12 | Title I | 23 | Music K-12 | 33 | Career/Sch-to-Work Sec | 43 | Science Elem | 53 | Reading Sec | 63 | Foreign/World Lang Sec | 73 | Instructional Tech |
| 6 | Athletic | 13 | Title V | 24 | Music Elem | 34 | Early Childhood Ed | 44 | Science Sec | 54 | Remedial Reading K-12 | 64 | Religious Education K-12 | 74 | Inservice Training |
| 7 | Health Services | 15 | Asst Superintendent | 25 | Music Sec | 35 | Health/Phys Education | 45 | Math K-12 | 55 | Remedial Reading Elem | 65 | Religious Education Elem | 75 | Marketing/Distributive |
| | | 16 | Instructional Media Svcs | 26 | Business Education | 36 | Guidance Services K-12 | 46 | Math Elem | 56 | Remedial Reading Sec | 66 | Religious Education Sec | 76 | Info Systems |
| | | 17 | Chief Operations Officer | 27 | Career & Tech Ed | 37 | Guidance Services Elem | 47 | Math Sec | 57 | Bilingual/ELL | 67 | School Board President | 77 | Psychological Assess |
| | | 18 | Chief Academic Officer | 28 | Technology Education | 38 | Guidance Services Sec | 48 | English/Lang Arts K-12 | 58 | Special Education K-12 | 68 | Teacher Personnel | 78 | Affirmative Action |

**TX—96**

| Public Schs..Principal | Grd | Prgm | Enr/#Cls | SN |
|---|---|---|---|---|
| Gatesville Elem Sch<br>2537 E Main St, Gatesville 76528<br>Keegan Webb | 1-3 | T | 630<br>22 | 58% 254/865-7262<br>Fax 254/248-0077 |
| Gatesville High Sch<br>205 S Lovers Ln, Gatesville 76528<br>Yancey Sanderson | 9-12 | AGTV | 840<br>50 | 44% 254/865-8281<br>Fax 254/865-2293 |
| Gatesville Intermediate Sch<br>311 Hornet Way, Gatesville 76528<br>Bridget Register | 4-6 | T | 617<br>30 | 55% 254/865-2526<br>Fax 254/865-2932 |
| Gatesville Junior High Sch<br>307 S Lovers Ln, Gatesville 76528<br>Cindy Venable | 7-8 | AT | 419<br>36 | 47% 254/865-8271<br>Fax 254/865-2252 |
| Gatesville Primary Sch<br>308 Hornet Way, Gatesville 76528<br>Mashara Streater | PK-K | T | 238<br>23 | 66% 254/865-7264<br>Fax 254/865-2160 |

- **Jonesboro Ind School Dist** PID: 01007714    254/463-2111
  14909 E State Hwy 36, Jonesboro 76538    Fax 254/463-2275

**Schools:** 1 \ **Teachers:** 23 \ **Students:** 330 \ **Special Ed Students:** 36 \ **College-Bound:** 50% \ **Ethnic:** Asian 1%, Hispanic 12%, Caucasian 87% \ **Exp:** $526 (High) \ **Poverty:** 20% \ **Title I:** $45,742 \ **Open-Close:** 08/17 - 05/21 \ **DTBP:** $303 (High)

| | | | |
|---|---|---|---|
| Matt Dossey ............................ 1,11,73,83 | Ashley Juggs ........................................ 2 |
| Keith Necessary .................................... 3* | Kendra Gustifsan ...................... 8,12,286* |
| Bethany Lejune ..................................... 36 | Brandi Surley ...................................... 59 |
| Chris Simon ......................................... 60 | Keith Taylor ........................................ 67 |

| Public Schs..Principal | Grd | Prgm | Enr/#Cls | SN |
|---|---|---|---|---|
| Jonesboro Sch<br>14909 E State Hwy 36, Jonesboro 76538<br>Kendra Gustin | PK-12 | TV | 330<br>30 | 53% 254/463-2111 |

- **Oglesby Ind School Dist** PID: 01007740    254/456-2271
  125 College Ave, Oglesby 76561    Fax 254/456-2522

**Schools:** 1 \ **Teachers:** 19 \ **Students:** 180 \ **Special Ed Students:** 13 \ **LEP Students:** 11 \ **College-Bound:** 50% \ **Ethnic:** Hispanic 29%, Native American: 1%, Caucasian 70% \ **Exp:** $527 (High) \ **Poverty:** 30% \ **Title I:** $90,607 \ **Open-Close:** 08/12 - 05/21 \ **DTBP:** $361 (High)

| | |
|---|---|
| David Maass ............................. 1,11,73 | Kalinda Westbrook ............................. 2 |
| Boone Brinkley ..................................... 3,5 | Jeb Dixon ............................................ 6 |
| Misti Sanders ...................... 8,12,69,286 | Angela Russell ................................... 57 |
| Kevin Harrington .................................. 58 | Jennifer Thompson .............................. 67 |
| Sheila Hoehn ....................................... 76 | |

| Public Schs..Principal | Grd | Prgm | Enr/#Cls | SN |
|---|---|---|---|---|
| Oglesby Sch<br>125 College Ave, Oglesby 76561<br>Misti Sanders | PK-12 | TV | 180<br>20 | 63% 254/456-2271<br>Fax 254/456-2916 |

## COTTLE COUNTY

## COTTLE PUBLIC SCHOOLS

- **Paducah Ind School Dist** PID: 01007776    806/492-3524
  810 Goodwin St, Paducah 79248    Fax 806/492-2432

**Schools:** 1 \ **Teachers:** 22 \ **Students:** 200 \ **Special Ed Students:** 36 \ **LEP Students:** 3 \ **College-Bound:** 90% \ **Ethnic:** African American 11%, Hispanic 43%, Native American: 1%, Caucasian 45% \ **Exp:** $618 (High) \ **Poverty:** 35% \ **Title I:** $129,173 \ **Open-Close:** 08/24 - 05/24 \ **DTBP:** $294 (High)

| | |
|---|---|
| Gary Waltman ................................ 1,83 | Irene Blount ....................................... 2 |
| Marty Smith ........................................... 3 | Elisa Love .......................................... 4 |
| John York ............................................ 6* | Leslie Hutchinson ............................... 8* |
| Denise Ford .......................... 11,294,296 | Brad Blount ........................................ 67 |

| Public Schs..Principal | Grd | Prgm | Enr/#Cls | SN |
|---|---|---|---|---|
| Paducah Sch<br>810 Goodwin Street, Paducah 79248<br>John York | PK-12 | TV | 200<br>50 | 64% 806/492-2009<br>Fax 806/492-2193 |

## CRANE COUNTY

## CRANE PUBLIC SCHOOLS

- **Crane Ind School Dist** PID: 01007817    432/558-1022
  511 W 8th St, Crane 79731    Fax 432/558-1025

**Schools:** 3 \ **Teachers:** 82 \ **Students:** 1,172 \ **Special Ed Students:** 93 \ **LEP Students:** 205 \ **College-Bound:** 51% \ **Ethnic:** Asian 1%, African American 2%, Hispanic 80%, Caucasian 18% \ **Exp:** $437 (High) \ **Poverty:** 13% \ **Title I:** $154,272 \ **Special Education:** $242,000 \ **Open-Close:** 08/10 - 05/21 \ **DTBP:** $350 (High)

| | |
|---|---|
| Jan Hunt ............................................... 1 | Leigh McCain ...................................... 2 |
| Monty King .......................................... 3,5 | Mendy McCarty ................................... 4 |
| Maria Hernandez ................................... 7 | Maria Hernandez ............................... 7* |
| Jamye Swinford ......8,11,15,31,69,74,275,294 | Shelley Garcia .................................... 58 |
| Alan Swinford ....................................... 67 | Thomas Valenzuela ....................... 73,295 |

| Public Schs..Principal | Grd | Prgm | Enr/#Cls | SN |
|---|---|---|---|---|
| Crane Elem Sch<br>300 W 7th St, Crane 79731<br>Linda Contreras | PK-5 | T | 499<br>24 | 54% 432/558-1050<br>Fax 432/558-1077 |
| Crane High Sch<br>509 W 8th St, Crane 79731<br>Stephen Cross | 9-12 | T | 329<br>30 | 43% 432/558-1030<br>Fax 432/558-1056 |
| Crane Middle Sch<br>302 W 10th St, Crane 79731<br>Arick Heredia | 6-8 | T | 253<br>20 | 63% 432/558-1040<br>Fax 432/558-1046 |

## CROCKETT COUNTY

### CROCKETT PUBLIC SCHOOLS

• **Crockett Co Cons Common SD** PID: 01007855
797 Avenue D, Ozona 76943

325/392-5501
Fax 325/392-5177

**Schools:** 3 \ **Teachers:** 62 \ **Students:** 720 \ **Special Ed Students:** 68 \ **LEP Students:** 108 \ **Ethnic:** Hispanic 76%, Native American: 1%, Caucasian 22% \ **Exp:** $621 (High) \ **Poverty:** 22% \ **Title I:** $237,778 \ **Open-Close:** 08/17 - 05/24 \ **DTBP:** $359 (High) \ 🇹

| | | | |
|---|---|---|---|
| Raul Chavarria | 1 | Lisa Harmsen | 2 |
| Chuy Martinez | 3 | Susan Webb | 4 |
| Anna Martinez | 5 | Jarryd Taylor | 6 |
| Farran Morris | 7,85 | Tamara McWilliams | 8,69 |
| Janina Savala | 11,57,288,296,298 | Dwight Childress | 67 |
| Keith Harmsen | 73,295 | Mari Sanchez | 76 |
| Connie Crenwelge | 280 | | |

| Public Schs..Principal | Grd | Prgm | Enr/#Cls | SN | |
|---|---|---|---|---|---|
| Ozona Elem Sch<br>1701 Avenue E, Ozona 76943<br>Erica Cruz | PK-5 | T | 347<br>19 | 56% | 325/392-5501<br>Fax 325/392-2327 |
| Ozona High Sch<br>605 Avenue E, Ozona 76943<br>**Tamara McWilliams** | 9-12 | ATV | 200<br>30 | 48% | 325/392-5501<br>Fax 325/392-3125 🇹 |
| Ozona Middle Sch<br>502 Avenue G, Ozona 76943<br>**Kristin Sesson** | 6-8 | T | 180<br>25 | 54% | 325/392-5501<br>Fax 325/392-2910 |

## CROSBY COUNTY

### CROSBY PUBLIC SCHOOLS

• **Crosbyton Cons Ind Sch Dist** PID: 01007908
204 S Harrison St, Crosbyton 79322

806/675-7331
Fax 806/675-2409

**Schools:** 2 \ **Teachers:** 38 \ **Students:** 330 \ **Special Ed Students:** 49 \ **LEP Students:** 3 \ **College-Bound:** 95% \ **Ethnic:** African American 3%, Hispanic 76%, Caucasian 21% \ **Exp:** $680 (High) \ **Poverty:** 45% \ **Title I:** $302,108 \ **Open-Close:** 08/17 - 05/20 \ **DTBP:** $348 (High)

| | | | |
|---|---|---|---|
| Shawn Mason | 1 | Gary Hardin | 2 |
| Gary Hamersley | 3,5 | Susan Guerrero | 4 |
| Colby Huseman | 6* | Shuntae Thomas | 7,83 |
| Stacy Mason | 11,69,77* | Alva Rodriguez | 57,271* |
| Meredith Caffey | 58 | Clifford Trull | 67 |
| Julie Harrington | 73,295 | | |

| Public Schs..Principal | Grd | Prgm | Enr/#Cls | SN | |
|---|---|---|---|---|---|
| Crosbyton Elem Sch<br>204 S Harrison St, Crosbyton 79322<br>**Rene Villegas** | PK-5 | T | 97<br>25 | 89% | 806/675-7331 |

| Crosbyton High Sch<br>204 S Harrison St, Crosbyton 79322<br>Hector Dominguez | 6-12 | TV | 125 | 77% | 806/675-7331 |

• **Lorenzo Ind School Dist** PID: 01007958
1003 4th Street, Lorenzo 79343

806/634-5591
Fax 806/634-5928

**Schools:** 2 \ **Teachers:** 30 \ **Students:** 250 \ **Special Ed Students:** 39 \ **LEP Students:** 18 \ **College-Bound:** 74% \ **Ethnic:** African American 3%, Hispanic 86%, Caucasian 11% \ **Exp:** $670 (High) \ **Poverty:** 39% \ **Title I:** $189,112 \ **Open-Close:** 08/26 - 05/21 \ **DTBP:** $354 (High)

| | | | |
|---|---|---|---|
| Kayla Morrisson | 1,11 | Joe Simpson | 2 |
| Omar Villegas | 3 | Dee Ware | 5 |
| Amanda Hare | 9,274 | Jessica Crabb | 10,273* |
| April Burguss | 16,82 | Angela Moreno | 31,54,69,83* |
| Gladice Salinas | 57 | Kristopher Lamm | 58 |
| Brad Aycock | 67 | Danny Thomas | 73* |

| Public Schs..Principal | Grd | Prgm | Enr/#Cls | SN | |
|---|---|---|---|---|---|
| Lorenzo Elem Sch<br>1003 4th Street, Lorenzo 79343<br>Jessica Crabb | PK-6 | T | 144<br>20 | 82% | 806/634-5593<br>Fax 806/634-8419 |
| Lorenzo Jr Sr High Sch<br>1003 4th Street, Lorenzo 79343<br>Jessica Crabb | 7-12 | T | 115<br>20 | 76% | 806/634-5592<br>Fax 806/634-5788 |

• **Ralls Ind School Dist** PID: 01007984
1082 4th St, Ralls 79357

806/253-2509
Fax 806/253-2508

**Schools:** 4 \ **Teachers:** 54 \ **Students:** 485 \ **Special Ed Students:** 63 \ **LEP Students:** 8 \ **College-Bound:** 59% \ **Ethnic:** African American 2%, Hispanic 75%, Caucasian 23% \ **Exp:** $562 (High) \ **Poverty:** 23% \ **Title I:** $174,080 \ **Open-Close:** 08/13 - 05/19 \ **DTBP:** $332 (High) \ 🇫

| | | | |
|---|---|---|---|
| **Dr Nathan Maxwell** | 1 | Bobby Casias | 5 |
| Xavier Rangel | 6 | Lori Peredia | 7,35,85* |
| Macy Cavazos | 8,11,57,58,83,288,296,298 | Brenda Prather | 10 |
| Miguel Salizar | 10* | Juan Calderon | 16,73,286,295* |
| Charla Mills | 59* | Aunie Sellers | 67 |
| Jill Calderon | 68 | Morgan Murry | 77 |
| Angelica Marquez | 271 | Lesley Wint | 280,285,752 |

| Public Schs..Principal | Grd | Prgm | Enr/#Cls | SN | |
|---|---|---|---|---|---|
| Ralls Elem Sch<br>1401 16th St, Ralls 79357<br>Amy Feaster | PK-5 | T | 265<br>18 | 84% | 806/253-2546<br>Fax 806/253-3112 |
| Ralls High Sch<br>1106 10th St, Ralls 79357<br>Miguel Salizar | 9-12 | AT | 78<br>20 | 80% | 806/253-2571<br>Fax 806/253-2609 |
| Ralls Middle Sch<br>1107 10th St, Ralls 79357<br>Brenda Prather | 6-8 | T | 119<br>12 | 81% | 806/253-2549<br>Fax 806/253-4031 |
| Ⓐ Recovery Education Campus<br>1107 Kent St, Ralls 79357<br>Marshal Herron | 9-12 | T | 5 | | 806/253-2549<br>Fax 806/253-4031 |

| | | | | | |
|---|---|---|---|---|---|
| 1 | Superintendent | 8 | Curric/Instruct K-12 | 19 | Chief Financial Officer |
| 2 | Bus/Finance/Purchasing | 9 | Curric/Instruct Elem | 20 | Art K-12 |
| 3 | Buildings And Grounds | 10 | Curric/Instruct Sec | 21 | Art Elem |
| 4 | Food Service | 11 | Federal Program | 22 | Art Sec |
| 5 | Transportation | 12 | Title I | 23 | Music K-12 |
| 6 | Athletic | 13 | Title V | 24 | Music Elem |
| 7 | Health Services | 14 | Asst Superintendent | 25 | Music Sec |
| | | 15 | Instructional Media Svcs | 26 | Business Education |
| | | 16 | Instructional Media Svcs | 27 | Career & Tech Ed |
| | | 17 | Chief Operations Officer | 28 | Technology Education |
| | | 18 | Chief Academic Officer | | |

| | |
|---|---|
| 29 Family/Consumer Science | 39 Social Studies K-12 |
| 30 Adult Education | 40 Social Studies Elem |
| 31 Career/Sch-to-Work K-12 | 41 Social Studies Sec |
| 32 Career/Sch-to-Work Elem | 42 Science K-12 |
| 33 Career/Sch-to-Work Sec | 43 Science Elem |
| 34 Early Childhood Ed | 44 Science Sec |
| 35 Health/Phys Education | 45 Math K-12 |
| 36 Business Education | 46 Math Elem |
| 37 Guidance Services Elem | 47 Math Sec |
| 38 Guidance Services Sec | 48 English/Lang Arts K-12 |

| | |
|---|---|
| 49 English/Lang Arts Elem | 59 Special Education Elem |
| 50 English/Lang Arts Sec | 60 Special Education Sec |
| 51 Reading K-12 | 61 Foreign/World Lang K-12 |
| 52 Reading Elem | 62 Foreign/World Lang Elem |
| 53 Reading Sec | 63 Foreign/World Lang Sec |
| 54 Remedial Reading K-12 | 64 Religious Education K-12 |
| 55 Remedial Reading Elem | 65 Religious Education Elem |
| 56 Remedial Reading Sec | 66 Religious Education Sec |
| 57 Bilingual/ELL | 67 School Board President |
| 58 Special Education K-12 | 68 Teacher Personnel |

| | |
|---|---|
| 69 Academic Assessment |
| 70 Research/Development |
| 71 Public Information |
| 72 Summer School |
| 73 Instructional Tech |
| 74 Inservice Training |
| 75 Marketing/Distributive |
| 76 Info Systems |
| 77 Psychological Assess |
| 78 Affirmative Action |

## CULBERSON COUNTY

### CULBERSON PUBLIC SCHOOLS

- **Culberson Co Allamoore Ind SD** PID: 01008029　　432/283-2245
  400 W 7th St, Van Horn 79855　　　　　　　　　　　Fax 432/283-9062

| | |
|---|---|
| **Schools:** 1 \ **Teachers:** 32 \ **Students:** 378 \ **Special Ed Students:** 32 \ **LEP Students:** 31 \ **College-Bound:** 39% \ **Ethnic:** Asian 2%, Hispanic 87%, Native American: 1%, Caucasian 10% \ **Exp:** $1,336 (High) \ **Poverty:** 33% \ **Title I:** $178,484 \ **Open-Close:** 08/26 - 05/28 \ **DTBP:** $372 (High) \ 🔵 🇹 |

| | | | |
|---|---|---|---|
| Kenneth Baugh | 1 | Marcial Gonzalez | 3 |
| Marie Borrego | 4 | Cornelio Garibay | 5 |
| Letty Hernandez | 67 | | |

| Public Schs..Principal | Grd | Prgm | Enr/#Cls | SN | |
|---|---|---|---|---|---|
| Van Horn Schools | PK-12 | TV | 378 | 78% | 432/283-2245 |
| 400 West 7th St, Van Horn 79855 | | | | | |
| Charles Gonzalez | | | | | 🔵 🇹 |

## DALLAM COUNTY

### DALLAM PUBLIC SCHOOLS

- **Dalhart Ind School Dist** PID: 01008067　　　806/244-7810
  701 E 10th St, Dalhart 79022　　　　　　　　　Fax 806/244-7822

| | |
|---|---|
| **Schools:** 4 \ **Teachers:** 127 \ **Students:** 1,700 \ **Special Ed Students:** 147 \ **LEP Students:** 269 \ **College-Bound:** 50% \ **Ethnic:** African American 1%, Hispanic 62%, Caucasian 36% \ **Exp:** $549 (High) \ **Poverty:** 13% \ **Title I:** $272,376 \ **Special Education:** $333,000 \ **Open-Close:** 08/19 - 05/27 \ **DTBP:** $339 (High) |

| | | | |
|---|---|---|---|
| Dr Joe Alcorta | 1,11 | Brian Walter | 2,19 |
| Joe Garcia | 3 | Ernest Fernandez | 4 |
| Frank Subeldoa | 5* | Joey Read | 6* |
| Sarah Nutter | 8 | Misty Bornemeier | 16,82 |
| Shannon Wilson | 16,82 | Christy Dovel | 38* |
| David Rivera | 58,275 | Robert Ledbetter | 67 |
| Brad Powell | 73,76,84,295 | Kurtis Abla | 88 |
| Rachael Rivera | 271 | | |

| Public Schs..Principal | Grd | Prgm | Enr/#Cls | SN | |
|---|---|---|---|---|---|
| Dalhart Elem Sch | PK-3 | T | 607 | 69% | 806/244-7350 |
| 1401 Tennessee Ave, Dalhart 79022 | | | 34 | | Fax 806/244-7352 |
| Shannon Marshall | | | | | |
| Dalhart High Sch | 9-12 | T | 506 | 42% | 806/244-7300 |
| 2100 Spirit Trl, Dalhart 79022 | | | 35 | | Fax 806/244-7307 |
| Scot Wright | | | | | |
| Dalhart Intermediate Sch | 4-5 | T | 242 | 64% | 806/244-7380 |
| 801 Oak Ave, Dalhart 79022 | | | 12 | | Fax 806/244-7387 |
| Misty Heiskell | | | | | 🔵 |

| Public Schs..Principal | Grd | Prgm | Enr/#Cls | SN | |
|---|---|---|---|---|---|
| Dalhart Junior High Sch | 6-8 | T | 406 | 55% | 806/244-7825 |
| 1802 E 16th St, Dalhart 79022 | | | 32 | | Fax 806/244-7835 |
| Staci Maddox | | | | | |

- **Texline Ind School Dist** PID: 01008108　　　806/362-4667
  302 E Pine Street, Texline 79087　　　　　　　Fax 806/362-4538

| | |
|---|---|
| **Schools:** 1 \ **Teachers:** 18 \ **Students:** 180 \ **Special Ed Students:** 17 \ **LEP Students:** 31 \ **College-Bound:** 85% \ **Ethnic:** African American 1%, Hispanic 51%, Caucasian 48% \ **Exp:** $1,101 (High) \ **Poverty:** 18% \ **Title I:** $55,579 \ **Open-Close:** 08/18 - 05/20 \ **DTBP:** $340 (High) |

| | | | |
|---|---|---|---|
| Terrell Jones | 1 | Debbie Carter | 2,84 |
| Stryker Green | 5* | Roff Perschbacher | 8,12,69,288* |
| Misty Luther | 16,82* | Misty Luther | 16,57,82 |
| Becky Claycomb | 31,90* | Megan Moore | 31,90 |
| Rayanne McGee | 31,58* | Jody Bezner | 67 |
| Karen Fernandez | 271 | | |

| Public Schs..Principal | Grd | Prgm | Enr/#Cls | SN | |
|---|---|---|---|---|---|
| Texline Sch | PK-12 | TV | 180 | 64% | 806/362-4284 |
| 302 E Pine Street, Texline 79087 | | | 16 | | Fax 806/362-4938 |
| Ross Perschbacher | | | | | |

### DALLAM CATHOLIC SCHOOLS

- **Diocese of Amarillo Ed Office** PID: 01047659
  Listing includes only schools located in this county. See District Index for location of Diocesan Offices.

| Catholic Schs..Principal | Grd | Prgm | Enr/#Cls | SN | |
|---|---|---|---|---|---|
| St Anthony's of Padua Elem | K-6 | | 113 | | 806/244-4811 |
| 410 E 13th St, Dalhart 79022 | | | 7 | | Fax 806/244-8062 |
| Shay Batenhorst | | | | | 🔵 🇹 |

### DALLAM PRIVATE SCHOOLS

| Private Schs..Principal | Grd | Prgm | Enr/#Cls | SN | |
|---|---|---|---|---|---|
| Dalhart Christian Academy | PK-6 | | 98 | | 806/244-6482 |
| 1000 E 16th St, Dalhart 79022 | | | 10 | | Fax 806/244-3542 |
| Debbie Dunham | | | | | |
| Stateline Christian Sch | 1-8 | | 41 | | 806/362-4320 |
| 220 Hershey Lane, Texline 79087 | | | 5 | | |
| Errol Smith | | | | | |

## DALLAS COUNTY

### DALLAS COUNTY SCHOOLS

- **Dallas Co Schools** PID: 02090673　　　　214/598-2200
  5151 Samuell Blvd, Dallas 75228

| | | | |
|---|---|---|---|
| Gary Lindsey | 1 | Paul King | 2 |
| Timothy Jones | 3 | Leigh Giddens | 5 |
| Leatha Mullins | 15,71 | Deanne Hullender | 16,70 |
| Gloria Levario | 67 | Jerry Martinez | 68 |

Michael Rogger ........................ 73　Scott Peters ........................74,77,91

| County Schs..Principal | Grd | Prgm | Enr/#Cls | SN |
|---|---|---|---|---|
| Ⓐ Acad of Academic Exc Youth Vlg<br>Ⓒ 1508 E Langdon Rd, Dallas 75241<br>Aubrey Hooper | 5-12 | | 72 | 214/698-2200<br>Fax 972/225-9737 |
| Ⓐ Dallas Co Jj Aae-Letot Ctr<br>Ⓒ 10505 Denton Dr, Dallas 75220<br>Marilena Zuppardo | 6-12 | T | 50 | 100% 214/956-2036<br>Fax 214/956-2010 |
| Ⓐ Dallas Co Jj Aae-Medlock<br>Ⓒ 1566 E Langdon Rd, Dallas 75241<br>Aubrey Hooper | 6-12 | T | 150<br>8 | 100% 972/225-9735<br>Fax 972/225-9763 |
| Ⓐ Dallas Co Jj Aae-SAU<br>Ⓒ 414 S R L Thornton Fwy, Dallas 75203<br>Jacqueline Bluitt | 6-12 | T | 50 | 100% 214/860-4370<br>Fax 214/860-4490 |
| Ⓐ Dallas Co Jj CS-Drc Campus<br>Ⓒ 1673 Terre Colony Ct, Dallas 75212<br>Daniel Guillary | 6-12 | T | 110 | 100% 214/637-6136<br>Fax 214/637-6779 |
| Ⓒ Dallas Co Jj CS-Main Camp<br>1673 Terre Colony Ct, Dallas 75212<br>Sheterric Malone | 5-12 | | 175 | 214/637-6136<br>Fax 214/637-6130 |

## DALLAS PUBLIC SCHOOLS

● **Advantage Academy Admin Office** PID: 11824891　214/276-5800
　618 W Wheatland Rd, Duncanville 75116　　　　Fax 214/276-5890

**Schools:** 4 \ **Teachers:** 89 \ **Students:** 1,650 \ **Special Ed Students:** 102 \
**LEP Students:** 376 \ **Ethnic:** Asian 2%, African American 27%, Hispanic 57%,
Caucasian 14% \ **Open-Close:** 08/28 - 06/01

| | | |
|---|---|---|
| Angela McDonald ........................ 1 | Wilma Mallory-Sneed ...........2,11,19,298 | |
| Kevin McDonald ....................3,5,17 | Manuel Ruiz ...........................3 | |
| Stella Sisneros ........................ 4 | Aimee Cooper ...........................8 | |
| Stephanie DeLuna ....................57 | Lisa Lanham ...................58,88,752 | |
| Marie Cox ........................68 | Sherri Busalacchi ...........................71 | |
| Marco Salazar ..........73,76,286,295 | Tammy Bailey ...........................79 | |
| Denise Clevenger ....................280 | | |

| Public Schs..Principal | Grd | Prgm | Enr/#Cls | SN |
|---|---|---|---|---|
| Ⓒ Advantage Acad-Grand Prairie E<br>300 W Pioneer Pkwy, Grand Prairie 75051<br>Roy Watts | 8-12 | V | 150 | 214/276-5800<br>Fax 972/237-7927 |
| Ⓒ Advantage Acad-Grand Prairie W<br>955 Freetown Rd, Grand Prairie 75051<br>Beverly Compton | PK-8 | T | 750 | 77% 214/276-5800<br>Fax 972/602-2212 |
| Ⓒ Advantage Acad-N Duncanville<br>4009 Joseph Hardin Dr, Dallas 75236<br>Donita White | PK-8 | AV | 500 | 214/276-5800<br>Fax 214/467-2510 |
| Ⓒ Advantage Academy-Waxahachie<br>701 W 287 Bypass, Waxahachie 75165<br>Aimee Barnes | PK-8 | | 335<br>20 | 972/937-9851<br>Fax 972/937-9876 |

● **Carrollton-Farmers Branch ISD** PID: 01008134　972/968-6100
　1445 N Perry Rd, Carrollton 75006　　　　Fax 972/968-6217

**Schools:** 37 \ **Teachers:** 1,711 \ **Students:** 24,500 \
**Special Ed Students:** 3,139 \ **LEP Students:** 7,157 \ **College-Bound:** 55%
\ **Ethnic:** Asian 12%, African American 17%, Hispanic 57%, Caucasian
13% \ **Exp:** $295 (Med) \ **Poverty:** 13% \ **Title I:** $5,480,889 \
**Special Education:** $5,502,000 \ **Open-Close:** 08/17 - 05/27 \ **DTBP:** $191
(High) \ 🅵 🅴

| | | |
|---|---|---|
| Dr John Chapman ........................ 1 | Gary Kerbow ........................2,19 | |
| Nikki Pendlay ........................ 2 | Malcolm Mulroney ........................3,17 | |
| Rachelle Sherrin ........................ 4 | David Hanna ........................ 5 | |
| Renee Putter ........................6,35 | Sandra Lieck ........................ 7 | |
| Dr Dana West ........................ 8,15,74,286 | Dr Pat Franklin ........................9,93 | |
| Tracy Smith ...................9,15,275 | Michelle Bailey ........................10,15,79 | |
| Kim Quinn ........................ 11 | Steve Bassett ........................ 11,15 | |
| Kimberly Guinn ...................12,69,294 | Dr Derrell Coleman ........................ 15,751 | |
| Scott Monroe ...................16,73,76,295 | Brett Farr ........................20,23 | |
| Jo Gillen ...........27,31,36,69,77,83,88,270 | Susan Kelly ........................34,54 | |
| Michael Ramirez ........................ 35 | Pier Larsen ........................ 39 | |
| Susan Shipp ...................42,280,285 | Karen Spaulding ........................46,277 | |
| Tonya Garvey ........................ 47 | Olivia Perez ...................57,61,89,271 | |
| Randi Wells ........................58,90 | Nancy Cline ........................ 67 | |
| Jason Liewehr ........................ 68 | Dr Randy Davis ........................ 68 | |
| Kathryn Schaeffer ........................69,81 | Pam Pena ........................71,75 | |
| Trudy Kelly ........................ 71 | Mario De La Rosa ........................ 91 | |
| Dr Robin Stout ........................ 98 | Pat Hester ........................ 274 | |
| Ashley Limvorratre ........................ 297 | | |

| Public Schs..Principal | Grd | Prgm | Enr/#Cls | SN |
|---|---|---|---|---|
| Annie Rainwater Elem Sch<br>1408 E Frankford Rd, Carrollton 75007<br>Charlotte Thomas | K-5 | T | 359<br>25 | 52% 972/968-2800<br>Fax 972/968-2810 |
| Barbara Bush Middle Sch<br>515 Cowboys Pkwy, Irving 75063<br>Matt Warnock | 6-8 | T | 677<br>60 | 62% 972/968-3700<br>Fax 972/968-3710 |
| Ⓐ Bea Salazar Sch<br>2416 Keller Springs Rd, Carrollton 75006<br>Melissa Wesley | K-12 | T | 150<br>12 | 79% 972/968-5900<br>Fax 972/968-5910<br>🅵 🆃 |
| Bernice Chatman Freeman ES<br>8757 Valley Ranch Pkwy W, Irving 75063<br>Robyn Campbell | PK-5 | | 612 | 35% 972/968-1700<br>Fax 972/968-1710<br>🅵 🆃 |
| Carrollton Elem Sch<br>1805 Pearl St, Carrollton 75006<br>Monica Koen | PK-5 | T | 572<br>25 | 85% 972/968-1200<br>Fax 972/968-1210 |
| Central Elem Sch<br>1600 S Perry Rd, Carrollton 75006<br>Luz Soto-Dimas | PK-5 | T | 569<br>21 | 90% 972/968-1300<br>Fax 972/968-1310 |
| Charles M Blalack Middle Sch<br>1706 E Peters Colony Rd, Carrollton 75007<br>Keith Davis | 6-8 | T | 1,044<br>85 | 59% 972/968-3500<br>Fax 972/968-3510 |
| Charlie C McKamy Elem Sch<br>3443 Briargrove Ln, Dallas 75287<br>Matthew Pruitt | PK-5 | T | 534<br>29 | 76% 972/968-2400<br>Fax 972/968-2410 |
| Country Place Elem Sch<br>2115 Raintree Dr, Carrollton 75006<br>**Amy Miller** | PK-5 | T | 356<br>20 | 46% 972/968-1400<br>Fax 972/968-1410 |
| Creekview High Sch<br>3201 Old Denton Rd, Carrollton 75007<br>Joe Lapuma | 9-12 | T | 1,866 | 52% 972/968-4800<br>Fax 972/968-4810 |
| Dale B Davis Elem Sch<br>3205 Dorchester Dr, Carrollton 75007<br>Lisa Williams | K-5 | T | 503<br>26 | 82% 972/968-1500<br>Fax 972/968-1510 |
| Dan F Long Middle Sch<br>2525 Frankford Rd, Dallas 75287<br>Charde Dockery | 6-8 | TV | 647<br>70 | 82% 972/968-4100<br>Fax 972/968-4110 |
| Dave Blair Elem Sch<br>14055 Heartside Pl, Farmers BRNCH 75234<br>Jose Ramos | K-5 | T | 539<br>47 | 87% 972/968-1000<br>Fax 972/968-1010 |
| DeWitt Perry Middle Sch<br>1709 E Belt Line Rd, Carrollton 75006<br>Adam Toy | 6-8 | TV | 1,000<br>60 | 77% 972/968-4400<br>Fax 972/968-4410 |
| E L Kent Elem Sch<br>1800 W Rosemeade Pkwy, Carrollton 75007<br>Debbie Williams | PK-5 | T | 529<br>22 | 46% 972/968-2000<br>Fax 972/968-2010 |
| Early College High Sch<br>3939 Valley View Ln Bldg P, Dallas 75244<br>Timothy Isaly | 9-12 | TV | 337<br>9 | 78% 972/968-6200<br>Fax 972/968-6270 |

| | | | | | | | | |
|---|---|---|---|---|---|---|---|---|
| **1** Superintendent | **8** Curric/Instruct K-12 | **19** Chief Financial Officer | **29** Family/Consumer Science | **39** Social Studies K-12 | **49** English/Lang Arts Elem | **59** Special Education Elem | **69** Academic Assessment |
| **2** Bus/Finance/Purchasing | **9** Curric/Instruct Elem | **20** Art K-12 | **30** Adult Education | **40** Social Studies Elem | **50** English/Lang Arts Sec | **60** Special Education Sec | **70** Research/Development |
| **3** Buildings And Grounds | **10** Curric/Instruct Sec | **21** Art Elem | **31** Career/Sch-to-Work K-12 | **41** Social Studies Sec | **51** Reading K-12 | **61** Foreign/World Lang K-12 | **71** Public Information |
| **4** Food Service | **11** Federal Program | **22** Art Sec | **32** Career/Sch-to-Work Elem | **42** Science K-12 | **52** Reading Elem | **62** Foreign/World Lang Elem | **72** Summer School |
| **5** Transportation | **12** Title I | **23** Music K-12 | **33** Career/Sch-to-Work Sec | **43** Science Elem | **53** Reading Sec | **63** Foreign/World Lang Sec | **73** Instructional Tech |
| **6** Athletic | **13** Title V | **24** Music Elem | **34** Early Childhood Ed | **44** Science Sec | **54** Remedial Reading K-12 | **64** Religious Education K-12 | **74** Inservice Training |
| **7** Health Services | **15** Asst Superintendent | **25** Music Sec | **35** Health/Phys Education | **45** Math K-12 | **55** Remedial Reading Elem | **65** Religious Education Elem | **75** Marketing/Distributive |
| | **16** Instructional Media Svcs | **26** Business Education | **36** Guidance Services K-12 | **46** Math Elem | **56** Remedial Reading Sec | **66** Religious Education Sec | **76** Info Systems |
| | **17** Chief Operations Officer | **27** Career & Tech Ed | **37** Guidance Services Elem | **47** Math Sec | **57** Bilingual/ELL | **67** School Board President | **77** Psychological Assess |
| | **18** Chief Academic Officer | **28** Technology Education | **38** Guidance Services Sec | **48** English/Lang Arts K-12 | **58** Special Education K-12 | **68** Teacher Personnel | **78** Affirmative Action |

| | Grd | Prgm | Enr | % | Phone |
|---|---|---|---|---|---|

**Farmers Branch Elem Sch** — PK-5 — T — 519 / 60 — 82% — 972/968-1600 — Fax 972/968-1610
13521 Tom Field Rd, Farmers BRNCH 75234
Shanah Brown

**Furneaux Elem Sch** — PK-5 — T — 402 / 18 — 67% — 972/968-1800 — Fax 972/968-1810
3210 Furneaux Ln, Carrollton 75007
Lori Parker

**Janie Stark Elem Sch** — PK-5 — T — 746 / 31 — 55% — 972/968-3300 — Fax 972/968-3310
12400 Josey Ln, Farmers BRNCH 75234
Jennifer Putman

**June R Thompson Elem Sch** — PK-5 — T — 421 / 24 — 71% — 972/968-3400 — Fax 972/968-3410
2915 Scott Mill Rd, Carrollton 75007
Robert Atchison

**Kathryn S McWhorter Elem Sch** — PK-5 — T — 560 / 30 — 87% — 972/968-2600 — Fax 972/968-2610
3678 Timberglen Rd, Dallas 75287
Eddie Reed

**L F Blanton Elem Sch** — K-5 — T — 427 / 28 — 79% — 972/968-1100 — Fax 972/968-1110
2525 Scott Mill Rd, Carrollton 75006
Patricia Badillo

**La Villita Elem Sch** — K-5 — 898 — 19% — 972/968-6900 — Fax 972/968-6910
1601 Camino Lago, Irving 75039
Dreama Mayfield

**Las Colinas Elem Sch** — K-5 — 579 / 30 — 25% — 972/968-2200 — Fax 972/968-2210
2200 Kinwest Pkwy, Irving 75063
**Shahnaj Ahmad**

**Ⓐ Mary Grimes Education Center** — 11-12 — V — 53 / 15 — 57% — 972/968-5600 — Fax 972/968-5610
1745 Hutton Dr, Carrollton 75006
Melissa Wesley

**McCoy Elem Sch** — K-5 — T — 456 / 23 — 33% — 972/968-2300 — Fax 972/968-2310
2425 McCoy Rd, Carrollton 75006
Dawn Rink

**McLaughlin Strickland ES** — K-5 — T — 535 / 22 — 89% — 972/968-5700 — Fax 972/968-2510
330 Fyke Rd, Farmers BRNCH 75234
**Victoria Cisneros**

**Newman Smith High Sch** — 9-12 — TV — 1,966 — 69% — 972/968-5200 — Fax 972/968-5210
2335 N Josey Ln, Carrollton 75006
Stephanie Jimenez

**R E Good Elem Sch** — PK-5 — T — 536 / 27 — 81% — 972/968-1900 — Fax 972/968-1910
1012 Study Ln, Carrollton 75006
**Agueda Paredes**

**R L Turner High Sch** — 9-12 — TV — 2,127 / 175 — 73% — 972/968-5400 — Fax 972/968-5410
1600 S Josey Ln, Carrollton 75006
**Adam Grinage**

**Ranchview High Sch** — 9-12 — TV — 910 — 52% — 972/968-5000 — Fax 972/968-5010
8401 Valley Ranch Pkwy E, Irving 75063
Sherie Skruch

**Riverchase Elem Sch** — PK-5 — T — 464 / 22 — 48% — 972/968-2900 — Fax 972/968-2910
272 S MacArthur Blvd, Coppell 75019
Pamela Henderson  f t

**Rosemeade Elem Sch** — K-5 — T — 389 / 19 — 41% — 972/968-3000 — Fax 972/968-3010
3550 Kimberly Dr, Carrollton 75007
Laura Gutierrez  f

**Sheffield Primary Elem Sch** — K-5 — T — 654 / 24 — 89% — 972/968-3100 — Fax 972/968-3110
18111 Kelly Blvd, Dallas 75287
**Ahveance Jones**

**Ted Polk Middle Sch** — 6-8 — TV — 1,040 / 30 — 74% — 972/968-4600 — Fax 972/968-4610
2001 Kelly Blvd, Carrollton 75006
Kelly O'Sullivan

**Tom Landry Elem Sch** — K-5 — TV — 280 / 25 — 79% — 972/968-2100 — Fax 972/968-2110
265 Red River Trl, Irving 75063
Stephanie Lopez  f t

**Vivian Field Middle Sch** — 6-8 — TV — 1,028 — 82% — 972/968-3900 — Fax 972/968-3910
13551 Dennis Ln, Farmers BRNCH 75234
Chad Hunter  f

---

• **Cedar Hill Ind School Dist** PID: 01008275 — 972/291-1581
285 Uptown Blvd Ste 300, Cedar Hill 75104 — Fax 972/291-5231

> **Schools:** 14 \ **Teachers:** 470 \ **Students:** 7,866 \ **Special Ed Students:** 649 \ **LEP Students:** 538 \ **College-Bound:** 55% \ **Ethnic:** Asian 1%, African American 69%, Hispanic 26%, Caucasian 4% \ **Exp:** $373 (High) \ **Poverty:** 15% \ **Title I:** $2,077,790 \ **Special Education:** $1,182,000 \ **Open-Close:** 08/12 - 05/21 \ **DTBP:** $204 (High) \ f t

| | | | |
|---|---|---|---|
| Dr Gerald Hudson | 1 | Sherra McGane | 2 |
| Josh Skains | 3 | Jimmy Blades | 5 |
| Gina Farmer | 6 | Pamela Reese-Taylor | 7* |
| Dr Charlotte Ford | 8 | Dr Darryl Henson | 15 |
| Kellie Spencer | 15 | Tellunce Graham | 15,79 |
| Violet Dean | 15,68,74,78 | Gilberto Prado | 19 |
| Tysha Lowe | 27,31 | Tracey Willyard | 28,73,95 |
| Lakimberly Wilson | 46 | Nicole Rose | 47 |
| Patrice Woodson | 49 | Holly Cunningham | 58 |
| Jennifer Lonsford | 58 | Cheryl Wesley | 67 |
| Bryan Ward | 69 | Jamie Brown | 71 |
| Neil Bolton | 76,295 | Chris Santos | 91 |
| Jimmy Hogg | 91 | Danyell Wells | 93 |
| Tierney Tinnin | 97 | | |

| Public Schs..Principal | Grd | Prgm | Enr/#Cls | SN |
|---|---|---|---|---|

**Besse Coleman Middle Sch** — 6-8 — T — 769 — 69% — 972/293-4505 — Fax 469/272-9445
1208 E Pleasant Run Rd, Cedar Hill 75104
Norman Jones  f t

**Bray Elem Sch** — PK-5 — T — 190 / 14 — 71% — 972/291-4231 — Fax 972/291-6098
218 N Broad St, Cedar Hill 75104
Eric Barnes  f t

**Cedar Hill 9th Grade Center** — 9-9 — 575 — 469/272-2050 — Fax 469/272-3443
1515 W Belt Line Rd, Cedar Hill 75104
Jason Miller

**Cedar Hill Collegiate High Sch** — 9-12 — 371 — 43% — 469/272-2021 — Fax 469/272-3445
1533 High Pointe Ln, Cedar Hill 75104
Deidrea Stevens

**Cedar Hill High Sch** — 10-12 — GTV — 1,707 — 60% — 469/272-2000 — Fax 972/293-7125
1 Longhorn Blvd, Cedar Hill 75104
Jason Miller

**Collegiate Academy Middle Sch** — 6-8 — T — 300 / 40 — 49% — 469/272-2021 — Fax 972/291-0646
1533 High Pointe Ln, Cedar Hill 75104
Heath Koenig  f

**Collegiate Prep Academy** — PK-5 — T — 500 — 47% — 972/293-4502 — Fax 972/291-5213
975 Pickard Dr, Cedar Hill 75104
Shay Whittaker

**Ⓐ Discipline Alt Education Pgrm** — K-12 — 50 / 8 — 972/293-4504 — Fax 972/291-7160
1515 W Belt Line Rd, Cedar Hill 75104
Patrick Nash  f t

**High Pointe Elem Sch** — PK-5 — T — 404 / 26 — 86% — 972/291-7874 — Fax 972/291-5695
1351 High Pointe Ln, Cedar Hill 75104
**Shay Whittaker**

**Highlands Elem Sch** — PK-5 — T — 604 / 40 — 86% — 972/291-0496 — Fax 972/291-5764
131 Sims Dr, Cedar Hill 75104
**Candice Griffin**  f

**Lake Ridge Elem Sch** — PK-5 — T — 289 — 66% — 972/293-4501 — Fax 972/291-5210
1020 Lake Ridge Pkwy, Cedar Hill 75104
Marquita McCullum  f t

**Plummer Elem Sch** — PK-5 — T — 607 / 25 — 83% — 972/291-4058 — Fax 972/291-4980
1203 S Clark Rd, Cedar Hill 75104
John Edmun

**W S Permenter Middle Sch** — 6-8 — TV — 800 — 74% — 972/291-5270 — Fax 972/291-5296
431 W Parkerville Rd, Cedar Hill 75104
John Ensley

**Waterford Oaks Elem Sch** — PK-5 — T — 532 / 26 — 77% — 972/291-5290 — Fax 972/293-2381
401 N Waterford Oaks Dr, Cedar Hill 75104
William Davis  f t

---

| | | | | | |
|---|---|---|---|---|---|
| 79 | Student Personnel | 91 | Safety/Security | 275 | Response To Intervention |
| 80 | Driver Ed/Safety | 92 | Magnet School | 277 | Remedial Math K-12 |
| 81 | Gifted/Talented | 93 | Parental Involvement | 280 | Literacy Coach |
| 82 | Video Services | 95 | Tech Prep Program | 285 | STEM |
| 83 | Substance Abuse Prev | 97 | Chief Information Officer | 286 | Digital Learning |
| 84 | Erate | 98 | Chief Technology Officer | 288 | Common Core Standards |
| 85 | AIDS Education | 270 | Character Education | 294 | Accountability |
| 88 | Alternative/At Risk | 271 | Migrant Education | 295 | Network System |
| 89 | Multi-Cultural Curriculum | 273 | Teacher Mentor | 296 | Title II Programs |
| 90 | Social Work | 274 | Before/After Sch | 297 | Webmaster |

| | | | |
|---|---|---|---|
| 298 | Grant Writer/Ptnrships | | |
| 750 | Chief Innovation Officer | | |
| 751 | Chief of Staff | | |
| 752 | Social Emotional Learning | | |

**Other School Types**
Ⓐ = Alternative School
Ⓒ = Charter School
Ⓜ = Magnet School
Ⓨ = Year-Round School

**School Programs**
A = Alternative Program
G = Adult Classes
M = Magnet Program
T = Title I Schoolwide
V = Career & Tech Ed Programs

New Schools are shaded
New Superintendents and Principals are bold
Personnel with email addresses are underscored

**Social Media**
f = Facebook
t = Twitter

## • Coppell Ind School Dist PID: 01008328
200 S Denton Tap Rd, Coppell 75019

214/496-6000
Fax 214/496-6036

**Schools:** 18 \ **Teachers:** 792 \ **Students:** 13,500 \ **Special Ed Students:** 869 \ **LEP Students:** 1,434 \ **College-Bound:** 61% \ **Ethnic:** Asian 51%, African American 4%, Hispanic 14%, Caucasian 30% \ **Poverty:** 3% \ **Title I:** $261,754 \ **Special Education:** $1,359,000 \ **Open-Close:** 08/17 - 05/26 \ **DTBP:** $173 (High) \ 🅵 🆃

| | | | |
|---|---|---|---|
| Brad Hunt | 1 | Diana Sircar | 2,19 |
| Justin Hill | 2 | Genaro Lopez | 3,5,91 |
| Jean Mosley | 4 | Kit Pehl | 6* |
| Dr Angie Applegate | 8,15,69 | Robyn Webb | 11,298 |
| Kristen Streeter | 15,68,79 | Greg Axelson | 17 |
| Evan Whitfield | 42 | Mary Kemper | 45 |
| Patricia Cheatham | 57 | Becky Ranibolt | 58 |
| Stephanie Flores | 58 | Thom Hulme | 67 |
| Kelly Mires | 68 | Amanda Simpson | 71,97 |
| Tamerah Ringo | 71 | Nancy Garvey | 73,286 |
| Steven McGilvary | 73,98 | Brooke Sims | 74 |
| Angela Brown | 75 | Carol Freese | 76 |
| Janice Duffney | 76 | Kathy Creek | 76 |
| Todd Sissom | 76 | Deana Dynis | 81 |
| Debbie Gauntt | 275 | Anita Delaisla | 280 |
| Jennifer Villines | 752 | | |

| Public Schs..Principal | Grd | Prgm | Enr/#Cls | SN |
|---|---|---|---|---|
| Barbara S Austin Elem Sch<br>161 S Moore Rd, Coppell 75019<br>**Kristan Perryman** | PK-5 | T | 680<br>28 | 30% 214/496-7300<br>Fax 214/496-7306 |
| Canyon Ranch Elem Sch<br>1205 Santa Fe Trl, Irving 75063<br>Ashley Minton | K-5 | | 700 | 214/496-7200 |
| Coppell High Sch<br>185 W Parkway Blvd, Coppell 75019<br>Laura Springer | 10-12 | V | 3,000<br>110 | 10% 214/496-6100<br>Fax 214/496-6166 🅵🆃 |
| Coppell HS 9th Grade<br>1301 Wrangler Cir, Coppell 75019<br>Cody Koontz | 9-9 | | 925 | 214/496-3800 |
| Coppell Middle School East<br>400 Mockingbird Ln, Coppell 75019<br>Steve Glover | 6-8 | V | 955<br>60 | 8% 214/496-6600<br>Fax 214/496-6603 🅵🆃 |
| Coppell Middle School North<br>120 Natches Trce, Coppell 75019<br>**Lorie Squalls** | 6-8 | TV | 983<br>60 | 9% 214/496-7100<br>Fax 214/496-7103 🅵🆃 |
| Coppell Middle School West<br>2701 Ranch Trail, Coppell 75019<br>Sarah Thornton | 6-8 | TV | 1,289<br>55 | 10% 214/496-8600<br>Fax 214/496-8606 |
| Cottonwood Creek Elem Sch<br>615 Minyard Dr, Coppell 75019<br>Dr Andra Penny | K-5 | | 439<br>26 | 5% 214/496-8300<br>Fax 214/496-8306 🅵🆃 |
| Denton Creek Elem Sch<br>250 Natches Trce, Coppell 75019<br>Shannon Edwards | PK-5 | T | 406<br>23 | 13% 214/496-8100<br>Fax 214/496-8106 🅵🆃 |
| Lakeside Elem Sch<br>1100 Village Pkwy, Coppell 75019<br>Gema Hall | PK-5 | | 514<br>20 | 5% 214/496-7600<br>Fax 214/496-7606 |
| Mockingbird Elem Sch<br>300 Mockingbird Ln, Coppell 75019<br>Laura Flynn | K-5 | | 484<br>25 | 7% 214/496-8200<br>Fax 214/496-8206 🅵🆃 |
| New Tech High Sch-Coppell<br>113 Samuel Blvd, Coppell 75019<br>Steffany Batik | 9-12 | | 247 | 8% 214/496-5900<br>Fax 214/496-5906 🅵🆃 |
| Richard J Lee Elem Sch<br>Olympus Blvd & Ranch Tr, Irving 75063<br>Chantel Kastorunis | PK-5 | | 730 | 5% 214/496-7900<br>Fax 214/496-7906 🅵 |
| Town Center Elem Sch<br>185 N Heartz Rd, Coppell 75019<br>Jennifer Martin | PK-5 | T | 494<br>23 | 10% 214/496-7800<br>Fax 214/496-7806 🆃 |
| Valley Ranch Elem Sch<br>9800 Rodeo Dr, Irving 75063<br>Cynthia Arterbery | PK-5 | | 575<br>20 | 4% 214/496-8500<br>Fax 214/496-8506 🅵🆃 |
| Ⓐ Victory Place at Coppell<br>550 N Denton Tap Rd, Coppell 75019<br>Jeff Minn | 6-12 | | 50<br>2 | 214/496-8032<br>Fax 214/496-8027 |
| W H Wilson Elem Sch<br>200 S Coppell Rd, Coppell 75019<br>Cooper Hilton | PK-5 | T | 402 | 24% 214/496-7500<br>Fax 214/496-7506 🅵🆃 |
| W W Pinkerton Elem Sch<br>260 Southwestern Blvd, Coppell 75019<br>Kristi Mikkelsen | PK-5 | | 289<br>18 | 4% 214/496-6800<br>Fax 214/496-6806 |

## • Dallas Ind School Dist PID: 01008354
9400 N Central Expy, Dallas 75231

972/925-3700
Fax 972/925-3701

**Schools:** 233 \ **Teachers:** 10,001 \ **Students:** 153,861 \ **Special Ed Students:** 13,737 \ **LEP Students:** 63,098 \ **College-Bound:** 87% \ **Ethnic:** Asian 1%, African American 22%, Hispanic 70%, Native American: 1%, Caucasian 6% \ **Exp:** $312 (High) \ **Poverty:** 25% \ **Title I:** $90,633,354 \ **Special Education:** $27,150,000 \ **Open-Close:** 09/08 - 06/18 \ **DTBP:** $194 (High) \ 🅵

| | | | |
|---|---|---|---|
| Dr Michael Hinojosa | 1 | David Bates | 3 |
| Scott Layne | 3,17 | Michael Rosenberger | 4 |
| Jaime Sandoval | 5 | Silvia Salinas | 6 |
| Jennifer Finley | 7 | Shannon Lee Trejo | 8,18 |
| Sequetta Marks | 11 | Dr Cecilia Oakeley | 15,69,70,294 |
| Sherry Christian | 15,88 | Gay Patrick | 16 |
| Dwayne Thompson | 19 | Tim Linley | 20,23 |
| Richard Grimsley | 27,31 | Alan Cohen | 34 |
| Barbara Johnson | 35 | Joann Jackson-Powell | 36 |
| Shalon Bond | 39 | Jenny Christian | 42,285 |
| Stej Sanchez | 45 | Arlena Gaynor | 48,51,280 |
| Amanda Clymer | 57 | Michelle Brown | 58 |
| Amy Anderton | 61 | Justin Henry | 67 |
| Dr Diedrae Bell-Hunter | 68 | Billy Snow | 70,750 |
| Dr Cynthia Wilson | 71,97* | Toni Cordova | 71 |
| Crystal Rentz | 72 | Jack Kelanic | 73,98* |
| Roland Antoine | 73,76,295 | Angie Gaylord | 74 |
| George Mallick | 76 | Dr Connie Rodriguez | 77,90 |
| Erik Nickerson | 79 | Mitch Morker | 81 |
| John Olin Lawton | 91 | Nancy Rubio | 92 |
| Charissa Govan | 275 | Jacquelyn Cumby | 286 |
| Brian Reed | 297 | Pamela Lear | 751 |
| Juony Valdespino-Gay | 752 | | |

| Public Schs..Principal | Grd | Prgm | Enr/#Cls | SN |
|---|---|---|---|---|
| Adelfa Botello Callejo ES<br>7817 Military Pkwy, Dallas 75227<br>**Christie Samuel** | PK-5 | T | 606 | 96% 972/892-5700<br>Fax 972/892-5701 |
| Adelle Turner Elem Sch<br>5505 S Polk St, Dallas 75232<br>**Derek Thomas** | PK-5 | T | 255<br>24 | 81% 972/794-6300<br>Fax 972/794-6301 |
| Alex Sanger Elem Sch<br>8410 San Leandro Dr, Dallas 75218<br>Hector Martinez | PK-8 | T | 708<br>27 | 78% 972/749-7600<br>Fax 972/749-7601 |
| Alex W Spence Middle Sch & Tag<br>4001 Capitol Ave, Dallas 75204<br>Shanna Jones | 6-8 | TV | 713<br>60 | 84% 972/925-2300<br>Fax 972/925-2301 |
| Ann Richards Steam Academy<br>3831 N Prairie Creek Rd, Dallas 75227<br>Natasha Shaw | 6-8 | TV | 1,322 | 96% 972/892-5400<br>Fax 972/892-5401 |
| Anne Frank Elem Sch<br>5201 Celestial Rd, Dallas 75254<br>Beverly Mullins | PK-5 | T | 1,119<br>55 | 77% 972/502-5900<br>Fax 972/502-5901 |

| | | | | | | | | |
|---|---|---|---|---|---|---|---|---|
| 1 | Superintendent | 8 | Curric/Instruct K-12 | 19 | Chief Financial Officer | 29 | Family/Consumer Science | |
| 2 | Bus/Finance/Purchasing | 9 | Curric/Instruct Elem | 20 | Art K-12 | 30 | Adult Education | |
| 3 | Buildings And Grounds | 10 | Curric/Instruct Sec | 21 | Art Elem | 31 | Career/Sch-to-Work K-12 | |
| 4 | Food Service | 11 | Federal Program | 22 | Art Sec | 32 | Career/Sch-to-Work Elem | |
| 5 | Transportation | 12 | Title I | 23 | Music K-12 | 33 | Career/Sch-to-Work Sec | |
| 6 | Athletic | 13 | Title V | 24 | Music Elem | 34 | Early Childhood Ed | |
| 7 | Health Services | 15 | Asst Superintendent | 25 | Music Sec | 35 | Health/Phys Education | |
| | | 16 | Instructional Media Svcs | 26 | Business Education | 36 | Guidance Services K-12 | |
| | | 17 | Chief Operations Officer | 27 | Career & Tech Ed | 37 | Guidance Services Elem | |
| | | 18 | Chief Academic Officer | 28 | Technology Education | 38 | Guidance Services Sec | |

| | | | | | | | |
|---|---|---|---|---|---|---|---|
| 39 | Social Studies K-12 | 49 | English/Lang Arts Elem | 59 | Special Education Elem | 69 | Academic Assessment |
| 40 | Social Studies Elem | 50 | English/Lang Arts Sec | 60 | Special Education Sec | 70 | Research/Development |
| 41 | Social Studies Sec | 51 | Reading K-12 | 61 | Foreign/World Lang K-12 | 71 | Public Information |
| 42 | Science K-12 | 52 | Reading Elem | 62 | Foreign/World Lang Elem | 72 | Summer School |
| 43 | Science Elem | 53 | Reading Sec | 63 | Foreign/World Lang Sec | 73 | Instructional Tech |
| 44 | Science Sec | 54 | Remedial Reading K-12 | 64 | Religious Education K-12 | 74 | Inservice Training |
| 45 | Math K-12 | 55 | Remedial Reading Elem | 65 | Religious Education Elem | 75 | Marketing/Distributive |
| 46 | Math Elem | 56 | Remedial Reading Sec | 66 | Religious Education Sec | 76 | Info Systems |
| 47 | Math Sec | 57 | Bilingual/ELL | 67 | School Board President | 77 | Psychological Assess |
| 48 | English/Lang Arts K-12 | 58 | Special Education K-12 | 68 | Teacher Personnel | 78 | Affirmative Action |

| School / Address / Principal | Grades | Prog | Enroll | % | Phone / Fax |
|---|---|---|---|---|---|
| Annie Webb Blanton Elem Sch<br>8915 Greenmound Ave, Dallas 75227<br>Alicia Iwasko | PK-5 | T | 579<br>40 | 96% | 972/794-1700<br>Fax 972/794-1701 |
| Anson Jones Elem Sch<br>3901 Meredith Ave, Dallas 75211<br>Guillermo Cortez | PK-5 | T | 603<br>55 | 96% | 972/794-4700<br>Fax 972/794-4701 |
| Arcadia Park Elem Sch<br>1300 N Justin Ave, Dallas 75211<br>Kelly O'Hara-Sanchez | PK-5 | T | 652<br>30 | 91% | 972/502-5300<br>Fax 972/502-5301 |
| Arlington Park ECC<br>5606 Wayside Dr, Dallas 75235<br>Mary Molinares | PK-PK | T | 101 | 90% | 972/749-5500 |
| Arthur Kramer Elem Sch<br>7131 Midbury Dr, Dallas 75230<br>Kate Walker | PK-5 | T | 628<br>25 | 68% | 972/794-8300<br>Fax 972/794-8301 |
| Arturo Salazar Elem Sch<br>1120 S Ravinia Dr, Dallas 75211<br>Nicole Bixby | PK-5 | T | 502 | 90% | 972/502-1800<br>Fax 972/502-1801 |
| Ascher Silberstein Elem Sch<br>5940 Hollis Ave, Dallas 75227<br>**Dr Erika Pasieczny** | PK-5 | T | 704<br>40 | 95% | 972/794-1900<br>Fax 972/794-1901 |
| B H Macon Elem Sch<br>650 Holcomb Rd, Dallas 75217<br>Antonio Verduzco | PK-5 | T | 540<br>32 | 96% | 972/794-1500<br>Fax 972/794-1501 |
| Ⓜ B T Washington Perform Arts HS<br>2501 Flora St, Dallas 75201<br>Scott Rudes | 9-12 | V | 999<br>45 | 32% | 972/925-1200<br>Fax 972/925-1201 |
| Ⓜ Barack Obama Male Ldrshp Acad<br>3030 Stag Rd, Dallas 75241<br>**Rashad Jackson** | 6-12 | T | 461 | 76% | 972/749-2100<br>Fax 972/749-2101   FB T |
| Barbara Jordan Elem Sch<br>1111 W Kiest Blvd, Dallas 75224<br>Lucy Hopkins | PK-5 | T | 624<br>50 | 99% | 972/925-8100<br>Fax 972/925-8101 |
| Ⓐ Barbara M Manns Daep Sch<br>3313 S Beckley Ave, Dallas 75224<br>Billy Bratton | K-12 | T | 125<br>17 | 80% | 972/925-7000<br>Fax 214/371-2860 |
| Bayles Elem Sch<br>2444 Telegraph Ave, Dallas 75228<br>Gloria Kennedy | PK-5 | T | 491<br>55 | 98% | 972/749-8900<br>Fax 972/749-8901 |
| Ben Milam Elem Sch<br>4200 McKinney Ave, Dallas 75205<br>Anna Galvan | PK-5 | T | 304 | 83% | 972/749-5600<br>Fax 972/749-5601 |
| Billy Earl Dade Middle Sch<br>2727 Al Lipscomb Way, Dallas 75215<br>Rockell Stewart | 6-8 | T | 879<br>28 | 100% | 972/749-3800<br>Fax 972/749-3801 |
| Birdie Alexander Elem Sch<br>1830 Goldwood Dr, Dallas 75232<br>**David Welch** | PK-5 | T | 343<br>20 | 98% | 972/749-3100<br>Fax 972/749-3101 |
| Boude Storey Middle Sch<br>3000 Maryland Ave, Dallas 75216<br>Jacqueline Rivers | 6-8 | TV | 528<br>63 | 98% | 972/925-8700<br>Fax 972/925-8701 |
| Bryan Adams High Sch<br>2101 Millmar Dr, Dallas 75228<br>Ryan Bott | 9-12 | TV | 2,166 | 88% | 972/502-4900<br>Fax 972/502-4901 |
| C A Tatum Elem Sch<br>3002 N Saint Augustine Dr, Dallas 75227<br>Enrique Rodriguez | K-5 | T | 467 | 97% | 972/502-2000<br>Fax 972/502-2001 |
| C F Carr Elem Sch<br>1952 Bayside St, Dallas 75212<br>Carlotta Hooks | PK-5 | T | 559<br>27 | 99% | 972/794-4300<br>Fax 972/794-4301 |
| Casa View Elem Sch<br>2100 N Farola Dr, Dallas 75228<br>Thania Garibay | PK-5 | T | 595 | 93% | 972/749-7700<br>Fax 972/749-7701 |
| Cedar Crest Elem Sch<br>2020 Mouser Ln, Dallas 75203<br>**Tara Berry** | PK-5 | T | 354<br>37 | 97% | 972/925-7400<br>Fax 972/925-7401   FB T |
| Celestino Mauricio Soto ES<br>4510 W Jefferson Blvd, Dallas 75211<br>Norma Barragan | PK-5 | T | 540 | 94% | 972/502-5100<br>Fax 972/502-5101 |
| Central Elem Sch<br>902 Shady Ln, Seagoville 75159<br>Julie Singleton | PK-5 | T | 587<br>28 | 92% | 972/749-6800<br>Fax 972/749-6801 |
| Cesar Chavez Learning Center<br>1710 N Carroll Ave, Dallas 75204<br>Sheryl Wilson | PK-5 | T | 690<br>60 | 100% | 972/925-1000<br>Fax 972/925-1001 |
| Chapel Hill Preparatory Sch<br>12717 Templeton Trl, Dallas 75234<br>Fabian Hypolite | PK-5 | T | 474<br>40 | 95% | 972/794-2400<br>Fax 972/794-2401 |
| Charles A Gill Elem Sch<br>10910 Ferguson Rd, Dallas 75228<br>Shawki Freelon | PK-5 | T | 790<br>65 | 93% | 972/749-8400<br>Fax 972/749-8401 |
| Charles Rice Learning Center<br>2425 Pine St, Dallas 75215<br>Jennifer Atkins | PK-5 | T | 542 | 96% | 972/749-1100<br>Fax 972/749-1101 |
| Ⓐ City Lab High Sch<br>912 S Ervay St, Dallas 75201<br>Lynn Smith | 9-12 | T | 80 | 60% | 972/749-2700 |
| Clara Oliver Elem Sch<br>4010 Idaho Ave, Dallas 75216<br>Cheryl Freeman | PK-5 | T | 274<br>15 | 96% | 972/749-3400<br>Fax 972/749-3401 |
| Clinton P Russell Elem Sch<br>3031 S Beckley Ave, Dallas 75224<br>Gerald Bennett | PK-5 | T | 672<br>17 | 91% | 972/925-8300<br>Fax 972/925-8301 |
| D A Hulcy Steam Middle Sch<br>9339 S Polk St, Dallas 75232<br>Jonica Lockwood | 6-8 | T | 533 | 64% | 214/932-7400 |
| Ⓜ Dallas Environmental Sci Acad<br>3531 N Westmoreland Rd, Dallas 75212<br>Aris Rider | 6-8 | TV | 460<br>6 | 86% | 972/794-3950<br>Fax 972/794-3951 |
| Dan D Rogers Elem Sch<br>5314 Abrams Rd, Dallas 75214<br>Marissa Limon | PK-5 | T | 507<br>50 | 78% | 972/794-8800<br>Fax 972/794-8801 |
| Daniel Webster Elem Sch<br>3815 S Franklin St, Dallas 75233<br>Clement Alexander | PK-5 | T | 406<br>40 | 96% | 972/794-6100<br>Fax 972/794-6101 |
| David G Burnet Elem Sch<br>3200 Kinkaid Dr, Dallas 75220<br>Sonia Loskot | PK-5 | T | 644<br>55 | 99% | 972/794-3000<br>Fax 972/794-3001 |
| David W Carter High Sch<br>1819 W Wheatland Rd, Dallas 75232<br>Jonathan Smith | 9-12 | TV | 1,181<br>79 | 76% | 214/932-5700<br>Fax 214/932-5701 |
| Downtown Montessori Sch<br>1901 Main St, Dallas 75201<br>**Dr Olga Korobovskaya** | PK-2 | | 250 | | 972/749-2500 |
| Ⓐ Dr Wright Lassiter Erly Clg HS<br>801 Main St, Dallas 75202<br>Michael St Ama | 9-12 | T | 246 | 74% | 214/860-2356<br>Fax 214/860-2359 |
| E B Comstock Middle Sch<br>7044 Hodde St, Dallas 75217<br>**Wesley Sellers** | 6-8 | TV | 798<br>100 | 99% | 972/794-1300<br>Fax 972/794-1301 |
| E D Walker Middle Sch<br>12532 Nuestra Dr, Dallas 75230<br>**Mrs Toole** | 6-8 | T | 738 | 88% | 972/502-6100<br>Fax 972/502-6101 |
| Ebby Halliday Elem Sch<br>10210 Teagarden Rd, Dallas 75217<br>Amy Ward | PK-5 | T | 666 | 95% | 972/925-1800<br>Fax 972/925-1811 |
| Edna Rowe Elem Sch<br>4918 Hovenkamp Dr, Dallas 75227<br>Sharon Alexander | PK-5 | T | 459<br>45 | 92% | 972/749-8800<br>Fax 972/749-8801 |
| Eduardo Mata Mont Sch<br>7420 La Vista Dr, Dallas 75214<br>Tomeka Williams | PK-3 | GT | 492<br>25 | 57% | 972/749-7500<br>Fax 972/749-7501 |

| School | Grades | Codes | Enroll | % | Phone / Fax |
|---|---|---|---|---|---|
| Edward H Cary Middle Sch<br>3978 Killion Dr, Dallas 75229<br>Naomi Salas | 6-8 | GTV | 590<br>83 | 94% | 972/502-7600<br>Fax 972/502-7601 |
| Edward Titche Elem Sch<br>9560 Highfield Dr, Dallas 75227<br>Damien Stovall | PK-5 | T | 659<br>70 | 99% | 972/794-2100<br>Fax 972/794-2101 |
| Edwin J Kiest Elem Sch<br>2611 Healey Dr, Dallas 75228<br>Gerardo Hernandez | PK-5 | T | 716<br>39 | 93% | 972/502-5600<br>Fax 972/502-5601 |
| Eladio Martinez Learning Ctr<br>4500 Bernal Dr, Dallas 75212<br>Josefina Murillo | PK-5 | T | 562<br>51 | 99% | 972/794-6900<br>Fax 972/794-6901 |
| Elisha M Pease Elem Sch<br>2914 Cummings St, Dallas 75216<br>Sharri Zachary | PK-5 | T | 517<br>22 | 99% | 214/932-3800<br>Fax 214/932-3801 |
| Emmett J Conrad High Sch<br>7502 Fair Oaks Ave, Dallas 75231<br>Temesghen Asmerom | 9-12 | TV | 1,290 | 82% | 972/502-2300<br>Fax 972/502-2301 |
| Esperanza Medrano Elementary<br>2221 Lucas Dr, Dallas 75219<br>Mario Mondragon | PK-5 | T | 395<br>40 | 96% | 972/794-3300<br>Fax 972/794-3301 |
| Everette Lee Degolyer Elem Sch<br>3453 Flair Dr, Dallas 75229<br>Tara Berry | PK-5 | T | 378<br>24 | 58% | 972/794-2800<br>Fax 972/794-2801 |
| F P Caillet Elem Sch<br>3033 Merrell Rd, Dallas 75229<br>Oscar Nandayapa | PK-5 | T | 592<br>32 | 92% | 972/794-3200<br>Fax 972/794-3201 |
| Felix Botello Elem Sch<br>225 S Marsalis Ave, Dallas 75203<br>Maria Puentemejia | PK-5 | T | 542 | 95% | 972/502-4600<br>Fax 972/502-4601 |
| Francisco Medrano Middle Sch<br>9815 Brockbank Dr, Dallas 75220<br>Theresa Sigurdson | 6-8 | T | 943 | 96% | 972/925-1300<br>Fax 972/925-1301 |
| Frank Guzick Elem Sch<br>5000 Berridge Ln, Dallas 75227<br>Adreana Davis | PK-5 | T | 656 | 96% | 972/502-3900<br>Fax 972/502-3901 |
| Ⓜ Franklin D Roosevelt High Sch<br>525 Bonnie View Rd, Dallas 75203<br>Troy Tyson | 9-12 | GTV | 727 | 94% | 972/925-6800<br>Fax 972/925-6801 |
| Franklin Int'l Exploratory MS<br>6920 Meadow Rd, Dallas 75230<br>Roger Ceballos | 6-8 | T | 1,103<br>60 | 82% | 972/502-7100<br>Fax 972/502-7101 |
| Frederick Douglass Elem Sch<br>226 N Jim Miller Rd, Dallas 75217<br>Tenisha Allen | PK-5 | T | 475<br>20 | 97% | 972/794-1400<br>Fax 972/794-1401 |
| Ⓒ Ⓨ Gabe P Allen Charter Sch<br>5220 Nomas St, Dallas 75212<br>Sheila Espinell | PK-5 | GMT | 471<br>30 | 98% | 972/794-5100<br>Fax 972/794-5101 |
| Geneva Heights Elem Sch<br>2911 Delmar Ave, Dallas 75206<br>Michael Ruiz | PK-5 | T | 402<br>24 | 66% | 972/749-7400<br>Fax 972/749-7401 |
| Ⓜ George B Dealey Mont Intl Acad<br>6501 Royal Ln, Dallas 75230<br>Beth Wing | PK-8 | | 604<br>35 | 25% | 972/794-8400<br>Fax 972/794-8401 |
| George H W Bush Elem Sch<br>3939 Spring Valley Rd, Addison 75001<br>Carol Crowling | PK-5 | T | 695 | 81% | 972/925-1700<br>Fax 972/925-1701 |
| George Peabody Elem Sch<br>3101 Raydell Pl, Dallas 75211<br>Sherri Rogers-Hall | PK-5 | T | 535<br>40 | 97% | 972/794-5200<br>Fax 972/794-5201 |
| George W Truett Elem Sch<br>1811 Gross Rd, Dallas 75228<br>Terre Evans | PK-5 | T | 1,103<br>70 | 98% | 972/749-8000<br>Fax 972/749-8001 |
| Gilbert Cuellar Jr Elem Sch<br>337 Pleasant Vista Dr, Dallas 75217<br>Lonnie Russell | PK-5 | T | 718<br>45 | 94% | 972/749-6400<br>Fax 972/749-6401 |
| H Grady Spruce High Sch<br>9733 Old Seagoville Rd, Dallas 75217<br>Francine Taylor | 9-12 | TV | 1,827<br>120 | 90% | 972/892-5500<br>Fax 972/892-5501 |
| H I Holland ES-Lisbon<br>4203 S Lancaster Rd, Dallas 75216<br>Shanieka McDonald | PK-5 | T | 355<br>30 | 97% | 972/749-1900<br>Fax 972/749-1901 |
| Harold Lang Middle Sch<br>1678 Chenault St, Dallas 75228<br>Kimberly Robinson | 6-8 | T | 870 | 90% | 972/925-2400<br>Fax 972/925-2401 |
| Harrell Budd Elem Sch<br>2121 S Marsalis Ave, Dallas 75216<br>Anita Barnes | PK-5 | T | 487<br>40 | 99% | 972/502-8400<br>Fax 972/502-8401 |
| Harry C Withers Elem Sch<br>3959 Northaven Rd, Dallas 75229<br>Wendy Miller | PK-5 | T | 434<br>27 | 50% | 972/794-5000<br>Fax 972/794-5001 |
| Harry Stone Montessori Academy<br>4747 Veterans Dr, Dallas 75216<br>Niki Jones | PK-8 | T | 638<br>28 | 58% | 972/794-3400<br>Fax 972/794-3401 |
| Hector P Garcia Middle Sch<br>700 E 8th St, Dallas 75203<br>David Lee | 6-8 | T | 781 | 92% | 972/502-5500<br>Fax 972/502-5501 |
| Henry B Gonzales Pla<br>6610 Lake June Rd, Dallas 75217<br>Reymundo Guajardo | PK-5 | T | 545 | 94% | 972/502-3300<br>Fax 972/502-3301 |
| Henry W Longfellow Academy<br>5314 Boaz St, Dallas 75209<br>Lorena Hernandez | 6-8 | TV | 429<br>32 | 77% | 972/749-5400<br>Fax 972/749-5401 |
| Herbert Marcus Elem Sch<br>2911 Northaven Rd, Dallas 75229<br>**Jonatan Romero** | PK-5 | GT | 744<br>45 | 97% | 972/794-2900<br>Fax 972/794-2901 |
| Highland Meadows Elem Sch<br>8939 Whitewing Ln, Dallas 75238<br>Jo'Anna Bahena | PK-5 | T | 702 | 98% | 972/502-5200<br>Fax 972/502-5201 |
| Hillcrest High Sch<br>9924 Hillcrest Rd, Dallas 75230<br>Joseph Sotelo | 9-12 | TV | 1,201<br>80 | 74% | 972/502-6800<br>Fax 972/502-6801 |
| Ignacio Zaragoza Elem Sch<br>4550 Worth St, Dallas 75246<br>Linda Olivarez | PK-5 | GT | 297 | 95% | 972/749-8600<br>Fax 972/749-8601 |
| Ignite Middle Sch<br>2211 Caddo St, Dallas 75204<br>Dr Michael Gayles | 6-8 | T | 160 | 71% | 972/794-7770 |
| Innovation Design Entrep Acad<br>4800 Ross Ave, Dallas 75204<br>Nakimia Hicks | 9-9 | | 207 | 85% | 972/794-6800 |
| J L Long Middle Sch<br>6116 Reiger Ave, Dallas 75214<br>Chandra Barnett | 6-8 | TV | 1,474<br>73 | 65% | 972/502-4700<br>Fax 972/502-4701 |
| J N Ervin Elem Sch<br>3722 Black Oak Dr, Dallas 75241<br>James Wallace | PK-5 | T | 501<br>50 | 100% | 972/749-3700<br>Fax 972/749-3701 |
| Ⓜ J P Starks Mst Vanguard<br>3033 Tips Blvd, Dallas 75216<br>**Lynette Howard** | PK-5 | T | 312<br>28 | 98% | 972/502-8800<br>Fax 972/502-8801 |
| Jack Lowe Sr Elem Sch<br>7000 Holly Hill Dr, Dallas 75231<br>Sandra Barrios | PK-5 | T | 621 | 100% | 972/502-1700<br>Fax 972/502-1701 |
| James Bowie Elem Sch<br>330 N Marsalis Ave, Dallas 75203<br>Caroline Wilson | PK-5 | T | 468<br>70 | 98% | 972/925-6600<br>Fax 972/925-6601 |
| James Madison High Sch<br>3000 Martin L King Blvd, Dallas 75215<br>Marian Willard | 9-12 | GTV | 490<br>50 | 89% | 972/925-2800<br>Fax 972/925-2801 |
| James S Hogg Elem Sch<br>1144 N Madison Ave, Dallas 75208<br>Jairo Casco | PK-5 | T | 271<br>55 | 91% | 972/502-8600<br>Fax 972/502-8601 |

| School | Grades | Programs | Enroll | % | Phone |
|---|---|---|---|---|---|
| Jerry Junkins Elem Sch<br>2808 Running Duke Dr, Carrollton 75006<br>Oscar Spurlock | PK-5 | T | 645 | 76% | 972/502-2400<br>Fax 972/502-2401 |
| Jill Stone-Vickery Meadow ES<br>6606 Ridgecrest Rd, Dallas 75231<br>Rosalinda Pratt | PK-5 | T | 335<br>25 | 99% | 972/502-7900<br>Fax 972/502-7901 |
| Jimmie Tyler Brashear Elem Sch<br>2959 S Hampton Rd, Dallas 75224<br>Sonja Barnes | PK-5 | T | 590 | 84% | 972/502-2600<br>Fax 972/502-2601 |
| John F Peeler Elem Sch<br>810 S Llewellyn Ave, Dallas 75208<br>Janie Carballo | PK-5 | T | 273<br>28 | 92% | 972/502-8300<br>Fax 972/502-8301 |
| John H Reagan Elem Sch<br>201 N Adams Ave, Dallas 75208<br>Ruth Roman | PK-5 | T | 345<br>36 | 95% | 972/502-8200<br>Fax 972/502-8201 |
| John Ireland Elem Sch<br>1515 N Jim Miller Rd, Dallas 75217<br>Stephanie Amaya | PK-5 | T | 495<br>40 | 99% | 972/749-4900<br>Fax 972/749-4901 |
| John J Pershing Elem Sch<br>5715 Meaders Ln, Dallas 75229<br>Dr Lourdes Figueroa | PK-5 | T | 404<br>36 | 93% | 972/794-8600<br>Fax 972/794-8601 |
| Ⓐ John L Patton Academic Center<br>3313 S Beckley Ave, Dallas 75224<br>Marlon Brooks | 9-12 | T | 210 | 78% | 214/932-5160<br>Fax 214/932-5149 |
| John Neely Bryan Elem Sch<br>2001 Deer Path Dr, Dallas 75216<br>Tonya Anderson | PK-5 | T | 391<br>30 | 99% | 972/502-8500<br>Fax 972/502-8501 |
| John Q Adams Elem Sch<br>8239 Lake June Rd, Dallas 75217<br>Maria Reyes | PK-5 | T | 724<br>50 | 97% | 972/794-1200<br>Fax 972/794-1201 |
| John W Carpenter Elem Sch<br>2121 Tosca Ln, Dallas 75224<br>Verna Farmer | PK-5 | T | 273<br>45 | 96% | 972/794-6000<br>Fax 972/794-6001 |
| John W Runyon Elem Sch<br>10750 Cradlerock Dr, Dallas 75217<br>Sherry Williams | PK-5 | T | 553<br>45 | 96% | 972/749-6100<br>Fax 972/749-6101 |
| Jose May Elem Sch<br>9818 Brockbank Dr, Dallas 75220<br>**Rossee Nava** | PK-5 | T | 675 | 98% | 972/749-4800<br>Fax 972/749-4801 |
| Joseph J Rhoads Learning Ctr<br>4401 S 2nd Ave, Dallas 75210<br>Chaundra Macklin | PK-5 | T | 642<br>40 | 98% | 972/749-1000<br>Fax 972/749-1001 |
| Ⓜ Judge Barefoot Sanders Law Mag<br>1201 E 8th St, Dallas 75203<br>Garet Feimster | 9-12 | TV | 409 | 75% | 972/925-5950<br>Fax 972/925-6010 |
| Julian T Saldivar Elem Sch<br>9510 Brockbank Dr, Dallas 75220<br>Edgar Jaramillo | PK-5 | T | 665<br>60 | 99% | 972/794-2000<br>Fax 972/794-2001 |
| Julius Dorsey Elem Sch<br>133 N Saint Augustine Dr, Dallas 75217<br>Rubinna Sanchez | PK-5 | T | 456<br>45 | 96% | 972/749-6300<br>Fax 972/749-6301 |
| Ⓜ Justin F Kimball High Sch<br>3606 S Westmoreland Rd, Dallas 75233<br>Llewellyn Smith | 9-12 | GTV | 1,454 | 79% | 972/502-2100<br>Fax 972/502-2101 |
| Ⓜ K B Polk Elem Sch<br>6911 Victoria Ave, Dallas 75209<br>Kourtnei Billups | PK-5 | T | 409<br>40 | 91% | 972/794-8900<br>Fax 972/794-8901 |
| Kathlyn Joy Gilliam Academy<br>1700 E Camp Wisdom Rd, Dallas 75241<br>Gayle Smith | 9-12 | T | 373 | 79% | 972/925-1400<br>Fax 972/925-1401 |
| Kennedy-Curry Middle Sch<br>6605 Sebring Dr, Dallas 75241<br>Patrice Ruffin-Brown | 6-8 | T | 762<br>28 | 90% | 972/925-1600<br>Fax 214/932-7901 |
| Kleberg Elem Sch<br>1450 Edd Rd, Dallas 75253<br>Amy Zbylut | PK-5 | T | 696<br>46 | 91% | 972/749-6500<br>Fax 972/749-6501 |
| Ⓜ L G Pinkston High Sch<br>2200 Dennison St, Dallas 75212<br>Marlon Brooks | 9-12 | TV | 906<br>70 | 96% | 972/502-2700<br>Fax 972/502-2701 |
| L L Hotchkiss Elem Sch<br>6929 Town North Dr, Dallas 75231<br>Rocio Bernal | PK-5 | T | 721<br>52 | 98% | 972/749-7000<br>Fax 972/749-7001 |
| L O Donald Elem Sch<br>1218 Phinney Ave, Dallas 75211<br>Kathryn Carter | PK-5 | T | 431<br>31 | 92% | 972/794-5300<br>Fax 972/794-5301 |
| L V Stockard Middle Sch<br>2300 S Ravinia Dr, Dallas 75211<br>Heather Holland | 6-8 | TV | 1,137<br>60 | 90% | 972/794-5700<br>Fax 972/794-5701 |
| Lakewood Elem Sch<br>3000 Hillbrook St, Dallas 75214<br>Kate Wilke | K-5 | | 942<br>41 | 7% | 972/749-7300<br>Fax 972/749-7301 |
| Larry G Smith Elem Sch<br>5299 Gus Thomasson Rd, Mesquite 75150<br>Lora Morris | PK-5 | T | 695 | 93% | 972/502-4800<br>Fax 972/502-4801 |
| Lee A McShan Jr Elem Sch<br>8307 Meadow Rd, Dallas 75231<br>Joseph Medaris | PK-5 | T | 715 | 98% | 972/502-3800<br>Fax 972/502-3801 |
| Leila P Cowart Elem Sch<br>1515 S Ravinia Dr, Dallas 75211<br>Lucia Salinas | PK-5 | T | 509<br>55 | 95% | 972/794-5500<br>Fax 972/794-5501 |
| Lenore Kirk Hall Elem Sch<br>2120 Keats Dr, Dallas 75211<br>Olga Romero | PK-5 | T | 506<br>38 | 94% | 972/794-5400<br>Fax 972/794-5401 |
| Leonides G Cigarroa Elem Sch<br>9990 Webb Chapel Rd, Dallas 75220<br>Douglas Burak | PK-5 | T | 534 | 99% | 972/502-2900<br>Fax 972/502-2901 |
| Leslie A Stemmons Elem Sch<br>2727 Knoxville St, Dallas 75211<br>Efrain Tovar | PK-5 | T | 711<br>40 | 90% | 972/794-4900<br>Fax 972/794-4901 |
| Lida Hooe Elem Sch<br>2419 Gladstone Dr, Dallas 75211<br>Fernando Rodriguez | PK-5 | T | 422<br>53 | 90% | 972/794-6700<br>Fax 972/794-6701 |
| Ⓜ Lincoln Humanities/Comm HS<br>2826 Elsie Faye Heggins St, Dallas 75215<br>Johnna Weaver | 9-12 | TV | 645 | 91% | 972/925-7600<br>Fax 972/925-7601 |
| Lorenzo De Zavala Elem Sch<br>3214 N Winnetka Ave, Dallas 75212<br>Melissa Gonzalez | PK-5 | T | 409<br>26 | 99% | 972/892-6400<br>Fax 972/892-6401 |
| Louise Wolff Kahn Elem Sch<br>610 N Franklin St, Dallas 75211<br>Monica Marquez | PK-5 | T | 555<br>41 | 93% | 972/502-1400<br>Fax 972/502-1401 |
| Ⓐ Manns High Middle School Daep<br>3313 S Beckley Ave, Dallas 75224<br>Billy Bratton | 6-8 | | 94<br>10 | 89% | 972/925-7000<br>Fax 972/925-7061 |
| Maple Lawn Elem Sch<br>3120 Inwood Rd, Dallas 75235<br>Oscar Aponte | PK-5 | T | 621<br>42 | 97% | 972/925-2500<br>Fax 972/925-2501 |
| Margaret B Henderson Elem Sch<br>2200 S Edgefield Ave, Dallas 75224<br>Ida Escobedo | PK-5 | T | 456<br>50 | 91% | 972/749-2900<br>Fax 972/749-2901 |
| Maria Moreno Elem Sch<br>2115 S Hampton Rd, Dallas 75224<br>Tammie Brooks | PK-5 | T | 360<br>60 | 95% | 972/502-3100<br>Fax 972/502-3101 |
| Mark Twain Elem Sch<br>724 Green Cove Ln, Dallas 75232<br>Pertricee Traylor | PK-5 | T | 217<br>40 | 97% | 972/749-3000<br>Fax 972/749-3001 |
| Martha Turner Reilly Elem Sch<br>11230 Lippitt Ave, Dallas 75218<br>**Nichole O'Neal** | PK-5 | T | 553<br>75 | 80% | 972/749-7800<br>Fax 972/749-7801 |
| Martin Luther King Jr Lrng Ctr<br>1817 Warren Ave, Dallas 75215<br>Romikianta Sneed | PK-5 | T | 418<br>36 | 100% | 972/502-8100<br>Fax 972/502-8101 |

| | | | | | | |
|---|---|---|---|---|---|---|
| 79 | Student Personnel | 91 | Safety/Security | 275 | Response To Intervention | 298 Grant Writer/Ptnrships |
| 80 | Driver Ed/Safety | 92 | Magnet School | 277 | Remedial Math K-12 | 750 Chief Innovation Officer |
| 81 | Gifted/Talented | 93 | Parental Involvement | 280 | Literacy Coach | 751 Chief of Staff |
| 82 | Video Services | 95 | Tech Prep Program | 285 | STEM | 752 Social Emotional Learning |
| 83 | Substance Abuse Prev | 97 | Chief Infomation Officer | 286 | Digital Learning | |
| 84 | Erate | 98 | Chief Technology Officer | 288 | Common Core Standards | Other School Types |
| 85 | AIDS Education | 270 | Character Education | 294 | Accountability | Ⓐ = Alternative School |
| 88 | Alternative/At Risk | 271 | Migrant Education | 295 | Network System | Ⓒ = Charter School |
| 89 | Multi-Cultural Curriculum | 273 | Teacher Mentor | 296 | Title II Programs | Ⓜ = Magnet School |
| 90 | Social Work | 274 | Before/After Sch | 297 | Webmaster | Ⓨ = Year-Round School |

**School Programs**
A = Alternative Program
G = Adult Classes
M = Magnet Program
T = Title I Schoolwide
V = Career & Tech Ed Programs

**Social Media**
 = Facebook
 = Twitter

New Schools are shaded
New Superintendents and Principals are bold
Personnel with email addresses are underscored

| School | Grades | Tech | Enroll | % | Phone |
|---|---|---|---|---|---|
| Martin Weiss Elem Sch<br>8601 Willoughby Blvd, Dallas 75232<br>Lakisha Merritt | PK-5 | T | 509<br>35 | 99% | 972/749-4000<br>Fax 972/749-4001 |
| Mary McLeod Bethune Elem Sch<br>1665 Duncanville Rd, Dallas 75211<br>Teresa Hernandez | PK-5 | T | 706<br>90 | 87% | 972/502-1300<br>Fax 972/502-1301 |
| Ⓐ Maya Angelou High Sch<br>3313 S Beckley Ave, Dallas 75224<br>Billy Bratton | 6-12 | V | 24<br>13 | | 972/925-7000<br>Fax 972/925-2201 |
| Mockingbird Elem Sch<br>5828 E Mockingbird Ln, Dallas 75206<br>Melanie Mans | K-5 | | 670<br>40 | 22% | 972/749-7200<br>Fax 972/749-7201 |
| Moises E Molina High Sch<br>2355 Duncanville Rd, Dallas 75211<br>Terry-Ann Rodriguez | 9-12 | T | 2,254<br>83 | 87% | 972/502-1000<br>Fax 972/502-1001 |
| Montessori Acad Hernandez ES<br>5555 Maple Ave, Dallas 75235<br>Lisa Vega | PK-3 | | 322<br>40 | 76% | 972/925-2700<br>Fax 972/925-2701 |
| Mt Auburn Steam Academy<br>6012 E Grand Ave, Dallas 75223<br>Brittany Swanson | PK-4 | T | 710<br>39 | 94% | 972/749-8500<br>Fax 972/749-8501 |
| Multiple Careers Magnet Center<br>4528 Rusk Ave, Dallas 75204<br>Lynn Smith | Spec | AV | 115<br>5 | | 972/925-2200<br>Fax 972/925-2201 |
| N W Harllee Early Chldhd Ctr<br>1216 E 8th St, Dallas 75203<br>Amber Shields | PK-2 | T | 220 | 92% | 972/925-6500<br>Fax 972/925-6501 |
| Nancy J Cochran Elem Sch<br>6000 Keeneland Pkwy, Dallas 75211<br>Jamila Steen | PK-5 | T | 438<br>20 | 97% | 972/794-4600<br>Fax 972/794-4601 |
| Nancy Moseley Elem Sch<br>10400 Rylie Rd, Dallas 75217<br>Carmen Derrick | PK-5 | T | 752<br>40 | 94% | 972/749-6700<br>Fax 972/749-6701 |
| Nathan Adams Elem Sch<br>12600 Welch Rd, Dallas 75244<br>Adrian Luna | PK-5 | T | 477<br>31 | 91% | 972/794-2600<br>Fax 972/794-2601 |
| Nathaniel Hawthorne Elem Sch<br>7800 Umphress Rd, Dallas 75217<br>Ana Fernandez | PK-5 | T | 420<br>57 | 95% | 972/749-4700<br>Fax 972/749-4701 |
| New Tech HS at BF Darrell<br>4730 S Lancaster Rd, Dallas 75216<br>Jameile Choice | 9-12 | TV | 271<br>70 | 92% | 214/932-7600<br>Fax 214/932-7601 |
| North Dallas High Sch<br>3120 N Haskell Ave, Dallas 75204<br>Katherine Wanserski-Eska | 9-12 | TV | 1,060<br>100 | 91% | 972/925-1500<br>Fax 972/925-1501 |
| North Lake Early Clg High Sch<br>1081 W Shady Grove Rd, Irving 75060<br>**Tristan Lysowski** | 9-9 | | 85 | | 972/502-7803 |
| Obadiah Knight Elem Sch<br>2615 Anson Rd, Dallas 75235<br>Blanca Rojo | PK-5 | GT | 459<br>42 | 92% | 972/749-5300<br>Fax 972/749-5301 |
| Oliver W Holmes Academy<br>2001 E Kiest Blvd, Dallas 75216<br>Sharron Jackson | 6-8 | TV | 715 | 99% | 972/925-8500<br>Fax 972/925-8501 |
| Oran M Roberts Elem Sch<br>4919 E Grand Ave, Dallas 75223<br>Kimberly Seymore | PK-5 | T | 565<br>25 | 94% | 972/749-8700<br>Fax 972/749-8701 |
| Paul L Dunbar Learning Center<br>4200 Metropolitan Ave, Dallas 75210<br>Alpher Garrett-Jones | PK-5 | T | 487 | 98% | 972/794-6600<br>Fax 972/794-6601 |
| Personalized Lrng Prep Houston<br>2827 Throckmorton St, Dallas 75219<br>Raymie Venable | PK-5 | T | 203<br>30 | 80% | 972/749-5800<br>Fax 972/749-5801 |
| Piedmont Global Academy<br>7625 Hume Dr, Dallas 75227<br>Letrice Portley | 6-8 | TV | 1,028<br>90 | 93% | 972/749-4100<br>Fax 972/749-4101 |
| Pleasant Grove Elem Sch<br>1614 N Saint Augustine Dr, Dallas 75217<br>Anabel Ruiz | PK-5 | T | 536<br>50 | 97% | 972/892-5000<br>Fax 972/892-5001 |
| Preston Hollow Elem Sch<br>6423 Walnut Hill Ln, Dallas 75230<br>Vincent Garcia | PK-5 | T | 449<br>22 | 84% | 972/794-8500<br>Fax 972/794-8501 |
| Ⓦ R M Sorrells Sch-Ed & Soc Srvs<br>1201 E 8th St Ste 111, Dallas 75203<br>Shelia Brown | 9-12 | TV | 306<br>9 | 71% | 972/925-5940<br>Fax 972/925-6004 |
| Ⓦ Rangel Women's Leadership Sch<br>1718 Robert B Cullum Blvd, Dallas 75210<br>Beverly Lusk | 6-12 | T | 269 | 71% | 972/749-5200<br>Fax 972/502-5201 |
| Raul Quintanilla Middle Sch<br>2700 Remond Dr, Dallas 75211<br>**Tameca Ward** | 6-8 | T | 691<br>70 | 94% | 972/502-3200<br>Fax 972/502-3201 |
| Reinhardt Elem Sch<br>10122 Losa Dr, Dallas 75218<br>Phoebe Montgomery | PK-5 | T | 515<br>36 | 88% | 972/749-7900<br>Fax 972/749 7901 |
| Richard Lagow Elem Sch<br>637 Edgeworth Dr, Dallas 75217<br>Jospeh Luedecke | PK-5 | T | 538<br>35 | 93% | 972/749-6600<br>Fax 972/749-6601 |
| Robert L Thornton Elem Sch<br>6011 Old Ox Rd, Dallas 75241<br>Christofor Stephens | PK-5 | T | 298<br>38 | 95% | 972/794-8000<br>Fax 972/794-8001 |
| Robert T Hill Middle Sch<br>505 Easton Rd, Dallas 75218<br>Candice Ruiz | 6-8 | TV | 862<br>50 | 88% | 972/502-5700<br>Fax 972/502-5701 |
| Ronald E McNair Elem Sch<br>3150 Bainbridge Ave, Dallas 75237<br>**Demetria Bell-Ellis** | PK-5 | T | 600<br>38 | 98% | 972/794-6200<br>Fax 972/794-6201 |
| Rosemont Elem & Prep Lang MS<br>719 N Montclair Ave, Dallas 75208<br>Marco Barker | 3-8 | T | 671<br>40 | 79% | 972/749-5000<br>Fax 972/749-5001 |
| Rosemont Primary Sch<br>1919 Stevens Forest Dr, Dallas 75208<br>Marco Barker | PK-2 | T | 540<br>32 | 65% | 972/502-3850<br>Fax 972/502-3851 |
| Rufus C Burleson Elem Sch<br>6300 Elam Rd, Dallas 75217<br>Lajoyce Johnson | PK-5 | T | 619<br>45 | 99% | 972/749-4500<br>Fax 972/749-4501 |
| S S Conner Elem Sch<br>3037 Green Meadow Dr, Dallas 75228<br>Kiashan King-Corbett | PK-5 | T | 586<br>38 | 98% | 972/749-8200<br>Fax 972/749-8201 |
| Sam Tasby Middle Sch<br>7001 Fair Oaks Ave, Dallas 75231<br>Audrey Delacruz | 6-8 | T | 919 | 98% | 972/502-1900<br>Fax 972/502-1901 |
| San Jacinto Elem Sch<br>7900 Hume Dr, Dallas 75227<br>Celia Sanchez | PK-5 | T | 470<br>50 | 98% | 972/749-4200<br>Fax 972/749-4201 |
| Sarah Zumwalt Middle Sch<br>2245 E Ledbetter Dr, Dallas 75216<br>**Bobby Nevels** | 6-8 | TV | 396<br>50 | 99% | 972/749-3600<br>Fax 972/749-3601 |
| Ⓦ Sch Health Prof-Townview Ctr<br>1201 E 8th St, Dallas 75203<br>Lasandra Sanders | 9-12 | TV | 549<br>30 | 74% | 972/925-5930<br>Fax 972/925-6007 |
| School for Talented & Gifted<br>9610 Bruton Rd, Dallas 75217<br>Ruby Ramirez | 4-7 | T | 300 | 86% | 972/794-1800<br>Fax 214/932-7521 |
| Seagoville Elem Sch<br>304 N Kaufman St, Seagoville 75159<br>Katrina Gibson | PK-5 | T | 624<br>45 | 89% | 972/892-7900<br>Fax 972/892-7901 ⓕⓔ |
| Ⓦ Seagoville High Sch<br>15920 Seagoville Rd, Dallas 75253<br>Angela West | 9-12 | ATV | 1,514<br>60 | 86% | 972/892-5900<br>Fax 972/892-5901 |
| Seagoville Middle Sch<br>950 N Woody Rd, Dallas 75253<br>Jesus Martinez | 6-8 | TV | 1,380<br>50 | 91% | 972/892-7100<br>Fax 972/892-7146 |

| School | Grades | Pgm | Enroll | % | Phone / Fax |
|---|---|---|---|---|---|
| Seagoville North Elem Sch<br>1906 Seagoville Rd, Seagoville 75159<br>Rocio Gardea | PK-5 | T | 775 | 91% | 972/892-5300 |
| Sidney Lanier Expressive Arts<br>1400 Walmsley Ave, Dallas 75208<br>Alyssa Peraza | PK-5 | T | 567<br>60 | 80% | 972/794-4400<br>Fax 972/794-4401 |
| Ⓜ Skyline High Sch<br>7777 Forney Rd, Dallas 75227<br>Dwain Simmons | 9-12 | TV | 4,229 | 75% | 972/502-3400<br>Fax 972/502-3401 |
| Solar Prep Sch for Girls-Bonhm<br>2617 N Henderson Ave, Dallas 75206<br>Nancy Bernardino | K-2 | T | 194 | 50% | 972/749-4300 |
| Solar Preparatory for Boys<br>1802 Moser Ave, Dallas 75206<br>Adriana Gonzalez | PK-2 | T | 220 | 50% | 972/794-7100 |
| South Oak Cliff High Sch<br>3601 S Marsalis Ave, Dallas 75216<br>Dr Willie Johnson | 9-12 | TV | 1,073 | 95% | 214/932-7000<br>Fax 214/932-7001 |
| Stephen C Foster Elem Sch<br>3700 Clover Ln, Dallas 75220<br>Irma Delaguardia | PK-5 | T | 595<br>54 | 93% | 972/794-8100<br>Fax 972/794-8101 |
| Stevens Park Elem Sch<br>2615 W Colorado Blvd, Dallas 75211<br>Roberto Gonzalez | PK-5 | T | 657<br>50 | 99% | 972/794-4200<br>Fax 972/794-4201 |
| Sudie Williams Tag Acad<br>4518 Pomona Rd, Dallas 75209<br>Michael Jackson | PK-5 | T | 215<br>19 | 38% | 972/794-8700<br>Fax 972/794-8701 |
| Sunset High Sch<br>2120 W Jefferson Blvd, Dallas 75208<br>Claudia Vega | 9-12 | TV | 2,026 | 79% | 972/502-1500<br>Fax 972/502-1501 |
| T G Terry Elem Sch<br>6661 Greenspan Ave, Dallas 75232<br>Alicia Bradley | PK-5 | T | 390<br>45 | 96% | 972/749-3200<br>Fax 972/749-3201 |
| T W Browne Middle Sch<br>3333 Sprague Dr, Dallas 75233<br>Lakisha Thomas | 6-8 | TV | 571<br>75 | 97% | 972/502-2500<br>Fax 972/502-2501 |
| Thelma E Page-Richardson ES<br>7203 Bruton Rd, Dallas 75217<br>Courtney Loy | PK-5 | T | 693 | 95% | 972/892-8100 |
| Thomas C Marsh Prep Academy<br>3838 Crown Shore Dr, Dallas 75244<br>Martha Bujanda | 6-8 | TV | 963<br>60 | 90% | 972/502-6600<br>Fax 972/502-6601 |
| Thomas J Rusk Middle Sch<br>2929 Inwood Rd, Dallas 75235<br>**Jennifer Scott \ Gabriel Hernandez \ Marina Guerra** | 6-8 | TV | 648<br>42 | 97% | 972/925-2000<br>Fax 972/925-2001 |
| Thomas Jefferson High Sch<br>2940 Singleton Blvd, Dallas 75212<br>Sandi Massey | 9-12 | V | 1,723<br>60 | | 972/502-7300<br>Fax 972/502-7301 |
| Thomas L Marsalis Elem Sch<br>5640 S Marsalis Ave, Dallas 75241<br>Kimberly Richardson | PK-5 | T | 421<br>37 | 91% | 972/749-3500<br>Fax 972/749-3501 |
| Thomas Tolbert Elem Sch<br>4000 Blue Ridge Blvd, Dallas 75233<br>Lakeisha Smith | PK-5 | T | 485<br>50 | 97% | 972/794-5900<br>Fax 972/794-5901 |
| Tom C Gooch Elem Sch<br>4030 Calculus Dr, Dallas 75244<br>Kermange Johnson | PK-5 | T | 433<br>19 | 91% | 972/794-2500<br>Fax 972/794-2501 |
| Tom W Field Elem Sch<br>2151 Royal Ln, Dallas 75229<br>Selena Deboskie | PK-5 | T | 203<br>37 | 94% | 972/794-2700<br>Fax 972/794-2701 |
| Ⓜ Townview Mag HS-Bus & Mngmnt<br>1201 E 8th St Ste 241, Dallas 75203<br>Israel Rivera | 9-12 | TV | 505<br>15 | 69% | 972/925-5920<br>Fax 972/925-6001 |
| Ⓜ Townview Mag HS-Sci & Eng<br>1201 E 8th St, Dallas 75203<br>Andrew Palacios | 9-12 | TV | 428 | 53% | 972/925-5960<br>Fax 972/925-6016 |
| Ⓜ Townview Mag HS-Talent & Gift<br>1201 E 8th St Ste 302, Dallas 75203<br>Arnoldo Zuniga | 9-12 | T | 359<br>16 | 35% | 972/925-5970<br>Fax 972/925-6018 |
| Trinidad Garza Early College<br>4849 W Illinois Ave W53A, Dallas 75211<br>Macario Hernandez | 9-12 | T | 438 | 87% | 214/860-3680<br>Fax 214/860-3689 |
| Trinity Hts Gifted & Talented<br>1515 Lynn Haven Ave, Dallas 75216<br>Marquetta Masters | K-6 | | 300 | | 972/925-7500 |
| Umphrey Lee Elem Sch<br>7808 Racine Dr, Dallas 75232<br>Stephanie McCloud | PK-5 | T | 483<br>32 | 98% | 972/749-3900<br>Fax 972/749-3901 |
| Urban Park Elem Sch<br>6901 Military Pkwy, Dallas 75227<br>Lisa Falcon | PK-5 | T | 607<br>52 | 97% | 972/794-1100<br>Fax 972/794-1101 |
| Victor H Hexter Elem Sch<br>9720 Waterview Rd, Dallas 75218<br>Dr Jennifer Jackson | PK-5 | T | 557<br>28 | 52% | 972/502-5800<br>Fax 972/502-5801 |
| Ⓐ Village Fair-Elem Daep<br>3313 S Beckley Ave, Dallas 75224<br>Billy Bratton | K-6 | | 4<br>10 | 91% | 972/925-7000<br>Fax 214/932-5161 |
| W A Blair Elem Sch<br>7720 Gayglen Dr, Dallas 75217<br>Umoja Turner | PK-5 | T | 590<br>35 | 96% | 972/794-1600<br>Fax 972/794-1601 |
| Ⓜ W B Travis Vanguard & Academy<br>3001 McKinney Ave, Dallas 75204<br>Tom Brandt | 4-8 | | 521<br>32 | 16% | 972/794-7500<br>Fax 972/794-7501 |
| W E Greiner Explor Arts Acad<br>501 S Edgefield Ave, Dallas 75208<br>Yvonne Rojas | 6-8 | TV | 1,796 | 77% | 972/925-7100<br>Fax 972/925-7101 |
| W H Adamson High Sch<br>309 E 9th St, Dallas 75203<br>Diana Nunez | 9-12 | TV | 1,620<br>60 | 94% | 972/749-1400<br>Fax 972/749-1401 |
| W H Gaston Middle Sch<br>9565 Mercer Dr, Dallas 75228<br>Janeen Whitmore | 6-8 | TV | 939<br>62 | 93% | 972/502-5400<br>Fax 972/502-5401 |
| W T White High Sch<br>4505 Ridgeside Dr, Dallas 75244<br>Elena Luna-Bates | 9-12 | TV | 2,207 | 70% | 972/502-6200<br>Fax 972/502-6201 |
| W W Bushman Elem Sch<br>4200 Bonnie View Rd, Dallas 75216<br>Yolanda Knight | PK-5 | T | 423<br>30 | 100% | 972/749-1800<br>Fax 972/749-1801 |
| W W Samuell High Sch<br>8928 Palisade Dr, Dallas 75217<br>Jennifer Tecklenburg | 9-12 | TV | 1,942<br>108 | 92% | 972/892-5100<br>Fax 972/892-5101 |
| Walnut Hill Elem Sch<br>10115 Midway Rd, Dallas 75229<br>Phillip Potter | PK-5 | T | 377<br>25 | 75% | 972/502-7800<br>Fax 972/502-7801 |
| Whitney M Young Jr Elem Sch<br>4601 Veterans Dr, Dallas 75216<br>Shabranda Mathis | PK-5 | T | 397<br>35 | 100% | 972/749-2000<br>Fax 972/749-2001 |
| William Anderson Elem Sch<br>620 N Saint Augustine Dr, Dallas 75217<br>Silvia Garcia | PK-5 | T | 678<br>45 | 98% | 972/749-6200<br>Fax 972/749-6201 |
| William B Miller Elem Sch<br>3111 Bonnie View Rd, Dallas 75216<br>**Chinqua Varner-Busby** | PK-5 | T | 292<br>22 | 98% | 972/502-8700<br>Fax 972/502-8701 |
| William H Atwell Law Academy<br>1303 Reynoldston Ln, Dallas 75232<br>Shondula Whitfield | 6-8 | TV | 785 | 99% | 972/794-6400<br>Fax 972/794-6401 |
| William Lipscomb Elem Sch<br>5801 Worth St, Dallas 75214<br>Michael Sandoval | PK-5 | T | 451<br>27 | 83% | 972/794-7300<br>Fax 972/794-7301 |
| Wilmer Early Chldhd Center<br>211 Walnut St, Wilmer 75172<br>Dr Sharonda Pruitt | PK-PK | | 73 | | 469/660-7296<br>Fax 214/932-7531 |

---

| 79 Student Personnel | 91 Safety/Security | 275 Response To Intervention | 298 Grant Writer/Ptnrships | **School Programs** | **Social Media** |
|---|---|---|---|---|---|
| 80 Driver Ed/Safety | 92 Magnet School | 277 Remedial Math K-12 | 750 Chief Innovation Officer | A = Alternative Program | |
| 81 Gifted/Talented | 93 Parental Involvement | 280 Literacy Coach | 751 Chief of Staff | G = Adult Classes | 🅵 = Facebook |
| 82 Video Services | 95 Tech Prep Program | 285 STEM | 752 Social Emotional Learning | M = Magnet Program | |
| 83 Substance Abuse Prev | 97 Chief Information Officer | 286 Digital Learning | | T = Title I Schoolwide | 🆃 = Twitter |
| 84 Erate | 98 Chief Technology Officer | 288 Common Core Standards | **Other School Types** | V = Career & Tech Ed Programs | |
| 85 AIDS Education | 270 Character Education | 294 Accountability | Ⓐ = Alternative School | | |
| 88 Alternative/At Risk | 271 Migrant Education | 295 Network System | Ⓒ = Charter School | **New Schools are shaded** | |
| 89 Multi-Cultural Curriculum | 273 Teacher Mentor | 296 Title II Programs | Ⓜ = Magnet School | **New Superintendents and Principals are bold** | |
| 90 Social Work | 274 Before/After Sch | 297 Webmaster | Ⓨ = Year-Round School | Personnel with email addresses are underscored | |

| | | | | | |
|---|---|---|---|---|---|
| Wilmer-Hutchins Elem Sch<br>7475 J J Lemmon Rd, Dallas 75241<br>**Samantha White** | PK-5 | T | 954 | 93% | 972/925-2600<br>Fax 972/925-2601 🇫 🇹 |
| Wilmer-Hutchins High Sch<br>5520 Langdon Rd, Dallas 75241<br>Jasen Campbell | 9-12 | T | 914 | 74% | 972/925-2900<br>Fax 972/925-2901 |
| Winnetka Elem Sch<br>1151 S Edgefield Ave, Dallas 75208<br>Lourdes Garduno | PK-5 | T | 884<br>54 | 93% | 972/749-5100<br>Fax 972/749-5101 |
| Woodrow Wilson High Sch<br>100 S Glasgow Dr, Dallas 75214<br>Michael Moran | 9-12 | TV | 1,951<br>80 | 47% | 972/502-4400<br>Fax 972/502-4401 |
| Young Mens Ldrshp Acad-Flornce<br>1625 N Masters Dr, Dallas 75217<br>Dr Christopher Barksdale | 6-8 | TV | 870<br>100 | 88% | 972/749-6000<br>Fax 972/749-6001 |
| Young Women Steam Acad-Blch Sp<br>710 Cheyenne Rd, Dallas 75217<br>Gabrelle Dickson | 6-8 | V | 1,199 | | 972/892-5800<br>Fax 972/892-5801 |
| Zan Wesley Holmes Jr Mid Sch<br>2939 Saint Rita Dr, Dallas 75233<br>Tangela Carter | 6-8 | T | 855 | 93% | 214/932-7800<br>Fax 214/932-7801 |

---

● **DeSoto Ind School Dist** PID: 01010242          972/223-6666
200 E Belt Line Rd, Desoto 75115                Fax 972/274-8968

**Schools:** 14 \ **Teachers:** 669 \ **Students:** 9,872 \ **Special Ed Students:** 876
\ **LEP Students:** 608 \ **Ethnic:** African American 77%, Hispanic 20%,
Caucasian 2% \ **Exp:** $334 (High) \ **Poverty:** 17% \ **Title I:** $2,831,020 \
**Special Education:** $1,291,000 \ **Open-Close:** 08/17 - 05/28 \ **DTBP:** $182
(High) \ 🇫

| | | | |
|---|---|---|---|
| Dandre Weaver | 1 | Bobby LaBorde | 2,15 |
| David Scott | 2 | William Wooten | 2 |
| Don Lester | 3 | Larry Davis | 6,35 |
| Rhonda Dalfonso | 7 | Dr Michelle Howard-Schwind | 8,15 |
| Dr Gabrielle Lemonier | 15 | Levatta Levels | 15,79 |
| Mia Stroy | 15,68 | Roberto Torres | 16,73,76,286,295 |
| Nicholas Johnson | 27,285 | Dr Akweta Hickman | 58,77 |
| Karen Daniel | 67 | Dr Darryl Cob | 68,78 |
| Kathy Ferrell | 69,294 | Tiffanie Blackman Jones | 71 |
| Darrell Baty | 73 | Buddy Watson | 295,297 |

| Public Schs..Principal | Grd | Prgm | Enr/#Cls | SN | |
|---|---|---|---|---|---|
| Amber Terrace Discovery ECC<br>224 Amber Ln, Desoto 75115<br>Keishla Coleman | PK-PK | T | 448<br>38 | 99% | 972/223-8757<br>Fax 972/274-8247 🇫 |
| Cockrell Hill Elem Sch<br>425 S Cockrell Hill Rd, Desoto 75115<br>Angela Robinson | K-5 | T | 587<br>25 | 74% | 972/230-1692<br>Fax 972/274-8081 |
| Ⓐ DeSoto Alt Sch<br>204 E Belt Line Rd, Desoto 75115<br>Homer Webb | K-12 | T | 121<br>11 | 73% | 972/223-2242<br>Fax 972/230-1735 |
| DeSoto High Sch<br>600 Eagle Dr, Desoto 75115<br>Shon Joseph | 9-12 | T | 3,102<br>127 | 67% | 972/230-0726<br>Fax 972/274-8115 |
| East Middle Sch<br>601 E Belt Line Rd, Desoto 75115<br>Deidre Hannible | 6-8 | T | 357<br>48 | 85% | 972/223-0690<br>Fax 972/274-8156 |
| Frank D Moates Elem Sch<br>1500 Heritage Blvd, Glenn Heights 75154<br>Alexandra Barton | K-5 | T | 482<br>50 | 83% | 972/230-2881<br>Fax 972/274-8073 |
| Ⓜ Katherine Johnson Tech Mag Sch<br>1200 Academy Way, Desoto 75115<br>Angela Batiste | K-5 | T | 544 | 80% | 972/274-8026 |
| McCowan Middle Sch<br>1500 Majestic Meadows Dr, Glenn Heights 75154<br>Kelli McWashington | 6-8 | T | 962 | 73% | 972/274-8090<br>Fax 972/274-8099 |

---

| | | | | | |
|---|---|---|---|---|---|
| Meadows Elem Sch<br>1016 the Meadows Pkwy, Desoto 75115<br>Leon Darden | K-5 | T | 434<br>38 | 88% | 972/224-0960<br>Fax 972/228-7908 |
| Northside Elem Sch<br>525 Ray Ave, Desoto 75115<br>Lori Mathis | K-5 | T | 392<br>24 | 81% | 972/224-6709<br>Fax 972/228-7925 🇫 |
| Ruby Young Elem Sch<br>707 N Young Blvd, Desoto 75115<br>Shanta Duren | K-5 | T | 425<br>24 | 73% | 972/223-6505<br>Fax 972/274-8221 🇫 |
| West Middle Sch<br>800 N Westmoreland Rd, Desoto 75115<br>Shana Hawthorne | 6-8 | T | 721<br>40 | 69% | 972/230-1820<br>Fax 972/274-8058 |
| Ⓐ Wings<br>210 E Belt Line Rd, Desoto 75115<br>Reginald Lewis | 9-12 | T | 31 | 53% | 972/274-8219 |
| Woodridge Elem Sch<br>1001 Woodridge Dr, Desoto 75115<br>Tarsha Lunkin | K-5 | T | 563<br>23 | 75% | 972/223-3800<br>Fax 972/274-8204 |

---

● **Duncanville Ind School Dist** PID: 01010292     972/708-2000
710 S Cedar Ridge Dr, Duncanville 75137          Fax 972/708-2020

**Schools:** 19 \ **Teachers:** 801 \ **Students:** 12,250 \
**Special Ed Students:** 1,157 \ **LEP Students:** 2,266 \ **Ethnic:** Asian 1%,
African American 40%, Hispanic 55%, Caucasian 3% \ **Exp:** $482 (High)
\ **Poverty:** 18% \ **Title I:** $3,880,551 \ **Special Education:** $2,314,000 \
**Open-Close:** 09/08 - 06/03 \ **DTBP:** $186 (High) \ 🇫 🇹

| | | | |
|---|---|---|---|
| Dr Marc Smith | 1 | Christi Courson | 2 |
| Dr Ed Bigbee | 2,19 | Joe Peterka | 3 |
| Donna Thomas | 4 | Brad Hamrick | 5 |
| Dwight Weaver | 6,35 | Eva Navarro | 7,85* |
| Cathy Sewell | 8,18 | Devin Hanes | 8 |
| Maria Zimora | 11 | Dr Karin Holacka | 15,79 |
| Kathleen Brown | 15,68 | Melissa Kates | 15,751 |
| Leslie Shimomura | 16 | Shawntee Cowan | 16,73,82,95,98,295 |
| Shalontae Payne | 27,31* | Erika Reyas | 34,296 |
| MacKenzie Casall | 36,58,77 | Ashley Evans | 41 |
| Rosey Sandoval | 57 | Cassandra Phillips | 67 |
| Alexis McClendon | 68 | Dr Samuel Nix | 69,270,286,288 |
| Tiara Richard | 71 | Sherri Smith | 74 |
| Melinda Turner | 76 | Julie Hargrove | 79 |
| Dr Norbert Whitaker | 79,93,271 | Nneka Bernard | 81* |
| Tijuana Hudson | 88* | Chavela Hampton | 91 |
| Kimberly Bauer | 297 | | |

| Public Schs..Principal | Grd | Prgm | Enr/#Cls | SN | |
|---|---|---|---|---|---|
| Acton Elem Sch<br>7095 W Wheatland Rd, Dallas 75249<br>**Jessica Linwood** | PK-4 | T | 543<br>22 | 85% | 972/708-2400<br>Fax 972/708-2424 🇫 🇹 |
| Alexander Elem Sch<br>510 Softwood Dr, Duncanville 75137<br>Erin Frye | PK-4 | T | 417<br>50 | 82% | 972/708-2500<br>Fax 972/708-2525 |
| Brandenburg Intermediate Sch<br>1903 Blueridge Dr, Duncanville 75137<br>Tamra Thompson | 5-6 | T | 473<br>43 | 80% | 972/708-3100<br>Fax 972/708-3131 🇫 🇹 |
| Byrd Middle Sch<br>1040 W Wheatland Rd, Duncanville 75116<br>Kendria Davis-Martin | 7-8 | T | 719<br>45 | 79% | 972/708-3400<br>Fax 972/708-3434 |
| C J & Anne Hyman Elem Sch<br>8441 Fox Creek Trl, Dallas 75249<br>Derrick Ross | PK-4 | T | 433<br>25 | 71% | 972/708-6700<br>Fax 972/708-6767 |
| Central Elem Sch<br>302 E Freeman St, Duncanville 75116<br>Ayanna Parker | PK-4 | T | 413<br>25 | 86% | 972/708-2600<br>Fax 972/708-2626 🇫 🇹 |
| Daniel Intermediate Sch<br>1007 Springwood Ln, Duncanville 75137<br>**Terrence Chase** | 5-6 | T | 628<br>28 | 82% | 972/708-3200<br>Fax 972/708-3232 |

---

| | | | | | | | |
|---|---|---|---|---|---|---|---|
| 1 | Superintendent | 8 | Curric/Instruct K-12 | 19 | Chief Financial Officer | 29 | Family/Consumer Science |
| 2 | Bus/Finance/Purchasing | 9 | Curric/Instruct Elem | 20 | Art K-12 | 30 | Adult Education |
| 3 | Buildings And Grounds | 10 | Curric/Instruct Sec | 21 | Art Elem | 31 | Career/Sch-to-Work K-12 |
| 4 | Food Service | 11 | Federal Program | 22 | Art Sec | 32 | Career/Sch-to-Work Elem |
| 5 | Transportation | 12 | Title I | 23 | Music K-12 | 33 | Career/Sch-to-Work Sec |
| 6 | Athletic | 13 | Title V | 24 | Music Elem | 34 | Early Childhood Ed |
| 7 | Health Services | 15 | Asst Superintendent | 25 | Music Sec | 35 | Health/Phys Education |
| | | 16 | Instructional Media Svcs | 26 | Business Education | 36 | Guidance Services K-12 |
| | | 17 | Chief Operations Officer | 27 | Career & Tech Ed | 37 | Guidance Services Elem |
| | | 18 | Chief Academic Officer | 28 | Technology Education | 38 | Guidance Services Sec |

| | | | | | | | |
|---|---|---|---|---|---|---|---|
| 39 | Social Studies K-12 | 49 | English/Lang Arts Elem | 59 | Special Education Elem | 69 | Academic Assessment |
| 40 | Social Studies Elem | 50 | English/Lang Arts Sec | 60 | Special Education Sec | 70 | Research/Development |
| 41 | Social Studies Sec | 51 | Reading K-12 | 61 | Foreign/World Lang K-12 | 71 | Public Information |
| 42 | Science K-12 | 52 | Reading Elem | 62 | Foreign/World Lang Elem | 72 | Summer School |
| 43 | Science Elem | 53 | Reading Sec | 63 | Foreign/World Lang Sec | 73 | Instructional Tech |
| 44 | Science Sec | 54 | Remedial Reading K-12 | 64 | Religious Education K-12 | 74 | Inservice Training |
| 45 | Math K-12 | 55 | Remedial Reading Elem | 65 | Religious Education Elem | 75 | Marketing/Distributive |
| 46 | Math Elem | 56 | Remedial Reading Sec | 66 | Religious Education Sec | 76 | Info Systems |
| 47 | Math Sec | 57 | Bilingual/ELL | 67 | School Board President | 77 | Psychological Assess |
| 48 | English/Lang Arts K-12 | 58 | Special Education K-12 | 68 | Teacher Personnel | 78 | Affirmative Action |

| | | | | | | |
|---|---|---|---|---|---|---|
| Duncanville High Sch | 9-12 | TV | 4,346 | 71% | 972/708-3700 | |
| 900 W Camp Wisdom Rd, Duncanville 75116 | | | | | Fax 972/708-3737 | |
| Michael McDonald \ **Napoleon Leiva** | | | | | | |
| Duncanville HS Collegiate Acad | 9-12 | | 210 | | 972/708-3885 | |
| 900 W Camp Wisdom Rd, Duncanville 75116 | | | | | Fax 972/708-3737 | |
| Pamela Thomas | | | | | | |
| Fairmeadows Elem Sch | PK-4 | T | 445 | 86% | 972/708-2700 | |
| 101 E Fairmeadows Dr, Duncanville 75116 | | | 26 | | Fax 972/708-2727 | |
| Sugey Villarreal | | | | | | 🇫 🇹 |
| G W Kennemer Middle Sch | 7-8 | T | 723 | 75% | 972/708-3600 | |
| 7101 W Wheatland Rd, Dallas 75249 | | | 60 | | Fax 972/708-3636 | |
| **Tambia Wesco** | | | | | | |
| Hardin Intermediate Sch | 5-6 | T | 632 | 87% | 972/708-3300 | |
| 426 E Freeman St, Duncanville 75116 | | | 30 | | Fax 972/708-3333 | |
| Melanie Lewis | | | | | | |
| Hastings Elem Sch | PK-4 | T | 587 | 89% | 972/708-2800 | |
| 602 W Center St, Duncanville 75116 | | | 28 | | Fax 972/708-2828 | |
| Wendy Simpson | | | | | | 🇫 🇹 |
| James Bilhartz Jr Elem Sch | PK-4 | T | 580 | 80% | 972/708-6600 | |
| 6700 Wandt Dr, Dallas 75236 | | | | | Fax 972/708-6666 | |
| Valerie Nelms-Harris | | | | | | 🇫 🇹 |
| Ⓐ Mary E Smithey Pace High Sch | 9-12 | T | 86 | 74% | 972/708-2470 | |
| 502 E Freeman St, Duncanville 75116 | | | 10 | | Fax 972/708-2474 | |
| Tijuana Hudson | | | | | | 🇫 🇹 |
| Merrifield Elem Sch | PK-4 | T | 440 | 88% | 972/708-2900 | |
| 102 E Vinyard Rd, Duncanville 75137 | | | 35 | | Fax 972/708-2929 | |
| **Dr Tanya Jones** | | | | | | |
| Reed Middle Sch | 7-8 | T | 618 | 81% | 972/708-3500 | |
| 530 E Freeman St, Duncanville 75116 | | | 60 | | Fax 972/708-3535 | |
| Bryan Byrd | | | | | | |
| Smith Elem Sch | PK-4 | T | 319 | 88% | 972/708-3000 | |
| 1010 Big Stone Gap Rd, Duncanville 75137 | | | 23 | | Fax 972/708-3030 | |
| Celee Stephens \ **Kellee Stephens** | | | | | | |
| Ⓐ Summit Education Center | K-12 | T | 140 | 84% | 972/708-2570 | |
| 900 S Cedar Ridge Dr, Duncanville 75137 | | | 6 | | Fax 972/708-2585 | |
| Mekasha Brown | | | | | | |

• **Garland Ind School Dist** PID: 01010395    972/494-8201
   501 S Jupiter Rd, Garland 75042    Fax 972/485-4936

Schools: 72 \ Teachers: 3,668 \ Students: 55,848 \
Special Ed Students: 4,951 \ LEP Students: 16,249 \ College-Bound: 52%
\ Ethnic: Asian 9%, African American 18%, Hispanic 52%, Native American:
2%, Caucasian 18% \ Exp: $524 (High) \ Poverty: 16% \ Title I: $15,782,105
\ Special Education: $9,835,000 \ Bilingual Education: $19,000 \
Open-Close: 08/10 - 06/08 \ DTBP: $190 (High) \ 🇹

| | |
|---|---|
| Dr Ricardo Lopez .............................1 | Allison Davenport ..........................2 |
| Brent Ringo ...............................2,19 | Bradford Trudeau ...........................4 |
| Holly Frias ....................................4 | Jack Younguin ...............................5 |
| Cliff Odenwald ..............................6 | Renee Kotsopoulos ....................7,85* |
| Dr Christi Allen ............................11 | Stacy Singleton ............................12 |
| Dr Gradyne Brown .....................15,68 | Shelley Garrett ..........................15,91 |
| Dr Jovan Wells ............................18 | Joseph Figarelli ......................20,23 |
| Erika Crump ................................27 | Stan Maige ...........................28,295 |
| Sandra Thompson .........................29 | Louise Gartrell ............................35 |
| Debbie Lee .................................36 | Tiffany Gilmore ...........................36 |
| John Hatch ..................................39 | Traci Vickery ...............................46 |
| Kim Webb ...................................47 | Michele Nichols ...........................49 |
| Myra Crump .............................49,93 | Mary Shelton ...............................50 |
| Zaida Saldivar .............................57 | Dr Debi Buchanan ........................58 |
| Veronica Joyner ...........................61 | Johnny Beach ..............................67 |
| Atticus Wisener ...........................68 | Rodney McHenry ..........................68 |
| Dr Kimberly Caddell ...............69,70,294 | Dr Mida Milligan ...........................71 |
| Tiffany Veno ................................71 | Cathy Barck .................................73 |
| Pam Holcomb ..............................73 | Nelson Orta .................................74 |
| Cheryl Jacobs ..............................75 | Amy Montgomery .........................76 |
| Bebetta Hemphill .........................79 | Cheryl Beard ................................81 |

| | |
|---|---|
| Tammy McDonald .............................92 | Matthew Yeager .............................98 |
| Dr Melissa Hill .................................273 | Leaann Schhade ...........................275 |
| Shermika Nelson-Fluker .....................298 | Susanna Russell ............................751 |

| Public Schs..Principal | Grd | Prgm | Enr/#Cls | SN | |
|---|---|---|---|---|---|
| Abbett Elem Sch | PK-5 | T | 605 | 46% | 972/675-3000 |
| 730 W Muirfield Rd, Garland 75044 | | | 30 | | Fax 972/675-3005 |
| Kelly Williams | | | | | |
| Ⓜ Austin Academy for Excellence | 6-8 | TV | 978 | 46% | 972/926-2620 |
| 1125 Beverly Dr, Garland 75040 | | | 48 | | Fax 972/926-2628 |
| John Fishpaw | | | | | |
| Back Elem Sch | PK-5 | T | 380 | 70% | 972/475-1884 |
| 7300 Bluebonnet Dr, Rowlett 75089 | | | 30 | | Fax 972/412-5245 |
| **Amanda Ramos** | | | | | |
| Ⓜ Beaver Tech Ctr-Math & Science | K-5 | T | 580 | 58% | 972/494-8301 |
| 3232 March Ln, Garland 75042 | | | 30 | | Fax 972/494-8702 |
| **Vicki Devantier** | | | | | |
| Bradfield Elem Sch | PK-5 | T | 488 | 84% | 972/494-8303 |
| 3817 Bucknell Dr, Garland 75042 | | | 22 | | Fax 972/494-8729 |
| **Cecilia Bados** | | | | | |
| Bullock Elem Sch | PK-5 | T | 508 | 86% | 972/494-8308 |
| 3909 Edgewood Dr, Garland 75042 | | | 30 | | Fax 972/494-8704 |
| Brian Trichell | | | | | |
| Bussey Middle Sch | 6-8 | GT | 931 | 90% | 972/494-8391 |
| 1204 Travis St, Garland 75040 | | | 50 | | Fax 972/494-8971 |
| Carol Goff | | | | | |
| Caldwell Elem Sch | PK-5 | T | 403 | 90% | 972/926-2500 |
| 3400 Saturn Rd, Garland 75041 | | | 20 | | Fax 972/926-2505 |
| Raelyn Scroggin | | | | | |
| Centerville Elem Sch | K-5 | T | 270 | 88% | 972/926-2510 |
| 600 Keen Dr, Garland 75041 | | | 16 | | Fax 972/926-2515 |
| Amie Pennington | | | | | 🇹 |
| Cisneros Pre-K Sch | PK-PK | T | 607 | 84% | 972/271-7160 |
| 2826 S 5th St, Garland 75041 | | | | | Fax 972/271-7165 |
| **Andy Kiser** | | | | | |
| Ⓜ Classical Center at Vial Sch | PK-5 | T | 484 | 52% | 972/240-3710 |
| 126 Creekview Dr, Garland 75043 | | | 31 | | Fax 972/240-3711 |
| Beatris Martinez | | | | | |
| Ⓜ Classical Center-Brandenburg | 6-8 | T | 1,192 | 61% | 972/926-2630 |
| 626 Nickens Rd, Garland 75043 | | | 50 | | Fax 972/926-2633 |
| Elise Mosty | | | | | 🇹 |
| Club Hill Elem Sch | PK-5 | T | 500 | 78% | 972/926-2520 |
| 1330 Colonel Dr, Garland 75043 | | | 35 | | Fax 972/926-2526 |
| Kerstin Allen | | | | | |
| Cooper Elem Sch | PK-5 | T | 460 | 79% | 972/675-3010 |
| 1200 Kingsbridge Dr, Garland 75040 | | | 28 | | Fax 972/675-3015 |
| Bobbie Carter | | | | | |
| Coyle Middle Sch | 6-8 | TV | 1,007 | 63% | 972/475-3711 |
| 4500 Skyline Dr, Rowlett 75088 | | | 60 | | Fax 972/412-7222 |
| **Kenneth Washington** | | | | | |
| Daugherty Elem Sch | PK-5 | T | 648 | 84% | 972/926-2530 |
| 500 W Miller Rd, Garland 75041 | | | 18 | | Fax 972/926-2535 |
| Bonnie Barrett | | | | | |
| Davis Elem Sch | PK-5 | T | 565 | 83% | 972/494-8205 |
| 1621 McCallum Dr, Garland 75042 | | | 23 | | Fax 972/494-8707 |
| Patricia Tatum | | | | | |
| Ethridge Elem Sch | K-5 | T | 727 | 77% | 972/675-3020 |
| 2301 Sam Houston Dr, Garland 75044 | | | | | Fax 972/675-3025 |
| **Jill Vincent** | | | | | |
| Freeman Elem Sch | PK-5 | T | 271 | 83% | 972/494-8371 |
| 1220 W Walnut St, Garland 75040 | | | 30 | | Fax 972/494-8835 |
| Kelly Garcia | | | | | |
| Garland High Sch | 9-12 | TV | 2,389 | 64% | 972/494-8492 |
| 310 S Garland Ave, Garland 75040 | | | | | Fax 972/494-8415 |
| Holly Hines | | | | | |

| School | Grades | | Enroll | % | Phone / Fax |
|---|---|---|---|---|---|
| George Washington Carver ES<br>2200 Wynn Joyce Rd, Garland 75043<br>Wendy Williams | PK-5 | T | 749 | 74% | 972/487-4415<br>Fax 972/240-8042 |
| Giddens Steadham Elem Sch<br>6200 Danridge Rd, Rowlett 75089<br>Jade Hobbs | PK-5 | T | 486<br>25 | 54% | 972/463-5887<br>Fax 972/463-7147 |
| Gilbreath-Reed Career Tech Ctr<br>4885 N George Bush Hwy, Garland 75040<br>Erika Crump | Voc | | 500 | | 972/487-4588<br>Fax 972/487-4589 |
| Ⓐ Gisd Alternative Ed Center<br>2015 S Country Club Rd, Garland 75041<br>Darrin Hemphill | K-12 | | 69<br>24 | 80% | 972/926-2691<br>Fax 972/926-2692 |
| Glen Couch Elem Sch<br>4349 Waterhouse Blvd, Garland 75043<br>Armenia Smith | PK-5 | T | 593 | 73% | 972/240-1801<br>Fax 972/240-9276 |
| Golden Meadows Elem Sch<br>1726 Travis St, Garland 75042<br>Jacqueline Rhymes | K-5 | T | 545<br>35 | 83% | 972/494-8373<br>Fax 972/494-8709 |
| Handley Elem Sch<br>3725 Broadway Blvd, Garland 75043<br>Cheryl Alexander | PK-5 | T | 365<br>24 | 83% | 972/926-2540<br>Fax 972/926-2545 |
| Heather Glen Elem Sch<br>5119 Heather Glen Dr, Garland 75043<br>Melissa True | PK-5 | T | 396<br>45 | 80% | 972/270-2881<br>Fax 972/681-0078 🇹 |
| Herfurth Elem Sch<br>7500 Miller Rd, Rowlett 75088<br>Jessica Hicks | PK-5 | T | 381<br>36 | 38% | 972/475-7994<br>Fax 972/475-7391 |
| Hickman Elem Sch<br>3114 Pinewood Dr, Garland 75044<br>**Karla Beltran** | PK-5 | T | 450 | 79% | 972/675-3150<br>Fax 972/675-3155 |
| Ⓜ Hillside Acad for Excellence<br>2014 Dairy Rd, Garland 75041<br>Sonya Palmer | PK-5 | T | 403<br>25 | 54% | 972/926-2550<br>Fax 972/926-2555 🇹 |
| Hudson Middle Sch<br>4405 Hudson Park, Sachse 75048<br>**Amber Hope** | 6-8 | T | 1,298<br>50 | 44% | 972/675-3070<br>Fax 972/675-3077 |
| Ⓜ Jackson Tech Ctr Math Science<br>1310 Bobbie Ln, Garland 75042<br>David Dunphy | 6-8 | TV | 1,375<br>50 | 61% | 972/494-8362<br>Fax 972/494-8802 |
| John W Armstrong Elem Sch<br>4750 Ben Davis Rd, Sachse 75048<br>Brandy Schneider | PK-5 | | 860<br>50 | 35% | 972/414-7480<br>Fax 972/414-7488 |
| Keeley Elem Sch<br>8700 Liberty Grove Rd, Rowlett 75089<br>Sheri Taylor | PK-5 | | 550<br>45 | 27% | 972/412-2140<br>Fax 972/412-7061 |
| Ⓜ Kimberlin Acad for Excellence<br>1520 Cumberland Dr, Garland 75040<br>Tammy Sullivan | PK-5 | | 420<br>35 | 30% | 972/926-2560<br>Fax 972/926-2565 |
| Lakeview Centennial High Sch<br>3505 Hayman Dr, Garland 75043<br>Maresa Bailey | 9-12 | TV | 2,404 | 63% | 972/240-3740<br>Fax 972/240-3750 🇹 |
| Liberty Grove Elem Sch<br>10201 Liberty Grove Rd, Rowlett 75089<br>**Debra Bottoms** | PK-5 | | 518<br>60 | 52% | 972/487-4416<br>Fax 214/227-5348 |
| Luna Elem Sch<br>1050 Lochness Ln, Garland 75044<br>Deborah Wilkerson | PK-5 | | 252<br>40 | 30% | 972/675-3040<br>Fax 972/675-3045 |
| Lyles Middle Sch<br>4655 S Country Club Rd, Garland 75043<br>Michael Bland | 6-8 | TV | 445<br>76 | 78% | 972/240-3720<br>Fax 972/240-3723 |
| Memorial Pathway Academy<br>2825 S 1st St, Garland 75041<br>James Thomas | 6-12 | V | 249<br>20 | | 972/926-2650<br>Fax 972/926-2651 |
| Montclair Elem Sch<br>5200 Marketplace Dr, Garland 75043<br>**Karla Massey** | PK-5 | T | 523<br>31 | 82% | 972/279-4041<br>Fax 972/681-0565 |
| Naaman Forest High Sch<br>4843 Naaman Forest Blvd, Garland 75040<br>Herbert Oneil | 9-12 | TV | 2,174<br>112 | 63% | 972/675-3091<br>Fax 972/675-3100 |
| Nita Pearson Elem Sch<br>5201 Nita Pearson Dr, Rowlett 75088<br>**Cherelle Wilson** | PK-5 | T | 658<br>65 | 63% | 972/463-7568<br>Fax 972/463-7623 |
| Norma Dorsey Elem Sch<br>6200 Dexham Rd, Rowlett 75089<br>Leslie Russell | PK-5 | T | 525<br>50 | 51% | 972/463-5595<br>Fax 972/463-1805 |
| North Garland High Sch<br>2109 W Buckingham Rd, Garland 75042<br>Michael Arreola | 9-12 | TV | 2,728 | 64% | 972/675-3120<br>Fax 972/675-3145 |
| Northlake Elem Sch<br>1626 Bosque Dr, Garland 75040<br>**Dr Metzinger Kathy** | PK-5 | T | 508<br>33 | 78% | 972/494-8359<br>Fax 972/494-8717 |
| O'Banion Middle Sch<br>700 Birchwood Dr, Garland 75043<br>**Earl Gilmore** | 6-8 | TV | 1,210<br>35 | 85% | 972/279-6103<br>Fax 972/613-9532 |
| Park Crest Elem Sch<br>2232 Parkcrest Dr, Garland 75041<br>Andrea Kleckner | K-5 | T | 321<br>30 | 81% | 972/926-2571<br>Fax 972/926-2575 |
| Parsons Pre-K Sch<br>2202 Richoak Dr, Garland 75044<br>Disa McEwen | PK-PK | T | 502 | 82% | 972/675-8065<br>Fax 972/675-8061 |
| Pathfinder Achievement Center<br>221 S 9th St, Garland 75040<br>**Danny Guillory** | Spec | T | 46<br>6 | | 972/494-8520<br>Fax 972/494-8629 |
| Routh Roach Elem Sch<br>1811 Mayfield Ave, Garland 75041<br>Aurora Trichell | PK-5 | T | 409<br>25 | 74% | 972/926-2580<br>Fax 972/926-2585 |
| Rowlett Elem Sch<br>3315 Carla Dr, Rowlett 75088<br>**Keith Ellis** | K-5 | T | 542<br>36 | 61% | 972/475-3380<br>Fax 972/412-4484 |
| Rowlett High Sch<br>4700 President George Bush Hwy, Rowlett 75088<br>**Carmen Blakey** | 9-12 | TV | 2,587 | 49% | 972/463-1712<br>Fax 972/412-2951 |
| Sachse High Sch<br>3901 Miles Rd, Sachse 75048<br>Shae Creel | 9-12 | TV | 2,798 | 39% | 972/414-7450<br>Fax 972/414-7458 |
| Sam Houston Middle Sch<br>2232 Sussex Dr, Garland 75041<br>Donald Hernandez | 6-8 | T | 1,009<br>48 | 86% | 972/926-2640<br>Fax 972/926-2647 |
| Schrade Middle Sch<br>6201 Danridge Rd, Rowlett 75089<br>Tobi Schmidt | 6-8 | T | 1,063<br>50 | 51% | 972/463-8790<br>Fax 972/463-8793 |
| Sellers Middle Sch<br>1009 Mars Dr, Garland 75040<br>**Janice Howard** | 6-8 | TV | 867<br>60 | 82% | 972/494-8337<br>Fax 972/494-8607 |
| Sewell Elem Sch<br>4400 Hudson Park, Sachse 75048<br>Kimberly Marsh | PK-5 | T | 561<br>32 | 47% | 972/675-3050<br>Fax 972/675-3053 |
| Shorehaven Elem Sch<br>600 Shorehaven Dr, Garland 75040<br>Krista McClure | PK-5 | T | 330<br>24 | 85% | 972/494-8346<br>Fax 972/494-8720 |
| Shugart Elem Sch<br>4726 Rosehill Rd, Garland 75043<br>Salina Allen | PK-5 | T | 505<br>47 | 77% | 972/240-3700<br>Fax 972/240-3701 |
| South Garland High Sch<br>600 Colonel Dr, Garland 75043<br>**Steven Ewing** | 9-12 | TV | 2,192<br>101 | 78% | 972/926-2700<br>Fax 972/926-2727 |
| Southgate Elem Sch<br>1115 Mayfield Ave, Garland 75041<br>Jennifer Fowler | PK-5 | T | 440<br>31 | 83% | 972/926-2590<br>Fax 972/926-2595 |
| Spring Creek Elem Sch<br>1510 Spring Creek Dr, Garland 75040<br>**Teresa McCutcheon** | PK-5 | T | 570<br>40 | 68% | 972/675-3060<br>Fax 972/675-3065 |

| | | | | | |
|---|---|---|---|---|---|
| 1 | Superintendent | 8 | Curric/Instruct K-12 | 19 | Chief Financial Officer |
| 2 | Bus/Finance/Purchasing | 9 | Curric/Instruct Elem | 20 | Art K-12 |
| 3 | Buildings And Grounds | 10 | Curric/Instruct Sec | 21 | Art Elem |
| 4 | Food Service | 11 | Federal Program | 22 | Art Sec |
| 5 | Transportation | 12 | Title I | 23 | Music K-12 |
| 6 | Athletic | 13 | Title V | 24 | Music Elem |
| 7 | Health Services | 15 | Asst Superintendent | 25 | Music Sec |
| | | 16 | Instructional Media Svcs | 26 | Business Education |
| | | 17 | Chief Operations Officer | 27 | Career & Tech Ed |
| | | 18 | Chief Academic Officer | 28 | Technology Education |

| | |
|---|---|
| 29 | Family/Consumer Science |
| 30 | Adult Education |
| 31 | Career/Sch-to-Work K-12 |
| 32 | Career/Sch-to-Work Elem |
| 33 | Career/Sch-to-Work Sec |
| 34 | Early Childhood Ed |
| 35 | Health/Phys Education |
| 36 | Guidance Services K-12 |
| 37 | Guidance Services Elem |
| 38 | Guidance Services Sec |

| | |
|---|---|
| 39 | Social Studies K-12 |
| 40 | Social Studies Elem |
| 41 | Social Studies Sec |
| 42 | Science K-12 |
| 43 | Science Elem |
| 44 | Science Sec |
| 45 | Math K-12 |
| 46 | Math Elem |
| 47 | Math Sec |
| 48 | English/Lang Arts K-12 |

| | |
|---|---|
| 49 | English/Lang Arts Elem |
| 50 | English/Lang Arts Sec |
| 51 | Reading K-12 |
| 52 | Reading Elem |
| 53 | Reading Sec |
| 54 | Remedial Reading K-12 |
| 55 | Remedial Reading Elem |
| 56 | Remedial Reading Sec |
| 57 | Bilingual/ELL |
| 58 | Special Education K-12 |

| | |
|---|---|
| 59 | Special Education Elem |
| 60 | Special Education Sec |
| 61 | Foreign/World Lang K-12 |
| 62 | Foreign/World Lang Elem |
| 63 | Foreign/World Lang Sec |
| 64 | Religious Education K-12 |
| 65 | Religious Education Elem |
| 66 | Religious Education Sec |
| 67 | School Board President |
| 68 | Teacher Personnel |

| | |
|---|---|
| 69 | Academic Assessment |
| 70 | Research/Development |
| 71 | Public Information |
| 72 | Summer School |
| 73 | Instructional Tech |
| 74 | Inservice Training |
| 75 | Marketing/Distributive |
| 76 | Info Systems |
| 77 | Psychological Assess |
| 78 | Affirmative Action |

| | | | | | | |
|---|---|---|---|---|---|---|
| **Stephens Elem Sch** | PK-5 | T | 618 | 72% | 972/463-5790 | |
| 3700 Cheyenne Dr, Rowlett 75088 | | | 44 | | Fax 972/463-5794 | |
| Jeffrey Waller | | | | | | |
| **Toler Elem Sch** | PK-5 | T | 534 | 75% | 972/226-3922 | |
| 3520 Guthrie Rd, Garland 75043 | | | 35 | | Fax 972/226-0262 | |
| Kerresha Strickland | | | | | | |
| **Vernal Lister Elem Sch** | PK-5 | T | 367 | 67% | 972/675-3030 | |
| 3131 Mars Dr, Garland 75040 | | | | | Fax 972/675-3036 | |
| **Danielle Riddick** | | | | | | |
| Ⓜ **Walnut Glen Academy Excellence** | K-5 | T | 413 | 58% | 972/494-8330 | |
| 3101 Edgewood Dr, Garland 75042 | | | 30 | | Fax 972/494-8725 | |
| Lisa Alexander | | | | | | |
| Ⓜ **Watson Tech Center Math & Sci** | PK-5 | T | 512 | 55% | 972/926-2600 | |
| 2601 Dairy Rd, Garland 75041 | | | 20 | | Fax 972/926-2606 | |
| **Adrian Leday** | | | | | | |
| **Weaver Elem Sch** | PK-5 | T | 554 | 75% | 972/494-8311 | |
| 805 Pleasant Valley Rd, Garland 75040 | | | 30 | | Fax 972/494-8721 | |
| Ernest Espino | | | | | | |
| **Webb Middle Sch** | 6-8 | TV | 1,193 | 71% | 972/675-3080 | |
| 1610 Spring Creek Dr, Garland 75040 | | | 55 | | Fax 972/675-3089 | |
| **Nikketta Wilson** | | | | | | |
| **Williams Elem Sch** | PK-5 | T | 228 | 84% | 972/926-2610 | |
| 1821 Oldgate Ln, Garland 75042 | | | 20 | | Fax 972/926-2615 | |
| **Lucas Pizana** | | | | | | |

● **Grand Prairie Ind School Dist** PID: 01010814　　　972/237-4000
2602 S Belt Line Rd, Grand Prairie 75052　　　　　　　Fax 972/237-5440

---

**Schools:** 42 \ **Teachers:** 1,900 \ **Students:** 29,334 \
**Special Ed Students:** 2,601 \ **LEP Students:** 8,407 \ **College-Bound:** 54%
\ **Ethnic:** Asian 3%, African American 19%, Hispanic 66%, Caucasian
11% \ **Exp:** $421 (High) \ **Poverty:** 17% \ **Title I:** $7,294,970 \
**Special Education:** $5,377,000 \ **Open-Close:** 08/17 - 05/20 \ **DTBP:** $45
(Low) \ 🛐 🇹

---

| | | | |
|---|---|---|---|
| Linda Ellis | 1 | Ray Wilks | 2 |
| Tracy Ray | 2,15 | Charte Stefka | 3 |
| Dominik Peterson | 4 | Dana Acock | 5* |
| Gary Bartel | 6 | Mary Lincomm | 7,85 |
| Dr Nuggett Cunningham | 8,15,69 | Patricia Lewis | 11,15 |
| Elna Davis | 15 | Susanna Ramirez | 15,34,93 |
| Traci Davis | 15 | Dr Vern Alexander | 15,72,79,294 |
| Tara Cahill | 16,286 | Troy Mathieu | 17 |
| Winston Minix | 27,31 | Dana Jackson | 36 |
| Magda Grape | 57 | Dr Dorothea Gordon | 58 |
| Aaron King | 67 | Karry Chapman | 68 |
| Melissa Steger | 69,76 | Sam Buchmeyer | 71 |
| Chris Malone | 73,98 | Bill Young | 76 |
| Rich Loffey | 79 | Kasie Roden | 285 |
| Mark Nobch | 295 | Teri Wilson | 751 |
| Blanca McGee | 752 | | |

| **Public Schs..Principal** | **Grd** | **Prgm** | **Enr/#Cls** | **SN** | | |
|---|---|---|---|---|---|---|
| **Austin Environ Sci Acad** | PK-5 | T | 480 | 91% | 972/343-4600 | |
| 815 NW 7th St, Grand Prairie 75050 | | | 27 | | Fax 972/343-4699 | |
| Tanya Gilliam | | | | | | |
| **Bonham Early Ed Sch** | PK-PK | T | 346 | 99% | 972/262-4255 | |
| 1301 E Coral Way, Grand Prairie 75051 | | | 15 | | Fax 972/522-3199 | |
| Rachel Mendoza | | | | | | |
| **Bowie Fine Arts Academy** | PK-5 | T | 542 | 94% | 972/262-7348 | |
| 425 Alice Dr, Grand Prairie 75051 | | | 32 | | Fax 972/264-6219 | |
| Ana Holland | | | | | | |
| **Bush Global Ldrshp Acad** | K-5 | T | 455 | 89% | 972/237-1628 | |
| 511 E Springdale Ln, Grand Prairie 75052 | | | 27 | | Fax 972/237-1059 | |
| Dina Jammer | | | | | | |
| **Colin Powell Elem Sch** | PK-5 | T | 450 | 42% | 972/642-3961 | |
| 5009 S Carrier Pkwy, Grand Prairie 75052 | | | 25 | | Fax 972/642-4049 | |
| Marchelle Sterling | | | | | | |

| | | | | | | |
|---|---|---|---|---|---|---|
| **Crockett Early Education Sch** | PK-PK | T | 597 | 94% | 972/262-5353 | |
| 1340 Skyline Rd, Grand Prairie 75051 | | | | | Fax 972/343-6299 | |
| Magdalena Garcia | | | | | | |
| Ⓐ **Crosswinds Accelerated HS** | 9-12 | T | 378 | 71% | 972/522-2950 | |
| 1100 N Carrier Pkwy, Grand Prairie 75050 | | | 40 | | Fax 972/522-2999 | |
| Dr Suzy Meyer | | | | | | |
| **Daniels Acad of Sci & Math** | K-5 | T | 381 | 93% | 972/264-7803 | |
| 801 SW 19th St, Grand Prairie 75051 | | | 34 | | Fax 972/343-4599 | |
| Marva Maynard-Walter | | | | | | |
| **Dezavala Environ Science Acad** | K-5 | T | 822 | 84% | 972/642-0448 | |
| 3410 Kirby Creek Dr, Grand Prairie 75052 | | | 26 | | Fax 972/264-9495 | |
| Mary Smith | | | | | | |
| **Dickinson Elem Sch** | PK-5 | T | 381 | 83% | 972/641-1664 | |
| 1902 Palmer Trl, Grand Prairie 75052 | | | 26 | | Fax 972/641-8601 | |
| Whitney Carlisle | | | | | | |
| **Digital Arts Tech Acad-Adams** | 6-8 | T | 733 | 86% | 972/262-1934 | |
| 833 W Tarrant Rd, Grand Prairie 75050 | | | 60 | | Fax 972/522-3099 | |
| Darwert Johnson | | | | | | |
| **Dubiski Career High Sch** | 9-12 | TV | 1,694 | 73% | 972/343-7800 | |
| 2990 S State Highway 161, Grand Prairie 75052 | | | | | Fax 972/343-7899 | |
| Larry Jones | | | | | | 🛐 🇹 |
| **Eisenhower Elem Sch** | PK-5 | T | 701 | 84% | 972/262-3717 | |
| 2102 N Carrier Pkwy, Grand Prairie 75050 | | | 24 | | Fax 972/264-9473 | |
| Dr Shelley Handcock | | | | | | 🛐 🇹 |
| **Fannin Middle Sch** | 6-8 | T | 670 | 92% | 972/262-8668 | |
| 301 NE 28th St, Grand Prairie 75050 | | | 24 | | Fax 972/343-4799 | |
| Roberto Lopez | | | | | | |
| **Florence Hill Elem Sch** | PK-5 | T | 594 | 68% | 972/264-0802 | |
| 4213 S Robinson Rd, Grand Prairie 75052 | | | 27 | | Fax 972/264-9475 | |
| Catherine Bridges | | | | | | |
| **Garcia Elem Sch** | PK-5 | T | 571 | 92% | 972/237-0001 | |
| 2444 Graham St, Grand Prairie 75050 | | | 41 | | Fax 972/237-9660 | |
| Martin Zamarripa | | | | | | |
| **Garner Fine Arts Academy** | PK-5 | T | 1,010 | 44% | 972/262-5000 | |
| 145 W Polo Rd, Grand Prairie 75052 | | | 40 | | Fax 972/522-3399 | |
| Alisha Crumley | | | | | | |
| © **Grand Prairie Collegiate Inst** | 6-12 | T | 272 | 63% | 972/343-3120 | |
| 1502 College St, Grand Prairie 75050 | | | | | Fax 972/343-3159 | |
| Darnisha Carreathers | | | | | | |
| **Grand Prairie Early Clg HS** | 9-12 | | 150 | | 972/809-5711 | |
| 101 Gopher Blvd, Grand Prairie 75050 | | | | | Fax 972/809-5775 | |
| Laigha Boyle | | | | | | |
| **Grand Prairie Fine Arts Acad** | 6-12 | T | 830 | 42% | 972/237-5603 | |
| 102 Gopher Blvd, Grand Prairie 75050 | | | | | Fax 972/343-6399 | |
| Maria Schell | | | | | | |
| **Grand Prairie High Sch** | 9-12 | TV | 2,942 | 84% | 972/809-5711 | |
| 101 High School Dr, Grand Prairie 75050 | | | 85 | | Fax 972/809-5775 | |
| Laigha Boyle | | | | | | |
| **Harry S Truman Middle Sch** | 6-8 | T | 617 | 79% | 972/641-7676 | |
| 1501 Coffeyville Trl, Grand Prairie 75052 | | | | | Fax 972/522-3999 | |
| Letycia Fowler | | | | | | |
| **Hobbs Williams Elem Sch** | K-5 | T | 641 | 86% | 972/522-2700 | |
| 1635 SE 14th St, Grand Prairie 75051 | | | 34 | | Fax 972/522-2799 | |
| **Mesias Trejo** | | | | | | 🛐 🇹 |
| **Jackson Middle Sch** | 6-8 | T | 1,036 | 82% | 972/264-2704 | |
| 3504 Corn Valley Rd, Grand Prairie 75052 | | | 45 | | Fax 972/343-7599 | |
| Robert Wallace | | | | | | 🛐 🇹 |
| Ⓐ **Johnson Daep** | 6-12 | | 21 | 80% | 972/262-7244 | |
| 650 Stonewall Dr, Grand Prairie 75052 | | | 18 | | Fax 972/264-9479 | |
| Kerry Rapier | | | | | | 🛐 🇹 |
| **Juan Seguin Elem Sch** | K-5 | T | 410 | 89% | 972/522-7100 | |
| 1450 SE 4th St, Grand Prairie 75051 | | | 45 | | Fax 972/522-7199 | |
| Amanda Rodriguez | | | | | | |
| **Lee Elem Sch** | K-5 | TV | 492 | 94% | 972/262-6785 | |
| 401 E Grand Prairie Rd, Grand Prairie 75051 | | | 89 | | Fax 972/343-6099 | |
| **Carla Carattini** | | | | | | |

---

| | | | | | |
|---|---|---|---|---|---|
| Marshall Leadership Academy<br>1160 W Warrior Trl, Grand Prairie 75052<br>Gordon Carlisle | PK-5 | T | 684<br>31 | 76% | 972/522-7200<br>Fax 972/522-7299 🅕🅣 |
| Mike Moseley Elem Sch<br>1851 W Camp Wisdom Rd, Grand Prairie 75052<br>Tuyet Huynh | PK-5 | T | 603 | 73% | 972/522-2800<br>Fax 972/522-2899 |
| Ochoa STEM Academy/Milam<br>2030 Proctor Dr, Grand Prairie 75051<br>Dinnah Escanilla | K-5 | T | 785<br>40 | 89% | 972/262-7131<br>Fax 972/264-9492 |
| Ronald Reagan Middle Sch<br>4616 Bardin Rd, Grand Prairie 75052<br>**Ami Potts** | 6-8 | T | 855 | 45% | 972/522-7300<br>Fax 972/522-7399 |
| Sallye Moore Clg&Career Prep<br>3150 Waterwood Dr, Grand Prairie 75052<br>Nichole Holland | PK-8 | T | 428<br>29 | 73% | 972/660-2261<br>Fax 972/343-4899 |
| Sam Rayburn Steam Acad<br>2800 Reforma Dr, Grand Prairie 75052<br>**Amanda Schmitter** | PK-5 | T | 490<br>22 | 83% | 972/264-8900<br>Fax 972/522-3899 |
| © School for the Highly Gifted<br>2990 S Highway 161, Grand Prairie 75052<br>Holly Mohler | 1-8 | | 106 | 34% | 972/343-7864 |
| South Grand Prairie 9th GR Ctr<br>305 W Warrior Trl, Grand Prairie 75052<br>Donnie Bartlett | 9-9 | | 889 | 75% | 972/264-1769<br>Fax 972/343-7698 |
| South Grand Prairie Echs<br>305 W Warrior Trl, Grand Prairie 75052<br>Dr Joanna Slaton | 9-12 | | 200 | | 972/343-7640<br>Fax 972/623-9051 |
| South Grand Prairie High Sch<br>301 W Warrior Trl, Grand Prairie 75052<br>Donna Grant | 10-12 | T | 2,368<br>103 | 62% | 972/343-1500<br>Fax 972/642-7902 🅣 |
| Travis World Language Academy<br>525 NE 15th St, Grand Prairie 75050<br>Veronica Kunschik | PK-8 | T | 740 | 94% | 972/262-2990<br>Fax 972/343-6198 |
| © Uplift Lee Prep Sch [331]<br>401 E Grand Prairie Rd, Grand Prairie 75051<br>Dani Erbert | K-6 | T | 223 | 78% | 972/262-6785 |
| Whitt Fine Arts Academy<br>3320 S Edelweiss Dr, Grand Prairie 75052<br>April Wyatt | PK-5 | T | 527<br>37 | 73% | 972/264-5024<br>Fax 972/343-4999 🅕🅣 |
| Young Mens Leadership Academy<br>2205 SE 4th St, Grand Prairie 75051<br>Joseph Melms | 6-8 | T | 703 | 89% | 972/264-8651<br>Fax 972/522-3699 |
| Young Womens Leadership Acad<br>1204 E Marshall Dr, Grand Prairie 75051<br>Janna Burns | 6-12 | T | 794 | 87% | 972/343-7400<br>Fax 972/343-7499 |

● **Highland Park Ind Sch Dist** PID: 01011038  214/780-3000
7015 Westchester Dr, Dallas 75205  Fax 214/780-3099

**Schools:** 8 \ **Teachers:** 440 \ **Students:** 7,000 \ **Special Ed Students:** 634 \ **LEP Students:** 86 \ **College-Bound:** 92% \ **Ethnic:** Asian 8%, African American 1%, Hispanic 6%, Caucasian 85% \ **Exp:** $251 (Med) \ **Poverty:** 3% \ **Title I:** $169,628 \ **Special Education:** $1,019,000 \ **Open-Close:** 08/20 - 05/27 \ **DTBP:** $173 (High)

| | | | |
|---|---|---|---|
| Dr Tom Trigg | 1 | Chase Park | 2 |
| Mary Witcher | 2 | Mike White | 2,15 |
| Shane Bryan | 3 | Lynn Prichard | 4 |
| Johnny Ringo | 6 | Lisa Wilson | 8,15 |
| Lydia Walden | 36,77,83,88 | Dr Laurie Gagne | 58 |
| Jim Hitzelberger | 67 | Brenda West | 68 |
| Dr Jamie Callahan | 69 | Jon Dahlander | 71,751 |
| Charlie Jackson | 73,76,98 | Lisa Ham | 73 |
| Kim Brooks | 81 | Mark Rowden | 91 |
| Mark Hunter | 295 | | |

| Public Schs..Principal | Grd | Prgm | Enr/#Cls | SN |
|---|---|---|---|---|
| Arch H McCulloch Interm Sch<br>3555 Granada Ave, Dallas 75205<br>Clifton Moran | 5-6 | | 1,086<br>50 | 214/780-3500<br>Fax 214/780-3599 |
| Highland Park High Sch<br>4220 Emerson Ave, Dallas 75205<br>**Jeremy Gilbert** | 9-12 | | 2,148 | 214/780-3700<br>Fax 214/780-3799 |
| Highland Park Middle Sch<br>3555 Granada Ave, Dallas 75205<br>**Jeremy Gilbert** | 7-8 | | 1,106<br>75 | 214/780-3600<br>Fax 214/780-3699 |
| John S Armstrong Elem Sch<br>3600 Cornell Ave, Dallas 75205<br>Betsy Cummins | K-4 | | 509<br>26 | 214/780-3100<br>Fax 214/780-3199 |
| John S Bradfield Elem Sch<br>4300 Southern Ave, Dallas 75205<br>Regina Dumar | PK-4 | | 594<br>31 | 214/780-3200<br>Fax 214/780-3299 |
| Michael M Boone Elem Sch<br>8385 Durham St, Dallas 75225<br>**Amanda Reyes** | K-4 | | 401 | 214/780-4100 |
| Robert S Hyer Elem Sch<br>8385 Durham St, Dallas 75225<br>Debbie Burt | PK-4 | | 649<br>35 | 214/780-3300<br>Fax 214/780-3399 |
| University Park Elem Sch<br>3505 Amherst Ave, Dallas 75225<br>Candace Judd | K-4 | | 657<br>30 | 214/780-3400<br>Fax 214/780-3402 |

● **Int'l Leadership of Texas Dist** PID: 12261400  972/479-9078
1820 N Glenville Dr, Richardson 75081  Fax 972/479-9129

**Schools:** 19 \ **Teachers:** 1,184 \ **Students:** 19,100 \
**Special Ed Students:** 978 \ **LEP Students:** 4,813 \ **Ethnic:** Asian 4%, African American 35%, Hispanic 52%, Caucasian 9% \ **Open-Close:** 08/13 - 05/20

| | | | |
|---|---|---|---|
| Eddie Conger | 1 | James Dworkin | 2,19 |
| Frank Crabill | 3 | Yolanda Banks | 4 |
| Rodney Minor | 5 | Laura Carrasco | 8,18 |
| Krystal Lovato | 12,298 | Anthony Palagonia | 15 |
| Dr Matilda Orozco | 15 | Rodney Cooksy | 15 |
| Bryndan Wright | 17 | Shannon Urbina | 58 |
| James Williams | 67 | Claudia Neira | 68 |
| Jason Sturgeon | 69 | Caitlin Madison | 71 |
| Joyce Wheeler | 73,98 | Angela Marcellus | 79 |
| Lucy Mariappa | 97 | Aaron Thorson | 751 |

| Public Schs..Principal | Grd | Prgm | Enr/#Cls | SN |
|---|---|---|---|---|
| © Int'l Ldrship TX-Lancaster<br>1900 W Pleasant Run Rd, Lancaster 75146<br>Senta Wilson | K-8 | T | 1,244 | 82% 469/862-4237 |
| © Int'l Ldrshp TX-Arlington ES<br>4950 S Bowen Rd, Arlington 76017<br>**Angel McKoy** | K-8 | T | 935 | 72% 817/496-0400 |
| © Int'l Ldrshp TX-Arlngtn GR PR<br>2851 Ragland Rd, Grand Prairie 75052<br>Quentyn Seamster | 9-10 | T | 215 | 65% 682/808-5960<br>Fax 817/635-3118 |
| © Int'l Ldrshp TX-College Sta<br>3610 Longmire Dr, College Sta 77845<br>Dr Heather McMahan | K-8 | T | 964 | 979/704-6027<br>Fax 979/704-5332 |
| © Int'l Ldrshp TX-East Ft Worth<br>5901 Boca Raton Blvd, Fort Worth 76112<br>**Michelle Porter** | K-8 | T | 1,166 | 71% 817/395-1766<br>Fax 817/446-4270 |
| © Int'l Ldrshp TX-Garland<br>3301 N Shiloh Rd, Garland 75044<br>Jade Esquivel | K-8 | T | 941 | 65% 972/414-8000<br>Fax 972/495-2405 |
| © Int'l Ldrshp TX-Garland HS<br>4413 N Shiloh Rd, Garland 75044<br>Karen Marx | 9-12 | T | 622 | 62% 972/414-3414<br>Fax 972/495-2234 |

© Int'l Ldrshp TX-Grand Prairie — K-8 — T — 1,402 — 73% — 469/348-7960
3501 S Great Southwest Pkwy, Grand Prairie 75052
Adrian Apodaca

© Int'l Ldrshp TX-Katy — K-8 — — 1,280 — — 281/394-9417
24406 Franz Rd, Katy 77493 — Fax 346/387-7044
Dr Sheri Hawthorn

© Int'l Ldrshp TX-Katy Westpark — 9-12 — T — 221 — — 832/222-9470
20055 Beechnut St, Richmond 77407 — Fax 832/222-9112
**Dr Laura Villaflor**

© Int'l Ldrshp TX-Keller — K-8 — — 457 — — 817/665-0646
2301 Heritage Trace Pkwy, Fort Worth 76177 — Fax 817/232-8220
Armando Rendon

© Int'l Ldrshp TX-Keller Saginaw — 9-12 — — 550 — 36% — 682/250-3701
10537 US Highway 287, Fort Worth 76131 — Fax 817/306-6039
Valerie Layne

© Int'l Ldrshp TX-Lanc-DeSoto HS — 9-9 — T — 44 — 86% — 469/786-2850
901 N Polk St, Desoto 75115 — Fax 972/231-7995
Marco DeLeon

© Int'l Ldrshp TX-N Richlnd Hill — K-8 — — 1,357 — — 817/576-9031
4131 Rufe Snow Dr, N Richlnd Hls 76180
**Gearoid Dubhghaill**

© Int'l Ldrshp TX-Orem — K-8 — T — 1,158 — 85% — 713/987-9435
5445 E Orem Dr, Houston 77048
Joshua Brown

© Int'l Ldrshp TX-Saginaw — K-8 — T — 1,326 — 52% — 682/250-3600
500 N Old Decatur Rd, Fort Worth 76179
Nanette Coleman

© Int'l Ldrshp TX-Westpark — K-8 — T — 1,300 — 78% — 346/203-4126
15300 Bellaire Blvd, Houston 77083 — Fax 281/933-8129
**Arelis Hilaire**

© Int'l Ldrshp TX-Windmill Lakes — K-8 — T — 1,285 — 63% — 832/667-0453
9898 Windmill Lakes Blvd, Houston 77075 — Fax 713/944-4344
Mayra Arreola

© Int'l Ldrshp TX-Wml-Orem HS — 9-9 — T — 60 — 77% — 832/649-6817
9901 Windmill Lakes Blvd, Houston 77075 — Fax 832/271-7410
Stephanie Mott

● **Irving Ind School Dist** PID: 01011105 — 972/600-5000
2621 W Airport Fwy, Irving 75062 — Fax 972/215-5003

**Schools:** 38 \ **Teachers:** 2,221 \ **Students:** 33,901 \
**Special Ed Students:** 2,740 \ **LEP Students:** 12,589 \ **College-Bound:** 60%
\ **Ethnic:** Asian 3%, African American 13%, Hispanic 73%, Native American:
2%, Caucasian 9% \ **Exp:** $465 (High) \ **Poverty:** 20% \ **Title I:** $10,641,623
\ **Special Education:** $6,441,000 \ **Open-Close:** 08/17 - 05/27 \ **DTBP:** $193
(High) \ 🅕 🅣

| Public Schs..Principal | Grd | Prgm | Enr/#Cls | SN |
|---|---|---|---|---|
| Austin Middle Sch<br>825 E Union Bower Rd, Irving 75061<br>Dr Channa Barrett | 6-8 | TV | 983<br>60 | 83% 972/600-3100<br>Fax 972/600-3105 |
| Ⓐ Barbara Cardwell Career Prep<br>101 E Union Bower Rd, Irving 75061<br>Lesley Kelley | 6-12 | TV | 354<br>60 | 68% 972/600-6140<br>Fax 972/273-6188<br>🅣 |
| Barton Elem Sch<br>2931 Conflans Rd, Irving 75061<br>**Christine Ruiz** | K-5 | T | 733<br>43 | 85% 972/600-4100<br>Fax 972/600-4110<br>🅣 |
| Bowie Middle Sch<br>600 E 6th St, Irving 75060<br>Natasha Stewart | 6-8 | TV | 925<br>70 | 77% 972/600-3000<br>Fax 972/600-3044 |
| Brandenburg Elem Sch<br>2800 Hillcrest Dr, Irving 75062<br>Netassha Rendon | PK-5 | T | 786<br>46 | 73% 972/600-7100<br>Fax 972/258-7199 |
| Britain Elem Sch<br>631 Edmondson Dr, Irving 75060<br>Mariela Magro-Malo | PK-5 | T | 635<br>60 | 84% 972/600-3800<br>Fax 972/600-3899<br>🅕 🅣 |
| Clifton Early Childhood Sch<br>3950 Pleasant Run Rd, Irving 75038<br>Leigh Ann McNeese | PK-PK | T | 603<br>17 | 85% 972/600-4200<br>Fax 972/261-2849 |
| Crockett Middle Sch<br>2431 Hancock St, Irving 75061<br>Bianca Johnson | 6-8 | TV | 953<br>87 | 80% 972/600-4700<br>Fax 972/313-4770<br>🅕 🅣 |
| Elliott Elem Sch<br>1900 S Story Rd, Irving 75060<br>Sheila Peragine | K-5 | T | 604<br>50 | 75% 972/600-4300<br>Fax 972/600-4316 |
| Farine Elem Sch<br>615 Metker St, Irving 75062<br>Norma Gonzalez-Perez | K-5 | T | 736<br>46 | 65% 972/600-7900<br>Fax 972/261-2799<br>🅣 |
| Franklin Monroe Gilbert ES<br>1501 E Pioneer Dr, Irving 75061<br>Claudia Ruiz | K-5 | T | 716<br>48 | 85% 972/600-0400<br>Fax 972/721-8480 |
| Hanes Elem Sch<br>2730 Cheyenne St, Irving 75062<br>Ed Henderson | K-5 | T | 644<br>36 | 73% 972/600-3600<br>Fax 972/261-2950 |
| Houston Middle Sch<br>3033 Country Club Dr W, Irving 75038<br>**Manny Espino** | 6-8 | T | 935 | 77% 972/600-7500<br>Fax 972/261-2399 |
| Irving High Sch<br>900 N O Connor Rd, Irving 75061<br>**Jeffrey Dorman** | 9-12 | GTV | 2,646<br>110 | 72% 972/600-6300<br>Fax 972/273-8319 |
| Irving Reg Day Sch Pgrm-Deaf<br>631 Edmondson Dr, Irving 75060<br>Sherry Clifton | Spec | | 50 | 972/600-3800<br>Fax 972/554-3899 |
| J O Davis Elem Sch<br>310 Davis Dr, Irving 75061<br>Angela Long | K-5 | T | 826<br>61 | 77% 972/600-4900<br>Fax 972/600-4949 |
| J O Schulze Elem Sch<br>1200 S Irving Heights Dr, Irving 75060<br>**Linda Torres-Rangel** | K-5 | T | 607<br>40 | 87% 972/600-3500<br>Fax 972/600-3599<br>🅕 |
| Jack E Singley Academy<br>4601 N MacArthur Blvd, Irving 75038<br>Melanie Kibodeaux | 9-12 | T | 1,712 | 68% 972/600-5300<br>Fax 972/600-5301 |
| John Haley Elem Sch<br>1100 Schulze Dr, Irving 75060<br>Lindsey Sanders | K-5 | T | 667<br>45 | 87% 972/600-6600<br>Fax 972/273-6608 |

**TX—113**

| School | Grades | Prgm | Enr/#Cls | % | Phone |
|---|---|---|---|---|---|
| John R Good Elem Sch<br>1200 E Union Bower Rd, Irving 75061<br>Alberto Zavala | K-5 | T | 720<br>56 | 86% | 972/600-3300<br>Fax 972/721-3379 |
| Johnston Elem Sch<br>2801 Rutgers Dr, Irving 75062<br>Stephen Pollard | K-5 | T | 815<br>50 | 78% | 972/600-7700<br>Fax 972/600-7799 |
| Kinkeade Early Childhood Sch<br>2333 Cameron Pl, Irving 75060<br>Jennifer McKee | PK-PK | T | 570<br>22 | 83% | 972/600-6500<br>Fax 972/600-6549 |
| Lady Bird Johnson Middle Sch<br>3601 W Pioneer Dr, Irving 75061<br>James Clark | 6-8 | T | 963 | 74% | 972/600-0500<br>Fax 972/986-6830 |
| Lamar Middle Sch<br>219 Crandall Rd, Irving 75060<br>Eric Ogle | 6-8 | T | 300<br>100 | 70% | 972/600-4400<br>Fax 972/600-4499 |
| Lee Elem Sch<br>1600 Carlisle St, Irving 75062<br>Angel Rico | K-5 | T | 613<br>50 | 76% | 972/600-7800<br>Fax 972/261-2629 |
| Lively Elem Sch<br>1800 Plymouth Dr W, Irving 75061<br>Fernando Vadillo | K-5 | T | 747 | 76% | 972/600-6700<br>Fax 972/273-6710 |
| Lorenzo De Zavala Middle Sch<br>707 W Pioneer Dr, Irving 75061<br>Trent Nickerson | 6-8 | TV | 928 | 78% | 972/600-6000<br>Fax 972/273-8924 |
| MacArthur High Sch<br>3700 N MacArthur Blvd, Irving 75062<br>Deeadra Brown | 9-12 | GTV | 2,770<br>120 | 61% | 972/600-7200<br>Fax 972/261-2299 |
| Nimitz High Sch<br>100 W Oakdale Rd, Irving 75060<br>Francisco Miranda | 9-12 | TV | 2,533<br>70 | 66% | 972/600-5700<br>Fax 972/273-8610 |
| Otis Brown Elem Sch<br>2501 10th St, Irving 75060<br>Maria Bloomfield | K-5 | T | 756<br>60 | 82% | 972/600-4000<br>Fax 972/600-4099 |
| Paul Keyes Elem Sch<br>1501 N Britain Rd, Irving 75061<br>Joe Estrada | K-5 | T | 634<br>52 | 89% | 972/600-3400<br>Fax 972/600-3405 |
| Pierce Early Childhood Sch<br>901 N Britain Rd, Irving 75061<br>Jennifer Dickson | PK-PK | T | 557<br>22 | 82% | 972/600-3700<br>Fax 972/554-3749 |
| Stipes Elem Sch<br>3100 Cross Timbers Dr, Irving 75060<br>Kelly Giddens | K-5 | T | 646 | 65% | 972/600-4500<br>Fax 972/600-4598 |
| Ⓐ Student Reassignment Ctr<br>1600 E Shady Grove Rd, Irving 75060<br>Scott Sralla | 6-12 | | 150<br>12 | | 972/600-3900<br>Fax 972/721-3205 |
| Thomas Haley Elem Sch<br>3601 Cheyenne St, Irving 75062<br>Henry Taylor | K-5 | T | 755<br>40 | 71% | 972/600-7000<br>Fax 972/261-2599 |
| Townley Elem Sch<br>1030 W Vilbig St, Irving 75060<br>Liz Munoz | K-5 | T | 709<br>50 | 76% | 972/600-6800<br>Fax 972/600-6877 |
| Townsell Elem Sch<br>3700 Pleasant Run Rd, Irving 75038<br>Amber Brooks | K-5 | T | 797 | 78% | 972/600-5500<br>Fax 972/255-6008 |
| Travis Middle Sch<br>1600 Finley Rd, Irving 75062<br>Denise Anderson | 6-8 | TV | 987<br>45 | 68% | 972/600-0100<br>Fax 972/261-2450 |

---

● **Lancaster Ind School Dist** PID: 01011337  972/218-1400
422 S Centre Ave, Lancaster 75146  Fax 972/218-1401

> **Schools:** 11 \ **Teachers:** 434 \ **Students:** 7,600 \ **Special Ed Students:** 610 \ **LEP Students:** 518 \ **College-Bound:** 65% \ **Ethnic:** African American 78%, Hispanic 20%, Caucasian 2% \ **Exp:** $267 (Med) \ **Poverty:** 21% \ **Title I:** $2,419,805 \ **Special Education:** $1,262,000 \ **Open-Close:** 08/17 - 05/27 \ **DTBP:** $19 (Low) \ Ⓕ Ⓣ

| | | | |
|---|---|---|---|
| Elijah Granger | 1 | Dana Mosley | 2 |
| Shonna Pumphrey | 2,19 | James Thomas | 3 |
| Dr John Price | 3,17 | Upenda Sibley | 4 |
| Dawn Rice | 5 | Beverly Humphrey | 6,71 |
| Karleen Watson | 7* | Shemeka Williams | 8,15 |
| Pamela Brown | 15,57,68,79,81 | Tonia Howard | 18,74 |
| Garry Williams | 20* | Sheila Benskin | 27,31 |
| Crystal Cromer | 58 | Susan Keen | 58 |
| Ellen Clark | 67 | Connie Isabel | 69 |
| Kelli Watson | 73 | Pamela Carroll | 78* |
| Clifford Wherley | 91 | Dr Kanesha Waites | 93 |
| Sonya Butler | 98,295 | Lisa Bacon | 274* |
| Lachele Washington | 275 | Dr Lamont Smith | 294 |

| Public Schs..Principal | Grd | Prgm | Enr/#Cls | SN |
|---|---|---|---|---|
| Beltline Elem Sch<br>1355 W Belt Line Rd, Lancaster 75146<br>Wendy Hawthrone | PK-5 | T | 495<br>29 | 94% 972/218-1608<br>Fax 972/218-1620<br>Ⓕ Ⓣ |
| Elsie Robertson Middle Sch<br>822 W Pleasant Run Rd, Lancaster 75146<br>Willisa House | 7-8 | TV | 1,028<br>51 | 85% 972/218-1660<br>Fax 972/218-3080 |
| GW Carver 6th GR STEM Lrng Ctr<br>1005 Westridge Ave, Lancaster 75146<br>**Rickyl Wesson** | 6-6 | T | 515 | 91% 972/218-1577<br>Fax 972/218-1589 |
| Houston Elem Sch<br>2929 Marquis Ln, Lancaster 75134<br>Tatanisha Stevenson | PK-5 | T | 703<br>18 | 92% 972/218-1513<br>Fax 972/218-1524<br>Ⓕ Ⓣ |
| Ⓐ J D Hall Learning Center<br>602 E 2nd St, Lancaster 75146<br>Antoinette Mathews | 1-12 | V | 60<br>5 | 972/218-1441<br>Fax 972/218-1442 |
| Lancaster High Sch<br>200 E Wintergreen Rd, Lancaster 75134<br>Eleanor Webb | 9-12 | GTV | 1,165 | 85% 972/218-1800<br>Fax 972/218-5797<br>Ⓕ Ⓣ |
| Lancaster STEM Early Clg HS<br>200 E Wintergreen Rd, Lancaster 75134<br>Anthony Thornhill | 9-12 | | 401 | 972/218-1861 |
| Pleasant Run Elem Sch<br>427 W Pleasant Run Rd, Lancaster 75146<br>**Marlon Waites** | PK-5 | T | 730<br>21 | 89% 972/218-1538<br>Fax 972/218-1550 |
| Rolling Hills Elem Sch<br>450 Rolling Hills Pl, Lancaster 75146<br>Cherish Pipkins | PK-5 | T | 428<br>24 | 90% 972/218-1525<br>Fax 972/218-1537 |
| Rosa Parks-Millbrook Sch<br>630 Millbrook Dr, Lancaster 75146<br>Yvonne Thornton | PK-5 | T | 415<br>27 | 87% 972/218-1564<br>Fax 972/218-1523 |
| West Main Elem Sch<br>531 W Main St, Lancaster 75146<br>Gail Wright | PK-5 | T | 718<br>15 | 89% 972/218-1551<br>Fax 972/218-1563 |

---

| | | | | | |
|---|---|---|---|---|---|
| 1 Superintendent | 19 Chief Financial Officer | 29 Family/Consumer Science | 39 Social Studies K-12 | 49 English/Lang Arts Elem | 59 Special Education Elem | 69 Academic Assessment |
| 2 Bus/Finance/Purchasing | 20 Art K-12 | 30 Adult Education | 40 Social Studies Elem | 50 English/Lang Arts Sec | 60 Special Education Sec | 70 Research/Development |
| 3 Buildings And Grounds | 21 Art Elem | 31 Career/Sch-to-Work K-12 | 41 Social Studies Sec | 51 Reading K-12 | 61 Foreign/World Lang K-12 | 71 Public Information |
| 4 Food Service | 22 Art Sec | 32 Career/Sch-to-Work Elem | 42 Science K-12 | 52 Reading Elem | 62 Foreign/World Lang Elem | 72 Summer School |
| 5 Transportation | 23 Music K-12 | 33 Career/Sch-to-Work Sec | 43 Science Elem | 53 Reading Sec | 63 Foreign/World Lang Sec | 73 Instructional Tech |
| 6 Athletic | 24 Music Elem | 34 Early Childhood Ed | 44 Science Sec | 54 Remedial Reading K-12 | 64 Religious Education K-12 | 74 Inservice Training |
| 7 Health Services | 25 Music Sec | 35 Health/Phys Education | 45 Math K-12 | 55 Remedial Reading Elem | 65 Religious Education Elem | 75 Marketing/Distributive |
| 8 Curric/Instruct K-12 | 16 Instructional Media Svcs | 26 Business Education | 36 Guidance Services K-12 | 46 Math Elem | 56 Remedial Reading Sec | 66 Religious Education Sec | 76 Info Systems |
| 9 Curric/Instruct Elem | 17 Chief Operations Officer | 27 Career & Tech Ed | 37 Guidance Services Elem | 47 Math Sec | 57 Bilingual/ELL | 67 School Board President | 77 Psychological Assess |
| 10 Curric/Instruct Sec | 18 Chief Academic Officer | 28 Technology Education | 38 Guidance Services Sec | 48 English/Lang Arts K-12 | 58 Special Education K-12 | 68 Teacher Personnel | 78 Affirmative Action |
| 11 Federal Program | | | | | | |
| 12 Title I | | | | | | |
| 13 Title V | | | | | | |
| 15 Asst Superintendent | | | | | | |

## • Mesquite Ind School Dist PID: 01011399

3819 Towne Crossing Blvd, Mesquite 75150

972/288-6411
Fax 972/882-7787

**Schools:** 48 \ **Teachers:** 2,632 \ **Students:** 38,266 \
**Special Ed Students:** 4,333 \ **LEP Students:** 10,007 \ **College-Bound:** 52%
\ **Ethnic:** Asian 1%, African American 25%, Hispanic 59%, Native American:
1%, Caucasian 13% \ **Exp:** $419 (High) \ **Poverty:** 19% \ **Title I:** $11,865,152
\ **Special Education:** $7,009,000 \ **Open-Close:** 08/17 - 05/26 \ **DTBP:** $184
(High) \ �facebook 🐦

| | |
|---|---|
| Dr David Vroonland ................................. 1 | Kathryn Bohling ......................... 2,3,15 |
| Peter Pape ......................................... 2,15 | Taylor Morris .................................... 2 |
| Scott Owens ......................................... 3 | Dr Karyn Cummings .......... 4,5,7,15,36,76,91 |
| Lara Stewart ......................................... 4 | Michelle Ramm .................................. 5 |
| Kody Groves ......................................... 6 | Macey Dossey ................................... 7 |
| Dr Treva Franklin ............ 8,11,15,20,23,27,34 | Jennifer Mobley ............................... 11 |
| Dr Angel Rivera ...................... 15,16,70,73 | Beth Nicholas ............. 15,57,58,69,72,73,275 |
| Mary Randall ................................. 15,68 | Mary Woodard ................................. 16 |
| Steve Andre ................................... 20,23 | Kristi Krajca ................................ 27,31 |
| Kim Edwards ...................................... 36 | Kim Johnson .................................... 58 |
| Gary Bingham ..................................... 67 | Donna McAda .................................. 69 |
| Laura Jobe .................................... 71,297 | Cara Jackson ............................... 73,286 |
| Debbie Tanton ............................... 74,273 | Alesia Austin .............................. 76,295 |
| Jennifer Reed ..................................... 88 | |

| Public Schs..Principal | Grd | Prgm | Enr/#Cls | SN | |
|---|---|---|---|---|---|
| A C New Middle Sch<br>3700 S Belt Line Rd, Mesquite 75181<br>Regina Jackson | 6-8 | TV | 912<br>40 | 91% | 972/882-5600<br>Fax 972/882-5620 |
| Achziger Elem Sch<br>3300 Ridge Ranch Rd, Mesquite 75181<br>Kristi Gregory | PK-5 | T | 879 | 74% | 972/290-4180<br>Fax 972/882-4190 |
| B J Smith Elem Sch<br>2300 Mesquite Valley Rd, Mesquite 75149<br>Charelene Goss | PK-5 | T | 391<br>35 | 62% | 972/882-7080<br>Fax 972/882-7090 |
| Ben Tisinger Elem Sch<br>1701 Hillcrest St, Mesquite 75149<br>Amanda Relf | PK-5 | T | 718<br>33 | 91% | 972/882-5120<br>Fax 972/882-5130 |
| Bonnie Gentry Elem Sch<br>1901 Twin Oaks Dr, Mesquite 75181<br>Rashunda Price | PK-6 | T | 916<br>35 | 74% | 972/290-4140<br>Fax 972/290-4150 |
| C W Beasley Elem Sch<br>919 Green Canyon Dr, Mesquite 75150<br>Kelly McCollom | PK-6 | T | 467<br>30 | 62% | 972/882-5160<br>Fax 972/882-5161 |
| Charles Tosch Elem Sch<br>2424 Larchmont Dr, Mesquite 75150<br>Amy Childress | PK-6 | T | 872<br>40 | 89% | 972/882-5000<br>Fax 972/882-5010 |
| Dr J C Cannaday Elem Sch<br>2701 Chisolm Trl, Mesquite 75150<br>Lauren Chism | K-6 | T | 564<br>27 | 81% | 972/882-5060<br>Fax 972/882-5070 |
| Dr James P Terry Middle Sch<br>2351 Edwards Church Rd, Mesquite 75181<br>Kelley Prewitt | 6-8 | T | 1,427<br>40 | 74% | 972/882-5650<br>Fax 972/882-5660 |
| Dr Joey Pirrung Elem Sch<br>1500 Creek Valley Rd, Mesquite 75181<br>Susan Brison | PK-5 | T | 368<br>30 | 70% | 972/882-7170<br>Fax 972/882-7189 |
| Dr John D Horn High Sch<br>3300 E Cartwright Rd, Mesquite 75181<br>Patrick Perkins | 9-12 | TV | 2,622<br>60 | 62% | 972/882-5200<br>Fax 972/882-5292 |
| Dr Linda Henrie Elem Sch<br>253 W Lawson Rd, Dallas 75253<br>**Elizabeth Felton** | PK-6 | T | 961 | 90% | 972/290-4200<br>Fax 972/290-4210 |
| Dr Ralph H Poteet High Sch<br>3300 Poteet Dr, Mesquite 75150<br>**Kelly Long** | 9-12 | TV | 1,791<br>53 | 58% | 972/882-5300<br>Fax 972/882-5355 |
| E S McKenzie Elem Sch<br>3535 Stephens Green Dr, Mesquite 75150<br>**Emmalee Langston** | K-6 | T | 538<br>30 | 84% | 972/882-5140<br>Fax 972/882-5151 |
| Ed Vanston Middle Sch<br>3230 Karla Dr, Mesquite 75150<br>Melissa Smith | 7-8 | TV | 805<br>30 | 82% | 972/882-5801<br>Fax 972/882-5848 |
| Elsie Shands Elem Sch<br>4836 Shands Dr, Mesquite 75150<br>Brandi Lewis | K-6 | T | 825<br>34 | 84% | 972/290-4020<br>Fax 972/290-4030 |
| Florence Black Elem Sch<br>328 Newsom Rd, Mesquite 75149<br>Darla Franklin | PK-6 | T | 639<br>30 | 80% | 972/882-7240<br>Fax 972/882-7250 |
| Frank B Agnew Middle Sch<br>729 Wilkinson Dr, Mesquite 75149<br>**Thomas Reed** | 7-8 | TV | 831 | 78% | 972/882-5750<br>Fax 972/882-5760 |
| Fred McWhorter Elem Sch<br>1700 Hickory Tree Rd, Mesquite 75149<br>Tammi Froning | PK-6 | T | 870<br>35 | 91% | 972/882-7020<br>Fax 972/882-7030 |
| G R Porter Elem Sch<br>517 Via Avenida, Mesquite 75150<br>Becky Rasco | PK-6 | T | 605<br>20 | 73% | 972/290-4000<br>Fax 972/290-4004 |
| Galloway Elem Sch<br>200 Clary Dr, Mesquite 75149<br>April Sarpy | PK-6 | T | 732 | 87% | 972/882-5101<br>Fax 972/882-5110 |
| Georgia Kimball Elem Sch<br>4010 Coryell Way, Mesquite 75150<br>Stacy Sheffield | K-6 | T | 242<br>19 | 65% | 972/290-4120<br>Fax 972/290-4130 |
| Hodges Elem Sch<br>14401 Spring Oak Dr, Balch Springs 75180<br>Dr Kim Broadway | PK-6 | T | 767<br>35 | 90% | 972/290-4040<br>Fax 972/290-4046 |
| I N Range Elem Sch<br>4060 Emerald Dr, Mesquite 75150<br>Kelly Locke | K-6 | T | 763<br>28 | 91% | 972/882-5180<br>Fax 972/882-5190 |
| J C Austin Elem Sch<br>3020 Poteet Dr, Mesquite 75150<br>Dr Jonathan Royle | PK-6 | T | 471<br>22 | 63% | 972/882-7220<br>Fax 972/882-7225 |
| J C Rugel Elem Sch<br>2701 Sybil Dr, Mesquite 75149<br>Dr Amanda Martin | K-6 | T | 458<br>21 | 81% | 972/882-7260<br>Fax 972/882-7270 |
| J H Florence Elem Sch<br>4600 Ashwood Dr, Mesquite 75150<br>Ladonna Gulley | PK-5 | T | 593<br>35 | 87% | 972/290-4080<br>Fax 972/290-4088 |
| Jay Thompson Elem Sch<br>2525 Helen Ln, Mesquite 75181<br>Bridget Mitchell | PK-5 | T | 524<br>38 | 65% | 972/882-7190<br>Fax 972/882-7197 |
| Joe Lawrence Elem Sch<br>3811 Richman Dr, Mesquite 75150<br>**Roshanda Jenkins** | PK-6 | T | 440<br>23 | 77% | 972/882-7000<br>Fax 972/882-7010 |
| John Hanby Elem Sch<br>480 Gross Rd, Mesquite 75149<br>Jessica Eaton | PK-5 | T | 837<br>50 | 90% | 972/882-5040<br>Fax 972/882-5050 |
| Judge Frank Berry Middle Sch<br>2675 Bear Dr, Mesquite 75181<br>Angela Wiggins | 6-8 | TV | 1,106<br>55 | 70% | 972/882-5850<br>Fax 972/882-5888 |
| Lanny Frasier Middle Sch<br>2250 W Scyene Rd, Mesquite 75149<br>Kristy Morse | 6-8 | T | 1,222 | 86% | 972/290-4300 |
| Mary Moss Elem Sch<br>1208 New Market Rd, Mesquite 75149<br>Michael Pierotti | K-6 | T | 434<br>33 | 77% | 972/882-7130<br>Fax 972/882-7146 |
| Ⓐ Mesquite Academy Aec of Choice<br>2704 Motley Dr, Mesquite 75150<br>Abram Joseph | 9-12 | GT | 167<br>15 | 75% | 972/882-7570<br>Fax 972/882-7169<br>facebook |
| Mesquite High Sch<br>300 E Davis St, Mesquite 75149<br>Gerald Sarpy | 9-12 | GTV | 2,642<br>100 | 73% | 972/882-7800<br>Fax 972/882-7876<br>facebook twitter |
| North Mesquite High Sch<br>18201 Lyndon B Johnson Fwy, Mesquite 75150<br>**Kenneth Washington** | 9-12 | TV | 2,591<br>115 | 77% | 972/882-7900<br>Fax 972/882-7908 |

| School | Grd | Prgm | Enr/#Cls | SN |
|---|---|---|---|---|
| R S Kimbrough Middle Sch<br>3900 N Galloway Ave, Mesquite 75150<br>Chris Brott | 7-8 | T | 825<br>50 | 69% 972/882-5900<br>Fax 972/882-5942 🅕 |
| Ruby Shaw Elem Sch<br>707 Purple Sage Trl, Mesquite 75149<br>Jennifer Dumaine | PK-6 | T | 884<br>34 | 73% 972/882-7060<br>Fax 972/882-7070 |
| S M Seabourn Elem Sch<br>2300 Sandy Ln, Mesquite 75149<br>Jewel Kern | PK-6 | T | 724<br>35 | 89% 972/882-7040<br>Fax 972/882-7050 |
| Sam Rutherford Elem Sch<br>1607 Sierra Dr, Mesquite 75149<br>Holly Grubbs | PK-5 | T | 673<br>35 | 80% 972/290-4060<br>Fax 972/290-4068 |
| Sue Ann Mackey Elem Sch<br>14900 N Spring Ridge Cir, Balch Springs 75180<br>Artha Noe | K-5 | T | 671<br>40 | 85% 972/290-4160<br>Fax 972/290-4179 |
| T H McDonald Middle Sch<br>2930 N Town East Blvd, Mesquite 75150<br>**Jordan Simmons** | 7-8 | TV | 1,002<br>30 | 87% 972/882-5700<br>Fax 972/882-5710 |
| Vernon Price Elem Sch<br>630 Stroud Ln, Garland 75043<br>Tomika Johnson | PK-6 | T | 451<br>24 | 85% 972/290-4100<br>Fax 972/290-4110 |
| W O Gray Elem Sch<br>3500 Pioneer Rd, Balch Springs 75180<br>Dr Jennifer LaPlante | PK-6 | T | 634<br>42 | 92% 972/882-7280<br>Fax 972/882-7288 |
| Walter E Floyd Elem Sch<br>3025 Hickory Tree Rd, Balch Springs 75180<br>Kelsey Bowles | PK-6 | T | 798<br>31 | 94% 972/882-7100<br>Fax 972/882-7110 |
| Walter Wilkinson Middle Sch<br>2100 Crest Park Dr, Mesquite 75149<br>**Tomika Johnson** | 6-8 | TV | 523<br>53 | 89% 972/882-5950<br>Fax 972/882-5988 |
| West Mesquite High Sch<br>2500 Memorial Blvd, Mesquite 75149<br>Karen Morris \ Dr Shelly Faulkner | 9-12 | TV | 2,095<br>87 | 80% 972/882-7600<br>Fax 972/882-7611 |
| ⓨ Zack Motley Elem Sch<br>3719 Moon Dr, Mesquite 75150<br>Dr Shawna Delamar | PK-6 | MT | 455<br>17 | 84% 972/882-5080<br>Fax 972/882-5090 |

● **Richardson Ind School Dist** PID: 01011624    469/593-0000
400 S Greenville Ave, Richardson 75081    Fax 469/593-0302

> **Schools:** 56 \ **Teachers:** 2,662 \ **Students:** 38,700 \
> **Special Ed Students:** 4,681 \ **LEP Students:** 9,686 \ **College-Bound:** 63%
> \ **Ethnic:** Asian 7%, African American 23%, Hispanic 39%, Caucasian
> 31% \ **Exp:** $160 (Low) \ **Poverty:** 16% \ **Title I:** $9,822,286 \
> **Special Education:** $6,966,000 \ **Open-Close:** 08/19 - 05/28 \ **DTBP:** $187
> (High) \ 🅕 🅣

| | | | |
|---|---|---|---|
| Dr Jeannie Stone | 1 | David Pate | 2,19 |
| Melody Greig | 2 | Sandra Hayes | 3,15 |
| Rose Ann Martin | 4 | Larry Hudson | 5 |
| Kevin Pitts | 6 | Kristin Benford | 7 |
| Dr Kristin Byno | 8,15 | Brenda Payne | 9,15 |
| Dr Kim Fuller | 11,298 | Dr Christopher Goodson | 15,68 |
| Tabitha Branum | 15 | Julie Briggs | 16* |
| Jeff Bradford | 20 | Henry Hall | 31,73,98 |
| Kellie Sellers | 35 | Ann Marie Yarbrough | 39 |
| Lakeisha Mitchell | 42 | Doug Planey | 47 |
| Jill Halton | 51 | Caroline Armstrong | 57 |
| Dr Cindy Lawrence | 58 | Jessica Sloan | 61 |
| Karen Clardy | 67 | Mary Welch | 68 |
| Nancy Kinzie | 68 | Dr Sandra Moore | 68,273 |
| Terry Harris | 68 | Rachel Walters | 69 |
| Tim Clark | 71 | Melissa Heller | 74,750 |
| Norma Comer | 76,295 | Craig Raley | 79 |
| Dr Matthew Gibbin | 79,83 | Monica Simonds | 81 |
| La'Evening Woodard | 91 | Michael Freeman | 92 |
| Kyndra Johnson | 285 | Adriana Sanchez | 286 |
| Jacob Cortez | 294 | Andy McCormick | 297 |

| Public Schs..Principal | Grd | Prgm | Enr/#Cls | SN |
|---|---|---|---|---|
| Aikin Elem Sch<br>12300 Pleasant Valley Dr, Dallas 75243<br>Roxanne Cheek | PK-6 | T | 713<br>— | 88% 469/593-1820<br>Fax 469/593-1763 🅕🅣 |
| Apollo Junior High Sch<br>1600 Apollo Rd, Richardson 75081<br>Yolanda Gaither | 7-8 | T | 316<br>150 | 59% 469/593-7900<br>Fax 469/593-7911 |
| ⓜ Arapaho Classical Magnet Sch<br>1300 Cypress Dr, Richardson 75080<br>Kristin Strickland | PK-6 | T | 501<br>24 | 24% 469/593-6400<br>Fax 469/593-6448 |
| Audelia Creek Elem Sch<br>12600 Audelia Rd, Dallas 75243<br>Martha Staufert | PK-6 | T | 617<br>— | 84% 469/593-2900<br>Fax 469/593-1763 |
| Berkner High Sch<br>1600 E Spring Valley Rd, Richardson 75081<br>Kristy Cage | 9-12 | TV | 2,621<br>130 | 55% 469/593-7000<br>Fax 469/593-7211 🅣 |
| Berkner STEM Academy<br>1600 E Spring Valley Rd, Richardson 75081<br>Elizabeth Swaner | 9-12 | | 99<br>— | 469/593-7000<br>Fax 469/593-7211 |
| Big Springs Elem Sch<br>3301 W Campbell Rd, Garland 75044<br>**Vince Dawes** | PK-6 | | 295<br>29 | 39% 469/593-8100<br>Fax 469/593-8114 |
| Bowie Elem Sch<br>7643 La Manga Dr, Dallas 75248<br>Chanda Ash | K-6 | | 645<br>40 | 12% 469/593-6000<br>Fax 469/593-6066 |
| Brentfield Elem Sch<br>6767 Brentfield Dr, Dallas 75248<br>Jason Myatt | PK-6 | | 714<br>28 | 8% 469/593-5740<br>Fax 469/593-5723 |
| Canyon Creek Elem Sch<br>2100 Copper Ridge Dr, Richardson 75080<br>Carol Mixon | PK-6 | | 243<br>20 | 10% 469/593-6500<br>Fax 469/593-8114 |
| Carolyn G Bukhair Elem Sch<br>13900 Esperanza Rd, Dallas 75240<br>Roxxy Griffin | 1-6 | T | 639<br>— | 92% 469/593-4900<br>Fax 469/593-4901 🅕🅣 |
| ⓐ Christa McAuliffe Learning Ctr<br>900 S Greenville Ave, Richardson 75081<br>Carmen Steward | 1-12 | T | 11<br>6 | 72% 469/593-5800<br>Fax 469/593-5805 |
| Dartmouth Elem Sch<br>417 Dartmouth Ln, Richardson 75081<br>Stacey Marx | PK-6 | | 399<br>22 | 35% 469/593-8400<br>Fax 469/593-8408 |
| Dobie Primary Sch<br>14040 Rolling Hills Ln, Dallas 75240<br>Kristyn Hart | PK-K | T | 494<br>35 | 93% 469/593-4100<br>Fax 469/593-4011 |
| Dover Elem Sch<br>700 Dover Dr, Richardson 75080<br>Jennifer Balch | PK-6 | T | 595<br>25 | 87% 469/593-4200<br>Fax 469/593-4201 |
| Forest Ln Acad of Arts & Comm<br>9663 Forest Ln, Dallas 75243<br>DeMarcus Watkins | PK-6 | T | 747<br>— | 92% 469/593-1850<br>Fax 469/593-1919 |
| Forest Meadow Jr High Sch<br>9373 Whitehurst Dr, Dallas 75243<br>Kerri Jones | 7-8 | T | 820<br>— | 65% 469/593-1500<br>Fax 469/593-1461 🅕🅣 |
| Forestridge Elem Sch<br>10330 Bunchberry Dr, Dallas 75243<br>Misty Wilson | PK-6 | | 665<br>47 | 77% 469/593-8500<br>Fax 469/593-8502 |
| Greenwood Hills Elem Sch<br>1313 W Shore Dr, Richardson 75080<br>Misti Lehman | K-6 | T | 436<br>25 | 79% 469/593-6100<br>Fax 469/593-6111 🅕🅣 |
| ⓜ Hamilton Park Pacesetter Mag<br>8301 Towns St, Dallas 75243<br>Michael Thomas | PK-6 | T | 623<br>54 | 63% 469/593-3900<br>Fax 469/593-3950 |
| Jess Harben Elem Sch<br>600 S Glenville Dr, Richardson 75081<br>Sharon Newman | PK-6 | T | 427<br>30 | 63% 469/593-8800<br>Fax 469/593-8801 |
| Lake Highlands Elem Sch<br>9501 Ferndale Rd, Dallas 75238<br>Emily Gruninger | PK-6 | T | 725<br>41 | 30% 469/593-2100<br>Fax 469/593-2088 |

| School / Address / Principal | Grd | Prgm | Enr/#Cls | SN | Phone/Fax |
|---|---|---|---|---|---|
| Lake Highlands High Sch<br>9449 Church Rd, Dallas 75238<br>Joshua Delich | 9-12 | TV | 2,728<br>50 | 53% | 469/593-1000<br>Fax 469/593-1030 � 🇫🇧 |
| Lake Highlands Jr High Sch<br>10301 Walnut Hill Ln, Dallas 75238<br>Carrie Breedlove | 7-8 | T | 787 | 54% | 469/593-1600<br>Fax 469/593-1606 |
| Liberty Junior High Sch<br>10330 Lawler Rd, Dallas 75243<br>Cecilia Galvan | 7-8 | T | 631<br>50 | 75% | 469/593-7888<br>Fax 469/593-7764 |
| Mark Twain Elem Sch<br>1200 Larkspur Dr, Richardson 75081<br>Catherine Kelly | PK-6 | T | 519<br>18 | 87% | 469/593-4800<br>Fax 469/593-4799 |
| Ⓜ Math Science & Tech Magnet Sch<br>450 Abrams Rd, Richardson 75081<br>Helena Lopez | PK-6 | T | 515<br>26 | 49% | 469/593-7300<br>Fax 469/593-7301 |
| Ⓐ Memorial Park Academy<br>410 S Greenville Ave, Richardson 75081<br>Bill Gallo | 9-12 | | 20 | | 469/593-0450<br>Fax 469/593-0451 |
| Merriman Park Elem Sch<br>7101 Winedale Dr, Dallas 75231<br>Pharah Hogan | PK-6 | T | 529<br>25 | 43% | 469/593-2800<br>Fax 469/593-2741 |
| Mohawk Elem Sch<br>1500 Mimosa Dr, Richardson 75080<br>Megan Cox | K-6 | | 470<br>17 | 7% | 469/593-6600<br>Fax 469/593-6610 |
| Moss Haven Elem Sch<br>9202 Moss Farm Ln, Dallas 75243<br>Philip Henderson | PK-6 | | 440<br>25 | 18% | 469/593-2200<br>Fax 469/593-2158 |
| Northlake Elem Sch<br>10059 Ravensway Dr, Dallas 75238<br>Mary Kellagher | PK-6 | T | 571<br>45 | 82% | 469/593-2300<br>Fax 469/593-2309 |
| Northrich Elem Sch<br>1301 Custer Rd, Richardson 75080<br>**Lindsey Gammaro** | PK-6 | T | 388<br>26 | 61% | 469/593-6200<br>Fax 469/593-6201 |
| Northwood Hills Elem Sch<br>14532 Meandering Way, Dallas 75254<br>David Lewis | PK-6 | T | 389<br>20 | 64% | 469/593-4300<br>Fax 469/593-4301 🇫🇧 |
| O Henry Elem Sch<br>4100 Tyree Dr, Garland 75042<br>Jennifer Wills | PK-6 | T | 447<br>24 | 82% | 469/593-8200<br>Fax 469/593-4201 |
| Parkhill Junior High Sch<br>16500 Shadybank Dr, Dallas 75248<br>Farrah Smock | 7-8 | T | 655<br>40 | 42% | 469/593-5600<br>Fax 469/593-5500 |
| Pearce High Sch<br>1600 N Coit Rd, Richardson 75080<br>Mike Evans | 9-12 | V | 1,221<br>65 | 33% | 469/593-5000<br>Fax 469/593-5169 |
| Prairie Creek Elem Sch<br>2120 E Prairie Creek Dr, Richardson 75080<br>Kyle Stuard | PK-6 | | 283<br>18 | 2% | 469/593-6300<br>Fax 469/593-6308 |
| Prestonwood Elem Sch<br>6525 La Cosa Dr, Dallas 75248<br>Pam Aitken | PK-6 | T | 414<br>16 | 41% | 469/593-6700<br>Fax 469/593-6712 |
| Richardson Heights Elem Sch<br>101 N Floyd Rd, Richardson 75081<br>Jenny Lanier | PK-6 | T | 441<br>26 | 67% | 469/593-4400<br>Fax 469/593-4401 |
| Richardson High Sch<br>1250 W Belt Line Rd, Richardson 75080<br>Christopher Choat | 9-12 | TV | 2,693<br>110 | 48% | 469/593-3000<br>Fax 469/593-3010 |
| Richardson North Jr High Sch<br>1820 N Floyd Rd, Richardson 75080<br>Joshua Eason | 7-8 | T | 694<br>50 | 43% | 469/593-5300 |
| Richardson Terrace Elem Sch<br>300 N Dorothy Dr, Richardson 75081<br>Michele Zupa | PK-6 | T | 530<br>35 | 68% | 469/593-8700<br>Fax 469/593-8781 |
| Ⓜ Richardson West Arts & Tech<br>1309 Holly Dr, Richardson 75080<br>Kimberly Kindred | 7-8 | T | 739<br>40 | 54% | 469/593-3700<br>Fax 469/593-3666 |
| Richland Elem Sch<br>550 Park Bend Dr, Richardson 75081<br>**Pharah Hogan** | PK-6 | T | 600<br>26 | 67% | 469/593-4650<br>Fax 469/593-4654 |
| Risd Academy<br>13630 Coit Rd, Dallas 75240<br>Rebeca Carrero | PK-6 | T | 825<br>48 | 92% | 469/593-3300<br>Fax 469/593-3307 |
| Skyview Elem Sch<br>9229 Meadowknoll Dr, Dallas 75243<br>Katrina Collins | PK-6 | T | 721<br>32 | 88% | 469/593-2400<br>Fax 469/593-4401 |
| Spring Creek Elem Sch<br>7667 Roundrock Rd, Dallas 75248<br>Sharon Erickson | PK-6 | | 339<br>20 | 17% | 469/593-4500<br>Fax 469/593-4501 |
| Spring Valley Elem Sch<br>13535 Spring Grove Ave, Dallas 75240<br>Brona Hudson | PK-6 | | 391<br>37 | 85% | 469/593-4600<br>Fax 469/593-4609 |
| Springridge Elem Sch<br>1801 E Spring Valley Rd, Richardson 75081<br>Katie Barrett | K-6 | T | 351<br>21 | 68% | 469/593-8600<br>Fax 469/593-8603 |
| Stults Road Elem Sch<br>8700 Stults Rd, Dallas 75243<br>**Jason Barnett \ Jennifer Balch** | PK-6 | T | 726<br>25 | 81% | 469/593-2500<br>Fax 469/593-2521 |
| Thurgood Marshall Elem Sch<br>9666 W Ferris Branch Blvd, Dallas 75243<br>Charmaine Curtis | PK-6 | T | 600 | 94% | 469/593-6800<br>Fax 469/593-6801 |
| Wallace Elem Sch<br>9921 Kirkhaven Dr, Dallas 75238<br>**Tonya Anderson** | PK-6 | T | 738 | 57% | 469/593-2600<br>Fax 469/593-2610 |
| Ⓜ Westwood JHS Math Sci Ldrshp<br>7630 Arapaho Rd, Dallas 75248<br>Jennie Bates | 7-8 | T | 671<br>60 | 54% | 469/593-3600<br>Fax 469/593-3508 |
| White Rock Elem Sch<br>9229 Chiswell Rd, Dallas 75238<br>Becky Stevens | PK-6 | | 799<br>24 | 11% | 469/593-2700<br>Fax 469/593-2706 |
| Yale Elem Sch<br>1900 E Collins Blvd, Richardson 75081<br>Carrie Greer | PK-6 | | 366<br>27 | 33% | 469/593-8300<br>Fax 469/593-8362 🇫🇧 |

---

● **Sunnyvale Ind School Dist** PID: 01012018   972/226-5974<br>417 E Tripp Rd, Sunnyvale 75182   Fax 972/226-6882

**Schools:** 3 \ **Teachers:** 124 \ **Students:** 2,200 \ **Special Ed Students:** 187 \ **LEP Students:** 81 \ **Ethnic:** Asian 24%, African American 10%, Hispanic 12%, Caucasian 54% \ **Exp:** $403 (High) \ **Poverty:** 5% \ **Title I:** $74,042 \ **Special Education:** $199,000 \ **Open-Close:** 08/18 - 06/01 \ **DTBP:** $350 (High)

Doug Williams ............ 1
Keith Adams ............ 3
John Settle ............ 6*
Erica Lawless ............ 11,58
Brad Cravens ............ 67
Buck Baskins ............ 73,76
Amy Tuttle ............ 294
Kyle Penn ............ 2,17,752
Karl Williams ............ 5
Christi Morgan ............ 8,15,79,298
Michael Fennig ............ 57*
Glenda McMahan ............ 69,88,270*
Jennifer Settle ............ 286

| Public Schs..Principal | Grd | Prgm | Enr/#Cls | SN | Phone/Fax |
|---|---|---|---|---|---|
| Sunnyvale Elem Sch<br>416 Hounsel Ln, Sunnyvale 75182<br>Brittany Dlabaj | PK-4 | T | 692 | 16% | 972/226-7601<br>Fax 972/226-4812 |
| Sunnyvale High Sch<br>222 N Collins Rd, Sunnyvale 75182<br>Brian Nickel | 9-12 | T | 552 | 15% | 972/203-4600<br>Fax 972/226-2834 |
| Sunnyvale Middle Sch<br>216 N Collins Rd, Sunnyvale 75182<br>Brandon Tunnell | 5-8 | T | 601<br>45 | 14% | 972/226-2922<br>Fax 972/226-0982 |

---

| | | | |
|---|---|---|---|
| 79 Student Personnel | 91 Safety/Security | 275 Response To Intervention | 298 Grant Writer/Ptnrships |
| 80 Driver Ed/Safety | 92 Magnet School | 277 Remedial Math K-12 | 750 Chief Innovation Officer |
| 81 Gifted/Talented | 93 Parental Involvement | 280 Literacy Coach | 751 Chief of Staff |
| 82 Video Services | 95 Tech Prep Program | 285 STEM | 752 Social Emotional Learning |
| 83 Substance Abuse Prev | 97 Chief Infomation Officer | 286 Digital Learning | |
| 84 Erate | 98 Chief Technology Officer | 288 Common Core Standards | **Other School Types** |
| 85 AIDS Education | 270 Character Education | 294 Accountability | Ⓐ = Alternative School |
| 88 Alternative/At Risk | 271 Migrant Education | 295 Network System | Ⓒ = Charter School |
| 89 Multi-Cultural Curriculum | 273 Teacher Mentor | 296 Title II Programs | Ⓜ = Magnet School |
| 90 Social Work | 274 Before/After Sch | 297 Webmaster | Ⓨ = Year-Round School |

**School Programs**
A = Alternative Program
G = Adult Classes
M = Magnet Program
T = Title I Schoolwide
V = Career & Tech Ed Programs

**Social Media**
🇫 = Facebook
🇧 = Twitter

New Schools are shaded
New Superintendents and Principals are bold
Personnel with email addresses are underscored

**TX—117**

## DALLAS CATHOLIC SCHOOLS

• **Diocese of Dallas Ed Office** PID: 01012367
3725 Blackburn St, Dallas 75219

214/528-2240
Fax 214/522-1753

**Schools: 35 \ Students: 14,823**

Listing includes only schools located in this county. See District Index for location of Diocesan Offices.

| Catholic Schs..Principal | Grd | Prgm | Enr/#Cls SN |
|---|---|---|---|
| Bishop Dunne Catholic Sch<br>3900 Rugged Dr, Dallas 75224<br>Mary Marchiony | 6-12 | | 624<br>40   214/339-6561<br>Fax 214/339-1438 |
| Bishop Lynch High Sch<br>9750 Ferguson Rd, Dallas 75228<br>Chad Riley | 9-12 | | 1,150<br>50   214/324-3607<br>Fax 214/324-3600 |
| Christ the King Sch<br>4100 Colgate Ave, Dallas 75225<br>Lisa Bosco | K-8 | | 430<br>18   214/365-1234<br>Fax 214/365-1236 |
| Cistercian Preparatory Sch<br>3660 Cistercian Rd, Irving 75039<br>Paul McCormick | 5-12 | | 347<br>22   469/499-5400<br>Fax 469/499-5440 |
| Good Shepherd Catholic Sch<br>214 S Garland Ave, Garland 75040<br>Gail Bassett | PK-8 | | 227<br>20   972/272-6533<br>Fax 972/272-0512 |
| Highlands Sch<br>1451 E Northgate Dr, Irving 75062<br>Dr Michael Pennell | PK-12 | | 400<br>32   972/554-1980<br>Fax 972/721-1691 |
| Holy Family Catholic Academy<br>2323 Cheyenne St, Irving 75062<br>Kathy Carruth | PK-8 | | 257<br>11   972/255-0205<br>Fax 972/252-0448 |
| Holy Trinity Catholic Sch<br>3815 Oak Lawn Ave, Dallas 75219<br>Marian Davis | PK-8 | | 150<br>11   214/526-5113<br>Fax 214/526-4524 |
| Immaculate Conception Sch<br>400 NE 17th St, Grand Prairie 75050<br>Linda Santos | PK-8 | | 135<br>22   972/264-8777<br>Fax 972/264-7742 |
| Jesuit College Prep Sch<br>12345 Inwood Rd, Dallas 75244<br>Thomas Garrison | 9-12 | | 1,090<br>47   972/387-8700<br>Fax 972/661-9349 |
| Mary Immaculate Sch<br>14032 Dennis Ln, Farmers BRNCH 75234<br>Sr Mary Zuberbueler | K-8 | | 430<br>21   972/243-7105<br>Fax 972/241-7678 |
| Mt Saint Michael Catholic Sch<br>4500 W Davis St, Dallas 75211<br>Renee Ozier | PK-8 | | 117<br>16   214/337-0244<br>Fax 214/339-1702 |
| Notre Dame Sch<br>2018 Allen St, Dallas 75204<br>Theresa Francis | Spec | | 150<br>12   214/720-3911<br>Fax 214/720-3913 |
| Our Lady of Perpetual Help Sch<br>7625 Cortland Ave, Dallas 75235<br>Maria Searle | K-8 | | 198<br>11   214/351-3396<br>Fax 214/351-9889 |
| Santa Clara Catholic Academy<br>321 Calumet Ave, Dallas 75211<br>Stephanie Matous | PK-8 | | 203<br>14   214/333-9423<br>Fax 214/333-2556 |
| St Bernard of Clairvaux Sch<br>1420 Old Gate Ln, Dallas 75218<br>Laurie Senecal | PK-8 | | 200<br>10   214/321-2897<br>Fax 214/321-4060 |
| St Cecilia Sch<br>635 Mary Cliff Rd, Dallas 75208<br>Lydia Torrez | PK-8 | | 215<br>11   214/948-8628<br>Fax 214/948-4956 |
| St Elizabeth of Hungary Sch<br>4019 S Hampton Rd, Dallas 75224<br>Jennifer Borth | PK-8 | | 250<br>24   214/331-5139<br>Fax 214/467-4346 |
| St Joseph Catholic Sch<br>600 S Jupiter Rd, Richardson 75081<br>Fran Thompson | K-8 | | 300<br>22   972/234-4679<br>Fax 972/692-4594 |
| St Mary of Carmel Sch<br>1716 Singleton Blvd, Dallas 75212<br>Kaitlyn Aguilar | PK-8 | | 159<br>10   214/748-2934<br>Fax 214/760-9052 |
| St Monica Catholic Sch<br>4140 Walnut Hill Ln, Dallas 75229<br>Phillip Riley | PK-8 | | 750<br>48   214/351-5688<br>Fax 214/352-2608 |
| St Patrick Sch<br>9635 Ferndale Rd, Dallas 75238<br>Julie Hendry | PK-8 | | 555<br>24   214/348-8070<br>Fax 214/503-7230 |
| St Paul the Apostle Sch<br>720 S Floyd Rd, Richardson 75080<br>Courtney Demakas | PK-8 | | 120<br>26   972/235-3263<br>Fax 972/690-1542 |
| St Philip & St Augustine Acad<br>8151 Military Pkwy, Dallas 75227<br>Dianne Brungardt | PK-8 | | 350<br>12   214/381-4973<br>Fax 214/381-0466 |
| St Pius X Sch<br>3030 Gus Thomasson Rd, Dallas 75228<br>Tana Scott | PK-8 | | 371<br>18   972/279-2339<br>Fax 972/613-2059 |
| St Rita Catholic Sch<br>12525 Inwood Rd, Dallas 75244<br>Michael Wixted | K-8 | G | 658<br>50   972/239-3203<br>Fax 972/934-0657 |
| St Thomas Aquinas Sch<br>3741 Abrams Rd, Dallas 75214<br>Lauren Roberts \ Jennifer Watts | PK-8 | | 863<br>44   214/826-0566<br>Fax 214/826-0251 |
| Ursuline Academy<br>4900 Walnut Hill Ln, Dallas 75229<br>Andrea Shurley | 9-12 | | 820<br>60   469/232-1800<br>Fax 469/232-1836 |

## DALLAS PRIVATE SCHOOLS

| Private Schs..Principal | Grd | Prgm | Enr/#Cls SN |
|---|---|---|---|
| Akiba Academy of Dallas<br>12324 Merit Dr, Dallas 75251<br>Danielle Rothenberg | PK-8 | | 356<br>  214/295-3400<br>Fax 214/295-3405 |
| Alcuin Montessori Sch<br>6144 Churchill Way, Dallas 75230<br>Paige Whitney \ Verna Salta \ Margaret Davis | PK-12 | | 535<br>25   972/239-1745<br>Fax 972/934-8727 |
| Ashleys Private Sch<br>310 W Belt Line Rd, Cedar Hill 75104<br>Michelle Emmert | PK-5 | | 125<br>972/291-1313 |
| Autism Treatment Center<br>10503 Metric Dr, Dallas 75243<br>Carolyn Garver | Spec | | 22<br>972/644-2076<br>Fax 972/644-5650 |
| Balch Springs Chrn Academy<br>11524 Seagoville Rd, Balch Springs 75180<br>Renia Peters | K-12 | | 100<br>17   972/286-8511<br>Fax 972/286-1379 |
| Bending Oaks High Sch<br>11884 Greenville Ave Ste 120, Dallas 75243<br>Beth Rule | 8-12 | A | 50<br>10   972/669-0000<br>Fax 972/232-2290 |
| Berean Christian Academy<br>1000 E 6th St, Irving 75060<br>Leon Adkins | K-6 | | 34<br>4   972/438-1440<br>Fax 972/554-6807 |
| Berne Acad Private Sch<br>1311 Johns Ave, Lancaster 75134<br>Theresa Smith | PK-12 | | 38<br>8   972/218-7373<br>Fax 972/218-7372 |

| | | | | | | | | | | | | |
|---|---|---|---|---|---|---|---|---|---|---|---|---|
| 1 | Superintendent | 8 | Curric/Instruct K-12 | 19 | Chief Financial Officer | 29 | Family/Consumer Science | 39 | Social Studies K-12 | 49 | English/Lang Arts Elem | 59 | Special Education Elem | 69 | Academic Assessment |
| 2 | Bus/Finance/Purchasing | 9 | Curric/Instruct Elem | 20 | Art K-12 | 30 | Adult Education | 40 | Social Studies Elem | 50 | English/Lang Arts Sec | 60 | Special Education Sec | 70 | Research/Development |
| 3 | Buildings And Grounds | 10 | Curric/Instruct Sec | 21 | Art Elem | 31 | Career/Sch-to-Work K-12 | 41 | Social Studies Sec | 51 | Reading K-12 | 61 | Foreign/World Lang K-12 | 71 | Public Information |
| 4 | Food Service | 11 | Federal Program | 22 | Art Sec | 32 | Career/Sch-to-Work Elem | 42 | Science K-12 | 52 | Reading Elem | 62 | Foreign/World Lang Elem | 72 | Summer School |
| 5 | Transportation | 12 | Title I | 23 | Music K-12 | 33 | Career/Sch-to-Work Sec | 43 | Science Elem | 53 | Reading Sec | 63 | Foreign/World Lang Sec | 73 | Instructional Tech |
| 6 | Athletic | 13 | Title V | 24 | Music Elem | 34 | Early Childhood Ed | 44 | Science Sec | 54 | Remedial Reading K-12 | 64 | Religious Education K-12 | 74 | Inservice Training |
| 7 | Health Services | 15 | Asst Superintendent | 25 | Music Sec | 35 | Health/Phys Education | 45 | Math K-12 | 55 | Remedial Reading Elem | 65 | Religious Education Elem | 75 | Marketing/Distributive |
| | | 16 | Instructional Media Svcs | 26 | Business Education | 36 | Guidance Services K-12 | 46 | Math Elem | 56 | Remedial Reading Sec | 66 | Religious Education Sec | 76 | Info Systems |
| | | 17 | Chief Operations Officer | 27 | Career & Tech Ed | 37 | Guidance Services Elem | 47 | Math Sec | 57 | Bilingual/ELL | 67 | School Board President | 77 | Psychological Assess |
| | | 18 | Chief Academic Officer | 28 | Technology Education | 38 | Guidance Services Sec | 48 | English/Lang Arts K-12 | 58 | Special Education K-12 | 68 | Teacher Personnel | 78 | Affirmative Action |

| School | Grades | Enroll/Staff | Phone/Fax |
|---|---|---|---|
| **Brighter Horizons Academy**<br>3145 Medical Plaza Dr, Garland 75044<br>Dr Iram Shaikh-Jilani | PK-12 | 800<br>45 | 972/675-2062<br>Fax 972/675-2063 |
| **Calvary Lutheran Sch**<br>9807 Church Rd, Dallas 75238<br>Jim Henrickson | PK-8 | 85<br>5 | 214/343-7457<br>Fax 214/348-1424 |
| **Calvary Temple Christian Acad**<br>3150 South Outline Road, Mesquite 75181<br>Betty Vickery | PK-12 | 60<br>4 | 972/286-4935<br>Fax 972/557-0045 |
| **Cambridge School of Dallas**<br>9330 N Central Expy, Dallas 75231<br>B Paul Wolfe | 6-12 | 100<br>12 | 214/357-2995<br>Fax 214/357-8008 |
| **Canterbury Collegiate Academy**<br>1708 N Westmoreland Rd, Desoto 75115<br>Misty Stern | K-12 | 200<br>37 | 214/672-9263 |
| **Cathedral of Life Chrn Sch**<br>12908 Seagoville Rd, Balch Springs 75180<br>David Gibbs | K-12 | 28<br>4 | 972/286-4845<br>Fax 972/287-4357 |
| **Classical School of Dallas**<br>9150 Garland Rd, Dallas 75218<br>Chuck Evans | PK-7 | 50 | 214/810-0341 |
| **Coram Deo Academy-Dallas**<br>7777 Lyndon B Johnson Fwy, Dallas 75251<br>Beverly Mullin | PK-8 | 100 | 972/385-6410 |
| **Covenant Sch**<br>7300 Valley View Ln, Dallas 75240<br>Charles Evans | K-12 | 512 | 214/358-5818<br>Fax 214/358-5809 |
| **Cristo Rey Dallas College Prep**<br>1064 N Saint Augustine Dr, Dallas 75217<br>Christine Roman | 9-11 | 378 | 469/844-7956 |
| **Cross of Christ Lutheran Sch**<br>512 N Cockrell Hill Rd, Desoto 75115<br>Lila Fusssell | PK-K | 85<br>6 | 972/223-9586 |
| **Crossroads Academy**<br>820 E Wintergreen Rd, Cedar Hill 75104<br>Cindy Lowe | 1-12 | 100 | 972/293-9093<br>Fax 972/293-9376 |
| **Dallas Academy**<br>950 Tiffany Way, Dallas 75218<br>Elizabeth Murski | 1-12 | 200<br>32 | 214/324-1481<br>Fax 214/327-8537 |
| **Dallas Christian Academy**<br>4025 N Central Expy, Dallas 75204<br>Maeli Dang | PK-12 | 140<br>12 | 214/528-6327<br>Fax 214/528-6450 |
| **Dallas Christian Sch**<br>1515 Republic Pkwy, Mesquite 75150<br>Courtney Pine \ Jennifer Webb | PK-12 | 866<br>40 | 972/270-5495<br>Fax 972/270-7581 |
| **Dallas International Sch**<br>6039 Churchill Way, Dallas 75230<br>Catherine Levy | PK-12 | 600 | 972/991-6379<br>Fax 972/991-6608 |
| **DeSoto Pvt Sch & Day Care Ctr**<br>301 E Belt Line Rd, Desoto 75115<br>Kenneth Larson | PK-6 | 400<br>40 | 972/223-6450<br>Fax 972/230-0629 |
| **Episcopal Sch Dallas-Mid Upper**<br>4100 Merrell Rd, Dallas 75229<br>Tracey Shirey \ Jonathan Chein \ Henry Heil | 5-12 | 651 | 214/358-4368<br>Fax 214/357-1232 |
| **Episcopal Sch of Dallas-Lower**<br>4344 Colgate Ave, Dallas 75225<br>Chelle Wabrek | PK-4 | 432<br>32 | 214/353-5818<br>Fax 214/353-5861 |
| **Fairhill Sch**<br>16150 Preston Rd, Dallas 75248<br>Caroline Stamos | Spec | 220<br>23 | 972/233-1026<br>Fax 972/233-8205 |
| **Family Christian Academy**<br>10715 Garland Rd, Dallas 75218<br>Richard Mitchell | K-6 | 61 | 214/324-4399<br>Fax 214/324-5549 |
| **Faustina Academy**<br>1621 W Grauwyler Rd, Irving 75061<br>Christina Mehaffey | PK-12 | 80 | 972/254-6726 |
| **Fellowship Collegiate Academy**<br>1821 W Camp Wisdom Rd, Dallas 75232<br>Karen Gosby | PK-8 | 350 | 214/672-9200<br>Fax 214/672-9201 |
| **Firewheel Christian Academy**<br>5500 Lavon Dr, Garland 75040<br>Stephanie Fuchs | PK-9 | 180<br>10 | 972/495-0851<br>Fax 972/495-3927 |
| **First Baptist Academy**<br>7894 Samuell Blvd, Dallas 75228<br>Julia Shoemake \ Joseph Davis | PK-12 | 366<br>25 | 972/453-1321 |
| **Fusion Academy-Dallas**<br>8128 Park Ln Ste 123, Dallas 75231<br>Christina Tipton | 6-12 | 50 | 214/363-4615 |
| **Gardner Preparatory Sch**<br>100 N Houston School Rd, Lancaster 75146<br>Lazonda Gardner | PK-1 | 50 | 972/275-1539 |
| **Garland Christian Academy**<br>1522 Lavon Dr, Garland 75040<br>Dr Cole Sandlin | PK-12 | 320<br>20 | 972/487-0043<br>Fax 972/276-4079 |
| **Glen Oaks Sch**<br>12105 Plano Rd, Dallas 75243<br>Donna Sharber | PK-K | 100<br>11 | 972/231-3135<br>Fax 972/644-6373 |
| **Good Shepherd Episcopal Sch**<br>11110 Midway Rd, Dallas 75229<br>Casey Martin \ Lori Rolke | PK-8 | 530<br>40 | 214/357-1610<br>Fax 214/357-4105 |
| **Grace Academy of Dallas**<br>11306A Inwood Rd, Dallas 75229<br>Jim Clarke | PK-6 | 220<br>17 | 214/696-5648<br>Fax 214/696-8713 |
| **Grace Fellowship Christian Sch**<br>3052 N Belt Line Rd, Sunnyvale 75182<br>Edris Carr | K-12 | 62 | 972/226-4499<br>Fax 972/226-0242 |
| **Greenhill Sch**<br>4141 Spring Valley Rd, Addison 75001<br>Michael Simpson \ Susan Palmer \ Trevor Worcester | PK-12 | 1,250 | 972/628-5400<br>Fax 972/404-8217 |
| **Highland PK Presbyterian Sch**<br>3821 University Blvd, Dallas 75205<br>Ashley Hickey | PK-5 | 280<br>21 | 214/525-6500<br>Fax 214/525-6501 |
| **Highlander Sch**<br>9120 Plano Rd, Dallas 75238<br>Jill Reed | PK-6 | 150<br>14 | 214/348-3220<br>Fax 214/341-0401 |
| **Hockaday Sch**<br>11600 Welch Rd, Dallas 75229<br>Randal Rhodus \ Linda Kramer \ Lisa Culbertson | PK-12 | 1,087<br>180 | 214/363-6311<br>Fax 214/360-6527 |
| **Iant Quranic Academy**<br>840 Abrams Rd, Richardson 75081<br>Mathew Moes | K-12 | 201 | 972/231-5698<br>Fax 972/231-6707 |
| **Iboc Christian Academy**<br>7710 S Westmoreland Rd, Dallas 75237<br>Sherrye Vaden | 1-3 | 75<br>10 | 972/572-4262<br>Fax 972/709-3888 |
| **Islamic School of Irving**<br>2555 Esters Rd, Irving 75062<br>Sadia Haq | PK-12 | 475 | 972/812-2230<br>Fax 972/257-8640 |
| **Kessler Sch**<br>1215 Turner Ave, Dallas 75208<br>Vanessa Ullmann | PK-6 | 140 | 214/942-2220<br>Fax 214/942-1223 |
| **Kiest Park Christian Academy**<br>2719 S Hampton Rd, Dallas 75224<br>Armida Ortega | PK-K | 69<br>6 | 214/331-1536<br>Fax 214/330-0469 |
| **Lake Cities Montessori Sch**<br>1935 E Centerville Rd, Garland 75041<br>Masi Adibi | PK-2 | 105 | 214/440-4930 |
| **Lakehill Preparatory Sch**<br>2720 Hillside Dr, Dallas 75214<br>John Trout \ Kaye Hauschild \ Bob Yttredahl | K-12 | 400<br>200 | 214/826-2931<br>Fax 214/826-4623 |
| **Lutheran High Sch**<br>8494 Stults Rd, Dallas 75243<br>Bradley Krause \ Todd Nitz | 7-12 | 200<br>32 | 214/349-8912<br>Fax 214/340-3095 |

| School | Grades | | Enroll | Phone |
|--------|--------|--|--------|-------|
| Meadow Oaks Academy<br>1412 S Belt Line Rd, Mesquite 75149<br>Nancy Albright | PK-5 | | 135 | 972/285-6895<br>Fax 972/285-7647 |
| Merit Academy<br>2825 Valley View Ln Ste 100, Dallas 75234<br>Darian Fowler | Spec | | 20 | 214/736-8375<br>Fax 214/377-4942 |
| Merrywood Sch<br>807 S Cockrell Hill Rd, Duncanville 75137<br>Peggy Ogden | PK-6 | | 200<br>17 | 972/298-0130<br>Fax 972/298-0277 |
| Mesorah High School for Girls<br>12712 Park Central Dr Ste B190, Dallas 75251<br>Avraham Kosowsky | 9-12 | | 45 | 214/420-1990<br>Fax 214/420-1993 |
| Momentous Sch<br>106 E 10th St, Dallas 75203<br>Sandy Nobles | PK-5 | | 248<br>18 | 214/915-1890 |
| New Life Christian Academy<br>2626 Gus Thomasson Rd, Dallas 75228<br>David Galvan | PK-12 | | 35 | 214/327-6522 |
| North Dallas Adventist Academy<br>2800 Custer Pkwy, Richardson 75080<br>Rosy Arizaga \ Becky Clark \ Melonie Wolfe | PK-12 | | 150<br>15 | 972/234-6322<br>Fax 972/234-6325 |
| Oak Crest Private Sch<br>1200 E Jackson Rd Bldg 2, Carrollton 75006<br>Hildegard Jessup | PK-8 | | 55 | 214/483-5400 |
| Oak Hill Academy<br>9407 Midway Rd, Dallas 75220<br>Elizabeth Willis \ Anne Acton \ Joya Jacob | PK-12 | | 140<br>12 | 214/353-8804<br>Fax 214/353-8839 |
| Our Redeemer Lutheran Sch<br>7611 Park Ln, Dallas 75225<br>Corey Moss | PK-6 | | 140<br>14 | 214/368-1371<br>Fax 214/368-1473 |
| Parish Episcopal Sch<br>4101 Sigma Rd, Dallas 75244<br>Laurel Ash \ Dr Jennifer Wilson \ William Jennings | PK-12 | | 1,100 | 972/239-8011<br>Fax 972/991-1237 |
| Parkside Baptist Academy<br>1729 Gross Rd, Mesquite 75149<br>Don Crutcher | K-12 | | 70 | 972/613-7833 |
| Preston Hollow Presby Sch<br>9800 Preston Rd, Dallas 75230<br>Patty McNally | K-6 | | 120<br>13 | 214/368-3886<br>Fax 214/368-2255 |
| Providence Christian Sch<br>5002 W Lovers Ln, Dallas 75209<br>Carol Chester \ Tag Green | K-8 | | 450 | 214/302-2800<br>Fax 214/357-6251 |
| Qalam Collegiate Academy<br>1111 Digital Dr # 101, Richardson 75081<br>Elora Bashir | 5-10 | | 19 | 972/437-2526<br>Fax 972/437-2524 |
| Radiant STEM Academy<br>2001 W Walnut Hill Ln, Irving 75038<br>Nuzhat Hye | PK-7 | | 275 | 214/245-5125 |
| Redeemer Montessori Sch<br>2700 Warren Cir, Irving 75062<br>Shannon Flowers | PK-6 | | 130<br>6 | 972/257-3517<br>Fax 972/258-9882 |
| Rise School of Dallas<br>600 Preston Rd, Dallas 75205<br>Kari Zerbe | Spec | | 56<br>5 | 214/373-7473<br>Fax 214/373-6545 |
| Scofield Christian Sch<br>7730 Abrams Rd, Dallas 75231<br>Dr Traci Tucker | PK-6 | | 100<br>10 | 214/349-6843<br>Fax 214/342-2061 |
| Shelton Sch<br>15720 Hillcrest Rd, Dallas 75248<br>Christine Davis \ Amy Kelton \ Jenny Cheatham | Spec | | 850 | 972/774-1772 |
| Southwest Adventist Jr Academy<br>1600 Bonnie View Rd, Dallas 75203<br>Kymberly Mayes | PK-8 | | 31<br>3 | 214/948-1666<br>Fax 214/948-1125 |
| St John's Episcopal Sch<br>848 Harter Rd, Dallas 75218<br>Jayme Johnson \ Pam Jordan | PK-8 | | 500<br>35 | 214/328-9131<br>Fax 214/320-0205 |
| St Mark's School of Texas<br>10600 Preston Rd, Dallas 75230<br>Sherri Darver \ Dean Clayman \ Colin Igoe | 1-12 | | 855 | 214/346-8000<br>Fax 214/346-8002 |
| St Philip's Episcopal Sch<br>1600 Pennsylvania Ave, Dallas 75215<br>Kellee Murrell | PK-6 | G | 255<br>20 | 214/421-5221<br>Fax 214/428-5371 |
| Stonegate Christian Academy<br>1705 Esters Rd, Irving 75061<br>Matt Maples | K-12 | | 151<br>21 | 972/790-0070 |
| The Humanist Academy<br>2925 Skyway Cir N V, Irving 75038<br>Vijay Shah | K-5 | | 16 | 972/646-1085 |
| The Westwood School-Upper<br>14240 Midway Rd, Dallas 75244<br>Heather Lourcey | 9-12 | | 60 | 972/239-8598<br>Fax 972/239-1028 |
| Trinity Christian Academy<br>17001 Addison Rd, Addison 75001<br>Anne Badger \ Scott Berthel \ Kyle Morrill | PK-12 | | 1,500 | 972/931-8325<br>Fax 972/931-8923 |
| Trinity Christian Sch<br>1231 E Pleasant Run Rd, Cedar Hill 75104<br>James Swearingin \ Debbie Durling | PK-12 | | 501<br>40 | 972/291-2505<br>Fax 972/291-4739 |
| Tyler Street Christian Academy<br>915 W 9th St, Dallas 75208<br>Kelly Betts | PK-12 | | 150<br>22 | 214/941-9717<br>Fax 214/941-0324 |
| Vanguard Preparatory Sch<br>4240 Sigma Rd, Dallas 75244<br>Becky Hodnett | Spec | | 100 | 972/404-1616<br>Fax 972/404-1641 |
| Wesley Prep Sch<br>9200 Inwood Rd, Dallas 75220<br>Carol Johnson | PK-6 | | 315 | 214/706-9568<br>Fax 214/346-3462 |
| West Dallas Community Sch<br>2300 Canada Dr, Dallas 75212<br>David Valverde | PK-8 | | 246<br>25 | 214/634-1927<br>Fax 214/688-1928 |
| Westwood Montessori/IB Sch<br>14340 Proton Rd, Dallas 75244<br>Heather Lourcey | PK-12 | | 250 | 972/239-8598<br>Fax 972/239-1028 |
| White Rock Montessori Sch<br>1601 Oates Dr, Dallas 75228<br>Connie Laufersky | PK-8 | | 175<br>7 | 214/324-5580<br>Fax 214/324-5671 |
| White Rock North Sch<br>9727 White Rock Trl, Dallas 75238<br>Amy Adams | PK-6 | | 325<br>15 | 214/348-7410<br>Fax 214/348-3109 |
| Winston Sch<br>5707 Royal Ln, Dallas 75229<br>Rebbie Evans | Spec | | 196<br>36 | 214/691-6950<br>Fax 214/691-1509 |
| Xavier Preparatory Sch<br>100 N Houston School Rd, Lancaster 75146<br>Lazonda Gardner | PK-3 | | 35 | 214/741-4485 |
| Yavneh Academy-Dallas<br>12324 Merit Dr, Dallas 75251<br>Maury Grebenau | 9-12 | | 130<br>13 | 214/295-3500<br>Fax 214/295-3505 |
| Zion Lutheran Sch<br>6121 E Lovers Ln, Dallas 75214<br>Jeff Thorman | PK-8 | | 294<br>10 | 214/363-1630<br>Fax 214/361-2049 |

## DALLAS REGIONAL CENTERS

- **Region 10 Ed Service Center** PID: 01012032    972/348-1700
  400 E Spring Valley Rd, Richardson 75081    Fax 972/231-3642

Gordon Taylor .......................................1,11    Sue Hayes ...........................................2,19
Mark Keahey ............................................4    Dr Dana West ...........................................8
Alison Fears ...........................................11    Jana Burns ............................................15
Dr Holly Bishop ......................................16    Angela Neal ...........................................34
Cathryn King .........................................58    Stephen Quisenberry ...........................68

| | | | | | | |
|--|--|--|--|--|--|--|
| 1 | Superintendent | 8 | Curric/Instruct K-12 | 19 | Chief Financial Officer | 29 Family/Consumer Science |
| 2 | Bus/Finance/Purchasing | 9 | Curric/Instruct Elem | 20 | Art K-12 | 30 Adult Education |
| 3 | Buildings And Grounds | 10 | Curric/Instruct Sec | 21 | Art Elem | 31 Career/Sch-to-Work K-12 |
| 4 | Food Service | 11 | Federal Program | 22 | Art Sec | 32 Career/Sch-to-Work Elem |
| 5 | Transportation | 12 | Title I | 23 | Music K-12 | 33 Career/Sch-to-Work Sec |
| 6 | Athletic | 13 | Title V | 24 | Music Elem | 34 Early Childhood Ed |
| 7 | Health Services | 15 | Asst Superintendent | 25 | Music Sec | 35 Health/Phys Education |
| | | 16 | Instructional Media Svcs | 26 | Business Education | 36 Guidance Services K-12 |
| | | 17 | Chief Operations Officer | 27 | Career & Tech Ed | 37 Guidance Services Elem |
| | | 18 | Chief Academic Officer | 28 | Technology Education | 38 Guidance Services Sec |

| | | | | | |
|--|--|--|--|--|--|
| 39 Social Studies K-12 | 49 English/Lang Arts Elem | 59 Special Education Elem | 69 Academic Assessment |
| 40 Social Studies Elem | 50 English/Lang Arts Sec | 60 Special Education Sec | 70 Research/Development |
| 41 Social Studies Sec | 51 Reading K-12 | 61 Foreign/World Lang K-12 | 71 Public Information |
| 42 Science K-12 | 52 Reading Elem | 62 Foreign/World Lang Elem | 72 Summer School |
| 43 Science Elem | 53 Reading Sec | 63 Foreign/World Lang Sec | 73 Instructional Tech |
| 44 Science Sec | 54 Remedial Reading K-12 | 64 Religious Education K-12 | 74 Inservice Training |
| 45 Math K-12 | 55 Remedial Reading Elem | 65 Religious Education Elem | 75 Marketing/Distributive |
| 46 Math Elem | 56 Remedial Reading Sec | 66 Religious Education Sec | 76 Info Systems |
| 47 Math Sec | 57 Bilingual/ELL | 67 School Board President | 77 Psychological Assess |
| 48 English/Lang Arts K-12 | 58 Special Education K-12 | 68 Teacher Personnel | 78 Affirmative Action |

## DAWSON COUNTY

## DAWSON PUBLIC SCHOOLS

- **Dawson Ind School Dist** PID: 01012795    806/489-7461
  Highway 137, Welch 79377    Fax 806/489-7463

> **Schools:** 1 \ **Teachers:** 10 \ **Students:** 140 \ **Special Ed Students:** 7
> \ **LEP Students:** 10 \ **College-Bound:** 100% \ **Ethnic:** Hispanic 70%,
> Caucasian 30% \ **Exp:** $629 (High) \ **Poverty:** 19% \ **Title I:** $20,196 \
> **Open-Close:** 08/19 - 05/21 \ **DTBP:** $362 (High)

| | | | | |
|---|---|---|---|---|
| Layne Steets .................................. 1,11,73 | Mike Hendricks .................................. 3,4,5* |
| Robbie Phipps .................................. 7* | Melanie Hayes .................................. 36,69,88* |
| Dana Mahan .................................. 58* | Kalith Brown .................................. 67 |
| Ruby Castro .................................. 271 | |

| Public Schs..Principal | Grd | Prgm | Enr/#Cls | SN |
|---|---|---|---|---|
| Dawson Sch | K-12 | TV | 140 | 64% 806/489-7461 |
| Highway 137, Welch 79377 | | | 13 | Fax 806/489-7546 |
| Jeffrey Fleenor | | | | |

- **Klondike Ind School Dist** PID: 01012824    806/462-7334
  2911 County Road H, Lamesa 79331    Fax 806/462-7333

> **Schools:** 1 \ **Teachers:** 24 \ **Students:** 249 \ **Special Ed Students:** 10 \
> **LEP Students:** 16 \ **College-Bound:** 90% \ **Ethnic:** African American 2%,
> Hispanic 31%, Native American: 1%, Caucasian 66% \ **Exp:** $642 (High) \
> **Poverty:** 17% \ **Title I:** $44,107 \ **Open-Close:** 08/13 - 05/14 \ **DTBP:** $255
> (High)

| | | | | |
|---|---|---|---|---|
| Steve McLaren .................................. 1,11 | Dalton Degraffenreid .................................. 2* |
| Dalton Degraffenreid .................................. 2,6 | Evaristo Acevedo .................................. 3* |
| Dolores Cobos .................................. 4* | Dolores Cobos .................................. 4 |
| Terry Morris .................................. 5* | Danielle Therwanger .................................. 8,83,288 |
| Julie Dossey .................. 36,69,88,270,271* | Hailey White .................................. 58* |
| Kenny Ferguson .................................. 67 | Randy Leonard .................................. 73,295* |

| Public Schs..Principal | Grd | Prgm | Enr/#Cls | SN |
|---|---|---|---|---|
| Klondike Sch | PK-12 | TV | 249 | 32% 806/462-7332 |
| 2911 County Road H, Lamesa 79331 | | | 15 | |
| Danielle Therwhanger | | | | |

- **Lamesa Ind School Dist** PID: 01012862    806/872-5461
  212 N Houston Ave, Lamesa 79331    Fax 806/872-6220

> **Schools:** 5 \ **Teachers:** 122 \ **Students:** 1,800 \ **Special Ed Students:** 220
> \ **LEP Students:** 104 \ **Ethnic:** Asian 1%, African American 4%, Hispanic
> 83%, Caucasian 12% \ **Exp:** $729 (High) \ **Poverty:** 28% \ **Title I:** $799,306 \
> **Open-Close:** 08/19 - 05/27 \ **DTBP:** $372 (High)

| | | | | |
|---|---|---|---|---|
| Jim Knight .................................. 1 | Liz Poage .................................. 2,294 |
| Sammy Sanchez .................................. 3,5,91 | Gary Pope .................................. 4 |
| Gregg Moreland .................................. 6* | Steve Ruiz .................................. 7* |
| Doug Morris ...... 8,11,57,83,286,288,296,298 | Keith Emfinger .................. 16,73,286,295* |
| Stacy Stewart .................. 34,58,77* | Amy Baker .................................. 36* |
| Kelli Merritt .................................. 67 | Chris Riggins .................................. 68* |

| Public Schs..Principal | Grd | Prgm | Enr/#Cls | SN |
|---|---|---|---|---|
| Lamesa High Sch | 9-12 | ATV | 128 | 69% 806/872-8385 |
| 600 N 14th St, Lamesa 79331 | | | 50 | Fax 806/872-6008 |
| Jerry Jerabek | | | | |
| Lamesa Middle Sch | 6-8 | TV | 334 | 80% 806/872-8301 |
| N Bryan St & S 1st St, Lamesa 79331 | | | 37 | Fax 806/872-2949 |
| Serapio Arguijo | | | | |
| Ⓐ Lamesa Success Academy | 9-12 | T | 29 | 82% 806/872-5410 |
| 212 N Houston Ave, Lamesa 79331 | | | | |
| David Ritchey | | | | |
| North Elem Sch | 3-5 | T | 397 | 75% 806/872-5428 |
| 601 N 14th St, Lamesa 79331 | | | 27 | Fax 806/872-8324 |
| Jennifer Stewart | | | | |
| South Elem Sch | PK-2 | T | 513 | 77% 806/872-5401 |
| 2000 S 8th St, Lamesa 79331 | | | 29 | Fax 806/872-9161 |
| **David Ritchey** | | | | |

- **Sands Consolidated ISD** PID: 01012941    432/353-4888
  101 1st St, Ackerly 79713    Fax 432/353-4650

> **Schools:** 1 \ **Teachers:** 20 \ **Students:** 247 \ **Special Ed Students:** 17
> \ **LEP Students:** 32 \ **College-Bound:** 80% \ **Ethnic:** Asian 1%, African
> American 1%, Hispanic 41%, Native American: 2%, Caucasian 56% \
> **Exp:** $711 (High) \ **Poverty:** 19% \ **Title I:** $37,814 \ **Open-Close:** 08/14 -
> 05/14 \ **DTBP:** $326 (High)

| | | | | |
|---|---|---|---|---|
| Wayne Henderson .................................. 1 | Amy Grumbles .................................. 2 |
| Chris Spivey .................................. 3* | Jana Spivey .................................. 4* |
| Fred Brown .................................. 5 | Lenny Morrow .................................. 8,12* |
| Tommy Stags .................................. 67 | Tana Howard .................................. 69,83,270* |
| Scott Ragle .................................. 73* | Debi Barraza .................................. 271* |

| Public Schs..Principal | Grd | Prgm | Enr/#Cls | SN |
|---|---|---|---|---|
| Sands Sch | PK-12 | TV | 247 | 55% 432/353-4744 |
| 101 1st St, Ackerly 79713 | | | 25 | |
| Lenny Morrow | | | | |

## DE WITT COUNTY

## DE WITT PUBLIC SCHOOLS

- **Cuero Ind School Dist** PID: 01013684    361/275-1900
  960 E Broadway St, Cuero 77954    Fax 361/275-8957

> **Schools:** 4 \ **Teachers:** 152 \ **Students:** 1,990 \ **Special Ed Students:** 234
> \ **LEP Students:** 71 \ **College-Bound:** 65% \ **Ethnic:** African American
> 11%, Hispanic 50%, Caucasian 38% \ **Exp:** $459 (High) \ **Poverty:** 26% \
> **Title I:** $582,961 \ **Special Education:** $474,000 \ **Open-Close:** 08/17 -
> 06/03 \ **DTBP:** $341 (High) \ 🇫 ⓣ

| | | | | |
|---|---|---|---|---|
| Dr Micah Dyer .................................. 1 | Mark Iacoponelli .................................. 2,15 |
| Dwayne Noack .................................. 3,91 | Sandra Hernandez .................................. 4 |
| Bo Daniel .................................. 5 | Jack Alverez .................................. 6 |
| Wanda Hays .................................. 7 | Dr Pamela Long Botham .................................. |
| 8,11,15,57,88,285,288,298 | |
| Jennifer Hudgeons .................................. 16 | Oscar Ray .................................. 16,73,286,295 |
| Stacey Porter .................................. 27* | Brittany Braden .................................. 36* |
| Megan Castillo .................................. 36* | Gina Rico .................................. 38 |

| | | | |
|---|---|---|---|
| 79 Student Personnel | 91 Safety/Security | 275 Response To Intervention | 298 Grant Writer/Ptnrships |
| 80 Driver Ed/Safety | 92 Magnet School | 277 Remedial Math K-12 | 750 Chief Innovation Officer |
| 81 Gifted/Talented | 93 Parental Involvement | 280 Literacy Coach | 751 Chief of Staff |
| 82 Video Services | 95 Tech Prep Program | 285 STEM | 752 Social Emotional Learning |
| 83 Substance Abuse Prev | 97 Chief Infomation Officer | 286 Digital Learning | |
| 84 Erate | 98 Chief Technology Officer | 288 Common Core Standards | Other School Types |
| 85 AIDS Education | 270 Character Education | 294 Accountability | Ⓐ = Alternative School |
| 88 Alternative/At Risk | 271 Migrant Education | 295 Network System | Ⓒ = Charter School |
| 89 Multi-Cultural Curriculum | 273 Teacher Mentor | 296 Title II Programs | Ⓜ = Magnet School |
| 90 Social Work | 274 Before/After Sch | 297 Webmaster | Ⓨ = Year-Round School |

School Programs
A = Alternative Program
G = Adult Classes
M = Magnet Program
T = Title I Schoolwide
V = Career & Tech Ed Programs

Social Media
🇫 = Facebook
ⓣ = Twitter

New Schools are shaded
New Superintendents and Principals are bold
Personnel with email addresses are underscored

TX—121

Kim Alverez .................................58,77
Connie Phillips .............................76,294
Ruby Rodriguez ...........................93

Courtney Moore ...........................67
Dave Truman ..............................84,295

| Public Schs..Principal | Grd | Prgm | Enr/#Cls | SN |
|---|---|---|---|---|
| Cuero High Sch<br>920 E Broadway St, Cuero 77954<br>**Kimberly Fleener** | 9-12 | ATV | 640<br>40 | 48% 361/275-1900<br>Fax 361/275-2430 |
| Cuero Junior High Sch<br>608 Jr High Dr, Cuero 77954<br>**Jennifer Dracos** | 6-8 | ATV | 473<br>32 | 61% 361/275-1900<br>Fax 361/275-6912 |
| Hunt Elem Sch<br>550 Industrial Blvd, Cuero 77954<br>**Bridgette Cerny** | 2-5 | AT | 547<br>21 | 66% 361/275-1900<br>Fax 361/275-3474 |
| John C French Elem Sch<br>611 E Prairie St, Cuero 77954<br>**Jennifer Bauer** | PK-1 | AT | 329<br>22 | 73% 361/275-1900<br>Fax 361/275-2698 |

• **Meyersville Ind School Dist** PID: 01013737
1897 Meyersville Rd, Meyersville 77974
361/277-5817
Fax 361/275-5034

**Schools:** 1 \ **Teachers:** 9 \ **Students:** 137 \ **Special Ed Students:** 9 \
**Ethnic:** African American 3%, Hispanic 21%, Caucasian 76% \ **Exp:** $650
(High) \ **Poverty:** 14% \ **Title I:** $37,009 \ **Open-Close:** 08/12 - 05/20 \
**DTBP:** $397 (High)

Kelly Dunn ...................................1,11
Gay Davis ............................16,57,73,295*

Kelly Washwell ...........................2,752
Johnny Jank ...............................67

| Public Schs..Principal | Grd | Prgm | Enr/#Cls | SN |
|---|---|---|---|---|
| Meyersville Elem Sch<br>1897 Meyersville Rd, Meyersville 77974<br>**Kelly Dunn** | PK-8 | T | 137<br>13 | 53% 361/275-3639 |

• **Nordheim Ind School Dist** PID: 01013751
500 Broadway, Nordheim 78141
361/938-5211
Fax 361/938-5266

**Schools:** 1 \ **Teachers:** 17 \ **Students:** 149 \ **Special Ed Students:** 9
\ **College-Bound:** 50% \ **Ethnic:** African American 3%, Hispanic 39%,
Caucasian 59% \ **Exp:** $517 (High) \ **Poverty:** 19% \ **Title I:** $27,812 \
**Open-Close:** 08/28 - 06/01 \ **DTBP:** $326 (High)

John Kevin Wilson ...........................1
Mary Castillo ..................................4
Pamela Remmers ...........................67

Kimberly Saunders ...........................2
Carlton Williams ...........................6*
Ron Squires ..................................73

| Public Schs..Principal | Grd | Prgm | Enr/#Cls | SN |
|---|---|---|---|---|
| Nordheim Sch<br>500 Broadway, Nordheim 78141<br>**Lisa Karnei** | PK-12 | TV | 149<br>14 | 62% 361/938-5211 |

• **Westhoff Ind School Dist** PID: 01013787
244 Lynch Ave, Westhoff 77994
830/236-5519
Fax 830/236-5583

**Schools:** 1 \ **Teachers:** 7 \ **Students:** 80 \ **Special Ed Students:** 4
\ **LEP Students:** 7 \ **Ethnic:** African American 1%, Hispanic 42%,
Caucasian 56% \ **Exp:** $725 (High) \ **Poverty:** 33% \ **Title I:** $33,922 \
**Open-Close:** 08/12 - 05/25 \ **DTBP:** $293 (High)

David Kennedy ...................1,11,73,83,84
Paddy Burwell ...............................67

Maryhelen Robles ...........................2

| Public Schs..Principal | Grd | Prgm | Enr/#Cls | SN |
|---|---|---|---|---|
| Westhoff Elem Sch<br>244 Lynch Ave, Westhoff 77994<br>David Kennedy | PK-8 | T | 80<br>8 | 69% 830/236-5519 |

• **Yoakum Ind School Dist** PID: 01013804
315 E Gonzales St, Yoakum 77995
361/293-3162
Fax 361/293-6678

**Schools:** 5 \ **Teachers:** 147 \ **Students:** 1,500 \ **Special Ed Students:** 249
\ **LEP Students:** 253 \ **College-Bound:** 50% \ **Ethnic:** African American
8%, Hispanic 66%, Caucasian 27% \ **Exp:** $534 (High) \ **Poverty:** 23% \
**Title I:** $529,630 \ **Special Education:** $6,000 \ **Open-Close:** 08/19 - 05/27 \
**DTBP:** $342 (High)

Tom Kelley .......................................1
Eric Thiry .........................................3
Bo Robinson ....................................6
Chad Rothbauer ......8,11,57,58,69,77,83,88
Kim Kvinta ....................................37*
Glen Kusak ....................................67

Chris Kvinta .....................2,15,71,91,271
Dwight Watson .................................5
Amanda Murphree ...........................7,85
Jason Fling ...............16,73,76,84,295,298
Courtney Zinke ...............................38*
Lynette Pate ..................................68,79

| Public Schs..Principal | Grd | Prgm | Enr/#Cls | SN |
|---|---|---|---|---|
| Yoakum High Sch<br>104 Poth St, Yoakum 77995<br>**Chris Wegener** | 9-12 | TV | 506<br>65 | 52% 361/293-3442<br>Fax 361/293-2145 |
| Yoakum Intermediate Sch<br>208 Aubrey St, Yoakum 77995<br>**Gabe Adamek** | 3-5 | T | 374<br>20 | 75% 361/293-3001<br>Fax 361/293-6562 |
| Yoakum Junior High Sch<br>103 McKinnon St, Yoakum 77995<br>**Patrick Frank** | 6-8 | TV | 353<br>25 | 77% 361/293-3111<br>Fax 361/293-5787 |
| Yoakum Primary Annex Sch<br>412 Simpson St, Yoakum 77995<br>**Pat Brewer** | PK-K | | 190<br>9 | 361/293-2011<br>Fax 361/293-6937 |
| Yoakum Primary Sch<br>800 W Grand Ave, Yoakum 77995<br>**Darrin Stansberry** | 1-2 | T | 233<br>13 | 82% 361/293-2011<br>Fax 361/293-2688 |

• **Yorktown Ind School Dist** PID: 01013866
331 W Main St, Yorktown 78164
361/564-2252
Fax 361/564-2254

**Schools:** 3 \ **Teachers:** 43 \ **Students:** 513 \ **Special Ed Students:** 61
\ **LEP Students:** 6 \ **Ethnic:** African American 2%, Hispanic 51%,
Caucasian 47% \ **Exp:** $524 (High) \ **Poverty:** 25% \ **Title I:** $182,978 \
**Open-Close:** 08/26 - 06/03 \ **DTBP:** $323 (High)

Katherine Kuenstler ...........................1
Jason Chapa ....................................3
Stacey Boldrin ..................................5
Brandi Olsovsky ..............................37
Joseph Fabaia .............................52,59
Blake Bryant ................................73,84

Erin Merts .....................2,11,30,271
Diana Trevino ..................................4
John Caffey .....................................6
Tracy Heafley .................................38
Nelda Sertuche ...............................67
Delia Ramirez .................................76

| Public Schs..Principal | Grd | Prgm | Enr/#Cls | SN |
|---|---|---|---|---|
| Yorktown Elem Sch<br>416 W 4th St, Yorktown 78164<br>**Laura Patek** | PK-5 | T | 243<br>18 | 59% 361/564-2252<br>Fax 361/564-2270 |
| Yorktown High Sch<br>417 W 4th St, Yorktown 78164<br>**Ashley Chandler** | 9-12 | T | 156<br>30 | 65% 361/564-2252<br>Fax 361/564-2274 |
| Yorktown Junior High Sch<br>418 W 4th St, Yorktown 78164<br>**Ashley Chandler** | 6-8 | T | 116<br>20 | 61% 361/564-2252<br>Fax 361/564-2289 |

| | | | | | | | | |
|---|---|---|---|---|---|---|---|---|
| **1** Superintendent | **8** Curric/Instruct K-12 | **19** Chief Financial Officer | **29** Family/Consumer Science | **39** Social Studies K-12 | **49** English/Lang Arts Elem | **59** Special Education Elem | **69** Academic Assessment |
| **2** Bus/Finance/Purchasing | **9** Curric/Instruct Elem | **20** Art K-12 | **30** Adult Education | **40** Social Studies Elem | **50** English/Lang Arts Sec | **60** Special Education Sec | **70** Research/Development |
| **3** Buildings And Grounds | **10** Curric/Instruct Sec | **21** Art Elem | **31** Career/Sch-to-Work K-12 | **41** Social Studies Sec | **51** Reading K-12 | **61** Foreign/World Lang K-12 | **71** Public Information |
| **4** Food Service | **11** Federal Program | **22** Art Sec | **32** Career/Sch-to-Work Elem | **42** Science K-12 | **52** Reading Elem | **62** Foreign/World Lang Elem | **72** Summer School |
| **5** Transportation | **12** Title I | **23** Music K-12 | **33** Career/Sch-to-Work Sec | **43** Science Elem | **53** Reading Sec | **63** Foreign/World Lang Sec | **73** Instructional Tech |
| **6** Athletic | **13** Title V | **24** Music Elem | **34** Early Childhood Ed | **44** Science Sec | **54** Remedial Reading K-12 | **64** Religious Education K-12 | **74** Inservice Training |
| **7** Health Services | **14** Asst Superintendent | **25** Music Sec | **35** Health/Phys Education | **45** Math K-12 | **55** Remedial Reading Elem | **65** Religious Education Elem | **75** Marketing/Distributive |
| | **15** Asst Superintendent | **26** Business Education | **36** Guidance Services K-12 | **46** Math Elem | **56** Remedial Reading Sec | **66** Religious Education Sec | **76** Info Systems |
| | **16** Instructional Media Svcs | **27** Career & Tech Ed | **37** Guidance Services Elem | **47** Math Sec | **57** Bilingual/ELL | **67** School Board President | **77** Psychological Assess |
| | **17** Chief Operations Officer | **28** Technology Education | **38** Guidance Services Sec | **48** English/Lang Arts K-12 | **58** Special Education K-12 | **68** Teacher Personnel | **78** Affirmative Action |

## DE WITT CATHOLIC SCHOOLS

- **Diocese of Victoria Ed Office** PID: 02181727
  Listing includes only schools located in this county. See District Index for location of Diocesan Offices.

| Catholic Schs..Principal | Grd | Prgm | Enr/#Cls | SN |
|---|---|---|---|---|
| St Michael Sch | PK-6 | | 73 | 361/274-3854 |
| 208 N McLeod St, Cuero 77954 | | | 9 | Fax 361/275-3135 |
| Jennifer Saenz | | | | |

## DEAF SMITH COUNTY

## DEAF SMITH PUBLIC SCHOOLS

- **Hereford Ind School Dist** PID: 01012989      806/363-7600
  601 N 25 Mile Ave, Hereford 79045      Fax 806/363-7699

**Schools:** 9 \ **Teachers:** 296 \ **Students:** 4,100 \ **Special Ed Students:** 393 \ **LEP Students:** 683 \ **Ethnic:** African American 1%, Hispanic 89%, Caucasian 10% \ **Exp:** $340 (High) \ **Poverty:** 24% \ **Title I:** $1,292,937 \ **Special Education:** $811,000 \ **Open-Close:** 08/12 - 05/28 \ **DTBP:** $157 (High) \ [f]

| | | | |
|---|---|---|---|
| Sheri Blankenship | 1 | Adianna Wolf | 2,11,296 |
| Joe Mendez | 3,16,17,73,84,286,295 | Joel Evertt | 3 |
| Ruth Evenson | 5 | Brenda Kitten | 6,35* |
| Don Delozier | 6,35 | Joy Kilian | 7,58,72 |
| Mark Stokes | 8,18,45,69,294 | Yolanda Gavina | 11,83,271,274 |
| Michelle Delozier | 28,30,31* | Ruth Vessels | 57 |
| Clay McNeely | 67 | Christie Volmer | 68 |

| Public Schs..Principal | Grd | Prgm | Enr/#Cls | SN | |
|---|---|---|---|---|---|
| Aikman Elem Sch | K-5 | T | 414 | 91% | 806/363-7640 |
| 900 Avenue K, Hereford 79045 | | | 22 | | |
| Sandra Maldonado | | | | | |
| Bluebonnet Elem Sch | K-5 | T | 430 | 94% | 806/363-7650 |
| 221 16th St, Hereford 79045 | | | 18 | | Fax 806/363-7657 |
| Andrea Brown | | | | | |
| Hcal | 9-12 | T | 67 | 61% | 806/363-7720 |
| 241 Avenue H, Hereford 79045 | | | | | |
| Tony Barker | | | | | |
| Hereford High Sch | 9-12 | GTV | 1,114 | 64% | 806/363-7620 |
| 200 Avenue F, Hereford 79045 | | | 50 | | Fax 806/363-7688 |
| Richard Sauceda | | | | | |
| Hereford Junior High Sch | 6-7 | TV | 600 | 86% | 806/363-7630 |
| 704 La Plata St, Hereford 79045 | | | 60 | | Fax 806/363-7697 |
| Cuca Salinas | | | | | |
| Hereford Preparatory Academy | 8-8 | T | 294 | 84% | 806/363-7740 |
| 704 La Plata St Ste B, Hereford 79045 | | | | | Fax 806/363-7637 |
| Linda Gonzalez | | | | | [f] |
| Northwest Elem Sch | K-5 | T | 483 | 81% | 806/363-7660 |
| 400 Moreman St, Hereford 79045 | | | 21 | | Fax 806/363-7662 |
| Nancy Neusch | | | | | [f] |
| Tierra Blanca Early Child Ctr | PK-PK | | 340 | | 806/363-7680 |
| 7615 Columbia Dr, Hereford 79045 | | | | | |
| Brenda Bice | | | | | |

| Public Schs..Principal | Grd | Prgm | Enr/#Cls | SN | |
|---|---|---|---|---|---|
| West Central Elem Sch | K-5 | T | 403 | 90% | 806/363-7690 |
| 120 Campbell St, Hereford 79045 | | | | | |
| Ortencia Mendez | | | | | |

- **Walcott Ind School Dist** PID: 01013086      806/289-5222
  4275 Highway 214, Hereford 79045      Fax 806/289-5224

**Schools:** 1 \ **Teachers:** 10 \ **Students:** 146 \ **Special Ed Students:** 16 \ **LEP Students:** 13 \ **Ethnic:** Hispanic 85%, Caucasian 15% \ **Exp:** $1,351 (High) \ **Poverty:** 16% \ **Open-Close:** 08/28 - 05/25 \ **DTBP:** $192 (High)

| | | | |
|---|---|---|---|
| Dr Bill McLaughlin | 1,11,288 | Leslynn Arfsten | 2 |
| Cindy Hernandez | 4 | Darla Bryant | 12,296* |
| Natalie Sims | 16,73* | Vickie Matthews | 57* |
| Tammy Northcutt | 59* | Lucy McGowan | 67 |
| Tonya Gruhlkey | 271* | | |

| Public Schs..Principal | Grd | Prgm | Enr/#Cls | SN | |
|---|---|---|---|---|---|
| Walcott Elem Sch | PK-6 | T | 146 | 61% | 806/289-5222 |
| 4275 Highway 214, Hereford 79045 | | | 8 | | |
| Tonya Gruhlkey | | | | | |

## DEAF SMITH CATHOLIC SCHOOLS

- **Diocese of Amarillo Ed Office** PID: 01047659
  Listing includes only schools located in this county. See District Index for location of Diocesan Offices.

| Catholic Schs..Principal | Grd | Prgm | Enr/#Cls | SN |
|---|---|---|---|---|
| St Anthony's Elem Sch | PK-6 | | 109 | 806/364-1952 |
| 120 W Park Ave, Hereford 79045 | | | 8 | Fax 806/364-7179 |
| Ana Copeland | | | | |

## DEAF SMITH PRIVATE SCHOOLS

| Private Schs..Principal | Grd | Prgm | Enr/#Cls | SN |
|---|---|---|---|---|
| Nazarene Christian Academy | K-6 | | 70 | 806/364-1697 |
| 1410 La Plata St, Hereford 79045 | | | 8 | Fax 806/364-7973 |
| Shannon Victor | | | | |

## DELTA COUNTY

## DELTA PUBLIC SCHOOLS

- **Cooper Ind School Dist** PID: 01013103      903/395-2111
  350 W McKinney Ave, Cooper 75432      Fax 903/395-2117

**Schools:** 2 \ **Teachers:** 63 \ **Students:** 800 \ **Special Ed Students:** 87 \ **LEP Students:** 14 \ **Ethnic:** African American 9%, Hispanic 15%, Native American: 1%, Caucasian 75% \ **Exp:** $529 (High) \ **Poverty:** 24% \ **Title I:** $254,145 \ **Open-Close:** 08/13 - 06/04 \ **DTBP:** $348 (High) \ [f] [t]

| | | | |
|---|---|---|---|
| Denicia Hohenberger | 1,11,57 | James Roan | 3 |
| Lafreceia Robinson | 4 | Denice Vaughn | 5 |

Rod Casterona .......................................... 6*
Richard Roan ........................................... 12*
Thomas Darden ....................................... 67
Charles Rutledge ..........................73,76,295
Jean Howard ............................................ 271*

Lou Ann Murray ...................................7,85*
Amber Norris .....................................15,286*
Neali Landers .......................................... 68
Charles Rutledge .................................... 76*

| Public Schs..Principal | Grd | Prgm | Enr/#Cls | SN |
|---|---|---|---|---|
| Cooper Elem Sch<br>1401 SW 8th St, Cooper 75432<br>Cody Gibson | PK-5 | T | 346<br>24 | 75% 903/395-2111<br>Fax 903/395-2019 |
| Cooper Jr Sr High Sch<br>823 FM 1528, Cooper 75432<br>Richard Roan | 6-12 | ATV | 412<br>40 | 55% 903/395-2111<br>Fax 903/395-2382 |

- **Fannindel Ind School Dist** PID: 01013141
  601 W Main St, Ladonia 75449
  903/367-7251
  Fax 903/367-7252

**Schools:** 2 \ **Teachers:** 18 \ **Students:** 200 \ **Special Ed Students:** 27 \ **LEP Students:** 5 \ **College-Bound:** 80% \ **Ethnic:** Asian 3%, African American 34%, Hispanic 9%, Caucasian 54% \ **Exp:** $318 (High) \ **Poverty:** 27% \ **Title I:** $92,994 \ **Open-Close:** 08/12 - 05/21 \ **DTBP:** $335 (High)

Brad Lane ............................... 1,11,73,83
Larry Braley ................................................ 5
Don Childress ........................................... 16*
Wanda White ........................................... 67

Discha Threlkelb ........................................ 2
Chiquita Wiburn-Hill ................8,88,288,752
Jana Stancil ............................................. 58

| Public Schs..Principal | Grd | Prgm | Enr/#Cls | SN |
|---|---|---|---|---|
| Fannindel Elem Sch<br>409 W Main St, Pecan Gap 75469<br>Marjory Eaton | PK-5 | T | 95<br>8 | 91% 903/359-6314<br>Fax 903/359-6315 |
| Fannindel High Sch<br>601 W Main St, Ladonia 75449<br>Jamie Babineaux | 6-12 | TV | 73<br>12 | 85% 903/367-7251 |

# DENTON COUNTY

## DENTON PUBLIC SCHOOLS

- **Argyle Ind School Dist** PID: 01013177
  800 Eagle Dr, Argyle 76226
  940/464-7241
  Fax 940/464-7297

**Schools:** 5 \ **Teachers:** 197 \ **Students:** 3,100 \ **Special Ed Students:** 309 \ **LEP Students:** 72 \ **College-Bound:** 90% \ **Ethnic:** Asian 3%, African American 2%, Hispanic 13%, Caucasian 82% \ **Exp:** $318 (High) \ **Poverty:** 4% \ **Title I:** $56,918 \ **Open-Close:** 08/17 - 05/21 \ **DTBP:** $326 (High)

Dr Telena Wright ........................................ 1
Thomas Ledford ........................................ 3
Albert Rutledge .......................................... 5
Deana Steeber ..8,11,18,280,285,288,296,298
Sam Slaton ............................................... 67
Paul Haggen ..................................77,88,275
Rick Herrin ............................................... 98

Elizabeth Stewart ................................2,19
Amy Bresnahan .......................................... 4
Todd Rogers ............................................... 6*
Greg Royar ........................... 16,73,76,295
Chris Daniel ............................................. 68
Paul Haggan ........................77,83,88,275*

| Public Schs..Principal | Grd | Prgm | Enr/#Cls | SN |
|---|---|---|---|---|
| Argyle High Sch<br>191 S Highway 377, Argyle 76226<br>John King | 9-12 | | 919<br>25 | 7% 940/262-7777<br>Fax 940/262-7783 |

| | Grd | Prgm | Enr/#Cls | SN |
|---|---|---|---|---|
| Argyle Intermediate Sch<br>800 Eagle Dr, Argyle 76226<br>**Dawn Jordan** | 4-5 | | 442 | 10% 940/464-5100<br>Fax 940/464-7245 |
| Argyle Middle Sch<br>6601 Canyon Falls Rd, Argyle 76226<br>Scott Gibson | 6-8 | | 770<br>32 | 9% 940/246-2126<br>Fax 940/262-4039 |
| Argyle West Elem Sch<br>1741 Old Justin Rd, Argyle 76226<br>Renee Funderburg | PK-5 | | 401 | 940/464-7241 |
| Hilltop Elem Sch<br>1050 Harrison Ln, Argyle 76226<br>**Dona Lumsden** | PK-3 | | 930<br>40 | 13% 940/464-0564<br>Fax 940/464-4017 |

- **Aubrey Ind School Dist** PID: 01013191
  415 Tisdell Ln, Aubrey 76227
  940/668-0060
  Fax 940/365-2627

**Schools:** 5 \ **Teachers:** 158 \ **Students:** 2,500 \ **Special Ed Students:** 205 \ **LEP Students:** 73 \ **College-Bound:** 60% \ **Ethnic:** African American 8%, Hispanic 18%, Native American: 1%, Caucasian 72% \ **Exp:** $494 (High) \ **Poverty:** 7% \ **Title I:** $161,076 \ **Open-Close:** 08/17 - 05/27 \ **DTBP:** $315 (High) \

Dr David Belding ...............................1,11
Eric Huff ............................................3,17
Sherri Clement ........................................ 4
Keith Ivy .................................................. 6
Joanie Rouk .............................................. 8
Terry McNabb ........................................ 15
Dr Joey Saxon ....................................... 67
Sandra Ungerwood ...........................83,85

Eric Hough ......................................2,19
Marilyn Hampton ....................................... 3
Yolanda Tarver .......................................... 5
Elizabeth Swaim ....................................... 7*
Dr Shannon Saylor .........................15,68,79
Monica Molinar ...............................57,271*
Chris Millican .................................73,295

| Public Schs..Principal | Grd | Prgm | Enr/#Cls | SN |
|---|---|---|---|---|
| Aubrey High Sch<br>510 Spring Hill Rd, Aubrey 76227<br>Matthew Gore | 9-12 | | 489<br>30 | 22% 940/668-3900<br>Fax 940/668-3903 |
| Aubrey Middle Sch<br>815 W Sherman Dr, Aubrey 76227<br>Karen Wright | 6-8 | | 772<br>12 | 27% 940/668-0200<br>Fax 940/668-0228 |
| Brockett Elem Sch<br>900 Chestnut St, Aubrey 76227<br>Courtney Siggers | K-5 | T | 488<br>30 | 34% 940/668-0036<br>Fax 940/668-0037 |
| Jackie Fuller Elem Sch<br>10825 Quicksilver Blvd, Aubrey 76227<br>**Kari Abrams** | PK-5 | | 300 | 940/668-3800<br>Fax 940/668-3801 |
| Monaco Elem Sch<br>9350 Cape Cod Blvd, Aubrey 76227<br>Barbara Pitt | PK-5 | T | 551<br>15 | 40% 940/668-0000<br>Fax 940/668-0001 |

- **Denton Ind School Dist** PID: 01013220
  1307 N Locust St, Denton 76201
  940/369-0000
  Fax 940/369-4982

**Schools:** 42 \ **Teachers:** 2,242 \ **Students:** 33,485 \ **Special Ed Students:** 3,368 \ **LEP Students:** 4,091 \ **College-Bound:** 59% \ **Ethnic:** Asian 4%, African American 17%, Hispanic 32%, Native American: 1%, Caucasian 47% \ **Exp:** $282 (Med) \ **Poverty:** 8% \ **Title I:** $3,150,050 \ **Special Education:** $5,567,000 \ **Open-Close:** 08/26 - 05/27 \ **DTBP:** $186 (High) \

Dr Jamie Wilson ........................................ 1
Jennifer Stewart ........................................ 2
Paul Andress ............................................ 3
Liz Raftery ................................................ 4
Kathy Malmberg ....................................... 7*
Dr Mike Mattingly ..................................8,15
Dr Lisa Thibodeaux ................................. 10
Dr Gwen Perkins ..................................... 15
Dr Lacey Rainey ...................................... 15

Dianna Casper ........................................... 2
Julie Simpson ............................................ 2
Chris Bomberger ....................................... 4
Jim Watson ............................................... 5
Dr Dan Ford .........................................8,74
Sandy Brown ............................................. 9
Chris Shade .............................11,296,298
Dr Jeff Russell ........................................ 15
Dr Richard Valenta ...........................15,751

| 1 | Superintendent | 8 | Curric/Instruct K-12 | 19 | Chief Financial Officer | 29 | Family/Consumer Science | 39 | Social Studies K-12 | 49 | English/Lang Arts Elem | 59 | Special Education Elem | 69 | Academic Assessment |
|---|---|---|---|---|---|---|---|---|---|---|---|---|---|---|---|
| 2 | Bus/Finance/Purchasing | 9 | Curric/Instruct Elem | 20 | Art K-12 | 30 | Adult Education | 40 | Social Studies Elem | 50 | English/Lang Arts Sec | 60 | Special Education Sec | 70 | Research/Development |
| 3 | Buildings And Grounds | 10 | Curric/Instruct Sec | 21 | Art Elem | 31 | Career/Sch-to-Work K-12 | 41 | Social Studies Sec | 51 | Reading K-12 | 61 | Foreign/World Lang K-12 | 71 | Public Information |
| 4 | Food Service | 11 | Federal Program | 22 | Art Sec | 32 | Career/Sch-to-Work Elem | 42 | Science K-12 | 52 | Reading Elem | 62 | Foreign/World Lang Elem | 72 | Summer School |
| 5 | Transportation | 12 | Title I | 23 | Music K-12 | 33 | Career/Sch-to-Work Sec | 43 | Science Elem | 53 | Reading Sec | 63 | Foreign/World Lang Sec | 73 | Instructional Tech |
| 6 | Athletic | 13 | Title V | 24 | Music Elem | 34 | Early Childhood Ed | 44 | Science Sec | 54 | Remedial Reading K-12 | 64 | Religious Education K-12 | 74 | Inservice Training |
| 7 | Health Services | 15 | Asst Superintendent | 25 | Music Sec | 35 | Health/Phys Education | 45 | Math K-12 | 55 | Remedial Reading Elem | 65 | Religious Education Elem | 75 | Marketing/Distributive |
| | | 16 | Instructional Media Svcs | 26 | Business Education | 36 | Guidance Services K-12 | 46 | Math Elem | 56 | Remedial Reading Sec | 66 | Religious Education Sec | 76 | Info Systems |
| | | 17 | Chief Operations Officer | 27 | Career & Tech Ed | 37 | Guidance Services Elem | 47 | Math Sec | 57 | Bilingual/ELL | 67 | School Board President | 77 | Psychological Assess |
| | | 18 | Chief Academic Officer | 28 | Technology Education | 38 | Guidance Services Sec | 48 | English/Lang Arts K-12 | 58 | Special Education K-12 | 68 | Teacher Personnel | 78 | Affirmative Action |

| Public Schs..Principal | Grd | Prgm | Enr/#Cls | SN | |
|---|---|---|---|---|---|
| Adkins Elem Sch<br>1701 Monahan Dr, Lantana 76226<br>Erin Vennell | PK-5 | | 359 | 11% | 940/369-1300<br>Fax 940/584-0857<br>🄵 🅃 |
| Alice Moore Alexander Elem Sch<br>800 Mack Dr, Denton 76209<br>Lindsay Henderson | PK-5 | T | 580<br>35 | 75% | 940/369-3500<br>Fax 940/369-4918 |
| Bettye Myers Middle Sch<br>131 N Garza Rd, Shady Shores 76208<br>Trey Peden | 6-8 | T | 858 | 60% | 940/369-1500<br>Fax 940/498-0050 |
| Billy Ryan High Sch<br>5101 E McKinney St, Denton 76208<br>Vernon Reeves | 9-12 | AGTV | 2,068 | 58% | 940/369-3000<br>Fax 940/369-4960 |
| Blanton Elem Sch<br>9501 Stacee Ln, Argyle 76226<br>Linda Bozeman | K-5 | | 488 | 4% | 940/369-0700<br>Fax 940/241-1423 |
| Borman Elem Sch<br>1201 Parvin St, Denton 76205<br>Emily McLarty | PK-5 | T | 382<br>40 | 81% | 940/369-2500<br>Fax 940/369-4903<br>🄵 |
| Braswell High Sch<br>26750 E University Ave, Aubrey 76227<br>**Decorian Hailey** | 9-12 | | 2,007 | 36% | 972/347-7700<br>Fax 972/347-6259 |
| Calhoun Middle Sch<br>709 W Congress St, Denton 76201<br>Paul Martinez | 6-8 | GTV | 736<br>70 | 65% | 940/369-2400<br>Fax 940/369-4939 |
| Catherine Bell Elem Sch<br>601 Villa Paloma Blvd, Little Elm 75068<br>Lauren Shapiro | PK-5 | | 692 | 40% | 972/347-7200<br>Fax 972/347-9990 |
| Cross Oaks Elem Sch<br>600 Liberty Rd, Crossroads 76227<br>Matthew Preston | PK-5 | T | 708 | 47% | 972/347-7100<br>Fax 940/440-9770<br>🄵 🅃 |
| Denton High Sch<br>1007 Fulton St, Denton 76201<br>Joel Hays | 9-12 | AGTV | 2,005<br>70 | 50% | 940/369-2000<br>Fax 940/369-4953 |
| Eugenia P Rayzor Elem Sch<br>377 Rayzor Rd, Argyle 76226<br>Mary Dunlevy | K-5 | | 385 | 5% | 940/369-4100<br>Fax 940/455-2658 |
| Evers Park Elem Sch<br>3300 Evers Pkwy, Denton 76207<br>Linda Cavazos-Tucker | K-5 | T | 590<br>44 | 72% | 940/369-2600<br>Fax 940/369-4906 |
| Ⓐ Fred Moore High Sch<br>815 Cross Timber St, Denton 76205<br>Jacqueline San Miguel | 9-12 | TV | 56<br>7 | 56% | 940/369-4000<br>Fax 940/369-4957 |
| Ginnings Elem Sch<br>2525 Yellowstone Pl, Denton 76209<br>Cornelius Anderson | K-5 | T | 570<br>35 | 82% | 940/369-2700<br>Fax 940/369-4909 |
| Gonzalez Sch for Young Chldrn<br>1212 Long Rd, Denton 76207<br>Felicia Sprayberry | PK-PK | | 337 | 99% | 940/369-4360<br>Fax 940/382-4285 |
| Harpool Middle Sch<br>9601 Stacee Ln, Argyle 76226<br>Jeff Smith | 6-8 | | 913 | 12% | 940/369-1700<br>Fax 940/241-1342 |
| Hodge Elem Sch<br>3900 Grant Pkwy, Denton 76208<br>Andrea Hare | PK-5 | T | 637<br>35 | 82% | 940/369-2800<br>Fax 940/369-4912<br>🄵 🅃 |
| Ⓐ Joe Dale Sparks Campus<br>210 S Woodrow Ln, Denton 76205<br>Anthony Sims | 4-12 | | 54 | 58% | 940/349-2468<br>Fax 940/304-3408 |
| John H Guyer High Sch<br>7501 Teasley Ln, Denton 76210<br>Dr Shaun Perry | 9-12 | | 2,618 | 21% | 940/369-1000<br>Fax 940/369-4965 |
| L A Nelson Elem Sch<br>3909 Teasley Ln, Denton 76210<br>Erika Timmons | PK-5 | | 565 | 36% | 940/369-1400<br>Fax 940/383-3534 |
| LaGrone Advanced Tech Complex<br>1504 Long Rd, Denton 76207<br>Marcus Bourland | Voc | | 850<br>20 | | 940/369-4850<br>Fax 940/380-0243 |
| Ⓐ Lester Davis Sch<br>1125 Davis St, Denton 76209<br>Ronnie Watkins | K-12 | T | 56<br>9 | 76% | 940/369-4050<br>Fax 940/369-4966 |
| McMath Middle Sch<br>1900 Jason Dr, Denton 76205<br>Dr Buddy Dunworth | 6-8 | T | 769<br>60 | 53% | 940/369-3300<br>Fax 940/369-4946 |
| McNair Elem Sch<br>1212 Hickory Creek Rd, Denton 76210<br>Lacey Hailey | PK-5 | T | 519<br>45 | 46% | 940/369-3600<br>Fax 940/369-4921 |
| Mildred M Hawk Elem Sch<br>2300 Oakmont Dr, Corinth 76210<br>Robin Brownell | PK-5 | | 561<br>36 | 12% | 940/369-1800<br>Fax 940/321-1872 |
| Navo Middle Sch<br>1701 Navo Rd, Aubrey 76227<br>Beth Kelly | 6-8 | V | 985 | 40% | 972/347-7500<br>Fax 940/304-3404 |
| Newton Rayzor Elem Sch<br>1400 Malone St, Denton 76201<br>Cecilia Holt | PK-5 | T | 606<br>25 | 56% | 940/369-3700<br>Fax 940/369-4924 |
| Paloma Creek Elem Sch<br>1600 Navo Rd, Aubrey 76227<br>Natalie Mead | PK-5 | T | 807<br>30 | 43% | 972/347-7300<br>Fax 972/346-9501 |
| Pecan Creek Elem Sch<br>4400 Lakeview Blvd, Denton 76208<br>Amanda Bomar | PK-5 | | 568 | 39% | 940/369-4400<br>Fax 940/369-4904 |
| Providence Elem Sch<br>1000 FM 2931, Aubrey 76227<br>Jairia Diggs | PK-5 | | 382 | 40% | 940/369-1900<br>Fax 940/365-2985 |
| Rodriguez Middle Sch<br>8650 Martop Rd, Aubrey 76227<br>Renee Koontz | 6-8 | T | 825 | 41% | 972/347-7050<br>Fax 972/987-4920 |
| Ronnie Crownover Middle Sch<br>1901 Creekside Dr, Corinth 76210<br>Charlene Parham | 6-8 | | 957 | 25% | 940/369-4700<br>Fax 940/321-0502 |
| Sam Houston Elem Sch<br>3100 Teasley Ln, Denton 76205<br>Teresa Andress | PK-5 | | 492<br>35 | 37% | 940/369-2900<br>Fax 940/369-4915 |
| Savannah Elem Sch<br>1101 Cotton Exchange Dr, Aubrey 76227<br>Michael McWilliams | PK-5 | | 622 | 25% | 972/347-7400<br>Fax 972/346-3352 |
| Stephens Elem Sch<br>133 N Garza Rd, Shady Shores 76208<br>Chris Rangel | PK-5 | T | 309 | 61% | 940/369-0800<br>Fax 940/321-1318 |
| Strickland Middle Sch<br>324 E Windsor Dr, Denton 76209<br>Kathleen Carmona | 6-8 | GT | 909 | 65% | 940/369-4200<br>Fax 940/369-4950 |
| Tomas Rivera Elem Sch<br>701 Newton St, Denton 76205<br>Marvyn White | PK-5 | T | 590<br>80 | 88% | 940/369-3800<br>Fax 940/369-4927 |
| Union Park Elem Sch<br>7401 Fieldwood Way, Aubrey 76227<br>Lorena Salas | PK-5 | | 450 | | 940/369-0900 |
| Wayne Stuart Ryan Elem Sch<br>201 W Ryan Rd, Denton 76210<br>Nicole Poole | PK-5 | T | 606 | 55% | 940/369-4600<br>Fax 940/369-4936 |
| Windle Sch for Young Children<br>901 Audra Ln, Denton 76209<br>Angela Hellman | PK-PK | T | 347<br>23 | 99% | 940/369-3900<br>Fax 940/369-4930 |

| Woodrow Wilson Elem Sch | PK-5 | T | 525 | 42% | 940/369-4500 |
|---|---|---|---|---|---|
| 1306 E Windsor Dr, Denton 76209 | | | 35 | | Fax 940/369-4933 |
| Caleb Leath | | | | | |

## • Krum Ind School Dist PID: 01013347
1200 Bobcat Blvd, Krum 76249

940/482-6000
Fax 940/482-3929

---

**Schools:** 5 \ **Teachers:** 158 \ **Students:** 2,100 \ **Special Ed Students:** 251 \
**LEP Students:** 189 \ **Ethnic:** Asian 1%, African American 2%, Hispanic 30%,
Native American: 1%, Caucasian 66% \ **Exp:** $343 (High) \ **Poverty:** 7% \
**Title I:** $148,308 \ **Open-Close:** 08/18 - 05/25 \ **DTBP:** $347 (High) \ [f]

---

| | | | |
|---|---|---|---|
| **Mike Davis** | 1 | Misty Ward | 2 |
| Bobby Carey | 3,5 | Ashley Doyal | 4 |
| Robby Clark | 6* | Nancy Shipley | 11,15 |
| Cheryl Eager | 16 | Amy Roesler | 37 |
| Michelle Vanzant | 38* | Terry Rahn | 58,88 |
| Eric Borchardt | 67 | Mark Sprague | 73 |
| Marilin Reeves | 274* | | |

| Public Schs..Principal | Grd | Prgm | Enr/#Cls | SN | |
|---|---|---|---|---|---|
| Blanche Dodd Elem Sch | 2-5 | T | 314 | 40% | 940/482-2603 |
| 915 E McCart St, Krum 76249 | | | 25 | | Fax 940/482-3368 |
| Patricia Bolz | | | | | [f] |
| Hattie Dyer Elem Sch | 2-5 | T | 305 | 43% | 940/482-2604 |
| 304 N 3rd St, Krum 76249 | | | 20 | | Fax 940/482-8203 |
| Lindsey Boone | | | | | |
| Krum Early Education Center | PK-1 | T | 249 | 53% | 940/482-2605 |
| 1513 Sequoia Dr, Krum 76249 | | | | | Fax 940/482-6232 |
| **Lyndi Stupka** | | | | | |
| Krum High Sch | 9-12 | V | 310 | 28% | 940/482-2601 |
| 700A Bobcat Blvd, Krum 76249 | | | 16 | | Fax 940/482-2997 |
| Michelle Pieniazek | | | | | [f] |
| Krum Middle Sch | 6-8 | | 496 | 36% | 940/482-2602 |
| 805 E McCart St, Krum 76249 | | | 30 | | Fax 940/482-6299 |
| Robert Butler | | | | | |

## • Lake Dallas Ind School Dist PID: 01013373
104 Swisher Rd, Lake Dallas 75065

940/497-4039
Fax 940/497-3737

---

**Schools:** 5 \ **Teachers:** 284 \ **Students:** 4,000 \
**Special Ed Students:** 470 \ **LEP Students:** 357 \ **College-Bound:** 65% \
**Ethnic:** Asian 2%, African American 9%, Hispanic 33%, Native American:
1%, Caucasian 55% \ **Exp:** $342 (High) \ **Poverty:** 6% \ **Title I:** $352,600 \
**Special Education:** $715,000 \ **Open-Close:** 08/26 - 05/27 \ **DTBP:** $175
(High)

---

| | | | |
|---|---|---|---|
| Dr Gayle Stinson | 1 | Anne Haehn | 2,11 |
| Wes Eversole | 2,15,19 | David Talbert | 3 |
| Stephanie Reese | 4 | Wendy Konz | 5 |
| Scott Head | 6* | Diane Ramirez | 7* |
| Charlie Lokie | 9,57,274 | Dr Marci Malcom | 15 |
| Sharon Simon | 16,82* | Dr Mark Ruggles | 58 |
| Lance Stacy | 67 | Stephanie Payne | 69 |
| Anthony Tosie | 71 | Mike Dabney | 73,286,297 |
| Robin Ballard | 73 | Mike Cromis | 88 |
| Gerry Hamilton | 295 | | |

| Public Schs..Principal | Grd | Prgm | Enr/#Cls | SN | |
|---|---|---|---|---|---|
| Corinth Elem Sch | PK-5 | T | 503 | 43% | 940/497-4010 |
| 3501 Cliff Oaks Dr, Corinth 76210 | | | 47 | | Fax 940/497-8479 |
| Randall Caldwell | | | | | |
| Lake Dallas Elem Sch | PK-5 | T | 571 | 66% | 940/497-2222 |
| 401 Main St, Lake Dallas 75065 | | | 16 | | Fax 940/497-2807 |
| **Larry Dominguez** | | | | | |

| Lake Dallas High Sch | 9-12 | AV | 1,314 | 37% | 940/497-4031 |
|---|---|---|---|---|---|
| 3016 Parkridge Dr, Corinth 76210 | | | 60 | | Fax 940/497-1524 |
| Dr Kristi Strickland | | | | | |
| Lake Dallas Middle Sch | 6-8 | T | 919 | 44% | 940/497-4037 |
| 325 E Hundley Dr, Lake Dallas 75065 | | | 120 | | Fax 940/497-4028 |
| Randall Caldwell | | | | | [t] |
| Shady Shores Elem Sch | PK-5 | T | 548 | 40% | 940/497-4035 |
| 300 Dobbs Rd, Shady Shores 76208 | | | | | Fax 940/497-4036 |
| Jennifer Bryant | | | | | |

## • Lewisville Ind School Dist PID: 01013402
1565 W Main St, Lewisville 75067

469/713-5200
Fax 972/350-9500

---

**Schools:** 71 \ **Teachers:** 3,667 \ **Students:** 52,300 \
**Special Ed Students:** 6,168 \ **LEP Students:** 8,152 \ **College-Bound:** 71%
\ **Ethnic:** Asian 15%, African American 12%, Hispanic 31%, Caucasian
42% \ **Exp:** $289 (Med) \ **Poverty:** 6% \ **Title I:** $5,604,253 \
**Special Education:** $8,092,000 \ **Open-Close:** 08/19 - 05/26 \ **DTBP:** $191
(High) \ [f] [t]

---

| | | | |
|---|---|---|---|
| Dr Kevin Rogers | 1 | Craig Martin | 2 |
| Rosemary Travino | 2 | Jason Hughes | 3 |
| Raymond Danilowicz | 4 | Tim Ford | 6 |
| Dr Joseph Coburn | 7,72,91 | Melanie Vincelette | 7 |
| Dr Robert Thornell | 8 | Adrienne Gall | 9 |
| Karen Sealy | 10 | Courtney Hart | 11 |
| Dr Lori Rapp | 15 | Brandi Dawson | 16 |
| Mark Youngs | 19 | Amanda Drinkwater | 20,23 |
| Jason Cooper | 31 | Heidi Veal | 34 |
| Trish Cuckler | 35 | Monya Crow | 36 |
| Koby Stringer | 40,49 | Dr Kelly Glos | 41 |
| Renee Marts | 43 | Jennifer Beimer | 44 |
| Lindsey Ferguson | 46 | Lori Doering | 47 |
| Sean Hood | 50 | Esther Montanez | 57 |
| Jorge Castillo | 57,69 | Dr Kathy Talbert | 58 |
| Annie Rivera | 63 | Katherine Sells | 67 |
| Sheila Smith | 68 | Dr Sarah Fitzhugh | 69,294 |
| Amanda Brim | 71 | Bryon Kolbeck | 73,98 |
| Dana Sons | 73 | Dr Shawna Miller | 74 |
| David Koonce | 76 | Jeffrey Kajs | 79 |
| Deborah Roby | 81 | Sharon Nobis | 81 |
| Matthew Garrett | 91 | Melissa Davis | 275 |
| Dr Jonas Greene | 285 | Michele Jacobsen | 286 |
| Chris Langford | 295 | Nick Rooney | 297 |

| Public Schs..Principal | Grd | Prgm | Enr/#Cls | SN | |
|---|---|---|---|---|---|
| Arbor Creek Middle Sch | 6-8 | | 825 | 22% | 469/713-5971 |
| 2109 Arbor Creek Dr, Carrollton 75010 | | | 50 | | Fax 972/350-9163 |
| Amy Obenhaus | | | | | |
| Bluebonnet Elem Sch | K-5 | | 484 | 6% | 469/713-5195 |
| 2000 Spinks Rd, Flower Mound 75028 | | | 17 | | Fax 972/350-9005 |
| Lana Fisher | | | | | [f][t] |
| Briarhill Middle Sch | 6-8 | | 870 | 9% | 469/713-5975 |
| 2100 Briarhill Blvd, Lewisville 75077 | | | 80 | | Fax 972/350-9167 |
| **Leslie Davenport** | | | | | [f][t] |
| Camey Elem Sch | PK-5 | T | 603 | 57% | 469/713-5951 |
| 4949 Arbor Glen Rd, The Colony 75056 | | | 30 | | Fax 972/350-9015 |
| Angela Cortez | | | | | |
| Castle Hills Elem Sch | K-5 | | 691 | 3% | 469/713-5952 |
| 1025 Holy Grail Dr, Lewisville 75056 | | | 35 | | Fax 972/350-9018 |
| Jaime Clark | | | | | |
| Central Elem Sch | PK-5 | T | 795 | 83% | 469/713-5976 |
| 400 High School Dr, Lewisville 75057 | | | 70 | | Fax 972/350-9019 |
| Lea Devers | | | | | |
| Collegiate Academy | 9-12 | | 401 | | 469/948-2507 |
| 4301 Blair Oaks Dr, The Colony 75056 | | | | | |
| **Kelly Kirkland** | | | | | |

---

| | | | | | | | |
|---|---|---|---|---|---|---|---|
| 1 Superintendent | 8 Curric/Instruct K-12 | 19 Chief Financial Officer | 29 Family/Consumer Science | 39 Social Studies K-12 | 49 English/Lang Arts Elem | 59 Special Education Elem | 69 Academic Assessment |
| 2 Bus/Finance/Purchasing | 9 Curric/Instruct Elem | 20 Art K-12 | 30 Adult Education | 40 Social Studies Elem | 50 English/Lang Arts Sec | 60 Special Education Sec | 70 Research/Development |
| 3 Buildings And Grounds | 10 Curric/Instruct Sec | 21 Art Elem | 31 Career/Sch-to-Work K-12 | 41 Social Studies Sec | 51 Reading K-12 | 61 Foreign/World Lang K-12 | 71 Public Information |
| 4 Food Service | 11 Federal Program | 22 Art Sec | 32 Career/Sch-to-Work Elem | 42 Science K-12 | 52 Reading Elem | 62 Foreign/World Lang Elem | 72 Summer School |
| 5 Transportation | 12 Title I | 23 Music K-12 | 33 Career/Sch-to-Work Sec | 43 Science Elem | 53 Reading Sec | 63 Foreign/World Lang Sec | 73 Instructional Tech |
| 6 Athletic | 13 Title V | 24 Music Elem | 34 Early Childhood Ed | 44 Science Sec | 54 Remedial Reading K-12 | 64 Religious Education K-12 | 74 Inservice Training |
| 7 Health Services | 15 Asst Superintendent | 25 Music Sec | 35 Health/Phys Education | 45 Math K-12 | 55 Remedial Reading Elem | 65 Religious Education Elem | 75 Marketing/Distributive |
| | 16 Instructional Media Svcs | 26 Business Education | 36 Guidance Services K-12 | 46 Math Elem | 56 Remedial Reading Sec | 66 Religious Education Sec | 76 Info Systems |
| | 17 Chief Operations Officer | 27 Career & Tech Ed | 37 Guidance Services Elem | 47 Math Sec | 57 Bilingual/ELL | 67 School Board President | 77 Psychological Assess |
| | 18 Chief Academic Officer | 28 Technology Education | 38 Guidance Services Sec | 48 English/Lang Arts K-12 | 58 Special Education K-12 | 68 Teacher Personnel | 78 Affirmative Action |

| School | Grades | Prog | Enroll | % | Phone / Fax | Social |
|---|---|---|---|---|---|---|
| **Coyote Ridge Elem Sch** <br>4520 Maumee Dr, Carrollton 75010 <br>Padgett Cervantes | PK-5 | | 544 | 34% | 469/713-5994 <br>Fax 972/350-9026 | |
| **Creek Valley Middle Sch** <br>4109 Creek Valley Blvd, Carrollton 75010 <br>Steffanie Webb | 6-8 | | 702 | 29% | 469/713-5184 <br>Fax 972/350-9172 | |
| **Creekside Elem Sch** <br>901 Valley View Dr, Lewisville 75067 <br>Rodney McGinnis | PK-5 | T | 433 <br>50 | 67% | 469/713-5953 <br>Fax 972/350-9027 | |
| **Degan Elem Sch** <br>1680 College Pkwy, Lewisville 75077 <br>Vanessa Stuart | PK-5 | T | 534 <br>40 | 61% | 469/713-5967 <br>Fax 972/350-9028 | |
| **Delay Middle Sch** <br>2103 Savage Ln, Lewisville 75057 <br>**Charde Dockery** | 6-8 | TV | 1,016 <br>78 | 88% | 469/713-5191 <br>Fax 972/350-9174 | |
| **Downing Middle Sch** <br>5555 Bridlewood Blvd, Flower Mound 75028 <br>Curt Martin | 6-8 | | 353 <br>55 | 7% | 469/713-5962 <br>Fax 972/350-9176 | |
| **Durham Middle Sch** <br>2075 S Edmonds Ln, Lewisville 75067 <br>Gary Holt | 6-8 | T | 855 | 69% | 469/713-5963 <br>Fax 972/350-9182 | |
| **Ethridge Elem Sch** <br>6001 Ethridge Dr, The Colony 75056 <br>Tasia Thompson | PK-5 | | 380 <br>35 | 33% | 469/713-5954 <br>Fax 972/350-9036 | f t |
| **Flower Mound 9th Grade Center** <br>3411A Peters Colony Rd, Flower Mound 75022 <br>Jeffrey Brown | 9-9 | A | 870 | | 469/713-5999 | |
| **Flower Mound Elem Sch** <br>4101 Churchill Dr, Flower Mound 75028 <br>Christy Van Scoyoc | PK-5 | | 420 <br>35 | 15% | 469/713-5955 <br>Fax 972/350-9046 | f t |
| **Flower Mound High Sch** <br>3411 Peters Colony Rd, Flower Mound 75022 <br>Chad Russell | 10-12 | V | 2,619 <br>150 | 5% | 469/713-5192 <br>Fax 972/350-9237 | |
| **Forest Vista Elem Sch** <br>900 Forest Vista Dr, Flower Mound 75028 <br>Dr Patrick Schott | PK-5 | | 492 <br>40 | 10% | 469/713-5194 <br>Fax 972/350-9047 | f t |
| **Forestwood Middle Sch** <br>2810 Morriss Rd, Flower Mound 75028 <br>**Jennifer Hawes** | 6-8 | V | 911 <br>60 | 9% | 469/713-5972 <br>Fax 972/350-9184 | |
| **Garden Ridge Elem Sch** <br>2220 S Garden Ridge Blvd, Flower Mound 75028 <br>Kelly Roden | PK-5 | | 347 <br>28 | 15% | 469/713-5956 <br>Fax 972/350-9052 | |
| **Griffin Middle Sch** <br>5105 N Colony Blvd, The Colony 75056 <br>Heather Garrison | 6-8 | GTV | 778 <br>30 | 50% | 469/713-5973 <br>Fax 972/350-9187 | |
| **Hebron 9th Grade Campus** <br>4211 Plano Pkwy, Carrollton 75010 <br>Amanda Werneke | 9-9 | | 985 | | 469/713-5996 <br>Fax 214/626-1630 | |
| **Hebron High Sch** <br>4207 Plano Pkwy, Carrollton 75010 <br>Amy Boughton | 10-12 | V | 1,648 | 22% | 469/713-5183 <br>Fax 972/350-9255 | f t |
| **Hebron Valley Elem Sch** <br>4108 Creek Valley Blvd, Carrollton 75010 <br>**Laura Zamora** | PK-5 | | 567 <br>40 | 20% | 469/713-5182 <br>Fax 972/350-9068 | |
| **Hedrick Middle Sch** <br>1526 Bellaire Blvd, Lewisville 75067 <br>Barbara Hamric | 6-8 | TV | 665 <br>55 | 71% | 469/713-5188 <br>Fax 972/350-9196 | |
| **Heritage Elem Sch** <br>100 Barnett Dr, Lewisville 75077 <br>Toby Maxson | PK-5 | | 471 <br>22 | 7% | 469/713-5985 <br>Fax 972/350-9072 | |
| **Highland Village Elem Sch** <br>301 Brazos Blvd, Lewisville 75077 <br>Leslye Mitchell | PK-5 | | 295 <br>24 | 15% | 469/713-5957 <br>Fax 972/350-9079 | |
| **Homestead Elem Sch** <br>1830 E Branch Hollow Dr, Carrollton 75007 <br>Sean Perry | PK-5 | | 481 <br>30 | 18% | 469/713-5181 <br>Fax 972/350-9083 | |
| **Huffines Middle Sch** <br>1440 N Valley Pkwy, Lewisville 75077 <br>Estella Rupard | 6-8 | T | 833 <br>50 | 54% | 469/713-5990 <br>Fax 972/350-9199 | |
| **Independence Elem Sch** <br>2511 Windhaven Pkwy, Lewisville 75056 <br>Theodora Winslow | PK-5 | T | 934 | 44% | 469/713-5212 <br>Fax 972/350-9479 | |
| **Indian Creek Elem Sch** <br>2050 Arbor Creek Dr, Carrollton 75010 <br>Lori Sowers | PK-5 | | 489 <br>43 | 38% | 469/713-5180 <br>Fax 972/350-9085 | f t |
| **Jackson Early Childhood Center** <br>1651 S Valley Pkwy, Lewisville 75067 <br>Virginia Gwyn | PK-PK | T | 687 <br>19 | 76% | 469/713-5986 <br>Fax 972/350-9103 | f t |
| **Lakeland Elem Sch** <br>800 Fox Ave, Lewisville 75067 <br>Vanesa Asbun | K-5 | T | 795 <br>33 | 87% | 469/713-5992 <br>Fax 972/350-9092 | |
| **Lakeview Middle Sch** <br>4300 Keys Dr, The Colony 75056 <br>Beri Deister | 6-8 | TV | 709 <br>75 | 50% | 469/713-5974 <br>Fax 972/350-9202 | f t |
| **Lamar Middle Sch** <br>4000 Timber Creek Rd, Flower Mound 75028 <br>Kristy Casal | 6-8 | V | 720 <br>75 | 19% | 469/713-5966 <br>Fax 972/350-9204 | |
| **Lewisville Elem Sch** <br>285 W Country Ridge Rd, Lewisville 75067 <br>Lakshmi Natividad | K-5 | T | 750 | 87% | 469/713-5995 <br>Fax 214/626-1620 | |
| **Lewisville High Sch** <br>1098 W Main St, Lewisville 75067 <br>**Jim Baker** | 11-12 | ATV | 1,921 | 61% | 469/713-5190 <br>Fax 972/350-9291 | |
| **Lewisville HS-B Harmon Campus** <br>1250 W Round Grove Rd, Lewisville 75067 <br>**Joi Cartmill** | 9-10 | | 1,256 | | 469/713-5201 <br>Fax 214/626-1680 | |
| **Lewisville HS-Killough** <br>1301 Summit Ave, Lewisville 75077 <br>Kyndra Tyler | 9-10 | V | 1,125 <br>70 | | 469/713-5987 <br>Fax 972/350-9304 | |
| Ⓐ **Lewisville Learning Center** <br>1601 S Edmonds Ln, Lewisville 75067 <br>Angie Deaton | 1-12 | T | 228 <br>21 | 54% | 469/713-5185 <br>Fax 972/350-9350 | |
| **Liberty Elem Sch** <br>4600 Quail Run, Flower Mound 75022 <br>Timothy Greenwell | PK-5 | | 520 <br>40 | 4% | 469/713-5958 <br>Fax 972/350-9098 | |
| **Lisd STEM Acad-Bridlewood** <br>4901 Remington Park Dr, Flower Mound 75028 <br>Robin Block | PK-5 | | 347 <br>20 | 4% | 469/713-5193 <br>Fax 972/350-9007 | |
| **Lisd STEM Acad-Donald** <br>2400 Forest Vista Dr, Flower Mound 75028 <br>Michelle Wooten | PK-5 | | 477 <br>35 | 10% | 469/713-5198 <br>Fax 972/350-9033 | f t |
| **Lisd STEM Acad-Polser** <br>1520 Polser Rd, Carrollton 75010 <br>Lisa Phelps | PK-5 | T | 411 <br>25 | 51% | 469/713-5978 <br>Fax 972/350-9134 | |
| **Marcus 9th Grade Center** <br>5707A Morriss Rd, Flower Mound 75028 <br>Chantell Upshaw | 9-9 | A | 824 | | 469/713-5998 | |
| **Marcus High Sch** <br>5707 Morriss Rd, Flower Mound 75028 <br>Will Skelton | 10-12 | GV | 2,421 <br>135 | 8% | 469/713-5196 <br>Fax 972/350-9313 | |
| **McAuliffe Elem Sch** <br>2300 Briarhill Blvd, Lewisville 75077 <br>Jennifer Mattingly | PK-5 | | 570 <br>50 | 5% | 469/713-5959 <br>Fax 972/350-9116 | |
| **McKamy Middle Sch** <br>2401 Old Settlers Rd, Flower Mound 75022 <br>Kelly Knight | 6-8 | V | 881 | 3% | 469/713-5991 <br>Fax 972/350-9477 | |
| **Michael G Killian Middle Sch** <br>2561 Parker Rd, Lewisville 75056 <br>**Dr Tina Krol** | 6-8 | | 996 | 24% | 469/713-5977 <br>Fax 469/350-9200 | |
| **Mill St Elem Sch** <br>601 S Mill St, Lewisville 75057 <br>**Deborah Bailey** | PK-5 | T | 246 <br>24 | 74% | 469/713-5965 <br>Fax 972/350-9024 | |

| School | Grd | Prgm | Enr/#Cls | SN | Phone |
|---|---|---|---|---|---|
| Morningside Elem Sch<br>6350 Paige Rd, The Colony 75056<br>Rita Bacque | K-5 | | 373<br>46 | 22% | 469/713-5970<br>Fax 972/350-9117 |
| Old Settlers Elem Sch<br>2525 Old Settlers Rd, Flower Mound 75022<br>Kelly Hayunga | PK-5 | | 491<br>40 | 6% | 469/713-5993<br>Fax 972/350-9126 |
| Owen Elem Sch<br>5640 Squires Dr, The Colony 75056<br>Jennifer Spitzer | PK-5 | T | 373<br>26 | 54% | 469/713-5950<br>Fax 972/350-9000<br>⬛⬛ |
| Parkway Elem Sch<br>2100 S Valley Pkwy, Lewisville 75067<br>Valerie Parsons | PK-5 | T | 434<br>50 | 56% | 469/713-5979<br>Fax 972/350-9132<br>⬛⬛ |
| Peters Colony Elem Sch<br>5101 Nash Dr, The Colony 75056<br>Rebecca Chirinos | PK-5 | T | 613<br>34 | 65% | 469/713-5179<br>Fax 972/350-9133 |
| Prairie Trail Elem Sch<br>5555 Timber Creek Rd, Flower Mound 75028<br>Wendi Vaughn | PK-5 | | 593<br>30 | 16% | 469/713-5980<br>Fax 972/350-9135<br>⬛⬛ |
| Purnell Support Center<br>136 W Purnell Rd, Lewisville 75057<br>Shawnda LaRocque | Spec | | 100 | | 469/713-5199<br>Fax 972/350-9393 |
| Rockbrook Elem Sch<br>2751 Rockbrook Dr, Lewisville 75067<br>Patrick Guy | PK-5 | T | 756 | 68% | 469/713-5968<br>Fax 972/350-9139 |
| Shadow Ridge Middle Sch<br>2050 Aberdeen Dr, Flower Mound 75028<br>Gary Gibson | 6-8 | | 694 | 5% | 469/713-5984<br>Fax 972/350-9215 |
| Southridge Elem Sch<br>495 W Corporate Dr, Lewisville 75067<br>Wyvona Ulman | K-5 | T | 637 | 75% | 469/713-5187<br>Fax 972/350-9140 |
| Stewart's Creek Elem Sch<br>4431 Augusta St, The Colony 75056<br>Andrea Smith | PK-5 | T | 337<br>20 | 60% | 469/713-5960<br>Fax 972/350-9145 |
| Tecc-East<br>2553 Parker Rd, Lewisville 75056<br>Adrian Moreno | Voc | | 450 | | 469/713-5211<br>Fax 214/626-1640 |
| Tesc-West<br>1250 A W FM 3040, Lewisville 75067<br>Justin Gilbreath | Voc | | 500<br>14 | | 469/713-5186<br>Fax 972/350-9342 |
| The Colony High Sch<br>4301 Blair Oaks Dr, The Colony 75056<br>Tim Baxter | 9-12 | GTV | 2,028<br>147 | 39% | 469/713-5178<br>Fax 972/350-9336 |
| Thomas O Hicks Elem Sch<br>3651 Compass Dr, Frisco 75034<br>**Misty Webb** | PK-5 | | 499<br>38 | 7% | 469/713-5981<br>Fax 972/350-9075 |
| Timber Creek Elem Sch<br>1900 Timber Creek Rd, Flower Mound 75028<br>Amy Acosta | PK-5 | | 435 | 29% | 469/713-5961<br>Fax 972/350-9146 |
| Valley Ridge Elem Sch<br>1604 N Garden Ridge Blvd, Lewisville 75077<br>Rachel Garrett | PK-5 | | 441<br>35 | 37% | 469/713-5982<br>Fax 972/350-9155 |
| Vickery Elem Sch<br>3301 Wager Rd, Flower Mound 75028<br>Adam Gray | K-5 | T | 474 | 55% | 469/713-5969<br>Fax 972/350-9157 |
| Virtual Learning Academy<br>5707 Morriss Rd, Flower Mound 75028<br>Dr Christopher Bigenho | 9-12 | | 300 | | 972/350-1870 |
| Wellington Elem Sch<br>3900 Kenwood Dr, Flower Mound 75022<br>Tami Braun | PK-5 | | 857<br>30 | 3% | 469/713-5989<br>Fax 972/350-9160 |

---

● **Little Elm Ind School Dist** PID: 01013490    972/947-9340
300 Lobo Ln, Little Elm 75068    Fax 972/294-1107

**Schools:** 9 \ **Teachers:** 470 \ **Students:** 8,100 \ **Special Ed Students:** 631 \ **LEP Students:** 1,312 \ **College-Bound:** 58% \ **Ethnic:** Asian 4%, African American 17%, Hispanic 40%, Caucasian 38% \ **Exp:** $468 (High) \ **Poverty:** 8% \ **Title I:** $633,502 \ **Special Education:** $980,000 \ **Open-Close:** 08/12 - 05/20 \ **DTBP:** $181 (High) \ ⬛ ⬛

| | | | |
|---|---|---|---|
| Daniel Gallagher | 1 | Anna Chavez | 2 |
| Grant Anderson | 2,15,19 | Danny Cogdell | 3 |
| Joel Moses | 3 | Carolyn Tarver | 4 |
| Sandra Howell | 6 | Toni Nelson | 7* |
| Dr Ashley Glover | 8 | Dr Cyndy Mika | 11,15,70,294 |
| Ross Roberts | 15,79 | Jeff Wiseman | 16,73,286 |
| Dr Tony Tipton | 27,31 | Cortney Clover | 58 |
| David Montemayor | 67 | Cleota Epps | 68 |
| Cecelia Jones | 71 | Patricia Robbins | 71 |
| Amanda Ball | 74 | Brandon Thompson | 76 |
| Kendall Euler | 76 | Billy Coburn | 91 |
| Clay Walker | 295 | | |

| Public Schs..Principal | Grd | Prgm | Enr/#Cls | SN | Phone |
|---|---|---|---|---|---|
| Brent Elem Sch<br>500 Witt Rd, Little Elm 75068<br>Karie Kuster | PK-5 | T | 758<br>13 | 52% | 972/947-9451<br>Fax 972/947-9330 |
| Cesar Chavez Elem Sch<br>2600 Hart Rd, Little Elm 75068<br>Elizabeth Miller | PK-5 | T | 623 | 45% | 972/947-9452<br>Fax 972/947-9331<br>⬛⬛ |
| Colin Powell 6th Grade Center<br>520 Lobo Ln, Little Elm 75068<br>Elizabeth Miller | 6-6 | | 421 | | 972/947-9446 |
| Hackberry Elem Sch<br>7200 Snug Harbor Cir, Frisco 75036<br>Stephen Richardson | PK-5 | T | 715 | 46% | 972/947-9453<br>Fax 972/947-9327 |
| Lakeside Middle Sch<br>400 Lobo Ln, Little Elm 75068<br>Kelley Carr | 7-8 | AT | 1,609<br>45 | 52% | 972/947-9445<br>Fax 972/292-3009 |
| Lakeview Elem Sch<br>1800 Waterside Dr, Little Elm 75068<br>John Wofford | K-5 | | 581 | 34% | 972/947-9454<br>Fax 972/947-9328 |
| Little Elm High Sch<br>1900 Walker Ln, Little Elm 75068<br>Dr Elizabeth Priddy | 9-12 | GT | 2,262<br>30 | 49% | 972/947-9443<br>Fax 972/947-9334 |
| Oak Point Elem Sch<br>401 Shahan Prairie Rd, Oak Point 75068<br>Kori Werth | PK-5 | T | 779 | 53% | 972/947-9455<br>Fax 972/947-9329 |
| Prestwick STEM Academy<br>3101 Stonefield, The Colony 75056<br>Christine Gibson | PK-8 | V | 733 | 12% | 972/947-9450<br>Fax 972/947-9326 |

---

● **Northwest Ind School Dist** PID: 01013517    817/215-0000
2001 Texan Dr, Justin 76247    Fax 817/215-0170

**Schools:** 31 \ **Teachers:** 1,598 \ **Students:** 25,000 \ **Special Ed Students:** 2,451 \ **LEP Students:** 1,175 \ **Ethnic:** Asian 5%, African American 9%, Hispanic 22%, Native American: 1%, Caucasian 64% \ **Exp:** $343 (High) \ **Poverty:** 5% \ **Title I:** $1,096,894 \ **Special Education:** $2,195,000 \ **Open-Close:** 08/20 - 05/28 \ **DTBP:** $164 (High) \ ⬛ ⬛

| | | | |
|---|---|---|---|
| Dr Ryder Warren | 1 | Brian Carter | 2,15,19 |
| Cara Carter | 2,16,19,73,76,95,286 | Tim McClure | 3,5,15 |
| Joel Johnson | 6,35 | Dr Mary Seltzer | 9 |
| Dr Logan Faris | 10 | Carri Eddy | 12,36,57,83,271,274 |
| Dr Kim Caley | 15,68 | Michael Griffien | 15 |
| Dr Kevin Lacefield | 20,27 | Cylynn Braswell | 27,31,285 |

---

| | | | | | | | |
|---|---|---|---|---|---|---|---|
| **1** Superintendent | **8** Curric/Instruct K-12 | **19** Chief Financial Officer | **29** Family/Consumer Science | **39** Social Studies K-12 | **49** English/Lang Arts Elem | **59** Special Education Elem | **69** Academic Assessment |
| **2** Bus/Finance/Purchasing | **9** Curric/Instruct Elem | **20** Art K-12 | **30** Adult Education | **40** Social Studies Elem | **50** English/Lang Arts Sec | **60** Special Education Sec | **70** Research/Development |
| **3** Buildings And Grounds | **10** Curric/Instruct Sec | **21** Art Elem | **31** Career/Sch-to-Work K-12 | **41** Social Studies Sec | **51** Reading K-12 | **61** Foreign/World Lang K-12 | **71** Public Information |
| **4** Food Service | **11** Federal Program | **22** Art Sec | **32** Career/Sch-to-Work Elem | **42** Science K-12 | **52** Reading Elem | **62** Foreign/World Lang Elem | **72** Summer School |
| **5** Transportation | **12** Title I | **23** Music K-12 | **33** Career/Sch-to-Work Sec | **43** Science Elem | **53** Reading Sec | **63** Foreign/World Lang Sec | **73** Instructional Tech |
| **6** Athletic | **13** Title V | **24** Music Elem | **34** Early Childhood Ed | **44** Science Sec | **54** Remedial Reading K-12 | **64** Religious Education K-12 | **74** Inservice Training |
| **7** Health Services | **15** Asst Superintendent | **25** Music Sec | **35** Health/Phys Education | **45** Math K-12 | **55** Remedial Reading Elem | **65** Religious Education Elem | **75** Marketing/Distributive |
| | **16** Instructional Media Svcs | **26** Business Education | **36** Guidance Services K-12 | **46** Math Elem | **56** Remedial Reading Sec | **66** Religious Education Sec | **76** Info Systems |
| | **17** Chief Operations Officer | **27** Career & Tech Ed | **37** Guidance Services Elem | **47** Math Sec | **57** Bilingual/ELL | **67** School Board President | **77** Psychological Assess |
| **TX—128** | **18** Chief Academic Officer | **28** Technology Education | **38** Guidance Services Sec | **48** English/Lang Arts K-12 | **58** Special Education K-12 | **68** Teacher Personnel | **78** Affirmative Action |

| Public Schs..Principal | Grd | Prgm | Enr/#Cls | SN | |
|---|---|---|---|---|---|
| Byron Nelson High Sch<br>2775 Bobcat Blvd, Trophy Club 76262<br>Ron Myers | 9-12 | | 2,499 | 12% | 817/698-5600<br>Fax 817/698-5670<br>⬛⬛ |
| Carl E Schluter Elem Sch<br>1220 Mesa Crest Dr, Haslet 76052<br>Kasey Rogers | PK-5 | | 669 | 15% | 817/698-3900<br>Fax 817/698-3970<br>⬛⬛ |
| Chisholm Trail Middle Sch<br>583 FM 3433, Rhome 76078<br>Matrice Raven | 6-8 | TV | 473<br>45 | 43% | 817/215-0600<br>Fax 817/215-0648 |
| Clara Love Elem Sch<br>16301 Elementary Dr, Justin 76247<br>Lisa Crosslin | PK-5 | T | 705 | 42% | 817/698-6600<br>Fax 817/698-6670<br>⬛⬛ |
| Ⓐ Denton Creek Sch<br>3505 Haynes Rd, Roanoke 76262<br>Dr Monty Brown | 9-12 | | 18<br>5 | | 817/215-0920<br>Fax 817/490-0329 |
| Gene Pike Middle Sch<br>2200 Texan Dr, Justin 76247<br>Christopher Jones | 6-8 | TV | 976<br>50 | 28% | 817/215-0400<br>Fax 817/215-0425 |
| Haslet Elem Sch<br>501 Schoolhouse Rd, Haslet 76052<br>Melissa Webber | PK-5 | | 453<br>39 | 18% | 817/215-0850<br>Fax 817/215-0870<br>⬛⬛ |
| J C Thompson Elem Sch<br>440 E Wishbone Ln, Haslet 76052<br>Leigh Romer | PK-5 | | 616 | 28% | 817/698-3800<br>Fax 817/698-3870<br>⬛⬛ |
| J Lyndal Hughes Elem Sch<br>13824 Lost Spurs Rd, Roanoke 76262<br>Jessica McDonald | PK-5 | | 688 | 26% | 817/698-1900<br>Fax 817/698-1915 |
| James Steele Accelerated HS<br>606 N Walnut St, Roanoke 76262<br>Todd Rogers | 9-12 | | 132 | 17% | 817/698-5800<br>Fax 817/698-5840<br>⬛⬛ |
| John M Tidwell Middle Sch<br>3937 Haslet Roanoke Rd, Roanoke 76262<br>Justin Vercher | 6-8 | V | 954 | 16% | 817/698-5900<br>Fax 817/698-5870<br>⬛⬛ |
| Justin Elem Sch<br>425 Boss Range Rd, Justin 76247<br>Dr Lisa Ransleben | PK-5 | | 638<br>21 | 27% | 817/215-0800<br>Fax 817/215-0840 |
| Kay Granger Elem Sch<br>12771 Saratoga Springs Cir, Keller 76244<br>Michelle McAdams | PK-5 | | 670 | 10% | 817/698-1100<br>Fax 817/698-1170<br>⬛⬛ |
| Lakeview Elem Sch<br>100 Village Trl, Trophy Club 76262<br>Erika Oster | PK-5 | | 590<br>15 | 5% | 817/215-0750<br>Fax 817/215-0770<br>⬛⬛ |
| Lance Thompson Elem Sch<br>821 Hawks Way, Argyle 76226<br>Amy Howell | PK-5 | | 500 | | 817/698-1800<br>Fax 817/698-1813 |
| Leo Adams Middle Sch<br>1069 Eagle Blvd, Haslet 76052<br>Dr Cynthia Webber | 6-8 | | 1,178 | 20% | 817/541-8000<br>Fax 817/541-8099 |
| Lizzie Curtis Elem Sch<br>9640 Belle Prairie Trl, Fort Worth 76177<br>Carrie Pierce | PK-5 | | 507 | 14% | 817/541-8901<br>Fax 817/541-8999 |
| Medlin Middle Sch<br>601 Parkview Dr, Trophy Club 76262<br>Paige Cantrell | 6-8 | V | 1,121<br>22 | 10% | 817/215-0500<br>Fax 817/215-0548 |
| Northwest High Sch<br>2301 Texan Dr, Justin 76247<br>Carrie Jackson | 9-12 | V | 1,816<br>114 | 26% | 817/215-0200<br>Fax 817/215-0251<br>⬛⬛ |

| Public Schs..Principal | Grd | Prgm | Enr/#Cls | SN | |
|---|---|---|---|---|---|
| Ⓐ Northwest Special Program Ctr<br>1800 Highway 114, Justin 76247<br>Susan Moore | 6-12 | | 85<br>5 | | 817/215-0900<br>Fax 817/215-0120<br>⬛⬛ |
| O A Peterson Elem Sch<br>2000 Winter Hawk Dr, Fort Worth 76177<br>Danielle Grimes | PK-5 | | 741 | 25% | 817/698-5000<br>Fax 817/698-5070<br>⬛⬛ |
| Prairie View Elem Sch<br>609 FM 3433, Rhome 76078<br>Yolanda Wallace | PK-5 | T | 357<br>20 | 51% | 817/215-0550<br>Fax 817/215-0598<br>⬛⬛ |
| Roanoke Elem Sch<br>1401 Lancelot Dr, Roanoke 76262<br>Kristi King | PK-5 | | 776<br>18 | 20% | 817/215-0650<br>Fax 817/215-0670 |
| Samuel Beck Elem Sch<br>401 Parkview Dr, Trophy Club 76262<br>Sandy Conklin | PK-5 | | 707<br>22 | 5% | 817/215-0450<br>Fax 817/215-0498<br>⬛⬛ |
| Sendera Ranch Elem Sch<br>1216 Diamond Back Ln, Haslet 76052<br>John Booles | PK-5 | | 556 | 22% | 817/698-3500<br>Fax 817/698-3515 |
| Seven Hills Elem Sch<br>654 FM 3433, Newark 76071<br>Kim Blackburn | PK-5 | | 518<br>34 | | 817/215-0700<br>Fax 817/215-0740 |
| Sonny & Allegra Nance ES<br>701 Tierra Vista Way, Fort Worth 76131<br>Penny Bowles | PK-5 | | 574 | 22% | 817/698-1950<br>Fax 817/698-1960<br>⬛ |
| Truett Wilson Middle Sch<br>14250 Sendera Ranch Blvd, Haslet 76052<br>Natalie Arnold | 6-8 | | 929 | 20% | 817/698-7900<br>Fax 817/698-7970<br>⬛⬛ |
| V R Eaton High Sch<br>1350 Eagle Blvd, Haslet 76052<br>**Stacy Miles** | 9-10 | | 1,603 | | 817/698-7300<br>Fax 817/698-7370 |
| W R Hatfield Elem Sch<br>2051 Texan Dr, Justin 76247<br>James Mahler | PK-5 | T | 328<br>21 | 25% | 817/215-0350<br>Fax 817/215-0369 |
| Wayne A Cox Elem Sch<br>1100 Litsey Rd, Roanoke 76262<br>Chrisa Oakley | PK-5 | | 578 | 12% | 817/698-7200<br>Fax 817/698-7270 |

● **Pilot Point Ind School Dist** PID: 01013581    940/686-8700
829 S Harrison St, Pilot Point 76258    Fax 940/686-8705

**Schools:** 4 \ **Teachers:** 111 \ **Students:** 1,400 \ **Special Ed Students:** 121 \ **LEP Students:** 333 \ **Ethnic:** African American 3%, Hispanic 49%, Native American: 1%, Caucasian 47% \ **Exp:** $311 (High) \ **Poverty:** 12% \ **Title I:** $234,739 \ **Open-Close:** 08/13 - 05/19 \ **DTBP:** $616 (High)

| Public Schs..Principal | Grd | Prgm | Enr/#Cls | SN | |
|---|---|---|---|---|---|
| Pilot Point Elem Sch<br>829 S Jefferson St, Pilot Point 76258<br>Rae Strittmatter | PK-2 | T | 291<br>28 | 70% | 940/686-8710<br>Fax 940/686-8715 |
| Pilot Point High Sch<br>1300 N Washington St, Pilot Point 76258<br>Todd Southard | 9-12 | TV | 432<br>33 | 47% | 940/686-8740<br>Fax 940/686-8745 |
| Pilot Point Intermediate Sch<br>501 Carol St, Pilot Point 76258<br>Darla Wooten | 3-6 | T | 387<br>25 | 57% | 940/686-8720<br>Fax 940/686-8725 |
| Pilot Point Middle Sch<br>828 S Harrison St, Pilot Point 76258<br>Robyn Leslie | 7-8 | T | 217<br>27 | 56% | 940/686-8730<br>Fax 940/686-8735 |

| | | | | | | |
|---|---|---|---|---|---|---|
| **79** Student Personnel | **91** Safety/Security | **275** Response To Intervention | **298** Grant Writer/Ptnrships | **School Programs** | **Social Media** | |
| **80** Driver Ed/Safety | **92** Magnet School | **277** Remedial Math K-12 | **750** Chief Innovation Officer | **A** = Alternative Program | | |
| **81** Gifted/Talented | **93** Parental Involvement | **280** Literacy Coach | **751** Chief of Staff | **G** = Adult Classes | ⬛ = Facebook | |
| **82** Video Services | **95** Tech Prep Program | **285** STEM | **752** Social Emotional Learning | **M** = Magnet Program | | |
| **83** Substance Abuse Prev | **97** Chief Infomation Officer | **286** Digital Learning | | **T** = Title I Schoolwide | ⬛ = Twitter | |
| **84** Erate | **98** Chief Technology Officer | **288** Common Core Standards | **Other School Types** | **V** = Career & Tech Ed Programs | | |
| **85** AIDS Education | **270** Character Education | **294** Accountability | Ⓐ = Alternative School | | | |
| **88** Alternative/At Risk | **271** Migrant Education | **295** Network System | Ⓒ = **Charter School** | New Schools are shaded | | |
| **89** Multi-Cultural Curriculum | **273** Teacher Mentor | **296** Title II Programs | Ⓜ = **Magnet School** | New Superintendents and Principals are bold | | |
| **90** Social Work | **274** Before/After Sch | **297** Webmaster | Ⓨ = **Year-Round School** | Personnel with email addresses are underscored | | |

## • Ponder Ind School Dist PID: 01013610
400 W Bailey St, Ponder 76259

940/479-8200
Fax 940/479-8209

> **Schools:** 3 \ **Teachers:** 102 \ **Students:** 1,600 \ **Special Ed Students:** 137 \
> **LEP Students:** 162 \ **Ethnic:** Asian 1%, African American 2%, Hispanic 29%,
> Native American: 1%, Caucasian 67% \ **Exp:** $743 (High) \ **Poverty:** 16% \
> **Title I:** $282,420 \ **Open-Close:** 08/25 - 05/27 \ **DTBP:** $316 (High)

| | | |
|---|---|---|
| Bruce Yeager | 1 | |
| Patrick McLarty | 3,5 | |
| Royce Reynolds | 6 | |
| Emily Manning | 11,34,57,59,274 | |
| Bart Stover | 27* | |
| Anne Ivy | 38,88* | |
| Chuck Woodall | 295 | |
| Kent Josselet | 2,15,286 | |
| Jeannie Delange | 4* | |
| Tara Allred | 8 | |
| Rhonda Brockett | 16,82* | |
| Richard Hooper | 31,73,297 | |
| Vangee Deussen | 67 | |

| Public Schs..Principal | Grd | Prgm | Enr/#Cls | SN |
|---|---|---|---|---|
| Ponder Elem Sch<br>401 W Bailey St, Ponder 76259<br>**Emily Manning** | PK-5 | T | 742<br>31 | 44% 940/479-8230<br>Fax 940/479-8239 |
| Ponder High Sch<br>300 W Bailey St, Ponder 76259<br>Dr Matthew Birdwell | 9-12 | AV | 434<br>30 | 30% 940/479-8210<br>Fax 940/479-8219 |
| Ponder Junior High Sch<br>501 Shaffner St, Ponder 76259<br>Shawn Simmons | 6-8 | TV | 374<br>22 | 40% 940/479-8220<br>Fax 940/479-8229 |

## • Sanger Ind School Dist PID: 01013646
601 Elm St, Sanger 76266

940/458-7438
Fax 940/458-5140

> **Schools:** 7 \ **Teachers:** 185 \ **Students:** 2,660 \ **Special Ed Students:** 331
> \ **LEP Students:** 212 \ **College-Bound:** 48% \ **Ethnic:** Asian 1%, African
> American 4%, Hispanic 29%, Native American: 1%, Caucasian 66% \
> **Exp:** $487 (High) \ **Poverty:** 8% \ **Title I:** $271,080 \ **Open-Close:** 08/12 -
> 05/27 \ **DTBP:** $183 (High) \ ⨍

| | | |
|---|---|---|
| Dr Tommy Hunter | 1 | |
| Dena Scheffler | 3 | |
| Terry Gleaton | 5 | |
| Leann Loyless | 8,270 | |
| Kim Phillips | 58 | |
| Natalie Key | 68 | |
| Tammy Austin | 73 | |
| Susan Kwast | 2 | |
| Paige Hachmeister | 4 | |
| Charles Galbreath | 6* | |
| Jennifer Mulkey | 11,57,296 | |
| Ken Scribner | 67 | |
| Leon Elsbecker | 73,295 | |

| Public Schs..Principal | Grd | Prgm | Enr/#Cls | SN |
|---|---|---|---|---|
| Butterfield Elem Sch<br>291 Indian Ln, Sanger 76266<br>Larry Beam | PK-5 | T | 578<br>56 | 46% 940/458-4377<br>Fax 940/458-5591 |
| Chisholm Trail Elem Sch<br>812 Keaton Rd N, Sanger 76266<br>Cari Cockrell | K-2 | T | 320<br>27 | 45% 940/458-5297<br>Fax 940/458-2537 |
| Clear Creek Intermediate Sch<br>1901 S Stemmons St, Sanger 76266<br>Sally Herrell | 3-5 | T | 388<br>24 | 47% 940/458-7476<br>Fax 940/458-2539 |
| Ⓐ Linda Tutt High Sch<br>404 Hughes St, Sanger 76266<br>**Anthony Love** | 9-12 | T | 30<br>3 | 46% 940/458-5701<br>Fax 940/458-3157 |
| Sanger 6th Grade Sch<br>508 N 7th St, Sanger 76266<br>Larry Shuman | 6-6 | T | 216<br>10 | 38% 940/458-3699<br>Fax 940/458-3795 |
| Sanger High Sch<br>100 Indian Ln, Sanger 76266<br>Jennifer Flaa | 9-12 | T | 421<br>40 | 41% 940/458-7497<br>Fax 940/458-4637 |
| Sanger Middle Sch<br>105 Berry St, Sanger 76266<br>Jim Cain | 7-8 | GT | 418<br>30 | 39% 940/458-7916<br>Fax 940/458-5111 |

## DENTON CATHOLIC SCHOOLS

## • Diocese of Fort Worth Ed Off PID: 01054339
Listing includes only schools located in this county. See District Index for
location of Diocesan Offices.

| Catholic Schs..Principal | Grd | Prgm | Enr/#Cls | SN |
|---|---|---|---|---|
| Immaculate Conception Catholic<br>2301 N Bonnie Brae St, Denton 76207<br>Elaine Schad | PK-8 | | 260<br>15 | 940/381-1155<br>Fax 940/381-1837 |

## DENTON PRIVATE SCHOOLS

| Private Schs..Principal | Grd | Prgm | Enr/#Cls | SN |
|---|---|---|---|---|
| Blossom Valley Academy<br>1252 College Pkwy, Lewisville 75077<br>Edith Lam | PK-PK | | 90<br>6 | 972/436-3613 |
| Christian Academy of America<br>175 Double Oaks Dr, Double Oak 75077<br>Karen Pulaski | K-12 | | 800 | 972/539-1458<br>Fax 972/539-9434 |
| Coram Deo Academy<br>4900 Wichita Trl, Flower Mound 75022<br>Polly Dwyer | K-12 | | 600 | 682/237-0232<br>Fax 972/692-5140 |
| Denton Calvary Academy<br>1910 E University Dr, Denton 76209<br>Stacey Baxter | K-12 | | 350 | 940/320-1944<br>Fax 940/591-9311 |
| Explorations Preparatory Sch<br>1501 Flower Mound Rd, Flower Mound 75028<br>Carolyn Hart | PK-8 | | 120 | 972/539-0601 |
| Frisco Montessori Academy<br>8890 Meadow Hill Dr, Frisco 75033<br>Jody Rosen | PK-8 | | 202<br>12 | 972/712-7400<br>Fax 972/712-6441 |
| Grace Covenant Academy<br>8000 Sanctuary Dr, Frisco 75033<br>Shannon Behrman | K-12 | | 158 | 972/836-9422<br>Fax 972/528-7297<br>⨍⨏ |
| Knowledge Seeker Christian Sch<br>1471 W Corporate Dr, Lewisville 75067<br>Sandra Goodrich | K-8 | | 6<br>2 | 972/353-3981 |
| Lakeland Christian Academy<br>397 S Stemmons Fwy, Lewisville 75067<br>Patti Nason \ Linroy Kilgore | PK-12 | | 500 | 972/219-3939<br>Fax 972/219-9601 |
| Liberty Baptist Sch<br>602 Manco Rd, Lewisville 75067<br>Doyle Moseley | K-12 | | 30<br>3 | 972/436-3493 |
| Liberty Christian Sch<br>1301 S Highway 377, Argyle 76226<br>Joe Belyeu \ Norman Parker \ Heather Lytle | PK-12 | | 1,300 | 940/294-2000<br>Fax 940/294-2035<br>⨍⨏ |
| Montessori Episcopal Sch<br>602 N Old Orchard Ln, Lewisville 75077<br>Tracey Reinhart | PK-K | | 70<br>10 | 972/221-3533 |
| Prince of Peace Christian Sch<br>4004 Midway Rd, Carrollton 75007<br>Todd Baringer \ Betsy Graham | PK-12 | | 1,000<br>50 | 972/447-0532<br>Fax 972/267-4202 |
| Selwyn College Prep Sch<br>2270 Copper Canyon Rd, Argyle 76226<br>Melissa Sayler \ Lisa Biles \ Mary Kosednar | PK-12 | | 150<br>20 | 940/382-6771<br>Fax 940/400-2593 |
| Temple Christian Academy<br>2501 Northshore Blvd, Flower Mound 75028<br>Todd Hickman | PK-12 | | 170<br>30 | 972/874-8700<br>Fax 972/539-4649 |
| Wellspring Christian Acad<br>1919 N Elm St, Denton 76201 | PK-5 | | 120 | 940/591-9900<br>Fax 940/387-1518 |

| | | | | | | | |
|---|---|---|---|---|---|---|---|
| **1** Superintendent | **8** Curric/Instruct K-12 | **19** Chief Financial Officer | **29** Family/Consumer Science | **39** Social Studies K-12 | **49** English/Lang Arts Elem | **59** Special Education Elem | **69** Academic Assessment |
| **2** Bus/Finance/Purchasing | **9** Curric/Instruct Elem | **20** Art K-12 | **30** Adult Education | **40** Social Studies Elem | **50** English/Lang Arts Sec | **60** Special Education Sec | **70** Research/Development |
| **3** Buildings And Grounds | **10** Curric/Instruct Sec | **21** Art Elem | **31** Career/Sch-to-Work K-12 | **41** Social Studies Sec | **51** Reading K-12 | **61** Foreign/World Lang K-12 | **71** Public Information |
| **4** Food Service | **11** Federal Program | **22** Art Sec | **32** Career/Sch-to-Work Elem | **42** Science K-12 | **52** Reading Elem | **62** Foreign/World Lang Elem | **72** Summer School |
| **5** Transportation | **12** Title I | **23** Music K-12 | **33** Career/Sch-to-Work Sec | **43** Science Elem | **53** Reading Sec | **63** Foreign/World Lang Sec | **73** Instructional Tech |
| **6** Athletic | **13** Title V | **24** Music Elem | **34** Early Childhood Ed | **44** Science Sec | **54** Remedial Reading K-12 | **64** Religious Education K-12 | **74** Inservice Training |
| **7** Health Services | **15** Asst Superintendent | **25** Music Sec | **35** Health/Phys Education | **45** Math K-12 | **55** Remedial Reading Elem | **65** Religious Education Elem | **75** Marketing/Distributive |
| | **16** Instructional Media Svcs | **26** Business Education | **36** Guidance Services K-12 | **46** Math Elem | **56** Remedial Reading Sec | **66** Religious Education Sec | **76** Info Systems |
| | **17** Chief Operations Officer | **27** Career & Tech Ed | **37** Guidance Services Elem | **47** Math Sec | **57** Bilingual/ELL | **67** School Board President | **77** Psychological Assess |
| | **18** Chief Academic Officer | **28** Technology Education | **38** Guidance Services Sec | **48** English/Lang Arts K-12 | **58** Special Education K-12 | **68** Teacher Personnel | **78** Affirmative Action |

## DICKENS COUNTY

### DICKENS PUBLIC SCHOOLS

- **Patton Springs Ind School Dist** PID: 01013933    806/689-2220
  1261 East FM 193, Afton 79220    Fax 806/689-2253

**Schools:** 1 \ **Teachers:** 11 \ **Students:** 97 \ **Special Ed Students:** 13 \
**College-Bound:** 100% \ **Ethnic:** African American 3%, Hispanic 44%,
Caucasian 53% \ **Exp:** $635 (High) \ **Poverty:** 45% \ **Title I:** $34,602 \
**Open-Close:** 08/19 - 05/21 \ **DTBP:** $350 (High)

| | | | |
|---|---|---|---|
| Bryan White ................................ 1,11,57 | Becky Hodges ......................................... 2 |
| Bruce Porter ........................................ 3* | Kristin Dockery ...................................... 4 |
| Bryan White .................................. 12,288* | Gary Bridge ......................................... 67 |
| James Stephens ................................. 73* | |

| Public Schs..Principal | Grd | Prgm | Enr/#Cls | SN |
|---|---|---|---|---|
| Patton Springs Sch | PK-12 | TV | 97 | 82% 806/689-2220 |
| 1261 East FM 193, Afton 79220 | | | 18 | Fax 806/689-2470 |
| Sandra Ramirez | | | | |

- **Spur Ind School Dist** PID: 01013969    806/271-3272
  800 Williams Ave, Spur 79370    Fax 806/271-4575

**Schools:** 1 \ **Teachers:** 28 \ **Students:** 235 \ **Special Ed Students:** 34
\ **LEP Students:** 3 \ **Ethnic:** African American 3%, Hispanic 45%,
Caucasian 51% \ **Exp:** $632 (High) \ **Poverty:** 21% \ **Title I:** $69,005 \
**Open-Close:** 08/17 - 05/21 \ **f**

| | |
|---|---|
| Craig Hamilton ...................................... 1 | Jodi Gonzalez ................................... 2,11 |
| Michael Norman .............................. 6,12* | Josh Watson .................................. 16,73* |
| Josh Watson ................................... 16,73 | Amy Tagle ......................................... 23 |
| Justin Been ....................................... 27 | Dana Conrad ..................................... 58* |
| Barry Ferguson ................................. 67 | Marcella Bilberry ........................... 83,85* |

| Public Schs..Principal | Grd | Prgm | Enr/#Cls | SN |
|---|---|---|---|---|
| Spur Sch | PK-12 | TV | 235 | 61% 806/271-3385 |
| 800 Williams Ave, Spur 79370 | | | 25 | |
| Jose Molina \ Michael Norman | | | | |

## DIMMIT COUNTY

### DIMMIT PUBLIC SCHOOLS

- **Carrizo Spgs Cons Ind SD** PID: 01014030    830/876-3503
  300 N 7th St, Carrizo Spgs 78834    Fax 830/876-3619

**Schools:** 4 \ **Teachers:** 148 \ **Students:** 2,200 \ **Special Ed Students:** 214
\ **LEP Students:** 125 \ **College-Bound:** 75% \ **Ethnic:** Hispanic 94%,
Caucasian 5% \ **Exp:** $659 (High) \ **Poverty:** 32% \ **Title I:** $1,259,120 \
**Special Education:** $346,000 \ **Open-Close:** 08/24 - 05/31 \ **DTBP:** $326
(High)

| | |
|---|---|
| Dr Osae Cervantes ......................... 1 | Jesse Muniz ...................................... 2 |
| Alejandro Orosco ......................... 3,5 | Juan Cela ......................................... 4 |
| Joaquin Escobar ............................. 6 | Maria Areal ............................... 8,288 |
| Sandra Uriegas ........................ 11,57 | Michael Uriegas ........ 33,68,78,79,91 |
| Nayda Rodriguez ........................... 38 | Roxanne Miranda ........................ 38* |
| Gilbert Morales ............................. 58 | Rodney Perez .............................. 67 |
| Marco Mendez ................... 73,76,295 | Eddie Cortez ................................ 91 |

| Public Schs..Principal | Grd | Prgm | Enr/#Cls | SN |
|---|---|---|---|---|
| Carrizo Springs Elem Sch | PK-3 | T | 747 | 81% 830/876-3513 |
| 605 N 9th St, Carrizo Spgs 78834 | | | 20 | Fax 830/876-4138 |
| Elisa Martinez | | | | |
| Carrizo Springs High Sch | 9-12 | AGTV | 623 | 74% 830/876-9393 |
| 335 Farm Rd 1917, Carrizo Spgs 78834 | | | 52 | Fax 830/876-9553 |
| Michelle Gonzalez | | | | |
| Carrizo Springs Interm Sch | 4-6 | T | 512 | 78% 830/876-3561 |
| 452 Highway 85, Carrizo Spgs 78834 | | | 15 | Fax 830/876-5132 |
| Mario Ruiz | | | | |
| Carrizo Springs Jr High Sch | 6-8 | T | 333 | 75% 830/876-2496 |
| 286 Farm Rd 1556, Carrizo Spgs 78834 | | | 45 | Fax 830/876-2497 |
| Maria Villarreal | | | | |

## DONLEY COUNTY

### DONLEY PUBLIC SCHOOLS

- **Clarendon Cons Ind Sch Dist** PID: 01014119    806/874-2062
  416 S Allen Street, Clarendon 79226    Fax 806/874-2579

**Schools:** 3 \ **Teachers:** 45 \ **Students:** 450 \ **Special Ed Students:** 45 \
**Ethnic:** African American 11%, Hispanic 13%, Caucasian 76% \ **Exp:** $533
(High) \ **Poverty:** 28% \ **Title I:** $167,750 \ **Special Education:** $50,000 \
**Open-Close:** 08/13 - 05/20 \ **DTBP:** $354 (High) \ **f**

| | |
|---|---|
| Jarod Bellar .................................... 1 | Kristen Brown ................................... 2 |
| Sarah Emerson ................................ 2 | Terry Ralston .................................... 3 |
| Pat Ritchie ..................................... 4* | Chad Hommel .................................. 5 |
| Clinit Coonkin .................................. 6 | Travis Victory .................................. 8 |
| Jenay Ashbrooke ................... 11,88,752 | Mike Word ................................. 11,93* |
| Melondy Lusk ................................. 58 | Wayne Hardin ................................ 67 |
| Butch Noble ............... 71,73,97,98,295* | Jen Bellard ................................... 298 |

| Public Schs..Principal | Grd | Prgm | Enr/#Cls | SN |
|---|---|---|---|---|
| Clarendon Elem Sch | PK-5 | T | 191 | 64% 806/874-3855 |
| 922 W 5th St, Clarendon 79226 | | | 20 | Fax 806/874-2082 |
| **Cynthia Bessent** | | | | |
| Clarendon High Sch | 9-12 | TV | 123 | 37% 806/874-2181 |
| 420 S Allen St, Clarendon 79226 | | | 16 | Fax 806/874-3428 |
| Larry Jeffers | | | | |
| Clarendon Junior High Sch | 6-8 | T | 114 | 53% 806/874-3232 |
| 922 W 5th St, Clarendon 79226 | | | 9 | Fax 806/874-9748 |
| Travis Victory | | | | |

## • Hedley Ind School Dist PID: 01014145

301 Jones St, Hedley 79237

806/856-5323
Fax 806/856-5372

**Schools:** 1 \ **Teachers:** 17 \ **Students:** 112 \ **Special Ed Students:** 11 \ **LEP Students:** 4 \ **College-Bound:** 4% \ **Ethnic:** Asian 1%, African American 2%, Hispanic 25%, Native American: 1%, Caucasian 72% \ **Exp:** $1,345 (High) \ **Poverty:** 16% \ **Title I:** $22,464 \ **Open-Close:** 08/13 - 06/04 \ **DTBP:** $392 (High)

| | | | |
|---|---|---|---|
| Garrett Baines | 1,11,57,73 | Tresa Alston | 2 |
| Eric Alston | 8 | Christi Willey | 58 |
| Dana Bell | 67 | Jennie Owens | 73,295* |

| Public Schs..Principal | Grd | Prgm | Enr/#Cls | SN | |
|---|---|---|---|---|---|
| Hedley Sch<br>301 Jones St, Hedley 79237<br>Eric Alston | PK-12 | TV | 112<br>19 | 76% | 806/856-5323 |

# DUVAL COUNTY

# DUVAL PUBLIC SCHOOLS

## • Benavides Ind School Dist PID: 01014171

106 W School St, Benavides 78341

361/256-3000
Fax 361/256-3002

**Schools:** 2 \ **Teachers:** 27 \ **Students:** 320 \ **Special Ed Students:** 41 \ **LEP Students:** 14 \ **College-Bound:** 50% \ **Ethnic:** Hispanic 100%, \ **Exp:** $1,030 (High) \ **Poverty:** 32% \ **Title I:** $171,620 \ **Open-Close:** 08/17 - 05/25 \ **DTBP:** $350 (High) \ **f**

| | | | |
|---|---|---|---|
| Dr Marisa Chapa | 1,11 | Christina Perez | 2,5 |
| Marcos Zubia | 6 | Melissa Rodriquez | 36,69,83,288 |
| Rosie Soliz | 58 | Jesse Abitua | 67 |
| Greg Perez | 73,84,285,286 | | |

| Public Schs..Principal | Grd | Prgm | Enr/#Cls | SN | |
|---|---|---|---|---|---|
| ⓨ Benavides Elem Sch<br>106 W School St, Benavides 78341<br>Dr Anacita Sugalan | PK-6 | MTV | 152<br>14 | 86% | 361/256-3030<br>Fax 361/256-3032<br>**f** |
| Benavides Secondary Sch<br>1025 Eagle Dr, Benavides 78341<br>Dr Anacita Sugalan | 7-12 | TV | 167<br>18 | 79% | 361/256-3040<br>Fax 361/256-3043<br>**f** |

## • Freer Ind School Dist PID: 01809196

905 S Norton St, Freer 78357

361/394-6025
Fax 361/394-5055

**Schools:** 3 \ **Teachers:** 61 \ **Students:** 701 \ **Special Ed Students:** 120 \ **LEP Students:** 33 \ **College-Bound:** 97% \ **Ethnic:** Hispanic 91%, Caucasian 8% \ **Exp:** $886 (High) \ **Poverty:** 30% \ **Title I:** $262,389 \ **Open-Close:** 08/04 - 05/20 \ **DTBP:** $380 (High)

| | | | |
|---|---|---|---|
| Conrad Cantu | 1 | Guadalupe Cude | 2,11,57,69,271,296 |
| Carolyn Stanfield | 4 | Linda Worsham | 5 |
| Francis Adami | 6 | Maria Cantu | 7* |
| Dr Frances Perez | 8,15,752 | Dina McQuagge | 33,38* |
| Susan Gallagos | 58 | Steve McQuagge | 67 |
| Karl Garcia | 73,84,295 | | |

| Public Schs..Principal | Grd | Prgm | Enr/#Cls | SN | |
|---|---|---|---|---|---|
| Freer High Sch<br>905 S Norton St, Freer 78357<br>Linda Hinojosa | 9-12 | ATV | 236<br>30 | 76% | 361/394-6717<br>Fax 361/394-5046 |
| Freer Junior High Sch<br>615 S Norton St, Freer 78357<br>Rosalva Campos | 6-8 | T | 182<br>22 | 73% | 361/394-7102<br>Fax 361/394-5016 |
| Norman Thomas Elem Sch<br>1404 S Norton St, Freer 78357<br>Ramon Garza | PK-5 | T | 404<br>21 | 74% | 361/394-6800<br>Fax 361/394-5014 |

## • Ramirez Common School Dist PID: 01014250

10492 School St, Realitos 78376

361/539-4343
Fax 361/539-4482

**Schools:** 1 \ **Teachers:** 3 \ **Students:** 37 \ **Special Ed Students:** 3 \ **LEP Students:** 10 \ **Ethnic:** Hispanic 100%, \ **Exp:** $529 (High) \ **Poverty:** 25% \ **Title I:** $17,918 \ **Open-Close:** 08/10 - 05/28 \ **DTBP:** $245 (High)

| | | | |
|---|---|---|---|
| Yliana Gonzalez | 1 | Dalia Bazan | 2 |
| George Chavera | 67 | | |

| Public Schs..Principal | Grd | Prgm | Enr/#Cls | SN | |
|---|---|---|---|---|---|
| Ramirez Elem Sch<br>10492 School St, Realitos 78376<br>Yliana Gonzalez | PK-6 | T | 37<br>5 | 89% | 361/539-4343 |

## • San Diego Ind School Dist PID: 01014274

609 W Labbe St, San Diego 78384

361/279-3382
Fax 361/279-1830

**Schools:** 3 \ **Teachers:** 101 \ **Students:** 1,385 \ **Special Ed Students:** 145 \ **LEP Students:** 22 \ **College-Bound:** 51% \ **Ethnic:** Hispanic 98%, Caucasian 2% \ **Exp:** $541 (High) \ **Poverty:** 40% \ **Title I:** $800,171 \ **Open-Close:** 08/10 - 05/28 \ **DTBP:** $346 (High)

| | | | |
|---|---|---|---|
| Dr Rodrigo Pena | 1 | Angelina Smith-Wick | 2 |
| Bo Ochoa | 6 | Yvonne Munoz | 8 |
| Gracie Pizzini | 11,15,79 | Rosalinda Flores | 16* |
| Rosie Solis | 58,76 | Librada Vela | 67 |
| Oscar Ruiz | 73* | | |

| Public Schs..Principal | Grd | Prgm | Enr/#Cls | SN | |
|---|---|---|---|---|---|
| Bernarda Jaime Jr High Sch<br>609 W Labbe St, San Diego 78384<br>Nita Vela | 6-8 | AT | 334<br>38 | 78% | 361/279-3382<br>Fax 361/279-1838 |
| Collins-Parr Elem Sch<br>600 S Reforma St, San Diego 78384<br>Monica Perez | PK-5 | AT | 664<br>28 | 85% | 361/279-3382<br>Fax 361/279-1822 |
| San Diego High Sch<br>235 S Highway 359, San Diego 78384<br>Claudette Garcia | 9-12 | ATV | 387<br>37 | 72% | 361/279-3544<br>Fax 361/279-1840 |

| | | | | | | |
|---|---|---|---|---|---|---|
| 1 Superintendent | 8 Curric/Instruct K-12 | 19 Chief Financial Officer | 29 Family/Consumer Science | 39 Social Studies K-12 | 49 English/Lang Arts Elem | 59 Special Education Elem | 69 Academic Assessment |
| 2 Bus/Finance/Purchasing | 9 Curric/Instruct Elem | 20 Art K-12 | 30 Adult Education | 40 Social Studies Elem | 50 English/Lang Arts Sec | 60 Special Education Sec | 70 Research/Development |
| 3 Buildings And Grounds | 10 Curric/Instruct Sec | 21 Art Elem | 31 Career/Sch-to-Work K-12 | 41 Social Studies Sec | 51 Reading K-12 | 61 Foreign/World Lang K-12 | 71 Public Information |
| 4 Food Service | 11 Federal Program | 22 Art Sec | 32 Career/Sch-to-Work Elem | 42 Science K-12 | 52 Reading Elem | 62 Foreign/World Lang Elem | 72 Summer School |
| 5 Transportation | 12 Title I | 23 Music K-12 | 33 Career/Sch-to-Work Sec | 43 Science Elem | 53 Reading Sec | 63 Foreign/World Lang Sec | 73 Instructional Tech |
| 6 Athletic | 13 Title V | 24 Music Elem | 34 Early Childhood Ed | 44 Science Sec | 54 Remedial Reading K-12 | 64 Religious Education K-12 | 74 Inservice Training |
| 7 Health Services | 15 Asst Superintendent | 25 Music Sec | 35 Health/Phys Education | 45 Math K-12 | 55 Remedial Reading Elem | 65 Religious Education Elem | 75 Marketing/Distributive |
| | 16 Instructional Media Svcs | 26 Business Education | 36 Guidance Services K-12 | 46 Math Elem | 56 Remedial Reading Sec | 66 Religious Education Sec | 76 Info Systems |
| | 17 Chief Operations Officer | 27 Career & Tech Ed | 37 Guidance Services Elem | 47 Math Sec | 57 Bilingual/ELL | 67 School Board President | 77 Psychological Assess |
| | 18 Chief Academic Officer | 28 Technology Education | 38 Guidance Services Sec | 48 English/Lang Arts K-12 | 58 Special Education K-12 | 68 Teacher Personnel | 78 Affirmative Action |

## EASTLAND COUNTY

## EASTLAND PUBLIC SCHOOLS

● **Cisco Independent Sch Dist** PID: 01014353  254/442-3056
1503 Liggett St, Cisco 76437  Fax 254/442-1412

**Schools:** 4 \ **Teachers:** 84 \ **Students:** 830 \ **Special Ed Students:** 105 \ **LEP Students:** 11 \ **College-Bound:** 95% \ **Ethnic:** Asian 1%, African American 2%, Hispanic 18%, Native American: 1%, Caucasian 77% \ **Exp:** $516 (High) \ **Poverty:** 25% \ **Title I:** $291,988 \ **Open-Close:** 08/17 - 05/28 \ **DTBP:** $386 (High) \ 🅵 🅴

| | | | |
|---|---|---|---|
| Dr Ryan Steel ...........................1,11 | Terri Hanlon ...........................2 |
| Derrick White ...........................3,5* | Lori Boyd ...........................4* |
| Brent West ...........................6* | Pam Duncan ...........................7* |
| Charlotte Weiser ...........................16,73* | Julie Patterson ...........................58,74,92* |
| Joe Petree ...........................67 | Cindy Tubb ...........................68 |
| Kathy Conring ...........................69,83* | Charlotte Weiser ...........................84 |

| Public Schs..Principal | Grd | Prgm | Enr/#Cls | SN | |
|---|---|---|---|---|---|
| Cisco Elem Sch<br>503 W 11th St, Cisco 76437<br>Sharon Wilcoxen | PK-5 | T | 370<br>26 | 63% | 254/442-1219<br>Fax 254/442-4836 |
| Cisco High Sch<br>1300 Pershing St, Cisco 76437<br>Julie Patterson | 9-12 | TV | 244<br>45 | 52% | 254/442-3051<br>Fax 254/442-2516 |
| Cisco Junior High Sch<br>1200 Pershing St, Cisco 76437<br>Tooter Draper | 6-8 | TV | 203<br>12 | 51% | 254/442-3004<br>Fax 254/442-1832 |
| Cisco Learning Center<br>804 Avenue H, Cisco 76437<br>Julie Patterson | 9-12 | AV | 12<br>2 | 75% | 254/442-4852<br>Fax 254/442-1917 |

● **Eastland Ind School Dist** PID: 01014406  254/631-5120
900 W Plummer St, Eastland 76448  Fax 254/631-5126

**Schools:** 3 \ **Teachers:** 88 \ **Students:** 1,000 \ **Special Ed Students:** 118 \ **LEP Students:** 74 \ **College-Bound:** 85% \ **Ethnic:** Asian 1%, African American 1%, Hispanic 27%, Caucasian 71% \ **Exp:** $586 (High) \ **Poverty:** 28% \ **Title I:** $402,966 \ **Special Education:** $7,000 \ **Open-Close:** 08/12 - 05/27 \ **DTBP:** $344 (High) \ 🅵 🅴

| | | |
|---|---|---|
| Jason Cochran ...........................1,83 | Mary Jones ...........................2 |
| Cala Willis ...........................4 | Brian Schafer ...........................5 |
| James Morton ...........................6* | Brandon Chesser ...........................12 |
| Jeremy Williams ...........................15 | Laurah Williams ...........................27* |
| David Hullman ...........................67 | |

| Public Schs..Principal | Grd | Prgm | Enr/#Cls | SN | |
|---|---|---|---|---|---|
| Eastland High Sch<br>900 W Plummer St Ste 101, Eastland 76448<br>Adam Bramlett | 9-12 | ATV | 355<br>40 | 45% | 254/631-5000<br>Fax 254/631-5025 |
| Eastland Middle Sch<br>900 W Plummer St, Eastland 76448<br>Jason Henry | 6-8 | T | 258<br>32 | 60% | 254/631-5040<br>Fax 254/631-5049 |
| Siebert Elem Sch<br>100 Little Maverick Trl, Eastland 76448<br>Brandon Chesser | PK-5 | T | 470<br>32 | 66% | 254/631-5080<br>Fax 254/631-5085 |

● **Gorman Ind School Dist** PID: 01014444  254/734-3171
114 W Lexington Street, Gorman 76454  Fax 254/734-3393

**Schools:** 3 \ **Teachers:** 28 \ **Students:** 287 \ **Special Ed Students:** 44 \ **LEP Students:** 14 \ **College-Bound:** 80% \ **Ethnic:** African American 1%, Hispanic 35%, Caucasian 64% \ **Exp:** $727 (High) \ **Poverty:** 16% \ **Title I:** $58,009 \ **Open-Close:** 08/19 - 05/27 \ **DTBP:** $350 (High)

| | | |
|---|---|---|
| Mike Winter ...........................1,11 | Randy Lewis ...........................3,5 |
| Lissa Young ...........................4 | Shellie Little ...........................7 |
| Latricia Hampton ...........................36,83,88* | Debra Sanchez ...........................57,271* |
| Vicki Brown ...........................58* | Eldin Straw ...........................67 |
| Dianne Snider ...........................68 | Denise Carlton ...........................73 |

| Public Schs..Principal | Grd | Prgm | Enr/#Cls | SN | |
|---|---|---|---|---|---|
| Gorman High Sch<br>114 W Lexington Street, Gorman 76454<br>**Karen Robinson** | 9-12 | TV | 77<br>13 | 66% | 254/734-3171<br>Fax 254/734-3425 🅵 🅴 |
| Gorman Middle Sch<br>114 W Lexington St, Gorman 76454<br>**Karen Robinson** | 6-8 | T | 73 | 71% | 254/734-3171<br>Fax 254/734-4729 🅵 🅴 |
| Maxfield Elem Sch<br>114 W Lexington Street, Gorman 76454<br>Fernando Sandoval | PK-5 | T | 137<br>13 | 73% | 254/734-3171<br>Fax 254/734-3445 🅵 🅴 |

● **Ranger Ind School Dist** PID: 01014470  254/647-1187
1842 E Loop 254, Ranger 76470  Fax 254/647-5215

**Schools:** 1 \ **Teachers:** 38 \ **Students:** 350 \ **Special Ed Students:** 60 \ **LEP Students:** 7 \ **College-Bound:** 60% \ **Ethnic:** African American 2%, Hispanic 24%, Caucasian 74% \ **Exp:** $616 (High) \ **Poverty:** 24% \ **Title I:** $161,457 \ **Open-Close:** 08/24 - 05/28 \ **DTBP:** $350 (High)

| | | |
|---|---|---|
| Mike Thompson ...........................1,73 | Joy Felan ...........................2 |
| Bobby Campbell ...........................6,35* | Lindsey Hawvermale ...........................8 |
| Michelle Arnold ...........................11* | June Guess ...........................16* |
| Nanette Edwards ...........................27,31* | Trey Felan ...........................36,69,85,270 |
| Karen Clifton ...........................67 | |

| Public Schs..Principal | Grd | Prgm | Enr/#Cls | SN | |
|---|---|---|---|---|---|
| Ranger Sch<br>1842 E Loop 254, Ranger 76470<br>Jessie Ellerbe | PK-12 | TV | 350<br>30 | 73% | 254/647-3216<br>Fax 254/647-1895 |

● **Rising Star Ind Sch Dist** PID: 01014511  254/643-1981
907 N Main St, Rising Star 76471  Fax 254/643-1922

**Schools:** 2 \ **Teachers:** 17 \ **Students:** 150 \ **Special Ed Students:** 15 \ **LEP Students:** 7 \ **Ethnic:** Asian 1%, African American 2%, Hispanic 20%, Caucasian 77% \ **Exp:** $950 (High) \ **Poverty:** 16% \ **Title I:** $74,118 \ **Open-Close:** 08/19 - 05/21 \ **DTBP:** $353 (High) \ 🅵 🅴

| | | |
|---|---|---|
| Mary Jane Atkins ...........................1 | Teresa Lawrence ...........................2 |
| Tracey Rutledge ...........................4 | Clint Miller ...........................6 |
| Creig Hopper ...........................58 | Howard Lawrence ...........................67 |

| Public Schs..Principal | Grd | Prgm | Enr/#Cls | SN | |
|---|---|---|---|---|---|
| Rising Star Elem Sch<br>113 W Newton St, Rising Star 76471<br>Mary Atkins | PK-6 | T | 83<br>10 | 73% | 254/643-2431<br>Fax 254/643-1002 |
| Rising Star High Sch<br>905 N Main St, Rising Star 76471<br>Randy Jones | 7-12 | TV | 76<br>11 | 67% | 254/643-3521<br>Fax 254/643-5408 |

# ECTOR COUNTY

## ECTOR PUBLIC SCHOOLS

• **Ector Co Ind School Dist** PID: 01014547     432/456-0000
  802 N Sam Houston Ave, Odessa 79761

**Schools:** 42 \ **Teachers:** 1,917 \ **Students:** 32,391 \
**Special Ed Students:** 2,870 \ **LEP Students:** 5,748 \ **College-Bound:** 55%
\ **Ethnic:** Asian 1%, African American 4%, Hispanic 77%, Caucasian
17% \ **Exp:** $456 (High) \ **Poverty:** 17% \ **Title I:** $8,556,318 \
**Special Education:** $5,521,000 \ **Open-Close:** 08/12 - 05/27 \ **DTBP:** $180
(High)

| Public Schs..Principal | Grd | Prgm | Enr/#Cls | SN |
|---|---|---|---|---|
| Ⓜ Austin Montessori Elem Sch<br>901 N Lee Ave, Odessa 79761<br>Tania Hagood | PK-5 | T | 354<br>30 | 63% 432/456-1029<br>Fax 432/456-1028 |
| Barbara Jordan Elem Sch<br>9400 Rainbow Dr, Odessa 79765<br>Scott Houston | K-5 | T | 771<br>55 | 41% 432/456-1299<br>Fax 432/456-1298 |
| Ⓜ Blackshear Magnet Elem Sch<br>501 S Dixie Blvd, Odessa 79761<br>Ms Rivera | K-5 | T | 683<br>30 | 72% 432/456-1279<br>Fax 432/456-1278 ⓕⓣ |
| Blanton Elem Sch<br>4101 Lynbrook Ave, Odessa 79762<br>**Stacey Ybarra** | PK-5 | T | 555<br>25 | 51% 432/456-1259<br>Fax 432/456-1258 |
| Bonham Middle Sch<br>2201 E 21st St, Odessa 79761<br>**Mareka Austin** | 6-8 | TV | 690 | 57% 432/456-0429<br>Fax 432/456-0428 ⓕⓣ |
| Bowie Middle Sch<br>500 W 21st St, Odessa 79761<br>**Brian Ellington** | 6-8 | TV | 1,247<br>65 | 57% 432/456-0439<br>Fax 432/456-0438 ⓕⓣ |
| Burleson Elem Sch<br>3900 Golder Ave, Odessa 79764<br>Tristan Specter | K-5 | T | 543<br>35 | 68% 432/456-1039<br>Fax 432/456-1038 |
| Burnet Elem Sch<br>3511 Maple Ave, Odessa 79762<br>**Maria Serrano** | K-5 | | 559<br>35 | 432/456-1049<br>Fax 432/456-1048 |
| Ⓜ Cameron Dual Lang Magnet Sch<br>2401 W 8th St, Odessa 79763<br>Jacob Bargas | PK-5 | T | 531<br>36 | 65% 432/456-1059<br>Fax 432/456-1058 ⓕⓣ |
| Carver Early Education Center<br>600 College Ave, Odessa 79761<br>Sherry Palmer | PK-PK | | 556<br>15 | 432/456-1069<br>Fax 432/456-1068 ⓣ |
| Crockett Middle Sch<br>2301 Conover Ave, Odessa 79763<br>Maribel Aranda | 6-8 | TV | 1,199<br>52 | 60% 432/456-0449<br>Fax 432/456-0448 |
| Dowling Elem Sch<br>1510 E 17th St, Odessa 79761<br>Kristabel Regalado | K-5 | T | 567<br>40 | 70% 432/456-1079<br>Fax 432/456-1078 |
| Dr Lee Buice Elem Sch<br>1800 E 87th St, Odessa 79765<br>Jessica Rickman | K-5 | T | 670 | 45% 432/456-1339 |
| © Ector Clg Prep Success Acad<br>Ⓜ 809 W Clements St, Odessa 79763<br>Charles Quintela | 6-8 | TV | 1,395<br>87 | 76% 432/456-0479<br>Fax 432/456-0478 |
| Ⓐ Ector Co Youth Alt Center<br>1299 E Yukon Rd, Odessa 79762<br>Adam Portillo | 6-12 | V | 104<br>15 | 432/456-0049<br>Fax 432/456-0048 ⓕ |
| Edward K Downing Elem Sch<br>1480 N Knox Ave, Odessa 79763<br>Marcos Lopez | K-5 | T | 708 | 73% 432/456-1319 |
| Ⓨ Gale Pond Alamo Steam Academy<br>801 E 23rd St, Odessa 79761<br>Regina Lee | PK-5 | MT | 308<br>25 | 62% 432/456-1019<br>Fax 432/456-1018 |
| George Buddy West Elem Sch<br>2225 W Sycamore Dr, Odessa 79763<br>Gisela Davila | PK-5 | T | 594 | 69% 432/456-1329 |
| George W Bush New Tech Odessa<br>300 E 29th St, Odessa 79762<br>Gerardo Ramirez | 9-12 | | 361<br>60 | 37% 432/456-6989<br>Fax 432/456-6988 |
| Goliad Elem Sch<br>501 E 52nd St, Odessa 79762<br>Cristabel Gonzales | K-5 | T | 552<br>32 | 75% 432/456-1109<br>Fax 432/456-1108 ⓕⓣ |
| Gonzales Elem Sch<br>2700 Disney St, Odessa 79761<br>Angie Moad | K-5 | T | 441<br>35 | 59% 432/456-1119<br>Fax 432/456-1118 ⓕⓣ |
| Ⓜ Hays Magnet Academy<br>1101 E Monahans St, Odessa 79761<br>Julie Marshall | PK-5 | T | 396<br>30 | 45% 432/456-1129<br>Fax 432/456-1128 |
| Ⓜ Ireland Elem Sch<br>4301 Dawn Ave, Odessa 79762<br>Katy Ochoa | K-5 | T | 576<br>38 | 55% 432/456-1149<br>Fax 432/456-1148 |
| Lamar Early Education Center<br>501 Lettie Lee, Odessa 79761<br>Maryjane Hutchins | PK-PK | T | 652<br>23 | 97% 432/456-1159<br>Fax 432/456-1158 |
| Lauro Cavazos Elem Sch<br>9301 W 16th St, Odessa 79763<br>Amanda Montelongo | K-5 | T | 807<br>36 | 72% 432/456-1309<br>Fax 432/456-1308 |
| Lyndon B Johnson Elem Sch<br>6401 Amber Dr, Odessa 79762<br>Alisha Holguin | K-5 | T | 711<br>60 | 52% 432/456-1289<br>Fax 432/456-1288 |
| Ⓜ Milam Magnet Elem Sch<br>640 College Ave, Odessa 79761<br>Natalie Fitzgerald | PK-5 | | 534<br>40 | 432/456-1169<br>Fax 432/456-1168 ⓕⓣ |
| Murry Fly Elem Sch<br>11688 W Westview Dr, Odessa 79764<br>Sammy Martinez | PK-5 | T | 824<br>38 | 71% 432/456-1269<br>Fax 432/456-1268 |
| Nimitz Middle Sch<br>4900 Maple Ave, Odessa 79762<br>Teresa Willison | 6-8 | V | 1,301<br>60 | 36% 432/456-0469<br>Fax 432/456-0468 ⓕⓣ |
| Ⓜ Noel Elem Sch<br>2200 Newcomb Dr, Odessa 79764<br>Jennie Chavez | 3-5 | T | 516<br>30 | 62% 432/456-1249<br>Fax 432/456-1248 |
| Odessa Career Tch Early Clg HS<br>201 W University Blvd, Odessa 79764<br>Karl Miller | 9-9 | | 174 | 36% 432/456-6409 |
| Odessa Collegiate Academy<br>4901 E University Blvd, Odessa 79762<br>Lindsey Lumpkin | 9-9 | | 140 | 432/456-6429<br>ⓕⓣ |

| | | | | | | |
|---|---|---|---|---|---|---|
| Odessa High Sch<br>1301 Dotsy Ave, Odessa 79763<br>Mauricio Marquez | 9-12 | TV | 3,850<br>100 | 44% | 432/456-0029<br>Fax 432/456-5264 | |
| Pease Elem Sch<br>1800 W 22nd St, Odessa 79763<br>Kamye Smith | K-5 | T | 602<br>50 | 76% | 432/456-1179<br>Fax 432/456-1178 | |
| Permian High Sch<br>1800 E 42nd St, Odessa 79762<br>**Dr Delesa Styles** | 9-12 | V | 3,817 | 34% | 432/456-0039<br>Fax 432/456-0038 | |
| Ⓜ Reagan Magnet Elem Sch<br>2321 E 21st St, Odessa 79761<br>**Jennifer Bizzell** | K-5 | | 576<br>33 | 28% | 432/456-1189<br>Fax 432/456-1188 | 🅕🅣 |
| Ross Elem Sch<br>4600 N Everglade Ave, Odessa 79762<br>Rebecca Phillips | K-5 | T | 427<br>32 | 69% | 432/456-1199<br>Fax 432/456-1198 | |
| Sam Houston Elem Sch<br>300 E 37th St, Odessa 79762<br>Crystal Marquez | K-5 | T | 534<br>30 | 82% | 432/456-1139<br>Fax 432/456-1138 | |
| San Jacinto Elem Sch<br>1000 W 19th St, Odessa 79763<br>Erin Bueno | K-5 | T | 506<br>34 | 72% | 432/456-1219<br>Fax 432/456-1218 | |
| Ⓜ Travis Magnet Elem Sch<br>1400 S Lee Ave, Odessa 79761<br>Linda Voss | K-5 | T | 333<br>23 | 73% | 432/456-1229<br>Fax 432/456-1228 | |
| Wilson & Young Middle Sch<br>601 E 38th St, Odessa 79762<br>Anthony Garza | 6-8 | V | 1,116<br>55 | 45% | 432/456-0459<br>Fax 432/456-0458 | |
| Ⓜ Zavala Magnet Elem Sch<br>1201 Clifford St, Odessa 79763<br>Tanya Galindo | K-5 | T | 611<br>38 | 85% | 432/456-1239<br>Fax 432/456-1238 | |

## ECTOR CATHOLIC SCHOOLS

● **Diocese of San Angelo Ed Off** PID: 01055929
Listing includes only schools located in this county. See District Index for location of Diocesan Offices.

| Catholic Schs..Principal | Grd | Prgm | Enr/#Cls | SN |
|---|---|---|---|---|
| St Mary's Central Catholic Sch<br>1703 Adams Ave, Odessa 79761<br>Pat Salcido | K-8 | | 300<br>13 | 432/337-6052<br>Fax 432/332-2942 |

## ECTOR PRIVATE SCHOOLS

| Private Schs..Principal | Grd | Prgm | Enr/#Cls | SN |
|---|---|---|---|---|
| Holy Cross Catholic HS<br>7601 N Grandview Ave, Odessa 79765<br>Carolyn Gonzalez | 9-12 | | 21 | 432/713-0143 |
| Montessori Mastery Sch-Odessa<br>1415 N Grandview Ave, Odessa 79761<br>Randy McGuire | 7-12 | | 50 | 432/631-2405 |
| Odessa Christian Sch<br>2000 Doran Dr, Odessa 79761<br>Pamela Walker | PK-8 | | 150<br>12 | 432/362-6311<br>Fax 432/550-7086 |
| St John's Episcopal Sch<br>401 W County Rd N, Odessa 79763<br>Emily McDoniel | PK-8 | | 220<br>13 | 432/337-6431<br>Fax 432/335-0815 |

## EDWARDS COUNTY

## EDWARDS PUBLIC SCHOOLS

● **Nueces Canyon Cons Ind SD** PID: 01014872
200 Taylor Street, Barksdale 78828

830/234-3514
Fax 830/234-3435

**Schools:** 2 \ **Teachers:** 30 \ **Students:** 264 \ **Special Ed Students:** 29 \ **LEP Students:** 4 \ **College-Bound:** 100% \ **Ethnic:** Hispanic 43%, Caucasian 56% \ **Exp:** $439 (High) \ **Poverty:** 42% \ **Title I:** $169,015 \ **Open-Close:** 08/19 - 05/21

| | | | |
|---|---|---|---|
| Kristi Powers | 1 | Billye Smith | 2 |
| Steven Smith | 3,5 | Wilma Reading | 4* |
| Leslie Caillet | 7* | Shawna Moore | 8,11,36,59,69,88,296* |
| Brett Vurner | 16,73,298 | Richard Kramer | 27* |
| Christi Collins | 58,83* | Toby Kramer | 59* |
| Danny Irwin | 67 | Tina Taylor | 286* |
| Tena Hunger | 297 | | |

| Public Schs..Principal | Grd | Prgm | Enr/#Cls | SN |
|---|---|---|---|---|
| Nueces Canyon Elem Sch<br>Highway 337, Camp Wood 78833<br>Shawna Moore | PK-6 | T | 158<br>12 | 74% 830/597-3218<br>Fax 830/597-6197 |
| Nueces Canyon Jr Sr High Sch<br>200 Taylor Street, Barksdale 78828<br>Shawna Moore | 7-12 | TV | 106<br>16 | 67% 830/234-3524<br>Fax 830/234-4129 |

● **Rocksprings Ind School Dist** PID: 01014901
201 N Highway 377, Rocksprings 78880

830/683-4137
Fax 830/683-4141

**Schools:** 1 \ **Teachers:** 24 \ **Students:** 289 \ **Special Ed Students:** 45 \ **LEP Students:** 19 \ **College-Bound:** 50% \ **Ethnic:** Hispanic 77%, Caucasian 23% \ **Exp:** $1,130 (High) \ **Poverty:** 33% \ **Title I:** $147,131 \ **Open-Close:** 08/21 - 05/28 \ **DTBP:** $443 (High)

| | | | |
|---|---|---|---|
| **Larry Taylor** | 1 | Patty Flores | 2 |
| Manuel Ramos | 6* | Brian McCraw | 8,12,57,69,88,270* |
| Daron Worrell | 11 | Leann Holt | 58 |
| Brady Hyde | 67 | Mario Gonzales | 73* |

| Public Schs..Principal | Grd | Prgm | Enr/#Cls | SN |
|---|---|---|---|---|
| Rocksprings Sch<br>201 N Highway 377, Rocksprings 78880<br>Brian McCraw | PK-12 | TV | 289<br>20 | 70% 830/683-2140<br>Fax 830/683-8141 |

| | | | | |
|---|---|---|---|---|
| 79 Student Personnel | 91 Safety/Security | 275 Response To Intervention | 298 Grant Writer/Ptnrships | School Programs |
| 80 Driver Ed/Safety | 92 Magnet School | 277 Remedial Math K-12 | 750 Chief Innovation Officer | A = Alternative Program |
| 81 Gifted/Talented | 93 Parental Involvement | 280 Literacy Coach | 751 Chief of Staff | G = Adult Classes |
| 82 Video Services | 95 Tech Prep Program | 285 STEM | 752 Social Emotional Learning | M = Magnet Program |
| 83 Substance Abuse Prev | 97 Chief Information Officer | 286 Digital Learning | | T = Title I Schoolwide |
| 84 Erate | 98 Chief Technology Officer | 288 Common Core Standards | Other School Types | V = Career & Tech Ed Programs |
| 85 AIDS Education | 270 Character Education | 294 Accountability | Ⓐ = Alternative School | |
| 88 Alternative/At Risk | 271 Migrant Education | 295 Network System | Ⓒ = Charter School | New Schools are shaded |
| 89 Multi-Cultural Curriculum | 273 Teacher Mentor | 296 Title II Programs | Ⓜ = Magnet School | New Superintendents and Principals are bold |
| 90 Social Work | 274 Before/After Sch | 297 Webmaster | Ⓨ = Year-Round School | Personnel with email addresses are underscored |

Social Media
🅕 = Facebook
🅣 = Twitter

**TX—135**

## EL PASO COUNTY

## EL PASO PUBLIC SCHOOLS

● **Anthony Ind School Dist** PID: 01015357
840 6th St, Anthony 79821

915/886-6500
Fax 915/886-2420

**Schools:** 3 \ **Teachers:** 58 \ **Students:** 795 \ **Special Ed Students:** 90 \ **LEP Students:** 197 \ **Ethnic:** Hispanic 97%, Caucasian 3% \ **Exp:** $1,300 (High) \ **Poverty:** 29% \ **Title I:** $283,005 \ **Special Education:** $122,000 \ **Open-Close:** 08/12 - 05/21 \ **DTBP:** $354 (High)

| | | | |
|---|---|---|---|
| Oscar Troncoso | 1 | Jissel Reyes | 2 |
| Rene Ramirez | 3,5 | Jesus Carrasco | 4 |
| Jaime Reyes | 5 | David Rueda | 6 |
| Sandy Honts | 8,11,58 | Karen Paterson | 16* |
| Angel Cuellar | 67 | Melissa Leos | 271* |
| Alex Ramirez | 295 | Raymond Carroll | 296 |

| Public Schs..Principal | Grd | Prgm | Enr/#Cls | SN |
|---|---|---|---|---|
| Anthony Elem Sch<br>610 6th St, Anthony 79821<br>Oralia Moseley | PK-5 | T | 376<br>36 | 100% 915/886-6510<br>Fax 915/886-3205 |
| Anthony High Sch<br>825 Wildcat Dr, Anthony 79821<br>Fernando Garnica | 9-12 | AGTV | 230<br>18 | 100% 915/886-6550<br>Fax 915/886-3876 |
| Anthony Middle Sch<br>813 6th St, Anthony 79821<br>Fernando Garnica | 6-8 | T | 189 | 100% 915/886-6530<br>Fax 915/886-3875 |

● **Canutillo Ind School Dist** PID: 01015383
7965 Artcraft Rd, El Paso 79932

915/877-7400
Fax 915/877-7525

**Schools:** 10 \ **Teachers:** 418 \ **Students:** 6,200 \ **Special Ed Students:** 602 \ **LEP Students:** 1,805 \ **College-Bound:** 54% \ **Ethnic:** African American 1%, Hispanic 94%, Caucasian 5% \ **Exp:** $619 (High) \ **Poverty:** 25% \ **Title I:** $1,847,469 \ **Special Education:** $871,000 \ **Open-Close:** 08/10 - 05/25 \ **DTBP:** $193 (High) \ 🅵 🅴

| | | | |
|---|---|---|---|
| Dr Pedro Galaviz | 1 | Martha Piekarski | 2,19 |
| Bruno Vasquez | 3,5 | Marco Macias | 4 |
| Scott Brooks | 6* | Dr Monica Reyes | 7,30,34,36,85,88,93 |
| Debra Kerney | 8* | Marnie Rocha | 15 |
| Tracy Andrews | 27* | Sandra Carrillo | 34 |
| Stacey Parker | 39 | Marlena Zimmerman | 42 |
| Nidia Avila | 45* | Yirah Valverde | 45 |
| Natalie Spalloni | 48 | Maria Silva | 57,271 |
| Carey Chambers | 58 | Sergio Coronado | 67 |
| Martha Carrasco | 68 | April Galaviz | 69,70,294 |
| Liza Rodriguez | 71 | Lucero Hernandez | 88 |
| Carlos Carrillo | 91* | Marisela Ramos | 271 |
| Albert Vega | 286 | | |

| Public Schs..Principal | Grd | Prgm | Enr/#Cls | SN |
|---|---|---|---|---|
| Bill Childress Elem Sch<br>7700 Cap Carter Rd, Vinton 79821<br>Reyna Salcedo | PK-5 | T | 386<br>60 | 77% 915/877-7701<br>Fax 915/877-7709<br>🅵🅴 |
| Canutillo Elem Sch<br>651 Canutillo Ave, Canutillo 79835<br>Julie Melendez | PK-5 | T | 497<br>40 | 82% 915/877-7600<br>Fax 915/877-7609 |

| Public Schs..Principal | Grd | Prgm | Enr/#Cls | SN |
|---|---|---|---|---|
| Canutillo High Sch<br>6675 S Desert Blvd, El Paso 79932<br>Teresa Clapsaddle | 9-12 | TV | 1,559<br>90 | 70% 915/877-7800<br>Fax 915/877-7807 |
| Canutillo Middle Sch<br>7311 Bosque Rd, Canutillo 79835<br>Christopher Judge | 6-8 | T | 660<br>60 | 62% 915/877-7900<br>Fax 915/877-7919 |
| Deanna Davenport Elem Sch<br>8401 Remington Rd, Canutillo 79835<br>Marta Strobach | PK-5 | T | 317<br>23 | 92% 915/886-6400<br>Fax 915/886-6407<br>🅵🅴 |
| Gonzalo & Sofia Garcia ES<br>6550 Westside Dr, El Paso 79932<br>Teresa Heimer | PK-5 | T | 507 | 58% 915/877-1200<br>Fax 915/877-1219<br>🅵🅴 |
| Jose Alderete Middle Sch<br>801 Talbot Ave, Canutillo 79835<br>Dr Oscar Rico | 6-8 | T | 637 | 74% 915/877-6600<br>Fax 915/877-6619<br>🅵🅴 |
| Jose Damian Elem Sch<br>6300 Strahan Rd, El Paso 79932<br>Jesus Barba | PK-5 | T | 577<br>40 | 63% 915/877-6800<br>Fax 915/877-6819<br>🅵 |
| Northwest Early College HS<br>6701 S Desert Blvd, El Paso 79932<br>Jesica Arellano | 9-12 | T | 371 | 49% 915/877-1700<br>Fax 915/877-7033<br>🅵🅴 |
| Silvestre & Reyes Elem Sch<br>7440 Northern Pass Dr, El Paso 79911<br>Dr Debra Kerney | PK-5 | T | 506 | 30% 915/877-1300<br>Fax 915/877-2319 |

● **Clint Ind School Dist** PID: 01015424
14521 Horizon Blvd, El Paso 79928

915/926-4000
Fax 915/926-4009

**Schools:** 14 \ **Teachers:** 654 \ **Students:** 11,522 \ **Special Ed Students:** 986 \ **LEP Students:** 3,876 \ **College-Bound:** 55% \ **Ethnic:** Hispanic 96%, Caucasian 4% \ **Exp:** $495 (High) \ **Poverty:** 33% \ **Title I:** $5,187,542 \ **Special Education:** $1,856,000 \ **Open-Close:** 07/27 - 06/03 \ **DTBP:** $161 (High) \ 🅵 🅴

| | | | |
|---|---|---|---|
| Dr Juan Martinez | 1 | Donna Cline | 2,19 |
| Sandra Odenburg | 3 | Paul Harrington | 4 |
| Jonathan Powell | 5* | Mike Mackeben | 6 |
| Jennifer Parker | 9 | Jim Littlejohn | 10,15 |
| Melissa Williams | 11 | Manuel Ayala | 15,69,294 |
| Veronica Booth | 27 | Jose Ramirez | 39 |
| William Swanson | 44 | Sandra Martinez | 48 |
| Victor Hernandez | 57 | Josephine Angerstein | 58 |
| Arlene Parada | 67 | Rene Chavez | 68 |
| Laura Cade | 71 | Manuel Verduzco | 73,98 |
| Noe Cantu | 73 | Sally Upchurch | 91 |

| Public Schs..Principal | Grd | Prgm | Enr/#Cls | SN |
|---|---|---|---|---|
| Carroll T Welch Elem Sch<br>14510 McMahon Ave, El Paso 79928<br>Alma Vasquez | PK-5 | AT | 788<br>45 | 93% 915/926-4400<br>Fax 915/852-7230 |
| Clint Early College Academy<br>13100 Alameda Ave, Clint 79836<br>Edmond Martinez | 9-9 | T | 342 | 75% 915/926-8100<br>Fax 915/851-3459 |
| Clint High Sch<br>13890 Alameda Ave, Clint 79836<br>Garrett Ritchey | 9-12 | AGTV | 694<br>60 | 80% 915/926-8300<br>Fax 915/851-5375<br>🅴 |
| Clint Junior High Sch<br>12625 Alameda Ave, Clint 79836<br>Noemi Hernandez | 6-8 | AGT | 538<br>15 | 85% 915/926-8000<br>Fax 915/851-3895 |
| Desert Hills Elem Sch<br>300 N Kenazo Ave, El Paso 79928<br>Adriana Cantu | PK-5 | AT | 1,032<br>45 | 79% 915/926-4500<br>Fax 915/852-3570 |
| East Montana Middle Sch<br>3490 Ascencion St, El Paso 79938<br>Juanita Guerra | 6-8 | AT | 670<br>68 | 90% 915/926-5200<br>Fax 915/855-0821 |

| # | | # | | # | | # | | # | | # | | # | |
|---|---|---|---|---|---|---|---|---|---|---|---|---|---|
| 1 | Superintendent | 8 | Curric/Instruct K-12 | 19 | Chief Financial Officer | 29 | Family/Consumer Science | 39 | Social Studies K-12 | 49 | English/Lang Arts Elem | 59 | Special Education Elem | 69 | Academic Assessment |
| 2 | Bus/Finance/Purchasing | 9 | Curric/Instruct Elem | 20 | Art K-12 | 30 | Adult Education | 40 | Social Studies Elem | 50 | English/Lang Arts Sec | 60 | Special Education Sec | 70 | Research/Development |
| 3 | Buildings And Grounds | 10 | Curric/Instruct Sec | 21 | Art Elem | 31 | Career/Sch-to-Work K-12 | 41 | Social Studies Sec | 51 | Reading K-12 | 61 | Foreign/World Lang K-12 | 71 | Public Information |
| 4 | Food Service | 11 | Federal Program | 22 | Art Sec | 32 | Career/Sch-to-Work Elem | 42 | Science K-12 | 52 | Reading Elem | 62 | Foreign/World Lang Elem | 72 | Summer School |
| 5 | Transportation | 12 | Title I | 23 | Music K-12 | 33 | Career/Sch-to-Work Sec | 43 | Science Elem | 53 | Reading Sec | 63 | Foreign/World Lang Sec | 73 | Instructional Tech |
| 6 | Athletic | 13 | Title V | 24 | Music Elem | 34 | Early Childhood Ed | 44 | Science Sec | 54 | Remedial Reading K-12 | 64 | Religious Education K-12 | 74 | Inservice Training |
| 7 | Health Services | 15 | Asst Superintendent | 25 | Music Sec | 35 | Health/Phys Education | 45 | Math K-12 | 55 | Remedial Reading Elem | 65 | Religious Education Elem | 75 | Marketing/Distributive |
| | | 16 | Instructional Media Svcs | 26 | Business Education | 36 | Guidance Services K-12 | 46 | Math Elem | 56 | Remedial Reading Sec | 66 | Religious Education Sec | 76 | Info Systems |
| | | 17 | Chief Operations Officer | 27 | Career & Tech Ed | 37 | Guidance Services Elem | 47 | Math Sec | 57 | Bilingual/ELL | 67 | School Board President | 77 | Psychological Assess |
| | | 18 | Chief Academic Officer | 28 | Technology Education | 38 | Guidance Services Sec | 48 | English/Lang Arts K-12 | 58 | Special Education K-12 | 68 | Teacher Personnel | 78 | Affirmative Action |

| School | Grd | Prgm | Enr/#Cls | SN | Phone |
|---|---|---|---|---|---|
| Frank Macias Elem Sch<br>14400 Golden Eagle Dr, Horizon City 79928<br>Liz Olga | PK-5 | AT | 906<br>43 | 92% | 915/926-4600<br>Fax 915/852-7547 |
| Horizon High Sch<br>14651 Horizon Blvd, El Paso 79928<br>Elena Acosta | 10-12 | AT | 1,555 | 86% | 915/926-4200<br>Fax 915/852-0357 |
| Horizon Middle Sch<br>400 N Kenazo Ave, El Paso 79928<br>Roxanne Ruiz | 6-7 | AT | 687 | 80% | 915/926-4700<br>Fax 915/852-9274 |
| Montana Vista Elem Sch<br>3550 Mark Jason Dr, El Paso 79938<br>Cain Castillo | PK-5 | AT | 460<br>40 | 94% | 915/926-5307<br>Fax 915/857-0631 |
| Mountain View High Sch<br>14964 Greg Dr, El Paso 79938<br>Roberto Trejo | 9-12 | AGTV | 835<br>85 | 87% | 915/926-5000<br>Fax 915/855-2503<br>🅵🅃 |
| Red Sands Elem Sch<br>4250 Oshea St, El Paso 79938<br>Carlos Villalobos | PK-5 | AT | 535 | 89% | 915/926-5400<br>Fax 915/855-8294 |
| Ricardo Estrada Middle Sch<br>851 Darrington Rd, El Paso 79928<br>Lorraine Vidales | 6-8 | AT | 741 | 85% | 915/926-4800<br>Fax 915/852-2455 |
| William D Surratt Elem Sch<br>12675 Alameda Ave, Clint 79836<br>Melissa Williams | PK-5 | AT | 908<br>40 | 88% | 915/926-8200<br>Fax 915/851-3489 |

## ● El Paso Ind School Dist   PID: 01015450          915/230-2000
6531 Boeing Dr, El Paso 79925

**Schools:** 86 \ **Teachers:** 3,900 \ **Students:** 57,315 \
**Special Ed Students:** 6,368 \ **LEP Students:** 16,151 \ **College-Bound:** 76%
\ **Ethnic:** Asian 1%, African American 4%, Hispanic 85%, Caucasian
10% \ **Exp:** $492 (High) \ **Poverty:** 28% \ **Title I:** $28,685,834 \
**Special Education:** $11,158,000 \ **Bilingual Education:** $84,000 \
**Open-Close:** 08/17 - 06/15 \ **DTBP:** $191 (High)

<table>
<tr><td>

Juan Cabrera .................................. 1,288<br>
Maria Pineda ................................................ 2<br>
Ernesto Ortiz ................................................ 3<br>
Laura Duran .................................................. 4<br>
Maria Kennedy .............................................. 6<br>
Kristine Ferret .............................................. 8<br>
Vincent Sheffield ................. 8,15,68,78<br>
Ana Torres .................................................. 15<br>
Patricia Cortez ..................................... 15,68<br>
Phillip Barraza .......................................20,23<br>
John Adams .............................................. 35<br>
Laila Ferris ...........................................57,61<br>
Brenda Booth ............................................. 69<br>
Victoria Orozco .......................................... 70<br>
Alice Ramos ............ 73,76,97,98,286,295<br>
Tony Flores ................................................. 73<br>
Manny Chavira ............................................ 91<br>
Jose Lopez ............................................... 751

</td><td>

Carmen Candelaria ........................... 2,3,15<br>
Ron Gatlin ..................................................... 2<br>
Nicholas Corona ........................................3,4,5<br>
Oscar Anchondo ............................................ 5<br>
Alana Bejarano ............................................. 7<br>
Dr Tamekia Brown ....................................8,18<br>
Nancy Tovar ...........................................9,15<br>
Laurie Enlue .........................................15,58<br>
Armando Loera ........................................... 16<br>
Eric Winkelman ...........................27,31,285<br>
Manuel Castruita ....................................36,88<br>
Bob Geske ................................................. 67<br>
Steve Clay .....................................69,70,294<br>
Melissa Martinez ........................................ 71<br>
Jesus Corral ............................................... 73<br>
Terry Funk .................................................. 76<br>
Ramon Lozano ..........................93,275,752

</td></tr>
</table>

| Public Schs..Principal | Grd | Prgm | Enr/#Cls | SN | Phone |
|---|---|---|---|---|---|
| Ⓐ About Face Alternative ES<br>1440 E Cliff Dr, El Paso 79902<br>Bertha Martinez | K-5 | | 44 | | 915/236-3150 |
| Ⓐ Delta Academy<br>6400 Delta Dr, El Paso 79905<br>Federico Rojas | 5-12 | T | 80<br>12 | 60% | 915/774-0447<br>Fax 915/881-1245 |
| Ⓐ Raymond Telles/Lafarelle MS<br>2851 Grant Ave Bldg A, El Paso 79930<br>Lorenzo Munoz | 6-12 | | 45<br>40 | | 915/236-7800<br>Fax 915/532-0540 |
| San Jacinto Adult Learning Ctr<br>1216 Olive Ave, El Paso 79901<br>Arturo Gonzalez | Adult | | 500<br>18 | | 915/230-3200<br>Fax 915/544-7163 |

| School | Grd | Prgm | Enr/#Cls | SN | Phone |
|---|---|---|---|---|---|
| YW Steam Research & Prep Acad<br>2231 Arizona Ave, El Paso 79930<br>Cynthia Ontiveros | 6-12 | T | 182 | 64% | 915/236-4830 |

## ● El Paso ISD-Elementary   PID: 11982247          915/230-2485
6531 Boeing Dr, El Paso 79925

**Juan Cabrera** .........................................1   Dr Blanca Garcia ................................. 15
Bob Geske ............................................ 67

| Public Schs..Principal | Grd | Prgm | Enr/#Cls | SN | Phone |
|---|---|---|---|---|---|
| Aoy Elem Sch<br>901 S Campbell St, El Paso 79901<br>**Mary Arnold** | PK-5 | T | 397<br>60 | 92% | 915/236-0175<br>Fax 915/313-0163 |
| Barron Elem Sch<br>11155 Whitey Ford St, El Paso 79934<br>Lidia Anguiano | PK-5 | T | 429 | 72% | 915/236-5075<br>Fax 915/822-1460 |
| Bliss Elem Sch<br>4401 Sheridan Rd, El Paso 79906<br>Narichica Handy | PK-5 | T | 449 | 62% | 915/236-5150<br>Fax 915/566-2806 |
| Bonham Elem Sch<br>7024 Cielo Vista Dr, El Paso 79925<br>Sandra Sanchez | PK-5 | T | 197<br>30 | 93% | 915/236-8150<br>Fax 915/778-0525 |
| Cielo Vista Elem Sch<br>9000 Basil Ct, El Paso 79925<br>Bertha Rodriguez | PK-5 | T | 380<br>20 | 63% | 915/236-8375<br>Fax 915/599-2965 |
| Clardy Elem Sch<br>5508 Delta Dr, El Paso 79905<br>**Michelle Corral** | PK-5 | T | 498<br>46 | 94% | 915/236-8450<br>Fax 915/778-1580 |
| Clendenin Elem Sch<br>2701 Harrison Ave, El Paso 79930<br>Martha Martinez | PK-5 | T | 442<br>30 | 91% | 915/236-5300<br>Fax 915/566-4459 |
| Coldwell Elem Sch<br>4101 Altura Ave, El Paso 79903<br>Jose Gijon | PK-5 | T | 492<br>65 | 88% | 915/236-8525<br>Fax 915/566-4634 |
| Collins Elem Sch<br>4860 Tropicana Ave, El Paso 79924<br>Leticia Ewing | PK-5 | T | 429<br>35 | 86% | 915/236-5375<br>Fax 915/759-7315 |
| Cooley Elem Sch<br>107 N Collingsworth St, El Paso 79905<br>Elizabeth Prangner | PK-5 | T | 408<br>54 | 95% | 915/236-8600<br>Fax 915/775-1272 |
| Crockett Elem Sch<br>3200 Wheeling Ave, El Paso 79930<br>Elco Ramos | PK-5 | T | 427<br>60 | 90% | 915/236-8675<br>Fax 915/566-4950 |
| Crosby Elem Sch<br>5411 Wren Ave, El Paso 79924<br>Alonzo Barraza | PK-5 | T | 441<br>60 | 93% | 915/236-5450<br>Fax 915/759-7409 |
| Douglass Elem Sch<br>101 S Eucalyptus St, El Paso 79905<br>**Alonzo Barraza** | PK-5 | GT | 198<br>33 | 96% | 915/236-8750<br>Fax 915/533-3716 |
| Dowell Elem Sch<br>5249 Bastille Ave, El Paso 79924<br>Yeni Ontiveros | PK-5 | T | 323<br>35 | 86% | 915/236-5525<br>Fax 915/759-7713 |
| Dr Joseph E Torres<br>10700 Rushing Rd, El Paso 79924<br>**Kathleen Ese** | PK-5 | T | 850<br>53 | 84% | 915/236-5225 |
| Dr Nixon Elem Sch<br>11141 Loma Roja Dr, El Paso 79934<br>Christine Miles | PK-5 | T | 704<br>50 | 68% | 915/236-5900<br>Fax 915/821-6582 |
| General Colin Powell Elem Sch<br>4750 Ellerthorpe Ave, El Paso 79904<br>Wilfred Veilleux | PK-5 | T | 671 | 71% | 915/774-7775<br>Fax 915/564-5086 |
| Green Elem Sch<br>5430 Buckley Dr, El Paso 79912<br>Charlotte Quintana | PK-5 | T | 347<br>45 | 74% | 915/236-3000<br>Fax 915/833-8794 |

Hart Elem Sch   PK-5   T   490   95% 915/412-5499
1110 S Park St, El Paso 79901   40   Fax 915/533-3726
Angelica Negrete

Hawkins Elem Sch   PK-5   T   297   98% 915/236-8900
5816 Stephenson Ave, El Paso 79905   32   Fax 915/775-2699
Adriana Ruiz

Herrera Elem Sch   PK-5   T   579   84% 915/230-5000
350 Coates Dr, El Paso 79932   Fax 915/581-2377
Diana Provencio

Hillside Elem Sch   PK-5   T   531   90% 915/236-0100
4500 Clifton Ave, El Paso 79903   42   Fax 915/566-5210
Cynthia Anderson

Hughey Elem Sch   PK-5   T   563   81% 915/236-0250
6201 Hughey Dr, El Paso 79925   40   Fax 915/779-6911
Lilia Aguilera

Johnson Elem Sch   PK-5   T   447   91% 915/236-3925
499 Cabaret Dr, El Paso 79912   80   Fax 915/581-0917
**Luz Perez**

Lamar Elem Sch   PK-5   T   370   98% 915/236-3150
1440 E Cliff Dr, El Paso 79902   35   Fax 915/534-0083
Bertha Martinez

Logan Elem Sch   PK-5   T   607   70% 915/236-5750
3200 Ellerthorpe Ave, El Paso 79904   36   Fax 915/236-5752
Nancy Hanson

Lundy Elem Sch   PK-5     647   23% 915/230-5075
6201 High Ridge Dr, El Paso 79912   Fax 915/584-1972
Lourdes Lugo

MacArthur Elem-Interm Sch   PK-8   T   853   75% 915/236-0625
8101 Whitus Dr, El Paso 79925   57   Fax 915/779-2281
Rose Martinez

Mesita Elem Sch   PK-5   T   1,107   58% 915/236-6850
3307 N Stanton St, El Paso 79902   35   Fax 915/532-2068
Laila Ferris

Milam Elem Sch   PK-5   T   710   66% 915/236-0325
5000 Luke St, El Paso 79908   21   Fax 915/562-6448
Wanda Johnson

Mitzi Bond Elem Sch   PK-5   T   609   54% 915/236-2925
250 Lindbergh Ave, El Paso 79932   49   Fax 915/581-1220
Rachel Villalobos

Moye Elem Sch   PK-5   T   404   94% 915/230-5300
4825 Alps Dr, El Paso 79904   35   Fax 915/751-7810
Jesus Medina

Newman Elem Sch   PK-5   T   410   87% 915/236-5825
10275 Alcan St, El Paso 79924   45   Fax 915/759-8306
Pauletta Howard

Olga Kohlberg Elem Sch   PK-5   T   595   64% 915/236-2850
1445 Nardo Goodman Dr, El Paso 79912   50   Fax 915/833-4628
Michelle Pringle

Park Elem Sch   PK-5   T   516   86% 915/236-5975
3601 Edgar Park Ave, El Paso 79904   37   Fax 915/759-8315
Carmen Dwyer

Paul Moreno Elem Sch   PK-5   T   463   96% 915/236-0400
2300 San Diego Ave, El Paso 79930   30   Fax 915/566-5163
Robert Pancoast

Polk Elem Sch   PK-5   T   700   49% 915/236-2775
940 Belvidere St, El Paso 79912   45   Fax 915/236-2849
Sandra Spivey

Putnam Elem Sch   PK-5   T   418   79% 915/236-3225
6508 Fiesta Dr, El Paso 79912   36   Fax 915/585-2304
Cynthia Sanchez

Rivera Elem Sch   PK-5   T   340   86% 915/236-3700
6445 Escondido Dr, El Paso 79912   35   Fax 915/585-2337
Cindy Contreras

Roberts Elem Sch   PK-5   T   372   97% 915/236-3775
341 Thorn Ave, El Paso 79932   35   Fax 915/585-2729
Rafael Guardado

Rosa Guerrero Elem Sch   PK-5   T   519   86% 915/236-3075
7530 Lakehurst Rd, El Paso 79912   53   Fax 915/581-4418
Jill Crossley

Rusk Elem Sch   PK-5   T   260   93% 915/236-0475
3601 N Copia St, El Paso 79930   40   Fax 915/565-1666
Monica Brinkley

Stanton Elem Sch   PK-5   T   429   89% 915/236-6125
5414 Hondo Pass Dr, El Paso 79924   45   Fax 915/759-9415
Dr Sarah Chavez-Gibson

Sunrise Mountain Elem Sch   PK-5   T   564   93% 915/236-5675
7710 Pandora St, El Paso 79904   60   Fax 915/759-8115
Terry Montes

Tippin Elem Sch   PK-5     513   28% 915/230-5150
6541 Bear Ridge Dr, El Paso 79912   Fax 915/833-2140
Gina Nunez

Tom Lea Elem Sch   PK-5     840   56% 915/230-5450
4851 Marcus Uribe Dr, El Paso 79934   Fax 915/821-3665
Michelle Casillas

Travis Elem Sch   PK-5   T   368   93% 915/236-6200
500 N Stevens St, El Paso 79930   37   Fax 915/565-2013
Armando Llanos

Western Hills Elem Sch   PK-5   T   414   73% 915/774-4060
530 Thunderbird Dr, El Paso 79912   32   Fax 915/875-0183
Cristina Benavides

Whitaker Elem Sch   PK-5   T   379   88% 915/236-6275
4700 Rutherford Dr, El Paso 79924   35   Fax 915/751-9436
Antoinette Carpenter

Zach White Elem Sch   PK-5   T   417   54% 915/236-2700
4256 Roxbury Dr, El Paso 79922   50   Fax 915/585-3619
Jocelyn Scott

Zavala Elem Sch   PK-5   T   230   94% 915/236-0550
51 N Hammett St, El Paso 79905   27   Fax 915/542-1761
Alma Brockhoff

- **El Paso ISD-High Schools** PID: 11982259   915/236-2500
  800 E Schuster Ave, El Paso 79902

**Juan Cabrera** .........................................1   Dr Carla Gonzales ................................. 15
Mary Ann Clark ...................................92*

| Public Schs..Principal | Grd | Prgm | Enr/#Cls | SN |
|---|---|---|---|---|
| Andress High Sch | 9-12 | TV | 1,496 | 77% 915/236-4000 |
| 5400 Sun Valley Dr, El Paso 79924 | | | 100 | Fax 915/757-6443 |
| Joseph Manago | | | | |
| Austin High Sch | 9-12 | TV | 1,330 | 83% 915/236-4200 |
| 3500 Memphis Ave, El Paso 79930 | | | 100 | Fax 915/566-7360 |
| Cynthia Ponce | | | | |
| Bowie High Sch | 9-12 | TV | 1,356 | 90% 915/236-7000 |
| 801 S San Marcial St, El Paso 79905 | | | 60 | Fax 915/532-1918 |
| Francisco Ordaz | | | | |
| Burges High Sch | 9-12 | TV | 1,553 | 77% 915/236-7200 |
| 7800 Edgemere Blvd, El Paso 79925 | | | 100 | Fax 915/771-6914 |
| Christopher Smith | | | | |
| Center for Career & Tech Ed | Voc | G | 850 | 915/236-7900 |
| 1170 N Walnut St, El Paso 79930 | | | 38 | Fax 915/544-5976 |
| Matthew Farley | | | | |
| Chapin High Sch | 9-12 | AT | 1,836 | 68% 915/236-4400 |
| 7000 Dyer St, El Paso 79904 | | | | Fax 915/565-9716 |
| Robert Marsh | | | | |
| Ⓐ College Career Technology Acad | 9-12 | GTV | 352 | 85% 915/236-7700 |
| 2851 Grant Ave, El Paso 79930 | | | 12 | Fax 915/585-4789 |
| Fred Rojas | | | | |
| Coronado High Sch | 9-12 | TV | 2,716 | 55% 915/236-2000 |
| 100 Champions Pl, El Paso 79912 | | | | Fax 915/587-6458 |
| Marc Escareno | | | | |

| | | | |
|---|---|---|---|
| 1 Superintendent | 8 Curric/Instruct K-12 | 19 Chief Financial Officer | 29 Family/Consumer Science |
| 2 Bus/Finance/Purchasing | 9 Curric/Instruct Elem | 20 Art K-12 | 30 Adult Education |
| 3 Buildings And Grounds | 10 Curric/Instruct Sec | 21 Art Elem | 31 Career/Sch-to-Work K-12 |
| 4 Food Service | 11 Federal Program | 22 Art Sec | 32 Career/Sch-to-Work Elem |
| 5 Transportation | 12 Title I | 23 Music K-12 | 33 Career/Sch-to-Work Sec |
| 6 Athletic | 13 Title V | 24 Music Elem | 34 Early Childhood Ed |
| 7 Health Services | 15 Asst Superintendent | 25 Music Sec | 35 Health/Phys Education |
| | 16 Instructional Media Svcs | 26 Business Education | 36 Guidance Services K-12 |
| | 17 Chief Operations Officer | 27 Career & Tech Ed | 37 Guidance Services Elem |
| | 18 Chief Academic Officer | 28 Technology Education | 38 Guidance Services Sec |

| | | | |
|---|---|---|---|
| 39 Social Studies K-12 | 49 English/Lang Arts Elem | 59 Special Education Elem | 69 Academic Assessment |
| 40 Social Studies Elem | 50 English/Lang Arts Sec | 60 Special Education Sec | 70 Research/Development |
| 41 Social Studies Sec | 51 Reading K-12 | 61 Foreign/World Lang K-12 | 71 Public Information |
| 42 Science K-12 | 52 Reading Elem | 62 Foreign/World Lang Elem | 72 Summer School |
| 43 Science Elem | 53 Reading Sec | 63 Foreign/World Lang Sec | 73 Instructional Tech |
| 44 Science Sec | 54 Remedial Reading K-12 | 64 Religious Education K-12 | 74 Inservice Training |
| 45 Math K-12 | 55 Remedial Reading Elem | 65 Religious Education Elem | 75 Marketing/Distributive |
| 46 Math Elem | 56 Remedial Reading Sec | 66 Religious Education Sec | 76 Info Systems |
| 47 Math Sec | 57 Bilingual/ELL | 67 School Board President | 77 Psychological Assess |
| 48 English/Lang Arts K-12 | 58 Special Education K-12 | 68 Teacher Personnel | 78 Affirmative Action |

| | | | | | |
|---|---|---|---|---|---|
| El Paso High Sch<br>800 E Schuster Ave, El Paso 79902<br>Mark Paz | 9-12 | T | 1,525<br>70 | 73% | 915/236-2500<br>Fax 915/532-2008 |
| Franklin High Sch<br>900 N Resler Dr, El Paso 79912<br>Mary Mena | 9-12 | TV | 2,871 | 54% | 915/236-2200<br>Fax 915/587-4094 |
| Franklin HS 9th Grade Center<br>825 E Redd Rd, El Paso 79912<br>Mary Mena | 9-9 | | 800 | | 915/236-2400<br>Fax 915/587-5059 |
| Irvin High Sch<br>9465 Roanoke Dr, El Paso 79924<br>Mary Anna Giba | 9-12 | GTV | 1,357<br>130 | 88% | 915/236-4600<br>Fax 915/757-6450 |
| Jefferson High Sch<br>4700 Alameda Ave, El Paso 79905<br>Jose Gallegos | 9-12 | TV | 1,116<br>150 | 93% | 915/236-7400<br>Fax 915/532-2033 |
| Ⓜ Silva Health Magnet High Sch<br>121 Val Verde St, El Paso 79905<br>Jose Gallegos | 9-12 | T | 749<br>41 | 61% | 915/236-7600<br>Fax 915/533-3695 |
| Transmountain Early College HS<br>9570 Gateway Blvd N, El Paso 79924<br>Barbara Brinkley-Lopez | 9-12 | T | 416 | 69% | 915/236-5000<br>Fax 915/751-2011 |

## • El Paso ISD-Middle Schools  PID: 11982261  915/230-2213
6531 Boeing Dr, El Paso 79925

Juan Cabrera ...................................1  Angela Henderson ................................. 15

| Public Schs..Principal | Grd | Prgm | Enr/#Cls | SN | |
|---|---|---|---|---|---|
| Armendariz Middle Sch<br>2231 Arizona Ave, El Paso 79930<br>Dr Cynthia Ontiveros | 6-8 | T | 523<br>52 | 92% | 915/236-4800<br>Fax 915/577-0848 |
| Bassett Middle Sch<br>4400 Elm St, El Paso 79930<br>Michael Mendoza | 6-8 | GTV | 678<br>78 | 83% | 915/236-6350<br>Fax 915/565-1562 |
| Brown Middle Sch<br>7820 Helen of Troy Dr, El Paso 79912<br>Corina Favela | 6-8 | T | 1,037 | 67% | 915/774-4080<br>Fax 915/581-6424 |
| Canyon Hills Middle Sch<br>8930 Eclipse St, El Paso 79904<br>Carlos Gomez | 6-8 | T | 753<br>61 | 85% | 915/236-6450<br>Fax 915/757-8067 |
| Dr Hornedo Middle Sch<br>6101 High Ridge Dr, El Paso 79912<br>Micaela Varela | 6-8 | V | 1,323 | 33% | 915/236-3300<br>Fax 915/581-7371 |
| Guillen Middle Sch<br>900 S Cotton St, El Paso 79901<br>Monica Lyons | 6-8 | T | 708<br>75 | 97% | 915/236-4900<br>Fax 915/532-1143 |
| H E Charles Middle Sch<br>4909 Trojan Dr, El Paso 79924<br>David Zamora | 6-8 | T | 578 | 83% | 915/236-6550<br>Fax 915/821-0505 |
| Henderson Middle Sch<br>301 Lisbon St, El Paso 79905<br>Jason Yturralde | 6-8 | TV | 721<br>100 | 95% | 915/236-0700<br>Fax 915/772-3425 |
| Lincoln Middle Sch<br>500 Mulberry Ave, El Paso 79932<br>Haidi Appel | 6-8 | T | 766<br>64 | 65% | 915/236-3400<br>Fax 915/581-1371 |
| Magoffin Middle Sch<br>4931 Hercules Ave, El Paso 79904<br>Yvonne Portillo | 6-8 | T | 715 | 90% | 915/774-4040<br>Fax 915/757-7675 |
| Morehead Middle Sch<br>5625 Confetti Dr, El Paso 79912<br>Peggy Gustafson | 6-8 | T | 640<br>90 | 81% | 915/236-3500<br>Fax 915/587-5355 |
| Nolan Richardson Middle Sch<br>11350 Loma Franklin Dr, El Paso 79934<br>Ragen Chappell | 6-8 | TV | 733<br>50 | 60% | 915/236-6650<br>Fax 915/822-8812 |
| Ross Middle Sch<br>6101 Hughey Dr, El Paso 79925<br>Jason Yturralde | 6-8 | T | 812<br>100 | 75% | 915/236-0800<br>Fax 915/771-6792 |

| | | | | | |
|---|---|---|---|---|---|
| Terrace Hills Middle Sch<br>4835 Blossom Ave, El Paso 79924<br>Leticia Ewing | 6-8 | T | 504 | 92% | 915/236-6750<br>Fax 915/759-0615 |
| Wiggs Middle Sch<br>1300 Circle Dr, El Paso 79902<br>Timothy Luther | 6-8 | T | 901<br>50 | 67% | 915/236-3600<br>Fax 915/533-2902 |

## • Fabens Ind School Dist  PID: 01016129  915/765-2600
821 NE G Ave, Fabens 79838  Fax 915/764-3115

> **Schools:** 5 \ **Teachers:** 165 \ **Students:** 2,000 \ **Special Ed Students:** 279
> \ **LEP Students:** 1,007 \ **Ethnic:** Hispanic 99%, Caucasian 1% \ **Exp:** $446
> (High) \ **Poverty:** 40% \ **Title I:** $1,649,255 \ **Open-Close:** 08/10 - 06/04 \
> **DTBP:** $507 (High)

Dr Veronica Vijil .........................1  Yvonne Coupland ...........................2
Javier Garay .........................3,5  Marclella Lererio ...........................4
Liz Ramirez .........................7  Jorge Saenz ...........................11,58
Michelle Gonzalez ...................15,288  Manuela Gutierrez ...........................16*
Veronica Martinez .........................16  Tamika Young ...........................31
Orlando Flores .........................67  Mario Dominguez ...................73,84,91
Audre Ortegan .........................79  Pedro Gonzalez ...........................83
George Faniez .........................752

| Public Schs..Principal | Grd | Prgm | Enr/#Cls | SN | |
|---|---|---|---|---|---|
| Cotton Vly Early College HS<br>600 NE 4th St, Fabens 79838<br>Dr Sam Hogue | 9-12 | | 250 | | 915/765-2609<br>Fax 915/764-4358 |
| Fabens Elem Sch<br>1200 Mike Maros St, Fabens 79838<br>Richard Lopez | PK-3 | T | 590<br>47 | 93% | 915/765-2650<br>Fax 915/765-2655 |
| Fabens High Sch<br>601 NE G Ave, Fabens 79838<br>Anthony Prado | 9-12 | ATV | 745<br>60 | 87% | 915/765-2620<br>Fax 915/764-4953 |
| Fabens Middle Sch<br>800 Walker St, Fabens 79838<br>Nancy Torres | 6-8 | T | 488<br>39 | 91% | 915/765-2630<br>Fax 915/764-7263 |
| O'Donnell Intermediate Sch<br>301 NE Camp St, Fabens 79838<br>Corina Ruiz | 4-5 | T | 325<br>45 | 90% | 915/765-2640<br>Fax 915/764-3339 |

## • San Elizario Ind School Dist  PID: 01016179  915/872-3900
1050 Chicken Ranch Rd, San Elizario 79849  Fax 915/872-3901

> **Schools:** 6 \ **Teachers:** 240 \ **Students:** 3,560 \ **Special Ed Students:** 408
> \ **LEP Students:** 1,762 \ **College-Bound:** 85% \ **Ethnic:** Hispanic
> 99%, \ **Exp:** $691 (High) \ **Poverty:** 41% \ **Title I:** $2,287,763 \
> **Special Education:** $697,000 \ **Open-Close:** 08/26 - 06/04 \ **DTBP:** $178
> (High)

Dr Jeannie Meza-Chavez .........................1  Norberto Rivas ...........................2,19
Jesus Martinez .........................3,5  Raul Jacques ...........................4
Christine Jakssch .........................6  Robert Gallegos ...................7,35,83,91
Rogelio Segovia ...............8,11,15,70,72,274  Bea Apeldace ...........................12,271
Beatriz Apodaca .........................12  Michael Rodriguez ...................27,36,69*
Georgina Diaz .........................39,48,81  Lisa Renegar ...........39,48,69,81,88,275,294
Debbie Cortez .........................42,45,277  Amanda Sanchez ...........................58
Sandra Licon .........................67  Blanca Cruz ...........................68
Alice Ramos ...................73,76,297*  Corina Lugo ...........................93*
Perla Magallon .........................95  Horacio Hernandez ...........................295
Vicente Rodriguez .........................295

| Public Schs..Principal | Grd | Prgm | Enr/#Cls | SN | |
|---|---|---|---|---|---|
| Alarcon Elem Sch<br>12501 Socorro Road, San Elizario 79849<br>Julissa Esquivel | 1-6 | T | 570<br>37 | 93% | 915/872-3930<br>Fax 915/872-3931 |

| | Grd | Prgm | Enr/#Cls | SN | |
|---|---|---|---|---|---|
| **Ann M Garcia-Enriquez Mid Sch**<br>12280 Socorro Rd, San Elizario 79849<br>April Marioni | 7-8 | T | 542<br>38 | 92% | 915/872-3960<br>Fax 915/872-3961 |
| **Borrego Elem Sch**<br>13300 Chicken Ranch Rd, San Elizario 79849<br>Teresa Wilks | 1-6 | T | 479<br>28 | 92% | 915/872-3910<br>Fax 915/872-3911 |
| **Josefa L Sambrano Elem Sch**<br>200 Herring Rd, San Elizario 79849<br>George Augustain | 1-6 | T | 493<br>27 | 93% | 915/872-3950<br>Fax 915/872-3951 |
| **Lorenzo G Loya Primary Sch**<br>13705 Socorro Road, San Elizario 79849<br>Norma Casillas | PK-K | T | 296<br>32 | 94% | 915/872-3940<br>Fax 915/872-3941 |
| **San Elizario High Sch**<br>13981 Socorro Rd, San Elizario 79849<br>Maribel Guillen | 9-12 | TV | 1,062<br>80 | 91% | 915/872-3970<br>Fax 915/872-3971 |

● **Socorro Ind School Dist** PID: 01016208     915/937-0000
12440 Rojas Dr, El Paso 79928                 Fax 915/937-0194

**Schools:** 50 \ **Teachers:** 2,804 \ **Students:** 44,992 \
**Special Ed Students:** 4,908 \ **LEP Students:** 10,197 \ **College-Bound:** 89%
\ **Ethnic:** Asian 1%, African American 2%, Hispanic 93%, Caucasian
4% \ **Exp:** $381 (High) \ **Poverty:** 24% \ **Title I:** $15,885,321 \
**Special Education:** $6,503,000 \ **Open-Close:** 07/27 - 06/03 \ **DTBP:** $164
(High) \ f t

| | | | |
|---|---|---|---|
| Dr Jose Espinoza | ...1 | Samuel Garcia | ...2 |
| Tony Reza | ...2,19 | David Carrasco | ...3 |
| Gabriel Crespo | ...3 | Tom Eyeington | ...3,15,17 |
| Shelly Chenausky | ...4 | Jimmy Calderon | ...6 |
| Rebecca Madrid | ...7 | Lucia Borrego | ...8,18 |
| Alisa Zapata-Farmer | ...9,15 | Carmen Crosse | ...10,15 |
| Dr Adam Starke | ...11 | Lorena Cartagena | ...12 |
| Cynthia Retona | ...15 | Marivel Macias | ...15,68,78 |
| Marcy Sparks | ...16 | Armando Martinez | ...20,23 |
| George Thomas | ...27,31 | Anthony Fraga | ...30 |
| Liza Marquez | ...34 | Tammi Mackeben | ...36 |
| Jeanette Limon | ...40 | Kimberly Baxter | ...41 |
| Danielle Navariz | ...43 | Frank McDonald | ...44 |
| Fabiola Jordan | ...45 | Veronica Reyes | ...57 |
| Richard Ortega | ...58,275 | Cynthia Najera | ...67 |
| Rudy Campoya | ...68 | Kelly McBain | ...70 |
| Daniel Escobar | ...71 | Hector Reyna | ...73,76,98,295,297 |
| Lupe Luhan | ...79 | Dr Magdalena Aguilar | ...88* |
| Jose Castorena | ...91 | Corina Goytia | ...271 |
| Ann Darnell | ...298 | | |

| Public Schs..Principal | Grd | Prgm | Enr/#Cls | SN | |
|---|---|---|---|---|---|
| ⊗ **Americas High Sch**<br>12101 Pellicano Dr, El Paso 79936<br>Patricia Cuevas | 9-12 | MT | 2,535 | 66% | 915/937-2800<br>Fax 915/855-6898 |
| ⊗ **Benito Martinez Elem Sch**<br>2640 Robert Wynn St, El Paso 79936<br>Greg Hatch | PK-5 | MT | 473<br>60 | 83% | 915/937-8000<br>Fax 915/937-8090 |
| ⊗ **Bill Sybert Sch**<br>11530 Edgemere Blvd, El Paso 79936<br>Gabriela Elliott | PK-8 | MT | 642 | 82% | 915/937-4400<br>Fax 915/851-7777 |
| **Cactus Trails Elem Sch**<br>14701 Ralph Seitsinger, El Paso 79938<br>Leslie Thomas | PK-5 | | 401 | | 915/938-2600 |
| ⊗ **Campestre Elem Sch**<br>11399 Socorro Rd, El Paso 79927<br>Jennifer Avila | PK-5 | MT | 465<br>49 | 92% | 915/937-7300<br>Fax 915/851-1715 |
| ⊗ **Capt Walter E Clarke Mid Sch**<br>1515 Bob Hope Dr, El Paso 79936<br>Ivan Ramirez | 6-8 | MT | 941<br>75 | 83% | 915/937-5600<br>Fax 915/857-3765 |
| **Chester Jordan Elem Sch**<br>13995 Jason Crandall Dr, El Paso 79938<br>Maribel Pidone | PK-5 | T | 1,035 | 69% | 915/937-8801<br>Fax 915/937-8889 |
| ⊗ **Col John O Ensor Middle Sch**<br>13600 Ryderwood Dr, El Paso 79928<br>Lisa Estrada | 6-8 | MT | 1,064<br>43 | 64% | 915/937-6000<br>Fax 915/851-7590 |
| ⊗ **Desert Wind Elem Sch**<br>1100 Colina De Paz, El Paso 79928<br>Leticia Terrazas | PK-8 | MT | 854 | 86% | 915/937-7800<br>Fax 915/851-7840 |
| ⊗ **Dr Sue Shook Elem Sch**<br>13777 Paseo Del Este Dr, El Paso 79928<br>Cristina Chavira | PK-5 | T | 853 | 68% | 915/937-7100<br>Fax 915/937-7197 |
| **Eastlake High Sch**<br>13000 Emerald Pass Ave, El Paso 79928<br>Gilbert Martinez | 9-12 | T | 2,245 | 70% | 915/937-3600<br>Fax 915/937-3799 |
| ⊗ **El Dorado High Sch**<br>12401 Edgemere Blvd, El Paso 79938<br>Vanessa Betancourt | 9-12 | MT | 2,062 | 75% | 915/937-3200<br>Fax 915/937-3290 |
| ⊗ **Elfida P Chavez Elem Sch**<br>11720 Pebble Hills Blvd, El Paso 79936<br>Rosemary Yates | PK-5 | MT | 686<br>42 | 80% | 915/937-8300<br>Fax 915/856-9993 |
| ⊗ **Ernesto Serna Elem Sch**<br>11471 Alameda Ave, El Paso 79927<br>Alejandro Olvera | K-8 | MT | 496<br>42 | 90% | 915/937-4800<br>Fax 915/851-7580 |
| ⊗ **Escontrias Early Childhood Ctr**<br>10400 Alameda Ave, El Paso 79927<br>Jesse Aguirre | PK-1 | MT | 362<br>17 | 87% | 915/937-4200<br>Fax 915/937-4212 |
| ⊗ **Escontrias Elem Sch**<br>205 Buford Rd, El Paso 79927<br>Jesse Aguirre | 2-5 | MT | 565<br>40 | 88% | 915/937-4100<br>Fax 915/937-9212 |
| ⊗ **H D Hilley Elem Sch**<br>693 N Rio Vista Rd, El Paso 79927<br>Fernando Miranda | PK-5 | MT | 535<br>40 | 85% | 915/937-8400<br>Fax 915/937-8490 |
| ⊗ **Helen Ball Elem Sch**<br>1950 Firehouse Dr, El Paso 79936<br>Ana Soto | PK-5 | MT | 654<br>41 | 79% | 915/937-8202<br>Fax 915/856-1478 |
| ⊗ **Horizon Heights Sch**<br>13601 Ryderwood Dr, El Paso 79928<br>Jenifer Hansen | PK-5 | MT | 849<br>40 | 66% | 915/937-7400<br>Fax 915/937-7497 |
| ⊗ **Hueco Elem Sch**<br>300 Old Hueco Tanks Rd, El Paso 79927<br>Daisy Garcia | PK-5 | MT | 490<br>35 | 89% | 915/937-7600<br>Fax 915/860-1125 |
| ⊗ **Hurshel Antwine Elem Sch**<br>3830 Rich Beem, El Paso 79938<br>Benjamin Baldner | 4-6 | MT | 1,023 | 72% | 915/937-6400<br>Fax 915/851-7830 |
| **James P Butler Elem Sch**<br>14251 Ralph Seitsinger, El Paso 79938<br>Rosa Avedician | PK-5 | T | 851 | 59% | 915/937-8900<br>Fax 915/937-8996 |
| ⊗ **Jane A Hambric Sch**<br>3535 Nolan Richardson Dr, El Paso 79936<br>Joanne Anguiano | PK-8 | MT | 980<br>75 | 87% | 915/937-4600<br>Fax 915/851-7560 |
| ⊗ **John Drugan Elem Sch**<br>12451 Pellicano Dr, El Paso 79928<br>Adalberto Garcia | PK-8 | MT | 1,096 | 58% | 915/937-6800<br>Fax 915/937-6815 |
| Ⓐ **Keys Academy**<br>⊗ 12380 Pine Springs Dr, El Paso 79928<br>Dr Magdalena Aguilar | 6-12 | MTV | 50 | 78% | 915/937-4000<br>Fax 915/937-4006 |
| Ⓐ **Keys Elem Academy**<br>205 Buford Rd, El Paso 79927<br>Jesse Aguirre | 1-5 | | 3 | | 915/937-4104<br>Fax 915/937-9212 |
| ⊗ **Loma Verde Elem Sch**<br>12150 Ted Houghton, El Paso 79936<br>Leslie Chavez | PK-5 | MT | 675 | 61% | 915/937-8600<br>Fax 915/851-7780 |
| ⊗ **Lujan-Chavez Elem Sch**<br>2200 Sun Country Dr, El Paso 79938<br>Jina Eksaengsri | PK-5 | MT | 1,096<br>30 | 67% | 915/937-8700<br>Fax 915/937-8790 |

| | | | |
|---|---|---|---|
| **1** Superintendent | **8** Curric/Instruct K-12 | **19** Chief Financial Officer | **29** Family/Consumer Science |
| **2** Bus/Finance/Purchasing | **9** Curric/Instruct Elem | **20** Art K-12 | **30** Adult Education |
| **3** Buildings And Grounds | **10** Curric/Instruct Sec | **21** Art Elem | **31** Career/Sch-to-Work K-12 |
| **4** Food Service | **11** Federal Program | **22** Art Sec | **32** Career/Sch-to-Work Elem |
| **5** Transportation | **12** Title I | **23** Music K-12 | **33** Career/Sch-to-Work Sec |
| **6** Athletic | **13** Title V | **24** Music Elem | **34** Early Childhood Ed |
| **7** Health Services | **14** Instructional Media Svcs | **25** Music Sec | **35** Health/Phys Education |
| | **15** Asst Superintendent | **26** Business Education | **36** Guidance Services K-12 |
| | **16** Instructional Media Svcs | **27** Career & Tech Ed | **37** Guidance Services Elem |
| | **17** Chief Operations Officer | **28** Technology Education | **38** Guidance Services Sec |
| | **18** Chief Academic Officer | | |

| | | | |
|---|---|---|---|
| **39** Social Studies K-12 | **49** English/Lang Arts Elem | **59** Special Education Elem | **69** Academic Assessment |
| **40** Social Studies Elem | **50** English/Lang Arts Sec | **60** Special Education Sec | **70** Research/Development |
| **41** Social Studies Sec | **51** Reading K-12 | **61** Foreign/World Lang K-12 | **71** Public Information |
| **42** Science K-12 | **52** Reading Elem | **62** Foreign/World Lang Elem | **72** Summer School |
| **43** Science Elem | **53** Reading Sec | **63** Foreign/World Lang Sec | **73** Instructional Tech |
| **44** Science Sec | **54** Remedial Reading K-12 | **64** Religious Education K-12 | **74** Inservice Training |
| **45** Math K-12 | **55** Remedial Reading Elem | **65** Religious Education Elem | **75** Marketing/Distributive |
| **46** Math Elem | **56** Remedial Reading Sec | **66** Religious Education Sec | **76** Info Systems |
| **47** Math Sec | **57** Bilingual/ELL | **67** School Board President | **77** Psychological Assess |
| **48** English/Lang Arts K-12 | **58** Special Education K-12 | **68** Teacher Personnel | **78** Affirmative Action |

| School | Grd | Prgm | Enr/#Cls | SN | Phone/Fax |
|---|---|---|---|---|---|
| Mission Early College High Sch<br>10700 Gateway Blvd E, El Paso 79927<br>Benjamin Ortega | 9-12 | T | 466 | 69% | 915/937-1200<br>Fax 915/860-2935 |
| Mission Ridge Elem Sch<br>150 Nonap Rd, El Paso 79928<br>Jesus Mendez | PK-5 | T | 739 | 81% | 915/938-2000<br>Fax 915/852-8559 |
| ⓨ Montwood High Sch<br>12000 Montwood Dr, El Paso 79936<br>Carlos Guerra | 9-12 | MTV | 2,722<br>110 | 68% | 915/937-2400<br>Fax 915/937-2422 |
| ⓨ Montwood Middle Sch<br>11710 Pebble Hills Blvd, El Paso 79936<br>Melissa Martinez | 6-8 | MT | 751<br>200 | 78% | 915/937-5800<br>Fax 915/856-9909 |
| Myrtle Cooper Elem Sch<br>1515 Rebecca Ann Dr, El Paso 79936<br>Alicia Miranda | PK-6 | T | 720<br>48 | 85% | 915/937-7700<br>Fax 915/855-7645 |
| ⓨ O'Shea Keleher Elem Sch<br>1800 Leroy Bonse Dr, El Paso 79936<br>Laura Lujan-Garcia | PK-5 | MT | 888<br>44 | 84% | 915/937-7200<br>Fax 915/921-1506 |
| Ⓐ Options High Sch<br>12380 Pine Springs Dr, El Paso 79928<br>Dr Magdalena Aguilar | 9-12 | T | 42 | 75% | 915/937-1300<br>Fax 915/859-2603 |
| ⓨ Paso Del Norte Sch<br>12300 Tierra Este Rd, El Paso 79938<br>Benjamin Baldner | K-5 | MT | 1,173 | 71% | 915/937-6200<br>Fax 915/851-7800 |
| Pebble Hill High Sch<br>14400 Pebble Hills Blvd, El Paso 79938<br>Ignacio Estorga | 9-12 | T | 2,466 | 61% | 915/937-9400<br>Fax 915/937-9498 |
| Purple Heart Elem Sch<br>14400 G R Campuzano Dr, El Paso 79938<br>Deana White | PK-5 | T | 776 | 77% | 915/938-2200 |
| ⓨ Robert R Rojas Elem Sch<br>500 Bauman Rd, El Paso 79927<br>Jennifer Marquez | PK-5 | MT | 456<br>35 | 86% | 915/937-8500<br>Fax 915/937-8590 |
| ⓨ Salvador H Sanchez Middle Sch<br>321 N Rio Vista Rd, El Paso 79927<br>Nathan Ballard | 6-8 | MTV | 641<br>25 | 93% | 915/937-5200<br>Fax 915/859-6636 |
| Sgt Jose Carrasco Elem Sch<br>14900 Tierra Mirage De, El Paso 79938<br>Jesus Sepulveda | PK-5 | T | 672 | 68% | 915/938-2400<br>Fax 915/938-2490 Ⓣ |
| ⓨ Sgt Roberto Ituarte Elem Sch<br>12860 Tierra Sonora, El Paso 79938<br>Lynnette Vidales | PK-5 | MT | 640 | 69% | 915/937-7000<br>Fax 915/937-7095 |
| ⓨ Sierra Vista Elem Sch<br>1501 Bob Hope Dr, El Paso 79936<br>Christine De La Cruz | PK-5 | MT | 573<br>55 | 77% | 915/937-8100<br>Fax 915/849-1263 |
| ⓨ Socorro High Sch<br>10150 Alameda Ave, El Paso 79927<br>Federico Tovar | 9-12 | GMTV | 2,446 | 85% | 915/937-2000<br>Fax 915/937-2394 |
| ⓨ Socorro Middle Sch<br>321 Bovee Rd, El Paso 79927<br>Mauro Guerrero | 6-8 | MT | 654<br>50 | 73% | 915/937-5000<br>Fax 915/859-6955 |
| Spc Rafael Hernando Middle Sch<br>3451 Rich Beem, El Paso 79938<br>Valerie Hairston | 6-8 | T | 1,103 | 77% | 915/937-9800<br>Fax 915/937-9898 Ⓕ Ⓣ |
| Ssg Manuel R Puentes Mid Sch<br>3216 Tim Foster, El Paso 79938<br>Monica Castro | 6-8 | T | 1,044 | 60% | 915/937-9200<br>Fax 915/856-7855 |
| ⓨ Sun Ridge Middle Sch<br>2210 Sun Country Dr, El Paso 79938<br>**David Herrera** | 6-8 | MT | 883<br>57 | 66% | 915/937-6600<br>Fax 915/851-7730 |
| Ⓐ ⓨ Vista Del Sol Sch<br>11851 Vista Del Sol Dr, El Paso 79936<br>Cynthia Velasquez | PK-5 | MT | 446<br>47 | 84% | 915/937-7500<br>Fax 915/937-7598 |
| ⓨ William D Slider Middle Sch<br>11700 School Ln, El Paso 79936<br>Manuel Rios | 6-8 | MT | 710<br>75 | 72% | 915/937-5400 |

## ● Tornillo Ind School Dist  PID: 01016260
19200 Cobb St, Tornillo 79853
915/765-3000
Fax 915/765-3099

**Schools:** 4 \ **Teachers:** 73 \ **Students:** 950 \ **Special Ed Students:** 69 \ **LEP Students:** 560 \ **College-Bound:** 70% \ **Ethnic:** Hispanic 100%, \ **Exp:** $829 (High) \ **Poverty:** 35% \ **Title I:** $572,308 \ **Special Education:** $199,000 \ **Open-Close:** 09/08 - 06/04 \ **DTBP:** $521 (High) \ Ⓕ Ⓣ

| | | | |
|---|---|---|---|
| Rosy Vega-Barrio | 1 | Davette Solice | 2 |
| Norma Aguirre | 4 | Cody Burris | 6* |
| Rodrigo Portillo | 8 | Racheal Aguilar | 31 |
| Maria Melchor | 36 | Lizatte Caroll | 57,68 |
| Gerogina Miramontes | 58 | Marlene Bullard | 67 |
| Carlos Garcia | 73,76* | Carmen Beasley | 271 |

| Public Schs..Principal | Grd | Prgm | Enr/#Cls | SN | |
|---|---|---|---|---|---|
| Tornillo Elem Sch<br>19200 Gaby Rd, Tornillo 79853<br>Myrna Lopez | PK-3 | T | 268<br>21 | 92% | 915/765-3100<br>Fax 915/765-3199 |
| Tornillo High Sch<br>430 D Oil Mill Rd, Tornillo 79853<br>Laura Roa | 9-12 | AGTV | 334<br>20<br>Ⓕ Ⓣ | 96% | 915/765-3500<br>Fax 915/765-3599 |
| Tornillo Intermediate Sch<br>410 A Oil Mill Rd, Tornillo 79853<br>Nadia De La Rosa | 4-6 | T | 256 | 93% | 915/765-3350<br>Fax 915/765-3399 |
| Tornillo Junior High Sch<br>300 Oil Mill Rd, Tornillo 79853<br>Marco Tristan | 7-8 | T | 263<br>22<br>Ⓕ | 95% | 915/765-3400<br>Fax 915/765-3499 |

## ● Ysleta Ind School Dist  PID: 01016296
9600 Sims Dr, El Paso 79925
915/434-0000
Fax 915/435-9561

**Schools:** 57 \ **Teachers:** 2,748 \ **Students:** 40,304 \ **Special Ed Students:** 5,167 \ **LEP Students:** 10,553 \ **College-Bound:** 58% \ **Ethnic:** African American 1%, Hispanic 95%, Caucasian 3% \ **Exp:** $428 (High) \ **Poverty:** 34% \ **Title I:** $19,905,490 \ **Special Education:** $7,941,000 \ **Open-Close:** 08/17 - 06/11 \ **DTBP:** $193 (High)

| | | | |
|---|---|---|---|
| Dr Xavier De La Torre | 1 | Christine Gerlach | 2 |
| Mary Haynie | 2 | Frances Yepez | 3 |
| Mario Rodriguez | 3,15 | Alan Crawford | 4 |
| Leo Benitez | 5 | Mario Gomez | 5 |
| Mike Williams | 6 | Sylvia Belmontes | 7,85 |
| Louisa Aguirre-Baeza | 8,15 | Diane Flores | 9 |
| Connie Vasquez | 11 | Sheila Elias | 11,298 |
| Brenda Chacon | 15,18 | Dr Catherine Kennedy | 15 |
| Irene Ahumada | 15 | Roberto Basurto | 15,79 |
| Rosa Menchaca | 15 | Lynly Leeper | 17,19 |
| Scott Thoreson | 20,23 | Fernando Marquez | 27,31* |
| Elizabeth Moya | 30* | Rita Tellez | 45 |
| Ana Esqueda | 57 | Dr Diana Otero | 58 |
| Reymundo Sanchez | 58 | Cruz Ochoa | 67 |
| Bobbi Russell-Garcia | 68 | Craig Lahrman | 68 |
| Jiovana Gutierrez | 68 | Patricia Ayala | 71 |
| Gloria Chavez | 73,76 | James Vasquez | 79 |
| Cynthia Corrales | 93* | Raul Medellin | 294 |
| Doug Chamlee | 295 | Lorena Olmos | 297 |

| Public Schs..Principal | Grd | Prgm | Enr/#Cls | SN | |
|---|---|---|---|---|---|
| Ⓜ Alicia R Chacon Int'l Lang Sch<br>ⓨ 920 Burgundy Dr, El Paso 79907<br>Ruben Cadena | K-8 | MT | 704<br>35 | 66% | 915/434-9200<br>Fax 915/859-2131 |
| Ascarate Elem Sch<br>7090 Alameda Ave, El Paso 79915<br>Claudia Ureno Olivaz | K-6 | T | 411<br>27 | 95% | 915/434-7400<br>Fax 915/772-8051 |

| School / Address / Contact | Grades | Code | Enr. | Tchrs | % | Phone | Fax |
|---|---|---|---|---|---|---|---|
| Bel Air High Sch, 731 N Yarbrough Dr, El Paso 79915 — Charles Garcia | 9-12 | GTV | 1,955 | | 77% | 915/434-2000 | Fax 915/593-6110 |
| Bel Air Middle Sch, 7909 Ranchland Dr, El Paso 79915 — Dana DeRouen | 7-8 | T | 814 | | 87% | 915/434-2200 | Fax 915/591-9439 |
| Capistrano Elem Sch, 240 Mecca Dr, El Paso 79907 — **Norma Myers** | K-5 | T | 410 | 34 | 95% | 915/434-8600 | Fax 915/860-2750 |
| Cedar Grove Elem Sch, 218 Barker Rd, El Paso 79915 — Dolores Acosta | PK-6 | T | 424 | 35 | 95% | 915/434-7600 | Fax 915/772-8092 |
| Ⓐ Cesar Chavez Academy, 7814 Alameda Ave, El Paso 79915 — **Daniel Gurany** | 7-12 | V | 42 | 15 | 98% | 915/434-9600 | Fax 915/779-2068 |
| Constance Hulbert Elem Sch, 7755 Franklin Dr, El Paso 79915 — James McIntyre | PK-6 | T | 411 | | 96% | 915/434-6900 | Fax 915/772-8166 |
| Del Norte Heights Elem Sch, 1800 Winslow Rd, El Paso 79915 — **Roxanne Merfa** | K-6 | T | 322 | 31 | 89% | 915/434-2400 | Fax 915/591-8862 |
| Del Valle Elem Sch, 9251 Escobar Dr, El Paso 79907 — **Maritza Balderrama** | PK-5 | T | 383 | | 90% | 915/434-9300 | Fax 915/434-9306 |
| Del Valle High Sch, 950 Bordeaux Dr, El Paso 79907 — Antonio Acuna | 9-12 | GT | 2,060 | 96 | 82% | 915/434-3000 | Fax 915/858-1427 |
| Del Valle Middle Sch, 8674 N Loop Dr, El Paso 79907 — Ida Perales | 6-8 | TV | 1,308 | 50 | 89% | 915/434-3300 | Fax 915/858-3615 |
| Desert View Middle Sch, 1641 Billie Marie Dr, El Paso 79936 — Javier Salgado | 6-8 | T | 348 | 41 | 74% | 915/434-5300 | Fax 915/591-9327 |
| Desertaire Elem Sch, 6301 Tiger Eye Dr, El Paso 79924 — Beth Harbison | PK-5 | T | 700 | 47 | 80% | 915/434-6400 | Fax 915/821-0634 |
| Dolphin Terrace Elem Sch, 9790 Pickerel Dr, El Paso 79924 — Lorraine Martinez | K-5 | T | 592 | 37 | 84% | 915/434-6500 | Fax 915/757-8073 |
| East Point Elem Sch, 2400 Zanzibar Rd, El Paso 79925 — **Claudia Poblano** | PK-6 | T | 787 | 48 | 75% | 915/434-4500 | Fax 915/591-8958 |
| Eastwood Heights Elem Sch, 10530 Janway Dr, El Paso 79925 — Raul Mendoza | PK-6 | T | 756 | 30 | 68% | 915/434-4600 | Fax 915/591-8960 |
| Eastwood High Sch, 2430 McRae Blvd, El Paso 79925 — James Boatright | 9-12 | GT | 1,620 | 100 | 59% | 915/434-4000 | Fax 915/594-8014 |
| Eastwood Knolls Elem Sch, 10000 Buckwood Ave, El Paso 79925 — Robert Martinez | PK-8 | T | 798 | 60 | 51% | 915/434-4400 | Fax 915/592-0339 |
| Eastwood Middle Sch, 2612 Chaswood St, El Paso 79935 — Sarah Venegas | 7-8 | T | 1,035 | 53 | 69% | 915/434-4300 | Fax 915/591-9426 |
| Edgemere Elem Sch, 10300 Edgemere Blvd, El Paso 79925 — **Graciela Maldonado** | PK-6 | T | 721 | | 79% | 915/434-4700 | Fax 915/590-8335 |
| Glen Cove Elem Sch, 10955 Sam Snead Dr, El Paso 79936 — Margarita Mendoza | PK-5 | T | 805 | 56 | 80% | 915/434-5500 | Fax 915/591-9024 |
| Ⓜ Hacienda Heights Elem Sch, 7530 Acapulco Ave, El Paso 79915 — **Sandra Perez** | PK-6 | T | 393 | 45 | 84% | 915/434-2500 | Fax 915/591-9044 |
| Indian Ridge Middle Sch, 11201 Pebble Hills Blvd, El Paso 79936 — Pauline Muele | 6-8 | T | 623 | 52 | 78% | 915/434-5400 | Fax 915/591-9447 |
| J M Hanks High Sch, 2001 N Lee Trevino Dr, El Paso 79936 — Enrique Herrera | 9-12 | AGTV | 1,641 | 115 | 72% | 915/434-5000 | Fax 915/598-4621 |
| Lancaster Elem Sch, 9230 Elgin Dr, El Paso 79907 — Veronica Frias | K-5 | T | 467 | | 85% | 915/434-3400 | Fax 915/860-2315 |
| Loma Terrace Elem Sch, 8200 Ryland Ct, El Paso 79907 — Alejandro Armendariz | PK-6 | T | 533 | 46 | 88% | 915/434-2600 | Fax 915/591-9111 |
| Mesa Vista Elem Sch, 8032 Alamo Ave, El Paso 79907 — Norma Sierra | PK-6 | T | 376 | 35 | 90% | 915/434-2700 | Fax 915/591-9171 |
| Mission Valley Elem Sch, 8674 N Loop Dr, El Paso 79907 — Veronica Alvidrez | K-6 | T | 688 | 42 | 87% | 915/434-3700 | Fax 915/860-0049 |
| North Loop Elem Sch, 412 Emerson St, El Paso 79915 — **Christopher Puga** | K-6 | T | 344 | 26 | 94% | 915/434-2800 | Fax 915/591-9202 |
| North Star Elem Sch, 5950 Sean Haggerty Dr, El Paso 79924 — Stephanie Lahrman | PK-5 | T | 478 | | 71% | 915/434-6700 | Fax 915/822-9386 |
| Parkland Elem Sch, 6330 Deer Ave, El Paso 79924 — **Dana Boyd** | K-5 | T | 575 | 30 | 89% | 915/434-6600 | Fax 915/757-9458 |
| Parkland High Sch, 5932 Quail Ave, El Paso 79924 — Penelope Bankston | 9-12 | GT | 1,622 | 56 | 78% | 915/434-6000 | Fax 915/755-2382 |
| Parkland Middle Sch, 6045 Nova Way, El Paso 79924 — Angela Reyna | 6-8 | TV | 1,340 | 38 | 82% | 915/434-6300 | Fax 915/757-6608 |
| Parkland Pre-K Center, 10080 Chick A Dee St, El Paso 79924 — Rita Lopez | PK-PK | T | 353 | | 81% | 915/435-7800 | Fax 915/435-7896 |
| Pasodale Elem Sch, 8253 McElroy Ave, El Paso 79907 — **Natalie Alvarez** | PK-5 | T | 679 | 57 | 88% | 915/434-8500 | Fax 915/858-1269 |
| Pebble Hills Elem Sch, 11145 Edgemere Blvd, El Paso 79936 — Irene Youngs | PK-5 | T | 743 | 48 | 81% | 915/434-5600 | Fax 915/591-9222 |
| Ⓐ Plato Academy, 8441 Alameda Ave, El Paso 79907 — Gloria Spencer | 11-12 | V | 100 | 9 | 78% | 915/434-9000 | Fax 915/590-6815 |
| Presa Elem Sch, 128 Presa Pl, El Paso 79907 — Wendy Banegas | PK-5 | T | 285 | 28 | 86% | 915/434-8700 | Fax 915/860-2810 |
| Ramona Elem Sch, 351 Nichols Rd, El Paso 79915 — **Darlene Solis** | K-6 | T | 274 | 40 | 80% | 915/434-7700 | Fax 915/772-8153 |
| Rio Bravo Middle Sch, 525 Greggerson Dr, El Paso 79907 — Sandra Calzada | 6-8 | T | 447 | 20 | 90% | 915/434-8400 | Fax 915/872-0269 |
| Riverside High Sch, 301 Midway Dr, El Paso 79915 — Daniel Gurany | 9-12 | TV | 1,098 | | 88% | 915/434-7000 | Fax 915/779-6983 |
| Riverside Middle Sch, 7615 Mimosa Ave, El Paso 79915 — Jacob Valtierra | 7-8 | T | 511 | 40 | 89% | 915/434-7300 | Fax 915/772-7549 |
| Robbin E L Washington Elem Sch, 3505 N Lee Trevino Dr, El Paso 79936 — Mauricio Cano | K-6 | T | 526 | 30 | 78% | 915/434-5900 | Fax 915/590-6535 |
| Sageland Elem Sch, 7901 Santa Monica Ct, El Paso 79915 — Rachael Blair | PK-6 | T | 564 | 27 | 84% | 915/434-4800 | Fax 915/591-9228 |
| Scotsdale Elem Sch, 2901 McRae Blvd, El Paso 79925 — Juan Guzman | PK-6 | T | 827 | 42 | 74% | 915/434-4800 | Fax 915/591-9270 |

| | | Grd | Prgm | Enr/#Cls | % | Phone |
|---|---|---|---|---|---|---|
| Ⓐ | Tejas School of Choice | 9-12 | MT | 73 | 92% | 915/434-9900 |
| Ⓨ | 7500 Alpha Ave, El Paso 79915 | | | 14 | | Fax 915/772-8366 |
| | Lucy Lozano-Lerma | | | | | |
| | Thomas Manor Elem Sch | PK-6 | T | 565 | 88% | 915/434-7500 |
| | 7900 Jersey St, El Paso 79915 | | | 40 | | Fax 915/858-0873 |
| | Sandra Stresow | | | | | |
| | Tierra Del Sol Elem Sch | PK-6 | T | 742 | 71% | 915/434-5800 |
| | 1832 Tommy Aaron Dr, El Paso 79936 | | | 39 | | Fax 915/591-9271 |
| | Michelle Romero | | | | | |
| | Valle Verde Early College HS | 9-12 | T | 403 | 65% | 915/434-1500 |
| | 919 Hunter Dr, El Paso 79915 | | | 11 | | Fax 915/594-7112 |
| | Paul Covey | | | | | |
| | Vista Hills Elem Sch | PK-6 | T | 607 | 77% | 915/434-5700 |
| | 10801 La Subida Dr, El Paso 79935 | | | 50 | | Fax 915/591-9305 |
| | Laura Calderon | | | | | |
| | Young Women's Leadership Acad | 6-7 | T | 231 | 44% | 915/434-1300 |
| | 8040 Yermoland Dr, El Paso 79907 | | | | | Fax 915/434-1399 |
| | Malinda Villalobos | | | | | |
| | Ysleta Community Learning Ctr | Adult | | 250 | | 915/434-9400 |
| | 121 Padres Dr, El Paso 79907 | | | 20 | | Fax 915/858-6307 |
| | Louis Martinez | | | | | |
| | Ysleta Elem Sch | K-5 | T | 477 | 88% | 915/434-8900 |
| | 8624 Dorbandt Cir, El Paso 79907 | | | 40 | | Fax 915/859-9311 |
| | Norma Osuna | | | | | |
| | Ysleta High Sch | 9-12 | AGTV | 1,434 | 90% | 915/434-8000 |
| | 8600 Alameda Ave, El Paso 79907 | | | | | Fax 915/858-3299 |
| | Silvia Rendon | | | | | |
| | Ysleta Middle Sch | 6-8 | TV | 622 | 95% | 915/434-8200 |
| | 8691 Independence Dr, El Paso 79907 | | | 43 | | Fax 915/858-0261 |
| | David Gonzalez | | | | | |
| Ⓨ | Ysleta Pre-K Center | PK-PK | MT | 730 | 84% | 915/434-9500 |
| | 7940 Craddock Ave, El Paso 79915 | | | 26 | | Fax 915/591-9325 |
| | Heather Karns | | | | | |

## EL PASO CATHOLIC SCHOOLS

● **Diocese of El Paso Ed Office**  PID: 01016703  915/872-8426
499 Saint Matthews St, El Paso 79907  Fax 915/872-8464

**Schools:** 11 \ **Students:** 2,700

Listing includes only schools located in this county. See District Index for location of Diocesan Offices.

Steve Sanchez ............................... 1,11,73

| Catholic Schs..Principal | Grd | Prgm | Enr/#Cls | SN | |
|---|---|---|---|---|---|
| Cathedral High Sch | 9-12 | | 400 | | 915/532-3238 |
| 1309 N Stanton St, El Paso 79902 | | | 36 | | Fax 915/533-8248 |
| Adolfo Sanchez | | | | | |
| Father Yermo Elem Sch | PK-6 | | 300 | | 915/532-6875 |
| 220 Washington St, El Paso 79905 | | | 11 | | Fax 915/532-2827 |
| Sr Angelica Omana | | | | | |
| Father Yermo High Sch | 9-12 | | 123 | | 915/533-3185 |
| 250 Washington St, El Paso 79905 | | | 25 | | |
| Sr Yamila Trejo | | | | | |
| Loretto Acad Elem Sch | PK-5 | | 220 | | 915/566-8400 |
| 4625 Clifton Ave, El Paso 79903 | | | 13 | | Fax 915/564-0563 |
| Jane German | | | | | |
| Loretto Acad-Middle High Sch | 6-12 | | 477 | | 915/566-8400 |
| 1300 Hardaway St, El Paso 79903 | | | 40 | | Fax 915/564-0563 |
| Homero Silva | | | | | |

| | | Grd | | Enr/#Cls | | Phone |
|---|---|---|---|---|---|---|
| | Most Holy Trinity Sch | PK-8 | | 103 | | 915/751-2566 |
| | 10000 Pheasant Rd, El Paso 79924 | | | 12 | | Fax 915/751-2596 |
| | Jim Horan | | | | | |
| | St Joseph Sch | K-8 | | 511 | | 915/566-1661 |
| | 1300 Lamar St, El Paso 79903 | | | 23 | | Fax 915/566-1664 |
| | Marcela Hernandez | | | | | |
| | St Matthews Catholic Sch | K-8 | | 300 | | 915/581-8801 |
| | 400 W Sunset Rd, El Paso 79922 | | | | | Fax 915/581-8816 |
| | Veronica De La Cruz | | | | | |
| | St Patrick Cathedral Sch | K-8 | | 170 | | 915/532-4142 |
| | 1111 N Stanton St, El Paso 79902 | | | 15 | | Fax 915/532-8297 |
| | Elizabeth Carreon | | | | | |
| | St Pius X Sch | K-8 | | 486 | | 915/262-4846 |
| | 1007 Geronimo Dr, El Paso 79905 | | | 16 | | Fax 915/225-0010 |
| | Ana Silva | | | | | |
| | St Raphael Catholic Sch | K-8 | | 400 | | 915/598-2241 |
| | 2310 Woodside Dr, El Paso 79925 | | | 28 | | Fax 915/598-3002 |
| | Graciela Fernandez | | | | | |

## EL PASO PRIVATE SCHOOLS

| Private Schs..Principal | Grd | Prgm | Enr/#Cls | SN | |
|---|---|---|---|---|---|
| Bridges Sch | Spec | | 46 | | 915/532-6647 |
| 4320 N Stanton St, El Paso 79902 | | | 13 | | Fax 915/532-8767 |
| Irma Keys | | | | | |
| Community of Faith Chrn Sch | PK-8 | | 53 | | 915/584-2561 |
| 4539 Emory Rd, El Paso 79922 | | | | | Fax 915/584-3529 |
| Blanca Mixer | | | | | |
| El Paso Adventist Jr Academy | PK-9 | | 43 | | 915/855-7312 |
| 3510 George Dieter Dr, El Paso 79936 | | | 5 | | Fax 915/855-0092 |
| Juanita Camacho | | | | | |
| El Paso Country Day Sch | PK-8 | | 50 | | 915/533-4492 |
| 220 E Cliff Dr, El Paso 79902 | | | 6 | | Fax 915/533-9626 |
| Dr Laura Alpern | | | | | |
| El Paso Jewish Academy | 1-8 | | 50 | | 915/833-0808 |
| 805 Cherry Hill Ln Frnt, El Paso 79912 | | | 8 | | Fax 915/833-0819 |
| Kara Jones | | | | | |
| El Paso NE Children's Ed Ctr | PK-5 | | 100 | | 915/751-9487 |
| 6301 Alabama St, El Paso 79904 | | | 10 | | |
| Mari Jo Hodges | | | | | |
| Escuela Montessori-Del Valle | PK-6 | | 100 | | 915/584-9215 |
| 212 W Sunset Rd, El Paso 79922 | | | | | Fax 915/587-6067 |
| Vanessa Miranda | | | | | |
| Faith Christian Academy | PK-12 | | 550 | | 915/594-3305 |
| 8960 Escobar Dr, El Paso 79907 | | | | | Fax 915/593-5474 |
| Shannon Nyeman | | | | | |
| Immanuel Christian Sch | PK-12 | | 550 | | 915/778-6160 |
| 1201 Hawkins Blvd, El Paso 79925 | | | | | Fax 915/772-8207 |
| Linda Johnson | | | | | |
| Jesus Chapel Sch | PK-12 | | 180 | | 915/593-1153 |
| 10200 Album Ave, El Paso 79925 | | | 14 | | Fax 915/593-1113 |
| Alba Wilcox | | | | | |
| La Paz Language Academy | K-12 | | 200 | | 915/584-5100 |
| 1035 Belvidere St Ste 200, El Paso 79912 | | | | | |
| Ely Ferreyra | | | | | |
| Lydia Patterson Institute | 7-12 | | 450 | | 915/533-8286 |
| 517 S Florence St, El Paso 79901 | | | 23 | | Fax 915/533-5236 |
| Ernesto Morales | | | | | |
| Maran-Ata Christian Academy | K-12 | | 60 | | 915/592-1909 |
| 8800 Cristo Viene Dr, El Paso 79907 | | | 8 | | Fax 915/592-0303 |
| Lizbeth Cabrera | | | | | |
| New World Montessori Sch | PK-6 | | 150 | | 915/593-8091 |
| 3510 N Yarbrough Dr, El Paso 79925 | | | 6 | | Fax 915/593-8268 |
| Francisco Portillo | | | | | |

| 79 | Student Personnel | 91 | Safety/Security | 275 | Response To Intervention | 298 | Grant Writer/Ptnrships | **School Programs** | | **Social Media** |
| 80 | Driver Ed/Safety | 92 | Magnet School | 277 | Remedial Math K-12 | 750 | Chief Innovation Officer | A = Alternative Program | | |
| 81 | Gifted/Talented | 93 | Parental Involvement | 280 | Literacy Coach | 751 | Chief of Staff | G = Adult Classes | f = Facebook |
| 82 | Video Services | 95 | Tech Prep Program | 285 | STEM | 752 | Social Emotional Learning | M = Magnet Program | |
| 83 | Substance Abuse Prev | 97 | Chief Infomation Officer | 286 | Digital Learning | | | T = Title I Schoolwide | t = Twitter |
| 84 | Erate | 98 | Chief Technology Officer | 288 | Common Core Standards | **Other School Types** | | V = Career & Tech Ed Programs | |
| 85 | AIDS Education | 270 | Character Education | 294 | Accountability | Ⓐ = Alternative School | | |
| 88 | Alternative/At Risk | 271 | Migrant Education | 295 | Network System | Ⓒ = Charter School | New Schools are shaded |
| 89 | Multi-Cultural Curriculum | 273 | Teacher Mentor | 296 | Title II Programs | Ⓜ = Magnet School | New Superintendents and Principals are bold |
| 90 | Social Work | 274 | Before/After Sch | 297 | Webmaster | Ⓨ = Year-Round School | Personnel with email addresses are underscored |

**TX—143**

| | | | |
|---|---|---|---|
| North Loop Christian Academy<br>8617 N Loop Dr, El Paso 79907<br>Valerie DeVine | K-12 | 97<br>7 | 915/859-8090<br>Fax 915/859-3290 |
| Northeast Christian Academy<br>9901 McCombs St, El Paso 79924<br>Lillian Ainsworth | PK-12 | 65<br>20 | 915/755-1155<br>Fax 915/755-8264 |
| Palm Tree Academy<br>143 Paragon Ln, El Paso 79912<br>Laura Kassim | PK-5 | 41 | 915/229-2190 |
| Radford Sch<br>2001 Radford St, El Paso 79903<br>John Doran | PK-12 | 175<br>24 | 915/565-2700<br>Fax 915/565-2730 |
| St Clement's Parish Sch<br>600 Montana Ave, El Paso 79902<br>Priscilla Pelking | PK-8 | 380<br>50 | 915/533-4248<br>Fax 915/544-1778 |
| St Mark's Sch<br>5005 Love Rd, El Paso 79922<br>Linda Smith | PK-8 | 300<br>30 | 915/581-2032<br>Fax 915/581-4701 |
| Wee Wisdom Kindergarten<br>1712 Weston Brent Ln, El Paso 79935<br>Claudia Labrado | PK-1 | 75<br>5 | 915/592-6036 |
| Western Hills Academy<br>524 Thunderbird Dr, El Paso 79912<br>Patricia Aguirre | PK-5 | 250<br>17 | 915/584-6642<br>Fax 915/833-2965 |

## EL PASO REGIONAL CENTERS

• **Region 19 Ed Service Center** PID: 01016246
6611 Boeing Dr, El Paso 79925

915/780-5052
Fax 915/780-6537

| | | | |
|---|---|---|---|
| Dr Armando Aguirre | 1 | Royce Cleveland | 2 |
| Sonia Eubank | 2,15 | Monica Gonzalez | 16,73 |
| Angie Haro | 27,73 | Amy Avina | 57 |
| Juan Alderete | 58 | | |

# ELLIS COUNTY

## ELLIS PUBLIC SCHOOLS

• **Avalon Ind School Dist** PID: 01014937
Highway 104 FM 55, Avalon 76623

972/627-3251
Fax 972/627-3220

**Schools:** 1 \ **Teachers:** 32 \ **Students:** 350 \ **Special Ed Students:** 46 \ **LEP Students:** 15 \ **Ethnic:** African American 2%, Hispanic 37%, Caucasian 61% \ **Exp:** $647 (High) \ **Poverty:** 14% \ **Title I:** $29,158 \ **Open-Close:** 08/13 - 05/21 \ **DTBP:** $92 (Med) \ 

| | | | |
|---|---|---|---|
| Khristopher Marshall | 1 | Alice Compton | 2 |
| James Cashion | 3 | Jody Tennery | 9,34* |
| Neva Delbosque | 11,57,88,273,275* | Dwayne Betik | 16,73,295* |
| Sandra Berniking | 58* | Todd Bruner | 67 |

| Public Schs..Principal | Grd | Prgm | Enr/#Cls | SN | |
|---|---|---|---|---|---|
| Avalon Sch<br>Highway 104 FM 55, Avalon 76623<br>Jody Tennery | PK-12 | AGT | 350<br>14 | 66% | 972/627-3251 |

• **Ennis Ind School Dist** PID: 01014963
303 W Knox St, Ennis 75119

972/872-7000
Fax 972/875-8667

**Schools:** 11 \ **Teachers:** 382 \ **Students:** 5,800 \ **Special Ed Students:** 613 \ **LEP Students:** 714 \ **Ethnic:** African American 13%, Hispanic 57%, Caucasian 30% \ **Exp:** $522 (High) \ **Poverty:** 22% \ **Title I:** $1,804,350 \ **Special Education:** $1,007,000 \ **Open-Close:** 08/13 - 05/21 \ **DTBP:** $214 (High) \ 

| | | | |
|---|---|---|---|
| Lloyd Treadwell | 1 | Laurie Walker | 2,11 |
| Lisa Fincher | 2,19,296,298 | Jason Gilstrap | 3,15,68 |
| David Gutierrez | 4 | Ryan McCabe | 5,285* |
| David Kilpatrick | 6 | Kathy Cikanek | 8,15,69 |
| Dr Lacey Padgett | 8 | Twilla Rex | 8,57,69,288 |
| Jennifer Nelson | 11,34,58 | James Sanders | 15,68 |
| Scott Short | 16,28,73,76,82,84,286 | Cliff Mathes | 58 |
| Mandi Chapman | 58 | Bramlet Beard | 67 |
| Bill Honza | 71 | Jeremy Scruggs | 83,91* |
| John Steele | 295 | | |

| Public Schs..Principal | Grd | Prgm | Enr/#Cls | SN | |
|---|---|---|---|---|---|
| Ⓐ Alamo Education Center<br>501 N Gaines St, Ennis 75119<br>Nelly Medrano-Allen | 6-12 | G | 115 | | 972/872-7333<br>Fax 972/875-3834 |
| David S Crockett ECC<br>1701 W Lampasas St, Ennis 75119<br>Dee-Dee Gryder | PK-K | T | 181 | 92% | 972/872-7131<br>Fax 972/872-9829 |
| Dorie Miller Interm Sch<br>2200 W Lampasas St, Ennis 75119<br>Lindsey Wood | 4-6 | T | 635<br>23 | 71% | 972/872-3775<br>Fax 972/872-9370 |
| Ennis High Sch<br>2301 Ensign Rd, Ennis 75119<br>Wade Bishop | 9-12 | TV | 1,670<br>65 | 67% | 972/872-3500<br>Fax 972/875-6337 |
| Ennis Junior High Sch<br>3101 Ensign Rd, Ennis 75119<br>Sheila Thomas-Boone | 7-8 | ATV | 877<br>55 | 72% | 972/872-3850<br>Fax 972/875-9044 |
| G W Carver Early Childhood Ctr<br>600 E Martin Luther King Dr, Ennis 75119<br>Susan Jones | PK-K | T | 206 | 96% | 972/872-3730<br>Fax 972/875-5038 |
| Jack Lummus Interm Sch<br>501 N Clay St, Ennis 75119<br>Rodney McNeill | 4-6 | T | 638 | 71% | 972/872-7060<br>Fax 972/875-8030 |
| James Bowie Elem Sch<br>501 Jeter Dr, Ennis 75119<br>John Peterson | 1-3 | T | 366<br>36 | 66% | 972/872-7234<br>Fax 972/875-3407 |
| Sam Houston Elem Sch<br>1701 S Hall St, Ennis 75119<br>Lori Redning | 1-3 | T | 307<br>25 | 85% | 972/872-7285<br>Fax 972/875-4816 |
| Stephen F Austin Elem Sch<br>1500 Austin Dr, Ennis 75119<br>Bobby White | 1-3 | T | 281<br>18 | 68% | 972/872-7190<br>Fax 972/875-7216 |
| William B Travis Elem Sch<br>200 N Shawnee St, Ennis 75119<br>Philip Black | 1-3 | T | 300<br>15 | 73% | 972/872-7455<br>Fax 972/875-4205 |

• **Ferris Ind School Dist** PID: 01015034
301 E 5th St, Ferris 75125

972/544-3858
Fax 972/544-2784

**Schools:** 5 \ **Teachers:** 191 \ **Students:** 2,400 \ **Special Ed Students:** 314 \ **LEP Students:** 715 \ **College-Bound:** 60% \ **Ethnic:** African American 6%, Hispanic 71%, Caucasian 22% \ **Exp:** $462 (High) \ **Poverty:** 18% \ **Title I:** $546,414 \ **Open-Close:** 08/21 - 05/28 \ **DTBP:** $353 (High) \ 

| | | | |
|---|---|---|---|
| James Hartman | 1 | William Wooten | 2,19 |
| Dondi Markgraf | 3 | Gay Clark | 4* |
| Brandon Layne | 6,35 | Kendra Gajdica | 9 |
| Jane Dvorak | 10,85 | Thomas Knight | 11,54,57,68,69,74,83,294 |

| | | | | | | |
|---|---|---|---|---|---|---|
| **1** Superintendent | **8** Curric/Instruct K-12 | **19** Chief Financial Officer | **29** Family/Consumer Science | **39** Social Studies K-12 | **49** English/Lang Arts Elem | **59** Special Education Elem | **69** Academic Assessment |
| **2** Bus/Finance/Purchasing | **9** Curric/Instruct Elem | **20** Art K-12 | **30** Adult Education | **40** Social Studies Elem | **50** English/Lang Arts Sec | **60** Special Education Sec | **70** Research/Development |
| **3** Buildings And Grounds | **10** Curric/Instruct Sec | **21** Art Elem | **31** Career/Sch-to-Work K-12 | **41** Social Studies Sec | **51** Reading K-12 | **61** Foreign/World Lang K-12 | **71** Public Information |
| **4** Food Service | **11** Federal Program | **22** Art Sec | **32** Career/Sch-to-Work Elem | **42** Science K-12 | **52** Reading Elem | **62** Foreign/World Lang Elem | **72** Summer School |
| **5** Transportation | **12** Title I | **23** Music K-12 | **33** Career/Sch-to-Work Sec | **43** Science Elem | **53** Reading Sec | **63** Foreign/World Lang Sec | **73** Instructional Tech |
| **6** Athletic | **13** Title V | **24** Music Elem | **34** Early Childhood Ed | **44** Science Sec | **54** Remedial Reading K-12 | **64** Religious Education K-12 | **74** Inservice Training |
| **7** Health Services | **15** Asst Superintendent | **25** Music Sec | **35** Health/Phys Education | **45** Math K-12 | **55** Remedial Reading Elem | **65** Religious Education Elem | **75** Marketing/Distributive |
| | **16** Instructional Media Svcs | **26** Business Education | **36** Guidance Services K-12 | **46** Math Elem | **56** Remedial Reading Sec | **66** Religious Education Sec | **76** Info Systems |
| | **17** Chief Operations Officer | **27** Career & Tech Ed | **37** Guidance Services Elem | **47** Math Sec | **57** Bilingual/ELL | **67** School Board President | **77** Psychological Assess |
| | **18** Chief Academic Officer | **28** Technology Education | **38** Guidance Services Sec | **48** English/Lang Arts K-12 | **58** Special Education K-12 | **68** Teacher Personnel | **78** Affirmative Action |

| | |
|---|---|
| Dr Melinda Domain ... 12,15,27,79,88,296,298 | Brett Browne ..................... 16,73,84,295 |
| Rebecca Strick ......................... 16,82 | Viana Armstrong .......................... 57 |
| Kevin Dixon ............................. 58 | Robert Scott ............................. 67 |
| Diana Lopez ............................. 76 | Michelle Beard ........................... 81 |
| Joshua Newman ......................... 91 | Donna Sooby ............................ 295 |
| John Nericua .......................... 295 | |

| Public Schs..Principal | Grd | Prgm | Enr/#Cls | SN | |
|---|---|---|---|---|---|
| Ferris High Sch<br>1025 E 8th St, Ferris 75125<br>Andru Gilbert | 9-12 | TV | 767<br>42 | 73% | 972/544-3737<br>Fax 972/544-3820 |
| Ferris Intermediate Sch<br>601 W FM Rd 664, Ferris 75125<br>Lance Keating | 4-6 | T | 374<br>48 | 83% | 972/544-8662<br>Fax 972/544-3085 |
| Ferris Junior High Sch<br>1002 E 8th St, Ferris 75125<br>C Lowery | 7-8 | T | 586<br>18 | 77% | 972/544-2279<br>Fax 972/544-2281 |
| Hazel Ingram Elem Sch<br>600 S Central St, Ferris 75125<br>Victoria Griffith | PK-K | GT | 398<br>23 | 93% | 972/544-3212<br>Fax 972/544-3405 |
| Lucy Mae McDonald Elem Sch<br>500 FM 983, Ferris 75125<br>Christopher Hawkins | 1-3 | T | 511<br>40 | 82% | 972/544-3405<br>Fax 972/544-2116<br>[f] [t] |

• **Italy Ind School Dist** PID: 01015072    972/483-1815
300 College, Italy 76651    Fax 972/483-6152

**Schools:** 2 \ **Teachers:** 51 \ **Students:** 600 \ **Special Ed Students:** 82 \ **LEP Students:** 43 \ **College-Bound:** 49% \ **Ethnic:** African American 13%, Hispanic 33%, Caucasian 54% \ **Exp:** $592 (High) \ **Poverty:** 12% \ **Title I:** $91,300 \ **Open-Close:** 08/18 - 05/27 \ **DTBP:** $350 (High) \ [f]

| | |
|---|---|
| Dr Michelle Schwind ..................... 1 | Natasha Blackburn ................ 2,11,298 |
| Michael Chambers ..................... 3,5 | Charles Tindol ........................... 6* |
| Deedee Hamilton ....................... 7* | Lee Joffre ................................. 8* |
| Cassie Joffre .......................... 16* | John Woody .............................. 31* |
| Angela Green .......................... 37* | Cheryl Allen ............................. 57* |
| Allen Richards ......................... 67 | Erica Miller ..................... 69,88,271* |
| Oscar McCawley .................. 73,285* | |

| Public Schs..Principal | Grd | Prgm | Enr/#Cls | SN | |
|---|---|---|---|---|---|
| Italy Jr Sr High Sch<br>300 College, Italy 76651<br>Jason Lawson | 6-12 | T | 281<br>40 | 61% | 972/483-7411<br>Fax 972/483-1500<br>[f] |
| Stafford Elem Sch<br>301 Harris St, Italy 76651<br>**Stafford Bray** | PK-5 | T | 304<br>23 | 71% | 972/483-6342<br>Fax 972/483-6892 |

• **Maypearl Ind School Dist** PID: 01015101    972/435-2116
309 Main St, Maypearl 76064    Fax 972/435-1001

**Schools:** 4 \ **Teachers:** 77 \ **Students:** 1,040 \ **Special Ed Students:** 90 \ **LEP Students:** 66 \ **College-Bound:** 75% \ **Ethnic:** Asian 1%, African American 2%, Hispanic 21%, Caucasian 76% \ **Exp:** $402 (High) \ **Poverty:** 6% \ **Title I:** $82,503 \ **Special Education:** $200,000 \ **Open-Close:** 08/13 - 05/21 \ **DTBP:** $350 (High) \ [f]

| | |
|---|---|
| Ritchie Bowling ......................... 1 | Leighanne McAlister ..................... 2 |
| Dale Cheek ............................ 3,5 | Robert Garcia ....................... 3,5,91 |
| Robin Leal ............................. 4* | Jason Wallen ..................... 6,83,270 |
| Lisa Hyles ............................. 8 | Barbara Pinson ......................... 16* |
| Debra Griffin .............. 36,83,85,270* | Barbara Truby ........................... 58 |
| Tricia Ikard ........................... 58 | Lynne Pipes ............................. 59* |
| Charles Frame ......................... 67 | Carole Upchurch .................. 73,295 |

| Public Schs..Principal | Grd | Prgm | Enr/#Cls | SN | |
|---|---|---|---|---|---|
| Lorene S Kirkpatrick Elem Sch<br>1024 W 4th, Maypearl 76064<br>Cristin Votaw | PK-5 | AT | 378<br>20 | 44% | 972/435-1010<br>Fax 972/435-1011 |
| Maypearl High Sch<br>600 Philips St Hwy 157, Maypearl 76064<br>Eric Janszen | 9-12 | AV | 380<br>36 | 35% | 972/435-1020<br>Fax 972/435-1021 |
| Maypearl Intermediate Sch<br>400 Panther Ln, Maypearl 76064<br>Jessica Lee | 5-6 | | 174 | | 972/435-1099<br>Fax 972/435-1098 |
| Maypearl Middle Sch<br>1025 4th St, Maypearl 76064<br>Matthew Garrison | 5-8 | AT | 360<br>12 | 44% | 972/435-1015<br>Fax 972/435-1016 |

• **Midlothian Ind School Dist** PID: 01015137    469/856-5000
100 Walter Stephenson Rd, Midlothian 76065

**Schools:** 11 \ **Teachers:** 576 \ **Students:** 9,500 \ **Special Ed Students:** 1,019 \ **LEP Students:** 335 \ **College-Bound:** 64% \ **Ethnic:** Asian 1%, African American 8%, Hispanic 23%, Caucasian 68% \ **Exp:** $321 (High) \ **Poverty:** 6% \ **Title I:** $527,427 \ **Special Education:** $1,199,000 \ **Open-Close:** 08/18 - 05/27 \ **DTBP:** $177 (High) \ [f] [t]

| | |
|---|---|
| Dr Lane Ledbetter ....................... 1 | Jim Norris ............................ 2,15 |
| Rola Fadel ............................. 3 | Peter Pajack ............................. 4 |
| Deanna Cannon ......................... 5 | John Crawford ........................... 6 |
| Becki Krsnak ........................... 9* | Nikki Nix ................................ 10 |
| Lisa Knight ............. 11,57,271,296,298 | Judy Walling ............................ 15 |
| Karen Fitzgerald ............... 15,71,76,750 | Kay Lynn Day ....................... 15,79 |
| Melissa Wolfe .......................... 58 | Matt Sanders ........................... 67 |
| Natalie Dennington ................. 69,294* | Leslie Garakani ..................... 73,98 |
| Tim Hicks .............................. 91* | Gregg Burcham ....................... 295 |

| Public Schs..Principal | Grd | Prgm | Enr/#Cls | SN | |
|---|---|---|---|---|---|
| Baxter Elem Sch<br>1050 Park Place Blvd, Midlothian 76065<br>Ryan Timm | PK-5 | | 606<br>36 | 35% | 469/856-6100<br>[f] |
| Dolores W McClatchey Elem Sch<br>6631 Shiloh Rd, Midlothian 76065<br>Stacy Germany | K-5 | | 635 | 11% | 469/856-6600 |
| Frank Seale Middle Sch<br>700 George Hopper Rd, Midlothian 76065<br>Kristopher Vernon | 6-8 | V | 1,168<br>63 | 23% | 972/775-6145<br>Fax 972/775-1502 |
| J A Vitovsky Elem Sch<br>333 Church St, Midlothian 76065<br>Hollye Walker | PK-5 | T | 654<br>30 | 58% | 469/856-6400<br>[f] |
| J R Irvin Elem Sch<br>600 S 5th St, Midlothian 76065<br>Joshua Roberts | K-5 | T | 338<br>21 | 26% | 469/856-6000 |
| LaRue Miller Elem Sch<br>2800 Sudith Ln, Midlothian 76065<br>Shannon West | PK-5 | | 718 | 13% | 469/856-6500 |
| Longbranch Elem Sch<br>6631 FM 1387, Midlothian 76065<br>Karena Blackwell | PK-5 | | 594<br>38 | 16% | 469/856-6200 |
| Midlothian Heritage High Sch<br>4000 FM 1387, Midlothian 76065<br>Krista Tipton | 9-12 | | 969 | 10% | 469/856-5400 |
| Midlothian High Sch<br>923 S 9th St, Midlothian 76065<br>Gary Gates | 9-12 | AV | 1,829<br>50 | 24% | 469/856-5100 |
| Mountain Peak Elem Sch<br>5201 FM 663, Midlothian 76065<br>Shannon Thompson | PK-5 | | 714<br>32<br>[f] | 19% | 469/856-6300 |
| Walnut Grove Middle Sch<br>990 N Walnut Grove Rd, Midlothian 76065<br>**Carly Woolery** | 6-8 | | 1,120 | 23% | 469/856-5700 |

## Milford Ind School Dist  PID: 01015187
205 3rd St, Milford 76670

972/493-2911
Fax 972/493-4600

**Schools:** 1 \ **Teachers:** 23 \ **Students:** 240 \ **Special Ed Students:** 38 \ **LEP Students:** 37 \ **College-Bound:** 50% \ **Ethnic:** African American 22%, Hispanic 37%, Caucasian 40% \ **Exp:** $589 (High) \ **Poverty:** 17% \ **Title I:** $58,875 \ **Open-Close:** 08/17 - 05/27 \ **DTBP:** $30 (Low)

| | | | |
|---|---|---|---|
| Vernon Orndorff | 1 | April Gilley | 2 |
| James Rigsby | 3 | Brandi Galindo | 4 |
| Ronny Crompton | 6* | Alton Chambers | 8,36,69,88* |
| Joann Dahl | 11,296 | Mark Jackson | 13* |
| Flossie Gowin | 57* | Larry Williams | 58 |
| Kimberly Cook | 67 | Kirk Price | 73,286,295* |

| Public Schs..Principal | Grd | Prgm | Enr/#Cls | SN |
|---|---|---|---|---|
| Milford Sch<br>205 3rd St, Milford 76670<br>**David Johnson** | PK-12 | TV | 240<br>24 | 69% 972/493-2921 |

## Palmer Ind School Dist  PID: 01015216
303 Bulldog Way, Palmer 75152

972/449-3389
Fax 972/845-2112

**Schools:** 3 \ **Teachers:** 87 \ **Students:** 1,300 \ **Special Ed Students:** 192 \ **LEP Students:** 118 \ **College-Bound:** 65% \ **Ethnic:** African American 2%, Hispanic 43%, Caucasian 55% \ **Exp:** $447 (High) \ **Poverty:** 13% \ **Title I:** $190,964 \ **Special Education:** $226,000 \ **Open-Close:** 08/17 - 05/20 \ **DTBP:** $157 (High) \ [f]

| | | | |
|---|---|---|---|
| Kevin Noack | 1 | Karla Cochrane | 2 |
| Lance McCarty | 3 | Sharee Satcher | 4 |
| Clifford Hurd | 5 | Dawn Waddle | 6 |
| Joanette Roybal | 7 | Brian Fry | 8,74,285,286,288 |
| Regina Farish | 11,58,69,296,298 | Allison Kemp | 29* |
| Leann Jones | 31* | Cassie Odem | 35* |
| Kirk DeCordova | 57* | Christen Vick | 67 |
| Stephen Michael | 73* | Roxanne Ncelhaney | 79 |

| Public Schs..Principal | Grd | Prgm | Enr/#Cls | SN |
|---|---|---|---|---|
| Palmer Elem Sch<br>113 W FM 813, Palmer 75152<br>**Melissa Cunningham** | PK-4 | T | 525<br>19 | 61% 972/449-3132<br>Fax 972/845-2019 |
| Palmer High Sch<br>422 W Jefferson St, Palmer 75152<br>Brian Warner | 9-12 | TV | 321<br>30 | 55% 972/449-3487<br>Fax 972/845-3517 [f] |
| Palmer Middle Sch<br>112 Farm Road 813 W, Palmer 75152<br>Kristin Middlebrooks | 4-8 | TV | 391<br>30 | 56% 972/449-3319<br>Fax 972/845-3380 |

## Red Oak Ind School Dist  PID: 01015242
109 W Red Oak Rd, Red Oak 75154

972/617-2941
Fax 972/617-4333

**Schools:** 8 \ **Teachers:** 381 \ **Students:** 6,000 \ **Special Ed Students:** 695 \ **LEP Students:** 620 \ **College-Bound:** 71% \ **Ethnic:** Asian 1%, African American 24%, Hispanic 38%, Native American: 1%, Caucasian 36% \ **Exp:** $308 (High) \ **Poverty:** 10% \ **Title I:** $684,639 \ **Special Education:** $1,028,000 \ **Open-Close:** 08/20 - 05/28 \ **DTBP:** $181 (High) \ [f] [t]

| | | | |
|---|---|---|---|
| Brenda Sanford | 1 | Dr Bill Johnston | 2,19 |
| Brent Stanford | 3,5 | Kevin Freels | 3,15,88 |
| Victoria Ybarra | 4 | Tammy Pickett | 5 |
| Chris Anderson | 6,35 | Sue Brown | 7 |
| Rebecca Waller | 8 | Scott Rodgers | 10 |
| Nancy Toney | 11,296,298 | Michelle Ailara | 15,68,79 |
| Lisa Menton | 27 | John Anderson | 67 |
| Catrina Reeves | 68 | Mike Bahr | 73,76,295 |

| | | | |
|---|---|---|---|
| Amy Linex | 76 | Phillip Prasifka | 83,91 |
| Allison Bell | 273 | Tia Wilson | 274 |
| Diane Case | 297 | | |

| Public Schs..Principal | Grd | Prgm | Enr/#Cls | SN |
|---|---|---|---|---|
| Donald T Shields Elem Sch<br>223 W Ovilla Rd, Glenn Heights 75154<br>**Allyson Bell** | K-4 | T | 545<br>32 | 46% 972/617-4799<br>Fax 972/617-4798 [f][t] |
| Eastridge Elem Sch<br>725 E Ovilla Rd, Red Oak 75154<br>Michelle Owen | PK-5 | T | 441<br>19 | 56% 972/617-2266<br>Fax 972/617-4759 |
| H A Wooden Elem Sch<br>200 Louise Ritter Blvd, Red Oak 75154<br>**Amy Weis** | PK-4 | T | 540<br>25 | 52% 972/617-2977<br>Fax 972/617-4760 |
| Ischolars Magnet Academy<br>109 W Red Oak Rd, Red Oak 75154<br>Tim Day | 3-9 | | 41 | 972/617-4747 |
| Red Oak Elem Sch<br>200 Valley Ridge Dr, Red Oak 75154<br>Megan Corns | PK-4 | T | 600<br>28 | 54% 972/617-3523<br>Fax 972/576-3423 |
| Red Oak High Sch<br>220 S State Highway 342, Red Oak 75154<br>**Howard Gatewood** | 9-12 | T | 1,885<br>60 | 41% 972/617-3535<br>Fax 972/617-4796 |
| Red Oak Middle Sch<br>154 Louise Ritter Blvd, Red Oak 75154<br>**Fabian Garcia** | 6-8 | T | 1,433<br>40 | 51% 972/617-0066<br>Fax 972/617-4786 |
| Russell Schupmann Elem Sch<br>401 E Ovilla Rd, Glenn Heights 75154<br>Ashley Jackson | PK-5 | T | 376<br>50 | 58% 972/617-2685<br>Fax 972/576-5784 |

## Waxahachie Ind School Dist  PID: 01015292
411 N Gibson St, Waxahachie 75165

972/923-4631
Fax 972/923-4759

**Schools:** 16 \ **Teachers:** 640 \ **Students:** 9,481 \ **Special Ed Students:** 1,174 \ **LEP Students:** 734 \ **Ethnic:** Asian 1%, African American 13%, Hispanic 35%, Native American: 1%, Caucasian 51% \ **Exp:** $450 (High) \ **Poverty:** 13% \ **Title I:** $1,459,089 \ **Special Education:** $1,158,000 \ **Open-Close:** 08/19 - 05/28 \ **DTBP:** $171 (High) \ [t]

| | | | |
|---|---|---|---|
| Bonny Cain | 1 | Ryan Kahlden | 2,15 |
| Jacob Perry | 3 | Kam Bridgers | 4 |
| Tiffany Rivera | 5 | Greg Reed | 6 |
| Melissa Bousquet | 7* | Lisa Mott | 8 |
| Julie Hastings | 11,298 | Letty Bernal | 12,13,296 |
| Lee Auvenshine | 15,68 | Dustin Binnicker | 27 |
| Melissa Cobb | 30 | Ginger Robinson | 36,69,294 |
| Dana James | 40 | Andrea Kline | 41 |
| Melissa Abadie | 43,285 | Theresa Smithey | 44 |
| Stace Johnson | 46 | Alison Frary | 47 |
| Tricia Peyrot | 49,52,55 | Audrey Thomas | 58 |
| Dusty Autrey | 67 | Jenny Bridges | 71 |
| Debbie Needham | 73 | Allison Mendelsohn | 76 |
| Jeff Robinson | 76 | Mike Morgan | 79 |
| Ashley Cieri | 286 | Eli Saenz | 295 |

| Public Schs..Principal | Grd | Prgm | Enr/#Cls | SN |
|---|---|---|---|---|
| Coleman Junior High Sch<br>1000 N Dallas Hwy, Waxahachie 75165<br>**Brad Andrews** | 6-8 | T | 899 | 45% 972/923-4790<br>Fax 972/923-4621 |
| Dunaway Elem Sch<br>600 S Highway 77, Waxahachie 75165<br>**Emily Camarena** | K-5 | T | 461<br>30 | 70% 972/923-4646<br>Fax 972/923-4752 [f] |
| Eddie Finley Jr High Sch<br>2401 Brown St, Waxahachie 75165<br>Derek Zandt | 6-8 | GTV | 603<br>56 | 52% 972/923-4680<br>Fax 972/923-4687 |
| Margaret L Felty Elem Sch<br>231 Park Place Blvd, Waxahachie 75165<br>**Rusty East** | K-5 | | 529 | 22% 972/923-4616<br>Fax 972/923-9394 [t] |

| | | | | | |
|---|---|---|---|---|---|
| Marvin Elem Sch<br>110 Brown St, Waxahachie 75165<br>Christy Bailey | K-5 | T | 366<br>31 | 60% | 972/923-4670<br>Fax 972/923-4677<br>t |
| Northside Elem Sch<br>801 Brown St, Waxahachie 75165<br>Stefani Foster | K-5 | T | 388<br>26 | 44% | 972/923-4610<br>Fax 972/923-4750<br>f |
| Oliver E Clift Elem Sch<br>650 Parks School House Rd, Waxahachie 75165<br>**Tanisha Malone** | K-5 | T | 504 | 68% | 972/923-4720<br>Fax 972/937-5367 |
| Robbie E Howard Jr High Sch<br>265 Broadhead Rd, Waxahachie 75165<br>Ryan Cavazos | 6-8 | T | 633 | 44% | 972/923-4771<br>Fax 972/923-3817 |
| Shackelford Elem Sch<br>1001 Butcher Rd, Waxahachie 75165<br>**Veronica Schaeffer** | K-5 | | 524<br>40 | 32% | 972/923-4666<br>Fax 972/923-4753 |
| Turner Prekindergarten Academy<br>614 N Getzendaner St, Waxahachie 75165<br>Stefani Foster | PK-PK | T | 223 | 78% | 972/923-4690<br>Fax 972/923-4699 |
| Waxahachie Challenge Academy<br>55 Northgate Dr, Waxahachie 75165<br>Dr Al Benskin | 9-12 | A | 15 | | 972/923-4695<br>Fax 972/923-4717 |
| Ⓐ Waxahachie Global High Sch<br>275 Indian Dr, Waxahachie 75165<br>Ken Lynch | 9-12 | | 352<br>3 | 32% | 972/923-4761<br>Fax 972/923-4738<br>f |
| Waxahachie High Sch<br>3001 US Hwy 287 Bypass, Waxahachie 75167<br>Tonya Harris | 9-12 | TV | 2,363<br>75 | 44% | 972/923-4600<br>Fax 972/923-4617 |
| Ⓐ Waxahachie HS of Choice<br>55 Northgate Dr, Waxahachie 75165<br>Ryan Cavazos | 9-12 | T | 32 | 37% | 972/923-4695<br>Fax 972/923-4717<br>t |
| Wedgeworth Elem Sch<br>405 Solon Rd, Waxahachie 75165<br>Tim Day | K-5 | T | 655<br>33 | 56% | 972/923-4640<br>Fax 972/923-4751 |
| Wilemon Steam Academy<br>600 W 2nd St, Waxahachie 75165<br>Kate Authier | K-5 | T | 399 | 50% | 972/923-4780 |

## ELLIS CATHOLIC SCHOOLS

● **Diocese of Dallas Ed Office** PID: 01012367
Listing includes only schools located in this county. See District Index for location of Diocesan Offices.

| Catholic Schs..Principal | Grd | Prgm | Enr/#Cls | SN | |
|---|---|---|---|---|---|
| St Joseph Catholic Sch<br>506 E Marvin Ave, Waxahachie 75165<br>Autumn Helland | PK-8 | | 130<br>15 | | 972/937-0956 |

## ELLIS PRIVATE SCHOOLS

| Private Schs..Principal | Grd | Prgm | Enr/#Cls | SN | |
|---|---|---|---|---|---|
| First Christian Day Sch<br>1109 Brown St, Waxahachie 75165<br>Debbie Aday | PK-8 | | 100<br>17 | | 972/937-1952<br>Fax 972/937-1997 |
| Ovilla Christian Sch<br>3251 Ovilla Rd, Red Oak 75154<br>Lezlie Rozier \ Steven Johnston | PK-12 | | 400<br>38 | | 972/617-1177<br>Fax 469/218-0135<br>f t |
| Waxahachie Preparatory Academy<br>1000 Butcher Rd, Waxahachie 75165<br>Michael Partain | K-12 | | 160 | | 972/937-0440 |

## ERATH COUNTY

## ERATH PUBLIC SCHOOLS

● **Bluff Dale Ind Sch Dist** PID: 01016997     254/728-3277
710 Church St, Bluff Dale 76433     Fax 254/728-3298

**Schools:** 1 \ **Teachers:** 19 \ **Students:** 222 \ **Special Ed Students:** 11 \
**Ethnic:** Hispanic 6%, Native American: 1%, Caucasian 93% \ **Exp:** $504 (High)
\ **Poverty:** 9% \ **Title I:** $20,793 \ **Open-Close:** 08/11 - 05/27

John Taylor .............................1,11,288    Kim Welch ...................................................2
James Barton .......................................67    Janie Ezray ........................................73,286

| Public Schs..Principal | Grd | Prgm | Enr/#Cls | SN | |
|---|---|---|---|---|---|
| Bluff Dale Elem Sch<br>710 W Church St, Bluff Dale 76433<br>**Frank Berngen** | PK-12 | T | 222<br>10 | 39% | 254/728-3277 |

● **Dublin Ind School Dist** PID: 01017018     254/445-3341
420 Post Oak St, Dublin 76446     Fax 254/445-3345

**Schools:** 3 \ **Teachers:** 102 \ **Students:** 1,121 \ **Special Ed Students:** 89
\ **LEP Students:** 205 \ **College-Bound:** 75% \ **Ethnic:** Asian 1%,
African American 1%, Hispanic 59%, Caucasian 39% \ **Exp:** $424 (High) \
**Poverty:** 21% \ **Title I:** $529,825 \ **Open-Close:** 08/04 - 05/13 \ f t

Rodney Schnider ...................................1    Ginny Moiser ................................................2
Clyde Shubert ...................................3,5    Nocona Estes ...........................................4*
Nancy Johnson ...................................7*    Mellissa Summers 8,11,31,57,273,286,288,296
Samantha Abila ...................................58    Jeff Weaver ...............................................67
Kassi Eads ........................................68,78    Paige Johnson .........................................69*
Craig Parks .......................................73,84    Melanie Blew ..........................................298

| Public Schs..Principal | Grd | Prgm | Enr/#Cls | SN | |
|---|---|---|---|---|---|
| Dublin Elem Sch<br>701 Thomas St, Dublin 76446<br>Kalley Mitchell | PK-3 | T | 348<br>27 | 74% | 254/445-2577<br>Fax 254/445-2750 |
| Dublin High Sch<br>2233 E State Highway 6, Dublin 76446<br>Norma Briseno \ Chesta Schneider | 7-12 | GTV | 504<br>24<br>f | 69% | 254/445-0362<br>Fax 254/445-1706 |
| Dublin Intermediate Sch<br>609 N Thomas, Dublin 76446<br>**Chesta Schneider** | 4-6 | T | 272<br>15 | 78% | 254/445-2618<br>Fax 254/445-3383 |

● **Huckabay Ind School Dist** PID: 01017056     254/968-5274
200 County Road 421, Stephenville 76401     Fax 254/965-3740

**Schools:** 1 \ **Teachers:** 21 \ **Students:** 250 \ **Special Ed Students:** 12
\ **LEP Students:** 3 \ **College-Bound:** 100% \ **Ethnic:** Hispanic 18%,
Native American: 1%, Caucasian 80% \ **Exp:** $403 (High) \ **Poverty:** 15% \
**Title I:** $40,915 \ **Open-Close:** 08/24 - 05/28 \ **DTBP:** $359 (High)

Troy Roberts ...................................1,83    Tammy Shipman .........................................2
Kayla Walls ..........................................6*    Bill Dow ...............................................11,67

---

| | | | |
|---|---|---|---|
| 79 Student Personnel | 91 Safety/Security | 275 Response To Intervention | 298 Grant Writer/Ptnrships |
| 80 Driver Ed/Safety | 92 Magnet School | 277 Remedial Math K-12 | 750 Chief Innovation Officer |
| 81 Gifted/Talented | 93 Parental Involvement | 280 Literacy Coach | 751 Chief of Staff |
| 82 Video Services | 95 Tech Prep Program | 285 STEM | 752 Social Emotional Learning |
| 83 Substance Abuse Prev | 97 Chief Information Officer | 286 Digital Learning | |
| 84 Erate | 98 Chief Technology Officer | 288 Common Core Standards | **Other School Types** |
| 85 AIDS Education | 270 Character Education | 294 Accountability | Ⓐ = Alternative School |
| 88 Alternative/At Risk | 271 Migrant Education | 295 Network System | Ⓒ = Charter School |
| 89 Multi-Cultural Curriculum | 273 Teacher Mentor | 296 Title II Programs | Ⓜ = Magnet School |
| 90 Social Work | 274 Before/After Sch | 297 Webmaster | Ⓨ = Year-Round School |

| | | |
|---|---|---|
| **School Programs** | | **Social Media** |
| A = Alternative Program | | f = Facebook |
| G = Adult Classes | | t = Twitter |
| M = Magnet Program | | |
| T = Title I Schoolwide | | |
| V = Career & Tech Ed Programs | | |

New Schools are shaded
New Superintendents and Principals are bold
Personnel with email addresses are underscored

| Public Schs..Principal | Grd | Prgm | Enr/#Cls | SN |
|---|---|---|---|---|
| Huckabay Sch<br>200 County Road 421, Stephenville 76401<br>Wes Corzine | PK-12 | TV | 250<br>24 | 32% 254/968-8476<br>Fax 254/965-3140 |

● **Lingleville Ind School Dist** PID: 01017082     254/968-2596
21261 N FM 219, Lingleville 76461     Fax 254/965-5821

> **Schools:** 1 \ **Teachers:** 27 \ **Students:** 282 \ **Special Ed Students:** 23
> \ **LEP Students:** 50 \ **College-Bound:** 50% \ **Ethnic:** Hispanic 51%,
> Caucasian 48% \ **Exp:** $567 (High) \ **Poverty:** 16% \ **Title I:** $77,721 \
> **Open-Close:** 08/24 - 05/28 \ **DTBP:** $367 (High)

| | | | |
|---|---|---|---|
| Curtis Haley ............................1,11 | Paula Hidditts ...........................2 |
| Oscar Rodriguez ..........................3* | Deecee McDougal 8,57,88,274,286,288,294,295 |
| Barbara Vaden .......................16,82* | Biscotti Ford .......................27,31 |
| Cheryl Hudson ......................36,83 | Karen Keith ...........................58^ |
| Larry Griffin .............................67 | Rhonda Bays ......................73,76* |

| Public Schs..Principal | Grd | Prgm | Enr/#Cls | SN |
|---|---|---|---|---|
| Lingleville Sch<br>21261 N FM 219, Lingleville 76461<br>Scott Wells | PK-12 | TV | 282<br>25 | 51% 254/968-2596 |

● **Morgan Mill Ind School Dist** PID: 01017111     254/968-4921
295 E FM 1188, Morgan Mill 76465     Fax 254/968-4814

> **Schools:** 1 \ **Teachers:** 13 \ **Students:** 125 \ **Special Ed Students:** 8 \
> **Ethnic:** Hispanic 18%, Caucasian 82% \ **Exp:** $1,142 (High) \ **Poverty:** 11% \
> **Title I:** $17,679 \ **Open-Close:** 08/10 - 05/27 \ **DTBP:** $318 (High)

| | |
|---|---|
| Wendy Sanders ...............1,11,288 | Crystal Richard ............................2 |
| Kellen Cervveto .........................6 | Tony Ballinger ..........................67 |
| Maggie Burton ...............270,271 | |

| Public Schs..Principal | Grd | Prgm | Enr/#Cls | SN |
|---|---|---|---|---|
| Morgan Mill Elem Sch<br>Highway 281, Morgan Mill 76465<br>Barrett Hutchison | PK-8 | T | 125<br>9 | 51% 254/968-4921 |

● **Stephenville Ind School Dist** PID: 01017135     254/968-7990
2655 W Overhill Dr, Stephenville 76401     Fax 254/968-5942

> **Schools:** 6 \ **Teachers:** 254 \ **Students:** 3,650 \ **Special Ed Students:** 336
> \ **LEP Students:** 361 \ **College-Bound:** 66% \ **Ethnic:** Asian 1%,
> African American 1%, Hispanic 35%, Caucasian 62% \ **Exp:** $526 (High)
> \ **Poverty:** 18% \ **Title I:** $859,188 \ **Special Education:** $678,000 \
> **Open-Close:** 08/12 - 05/14 \ **DTBP:** $158 (High) \ 📱

| | |
|---|---|
| Matt Underwood ...........................1 | Terri Hodges ............................2 |
| Keith Starnes ........................3,91 | Melissa Blackwell ....................3 |
| Cheryl Dowell ...........................4 | David Woods ...........................5 |
| Kelly McGinn .......................8,288 | Renee Goodwin ............13,69,294 |
| Shelby Womack .................27,73* | Michelle McNutt ......................57 |
| Penny Hampton ......................58 | Dr Ann Calahan ......................67 |
| Kathy Hampton .....................68* | Luke Reagor ........................73* |
| Julie Griffin ..........................76 | Audrey Warren ......................80 |
| Ronda Monson ......................298 | |

| Public Schs..Principal | Grd | Prgm | Enr/#Cls | SN |
|---|---|---|---|---|
| Central Elem Sch<br>780 W Washington St, Stephenville 76401<br>Esther Tucker | PK-K | T | 427<br>25 | 55% 254/965-3716<br>Fax 254/965-5319<br>📱 |
| Chamberlin Elem Sch<br>1601 W Frey St, Stephenville 76401<br>Jennifer Salyards | 1-2 | T | 520<br>28 | 48% 254/968-2311<br>Fax 254/968-5399 |

| Public Schs..Principal | Grd | Prgm | Enr/#Cls | SN |
|---|---|---|---|---|
| Gilbert Intermediate Sch<br>950 N Dale Ave, Stephenville 76401<br>Victor Sauceda | 5-6 | T | 577<br>40 | 46% 254/968-4664<br>Fax 254/968-8696 |
| Henderson Junior High Sch<br>2798 W Frey St, Stephenville 76401<br>Brad Burleson | 7-8 | T | 590<br>50 | 48% 254/968-6967<br>Fax 254/965-7018 |
| Hook Elem Sch<br>1067 W Jones St, Stephenville 76401<br>Daresa Rhine | 3-4 | T | 535<br>24 | 50% 254/968-3213<br>Fax 254/968-6758 |
| Stephenville High Sch<br>2650 W Overhill Dr, Stephenville 76401<br>Stephanie Traweek | 9-12 | GV | 1,048<br>54 | 38% 254/968-4141<br>Fax 254/968-4897 |

● **Three Way Ind School Dist** PID: 01017185     254/965-6496
247 County Road 207, Stephenville 76401     Fax 254/965-3357

> **Schools:** 2 \ **Teachers:** 16 \ **Students:** 190 \ **Special Ed Students:** 4 \
> **LEP Students:** 24 \ **Ethnic:** Hispanic 51%, Caucasian 49% \ **Exp:** $559 (High)
> \ **Poverty:** 10% \ **Title I:** $11,466 \ **Open-Close:** 08/19 - 05/25 \ **DTBP:** $362
> (High)

| | |
|---|---|
| Paul Ryan ..........................1,11,84 | Jennifer Bailey ........................2 |
| Troy Sparks ...........................5 | Allison Wright .......................59* |
| Tracie Hankins ........................67 | Carlos Ortiz ...........................73 |

| Public Schs..Principal | Grd | Prgm | Enr/#Cls | SN |
|---|---|---|---|---|
| Three Way Elem Sch<br>247 County Road 207, Stephenville 76401<br>Kayla Sparks | PK-8 | T | 165<br>9 | 76% 254/965-6496 |
| Threeway High Sch<br>247 County Road 207, Stephenville 76401<br>Randall Ryan | 9-10 | | 47 | 254/965-9496 |

## ERATH PRIVATE SCHOOLS

| Private Schs..Principal | Grd | Prgm | Enr/#Cls | SN |
|---|---|---|---|---|
| Stephenville Christian Sch<br>1120 County Road 351, Stephenville 76401<br>Greg Judy | PK-6 | | 57<br>5 | 254/965-4821 |

## FALLS COUNTY

## FALLS PUBLIC SCHOOLS

● **Chilton Ind School Dist** PID: 01017202     254/546-1200
905 Durango Ave, Chilton 76632     Fax 254/546-1201

> **Schools:** 1 \ **Teachers:** 38 \ **Students:** 540 \ **Special Ed Students:** 70
> \ **LEP Students:** 89 \ **College-Bound:** 60% \ **Ethnic:** African American
> 18%, Hispanic 63%, Caucasian 19% \ **Exp:** $577 (High) \ **Poverty:** 25% \
> **Title I:** $142,056 \ **Open-Close:** 08/24 - 05/21 \ **DTBP:** $342 (High)

| | |
|---|---|
| Brandon Hubbard ....................1,11 | Lahoma Taylor ........................2 |
| Willis Childers ...........................3 | Robert Judie ...........................5 |
| Chris James ............................6* | Leslie Harris ..............8,12,69,88* |
| Gloria Pamplin ........................57 | Keimesha Alexander .............58* |
| Rodney Hall ...........................67 | Ronnie Lawson ...............73,286* |

| | | | | | | | |
|---|---|---|---|---|---|---|---|
| **1** | Superintendent | **8** | Curric/Instruct K-12 | **19** | Chief Financial Officer | **29** | Family/Consumer Science |
| **2** | Bus/Finance/Purchasing | **9** | Curric/Instruct Elem | **20** | Art K-12 | **30** | Adult Education |
| **3** | Buildings And Grounds | **10** | Curric/Instruct Sec | **21** | Art Elem | **31** | Career/Sch-to-Work K-12 |
| **4** | Food Service | **11** | Federal Program | **22** | Art Sec | **32** | Career/Sch-to-Work Elem |
| **5** | Transportation | **12** | Title I | **23** | Music K-12 | **33** | Career/Sch-to-Work Sec |
| **6** | Athletic | **13** | Title V | **24** | Music Elem | **34** | Early Childhood Ed |
| **7** | Health Services | **14** | Assistant Superintendent | **25** | Music Sec | **35** | Health/Phys Education |
| | | **15** | Asst Superintendent | **26** | Business Education | **36** | Guidance Services K-12 |
| | | **16** | Instructional Media Svcs | **27** | Career & Tech Ed | **37** | Guidance Services Elem |
| | | **17** | Chief Operations Officer | **28** | Technology Education | **38** | Guidance Services Sec |
| | | **18** | Chief Academic Officer | | | | |

| | | | |
|---|---|---|---|
| **39** Social Studies K-12 | **49** English/Lang Arts Elem | **59** Special Education Elem | **69** Academic Assessment |
| **40** Social Studies Elem | **50** English/Lang Arts Sec | **60** Special Education Sec | **70** Research/Development |
| **41** Social Studies Sec | **51** Reading K-12 | **61** Foreign/World Lang K-12 | **71** Public Information |
| **42** Science K-12 | **52** Reading Elem | **62** Foreign/World Lang Elem | **72** Summer School |
| **43** Science Elem | **53** Reading Sec | **63** Foreign/World Lang Sec | **73** Instructional Tech |
| **44** Science Sec | **54** Remedial Reading K-12 | **64** Religious Education K-12 | **74** Inservice Training |
| **45** Math K-12 | **55** Remedial Reading Elem | **65** Religious Education Elem | **75** Marketing/Distributive |
| **46** Math Elem | **56** Remedial Reading Sec | **66** Religious Education Sec | **76** Info Systems |
| **47** Math Sec | **57** Bilingual/ELL | **67** School Board President | **77** Psychological Assess |
| **48** English/Lang Arts K-12 | **58** Special Education K-12 | **68** Teacher Personnel | **78** Affirmative Action |

Latrice Canada ........................................ 76

| Public Schs..Principal | Grd | Prgm | Enr/#Cls | SN | |
|---|---|---|---|---|---|
| Chilton Sch<br>905 Durango Ave, Chilton 76632<br>Gladys Graves \ Leon Darden | PK-12 | TV | 540<br>54 | 87% | 254/546-1200 |

● **Marlin Ind School Dist** PID: 01017238
130 Coleman St, Marlin 76661
254/883-3585
Fax 254/883-6612

> **Schools:** 3 \ **Teachers:** 74 \ **Students:** 821 \ **Special Ed Students:** 95
> \ **LEP Students:** 127 \ **College-Bound:** 75% \ **Ethnic:** African American
> 57%, Hispanic 34%, Caucasian 8% \ **Exp:** $366 (High) \ **Poverty:** 31% \
> **Title I:** $660,093 \ **Special Education:** $330,000 \ **Open-Close:** 08/20 -
> 05/28 \ **DTBP:** $335 (High)

| | | | |
|---|---|---|---|
| Jean Bahney ..........................1 | Pat Lewis .............................2,19 | | |
| Vince Margoitta ...................3,5* | Barbara Brown ......................4 | | |
| Marshall Higgins ..................5 | Remy Hodge .........................8 | | |
| Dr Michael Seabolt ............. 11 | Remy Godfrey ...................... 15 | | |
| Adam LeJeune ..............16,288 | Nancy Laster ....................... 16* | | |
| Edward Rogers ...................36* | Billy Johnson ....................... 67 | | |
| Rockney Terry .....................73* | | | |

| Public Schs..Principal | Grd | Prgm | Enr/#Cls | SN | |
|---|---|---|---|---|---|
| Marlin Elem Sch<br>602 Donnaho St, Marlin 76661<br>Kimberly McKnight | PK-5 | AT | 414<br>33 | 100% | 254/883-3232<br>Fax 254/883-5237 |
| Marlin High Sch<br>1400 Capps St, Marlin 76661<br>Pamela Thomas | 9-12 | ATV | 224<br>22 | 100% | 254/883-2394<br>Fax 254/883-3470 |
| Marlin Middle Sch<br>678 Success Dr, Marlin 76661<br>Patti Ward | 6-8 | AT | 183<br>17 | 99% | 254/883-9241<br>Fax 254/883-6491 |

● **Rosebud-Lott Ind School Dist** PID: 01017276
1789 US Highway 77, Lott 76656
254/583-4510
Fax 254/583-4469

> **Schools:** 3 \ **Teachers:** 55 \ **Students:** 637 \ **Special Ed Students:** 95
> \ **LEP Students:** 24 \ **Ethnic:** African American 12%, Hispanic 35%,
> Caucasian 53% \ **Exp:** $491 (High) \ **Poverty:** 20% \ **Title I:** $231,418 \
> **Open-Close:** 08/19 - 05/20 \ **DTBP:** $273 (High)

| | | | |
|---|---|---|---|
| Dr Steve Brownlee ...................1 | Valerie Gausemeier ...................2* | | |
| Robby Sims ...........................3 | Steffanie Stone ....................... 4 | | |
| Tony Stone ............................5 | Brad Ballard ..........................6* | | |
| Natalie Parcus ................11,288 | Julie Bennett ......................... 67 | | |
| Larry Dutcher .......................73 | Randall Jennings ................... 73 | | |

| Public Schs..Principal | Grd | Prgm | Enr/#Cls | SN | |
|---|---|---|---|---|---|
| Rosebud-Lott Elem Sch<br>1813 US Highway 77, Lott 76656<br>Alushka Driska | PK-6 | T | 321<br>9 | 76% | 254/583-7965<br>Fax 254/583-2642 |
| Rosebud-Lott High Sch<br>1789 US Highway 77, Lott 76656<br>Jerrod Barton | 9-12 | T | 221 | 40% | 254/583-7967<br>Fax 254/583-1130 |
| Rosebud-Lott Middle Sch<br>1789 US Highway 77, Lott 76656<br>Phil Johanson | 7-8 | ATV | 95<br>45 | 59% | 254/583-7962<br>Fax 254/583-2904 |

● **Westphalia Ind School Dist** PID: 01017329
124 County Road 3000, Lott 76656
254/584-4988
Fax 254/584-2963

> **Schools:** 1 \ **Teachers:** 13 \ **Students:** 155 \ **Special Ed Students:** 18
> \ **LEP Students:** 3 \ **Ethnic:** African American 1%, Hispanic 11%, Native
> American: 1%, Caucasian 88% \ **Exp:** $583 (High) \ **Poverty:** 12% \
> **Open-Close:** 08/13 - 05/26 \ **DTBP:** $352 (High)

| | | | |
|---|---|---|---|
| Robert Hudson ......................1,11 | Shelley Thornton ...........................2 | | |
| Robert Hudson ...........6,69,83,270* | Kimberly Nejtek .........................57,59* | | |
| Michelle Weaver ...................... 67 | Michael Johnson ......................73,76,295* | | |

| Public Schs..Principal | Grd | Prgm | Enr/#Cls | SN | |
|---|---|---|---|---|---|
| Westphalia Sch<br>124 County Road 3000, Lott 76656<br>Robert Hudson | K-8 | T | 155<br>12 | 21% | 254/584-4988 |

## FANNIN COUNTY

---

## FANNIN PUBLIC SCHOOLS

---

● **Bonham Ind School Dist** PID: 01017367
1005 Chestnut St, Bonham 75418
903/583-5526
Fax 903/583-8463

> **Schools:** 5 \ **Teachers:** 132 \ **Students:** 1,850 \ **Special Ed Students:** 261
> \ **LEP Students:** 229 \ **College-Bound:** 44% \ **Ethnic:** Asian 1%, African
> American 8%, Hispanic 30%, Native American: 1%, Caucasian 61% \
> **Exp:** $481 (High) \ **Poverty:** 18% \ **Title I:** $510,854 \ **Open-Close:** 08/20 -
> 06/04 \ **DTBP:** $356 (High) \ 🇫 🇹

| | | | |
|---|---|---|---|
| **Kelly Trompler** .........................1 | Alicia Lang ..............................2 | | |
| Bill Wakefield ......................3,17,91 | Claude Lewis ..........................3 | | |
| Phyllis Kinnaird ........................4 | Concan Humphrey ...................5 | | |
| Ryan Crock ...............................6 | Heather Lawson ...................... 7 | | |
| Traci Daniel ........8,11,57,83,285,288,294 | Angie Richardson ................. 13,58 | | |
| April Peterson .........................16* | Rory Hilliard ........................... 34 | | |
| Suzanne Kennedy ..................34* | Chance Roberts ..................... 67 | | |

| Public Schs..Principal | Grd | Prgm | Enr/#Cls | SN | |
|---|---|---|---|---|---|
| Bailey Inglish Erly Chldhd Ctr<br>201 E 10th St, Bonham 75418<br>Rory Hillard | PK-PK | T | 205<br>8 | 94% | 903/583-8141<br>Fax 903/583-0025 |
| Bonham High Sch<br>1002 War Path St, Bonham 75418<br>Panchi Scown | 9-12 | ATV | 489<br>60 | 63% | 903/583-5567<br>Fax 903/583-5560 |
| Finley-Oates Elem Sch<br>1901 Albert Broadfoot St, Bonham 75418<br>Mary Lou Fox | K-3 | T | 521<br>31 | 65% | 903/640-4090<br>Fax 903/640-8140 |
| I W Evans Intermediate Sch<br>1300 N Main St, Bonham 75418<br>Karli Fowler | 4-6 | T | 407<br>21 | 68% | 903/583-2914<br>Fax 903/640-1056<br>🇫 |
| L H Rather Junior High Sch<br>1201 N Main St, Bonham 75418<br>Traci Daniel | 7-8 | TV | 268<br>25 | 63% | 903/583-7474<br>Fax 903/583-3713<br>🇫 🇹 |

## Dodd City Ind School Dist PID: 01017422
602 N Main St, Dodd City 75438

903/583-7585
Fax 903/583-9545

**Schools:** 1 \ **Teachers:** 30 \ **Students:** 364 \ **Special Ed Students:** 28 \
**LEP Students:** 11 \ **College-Bound:** 75% \ **Ethnic:** Asian 1%, Hispanic 8%,
Native American: 1%, Caucasian 91% \ **Exp:** $622 (High) \ **Poverty:** 9% \
**Title I:** $25,402 \ **Open-Close:** 08/17 - 05/20 \ **DTBP:** $346 (High)

| | | | |
|---|---|---|---|
| Craig Reed | 1,83 | Lesia Bridges | 2,15 |
| Alex Stevenson | 6* | Alisha Hale | 7 |
| Angie Freeman | 13,31,36,69,77,88* | Juliana Wild | 57* |
| Thomas Lackey | 67 | Tyler White | 73,286,295* |
| Joanna Collida | 274* | | |

| Public Schs..Principal | Grd | Prgm | Enr/#Cls | SN | |
|---|---|---|---|---|---|
| Dodd City Sch<br>602 N Main St, Dodd City 75438<br>Bruce Maupin \ Joanna Collida | PK-12 | TV | 364<br>23 | 41% | 903/583-7585 |

## Ector Ind School Dist PID: 01017458
301 S Main St, Ector 75439

903/961-2355
Fax 903/961-2110

**Schools:** 1 \ **Teachers:** 23 \ **Students:** 260 \ **Special Ed Students:** 40
\ **LEP Students:** 3 \ **College-Bound:** 85% \ **Ethnic:** Hispanic 7%,
Caucasian 93% \ **Exp:** $508 (High) \ **Poverty:** 17% \ **Title I:** $47,635 \
**Open-Close:** 08/20 - 06/11 \ **DTBP:** $325 (High)

| | | | |
|---|---|---|---|
| Jennifer Morris | 1 | Deborah Williams | 2 |
| Joe Detiller | 3* | Roger Morris | 5,275* |
| Blake Turner | 6 | Dawn Bohannon | 16,73* |
| Betty Day | 58* | John Harris | 67 |
| Jeff Glaser | 295* | | |

| Public Schs..Principal | Grd | Prgm | Enr/#Cls | SN | |
|---|---|---|---|---|---|
| Ector Sch<br>301 S Main St, Ector 75439<br>Bradford Evans \ **Justin Bankston** | K-12 | T | 260<br>20 | 68% | 903/961-2355 |

## Honey Grove Ind School Dist PID: 01017472
1206 17th St, Honey Grove 75446

903/378-2264
Fax 903/900-4935

**Schools:** 3 \ **Teachers:** 45 \ **Students:** 614 \ **Special Ed Students:** 97 \
**LEP Students:** 49 \ **Ethnic:** African American 8%, Hispanic 23%, Native
American: 1%, Caucasian 68% \ **Exp:** $506 (High) \ **Poverty:** 27% \
**Title I:** $216,876 \ **Open-Close:** 09/02 - 06/04 \ **DTBP:** $350 (High)

| | | | |
|---|---|---|---|
| Todd Morrison | 1,11 | Lori Lane | 2 |
| J Caraway | 3* | Margo Oats | 4* |
| Glenn Schulte | 6 | Joy Stroud | 7* |
| Ashley Odom | 8,12 | Joshua Edmondson | 16,73* |
| Zeb Tindel | 31 | Lyn Scott | 36,69,77,752 |
| Sandra Rubio | 57* | Angie Richardson | 58 |
| Josh Russell | 67 | Christy Caraway | 68 |
| Jamie Humphries | 76 | Rob Oconner | 84,298 |

| Public Schs..Principal | Grd | Prgm | Enr/#Cls | SN | |
|---|---|---|---|---|---|
| Honey Grove Elem Sch<br>1206 17th St, Honey Grove 75446<br>Ashley Odom | PK-5 | T | 269<br>25 | 68% | 903/378-2264<br>Fax 903/900-4725 |
| Honey Grove High Sch<br>1208 17th St, Honey Grove 75446<br>Tammy Mariani | 9-12 | TV | 208<br>23 | 47% | 903/378-2264<br>Fax 903/900-4725 |
| Honey Grove Middle Sch<br>1204 17th St, Honey Grove 75446<br>Lee Frost | 6-8 | T | 137<br>11 | 63% | 903/378-2264<br>Fax 903/900-4725 |

## Leonard Ind School Dist PID: 01017501
1 Tiger Aly, Leonard 75452

903/587-2318
Fax 903/587-2845

**Schools:** 4 \ **Teachers:** 65 \ **Students:** 878 \ **Special Ed Students:** 84 \
**LEP Students:** 49 \ **College-Bound:** 56% \ **Ethnic:** African American 2%,
Hispanic 20%, Native American: 1%, Caucasian 77% \ **Exp:** $665 (High) \
**Poverty:** 16% \ **Title I:** $149,547 \ **Open-Close:** 08/17 - 05/27 \ **DTBP:** $341
(High)

| | | | |
|---|---|---|---|
| Brad Maxwell | 1 | Janna Layman | 2,298 |
| Dwain Campbell | 3,5 | Sherry Cooper | 4* |
| Shane Fletcher | 6* | Nancy Zachary | 7* |
| Jeff Johnson | 11,15,296 | Pam McCarley | 16* |
| John Davis | 27 | Kacie Littrell | 31,36,58,69,83,88* |
| Billy Watson | 67 | Kim Wheeler | 73,295* |
| Tracy Howell | 271* | | |

| Public Schs..Principal | Grd | Prgm | Enr/#Cls | SN | |
|---|---|---|---|---|---|
| Leonard Elem Sch<br>300 E Mulberry St, Leonard 75452<br>Regina Blain | PK-3 | T | 266<br>17 | 59% | 903/587-2316<br>Fax 903/587-2392 |
| Leonard High Sch<br>1000 2N Poplar St, Leonard 75452<br>Tammy Hutchings | 9-12 | TV | 277<br>30 | 48% | 903/587-3556<br>Fax 903/587-8011 |
| Leonard Intermediate Sch<br>600 E Hackberry, Leonard 75452<br>Sarah Day | 4-5 | T | 118<br>7 | 65% | 903/587-8303<br>Fax 903/587-4414 |
| Leonard Junior High Sch<br>500 E Hackberry St, Leonard 75452<br>**Jacob Gregory** | 6-8 | T | 217<br>16 | 61% | 903/587-2315<br>Fax 903/587-2228 |

## Sam Rayburn Ind School Dist PID: 01017549
9363 E FM 273, Ivanhoe 75447

903/664-2255
Fax 903/664-2406

**Schools:** 1 \ **Teachers:** 52 \ **Students:** 525 \ **Special Ed Students:** 58
\ **LEP Students:** 24 \ **College-Bound:** 10% \ **Ethnic:** African American
1%, Hispanic 8%, Caucasian 90% \ **Exp:** $694 (High) \ **Poverty:** 16% \
**Title I:** $88,811 \ **Open-Close:** 08/17 - 05/21 \ **DTBP:** $366 (High)

| | | | |
|---|---|---|---|
| Steve Arthur | 1 | Tracie Ivey | 2,12 |
| Kyle Baker | 3* | Wendy Keeton | 8,11,69,73,271,275,286,295* |
| Kim Hopkins | 16* | Stephanie Klein | 37* |
| Christy Chambliss | 38 | Lavonda Hilliard | 57 |
| Chris Flippo | 67 | | |

| Public Schs..Principal | Grd | Prgm | Enr/#Cls | SN | |
|---|---|---|---|---|---|
| Sam Rayburn Sch<br>9363 E FM 273, Ivanhoe 75447<br>Julie Symanik \ **Stephanie Laisy** | PK-12 | TV | 525<br>30 | 39% | 903/664-2165 |

## Savoy Ind School Dist PID: 01017575
302 W Hayes St, Savoy 75479

903/965-5262
Fax 903/965-7282

**Schools:** 2 \ **Teachers:** 27 \ **Students:** 320 \ **Special Ed Students:** 38 \
**LEP Students:** 5 \ **Ethnic:** Asian 1%, African American 1%, Hispanic 12%,
Native American: 2%, Caucasian 84% \ **Exp:** $552 (High) \ **Poverty:** 14% \
**Title I:** $46,162 \ **Open-Close:** 08/17 - 05/27 \ **DTBP:** $305 (High)

| | | | |
|---|---|---|---|
| Brian Neal | 1 | Denise Pugh | 2,76 |
| Joe Baca | 3,5* | Georgina Green | 4* |
| Clay Wilson | 6* | Michael Smith | 10* |
| Stephanie Sweet | 58* | Terry Lewis | 67 |
| Rapee Sritairat | 73,84 | Rapee Sriritarat | 295* |

---

| | | | | | | | |
|---|---|---|---|---|---|---|---|
| 1 | Superintendent | 8 | Curric/Instruct K-12 | 19 | Chief Financial Officer | 29 | Family/Consumer Science |
| 2 | Bus/Finance/Purchasing | 9 | Curric/Instruct Elem | 20 | Art K-12 | 30 | Adult Education |
| 3 | Buildings And Grounds | 10 | Curric/Instruct Sec | 21 | Art Elem | 31 | Career/Sch-to-Work K-12 |
| 4 | Food Service | 11 | Federal Program | 22 | Art Sec | 32 | Career/Sch-to-Work Elem |
| 5 | Transportation | 12 | Title I | 23 | Music K-12 | 33 | Career/Sch-to-Work Sec |
| 6 | Athletic | 13 | Title V | 24 | Music Elem | 34 | Early Childhood Ed |
| 7 | Health Services | 14 | Asst Superintendent | 25 | Music Sec | 35 | Health/Phys Education |
| | | 15 | | 26 | Business Education | 36 | Guidance Services K-12 |
| | | 16 | Instructional Media Svcs | 27 | Career & Tech Ed | 37 | Guidance Services Elem |
| | | 17 | Chief Operations Officer | 28 | Technology Education | 38 | Guidance Services Sec |
| | | 18 | Chief Academic Officer | | | | |

| | | | | | | | |
|---|---|---|---|---|---|---|---|
| 39 | Social Studies K-12 | 49 | English/Lang Arts Elem | 59 | Special Education Elem | 69 | Academic Assessment |
| 40 | Social Studies Elem | 50 | English/Lang Arts Sec | 60 | Special Education Sec | 70 | Research/Development |
| 41 | Social Studies Sec | 51 | Reading K-12 | 61 | Foreign/World Lang K-12 | 71 | Public Information |
| 42 | Science K-12 | 52 | Reading Elem | 62 | Foreign/World Lang Elem | 72 | Summer School |
| 43 | Science Elem | 53 | Reading Sec | 63 | Foreign/World Lang Sec | 73 | Instructional Tech |
| 44 | Science Sec | 54 | Remedial Reading K-12 | 64 | Religious Education K-12 | 74 | Inservice Training |
| 45 | Math K-12 | 55 | Remedial Reading Elem | 65 | Religious Education Elem | 75 | Marketing/Distributive |
| 46 | Math Elem | 56 | Remedial Reading Sec | 66 | Religious Education Sec | 76 | Info Systems |
| 47 | Math Sec | 57 | Bilingual/ELL | 67 | School Board President | 77 | Psychological Assess |
| 48 | English/Lang Arts K-12 | 58 | Special Education K-12 | 68 | Teacher Personnel | 78 | Affirmative Action |

| Public Schs..Principal | Grd | Prgm | Enr/#Cls | SN |
|---|---|---|---|---|
| Savoy Elem Sch<br>302 W Hayes St, Savoy 75479<br>Danny Henderson | PK-6 | T | 181<br>11 | 61% 903/965-7738<br>Fax 903/965-4389 |
| Savoy High Sch<br>605 E Hayes St, Savoy 75479<br>Michael Smith | 7-12 | TV | 141 | 44% 903/965-4024<br>Fax 903/965-5608 |

### • Trenton Ind School Dist  PID: 01017604
702 S Ballentine St, Trenton 75490

903/989-2245
Fax 903/989-2767

**Schools:** 3 \ **Teachers:** 45 \ **Students:** 573 \ **Special Ed Students:** 59 \ **LEP Students:** 34 \ **College-Bound:** 51% \ **Ethnic:** African American 2%, Hispanic 21%, Native American: 1%, Caucasian 76% \ **Exp:** $325 (High) \ **Poverty:** 12% \ **Title I:** $92,417 \ **Open-Close:** 08/17 - 05/20 \ **DTBP:** $367 (High) \ 

| | | | |
|---|---|---|---|
| **Jeremy Strickland** .................................1 | **Kimberly Anderson** ....................................2 | | |
| Sonya McTee ..........................................4 | Mike Jones ...............................................6* | | |
| Kevin Cannon .................9,11,59,69,79,296* | Brenda Hines ..............................................16 | | |
| Amy Shaw ..........................31,83,85,88,273* | Jarret Tucker ...................................57,271* | | |
| Henry Baker ...........................................67 | Todd Gruhn ........................................70,73* | | |
| Jamie Doan ...........................................270 | | | |

| Public Schs..Principal | Grd | Prgm | Enr/#Cls | SN |
|---|---|---|---|---|
| Trenton Elem Sch<br>105 Witherspoon St, Trenton 75490<br>Mandi Alexander | PK-4 | T | 213<br>15 | 46% 903/989-2244<br>Fax 903/989-2415 |
| Trenton High Sch<br>2289 Farm Market 815, Trenton 75490<br>Jeremy Strickland \ **Stephen Foster** | 9-12 | AV | 185<br>15 | 38% 903/989-2242<br>Fax 903/989-5173 |
| Trenton Middle Sch<br>500 Ballentine St, Trenton 75490<br>Trent Hamilton | 5-8 | AT | 175 | 33% 903/989-2243<br>Fax 903/989-2668 |

## FAYETTE COUNTY

## FAYETTE PUBLIC SCHOOLS

### • Fayetteville Ind School Dist  PID: 01017666
618 N Rusk St, Fayetteville 78940

979/378-4242
Fax 979/378-4246

**Schools:** 1 \ **Teachers:** 20 \ **Students:** 260 \ **Special Ed Students:** 14 \ **LEP Students:** 11 \ **College-Bound:** 75% \ **Ethnic:** African American 2%, Hispanic 17%, Caucasian 81% \ **Exp:** $944 (High) \ **Poverty:** 14% \ **Title I:** $32,044 \ **Open-Close:** 08/17 - 05/18 \ **DTBP:** $37 (Low)

| | |
|---|---|
| Jeff Harvey ................................1,11,83 | Michelle Bertsch ....................................2 |
| Clint Jaeger ..........................................6* | Brynn Lopez ......................8,36,270,273 |
| Ray Brothers .....................16,31,73,295 | Lisa Dyer ..........................................57* |
| Lisa Simpson .........................................67 | |

| Public Schs..Principal | Grd | Prgm | Enr/#Cls | SN |
|---|---|---|---|---|
| Fayetteville Sch<br>618 N Rusk St, Fayetteville 78940<br>Brynn Lopez | PK-12 | V | 260<br>22 | 31% 979/378-4242 |

### • Flatonia Ind School Dist  PID: 01017692
400 E 4th St, Flatonia 78941

361/865-2941
Fax 361/865-2940

**Schools:** 3 \ **Teachers:** 56 \ **Students:** 580 \ **Special Ed Students:** 66 \ **LEP Students:** 26 \ **College-Bound:** 40% \ **Ethnic:** African American 4%, Hispanic 56%, Caucasian 40% \ **Exp:** $578 (High) \ **Poverty:** 19% \ **Title I:** $139,234 \ **Open-Close:** 08/19 - 05/27 \ **DTBP:** $427 (High)

| | |
|---|---|
| Dr Andy Reddock ......................................1 | Rodney Stryk ........................................2* |
| Rodney Stryk ....................................2,3,5 | Chris Freytag ......................................6* |
| Ashley Grahmann ....................................8* | Robin Branecky ......................................11* |
| Deanne Holloway .............................16,73* | Delia Moeller ...............................16,73* |
| Tim Rowell ...........................................67 | Marianna Herrera ..............................271* |

| Public Schs..Principal | Grd | Prgm | Enr/#Cls | SN |
|---|---|---|---|---|
| Flatonia Elem Sch<br>400 E 4th St, Flatonia 78941<br>Laura Kutac | PK-5 | T | 201<br>20 | 57% 361/865-2941<br>Fax 361/865-2945 |
| Flatonia High Sch<br>400 E 4th St, Flatonia 78941<br>Tandy Betak | 6-12 | ATV | 131<br>20 | 55% 361/865-2941<br>Fax 361/865-2944 |
| Whispering Hills Achieve Ctr<br>4110 FM 609, Flatonia 78941<br>Robin Branecky | Spec | | 13 | 77% 361/865-3083 |

### • La Grange Ind School Dist  PID: 01017721
560 N Monroe St, La Grange 78945

979/968-7000
Fax 979/968-8155

**Schools:** 3 \ **Teachers:** 142 \ **Students:** 2,350 \ **Special Ed Students:** 175 \ **LEP Students:** 243 \ **College-Bound:** 56% \ **Ethnic:** African American 10%, Hispanic 36%, Caucasian 54% \ **Exp:** $432 (High) \ **Poverty:** 19% \ **Title I:** $471,322 \ **Open-Close:** 08/13 - 05/27 \ **DTBP:** $268 (High) \ 

| | |
|---|---|
| Bill Wagner ...............................................1 | Sharon Muzny ....................................3,5 |
| Matt Kates ...............................................6 | Kari Willrich ...........................................7 |
| Tracy Head ...............................................8 | Nicole Ramirez ......................................11 |
| Stacy Eilers ...........................................15 | Dianna Fitzpatrick ................................19 |
| Kathryn Wyman ....................................58 | Gary Drab ..............................................67 |
| David Bennett ........................................73 | Stephanie Kates ....................................81 |

| Public Schs..Principal | Grd | Prgm | Enr/#Cls | SN |
|---|---|---|---|---|
| La Grange Elem Sch<br>192 S Vail St, La Grange 78945<br>Ray Morrow | PK-6 | | 1,439<br>21 | 979/968-4700<br>Fax 979/968-5694 |
| La Grange High Sch<br>820 S Vail St, La Grange 78945<br>John Pineda | 9-12 | TV | 608<br>40 | 46% 979/968-4800<br>Fax 979/968-6744 |
| La Grange Middle Sch<br>820 S Vail St, La Grange 78945<br>Sarah Otto | 7-8 | T | 303<br>23 | 56% 979/968-4747<br>Fax 979/968-6012 |

### • Round Top-Carmine Ind Sch Dist  PID: 01017771
378 Centennial St, Carmine 78932

979/278-3252
Fax 979/278-3063

**Schools:** 2 \ **Teachers:** 25 \ **Students:** 267 \ **Special Ed Students:** 25 \ **LEP Students:** 23 \ **College-Bound:** 92% \ **Ethnic:** African American 4%, Hispanic 26%, Caucasian 69% \ **Exp:** $321 (High) \ **Poverty:** 14% \ **Title I:** $30,447 \ **Open-Close:** 08/20 - 05/20 \ **DTBP:** $337 (High)

| | |
|---|---|
| Brandon Schovajsa ......................1,11,83 | Gwen Stork ...............................................2 |
| Rachelle Kuecker ......................6,10,88* | Kathryn Schoen ......................................9* |
| Andrea White ..................................57,271 | Calvin Krause ........................................67 |

| Public Schs..Principal | Grd | Prgm | Enr/#Cls | SN |
|---|---|---|---|---|
| Round Top Carmine Elem Sch<br>608 N Washington St, Round Top 78954<br>Kathryn Schoen | PK-6 | T | 151<br>14 | 50% 979/249-3200<br>Fax 979/249-4084 |
| Round Top Carmine High Sch<br>378 Centennial St, Carmine 78932<br>**Rachelle Kuecker** | 7-12 | | 116<br>20 | 30% 979/278-3252 |

---

- **Schulenburg Ind School Dist** PID: 01017800    979/743-3448
  521 Shorthorn Dr, Schulenburg 78956    Fax 979/743-4721

**Schools:** 2 \ **Teachers:** 65 \ **Students:** 700 \ **Special Ed Students:** 112 \
**LEP Students:** 62 \ **Ethnic:** Asian 1%, African American 15%, Hispanic 43%,
Caucasian 40% \ **Exp:** $376 (High) \ **Poverty:** 22% \ **Title I:** $225,687 \
**Open-Close:** 08/19 - 05/27 \ **DTBP:** $343 (High)

| | | | |
|---|---|---|---|
| Duane Limbaugh ...................................1 | Lynne Machac .........................................2 |
| Cindy Kalina .....................................7,85* | Kristi McBride ...........................8,11,16,286 |
| Brad Lux ...............................................27* | Misti Tucker ......................................31,36 |
| Deanna Moore ....................................58 | Craig Schultz .........................................67 |
| Charles Henke ....................................69* | Nick Sanchez ...............................73,295 |

| Public Schs..Principal | Grd | Prgm | Enr/#Cls | SN |
|---|---|---|---|---|
| Schulenburg Elem Sch<br>300 Bucek St, Schulenburg 78956<br>**Kristi McBride** | PK-5 | AT | 302<br>25 | 71% 979/743-4221<br>Fax 979/743-4864 |
| Schulenburg High Sch<br>503 College St, Schulenburg 78956<br>Callene Zapalac \ Charles Henke | 6-12 | ATV | 388<br>25 | 46% 979/743-3605<br>Fax 979/743-2428 |

# FAYETTE CATHOLIC SCHOOLS

- **Diocese of Austin Ed Office** PID: 01420568
  Listing includes only schools located in this county. See District Index for
  location of Diocesan Offices.

| Catholic Schs..Principal | Grd | Prgm | Enr/#Cls | SN |
|---|---|---|---|---|
| Sacred Heart Catholic Sch<br>545 E Pearl St, La Grange 78945<br>Ladonna Voelkel | PK-6 | | 139<br>20 | 979/968-3223<br>Fax 979/968-3215 |
| St Rose of Lima Sch<br>405 Black St, Schulenburg 78956<br>Roseanne Gallia | PK-8 | | 166<br>10 | 979/743-3080<br>Fax 979/743-4228 |

- **Diocese of Victoria Ed Office** PID: 02181727
  Listing includes only schools located in this county. See District Index for
  location of Diocesan Offices.

---

- **Roby Cons Ind School Dist** PID: 01017886    325/776-2222
  141 S College St, Roby 79543    Fax 325/267-2622

**Schools:** 2 \ **Teachers:** 29 \ **Students:** 277 \ **Special Ed Students:** 26
\ **LEP Students:** 14 \ **College-Bound:** 97% \ **Ethnic:** African American
2%, Hispanic 28%, Caucasian 70% \ **Exp:** $742 (High) \ **Poverty:** 17% \
**Title I:** $52,191 \ **Open-Close:** 08/21 - 05/25 \ **DTBP:** $420 (High)

| | | | |
|---|---|---|---|
| Keith Cook ........................................1,11 | Kandra Lakey .........................................2 |
| Christi Adkinson ..................................4 | Eli Sepeda ...............................................5 |
| Angel Pantoja ......................................6 | Jason Carter ................8,69,73,285,296,298* |
| Tempie West ......................................16* | Lisa Stuart ..........................................52* |
| Linda De La Santos ........................57,271 | Terry Orr .............................................58* |
| Jeff Posey ...........................................67 | Chrystal Loomis ................83,85,88,270,273 |

| Public Schs..Principal | Grd | Prgm | Enr/#Cls | SN |
|---|---|---|---|---|
| Roby Elem Sch<br>141 S College St, Roby 79543<br>Misty McWilliams | PK-8 | T | 213<br>17 | 45% 325/776-2222 |
| Roby High Sch<br>141 S College St, Roby 79543<br>Jason Carter | 9-12 | T | 64 | 41% 325/776-2223 |

- **Rotan Ind School Dist** PID: 01017915    325/735-2332
  102 N McKinley Ave, Rotan 79546    Fax 325/735-2686

**Schools:** 2 \ **Teachers:** 25 \ **Students:** 240 \ **Special Ed Students:** 27
\ **LEP Students:** 3 \ **College-Bound:** 90% \ **Ethnic:** African American
5%, Hispanic 50%, Caucasian 45% \ **Exp:** $741 (High) \ **Poverty:** 20% \
**Title I:** $73,328 \ **Special Education:** $19,000 \ **Open-Close:** 08/20 - 05/25 \
**DTBP:** $350 (High) \ **f**

| | | | |
|---|---|---|---|
| Greg Decker .......................................1,84 | Shelby Grooban .......................................2 |
| Jody Helms ...........................................9* | Scott Allen ...............................................9 |
| Britt Sipe ................................31,36,67,83 | Dera Gonzalez .......................................57 |
| Randy Hodges ....................................73 | |

| Public Schs..Principal | Grd | Prgm | Enr/#Cls | SN |
|---|---|---|---|---|
| Rotan Elem Sch<br>102 N McKinley Ave, Rotan 79546<br>Jody Helms | PK-5 | T | 118<br>15 | 72% 325/735-3182 |
| Rotan High Sch<br>102 N McKinley Ave, Rotan 79546<br>Bradley Hayhurst | 6-12 | TV | 122<br>19 | 61% 325/735-3041 |

---

| | | | | |
|---|---|---|---|---|
| **1** Superintendent | **8** Curric/Instruct K-12 | **19** Chief Financial Officer | **29** Family/Consumer Science | **39** Social Studies K-12 |
| **2** Bus/Finance/Purchasing | **9** Curric/Instruct Elem | **20** Art K-12 | **30** Adult Education | **40** Social Studies Elem |
| **3** Buildings And Grounds | **10** Curric/Instruct Sec | **21** Art Elem | **31** Career/Sch-to-Work K-12 | **41** Social Studies Sec |
| **4** Food Service | **11** Federal Program | **22** Art Sec | **32** Career/Sch-to-Work Elem | **42** Science K-12 |
| **5** Transportation | **12** Title I | **23** Music K-12 | **33** Career/Sch-to-Work Sec | **43** Science Elem |
| **6** Athletic | **13** Title V | **24** Music Elem | **34** Early Childhood Ed | **44** Science Sec |
| **7** Health Services | **14** Asst Superintendent | **25** Music Sec | **35** Health/Phys Education | **45** Math K-12 |
| | **15** Instructional Media Svcs | **26** Business Education | **36** Guidance Services K-12 | **46** Math Elem |
| | **16** Instructional Media Svcs | **27** Career & Tech Ed | **37** Guidance Services Elem | **47** Math Sec |
| | **17** Chief Operations Officer | **28** Technology Education | **38** Guidance Services Sec | **48** English/Lang Arts K-12 |
| | **18** Chief Academic Officer | | | |

| | | | |
|---|---|---|---|
| **49** English/Lang Arts Elem | **59** Special Education Elem | **69** Academic Assessment |
| **50** English/Lang Arts Sec | **60** Special Education Sec | **70** Research/Development |
| **51** Reading K-12 | **61** Foreign/World Lang K-12 | **71** Public Information |
| **52** Reading Elem | **62** Foreign/World Lang Elem | **72** Summer School |
| **53** Reading Sec | **63** Foreign/World Lang Sec | **73** Instructional Tech |
| **54** Remedial Reading K-12 | **64** Religious Education K-12 | **74** Inservice Training |
| **55** Remedial Reading Elem | **65** Religious Education Elem | **75** Marketing/Distributive |
| **56** Remedial Reading Sec | **66** Religious Education Sec | **76** Info Systems |
| **57** Bilingual/ELL | **67** School Board President | **77** Psychological Assess |
| **58** Special Education K-12 | **68** Teacher Personnel | **78** Affirmative Action |

## FLOYD COUNTY

### FLOYD PUBLIC SCHOOLS

● **Floydada Ind School Dist** PID: 01017977 806/983-3498
226 W California St, Floydada 79235 Fax 806/983-5739

**Schools:** 2 \ **Teachers:** 65 \ **Students:** 700 \ **Special Ed Students:** 66 \ **LEP Students:** 62 \ **College-Bound:** 70% \ **Ethnic:** African American 4%, Hispanic 82%, Caucasian 15% \ **Exp:** $1,273 (High) \ **Poverty:** 30% \ **Title I:** $318,819 \ **Special Education:** $170,000 \ **Open-Close:** 08/17 - 05/20 \ **DTBP:** $335 (High)

| | | | |
|---|---|---|---|
| Dr Gilbert Trevino | 1 | Alicia Bice | 2 |
| Todd Bandy | 6* | Monica Smith | 8 |
| Rex Holcombe | 11,57,73,81,84,271,295,296 | Alejandra Ramirez | 27,75* |
| Jim Hobbs | 34,58 | Jennifer Gonzalez | 37,83,88,752* |
| Kristie Rehkopf | 38,69,288* | Lyle Miller | 67 |
| Kelly Pachiano | 71 | Chrisntina Schesshir | 79 |
| Michael King | 286 | | |

| Public Schs..Principal | Grd | Prgm | Enr/#Cls | SN | |
|---|---|---|---|---|---|
| A B Duncan Elem Sch<br>1011 S 8th St, Floydada 79235<br>**Monica Smith** | PK-6 | T | 381<br>14 | 83% | 806/983-5332<br>Fax 806/983-4950 |
| Floydada High Sch<br>1 Whirlwind Aly, Floydada 79235<br>Wayne Morren | 7-12 | TV | 154<br>32 | 72% | 806/983-2340<br>Fax 806/983-5843 |

● **Lockney Independent Sch Dist** PID: 01018024 806/652-2104
601 W Poplar St, Lockney 79241 Fax 806/652-4920

**Schools:** 3 \ **Teachers:** 45 \ **Students:** 450 \ **Special Ed Students:** 47 \ **LEP Students:** 22 \ **College-Bound:** 95% \ **Ethnic:** African American 1%, Hispanic 78%, Caucasian 21% \ **Exp:** $520 (High) \ **Poverty:** 31% \ **Title I:** $201,838 \ **Open-Close:** 08/24 - 05/21

| | | | |
|---|---|---|---|
| Jim Baum | 1 | Kenton Hooten | 3,5 |
| Calixta Sustaita | 4 | Stacy Ward | 6 |
| Britney Dunniven | 7 | Carol Lane | 8,69,74 |
| Naiomo Jones | 11 | Darryn Perryman | 27 |
| Mike Lass | 67 | Chris Pritchard | 73,295 |
| Mindy Petty | 83,85* | Shana Hallmark | 88,294* |
| Jeffrey Hallmark | 270* | Robin Sherman | 280* |
| Sandra Cummings | 286* | | |

| Public Schs..Principal | Grd | Prgm | Enr/#Cls | SN | |
|---|---|---|---|---|---|
| Lockney Elem Sch<br>310 SW 8th St, Lockney 79241<br>**Micheal Michaleson** | PK-5 | T | 210<br>16 | 82% | 806/652-3321<br>Fax 806/652-2956<br>f |
| Lockney High Sch<br>410 SW 4th St, Lockney 79241<br>**Michelle Southard** | 9-12 | TV | 124<br>25 | 81% | 806/652-3325<br>Fax 806/652-4945 |
| Lockney Junior High Sch<br>406 W Willow St, Lockney 79241<br>Monte Setliff | 6-8 | T | 116<br>12 | 75% | 806/652-2236 |

## FOARD COUNTY

### FOARD PUBLIC SCHOOLS

● **Crowell Ind School Dist** PID: 01018086 940/684-1403
400 E Logan Street, Crowell 79227 Fax 940/684-1616

**Schools:** 2 \ **Teachers:** 21 \ **Students:** 230 \ **Special Ed Students:** 37 \ **LEP Students:** 3 \ **College-Bound:** 94% \ **Ethnic:** Asian 2%, African American 3%, Hispanic 43%, Caucasian 53% \ **Exp:** $920 (High) \ **Poverty:** 27% \ **Title I:** $73,827 \ **Open-Close:** 08/19 - 05/27 \ **DTBP:** $328 (High) \ f t

| | | | |
|---|---|---|---|
| **Dr Donald Rhodes** | 1 | Nora Urquizo | 4* |
| Chuck Chatfield | 5 | Megan Clifton | 16* |
| Stephanie Bearden | 58* | Joe Haynie | 67 |

| Public Schs..Principal | Grd | Prgm | Enr/#Cls | SN | |
|---|---|---|---|---|---|
| Crowell Elem Sch<br>400 E Logan St, Crowell 79227<br>Christie Flinn | PK-8 | | 119<br>15 | | 940/684-1878 |
| Crowell High Sch<br>400 E Logan Street, Crowell 79227<br>Nathan Hayes | 9-12 | TV | 98<br>15 | 70% | 940/684-1331<br>Fax 940/684-1978 |

## FORT BEND COUNTY

### FORT BEND PUBLIC SCHOOLS

● **Ft Bend Ind School Dist** PID: 01018115 281/634-1000
16431 Lexington Blvd, Sugar Land 77479 Fax 281/634-1700

**Schools:** 82 \ **Teachers:** 4,662 \ **Students:** 79,076 \ **Special Ed Students:** 6,702 \ **LEP Students:** 11,170 \ **College-Bound:** 94% \ **Ethnic:** Asian 27%, African American 28%, Hispanic 27%, Caucasian 17% \ **Exp:** $241 (Med) \ **Poverty:** 10% \ **Title I:** $16,168,727 \ **Special Education:** $10,817,000 \ **Open-Close:** 08/17 - 05/26 \ **DTBP:** $191 (High) \ t

| | | | |
|---|---|---|---|
| Dr Charles Dupre | 1 | Brenda Essberg | 2 |
| Bryan Gwinn | 2,19 | David Moore | 3 |
| Oscar Perez | 3,17 | Elizabeth Strodtbeck | 4 |
| Gustavo Rodriguez | 5 | Micheal Bradsfield | 5 |
| Dena Scott | 6 | Maria Johnson | 7 |
| Diana Sayavedra | 8,31,69,79 | Kwabera Meisah | 9,15 |
| Brett Lemley | 10,15 | Susan Voradakis | 10,69 |
| Deirdre Holloway | 11 | Dr Anthony Indelicato | 15,70,751 |
| Carmela Levy-David | 15,34 | Joe Rodriguez | 15 |
| Dr Xochitl Rodriguez | 15,79 | Tamiko Brown | 16 |
| Beth Martinez | 18 | James Drew | 20 |
| Meredith Watassek | 27* | Steven Shiels | 36,79,90,270,271 |
| Kelly Fox | 38* | Angela Tran | 57 |
| Dr Deena Hill | 58 | Jason Burdine | 67 |
| Gwyn Touchet | 68 | Kermit Spears | 68 |
| Kim Davis | 70 | Long Pham | 71,97 |
| Veronica Sopher | 71 | Mitzi Patin | 73,76 |

| | | | | School Programs | Social Media |
|---|---|---|---|---|---|
| 79 Student Personnel | 91 Safety/Security | 275 Response To Intervention | 298 Grant Writer/Ptnrships | **A** = Alternative Program | |
| 80 Driver Ed/Safety | 92 Magnet School | 277 Remedial Math K-12 | 750 Chief Innovation Officer | **G** = Adult Classes | f = Facebook |
| 81 Gifted/Talented | 93 Parental Involvement | 280 Literacy Coach | 751 Chief of Staff | **M** = Magnet Program | |
| 82 Video Services | 95 Tech Prep Program | 285 STEM | 752 Social Emotional Learning | **T** = Title I Schoolwide | t = Twitter |
| 83 Substance Abuse Prev | 97 Chief Infomation Officer | 286 Digital Learning | | **V** = Career & Tech Ed Programs | |
| 84 Erate | 98 Chief Technology Officer | 288 Common Core Standards | Other School Types | | |
| 85 AIDS Education | 270 Character Education | 294 Accountability | Ⓐ = Alternative School | | |
| 88 Alternative/At Risk | 271 Migrant Education | 295 Network System | Ⓒ = Charter School | New Schools are shaded | |
| 89 Multi-Cultural Curriculum | 273 Teacher Mentor | 296 Title II Programs | Ⓜ = Magnet School | New Superintendents and Principals are bold | |
| 90 Social Work | 274 Before/After Sch | 297 Webmaster | Ⓨ = Year-Round School | Personnel with email addresses are underscored | |

# Fort Bend County

**Market Data Retrieval**

Crystal Wilson ............ 81  
David Rider ............ 91  
Cathy Collins ............ 274*  
Lynette Meyer ............ 286  
Amanda Salazar ............ 298  
Michael Ewing ............ 88  
Pamela Shaw ............ 93  
Lisa Coston ............ 280  
Audra Ude ............ 294

| Public Schs..Principal | Grd | Prgm | Enr/#Cls | SN | |
|---|---|---|---|---|---|
| Anne Sullivan Elem Sch<br>17828 Winding Waters Ln, Sugar Land 77479<br>**Donna Whisonant** | PK-5 | | 1,310 | 6% | 281/327-2860<br>Fax 281/327-2861 |
| Arizona Fleming Elem Sch<br>14850 Bissonnet St, Houston 77083<br>Porsha Dudley | PK-5 | T | 631 | 78% | 281/634-4600<br>Fax 281/634-4615 |
| Armstrong Elem Sch<br>3440 Independence Blvd, Missouri City 77459<br>Nancy Sanchez | PK-5 | T | 492 | 91% | 281/634-9410<br>Fax 281/327-9409 |
| Austin Parkway Elem Sch<br>4400 Austin Pkwy, Sugar Land 77479<br>Audrey Macklin | K-5 | | 688<br>29 | 21% | 281/634-4001<br>Fax 281/634-4014 |
| Barbara Jordan Elem Sch<br>17800 W Oaks Village Dr, Richmond 77407<br>**Kimberly Charles** | PK-5 | T | 438 | 63% | 281/634-2800<br>Fax 281/634-2801 |
| Barrington Place Elem Sch<br>2100 Squire Dobbins Dr, Sugar Land 77478<br>Ruth Riha | PK-5 | T | 512<br>38 | 49% | 281/634-4040<br>Fax 281/634-4057 |
| Billy Baines Middle Sch<br>9000 Sienna Ranch Rd, Missouri City 77459<br>**Elizabeth Williams** | 6-8 | V | 1,212 | 29% | 281/634-6870<br>Fax 281/634-6880 |
| Blue Ridge Elem Sch<br>6241 McHard Rd, Houston 77053<br>**Sonya Evans-Williams** | PK-5 | T | 219<br>43 | 87% | 281/634-4520<br>Fax 281/634-4533 |
| Brazos Bend Elem Sch<br>621 Cunningham Creek Blvd, Sugar Land 77479<br>Stephanie Viado | PK-5 | T | 589<br>47 | 33% | 281/634-5180<br>Fax 281/327-5182 |
| Briargate Elem Sch<br>15817 Blueridge Rd, Missouri City 77489<br>Dr Latoya Garrett | PK-5 | T | 353<br>36 | 93% | 281/634-4560<br>Fax 281/634-4576 |
| Clements High Sch<br>4200 Elkins Rd, Sugar Land 77479<br>David Yaffie | 9-12 | V | 2,548<br>110 | 13% | 281/634-2150<br>Fax 281/634-2168 |
| Colony Bend Elem Sch<br>2720 Planters St, Sugar Land 77479<br>**Stacy Brown** | PK-5 | | 538<br>25 | 32% | 281/634-4080<br>Fax 281/634-4092 |
| Colony Meadows Elem Sch<br>4510 Sweetwater Blvd, Sugar Land 77479<br>Melissa Bolding | PK-5 | | 667 | 12% | 281/634-4120<br>Fax 281/634-4136 |
| Commonwealth Elem Sch<br>4909 Commonwealth Blvd, Sugar Land 77479<br>Latecha Bogle | PK-5 | | 876<br>39 | 6% | 281/634-5120<br>Fax 281/634-5140 |
| Cornerstone Elem Sch<br>1800 Chatham Ave, Sugar Land 77479<br>Margaret Murphy | PK-5 | | 981<br>33 | 5% | 281/634-6400<br>Fax 281/327-6400 |
| David Crockett Middle Sch<br>19001 Beechnut St, Richmond 77407<br>Dr Tonya Curtis | 6-8 | T | 958 | 61% | 281/634-6380<br>Fax 281/327-6380 |
| Donald Leonetti Elem Sch<br>1757 Waters Lake Blvd, Missouri City 77459<br>Joy Schwinger | PK-5 | | 541 | 12% | 281/327-3190<br>Fax 281/327-3191 |
| Dulles Elem Sch<br>630 Dulles Ave, Sugar Land 77478<br>Kyella Griffin | PK-5 | T | 601<br>27 | 54% | 281/634-5830<br>Fax 281/634-5843 |
| Dulles High Sch<br>550 Dulles Ave, Sugar Land 77478<br>Melissa King-Knowles | 9-12 | V | 2,558<br>110 | 36% | 281/634-5600<br>Fax 281/634-5634 |
| Dulles Middle Sch<br>500 Dulles Ave, Sugar Land 77478<br>Dee Knox | 6-8 | TV | 1,449<br>80 | 49% | 281/634-5750<br>Fax 281/634-5781 |
| E A Jones Elem Sch<br>302 Martin Ln, Missouri City 77489<br>Carlo Leiva | PK-5 | T | 601<br>30 | 87% | 281/634-4960<br>Fax 281/634-4974 |
| Edgar Glover Elem Sch<br>1510 Columbia Blue Dr, Missouri City 77489<br>Nikki Roberts | PK-5 | T | 373<br>42 | 81% | 281/634-4920<br>Fax 281/634-4934 |
| Elkins High Sch<br>7007 Knights Ct, Missouri City 77459<br>**Cynthia Ward** | 9-12 | V | 2,389 | 28% | 281/634-2600<br>Fax 281/634-2674 |
| Ⓐ Ferndell Henry Center for Lrng<br>7447 FM 521 Rd, Rosharon 77583<br>Trevor Lemon | 6-12 | T | 200 | 66% | 281/327-6000<br>Fax 281/327-6001 |
| First Colony Middle Sch<br>3225 Austin Pkwy, Sugar Land 77479<br>Courtney Muceus | 6-8 | V | 663<br>85 | 25% | 281/634-3240<br>Fax 281/634-3267 |
| Fort Settlement Middle Sch<br>5440 Elkins Rd, Sugar Land 77479<br>Michael Hejducek | 6-8 | | 1,540<br>70 | 8% | 281/634-6440<br>Fax 281/634-6456 |
| George Bush High Sch<br>6707 FM 1464 Rd, Richmond 77407<br>Felicia James | 9-12 | TV | 2,482 | 65% | 281/634-6060<br>Fax 281/634-6066 |
| Heritage Rose Elem Sch<br>636 Glendale Lakes Dr, Rosharon 77583<br>Gabriella Garza | PK-5 | T | 1,008 | 78% | 281/327-5400<br>Fax 281/327-5401 |
| Highlands Elem Sch<br>2022 Colonist Park Dr, Sugar Land 77478<br>Angela Dow | PK-5 | | 631<br>48 | 30% | 281/634-4160<br>Fax 281/634-4176 |
| Ⓦ Hightower High Sch<br>3333 Hurricane Ln, Missouri City 77459<br>John Montelongo | 9-12 | TV | 2,024<br>75 | 57% | 281/634-5240<br>Fax 281/634-5333 |
| Hodges Bend Middle Sch<br>16510 Bissonnet St, Houston 77083<br>Rachel Cortez | 6-8 | TV | 1,075<br>70 | 77% | 281/634-3000<br>Fax 281/634-3028 |
| Hunters Glen Elem Sch<br>695 Independence Blvd, Missouri City 77489<br>**Lavanta Williams** | PK-5 | T | 431<br>50 | 83% | 281/634-4640<br>Fax 281/634-4656 |
| I H Kempner High Sch<br>14777 Voss Rd, Sugar Land 77498<br>Lori Oliver | 9-12 | TV | 2,095<br>120 | 52% | 281/634-2300<br>Fax 281/634-2378 |
| James Bowie Middle Sch<br>700 Plantation Dr, Richmond 77406<br>Brian Shillingburg | 6-8 | | 1,350 | 32% | 281/327-6200<br>Fax 281/327-6201 |
| James Neill Elem Sch<br>3830 Harvest Corner Dr, Richmond 77406<br>Lori Hoeffken | PK-5 | | 689 | 30% | 281/327-3760<br>Fax 281/327-3761 |
| James Patterson Elem Sch<br>18702 Beechnut St, Richmond 77407<br>**Angela Wallace** | PK-5 | T | 719 | 53% | 281/327-4260<br>Fax 281/327-4261 |
| James Reese Career Tech Center<br>12300 University Blvd, Sugar Land 77479<br>Kelley Kirila | Voc | | 500 | | 281/327-7300 |
| Juan Seguin Elem Sch<br>7817 Grand Mission Blvd, Richmond 77407<br>Fidel Wells | PK-5 | T | 416 | 40% | 281/634-9850<br>Fax 281/327-7029 |
| Lake Olympia Middle Sch<br>3100 Lake Olympia Pkwy, Missouri City 77459<br>Deidra Lyons-Lewis | 6-8 | TV | 1,253 | 66% | 281/634-3520<br>Fax 281/634-3549 |
| Lakeview Elem Sch<br>314 Lakeview Dr, Sugar Land 77498<br>Alena McClanahan | PK-5 | T | 448<br>44 | 53% | 281/634-4200<br>Fax 281/634-4214 |
| Lantern Lane Elem Sch<br>3323 Mission Valley Dr, Missouri City 77459<br>**Justin Kowrach** | PK-5 | T | 409<br>35 | 77% | 281/634-4680<br>Fax 281/634-4694 |
| Lexington Creek Elem Sch<br>2335 Dulles Ave, Missouri City 77459<br>Christina Hopkins | PK-5 | | 482<br>45 | 36% | 281/634-5000<br>Fax 281/634-5014 |

| | | | | | | | |
|---|---|---|---|---|---|---|---|
| 1 Superintendent | 8 Curric/Instruct K-12 | 19 Chief Financial Officer | 29 Family/Consumer Science | 39 Social Studies K-12 | 49 English/Lang Arts Elem | 59 Special Education Elem | 69 Academic Assessment |
| 2 Bus/Finance/Purchasing | 9 Curric/Instruct Elem | 20 Art K-12 | 30 Adult Education | 40 Social Studies Elem | 50 English/Lang Arts Sec | 60 Special Education Sec | 70 Research/Development |
| 3 Buildings And Grounds | 10 Curric/Instruct Sec | 21 Art Elem | 31 Career/Sch-to-Work K-12 | 41 Social Studies Sec | 51 Reading K-12 | 61 Foreign/World Lang K-12 | 71 Public Information |
| 4 Food Service | 11 Federal Program | 22 Art Sec | 32 Career/Sch-to-Work Elem | 42 Science K-12 | 52 Reading Elem | 62 Foreign/World Lang Elem | 72 Summer School |
| 5 Transportation | 12 Title I | 23 Music K-12 | 33 Career/Sch-to-Work Sec | 43 Science Elem | 53 Reading Sec | 63 Foreign/World Lang Sec | 73 Instructional Tech |
| 6 Athletic | 13 Title V | 24 Music Elem | 34 Early Childhood Ed | 44 Science Sec | 54 Remedial Reading K-12 | 64 Religious Education K-12 | 74 Inservice Training |
| 7 Health Services | 14 Title V | 25 Music Sec | 35 Health/Phys Education | 45 Math K-12 | 55 Remedial Reading Elem | 65 Religious Education Elem | 75 Marketing/Distributive |
| | 15 Asst Superintendent | 26 Business Education | 36 Guidance Services K-12 | 46 Math Elem | 56 Remedial Reading Sec | 66 Religious Education Sec | 76 Info Systems |
| | 16 Instructional Media Svcs | 27 Career & Tech Ed | 37 Guidance Services Elem | 47 Math Sec | 57 Bilingual/ELL | 67 School Board President | 77 Psychological Assess |
| | 17 Chief Operations Officer | 28 Technology Education | 38 Guidance Services Sec | 48 English/Lang Arts K-12 | 58 Special Education K-12 | 68 Teacher Personnel | 78 Affirmative Action |
| | 18 Chief Academic Officer | | | | | | |

**TX—154**

| School | Grades | Prog | Students/Teachers | % | Phone/Fax |
|---|---|---|---|---|---|
| Lula Belle Goodman Elem Sch<br>1100 W Sycamore St, Fresno 77545<br>Dr Felicia Bolden | PK-5 | T | 722<br>40 | 80% | 281/634-5985<br>Fax 281/634-6000 |
| Macario Garcia Middle Sch<br>18550 Old Richmond Rd, Sugar Land 77498<br>Dr Cory Collins | 6-8 | TV | 1,264<br>85 | 39% | 281/634-3160<br>Fax 281/634-3166 |
| Madden Elem Sch<br>17727 Abermore Ln, Richmond 77407<br>Kristi Durham | PK-5 | | 863 | 16% | 281/327-2740<br>Fax 281/327-2742 |
| Malala Yousafzai Elem Sch<br>11770 W Aliana Trace Dr, Richmond 77407<br>Lisa Langston | K-6 | | 401 | | 281/327-5700 |
| Mary Austin Holley Elem Sch<br>16655 Bissonnet St, Houston 77083<br>Laureen Sanford | PK-5 | T | 808<br>46 | 78% | 281/634-3850<br>Fax 281/634-3856 |
| McAuliffe Middle Sch<br>16650 S Post Oak Rd, Houston 77053<br>Andre Roberson | 6-8 | TV | 630<br>85 | 91% | 281/634-3360<br>Fax 281/634-3393 |
| Meadows Elem Sch<br>12037 Pender Ln, Meadows Place 77477<br>Courtney Dickey | K-5 | T | 361<br>20 | 54% | 281/634-4720<br>Fax 281/634-4734 |
| Mission Bend Elem Sch<br>16200 Beechnut St, Houston 77083<br>Jill Gumbs | PK-5 | T | 329<br>46 | 77% | 281/634-4240<br>Fax 281/634-4250 |
| Mission Glen Elem Sch<br>16053 Mission Glen Dr, Houston 77083<br>**Jacob Nichols** | PK-5 | T | 475<br>30 | 75% | 281/634-4280<br>Fax 281/634-4296 |
| Mission West Elem Sch<br>7325 Clodine Reddick Rd, Houston 77083<br>Jorge Pena | PK-5 | T | 646<br>40 | 78% | 281/634-4320<br>Fax 281/634-4334 |
| Missouri City Middle Sch<br>202 Martin Ln, Missouri City 77489<br>Tasha Hamilton \ Tania Campbell \ **Jeannie Miles-Essone** | 6-8 | TV | 1,041<br>72 | 85% | 281/634-3440<br>Fax 281/634-3473 |
| Oakland Elem Sch<br>4455 Waterside Estates Dr D, Richmond 77406<br>Nancy Hummel | PK-5 | | 710 | 27% | 281/634-3730<br>Fax 281/634-3738 |
| Oyster Creek Elem Sch<br>16425 Mellow Oaks Ln, Sugar Land 77498<br>Deanna Olson | K-5 | T | 976<br>42 | 42% | 281/634-5910<br>Fax 281/634-5925<br>🅣 |
| Palmer Elem Sch<br>4208 Crow Valley Dr, Missouri City 77459<br>Kellie Clay | PK-5 | T | 498<br>40 | 43% | 281/634-4760<br>Fax 281/634-4773 |
| Pecan Grove Elem Sch<br>3330 Old South Dr, Richmond 77406<br>Dr Trenae Hill | PK-5 | T | 735<br>50 | 24% | 281/634-4800<br>Fax 281/634-4814 |
| Ⓐ Progressive High Sch<br>1555 Independence Blvd, Missouri City 77489<br>Lisa Jones | 10-12 | | 150<br>6 | | 281/634-2900<br>Fax 281/634-2913 |
| Quail Valley Elem Sch<br>3500 Quail Village Dr, Missouri City 77459<br>Carla Patton | PK-5 | T | 410<br>22 | 49% | 281/634-5040<br>Fax 281/634-5054 |
| Quail Valley Middle Sch<br>3019 FM 1092 Rd, Missouri City 77459<br>Jeffrey Post | 6-8 | V | 1,101<br>55 | 34% | 281/634-3600<br>Fax 281/634-3632 |
| Ridge Point High Sch<br>500 Waters Lake Blvd, Missouri City 77459<br>Leonard Brogan | 9-12 | V | 2,799 | 22% | 281/327-5200<br>Fax 281/327-5201 |
| Ridgegate Elem Sch<br>6015 W Ridgecreek Dr, Houston 77053<br>Marta Rivas | PK-5 | T | 533<br>55 | 92% | 281/634-4840<br>Fax 281/634-4855 |
| Ridgemont Early Literacy Ctr<br>5353 Ridge Creek Cir, Houston 77053<br>Venitra Senegal | PK-1 | | 498 | | 281/634-9810 |
| Ridgemont Elem Sch<br>4910 Raven Ridge Dr, Houston 77053<br>Framy Diaz | 2-5 | T | 335<br>43 | 95% | 281/634-4880<br>Fax 281/634-4896 |
| Rita Drabek Elem Sch<br>11325 Lake Woodbridge Dr, Sugar Land 77498<br>Wendy Nunez | PK-5 | | 755 | 40% | 281/634-6570<br>Fax 281/634-6572 |
| Ronald Thornton Middle Sch<br>1909 Waters Lake Blvd, Missouri City 77459<br>Jeanna Sniffin | 6-8 | | 1,108 | 25% | 281/327-3870<br>Fax 281/327-3871 |
| Rosa Parks Elem Sch<br>19101 Chimney Rock Rd, Fresno 77545<br>Amber Kent | PK-5 | T | 546 | 69% | 281/634-6390<br>Fax 281/327-6390 |
| Sartartia Middle Sch<br>8125 Homeward Way, Sugar Land 77479<br>Cholly Oglesby | 6-8 | | 1,326<br>50 | 16% | 281/634-6310<br>Fax 281/634-6373 |
| Scanlan Oaks Elem Sch<br>9000 Camp Sienna Trl, Missouri City 77459<br>Lori Craig | PK-5 | | 826<br>44 | 4% | 281/634-3950<br>Fax 281/634-3915 |
| Schiff Elem Sch<br>7400 Discovery Ln, Missouri City 77459<br>Lucretia Deflora | PK-5 | | 710 | 21% | 281/634-9450<br>Fax 281/327-9449<br>🅣 |
| Settlers Way Elem Sch<br>3015 Settlers Way Blvd, Sugar Land 77479<br>Danny Emery | PK-5 | | 664<br>26 | 28% | 281/634-4360<br>Fax 281/634-4376<br>🅣 |
| Sienna Crossing Elem Sch<br>10011 Steep Bank Trce, Missouri City 77459<br>Rachel Rosier | PK-5 | | 925<br>40 | 10% | 281/634-3680<br>Fax 281/634-3799 |
| Stephen F Austin High Sch<br>3434 Pheasant Creek Dr, Sugar Land 77498<br>Dr Rizvan Quadri | 9-12 | V | 2,200 | 30% | 281/634-2000<br>Fax 281/634-2074 |
| Sugar Land Middle Sch<br>321 7th St, Sugar Land 77498<br>Keith Fickel | 6-8 | TV | 1,221<br>88 | 54% | 281/634-3080<br>Fax 281/327-6599 |
| Sugar Mill Elem Sch<br>13707 Jess Pirtle Blvd, Sugar Land 77498<br>Jaimie Geis | PK-5 | T | 474<br>32 | 46% | 281/634-4440<br>Fax 281/634-4459<br>🅣 |
| Technical Education Center<br>540 Dulles Ave, Sugar Land 77478<br>Kennith Kendziora | Voc | | 500<br>10 | | 281/634-5671<br>Fax 281/634-5700 |
| Thurgood Marshall High Sch<br>1220 Buffalo Run, Missouri City 77489<br>Dr Ogechi Uwaga-Sanders | 9-12 | TV | 1,246 | 77% | 281/634-6630<br>Fax 281/634-6650 |
| Townewest Elem Sch<br>13927 Old Richmond Rd, Sugar Land 77498<br>Erika Edmond | PK-5 | T | 627<br>37 | 80% | 281/634-4480<br>Fax 281/634-4494 |
| Walker Station Elem Sch<br>6200 Homeward Way, Sugar Land 77479<br>Kate Kargbo | PK-5 | | 784<br>59 | 13% | 281/634-4400<br>Fax 281/634-4413 |
| Walter Moses Burton Elem Sch<br>1625 Hunter Green Ln, Fresno 77545<br>Lakisha Anthony | PK-5 | T | 377<br>50 | 70% | 281/634-5080<br>Fax 281/634-5094 |
| William B Travis High Sch<br>11111 Harlem Rd, Richmond 77406<br>Sarah LaBerge | 9-12 | V | 2,631 | 29% | 281/634-7000<br>Fax 281/634-7010 |
| Willowridge High Sch<br>16301 Chimney Rock Rd, Houston 77053<br>Terence Hayden | 9-12 | TV | 1,267<br>105 | 82% | 281/634-2450<br>Fax 281/634-2513 |

- **Katy Ind School Dist** PID: 01026227    281/396-6000
  6301 S Stadium Ln, Katy 77494    Fax 281/644-1849

**Schools:** 72 \ **Teachers:** 5,274 \ **Students:** 84,299 \
**Special Ed Students:** 8,635 \ **LEP Students:** 12,321 \ **College-Bound:** 75%
\ **Ethnic:** Asian 16%, African American 12%, Hispanic 37%, Caucasian
35% \ **Exp:** $331 (High) \ **Poverty:** 10% \ **Title I:** $11,305,410 \
**Special Education:** $9,238,000 \ **Bilingual Education:** $54,000 \
**Open-Close:** 08/19 - 05/21 \ **DTBP:** $179 (High) \ 🅕 🅣

Dr Ken Gregorski ........................ 1   Chris Smith ........................... 2,19

---

| Public Schs..Principal | Grd | Prgm | Enr/#Cls | SN | |
|---|---|---|---|---|---|
| Amy Campbell Elem Sch<br>3701 Cross Creek Bnd, Fulshear 77441<br>Jaime Shipley | PK-5 | | 756 | 11% | 281/234-4500<br>Fax 281/644-1890 |
| Bear Creek Elem Sch<br>4815 Hickory Downs Dr, Houston 77084<br>Stephanie McElroy | PK-5 | T | 599<br>36 | 71% | 281/237-5600<br>Fax 281/644-1500 |
| Beckendorff Junior High Sch<br>8200 S Fry Rd, Katy 77494<br>Paul Moussavi | 6-8 | | 1,699 | 10% | 281/237-8800<br>Fax 281/644-1635 |
| Bonnie Holland Elem Sch<br>23720 Seven Meadows Pkwy, Katy 77494<br>Linnea Griffith | PK-5 | | 1,092 | 18% | 281/234-0500<br>Fax 281/644-1695 |
| Cardiff Junior High Sch<br>3900 Dayflower Dr, Katy 77449<br>Bryan Rounds | 6-8 | T | 951 | 74% | 281/234-0600<br>Fax 281/644-1855 |
| Catherine Bethke Elem Sch<br>4535 E Ventana Pkwy, Katy 77493<br>Carrie Lowery | PK-5 | T | 1,131 | 38% | 281/234-4200<br>Fax 281/644-1935 |
| Cimarron Elem Sch<br>1100 S Peek Rd, Katy 77450<br>Youshawna Hunt | PK-5 | T | 542<br>41 | 45% | 281/237-6900<br>Fax 281/644-1505 |
| Cinco Ranch High Sch<br>23440 Cinco Ranch Blvd, Katy 77494<br>James Cross | 9-12 | V | 3,172<br>100 | 19% | 281/237-7000<br>Fax 281/644-1734 |
| Cinco Ranch Junior High Sch<br>23420 Cinco Ranch Blvd, Katy 77494<br>Mona Salinas | 6-8 | | 1,272 | 23% | 281/237-7300<br>Fax 281/644-1640 |
| Diane Winborn Elem Sch<br>22555 Prince George St, Katy 77449<br>Leah Lowry | PK-5 | T | 695<br>75 | 49% | 281/237-6650<br>Fax 281/644-1510 |
| Edna Mae Fielder Elem Sch<br>2100 Greenway Village Dr, Katy 77494<br>Mark Kampwerth | PK-5 | | 950<br>55 | 24% | 281/237-6450<br>Fax 281/664-1515 |
| Franz Elem Sch<br>2751 N Westgreen Blvd, Katy 77449<br>Yvette Sylvan | PK-5 | T | 1,003 | 66% | 281/237-8600<br>Fax 281/644-1520 |
| Fred and Patti Shafer ES<br>5150 Ranch Point Dr, Katy 77494<br>Shannon Smith | PK-5 | | 985 | 10% | 281/234-1900<br>Fax 281/644-1880 |
| Garland McMeans Junior HS<br>21000 Westheimer Pkwy, Katy 77450<br>Steve Guzzetta | 6-8 | V | 1,136 | 22% | 281/237-8000<br>Fax 281/644-1660 |
| Hazel S Pattison Elem Sch<br>19910 Stonelodge Dr, Katy 77450<br>Debbie Barker | PK-5 | | 1,020<br>42 | 15% | 281/237-5450<br>Fax 281/644-1575 |
| James E Randolph Elem Sch<br>5303 Flewellen Oaks Ln, Fulshear 77441<br>Michelle Gaskamp | PK-5 | | 923 | 3% | 281/234-3800<br>Fax 281/644-1930 |
| James E Taylor High Sch<br>20700 Kingsland Blvd, Katy 77450<br>Dr Melinda Stone | 9-12 | V | 2,884<br>100 | 24% | 281/237-3100<br>Fax 281/644-1762 |
| James Williams Elem Sch<br>3900 S Peek Rd, Katy 77450<br>Angel Bateman | PK-5 | | 803 | 21% | 281/237-7200<br>Fax 281/644-1545 |
| Jean & Betty Schmalz Elem Sch<br>18605 Green Land Way, Houston 77084<br>Charlotte Gilder | PK-5 | GT | 1,173 | 62% | 281/237-4500<br>Fax 281/644-1615 |
| Jeanette Hayes Elem Sch<br>21203 Park Timbers Ln, Katy 77450<br>Heather Mulcahy | PK-5 | | 670<br>42 | 26% | 281/237-3200<br>Fax 281/644-1541 |
| Jo Ella Exley Elem Sch<br>21800 Westheimer Pkwy, Katy 77450<br>Juli Noeldner | PK-5 | | 1,036 | 23% | 281/237-8400<br>Fax 281/644-1535 |
| Joe M Adams Junior High Sch<br>4141 Cross Creek Bnd, Fulshear 77441<br>Elisabeth Brodt | 6-8 | | 135 | | 281/234-3400<br>Fax 281/644-3805 |
| Jordan High Sch<br>27500 Fulshear Bend Dr, Fulshear 77441<br>Dr Ethan Crowell | 9-12 | | 1,000 | | 281/234-9000 |
| Katy Elem Sch<br>5726 George Bush Dr, Katy 77493<br>Beth Grimet | PK-5 | | 628<br>48 | 22% | 281/237-6550<br>Fax 281/644-1550 |
| Katy High Sch<br>6331 Highway Blvd, Katy 77494<br>Dr Richard Hull | 9-12 | V | 3,377<br>175 | 31% | 281/237-6700<br>Fax 281/644-1703 |
| Katy Junior High Sch<br>5350 Franz Rd, Katy 77493<br>Dr Jacob LeBlanc | 6-8 | TV | 1,085<br>68 | 44% | 281/237-6800<br>Fax 281/644-1645 |
| Keiko Davidson Elem Sch<br>26906 Pine Mill Rnch, Katy 77494<br>Jessie Miller | PK-5 | | 1,139 | 8% | 281/234-2500<br>Fax 281/644-1925 |
| Loraine T Golbow Elem Sch<br>3535 Lakes of Bridgewater Dr, Katy 77449<br>Jessica Hale | PK-5 | T | 790<br>54 | 53% | 281/237-5350<br>Fax 281/644-1525 |
| Ⓐ Martha Raines High Sch<br>1732 Katyland Dr, Katy 77493<br>Dr Diego Linares | 10-12 | T | 190 | 54% | 281/237-1500<br>Fax 281/644-1780 |
| Maurice Wolfe Elem Sch<br>502 Addicks Howell Rd, Houston 77079<br>Anna Hinojosa | PK-5 | T | 149<br>24 | 54% | 281/237-2250<br>Fax 281/644-1620 |
| Mayde Creek Elem Sch<br>2698 Greenhouse Rd, Houston 77084<br>Felicia Sheedy | PK-5 | T | 804<br>60 | 68% | 281/237-3950<br>Fax 281/644-1555 |
| Mayde Creek High Sch<br>19202 Groschke Rd, Houston 77084<br>Ronnie Edwards | 9-12 | TV | 2,744<br>200 | 64% | 281/237-3000<br>Fax 281/644-1721 |
| Mayde Creek Junior High Sch<br>2700 Greenhouse Rd, Houston 77084<br>Dr David Paz | 6-8 | TV | 1,141<br>60 | 69% | 281/237-3900<br>Fax 281/644-1650 |
| Maydell Jenks Elem Sch<br>27602 Westridge Creek Ln, Katy 77494<br>Troy Kemp | PK-5 | | 1,296 | 11% | 281/234-4100<br>Fax 281/644-1940 |
| Memorial Parkway Elem Sch<br>21603 Park Tree Ln, Katy 77450<br>Dr Doreen Martinez | PK-5 | T | 865<br>32 | 54% | 281/237-5850<br>Fax 281/644-1560 |
| Memorial Parkway Jr High Sch<br>21203 Highland Knolls Dr, Katy 77450<br>Dr Emily Craig | 6-8 | TV | 527<br>80 | 37% | 281/237-5800<br>Fax 281/644-1665 |
| Michael L Griffin Elem Sch<br>7800 S Fry Rd, Katy 77494<br>Jackie Keithan | PK-5 | | 990 | 9% | 281/237-8700<br>Fax 281/644-1850 |
| Miller Career & Tech Center<br>1734 Katyland Dr, Katy 77493<br>Russell Faldyn | Voc | | 275<br>25 | | 281/237-6300<br>Fax 281/644-1775 |
| Morton Ranch Elem Sch<br>2502 N Mason Rd, Katy 77449<br>Deborah Hubble | PK-5 | T | 981 | 56% | 281/234-0300<br>Fax 281/644-1685 |

| | | | |
|---|---|---|---|
| 1 | Superintendent | 8 | Curric/Instruct K-12 |
| 2 | Bus/Finance/Purchasing | 9 | Curric/Instruct Elem |
| 3 | Buildings And Grounds | 10 | Curric/Instruct Sec |
| 4 | Food Service | 11 | Federal Program |
| 5 | Transportation | 12 | Title I |
| 6 | Athletic | 13 | Title V |
| 7 | Health Services | 15 | Asst Superintendent |
| | | 16 | Instructional Media Svcs |
| | | 17 | Chief Operations Officer |
| | | 18 | Chief Academic Officer |

| | |
|---|---|
| 19 | Chief Financial Officer |
| 20 | Art K-12 |
| 21 | Art Elem |
| 22 | Art Sec |
| 23 | Music K-12 |
| 24 | Music Elem |
| 25 | Music Sec |
| 26 | Business Education |
| 27 | Career & Tech Ed |
| 28 | Technology Education |

| | |
|---|---|
| 29 | Family/Consumer Science |
| 30 | Adult Education |
| 31 | Career/Sch-to-Work K-12 |
| 32 | Career/Sch-to-Work Elem |
| 33 | Career/Sch-to-Work Sec |
| 34 | Early Childhood Ed |
| 35 | Health/Phys Education |
| 36 | Guidance Services K-12 |
| 37 | Guidance Services Elem |
| 38 | Guidance Services Sec |

| | |
|---|---|
| 39 | Social Studies K-12 |
| 40 | Social Studies Elem |
| 41 | Social Studies Sec |
| 42 | Science K-12 |
| 43 | Science Elem |
| 44 | Science Sec |
| 45 | Math K-12 |
| 46 | Math Elem |
| 47 | Math Sec |
| 48 | English/Lang Arts K-12 |

| | |
|---|---|
| 49 | English/Lang Arts Elem |
| 50 | English/Lang Arts Sec |
| 51 | Reading K-12 |
| 52 | Reading Elem |
| 53 | Reading Sec |
| 54 | Remedial Reading K-12 |
| 55 | Remedial Reading Elem |
| 56 | Remedial Reading Sec |
| 57 | Bilingual/ELL |
| 58 | Special Education K-12 |

| | |
|---|---|
| 59 | Special Education Elem |
| 60 | Special Education Sec |
| 61 | Foreign/World Lang K-12 |
| 62 | Foreign/World Lang Elem |
| 63 | Foreign/World Lang Sec |
| 64 | Religious Education K-12 |
| 65 | Religious Education Elem |
| 66 | Religious Education Sec |
| 67 | School Board President |
| 68 | Teacher Personnel |

| | |
|---|---|
| 69 | Academic Assessment |
| 70 | Research/Development |
| 71 | Public Information |
| 72 | Summer School |
| 73 | Instructional Tech |
| 74 | Inservice Training |
| 75 | Marketing/Distributive |
| 76 | Info Systems |
| 77 | Psychological Assess |
| 78 | Affirmative Action |

| | | | | | | |
|---|---|---|---|---|---|---|
| Morton Ranch High Sch<br>21000 Franz Rd, Katy 77449<br>Julie Hinson | 9-12 | T | 2,834 | 60% | 281/237-7800<br>Fax 281/644-1747 | |
| Morton Ranch Jr High Sch<br>2498 N Mason Rd, Katy 77449<br>Dr Sanee Bell | 6-8 | T | 1,190 | 65% | 281/237-7400<br>Fax 281/644-1670 | |
| Nottingham Country Elem Sch<br>20500 Kingsland Blvd, Katy 77450<br>Tracy Stroud | PK-5 | | 666 | 23% | 281/237-5500<br>Fax 281/644-1566 | |
| Obra D Tompkins High Sch<br>4400 Falcon Landing Blvd, Katy 77494<br>Mark Grisdale | 9-12 | | 3,750 | 8% | 281/234-1000<br>Fax 281/644-1910 | |
| Odessa Kilpatrick Elem Sch<br>26100 Cinco Ranch Blvd, Katy 77494<br>Malynn Rodriguez | PK-5 | | 1,174 | 7% | 281/237-7600<br>Fax 281/664-1570 | |
| Olga Leonard Elem Sch<br>2602 Winchester Ranch Trail, Katy 77493<br>Stephanie Vaughan | PK-5 | | 670 | | 281/234-4600<br>Fax 281/644-3810 | |
| Ⓐ Opportunity Awareness Center<br>1732 Katyland Dr, Katy 77493<br>Dr Diego Linares | 6-12 | T | 72<br>12 | 54% | 281/237-6350<br>Fax 281/644-1780 | |
| Patricia Paetow High Sch<br>23111 Stockdick Rd, Katy 77493<br>Mindy Dickerson | 9-12 | T | 725 | 51% | 281/234-4900 | |
| Polly Ann McRoberts Elem Sch<br>3535 Fry Rd, Katy 77449<br>Rahsan Smith | PK-5 | T | 760<br>55 | 63% | 281/237-2000<br>Fax 281/644-1580 | |
| Ray & Jamie Wolman Elem Sch<br>28727 N Firethorne Rd, Katy 77494<br>Kelly Ricks | PK-5 | | 979 | 6% | 281/234-1700<br>Fax 281/644-1875 | |
| Rhoads Elem Sch<br>19711 Clay Rd, Katy 77449<br>Amanda Weaver | PK-5 | T | 999 | 68% | 281/237-8500<br>Fax 281/644-1590 | |
| Robert & Felice Bryant ES<br>29801 Kingsland Blvd, Katy 77494<br>Dr William Rhodes | PK-5 | | 716 | | 281/234-4300<br>Fax 281/644-1965 | |
| Robert E King Elem Sch<br>1901 Charlton House Ln, Katy 77493<br>Tammi Wilhelm | PK-5 | T | 989 | 51% | 281/237-6850<br>Fax 281/644-1595 | |
| Robert R Shaw Ctr for Steam<br>1730 Katyland Dr, Katy 77493<br>Steve Adams | 6-12 | | 401 | | 281/396-7652 | |
| Roberta Rylander Elem Sch<br>24831 Westheimer Pkwy, Katy 77494<br>Cheryl Glasser | PK-5 | | 1,086 | 23% | 281/237-8300<br>Fax 281/644-1600 | |
| Rodger & Ellen Beck Jr HS<br>5200 S Fry Rd, Katy 77450<br>Carra Daniels | 6-8 | TV | 1,001<br>57 | 20% | 281/237-3300<br>Fax 281/644-1630 | |
| Roosevelt Alexander Elem Sch<br>6161 S Fry Rd, Katy 77494<br>Dr Charmaine Hobin | PK-5 | | 954<br>35 | 8% | 281/237-7100<br>Fax 281/644-1585 | |
| Seven Lakes High Sch<br>9251 S Fry Rd, Katy 77494<br>Kerri Finnesand | 9-12 | V | 3,617 | 12% | 281/237-2800<br>Fax 281/644-1785 | |
| Seven Lakes Junior High Sch<br>6026 Katy Gaston Rd, Katy 77494<br>Kristin Harper | 6-8 | | 2,032 | 9% | 281/234-2100<br>Fax 281/644-1885 | |
| Ⓐ Simon Youth Academy<br>5000 Katy Mills Cir, Katy 77494<br>Heather Devires | 9-12 | | 51 | | 281/396-6046<br>Fax 281/644-3800 | |
| Stan C Stanley Elem Sch<br>26633 Cinco Terrace Dr, Katy 77494<br>Rebecca Wingfield | PK-5 | | 1,004 | 6% | 281/234-1400<br>Fax 281/644-1865 | |
| Stockdick Jr High Sch<br>4777 Peek Rd, Katy 77449<br>**Dr Ann Lalime** | 6-8 | T | 903 | 48% | 281/234-2700<br>Fax 281/644-1970 | |
| Sue Creech Elem Sch<br>5905 S Mason Rd, Katy 77450<br>Sally Gupton | PK-5 | T | 777<br>53 | 28% | 281/237-8850<br>Fax 281/644-1605 | |
| Sundown Elem Sch<br>20100 Saums Rd, Katy 77449<br>Martha Pulido | PK-5 | GT | 781<br>50 | 74% | 281/237-5400<br>Fax 281/644-1610 | |
| T H McDonald Junior High Sch<br>3635 Lakes of Bridgewater Dr, Katy 77449<br>Carrie Caruso | 6-8 | TV | 902 | 66% | 281/237-5300<br>Fax 281/644-1655 | |
| Tays Junior High Sch<br>26721 Hawks Prairie Blvd, Katy 77494<br>Dr Kris Mitzner | 6-8 | | 1,377 | 7% | 281/234-2400<br>Fax 281/644-1945 | |
| Tom Wilson Elem Sch<br>5200 Falcon Landing Blvd, Katy 77494<br>Rhonda Henderson | PK-5 | | 1,043 | 7% | 281/234-1600<br>Fax 281/644-1870 | |
| Ursula Stephens Elem Sch<br>2715 Fry Rd, Katy 77449<br>Michael Schwartz | PK-5 | T | 723 | 67% | 281/234-0200<br>Fax 281/644-1680 | |
| West Memorial Elem Sch<br>22605 Provincial Blvd, Katy 77450<br>Rebecca Marron | PK-5 | T | 820<br>40 | 50% | 281/237-6600<br>Fax 281/644-1625 | |
| West Memorial Jr High Sch<br>22311 Provincial Blvd, Katy 77450<br>Gina Cobb | 6-8 | TV | 591<br>60 | 53% | 281/237-6400<br>Fax 281/644-1675 | |
| Woodcreek Elem Sch<br>1155 Woodcreek Bend Ln, Katy 77494<br>Ronnie Mosher | PK-5 | | 1,196<br>45 | 10% | 281/234-0100<br>Fax 281/644-1690<br>f | |
| Woodcreek Junior High Sch<br>1801 Woodcreek Bend Ln, Katy 77494<br>**Dr Andrew Lowry** | 6-8 | | 1,587 | 10% | 281/234-0800<br>Fax 281/644-1860 | |
| Zelma Hutsell Elem Sch<br>5360 Franz Rd, Katy 77493<br>**Margie Blount** | PK-5 | GT | 727<br>60 | 66% | 281/237-6500<br>Fax 281/644-1530 | |

● **Lamar Cons Ind School Dist** PID: 01018232    832/223-0000
3911 Avenue I, Rosenberg 77471    Fax 832/223-0002

**Schools:** 46 \ **Teachers:** 2,076 \ **Students:** 34,806 \
**Special Ed Students:** 3,351 \ **LEP Students:** 4,276 \ **College-Bound:** 89%
\ **Ethnic:** Asian 7%, African American 20%, Hispanic 44%, Caucasian
28% \ **Exp:** $281 (Med) \ **Poverty:** 11% \ **Title I:** $4,888,444 \
**Special Education:** $4,112,000 \ **Open-Close:** 08/24 - 05/27 \ **DTBP:** $189
(High) \ f t

| | | | |
|---|---|---|---|
| Dr Thomas Randle | 1 | Lamanda Nipps | 2 |
| Michelle Reynolds | 2 | Yvonne Dawson | 2 |
| Aaron Morgan | 3 | Christopher Juntti | 3,4,5,15,73 |
| Kevin McKeever | 3 | Monica Tomas | 4 |
| Mike Jones | 5 | Nicole Nelson | 6 |
| Dr Jennifer Roberts | 7,79 | Katie Marchena | 8 |
| Diane Parks | 9,15 | Dr Andree Osagie | 10,15 |
| Dr Jon Maxwell | 11,27,69,70,79,81,294 | Dr Marva Oneal | 11 |
| Dr Chad Jones | 16,286 | Dr Teresa Mossige | 18 |
| Jill Ludwig | 19 | Ram Estrada | 20,23 |
| Joel Garrett | 27,31 | Brian Moore | 36,69,70,294 |
| Kevin McCune | 39 | Michael Harvey | 42 |
| Lana Kettler | 46 | Andria Olson | 47 |
| Theresa Gage | 49,52 | Julie McGuane | 50,53 |
| Gloria Stewart-Kooper | 57 | Keonta Jackson | 58 |
| Tiffany Mathis | 58 | Joy Williams | 67 |
| Dr Kathleen Bowen | 68 | Mike Rockwood | 71,751 |
| Alan Voight | 73 | Jamie Vincek | 74 |
| David Eakin | 76,95 | Valerie Anderson | 81 |
| Dr Melissa Smith | 88 | Dallis Warren | 91 |
| David Jacobson | 97,98 | Kimberly Flores | 275 |
| David Banks | 295 | | |

| | | | | |
|---|---|---|---|---|
| 79 | Student Personnel | 91 | Safety/Security | |
| 80 | Driver Ed/Safety | 92 | Magnet School | |
| 81 | Gifted/Talented | 93 | Parental Involvement | |
| 82 | Video Services | 95 | Tech Prep Program | |
| 83 | Substance Abuse Prev | 97 | Chief Information Officer | |
| 84 | Erate | 98 | Chief Technology Officer | |
| 85 | AIDS Education | 270 | Character Education | |
| 88 | Alternative/At Risk | 271 | Migrant Education | |
| 89 | Multi-Cultural Curriculum | 273 | Teacher Mentor | |
| 90 | Social Work | 274 | Before/After Sch | |

| | | | |
|---|---|---|---|
| 275 | Response To Intervention | 298 | Grant Writer/Ptnrships |
| 277 | Remedial Math K-12 | 750 | Chief Innovation Officer |
| 280 | Literacy Coach | 751 | Chief of Staff |
| 285 | STEM | 752 | Social Emotional Learning |
| 286 | Digital Learning | | |
| 288 | Common Core Standards | | **Other School Types** |
| 294 | Accountability | | Ⓐ = Alternative School |
| 295 | Network System | | Ⓒ = Charter School |
| 296 | Title II Programs | | Ⓜ = Magnet School |
| 297 | Webmaster | | Ⓨ = Year-Round School |

**School Programs**
A = Alternative Program
G = Adult Classes
M = Magnet Program
T = Title I Schoolwide
V = Career & Tech Ed Programs

**Social Media**
f = Facebook
t = Twitter

New Schools are shaded
**New Superintendents and Principals are bold**
Personnel with email addresses are underscored

| Public Schs..Principal | Grd | Prgm | Enr/#Cls | SN | |
|---|---|---|---|---|---|
| ⓐ 1621 Place Sch<br>117 Lane Dr Ste 14, Rosenberg 77471<br>Randall Donnell | 9-12 | V | 77<br>3 | 832/223-0950<br>Fax 832/223-0951 | 📘📕 |
| Adolphus Elem Sch<br>7910 Winston Ranch Pkwy, Richmond 77406<br>Stacy Boarman | PK-5 | | 676 | 19% 832/223-4700<br>Fax 832/223-4701 | 📘📕 |
| ⓐ Alternative Learning Center<br>1708 Avenue M, Rosenberg 77471<br>**Dr Melissia Smith** | K-12 | V | 80<br>15 | 69% 832/223-0900<br>Fax 832/223-0901 | |
| Arredondo Elem Sch<br>6110 August Green Dr, Richmond 77469<br>Amber Barbarow | PK-5 | T | 817 | 55% 832/223-4800<br>Fax 832/223-4801 | |
| Austin Elem Sch<br>1630 Pitts Rd, Richmond 77406<br>Bud Whileyman | PK-5 | | 631<br>43 | 34% 832/223-1000<br>Fax 832/223-1001 | |
| Beasley Elem Sch<br>7511 Avenue J, Beasley 77417<br>Laura Haugvoll | PK-5 | T | 380<br>11 | 86% 832/223-1100<br>Fax 832/223-1101 | |
| Bentley Elem Sch<br>9910 FM 359 Rd, Richmond 77406<br>Jill Nehls | PK-5 | | 692 | 26% 832/223-4900<br>Fax 832/222-4901 | |
| Bowie Elem Sch<br>2304 Bamore Rd, Rosenberg 77471<br>Belynda Billings | PK-5 | T | 498<br>43 | 80% 832/223-1200<br>Fax 832/223-1201 | 📘📕 |
| Briscoe Junior High Sch<br>4300 FM 723 Rd, Richmond 77406<br>Jennifer Zebold | 7-8 | | 891 | 31% 832/223-4000<br>Fax 832/223-4001 | |
| Campbell Elem Sch<br>1000 Shadow Bend Dr, Sugar Land 77479<br>Michelle Koerth | PK-5 | | 489<br>38 | 7% 832/223-1300<br>Fax 832/223-1301 | |
| Culver Elem Sch<br>3131 Learning Tree Lane, Rosenberg 77471<br>Carla Thomas | K-5 | | 615 | 832/223-5600<br>Fax 832/223-5601 | |
| Dean Leaman Junior High Sch<br>9320 Charger Way, Fulshear 77441<br>Michael Semmler | 6-8 | | 753 | 21% 832/223-5200<br>Fax 832/223-5201 | |
| Don Carter Elem Sch<br>7800 A Meyers Rd, Richmond 77469<br>Henva Medlow | PK-5 | | 670 | 27% 832/223-5500<br>Fax 832/223-5501 | |
| ⓐ Fort Bend Alternative Sch<br>3404 Avenue F, Rosenberg 77471<br>Randall Donnell | 6-12 | | 60<br>3 | 65% 281/239-3431<br>Fax 281/341-5293 | |
| Frost Elem Sch<br>3306 Skinner Ln, Richmond 77406<br>Shannon Hood | PK-5 | | 603<br>27 | 19% 832/223-1500<br>Fax 832/223-1501 | |
| Fulshear High Sch<br>9302 Charger Way, Fulshear 77441<br>Daniel Ward | 9-12 | | 400 | 19% 832/223-5000<br>Fax 832/223-5001 | |
| George Junior High Sch<br>4601 Airport Ave, Rosenberg 77471<br>Stephen Judice | 7-8 | T | 1,066<br>80 | 74% 832/223-3600<br>Fax 832/223-3601 | |
| George Ranch High Sch<br>8181 FM 762 Rd, Richmond 77469<br>Heather Patterson | 9-12 | V | 2,674 | 24% 832/223-4200<br>Fax 832/223-4201 | 📘📕 |
| Huggins Elem Sch<br>1 Huggins Dr, Fulshear 77441<br>Bethany Cunningham | PK-5 | | 696<br>30 | 17% 832/223-1600<br>Fax 832/223-1601 | |
| Hutchinson Elem Sch<br>3602 Richmond Pkwy, Richmond 77469<br>Mark Melendez | PK-5 | | 632 | 41% 832/223-1700<br>Fax 832/223-1701 | 📘📕 |
| Jackson Elem Sch<br>301 3rd St, Rosenberg 77471<br>Tracy Mills | PK-5 | T | 347<br>30 | 94% 832/223-1800<br>Fax 832/223-1801 | |
| Jane Long Elem Sch<br>907 Main St, Richmond 77469<br>Risa Crosby | PK-5 | T | 590<br>35 | 81% 832/223-1900<br>Fax 832/223-1901 | |
| Jane Wessendorff Middle Sch<br>5201 Mustang Ave, Rosenberg 77471<br>Lorana Callis | 6-6 | T | 404<br>32 | 832/223-3300<br>Fax 832/223-3301 | |
| Joe Hubenak Elem Sch<br>11344 Rancho Bella Pkwy, Richmond 77406<br>Ernie Bainbridge | PK-5 | | 950 | 31% 832/223-2900<br>Fax 832/223-2901 | 📘📕 |
| Lamar Consolidated High Sch<br>4606 Mustang Ave, Rosenberg 77471<br>Kaye Williams | 9-12 | TV | 1,735<br>100 | 56% 832/223-3000<br>Fax 832/223-3001 | |
| Lamar Junior High Sch<br>4814 Mustang Ave, Rosenberg 77471<br>Creighton Jaster | 7-8 | T | 848 | 69% 832/223-3200<br>Fax 832/223-3201 | |
| Lindsey Elem Sch<br>2431 Joan Collier Trce, Katy 77494<br>Heather Williams | PK-5 | | 683 | 27% 832/223-5400<br>Fax 832/223-5401 | |
| McNeill Elem Sch<br>7300 S Mason Rd, Richmond 77407<br>Toni Scott | PK-5 | | 764 | 40% 832/223-2800<br>Fax 832/223-2801 | |
| Meyer Elem Sch<br>1930 J Meyer Rd, Richmond 77469<br>Kevin Smith | PK-5 | T | 813<br>45 | 66% 832/223-2000<br>Fax 832/223-2001 | 📕 |
| Navarro Middle Sch<br>4700 Avenue N, Rosenberg 77471<br>**Toshila Darjean** | 6-6 | | 513<br>35 | 832/223-3700<br>Fax 832/223-3701 | 📘📕 |
| Polly Ryon Middle Sch<br>7901 FM 762 Rd, Richmond 77469<br>Kevin Croft | 6-6 | | 679 | 832/223-4500<br>Fax 832/223-4501 | |
| Randolph Foster High Sch<br>4400 FM 723 Rd, Richmond 77406<br>Gerard Kipping | 9-12 | V | 1,912<br>102 | 30% 832/223-3800<br>Fax 832/223-3801 | 📘📕 |
| Reading Junior High Sch<br>8101 FM 762 Rd, Richmond 77469<br>Dr Sonya Sanzo | 6-8 | | 2,026 | 26% 832/223-4400<br>Fax 832/223-4401 | |
| Roberts Middle Sch<br>9230 Charger Way, Fulshear 77441<br>Janice Harvey | 6-6 | | 415 | 832/223-5300 | |
| Seguin Early Child Hood Ctr<br>605 Mabel St, Richmond 77469<br>Mary Ellen Rocha | PK-PK | T | 311<br>30 | 100% 832/223-2200<br>Fax 832/223-2201 | |
| Smith Elem Sch<br>2014 Lamar Dr, Richmond 77469<br>Keschia Jones | PK-5 | T | 443<br>39 | 86% 832/223-2300<br>Fax 832/223-2301 | |
| Susannah Dickinson Elem Sch<br>7110 Greatwood Pkwy, Sugar Land 77479<br>Karen Mumphord | PK-5 | | 436<br>42 | 10% 832/223-1400<br>Fax 832/223-1401 | |
| T L Pink Elem Sch<br>1001 Collins Rd, Richmond 77469<br>Tiffany Foster | K-5 | T | 560<br>45 | 94% 832/223-2100<br>Fax 832/223-2101 | |
| Tammaron Elem Sch<br>29616 Rileys Ridge, Katy 77494<br>**Mark Melendez** | PK-5 | | 538 | 832/223-5700<br>Fax 832/223-5701 | |
| Taylor Ray Elem Sch<br>2611 Avenue N, Rosenberg 77471<br>Ben Perez | PK-5 | T | 622<br>34 | 88% 832/223-2400<br>Fax 832/223-2401 | |
| Terry High Sch<br>5500 Avenue N, Rosenberg 77471<br>Juan Nava | 9-12 | TV | 2,117<br>95 | 68% 832/223-3400<br>Fax 832/223-3401 | 📘📕 |
| Thomas Elem Sch<br>6822 Irby Cobb Blvd, Richmond 77469<br>Vicki Stevenson | PK-5 | T | 780 | 56% 832/223-4600<br>Fax 832/223-4601 | |
| Travis Elem Sch<br>2700 Avenue K, Rosenberg 77471<br>Jearine Jordan | PK-5 | T | 425<br>34 | 82% 832/223-2500<br>Fax 832/223-2501 | |
| Wertheimer Middle Sch<br>4240 FM 723 Rd, Rosenberg 77471<br>Sharyn Kitto | 6-6 | | 428 | 832/223-4100<br>Fax 832/223-4101 | 📘📕 |

| | | | | | | | |
|---|---|---|---|---|---|---|---|
| 1 | Superintendent | 8 | Curric/Instruct K-12 | 19 | Chief Financial Officer | 29 | Family/Consumer Science |
| 2 | Bus/Finance/Purchasing | 9 | Curric/Instruct Elem | 20 | Art K-12 | 30 | Adult Education |
| 3 | Buildings And Grounds | 10 | Curric/Instruct Sec | 21 | Art Elem | 31 | Career/Sch-to-Work K-12 |
| 4 | Food Service | 11 | Federal Program | 22 | Art Sec | 32 | Career/Sch-to-Work Elem |
| 5 | Transportation | 12 | Title I | 23 | Music K-12 | 33 | Career/Sch-to-Work Sec |
| 6 | Athletic | 13 | Title V | 24 | Music Elem | 34 | Early Childhood Ed |
| 7 | Health Services | 14 | Asst Superintendent | 25 | Music Sec | 35 | Health/Phys Education |
| | | 15 | Instructional Media Svcs | 26 | Business Education | 36 | Guidance Services K-12 |
| | | 16 | Chief Operations Officer | 27 | Career & Tech Ed | 37 | Guidance Services Elem |
| | | 17 | Chief Academic Officer | 28 | Technology Education | 38 | Guidance Services Sec |

| | | | | | |
|---|---|---|---|---|---|
| 39 | Social Studies K-12 | 49 | English/Lang Arts Elem | 59 | Special Education Elem |
| 40 | Social Studies Elem | 50 | English/Lang Arts Sec | 60 | Special Education Sec |
| 41 | Social Studies Sec | 51 | Reading K-12 | 61 | Foreign/World Lang K-12 |
| 42 | Science K-12 | 52 | Reading Elem | 62 | Foreign/World Lang Elem |
| 43 | Science Elem | 53 | Reading Sec | 63 | Foreign/World Lang Sec |
| 44 | Science Sec | 54 | Remedial Reading K-12 | 64 | Religious Education K-12 |
| 45 | Math K-12 | 55 | Remedial Reading Elem | 65 | Religious Education Elem |
| 46 | Math Elem | 56 | Remedial Reading Sec | 66 | Religious Education Sec |
| 47 | Math Sec | 57 | Bilingual/ELL | 67 | School Board President |
| 48 | English/Lang Arts K-12 | 58 | Special Education K-12 | 68 | Teacher Personnel |

| | |
|---|---|
| 69 | Academic Assessment |
| 70 | Research/Development |
| 71 | Public Information |
| 72 | Summer School |
| 73 | Instructional Tech |
| 74 | Inservice Training |
| 75 | Marketing/Distributive |
| 76 | Info Systems |
| 77 | Psychological Assess |
| 78 | Affirmative Action |

| | | | | | |
|---|---|---|---|---|---|
| William Velasquez Elem Sch<br>402 Macek Rd, Richmond 77469<br>Brian Gibson | PK-5 | T | 549 | 54% | 832/223-2600<br>Fax 832/223-2601<br>🇫 🇹 |
| Williams Elem Sch<br>5111 FM 762 Rd, Richmond 77469<br>Anitra Wilson | PK-5 | | 385 | 43% | 832/223-2700<br>Fax 832/223-2701 |

● **Needville Ind School Dist** PID: 01018347    979/793-4158
16227 Highway 36, Needville 77461    Fax 979/793-3823

> **Schools:** 4 \ **Teachers:** 207 \ **Students:** 3,228 \ **Special Ed Students:** 372
> \ **LEP Students:** 260 \ **College-Bound:** 68% \ **Ethnic:** African American
> 3%, Hispanic 48%, Caucasian 48% \ **Exp:** $538 (High) \ **Poverty:** 10% \
> **Title I:** $348,672 \ **Open-Close:** 08/24 - 05/27 \ **DTBP:** $155 (High) \ 🇫

| | | | |
|---|---|---|---|
| Curtis Rhodes | 1 | Dovie Peschel | 2,15 |
| Rodney Wieghat | 3,5 | Michael Giles | 6 |
| Beth Briscoe | 8,11,15,69,271 | Melissa Rhodes | 16* |
| Chris Janicek | 67 | Charles Roehling | 68 |
| Corey Kelly | 73 | Joseph Wappel | 91 |
| Nick Stockton | 295* | | |

| Public Schs..Principal | Grd | Prgm | Enr/#Cls | SN | |
|---|---|---|---|---|---|
| Needville Elem Sch<br>3600 Margaret St, Needville 77461<br>Stacey Stavinoha | PK-4 | T | 1,255<br>40 | 47% | 979/793-4241<br>Fax 979/793-2299 |
| Needville High Sch<br>100 Fritzella Rd, Needville 77461<br>Steve Adamson | 9-12 | AV | 768<br>80 | 35% | 979/793-4158<br>Fax 979/793-5590 |
| Needville Junior High Sch<br>16413 Fritzella Road, Needville 77461<br>Brett Pohler | 7-8 | T | 213<br>17 | 39% | 979/793-4250<br>Fax 979/793-4575 |
| Needville Middle Sch<br>16411 Fritzella Rd, Needville 77461<br>Shannon Jedlicka | 5-6 | T | 473<br>50 | 44% | 979/793-3027<br>Fax 979/793-7665 |

● **Stafford Municipal Sch Dist** PID: 02228624    281/261-9200
1625 Staffordshire Rd, Stafford 77477    Fax 281/261-9249

> **Schools:** 7 \ **Teachers:** 219 \ **Students:** 3,600 \ **Special Ed Students:** 306
> \ **LEP Students:** 636 \ **College-Bound:** 57% \ **Ethnic:** Asian 6%,
> African American 42%, Hispanic 48%, Caucasian 4% \ **Exp:** $307 (High)
> \ **Poverty:** 12% \ **Title I:** $458,675 \ **Special Education:** $605,000 \
> **Open-Close:** 08/19 - 05/26 \ **DTBP:** $181 (High)

| | | | |
|---|---|---|---|
| Dr Robert Bostic | 1 | Daniel Flores | 2 |
| Jaci Phenix | 3 | Danny McDonald | 4 |
| Greg Jerkins | 5 | Ken Savanah | 6 |
| Carlota Allen | 8,273,285 | Charmaine Garcia | 11,58,275 |
| Dr Teresa Sazedj | 13,78,296 | Marva Rasberry | 16,57,69,74,88,270,288,294 |
| Steve Perez | 16 | Christopher Caldwell | 67 |
| Jorge Rodguiez | 73,295 | Cherise Roberts | 298 |

| Public Schs..Principal | Grd | Prgm | Enr/#Cls | SN | |
|---|---|---|---|---|---|
| Ⓐ Quest Academy<br>1625 Staffordshire Rd, Stafford 77477<br>Carlotta Allen | 10-11 | | 20 | | 281/261-9200 |
| Ⓐ Stafford Alt Ed Campus<br>1625 Staffordshire Rd, Stafford 77477<br>Carlotta Jenkins | 6-12 | | 25<br>2 | | 281/261-9270<br>Fax 281/208-6118 |
| Stafford Elem Sch<br>1625 Staffordshire Rd, Stafford 77477<br>Twyla Hynes | 2-4 | T | 777<br>40 | 79% | 281/261-9229<br>Fax 281/261-9262 |
| Stafford High Sch<br>1625 Staffordshire Rd, Stafford 77477<br>Raymond Root | 9-12 | ATV | 1,069<br>40 | 67% | 281/261-9239<br>Fax 281/261-9347 |

| | | | | | |
|---|---|---|---|---|---|
| Stafford Intermediate Sch<br>1625 Staffordshire Rd, Stafford 77477<br>Desiree James | 5-6 | T | 564<br>30 | 71% | 281/208-6100<br>Fax 281/208-6111 |
| Stafford Middle Sch<br>1625 Staffordshire Rd, Stafford 77477<br>Ginny Gayle | 7-8 | T | 542<br>64 | 70% | 281/261-9215<br>Fax 281/261-9349 |
| Stafford Primary Sch<br>1625 Staffordshire Rd, Stafford 77477<br>Twyla Hynes | PK-1 | T | 460<br>38 | 78% | 281/261-9203<br>Fax 281/261-9348 |

---

## FORT BEND CATHOLIC SCHOOLS

● **Archdiocese Galveston-Houston** PID: 01027855
Listing includes only schools located in this county. See District Index for
location of Diocesan Offices.

| Catholic Schs..Principal | Grd | Prgm | Enr/#Cls | SN | |
|---|---|---|---|---|---|
| Holy Rosary Sch<br>1426 George St, Rosenberg 77471<br>Linda Bradford | PK-8 | | 200<br>13 | | 281/342-5813<br>Fax 281/344-1107 |
| St Laurence Catholic Sch<br>2630 Austin Pkwy, Sugar Land 77479<br>Suzanne Barto | PK-8 | | 680<br>32 | | 281/980-0500<br>Fax 281/980-0026 |
| St Theresa Sch<br>705 St Theresa Blvd, Sugar Land 77498<br>Dr Mark Newcomb | K-5 | | 70 | | 281/494-1156<br>Fax 281/242-1393 |

---

## FORT BEND PRIVATE SCHOOLS

| Private Schs..Principal | Grd | Prgm | Enr/#Cls | SN | |
|---|---|---|---|---|---|
| Bakers Preparatory Sch<br>504 Murphy Rd Ste H, Stafford 77477<br>Dianna Baker | PK-5 | | 90<br>7 | | 281/403-2100<br>Fax 281/403-2101 |
| Calvary Episcopal Sch<br>1201 Austin St, Richmond 77469<br>Malcolm Smith | PK-12 | | 180<br>20 | | 281/342-3161<br>Fax 281/232-9449 |
| Everest Academy<br>610 Brand Ln, Stafford 77477<br>Farah Naz | PK-9 | | 620 | | 281/261-3030<br>Fax 281/806-5944 |
| Excel Adventist Academy<br>7950 W Fuqua Dr, Missouri City 77489<br>H Phillip Henry | PK-8 | | 46<br>5 | | 281/835-0770<br>Fax 281/835-1275 |
| Focus Academy<br>130 Industrial Blvd Ste 130, Sugar Land 77478<br>Jacquelyn Mulkey | 6-12 | | 15 | | 281/240-0663 |
| Fort Bend Baptist Academy ES<br>1201 Lakeview Dr, Sugar Land 77478<br>Margie Meyer | PK-5 | | 320<br>23 | | 281/263-9100<br>Fax 281/263-9102 |
| Fort Bend Christian Academy MS<br>1201 Lakeview Dr, Sugar Land 77478<br>Ron Bell | 5-8 | | 265<br>18 | | 281/263-9191<br>Fax 281/263-9193 |
| Fort Bend Christian Academy-HS<br>1250 7th St, Sugar Land 77478<br>Joshua Gettys | 9-12 | | 350<br>22 | | 281/263-9175<br>Fax 281/263-9199 |
| Fusion Academy-Sugarland<br>13440 University Blvd Ste 260, Sugar Land 77479<br>Shayne Horan | 6-12 | | 50 | | 281/207-9506 |
| Global Innovation Sch<br>2553 Cordes Dr, Sugar Land 77479<br>Huda Ahmed | PK-12 | G | 170<br>15 | | 281/980-5800<br>Fax 281/980-6106 |

---

| | | | |
|---|---|---|---|
| Honor Roll Sch<br>4111 Sweetwater Blvd, Sugar Land 77479<br>Doris Quintero | PK-8 | 600<br>37 | 281/265-7888<br>Fax 281/265-7880 |
| Living Water Christian Sch<br>4808 Airport Ave, Rosenberg 77471<br>Gamila Frank | PK-12 | 100<br>13 | 281/342-6336<br>Fax 281/342-9951 |
| Logos Preparatory Academy<br>13303 Southwest Fwy, Sugar Land 77478<br>Tammy McIlvoy | K-12 | 500 | 281/565-6467<br>Fax 713/456-2306 |
| Simonton Christian Academy<br>9703 FM 1489, Simonton 77476<br>Amy Oglesby | PK-8 | 45<br>6 | 281/346-2303<br>Fax 281/346-2393 |
| Southminster Sch<br>4200 Cartwright Rd, Missouri City 77459<br>Tiera Pennix | PK-6 | 250 | 281/261-8872<br>Fax 281/499-4430 |
| Towne Creek Sch<br>3311 Williamsburg Ln, Missouri City 77459<br>Judy Feinsteen | PK-K | 200<br>15 | 281/499-8030<br>Fax 281/261-7846 |
| Walden Sch<br>16103 Lexington Blvd Ste A, Sugar Land 77479<br>Mike McGilvray | PK-2 | 150 | 281/980-0022<br>Fax 281/980-0040 |
| Westlake Lutheran Academy<br>23300 Bellaire Blvd, Richmond 77406<br>Tim Wainright | PK-8 | 186 | 281/341-9910<br>Fax 281/341-9915 |

## FRANKLIN COUNTY

## FRANKLIN PUBLIC SCHOOLS

- **Mount Vernon Ind School Dist** PID: 01018385    903/537-2546
  501 Texas Highway 37, Mount Vernon 75457    Fax 903/537-4784

**Schools:** 3 \ **Teachers:** 123 \ **Students:** 1,570 \ **Special Ed Students:** 159 \ **LEP Students:** 157 \ **Ethnic:** Asian 1%, African American 5%, Hispanic 26%, Caucasian 68% \ **Exp:** $580 (High) \ **Poverty:** 19% \ **Title I:** $388,942 \ **Special Education:** $388,000 \ **Open-Close:** 08/17 - 05/20 \ **DTBP:** $348 (High) \

| | | |
|---|---|---|
| Jason McCullough ....................................1 | Barbara Shurbet ..........................................2 | |
| Shelley Black ............................................4 | Bobby Thompson .........................................5 | |
| Art Briles ...................................................6 | Chandra White ...........................8,11,15,288 | |
| Diane Ramsay .............................13,16,286* | Jason Glover .............................................31* | |
| Lacey Stephens ...............36,83,85,88,285* | Craig Watson ............................................58* | |
| Aaron Sanders ........................................67 | Jennifer Sumrow .....................................69,79 | |
| Anthony Eilers .................................73,295 | Dara Fisk ...................................................77* | |

| Public Schs..Principal | Grd | Prgm | Enr/#Cls | SN | |
|---|---|---|---|---|---|
| Mount Vernon Elem Sch<br>501 Texas Highway 37, Mount Vernon 75457<br>**Rhonda Orren** | PK-4 | T | 553<br>30 | 68% | 903/537-2266<br>Fax 903/537-3815 |
| Mount Vernon High Sch<br>501 Texas Highway 37, Mount Vernon 75457<br>Jason Glover | 9-12 | TV | 499<br>30 | 52% | 903/537-3700<br>Fax 903/537-2536 |
| Mount Vernon Middle Sch<br>501 Texas Highway 37, Mount Vernon 75457<br>James Payne | 5-8 | TV | 518<br>15 | 58% | 903/537-2267<br>Fax 903/537-3601 |

## FREESTONE COUNTY

## FREESTONE PUBLIC SCHOOLS

- **Dew Ind School Dist** PID: 01018438    903/389-2828
  606 County Road 481, Teague 75860    Fax 903/389-5104

**Schools:** 1 \ **Teachers:** 16 \ **Students:** 155 \ **Special Ed Students:** 13 \ **LEP Students:** 4 \ **Ethnic:** African American 9%, Hispanic 10%, Caucasian 81% \ **Exp:** $526 (High) \ **Poverty:** 14% \ **Title I:** $23,572 \ **Open-Close:** 08/14 - 05/21 \ **DTBP:** $361 (High) \

| | | |
|---|---|---|
| Darrell Evans ........................................1,11 | Nolan Glass ..................................................2 | |
| Charlotte Winkler ......................................4* | Nicole Sifford ...............................................7 | |
| Christie Fishbeck .................16,73,295,297* | Ginny Blackwell ...................................57,271* | |
| David Fowler ............................................67 | | |

| Public Schs..Principal | Grd | Prgm | Enr/#Cls | SN | |
|---|---|---|---|---|---|
| Dew Elem Sch<br>606 County Road 481, Teague 75860<br>Darrell Evans | PK-8 | T | 155<br>7 | 62% | 903/389-2828 |

- **Fairfield Ind School Dist** PID: 01018452    903/389-2532
  615 Post Oak Rd, Fairfield 75840    Fax 903/389-7050

**Schools:** 4 \ **Teachers:** 146 \ **Students:** 1,800 \ **Special Ed Students:** 124 \ **LEP Students:** 95 \ **Ethnic:** Asian 1%, African American 15%, Hispanic 26%, Caucasian 57% \ **Exp:** $428 (High) \ **Poverty:** 13% \ **Title I:** $321,586 \ **Open-Close:** 08/13 - 05/26 \ **DTBP:** $375 (High)

| | | |
|---|---|---|
| Jason Adams ............................................1 | Sharon Gibson ..............................................2 | |
| Ron Harris .................................................3 | Crystal Thill ..................................................4 | |
| Bryan Gawryszwski ........................5,79,294 | John Bachtel ...............................................6* | |
| Melissa Cox ..........8,11,15,57,69,280,296,298 | Eric Chavers ................................................67 | |
| Lisa Tate ..................................................68 | Arland Thill ............................................73,295 | |
| Robin Smith ..............................................76 | Billy Barlow ................................................91 | |
| Clif Allen ................................................295 | | |

| Public Schs..Principal | Grd | Prgm | Enr/#Cls | SN | |
|---|---|---|---|---|---|
| Fairfield Elem Sch<br>330 W Main St, Fairfield 75840<br>Sheila Ransom | PK-2 | T | 392<br>40 | 63% | 903/389-2148<br>Fax 903/389-5314 |
| Fairfield High Sch<br>631 Post Oak Rd, Fairfield 75840<br>Sonya Gibson | 9-12 | TV | 521<br>42 | 48% | 903/389-4177<br>Fax 903/389-5453 |
| Fairfield Intermediate Sch<br>605 N Fairway St, Fairfield 75840<br>Shetonia Scires | 3-5 | T | 403 | 52% | 903/389-7095<br>Fax 903/389-7101 |
| Fairfield Junior High Sch<br>701 Post Oak Rd, Fairfield 75840<br>**Daniel Johnson** | 6-8 | T | 436<br>37 | 52% | 903/389-4210<br>Fax 903/389-5454 |

| | | | | | | | | | |
|---|---|---|---|---|---|---|---|---|---|
| 1 Superintendent | 8 Curric/Instruct K-12 | 19 Chief Financial Officer | 29 Family/Consumer Science | 39 Social Studies K-12 | 49 English/Lang Arts Elem | 59 Special Education Elem | 69 Academic Assessment |
| 2 Bus/Finance/Purchasing | 9 Curric/Instruct Elem | 20 Art K-12 | 30 Adult Education | 40 Social Studies Elem | 50 English/Lang Arts Sec | 60 Special Education Sec | 70 Research/Development |
| 3 Buildings And Grounds | 10 Curric/Instruct Sec | 21 Art Elem | 31 Career/Sch-to-Work K-12 | 41 Social Studies Sec | 51 Reading K-12 | 61 Foreign/World Lang K-12 | 71 Public Information |
| 4 Food Service | 11 Federal Program | 22 Art Sec | 32 Career/Sch-to-Work Elem | 42 Science K-12 | 52 Reading Elem | 62 Foreign/World Lang Elem | 72 Summer School |
| 5 Transportation | 12 Title I | 23 Music K-12 | 33 Career/Sch-to-Work Sec | 43 Science Elem | 53 Reading Sec | 63 Foreign/World Lang Sec | 73 Instructional Tech |
| 6 Athletic | 13 Title V | 24 Music Elem | 34 Early Childhood Ed | 44 Science Sec | 54 Remedial Reading K-12 | 64 Religious Education K-12 | 74 Inservice Training |
| 7 Health Services | 15 Asst Superintendent | 25 Music Sec | 35 Health/Phys Education | 45 Math K-12 | 55 Remedial Reading Elem | 65 Religious Education Elem | 75 Marketing/Distributive |
| | 16 Instructional Media Svcs | 26 Business Education | 36 Guidance Services K-12 | 46 Math Elem | 56 Remedial Reading Sec | 66 Religious Education Sec | 76 Info Systems |
| **TX—160** | 17 Chief Operations Officer | 27 Career & Tech Ed | 37 Guidance Services Elem | 47 Math Sec | 57 Bilingual/ELL | 67 School Board President | 77 Psychological Assess |
| | 18 Chief Academic Officer | 28 Technology Education | 38 Guidance Services Sec | 48 English/Lang Arts K-12 | 58 Special Education K-12 | 68 Teacher Personnel | 78 Affirmative Action |

- **Teague Ind School Dist** PID: 01018505    254/739-1300
  420 N 10th Ave, Teague 75860    Fax 254/739-5223

**Schools:** 5 \ **Teachers:** 91 \ **Students:** 1,160 \ **Special Ed Students:** 126 \ **LEP Students:** 83 \ **College-Bound:** 59% \ **Ethnic:** African American 13%, Hispanic 32%, Caucasian 55% \ **Exp:** $430 (High) \ **Poverty:** 24% \ **Title I:** $379,546 \ **Special Education:** $199,000 \ **Open-Close:** 08/14 - 05/28 \ **DTBP:** $342 (High)

| | | | |
|---|---|---|---|
| Chris Skinner | 1 | Emily Evans | 2 |
| Carlos Perales | 3 | Debra Lively | 4* |
| Donnie Osborn | 6* | Kella Redic | 7* |
| Ray Matthews | 15 | Lynne Kilman | 16* |
| Christina Fuller | 57* | Jeff Gonzales | 67 |
| Elizabeth Hernandez | 69 | Brent Holmes | 73,295* |
| Cathy Schmidt | 288,296* | | |

| Public Schs..Principal | Grd | Prgm | Enr/#Cls | SN | |
|---|---|---|---|---|---|
| Teague Elem Sch<br>420 N 10th Ave, Teague 75860<br>Crystal Adams | PK-3 | T | 355<br>23 | 67% | 254/739-1350<br>Fax 254/739-3605 |
| Teague High Sch<br>420 Highway Loop 225, Teague 75860<br>Tracie Ezell | 9-12 | T | 410<br>20 | 53% | 254/739-1500<br>Fax 254/739-2724 |
| Teague Intermediate Sch<br>420 Highway Loop 225, Teague 75860<br>Vickey Little | 4-5 | | 188<br>17 | | 254/739-3303<br>Fax 254/739-3561 |
| Teague Junior High Sch<br>420 Highway Loop 225, Teague 75860<br>Drake Paris | 6-8 | T | 262<br>25 | 64% | 254/739-1350<br>Fax 254/739-5896 |
| Ⓐ Teague Lion Academy<br>420 N 10th Ave, Teague 75860<br>Cathy Schmidt | 7-12 | T | 20 | 100% | 254/739-1444 |

- **Wortham Ind School Dist** PID: 01018543    254/765-3095
  201 S 4th St, Wortham 76693    Fax 254/765-3473

**Schools:** 3 \ **Teachers:** 39 \ **Students:** 500 \ **Special Ed Students:** 36 \ **LEP Students:** 16 \ **Ethnic:** African American 12%, Hispanic 20%, Caucasian 68% \ **Exp:** $575 (High) \ **Poverty:** 18% \ **Title I:** $92,643 \ **Open-Close:** 08/13 - 05/21 \ **DTBP:** $404 (High)

| | | | |
|---|---|---|---|
| Melissa Bosley | 1,11 | Sherry Shivers | 2 |
| David Hayes | 8,271,273* | Sara Boyd | 16,73 |
| Deanna Whaley | 37,69 | Krystal Duke | 38 |
| Amanda Calame | 57 | Jeff Jones | 67 |
| Amy Miller | 83,85* | | |

| Public Schs..Principal | Grd | Prgm | Enr/#Cls | SN | |
|---|---|---|---|---|---|
| Wortham Elem Sch<br>200 S 5th St, Wortham 76693<br>Dee Allen | PK-5 | T | 223<br>13 | 72% | 254/765-3080<br>Fax 254/765-3512 |
| Wortham High Sch<br>109 S 5th St, Wortham 76693<br>David Hayes | 9-12 | ATV | 133 | 62% | 254/765-3094 |
| Wortham Middle Sch<br>200 S 5th St, Wortham 76693<br>David Hayes | 6-8 | T | 123<br>6 | 54% | 254/765-3523<br>Fax 254/765-3512 |

## FRIO PUBLIC SCHOOLS

- **Dilley Ind School Dist** PID: 01018579    830/965-1912
  245 W FM 117, Dilley 78017    Fax 830/965-4069

**Schools:** 4 \ **Teachers:** 76 \ **Students:** 950 \ **Special Ed Students:** 131 \ **LEP Students:** 34 \ **College-Bound:** 50% \ **Ethnic:** Asian 1%, Hispanic 90%, Caucasian 9% \ **Exp:** $562 (High) \ **Poverty:** 36% \ **Title I:** $487,971 \ **Open-Close:** 08/10 - 05/27 \ **DTBP:** $349 (High)

| | | | |
|---|---|---|---|
| **Dr Maria Leo** | 1 | Regina Sambrano | 2 |
| Javier Torres | 3 | Raul Ramirez | 5 |
| Steve Lozano | 11 | Ruben Pecina | 58 |
| Aida Chapa | 67 | Matthew Agular | 73 |

| Public Schs..Principal | Grd | Prgm | Enr/#Cls | SN | |
|---|---|---|---|---|---|
| Dilley Early Clg High Sch<br>245 W FM 117, Dilley 78017<br>Jadie Matthew | 11-12 | | 100 | | 830/965-1814 |
| Dilley Elem Sch<br>226 W Curtis St, Dilley 78017<br>**Adam Martinez** | PK-5 | T | 424<br>40 | 87% | 830/965-1313<br>Fax 830/965-1178 |
| Dilley High Sch<br>230 W FM 117, Dilley 78017<br>Roger Solis | 9-12 | AGTV | 294<br>25 | 73% | 830/965-1814<br>Fax 830/965-1276 |
| Mary Harper Middle Sch<br>208 W Curtis St, Dilley 78017<br>Jennifer Torres | 6-8 | T | 222<br>19 | 82% | 830/965-2195<br>Fax 830/965-2171<br>🇫 🇹 |

- **Pearsall Ind School Dist** PID: 01018610    830/334-8001
  318 Berry Ranch Rd, Pearsall 78061    Fax 830/334-8007

**Schools:** 4 \ **Teachers:** 147 \ **Students:** 2,100 \ **Special Ed Students:** 226 \ **LEP Students:** 125 \ **Ethnic:** African American 1%, Hispanic 94%, Caucasian 5% \ **Exp:** $268 (Med) \ **Poverty:** 30% \ **Title I:** $1,006,297 \ **Open-Close:** 08/12 - 05/27 \ **DTBP:** $362 (High) \ 🇫 🇹

| | | | |
|---|---|---|---|
| Dr Norbert Rodriguez | 1 | Teresa Trevino | 2 |
| Andres Cuevas | 3 | Jesse Ontiveros | 3 |
| Jesse Hinojosa | 5,73,295 | Edward Bocanegra | 6 |
| Sonya Martinez | 8,68,69,79 | Ruben Pesina | 11,57,58,88,271,288,296 |
| Tommy Navarro | 67 | Chris Marquez | 91 |

| Public Schs..Principal | Grd | Prgm | Enr/#Cls | SN | |
|---|---|---|---|---|---|
| Pearsall High Sch<br>1990 Maverick Dr, Pearsall 78061<br>Varghese Panachakunnil | 9-12 | AGTV | 599<br>40 | 80% | 830/334-8011<br>Fax 830/334-5018 |
| Pearsall Intermediate Sch<br>415 E Florida St, Pearsall 78061<br>**Brian Hicks** | 3-5 | T | 517<br>60 | 85% | 830/334-3316<br>Fax 830/334-5006 |
| Pearsall Junior High Sch<br>607 E Alabama St, Pearsall 78061<br>Devon Zamzow | 6-8 | ATV | 474<br>40 | 78% | 830/334-8021<br>Fax 830/334-8025 |
| Ted Flores Elem Sch<br>321 W Pena St, Pearsall 78061<br>Linda Chavera | PK-2 | T | 461<br>38 | 81% | 830/334-4108<br>Fax 830/334-5047 |

| | | | | | |
|---|---|---|---|---|---|
| 79 Student Personnel | 91 Safety/Security | 275 Response To Intervention | 298 Grant Writer/Ptnrships | **School Programs** | **Social Media** |
| 80 Driver Ed/Safety | 92 Magnet School | 277 Remedial Math K-12 | 750 Chief Innovation Officer | A = Alternative Program | |
| 81 Gifted/Talented | 93 Parental Involvement | 280 Literacy Coach | 751 Chief of Staff | G = Adult Classes | 🇫 = Facebook |
| 82 Video Services | 95 Tech Prep Program | 285 STEM | 752 Social Emotional Learning | M = Magnet Program | |
| 83 Substance Abuse Prev | 97 Chief Information Officer | 286 Digital Learning | | T = Title I Schoolwide | 🇹 = Twitter |
| 84 Erate | 98 Chief Technology Officer | 288 Common Core Standards | **Other School Types** | V = Career & Tech Ed Programs | |
| 85 AIDS Education | 270 Character Education | 294 Accountability | Ⓐ = Alternative School | | |
| 88 Alternative/At Risk | 271 Migrant Education | 295 Network System | Ⓒ = Charter School | **New Schools are shaded** | |
| 89 Multi-Cultural Curriculum | 273 Teacher Mentor | 296 Title II Programs | Ⓜ = Magnet School | **New Superintendents and Principals are bold** | |
| 90 Social Work | 274 Before/After Sch | 297 Webmaster | Ⓨ = Year-Round School | **Personnel with email addresses are underscored** | |

## FRIO PRIVATE SCHOOLS

| Private Schs..Principal | Grd | Prgm | Enr/#Cls | SN |
|---|---|---|---|---|
| Faith Christian Academy | 2-11 | | 35 | 830/965-1324 |
| 124 E Leona St, Dilley 78017 | | | 1 | Fax 830/965-1096 |
| Janeen Hartsfield | | | | |

# GAINES COUNTY

## GAINES PUBLIC SCHOOLS

• **Loop Ind School Dist** PID: 01018684          806/487-6412
1441 Highway 303, Loop 79342                     Fax 806/487-6420

**Schools:** 1 \ **Teachers:** 17 \ **Students:** 124 \ **Special Ed Students:** 9
\ **LEP Students:** 10 \ **College-Bound:** 100% \ **Ethnic:** Hispanic 39%,
Caucasian 61% \ **Exp:** $948 (High) \ **Poverty:** 12% \ **Title I:** $20,972 \
**Open-Close:** 08/19 - 05/21 \ **DTBP:** $400 (High)

| | | | |
|---|---|---|---|
| Heath Blackman | 1,11,288 | Deanne Bratcher | 2 |
| Rebecca Sescota | 4 | Vanetta Blackmon | 8,69,88* |
| Charla Scott | 16,27* | Kim McCoral | 58* |
| Norman Crow | 67 | | |

| Public Schs..Principal | Grd | Prgm | Enr/#Cls | SN | |
|---|---|---|---|---|---|
| Loop Sch | PK-12 | TV | 124 | 55% | 806/487-6412 |
| 1441 Highway 303, Loop 79342 | | | 22 | | |
| Heath Blackmon | | | | | 🔲 |

• **Seagraves Ind School Dist** PID: 01018713          806/387-2035
1301 16th St, Seagraves 79359                    Fax 806/387-2944

**Schools:** 3 \ **Teachers:** 43 \ **Students:** 547 \ **Special Ed Students:** 45
\ **LEP Students:** 122 \ **College-Bound:** 58% \ **Ethnic:** African American
7%, Hispanic 80%, Caucasian 13% \ **Exp:** $920 (High) \ **Poverty:** 25% \
**Title I:** $322,715 \ **Open-Close:** 08/19 - 05/28 \ **DTBP:** $350 (High) \ 🔲

| | | | |
|---|---|---|---|
| Joshua Goen | 1,83 | Traci Garza | 2 |
| Ruben Valles | 3,5 | Armando Minjarez | 6 |
| Jennifer Floyd | 7,85* | Daylan Sellers | 10* |
| Michelle Davila | 11,296,298 | Scott Beck | 28,73* |
| Angel Davila | 37 | Mary Heryford | 38 |
| Rose Flores | 57* | Michelle Bright | 58 |
| Wesley Rodgers | 67 | Melinda Martinez | 76 |

| Public Schs..Principal | Grd | Prgm | Enr/#Cls | SN | |
|---|---|---|---|---|---|
| Seagraves Elem Sch | PK-5 | | 320 | | 806/387-2015 |
| 1300 Avenue J, Seagraves 79359 | | | 35 | | Fax 806/387-3339 |
| **Jeff Fleenor** | | | | | 🔲 |
| Seagraves High Sch | 9-12 | ATV | 166 | 78% | 806/387-2520 |
| 1801 Avenue K, Seagraves 79359 | | | 20 | | |
| Daylan Sellers | | | | | 🔲 |
| Seagraves Junior High Sch | 6-8 | | 144 | | 806/387-2646 |
| 1605 Avenue K, Seagraves 79359 | | | 16 | | Fax 806/387-2451 |
| Jame Humphries | | | | | 🔲 |

• **Seminole Ind School Dist** PID: 01018751          432/758-3662
207 SW 6th St, Seminole 79360                    Fax 432/758-9833

**Schools:** 6 \ **Teachers:** 224 \ **Students:** 2,619 \ **Special Ed Students:** 234 \
**LEP Students:** 416 \ **Ethnic:** Asian 1%, African American 1%, Hispanic 51%,
Caucasian 48% \ **Exp:** $492 (High) \ **Poverty:** 21% \ **Title I:** $1,199,079 \
**Special Education:** $514,000 \ **Open-Close:** 08/13 - 05/20 \ **DTBP:** $379
(High) \ 🔲 🔲

| | | | |
|---|---|---|---|
| Kyle Lynch | 1 | Jay Lashaway | 2 |
| Bryan Ritchie | 3 | Cindy Therwhanger | 4 |
| Arsenio Ramirez | 5 | David Williams | 6 |
| Cheryl Houston | 7,85* | Dr Sylvia Suarez | 8,11,15,57,280,288,296 |
| Jeanet Lambert | 30 | Cindy Franklin | 58 |
| Shane Wimmer | 67 | Tasha Garcia | 69* |
| Stephanie Stone | 73,286,297 | Chris Brattain | 88 |

| Public Schs..Principal | Grd | Prgm | Enr/#Cls | SN | |
|---|---|---|---|---|---|
| Seminole Elem Sch | 4-5 | T | 457 | 56% | 432/758-3615 |
| 401 SW Avenue B, Seminole 79360 | | | 21 | | Fax 432/758-9064 |
| Aine Lopez | | | | | |
| Seminole High Sch | 9-12 | T | 171 | 42% | 432/758-5873 |
| 2100 NW Avenue D, Seminole 79360 | | | 80 | | Fax 432/758-8146 |
| Robert Chappell | | | | | |
| Seminole Junior High Sch | 6-8 | T | 694 | 55% | 432/758-9431 |
| 600 NW Avenue J, Seminole 79360 | | | 50 | | Fax 432/758-5795 |
| Randy Hicks | | | | | |
| Seminole Primary Sch | 2-3 | T | 437 | 58% | 432/758-5841 |
| 508 SW Avenue D, Seminole 79360 | | | 18 | | Fax 432/758-5299 |
| Kathy Moore | | | | | |
| Seminole Success Center | 6-12 | T | 34 | 59% | 432/758-2772 |
| 206 SW 3rd St, Seminole 79360 | | | 6 | | Fax 432/758-9917 |
| Seth Davis | | | | | |
| Young Elem Sch | PK-1 | T | 427 | 67% | 432/758-3636 |
| 2100 SW Avenue B, Seminole 79360 | | | 35 | | Fax 432/758-2066 |
| Sherry Warren | | | | | |

# GALVESTON COUNTY

## GALVESTON PUBLIC SCHOOLS

• **Clear Creek Ind School Dist** PID: 01018816          281/284-0000
2425 E Main St, League City 77573                Fax 281/284-9901

**Schools:** 46 \ **Teachers:** 2,532 \ **Students:** 42,042 \
**Special Ed Students:** 4,487 \ **LEP Students:** 4,521 \ **College-Bound:** 80%
\ **Ethnic:** Asian 10%, African American 9%, Hispanic 33%, Caucasian
48% \ **Exp:** $232 (Med) \ **Poverty:** 9% \ **Title I:** $5,705,110 \
**Special Education:** $5,914,000 \ **Open-Close:** 08/18 - 05/27 \ **DTBP:** $193
(High)

| | | | |
|---|---|---|---|
| Dr Greg Smith | 1 | Paul McLarty | 2,3,15 |
| Paul Miller | 3 | Fred Walker | 4 |
| Wendell Johns | 5 | Debbie Fuchs | 6,35 |
| Dr Steven Ebell | 8,15 | Holly Hughes | 9,15 |
| Karen Engle | 10,15* | Dr Casey O'Pry | 15,68,273 |
| Sue Ferrell | 16 | Greg Goodman | 20,23 |
| Dana Morgan | 27,31 | Christy Lawrence | 34* |
| Dava West | 36 | Marny Doepken | 39* |
| Anne Smith | 43 | Lisa Wooley | 44 |
| Rachel Powell | 46,277 | Lana Zimmer | 47 |

| | | | | | | | |
|---|---|---|---|---|---|---|---|
| 1 | Superintendent | 8 | Curric/Instruct K-12 | 19 | Chief Financial Officer | 29 | Family/Consumer Science |
| 2 | Bus/Finance/Purchasing | 9 | Curric/Instruct Elem | 20 | Art K-12 | 30 | Adult Education |
| 3 | Buildings And Grounds | 10 | Curric/Instruct Sec | 21 | Art Elem | 31 | Career/Sch-to-Work K-12 |
| 4 | Food Service | 11 | Federal Program | 22 | Art Sec | 32 | Career/Sch-to-Work Elem |
| 5 | Transportation | 12 | Title I | 23 | Music K-12 | 33 | Career/Sch-to-Work Sec |
| 6 | Athletic | 13 | Title V | 24 | Music Elem | 34 | Early Childhood Ed |
| 7 | Health Services | 15 | Asst Superintendent | 25 | Music Sec | 35 | Health/Phys Education |
| | | 16 | Instructional Media Svcs | 26 | Business Education | 36 | Guidance Services K-12 |
| | | 17 | Chief Operations Officer | 27 | Career & Tech Ed | 37 | Guidance Services Elem |
| | | 18 | Chief Academic Officer | 28 | Technology Education | 38 | Guidance Services Sec |

| | | | | | | | |
|---|---|---|---|---|---|---|---|
| 39 | Social Studies K-12 | 49 | English/Lang Arts Elem | 59 | Special Education Elem | 69 | Academic Assessment |
| 40 | Social Studies Elem | 50 | English/Lang Arts Sec | 60 | Special Education Sec | 70 | Research/Development |
| 41 | Social Studies Sec | 51 | Reading K-12 | 61 | Foreign/World Lang K-12 | 71 | Public Information |
| 42 | Science K-12 | 52 | Reading Elem | 62 | Foreign/World Lang Elem | 72 | Summer School |
| 43 | Science Elem | 53 | Reading Sec | 63 | Foreign/World Lang Sec | 73 | Instructional Tech |
| 44 | Science Sec | 54 | Remedial Reading K-12 | 64 | Religious Education K-12 | 74 | Inservice Training |
| 45 | Math K-12 | 55 | Remedial Reading Elem | 65 | Religious Education Elem | 75 | Marketing/Distributive |
| 46 | Math Elem | 56 | Remedial Reading Sec | 66 | Religious Education Sec | 76 | Info Systems |
| 47 | Math Sec | 57 | Bilingual/ELL | 67 | School Board President | 77 | Psychological Assess |
| 48 | English/Lang Arts K-12 | 58 | Special Education K-12 | 68 | Teacher Personnel | 78 | Affirmative Action |

| Public Schs..Principal | Grd | Prgm | Enr/#Cls | SN | |
|---|---|---|---|---|---|
| Armand Bayou Elem Sch<br>16000 Hickory Knoll Dr, Houston 77059<br>Jenny Thomas | PK-5 | T | 576<br>31 | 40% | 281/284-5100<br>Fax 281/284-5106 |
| Art & Pat Goforth Elem Sch<br>2610 Webster St, League City 77573<br>Mark Smith | PK-5 | | 897 | 22% | 281/284-6000<br>Fax 281/284-6006 |
| Bayside Intermediate Sch<br>4430 Village Way, League City 77573<br>James Thomas | 6-8 | | 874 | 18% | 281/284-3000<br>Fax 281/284-3005 |
| Brookside Intermediate Sch<br>3535 E FM 528 Rd, Friendswood 77546<br>Lauren Ambeau | 6-8 | TV | 892<br>88 | 35% | 281/284-3600<br>Fax 281/284-3605 |
| Brookwood Elem Sch<br>16850 Middlebrook Dr, Houston 77059<br>Kathryn Gouger | PK-5 | | 713 | 40% | 281/284-5600<br>Fax 281/284-5605 |
| C D Landolt Elem Sch<br>2104 Pilgrims Point Dr, Friendswood 77546<br>Debra Reno | PK-5 | T | 803<br>37 | 46% | 281/284-5200<br>Fax 281/284-5206 |
| Clear Brook High Sch<br>4607 FM 2351 Rd, Friendswood 77546<br>Michele Staley | 9-12 | V | 2,258<br>120 | 24% | 281/284-2100<br>Fax 281/284-2105 |
| Clear Connections Online Acad<br>2425 E Main St, League City 77573<br>**Adrian Washburn** | K-12 | | 100 | | 281/284-0000 |
| Clear Creek High Sch<br>2305 E Main St, League City 77573<br>James Majewski | 9-12 | GV | 2,391 | 24% | 281/284-1700<br>Fax 281/284-1705 |
| Clear Creek Intermediate Sch<br>2451 E Main St, League City 77573<br>Kimberly Brouillard | 6-8 | T | 503 | 46% | 281/284-2300<br>Fax 281/284-2306 |
| Clear Falls High Sch<br>4380 Village Way, League City 77573<br>Paul House | 9-12 | V | 2,773 | 13% | 281/284-1100<br>Fax 281/284-1106 |
| Clear Horizons Early Clg HS<br>13735 Beamer Rd Box 613, Houston 77089<br>Marshall Ponce | 9-12 | | 443 | 33% | 281/929-4657<br>Fax 281/284-9960 |
| Clear Lake City Elem Sch<br>1707 Fairwind Rd, Houston 77062<br>Jepsey Kimble | PK-5 | T | 542<br>26 | 46% | 281/284-4200<br>Fax 281/284-4205 |
| Clear Lake High Sch<br>2929 Bay Area Blvd, Houston 77058<br>David Drake | 9-12 | V | 2,325 | 21% | 281/284-1900<br>Fax 281/286-3249 |
| Clear Lake Intermediate Sch<br>15545 El Camino Real, Houston 77062<br>Lonnie Leal | 6-8 | V | 930<br>70 | 34% | 281/284-3200<br>Fax 281/284-3205 |
| Ⓐ Clear Path Alt High Sch<br>1001 Magnolia St, Webster 77598<br>Jerry Herd | 6-12 | | 150 | | 281/284-1600<br>Fax 281/284-1605 |
| Clear Springs High Sch<br>501 Palomino St, League City 77573<br>Michael Houston | 9-12 | | 2,815 | 14% | 281/284-1300<br>Fax 281/284-1305 |
| Ⓐ Clear View High Sch<br>400 S Walnut St, Webster 77598<br>Monica Speaks | 9-12 | | 153<br>22 | 32% | 281/284-1500<br>Fax 281/284-1505 |
| Creekside Intermediate Sch<br>4320 W Main St, League City 77573<br>Mandy Scott | 6-8 | V | 915<br>50 | 19% | 281/284-3500<br>Fax 281/284-3505 |
| Darwin L Gilmore Elem Sch<br>3552 W League City Pkwy, League City 77573<br>Suzanne Jones | PK-5 | | 874 | 19% | 281/284-6400<br>Fax 281/284-6405 |
| Ⓜ Ed White E-STEM Magnet Sch<br>1708 Les Talley Dr, El Lago 77586<br>Matthew Paulson | PK-5 | | 542<br>27 | 23% | 281/284-4300<br>Fax 281/284-4305 |
| Falcon Pass Elem Sch<br>2465 Falcon Pass Dr, Houston 77062<br>Monica Giuffre | PK-5 | | 613 | 40% | 281/284-6200<br>Fax 281/284-6205 |
| Florence Campbell Sch<br>6605 W Elem Pkwy, League City 77573<br>Erin Tite | PK-5 | | 700 | | 281/284-6600<br>Fax 281/284-6605 |
| G H Whitcomb Elem Sch<br>900 Reseda Dr, Houston 77062<br>Diana Kattner | PK-5 | T | 574<br>36 | 60% | 281/284-4900<br>Fax 281/284-4906 |
| G W Robinson Elem Sch<br>451 Kirby Rd, Seabrook 77586<br>Yolanda Jones | PK-5 | | 414 | 23% | 281/284-6500<br>Fax 281/284-6505 |
| Henry Bauerschlag Elem Sch<br>2051 W League City Pkwy, League City 77573<br>Kelly Chapman | PK-5 | | 949 | 13% | 281/284-6100<br>Fax 281/284-6105 |
| I W & Eleanor Hyde Elem Sch<br>3700 FM 518 Rd E, League City 77573<br>Suzanne Saunders | PK-5 | | 653<br>36 | 26% | 281/284-5800<br>Fax 281/284-5805 |
| James F Bay Elem Sch<br>1502 Bayport Blvd, Seabrook 77586<br>Deborah Johnson | PK-5 | T | 723<br>42 | 44% | 281/284-4600<br>Fax 281/284-4606 |
| James H Ross Elem Sch<br>2401 W Main St, League City 77573<br>Kelly Sawchak-Mooney | PK-5 | T | 577<br>40 | 42% | 281/284-4500 |
| John F Ward Elem Sch<br>1440 Bouldercrest Dr, Houston 77062<br>Elizabeth Pawlowski | PK-5 | | 480<br>36 | 35% | 281/284-5400<br>Fax 281/284-5405 |
| Lavace Stewart Elem Sch<br>330 Marina Bay Dr, Kemah 77565<br>Dr Britani Moses | PK-5 | T | 810<br>35 | 58% | 281/284-4700<br>Fax 281/284-4706 |
| League City Elem Sch<br>520 E Walker, League City 77573<br>Xan Wood | PK-5 | T | 425 | 69% | 281/284-4400<br>Fax 281/284-4405 |
| League City Intermediate Sch<br>2588 Webster St, League City 77573<br>Kimberly Brouillard | 6-8 | V | 1,066<br>50 | 14% | 281/284-3400<br>Fax 281/284-3405 |
| Lloyd R Ferguson Elem Sch<br>1910 S Compass Rose Blvd, League City 77573<br>Paige Hutchinson | PK-5 | | 599<br>55 | 21% | 281/284-5500<br>Fax 281/284-5505 |
| Margaret S McWhirter Elem Sch<br>300 Pennsylvania St, Webster 77598<br>Dr Michael Marquez | PK-5 | T | 796<br>50 | 73% | 281/284-4800<br>Fax 281/284-4805 |
| North Pointe Elem Sch<br>3200 Almond Creek Dr, Houston 77059<br>Diana Kattner | PK-5 | | 731<br>45 | 38% | 281/284-5900<br>Fax 281/284-5905 |
| P H Greene Elem Sch<br>2903 Friendswood Link Rd, Webster 77598<br>Lesa Gaffey | PK-5 | T | 679 | 47% | 281/284-5000<br>Fax 281/284-5005 |
| Ralph Parr Elem Sch<br>1315 Highway 3 S, League City 77573<br>Jane Kelling | PK-5 | | 707 | 29% | 281/284-4100<br>Fax 281/284-4105 |
| Sandra Mossman Elem Sch<br>4050 Village Way, League City 77573<br>Sara Konesheck | PK-5 | | 849 | 13% | 281/284-4000<br>Fax 281/284-4005 |
| Seabrook Intermediate Sch<br>2401 N Meyer Ave, Seabrook 77586<br>Sharon Lopez | 6-8 | | 958<br>60 | 16% | 281/284-3100<br>Fax 281/284-3107 |
| Space Center Intermediate Sch<br>17400 Saturn Ln, Houston 77058<br>Ann Thornton | 6-8 | V | 1,030<br>75 | 39% | 281/284-3300<br>Fax 281/284-3305 |

| | | | | | |
|---|---|---|---|---|---|
| Victory Lakes Intermediate Sch<br>2880 W Walker St, League City 77573<br>Leatrice Sanders | 6-8 | | 1,126 | 17% | 281/284-3700<br>Fax 281/284-3705 |
| Walter Hall Elem Sch<br>5931 Meadowside St, League City 77573<br>Stephanie King | PK-5 | | 724<br>36 | 13% | 281/284-5300<br>Fax 281/284-5305 |
| Weber Elem Sch<br>11955 Blackhawk Blvd, Houston 77089<br>Cheryl Chaney | PK-5 | T | 850<br>42 | 40% | 281/284-6300<br>Fax 281/284-6305 |
| Wedgewood Elem Sch<br>4000 Friendswood Link Rd, Friendswood 77546<br>Buffie Johnson | PK-5 | T | 729 | 47% | 281/284-5700<br>Fax 281/284-5705 |
| Westbrook Intermediate Sch<br>302 W El Dorado Blvd, Friendswood 77546<br>Stephanie Cooper | 6-8 | | 1,141 | 27% | 281/284-3800<br>Fax 281/284-3805 |

● **Dickinson Ind School Dist** PID: 01018969      281/229 6000
2218 FM 517 Rd E, Dickinson 77539              Fax 281/229-6011

**Schools:** 14 \ **Teachers:** 769 \ **Students:** 10,400 \
**Special Ed Students:** 1,314 \ **LEP Students:** 1,571 \ **Ethnic:** Asian 2%,
African American 17%, Hispanic 52%, Caucasian 29% \ **Exp:** $370 (High)
\ **Poverty:** 18% \ **Title I:** $2,479,690 \ **Special Education:** $1,578,000 \
**Open-Close:** 08/24 - 05/27 \ **DTBP:** $186 (High) \ [f]

| | | | |
|---|---|---|---|
| Carla Voelkel ........... 1 | | Ryan Boone ........... 2,3,15 |
| Jimmy Anderson ........... 3 | | Judy Lee ........... 4 |
| Brian Cmaidalka ........... 5 | | John Snelson ........... 6* |
| Robert Cobb ........... 15 | | Laurie Rodriguez ........... 58,77 |
| David Swartz ........... 67 | | Kimberly Rich ........... 68,79 |
| Dr Jeff Pack ........... 69,294 | | Tammy Dowdy ........... 71 |
| Melissa Williams-Scott ........... 76* | | Wendy Chide ........... 88* |
| Jo Allen ........... 90* | | |

| Public Schs..Principal | Grd | Prgm | Enr/#Cls | SN | |
|---|---|---|---|---|---|
| Barber Middle Sch<br>5651 FM 517 Rd E, Dickinson 77539<br>Lindsey Suarez | 5-6 | T | 709 | 64% | 281/229-6900<br>Fax 281/229-6901 |
| Bay Colony Elem Sch<br>101 Bay Colony Elementary Dr, Dickinson 77539<br>Amy Smith | PK-4 | T | 695<br>45 | 54% | 281/229-6200<br>Fax 281/229-6201 |
| Calder Road Elem Sch<br>6511 Calder Dr, Dickinson 77539<br>Sophia Acevedo | PK-4 | T | 568 | 55% | 281/229-7500<br>Fax 281/229-7501 |
| Ⓐ Dickinson Alt Lrng Center<br>2805 Oak Park St, Dickinson 77539<br>**Valerie Martinez** | 9-12 | T | 64<br>4 | 68% | 281/229-6300<br>Fax 281/229-6351 |
| Dickinson High Sch<br>3800 Baker Dr, Dickinson 77539<br>Dr Billye Smith | 9-12 | TV | 3,006 | 60% | 281/229-6400<br>Fax 281/229-6401 |
| Dunbar Middle Sch<br>2901 23rd St, Dickinson 77539<br>Temeka Brown | 5-6 | T | 652<br>26 | 83% | 281/229-6600<br>Fax 281/229-6601 |
| Elva C Lobit Middle Sch<br>1251 FM 517 Rd W, Dickinson 77539<br>Terri Bruce | 5-6 | T | 209 | 52% | 281/229-7700 |
| Hughes Road Elem Sch<br>11901 Hughes Rd, Dickinson 77539<br>**Kelly Colburn** | PK-4 | T | 664<br>36 | 67% | 281/229-6700<br>Fax 281/229-6701 |
| Jake Silbernagel Elem Sch<br>4201 25th St, Dickinson 77539<br>Leslie Tracy-Burke | PK-4 | T | 676<br>35 | 81% | 281/229-6800<br>Fax 281/229-6801 |
| Kenneth E Little Elem Sch<br>622 Oklahoma Ave, Bacliff 77518<br>Brooke Newell | PK-4 | T | 703<br>60 | 81% | 281/229-7000<br>Fax 281/229-7001 |

| | | | | | |
|---|---|---|---|---|---|
| Kranz Junior High Sch<br>12850 FM 3436 Rd, Dickinson 77539<br>Kim Kelley | 7-8 | T | 924 | 65% | 281/309-3600 |
| Louis G Lobit Elem Sch<br>1251 FM 517 Rd W, Dickinson 77539<br>Stephanie Williams | PK-4 | T | 544 | 41% | 281/229-7600 |
| R D McAdams Junior High Sch<br>11415 Hughes Rd, Dickinson 77539<br>Rachelle Beafneaux | 7-8 | T | 373<br>55 | 63% | 281/229-7100<br>Fax 281/229-7101 |
| San Leon Elem Sch<br>2655 Broadway St, Dickinson 77539<br>Sherri Blackburn \ Diana Medina | PK-4 | T | 626<br>50 | 78% | 281/229-7400<br>Fax 281/229-7401 |

● **Friendswood Ind Sch Dist** PID: 01019028      281/482-1267
302 Laurel Dr, Friendswood 77546              Fax 281/996-2513

**Schools:** 6 \ **Teachers:** 372 \ **Students:** 6,000 \ **Special Ed Students:** 656
\ **LEP Students:** 122 \ **College-Bound:** 98% \ **Ethnic:** Asian 6%,
African American 2%, Hispanic 20%, Caucasian 72% \ **Exp:** $213 (Med)
\ **Poverty:** 6% \ **Title I:** $429,210 \ **Special Education:** $942,000 \
**Open-Close:** 08/14 - 05/21 \ **DTBP:** $181 (High) \ [f] [t]

| | | | |
|---|---|---|---|
| Thad Roher ........... 1 | | Amber Petree ........... 2 |
| David Moynihan ........... 4 | | Dean Lewis ........... 5 |
| Robert Koopman ........... 6* | | Dahria Driskall ........... 13,58 |
| Diane Myers ........... 15 | | Susan Kirkpatricke ........... 27 |
| Tony Hopkins ........... 67 | | Lynn Tunnel ........... 68 |
| Dana Owen ........... 71,76 | | Mark Griffon ........... 72* |
| Mike Gasiorowski ........... 76 | | Erich Kreiter ........... 91 |
| Tonia Meadows ........... 286,295 | | Brian Smith ........... 295 |

| Public Schs..Principal | Grd | Prgm | Enr/#Cls | SN | |
|---|---|---|---|---|---|
| C W Cline Elem Sch<br>505 Briarmeadow Ave, Friendswood 77546<br>Barry Clifford | PK-2 | | 499<br>37 | 7% | 281/482-1201<br>Fax 281/996-2557 |
| Friendswood High Sch<br>702 Greenbriar Ave, Friendswood 77546<br>Mark Griffon | 9-12 | | 2,098 | 7% | 281/482-3413<br>Fax 281/996-2523 |
| Friendswood Junior High Sch<br>1000 Manison Pkwy, Friendswood 77546<br>Dana Drew | 6-8 | | 1,425<br>65 | 9% | 281/996-6200<br>Fax 281/996-6262 |
| Westwood-Bales Elem Sch<br>506 W Edgewood Dr, Friendswood 77546<br>Kristin Moffitt | PK-2 | T | 595<br>37 | 22% | 281/482-3341<br>Fax 281/996-2594 |
| Windsong Intermediate Sch<br>2100 W Parkwood Ave, Friendswood 77546<br>**Wendy McAshlan** | 3-5 | | 450<br>28 | 5% | 281/482-0111<br>Fax 281/996-2594 |
| Zue S Bales Intermediate Sch<br>211 Stadium Ln, Friendswood 77546<br>J T Patton | 3-5 | T | 632 | 16% | 281/482-8255<br>Fax 281/996-2551 |

● **Galveston Ind School Dist** PID: 01019078      409/766-5100
3904 Avenue T, Galveston 77550              Fax 409/762-8391

**Schools:** 11 \ **Teachers:** 445 \ **Students:** 7,000 \ **Special Ed Students:** 616
\ **LEP Students:** 1,143 \ **College-Bound:** 71% \ **Ethnic:** Asian 2%,
African American 24%, Hispanic 46%, Caucasian 28% \ **Exp:** $390 (High)
\ **Poverty:** 23% \ **Title I:** $2,292,129 \ **Special Education:** $1,771,000 \
**Bilingual Education:** $60,000 \ **Open-Close:** 08/24 - 05/27 \ **DTBP:** $159
(High)

| | | | |
|---|---|---|---|
| Dr Kelli Moulton ........... 1 | | Paul Byers ........... 3 |
| Jennifer Douglas ........... 4 | | John Pruitt ........... 5 |
| Walter Fortune ........... 6,35 | | Dr Annette Scott ........... 8,11,15 |
| Elizabeth Bennett ........... 9* | | Molly Allmond-Helmer ........... 10* |
| Mariana Mueller ........... 16,73 | | Eric Paul ........... 27 |

| | | | | | | | |
|---|---|---|---|---|---|---|---|
| 1 | Superintendent | 8 | Curric/Instruct K-12 | 19 | Chief Financial Officer | 29 | Family/Consumer Science |
| 2 | Bus/Finance/Purchasing | 9 | Curric/Instruct Elem | 20 | Art K-12 | 30 | Adult Education |
| 3 | Buildings And Grounds | 10 | Curric/Instruct Sec | 21 | Art Elem | 31 | Career/Sch-to-Work K-12 |
| 4 | Food Service | 11 | Federal Program | 22 | Art Sec | 32 | Career/Sch-to-Work Elem |
| 5 | Transportation | 12 | Title I | 23 | Music K-12 | 33 | Career/Sch-to-Work Sec |
| 6 | Athletic | 13 | Title V | 24 | Music Elem | 34 | Early Childhood Ed |
| 7 | Health Services | 14 | Title I | 25 | Music Sec | 35 | Health/Phys Education |
| | | 15 | Asst Superintendent | 26 | Business Education | 36 | Guidance Services K-12 |
| | | 16 | Instructional Media Svcs | 27 | Career & Tech Ed | 37 | Guidance Services Elem |
| | | 17 | Chief Operations Officer | 28 | Technology Education | 38 | Guidance Services Sec |
| | | 18 | Chief Academic Officer | | | | |

| | | | | | | | |
|---|---|---|---|---|---|---|---|
| 39 | Social Studies K-12 | 49 | English/Lang Arts Elem | 59 | Special Education Elem | 69 | Academic Assessment |
| 40 | Social Studies Elem | 50 | English/Lang Arts Sec | 60 | Special Education Sec | 70 | Research/Development |
| 41 | Social Studies Sec | 51 | Reading K-12 | 61 | Foreign/World Lang K-12 | 71 | Public Information |
| 42 | Science K-12 | 52 | Reading Elem | 62 | Foreign/World Lang Elem | 72 | Summer School |
| 43 | Science Elem | 53 | Reading Sec | 63 | Foreign/World Lang Sec | 73 | Instructional Tech |
| 44 | Science Sec | 54 | Remedial Reading K-12 | 64 | Religious Education K-12 | 74 | Inservice Training |
| 45 | Math K-12 | 55 | Remedial Reading Elem | 65 | Religious Education Elem | 75 | Marketing/Distributive |
| 46 | Math Elem | 56 | Remedial Reading Sec | 66 | Religious Education Sec | 76 | Info Systems |
| 47 | Math Sec | 57 | Bilingual/ELL | 67 | School Board President | 77 | Psychological Assess |
| 48 | English/Lang Arts K-12 | 58 | Special Education K-12 | 68 | Teacher Personnel | 78 | Affirmative Action |

| | |
|---|---|
| Mary Patrick ............................34,58 | Desiree Hartnett .................................57 |
| Jessica Swenson ..........................58* | Jessica Edwards ..................................58 |
| Anthony Brown ..............................67 | Dyann Polzin ..................................68,71 |
| Dr Keri Launius .............................74 | John Mathis ..........................76,84,295 |
| Netobia Taylor ...............................76 | Leeroy Amador ....................................91 |

| Public Schs..Principal | Grd | Prgm | Enr/#Cls | SN | |
|---|---|---|---|---|---|
| Aim College & Career Prep Acad<br>3014 Sealy St, Galveston 77550<br>Cheryl Rutledge | 6-12 | | 26 | | 409/761-6302<br>Fax 409/770-0918 |
| ⓜ Austin Middle Sch<br>1514 N 1/2, Galveston 77550<br>Matthew Neighbors | 5-8 | ATV | 565<br>35 | 57% | 409/761-3500<br>Fax 409/465-5946 |
| Ball High Sch<br>4115 Avenue O, Galveston 77550<br>Joseph Pillar | 9-12 | TV | 1,543 | 71% | 409/766-5700<br>Fax 409/766-5766 |
| Burnet Early Childhood Univ ES<br>5501 Avenue S, Galveston 77551<br>Beatriz Rodriguez | PK-4 | T | 536 | 85% | 409/761-6470 |
| Central Media Arts Academy<br>3014 Sealy St, Galveston 77550<br>Monique Lewis | 5-8 | TV | 602<br>46 | 89% | 409/761-6200<br>Fax 409/765-2141<br>f |
| Collegiate Academy at Weis<br>7100 Stewart Rd, Galveston 77551<br>Cornelius Phelps | 5-8 | T | 718 | 79% | 409/761-6100<br>Fax 409/770-0339<br>f |
| Crenshaw Elem & Mid Sch<br>416 Highway 87, Crystal Beach 77650<br>Tracie Camp | PK-8 | | 133 | | 409/761-6350<br>f |
| Greta Oppe Elem Sch<br>2915 81st St, Galveston 77554<br>Alice Prets | PK-4 | T | 648 | 55% | 409/761-6500<br>Fax 409/744-1905 |
| L A Morgan Elem Sch<br>1410 37th St, Galveston 77550<br>Divya Nagpal | PK-4 | T | 563<br>28 | 94% | 409/761-6700<br>Fax 409/763-0122 |
| Parker Elem Sch<br>6802 Jones Dr, Galveston 77551<br>Elizabeth Murphy | PK-4 | T | 603<br>32 | 79% | 409/761-6600<br>Fax 409/744-8312 |
| © Rosenberg Elem Sch<br>721 10th St, Galveston 77550<br>Cathy Van Ness | PK-2 | | 209 | | 409/761-6800<br>Fax 409/765-5674 |

## ● High Island Ind Sch Dist PID: 01019250
2113 6th St, High Island 77623

409/286-5317
Fax 409/286-5351

> **Schools:** 1 \ **Teachers:** 12 \ **Students:** 135 \ **Special Ed Students:** 14 \
> **College-Bound:** 50% \ **Ethnic:** Asian 1%, African American 1%, Hispanic 9%,
> Native American: 4%, Caucasian 85% \ **Exp:** $714 (High) \ **Poverty:** 13% \
> **Title I:** $15,668 \ **Special Education:** $1,000 \ **Open-Close:** 08/26 - 05/28 \
> **DTBP:** $378 (High)

| | |
|---|---|
| Travis Grubbs ............................1 | Crystal Larson ...........................................2 |
| Sabrina Bobino ...........................5* | John Jackson ...........................................6* |
| Amanda Jackson ...........8,11,57,88,273* | Benny Barrow .........................................67 |
| Zach Rothwell ...........................73 | |

| Public Schs..Principal | Grd | Prgm | Enr/#Cls | SN | |
|---|---|---|---|---|---|
| High Island Sch<br>2113 6th St, High Island 77623<br>Travis Grubbs | PK-12 | T | 135<br>25 | 98% | 409/286-5313<br>Fax 409/286-2120 |

## ● Hitchcock Ind School Dist PID: 01019274
7801 Neville Ave, Hitchcock 77563

409/316-6545
Fax 409/986-5141

> **Schools:** 4 \ **Teachers:** 114 \ **Students:** 1,600 \ **Special Ed Students:** 219
> \ **LEP Students:** 103 \ **College-Bound:** 55% \ **Ethnic:** African American
> 42%, Hispanic 32%, Caucasian 25% \ **Exp:** $352 (High) \ **Poverty:** 24% \
> **Title I:** $519,431 \ **Bilingual Education:** $16,000 \ **Open-Close:** 08/17 -
> 05/27 \ **DTBP:** $520 (High) \ f t

| | |
|---|---|
| Travis Edwards ................................1 | Jennifer Donovan .......................2,19,296 |
| Christopher Armacost ...........3,73,84,97,98 | Bridget Ford ...........................................5 |
| Craig Smith ..................................6* | Kathy Potts .............................................7* |
| Kay Painter ...................................8 | Sarah Roach ...........................................12 |
| Evangelina Guerra ..........................58 | Chad Allen ..............................................67 |
| Sharanda Harrison .........................68 | Patrick Faour ..................................69,294 |
| Vicki Raveeno ..............................752 | |

| Public Schs..Principal | Grd | Prgm | Enr/#Cls | SN | |
|---|---|---|---|---|---|
| Crosby Middle Sch<br>6625 FM 2004 Rd, Hitchcock 77563<br>Cherissa Crawford | 6-8 | AT | 312<br>22 | 75% | 409/316-6542<br>Fax 409/986-9254<br>t |
| Hitchcock High Sch<br>6629 FM 2004 Rd, Hitchcock 77563<br>Laurie Gilcrease | 9-12 | ATV | 361<br>30 | 70% | 409/316-6544<br>Fax 409/986-9339 |
| Hitchcock Primary Sch<br>5901 FM 2004 Rd, Hitchcock 77563<br>Constance White | PK-2 | T | 392 | 85% | 409/316-6467<br>Fax 409/986-3168<br>f t |
| Stewart Elem Sch<br>7013 Stewart St, Hitchcock 77563<br>Lisa Fain | 3-5 | T | 392<br>29 | 80% | 409/316-6543<br>Fax 409/986-5563 |

## ● Santa Fe Ind School Dist PID: 01019432
4133 Warpath Ave, Santa Fe 77510

409/925-3526
Fax 409/925-4002

> **Schools:** 5 \ **Teachers:** 270 \ **Students:** 4,794 \
> **Special Ed Students:** 491 \ **LEP Students:** 186 \ **College-Bound:** 75% \
> **Ethnic:** Asian 1%, African American 1%, Hispanic 22%, Native American:
> 1%, Caucasian 76% \ **Exp:** $198 (Low) \ **Poverty:** 9% \ **Title I:** $480,283 \
> **Special Education:** $714,000 \ **Open-Close:** 08/13 - 05/27 \ **DTBP:** $181
> (High) \ f

| | |
|---|---|
| Dr Leigh Wall ................................1 | Lee Townsend ....................................2,19 |
| Marianne Junco .............................2 | Bob Atkins .............................................3 |
| Cherie Bowers ...............................4 | David McMillian ......................................5 |
| Mark McKinney ..............................6 | Mark Kanipes .........................................6 |
| Dr Jackie Shulman ................8,12,34,288 | Dr Jacqueline Shuman ...........................15 |
| Rick Morril .............................28,73 | Kathy Oliver ..........................................58 |
| Rusty Norman ...............................67 | Patti Hanssard ..............................68,71,79 |
| Lois Jones ...................................90 | Walter Braun ..........................................91 |
| Belinda Slawson ...........................274 | Sara Ryan ............................................294* |

| Public Schs..Principal | Grd | Prgm | Enr/#Cls | SN | |
|---|---|---|---|---|---|
| Dan J Kubacak Elem Sch<br>4131 Warpath Ave, Santa Fe 77510<br>**Harold Payne** | 5-5 | T | 1,065<br>32 | 52% | 409/925-9600<br>Fax 409/927-8262 |
| Roy J Wollam Elem Sch<br>3400 Avenue S, Santa Fe 77510<br>Michelle Pourchot | PK-5 | T | 1,119<br>37 | 56% | 409/925-2770<br>Fax 409/925-4276 |
| Santa Fe High Sch<br>16000 Highway 6, Santa Fe 77517<br>Rachel Harris | 9-12 | AGV | 293 | 32% | 409/927-3100<br>Fax 409/925-2773<br>f |
| Santa Fe Junior High Sch<br>4132 Warpath Ave, Santa Fe 77510<br>**Dr Florence Adkins** | 6-8 | T | 1,082 | 44% | 409/925-9300<br>Fax 409/927-4106 |
| William F Barnett Elem Sch<br>11818 Highway 1764, Santa Fe 77510<br>Destini Martin | PK-5 | | 401 | | 409/925-9700 |

- **Texas City Ind School Dist** PID: 01019470    409/916-0100
1700 9th Ave N, Texas City 77590    Fax 409/942-2655

**Schools:** 14 \ **Teachers:** 544 \ **Students:** 9,000 \ **Special Ed Students:** 891
\ **LEP Students:** 744 \ **College-Bound:** 94% \ **Ethnic:** African American
33%, Hispanic 40%, Native American: 1%, Caucasian 25% \ **Exp:** $465 (High)
\ **Poverty:** 23% \ **Title I:** $3,518,626 \ **Special Education:** $1,718,000 \
**Open-Close:** 08/24 - 06/03 \ **DTBP:** $198 (High)

| | |
|---|---|
| Dr Melissa Duarte .....1 | Margaret Lee .....2,15 |
| Marion Godeaux .....3 | Tammy Shafer .....3 |
| John Vandever .....4 | Leonard Bradley .....5 |
| Anne Anderson .....8 | Susan Myers .....8,15,16,36,274 |
| Sherri Simmons .....10 | Dr Terri Burchfield .....12,15,69,79,273,296 |
| Marcus Higgs .....15,68,78 | Mark Lyon .....20,23 |
| Donna Peterson .....58* | Donna Peterson .....58,752 |
| Dickey Campbell .....67 | Christina Hall-Payne .....70,298 |
| Melissa Tortorici .....71 | James Banks .....73 |
| Tray White .....73,76,295,297 | Nathan Jackson .....79 |
| Mike Matranga .....91 | Lisa Campbell .....294 |

| Public Schs..Principal | Grd | Prgm | Enr/#Cls | SN |
|---|---|---|---|---|
| Blocker Middle Sch<br>1800 9th Ave N, Texas City 77590<br>Anthony Furman | 7-8 | T | 897<br>63 | 68% 409/916-0700<br>Fax 409/942-2755 |
| Calvin Vincent ECC<br>1805 13th Ave N, Texas City 77590<br>Susan Wilson | PK-PK | T | 299 | 98% 409/916-0512<br>Fax 409/916-0596 |
| Guajardo Elem Sch<br>2300 21st St N, Texas City 77590<br>Debbie Fuller | K-4 | T | 446<br>32 | 83% 409/916-0300<br>Fax 409/942-2839 |
| Heights Elem Sch<br>300 N Logan St, Texas City 77590<br>Erica Allen | K-4 | T | 450<br>30 | 88% 409/916-0500<br>Fax 409/942-2450 |
| Industrial Trades Center<br>1400 9th Ave N, Texas City 77590<br>Richard Chapa | Voc | | 200 | 409/916-0710 |
| Kohfeldt Elem Sch<br>1705 13th Ave N, Texas City 77590<br>Matthew Salley | K-4 | T | 528<br>27 | 84% 409/916-0400<br>Fax 409/916-0496 |
| La Marque Elem Sch<br>1217 Vauthier St, La Marque 77568<br>Sharon Williams | 2-4 | T | 574<br>20 | 88% 409/908-5056<br>Fax 409/908-5044 |
| La Marque High Sch<br>397 Duroux Rd, La Marque 77568<br>Ricky Nicholson | 9-12 | TV | 559<br>78 | 78% 409/938-4261<br>Fax 409/908-5036 |
| La Marque Middle Sch<br>1431 Bayou Rd, La Marque 77568<br>Dr Florence Adkins | 5-8 | TV | 737<br>75 | 83% 409/938-4286 |
| La Marque Primary Sch<br>100 Lake Rd, La Marque 77568<br>Patti Martin | PK-1 | T | 457<br>21 | 84% 409/935-3020<br>Fax 409/908-5022 |
| Levi Fry Intermediate Sch<br>300 25th Ave N, Texas City 77590<br>Felica Garrett | 5-6 | T | 922 | 83% 409/916-0600<br>Fax 409/916-0696 |
| Roosevelt-Wilson Elem Sch<br>301 16th Ave N, Texas City 77590<br>Wendy Patterson | PK-4 | T | 536<br>28 | 85% 409/916-0200<br>Fax 409/916-0296 |
| Texas City High Sch<br>1431 9th Ave N, Texas City 77590<br>Lincoln Hypolite | 9-12 | TV | 1,887 | 61% 409/916-0800 |
| Ⓐ Woodrow Wilson Daep Sch<br>1508 6th St N, Texas City 77590<br>Donald Jones | 5-12 | | 13<br>10 | 72% 409/916-0280<br>Fax 409/942-2462 |

# GALVESTON CATHOLIC SCHOOLS

- **Archdiocese Galveston-Houston** PID: 01027855
Listing includes only schools located in this county. See District Index for
location of Diocesan Offices.

| Catholic Schs..Principal | Grd | Prgm | Enr/#Cls | SN |
|---|---|---|---|---|
| Holy Family Catholic Sch<br>2601 Avenue N, Galveston 77550<br>Nadia Canino | PK-8 | | 130<br>10 | 409/765-6607<br>Fax 409/765-5154 |
| O'Connell High Sch<br>1320 Tremont St, Galveston 77550<br>Patti Abbot | 9-12 | | 128<br>20 | 409/765-5534<br>Fax 409/765-5536 |
| Our Lady of Fatima Sch<br>1600 9th Ave N, Texas City 77590<br>Jennifer Lopez | PK-8 | | 80<br>10 | 409/945-3326<br>Fax 409/945-3389 |
| Our Lady of Lourdes Cath Sch<br>10114 Highway 6, Hitchcock 77563<br>Dr Emilie Robert | PK-6 | | 70<br>8 | 409/925-3224<br>Fax 409/925-9900 |
| St Mary Catholic Sch<br>1612 E Walker St, League City 77573<br>Laura Halbardier | PK-8 | | 220<br>30 | 281/332-4014<br>Fax 281/332-5148 |
| True Cross Catholic Sch<br>400 FM 517 Rd E, Dickinson 77539<br>Yolanda Agrella | PK-8 | | 160<br>11 | 281/337-5212<br>Fax 832/738-1682 |

# GALVESTON PRIVATE SCHOOLS

| Private Schs..Principal | Grd | Prgm | Enr/#Cls | SN |
|---|---|---|---|---|
| Bay Area Christian Sch<br>4800 W Main St, League City 77573<br>Linda Mudgett \ Les Rainey \ Melissa Fuqua | K-12 | | 800<br>40 | 281/332-4814<br>Fax 281/554-5495 |
| Galloway Sch<br>3200 W Bay Area Blvd, Friendswood 77546<br>Robin Williams | K-5 | | 180<br>23 | 281/338-9510<br>Fax 281/338-9530 |
| Lord of Life Lutheran Sch<br>4425 FM 2351 Rd, Friendswood 77546<br>Andy Van Weele | PK-8 | | 52<br>3 | 281/482-0481<br>Fax 281/648-4189 |
| Pine Drive Christian Sch<br>6601 FM 2004 Rd, Hitchcock 77563<br>Lynn Deitz | PK-12 | | 45<br>10 | 281/534-4881 |
| Satori Elem Sch<br>2503 Sealy St, Galveston 77550<br>Claire Wilkins | PK-6 | | 45 | 409/763-7022 |
| Trinity Episcopal Sch<br>720 Tremont St, Galveston 77550<br>Mark Ravelli | PK-8 | | 202<br>15 | 409/765-9391<br>Fax 409/762-7000 |

| | | | |
|---|---|---|---|
| 1 Superintendent | 19 Chief Financial Officer | 39 Family/Consumer Science | 59 Special Education Elem | 69 Academic Assessment |
| 2 Bus/Finance/Purchasing | 8 Curric/Instruct K-12 | 29 Family/Consumer Science | 49 English/Lang Arts Elem | 70 Research/Development |
| 3 Buildings And Grounds | 9 Curric/Instruct Elem | 20 Art K-12 | 30 Adult Education | 40 Social Studies Elem | 50 English/Lang Arts Sec | 60 Special Education Sec | 71 Public Information |
| 4 Food Service | 10 Curric/Instruct Sec | 21 Art Elem | 31 Career/Sch-to-Work K-12 | 41 Social Studies Sec | 51 Reading K-12 | 61 Foreign/World Lang K-12 | 72 Summer School |
| 5 Transportation | 11 Federal Program | 22 Art Sec | 32 Career/Sch-to-Work Elem | 42 Science K-12 | 52 Reading Elem | 62 Foreign/World Lang Elem | 73 Instructional Tech |
| 6 Athletic | 12 Title I | 23 Music K-12 | 33 Career/Sch-to-Work Sec | 43 Science Elem | 53 Reading Sec | 63 Foreign/World Lang Sec | 74 Inservice Training |
| 7 Health Services | 13 Title V | 24 Music Elem | 34 Early Childhood Ed | 44 Science Sec | 54 Remedial Reading K-12 | 64 Religious Education K-12 | 75 Marketing/Distributive |
| | 15 Asst Superintendent | 25 Music Sec | 35 Health/Phys Education | 45 Math K-12 | 55 Remedial Reading Elem | 65 Religious Education Elem | 76 Info Systems |
| | 16 Instructional Media Svcs | 26 Business Education | 36 Guidance Services K-12 | 46 Math Elem | 56 Remedial Reading Sec | 66 Religious Education Sec | 77 Psychological Assess |
| | 17 Chief Operations Officer | 27 Career & Tech Ed | 37 Guidance Services Elem | 47 Math Sec | 57 Bilingual/ELL | 67 School Board President | 78 Affirmative Action |
| | 18 Chief Academic Officer | 28 Technology Education | 38 Guidance Services Sec | 48 English/Lang Arts K-12 | 58 Special Education K-12 | 68 Teacher Personnel | |

| GARZA COUNTY | GILLESPIE COUNTY |
|---|---|

## GARZA PUBLIC SCHOOLS

## GILLESPIE PUBLIC SCHOOLS

● **Post Ind School Dist** PID: 01019597          806/495-3343
501 S Avenue K, Post 79356                       Fax 806/495-2945

**Schools:** 3 \ **Teachers:** 81 \ **Students:** 566 \ **Special Ed Students:** 85 \
**LEP Students:** 57 \ **Ethnic:** African American 4%, Hispanic 65%, Native
American: 1%, Caucasian 30% \ **Exp:** $544 (High) \ **Poverty:** 23% \
**Title I:** $242,769 \ **Special Education:** $226,000 \ **Open-Close:** 08/14 -
05/21 \ **DTBP:** $344 (High) \ 🅣

| | | | |
|---|---|---|---|
| Heath Dickson | 1 | Gary Graves | 3 |
| Debbie Line | 4* | Ollie Abaraham | 5 |
| Michael Pittman | 6* | Joanne Travis | 7 |
| Kim Mills-Oller | 8,11,15,69,270,273 | Lizette Hastey | 37* |
| Serena Voss | 38,83,88* | Tonya Dunn | 38* |
| Regina Wise | 58 | Mike Holly | 67 |
| Coty Tidwell | 73 | Bobby Dean | 91 |
| Randon Torres | 295 | | |

| Public Schs..Principal | Grd | Prgm | Enr/#Cls | SN | |
|---|---|---|---|---|---|
| Post Elem Sch | PK-5 | T | 370 | 75% | 806/495-3414 |
| 211 W 8th St, Post 79356 | | | 32 | | Fax 806/495-2381 |
| Cassandra Petty | | | | | |
| Post High Sch | 9-12 | TV | 126 | 57% | 806/495-2770 |
| 307 W 4th St, Post 79356 | | | 40 | | Fax 806/495-2792 |
| Shelly Crow | | | | | |
| Post Middle Sch | 6-8 | T | 70 | 67% | 806/495-2874 |
| 405 W 8th St, Post 79356 | | | 24 | | Fax 806/495-2426 |
| Robert Wilson | | | | | |

● **Southland Ind School Dist** PID: 01019638          806/996-5339
190 Eighth St, Southland 79364                        Fax 806/496-2745

**Schools:** 1 \ **Teachers:** 15 \ **Students:** 123 \ **Special Ed Students:** 14 \
**College-Bound:** 65% \ **Ethnic:** Hispanic 53%, Caucasian 47% \ **Exp:** $1,214
(High) \ **Poverty:** 19% \ **Title I:** $1,647 \ **Open-Close:** 08/21 - 05/21 \
**DTBP:** $543 (High)

| | | | |
|---|---|---|---|
| Toby Miller | 1 | Wyanza Basinger | 2 |
| Justin Hyndran | 3,5* | Bethany Miller | 11,296 |
| Martha Angerer | 58 | Joe Basinger | 67 |
| Phillip Maldonado | 271* | | |

| Public Schs..Principal | Grd | Prgm | Enr/#Cls | SN | |
|---|---|---|---|---|---|
| Southland Sch | K-12 | TV | 123 | 92% | 806/996-5339 |
| 190 Eighth St, Southland 79364 | | | 25 | | |
| Gregg Johnson | | | | | 🅕 🅣 |

● **Doss Consolidated Common SD** PID: 01019664          830/669-2411
11431 Ranch Road 648, Doss 78618                         Fax 830/669-2303

**Schools:** 1 \ **Teachers:** 3 \ **Students:** 25 \ **Special Ed Students:** 3 \
**Ethnic:** Asian 5%, Hispanic 25%, Caucasian 70% \ **Exp:** $2,779 (High) \
**Poverty:** 6% \ **Open-Close:** 08/24 - 05/27 \ **DTBP:** $175 (High)

| | | | |
|---|---|---|---|
| Mark Stroeher | 1 | Pam Seippe | 2,11,19,73,286,288,296,298 |
| Shawn Sattler | 67 | | |

| Public Schs..Principal | Grd | Prgm | Enr/#Cls | SN |
|---|---|---|---|---|
| Doss Elem Sch | PK-8 | | 25 | 830/669-2411 |
| 11431 Ranch Road 648, Doss 78618 | | | 4 | |
| Mark Stroeher | | | | |

● **Fredericksburg Ind School Dist** PID: 01019688          830/997-9551
234 Friendship Ln, Fredericksbrg 78624                       Fax 830/997-6164

**Schools:** 6 \ **Teachers:** 217 \ **Students:** 3,200 \ **Special Ed Students:** 338
\ **LEP Students:** 392 \ **Ethnic:** Asian 1%, Hispanic 50%, Caucasian
49% \ **Exp:** $285 (Med) \ **Poverty:** 14% \ **Title I:** $590,287 \
**Special Education:** $174,000 \ **Open-Close:** 08/24 - 05/27

| | | | |
|---|---|---|---|
| Dr Jeff Brasher | 1 | Jill Minschu | 2,15 |
| Brandon Porter | 3 | Donnie Finn | 3,11,15,79,91 |
| Joyce Fox | 4 | Evelyn Peese | 5 |
| Lance Moffett | 6 | Judy Mayo | 7 |
| Robin Denington | 8,16,69,74,277,285,294,752 | Patricia Rivera | 11,57,81,271,298 |
| Debbie Lewis | 29 | Joan Kramer | 30* |
| Rachelle Malenack | 30 | Holly Cunningham | 34,58,275 |
| Dr Lance Love | 67 | Stacy Rush | 68 |
| Carl Oneil | 73* | Michelle Williams | 73 |
| Daylan Kirtchner | 88 | | |

| Public Schs..Principal | Grd | Prgm | Enr/#Cls | SN | |
|---|---|---|---|---|---|
| Fredericksburg Elem Sch | 1-5 | T | 1,061 | 61% | 830/997-9595 |
| 1608 N Adams St, Fredericksbrg 78624 | | | 50 | | Fax 830/997-7209 |
| **Laura Flack** | | | | | |
| Fredericksburg High Sch | 9-12 | AV | 989 | 40% | 830/997-7551 |
| 1107 S State Highway 16, Fredericksbrg 78624 | | | | | Fax 830/997-8583 |
| Joe Gonzalez | | | | | |
| Fredericksburg Middle Sch | 6-8 | T | 684 | 52% | 830/997-7657 |
| 110 W Travis St, Fredericksbrg 78624 | | | | | Fax 830/997-1927 |
| Sheryl Wallace | | | | | |
| Fredericksburg Primary Sch | PK-K | T | 347 | 71% | 830/997-7421 |
| 1110 S Adams St, Fredericksbrg 78624 | | | 20 | | Fax 830/990-0002 |
| Wendy Dietrich | | | | | |
| Ⓐ Gillespie County High Sch | 10-12 | T | 25 | 43% | 830/990-4598 |
| 1110 S Adams St, Fredericksbrg 78624 | | | 2 | | |
| Dalen Kirchner | | | | | |
| Stonewall Elem Sch | K-5 | | 93 | 31% | 830/990-4599 |
| 220 Peach St, Stonewall 78671 | | | 6 | | Fax 830/990-4549 |
| Amie Chalberg | | | | | |

---

| | | | | | |
|---|---|---|---|---|---|
| **79** Student Personnel | **91** Safety/Security | **275** Response To Intervention | **298** Grant Writer/Ptnrships | **School Programs** | **Social Media** |
| **80** Driver Ed/Safety | **92** Magnet School | **277** Remedial Math K-12 | **750** Chief Innovation Officer | A = **Alternative Program** | |
| **81** Gifted/Talented | **93** Parental Involvement | **280** Literacy Coach | **751** Chief of Staff | G = **Adult Classes** | 🅕 = Facebook |
| **82** Video Services | **95** Tech Prep Program | **285** STEM | **752** Social Emotional Learning | M = **Magnet Program** | |
| **83** Substance Abuse Prev | **97** Chief Information Officer | **286** Digital Learning | | T = **Title I Schoolwide** | 🅣 = Twitter |
| **84** Erate | **98** Chief Technology Officer | **288** Common Core Standards | **Other School Types** | V = **Career & Tech Ed Programs** | |
| **85** AIDS Education | **270** Character Education | **294** Accountability | Ⓐ = **Alternative School** | | |
| **88** Alternative/At Risk | **271** Migrant Education | **295** Network System | Ⓒ = **Charter School** | **New Schools are shaded** | |
| **89** Multi-Cultural Curriculum | **273** Teacher Mentor | **296** Title II Programs | Ⓜ = **Magnet School** | **New Superintendents and Principals are bold** | |
| **90** Social Work | **274** Before/After Sch | **297** Webmaster | Ⓨ = **Year-Round School** | Personnel with email addresses are underscored | |

**TX—167**

• **Harper Ind School Dist** PID: 01019731
23122 W Highway 290, Harper 78631

830/864-4044
Fax 830/864-4748

---

**Schools:** 3 \ **Teachers:** 50 \ **Students:** 557 \ **Special Ed Students:** 50 \
**LEP Students:** 4 \ **Ethnic:** Hispanic 11%, Caucasian 88% \ **Exp:** $427 (High)
\ **Poverty:** 12% \ **Title I:** $74,092 \ **Open-Close:** 08/14 - 05/21 \ **DTBP:** $323
(High)

---

| | | | |
|---|---|---|---|
| Bonnie Stewart | ...1 | Tina Bernhard | ...2,68 |
| Dean Eckert | ...3,5* | Dean Eckert | ...3,5 |
| Deborah Pascarella | ...4 | Bonnie Stewart | ...8,11,69,74,294,296* |
| Jay Harper | ...9,58* | Aaron Brooks | ...11* |
| Toni Marschall | ...16* | Nancy Cantwell | ...57,271* |
| Juanice Grona | ...67 | Bill Long | ...73,295 |

| Public Schs..Principal | Grd | Prgm | Enr/#Cls | SN | |
|---|---|---|---|---|---|
| Harper Elem Sch<br>23122 W Highway 290, Harper 78631<br>Billy Harper | PK-4 | T | 186<br>15 | 45% | 830/864-4044 |
| Harper High Sch<br>23122 W Highway 290, Harper 78631<br>Bonnie Stewart | 9-12 | T | 182<br>20 | 27% | 830/864-4044 |
| Harper Middle Sch<br>23122 W Hwy 290, Harper 78631<br>Julie Fiedler | 5-8 | T | 189<br>| 35% | 830/864-4044 |

## GILLESPIE CATHOLIC SCHOOLS

• **Archdiocese San Antonio Ed Off** PID: 00999724
Listing includes only schools located in this county. See District Index for
location of Diocesan Offices.

| Catholic Schs..Principal | Grd | Prgm | Enr/#Cls | SN | |
|---|---|---|---|---|---|
| St Mary Elem Sch<br>202 S Orange St, Fredericksbrg 78624<br>John Mein | PK-8 | | 300<br>19 | | 830/997-3914<br>Fax 830/997-2382<br>**f** |

## GILLESPIE PRIVATE SCHOOLS

| Private Schs..Principal | Grd | Prgm | Enr/#Cls | SN | |
|---|---|---|---|---|---|
| Ambleside School of Fredericks<br>406 Post Oak Rd, Fredericksbrg 78624<br>Russ York | K-12 | | 110<br>7 | | 830/990-9059 |
| Heritage Sch<br>310 Smokehouse Rd, Fredericksbrg 78624<br>Christopher Acton | K-12 | | 200<br>13 | | 830/997-6597<br>Fax 830/997-4900 |

---

## GLASSCOCK COUNTY

## GLASSCOCK PUBLIC SCHOOLS

• **Glasscock Co Ind School Dist** PID: 01019781
240 Bearkat Ln, Garden City 79739

432/354-2230
Fax 432/354-2503

---

**Schools:** 1 \ **Teachers:** 34 \ **Students:** 292 \ **Special Ed Students:** 27
\ **LEP Students:** 21 \ **College-Bound:** 100% \ **Exp:** $1,345 (High) \
**Poverty:** 12% \ **Title I:** $34,376 \ **Open-Close:** 08/20 - 05/20 \ **DTBP:** $899
(High)

---

| | | | |
|---|---|---|---|
| Scott Bicknell | ...1,83,288 | Kristy Fuchs | ...2,11,296 |
| Reeann McKinnon | ...4* | Jeff Jones | ...6 |
| Tiffany Parker | ...8,31,69,270* | Wayland Pierce | ...8,12,88,274* |
| Holly McDermott | ...27* | Sasha Goodwin | ...35,85* |
| Laura Dieringer | ...51,54* | Bea Correa | ...57* |
| Paula Ringo | ...58* | Sharon McDonald | ...58* |
| Doug Jost | ...67 | David Wood | ...73,286 |

| Public Schs..Principal | Grd | Prgm | Enr/#Cls | SN | |
|---|---|---|---|---|---|
| Glasscock Co Sch<br>240 Bearkat Ln, Garden City 79739<br>Wayland Pierce \ Brian Hastings | PK-12 | V | 292<br>30 | | 432/354-2244<br>Fax 432/354-2611 |

---

## GOLIAD COUNTY

## GOLIAD PUBLIC SCHOOLS

• **Goliad Ind School Dist** PID: 01019810
161 N Welch St, Goliad 77963

361/645-3259
Fax 361/645-3614

---

**Schools:** 3 \ **Teachers:** 93 \ **Students:** 1,325 \ **Special Ed Students:** 145
\ **LEP Students:** 25 \ **Ethnic:** African American 5%, Hispanic 48%,
Caucasian 46% \ **Exp:** $506 (High) \ **Poverty:** 21% \ **Title I:** $324,478 \
**Open-Close:** 08/19 - 05/20 \ **DTBP:** $336 (High)

---

| | | | |
|---|---|---|---|
| Stacy Acklery | ...1 | Caroly Estes | ...2 |
| David Hill | ...3 | Brenda Gohnert | ...4 |
| Kevin Salazar | ...6 | Kristen Russell | ...7 |
| Brandon Enos | ...8,15 | Patricia Huber | ...9,34* |
| Debra Bauer | ...11 | Brandon Huber | ...67 |
| David Luna | ...73,295 | | |

| Public Schs..Principal | Grd | Prgm | Enr/#Cls | SN | |
|---|---|---|---|---|---|
| Goliad Elem Sch<br>142 W High St, Goliad 77963<br>Patricia Huber | PK-6 | T | 731<br>40 | 57% | 361/645-3206<br>Fax 361/645-2336 |
| Goliad High Sch<br>749 Tiger Drive, Goliad 77963<br>Brandon Enos | 9-12 | ATV | 405<br>59 | 42% | 361/645-3257<br>Fax 361/645-8039 |
| Goliad Middle Sch<br>659 Tiger Dr, Goliad 77963<br>Sandy Fellers | 7-8 | T | 194<br>23 | 55% | 361/645-3146<br>Fax 361/645-8040 |

---

| | | | | | | | |
|---|---|---|---|---|---|---|---|
| 1 | Superintendent | 8 | Curric/Instruct K-12 | 19 | Chief Financial Officer | 29 | Family/Consumer Science |
| 2 | Bus/Finance/Purchasing | 9 | Curric/Instruct Elem | 20 | Art K-12 | 30 | Adult Education |
| 3 | Buildings And Grounds | 10 | Curric/Instruct Sec | 21 | Art Elem | 31 | Career/Sch-to-Work K-12 |
| 4 | Food Service | 11 | Federal Program | 22 | Art Sec | 32 | Career/Sch-to-Work Elem |
| 5 | Transportation | 12 | Title I | 23 | Music K-12 | 33 | Career/Sch-to-Work Sec |
| 6 | Athletic | 13 | Title V | 24 | Music Elem | 34 | Early Childhood Ed |
| 7 | Health Services | 15 | Asst Superintendent | 25 | Music Sec | 35 | Health/Phys Education |
| | | 16 | Instructional Media Svcs | 26 | Business Education | 36 | Guidance Services K-12 |
| | | 17 | Chief Operations Officer | 27 | Career & Tech Ed | 37 | Guidance Services Elem |
| | | 18 | Chief Academic Officer | 28 | Technology Education | 38 | Guidance Services Sec |

| | | | | | | | |
|---|---|---|---|---|---|---|---|
| 39 | Social Studies K-12 | 49 | English/Lang Arts Elem | 59 | Special Education Elem | 69 | Academic Assessment |
| 40 | Social Studies Elem | 50 | English/Lang Arts Sec | 60 | Special Education Sec | 70 | Research/Development |
| 41 | Social Studies Sec | 51 | Reading K-12 | 61 | Foreign/World Lang K-12 | 71 | Public Information |
| 42 | Science K-12 | 52 | Reading Elem | 62 | Foreign/World Lang Elem | 72 | Summer School |
| 43 | Science Elem | 53 | Reading Sec | 63 | Foreign/World Lang Sec | 73 | Instructional Tech |
| 44 | Science Sec | 54 | Remedial Reading K-12 | 64 | Religious Education K-12 | 74 | Inservice Training |
| 45 | Math K-12 | 55 | Remedial Reading Elem | 65 | Religious Education Elem | 75 | Marketing/Distributive |
| 46 | Math Elem | 56 | Remedial Reading Sec | 66 | Religious Education Sec | 76 | Info Systems |
| 47 | Math Sec | 57 | Bilingual/ELL | 67 | School Board President | 77 | Psychological Assess |
| 48 | English/Lang Arts K-12 | 58 | Special Education K-12 | 68 | Teacher Personnel | 78 | Affirmative Action |

| | | | | | |
|---|---|---|---|---|---|
| Nixon-Smiley High Sch | 9-12 | T | 88 | 83% | 830/582-1536 |
| 800 N Rancho Rd, Nixon 78140 | | | 24 | | Fax 830/582-2168 |
| Jim Weaver | | | | | f |

| | | | | | |
|---|---|---|---|---|---|
| Nixon-Smiley Middle Sch | 5-8 | T | 306 | 80% | 830/582-1536 |
| 800 N Rancho Rd, Nixon 78140 | | | 36 | | Fax 830/582-2258 |
| Anita Van Auken | | | | | |

## GONZALES COUNTY

### GONZALES PUBLIC SCHOOLS

- **Gonzales Ind School Dist** PID: 01019860    830/672-9551
  1711 N Sarah DeWitt Dr, Gonzales 78629    Fax 830/672-7159

**Schools:** 6 \ **Teachers:** 182 \ **Students:** 2,875 \ **Special Ed Students:** 333 \ **LEP Students:** 501 \ **Ethnic:** African American 8%, Hispanic 67%, Caucasian 25% \ **Exp:** $352 (High) \ **Poverty:** 25% \ **Title I:** $1,048,855 \ **Special Education:** $594,000 \ **Open-Close:** 08/17 - 05/26 \ **DTBP:** $154 (High)

| | | | |
|---|---|---|---|
| John Schumacker | .....1 | Amanda Smith | 2,19,81 |
| Gene Kridler | .3,5,17 | Michael Waldie | 6,35 |
| Dr Renee Fairchild | 16,28,73,76,82,297 | Glenn Menking | 67 |
| Haley Ratliff | 68 | Robin Trojcak | 71 |
| Dr Lydia Bartlett | 271,296 | Erin Lebuhn | 752 |

| Public Schs..Principal | Grd | Prgm | Enr/#Cls | SN | |
|---|---|---|---|---|---|
| ⓨ East Avenue Primary Sch | 1-2 | MT | 410 | 81% | 830/672-2826 |
| 1615 Saint Louis St, Gonzales 78629 | | | 40 | | Fax 830/672-6161 |
| Damaris Womack | | | | | |
| Gonzales Elem Sch | 3-4 | T | 430 | 77% | 830/672-1467 |
| 1600 Saint Andrew St, Gonzales 78629 | | | 35 | | Fax 830/672-5758 |
| Jim Workman | | | | | |
| Gonzales High Sch | 9-12 | ATV | 824 | 62% | 830/672-7535 |
| 1801 N Sarah DeWitt Dr, Gonzales 78629 | | | 46 | | Fax 830/672-8273 |
| Michael Garcia | | | | | |
| Gonzales Junior High Sch | 7-8 | T | 441 | 73% | 830/672-8641 |
| 426 N College St, Gonzales 78629 | | | 34 | | Fax 830/672-6446 |
| Roque Thompson | | | | | |
| Gonzales Primary Academy | PK-K | T | 350 | 85% | 830/519-4110 |
| 222 N Saint Joseph St, Gonzales 78629 | | | | | Fax 830/519-4112 |
| **Brandi Bell** | | | | | |
| North Avenue Interm Sch | 5-6 | T | 429 | 77% | 830/672-9557 |
| 1032 N Saint Joseph St, Gonzales 78629 | | | 23 | | Fax 830/672-4350 |
| Wanda Fryer | | | | | |

- **Nixon-Smiley Cons Ind Sch Dist** PID: 01019937    830/582-1536
  800 N Rancho Rd, Nixon 78140    Fax 830/582-1920

**Schools:** 3 \ **Teachers:** 84 \ **Students:** 1,076 \ **Special Ed Students:** 163 \ **LEP Students:** 164 \ **College-Bound:** 6% \ **Ethnic:** African American 1%, Hispanic 79%, Caucasian 20% \ **Exp:** $488 (High) \ **Poverty:** 21% \ **Title I:** $367,880 \ **Special Education:** $170,000 \ **Open-Close:** 09/01 - 05/28 \ **DTBP:** $337 (High) \ f

| | | | |
|---|---|---|---|
| Cathy Lauer | 1,11,83 | Jeff VanAuken | 2,3,5 |
| Bobby Newman | 3 | Lora Torres | 4 |
| Carlton McKinney | 6* | Jane Dwyer | 8,57,69,88,273,286,288,298 |
| Debbie Coleman | 16* | Jacki Tramell | 58 |
| Richard Lott | 67 | Israel Jimenez | 68 |
| Sarah Loer | 73* | Brittany Rogers | 274* |
| Susan Bell | 274 | | |

| Public Schs..Principal | Grd | Prgm | Enr/#Cls | SN | |
|---|---|---|---|---|---|
| Nixon-Smiley Elem Sch | PK-4 | T | 404 | 83% | 830/582-1536 |
| 500 Anglin Rd, Smiley 78159 | | | 25 | | Fax 830/587-6558 |
| Lundy Atkins | | | | | |

- **Waelder Ind School Dist** PID: 01020003    830/788-7161
  201 US Hwy 90 West, Waelder 78959    Fax 830/788-7429

**Schools:** 1 \ **Teachers:** 30 \ **Students:** 317 \ **Special Ed Students:** 36 \ **LEP Students:** 67 \ **College-Bound:** 90% \ **Ethnic:** African American 11%, Hispanic 81%, Caucasian 8% \ **Exp:** $425 (High) \ **Poverty:** 20% \ **Title I:** $115,312 \ **Open-Close:** 08/24 - 05/21 \ **DTBP:** $341 (High) \ f t

| | | | |
|---|---|---|---|
| Jon Orozlo | 1,11,73,83 | Tiana Landry | 2* |
| Annie Pustejovsky | 4 | Jacob Garcia | 6* |
| Dora Noyola | 67 | Juanita Melchor | 76 |

| Public Schs..Principal | Grd | Prgm | Enr/#Cls | SN | |
|---|---|---|---|---|---|
| Waelder Sch | PK-12 | T | 317 | 92% | 830/788-7221 |
| 109 N Ave C, Waelder 78959 | | | 10 | | Fax 830/788-7323 |
| **Darren Kesselus** \ Dr Ron Lilie | | | | | t |

### GONZALES PRIVATE SCHOOLS

| Private Schs..Principal | Grd | Prgm | Enr/#Cls | SN | |
|---|---|---|---|---|---|
| Emmanuel Christian Sch | PK-12 | | 23 | | 830/519-4086 |
| 1214 Saint Louis St, Gonzales 78629 | | | 2 | | |
| Carla Holmes | | | | | |

## GRAY COUNTY

### GRAY PUBLIC SCHOOLS

- **Grandview-Hopkins Ind Sch Dist** PID: 01020053    806/669-3831
  11676 FM 293, Groom 79039    Fax 806/669-3044

**Schools:** 1 \ **Teachers:** 6 \ **Students:** 50 \ **Special Ed Students:** 5 \ **Ethnic:** African American 2%, Hispanic 14%, Caucasian 84% \ **Exp:** $735 (High) \ **Poverty:** 23% \ **Open-Close:** 08/21 - 05/21

| | | | |
|---|---|---|---|
| Kent Hargis | 1,11,288 | Roselle Collingsworth | 4 |
| Ryan Davis | 67 | | |

| Public Schs..Principal | Grd | Prgm | Enr/#Cls | SN | |
|---|---|---|---|---|---|
| Grandview-Hopkins Elem Sch | K-6 | | 50 | 24% | 806/669-3831 |
| 11676 FM 293, Groom 79039 | | | 6 | | |
| John Wilson | | | | | |

• **Lefors Ind School Dist** PID: 01020077　　　　806/835-2533
209 E 5th Street, Lefors 79054　　　　　　　　　Fax 866/897-9637

**Schools:** 1 \ **Teachers:** 15 \ **Students:** 168 \ **Special Ed Students:** 19 \
**LEP Students:** 3 \ **College-Bound:** 80% \ **Ethnic:** Asian 1%, Hispanic 14%,
Native American: 1%, Caucasian 85% \ **Exp:** $919 (High) \ **Poverty:** 31% \
**Title I:** $50,210 \ **Special Education:** $4,000 \ **Open-Close:** 08/17 - 05/21 \
**DTBP:** $295 (High) \ 🇫 🇹

| | | |
|---|---|---|
| Kelley Porter ...............1,11,73 | Morgan McBee ....................2 |
| Ron Smith ..............................3 | Kendra Jazwinski ................4 |
| Johnny Woodard ...................5 | Joe Rally ..............................6* |
| Alicia Forsyth ...........8,11,57,288* | Lindy Jackson ....................67 |
| Tonya Lock ........................271 | Kristin Campos ................286 |

| Public Schs..Principal | Grd | Prgm | Enr/#Cls | SN | |
|---|---|---|---|---|---|
| Lefors Sch<br>209 E 5th Street, Lefors 79054<br>Alicia Forsyth | PK-12 | TV | 168<br>30 | 57% | 806/835-2533 |

• **McLean Ind School Dist** PID: 01020106　　　806/779-2301
4th & Rowe Streets, McLean 79057　　　　　　　Fax 806/779-2248

**Schools:** 1 \ **Teachers:** 20 \ **Students:** 236 \ **Special Ed Students:** 29
\ **LEP Students:** 3 \ **College-Bound:** 75% \ **Ethnic:** African American
1%, Hispanic 23%, Caucasian 76% \ **Exp:** $468 (High) \ **Poverty:** 23% \
**Title I:** $61,818 \ **Open-Close:** 08/14 - 05/21 \ **DTBP:** $162 (High)

| | | |
|---|---|---|
| Oscar Muniz .............................1 | Amy Calvert ..........................2,71 |
| Rhonda Sparling ...................4* | Clint Linman .............................6 |
| Tammy Hanes ...................7,271* | Shelly Henderson ...........54,280* |
| Diana Watson ........................57* | Sherri Haynes ......................67 |

| Public Schs..Principal | Grd | Prgm | Enr/#Cls | SN | |
|---|---|---|---|---|---|
| McLean Sch<br>4th & Rowe Streets, McLean 79057<br>**Robert Villegas** \ **Bradley Rainer** | PK-12 | TV | 236<br>16 | 54% | 806/779-2301 |

• **Pampa Ind School Dist** PID: 01020132　　　806/669-4700
1233 N Hobart St, Pampa 79065　　　　　　　　Fax 806/665-0506

**Schools:** 7 \ **Teachers:** 230 \ **Students:** 3,500 \ **Special Ed Students:** 428
\ **LEP Students:** 545 \ **Ethnic:** Asian 1%, African American 3%, Hispanic
50%, Caucasian 46% \ **Exp:** $359 (High) \ **Poverty:** 19% \ **Title I:** $913,134 \
**Open-Close:** 08/19 - 05/28 \ **DTBP:** $154 (High)

| | | |
|---|---|---|
| Tanya Larkin ..............................1 | Anita Russell .............................2 |
| Bill Hieronymus ........................5 | Stuart Smith .............................5 |
| Greg Poynor ..............................6 | Tamara Gutierrez .....................7* |
| Pam Mitchell .............8,11,15,30,72 | Kelly Vigil ..............................16* |
| Mark Murray .......................27,31* | Brittany Stark ................38,83,90* |
| Mark Elms .............................47* | Tatiana Greer ..................57,271* |
| Susan Furgeson ...............58,81,88 | Matt Brock .............................67 |
| Nathan Maxwell ..........68,74,78,273 | Molly Brinkley ........................73 |
| Melody Baker ..........................76 | Jana Williamson .....................93 |
| Dennis Boyd ...........................295 | |

| Public Schs..Principal | Grd | Prgm | Enr/#Cls | SN | |
|---|---|---|---|---|---|
| Austin Elem Sch<br>1900 Duncan St, Pampa 79065<br>Kristal Floyd | K-5 | T | 336<br>21 | 36% | 806/669-4760<br>Fax 806/669-4731 |
| Lamar Elem Sch<br>1234 S Nelson St, Pampa 79065<br>Troy McClendon | PK-5 | T | 581<br>30 | 84% | 806/669-4880<br>Fax 806/669-4735 |

| Public Schs..Principal | Grd | Prgm | Enr/#Cls | SN | |
|---|---|---|---|---|---|
| Pampa High Sch<br>111 E Harvester Ave, Pampa 79065<br>Hugh Piatt | 9-12 | TV | 453<br>130 | 49% | 806/669-4800<br>Fax 806/669-4826 |
| Pampa Junior High Sch<br>4000 Bad Cattle Co Rd, Pampa 79065<br>Jamie Winborne | 6-8 | T | 772<br>75 | 59% | 806/669-4900<br>Fax 806/669-4742 |
| Ⓐ Pampa Learning Center<br>111 E Harvester Ave, Pampa 79065<br>Carrie Williams | 9-12 | T | 41<br>2 | 60% | 806/669-4750<br>Fax 806/669-4734 |
| Travis Elem Sch<br>2300 Primrose Ln, Pampa 79065<br>Byron May | K-5 | T | 367<br>20 | 51% | 806/669-4950<br>Fax 806/669-4737 |
| Wilson Elem Sch<br>801 E Browning Ave, Pampa 79065<br>Keana Daughtry | K-5 | T | 380<br>19 | 84% | 806/669-4930<br>Fax 806/669-4736 |

## GRAY PRIVATE SCHOOLS

| Private Schs..Principal | Grd | Prgm | Enr/#Cls | SN | |
|---|---|---|---|---|---|
| Community Christian Sch<br>409 N Frost St, Pampa 79065<br>Marsha Richardson | PK-8 | | 71<br>8 | | 806/665-3393<br>Fax 806/665-4105 |

## GRAYSON COUNTY

## GRAYSON PUBLIC SCHOOLS

• **Bells Ind School Dist** PID: 01020235　　　903/965-7721
1550 Ole Ambrose Rd, Bells 75414　　　　　　　Fax 903/965-7036

**Schools:** 3 \ **Teachers:** 70 \ **Students:** 850 \ **Special Ed Students:** 99 \
**LEP Students:** 10 \ **Ethnic:** African American 1%, Hispanic 11%, Native
American: 2%, Caucasian 86% \ **Exp:** $446 (High) \ **Poverty:** 9% \
**Title I:** $77,710 \ **Open-Close:** 08/19 - 05/20 \ **DTBP:** $290 (High)

| | | |
|---|---|---|
| Tricia Meek .............................1,11 | Marilyn Steger ....................2,19 |
| Jackie Eller ..............................3 | Will Steger ..........................3,5* |
| Shannon Keating .....................4 | Dale West ...............................6 |
| Deborah Williams ..........7,35,85* | Josh Weger .........................12,15 |
| Pamela Pettit ......................16,82* | Eddie Brewer .........................17 |
| Clay Rolen ..........31,58,77,88,93 | E Pettit .................................67 |
| April Bellows ..........................69 | Ross Chlapecka ......73,76,84,97,98,286 |

| Public Schs..Principal | Grd | Prgm | Enr/#Cls | SN | |
|---|---|---|---|---|---|
| Bells Elem Sch<br>110 Scott Rd, Bells 75414<br>Yalonda Ivers | PK-5 | T | 371 | 48% | 903/965-3601<br>Fax 903/965-0140 |
| Bells High Sch<br>1500 Ole Ambrose Rd, Bells 75414<br>Clay Rolen | 9-12 | V | 281<br>30 | 28% | 903/965-3603<br>Fax 903/965-5205 |
| Pritchard Junior High Sch<br>1510 Ole Ambrose Rd, Bells 75414<br>Will Steger | 6-8 | | 206<br>18 | 33% | 903/965-3602<br>Fax 903/965-7428 |

| | | | | | | |
|---|---|---|---|---|---|---|
| 1 Superintendent | 8 Curric/Instruct K-12 | 19 Chief Financial Officer | 29 Family/Consumer Science | 39 Social Studies K-12 | 49 English/Lang Arts Elem | 59 Special Education Elem | 69 Academic Assessment |
| 2 Bus/Finance/Purchasing | 9 Curric/Instruct Elem | 20 Art K-12 | 30 Adult Education | 40 Social Studies Elem | 50 English/Lang Arts Sec | 60 Special Education Sec | 70 Research/Development |
| 3 Buildings And Grounds | 10 Curric/Instruct Sec | 21 Art Elem | 31 Career/Sch-to-Work K-12 | 41 Social Studies Sec | 51 Reading K-12 | 61 Foreign/World Lang K-12 | 71 Public Information |
| 4 Food Service | 11 Federal Program | 22 Art Sec | 32 Career/Sch-to-Work Elem | 42 Science K-12 | 52 Reading Elem | 62 Foreign/World Lang Elem | 72 Summer School |
| 5 Transportation | 12 Title I | 23 Music K-12 | 33 Career/Sch-to-Work Sec | 43 Science Elem | 53 Reading Sec | 63 Foreign/World Lang Sec | 73 Instructional Tech |
| 6 Athletic | 13 Title V | 24 Music Elem | 34 Early Childhood Ed | 44 Science Sec | 54 Remedial Reading K-12 | 64 Religious Education K-12 | 74 Inservice Training |
| 7 Health Services | 15 Asst Superintendent | 25 Music Sec | 35 Health/Phys Education | 45 Math K-12 | 55 Remedial Reading Elem | 65 Religious Education Elem | 75 Marketing/Distributive |
| | 16 Instructional Media Svcs | 26 Business Education | 36 Guidance Services K-12 | 46 Math Elem | 56 Remedial Reading Sec | 66 Religious Education Sec | 76 Info Systems |
| | 17 Chief Operations Officer | 27 Career & Tech Ed | 37 Guidance Services Elem | 47 Math Sec | 57 Bilingual/ELL | 67 School Board President | 77 Psychological Assess |
| | 18 Chief Academic Officer | 28 Technology Education | 38 Guidance Services Sec | 48 English/Lang Arts K-12 | 58 Special Education K-12 | 68 Teacher Personnel | 78 Affirmative Action |

## Collinsville Ind School Dist PID: 01020261
500 Reeves St, Collinsville 76233

903/429-6272
Fax 903/429-6665

**Schools:** 2 \ **Teachers:** 43 \ **Students:** 540 \ **Special Ed Students:** 47 \ **LEP Students:** 33 \ **College-Bound:** 60% \ **Ethnic:** African American 1%, Hispanic 20%, Native American: 1%, Caucasian 77% \ **Exp:** $425 (High) \ **Poverty:** 10% \ **Title I:** $63,841 \ **Open-Close:** 08/19 - 05/27 \ **DTBP:** $377 (High) \ 🅕

| | | | |
|---|---|---|---|
| Mark Dykes | 1 | Galen Ewton | 2 |
| Laurie Bishop | 4* | Garrett Patterson | 6 |
| Dawn Weaver | 7,85* | Ken Kemp | 16,73,295* |
| Katie Brock | 37 | Justin McDonnell | 67 |
| Melissa Baggs | 69,83,88* | Susan Stokes | 280 |
| Jeremy Harpole | 298 | | |

| Public Schs..Principal | Grd | Prgm | Enr/#Cls | SN |
|---|---|---|---|---|
| Collinsville Elem Sch<br>500 Reeves St, Collinsville 76233<br>Catherine Shackelford | PK-6 | T | 258<br>6 | 67% 903/429-3077<br>Fax 903/429-1004 |
| Collinsville High Sch<br>202 N Broadway St, Collinsville 76233<br>**Kim Patterson** | 7-12 | T | 237<br>24 | 48% 903/429-6164<br>Fax 903/429-6493 🅕 |

## Denison Ind School Dist PID: 01020297
1201 S Rusk Ave, Denison 75020

903/462-7000
Fax 903/462-7002

**Schools:** 9 \ **Teachers:** 335 \ **Students:** 3,885 \ **Special Ed Students:** 664 \ **LEP Students:** 299 \ **Ethnic:** Asian 1%, African American 11%, Hispanic 22%, Native American: 2%, Caucasian 64% \ **Exp:** $683 (High) \ **Poverty:** 17% \ **Title I:** $1,106,267 \ **Special Education:** $1,005,000 \ **Open-Close:** 08/13 - 05/20 \ **DTBP:** $155 (High) \ 🅣

| | | | |
|---|---|---|---|
| Dr Henry Scott | 1 | Cortney Hunkapillar | 2 |
| Randy Reid | 2,15,91 | David Self | 3 |
| Debbie Hosford | 4 | Randy Taylor | 5 |
| Chad Rogers | 6* | Heidi Lyons | 7* |
| Shonda Cannon | 8,45,51,74,273,298 | Amy Neidert | 9 |
| Laurie Brand | 10 | Renee Burroughs | 10 |
| Dr David Kirkbride | 13,15,68,78,79,83,294,296 | Dr Cavin Boettger | 31* |
| Regina Prigge | 36,69,271,294 | Lori May | 58,77 |
| David Hawley | 67 | Brian Eaves | 71* |
| Dr Dickie Deel | 73,295,297 | | |

| Public Schs..Principal | Grd | Prgm | Enr/#Cls | SN |
|---|---|---|---|---|
| B McDaniel Intemediate Sch<br>400 S Lillis Ln, Denison 75020<br>Alvis Dunlap | 5-6 | T | 705<br>52 | 67% 903/462-7200<br>Fax 903/462-7328 |
| Denison High Sch<br>4200 N State Highway 91, Denison 75020<br>Dr Cavin Boettger | 9-12 | TV | 267<br>71 | 57% 903/462-7125<br>Fax 903/462-7217 |
| Henry Scott Middle Sch<br>1901 S Mirick Ave, Denison 75020<br>John Parker | 7-8 | T | 718 | 66% 903/462-7180<br>Fax 903/462-7342 |
| Houston Elem Sch<br>1100 W Morgan St, Denison 75020<br>Kyle Uber | PK-4 | T | 159<br>17 | 77% 903/462-7300<br>Fax 903/462-7419 |
| Hyde Park Elem Sch<br>1701 S Hyde Park Ave, Denison 75020<br>Shea Klas | PK-5 | T | 470<br>15 | 58% 903/462-7350<br>Fax 903/462-7455 |
| Lamar Elem Sch<br>1000 S 5th Ave, Denison 75021<br>Gena Jackson | PK-4 | T | 468<br>21 | 75% 903/462-7400<br>Fax 903/462-7495 🅣 |
| Mayes Elem Sch<br>201 Jennie Ln, Denison 75020<br>Natalie Hicks | PK-4 | T | 462<br>14 | 70% 903/462-7500<br>Fax 903/462-7563 |

## Pathways High Sch (Ⓐ)
318 W Morgan St, Denison 75020
Lance San Millan

| | Grd | Prgm | Enr/#Cls | SN |
|---|---|---|---|---|
| | 9-12 | T | 14<br>2 | 68% 903/462-7150<br>Fax 903/462-7226 |

## Terrell Elem Sch
230 W M L King Jr Blvd, Denison 75020
Amy Neidert

| | Grd | Prgm | Enr/#Cls | SN |
|---|---|---|---|---|
| | PK-4 | T | 269<br>30 | 81% 903/462-7550<br>Fax 903/462-7609 |

## Gunter Ind School Dist PID: 01020443
213 Preston Gln, Gunter 75058

903/433-4750
Fax 903/433-1053

**Schools:** 3 \ **Teachers:** 92 \ **Students:** 1,000 \ **Special Ed Students:** 73 \ **LEP Students:** 64 \ **College-Bound:** 95% \ **Ethnic:** Asian 1%, African American 1%, Hispanic 23%, Native American: 1%, Caucasian 75% \ **Exp:** $482 (High) \ **Poverty:** 7% \ **Title I:** $55,002 \ **Open-Close:** 08/19 - 05/26 \ **DTBP:** $317 (High)

| | | | |
|---|---|---|---|
| Dr Jill Siler | 1 | Brittany Floyd | 2 |
| Kelley Teems | 3,296 | Caleb Bell | 5 |
| Jacob Fieszel | 6* | Dara Arrington | 8,11,296 |
| Jacob Waggoner | 38,83* | Elsie Wetzel | 57,271 |
| Christy Nolen | 58 | Scott Meyerdirk | 67 |
| Heidi Carruthers | 68 | Melissa Kelly | 73 |
| David Kobosky | 295* | | |

| Public Schs..Principal | Grd | Prgm | Enr/#Cls | SN |
|---|---|---|---|---|
| Gunter Elem Sch<br>200 Elm St, Gunter 75058<br>Heather Hale | PK-4 | T | 328<br>15 | 40% 903/433-5315<br>Fax 903/433-1184 |
| Gunter High Sch<br>1102 N Preston Rd, Gunter 75058<br>Chris Dodd \ **Kensie Woods** | 9-12 | V | 305<br>30 | 21% 903/433-1542<br>Fax 903/433-1492 |
| Gunter Middle Sch<br>410 Tiger Ln, Gunter 75058<br>**Chris Dodd** | 5-8 | | 280<br>20 | 28% 903/433-1545<br>Fax 903/433-9306 |

## Howe Ind School Dist PID: 01020479
105 W Tutt St, Howe 75459

903/532-3228
Fax 903/532-3205

**Schools:** 4 \ **Teachers:** 90 \ **Students:** 1,100 \ **Special Ed Students:** 151 \ **LEP Students:** 113 \ **College-Bound:** 64% \ **Ethnic:** African American 2%, Hispanic 23%, Native American: 1%, Caucasian 74% \ **Exp:** $375 (High) \ **Poverty:** 17% \ **Title I:** $228,438 \ **Open-Close:** 08/19 - 05/28 \ **DTBP:** $338 (High) \ 🅕

| | | | |
|---|---|---|---|
| Kevin Wilson | 1 | Julie Snapp | 2 |
| Ricky Brinlee | 3,5 | Lesia Kirland | 4 |
| Bill Jehlings | 6* | Darla Williams | 8,11,15,58,69* |
| Melissa Atchison | 16 | Mary Claire Woodard | 31* |
| K'Lain Ashlock | 37* | Pauli Stephens | 38 |
| Clint Catching | 67 | Joe Gandillon | 73,76,298* |

| Public Schs..Principal | Grd | Prgm | Enr/#Cls | SN |
|---|---|---|---|---|
| Howe High Sch<br>200 Ponderosa Rd, Howe 75459<br>Phil Kempson | 9-12 | AV | 372<br>25 | 37% 903/745-4400<br>Fax 903/745-4401 🅕 |
| Howe Intermediate Sch<br>315 Roberts St, Howe 75459<br>Tammy Witten | 3-5 | AT | 300<br>26 | 53% 903/745-4200<br>Fax 903/745-4201 |
| Howe Middle Sch<br>300 Beatrice St, Howe 75459<br>Clayton Wilson | 6-8 | AT | 250<br>24 | 46% 903/745-4300<br>Fax 903/745-4301 |
| Summit Hill Elem Sch<br>701 Summit Hill Pkwy, Howe 75459<br>Clarissa Doty | PK-2 | | 200 | 903/745-4100<br>Fax 903/745-4101 |

| | | | | | |
|---|---|---|---|---|---|
| 79 Student Personnel | 91 Safety/Security | 275 Response To Intervention | 298 Grant Writer/Ptnrships | **School Programs** | **Social Media** |
| 80 Driver Ed/Safety | 92 Magnet School | 277 Remedial Math K-12 | 750 Chief Innovation Officer | **A** = Alternative Program | |
| 81 Gifted/Talented | 93 Parental Involvement | 280 Literacy Coach | 751 Chief of Staff | **G** = Adult Classes | 🅕 = Facebook |
| 82 Video Services | 95 Tech Prep Program | 285 STEM | 752 Social Emotional Learning | **M** = Magnet Program | |
| 83 Substance Abuse Prev | 97 Chief Infomation Officer | 286 Digital Learning | | **T** = Title I Schoolwide | 🅣 = Twitter |
| 84 Erate | 98 Chief Technology Officer | 288 Common Core Standards | **Other School Types** | **V** = Career & Tech Ed Programs | |
| 85 AIDS Education | 270 Character Education | 294 Accountability | Ⓐ = Alternative School | | |
| 88 Alternative/At Risk | 271 Migrant Education | 295 Network System | Ⓒ = Charter School | New Schools are shaded | |
| 89 Multi-Cultural Curriculum | 273 Teacher Mentor | 296 Title II Programs | Ⓜ = Magnet School | New Superintendents and Principals are bold | |
| 90 Social Work | 274 Before/After Sch | 297 Webmaster | Ⓨ = Year-Round School | Personnel with email addresses are underscored | |

**TX—171**

## • Pottsboro Ind School Dist PID: 01020510
105 Cardinal Ln, Pottsboro 75076

903/771-0083
Fax 903/786-9085

---

**Schools:** 3 \ **Teachers:** 96 \ **Students:** 1,384 \ **Special Ed Students:** 128 \
**LEP Students:** 12 \ **College-Bound:** 70% \ **Ethnic:** Asian 1%, Hispanic 7%,
Native American: 3%, Caucasian 88% \ **Exp:** $532 (High) \ **Poverty:** 12% \
**Title I:** $203,190 \ **Open-Close:** 08/20 - 05/27 \ **DTBP:** $361 (High)

---

| | | |
|---|---|---|
| Dr Kevin Matthews ...1 | Janet Wilson ...2* | |
| Paul Wickett ...3 | Cathy Griffith ...4* | |
| Curtis Hendrickson ...5 | Matt Poe ...6 | |
| Debbie Ritchie ...8,11 | Josh Recer ...15 | |
| Angie Slate ...16,82* | Jim Copeland ...67 | |
| Jason Brown ...73,286,295* | | |

| Public Schs..Principal | Grd | Prgm | Enr/#Cls | SN |
|---|---|---|---|---|
| Pottsboro Elem Sch<br>525 Highway 120, Pottsboro 75076<br>Danielle Curry | PK-4 | T | 504<br>23 | 51% 903/771-2981<br>Fax 903/786-4903 |
| Pottsboro High Sch<br>901 E FM 120, Pottsboro 75076<br>**Danielle Curry** | 9-12 | | 402<br>40 | 30% 903/771-0085<br>Fax 903/786-6349 |
| Pottsboro Middle Sch<br>207 Cardinal Lane, Pottsboro 75076<br>Gerald Springer | 5-8 | T | 478<br>36 | 40% 903/771-2982<br>Fax 903/786-4902 |

## • S & S Cons Ind School Dist PID: 01020560
1 Ram Dr, Sadler 76264

903/564-6051
Fax 903/564-3492

---

**Schools:** 3 \ **Teachers:** 73 \ **Students:** 896 \ **Special Ed Students:** 103 \
**LEP Students:** 29 \ **Ethnic:** Asian 1%, Hispanic 12%, Native American: 2%,
Caucasian 85% \ **Exp:** $450 (High) \ **Poverty:** 12% \ **Title I:** $146,574 \
**Open-Close:** 08/20 - 05/25 \ **DTBP:** $359 (High)

---

| | | |
|---|---|---|
| Roger Reed ...1 | Stephanie Maher ...2 | |
| Corgie Fisher ...3,5 | Deanne Caffey ...4 | |
| Josh Aleman ...6 | Lance Johnson ...11,83 | |
| Chris Lopez ...67 | Dustin Wilson ...73* | |

| Public Schs..Principal | Grd | Prgm | Enr/#Cls | SN |
|---|---|---|---|---|
| S & S Cons High Sch<br>404 S Main St, Sadler 76264<br>**Scott Johnston** | 9-12 | TV | 275<br>20 | 45% 903/564-3768<br>Fax 903/564-7308 |
| S & S Cons Middle Sch<br>200 Ram Ave, Sadler 76264<br>Greg Pierce | 6-8 | T | 208<br>15 | 50% 903/564-7626<br>Fax 903/564-7857 |
| S & S Elem Sch<br>4217 Elementary Dr, Southmayd 76268<br>Shanna Reynolds | PK-5 | T | 413<br>27 | 57% 903/893-0767<br>Fax 903/891-9338 |

## • Sherman Ind School Dist PID: 01020596
2701 N Loy Lake Rd, Sherman 75090

903/891-6400
Fax 903/891-6407

---

**Schools:** 12 \ **Teachers:** 557 \ **Students:** 7,500 \ **Special Ed Students:** 913
\ **LEP Students:** 1,613 \ **College-Bound:** 56% \ **Ethnic:** Asian 3%,
African American 13%, Hispanic 45%, Native American: 1%, Caucasian
37% \ **Exp:** $358 (High) \ **Poverty:** 19% \ **Title I:** $1,899,965 \
**Special Education:** $1,415,000 \ **Bilingual Education:** $61,000 \
**Open-Close:** 08/17 - 05/27 \ **DTBP:** $157 (High) \ f

---

| | | |
|---|---|---|
| Dr David Hicks ...1 | Mandi Lewis ...2 | |
| Dr Tyson Bennett ...2,15 | Scott Conrad ...3 | |
| Mandy Stephens ...4 | Brett Counte ...5,91 | |
| Bob Jones ...6 | Stacy Phillips ...7,36,69,83,275 | |
| Susan Whitenack ...8,11,88,286,288,296,298 | Dr Kelly Flowers ...9 | |
| Blake Hays ...10 | Dr Tamy Smalskas ...15,31 | |

---

| | | |
|---|---|---|
| Kimberly Simpson ...16,71 | Katherine Morris ...27* | |
| Stephanie Lippard ...54,57,74,77,271,273,277 | Kaye Allen ...58,85 | |
| Tim Millerick ...67 | Jill O'Neal ...68,79 | |
| Mignon Plyler ...73,295 | Chris Cooper ...76 | |
| Colin Bell ...295 | Sean Vanderveer ...297 | |

| Public Schs..Principal | Grd | Prgm | Enr/#Cls | SN |
|---|---|---|---|---|
| Crutchfield Elem Sch<br>521 S Dewey Ave, Sherman 75090<br>Leda Roelke | K-4 | T | 403<br>22 | 80% 903/891-6565<br>Fax 903/891-6570 |
| Dillingham Intermediate Sch<br>1701 Gallagher Dr, Sherman 75090<br>Pamela Voss | 5-6 | T | 1,161<br>55 | 69% 903/891-6495<br>Fax 903/891-6499 |
| Fairview Elem Sch<br>501 W Taylor St, Sherman 75092<br>Michelle Eackles \ **Daniel Matejko** | K-4 | T | 425<br>60 | 60% 903/891-6580<br>Fax 903/891-6585 |
| Fred Douglass Early Chldhd Ctr<br>505 E College St, Sherman 75090<br>Deloris Dowell | PK-PK | T | 322<br>13 | 99% 903/891-6545<br>Fax 903/891-6549<br>f |
| Jefferson Elem Sch<br>608 N Lee Ave, Sherman 75090<br>Nancy Jung | K-4 | T | 189<br>12 | 92% 903/891-6610<br>Fax 903/891-6615 |
| Percy Neblitt Elem Sch<br>1505 Gallagher Dr, Sherman 75090<br>Kelli Abohosh | K-4 | T | 483 | 73% 903/891-6670<br>Fax 903/893-0263<br>f |
| Ⓐ Perrin Alt Learning Center<br>81 Vandenburg Dr, Denison 75020<br>Jimmy May | 9-12 | T | 60 | 68% 903/891-6680<br>Fax 903/786-4766 |
| Piner Middle Sch<br>402 W Pecan St, Sherman 75090<br>Amy Porter | 7-8 | T | 485<br>40 | 65% 903/891-6470<br>Fax 903/891-6475 |
| Sherman High Sch<br>2201 E Lamar St, Sherman 75090<br>Jennifer Politi \ **Jeffrey Chancellor** | 9-12 | TV | 1,884 | 55% 903/891-6440<br>Fax 903/891-6446 |
| Sory Elem Sch<br>120 Binkley Park Dr, Sherman 75092<br>Steven Traw | K-4 | T | 624 | 62% 903/891-6650<br>Fax 903/892-6307<br>f |
| Wakefield Elem Sch<br>400 Sunset Blvd, Sherman 75092<br>Eartha Linson | PK-4 | T | 251<br>40 | 61% 903/891-6595<br>Fax 903/891-6600 |
| Washington Elem Sch<br>815 S Travis St, Sherman 75090<br>Amy Pesina \ **Heather Wood** | PK-4 | T | 406<br>22 | 86% 903/891-6700<br>Fax 903/893-0141<br>f |

## • Tioga Ind School Dist PID: 01020699
405 N Florence St, Tioga 76271

940/437-2366
Fax 940/437-9986

---

**Schools:** 1 \ **Teachers:** 55 \ **Students:** 639 \ **Special Ed Students:** 44
\ **LEP Students:** 34 \ **College-Bound:** 50% \ **Ethnic:** Hispanic 20%,
Caucasian 79% \ **Exp:** $607 (High) \ **Poverty:** 13% \ **Title I:** $39,839 \
**Open-Close:** 08/14 - 05/21 \ **DTBP:** $410 (High)

---

| | | |
|---|---|---|
| Dr Charles Holloway ...1 | Nancy Whitworth ...2 | |
| Vickie McNaird ...4* | Cody Patton ...6* | |
| Diane Mincher ...11,88* | Josh Ballinger ...15 | |
| Jana Smith ...57,271 | Paul Rodarmer ...67 | |
| Elias Khalaf ...73* | | |

| Public Schs..Principal | Grd | Prgm | Enr/#Cls | SN |
|---|---|---|---|---|
| Tioga Sch<br>405 N Florence St, Tioga 76271<br>Jana Smith \ Erica Waller | PK-12 | T | 639<br>12 | 37% 940/437-2366<br>Fax 940/202-2587 |

- **Tom Bean Ind School Dist** PID: 01020716     903/546-6076
100 E Garner St, Tom Bean 75489     Fax 903/546-6104

**Schools:** 3 \ **Teachers:** 51 \ **Students:** 620 \ **Special Ed Students:** 69 \
**LEP Students:** 21 \ **Ethnic:** African American 2%, Hispanic 10%, Native
American: 1%, Caucasian 87% \ **Exp:** $264 (Med) \ **Poverty:** 10% \
**Title I:** $96,253 \ **Open-Close:** 08/19 - 05/24 \ **DTBP:** $353 (High)

| | |
|---|---|
| Kelly Lusk ...............1 | Jennifer Parrish ...............2 |
| Pam Piper ...............3 | Florence Penrod ...............4* |
| Tiffany Yale ...............7 | Cheryl Jones ...............16,73,82 |
| Marcy Chapman ...............27* | Chad Ashlock ...............38 |
| Wanda Johnson ...............58* | Jesse Farrer ...............67 |
| Jan Woods-Meals ...............73 | Bobbie Moran ...............76 |

| Public Schs..Principal | Grd | Prgm | Enr/#Cls | SN |
|---|---|---|---|---|
| Tom Bean Elem Sch<br>105 Eubanks St, Tom Bean 75489<br>Patrice Counts | PK-5 | T | 255<br>19 | 57% 903/546-6333<br>Fax 903/546-6572 |
| Tom Bean High Sch<br>7719 State Hwy 11, Tom Bean 75489<br>Sara McCarty | 9-12 | TV | 200<br>26 | 42% 903/546-6319<br>Fax 903/546-6426 |
| Tom Bean Middle Sch<br>289 Franklin Rd, Tom Bean 75489<br>Sara McCarty | 6-8 | T | 172<br>18 | 48% 903/546-6161<br>Fax 903/546-6798 |

- **Van Alstyne Ind School Dist** PID: 01020742     903/482-8802
1096 N Waco St, Van Alstyne 75495     Fax 903/482-6086

**Schools:** 4 \ **Teachers:** 111 \ **Students:** 1,576 \ **Special Ed Students:** 157
\ **LEP Students:** 44 \ **College-Bound:** 60% \ **Ethnic:** Asian 1%, African
American 2%, Hispanic 15%, Native American: 1%, Caucasian 82% \
**Exp:** $531 (High) \ **Poverty:** 9% \ **Title I:** $142,415 \ **Open-Close:** 08/13 -
05/20 \ **DTBP:** $338 (High) \ [f]

| | |
|---|---|
| Dr David Brown ...............1 | Reene Maples ...............2,11 |
| Lannie Barnes ...............3,5 | Denise Richardson ...............4* |
| Mikeal Miller ...............6* | Jamie Martinez ...............8,12,57 |
| Devin Hill ...............16* | Sara Williams ...............37* |
| Randall Morgan ...............67 | Kenneth Daniel ...............73 |

| Public Schs..Principal | Grd | Prgm | Enr/#Cls | SN |
|---|---|---|---|---|
| Bob & Lola Sandford Elem Sch<br>300 Williamsburg Dr, Van Alstyne 75495<br>Sherry Stillman | PK-4 | | 263 | 35% 903/712-1900<br>Fax 903/712-4199 |
| John & Nelda Partin Elem Sch<br>201 Newport Dr, Van Alstyne 75495<br>Kristina Odom | PK-4 | T | 261<br>26 | 21% 903/482-8805<br>Fax 903/482-8820<br>[f] |
| Van Alstyne High Sch<br>1722 N Waco St, Van Alstyne 75495<br>Craig Dennis | 9-12 | V | 484<br>25 | 23% 903/482-8803<br>Fax 903/482-8885<br>[f] |
| Van Alstyne Middle Sch<br>1314 N Waco St, Van Alstyne 75495<br>Kelly Moore | 5-8 | | 568<br>40 | 27% 903/482-8804<br>Fax 903/482-8890<br>[f] |

- **Whitesboro Ind School Dist** PID: 01020780     903/564-4200
115 4th St, Whitesboro 76273     Fax 903/564-9303

**Schools:** 4 \ **Teachers:** 106 \ **Students:** 1,540 \ **Special Ed Students:** 174
\ **LEP Students:** 77 \ **Ethnic:** African American 1%, Hispanic 17%, Native
American: 2%, Caucasian 80% \ **Exp:** $366 (High) \ **Poverty:** 13% \
**Title I:** $329,804 \ **Open-Close:** 08/21 - 05/21 \ **DTBP:** $547 (High)

| | |
|---|---|
| Ryan Harper ...............1 | Jamie Brooks ...............2 |
| Ken Carden ...............3 | Alicia Tracy ...............4* |
| Alicia Tracy ...............4 | Mike Pack ...............5* |

| | | | |
|---|---|---|---|
| Cody Fagan ...............6* | Jodie Tucker ...............8 |
| Mattew Davenport ...............8,15 | Sharon Bryan ...............16* |
| Donna Boiles ...............36,69,77* | Justin Boren ...............67 |
| Michael Peterson ...............73,295* | D M Hampton ...............91 |

| Public Schs..Principal | Grd | Prgm | Enr/#Cls | SN |
|---|---|---|---|---|
| J W Hayes Primary Sch<br>117 4th St, Whitesboro 76273<br>Patti Achimon | PK-2 | T | 333<br>28 | 59% 903/564-4281<br>Fax 903/564-4123 |
| Whitesboro High Sch<br>1 Bearcat Dr, Whitesboro 76273<br>Marlene Robinson | 9-12 | | 470<br>30 | 43% 903/564-4114<br>Fax 903/564-4288 |
| Whitesboro Intermediate Sch<br>211 N College St, Whitesboro 76273<br>**Kacy Kupper** | 3-5 | T | 370<br>18 | 55% 903/564-4180<br>Fax 903/564-6808 |
| Whitesboro Middle Sch<br>600 4th St, Whitesboro 76273<br>**Aaron Dodson** | 6-8 | T | 367<br>30 | 54% 903/564-4236<br>Fax 903/564-5939 |

- **Whitewright Ind School Dist** PID: 01020821     903/364-2155
315 A Highland Dr, Whitewright 75491     Fax 903/364-2839

**Schools:** 3 \ **Teachers:** 64 \ **Students:** 823 \ **Special Ed Students:** 66 \
**LEP Students:** 34 \ **Ethnic:** Asian 1%, African American 5%, Hispanic 13%,
Native American: 1%, Caucasian 80% \ **Exp:** $705 (High) \ **Poverty:** 10% \
**Title I:** $140,038 \ **Open-Close:** 08/19 - 05/27 \ **DTBP:** $105 (High)

| | |
|---|---|
| Brian Garner ...............1 | Chelsea Menjivar ...............2,19 |
| Mario Carpio ...............3 | Donna Lucas ...............4 |
| Bobby Worthy ...............5,8,11,57,74,273,288,294 | Kevin Wiggins ...............6 |
| Ashley Womble ...............9,93 | Lisa Lawson ...............16,286* |
| Linda Jester ...............67 | Nicholas Helge ...............73 |
| Judy Sims ...............91 | Mike Stephens ...............91 |

| Public Schs..Principal | Grd | Prgm | Enr/#Cls | SN |
|---|---|---|---|---|
| Whitewright Elem Sch<br>305 W Highland Dr, Whitewright 75491<br>**Allyson Price** | PK-5 | T | 353<br>22 | 53% 903/364-2155<br>Fax 903/364-5799 |
| Whitewright High Sch<br>304 Echols Ln, Whitewright 75491<br>**Chad Long** \ Steve Morrow | 9-12 | V | 285<br>21 | 34% 903/364-2155<br>Fax 903/364-2579 |
| Whitewright Middle Sch<br>315 W Highland Dr, Whitewright 75491<br>Charles Nash | 6-8 | T | 185<br>17 | 40% 903/364-2155<br>Fax 903/364-5263 |

## GRAYSON CATHOLIC SCHOOLS

- **Diocese of Dallas Ed Office** PID: 01012367
Listing includes only schools located in this county. See District Index for
location of Diocesan Offices.

| Catholic Schs..Principal | Grd | Prgm | Enr/#Cls | SN |
|---|---|---|---|---|
| St Marys Catholic Sch<br>713 S Travis St, Sherman 75090<br>Dr Danny Ledbetter | PK-8 | | 170<br>14 | 903/893-2127<br>Fax 903/893-3233<br>[f] |

| | | | |
|---|---|---|---|
| **79** Student Personnel | **91** Safety/Security | **275** Response To Intervention | **298** Grant Writer/Ptnrships |
| **80** Driver Ed/Safety | **92** Magnet School | **277** Remedial Math K-12 | **750** Chief Innovation Officer |
| **81** Gifted/Talented | **93** Parental Involvement | **280** Literacy Coach | **751** Chief of Staff |
| **82** Video Services | **95** Tech Prep Program | **285** STEM | **752** Social Emotional Learning |
| **83** Substance Abuse Prev | **97** Chief Information Officer | **286** Digital Learning | |
| **84** Erate | **98** Chief Technology Officer | **288** Common Core Standards | **Other School Types** |
| **85** AIDS Education | **270** Character Education | **294** Accountability | Ⓐ = Alternative School |
| **88** Alternative/At Risk | **271** Migrant Education | **295** Network System | Ⓒ = Charter School |
| **89** Multi-Cultural Curriculum | **273** Teacher Mentor | **296** Title II Programs | Ⓜ = Magnet School |
| **90** Social Work | **274** Before/After Sch | **297** Webmaster | Ⓨ = Year-Round School |

**School Programs**
A = Alternative Program
G = Adult Classes
M = Magnet Program
T = Title I Schoolwide
V = Career & Tech Ed Programs

**Social Media**
[f] = Facebook
[t] = Twitter

New Schools are shaded
New Superintendents and Principals are bold
Personnel with email addresses are underscored

## GRAYSON PRIVATE SCHOOLS

| Private Schs..Principal | Grd | Prgm | Enr/#Cls | SN |
|---|---|---|---|---|
| Grayson Christian Sch<br>4400 US Highway 82 E, Sherman 75090<br>Greg Rostyne | PK-12 | | 168<br>6 | 903/892-3304<br>Fax 903/868-2546 |
| Liberty Christian Academy<br>120 W Mulberry St, Sherman 75090<br>Katie Gresham | K-12 | | 36 | 903/328-6037 |
| Montessori Academy-North Texas<br>906 Cottonwood Dr, Sherman 75090<br>Angela Majors | PK-6 | | 120 | 903/893-3500<br>Fax 972/767-0999 |
| St Luke Sch<br>427 W Woodard St, Denison 75020<br>Cheryl Matsumoto | PK-5 | | 60<br>5 | 903/465-2653<br>Fax 903/465-1428 |
| Texoma Christian Sch<br>3500 W Houston St, Sherman 75092<br>Linda Yeilding | PK-12 | | 300<br>30 | 903/893-7076<br>Fax 903/891-8486 |
| Unity Christian Sch<br>1901 Woodlawn Blvd, Denison 75020<br>Harry Shomaker | 3-12 | | 6 | 903/465-1909 |

# GREGG COUNTY

## GREGG PUBLIC SCHOOLS

● **Gladewater Ind School Dist** PID: 01020857
200 Broadway Ave, Gladewater 75647
903/845-6991
Fax 903/845-6994

**Schools:** 4 \ **Teachers:** 146 \ **Students:** 1,700 \ **Special Ed Students:** 246 \ **LEP Students:** 114 \ **Ethnic:** Asian 1%, African American 22%, Hispanic 19%, Caucasian 58% \ **Exp:** $244 (Med) \ **Poverty:** 23% \ **Title I:** $677,908 \ **Open-Close:** 08/12 - 05/28 \ **DTBP:** $539 (High) \

| | | | |
|---|---|---|---|
| Sedric Clark ....................................1 | Glenda Hickey ........................2,19,84 |
| Lesa Lynn .......................................2 | Kim Chatman ..........................3,17,83 |
| Matt McIntosh ................................3 | Darla Allen ....................................4 |
| Steve McFarland ............................5 | Scott Clower ..................................6 |
| Jimmy Lightfoot ...............8,12,15,79,296 | Dr Peggy Oden ..............................58 |
| Jon Keller ......................................67 | Avon Bateman ...............................73 |

| Public Schs..Principal | Grd | Prgm | Enr/#Cls | SN |
|---|---|---|---|---|
| Gladewater High Sch<br>2201 W Gay Ave, Gladewater 75647<br>Cathy Bedair | 9-12 | TV | 504<br>45 | 66% 903/845-5591<br>Fax 903/845-3694 |
| Gladewater Middle Sch<br>414 S Loop 485, Gladewater 75647<br>Chris Langford | 6-8 | T | 393<br>40 | 73% 903/845-2243<br>Fax 903/844-1738 |
| Gladewater Primary Sch<br>100 W Gay Ave, Gladewater 75647<br>Amanda Langford | PK-1 | T | 369<br>22 | 77% 903/845-2254<br>Fax 903/845-5411 |
| Weldon Elem Sch<br>314 E Saunders St, Gladewater 75647<br>Darren Richardson | 2-5 | T | 533<br>21 | 77% 903/845-6921<br>Fax 903/845-6923 |

● **Kilgore Ind School Dist** PID: 01020900
301 N Kilgore St, Kilgore 75662
903/988-3900
Fax 903/983-3212

**Schools:** 5 \ **Teachers:** 280 \ **Students:** 4,086 \ **Special Ed Students:** 331 \ **LEP Students:** 688 \ **Ethnic:** Asian 1%, African American 14%, Hispanic 36%, Caucasian 49% \ **Exp:** $514 (High) \ **Poverty:** 19% \ **Title I:** $940,872 \ **Special Education:** $808,000 \ **Open-Close:** 08/19 - 05/27 \ **DTBP:** $184 (High) \

| | | | |
|---|---|---|---|
| Dr Andrew Baker ...............................1 | Revard Pfeffer .......................2,19,298 |
| Michael Brown ...............................3,5 | Jennie Hammerbacher ...................4 |
| Mike Wood ......................................6 | Zevely Hatcher ...............................8 |
| Richard Nash ...........................11,15 | Jerry Stuart ...................................27 |
| Danny Stanley ....................57,69,81* | Gina Akin .......................................58 |
| Reggie Henson ..............................67 | Amy Broadus .................................68 |
| Mark Lane ................73,82,295,297* | Heather Chism .............................295 |

| Public Schs..Principal | Grd | Prgm | Enr/#Cls | SN |
|---|---|---|---|---|
| Chandler Elem Sch<br>2500 Chandler St, Kilgore 75662<br>Cynthia Lindley | 2-3 | T | 636<br>41 | 72% 903/988-3904<br>Fax 903/986-8026 |
| Kilgore High Sch<br>711 N Longview St, Kilgore 75662<br>Charles Presley | 9-12 | TV | 1,109<br>70 | 56% 903/988-3901<br>Fax 903/984-0571 |
| Kilgore Intermediate Sch<br>2300 Whipperwill St, Kilgore 75662<br>Kim Slayter | 4-5 | T | 618<br>24 | 68% 903/988-3903<br>Fax 903/984-7879 |
| Kilgore Middle Sch<br>455 Baughman Rd, Kilgore 75662<br>Jennifer Gholson | 6-8 | T | 924<br>46 | 66% 903/988-3902<br>Fax 903/984-6225 |
| Kilgore Primary Sch<br>255 Baughman Rd, Kilgore 75662<br>Rebecca Montgomery | PK-1 | T | 799<br>26 | 79% 903/988-3905<br>Fax 903/984-2176 |

● **Longview Ind School Dist** PID: 01020986
1301 E Young St, Longview 75602
903/381-2200
Fax 903/753-5389

**Schools:** 13 \ **Teachers:** 589 \ **Students:** 8,700 \ **Special Ed Students:** 662 \ **LEP Students:** 1,634 \ **Ethnic:** Asian 2%, African American 35%, Hispanic 43%, Native American: 1%, Caucasian 20% \ **Exp:** $659 (High) \ **Poverty:** 21% \ **Title I:** $2,715,241 \ **Special Education:** $1,743,000 \ **Open-Close:** 08/17 - 05/25 \ **DTBP:** $158 (High) \

| | | | |
|---|---|---|---|
| Dr James Wilcox .................................1 | Joey Jones .................................2,19 |
| Mike Gipson ....................................3 | Phyllis Dozier .................................4 |
| John King .....................................6,35* | Dennis Williams .......7,15,79,83,88,91,275 |
| Beth Bassett ..........8,39,42,45,48,51,277,280 | Horace Williams ....9,15,36,69,77,286,294 |
| Melanie Pondant ............................10 | Sheri Broadwater ...............11,54,298 |
| Jennifer Smith ...........................16,73* | Brian Kasper ...............................31* |
| Dr Maureen Lewis ..........................58 | Virginia Northcutt ...........................67 |
| Dr Jody Clements .............68,74,93,296 | Loretta Martin ...............................68 |
| Catina Love ....................................69 | Matthew Prosser ............................71 |
| Brian Pitts ...............................73,295 | Glen Pierce ...................................76 |
| Latitia Wilson ................................294 | |

| Public Schs..Principal | Grd | Prgm | Enr/#Cls | SN |
|---|---|---|---|---|
| Bramlette Elem Sch<br>111 Tupelo Dr, Longview 75601<br>Nikita Mumphrey | 1-5 | | 458<br>28 | 903/803-5600<br>Fax 903/803-5601 |
| East Texas Mont Prep Academy<br>400 N Eastman Rd, Longview 75601<br>Dr Jacqueline Burnett | PK-K | T | 509 | 93% 903/803-5000 |
| Ⓜ Everhart Mgnt Acad/Cltrl Study<br>2919 Tryon Rd, Longview 75605<br>Cassandria James | 1-5 | | 742<br>16 | 903/803-5400<br>Fax 903/803-5401 |

| | | | | | | | | | | |
|---|---|---|---|---|---|---|---|---|---|---|
| 1 | Superintendent | 8 | Curric/Instruct K-12 | 19 | Chief Financial Officer | 29 | Family/Consumer Science | 39 | Social Studies K-12 | 49 | English/Lang Arts Elem |
| 2 | Bus/Finance/Purchasing | 9 | Curric/Instruct Elem | 20 | Art K-12 | 30 | Adult Education | 40 | Social Studies Elem | 50 | English/Lang Arts Sec |
| 3 | Buildings And Grounds | 10 | Curric/Instruct Sec | 21 | Art Elem | 31 | Career/Sch-to-Work K-12 | 41 | Social Studies Sec | 51 | Reading K-12 |
| 4 | Food Service | 11 | Federal Program | 22 | Art Sec | 32 | Career/Sch-to-Work Elem | 42 | Science K-12 | 52 | Reading Elem |
| 5 | Transportation | 12 | Title I | 23 | Music K-12 | 33 | Career/Sch-to-Work Sec | 43 | Science Elem | 53 | Reading Sec |
| 6 | Athletic | 13 | Title V | 24 | Music Elem | 34 | Early Childhood Ed | 44 | Science Sec | 54 | Remedial Reading K-12 |
| 7 | Health Services | 15 | Asst Superintendent | 25 | Music Sec | 35 | Health/Phys Education | 45 | Math K-12 | 55 | Remedial Reading Elem |
| | | 16 | Instructional Media Svcs | 26 | Business Education | 36 | Guidance Services K-12 | 46 | Math Elem | 56 | Remedial Reading Sec |
| | | 17 | Chief Operations Officer | 27 | Career & Tech Ed | 37 | Guidance Services Elem | 47 | Math Sec | 57 | Bilingual/ELL |
| | | 18 | Chief Academic Officer | 28 | Technology Education | 38 | Guidance Services Sec | 48 | English/Lang Arts K-12 | 58 | Special Education K-12 |

| | | | |
|---|---|---|---|
| 59 | Special Education Elem | 69 | Academic Assessment |
| 60 | Special Education Sec | 70 | Research/Development |
| 61 | Foreign/World Lang K-12 | 71 | Public Information |
| 62 | Foreign/World Lang Elem | 72 | Summer School |
| 63 | Foreign/World Lang Sec | 73 | Instructional Tech |
| 64 | Religious Education K-12 | 74 | Inservice Training |
| 65 | Religious Education Elem | 75 | Marketing/Distributive |
| 66 | Religious Education Sec | 76 | Info Systems |
| 67 | School Board President | 77 | Psychological Assess |
| 68 | Teacher Personnel | 78 | Affirmative Action |

| School | Grd | Prgm | Enr/#Cls | SN | Phone |
|---|---|---|---|---|---|
| ⓜ Forest Park Middle Sch<br>1644 N Eastman Rd, Longview 75601<br>Dr Wilbert Andrews | 6-8 | T | 169<br>50 | 86% | 903/446-2510<br>Fax 903/446-2501 |
| Foster Middle Sch<br>1504 S Martin Luther King Blvd, Longview 75602<br>Ryan Carroll | 6-8 | T | 765<br>60 | 72% | 903/446-2710<br>Fax 903/758-2052 |
| ⓜ Hudson Pep Elem Sch<br>1311 Lilly St, Longview 75602<br>Sue Wilson | 1-5 | T | 591<br>19 | 34% | 903/803-5100<br>Fax 903/803-5101 ⓣ |
| Johnston-McQueen Elem Sch<br>422 FM 2751, Longview 75605<br>**Dr Jennifer Bailey** | PK-5 | T | 709<br>23 | 65% | 903/803-5300<br>Fax 903/663-2135 |
| Judson Steam Academy<br>5745 Judson Rd, Longview 75605<br>Melanie Pandant | 6-8 | | 562<br>30 | | 903/446-2610<br>Fax 903/663-2604 ⓣ |
| ⓐ Longview Early Graduation HS<br>410 S Green St, Longview 75601<br>Kristi Means | 9-12 | | 250<br>5 | | 903/381-3921<br>Fax 903/381-3925 |
| Longview High Sch<br>201 E Tomlinson Pwky, Longview 75605<br>James Brewer | 9-12 | GTV | 2,145 | 61% | 903/663-1301<br>Fax 903/663-7180 |
| Ned E Williams Elem Sch<br>5230 Estes Pkwy, Longview 75603<br>Melanie Hamilton | 1-5 | T | 402 | 90% | 903/803-5500<br>Fax 903/803-5501 |
| South Ward Elem Sch<br>1011 S Mobberly Ave, Longview 75602<br>Joaquin Guerrero | 1-5 | T | 397<br>30 | 94% | 903/803-5200<br>Fax 903/753-2961 |
| Ware Elem Sch<br>601 W Garfield Dr, Longview 75602<br>**Josh Worsham** | 1-5 | T | 514<br>30 | 96% | 903/803-5700<br>Fax 903/758-7872 ⓣ |

---

● **Pine Tree Ind School Dist** PID: 01021148
1701 Pine Tree Rd, Longview 75604
903/295-5000
Fax 903/295-5004

**Schools:** 8 \ **Teachers:** 317 \ **Students:** 4,700 \ **Special Ed Students:** 441 \ **LEP Students:** 655 \ **Ethnic:** Asian 1%, African American 25%, Hispanic 38%, Caucasian 36% \ **Exp:** $368 (High) \ **Poverty:** 19% \ **Title I:** $1,320,679 \ **Special Education:** $593,000 \ **Open-Close:** 08/19 - 05/26 \ **DTBP:** $153 (High) \ 🅵 ⓣ

| | | | |
|---|---|---|---|
| Steve Clugston | 1 | Nikki Benoit | 2 |
| Salena Jackson | 2,15 | David Peurifoy | 3 |
| Tony Hollins | 3,15 | Michelle Mitchell | 4 |
| Jack Irvin | 5,91 | Penny Pike | 5 |
| Jody Berryhill | 6 | Dr Eric Cederstorm | 8,15,68 |
| Dr Lisa Mullins | 8,39,48 | Robin White | 8,44,47,285 |
| Michele Walker | 11,57 | Dr Valerie Baxter | 15 |
| Tina Luman | 16,82* | Lee Branson | 20,23 |
| Daniel Stuard | 58 | Kalli VanMeter | 58 |
| Frank Richard | 67 | Melanie Ferguson | 68 |
| Debbie Terry | 69,288,294 | Mary Whitton | 71 |
| Todd Yohn | 73 | Amber Hargrove | 76 |
| Donna Pruitt | 93 | Stephen Taft | 286,295 |

| Public Schs..Principal | Grd | Prgm | Enr/#Cls | SN |
|---|---|---|---|---|
| Birch Elem Sch<br>815 Birch St, Longview 75604<br>**Sharon Smith** \ Derrick Conley | 1-4 | T | 648<br>37 | 72% 903/295-5120<br>Fax 903/295-5126 |
| ⓐ Excel High Sch<br>850 Northwest Dr, Longview 75604<br>Cleotis Wadley | 9-12 | GT | 55 | 63% 903/295-6753 |
| ⓐ Pace Alternative Campus<br>1701 Pine Tree Rd, Longview 75604<br>Shalonda Adams | K-12 | | 25 | 903/295-5130<br>Fax 903/295-5145 |
| Parkway Elem Sch<br>601 Pt Pkwy, Longview 75608<br>Melanie Keoun | 1-4 | T | 684<br>34 | 72% 903/295-5151<br>Fax 903/295-5155 |

---

| School | Grd | Prgm | Enr/#Cls | SN | Phone |
|---|---|---|---|---|---|
| Pine Tree Junior High Sch<br>2100 NW Loop 281, Longview 75604<br>Vanessa Robinson | 7-8 | T | 709<br>27 | 66% | 903/295-5081<br>Fax 903/295-5082 |
| Pine Tree Middle Sch<br>600 Pt Parkway, Longview 75604<br>Mickey White | 5-6 | T | 691<br>50 | 68% | 903/295-5160<br>Fax 903/295-5162 |
| Pine Tree Primary Sch<br>1808 Silver Falls Rd, Longview 75604<br>**Ruthie Walker** | PK-K | T | 518<br>24 | 76% | 903/295-5095<br>Fax 903/295-5098 |
| Pine Tree Senior High Sch<br>900 Northwest Dr, Longview 75604<br>Cindy Gabehart | 9-12 | GTV | 588<br>80 | 55% | 903/295-5031<br>Fax 903/295-5029 |

---

● **Sabine Ind School Dist** PID: 01021215
5424 FM 1252 W, Gladewater 75647
903/984-8564
Fax 903/984-6108

**Schools:** 3 \ **Teachers:** 105 \ **Students:** 1,495 \ **Special Ed Students:** 155 \ **LEP Students:** 114 \ **College-Bound:** 95% \ **Ethnic:** Asian 1%, African American 5%, Hispanic 22%, Caucasian 72% \ **Exp:** $469 (High) \ **Poverty:** 12% \ **Title I:** $190,346 \ **Open-Close:** 08/19 - 05/26 \ **DTBP:** $553 (High)

| | | | |
|---|---|---|---|
| Stacey Bryce | 1 | Kevin Yandell | 2 |
| Ken Wilson | 3 | Sunnie Caldwell | 4 |
| Paul Allen | 5 | Rex Sharp | 6 |
| Amanda Madden | 7* | Shelley Yates | 8,11,83,285,286,288,294,298 |
| Teri Bass | 9,34* | Cyndi Bryce | 16,82* |
| Anna Hamilton | 22* | Tiffany Braxton | 37* |
| Vicki Thornton | 58,77 | Tony Raymond | 67 |
| Randy Cox | 73 | Shawn Whited | 73 |

| Public Schs..Principal | Grd | Prgm | Enr/#Cls | SN |
|---|---|---|---|---|
| Sabine Elem Sch<br>645 Access Rd, Kilgore 75662<br>Teri Bass | PK-5 | T | 708<br>30 | 53% 903/984-5320<br>Fax 903/984-4101 |
| Sabine High Sch<br>5424 FM 1252 W, Gladewater 75647<br>Monty Pepper | 9-12 | ATV | 433<br>35 | 45% 903/984-8587<br>Fax 903/986-1103 |
| Sabine Middle Sch<br>5424 FM 1252 W, Gladewater 75647<br>Stanton Reaves | 6-8 | T | 354<br>25 | 45% 903/984-4767<br>Fax 903/984-8823 |

---

● **Spring Hill Ind School Dist** PID: 01021253
3101 Spring Hill Rd, Longview 75605
903/759-4404
Fax 903/297-0141

**Schools:** 4 \ **Teachers:** 145 \ **Students:** 2,100 \ **Special Ed Students:** 160 \ **LEP Students:** 100 \ **College-Bound:** 70% \ **Ethnic:** Asian 2%, African American 16%, Hispanic 17%, Native American: 1%, Caucasian 65% \ **Exp:** $475 (High) \ **Poverty:** 14% \ **Title I:** $343,023 \ **Special Education:** $10,000 \ **Open-Close:** 08/12 - 05/21 \ **DTBP:** $332 (High)

| | | | |
|---|---|---|---|
| Dr Wayne Guidry | 1 | Martin Cobb | 2,19 |
| Toby Pleasant | 3 | Janet Albright | 4 |
| David Fleming | 5 | Weston Griffis | 6 |
| Penny Fleet | 8,15,74* | Mark White | 67 |
| Connie Johnson | 69 | Steve Hardy | 73 |
| Chenena Martin | 76 | Roger Askew | 91 |
| Amy Doron | 270 | Adrian Knight | 294 |
| Kyle Linthicum | 295 | | |

| Public Schs..Principal | Grd | Prgm | Enr/#Cls | SN |
|---|---|---|---|---|
| Spring Hill High Sch<br>3101 Spring Hill Rd, Longview 75605<br>Rusty Robinett | 9-12 | V | 543<br>27 | 33% 903/446-3300<br>Fax 903/323-7766 |

---

| | Grd | Prgm | Enr/#Cls | SN |
|---|---|---|---|---|
| Spring Hill Intermediate Sch<br>3101 Spring Hill Rd, Longview 75605<br>Dana Robertson | 3-5 | T | 504<br>14 | 51% 903/323-7701<br>Fax 903/323-7762 |
| Spring Hill Junior High Sch<br>3101 Spring Hill Rd, Longview 75605<br>David Lynch | 6-8 | T | 476<br>35 | 45% 903/323-7718<br>Fax 903/323-7765 |
| Spring Hill Primary Sch<br>2700 Spring Hill Rd, Longview 75605<br>Deanna Turner | PK-2 | T | 496<br>27 | 55% 903/323-7848<br>Fax 903/323-7847 |

● **White Oak Ind School Dist** PID: 01021306     903/291-2200
200 S White Oak Rd, White Oak 75693     Fax 903/291-2222

> **Schools:** 4 \ **Teachers:** 117 \ **Students:** 1,496 \ **Special Ed Students:** 174
> \ **LEP Students:** 16 \ **Ethnic:** Asian 1%, African American 4%, Hispanic 8%,
> Native American: 1%, Caucasian 86% \ **Exp:** $454 (High) \ **Poverty:** 17% \
> **Title I:** $317,764 \ **Open-Close:** 08/10 - 05/19 \ **DTBP:** $522 (High) \ 🅣

| | | | |
|---|---|---|---|
| **Brian Gray** .............1 | Tami Demers .............2 |
| Barry Henson .............3 | Laurie Ferguson .............4* |
| Stacy Anderson .............5 | Kris Iske .............6 |
| Susan Willis .............7* | Mitzi Neely .............8,11,57,83,88,273,294,296 |
| Carol Stewart .............16* | Megan Lawson .............19 |
| Vicki Thorton .............34,58 | Dr David Ummel .............67 |
| Scott Floyd .............73,295 | Deanna Boothe .............84 |

| Public Schs..Principal | Grd | Prgm | Enr/#Cls | SN |
|---|---|---|---|---|
| White Oak High Sch<br>200 S White Oak Rd, White Oak 75693<br>Donna Jennings | 9-12 | V | 413<br>46 | 35% 903/291-2004<br>Fax 903/291-2034 |
| White Oak Intermediate Sch<br>200 S White Oak Rd, White Oak 75693<br>Jennifer Rock | 3-5 | T | 355<br>16 | 42% 903/291-2101<br>Fax 903/291-2196 |
| White Oak Middle Sch<br>200 S White Oak Rd, White Oak 75693<br>Becky Balboa | 6-8 | TV | 368<br>27 | 40% 903/291-2055<br>Fax 903/291-2035 |
| White Oak Primary Sch<br>200 S White Oak Rd, White Oak 75693<br>Claire Koonce | PK-2 | T | 363<br>17 | 40% 903/291-2160<br>Fax 903/291-2132 |

## GREGG CATHOLIC SCHOOLS

● **Diocese of Tyler Ed Office** PID: 03014660
Listing includes only schools located in this county. See District Index for location of Diocesan Offices.

| Catholic Schs..Principal | Grd | Prgm | Enr/#Cls | SN |
|---|---|---|---|---|
| St Mary's Catholic Sch<br>405 Hollybrook Dr, Longview 75605<br>Dr Darbie Safford | PK-12 | | 200<br>19 | 903/753-1657<br>Fax 903/758-7347 |

## GREGG PRIVATE SCHOOLS

| Private Schs..Principal | Grd | Prgm | Enr/#Cls | SN |
|---|---|---|---|---|
| Christian Heritage Sch<br>2715 FM 1844, Longview 75605<br>Stephanie Jones | K-12 | | 250<br>20 | 903/663-4151<br>Fax 903/663-4587 |
| Crisman Sch<br>2455 N Eastman Rd, Longview 75605<br>Laura Lea Blanks | Spec | | 40<br>7 | 903/758-9741<br>Fax 903/758-9767 |

| | Grd | | Enr/#Cls | SN |
|---|---|---|---|---|
| East Texas Christian Sch<br>5621 S FM 2087, Longview 75603<br>Chandra Watson | PK-12 | | 130<br>14 | 903/757-7891<br>Fax 903/619-0349 |
| Longview Christian Academy<br>2200 W Loop 281, Longview 75604<br>Jaime Castillo | K-12 | | 150<br>15 | 903/759-0626 |
| Longview Christian Sch<br>1236 Pegues Pl, Longview 75601<br>Karen Williams | K-12 | | 250<br>15 | 903/297-3501<br>Fax 903/663-4448 |
| Trinity School of Texas<br>215 N Teague St, Longview 75601<br>Gary Whitwell | PK-12 | | 282<br>45 | 903/753-0612<br>Fax 903/753-4812 |

## GREGG REGIONAL CENTERS

● **Region 7 Ed Service Center** PID: 01021291     903/988-6700
1909 N Longview St, Kilgore 75662     Fax 903/988-6708

| | | | |
|---|---|---|---|
| Elizabeth Abernethy .............1 | Carrie Holland .............2,15 |
| Katie Chenoweth .............2,68,71 | Ronnie Hemann .............3,15,68 |
| Elaine Revell .............4 | Dr Sheron Darragh .............8,74 |
| Diana McBurnett .............11,58 | Viki Sparks .............11 |
| Dr Beverly Beran .............58 | Leesa Green .............69,294 |
| Barbara Bruhn .............73,76,286 | Henryette Lovely .............78 |

## GRIMES COUNTY

## GRIMES PUBLIC SCHOOLS

● **Anderson-Shiro Cons Ind SD** PID: 01021344     936/873-4500
458 FM 149 Rd W, Anderson 77830     Fax 936/873-4515

> **Schools:** 2 \ **Teachers:** 68 \ **Students:** 879 \ **Special Ed Students:** 81
> \ **LEP Students:** 42 \ **College-Bound:** 48% \ **Ethnic:** Asian 1%,
> African American 7%, Hispanic 17%, Caucasian 75% \ **Exp:** $312 (High)
> \ **Poverty:** 13% \ **Title I:** $82,503 \ **Special Education:** $35,000 \
> **Open-Close:** 08/12 - 05/28 \ **DTBP:** $320 (High) \ 🅕 🅣

| | | | |
|---|---|---|---|
| Scott Beene .............1 | Blake Vezurk .............2 |
| Julie Yargo .............4 | Brad Hodges .............6* |
| Carolyn Fiaschetti .............11 | Christy Nienstedt .............38* |
| Lonnie Owen .............67 | Brenda McDonald .............73,286* |
| Melisa Walla .............83 | |

| Public Schs..Principal | Grd | Prgm | Enr/#Cls | SN |
|---|---|---|---|---|
| Anderson-Shiro Elem Sch<br>458 FM 149 Rd W, Anderson 77830<br>Marcy Pavlock | PK-5 | T | 403<br>14 | 50% 936/873-4525<br>Fax 936/873-4530<br>🅕 |
| Anderson-Shiro Jr Sr High Sch<br>458 FM 149 Rd W, Anderson 77830<br>Dwayne Ross | 6-12 | TV | 476<br>35 | 37% 936/873-4550<br>Fax 936/873-4575 |

| | | | | | | | |
|---|---|---|---|---|---|---|---|
| **1** Superintendent | **8** Curric/Instruct K-12 | **19** Chief Financial Officer | **29** Family/Consumer Science | **39** Social Studies K-12 | **49** English/Lang Arts Elem | **59** Special Education Elem | **69** Academic Assessment |
| **2** Bus/Finance/Purchasing | **9** Curric/Instruct Elem | **20** Art K-12 | **30** Adult Education | **40** Social Studies Elem | **50** English/Lang Arts Sec | **60** Special Education Sec | **70** Research/Development |
| **3** Buildings And Grounds | **10** Curric/Instruct Sec | **21** Art Elem | **31** Career/Sch-to-Work K-12 | **41** Social Studies Sec | **51** Reading K-12 | **61** Foreign/World Lang K-12 | **71** Public Information |
| **4** Food Service | **11** Federal Program | **22** Art Sec | **32** Career/Sch-to-Work Elem | **42** Science K-12 | **52** Reading Elem | **62** Foreign/World Lang Elem | **72** Summer School |
| **5** Transportation | **12** Title I | **23** Music K-12 | **33** Career/Sch-to-Work Sec | **43** Science Elem | **53** Reading Sec | **63** Foreign/World Lang Sec | **73** Instructional Tech |
| **6** Athletic | **13** Title V | **24** Music Elem | **34** Early Childhood Ed | **44** Science Sec | **54** Remedial Reading K-12 | **64** Religious Education K-12 | **74** Inservice Training |
| **7** Health Services | **15** Asst Superintendent | **25** Music Sec | **35** Health/Phys Education | **45** Math K-12 | **55** Remedial Reading Elem | **65** Religious Education Elem | **75** Marketing/Distributive |
| | **16** Instructional Media Svcs | **26** Business Education | **36** Guidance Services K-12 | **46** Math Elem | **56** Remedial Reading Sec | **66** Religious Education Sec | **76** Info Systems |
| **TX—176** | **17** Chief Operations Officer | **27** Career & Tech Ed | **37** Guidance Services Elem | **47** Math Sec | **57** Bilingual/ELL | **67** School Board President | **77** Psychological Assess |
| | **18** Chief Academic Officer | **28** Technology Education | **38** Guidance Services Sec | **48** English/Lang Arts K-12 | **58** Special Education K-12 | **68** Teacher Personnel | **78** Affirmative Action |

## Iola Ind School Dist PID: 01021370

7282 Fort Worth Ave, Iola 77861

936/394-2361
Fax 936/394-2132

**Schools:** 2 \ **Teachers:** 43 \ **Students:** 527 \ **Special Ed Students:** 47 \ **LEP Students:** 5 \ **College-Bound:** 63% \ **Ethnic:** African American 3%, Hispanic 18%, Caucasian 79% \ **Exp:** $350 (High) \ **Poverty:** 18% \ **Title I:** $109,723 \ **Open-Close:** 08/19 - 05/28 \ **DTBP:** $354 (High)

| | | |
|---|---|---|
| Scott Martindale .....1 | Sharon Choiniere .....2 | |
| Dave Jordan .....3 | Linda Evans .....4 | |
| Sean Callahan .....5 | Pete Martinez .....6,83,88* | |
| Cindy Braaton .....7* | Tammy Brinkman .....11,271,273* | |
| Jamie McDougald .....16,85* | Mike McManners .....27 | |
| Lindsay Harris .....31,270* | Joan McKown .....54* | |
| Gail Swanlund .....57* | Doug Richards .....58,69* | |
| Renae Rains .....59* | Harvey Cannon .....60 | |
| Jason Gooch .....67 | Monica Hurst .....73,295* | |

| Public Schs..Principal | Grd | Prgm | Enr/#Cls | SN |
|---|---|---|---|---|
| Iola Elem Sch<br>7282 Fort Worth Ave, Iola 77861<br>Kristin Sajewski | PK-6 | T | 313<br>20 | 39% 936/394-2361<br>Fax 936/394-2051 |
| Iola Junior Senior High Sch<br>7282 Fort Worth Ave, Iola 77861<br>Dwayne Ross | 7-12 | T | 214<br>35 | 35% 936/394-2361<br>Fax 936/394-4700 |

## Navasota Ind School Dist PID: 01021409

705 E Washington Ave, Navasota 77868

936/825-4200
Fax 936/825-4297

**Schools:** 6 \ **Teachers:** 236 \ **Students:** 3,000 \ **Special Ed Students:** 288 \ **LEP Students:** 567 \ **College-Bound:** 100% \ **Ethnic:** African American 20%, Hispanic 48%, Native American: 1%, Caucasian 30% \ **Exp:** $559 (High) \ **Poverty:** 23% \ **Title I:** $1,008,125 \ **Open-Close:** 08/31 - 05/28 \ **DTBP:** $168 (High) \ 🇫 🇹

| | | |
|---|---|---|
| Dr Stu Musick .....1 | Valorie Moore .....2 | |
| Jeff Neblett .....3 | Wyvetta Franklin .....4 | |
| Kacey Dacous .....6,35* | Kathleen Busa .....7* | |
| Amberly Kolby .....8,69 | Jeanie Nickle .....8,16 | |
| Vanakan Leggett .....12 | Ronnie Gonzalez .....15,17 | |
| Tracy Brewer .....15,68,79 | Nancy Bouliane .....16* | |
| Francisco Perez .....27,73,98 | Beth Klammer .....39,48 | |
| Julie Horn .....42,45 | Jenny Boyer .....58 | |
| Tim Harris .....67 | Jeff Dyer .....68 | |

| Public Schs..Principal | Grd | Prgm | Enr/#Cls | SN |
|---|---|---|---|---|
| Brule Elem Sch<br>203 Brosig Ave, Navasota 77868<br>Vanikin Leggett | 4-5 | T | 384<br>30 | 82% 936/825-4275<br>Fax 936/825-8523 |
| High Point Elem Sch<br>11937 Highway 105 E, Navasota 77868<br>John Bathke | PK-5 | T | 417 | 76% 936/825-1130<br>Fax 936/894-3195<br>🇫🇹 |
| John C Webb Elem Sch<br>1605 Neal St, Navasota 77868<br>Emily Nichols | PK-3 | T | 750<br>26 | 82% 936/825-1120<br>Fax 936/825-2802 |
| Navasota High Sch<br>9238 Highway 90 S, Navasota 77868<br>Kristi Ramsey | 9-12 | T | 767<br>40 | 71% 936/825-4250<br>Fax 936/825-4293 |
| Navasota Junior High Sch<br>9038 Highway 90 S, Navasota 77868<br>Monica Guerrero | 6-8 | T | 652<br>50 | 79% 936/825-4225<br>Fax 936/825-4260 |
| Ⓐ W B Bizzell Academy<br>1604 Stacey St, Navasota 77868<br>**Jamie Bates** | 9-12 | T | 34 | 68% 936/825-4296 |

## Richards Ind School Dist PID: 01021459

9477 Panther Dr, Richards 77873

936/851-2364
Fax 936/851-2210

**Schools:** 1 \ **Teachers:** 17 \ **Students:** 180 \ **Special Ed Students:** 13 \ **LEP Students:** 3 \ **College-Bound:** 50% \ **Ethnic:** African American 9%, Hispanic 7%, Caucasian 84% \ **Exp:** $649 (High) \ **Poverty:** 21% \ **Title I:** $70,391 \ **Open-Close:** 08/24 - 05/28 \ **DTBP:** $327 (High)

| | | |
|---|---|---|
| William Boyce .....1,11 | Joy Boyce .....2 | |
| Justin Bane .....6* | Justin Bane .....6 | |
| William Boyce .....8,57,73,74,271,295* | John Portwood .....18 | |
| Jason Bay .....67 | | |

| Public Schs..Principal | Grd | Prgm | Enr/#Cls | SN |
|---|---|---|---|---|
| Richards Independent Sch<br>9477 Panther Dr, Richards 77873<br>John Portwood | PK-12 | TV | 180<br>16 | 58% 936/851-2364 |

## GRIMES CATHOLIC SCHOOLS

## Archdiocese Galveston-Houston PID: 01027855

Listing includes only schools located in this county. See District Index for location of Diocesan Offices.

| Catholic Schs..Principal | Grd | Prgm | Enr/#Cls | SN |
|---|---|---|---|---|
| Sch of Environmental Education<br>FM Rd 1774, Plantersville 77363<br>Michael Richmond | 5-5 | | 1,200 | 936/894-2141 |

## GUADALUPE COUNTY

## GUADALUPE PUBLIC SCHOOLS

## Marion Ind School Dist PID: 01021485

211 W Otto St, Marion 78124

830/914-2803
Fax 830/420-3268

**Schools:** 4 \ **Teachers:** 104 \ **Students:** 1,500 \ **Special Ed Students:** 138 \ **LEP Students:** 54 \ **Ethnic:** African American 2%, Hispanic 41%, Caucasian 57% \ **Exp:** $472 (High) \ **Poverty:** 11% \ **Title I:** $169,916 \ **Special Education:** $244,000 \ **Open-Close:** 08/12 - 05/28 \ **DTBP:** $350 (High)

| | | |
|---|---|---|
| Kelly Lindholm .....1,83 | Bill Orr .....2 | |
| Joe Allen .....3 | Marie Brooks .....4 | |
| Ryne Miller .....6 | Cesily Peeples .....8 | |
| Daniel Terrazas .....11,57,58* | Courtney Junkin .....16,297 | |
| Dr Kevin Kunde .....67 | Jon Lindholm .....68 | |
| Jason Causey .....73 | Debralee Richardson .....286 | |

| Public Schs..Principal | Grd | Prgm | Enr/#Cls | SN |
|---|---|---|---|---|
| Marion High Sch<br>506 Bulldog Ln, Marion 78124<br>Stacia Snyder | 9-12 | AV | 235<br>52 | 38% 830/914-1075<br>Fax 830/420-3639 |
| Marion Middle Sch<br>506 S Center St, Marion 78124<br>**Jeff Stevens** | 6-8 | TV | 356<br>30 | 39% 830/914-1070<br>Fax 830/420-3206 |

| | | | | |
|---|---|---|---|---|
| 79 Student Personnel | 91 Safety/Security | 275 Response To Intervention | 298 Grant Writer/Ptnrships | **School Programs** |
| 80 Driver Ed/Safety | 92 Magnet School | 277 Remedial Math K-12 | 750 Chief Innovation Officer | A = Alternative Program |
| 81 Gifted/Talented | 93 Parental Involvement | 280 Literacy Coach | 751 Chief of Staff | G = Adult Classes |
| 82 Video Services | 95 Tech Prep Program | 285 STEM | 752 Social Emotional Learning | M = Magnet Program |
| 83 Substance Abuse Prev | 97 Chief Information Officer | 286 Digital Learning | | T = Title I Schoolwide |
| 84 Erate | 98 Chief Technology Officer | 288 Common Core Standards | **Other School Types** | V = Career & Tech Ed Programs |
| 85 AIDS Education | 270 Character Education | 294 Accountability | Ⓐ = Alternative School | |
| 88 Alternative/At Risk | 271 Migrant Education | 295 Network System | Ⓒ = Charter School | **Social Media** |
| 89 Multi-Cultural Curriculum | 273 Teacher Mentor | 296 Title II Programs | Ⓜ = Magnet School | 🇫 = Facebook |
| 90 Social Work | 274 Before/After Sch | 297 Webmaster | Ⓨ = Year-Round School | 🇹 = Twitter |

New Schools are shaded
New Superintendents and Principals are bold
Personnel with email addresses are underscored

**TX—177**

| | | | | | |
|---|---|---|---|---|---|
| Norma Krueger Elem Sch-Karrer<br>213 W Huebinger St, Marion 78124<br>Paul Goetzke | 3-5 | T | 308 | 46% | 830/914-1065<br>Fax 830/420-3258 |
| Norma Krueger Elem Sch<br>306 S Cunningham St, Marion 78124<br>Rachel Robertson | PK-2 | T | 381<br>43 | 51% | 830/914-1060<br>Fax 830/420-3776 |

● **Navarro Ind School Dist** PID: 01021526    830/372-1930
6450 N State Highway 123, Seguin 78155    Fax 830/372-1853

**Schools:** 4 \ **Teachers:** 129 \ **Students:** 1,909 \ **Special Ed Students:** 161 \ **LEP Students:** 79 \ **Ethnic:** Asian 1%, African American 2%, Hispanic 42%, Caucasian 56% \ **Exp:** $692 (High) \ **Poverty:** 8% \ **Title I:** $151,255 \ **Special Education:** $259,000 \ **Open-Close:** 08/19 - 05/27 \ **DTBP:** $351 (High) \ 🅵

| | | | |
|---|---|---|---|
| **Wendi Russell** ...... 1 | Jo Ann Speed ...... 2 |
| Martin Mueck ...... 3 | Carlett Drabek ...... 4 |
| Kelly Hyde ...... 5 | Less Goad ...... 6* |
| Lacey Gosch ...... 8,11,57,271,273,288,294 | Becky Newton ...... 58 |
| Greg Gilcrease ...... 67 | Alissa Elley ...... 73,286,295,298 |
| Luke Morales ...... 91* | David Hyde ...... 295 |

| Public Schs..Principal | Grd | Prgm | Enr/#Cls | SN | |
|---|---|---|---|---|---|
| Navarro Elem Sch<br>380 Link Rd, Seguin 78155<br>Laurel Wilson | PK-3 | T | 514<br>29 | 45% | 830/372-1933<br>Fax 830/379-3145 |
| Navarro High Sch<br>6350 N State Highway 123, Seguin 78155<br>**Clay Scarborough** | 9-12 | | 638<br>33 | 27% | 830/372-1931<br>Fax 830/401-5570 |
| Navarro Intermediate Sch<br>300 Link Rd, Seguin 78155<br>**Wendy McMullen** | 4-6 | T | 433<br>23 | 41% | 830/372-1943<br>Fax 830/379-3170 |
| Navarro Junior High Sch<br>6450 N State Highway 123, Seguin 78155<br>Luke Morales | 7-8 | | 324 | 32% | 830/401-5550<br>Fax 830/379-3135<br>🅵 |

● **Schertz-Cibolo-Univ City ISD** PID: 01021552    210/945-6200
1060 Elbel Rd, Schertz 78154    Fax 210/945-6292

**Schools:** 17 \ **Teachers:** 936 \ **Students:** 15,925 \ **Special Ed Students:** 1,647 \ **LEP Students:** 596 \ **College-Bound:** 46% \ **Ethnic:** Asian 2%, African American 12%, Hispanic 45%, Caucasian 40% \ **Exp:** $338 (High) \ **Poverty:** 6% \ **Title I:** $1,086,170 \ **Special Education:** $2,410,000 \ **Open-Close:** 08/13 - 05/27 \ **DTBP:** $185 (High) \ 🅵 🆃

| | | | |
|---|---|---|---|
| **Dr Clark Ealy** ...... 1 | Angie Mocygemba ...... 2 |
| Matt Rivera ...... 2 | J D Mosley ...... 3 |
| Wayne Pruski ...... 3,4,5,19 | Maggie Cornejo ...... 4 |
| Francisco Perez ...... 5 | Scott Lehnhoff ...... 6,35 |
| David Thein ...... 7 | Ernie Reynolds ...... 7,10,91 |
| Dr Damon Edwards ...... 8,15,68,73 | Kelly Kovacs ...... 8,11,18,27,58,74 |
| Serena Georges-Penny ...... 8,74 | Veronica Goldhorn ...... 9 |
| Mike Lipe ...... 20,23 | Amy Massey ...... 27 |
| Cassandra Gracia ...... 27,31,36,69 | Marypaz Buitron ...... 57 |
| Kimberly Ferguson ...... 58 | Amy Driesbach ...... 67 |
| Linda Cannon ...... 68 | Araceli Trejo ...... 69,294 |
| Ed Suarez ...... 71 | Dr Karla Burkholder ...... 73 |
| Karen Blevins ...... 81 | Ryan Clark ...... 91 |

| Public Schs..Principal | Grd | Prgm | Enr/#Cls | SN | |
|---|---|---|---|---|---|
| Ⓐ A L Steele Enhanced Lrng Ctr<br>204 Wright Ave, Schertz 78154<br>Lisa Newman | 9-12 | | 70<br>7 | 38% | 210/945-6401<br>Fax 210/945-6410<br>🅵 🆃 |

| | | | | | |
|---|---|---|---|---|---|
| Barbara C Jordan Interm Sch<br>515 Thistle Creek Dr, Cibolo 78108<br>Tina Curtis | 5-6 | | 738<br>32 | 26% | 210/619-4250<br>Fax 210/619-4277 |
| Byron P Steele II High Sch<br>1300 FM 1103, Cibolo 78108<br>Jana Cervantes | 9-12 | V | 1,211 | 21% | 210/619-4000<br>Fax 210/619-4057<br>🅵 🆃 |
| Cibolo Valley Elem Sch<br>4093 Green Valley Rd, Cibolo 78108<br>Rhonda Jungmichel | PK-4 | | 912 | 27% | 210/619-4700<br>Fax 210/619-4740 |
| Ⓐ Daep<br>301 Main St, Schertz 78154<br>Stacy Serna | K-12 | | 53 | | 210/945-6413<br>Fax 210/945-6415 |
| Elaine S Schlather Interm Sch<br>230 Elaines Schlather Pkwy, Cibolo 78108<br>Yvette Ross | 5-6 | | 802 | 24% | 210/619-4300<br>Fax 210/619-4340 |
| Green Valley Elem Sch<br>1694 Green Valley Rd, Schertz 78154<br>Amy Denman | PK-4 | | 668<br>33 | 32% | 210/619-4450<br>Fax 210/619-4478 |
| J Frank Dobie Jr High Sch<br>395 W Borgfeld Rd, Cibolo 78108<br>Vernon Simmons | 7-8 | AV | 1,255<br>63 | 26% | 210/619-4100<br>Fax 210/619-4142<br>🅵 🆃 |
| John A Sippel Elem Sch<br>420 Fairlawn Ave, Schertz 78154<br>Clarie Bristow | PK-4 | | 777 | 31% | 210/619-4600<br>Fax 210/619-4630 |
| Laura Ingalls Wilder Inter Sch<br>806 Savannah Dr, Schertz 78154<br>Sarah Dauphinais | 5-6 | T | 804<br>38 | 42% | 210/619-4200<br>Fax 210/619-4220 |
| Maxine & Lutrell Watts ES<br>100 Deer Meadow Blvd, Cibolo 78108<br>Deanna Jackson | PK-4 | | 584 | 37% | 210/619-4400<br>Fax 210/619-4419 |
| Norma J Paschal Elem Sch<br>590 Savannah Dr, Schertz 78154<br>Allison Miller | PK-4 | | 708<br>36 | 23% | 210/619-4500<br>Fax 210/619-4518 |
| O G Wiederstein Elem Sch<br>171 W Borgfeld Rd, Cibolo 78108<br>Luis Chavez | PK-4 | | 643<br>20 | 30% | 210/619-4550<br>Fax 210/619-4590<br>🅵 🆃 |
| Ray D Corbett Junior High Sch<br>12000 Ray Corbett Dr, Schertz 78154<br>Rashad Ray | 7-8 | V | 1,148<br>45 | 35% | 210/619-4150<br>Fax 210/619-4190 |
| Rose Garden Elem Sch<br>10414 E FM 1518 N, Schertz 78154<br>Sarah Reed | PK-4 | | 586<br>28 | | 210/619-4350<br>Fax 210/619-4369 |
| Samuel Clemens High Sch<br>1001 Elbel Rd, Schertz 78154<br>Amy Sirizzotti | 9-12 | V | 2,631<br>120 | 25% | 210/945-6501<br>Fax 210/945-6590<br>🅵 🆃 |
| Schertz Elem Sch<br>701 Curtiss Ave, Schertz 78154<br>Geri Pope | PK-4 | T | 677<br>23 | 56% | 210/619-4650<br>Fax 210/619-4690 |

● **Seguin Ind School Dist** PID: 01021631    830/401-8600
1221 E Kingsbury St, Seguin 78155    Fax 830/379-0392

**Schools:** 13 \ **Teachers:** 464 \ **Students:** 7,048 \ **Special Ed Students:** 841 \ **LEP Students:** 634 \ **College-Bound:** 37% \ **Ethnic:** African American 5%, Hispanic 71%, Caucasian 24% \ **Exp:** $284 (Med) \ **Poverty:** 17% \ **Title I:** $1,896,802 \ **Special Education:** $1,729,000 \ **Open-Close:** 08/10 - 05/11 \ **DTBP:** $184 (High) \ 🅵 🆃

| | | | |
|---|---|---|---|
| Dr Matthew Gutierrez ...... 1 | Anthony Hillberg ...... 2,88,298 |
| James Pizana ...... 3,5,79,91 | Robert Gonzales ...... 3 |
| Jacob Galvin ...... 4 | Phia Rigney ...... 5 |
| Travis Bush ...... 6* | Cynthia Borden ...... 8,11,57,69,77,83,294 |
| Mark Cantu ...... 9,15,288 | Cynthia Moreno ...... 15,68 |
| Bill Lewis ...... 16,73,76 | Pete Silvius ...... 35 |
| Nilda Vella ...... 42 | David Hall ...... 45 |
| Andrea Jaramillo ...... 48 | Halcy Dean ...... 58 |
| Haley Martinez ...... 58* | Cinde Thomas-Jimenez ...... 67 |

| | | | |
|---|---|---|---|
| **1** Superintendent | **8** Curric/Instruct K-12 | **19** Chief Financial Officer | **29** Family/Consumer Science |
| **2** Bus/Finance/Purchasing | **9** Curric/Instruct Elem | **20** Art K-12 | **30** Adult Education |
| **3** Buildings And Grounds | **10** Curric/Instruct Sec | **21** Art Elem | **31** Career/Sch-to-Work K-12 |
| **4** Food Service | **11** Federal Program | **22** Art Sec | **32** Career/Sch-to-Work Elem |
| **5** Transportation | **12** Title I | **23** Music K-12 | **33** Career/Sch-to-Work Sec |
| **6** Athletic | **13** Title V | **24** Music Elem | **34** Early Childhood Ed |
| **7** Health Services | **15** Asst Superintendent | **25** Music Sec | **35** Health/Phys Education |
| | **16** Instructional Media Svcs | **26** Business Education | **36** Guidance Services K-12 |
| | **17** Chief Operations Officer | **27** Career & Tech Ed | **37** Guidance Services Elem |
| | **18** Chief Academic Officer | **28** Technology Education | **38** Guidance Services Sec |

| | | | |
|---|---|---|---|
| **39** Social Studies K-12 | **49** English/Lang Arts Elem | **59** Special Education Elem | **69** Academic Assessment |
| **40** Social Studies Elem | **50** English/Lang Arts Sec | **60** Special Education Sec | **70** Research/Development |
| **41** Social Studies Sec | **51** Reading K-12 | **61** Foreign/World Lang K-12 | **71** Public Information |
| **42** Science K-12 | **52** Reading Elem | **62** Foreign/World Lang Elem | **72** Summer School |
| **43** Science Elem | **53** Reading Sec | **63** Foreign/World Lang Sec | **73** Instructional Tech |
| **44** Science Sec | **54** Remedial Reading K-12 | **64** Religious Education K-12 | **74** Inservice Training |
| **45** Math K-12 | **55** Remedial Reading Elem | **65** Religious Education Elem | **75** Marketing/Distributive |
| **46** Math Elem | **56** Remedial Reading Sec | **66** Religious Education Sec | **76** Info Systems |
| **47** Math Sec | **57** Bilingual/ELL | **67** School Board President | **77** Psychological Assess |
| **48** English/Lang Arts K-12 | **58** Special Education K-12 | **68** Teacher Personnel | **78** Affirmative Action |

| Public Schs..Principal | Grd | Prgm | Enr/#Cls | SN |
|---|---|---|---|---|
| A J Briesemeister Mid Sch 1616 W Court St, Seguin 78155 Benjamin Grijalva | 6-8 | T | 778 40 | 75% 830/401-8711 Fax 830/379-0615 |
| Ball Early Childhood Center 812 Shannon Ave, Seguin 78155 Rhonda Jubela | PK-K | T | 490 18 | 99% 830/401-1281 Fax 830/379-5590 |
| F C Weinert Elem Sch 1111 Bruns St, Seguin 78155 Mary Hernandez | K-5 | T | 475 37 | 66% 830/401-1241 Fax 830/372-2720 ⓕⓣ |
| George Vogel Elem Sch 16121 FM 725, Seguin 78155 Laura Flack | K-5 | T | 405 24 | 69% 830/401-8745 Fax 830/372-2174 |
| Jefferson Avenue Elem Sch 215 Short Ave, Seguin 78155 Merry White | K-5 | T | 299 28 | 88% 830/401-8727 Fax 830/379-0950 |
| Jim Barnes Middle Sch 1539 Joe Carrillo St, Seguin 78155 Jason Schmidt | 6-8 | T | 876 | 62% 830/401-8756 Fax 830/379-4239 |
| Ⓐ Lizzie Burgess Alt Sch 225 N Saunders St, Seguin 78155 Erma Freeman | 2-12 | | 40 14 | 85% 830/379-1108 Fax 830/379-0088 |
| McQueeney Elem Sch 8860 FM 725, Mc Queeney 78123 Meredith Stadler | K-5 | T | 281 28 | 83% 830/401-8738 Fax 830/557-6981 ⓕⓣ |
| Ⓐ Mercer-Blumberg Learning Ctr 1205 E Kingsbury St, Seguin 78155 Jay Law | 9-12 | T | 150 10 | 79% 830/401-8690 Fax 830/379-1362 |
| Oralia R Rodriguez Elem Sch 1567 W Kingsbury St, Seguin 78155 Yolanda Grijalva | K-5 | T | 551 | 82% 830/401-8774 Fax 830/386-0001 |
| Robert F Koennecke Elem Sch 1441 Joe Carrillo St, Seguin 78155 Cassie Koehler | K-5 | T | 539 40 | 67% 830/401-8741 Fax 830/372-3317 |
| Seguin High Sch 1315 E Cedar St, Seguin 78155 Hector Esquivel | 9-12 | TV | 1,985 | 58% 830/401-8000 Fax 830/372-9851 |
| Vincent Patlan Elem Sch 2501 Breustedt St, Seguin 78155 Linda Guzman | K-5 | T | 419 44 | 83% 830/401-1221 Fax 830/372-4565 ⓕⓣ |

## GUADALUPE CATHOLIC SCHOOLS

• **Archdiocese San Antonio Ed Off** PID: 00999724
Listing includes only schools located in this county. See District Index for location of Diocesan Offices.

| Catholic Schs..Principal | Grd | Prgm | Enr/#Cls | SN |
|---|---|---|---|---|
| Our Lady-Perpetual Help Sch 16075 N Evans Rd, Selma 78154 Amanda Miller | PK-8 | | 511 18 | 210/651-6811 Fax 210/651-5516 |
| St James Catholic Sch 507 S Camp St, Seguin 78155 Johanna Lopez | PK-8 | | 180 13 | 830/379-2878 Fax 830/379-0047 |

## GUADALUPE PRIVATE SCHOOLS

| Private Schs..Principal | Grd | Prgm | Enr/#Cls | SN |
|---|---|---|---|---|
| Lifegate Christian Sch 395 Lifegate Ln, Seguin 78155 Mark Peters | K-12 | | 174 12 | 830/372-0850 Fax 830/372-0895 |
| River City Believers Academy 16765 Lookout Rd, Selma 78154 Dr Victor Fordyce | PK-12 | | 147 | 210/656-2999 |
| Seguin Christian Academy 1456 E Kingsbury St, Seguin 78155 Allison Haeussler | K-10 | | 40 7 | 830/433-4131 |

# HALE COUNTY

## HALE PUBLIC SCHOOLS

• **Abernathy Ind School Dist** PID: 01021746
505 7th St, Abernathy 79311
806/298-2563
Fax 806/298-2400

**Schools:** 3 \ **Teachers:** 68 \ **Students:** 850 \ **Special Ed Students:** 57 \ **LEP Students:** 15 \ **Ethnic:** African American 1%, Hispanic 55%, Caucasian 43% \ **Exp:** $693 (High) \ **Poverty:** 16% \ **Title I:** $162,397 \ **Open-Close:** 08/19 - 05/21 \ **DTBP:** $359 (High) \ ⓣ

| Public Schs..Principal | Grd | Prgm | Enr/#Cls | SN |
|---|---|---|---|---|
| Abernathy Elem Sch 505 7th St, Abernathy 79311 Jenci Chambers | PK-5 | T | 320 34 | 55% 806/298-4930 Fax 806/298-4995 |
| Abernathy High Sch 505 7th St, Abernathy 79311 Ezra Chambers | 9-12 | TV | 238 25 | 42% 806/298-2563 Fax 806/298-4653 |
| Abernathy Middle Sch 505 7th St, Abernathy 79311 Kelly Carlisle | 6-8 | T | 188 18 | 53% 806/298-4921 Fax 806/298-4775 |

• **Cotton Center Ind School Dist** PID: 01021784
2345 Farm Rd 179, Cotton Center 79021
806/879-2160
Fax 806/879-2175

**Schools:** 1 \ **Teachers:** 15 \ **Students:** 125 \ **Special Ed Students:** 9 \ **LEP Students:** 5 \ **College-Bound:** 75% \ **Ethnic:** Hispanic 58%, Caucasian 42% \ **Exp:** $605 (High) \ **Poverty:** 25% \ **Title I:** $29,985 \ **Open-Close:** 08/26 - 05/21 \ **DTBP:** $350 (High) \ ⓕ ⓣ

---

| | | | | | | |
|---|---|---|---|---|---|---|
| 79 | Student Personnel | 91 | Safety/Security | 275 | Response To Intervention | |
| 80 | Driver Ed/Safety | 92 | Magnet School | 277 | Remedial Math K-12 | |
| 81 | Gifted/Talented | 93 | Parental Involvement | 280 | Literacy Coach | |
| 82 | Video Services | 95 | Tech Prep Program | 285 | STEM | |
| 83 | Erate | 97 | Chief Information Officer | 286 | Digital Learning | |
| 84 | Erate | 98 | Chief Technology Officer | 288 | Common Core Standards | |
| 85 | AIDS Education | 270 | Character Education | 294 | Accountability | |
| 88 | Alternative/At Risk | 271 | Migrant Education | 295 | Network System | |
| 89 | Multi-Cultural Curriculum | 273 | Teacher Mentor | 296 | Title II Programs | |
| 90 | Social Work | 274 | Before/After Sch | 297 | Webmaster | |

| | |
|---|---|
| 298 Grant Writer/Ptnrships | **School Programs** |
| 750 Chief Innovation Officer | A = Alternative Program |
| 751 Chief of Staff | G = Adult Classes |
| 752 Social Emotional Learning | M = Magnet Program |
| | T = Title I Schoolwide |
| **Other School Types** | V = Career & Tech Ed Programs |
| Ⓐ = Alternative School | |
| Ⓒ = Charter School | **New Schools are shaded** |
| Ⓜ = Magnet School | **New Superintendents and Principals are bold** |
| Ⓨ = Year-Round School | Personnel with email addresses are underscored |

**Social Media**
ⓕ = Facebook
ⓣ = Twitter

| Public Schs..Principal | Grd | Prgm | Enr/#Cls | SN |
|---|---|---|---|---|
| Cotton Center Sch<br>2345 Farm Rd 179, Cotton Center 79021<br>**Ryan Bobo** | PK-12 | TV | 125<br>30 | 71% 806/879-2176 |

---

● **Hale Center Ind School Dist** PID: 01021813    806/839-2451
103 W Cleveland St, Hale Center 79041    Fax 806/839-2195

---

**Schools:** 3 \ **Teachers:** 53 \ **Students:** 628 \ **Special Ed Students:** 55 \
**LEP Students:** 45 \ **College-Bound:** 59% \ **Ethnic:** African American 2%,
Hispanic 71%, Native American: 1%, Caucasian 26% \ **Exp:** $750 (High) \
**Poverty:** 28% \ **Title I:** $225,387 \ **Open-Close:** 08/18 - 05/17 \ **DTBP:** $350
(High) \ 🇫 🇹

---

| | | | |
|---|---|---|---|
| Steven Pyburn ....................1 | Erica Garcia ....................4* |
| Joe Betancur ....................5 | Jeff Smith ....................6 |
| Monika Berry ....................11,57,271 | Laurie Johnson ....................38,83* |
| Pam Johnson ....................67 | Bryan McGan ....................73 |

| Public Schs..Principal | Grd | Prgm | Enr/#Cls | SN |
|---|---|---|---|---|
| Akin Elem Sch<br>1105 Ave K, Hale Center 79041<br>Jeff Hutton | PK-4 | T | 247<br>16 | 73% 806/839-2121<br>Fax 806/839-4404 |
| Carr Middle Sch<br>410 W 12th St, Hale Center 79041<br>Alan Berry | 5-8 | T | 182<br>13 | 73% 806/839-2141<br>Fax 806/839-4417 |
| Hale Center High Sch<br>411 Owl Dr, Hale Center 79041<br>Carlon Branson | 9-12 | ATV | 173<br>24 | 62% 806/839-2452<br>Fax 806/839-2059 |

---

● **Petersburg Ind School Dist** PID: 01021863    806/667-3585
1411 W 4th St, Petersburg 79250    Fax 806/667-3463

---

**Schools:** 1 \ **Teachers:** 26 \ **Students:** 280 \ **Special Ed Students:** 38 \
**LEP Students:** 33 \ **College-Bound:** 95% \ **Ethnic:** African American 1%,
Hispanic 71%, Native American: 1%, Caucasian 27% \ **Exp:** $547 (High) \
**Poverty:** 20% \ **Title I:** $81,977 \ **Open-Close:** 08/19 - 05/20 \ **DTBP:** $408
(High)

---

| | |
|---|---|
| Dr Brian Bibb ....................1,11,73 | Darlenea Robertson ....................2 |
| Donna Carnigney ....................8,57,58,271,274* | Corina Reyes ....................36* |
| Chad Byrd ....................67 | Menivra Orozco ....................98 |

| Public Schs..Principal | Grd | Prgm | Enr/#Cls | SN |
|---|---|---|---|---|
| Petersburg Sch<br>1411 W 4th St, Petersburg 79250<br>**Todd Newberry \ Cash Fortune** | PK-12 | T | 280<br>14 | 75% 806/667-3585 |

---

● **Plainview Ind School Dist** PID: 01021904    806/296-6392
2417 Yonkers St, Plainview 79072    Fax 806/293-6000

---

**Schools:** 10 \ **Teachers:** 359 \ **Students:** 4,717 \ **Special Ed Students:** 566
\ **LEP Students:** 357 \ **College-Bound:** 44% \ **Ethnic:** African American
4%, Hispanic 80%, Caucasian 16% \ **Exp:** $318 (High) \ **Poverty:** 25% \
**Title I:** $1,809,155 \ **Special Education:** $1,133,000 \ **Open-Close:** 08/12 -
05/21 \ **DTBP:** $155 (High) \ 🇫

---

| | |
|---|---|
| Dr H T Sanchez ....................1 | Becca Dunlap ....................2 |
| Doris Chapa ....................2 | Luis Trujillo ....................2 |
| Victor Hernandez ....................2 | Charles Mooney ....................3 |
| David Lopez ....................3 | Manuel Marin ....................3 |
| Lorrie Coats ....................5 | Ryan Rhoades ....................6* |
| Robin Straley ....................8 | Garrett Katrina ....................9 |
| Edna Garcia ....................11,57,93,271 | Greg Brown ....................15 |
| Susan Flippin ....................16 | Sylvia Delagarza ....................67 |

---

| | |
|---|---|
| Brandy Merrick ....................68 | Robin Forbes-Salazar ....................69,72,294* |
| Alissa Carter ....................73 | Dr Brent Richburg ....................73,76,84 |
| Jeff De La Garza ....................79 | Anita Flores ....................271 |
| Wayne Jennings ....................295 | |

| Public Schs..Principal | Grd | Prgm | Enr/#Cls | SN |
|---|---|---|---|---|
| Ⓐ Ash High Sch<br>908 Ash St, Plainview 79072<br>Rodney Wallace | 9-12 | | 83<br>15 | 806/293-6010<br>Fax 806/296-4183 |
| College Hill Elem Sch<br>707 Canyon St, Plainview 79072<br>Lori Glenn | PK-5 | T | 383<br>18 | 72% 806/293-6035<br>Fax 806/296-4102 |
| Coronado Middle Sch<br>2501 Joliet St, Plainview 79072<br>Rachel Long | 6-8 | T | 642<br>36 | 75% 806/293-6020<br>Fax 806/296-4177 |
| Edgemere Elem Sch<br>2600 W 20th St, Plainview 79072<br>Leslie Richburg | PK-5 | T | 432<br>24 | 81% 806/293-6040<br>Fax 806/296-4103 |
| Estacado Middle Sch<br>2200 W 20th St, Plainview 79072<br>Ritchie Thornton | 6-8 | T | 639<br>33 | 77% 806/293-6015<br>Fax 806/296-4169 🇫 |
| Highland Elem Sch<br>1707 W 11th St, Plainview 79072<br>Deborah Alcozer | PK-5 | T | 409<br>20 | 80% 806/293-6045<br>Fax 806/296-4169 🇫 |
| Hillcrest Elem Sch<br>315 SW Alpine Dr, Plainview 79072<br>Yesenia Pardo | PK-5 | T | 413<br>21 | 89% 806/293-6050<br>Fax 806/296-4106 |
| La Mesa Elem Sch<br>600 S Ennis St, Plainview 79072<br>Vickie Young | PK-5 | T | 534<br>27 | 68% 806/293-6055<br>Fax 806/296-9425 |
| Plainview High Sch<br>1501 Quincy St, Plainview 79072<br>Brandt Reagan | 9-12 | TV | 307<br>40 | 70% 806/293-6005<br>Fax 806/296-4069 |
| Thunderbird Elem Sch<br>1200 W 32nd St, Plainview 79072<br>**Edna Garcia** | PK-5 | T | 447<br>25 | 85% 806/293-6060<br>Fax 806/296-4125 |

---

## HALE PRIVATE SCHOOLS

| Private Schs..Principal | Grd | Prgm | Enr/#Cls | SN |
|---|---|---|---|---|
| Plainview Christian Academy<br>310 S Ennis St, Plainview 79072<br>Jennifer Harrell | PK-12 | | 213<br>14 | 806/296-6034<br>Fax 806/686-0988 |

---

## HALL COUNTY

---

## HALL PUBLIC SCHOOLS

---

● **Memphis Ind School Dist** PID: 01022087    806/259-5900
1501 High St, Memphis 79245    Fax 806/259-2515

---

**Schools:** 4 \ **Teachers:** 43 \ **Students:** 400 \ **Special Ed Students:** 68
\ **LEP Students:** 64 \ **Ethnic:** African American 7%, Hispanic 61%,
Caucasian 32% \ **Exp:** $538 (High) \ **Poverty:** 35% \ **Title I:** $254,713 \
**Special Education:** $41,000 \ **Open-Close:** 08/20 - 05/28 \ **DTBP:** $336
(High) \ 🇫

---

| | |
|---|---|
| William Alexander ....................1 | Brenda Alexander ....................2,19 |

---

| | | | | | | | | |
|---|---|---|---|---|---|---|---|---|
| 1 | Superintendent | 8 | Curric/Instruct K-12 | 19 | Chief Financial Officer | 29 | Family/Consumer Science | 39 Social Studies K-12 | 49 English/Lang Arts Elem | 59 Special Education Elem | 69 Academic Assessment |
| 2 | Bus/Finance/Purchasing | 9 | Curric/Instruct Elem | 20 | Art K-12 | 30 | Adult Education | 40 Social Studies Elem | 50 English/Lang Arts Sec | 60 Special Education Sec | 70 Research/Development |
| 3 | Buildings And Grounds | 10 | Curric/Instruct Sec | 21 | Art Elem | 31 | Career/Sch-to-Work K-12 | 41 Social Studies Sec | 51 Reading K-12 | 61 Foreign/World Lang K-12 | 71 Public Information |
| 4 | Food Service | 11 | Federal Program | 22 | Art Sec | 32 | Career/Sch-to-Work Elem | 42 Science K-12 | 52 Reading Elem | 62 Foreign/World Lang Elem | 72 Summer School |
| 5 | Transportation | 12 | Title I | 23 | Music K-12 | 33 | Career/Sch-to-Work Sec | 43 Science Elem | 53 Reading Sec | 63 Foreign/World Lang Sec | 73 Instructional Tech |
| 6 | Athletic | 13 | Title V | 24 | Music Elem | 34 | Early Childhood Ed | 44 Science Sec | 54 Remedial Reading K-12 | 64 Religious Education K-12 | 74 Inservice Training |
| 7 | Health Services | 14 | Asst Superintendent | 25 | Music Sec | 35 | Health/Phys Education | 45 Math K-12 | 55 Remedial Reading Elem | 65 Religious Education Elem | 75 Marketing/Distributive |
| | | 15 | Asst Superintendent | 26 | Business Education | 36 | Guidance Services K-12 | 46 Math Elem | 56 Remedial Reading Sec | 66 Religious Education Sec | 76 Info Systems |
| | | 16 | Instructional Media Svcs | 27 | Career & Tech Ed | 37 | Guidance Services Elem | 47 Math Sec | 57 Bilingual/ELL | 67 School Board President | 77 Psychological Assess |
| | | 17 | Chief Operations Officer | 28 | Technology Education | 38 | Guidance Services Sec | 48 English/Lang Arts K-12 | 58 Special Education K-12 | 68 Teacher Personnel | 78 Affirmative Action |
| | | 18 | Chief Academic Officer | | | | | | | |

Donnie Bridges ............................................ 3
Tony Zuniga ................................................ 5
Kellie Maddox ............................................ 7*
Sarah Cook ................................................ 67
Kitsy Pepper ............................................. 298

Sherree Foster ........................................... 4
David Jurado ............................................. 6*
Leighann Hawthorne ................................. 8
Jennifer Lindsey ............................. 295,298*

| Public Schs..Principal | Grd | Prgm | Enr/#Cls | SN | |
|---|---|---|---|---|---|
| Austin Elem Sch<br>519 N 9th St, Memphis 79245<br>**Leighann Hawthorne** | 3-5 | T | 93<br>7 | 82% | 806/259-5930<br>Fax 806/259-2786 |
| Memphis High Sch<br>1501 High St, Memphis 79245<br>**Dick Hutcherson** | 9-12 | TV | 152<br>18 | 65% | 806/259-5910<br>Fax 806/259-3026 |
| Memphis Middle Sch<br>1120 N 16th St, Memphis 79245<br>**Kennith Hardin** | 6-8 | T | 104<br>10 | 67% | 806/259-5920<br>Fax 806/259-2051 |
| Travis Elem Sch<br>710 N 12th St, Memphis 79245<br>**Vicki Davis** | PK-2 | T | 139<br>15 | 88% | 806/259-5940<br>Fax 806/259-3119 |

• **Turkey-Quitaque Cons Ind SD** PID: 01022130
11826 Highway 86, Turkey 79261

806/455-1411
Fax 806/455-1718

Schools: 1 \ Teachers: 21 \ Students: 185 \ Special Ed Students: 21 \ LEP Students: 13 \ Ethnic: African American 2%, Hispanic 37%, Caucasian 61% \ Exp: $391 (High) \ Poverty: 29% \ Title I: $87,135 \ Open-Close: 08/19 - 05/20 \ DTBP: $276 (High)

Jackie Jenkins ......................................1,11
Kristi Maynard ...........................................4
John Stanaland ..........................................6
Garrett Watson .........................................58

Donna Pigg .................................................2
Matt Edwards ............................................5*
Shadi Buchanan .................. 16,73,76,97,98
Chris Tucker ..............................................67

| Public Schs..Principal | Grd | Prgm | Enr/#Cls | SN | |
|---|---|---|---|---|---|
| Valley Sch<br>11826 Highway 86, Turkey 79261<br>**Brandon Smith** | PK-12 | TV | 185<br>26 | 59% | 806/455-1411 |

## HAMILTON COUNTY

## HAMILTON PUBLIC SCHOOLS

• **Hamilton Ind School Dist** PID: 01022166
400 S College St, Hamilton 76531

254/386-3149
Fax 254/386-8885

Schools: 3 \ Teachers: 75 \ Students: 789 \ Special Ed Students: 114 \ LEP Students: 42 \ College-Bound: 51% \ Ethnic: Hispanic 21%, Caucasian 78% \ Exp: $559 (High) \ Poverty: 23% \ Title I: $252,139 \ Open-Close: 08/13 - 05/20 \ DTBP: $337 (High)

Clay Tarpley ..............................................1
Casey Jones ..............................................6
Jennifer Zschiesche ........................ 8,15,73
Misti Polster ...........................................57*
Lisa Parrish .............................................69*

Ken Alexander ......................................2,11
Wendy Cude ....................................7,35,85*
James Sloane .........................................12*
T Medlock .................................................67

| Public Schs..Principal | Grd | Prgm | Enr/#Cls | SN | |
|---|---|---|---|---|---|
| Ann Whitney Elem Sch<br>400 S College St, Hamilton 76531<br>**James Slone** | PK-5 | T | 384<br>29 | 54% | 254/386-8166<br>Fax 254/386-3316 |

| | | | | | |
|---|---|---|---|---|---|
| Hamilton High Sch<br>611 S College St, Hamilton 76531<br>**Gina Poe** | 9-12 | ATV | 234<br>35 | 47% | 254/386-8167<br>Fax 254/386-4677 |
| Hamilton Junior High Sch<br>400 S College St, Hamilton 76531<br>**Mona Gloff** | 6-8 | T | 171<br>10 | 50% | 254/386-8168<br>Fax 254/386-4677 |

• **Hico Ind School Dist** PID: 01022192
901 Cedar St, Hico 76457

254/796-2182
Fax 254/796-2446

Schools: 2 \ Teachers: 51 \ Students: 563 \ Special Ed Students: 63 \ LEP Students: 48 \ College-Bound: 42% \ Ethnic: African American 1%, Hispanic 22%, Caucasian 77% \ Exp: $576 (High) \ Poverty: 20% \ Title I: $159,333 \ Open-Close: 08/12 - 06/01 \ DTBP: $409 (High) \ 🅵 🅣

Jon Hartgraves ............................. 1,11,84
Joni Broumbley ...........................................4
Rodney Thornton .......................................6*
Eric Kale ..................................................27*
Dana Broumley .........................................37*
Keith Broumley ..........................................67
David Oneill ............................................286*

Keith Elrod ..........................................2,298
David Wilkins ............................................5
Lavern Tooley .......................................7,85*
Deborah McGavock ....................31,36,69*
Brian Hunt ................................................57
Sherry Gerber ..........................................73*

| Public Schs..Principal | Grd | Prgm | Enr/#Cls | SN | |
|---|---|---|---|---|---|
| Hico Elem Sch<br>805 Tiger Rd, Hico 76457<br>**Brian Hunt** | PK-5 | T | 273<br>19 | 49% | 254/796-2183<br>Fax 254/796-4214 |
| Hico Secondary Sch<br>901 Cedar St, Hico 76457<br>**Dixie Watson** | 6-12 | TV | 290<br>16 | 58% | 254/796-2184 |

## HANSFORD COUNTY

## HANSFORD PUBLIC SCHOOLS

• **Gruver Ind School Dist** PID: 01022257
601 Garrett Ave, Gruver 79040

806/733-2001
Fax 806/733-5416

Schools: 3 \ Teachers: 47 \ Students: 450 \ Special Ed Students: 39 \ LEP Students: 80 \ College-Bound: 80% \ Ethnic: Hispanic 48%, Caucasian 51% \ Exp: $586 (High) \ Poverty: 9% \ Title I: $35,358 \ Open-Close: 08/18 - 05/21 \ DTBP: $178 (High)

Wade Callaway ...........................................1
Sahala Gaillard ..........................................7*
Kelly Hart ................................................16*
Carolyn Adams ........................................60*
Raquel Whitehead ....................69,88,270*

Karen Fischer .......................................2,11
Amber Holland ..........................................9*
Jill Butler ..................................................57
Mike Yanke ...............................................67
Holly McLean ............................................73

| Public Schs..Principal | Grd | Prgm | Enr/#Cls | SN | |
|---|---|---|---|---|---|
| Gruver Elem Sch<br>401 Garrett St, Gruver 79040<br>**Amber Holland** | PK-4 | T | 140<br>14 | 44% | 806/733-2031<br>Fax 806/733-5412 |
| Gruver High Sch<br>601 Garrett Ave, Gruver 79040<br>**Kimberly Conyers** | 9-12 | GTV | 151<br>20 | 52% | 806/733-2477<br>Fax 806/733-2596 |
| Gruver Junior High Sch<br>600 Garrett St, Gruver 79040<br>**Lexy Glass** | 5-8 | T | 151<br>13 | 46% | 806/733-2081<br>Fax 806/733-5523 |

## • Pringle-Morse Cons ISD PID: 01022295
100 S 5th St, Morse 79062

806/733-2507
Fax 806/733-2351

**Schools:** 1 \ **Teachers:** 13 \ **Students:** 125 \ **Special Ed Students:** 10 \
**LEP Students:** 27 \ **Ethnic:** Hispanic 61%, Native American: 4%, Caucasian
35% \ **Exp:** $609 (High) \ **Poverty:** 9% \ **Title I:** $1,016 \ **Open-Close:** 08/12
- 05/18 \ **DTBP:** $398 (High)

| | | |
|---|---|---|
| Scott Burrow .....................1,11,73 | Paige Speck .....................2,12,84,97,298 | |
| Jerahiah Martinez .....................3 | Janice McCloy .....................4 | |
| Jeff Forrest .....................6* | Monica Schmidt .....................16* | |
| Shannon Lane .....................57* | James Lieb .....................67 | |
| Shannon Lane .....................88 | Viann Clark .....................271 | |
| Cindy Lied .....................280 | Sadie Delacruz .....................295* | |

| Public Schs..Principal | Grd | Prgm | Enr/#Cls | SN | |
|---|---|---|---|---|---|
| Pringle-Morse Sch<br>100 S 5th St, Morse 79062<br>Scott Burrow | PK-12 | T | 125<br>13 | 72% | 806/733-2507 |

## • Spearman Ind School Dist PID: 01022312
403 E 11th Ave, Spearman 79081

806/659-3233
Fax 806/659-2079

**Schools:** 3 \ **Teachers:** 80 \ **Students:** 834 \ **Special Ed Students:** 60 \
**LEP Students:** 164 \ **Ethnic:** Hispanic 69%, Caucasian 31% \ **Exp:** $422
(High) \ **Poverty:** 20% \ **Title I:** $189,184 \ **Open-Close:** 08/10 - 05/14 \
**DTBP:** $353 (High) \ f t

| | | |
|---|---|---|
| Clay Montgomery .....................1 | Brenda Ferguson .....................2,11 | |
| Bernice Flores .....................4* | Joe Martinez .....................5 | |
| Aaron Witten .....................6 | Sally Swan .....................7,35,83,85* | |
| Sandi Wheeler .....................10,88,270 | Bonnie Morton .....................16,82 | |
| Shane Whiteley .....................16* | Krista Baird .....................31,36,69* | |
| Mary Nine .....................58 | Dr Mark Garnett .....................67 | |
| Kristen Shieldknight .....................73 | Brianne Eslick .....................95 | |

| Public Schs..Principal | Grd | Prgm | Enr/#Cls | SN | |
|---|---|---|---|---|---|
| Gus Birdwell Elem Sch<br>511 Townsend St, Spearman 79081<br>Alexis Beck | PK-5 | T | 412<br>32 | 65% | 806/659-2565<br>Fax 806/659-2257 |
| Spearman High Sch<br>403 E 11th Ave, Spearman 79081<br>**Sandi Wheeler** | 9-12 | ATV | 265<br>27 | 62% | 806/659-2584<br>Fax 806/659-3824 |
| Spearman Junior High Sch<br>313 W 5th Ave, Spearman 79081<br>Starla Whiteley | 6-8 | T | 186<br>14 | 60% | 806/659-2563<br>Fax 806/659-2243 |

# HARDEMAN COUNTY

## HARDEMAN PUBLIC SCHOOLS

## • Chillicothe ISD School Dist PID: 01022350
1610 S 6th St, Chillicothe 79225

940/852-5391
Fax 940/852-5269

**Schools:** 2 \ **Teachers:** 20 \ **Students:** 200 \ **Special Ed Students:** 20
\ **LEP Students:** 46 \ **College-Bound:** 60% \ **Ethnic:** African American
2%, Hispanic 49%, Native American: 1%, Caucasian 48% \ **Exp:** $435
(High) \ **Poverty:** 23% \ **Title I:** $78,669 \ **Special Education:** $11,000 \
**Open-Close:** 08/17 - 05/28 \ **DTBP:** $357 (High) \ f t

| | | |
|---|---|---|
| Todd Wilson .....................1,11 | Tammy Daniel .....................2 | |
| Steve Cheek .....................3 | Susan Pautsky .....................4 | |
| Donna Prince .....................36,69,83,85,88 | Mark Williams .....................67 | |
| Phyllis Heath .....................73* | | |

| Public Schs..Principal | Grd | Prgm | Enr/#Cls | SN | |
|---|---|---|---|---|---|
| Chillicothe Elem Sch<br>400 Ave L, Chillicothe 79225<br>Brenda Dunlap | PK-6 | T | 113<br>7 | 89% | 940/852-5521<br>Fax 940/852-5012 |
| Chillicothe High Sch<br>1610 S 6th St, Chillicothe 79225<br>Tony Martinez | 7-12 | TV | 87<br>20 | 76% | 940/852-5391<br>Fax 940/852-5465 |

## • Quanah Ind School Dist PID: 01022398
801 Elbert St, Quanah 79252

940/663-2281
Fax 940/663-2875

**Schools:** 3 \ **Teachers:** 53 \ **Students:** 525 \ **Special Ed Students:** 75
\ **LEP Students:** 8 \ **College-Bound:** 70% \ **Ethnic:** Asian 1%, African
American 2%, Hispanic 31%, Caucasian 65% \ **Exp:** $621 (High) \
**Poverty:** 24% \ **Title I:** $152,893 \ **Open-Close:** 08/21 - 05/21 \ **DTBP:** $355
(High) \ f

| | | |
|---|---|---|
| **Tom Johnson** .....................1 | Jim Jones .....................2 | |
| Armando Leal .....................3 | Lynn Isnhower .....................4 | |
| Jason Kole .....................6* | Amy Bibler .....................10,38,57 | |
| Rusty Brawley .....................11,58 | John White .....................16,73,295,297* | |
| Carol Johnson .....................83* | | |

| Public Schs..Principal | Grd | Prgm | Enr/#Cls | SN | |
|---|---|---|---|---|---|
| Quanah High Sch<br>501 W 7th St, Quanah 79252<br>Amy Bibler | 9-12 | ATV | 149<br>20 | 76% | 940/663-2791<br>Fax 940/663-6447 |
| Reagan Elem Sch<br>205 E 8th St, Quanah 79252<br>**Connie Miller** | PK-5 | T | 226<br>23 | 78% | 940/663-2171<br>Fax 940/663-2209 |
| Travis Middle Sch<br>600 W 7th St, Quanah 79252<br>Virginia Turner | 6-8 | T | 125<br>10 | 83% | 940/663-2226<br>Fax 940/663-6361 |

# HARDIN COUNTY

## HARDIN PUBLIC SCHOOLS

## • Hardin Jefferson Ind Sch Dist PID: 01022439
520 W Herring St, Sour Lake 77659

409/981-6400
Fax 409/287-2287

**Schools:** 4 \ **Teachers:** 162 \ **Students:** 2,300 \ **Special Ed Students:** 229
\ **LEP Students:** 96 \ **College-Bound:** 68% \ **Ethnic:** Asian 1%, African
American 12%, Hispanic 10%, Caucasian 77% \ **Exp:** $521 (High) \
**Poverty:** 11% \ **Title I:** $231,934 \ **Special Education:** $126,000 \
**Open-Close:** 08/12 - 05/28 \ **DTBP:** $347 (High) \ f t

| | | |
|---|---|---|
| Brad McEachern .....................1 | Brad Boullion .....................2,3 | |
| Courtney Bulion .....................4* | Katie Kibodeaux .....................5 | |
| Dwayne DeBoise .....................6 | Dr Steven Cox .....................11,15,57 | |
| Christian Kemp .....................28 | Deena Van Pelt .....................58 | |
| Michelle Yentzen .....................67 | Mandy Fortenberry .....................71 | |
| Lucas Turner .....................73,295,297 | Courtney Bagwell .....................76,84 | |
| Randy Obannion .....................91 | | |

| | | | | | |
|---|---|---|---|---|---|
| 1 Superintendent | 19 Chief Financial Officer | 29 Family/Consumer Science | 39 Social Studies K-12 | 49 English/Lang Arts Elem | 59 Special Education Elem | 69 Academic Assessment |
| 2 Bus/Finance/Purchasing | 9 Curric/Instruct Elem | 20 Art K-12 | 30 Adult Education | 40 Social Studies Elem | 50 English/Lang Arts Sec | 60 Special Education Sec | 70 Research/Development |
| 3 Buildings And Grounds | 10 Curric/Instruct Sec | 21 Art Elem | 31 Career/Sch-to-Work K-12 | 41 Social Studies Sec | 51 Reading K-12 | 61 Foreign/World Lang K-12 | 71 Public Information |
| 4 Food Service | 11 Federal Program | 22 Art Sec | 32 Career/Sch-to-Work Elem | 42 Science K-12 | 52 Reading Elem | 62 Foreign/World Lang Elem | 72 Summer School |
| 5 Transportation | 12 Title I | 23 Music K-12 | 33 Career/Sch-to-Work Sec | 43 Science Elem | 53 Reading Sec | 63 Foreign/World Lang Sec | 73 Instructional Tech |
| 6 Athletic | 13 Title V | 24 Music Elem | 34 Early Childhood Ed | 44 Science Sec | 54 Remedial Reading K-12 | 64 Religious Education K-12 | 74 Inservice Training |
| 7 Health Services | 15 Asst Superintendent | 25 Music Sec | 35 Health/Phys Education | 45 Math K-12 | 55 Remedial Reading Elem | 65 Religious Education Elem | 75 Marketing/Distributive |
| | 16 Instructional Media Svcs | 26 Business Education | 36 Guidance Services K-12 | 46 Math Elem | 56 Remedial Reading Sec | 66 Religious Education Sec | 76 Info Systems |
| 8 Curric/Instruct K-12 | 17 Chief Operations Officer | 27 Career & Tech Ed | 37 Guidance Services Elem | 47 Math Sec | 57 Bilingual/ELL | 67 School Board President | 77 Psychological Assess |
| | 18 Chief Academic Officer | 28 Technology Education | 38 Guidance Services Sec | 48 English/Lang Arts K-12 | 58 Special Education K-12 | 68 Teacher Personnel | 78 Affirmative Action |

| Public Schs..Principal | Grd | Prgm | Enr/#Cls | SN |
|---|---|---|---|---|
| China Elem Sch<br>605 Henderson Ave, China 77613<br>Dianne Timberlake | PK-5 | T | 434<br>20 | 51% 409/981-6410<br>Fax 409/752-3623<br>f |
| Hardin-Jefferson High Sch<br>3155 Highway 326 S, Sour Lake 77659<br>Patrick Brown | 9-12 | TV | 700<br>40 | 36% 409/981-6430<br>Fax 409/287-2558 |
| Henderson Middle Sch<br>3025 Highway 326 S, Sour Lake 77659<br>Darrell Westfall | 6-8 | T | 524<br>40 | 50% 409/981-6420<br>Fax 409/287-1235<br>f |
| Sour Lake Elem Sch<br>1055 Highway 326, Sour Lake 77659<br>Danny McFarland | PK-5 | T | 601<br>60 | 49% 409/981-6440<br>Fax 409/287-3987 |

● **Kountze Ind School Dist** PID: 01022491
160 W Vaughn St, Kountze 77625

409/246-3352
Fax 409/246-3217

**Schools:** 4 \ **Teachers:** 95 \ **Students:** 767 \ **Special Ed Students:** 103 \ **LEP Students:** 35 \ **College-Bound:** 53% \ **Ethnic:** African American 13%, Hispanic 8%, Native American: 1%, Caucasian 78% \ **Exp:** $504 (High) \ **Poverty:** 21% \ **Title I:** $378,057 \ **Open-Close:** 08/24 - 05/28 \ **DTBP:** $15 (Low)

| | | | |
|---|---|---|---|
| Shane Reyenga | 1 | Philip Welch | 2,19 |
| Elizabeth Jordan | 4* | John French | 5 |
| Sherry Allen | 7* | Shane Reyenga | 8,11,15,69* |
| Teresa Matthews | 16* | Steve Eppes | 67 |
| Spencer Matthews | 73,295 | | |

| Public Schs..Principal | Grd | Prgm | Enr/#Cls | SN |
|---|---|---|---|---|
| Kountze Elem Sch<br>565 Park St, Kountze 77625<br>Thomas Cooley | PK-3 | T | 335<br>41 | 69% 409/246-3877<br>Fax 409/246-4138 |
| Kountze High Sch<br>1488 FM 1293 Rd, Kountze 77625<br>Dr Chet Deaver | 9-12 | ATV | 79<br>40 | 42% 409/246-3474<br>Fax 409/246-8180 |
| Kountze Intermediate Sch<br>150 Vaughn St, Kountze 77625<br>Connie Joubert | 4-6 | T | 275 | 61% 409/246-8230<br>Fax 409/246-3857 |
| Kountze Middle Sch<br>1676 FM 1293 Rd, Kountze 77625<br>**Michael Hatton** | 7-8 | T | 78<br>20 | 54% 409/246-3551<br>Fax 409/246-8907 |

● **Lumberton Ind School Dist** PID: 01022544
121 S Main St, Lumberton 77657

409/923-7580
Fax 409/755-7848

**Schools:** 5 \ **Teachers:** 259 \ **Students:** 3,437 \ **Special Ed Students:** 371 \ **LEP Students:** 75 \ **College-Bound:** 58% \ **Ethnic:** Asian 1%, Hispanic 9%, Native American: 1%, Caucasian 89% \ **Exp:** $490 (High) \ **Poverty:** 11% \ **Title I:** $433,138 \ **Special Education:** $85,000 \ **Open-Close:** 08/11 - 05/26 \ **DTBP:** $179 (High)

| | | | |
|---|---|---|---|
| Dr Tony Tipton | 1 | Abby Zernial | 2 |
| Lori Mack | 2 | Ricci Pampolina | 3 |
| Katie Baker | 4 | Roy Coleman | 5 |
| Chris Babin | 6 | Amy Morgan | 7,85* |
| Cynthia Lawrence | 8 | Mandy Babin | 8 |
| Patty Crouch | 11,15,91,285,288,296 | Candace Koran | 16,82 |
| Ticia McBride | 57 | James Kersh | 67 |
| Anna Miller | 71 | Mary Johnson | 73,286,297* |
| Mike Buffington | 80 | Daniel Cazares | 84,295 |
| Gretchen Scoggins | 298 | | |

| Public Schs..Principal | Grd | Prgm | Enr/#Cls | SN |
|---|---|---|---|---|
| Early Childhood Sch<br>1020 S Main St, Lumberton 77657<br>John Wing | PK-K | T | 405<br>23 | 51% 409/923-7695<br>Fax 409/755-6607 |
| Lumberton High Sch<br>103 S Lhs Dr, Lumberton 77657<br>John White | 9-12 | AV | 871<br>98 | 26% 409/923-7890<br>Fax 409/755-6576 |
| Lumberton Intermediate Sch<br>107 S Lhs Dr, Lumberton 77657<br>Paige Wing | 4-6 | T | 963<br>40 | 37% 409/923-7790<br>Fax 409/923-7764 |
| Lumberton Middle Sch<br>123 S Main St, Lumberton 77657<br>Travis Edgerton | 7-8 | T | 289<br>47 | 33% 409/923-7581<br>Fax 409/751-0641 |
| Lumberton Primary Sch<br>128 E Candlestick Dr, Lumberton 77657<br>Katherine Waldrop | 1-3 | T | 909<br>45 | 40% 409/923-7490<br>Fax 409/923-7444 |

● **Silsbee Ind School Dist** PID: 01022582
415 Highway 327 W, Silsbee 77656

409/980-7800
Fax 409/980-7897

**Schools:** 4 \ **Teachers:** 203 \ **Students:** 2,800 \ **Special Ed Students:** 430 \ **LEP Students:** 44 \ **Ethnic:** African American 18%, Hispanic 8%, Native American: 1%, Caucasian 73% \ **Exp:** $437 (High) \ **Poverty:** 21% \ **Title I:** $843,472 \ **Special Education:** $741,000 \ **Open-Close:** 08/31 - 05/26 \ **DTBP:** $181 (High)

| | | | |
|---|---|---|---|
| Dr Gregg Weiss | 1 | Lynda Parks | 3 |
| Michael Tomas | 3,5 | Michelle Johnson | 4 |
| Randy Smith | 6* | Michelle Hardy | 7* |
| Sherrie Thornhill | 8,15,68,288,296 | Catherine Whitehead | 11,69 |
| Judy Honeycutt | 27,95* | Dr Vicky Brantley | 34,58,79 |
| Tammy McDuff | 57,271* | Sam Edd Harrell | 67 |
| Daniel Elizondo | 71 | Jamie Youngblood | 73,81 |
| Lester Perrin | 84,295 | Kenny Davenport | 91 |

| Public Schs..Principal | Grd | Prgm | Enr/#Cls | SN |
|---|---|---|---|---|
| Edwards-Johnson Memorial MS<br>1140 Highway 327 E, Silsbee 77656<br>**Amanda Jenkins** | 6-8 | GTV | 628 | 61% 409/980-7870<br>Fax 409/980-7884 |
| Laura Reeves Primary Sch<br>695 Woodrow St, Silsbee 77656<br>Terry Deaver | PK-K | T | 349<br>25 | 71% 409/980-7850<br>Fax 409/980-7868 |
| Silsbee Elem Sch<br>770 S 7th St, Silsbee 77656<br>Terry Deaver | 1-5 | T | 1,180<br>36 | 62% 409/980-7856<br>Fax 409/980-7861 |
| Silsbee High Sch<br>1575 Highway 96 N, Silsbee 77656<br>Scott Schwartz | 9-12 | AGTV | 615 | 49% 409/980-7877<br>Fax 409/980-7881 |

● **West Hardin Co Cons Sch Dist** PID: 01022659
39227 Highway 105, Saratoga 77585

936/274-5061
Fax 936/274-4321

**Schools:** 2 \ **Teachers:** 40 \ **Students:** 525 \ **Special Ed Students:** 47 \ **LEP Students:** 3 \ **College-Bound:** 56% \ **Ethnic:** Hispanic 3%, Caucasian 97% \ **Exp:** $819 (High) \ **Poverty:** 9% \ **Title I:** $57,948 \ **Open-Close:** 08/19 - 05/27 \ **DTBP:** $335 (High)

| | | | |
|---|---|---|---|
| Dr Jim Armstrong | 1 | Penny White | 2* |
| Patti Graham | 3,5* | Kathy Lofton | 4* |
| Kenny Holfpauir | 6* | Tammy Adams | 7* |
| D'Wanna Rasnick | 8,11,69 | Charlene Zwahr | 16,82* |
| Gina Strahan | 52,55 | Stephanie Battle | 57,58 |
| Scotty Hughes | 67 | Shawn Buser | 73,273,295* |

| Public Schs..Principal | Grd | Prgm | Enr/#Cls | SN |
|---|---|---|---|---|
| West Hardin Elem Sch<br>39227 Highway 105, Saratoga 77585<br>Tiffany Merriweather | PK-5 | T | 321<br>14 | 74% 936/274-5061 |
| West Hardin High Sch<br>39227 Highway 105, Saratoga 77585<br>Michael Smith | 7-12 | T | 239<br>20 | 49% 936/274-5061<br>Fax 936/274-5671 |

## HARRIS COUNTY

## HARRIS COUNTY SCHOOLS

### • Harris Co Dept of Ed PID: 02091055
6300 Irvington Blvd, Houston 77022

713/694-6300
Fax 713/696-0730

| | | |
|---|---|---|
| James Colbert ............1 | Jesus Amezcua ...............2,15 | |
| Rosa Maria Torres ............2 | Greg Lookabaugh ...............3 | |
| Kimberly McLeod ............8,15 | Jonathan Parker ...............15 | |
| Eduardo Honold ............30 | Louis Evans ...............67 | |
| Natasha Truitt ............68 | Darlene Breaux ...............70 | |
| Tammy Lanier ............71 | Arthur Vu ...............73 | |
| Ecomet Burley ............91 | Helen Spencer ...............295 | |
| Gayla Rawlinson ............298 | | |

| County Schs..Principal | Grd | Prgm | Enr/#Cls | SN |
|---|---|---|---|---|
| Academic Behavior Center-East<br>7703 South Loop E, Houston 77012<br>Donna Trevino-Jones | Spec | | 119<br>24 | 713/242-8036<br>Fax 713/645-5773 |
| Academic Behavior Sch-West<br>7800 Westglen Dr, Houston 77063<br>Dr Victor Keys | Spec | | 109<br>18 | 713/339-9411<br>Fax 713/978-7662 |
| Ⓐ Harris Co Detention Center<br>1200 Congress St, Houston 77002<br>Chris Garcia | 3-12 | T | 184<br>16 | 98% 713/222-4100<br>Fax 713/222-4360 |
| Ⓒ Harris Co Youth Village<br>210 J W Mills Dr, Seabrook 77586<br>Diane Hubbell | 6-12 | TV | 65<br>12 | 94% 281/326-2521<br>Fax 713/222-4749 |
| Ⓐ Highpoint School East<br>8003 E Sam Houston Pkwy N, Houston 77049<br>Marion Cooksey | 6-12 | V | 250<br>17 | 713/696-2160<br>Fax 713/696-2161 |
| Ⓐ Highpoint School North<br>11902 Spears Rd, Houston 77067<br>David Oquin | 6-12 | | 250<br>12 | 713/696-2195<br>Fax 713/696-2196 |

## HARRIS PUBLIC SCHOOLS

### • Aldine Ind School Dist PID: 01022697
2520 WW Thorne Blvd, Houston 77073

281/449-1011
Fax 281/449-4911

**Schools:** 82 \ **Teachers:** 4,128 \ **Students:** 67,331 \
**Special Ed Students:** 5,449 \ **LEP Students:** 21,075 \ **College-Bound:** 75%
\ **Ethnic:** Asian 1%, African American 23%, Hispanic 74%, Caucasian
2% \ **Exp:** $139 (Low) \ **Poverty:** 31% \ **Title I:** $35,755,244 \
**Special Education:** $14,118,000 \ **Bilingual Education:** $6,000 \
**Open-Close:** 08/17 - 05/27 \ **DTBP:** $192 (High) \ 🅕 🅣

| | | |
|---|---|---|
| Dr Latonya Goffney ...............1 | Dr Tamika Stephens ............2,19 | |
| Twiana Collier ...............2 | Milo Ortiz ...............3 | |
| Dani Sheffield ...............4 | Dr Jill Metcalf ...............5 | |

| | | |
|---|---|---|
| Dean Colbert ...............6 | Maisha Guillory ...............7 |
| Carlos Barron ...............10 | Perla Davilla ...............11 |
| Dr Charlotte Davis ...............15,79,275 | Cynthia Buchanan ...............16 |
| Dr Todd Davis ...............18 | Dr Michaelann Kelley ...............20 |
| Refugio Rodriguez ...............23 | Franklin Higgins ...............27,31 |
| Gwendolyn Lockett ...............40 | Tracy Mansfield ...............43 |
| Xandra Earlie ...............44 | Chantay Smith ...............46 |
| Lisa Edwards ...............49 | Charity Bostick ...............50 |
| Betsy Haisler ...............57 | Katherine Seals ...............58 |
| Steve Mead ...............67 | Dawn Rodriguez ...............69,70,294 |
| Denise Simons ...............69 | Rachel Haller ...............69 |
| Mike Keeney ...............71 | Sheleah Reed ...............71 |
| Cynthia Bingman ...............73,76,295 | Akilah Willery ...............74 |
| Nikki Reid ...............91 | Olivia Boatner ...............92 |
| Deborah McNeely ...............275 | |

### • Aldine ISD-Elem Sch Team 1 PID: 12107347
2520 WW Thorne Blvd, Houston 77073

281/985-6467

Latonia Amerson ...............15

| Public Schs..Principal | Grd | Prgm | Enr/#Cls | SN |
|---|---|---|---|---|
| ⓦ A B Anderson Academy<br>7401 Wheatley St, Houston 77088<br>Dr Eunetra Simpson | 1-4 | T | 516<br>37 | 88% 281/878-0370<br>Fax 281/591-8549 |
| ⓦ Earl & Hazel Harris Academy<br>3130 Holder Forest Dr, Houston 77088<br>Norman Dionisio | 1-5 | T | 596<br>45 | 95% 281/878-7900<br>Fax 281/878-7913 |
| Gloria B Sammons Elem Sch<br>2301 Frick Rd, Houston 77038<br>Georgina Foroi | 1-5 | T | 524<br>30 | 85% 281/878-0955<br>Fax 281/591-8546 |
| ⓦ J Ruth Smith Academy<br>5815 W Little York Rd, Houston 77091<br>Ida Carter | 1-5 | T | 641<br>65 | 92% 713/613-7650<br>Fax 713/613-7653 |
| Kujawa Elem Sch<br>7007 Fallbrook Dr, Houston 77086<br>Kimberly Jenkins | 1-5 | T | 681<br>35 | 89% 281/878-1530<br>Fax 281/878-1536 |
| ⓦ Lola Mae Carter Academy<br>3111 Fallbrook Dr, Houston 77038<br>Lee Wold | 1-5 | T | 656<br>50 | 90% 281/878-7760<br>Fax 281/878-7767 |
| Stehlik Elem Sch<br>400 West Rd, Houston 77038<br>Karen Wilkerson | 1-5 | T | 692 | 93% 281/878-0300<br>Fax 281/878-0305 |
| Thomas B Gray Elem Sch<br>700 West Rd, Houston 77038<br>Scott Dubberke | 1-5 | T | 602<br>100 | 91% 281/878-0660<br>Fax 281/878-0664 |
| Voyde Caraway Elem Sch<br>3031 Ellington St, Houston 77088<br>Dr Andrenetta Marshall | 1-5 | T | 548<br>55 | 90% 281/878-0320<br>Fax 281/878-0326 |
| William R Carmichael Elem Sch<br>6902 Silver Star Dr, Houston 77086<br>Monica Stogsdill | 1-5 | T | 511<br>40 | 85% 281/878-0345<br>Fax 281/878-0379 |
| Willie B Ermel Elem Sch<br>7103 Woodsman Trl, Houston 77040<br>Dr Martha Escalante | 1-5 | T | 512<br>37 | 91% 713/466-5220<br>Fax 713/856-4256 |
| Wilson Elem Sch<br>3131 Fallbrook Dr, Houston 77038<br>Dana Baker | 1-5 | T | 440<br>58 | 90% 281/878-0990<br>Fax 281/878-0995 |

### • Aldine ISD-Elem Sch Team 2 PID: 12107359
2520 WW Thorne Blvd, Houston 77073

281/985-6159

Dr Faviola Cantu ...............15

| Public Schs..Principal | Grd | Prgm | Enr/#Cls | SN |
|---|---|---|---|---|
| Beulah E Johnson Elem Sch<br>13901 Homestead Rd, Humble 77396<br>Pamela Johnson | 1-5 | | 710<br>40 | 281/985-6510<br>Fax 281/985-6494 |

| | | | | | | | |
|---|---|---|---|---|---|---|---|
| 1 | Superintendent | 8 | Curric/Instruct K-12 | 19 | Chief Financial Officer | 29 | Family/Consumer Science |
| 2 | Bus/Finance/Purchasing | 9 | Curric/Instruct Elem | 20 | Art K-12 | 30 | Adult Education |
| 3 | Buildings And Grounds | 10 | Curric/Instruct Sec | 21 | Art Elem | 31 | Career/Sch-to-Work K-12 |
| 4 | Food Service | 11 | Federal Program | 22 | Art Sec | 32 | Career/Sch-to-Work Elem |
| 5 | Transportation | 12 | Title I | 23 | Music K-12 | 33 | Career/Sch-to-Work Sec |
| 6 | Athletic | 13 | Title V | 24 | Music Elem | 34 | Early Childhood Ed |
| 7 | Health Services | 15 | Asst Superintendent | 25 | Music Sec | 35 | Health/Phys Education |
| | | 16 | Instructional Media Svcs | 26 | Business Education | 36 | Guidance Services K-12 |
| | | 17 | Chief Operations Officer | 27 | Career & Tech Ed | 37 | Guidance Services Elem |
| | | 18 | Chief Academic Officer | 28 | Technology Education | 38 | Guidance Services Sec |

| | | | | | | | |
|---|---|---|---|---|---|---|---|
| 39 | Social Studies K-12 | 49 | English/Lang Arts Elem | 59 | Special Education Elem | 69 | Academic Assessment |
| 40 | Social Studies Elem | 50 | English/Lang Arts Sec | 60 | Special Education Sec | 70 | Research/Development |
| 41 | Social Studies Sec | 51 | Reading K-12 | 61 | Foreign/World Lang K-12 | 71 | Public Information |
| 42 | Science K-12 | 52 | Reading Elem | 62 | Foreign/World Lang Elem | 72 | Summer School |
| 43 | Science Elem | 53 | Reading Sec | 63 | Foreign/World Lang Sec | 73 | Instructional Tech |
| 44 | Science Sec | 54 | Remedial Reading K-12 | 64 | Religious Education K-12 | 74 | Inservice Training |
| 45 | Math K-12 | 55 | Remedial Reading Elem | 65 | Religious Education Elem | 75 | Marketing/Distributive |
| 46 | Math Elem | 56 | Remedial Reading Sec | 66 | Religious Education Sec | 76 | Info Systems |
| 47 | Math Sec | 57 | Bilingual/ELL | 67 | School Board President | 77 | Psychological Assess |
| 48 | English/Lang Arts K-12 | 58 | Special Education K-12 | 68 | Teacher Personnel | 78 | Affirmative Action |

| Public Schs..Principal | Grd | Prgm | Enr/#Cls | SN |
|---|---|---|---|---|
| Douglas B Bussey Elem Sch<br>11555 Airline Dr, Houston 77037<br>Kathleen Sandoval | 1-5 | T | 583<br> | 92% 281/878-1501<br>Fax 281/878-1506 |
| Evelyn S Thompson Elem Sch<br>220 Casa Grande Dr, Houston 77060<br>Nereida Ochoa | 1-5 | T | 571<br>38 | 94% 281/878-0333<br>Fax 281/878-0339 |
| Gus A Oleson Elem Sch<br>12345 Vickery St, Houston 77039<br>Nadia Stafford | 1-5 | T | 735<br>50 | 94% 281/985-6530<br>Fax 281/985-6143 |
| Hill Elem Sch<br>2625 W Mount Houston Rd, Houston 77038<br>**Constance White** | 1-5 | T | 641<br> | 90% 281/878-7775<br>Fax 281/878-7779 |
| ⓜ Inez Carroll Academy<br>423 W Gulf Bank Rd, Houston 77037<br>Jennifer Price | 1-5 | T | 796<br>54 | 88% 281/878-0340<br>Fax 281/591-8527 |
| Kenneth D Black Elem Sch<br>160 Mill Stream Ln, Houston 77060<br>Ash Kirk | 1-5 | T | 531<br>45 | 94% 281/878-0350<br>Fax 281/878-0389 |
| Lawrence A Eckert Elem Sch<br>1430 Aldine Meadows Rd, Houston 77032<br>Mark Herndon | 1-5 | T | 663<br>50 | 91% 281/985-6380<br>Fax 281/985-6117 |
| Mary Walke Stephens Elem Sch<br>2402 Aldine Mail Route Rd, Houston 77039<br>Shauna Showers | 1-5 | T | 669<br>47 | 89% 281/985-6560<br>Fax 281/985-6564 |
| Orange Grove Elem Sch<br>4514 Mount Houston Rd, Houston 77093<br>**Fernanda Flores-Bolivar** | 1-5 | T | 804<br>42 | 90% 281/985-6540<br>Fax 281/985-6544 |
| ⓜ Reed Academy<br>1616 Lauder Rd, Houston 77039<br>Astar Jones | 1-5 | V | 837<br>65 | 281/985-6670<br>Fax 281/985-6679 |
| Vera Escamilla Elem Sch<br>5241 Mount Houston Rd, Houston 77093<br>Susan Rehan | 1-5 | T | 842<br>65 | 94% 281/985-6390<br>Fax 281/985-6137 |
| Weaver Odom Elem Sch<br>14701 Henry Rd, Houston 77060<br>Delilah St Julian | 1-5 | T | 456<br>43 | 94% 281/878-0390<br>Fax 281/878-0397 |

● **Aldine ISD-Elem Sch Team 3** PID: 12107361    281/985-6956
2520 WW Thorne Blvd, Houston 77073

Latoya Wynne ...................................... 15

| Public Schs..Principal | Grd | Prgm | Enr/#Cls | SN |
|---|---|---|---|---|
| Clifford Dunn Elem Sch<br>2003 WW Thorne Blvd, Houston 77073<br>**Terese Pollard** | 1-5 | T | 501<br>54 | 82% 281/233-4320<br>Fax 281/233-4328 |
| Cypresswood Elem Sch<br>6901 Cypresswood Point Ave, Humble 77338<br>Innetta Carter | 1-5 | T | 937<br> | 80% 281/227-3370<br>Fax 281/446-4039 |
| Ellen B Lane Sch<br>2001 Aldine Bender Rd, Houston 77032<br>Dale Prioleau | Spec | A | 117<br>34 | 61% 281/985-6350<br>Fax 281/985-6358 |
| ⓜ Grace Raymond Academy<br>1605 Connorvale Rd, Houston 77039<br>Tannessa Maddox | 1-5 | T | 672<br>45 | 93% 281/985-6550<br>Fax 281/985-6555 |
| Greenspoint Elem Sch<br>18028 Chisholm Trl, Houston 77060<br>Tami Schuler | 1-5 | T | 700<br> | 91% 281/985-7800 |
| Jones Elem Sch<br>7903 Forest Point Dr, Humble 77338<br>Cheryl Fontenot | 1-5 | T | 813<br> | 77% 281/446-6168<br>Fax 281/985-6022 |
| Marcella Elem Sch<br>16250 Cotillion Dr, Houston 77060<br>Demedia Edwards | 1-5 | T | 638<br> | 92% 281/878-0860<br>Fax 281/878-0805 |
| O V Calvert Elem Sch<br>1925 Marvell Dr, Houston 77032<br>Cheryl LaFleur | 1-5 | T | 313<br>40 | 94% 281/985-6360<br>Fax 281/985-6364 |

| Public Schs..Principal | Grd | Prgm | Enr/#Cls | SN |
|---|---|---|---|---|
| Oticel Parker Elem Sch<br>19850 E Hardy Rd, Houston 77073<br>Candace Hardin | 1-5 | | 625<br>45 | 281/233-8930<br>Fax 281/233-8935 |
| R C Conley Elem Sch<br>3345 W Greens Rd, Houston 77066<br>Dr Lashawn Hodge | 1-5 | T | 532<br>30 | 89% 281/537-5418<br>Fax 281/895-5005 |
| Rick Ogden Elem Sch<br>21919 Rayford Rd, Humble 77338<br>**Ashley Johnson** | 1-5 | T | 665<br> | 87% 281/233-8901<br>Fax 281/233-8907 |
| Spence Elem Sch<br>1300 Gears Rd, Houston 77067<br>Susana Bazan | 1-5 | T | 656<br> | 93% 281/539-4050<br>Fax 281/539-4054 |
| Thomas B Francis Elem Sch<br>6525 Greens Rd, Humble 77396<br>Dr Dana Stelly | 1-5 | | 813<br>43 | 281/985-6500 |

● **Aldine ISD-High Sch Team** PID: 12107397    281/985-6427
2520 WW Thorne Blvd, Houston 77073

Todd Lindeman ...................................... 15

| Public Schs..Principal | Grd | Prgm | Enr/#Cls | SN |
|---|---|---|---|---|
| Aldine 9th Grade Sch<br>10650 North Fwy, Houston 77037<br>Dr Kanisha Wiley | 9-9 | TV | 703<br>43 | 87% 281/878-6800<br>Fax 281/878-6824 |
| Aldine Senior HS<br>11101 Airline Dr, Houston 77037<br>Walter Stewart | 9-12 | TV | 2,327<br>125 | 86% 281/448-5231<br>Fax 281/878-0641 |
| Blanson Cte High Sch<br>311 West Rd, Houston 77038<br>Benjamin Ibarra | 9-12 | TV | 401<br> | 84% 281/591-4950 |
| ⓜ Carver High Sch<br>2100 S Victory Dr, Houston 77088<br>Patricia Ross | 9-12 | TV | 776<br> | 76% 281/878-0310<br>Fax 281/591-8579 |
| Chester W Nimitz High Sch<br>2005 WW Thorne Blvd, Houston 77073<br>Dr Crystal Watson | 9-12 | TV | 1,933<br>120 | 73% 281/443-7480<br>Fax 281/233-4331 |
| Davis 9th Grade Sch<br>12211 Ella Blvd, Houston 77067<br>James Metcalf | 9-9 | T | 850<br> | 88% 281/873-1800 |
| Davis Senior High Sch<br>12525 Ella Blvd, Houston 77067<br>**Anthony Watkins** | 10-12 | T | 2,621<br> | 81% 281/539-4070<br>Fax 281/539-4075 |
| Douglas MacArthur High Sch<br>4400 Aldine Mail Route Rd, Houston 77039<br>Heather Peterson | 10-12 | TV | 2,830<br> | 87% 281/985-6330<br>Fax 281/985-6294 |
| Dwight D Eisenhower High Sch<br>7922 Antoine Dr, Houston 77088<br>**Mandele Davis** | 10-12 | TV | 1,750<br>110 | 65% 281/878-0900<br>Fax 281/448-2936 |
| Eisenhower Ninth Grade Sch<br>3550 W Gulf Bank Rd, Houston 77088<br>Jane Ocanas | 9-9 | TV | 603<br>60 | 84% 281/878-7700<br>Fax 281/878-7736 |
| MacArthur 9th Grade Sch<br>12111 Gloger St, Houston 77039<br>**Dr Yul Everline** | 9-9 | T | 918<br>25 | 91% 281/985-7400<br>Fax 281/219-2444 |
| Nimitz 9th Grade Sch<br>2425 WW Thorne Blvd, Houston 77073<br>Aisley Adams | 9-9 | T | 681<br>43 | 81% 281/209-8200<br>Fax 281/209-8220 |
| Rose M Avalos P-Tech Sch<br>2430 Aldine Mail Route Rd, Houston 77039<br>Diana Delpilar | 9-12 | | 126<br> | 281/985-2100<br>Fax 281/985-2119 |
| Victory Early College HS<br>4141 Victory Dr, Houston 77088<br>Dr Phyllis Cormier | 9-12 | T | 399<br> | 80% 281/810-5675<br>Fax 281/810-5698 |
| W T Hall Education Center<br>15014 Aldine Westfield Rd, Houston 77032<br>Marcie Strahan | 9-12 | AGT | 127<br> | 77% 281/985-7446<br>Fax 281/985-7453 |

- **Aldine ISD-Middle Sch Team** PID: 12107385     281/985-6689
2520 WW Thorne Blvd, Houston 77073

Latonia Amerson ................................ 15

| Public Schs..Principal | Grd | Prgm | Enr/#Cls | SN | |
|---|---|---|---|---|---|
| Ⓐ Aldine Education Center<br>1702 Aldine Bender Rd, Houston 77032<br>Gerald Schattle | 1-12 | | 384<br>24 | | 281/985-6685<br>Fax 281/985-6688 |
| Aldine Middle Sch<br>14908 Aldine Westfield Rd, Houston 77032<br>Christi Vanwassenhove | 6-8 | T | 952<br>70 | 91% | 281/985-6580<br>Fax 281/985-6480 |
| Ⓦ Charles R Drew Academy<br>1910 W Little York Rd, Houston 77091<br>**Christopher Walker** | 6-8 | T | 583<br>30 | 86% | 281/878-0360<br>Fax 281/447-4694 |
| Floyd Hoffman Middle Sch<br>6101 W Little York Rd, Houston 77091<br>Jeana Morrison-Adams | 6-8 | TV | 1,027<br>83 | 77% | 713/613-7670<br>Fax 713/613-7675 |
| Garcia Middle Sch<br>11000 Rosslyn Rd, Houston 77038<br>Todd Roede | 6-8 | T | 1,177 | 87% | 281/878-3730<br>Fax 281/878-3749 |
| Ⓦ Jewel S Houston Academy<br>8103 Carver Rd, Houston 77088<br>**Dr Cedric Stewart** | 6-8 | T | 604 | 86% | 281/878-7745<br>Fax 281/878-7755 |
| Jones Middle Sch<br>20155 Townsen Blvd, Humble 77338<br>Marcus Pruitt | 6-8 | T | 1,265 | 83% | 281/985-3720<br>Fax 281/985-3739 |
| Mattie A Teague Middle Sch<br>21700 Rayford Rd, Humble 77338<br>**Kimberly Dussette** | 6-8 | T | 1,268<br>64 | 85% | 281/233-4310<br>Fax 281/233-4318 |
| Mattie B Hambrick Middle Sch<br>4600 Aldine Mail Route Rd, Houston 77039<br>Rebecca Sanford | 6-8 | T | 1,246<br>80 | 94% | 281/985-6570<br>Fax 281/442-9036 |
| Mead Middle Sch<br>3500 Lauder Rd, Houston 77039<br>Jessica Scott | 6-8 | T | 1,202 | 88% | 281/985-3700<br>Fax 281/985-3719 |
| Plummer Middle Sch<br>11429 Spears Rd, Houston 77067<br>Andrea Cain | 6-8 | T | 1,120 | 90% | 281/539-4000<br>Fax 281/539-4017 |
| Ray L Shotwell Middle Sch<br>6515 Trail Valley Way, Houston 77086<br>Denise Winchester | 6-8 | T | 1,193<br>61 | 86% | 281/878-0960<br>Fax 281/591-8564 |
| Thomas J Stovall Middle Sch<br>11201 Airline Dr, Houston 77037<br>Elsa Wright | 6-8 | T | 1,016<br>74 | 88% | 281/878-0670<br>Fax 281/449-0396 |
| Ⓦ Thomas S Grantham Academy<br>13300 Chrisman Rd, Houston 77039<br>**Ivan Hepworth** | 6-8 | TV | 1,140<br>80 | 88% | 281/985-6590<br>Fax 281/985-6595 |
| Vernon & Kathy Lewis Mid Sch<br>21255 W Hardy Rd, Houston 77073<br>**Tonya Clark-Antwine** | 6-8 | T | 1,141 | 89% | 281/209-8257<br>Fax 281/209-8267 |

- **Aldine ISD-Primary Team** PID: 12368280     281/449-1011
2520 WW Thorne Blvd, Houston 77073

Patricia Rodriguez ................................ 15

| Public Schs..Principal | Grd | Prgm | Enr/#Cls | SN | |
|---|---|---|---|---|---|
| Bill Worsham Elem Sch<br>3007 Hartwick Rd, Houston 77093<br>Sandra Doria | 1-5 | T | 679<br>56 | 90% | 281/985-6520<br>Fax 281/985-6524 |
| De Santiago EC-PK-K Sch<br>1420 Aldine Meadows Rd, Houston 77032<br>Dr Maria Galindo | PK-K | T | 724<br>38 | 96% | 281/985-7500<br>Fax 281/985-7509 |
| Garcia-Leza EC-PK-K Sch<br>5311 Mount Houston Rd, Houston 77093<br>Patricia Willis | PK-K | T | 850 | 95% | 281/985-6037<br>Fax 281/985-6044 |

| | Grd | Prgm | Enr/#Cls | SN | |
|---|---|---|---|---|---|
| Griggs EC-PK-K Sch<br>801 Regional Park Dr, Houston 77060<br>**Tonya Porter Brisker** | PK-K | T | 865 | 96% | 281/985-3760<br>Fax 281/985-3779 |
| Hinojosa EC-PK-K Sch<br>1620 Lauder Rd, Houston 77039<br>Denise Meister | PK-K | T | 753<br>36 | 92% | 281/985-4750<br>Fax 281/985-4754 |
| Jones EC-PK-K Sch<br>8003 Forest Point Dr, Humble 77338<br>Rosalind Burns | PK-K | T | 891 | 88% | 281/446-1576<br>Fax 281/985-6010 |
| Keeble EC-PK-K Sch<br>203 W Gulf Bank Rd, Houston 77037<br>**Dr Andrenetta Marshall** | PK-K | T | 785<br>50 | 95% | 281/878-6860<br>Fax 281/878-6869 |
| Kujawa EC-PK-K Sch<br>7111 Fallbrook Dr, Houston 77086<br>Andrea Davis | PK-K | T | 803 | 94% | 281/878-1514<br>Fax 281/878-1545 |
| Magrill EC-PK-K Sch<br>21701 Rayford Rd, Humble 77338<br>Mark Malo | PK-K | | 729<br>48 | | 281/233-4300<br>Fax 281/233-4303 |
| Ralph G Goodman Elem Sch<br>9325 Deer Trail Dr, Houston 77088<br>**Ladon Ward** | 1-5 | T | 404<br>54 | 92% | 281/878-0355<br>Fax 281/878-0330 |
| Ⓦ Reece EC-PK-K Sch<br>2223 Esther Dr, Houston 77088<br>Sharla Rogers | PK-K | T | 466<br>28 | 94% | 281/878-0800<br>Fax 281/878-0808 |
| Ⓦ Stovall EC-PK-K Sch<br>3025 Ellington St, Houston 77088<br>**Jeremy Ames** | PK-K | | 561<br>45 | | 281/591-8500<br>Fax 281/591-8507 |
| Vardeman EC-PK-K Sch<br>3302 Connorvale Rd, Houston 77039<br>Orfelinda Todd | PK-K | T | 744 | 92% | 281/985-3740<br>Fax 281/985-3759 |
| Vines EC-PK-K Sch<br>7220 Inwood Park Dr, Houston 77088<br>Linda Reed | PK-K | T | 628<br>26 | 97% | 281/878-7950<br>Fax 281/878-7959 |

- **Alief Ind School Dist** PID: 01022972     281/498-8110
4250 Cook Rd, Houston 77072     Fax 281/988-3037

> **Schools:** 46 \ **Teachers:** 3,260 \ **Students:** 46,000 \
> **Special Ed Students:** 3,527 \ **LEP Students:** 18,320 \ **College-Bound:** 80%
> \ **Ethnic:** Asian 12%, African American 29%, Hispanic 55%, Native American:
> 1%, Caucasian 4% \ **Exp:** $511 (High) \ **Poverty:** 31% \ **Title I:** $28,846,781
> \ **Special Education:** $7,705,000 \ **Bilingual Education:** $126,000 \
> **Open-Close:** 08/06 - 06/03 \ **DTBP:** $189 (High) \ Ⓔ

| | | | |
|---|---|---|---|
| H D Chambers ..................................... 1 | | Charles Woods ............................... 2,15 | |
| Deanna Wentz ................................. 2,15 | | Jeff Delisle ............................................ 3 | |
| Heather Hayes-Ramirez ......................... 4 | | Richard Torres ..................................... 5 | |
| Scott Moehlig ....................................... 6 | | Carleen Johnson ................................... 7 | |
| Ava Montgomery ............................... 8,15 | | Kathy Jahn ............................................ 8 | |
| Karla Kessler ...................... 11,296,298 | | Dr Elizabeth Veloz-Powell ................. 15,68 | |
| Charla Hollingsworth .................. 16,280* | | Renford Joseph ............................... 20,23 | |
| Jennifer Baker ..................................... 27 | | Kimberly Crow ........................... 27,70,750 | |
| Mari Martinez ..................................... 34* | | Dr Elvia Baldwin .................................. 36 | |
| Gretchen Gaskins ............................... 39 | | Gelyn Roble ........................................ 43 | |
| Dr Karen Jacobs ........................... 44,285 | | Bridget McKinney ............................... 46 | |
| Anne Hoskin ....................................... 47 | | Michelle Patterson ............................. 49 | |
| Joann Williams .................................... 50 | | Patricia Cantu ............................... 57,271 | |
| Nicole Roberts .................................... 58 | | Ann Williams ...................................... 67 | |
| Darrell Alexander ................................ 68 | | Kimberly Smith ................................... 71 | |
| Wally Rakestraw ............................ 73,295 | | Janine Hoke ....................................... 74 | |
| Al Reaves .......................................... 76 | | Dr Jackie Armwood ............................. 79 | |
| Dr Tracy Scholz .................................. 81 | | Dan Turner ......................................... 91 | |
| Tameka Anderson .............................. 274 | | Joni Maniatis ..................................... 275 | |
| Pamela Lowe ..................................... 286 | | | |

| | | | | | | | |
|---|---|---|---|---|---|---|---|
| 1 | Superintendent | 8 | Curric/Instruct K-12 | 19 | Chief Financial Officer | 29 | Family/Consumer Science |
| 2 | Bus/Finance/Purchasing | 9 | Curric/Instruct Elem | 20 | Art K-12 | 30 | Adult Education |
| 3 | Buildings And Grounds | 10 | Curric/Instruct Sec | 21 | Art Elem | 31 | Career/Sch-to-Work K-12 |
| 4 | Food Service | 11 | Federal Program | 22 | Art Sec | 32 | Career/Sch-to-Work Elem |
| 5 | Transportation | 12 | Title I | 23 | Music K-12 | 33 | Career/Sch-to-Work Sec |
| 6 | Athletic | 13 | Title V | 24 | Music Elem | 34 | Early Childhood Ed |
| 7 | Health Services | 14 | Asst Superintendent | 25 | Music Sec | 35 | Health/Phys Education |
| | | 15 | Instructional Media Svcs | 26 | Business Education | 36 | Guidance Services K-12 |
| | | 16 | Instructional Media Svcs | 27 | Career & Tech Ed | 37 | Guidance Services Elem |
| | | 17 | Chief Operations Officer | 28 | Technology Education | 38 | Guidance Services Sec |
| | | 18 | Chief Academic Officer | | | | |

| | | | | | | | |
|---|---|---|---|---|---|---|---|
| 39 | Social Studies K-12 | 49 | English/Lang Arts Elem | 59 | Special Education Elem | 69 | Academic Assessment |
| 40 | Social Studies Elem | 50 | English/Lang Arts Sec | 60 | Special Education Sec | 70 | Research/Development |
| 41 | Social Studies Sec | 51 | Reading K-12 | 61 | Foreign/World Lang K-12 | 71 | Public Information |
| 42 | Science K-12 | 52 | Reading Elem | 62 | Foreign/World Lang Elem | 72 | Summer School |
| 43 | Science Elem | 53 | Reading Sec | 63 | Foreign/World Lang Sec | 73 | Instructional Tech |
| 44 | Science Sec | 54 | Remedial Reading K-12 | 64 | Religious Education K-12 | 74 | Inservice Training |
| 45 | Math K-12 | 55 | Remedial Reading Elem | 65 | Religious Education Elem | 75 | Marketing/Distributive |
| 46 | Math Elem | 56 | Remedial Reading Sec | 66 | Religious Education Sec | 76 | Info Systems |
| 47 | Math Sec | 57 | Bilingual/ELL | 67 | School Board President | 77 | Psychological Assess |
| 48 | English/Lang Arts K-12 | 58 | Special Education K-12 | 68 | Teacher Personnel | 78 | Affirmative Action |

| Public Schs..Principal | Grd | Prgm | Enr/#Cls | SN | |
|---|---|---|---|---|---|
| A J Martin Elem Sch<br>11718 Hendon Ln, Houston 77072<br>Dr Ting-Ling Sha | PK-4 | T | 880<br>45 | 89% | 281/983-8363<br>Fax 281/983-7705 |
| Albright Middle Sch<br>6315 Winkleman Rd, Houston 77083<br>Lori Wyatt | 7-8 | TV | 1,187<br>65 | 79% | 281/983-8411<br>Fax 281/983-8443 |
| Alexander Elem Sch<br>8500 Brookwulf Dr, Houston 77072<br>Kathleen Difelice | PK-4 | T | 716<br>50 | 88% | 281/983-8300<br>Fax 281/983-8454 |
| Alief Ctr for Advanced Careers<br>12160 Richmond Ave, Houston 77082<br>Sampson Kim | Voc | | 800 | | 281/988-3550 |
| Alief Early College High Sch<br>2811 Hayes Rd, Houston 77082<br>Brandi Brotherton | 9-12 | T | 402 | 74% | 281/988-3010<br>Fax 281/496-4593 |
| ⓐ Alief Learning Center<br>4427 Belle Park Dr, Houston 77072<br>Mindy Robertson | K-12 | V | 99<br>10 | 88% | 281/983-8000<br>Fax 281/983-7701 |
| Alief Middle Sch<br>4415 Cook Rd, Houston 77072<br>Sergio Lopez | 6-8 | TV | 1,003 | 87% | 281/983-8422<br>Fax 281/983-8053 |
| Alief Taylor High Sch<br>7555 Howell Sugar Land Rd, Houston 77083<br>Mary Williams \ **William Price** | 9-12 | T | 3,112 | 74% | 281/988-3500<br>Fax 281/561-7214 |
| Best Elem Sch<br>10000 Centre Pkwy, Houston 77036<br>Renee Canales | PK-4 | T | 753<br>55 | 97% | 713/988-6445<br>Fax 713/272-3211 |
| Boone Elem Sch<br>11400 Bissonnet St, Houston 77099<br>Angela Chapman | PK-4 | T | 802<br>40 | 93% | 281/983-8308<br>Fax 281/988-3015 |
| Budewig Intermediate Sch<br>12570 Richmond Ave, Houston 77082<br>Heather Turner | 5-6 | T | 1,337 | 84% | 281/988-3200<br>Fax 281/497-7293 |
| Bush Elem Sch<br>9730 Stroud Dr, Houston 77036<br>Gloria Harris-Price \ Jesenia Mancines | PK-4 | T | 873<br>51 | 94% | 713/272-3220<br>Fax 713/272-3230 |
| Chambers Elem Sch<br>10700 Carvel Ln, Houston 77072<br>Jannae Jernberg | PK-4 | T | 699<br>60 | 93% | 281/983-8313<br>Fax 281/988-3013 |
| Chancellor Elem Sch<br>4350 Boone Rd, Houston 77072<br>Lisa Saarie | PK-5 | T | 950<br>56 | 88% | 281/983-8318<br>Fax 281/983-8033 |
| Collins Elem Sch<br>9829 Town Park Dr, Houston 77036<br>Courtney Marshall | PK-5 | T | 928<br>100 | 96% | 713/272-3250<br>Fax 713/272-3260 |
| ⓐ Crossroads Alt Tech Sch<br>12360 Bear Ram Rd, Houston 77072<br>Tremayne Wickliffe | 9-12 | | 39 | | 281/988-3266<br>Fax 281/988-3277 |
| Cummings Elem Sch<br>10455 S Kirkwood Rd, Houston 77099<br>Jeanette Byrd | PK-4 | T | 379<br>50 | 89% | 281/983-8328<br>Fax 281/988-3051 |
| Elsik 9th Grade Center<br>6767 S Dairy Ashford Rd, Houston 77072<br>Gina Sprang | 9-9 | V | 1,000<br>75 | | 281/988-3239<br>Fax 281/988-3319 |
| Elsik High Sch<br>12601 High Star Dr, Houston 77072<br>Tina Elzy | 9-12 | AGTV | 4,266 | 79% | 281/988-3150<br>Fax 281/530-7058 |
| Hastings 9th Grade Center<br>6750 Cook Rd, Houston 77072<br>Janie Saxton | 9-9 | V | 1,100 | | 281/988-3139<br>Fax 281/988-3419 |
| Hastings High Sch<br>4410 Cook Rd, Houston 77072<br>Lynette Miller | 9-12 | TV | 3,998<br>169 | 77% | 281/988-3110<br>Fax 281/561-5763 |
| Hearne Elem Sch<br>13939 Rio Bonito Rd, Houston 77083<br>Johanna Sanchez | PK-4 | T | 827<br>42 | 89% | 281/983-8333<br>Fax 281/988-3020 |
| Heflin Elem Sch<br>3303 Synott Rd, Houston 77082<br>Robin Human | PK-4 | T | 812<br>36 | 86% | 281/531-1144<br>Fax 281/988-3014 |
| Hicks Elem Sch<br>8520 Hemlock Hill Dr, Houston 77083<br>Mary Kesler | PK-4 | T | 755<br>57 | 85% | 281/983-8040<br>Fax 281/988-3017 |
| Holmquist Elem Sch<br>15040 Westpark Dr, Houston 77082<br>Kimberly Toney | PK-4 | T | 1,160 | 84% | 281/988-3024<br>Fax 281/556-1050 |
| Holub Middle Sch<br>9515 S Dairy Ashford Rd, Houston 77099<br>Pauline Beckley | 7-8 | TV | 897<br>80 | 86% | 281/983-8433<br>Fax 281/983-8398 |
| Horn Elem Sch<br>10734 Bissonnet St, Houston 77099<br>Alicia Leyva \ Mary Starling | PK-4 | T | 936 | 94% | 281/988-3223<br>Fax 281/530-5262 |
| Kennedy Elem Sch<br>10200 Huntington Place Dr, Houston 77099<br>Sara Caldwell | PK-4 | T | 728<br>62 | 91% | 281/983-8338<br>Fax 281/983-8390 |
| Kerr High Sch<br>8150 Howell Sugar Land Rd, Houston 77083<br>Vinson Lewis | 9-12 | T | 796<br>28 | 67% | 281/983-8484<br>Fax 281/983-8014 |
| Killough Middle Sch<br>7600 Synott Rd, Houston 77083<br>Bertran Bilton | 7-8 | TV | 998 | 86% | 281/983-8444<br>Fax 281/983-8067 |
| Klentzman Intermediate Sch<br>11100 Stancliff Rd, Houston 77099<br>Courtney Holman | 5-6 | T | 985<br>54 | 92% | 281/983-8477<br>Fax 281/983-8373 |
| Landis Elem Sch<br>10255 Spice Ln, Houston 77072<br>Kelli Upshaw | PK-4 | T | 743<br>50 | 95% | 281/983-8343<br>Fax 281/983-8072 |
| Liestman Elem Sch<br>7610 Synott Rd, Houston 77083<br>Noe Galindo | PK-4 | T | 793<br>45 | 83% | 281/983-8348<br>Fax 281/988-3047 |
| Mahanay Elem Sch<br>13215 High Star Dr, Houston 77083<br>Carmilla Nandlal | PK-4 | T | 603<br>30 | 87% | 281/983-8355<br>Fax 281/983-8083 |
| Mata Intermediate Sch<br>9225 S Dairy Ashford Rd, Houston 77099<br>Amy Coleman | 5-6 | T | 875<br>48 | 89% | 281/983-7800<br>Fax 281/983-7810 |
| Miller Intermediate Sch<br>15025 Westpark Dr, Houston 77082<br>Seymour Stewart | 5-6 | T | 963 | 81% | 281/531-3430<br>Fax 281/988-3057 |
| O'Donnell Middle Sch<br>14041 Alief Clodine Rd, Houston 77082<br>Amador Velasquez | 7-8 | TV | 1,375 | 83% | 281/495-6000<br>Fax 281/568-5029 |
| Olle Middle Sch<br>9200 Boone Rd, Houston 77099<br>Nelda Billescas | 7-8 | TV | 1,064<br>66 | 91% | 281/983-8455<br>Fax 281/983-8077 |
| Outley Elem Sch<br>12355 Richmond Ave, Houston 77082<br>Sharonda Ross-Newby | PK-4 | T | 1,164<br>55 | 76% | 281/584-0655<br>Fax 281/988-3042 |
| Owens Intermediate Sch<br>6900 Turtlewood Dr, Houston 77072<br>Lorena Augustus | 5-6 | T | 979<br>70 | 91% | 281/983-8466<br>Fax 281/988-3052 |
| Petrosky Elem Sch<br>6703 Winkleman Rd, Houston 77083<br>Bernadette Bentley | PK-4 | T | 481<br>32 | 77% | 281/983-8366<br>Fax 281/988-3043 |
| Rees Elem Sch<br>16305 Kensley Dr, Houston 77082<br>Paul Baez | PK-4 | T | 582 | 81% | 281/531-1444<br>Fax 281/988-3044 |
| Smith Elem Sch<br>11300 Stancliff Rd, Houston 77099<br>Jennifer Silva | PK-4 | T | 826 | 93% | 281/983-8380<br>Fax 281/983-7710 |
| Sneed Elem Sch<br>9855 Pagewood Ln, Houston 77042<br>Kristen Creeggan | PK-4 | T | 1,086 | 93% | 713/789-6979<br>Fax 713/260-7307 |

| | | | | | | | |
|---|---|---|---|---|---|---|---|
| 79 | Student Personnel | 91 | Safety/Security | 275 | Response To Intervention | 298 | Grant Writer/Ptnrships |
| 80 | Driver Ed/Safety | 92 | Magnet School | 277 | Remedial Math K-12 | 750 | Chief Innovation Officer |
| 81 | Gifted/Talented | 93 | Parental Involvement | 280 | Literacy Coach | 751 | Chief of Staff |
| 82 | Video Services | 95 | Tech Prep Program | 285 | STEM | 752 | Social Emotional Learning |
| 83 | Substance Abuse Prev | 97 | Chief Infomation Officer | 286 | Digital Learning | | |
| 84 | Erate | 98 | Chief Technology Officer | 288 | Common Core Standards | | **Other School Types** |
| 85 | AIDS Education | 270 | Character Education | 294 | Accountability | ⓐ | = Alternative School |
| 88 | Alternative/At Risk | 271 | Migrant Education | 295 | Network System | ⓒ | = Charter School |
| 89 | Multi-Cultural Curriculum | 273 | Teacher Mentor | 296 | Title II Programs | Ⓜ | = Magnet School |
| 90 | Social Work | 274 | Before/After Sch | 297 | Webmaster | Ⓨ | = Year-Round School |

**School Programs**
A = Alternative Program
G = Adult Classes
M = Magnet Program
T = Title I Schoolwide
V = Career & Tech Ed Programs

**Social Media**
 = Facebook
 = Twitter

New Schools are shaded
New Superintendents and Principals are bold
Personnel with email addresses are underscored

| | | | | | |
|---|---|---|---|---|---|
| Youens Elem Sch<br>12141 High Star Dr, Houston 77072<br>**Tessia Brixey \ Sancionett Rose** | PK-5 | T | 900<br>50 | 94% | 281/983-8383<br>Fax 281/988-3046 [f] |
| Youngblood Intermediate Sch<br>8410 Dairy View Ln, Houston 77072<br>Gwendolyn Sandles | 5-6 | T | 1,057<br>47 | 82% | 281/983-8020<br>Fax 281/988-3056 |

## • Channelview Ind School Dist   PID: 01023079

828 Sheldon Rd, Channelview 77530

281/452-8002
Fax 281/457-9075

> **Schools:** 13 \ **Teachers:** 547 \ **Students:** 9,700 \ **Special Ed Students:** 940 \ **LEP Students:** 2,932 \ **College-Bound:** 53% \ **Ethnic:** Asian 1%, African American 11%, Hispanic 80%, Native American: 1%, Caucasian 7% \ **Exp:** $349 (High) \ **Poverty:** 21% \ **Title I:** $2,743,187 \ **Special Education:** $1,514,000 \ **Open-Close:** 08/14 - 05/21 \ **DTBP:** $181 (High)

| | | | |
|---|---|---|---|
| Greg Ollis | 1 | Kris Lynn | 2,15 |
| Michael Lyons | 3 | David Bienvenu | 4 |
| Jared Diehl | 5 | William Jennings | 6,7,35,85 |
| Dr Don Beck | 8,15 | Heather Gilpin | 9 |
| Pam Latiolais | 10 | Patricia Glaeser | 11,286,288,294,296,298 |
| Mike Niemeyer | 15 | Jennifer Carnathan | 19 |
| Jennifer Tunink | 20,23 | Mia Young | 27,31 |
| Magdalena Garcia | 57 | Gloria Roach | 58 |
| Patrick Lacy | 67 | Kay Kerr | 68,79 |
| Karen Bryant | 69,70 | Lakeisha LeBlanc | 71 |
| Darrell Cheney | 73,84 | Raquel Ochoa | 76 |
| Ruth Dougherty | 76 | Gregg Board | 91 |
| Marion Barnes | 295 | | |

| Public Schs..Principal | Grd | Prgm | Enr/#Cls | SN | |
|---|---|---|---|---|---|
| Alice Johnson Jr High Sch<br>15500 Proctor St, Channelview 77530<br>Jules Pichon | 6-8 | T | 1,151<br>68 | 87% | 281/452-8030<br>Fax 281/452-1022 |
| Anthony Aguirre Junior HS<br>15726 Wallisville Rd, Houston 77049<br>Eric Lathan | 6-8 | T | 1,061 | 78% | 281/860-3300<br>Fax 281/860-3320 |
| B H Hamblen Elem Sch<br>1019 Dell Dale St, Channelview 77530<br>Jose Lopez | K-5 | T | 874<br>43 | 77% | 281/457-8720<br>Fax 281/457-8724 |
| Barrett-Lee Early Chldhd Ctr<br>911 Sheldon Rd, Channelview 77530<br>Emily Laird | PK-PK | T | 398 | 86% | 281/860-3827<br>Fax 281/860-3810 |
| Channelview High Sch<br>1100 Sheldon Rd, Channelview 77530<br>Robert Laird | 10-12 | TV | 1,798 | 79% | 281/452-1450<br>Fax 281/457-7346 |
| Crenshaw Elem Sch<br>16204 Wood Dr, Channelview 77530<br>Audry Lane | K-5 | T | 551<br>30 | 93% | 281/457-3080<br>Fax 281/457-5434 |
| De Zavala Elem Sch<br>16150 2nd St, Channelview 77530<br>Ruben Rodriguez | K-5 | T | 566<br>30 | 94% | 281/452-6008<br>Fax 281/452-3562 |
| Ⓐ Endeavor HS-J F Campbell Ctr<br>915 Sheldon Rd, Channelview 77530<br>Mark Sims | 9-12 | T | 112<br>6 | 54% | 281/860-3800<br>Fax 281/860-3826 |
| H C Schochler Elem Sch<br>910 Deerpass Dr, Channelview 77530<br>Ann Marie Garza | K-5 | T | 467<br>28 | 87% | 281/452-2880<br>Fax 281/452-3709 |
| Harvey S Brown Elem Sch<br>16550 Wallisville Rd, Houston 77049<br>Troy Michaud | K-5 | T | 730<br>47 | 56% | 281/860-1400<br>Fax 281/860-9916 |
| L W Kolarik 9th Grade Center<br>1120 Sheldon Rd, Channelview 77530<br>Steve McCanless | 9-9 | V | 673 | | 713/378-3400<br>Fax 713/378-3498 |

| | | | | | |
|---|---|---|---|---|---|
| McMullan Elem Sch<br>1290 Dell Dale St, Channelview 77530<br>Gina Ervin | K-5 | T | 557<br>29 | 89% | 281/452-1154<br>Fax 281/452-1367 |
| Viola Cobb Elem Sch<br>915 Dell Dale St, Channelview 77530<br>Lizette Castelline | K-5 | T | 437 | 81% | 281/452-7788<br>Fax 281/452-7413 |

## • Crosby Ind School Dist   PID: 01023134

706 Runneburg Rd, Crosby 77532

281/328-9200
Fax 281/328-9208

> **Schools:** 7 \ **Teachers:** 408 \ **Students:** 6,350 \ **Special Ed Students:** 602 \ **LEP Students:** 857 \ **College-Bound:** 50% \ **Ethnic:** African American 15%, Hispanic 41%, Caucasian 43% \ **Exp:** $62 (Low) \ **Poverty:** 17% \ **Title I:** $1,156,881 \ **Special Education:** $903,000 \ **Open-Close:** 08/13 - 05/27 \ **DTBP:** $158 (High) \ [f] [t]

| | | | |
|---|---|---|---|
| Dr Scott Davis | 1 | Lisa Jones | 2,11,19 |
| Chuck Murray | 3,91 | Rusty Hollingsworth | 3 |
| Teresa Evans | 4 | Renee Davis | 5 |
| Jerry Prieto | 6 | Sherry Long | 9,37 |
| Todd Hicks | 10,74,273,286 | Karen Grey | 15,68 |
| Dr Patricia Kay | 15,31,68 | Christie Davis | 34 |
| Mary Gill | 46 | Dr Brenda Aleman | 47 |
| Vicki Randolph | 49,52,54 | Tamara Meigh | 50 |
| Hamie Ornelas | 57 | Karla McGee | 58 |
| Randy Condra | 67 | Shelley Rena | 69 |
| Viviana Killion | 71 | Amy Davis | 73,98,295,297 |
| Jenny Kanierin | 298 | | |

| Public Schs..Principal | Grd | Prgm | Enr/#Cls | SN | |
|---|---|---|---|---|---|
| Barrett Elem Sch<br>815 FM 1942 Rd, Crosby 77532<br>Karen Walthall | 1-5 | T | 463<br>34 | 64% | 281/328-9320<br>Fax 281/328-9374 |
| Charles R Drew Elem Sch<br>223 Red Oak Ave, Crosby 77532<br>Christy Tisdom | 1-5 | T | 492<br>33 | 85% | 281/328-9306<br>Fax 281/328-3490 |
| Crosby Elem Sch<br>14705 FM 2100 Rd, Crosby 77532<br>Dana Kratky | 1-5 | T | 744 | 46% | 281/328-9360<br>Fax 281/328-9213 |
| Crosby High Sch<br>14703 FM 2100 Rd, Crosby 77532<br>Dustin Bromley | 9-12 | AGTV | 1,432<br>100 | 47% | 281/328-9237<br>Fax 281/328-0506 |
| Crosby Kindergarten Center<br>805 Runneburg Rd, Crosby 77532<br>Kriste Davis | PK-K | T | 715<br>27 | 59% | 281/328-9370<br>Fax 281/328-9379 |
| Crosby Middle Sch<br>14703 FM 2100 Rd, Crosby 77532<br>Colette Vallot | 6-8 | AT | 493<br>40 | 51% | 281/328-9264<br>Fax 281/328-9356 |
| Newport Elem Sch<br>430 N Diamondhead Blvd, Crosby 77532<br>Christy Covan | 1-5 | T | 714<br>60 | 47% | 281/328-9330<br>Fax 281/328-9378 |

## • Cypress-Fairbanks Ind Sch Dist   PID: 01023184

10300 Jones Rd, Houston 77065

281/897-4000
Fax 281/517-2125

> **Schools:** 92 \ **Teachers:** 7,262 \ **Students:** 113,256 \ **Special Ed Students:** 9,965 \ **LEP Students:** 14,860 \ **College-Bound:** 64% \ **Ethnic:** Asian 10%, African American 19%, Hispanic 46%, Native American: 1%, Caucasian 25% \ **Exp:** $163 (Low) \ **Poverty:** 15% \ **Title I:** $30,904,100 \ **Special Education:** $17,044,000 \ **Open-Close:** 09/08 - 06/03 \ **DTBP:** $187 (High) \ [f] [t]

| | | | |
|---|---|---|---|
| Dr Mark Henry | 1 | Connie Morgenroth | 2,15 |
| Melissa McAnear | 2 | Roy Sprague | 3,15,17 |
| Darin Crawford | 4 | Kayne Smith | 5 |
| Raymond Zepeda | 6,35 | Sydne Marshall | 7 |
| Barbara Levandoski | 8,15,34,58 | Denise Kubecka | 8,15,27 |

| Public Schs..Principal | Grd | Prgm | Enr/#Cls | SN | |
|---|---|---|---|---|---|
| A Robison Elem Sch 17100 Robison Woods Rd, Cypress 77429 Kelly Gerletti | PK-5 | | 998 | 34% | 281/213-1700 Fax 281/213-1705 |
| Adaptive Behavior Center 12508 Windfern Rd, Houston 77064 Chad Perry | Spec | | 20 9 | | 281/897-4174 Fax 281/517-2884 ⓕⓔ |
| Ⓐ Alternative Lrng Ctr-East 12508 Windfern Rd, Houston 77064 Rashad Godbolt | 6-12 | | 100 21 | | 281/897-4171 Fax 281/897-4170 |
| Ⓐ Alternative Lrng Ctr-West 19350 Rebel Yell Dr, Katy 77449 Stacie Wicke | 6-12 | | 100 | | 281/855-4310 Fax 281/855-4307 |
| Andre Elem Sch 8111 Fry Rd, Cypress 77433 Laura Novacinski | PK-5 | T | 915 | 55% | 281/463-5500 Fax 281/463-5507 |
| Arnold Middle Sch 11111 Telge Rd, Cypress 77429 Jodi White | 6-8 | TV | 1,526 85 | 58% | 281/897-4700 Fax 281/517-6857 |
| Ault Elem Sch 21010 Maple Village Dr, Cypress 77433 Jeff Lacoke | PK-5 | | 1,050 | 35% | 281/373-2800 Fax 281/373-2823 |
| B F Adam Elem Sch 11303 Honey Grove Ln, Houston 77065 Stephanie Thomas | PK-5 | T | 870 | 60% | 281/897-4485 Fax 281/517-2089 |
| Bane Elem Sch 5804 Premier St, Houston 77040 Cesar Diaz | PK-5 | T | 877 | 95% | 713/460-6140 Fax 713/460-7847 |
| Birkes Elem Sch 8500 Queenston Blvd, Houston 77095 Stacie Everson | PK-5 | | 1,117 | 37% | 281/345-3300 Fax 281/345-3305 |
| Black Elem Sch 14155 Grant Rd, Cypress 77429 Kyla Mote | PK-5 | | 1,136 | 39% | 281/320-7145 Fax 281/320-7144 |
| Bleyl Middle Sch 10800 Mills Rd, Houston 77070 Michelle Provo | 6-8 | TV | 1,620 90 | 67% | 281/897-4340 Fax 281/897-4353 |
| Bridgeland High Sch 10707 Mason Rd, Cypress 77433 Michael Smith | 9-12 | | 1,276 | 14% | 832/349-7600 Fax 832/349-7610 |
| Campbell Middle Sch 11415 Bobcat Rd, Houston 77064 Dr Laura Perry | 6-8 | TV | 1,293 80 | 79% | 281/897-4300 Fax 281/807-8634 ⓕⓔ |
| Cook Middle Sch 9111 Wheatland Dr, Houston 77064 Martin Drayton | 6-8 | TV | 1,578 | 63% | 281/897-4400 Fax 281/517-2657 |
| Copeland Elem Sch 18018 Forest Heights Dr, Houston 77095 Ann Melancon | PK-5 | | 1,000 50 | 41% | 281/856-1400 Fax 281/463-5510 |
| Cy-Fair High Sch 22602 Northwest Fwy, Cypress 77429 Ana Martin | 9-12 | TV | 3,391 150 | 36% | 281/897-4600 Fax 281/517-6530 |
| Cypress Creek High Sch 9815 Grant Rd, Houston 77070 Vicki Snokhous | 9-12 | TV | 3,218 | 53% | 281/897-4200 Fax 281/897-4193 ⓕⓔ |
| Cypress Falls High Sch 9811 Huffmeister Rd, Houston 77095 Becky Denton | 9-12 | TV | 2,989 | 56% | 281/856-1000 Fax 281/856-1445 |
| Cypress Lakes High Sch 5750 Greenhouse Rd, Katy 77449 Sarah Harty | 9-12 | T | 3,333 | 67% | 281/856-3800 Fax 281/856-3808 |
| Cypress Park High Sch 7425 Westgreen Blvd, Cypress 77433 Chris Hecker | 9-12 | T | 551 | 73% | 346/227-6000 |
| Cypress Ranch High Sch 10700 Fry Rd, Cypress 77433 Michael Maness | 9-12 | | 2,592 | 21% | 281/373-2300 Fax 281/213-1976 |
| Cypress Ridge High Sch 7900 N Eldridge Pkwy, Houston 77041 Stephanie Meshell | 9-12 | TV | 3,088 | 69% | 281/807-8045 |
| Cypress Springs High Sch 7909 Fry Rd, Cypress 77433 Dr Cheryl Henry | 9-12 | TV | 2,123 | 65% | 281/345-3000 Fax 281/345-3010 ⓕⓔ |
| Cypress Woods High Sch 13550 Woods Spillane Blvd, Cypress 77429 Garold Kinninger | 9-12 | AV | 3,334 | 21% | 281/213-1800 Fax 281/213-1827 ⓕⓔ |
| Danish Elem Sch 11850 Fallbrook Dr, Houston 77065 Kelly Dalton | PK-5 | T | 961 | 77% | 281/955-4981 Fax 281/955-4994 |
| David Anthony Middle Sch 10215 Greenhouse Rd, Cypress 77433 Vivian Bennett | 6-8 | TV | 1,722 | 48% | 281/373-5660 Fax 281/373-2560 |
| Dean Middle Sch 14104 Reo St, Houston 77040 **Hoang Pham** | 6-8 | TV | 1,384 | 87% | 713/460-6153 Fax 713/460-6197 |
| Dorothy Carlton Center 13550 Woods Spillane Blvd, Cypress 77429 Rhonda Turns | Spec | | 92 15 | | 281/213-1950 Fax 281/213-1951 ⓕⓔ |
| Duryea Elem Sch 20150 Arbor Creek Dr, Katy 77449 Tomicka Williams | PK-5 | T | 857 | 82% | 281/856-5174 Fax 281/856-5179 |
| Emery Elem Sch 19636 Plantation Myrtle, Katy 77449 Dr Michelle Merricks | PK-5 | T | 1,103 | 74% | 281/855-9080 Fax 281/855-9380 |
| Emmott Elem Sch 11750 Steeple Way Blvd, Houston 77065 Jessica Hernandez | PK-5 | T | 793 | 75% | 281/897-4500 Fax 281/897-3888 |
| Farney Elem Sch 14425 Barker Cypress Rd, Cypress 77429 Dr Patricia Reilly | PK-5 | | 993 65 | 37% | 281/373-2850 Fax 281/373-2855 |
| Fiest Elem Sch 8425 Pine Falls Dr, Houston 77095 Jeanette Gerault | PK-5 | T | 1,021 60 | 63% | 281/463-5838 Fax 281/856-1174 |
| Francone Elem Sch 11250 Perry Rd, Houston 77064 Melissa Martin | PK-5 | T | 900 | 83% | 281/897-4512 Fax 281/897-4518 ⓕⓔ |
| Frazier Elem Sch 8300 Little River Rd, Houston 77064 Michael Pagano | PK-5 | T | 637 46 | 88% | 713/896-3475 Fax 713/896-5013 ⓔ |
| Gleason Elem Sch 9203 Willowbridge Park Blvd, Houston 77064 Christine Melancon | PK-5 | T | 962 | 53% | 281/517-6800 Fax 281/517-6805 |
| Goodson Middle Sch 17333 Huffmeister Rd, Cypress 77429 Richard Dixon | 6-8 | V | 1,450 50 | 33% | 281/373-2350 Fax 281/373-2355 |
| Hairgrove Elem Sch 7120 N Eldridge Pkwy, Houston 77041 Darynda Klein | PK-5 | T | 740 54 | 85% | 713/896-5015 Fax 713/896-5020 |

| School | Grades | | Enrollment | % | Phone |
|---|---|---|---|---|---|

Hamilton Elem Sch
12050 Old Kluge Rd, Cypress 77429
Sage Papaioannou — PK-5 — 1,006 — 15% 281/370-0990 — Fax 281/320-7067

Hamilton Middle Sch
12330 Kluge Rd, Cypress 77429
Kim Sempe — 6-8 — 1,520 / 69 — 25% 281/320-7000 — Fax 281/320-7033 [t]

Hemmenway Elem Sch
20400 W Little York Rd, Katy 77449
Dr Renee Silliman — PK-5 — T — 1,070 — 77% 281/856-9870 [f][t]

Holbrook Elem Sch
6402 Langfield Rd, Houston 77092
**Becky Mendez** — PK-5 — T — 983 — 90% 713/460-6165 — Fax 713/460-7866

Holmsley Elem Sch
7315 Hudson Oaks Dr, Houston 77095
Ana Diaz — PK-5 — T — 889 — 71% 281/463-5885 — Fax 281/463-5529

Hoover Elem Sch
6425 Greenhouse Rd, Katy 77449
Michelle Rice — PK-2 — T — 837 — 81% 832/667-7301 — Fax 832/667-7310

Hopper Middle Sch
7811 Fry Rd, Cypress 77433
Wendi Witthaus — 6-8 — T — 1,315 — 80% 281/463-5353 — Fax 281/463-5354

Horne Elem Sch
14950 W Little York Rd, Houston 77084
Tracey Bennett — PK-5 — T — 962 / 60 — 80% 281/463-5954 — Fax 281/856-1451 [f][t]

Jan Aragon Middle Sch
16823 West Rd, Houston 77095
Maria Mamaux — 6-8 — TV — 1,549 — 42% 281/856-5100 — Fax 281/856-5105

Jersey Village High Sch
7600 Solomon St, Jersey Vlg 77040
Maggie Wiley — 9-12 — TV — 3,515 — 56% 713/896-3400 — Fax 713/849-6710

Joan Postma Elem Sch
18425 West Rd, Cypress 77433
Teresa Bell — PK-5 — 1,045 — 38% 281/345-3660 — Fax 281/345-3545

Jowell Elem Sch
6355 Greenhouse Rd, Katy 77449
Kimberly Criswell — 3-5 — T — 677 / 37 — 81% 281/463-5966 — Fax 281/345-3628

Kahla Middle Sch
16212 W Little York Rd, Houston 77084
Virgil Maddox — 6-8 — TV — 1,336 — 76% 281/345-3260 — Fax 281/856-5275

Keith Elem Sch
20550 Fairfield Green Blvd, Cypress 77433
Dawn Tryon — PK-5 — 1,023 — 21% 281/213-1744 — Fax 281/213-1749

Kirk Elem Sch
12421 Tanner Rd, Houston 77041
Jennifer Bell — PK-5 — 889 / 50 — 76% 713/849-8250 — Fax 713/849-8255

Labay Middle Sch
15435 Willow River Dr, Houston 77095
**Lanette Bellamy** — 6-8 — TV — 1,334 — 67% 281/463-5800 — Fax 281/463-5939

Lamkin Elem Sch
11521 Telge Rd, Cypress 77429
Gale Parker — PK-5 — T — 850 / 45 — 60% 281/897-4775 — Fax 281/807-8163

Langham Creek High Sch
17610 FM 529 Rd, Houston 77095
**Jose Martinez** — 9-12 — TV — 2,980 — 50% 281/463-5400 — Fax 281/345-3509 [f][t]

Lee Elem Sch
12900 W Little York Rd, Houston 77041
Susan Epperson — PK-5 — T — 905 — 69% 713/849-8281 — Fax 713/849-8249

Ⓐ Leonard Brautigam Center
13102 Jones Rd, Houston 77070
Martha Strother — 11-12 — GV — 250 / 23 — 281/807-8684 — Fax 281/807-8693

Lieder Elem Sch
17003 Kieth Harrow Blvd, Houston 77084
Dinah McMichael — PK-5 — T — 870 / 43 — 84% 281/463-5928 — Fax 281/463-5531

Lowery Elem Sch
15950 Ridge Park Dr, Houston 77095
April Wright — PK-5 — T — 910 — 48% 281/463-5900 — Fax 281/463-5516

M Robinson Elem Sch
4321 Westfield Village Dr D, Katy 77449
Rocio Braley — PK-5 — T — 1,188 — 77% 281/855-1240 — Fax 281/855-0740

Matzke Elem Sch
10002 Mills Rd, Houston 77070
Cathy Jacobs — PK-5 — T — 1,055 / 45 — 67% 281/897-4450 — Fax 281/897-4454

McFee Elem Sch
19315 Plantation Cove Ln, Katy 77449
Sharon Whitfield — PK-5 — T — 1,102 — 83% 281/463-5380 — Fax 281/463-5680

Metcalf Elem Sch
6100 Queenston Blvd, Houston 77084
John Steward — PK-5 — T — 739 / 50 — 80% 281/856-1152 — Fax 281/856-1154

Millsap Elem Sch
12424 Huffmeister Rd, Cypress 77429
Joy Dauphin — PK-5 — T — 861 / 46 — 57% 281/897-4470 — Fax 281/807-8635

Moore Elem Sch
13734 Lakewood Forest Dr, Houston 77070
Patricia Myers — PK-5 — T — 914 / 42 — 39% 281/370-4040 — Fax 281/320-7978

Owens Elem Sch
7939 Jackrabbit Rd, Houston 77095
Amy Frank — PK-5 — T — 873 — 73% 281/463-5915 — Fax 281/463-5526

Pope Elem Sch
19019 N Bridgeland Lake Pkwy, Cypress 77433
Elizabeth Bradley — PK-5 — 1,022 — 6% 281/373-2340 — Fax 281/373-2341

Post Elem Sch
7600 Equador St, Houston 77040
Karen Stockton — PK-5 — 910 / 50 — 69% 713/896-3488 — Fax 713/896-3497

Ramona Bang Elem Sch
8900 Rio Grande Dr, Houston 77064
Erwann Wilson — PK-5 — T — 950 / 44 — 68% 281/897-4760 — Fax 281/517-2095

Reed Elem Sch
8700 Tami Renee Ln, Houston 77040
**Karen Richardson** — PK-5 — T — 924 / 52 — 80% 713/896-5035 — Fax 713/896-5051

Rennell Elem Sch
19500 Tuckerton Rd, Cypress 77433
Meredith Akers — PK-5 — 1,108 — 18% 281/213-1550

Rowe Middle Sch
7611 Westgreen Blvd, Cypress 77433
**Stacia Carew** — 6-8 — 450 — 346/227-6220 — Fax 346/227-6221

Sadie Woodard Elem Sch
17501 Cypress North Houston Rd, Cypress 77433
Susan Brenz — PK-5 — T — 1,092 — 45% 281/373-2303 — Fax 281/373-2304

Salyards Middle Sch
21757 Fairfield Place Dr, Cypress 77433
Liz Wood — 6-8 — 1,601 — 17% 281/373-2400

Sampson Elem Sch
16002 Coles Crossing Dr, Cypress 77429
Heather Motzny — PK-5 — 976 — 8% 281/213-1600 — Fax 281/213-1605

Sheridan Elem Sch
19790 Kieth Harrow Blvd, Katy 77449
Rene McIntyre — PK-5 — T — 1,189 / 60 — 74% 281/856-1420 — Fax 281/856-1461

Smith Middle Sch
10300 Warner Smith Blvd, Cypress 77433
Rebecca Koop — 6-8 — 1,633 — 12% 281/213-1010 — Fax 281/213-1019

Spillane Middle Sch
13403 Woods Spillane Blvd, Cypress 77429
Jamie Brotemarkle — 6-8 — V — 1,585 — 21% 281/213-1645 — Fax 281/213-1799

Swenke Elem Sch
22400 Fairfield Place Dr, Cypress 77433
Dr Elizabeth Miller — PK-5 — 1,114 — 7% 281/213-1200

T S Hancock Elem Sch
13801 Schroeder Rd, Houston 77070
Lissa Archuletta — PK-5 — T — 896 / 35 — 72% 281/897-4523 — Fax 281/807-8166

Thornton Middle Sch
19802 Kieth Harrow Blvd, Katy 77449
Reginal Mitchell — 6-8 — TV — 1,927 — 76% 281/856-1500 — Fax 281/856-1548

---

1 Superintendent
2 Bus/Finance/Purchasing
3 Buildings And Grounds
4 Food Service
5 Transportation
6 Athletic
7 Health Services
8 Curric/Instruct K-12
9 Curric/Instruct Elem
10 Curric/Instruct Sec
11 Federal Program
12 Title I
13 Title V
14 Asst Superintendent
16 Instructional Media Svcs
17 Chief Operations Officer
18 Chief Academic Officer
19 Chief Financial Officer
20 Art K-12
21 Art Elem
22 Art Sec
23 Music K-12
24 Music Elem
25 Music Sec
26 Business Education
27 Career & Tech Ed
28 Technology Education
29 Family/Consumer Science
30 Adult Education
31 Career/Sch-to-Work K-12
32 Career/Sch-to-Work Elem
33 Career/Sch-to-Work Sec
34 Early Childhood Ed
35 Health/Phys Education
36 Guidance Services K-12
37 Guidance Services Elem
38 Guidance Services Sec
39 Social Studies K-12
40 Social Studies Elem
41 Social Studies Sec
42 Science K-12
43 Science Elem
44 Science Sec
45 Math K-12
46 Math Elem
47 Math Sec
48 English/Lang Arts K-12
49 English/Lang Arts Elem
50 English/Lang Arts Sec
51 Reading K-12
52 Reading Elem
53 Reading Sec
54 Remedial Reading K-12
55 Remedial Reading Elem
56 Remedial Reading Sec
57 Bilingual/ELL
58 Special Education K-12
59 Special Education Elem
60 Special Education Sec
61 Foreign/World Lang K-12
62 Foreign/World Lang Elem
63 Foreign/World Lang Sec
64 Religious Education K-12
65 Religious Education Elem
66 Religious Education Sec
67 School Board President
68 Teacher Personnel
69 Academic Assessment
70 Research/Development
71 Public Information
72 Summer School
73 Instructional Tech
74 Inservice Training
75 Marketing/Distributive
76 Info Systems
77 Psychological Assess
78 Affirmative Action

| School | Grd | Prgm | Enr/#Cls | SN | Phone |
|---|---|---|---|---|---|
| Tipps Elem Sch<br>5611 Queenston Blvd, Houston 77084<br>Kari Hough | PK-5 | T | 966 | 89% | 281/345-3350<br>Fax 281/345-3355 |
| Truitt Middle Sch<br>6600 Addicks Satsuma Rd, Houston 77084<br>Yvette Garcia | 6-8 | TV | 1,478 | 73% | 281/856-1100<br>Fax 281/856-1104 |
| Walker Elem Sch<br>6424 Settlers Village Dr, Katy 77449<br>Kim Dameron | PK-5 | T | 907 | 78% | 281/345-3200<br>Fax 281/345-3205 |
| Warner Elem Sch<br>10400 Warner Smith Blvd, Cypress 77433<br>Schonda Kidd | PK-5 | | 1,097 | 11% | 281/213-1650<br>Fax 281/213-1651 |
| Watkins Middle Sch<br>4800 Cairnvillage St, Houston 77084<br>Dr Jose Martinez | 6-8 | TV | 1,438 | 73% | 281/463-5850<br>Fax 281/856-1583 |
| Wells Elem Sch<br>10607 Mason Rd, Cypress 77433<br>Cheryl Fisher | PK-5 | | 1,001 | 8% | 832/349-7400<br>Fax 832/349-7410 |
| Willbern Elem Sch<br>10811 Goodspring Dr, Houston 77064<br>Connye Roberson | PK-5 | T | 904 | 76% | 281/897-3820<br>Fax 281/517-2162 |
| Wilson Elem Sch<br>18015 Kieth Harrow Blvd, Houston 77084<br>Tamera Felder | PK-5 | T | 903<br>40 | 61% | 281/463-5941<br>Fax 281/463-5944 |
| Yeager Elem Sch<br>13615 Champion Forest Dr, Houston 77069<br>Laura Barrett | PK-5 | T | 928<br>60 | 69% | 281/440-4914<br>Fax 281/587-7531 |

● **Deer Park Ind School Dist** PID: 01023316  832/668-7000
2800 Texas Ave, Deer Park 77536  Fax 281/930-4638

> **Schools:** 16 \ **Teachers:** 819 \ **Students:** 13,000 \
> **Special Ed Students:** 1,484 \ **LEP Students:** 1,450 \ **College-Bound:** 61%
> \ **Ethnic:** Asian 1%, African American 3%, Hispanic 59%, Caucasian
> 37% \ **Exp:** $176 (Low) \ **Poverty:** 15% \ **Title I:** $2,262,771 \
> **Special Education:** $2,019,000 \ **Open-Close:** 08/19 - 05/27 \ **DTBP:** $185
> (High) \ **t**

| | | | |
|---|---|---|---|
| Victor White | 1 | David Edgar | 2,15 |
| John Knowlton | 2 | Stacey McDowell | 2 |
| Michelle Keener | 4 | Jeff Greene | 5 |
| Darren Chandler | 6 | Ronda Kouba | 8,15,296 |
| Donna Yost | 11 | Pam McClean | 13,58,77,83 |
| Janet Byers | 15,79,91 | Peaches McCroskey | 15,68 |
| Jason Dove | 20,23 | David Berrier | 27,31 |
| Michele Deutschendorf | 34,60 | Kathryn Andrews | 39,81 |
| Denise Haynes | 42 | Becky Stack | 45 |
| Cindy Hart | 45 | Jessica Reyna | 48 |
| Lisa Mayer | 48* | Misti Mead | 60 |
| Lynn Kirkpatrick | 67 | Kathy Owens | 69,294* |
| Dr Steven Travis | 70 | Matt Lucas | 71 |
| Kari Murphy | 73,286,295 | Sue Pike | 76 |
| Denise Batchelor | 88 | | |

| Public Schs..Principal | Grd | Prgm | Enr/#Cls | SN | |
|---|---|---|---|---|---|
| Deepwater Elem Sch<br>309 Glenmore Dr, Pasadena 77503<br>Angie Cabaniss | 3-5 | T | 761<br>36 | 78% | 832/668-8300<br>Fax 713/475-6150 |
| Deepwater Junior High Sch<br>501 Glenmore Dr, Pasadena 77503<br>Rosa Ramos | 6-8 | T | 438<br>60 | 85% | 832/668-7600<br>Fax 713/475-6138 |
| Deer Park Elem Sch<br>2920 Luella Ave, Deer Park 77536<br>Whitney Rich | K-5 | | 785<br>35 | 27% | 832/668-8000<br>Fax 281/930-4930 |
| Deer Park High Sch-N Campus<br>402 Ivy Ave, Deer Park 77536<br>**Kirk Taylor** | 9-9 | | 1,073 | | 832/668-7300<br>Fax 281/930-4840 |
| Deer Park High Sch-S Campus<br>710 W San Augustine St, Deer Park 77536<br>Steve Corry | 10-12 | GTV | 2,647 | 42% | 832/668-7200<br>Fax 281/930-4894 **t** |
| Deer Park Junior High Sch<br>410 E 9th St, Deer Park 77536<br>Dr Tiffany Regan | 6-8 | | 894 | 32% | 832/668-7500<br>Fax 281/930-4726 |
| Ⓐ Deerpark HS Wolters Campus<br>204 Ivy Ave, Deer Park 77536<br>Clyde Skarke | 9-12 | | 153<br>18 | | 832/668-7400<br>Fax 281/930-0525 |
| Ⓐ Disciplinary Alt Ed Program<br>601 E 8th St, Deer Park 77536<br>Paul Moore | 6-12 | | 25<br>2 | | 832/668-7407<br>Fax 281/930-0064 |
| Early Childhood Center<br>401 Luella Dr, Pasadena 77503<br>Jenny Sisco-Martinez | PK-PK | T | 364 | 57% | 832/668-8390<br>Fax 832/668-8395 |
| Fairmont Elem Sch<br>4315 Heathfield Dr, Pasadena 77505<br>Lea Boswell | K-5 | | 802<br>42 | 26% | 832/668-8500<br>Fax 281/998-4411 |
| Fairmont Junior High Sch<br>4911 Holly Bay Ct, Pasadena 77505<br>Neil Munro | 6-8 | T | 716<br>42 | 35% | 832/668-7800<br>Fax 281/998-4456 |
| J P Bonnette Jr High Sch<br>5010 W Pasadena Blvd, Deer Park 77536<br>John Wegman | 6-8 | TV | 820<br>55 | 49% | 832/668-7700<br>Fax 281/930-4756 |
| J P Dabbs Elem Sch<br>302 E Lambuth Ln, Deer Park 77536<br>Mandy Davis | K-5 | T | 683<br>45 | 54% | 832/668-8100<br>Fax 281/930-4910 |
| Parkwood Elem Sch<br>404 Parkwood Dr, Pasadena 77503<br>Debbie Yampey | K-2 | T | 667<br>45 | 80% | 832/668-8200<br>Fax 713/475-6180 |
| San Jacinto Elem Sch<br>1302 E 13th St, Deer Park 77536<br>Robin Evans | K-5 | T | 898<br>31 | 41% | 832/668-7900<br>Fax 281/930-4950 **t** |
| W A Carpenter Elem Sch<br>5002 W Pasadena Blvd, Deer Park 77536<br>**Blanca Galvan** | K-5 | T | 824<br>42 | 50% | 832/668-8400<br>Fax 281/930-4970 |

● **Galena Park Ind School Dist** PID: 01023419  832/386-1000
14705 Woodforest Blvd, Houston 77015  Fax 832/386-1100

> **Schools:** 27 \ **Teachers:** 1,359 \ **Students:** 21,045 \
> **Special Ed Students:** 2,011 \ **LEP Students:** 7,030 \ **College-Bound:** 55%
> \ **Ethnic:** Asian 1%, African American 15%, Hispanic 80%, Caucasian
> 4% \ **Exp:** $290 (Med) \ **Poverty:** 29% \ **Title I:** $9,391,056 \
> **Special Education:** $3,989,000 \ **Open-Close:** 09/08 - 06/10 \ **DTBP:** $185
> (High) \ **f** **t**

| | | | |
|---|---|---|---|
| **Dr John Moore** | 1 | Dina Edgar | 2,15 |
| Sonya George | 2,3,15,19,68 | Brian Aubin | 4 |
| Kenneth Bush | 5 | Vivian Dancy | 6 |
| Dr Seretha Augustine | 7,36,58,79 | Elizabeth Lalor | 8,15,74,79 |
| Amy Cole | 11 | Dr David Harris | 15 |
| Holli Malloy | 15 | Dr Mechelle Epps | 15 |
| Michael McKay | 15,68 | Terri Moore | 15,74,79,294 |
| Dr Wanna Giacona | 15 | Sam Harris | 20,23 |
| Dr Marley Morris | 27,31 | Veronica Martinez | 34,57 |
| Chad Perry | 58 | Ramon Garza | 67 |
| Dolly Mayeaux | 69,294 | Cherrhunda Johnson | 71 |
| Michelle Young | 73,286 | Donna Pruitt | 76 |
| Ella Moreaux | 76 | Dr Kareen Brown | 81 |
| Bryan Clements | 91 | Marisa Martinez | 271 |
| Livia Callahan | 275 | Nicole Johns | 275 |
| Adrian Hernendez | 295 | Anna Gonzalez | 298 |
| Vanessa Squirrell | 752 | | |

---

| Public Schs..Principal | Grd | Prgm | Enr/#Cls | SN |
|---|---|---|---|---|
| Ⓐ Accelerated Center for Ed<br>13801 Hollypark Dr, Houston 77015<br>Julien Guillory | 9-12 | | 9<br>8 | 832/386-3672<br>Fax 832/386-3671 ⨍⨎ |
| Ⓐ Center for Success<br>13801 Hollypark Dr, Houston 77015<br>Sherrhonda Johnson | 6-12 | | 70<br>6 | 832/386-3637<br>Fax 832/386-3631 |
| Cimarron Elem Sch<br>816 Cimarron St, Houston 77015<br>Cynthia Galaviz | PK-5 | AT | 670<br>63 | 91% 832/386-3240<br>Fax 832/386-3241 ⨍⨎ |
| Cloverleaf Elem Sch<br>1035 Frankie St, Houston 77015<br>Lee Brown | PK-5 | T | 672<br>49 | 95% 832/386-3200<br>Fax 832/386-3201 ⨍⨎ |
| Cobb Sixth Grade Campus<br>6722 Uvalde Rd, Houston 77049<br>Adrian Hurtado | 6-6 | T | 1,155<br>60 | 87% 832/386-2100<br>Fax 832/386-2101 |
| Dr Shirley J Williamson ES<br>6720 New Forest Pkwy, Houston 77049<br>Dr Jonathan Sutton | PK-5 | T | 680 | 79% 832/386-4000<br>Fax 832/386-4025 ⨍⨎ |
| Galena Park Cte Early Clg HS<br>5800 Uvalde Rd Bldg N, Houston 77049<br>Jeff Hutchinson | 9-12 | V | 125 | 281/459-7198<br>Fax 281/459-7113 |
| Galena Park Elem Sch<br>401 N Main St, Galena Park 77547<br>Jaime Rocha | PK-5 | T | 538<br>50 | 89% 832/386-1670<br>Fax 832/386-1692 |
| Galena Park High Sch<br>1000 Keene St, Galena Park 77547<br>Kimberly Martin | 9-12 | GTV | 1,843<br>80 | 84% 832/386-2800<br>Fax 832/386-2802 ⨍⨎ |
| Galena Park Middle Sch<br>400 Keene St, Galena Park 77547<br>Lee Ramirez | 6-8 | TV | 1,064 | 88% 832/386-1700<br>Fax 832/386-1738 |
| Green Valley Elem Sch<br>13350 Woodforest Blvd, Houston 77015<br>Grace Devost | PK-5 | T | 677<br>55 | 93% 832/386-4390<br>Fax 832/386-4391 |
| Jacinto City Elem Sch<br>10910 Wiggins St, Houston 77029<br>Becky Gardea | PK-5 | T | 624<br>49 | 89% 832/386-4600<br>Fax 832/386-4601 |
| James B Havard Elem Sch<br>15150 Wallisville Rd, Houston 77049<br>Lisa Hamblen | PK-5 | T | 669<br>43 | 73% 832/386-3710<br>Fax 832/386-3711 ⨍⨎ |
| MacArthur Elem Sch<br>1801 N Main St, Galena Park 77547<br>Maria Munoz | PK-5 | T | 708<br>45 | 89% 832/386-4630<br>Fax 832/386-4631 ⨍⨎ |
| Normandy Crossing Elem Sch<br>12500 Normandy Crossing Dr, Houston 77015<br>Irene Benzor | PK-5 | T | 575<br>50 ⨍⨎ | 88% 832/386-1600<br>Fax 832/386-1642 |
| North Shore 10th Grade Ctr<br>353 N Castlegory Rd # 3, Houston 77049<br>Kenneth Bryant | 10-10 | V | 1,072 | 832/386-4880<br>Fax 832/386-4881 |
| North Shore Elem Sch<br>14310 Duncannon Dr, Houston 77015<br>Esmeralda Perez | PK-5 | T | 917<br>55 | 89% 832/386-4660<br>Fax 832/386-4661 ⨍⨎ |
| North Shore Middle Sch<br>120 Castlegory Rd, Houston 77015<br>Dr Christopher Eckford | 7-8 | TV | 1,380 | 83% 832/386-2600<br>Fax 832/386-2643 |
| North Shore Ninth Grade Center<br>13501 Hollypark Dr, Houston 77015<br>David Pierson | 9-9 | AV | 1,166<br>50 | 832/386-3400<br>Fax 832/386-3401 |
| North Shore Senior High Sch<br>353 N Castlegory Rd, Houston 77049<br>Dr Joe Coleman | 11-12 | TV | 2,500 | 82% 832/386-4100<br>Fax 832/386-4101 |
| Purple Sage Elem Sch<br>6500 Purple Sage Rd, Houston 77049<br>Wendy McGee | PK-5 | T | 462 | 88% 832/386-3100<br>Fax 832/386-3106 |
| Pyburn Elem Sch<br>12302 Coulson St, Houston 77015<br>Conrad Rivera | PK-5 | T | 541<br>27 | 85% 832/386-3150<br>Fax 832/386-3168 |

| Public Schs..Principal | Grd | Prgm | Enr/#Cls | SN |
|---|---|---|---|---|
| Sam Houston Elem Sch<br>4101 E Sam Houston Pkwy N, Houston 77015<br>Michelle Cavazos | PK-5 | T | 826<br>48 | 93% 832/386-4430<br>Fax 832/386-4431 |
| Tice Elem Sch<br>14120 Wallisville Rd, Houston 77049<br>Toshia Gouard | PK-5 | T | 604<br>50 | 89% 832/386-4050<br>Fax 832/386-4053 |
| W C Cunningham Middle Sch<br>14110 Wallisville Rd, Houston 77049<br>Shaunte Morris | 7-8 | TV | 962 | 87% 832/386-4470<br>Fax 832/386-4471 |
| Woodland Acres Elem Sch<br>12936 Sarahs Ln, Houston 77015<br>Sandra Rodriguez | PK-5 | T | 412<br>50 | 78% 832/386-2220<br>Fax 832/386-2221 ⨍⨎ |
| Woodland Acres Middle Sch<br>12947 Myrtle Ln, Houston 77015<br>Manuel Escalante | 6-8 | TV | 194<br>40 | 85% 832/386-4700<br>Fax 832/386-4701 ⨍⨎ |

● **Goose Creek Cons Ind Sch Dist** PID: 01023562   281/420-4800
4544 I-10 E, Baytown 77521   Fax 281/420-4854

**Schools:** 28 \ **Teachers:** 1,534 \ **Students:** 24,000 \
**Special Ed Students:** 2,525 \ **LEP Students:** 3,788 \ **College-Bound:** 75%
\ **Ethnic:** Asian 2%, African American 16%, Hispanic 64%, Caucasian
18% \ **Exp:** $339 (High) \ **Poverty:** 21% \ **Title I:** $7,093,216 \
**Special Education:** $3,632,000 \ **Open-Close:** 09/08 - 06/11 \ **DTBP:** $181
(High) \ 🇹

| | | | | |
|---|---|---|---|---|
| Randal O'Brien | 1 | Joseph Villalba | 2 |
| Margie Grimes | 2,19 | Renea Dobbs | 2 |
| Billy Gray | 3 | Natalie Edwards | 4 |
| Rick Walterscheid | 5 | Bernard Mulvaney | 6 |
| Patricia Pina | 7 | Becky Robins | 8 |
| Susan Jackson | 8,15,296 | Ginger McKay | 11,298 |
| Anthony Price | 15 | Eloy Chapa | 15,68 |
| Susan Chiboroski | 20,23 | Renae Dillon | 27,92* |
| Dr Precious Reimonenq | 31,36 | Hollie Pharris | 34,88 |
| Faith Longorio | 39 | Kevin Wrobleski | 42 |
| Kami Hale | 48,61 | Pilar Moreno-Recio | 57 |
| Janna Crow | 58,77 | Natalie Hudson | 58 |
| Augustine Loredo | 67 | Ron Wyatt | 68 |
| Tyrone Sylvester | 68 | David Yannotta | 69,294 |
| Susan Passmore | 71 | Matt Flood | 73,76,98 |
| Steve Koester | 73,286 | Christi Leath | 74,81,273 |
| Araceli Delacruz | 79 | Lisa Vaughan | 90 |
| Tony Alfaro | 91 | Jane Paris | 271 |
| Lindsey Marek | 285* | Mima Trujillo | 297 |

| Public Schs..Principal | Grd | Prgm | Enr/#Cls | SN |
|---|---|---|---|---|
| Alamo Elem Sch<br>6100 N Main St, Baytown 77521<br>**Leah Abbate** | PK-5 | T | 769<br>25 | 77% 281/420-4595<br>Fax 281/420-4905 |
| Ashbel Smith Elem Sch<br>403 E James St, Baytown 77520<br>Katherine Cruz | PK-5 | T | 650<br>40 | 84% 281/420-4615<br>Fax 281/420-4940 |
| Baytown Junior High Sch<br>7707 Bayway Dr, Baytown 77520<br>Brian Aiken | 6-8 | TV | 649<br>55 | 82% 281/420-4560<br>Fax 281/420-4908 |
| Bonnie P Hopper Primary Sch<br>405 E Houston St, Highlands 77562<br>Maria Rosas | PK-1 | T | 397<br>30 | 75% 281/420-4685<br>Fax 281/426-5179 |
| Cedar Bayou Junior High Sch<br>2610 Elvinta St, Baytown 77520<br>Renee Meyer | 6-8 | TV | 1,085<br>60 | 73% 281/420-4570<br>Fax 281/420-4569 |
| David Crockett Elem Sch<br>4500 Barkaloo Rd, Baytown 77521<br>Michelle James | PK-5 | T | 673<br>35 | 67% 281/420-4645<br>Fax 281/420-4649 |
| Dr Antonio Banuelos Elem Sch<br>7770 Eastpoint Blvd, Baytown 77521<br>Carrie Smith | PK-5 | T | 797 | 59% 281/420-1230<br>Fax 281/421-3480 |

| | | | | | | | |
|---|---|---|---|---|---|---|---|
| 1 | Superintendent | 8 | Curric/Instruct K-12 | 19 | Chief Financial Officer | 29 | Family/Consumer Science |
| 2 | Bus/Finance/Purchasing | 9 | Curric/Instruct Elem | 20 | Art K-12 | 30 | Adult Education |
| 3 | Buildings And Grounds | 10 | Curric/Instruct Sec | 21 | Art Elem | 31 | Career/Sch-to-Work K-12 |
| 4 | Food Service | 11 | Federal Program | 22 | Art Sec | 32 | Career/Sch-to-Work Elem |
| 5 | Transportation | 12 | Title I | 23 | Music K-12 | 33 | Career/Sch-to-Work Sec |
| 6 | Athletic | 13 | Title V | 24 | Music Elem | 34 | Early Childhood Ed |
| 7 | Health Services | 15 | Asst Superintendent | 25 | Music Sec | 35 | Health/Phys Education |
| | | 16 | Instructional Media Svcs | 26 | Business Education | 36 | Guidance Services K-12 |
| | | 17 | Chief Operations Officer | 27 | Career & Tech Ed | 37 | Guidance Services Elem |
| | | 18 | Chief Academic Officer | 28 | Technology Education | 38 | Guidance Services Sec |

| | | | | | |
|---|---|---|---|---|---|
| 39 | Social Studies K-12 | 49 | English/Lang Arts Elem | 59 | Special Education Elem |
| 40 | Social Studies Elem | 50 | English/Lang Arts Sec | 60 | Special Education Sec |
| 41 | Social Studies Sec | 51 | Reading K-12 | 61 | Foreign/World Lang K-12 |
| 42 | Science K-12 | 52 | Reading Elem | 62 | Foreign/World Lang Elem |
| 43 | Science Elem | 53 | Reading Sec | 63 | Foreign/World Lang Sec |
| 44 | Science Sec | 54 | Remedial Reading K-12 | 64 | Religious Education K-12 |
| 45 | Math K-12 | 55 | Remedial Reading Elem | 65 | Religious Education Elem |
| 46 | Math Elem | 56 | Remedial Reading Sec | 66 | Religious Education Sec |
| 47 | Math Sec | 57 | Bilingual/ELL | 67 | School Board President |
| 48 | English/Lang Arts K-12 | 58 | Special Education K-12 | 68 | Teacher Personnel |

| | |
|---|---|
| 69 | Academic Assessment |
| 70 | Research/Development |
| 71 | Public Information |
| 72 | Summer School |
| 73 | Instructional Tech |
| 74 | Inservice Training |
| 75 | Marketing/Distributive |
| 76 | Info Systems |
| 77 | Psychological Assess |
| 78 | Affirmative Action |

| | | | | | |
|---|---|---|---|---|---|
| Dr Johnny T Clark Jr Elem Sch<br>6033 N Highway 146, Baytown 77523<br>Kemberly Scheidt | PK-5 | | 704 | | 281/420-7450 |
| George H Gentry Jr High Sch<br>1919 E Archer Rd, Baytown 77521<br>Kathryn Holland | 6-8 | TV | 1,117<br>47 | 55% | 281/420-4590<br>Fax 281/420-4909 |
| George W Carver Elem Sch<br>600 S Pruett St, Baytown 77520<br>Angela Mancini | PK-5 | T | 609<br>50 | 89% | 281/420-4600<br>Fax 281/420-4983 |
| Goose Creek Memorial High Sch<br>6001 E Wallisville Rd, Baytown 77521<br>Susan Jackson | 9-12 | T | 2,088 | 54% | 281/421-4400<br>Fax 281/421-4444 |
| Harlem Elem Sch<br>3333 I-10, Baytown 77521<br>Betty Baca | PK-5 | T | 580<br>75 | 89% | 281/420-4910<br>Fax 281/426-5358 |
| Highlands Elem Sch<br>200 E Wallisville Rd, Highlands 77562<br>Blanca Capetillo | 2-5 | T | 832<br>42 | 72% | 281/420-4900<br>Fax 281/426-5099 |
| Highlands Junior High Sch<br>1212 E Wallisville Rd, Highlands 77562<br>Gary Guy | 6-8 | TV | 1,185<br>33 | 62% | 281/420-4695<br>Fax 281/426-4301 t |
| Horace Mann Junior High Sch<br>310 S Highway 146, Baytown 77520<br>Christie Speights | 6-8 | TV | 990 | 85% | 281/420-4585<br>Fax 281/420-4664 |
| Impact Early College High Sch<br>1415 Market St, Baytown 77520<br>Laura Reyes | 9-12 | | 402 | | 281/420-4802<br>Fax 832/556-5781 |
| James Bowie Elem Sch<br>2200 Clayton Dr, Baytown 77520<br>Regina Patrick-Sims | PK-5 | T | 764<br>37 | 75% | 281/420-4605<br>Fax 281/420-4609 |
| John M Stuart Career Tech HS<br>302 W Wye Dr, Baytown 77521<br>Dr Cap Roder | Voc | | 450<br>16 | | 281/420-4550<br>Fax 281/420-4553 |
| Lorenzo De Zavala Elem Sch<br>305 Tri City Beach Rd, Baytown 77520<br>**Bart Cobb** | PK-5 | T | 752<br>46 | 81% | 281/420-4920<br>Fax 281/420-4342 |
| Miraibeau B Lamar Elem Sch<br>816 N Pruett St, Baytown 77520<br>Maria Rosas Gonzalez | PK-5 | T | 672<br>75 | 86% | 281/420-4625<br>Fax 281/420-4626 |
| Ⓐ Peter E Hyland Center<br>1906 Decker Dr, Baytown 77520<br>Michelle Verdun | 9-12 | T | 150<br>11 | 70% | 281/420-4555<br>Fax 281/420-4629 |
| Ⓐ Point Alternative Center<br>401 Jones Rd, Highlands 77562<br>Tricia Times | 6-12 | | 75 | | 281/420-4630<br>Fax 281/420-2680 |
| Robert E Lee High Sch<br>1809 Market St, Baytown 77520<br>Joseph Farnsworth | 9-12 | TV | 1,757 | 78% | 281/420-4535<br>Fax 281/420-4548 |
| Ross S Sterling High Sch<br>300 W Baker Rd, Baytown 77521<br>Nathan Chaddick | 9-12 | TV | 2,233 | 58% | 281/420-4500<br>Fax 281/420-4974 |
| San Jacinto Elem Sch<br>2615 Virginia St, Baytown 77520<br>Rachel McAdam | PK-5 | T | 443<br>35 | 85% | 281/420-4670<br>Fax 281/420-4599 |
| Stephen F Austin Elem Sch<br>3022 Massey Tompkins Rd, Baytown 77521<br>Michelle Duhon | PK-5 | T | 723<br>44 | 60% | 281/420-4620<br>Fax 281/420-4899 |
| Victoria Walker Elem Sch<br>4711 Seabird St, Baytown 77521<br>Monica Juarez | PK-5 | T | 849 | 51% | 281/421-1800<br>Fax 281/421-3489 |
| William B Travis Elem Sch<br>100 Robin Rd, Baytown 77520<br>Adrienne Tessar | PK-5 | T | 807<br>44 | 70% | 281/420-4660<br>Fax 281/420-4986 |

## ● Houston Ind School Dist   PID: 01023770

4400 W 18th St, Houston 77092

713/556-6000
Fax 713/556-6323

**Schools:** 276 \ **Teachers:** 11,967 \ **Students:** 207,809 \
**Special Ed Students:** 15,792 \ **LEP Students:** 59,917 \ **College-Bound:** 75% \ **Ethnic:** Asian 4%, African American 24%, Hispanic 63%, Caucasian 9% \ **Exp:** $245 (Med) \ **Poverty:** 30% \ **Title I:** $143,675,881 \
**Special Education:** $37,903,000 \ **Bilingual Education:** $215,000 \
**Open-Close:** 09/08 - 06/11 \ **DTBP:** $198 (High) \ f t

| | | | |
|---|---|---|---|
| Dr Grenita Lathan | 1 | Sherrie Robinson | 2 |
| Timothy Momanyi | 2 | Alishia Jolivette | 3 |
| Betti Wiggins | 4 | John Wilcots | 5 |
| Andre Walker | 6 | Lisa Jones | 7 |
| Margarita Gardea | 9 | Dr Montra Rogers | 10 |
| Pamela Evans | 11,296 | Wanda Thomas | 11 |
| Anna White | 15,57,271 | Dr Kennith Davis | 15,78 |
| Dr Lachlin Verrett | 15,58 | Kallie Benes | 16 |
| Eugene Salzar | 17 | Yolanda Rodriguez | 18 |
| Glenn Reed | 19 | Wenden Sanders | 20,23 |
| Marisol Castruita | 34 | Felecia Caeser-White | 35 |
| Glenda Calloway | 36,79 | Denise Carter | 40 |
| Jamie Filipow | 41 | Donelle Williams | 43 |
| Dr Hortense Campbell | 44 | Nalsy Perez | 46 |
| Alyssa Howell | 47 | Marisa Hartling | 53 |
| Jessica Chevalier | 57,280 | Stephen Winton | 57 |
| Gabi Frunza-Tanca | 61 | Sue Deigaard | 67 |
| Julia Dimmitt | 68 | James Metoyer | 69 |
| Rebecca Suarez | 71 | Adrian Acosta | 73 |
| Felicia Adams | 73 | Anetta Modest | 74 |
| Tia Lockesimmons | 81 | Pedro Lopez | 91 |
| Justin Fuenties | 92 | Scott Gilhousen | 98 |
| Magda Galindo | 271 | Jonnelle Hollins | 274 |
| Rene Flores | 285 | Dr Allison Matney | 294 |
| Angela Brooks | 298 | Rick Cruz | 750 |
| Silvia Trinh | 751 | Dr Roberta Scott | 752 |

## ● Houston ISD-Achieve 180   PID: 12310958

400 W 18th St, Houston 77008

713/556-7102

Nicole Moore Morrison ......................... 15

| Public Schs..Principal | Grd | Prgm | Enr/#Cls | SN |
|---|---|---|---|---|
| A G Hilliard Elem Sch<br>8115 E Houston Rd, Houston 77028<br>Erika Kimble | PK-5 | T | 531<br>30 | 98% 713/635-3085<br>Fax 713/635-7905 |
| Ⓜ Attucks Middle Sch<br>4330 Bellfort St, Houston 77051<br>Shani Wyllie | 6-8 | TV | 464<br>50 | 90% 713/732-3670<br>Fax 713/732-3677 |
| Ⓜ B T Washington High Sch<br>4204 Yale St, Houston 77018<br>Carlos Phillips | 9-12 | TV | 758 | 95% 713/696-6600<br>Fax 713/696-6657 |
| Blackshear Elem Sch<br>2900 Holman St, Houston 77004<br>Alicia Lewis | PK-5 | T | 418<br>35 | 100% 713/942-1481<br>Fax 713/942-1486 f |
| Blanche K Bruce Elem Sch<br>510 Jensen Dr, Houston 77020<br>Dr Shawn Nickerson | PK-5 | T | 495<br>30 | 98% 713/226-4560<br>Fax 713/226-4562 |
| Cullen Middle Sch<br>6900 Scott St, Houston 77021<br>Jacqueline Thompson | 6-8 | TV | 352<br>52 | 97% 713/746-8180<br>Fax 713/746-8181 |
| Deady Middle Sch<br>2500 Broadway St, Houston 77012<br>Opal Harrison | 6-8 | TV | 669 | 95% 713/845-7411<br>Fax 713/649-5645 |
| Dogan Elem Sch<br>4202 Liberty Rd, Houston 77026<br>Margarita Tovar | PK-5 | T | 607<br>35 | 100% 713/671-4110<br>Fax 713/671-4114 |

TX—193

| | | | | | | |
|---|---|---|---|---|---|---|
| Foerster Elem Sch<br>14200 Fonmeadow Dr, Houston 77035<br>Dr Latreia Woodard | PK-5 | T | 723<br>44 | 99% | 713/726-3604<br>Fax 713/726-3629 | |
| Fondren Elem Sch<br>12405 Carlsbad St, Houston 77085<br>**Edgar Contreras** | PK-5 | T | 314<br>30 | 97% | 713/726-3611<br>Fax 713/726-2252 | |
| Forest Brook Middle Sch<br>7525 Tidwell Rd, Houston 77016<br>Tannisha Gentry \ **Ashley Jenkins** | 6-8 | T | 828 | 99% | 713/631-7720<br>Fax 713/636-4114 | |
| Gregory-Lincoln Education Ctr<br>1101 Taft St, Houston 77019<br>Angel Wilson | PK-8 | AT | 740<br>30 | 88% | 713/942-1400<br>Fax 713/942-1406 | |
| High School Ahead Acad MS<br>5320 Yale St, Houston 77091<br>Ericka Austin | 6-8 | T | 205 | 99% | 713/696-2643<br>Fax 713/696-2999 | |
| © Highland Heights Elem Sch<br>865 Paul Quinn St, Houston 77091<br>John Flowers | PK-5 | T | 517<br>25 | 96% | 713/696-2920<br>Fax 713/696-2922 | |
| Holland Middle Sch<br>1600 Gellhorn Dr, Houston 77029<br>Pablo Resendiz | 6-8 | T | 673 | 89% | 713/671-3860<br>Fax 713/671-3874 | |
| James Butler Bonham Elem Sch<br>8302 Braes River Dr, Houston 77074<br>Erica Tran | PK-5 | T | 946<br>70 | 98% | 713/778-3480<br>Fax 713/778-3482 | |
| ⓦ Kashmere High Sch<br>6900 Wileyvale Rd, Houston 77028<br>Reginald Bush | 9-12 | GTV | 777 | 98% | 713/636-6400<br>Fax 713/636-6433 | |
| L L Pugh Elem Sch<br>1147 Kress St, Houston 77020<br>Jorge Ortiz | PK-5 | T | 390<br>18 | 95% | 713/671-3820<br>Fax 713/671-3825 | |
| Lawson Middle Sch<br>14000 Stancliff St, Houston 77045<br>**Keoshya Dunn** | 6-8 | TV | 1,210<br>70 | 96% | 713/434-5600<br>Fax 713/434-5608 | |
| © Liberty High Sch<br>8330 Triola Ln, Houston 77036<br>Monico Rivas | 11-12 | | 361 | | 713/458-5555<br>Fax 713/458-5567 | |
| Looscan Elem Sch<br>3800 Robertson St, Houston 77009<br>Alvaro Montelongo | PK-5 | T | 326<br>21 | 96% | 713/696-2760<br>Fax 713/696-2765 | |
| © M C Williams Middle Sch<br>6100 Knox St, Houston 77091<br>Roshanda Griffin | 6-8 | TV | 496 | 99% | 713/696-2600<br>Fax 713/696-2604 | |
| © Mabel B Wesley Elem Sch<br>800 Dillard St, Houston 77091<br>Thomas Cotter | PK-5 | T | 344<br>40 | 100% | 713/696-2860<br>Fax 713/696-2866 | |
| Mading Elem Sch<br>8511 Crestmont St, Houston 77033<br>**Angela Gaddis** \ **Tabitha Dudley** | PK-5 | T | 433<br>27 | 94% | 713/732-3560<br>Fax 713/732-3563 | |
| Madison High Sch<br>13719 White Heather Dr, Houston 77045<br>Carlotta Brown | 9-12 | TV | 1,736<br>80 | 77% | 713/433-9801<br>Fax 713/434-5242 | |
| Montgomery Elem Sch<br>4000 Simsbrook Dr, Houston 77045<br>Dr Faye McNeil | PK-5 | T | 551<br>45 | 88% | 713/434-5640<br>Fax 713/434-5643 | |
| North Forest High Sch<br>10726 Mesa Dr, Houston 77078<br>Connie Smith | 9-12 | TV | 993 | 92% | 713/636-4300<br>Fax 713/636-8116 | |
| Patrick Henry Middle Sch<br>10702 E Hardy Rd, Houston 77093<br>Jason Davila | 6-8 | TV | 829<br>72 | 93% | 713/696-2650<br>Fax 713/696-2657 | |
| Sharpstown High Sch<br>7504 Bissonnet St, Houston 77074<br>Daniel De Leon | 9-12 | TV | 1,689 | 95% | 713/771-7215<br>Fax 713/773-6103 | |
| Stevens Elem Sch<br>1910 La Monte Ln, Houston 77018<br>Erin Trent | PK-5 | T | 648<br>40 | 100% | 713/613-2546<br>Fax 713/613-2541 | |

| | | | | | | |
|---|---|---|---|---|---|---|
| Sugar Grove Academy<br>8405 Bonhomme Rd, Houston 77074<br>Orlando Reyna | 6-8 | T | 678<br>40 | 97% | 713/271-0214<br>Fax 713/771-9342 | |
| © Texas Connections Academy [190]<br>10550 Richmond Ave Ste 140, Houston 77042<br>**Benjamin Chaplin** \ **Brita Lindsey** | 3-12 | T | 5,680 | 40% | 281/661-8293<br>Fax 713/780-2487 | |
| Wheatley High Sch<br>4801 Providence St, Houston 77020<br>Joseph Williams | 9-12 | TV | 873<br>70 | 94% | 713/671-3900<br>Fax 713/671-3951 | |
| Woodson PK-5 Sch<br>10720 Southview St, Houston 77047<br>**Gina Wilkins** | PK-5 | T | 643<br>200 | 100% | 713/732-3600<br>Fax 713/732-3606 | |
| ⓦ Worthing High Sch<br>9215 Scott St, Houston 77051<br>**Everett Hare** | 9-12 | TV | 781<br>67 | 100% | 713/733-3433<br>Fax 713/731-5537 | |
| ⓦ Yates High Sch<br>3650 Alabama St, Houston 77004<br>**Tiffany Guillory** | 9-12 | TV | 874<br>80 | 82% | 713/748-5400<br>Fax 713/746-8206 | |
| © Young Scholars Acad Excellence<br>1809 Louisiana St, Houston 77002<br>Anella Coleman | PK-8 | T | 129<br>15 | 86% | 713/654-1400<br>Fax 713/654-1401 | |

● **Houston ISD-East Area** PID: 12170253     713/556-8998
4400 W 18th St, Houston 77092

Geovanny Ponce ..................................... 15

| Public Schs..Principal | Grd | Prgm | Enr/#Cls | SN | |
|---|---|---|---|---|---|
| Austin High Sch<br>1700 Dumble St, Houston 77023<br>Steve Guerrero | 9-12 | TV | 1,685 | 93% | 713/924-1600<br>Fax 713/923-3157 |
| Bonner Elem Sch<br>8100 Elrod St, Houston 77017<br>Klinger Casquete | PK-5 | T | 790<br>55 | 96% | 713/943-5740<br>Fax 713/943-5741 |
| Briscoe Elem Sch<br>321 Forest Hill Blvd, Houston 77011<br>Daniel Hernandez | PK-5 | T | 262<br>43 | 93% | 713/924-1740<br>Fax 713/924-1742 |
| Burnet Elem Sch<br>5403 Canal St, Houston 77011<br>Ana Cantu | PK-5 | T | 486<br>40 | 95% | 713/924-1780<br>Fax 713/924-1783 |
| © Cage Charter Elem Sch<br>4528 Leeland St, Houston 77023<br>Dr Lisa Patenotte | PK-5 | T | 520<br>40 | 86% | 713/924-1700<br>Fax 713/924-1704 |
| Carrillo Elem Sch<br>960 S Wayside Dr, Houston 77023<br>Mary Hallinan | PK-5 | T | 492<br>40 | 83% | 713/924-1870<br>Fax 713/924-1873 |
| Charles H Milby High Sch<br>1601 Broadway St, Houston 77012<br>Ruth Ruiz | 9-12 | GTV | 1,903 | 93% | 713/928-7401<br>Fax 713/928-7474 |
| Chavez High Sch<br>8501 Howard Dr, Houston 77017<br>Luis Landa | 9-12 | TV | 2,882 | 87% | 713/495-6950<br>Fax 713/495-6988 |
| ⓦ Crespo Elem Sch<br>7500 Office City Dr, Houston 77012<br>Mayra Ramon | PK-5 | T | 766<br>40 | 96% | 713/845-7492<br>Fax 713/847-4716 |
| Davila Elem Sch<br>7610 Dahlia St, Houston 77012<br>**Avisay Cerda** | PK-5 | T | 403<br>52 | 94% | 713/924-1851<br>Fax 713/924-1853 |
| De Zavala Elem Sch<br>7521 Avenue H, Houston 77012<br>Victoria Martinez | PK-5 | T | 542<br>36 | 91% | 713/924-1888<br>Fax 713/924-1891 |
| East Early College High Sch<br>220 N Milby St, Houston 77003<br>Stephanie Square | 9-12 | T | 476 | 88% | 713/847-4809<br>Fax 713/847-4813 |
| © Eastwood Academy<br>1315 Dumble St, Houston 77023<br>Brandi Lira | 9-12 | T | 432<br>14 | 76% | 713/924-1697<br>Fax 713/924-1715 |

| | | | | | |
|---|---|---|---|---|---|
| 1 | Superintendent | 8 | Curric/Instruct K-12 | 19 | Chief Financial Officer |
| 2 | Bus/Finance/Purchasing | 9 | Curric/Instruct Elem | 20 | Art K-12 |
| 3 | Buildings And Grounds | 10 | Curric/Instruct Sec | 21 | Art Elem |
| 4 | Food Service | 11 | Federal Program | 22 | Art Sec |
| 5 | Transportation | 12 | Title I | 23 | Music K-12 |
| 6 | Athletic | 13 | Title V | 24 | Music Elem |
| 7 | Health Services | 15 | Asst Superintendent | 25 | Music Sec |
| | | 16 | Instructional Media Svcs | 26 | Business Education |
| | | 17 | Chief Operations Officer | 27 | Career & Tech Ed |
| | | 18 | Chief Academic Officer | 28 | Technology Education |

| | | | | | | | | |
|---|---|---|---|---|---|---|---|---|
| 29 | Family/Consumer Science | 39 | Social Studies K-12 | 49 | English/Lang Arts Elem | 59 | Special Education Elem | 69 | Academic Assessment |
| 30 | Adult Education | 40 | Social Studies Elem | 50 | English/Lang Arts Sec | 60 | Special Education Sec | 70 | Research/Development |
| 31 | Career/Sch-to-Work K-12 | 41 | Social Studies Sec | 51 | Reading K-12 | 61 | Foreign/World Lang K-12 | 71 | Public Information |
| 32 | Career/Sch-to-Work Elem | 42 | Science K-12 | 52 | Reading Elem | 62 | Foreign/World Lang Elem | 72 | Summer School |
| 33 | Career/Sch-to-Work Sec | 43 | Science Elem | 53 | Reading Sec | 63 | Foreign/World Lang Sec | 73 | Instructional Tech |
| 34 | Early Childhood Ed | 44 | Science Sec | 54 | Remedial Reading K-12 | 64 | Religious Education K-12 | 74 | Inservice Training |
| 35 | Health/Phys Education | 45 | Math K-12 | 55 | Remedial Reading Elem | 65 | Religious Education Elem | 75 | Marketing/Distributive |
| 36 | Guidance Services K-12 | 46 | Math Elem | 56 | Remedial Reading Sec | 66 | Religious Education Sec | 76 | Info Systems |
| 37 | Guidance Services Elem | 47 | Math Sec | 57 | Bilingual/ELL | 67 | School Board President | 77 | Psychological Assess |
| 38 | Guidance Services Sec | 48 | English/Lang Arts K-12 | 58 | Special Education K-12 | 68 | Teacher Personnel | 78 | Affirmative Action |

| School | Grd | Prgm | Enr/#Cls | SN | Phone |
|---|---|---|---|---|---|
| Edison Middle Sch<br>6901 Avenue I, Houston 77011<br>Karina Lopez | 6-8 | TV | 654<br>33 | 97% | 713/924-1800<br>Fax 713/924-1316 |
| Franklin Elem Sch<br>7101 Canal St, Houston 77011<br>Tammie Moran | PK-5 | T | 431<br>50 | 99% | 713/924-1820<br>Fax 713/924-1823 |
| Furr High Sch<br>520 Mercury Dr, Houston 77013<br>Steven Stapleton | 9-12 | TV | 1,035<br>55 | 94% | 713/675-1118<br>Fax 713/671-3612 🇹 |
| Gallegos Elem Sch<br>7415 Harrisburg Blvd, Houston 77011<br>**Norma Gonzalez** | PK-5 | T | 357<br>35 | 98% | 713/924-1830<br>Fax 713/924-1833 🇹 |
| Ⓐ High School for Law & Justice<br>Ⓜ 3505 Coyle St, Houston 77003<br>Stacy Garcia | 9-12 | T | 469<br>49 | 83% | 713/867-5100<br>Fax 713/802-4600 |
| J Henderson Elem Sch<br>1800 Dismuke St, Houston 77023<br>Maria Guerra | PK-5 | T | 783<br>45 | 98% | 713/924-1730<br>Fax 713/924-1735 |
| J R Harris Elem Sch<br>801 Broadway St, Houston 77012<br>**Jessica Rivero** | PK-5 | T | 411<br>37 | 100% | 713/924-1860<br>Fax 713/924-1863 |
| Judson Robinson Elem Sch<br>12425 Wood Forest Dr, Houston 77013<br>Ana Aguilar | PK-5 | T | 521 | 97% | 713/450-7108<br>Fax 713/450-7129 |
| Lantrip Elem Sch<br>100 Telephone Rd, Houston 77023<br>Magdalena Strickland | PK-5 | T | 720<br>45 | 77% | 713/924-1670<br>Fax 713/924-1672 |
| Laurenzo ECC<br>205 N Delmar St, Houston 77011<br>**Janet Benavides** | PK-K | T | 344<br>14 | 100% | 713/924-0350<br>Fax 713/924-0390 🇫🇹 |
| Lewis Elem Sch<br>6745 Tipperary Ln, Houston 77061<br>Jorge Rodriguez | 1-5 | T | 791<br>45 | 98% | 713/845-7453<br>Fax 713/847-4711 |
| Ⓐ Middle College at HCC Fraga<br>301 N Drennan St, Houston 77003<br>Jose Santos | 9-12 | T | 128 | 86% | 713/228-3408<br>Fax 713/228-3418 |
| Ⓐ Middle College at HCC Gulfton<br>5407 Gulfton St Ste 219, Houston 77081<br>Holly Gibson | 9-12 | T | 162 | 98% | 713/662-2551<br>Fax 713/662-2572 |
| Ⓐ Mount Carmel Academy<br>Ⓒ 7155 Ashburn St, Houston 77061<br>Maureen Giacchino | 9-12 | T | 340 | 72% | 713/643-2008<br>Fax 713/645-0078 |
| Navarro Mid Sch<br>5100 Polk St, Houston 77023<br>**Emeterio Cruz** | 6-8 | TV | 682 | 96% | 713/924-1760<br>Fax 713/924-1768 |
| Oates Elem Sch<br>10044 Wallisville Rd, Houston 77013<br>Melissa Melchor | PK-5 | T | 386<br>22 | 100% | 713/671-3800<br>Fax 713/671-3803 |
| Ortiz Middle Sch<br>6767 Telephone Rd, Houston 77061<br>Marlen Martinez | 6-8 | T | 1,067 | 96% | 713/845-5650<br>Fax 713/845-5646 |
| Park Place Elem Sch<br>8235 Park Place Blvd, Houston 77017<br>**Nimmi Thomas** | PK-5 | T | 951<br>45 | 94% | 713/845-7458<br>Fax 713/845-7460 |
| Patterson Elem Sch<br>5302 Allendale Rd, Houston 77017<br>**Luis Saenz** | PK-5 | T | 931<br>55 | 90% | 713/943-5750<br>Fax 713/943-5755 |
| Pleasantville Elem Sch<br>1431 Gellhorn Dr, Houston 77029<br>**Samyra Rogers** | PK-5 | T | 266<br>31 | 94% | 713/671-3840<br>Fax 713/671-3844 |
| Port Houston Elem Sch<br>1800 McCarty St, Houston 77029<br>Victor Garcia | PK-5 | T | 292<br>18 | 97% | 713/671-3890<br>Fax 713/671-3893 |
| Project Chrysalis Middle Sch<br>4528 Leeland St, Houston 77023<br>**Lisa Rodriguez** | 6-8 | T | 279 | 77% | 713/924-1700<br>Fax 713/924-1704 |
| R P Harris Elem Sch<br>1262 Mae Dr, Houston 77015<br>Erica Avie | PK-5 | T | 569 | 100% | 713/450-7100<br>Fax 713/450-7103 |
| Rucker Elem Sch<br>5201 Vinett Ave, Houston 77017<br>Eileen Puente | PK-5 | T | 428<br>50 | 94% | 713/845-7467<br>Fax 713/845-5083 |
| Sanchez Elem Sch<br>2700 Berkley St, Houston 77012<br>**Ricardo Mena** | PK-5 | T | 581<br>50 | 99% | 713/845-7472<br>Fax 713/847-4755 🇫 |
| Southmayd Elem Sch<br>1800 Coral St, Houston 77012<br>Sandra Cisneros | PK-5 | T | 581<br>32 | 94% | 713/924-1720<br>Fax 713/924-1722 |
| Tijerina Elem Sch<br>6501 Sherman St, Houston 77011<br>**Alesander Olaizola** | PK-5 | T | 342<br>45 | 95% | 713/924-1790<br>Fax 713/924-1792 🇫 |
| W I Stevenson Middle Sch<br>9595 Winkler Dr, Houston 77017<br>Christyn McCloskey | 6-8 | T | 1,446<br>80 | 90% | 713/943-5700<br>Fax 713/943-5711 |
| Whittier Elem Sch<br>10511 La Crosse St, Houston 77029<br>Lori Lueptow | PK-5 | T | 526<br>38 | 98% | 713/671-3810<br>Fax 713/671-3812 |

• **Houston ISD-North Area** PID: 12170239   713/556-8998
4400 W 18th St, Houston 77092

Staci Taylor ............................................. 15

| Public Schs..Principal | Grd | Prgm | Enr/#Cls | SN | |
|---|---|---|---|---|---|
| Atherton Elem Sch<br>2011 Solo St, Houston 77020<br>Albert Lemons | PK-6 | T | 585<br>28 | 100% | 713/671-4100<br>Fax 713/671-4526 |
| Barrick Elem Sch<br>12001 Winfrey Ln, Houston 77076<br>Yolanda Garrido | PK-5 | T | 657<br>38 | 94% | 281/405-2500<br>Fax 281/405-2502 |
| Berry Elem Sch<br>2310 Berry Rd, Houston 77093<br>Philip Steuernagel | PK-5 | T | 799<br>27 | 100% | 713/696-2700<br>Fax 713/696-2701 |
| Burbank Elem Sch<br>216 Tidwell Rd, Houston 77022<br>**Heather Luebbers** | PK-5 | T | 912<br>40 | 96% | 713/696-2690<br>Fax 713/696-2691 |
| Burbank Middle Sch<br>315 Berry Rd, Houston 77022<br>David Knittle | 6-8 | TV | 1,464<br>85 | 96% | 713/696-2720<br>Fax 713/696-2723 |
| Burrus Elem Sch<br>701 E 33rd St, Houston 77022<br>Jessie Woods | PK-5 | T | 454<br>45 | 95% | 713/867-5180<br>Fax 713/867-5182 |
| Codwell Elem Sch<br>5225 Tavenor Ln, Houston 77048<br>Kristy Love | PK-5 | T | 410<br>40 | 91% | 713/732-3580<br>Fax 713/732-3582 |
| Cook Jr Elem Sch<br>7115 Lockwood Dr, Houston 77016<br>**Shundra Harris-Mosley** | PK-5 | T | 625<br>10 | 100% | 713/636-6040<br>Fax 713/636-6088 |
| Coop Elem Sch<br>10130 Aldine Westfield Rd, Houston 77093<br>Tudon Martinez | PK-5 | T | 736<br>47 | 98% | 713/696-2630<br>Fax 713/696-2633 |
| De Chaumes Elem Sch<br>155 Cooper Rd, Houston 77076<br>Enedith Silerio | PK-5 | T | 841<br>36 | 99% | 713/696-2676<br>Fax 713/696-2680 |
| Durkee Elem Sch<br>7301 Nordling Rd, Houston 77076<br>Alicia Puente-Sanchez | PK-5 | T | 574<br>58 | 97% | 713/696-2835<br>Fax 713/696-2837 |
| Eliot Elem Sch<br>6411 Laredo St, Houston 77020<br>**Matthew Schwer \ Zandra Aguilar** | PK-5 | T | 605<br>44 | 96% | 713/671-3670<br>Fax 713/671-3676 |
| Elmore Elem Sch<br>8200 Tate St, Houston 77028<br>Joyce Fugit | PK-5 | T | 588 | 98% | 713/672-7466<br>Fax 713/671-3565 |

| | | | | | |
|---|---|---|---|---|---|
| Farias Early Childhood Center<br>515 E Rittenhouse St, Houston 77076<br>Maria Solis | PK-PK | T | 434<br>20 | 100% 713/691-8730<br>Fax 713/691-8746 | |
| Fleming Middle Sch<br>4910 Collingsworth St, Houston 77026<br>Yolanda Bruce | 6-8 | TV | 486<br>48 | 95% 713/671-4170<br>Fax 713/671-4176 | |
| Fonville Middle Sch<br>725 E Little York Rd, Houston 77076<br>Irma Sandate | 6-8 | TV | 808<br>60 | 88% 713/696-2825<br>Fax 713/696-2829 | |
| Fonwood Early Childhood Center<br>9709 Mesa Dr, Houston 77078<br>Christina Jordan | PK-K | T | 555 | 99% 713/633-0781<br>Fax 713/636-7940 | |
| Garcia Elem Sch<br>9550 Aldine Westfield Rd, Houston 77093<br>Linda Bellard | PK-5 | T | 593<br>45 | 100% 713/696-2900<br>Fax 713/696-2904 | |
| ⓐ Harper Daep Sch<br>4425 N Shepherd Dr, Houston 77018<br>Raymond Glass | 6-12 | V | 14<br>35 | 57% 713/802-4760<br>Fax 281/986-6475 | |
| Herrera Elem Sch<br>525 Bennington St, Houston 77022<br>Christopher Carnes | PK-5 | T | 888<br>40 | 99% 713/696-2800<br>Fax 713/696-2804 | |
| Janowski Elem Sch<br>7500 Bauman Rd, Houston 77022<br>Myrna Bazan | PK-5 | T | 550<br>50 | 95% 713/696-2844<br>Fax 713/696-2847 | |
| Joe E Moreno Elem Sch<br>620 E Canino Rd, Houston 77037<br>Adriana Castro | PK-5 | T | 752 | 100% 281/405-2150<br>Fax 281/405-2176 | |
| Kashmere Gardens Elem Sch<br>4901 Lockwood Dr, Houston 77026<br>Marques Collins | PK-5 | T | 391<br>28 | 99% 713/671-4160<br>Fax 713/671-4163 | |
| Kennedy Elem Sch<br>400 Victoria Dr, Houston 77022<br>Haydee Cavazos | PK-5 | T | 702<br>25 | 98% 713/696-2686<br>Fax 713/696-2689 | |
| ⓜ Key Middle Sch<br>4000 Kelley St, Houston 77026<br>Erika Carter | 6-8 | T | 688 | 93% 713/636-6000<br>Fax 713/636-6008 | |
| Lyons Elem Sch<br>800 Roxella St, Houston 77076<br>Olivia Casares | PK-5 | T | 1,002<br>35 | 93% 713/696-2870<br>Fax 713/696-2877 | |
| Marshall Elem Sch<br>6200 Winfield Rd, Houston 77050<br>Lauren Price | PK-5 | T | 944<br>34 | 98% 281/636-4606<br>Fax 281/986-6475 | |
| McGowen Elem Sch<br>6820 Homestead Rd, Houston 77028<br>Jeffrey Whitaker \ **Jessie Woods** | PK-5 | T | 452<br>25 | 98% 713/636-6979<br>Fax 713/636-6983 | |
| McReynolds Middle Sch<br>5910 Market St, Houston 77020<br>Jasmine Giron \ **Philip Steuernagel** | 6-8 | TV | 595<br>40 | 100% 713/671-3650<br>Fax 713/671-3657 | |
| ⓜ Mickey Leland Clg Prep for Men<br>1700 Gregg St, Houston 77020<br>Dameion Crook | 6-12 | T | 501 | 61% 713/226-2668<br>Fax 713/266-4923 | |
| N Q Henderson Elem Sch<br>701 Solo St, Houston 77020<br>Alana Holloway | PK-5 | T | 321<br>38 | 100% 713/671-4195<br>Fax 713/671-4197 | |
| Northline Elem Sch<br>821 E Witcher Ln, Houston 77076<br>Mario Sandoval | PK-5 | T | 560<br>44 | 99% 713/696-2890<br>Fax 713/696-2894 | |
| ⓒ Osborne Elem Sch<br>800 Ringold St, Houston 77088<br>**Mikia Barnes** | PK-5 | T | 407<br>30 | 99% 281/405-2525<br>Fax 281/405-2528 | |
| Paige Elem Sch<br>7501 Curry Rd, Houston 77093<br>Iliana Perez | PK-5 | T | 462<br>35 | 99% 713/696-2855<br>Fax 713/696-2858 | |
| R L Isaacs Elem Sch<br>3830 Pickfair St, Houston 77026<br>Lajuana Armstrong | PK-5 | T | 304<br>19 | 98% 713/671-4120<br>Fax 713/671-4122 | |

| | | | | | |
|---|---|---|---|---|---|
| Raul C Martinez Elem Sch<br>7211 Market St, Houston 77020<br>Keri Ward | PK-5 | T | 539<br>44 | 96% 713/671-3680<br>Fax 713/671-3684 | |
| Ross Elem Sch<br>2819 Bay St, Houston 77026<br>Treasure West | PK-5 | T | 372<br>28 | 95% 713/226-4550<br>Fax 713/226-4554 | |
| Scarborough Elem Sch<br>3021 Little York Rd, Houston 77093<br>Miriam Medina | PK-5 | T | 681<br>44 | 96% 713/696-2710<br>Fax 713/696-2712 | |
| Scroggins Elem Sch<br>400 Boyles St, Houston 77020<br>Dianna Balderas | PK-5 | T | 523<br>30 | 94% 713/671-4130<br>Fax 713/671-4133 | |
| Shadydale Elem Sch<br>5905 Tidwell Rd, Houston 77016<br>**Teri Hampton** | PK-5 | T | 897<br>36 | 100% 713/633-5150<br>Fax 713/636-7925 | |
| Shearn Elem Sch<br>9802 Stella Link Rd, Houston 77025<br>Mayra Romero | PK-5 | T | 603<br>25 | 94% 713/295-5236<br>Fax 713/295-5253 | |
| Sherman Elem Sch<br>1909 McKee St, Houston 77009<br>**Racquel Rosenbaum** | PK-5 | T | 570<br>15 | 94% 713/226-2627<br>Fax 713/236-8417 | |

● **Houston ISD-Northwest Area** PID: 12179974       713/556-8999
  4400 W 18th St, Houston 77092

Cesar Martinez ....................................... 15

| Public Schs..Principal | Grd | Prgm | Enr/#Cls | SN | |
|---|---|---|---|---|---|
| ⓜ Arabic Immersion Magnet Sch<br>812 W 28th St, Houston 77008<br>Mahassen Ballouli | PK-4 | T | 346 | 55% 713/556-8940<br>Fax 713/556-8944 | |
| ⓐ Barbara Jordan Career Center<br>5800 Eastex Fwy, Houston 77026<br>**John McAlpine** | 11-12 | V | 150<br>120 | 713/636-6900<br>Fax 713/636-6917 | |
| Benbrook Elem Sch<br>4026 Bolin Rd, Houston 77092<br>Dana Darden | PK-5 | T | 588<br>21 | 87% 713/613-2502<br>Fax 713/613-2281 | |
| Black Middle Sch<br>1575 Chantilly Ln, Houston 77018<br>Rhonda Honore | 6-8 | T | 1,233<br>70 | 57% 713/613-2505<br>Fax 713/613-2533 | |
| Browning Elem Sch<br>607 Northwood St, Houston 77009<br>**Annie Garcia** | PK-5 | T | 489<br>40 | 93% 713/867-5140<br>Fax 713/867-5148 | |
| ⓜ Carnegie Vanguard High Sch<br>1501 Taft St, Houston 77019<br>Ramon Moss | 9-12 | T | 808<br>20 | 31% 713/732-3690<br>Fax 713/732-3694 | |
| ⓒ Challenge Early Clg High Sch<br>5601 West Loop S, Houston 77081<br>Tonya Miller | 9-12 | T | 463 | 76% 713/664-9712<br>Fax 713/664-9780 | |
| Clemente Martinez Elem Sch<br>901 Hays St, Houston 77009<br>Alejandro Lopez | PK-5 | T | 412<br>43 | 98% 713/224-1424<br>Fax 713/224-1304 | |
| ⓐ Community Services Sch<br>1102 Telephone Rd, Houston 77023<br>Cicely Williams | PK-12 | T | 154 | 69% 713/967-5285<br>Fax 713/967-5223 | |
| ⓒ Crockett Charter Elem Sch<br>2112 Crockett St, Houston 77007<br>Priscilla Rivas | PK-5 | T | 582<br>15 | 73% 713/802-4780<br>Fax 713/802-4783 | |
| ⓐ Debakey High Sch-Health Prof<br>ⓜ 2545 Pressler St, Houston 77030<br>Agnes Perry | 9-12 | TV | 891<br>50 | 44% 713/741-2410<br>Fax 713/746-5211 | |
| ⓜ Durham Elem Sch<br>4803 Brinkman St, Houston 77018<br>Carrie Flores | PK-5 | T | 571<br>23 | 60% 713/613-2527<br>Fax 713/613-2515 | |
| Field Elem Sch<br>703 E 17th St, Houston 77008<br>John Hendrickson | PK-5 | T | 461<br>25 | 71% 713/867-5190<br>Fax 713/867-5194 | |

| | | | |
|---|---|---|---|
| 1 Superintendent | 8 Curric/Instruct K-12 | 19 Chief Financial Officer | 29 Family/Consumer Science |
| 2 Bus/Finance/Purchasing | 9 Curric/Instruct Elem | 20 Art K-12 | 30 Adult Education |
| 3 Buildings And Grounds | 10 Curric/Instruct Sec | 21 Art Elem | 31 Career/Sch-to-Work K-12 |
| 4 Food Service | 11 Federal Program | 22 Art Sec | 32 Career/Sch-to-Work Elem |
| 5 Transportation | 12 Title I | 23 Music K-12 | 33 Career/Sch-to-Work Sec |
| 6 Athletic | 13 Title V | 24 Music Elem | 34 Early Childhood Ed |
| 7 Health Services | 15 Asst Superintendent | 25 Music Sec | 35 Health/Phys Education |
| | 16 Instructional Media Svcs | 26 Business Education | 36 Guidance Services K-12 |
| | 17 Chief Operations Officer | 27 Career & Tech Ed | 37 Guidance Services Elem |
| **TX—196** | 18 Chief Academic Officer | 28 Technology Education | 38 Guidance Services Sec |

| | | | |
|---|---|---|---|
| 39 Social Studies K-12 | 49 English/Lang Arts Elem | 59 Special Education Elem | 69 Academic Assessment |
| 40 Social Studies Elem | 50 English/Lang Arts Sec | 60 Special Education Sec | 70 Research/Development |
| 41 Social Studies Sec | 51 Reading K-12 | 61 Foreign/World Lang K-12 | 71 Public Information |
| 42 Science K-12 | 52 Reading Elem | 62 Foreign/World Lang Elem | 72 Summer School |
| 43 Science Elem | 53 Reading Sec | 63 Foreign/World Lang Sec | 73 Instructional Tech |
| 44 Science Sec | 54 Remedial Reading K-12 | 64 Religious Education K-12 | 74 Inservice Training |
| 45 Math K-12 | 55 Remedial Reading Elem | 65 Religious Education Elem | 75 Marketing/Distributive |
| 46 Math Elem | 56 Remedial Reading Sec | 66 Religious Education Sec | 76 Info Systems |
| 47 Math Sec | 57 Bilingual/ELL | 67 School Board President | 77 Psychological Assess |
| 48 English/Lang Arts K-12 | 58 Special Education K-12 | 68 Teacher Personnel | 78 Affirmative Action |

| School | Grd | Prgm | Enr/#Cls | SN | Phone |
|--------|-----|------|----------|----|----|
| Garden Oaks Montessori<br>901 Sue Barnett Dr, Houston 77018<br>Lindsey Pollock | PK-8 | T | 850<br>30 | 39% | 713/696-2930<br>Fax 713/696-2932 🄵 |
| ⓜ Hamilton Middle Sch<br>139 E 20th St, Houston 77008<br>Robert Johnson | 6-8 | TV | 1,266<br>55 | 84% | 713/802-4725<br>Fax 713/802-4731 |
| ⓜ Harvard Elem Sch<br>810 Harvard St, Houston 77007<br>Laura Alaniz | PK-5 | | 656<br>27 | 16% | 713/867-5210<br>Fax 713/867-5215 |
| Heights High Sch<br>413 E 13th St, Houston 77008<br>Wendy Hampton | 9-12 | TV | 2,377<br>90 | 70% | 713/865-4400<br>Fax 713/802-4749 |
| Helms Elem Sch<br>503 W 21st St, Houston 77008<br>**Lola Perejon** | PK-5 | T | 473<br>25 | 70% | 713/867-5130<br>Fax 713/867-5133 🄵 |
| Hogg Middle Sch<br>1100 Merrill St, Houston 77009<br>Vanessa Saldana | 6-8 | TV | 984<br>90 | 51% | 713/802-4700<br>Fax 713/802-4708 🄵 🅃 |
| Houston Academy Int'l Studies<br>1810 Stuart St, Houston 77004<br>Melissa Jacobs | 9-12 | TV | 495 | 66% | 713/942-1430<br>Fax 713/942-1433 |
| Jefferson Elem Sch<br>5000 Sharman St, Houston 77009<br>Lilly Rincon | PK-5 | T | 432<br>30 | 93% | 713/696-2778<br>Fax 713/696-2784 |
| Ketelsen Elem Sch<br>600 Quitman St, Houston 77009<br>**Christina Aguirre** | PK-5 | T | 579<br>12 | 90% | 713/220-5050<br>Fax 713/220-5074 |
| ⓜ Kinder HS Perform & Visual Art<br>790 Austin St, Houston 77002<br>Dr R Scott Allen | 9-12 | | 752<br>60 | 18% | 713/942-1960<br>Fax 713/942-1968 🄵 🅃 |
| Love Elem Sch<br>1120 W 13th St, Houston 77008<br>**Eden Bass** | PK-5 | T | 377<br>19 | 86% | 713/867-0840<br>Fax 713/867-0841 |
| Marshall<br>Mid Acad of Fine Arts, Houston 77009<br>Dr Queinnise Miller | 6-8 | GTV | 794<br>70 | 97% | 713/226-2600<br>Fax 713/226-2605 |
| North Houston Early College HS<br>8001 Fulton St Bldg C, Houston 77022<br>**Samantha Brooks** | 9-12 | T | 484 | 85% | 713/696-6168<br>Fax 713/696-6172 |
| ⓜ Northside High Sch<br>1101 Quitman St, Houston 77009<br>Cecilia Gonzales | 9-12 | TV | 1,540<br>76 | 94% | 713/226-4900<br>Fax 713/226-4999 |
| ⓜ Oak Forest Elem Sch<br>1401 W 43rd St, Houston 77018<br>Andrew Casler | PK-5 | | 859<br>37 | 18% | 713/613-2536<br>Fax 713/613-2244 |
| ⓜ Rice Sch<br>7550 Seuss Dr, Houston 77025<br>Kimberly Hobbs | K-8 | T | 1,143<br>65 | 62% | 713/349-1800<br>Fax 713/349-1828 |
| ⓜ Roosevelt Elem Sch<br>6700 Fulton St, Houston 77022<br>Lisa McManus | PK-5 | T | 645<br>40 | 84% | 713/696-2820<br>Fax 713/696-2821 |
| Ruby Sue Clifton Middle Sch<br>6001 Golden Forest Dr, Houston 77092<br>Georgina Castilleja | 6-8 | T | 705 | 92% | 713/613-2516<br>Fax 713/613-2523 |
| Sam Houston Math Sci Tech HS<br>9400 Irvington Blvd, Houston 77076<br>Alan Summers | 9-12 | TV | 2,612<br>170 | 96% | 713/696-0200<br>Fax 713/696-8984 |
| Scarborough High Sch<br>4141 Costa Rica Rd, Houston 77092<br>Roderick Trevino | 9-12 | TV | 752<br>53 | 92% | 713/613-2200<br>Fax 713/613-2205 🄵 |
| Sinclair Elem Sch<br>6410 Grovewood Ln, Houston 77008<br>Lee Mashburn | PK-5 | T | 577<br>28 | 42% | 713/867-5161<br>Fax 713/867-5162 |
| Smith Elem Sch<br>4802 Chrystell Ln, Houston 77092<br>Melinda Daugherty | PK-5 | T | 862<br>45 | 100% | 713/613-2542<br>Fax 713/613-2578 |

| School | Grd | Prgm | Enr/#Cls | SN | Phone |
|--------|-----|------|----------|----|----|
| ⓜ Travis Elem Sch<br>3311 Beauchamp St, Houston 77009<br>Thomas Day | PK-5 | | 687<br>30 | 21% | 713/802-4790<br>Fax 713/802-4795 |
| Wainwright Elem Sch<br>5330 Milwee St, Houston 77092<br>**Ryan Hutchings** | PK-5 | T | 519<br>30 | 93% | 713/613-2550<br>Fax 713/613-2549 🄵 |
| Waltrip High Sch<br>1900 W 34th St, Houston 77018<br>Michael Niggli | 9-12 | TV | 1,902<br>97 | 67% | 713/688-1361<br>Fax 713/556-4297 |
| ⓜ Young Womens College Prep Acad<br>1906 Cleburne St, Houston 77004<br>April Williams | 6-12 | T | 477 | 96% | 713/942-1441<br>Fax 713/942-1448 |

● **Houston ISD-South Area**  PID: 12170241       713/556-4447
4400 W 18th St, Houston 77092

Dr Kenneth Davis ................................... 15

| Public Schs..Principal | Grd | Prgm | Enr/#Cls | SN | Phone |
|--------|-----|------|----------|----|----|
| Alcott Elem Sch<br>5859 Bellfort St, Houston 77033<br>Kim Williams | PK-5 | T | 232<br>30 | 94% | 713/732-3540<br>Fax 713/732-3542 |
| Almeda Elem Sch<br>14226 Almeda School Rd, Houston 77047<br>Gerardo Medina | PK-5 | T | 839<br>40 | 99% | 713/434-5620<br>Fax 713/434-5622 |
| Bastian Elem Sch<br>5051 Bellfort St, Houston 77033<br>**Alana Holloway** | PK-5 | T | 708<br>25 | 99% | 713/732-5830<br>Fax 713/732-5837 |
| ⓜ Baylor Clg of Medicine Acad<br>2610 Elgin St, Houston 77004<br>Tanya Edwards | 6-8 | T | 728 | 66% | 713/942-1932<br>Fax 713/942-1943 |
| Bellfort Acad Early Chldhd Ctr<br>7647 Bellfort St, Houston 77061<br>Darcele Lofton | PK-K | T | 339 | 99% | 713/640-0950<br>Fax 713/640-0957 |
| Billy Reagan K-8 Educ Ctr<br>4842 Anderson Rd, Houston 77053<br>Dr Tabitha Davis | PK-8 | T | 1,004 | 97% | 713/556-9575<br>Fax 713/556-9576 |
| Biotech Academy-Rusk<br>2805 Garrow St, Houston 77003<br>**Jesse Herrera** | 6-8 | T | 484<br>25 | 99% | 713/226-4543<br>Fax 713/226-4546 |
| Brookline Elem Sch<br>6301 South Loop E, Houston 77087<br>Rick Nagir | PK-5 | T | 897<br>56 | 100% | 713/845-7400<br>Fax 713/847-4717 🄵 🅃 |
| Cornelius Elem Sch<br>7475 Westover St, Houston 77087<br>Zaira Gomez | PK-5 | T | 867<br>58 | 92% | 713/845-7405<br>Fax 713/845-7448 |
| ⓜ Energy Institute High Sch<br>3501 Southmore Blvd, Houston 77004<br>Lori Lambropulos | 9-12 | T | 764 | 56% | 713/802-4620<br>Fax 713/556-9840 |
| Foster Elem Sch<br>3919 Ward St, Houston 77021<br>Traci Lightfoot | PK-5 | T | 436<br>21 | 99% | 713/746-8260<br>Fax 713/746-8263 |
| Frost Elem Sch<br>5002 Almeda Genoa Rd, Houston 77048<br>**Cedric Starks** | PK-5 | T | 615<br>32 | 99% | 713/732-3490<br>Fax 713/732-3497 |
| Garden Villas Elem Sch<br>7185 Santa Fe Dr, Houston 77061<br>Kimberly Thompson | PK-5 | T | 691<br>62 | 91% | 713/845-7484<br>Fax 713/645-0028 |
| Golfcrest Elem Sch<br>7414 Fairway Dr, Houston 77087<br>**Miguel Blanco** | PK-5 | T | 656<br>42 | 98% | 713/845-7425<br>Fax 713/847-4705 |
| Gregg Elem Sch<br>6701 Roxbury Rd, Houston 77087<br>David Jackson | PK-5 | T | 553<br>36 | 99% | 713/845-7432<br>Fax 713/847-4708 |
| Grissom Elem Sch<br>4900 Simsbrook Dr, Houston 77045<br>Meagan Edwards | PK-5 | T | 527<br>34 | 96% | 713/434-5660<br>Fax 713/434-5664 |

**TX—197**

| | | | | | |
|---|---|---|---|---|---|
| Hartman Middle Sch<br>7111 Westover St, Houston 77087<br>Gerrol Johnson | 6-8 | TV | 1,263<br>85 | 93% | 713/845-7435<br>Fax 713/847-4706 |
| Hartsfield Elem Sch<br>5001 Perry St, Houston 77021<br>Travis Johnson | PK-5 | T | 407<br>14 | 100% | 713/746-8280<br>Fax 713/746-8283 |
| James Deanda Elem Sch<br>7980 Almeda Genoa Rd, Houston 77075<br>Lauren Mailhiot | PK-5 | T | 685 | 94% | 713/556-9550<br>Fax 713/556-9552 |
| James R Reynolds Elem Sch<br>9601 Rosehaven Dr, Houston 77051<br>**Renesiaha Marshall** | PK-5 | T | 467<br>50 | 96% | 713/731-5590<br>Fax 713/731-5598 |
| Jean Hines-Caldwell Elem Sch<br>5515 W Orem Dr, Houston 77085<br>Juanette Green | PK-5 | T | 781<br>43 | 85% | 713/726-3700<br>Fax 713/726-3724 |
| Jones Futures Academy<br>7414 Saint LO Rd, Houston 77033<br>Nirmol Lim | 9-12 | TV | 390 | 90% | 713/733-1111<br>Fax 713/732-3450 |
| Juan N Seguin Elem Sch<br>5905 Waltrip St, Houston 77087<br>Mayte Garcia-Olivo | PK-5 | T | 544 | 96% | 713/845-5600<br>Fax 713/845-5615 |
| Kelso Elem Sch<br>5800 Southmund St, Houston 77033<br>Shanda Walker | PK-5 | T | 448<br>27 | 96% | 713/845-7451<br>Fax 713/847-4710 |
| King Early Childhood Center<br>3930 W Fuqua St, Houston 77045<br>Tremeka Collins | PK-K | | 395 | 100% | 713/797-7900<br>Fax 713/797-7904 |
| Law Elem Sch<br>12401 S Coast Dr, Houston 77047<br>Derrick Estes | PK-5 | T | 688<br>40 | 98% | 713/732-3630<br>Fax 713/732-3633 |
| Ⓜ Lockhart Elem Sch<br>3200 Rosedale St, Houston 77004<br>**Cameshia Emerson** | PK-5 | T | 589<br>23 | 100% | 713/942-1950<br>Fax 713/942-1953 |
| Mitchell Elem Sch<br>10900 Gulfdale Dr, Houston 77075<br>**Elizabeth Guajardo** | PK-5 | T | 384<br>42 | 92% | 713/991-8190<br>Fax 713/991-8193 |
| Peck Elem Sch<br>5001 Martin Luther King Blvd, Houston 77021<br>Myra Bell | PK-5 | T | 528<br>35 | 97% | 713/845-7463<br>Fax 713/847-4701 |
| Petersen Elem Sch<br>14404 Waterloo Dr, Houston 77045<br>Danitra Arredondo | PK-5 | T | 419<br>20 | 92% | 713/434-5630<br>Fax 713/434-5634<br>f |
| Ruby Thompson Elem Sch<br>6121 Tierwester St, Houston 77021<br>Erica Brame | PK-5 | T | 413<br>43 | 100% | 713/746-8250<br>Fax 713/746-8104 |
| South Early College High Sch<br>1930 Airport Blvd, Houston 77051<br>Steve Gourrier | 9-12 | T | 395<br>14 | 92% | 713/732-3623<br>Fax 713/732-3425 |
| Ⓜ Sterling Aviation High Sch<br>11625 Martindale Rd, Houston 77048<br>Sabrina Cuby | 9-12 | TV | 1,483<br>67 | 96% | 713/991-0510<br>Fax 713/991-8111 |
| Thomas Middle Sch<br>5655 Selinsky Rd, Houston 77048<br>**Nicole Haskins** | 6-8 | TV | 594 | 100% | 713/732-3500<br>Fax 713/732-3511 |
| © Tsu Charter Lab Sch<br>3100 Cleburne St, Houston 77004<br>Debbra Collins | PK-2 | T | 100 | 96% | 713/313-6754<br>Fax 713/313-6745 |
| W P Hobby Elem Sch<br>4021 Woodmont Dr, Houston 77045<br>Dimitrie Rainey | PK-5 | T | 830<br>32 | 99% | 713/434-5650<br>Fax 713/434-5652 |
| Westbury High Sch<br>11911 Chimney Rock Rd, Houston 77035<br>**Jerri Nixon** | 9-12 | TV | 2,341 | 93% | 713/723-6015<br>Fax 713/726-2165 |
| Ⓜ Whidby Elem Sch<br>7625 Springhill St, Houston 77021<br>Mimi Lam | PK-5 | T | 590<br>36 | 92% | 713/746-8170<br>Fax 713/746-8173 |

| | | | | | |
|---|---|---|---|---|---|
| Ⓜ Windsor Village Elem Sch<br>14440 Polo St, Houston 77085<br>Shantelle Louis | PK-5 | T | 757<br>40 | 90% | 713/726-3642<br>Fax 713/726-3647 |
| Young Elem Sch<br>3555 Bellfort St, Houston 77051<br>Shanica Smith | PK-5 | T | 301<br>28 | 96% | 713/732-3590<br>Fax 713/732-3592 |

● **Houston ISD-West Area**  PID: 12170265  713/556-9123
4400 W 18th St, Houston 77092

James McSwain ..................................... 15

| Public Schs..Principal | Grd | Prgm | Enr/#Cls | | SN |
|---|---|---|---|---|---|
| A A Milne Elem Sch<br>7800 Portal Dr, Houston 77071<br>**Bronchell Johnson** | PK-5 | T | 559<br>70 | 98% | 713/778-3420<br>Fax 713/778-3424 |
| © Anderson Elem Sch<br>5727 Ludington Dr, Houston 77035<br>Dr Deshonta Everett | PK-5 | T | 758<br>60 | 88% | 713/726-3600<br>Fax 713/726-3603 |
| Ashford Elem Sch<br>1815 Shannon Valley Dr, Houston 77077<br>**Kylene Vasquez** | PK-5 | T | 584<br>35 | 80% | 281/368-2120<br>Fax 713/368-2123<br>t |
| Barbara Bush Elem Sch<br>13800 Westerloch Dr, Houston 77077<br>Theresa Rose | PK-5 | | 881<br>50 | 15% | 281/368-2150<br>Fax 713/368-2153 |
| Bell Elem Sch<br>12323 Shaftsbury Dr, Houston 77031<br>Brishaun Sutton | PK-5 | T | 706<br>45 | 84% | 281/983-2800<br>Fax 281/983-2802 |
| Ⓜ Bellaire High Sch<br>5100 Maple St, Bellaire 77401<br>Michael McDonough | 9-12 | TV | 3,307 | 49% | 713/295-3704<br>Fax 713/295-3763 |
| Benavidez Elem Sch<br>6262 Gulfton St, Houston 77081<br>Dorcas Parra-Malek | PK-5 | T | 1,024<br>65 | 99% | 713/778-3350<br>Fax 713/778-3358 |
| Braeburn Elem Sch<br>7707 Rampart St, Houston 77081<br>Amanda Rodgers | PK-5 | | 638<br>55 | | 713/295-5210<br>Fax 713/295-5289 |
| Briargrove Elem Sch<br>6145 San Felipe St, Houston 77057<br>**Kelli McDonald** | PK-5 | | 881<br>45 | 35% | 713/917-3600<br>Fax 713/917-3601 |
| © Briarmeadow Charter Sch<br>3601 Dunvale Rd, Houston 77063<br>Peter Heinze | PK-8 | T | 606<br>20 | 52% | 713/458-5500<br>Fax 713/458-5506<br>t |
| Condit Elem Sch<br>7000 S 3rd St, Bellaire 77401<br>Daniel Greenberg | PK-5 | | 770<br>32 | 35% | 713/295-5255<br>Fax 713/668-5738 |
| Cunningham Elem Sch<br>5100 Gulfton St, Houston 77081<br>Karen Harris | PK-5 | T | 696<br>42 | 93% | 713/295-5223<br>Fax 713/668-6217 |
| E White Elem Sch<br>9001 Triola Ln, Houston 77036<br>Paulette Caston | PK-5 | T | 759<br>38 | 95% | 713/778-3490<br>Fax 713/778-3493 |
| Eleanor Tinsley Elem Sch<br>11035 Bob White Dr, Houston 77096<br>Mythesia Johnson | PK-5 | T | 704 | 97% | 713/778-8400<br>Fax 713/778-8405 |
| Elrod Elem Sch<br>6230 Dumfries Dr, Houston 77096<br>**Michael Hutchins** | PK-5 | T | 763<br>64 | 93% | 713/778-3330<br>Fax 713/778-3333 |
| Emerson Elem Sch<br>9533 Skyline Dr, Houston 77063<br>Alexander Rodriguez | PK-5 | T | 920<br>60 | 93% | 713/917-3630<br>Fax 713/917-3634 |
| © Energized for Excellence ECC<br>6400 Southwest Fwy, Houston 77074<br>Jose Cintron | PK-PK | T | 667 | 94% | 281/779-4411<br>Fax 713/779-4414 |
| © Energized for Excellence ES<br>6201 Bissonnet St, Houston 77081<br>Claudia Chavez-Pinto | K-5 | T | 1,682<br>56 | 98% | 713/773-3600<br>Fax 713/773-3630<br>f t |

| | | | |
|---|---|---|---|
| 1 Superintendent | 8 Curric/Instruct K-12 | 19 Chief Financial Officer | 29 Family/Consumer Science |
| 2 Bus/Finance/Purchasing | 9 Curric/Instruct Elem | 20 Art K-12 | 30 Adult Education |
| 3 Buildings And Grounds | 10 Curric/Instruct Sec | 21 Art Elem | 31 Career/Sch-to-Work K-12 |
| 4 Food Service | 11 Federal Program | 22 Art Sec | 32 Career/Sch-to-Work Elem |
| 5 Transportation | 12 Title I | 23 Music K-12 | 33 Career/Sch-to-Work Sec |
| 6 Athletic | 13 Title V | 24 Music Elem | 34 Early Childhood Ed |
| 7 Health Services | 15 Asst Superintendent | 25 Music Sec | 35 Health/Phys Education |
| | 16 Instructional Media Svcs | 26 Business Education | 36 Guidance Services K-12 |
| | 17 Chief Operations Officer | 27 Career & Tech Ed | 37 Guidance Services Elem |
| | 18 Chief Academic Officer | 28 Technology Education | 38 Guidance Services Sec |

| | | | |
|---|---|---|---|
| 39 Social Studies K-12 | 49 English/Lang Arts Elem | 59 Special Education Elem | 69 Academic Assessment |
| 40 Social Studies Elem | 50 English/Lang Arts Sec | 60 Special Education Sec | 70 Research/Development |
| 41 Social Studies Sec | 51 Reading K-12 | 61 Foreign/World Lang K-12 | 71 Public Information |
| 42 Science K-12 | 52 Reading Elem | 62 Foreign/World Lang Elem | 72 Summer School |
| 43 Science Elem | 53 Reading Sec | 63 Foreign/World Lang Sec | 73 Instructional Tech |
| 44 Science Sec | 54 Remedial Reading K-12 | 64 Religious Education K-12 | 74 Inservice Training |
| 45 Math K-12 | 55 Remedial Reading Elem | 65 Religious Education Elem | 75 Marketing/Distributive |
| 46 Math Elem | 56 Remedial Reading Sec | 66 Religious Education Sec | 76 Info Systems |
| 47 Math Sec | 57 Bilingual/ELL | 67 School Board President | 77 Psychological Assess |
| 48 English/Lang Arts K-12 | 58 Special Education K-12 | 68 Teacher Personnel | 78 Affirmative Action |

© Energized for Excellence MS | 6-8 | T | 522 | 98% 713/773-3600
6107 Bissonnet St, Houston 77081 | | | | Fax 713/773-3630
Arlene Kho

© Energized for STEM Acad Ctrl | 9-12 | | 315 | 713/641-1630
9220 Jutland Rd, Houston 77033 | | | | Fax 713/641-1669
**Shavon Clark**

© Energized for STEM Academy HS | 9-12 | T | 200 | 100% 713/641-1630
9220 Jutland Rd, Houston 77033
Shavon Clark

© Energized for STEM Academy MS | 6-8 | T | 218 | 100% 713/773-3600
7055 Beechnut St, Houston 77074 | | | | Fax 713/773-3630
**Arlene Kho**

Fondren Middle Sch | 6-8 | TV | 1,013 | 97% 713/778-3360
6333 S Braeswood Blvd, Houston 77096 | | | 66 | Fax 713/778-3362
Tiffany Narcisse

Gross Elem Sch | PK-5 | T | 632 | 100% 713/778-8450
12583 S Gessner Rd, Houston 77071 | | | 40 | Fax 713/778-8454
Tracie Hart-Jackson

Halpin Early Chldhd Lrng Ctr | PK-K | T | 432 | 97% 713/778-6720
10901 Sandpiper Dr, Houston 77096 | | | 20 | Fax 713/778-6724
Constance Lathan

HCC Life Skills | 12-12 | T | 61 | 34% 713/718-6882
1301 Alabama St, Houston 77004 | | | | Fax 713/718-6179
Shawna Punch

Ⓜ Herod Elem Sch | PK-5 | T | 818 | 51% 713/778-3315
5627 Jason St, Houston 77096 | | | | Fax 713/778-3317
**Gina Collon-Hernand** | | | | f

Ⓜ Horn Elem Sch | PK-5 | | 805 | 11% 713/295-5264
4530 Holly St, Bellaire 77401 | | | 20 | Fax 713/295-5286
Vanessa Flores | | | | f t

© Inspired for Excellence Acad W | 5-8 | T | 227 | 98% 832/834-5295
12525 Fondren Rd Ste N, Houston 77035 | | | | Fax 832/834-5687
Letha Gilmore

Ⓜ Jewel Askew Elem Sch | PK-5 | T | 907 | 71% 281/368-2100
11200 Wood Lodge Dr, Houston 77077 | | | 52 | Fax 281/368-2103
Ebony Cumby

Ⓐ Jjaep Sch | 4-12 | | 12 | 83% 713/394-4000
© 2525 Murworth Dr Ste 100, Houston 77054 | | | | Fax 713/556-7282
Luis Gavito

Ⓜ Kolter Elem Sch | PK-5 | | 626 | 22% 713/726-3630
9710 Runnymeade Dr, Houston 77096 | | | 20 | Fax 713/726-3663
Julianne Dickinson

Ⓜ Lamar High Sch | 9-12 | TV | 3,062 | 45% 713/522-5960
3325 Westheimer Rd, Houston 77098 | | | 100 | Fax 713/535-3769
Rita Graves

© Lanier Middle Sch | 6-8 | A | 1,464 | 24% 713/942-1900
2600 Woodhead St, Houston 77098 | | | 100 | Fax 713/942-1907
Dave Wheat

Las Americas Newcomer Mid Sch | 4-8 | T | 198 | 99% 713/773-5300
6501 Bellaire Blvd, Houston 77074 | | | 6 | Fax 713/773-5303
Maria Moreno

Ⓜ Long Academy | 6-12 | TV | 896 | 98% 713/778-3380
6501 Bellaire Blvd, Houston 77074 | | | | Fax 713/778-3387
**Benigno Soto**

Longfellow Elem Sch | PK-5 | T | 737 | 71% 713/295-5268
3617 Norris Dr, Houston 77025 | | | 30 | Fax 713/295-5257
Katherine Keafer

Louie Welch Middle Sch | 6-8 | TV | 727 | 92% 713/778-3300
11544 S Gessner Rd, Houston 77071 | | | 92 | Fax 713/995-6067
Rosa Hernandez

Lovett Elem Sch | PK-5 | | 631 | 36% 713/295-5258
8814 S Rice Ave, Houston 77096 | | | 29 | Fax 713/295-5291
Dawn Thompson

MacGregor Elem Sch | PK-5 | T | 586 | 72% 713/942-1990
4801 La Branch St, Houston 77004 | | | 55 | Fax 713/942-1993
Tara Garrett

Ⓜ Mandarin Immersion Magnet Sch | PK-8 | | 748 | 20% 713/295-5276
5445 W Alabama St, Houston 77056 | | | | Fax 713/556-3598
Chung Ying

Margaret Long Wisdom High Sch | 9-12 | T | 2,023 | 99% 713/787-1700
6529 Beverlyhill St, Houston 77057 | | | 150 | Fax 713/787-1723
Michelle Wagner

Ⓜ Mark Twain Elem Sch | PK-5 | | 869 | 16% 713/295-5230
7500 Braes Blvd, Houston 77025 | | | 34 | Fax 713/295-5283
Melissa Patin

Mark White Elem Sch | PK-5 | T | 679 | 72% 713/556-6571
2515 Old Farm Rd, Houston 77063 | | | | Fax 713/556-7497
Lisa Hernandez

McNamara Elem Sch | PK-5 | T | 934 | 97% 713/778-3460
8714 McAvoy Dr, Houston 77074 | | | 38 | Fax 713/778-3431
Toufic Elachkar

Memorial Elem Sch | PK-5 | T | 340 | 76% 713/867-5150
6401 Arnot St, Houston 77007 | | | 24 | Fax 713/867-5151
Maria Garcia

Meyerland Perf-Visual Arts MS | 6-8 | TV | 1,574 | 63% 713/726-3616
10410 Manhattan Dr, Houston 77096 | | | | Fax 713/726-3622
Auden Sarabia

Mistral Early Childhood Center | PK-PK | T | 355 | 99% 713/773-6253
6203 Jessamine St, Houston 77081 | | | | Fax 713/773-6257
Kristina Davis-Troutman

Neff Early Learning Center | PK-1 | T | 661 | 91% 713/778-3470
8200 Carvel Ln, Houston 77036 | | | | Fax 713/778-3473
Santrice Jones

Neff Elem Sch | 2-5 | T | 783 | 93% 713/556-9566
8301 Neff St, Houston 77036 | | | | Fax 713/556-9567
Amanda Wingard

Parker Elem Sch | PK-5 | T | 883 | 46% 713/726-3634
10626 Atwell Dr, Houston 77096 | | | 36 | Fax 713/726-3660
Chavis Mitchell | | | | f t

Paul Revere Middle Sch | 6-8 | T | 1,228 | 78% 713/917-3500
10502 Briar Forest Dr, Houston 77042 | | | 65 | Fax 713/917-3505
Monijit Katial

Pershing Middle Sch | 6-8 | TV | 1,771 | 52% 713/295-5240
3838 Blue Bonnet Blvd, Houston 77025 | | | | Fax 713/295-5252
Steven Shetzer | | | | f t

Pilgrim Academy | PK-8 | T | 1,135 | 98% 713/458-4672
6302 Skyline Dr, Houston 77057 | | | 34 | Fax 713/458-4693
Diana Castillo | | | | f t

Pin Oak Middle Sch | 6-8 | | 1,213 | 38% 713/295-6500
4601 Glenmont St, Bellaire 77401 | | | | Fax 713/295-6511
Michelle Shoulders | | | | f t

Piney Point Elem Sch | PK-5 | T | 1,181 | 98% 713/917-3610
8921 Pagewood Ln, Houston 77063 | | | 45 | Fax 713/917-3613
Bobbie Swaby | | | | f

Poe Elem Sch | PK-5 | | 863 | 26% 713/535-3780
5100 Hazard St, Houston 77098 | | | 36 | Fax 713/535-3784
Jeffrey Amerson

Ray Daily Elem Sch | PK-5 | T | 768 | 59% 281/368-2111
12909 Briar Forest Dr, Houston 77077 | | | | Fax 281/368-7463
Cindy Tiet

Ⓜ River Oaks Elem Sch | PK-5 | | 674 | 8% 713/942-1460
2008 Kirby Dr, Houston 77019 | | | 20 | Fax 713/942-1463
Dr Keri Fovargue

Roberts Elem Sch | PK-5 | | 756 | 15% 713/295-5272
6000 Greenbriar Dr, Houston 77030 | | | 29 | Fax 713/295-5282
Trealla Epps | | | | t

S C Red Elem Sch | PK-5 | | 598 | 70% 713/726-3638
4520 Tonawanda Dr, Houston 77035 | | | 35 | Fax 713/726-3698
Octaviano Trevino

School at St George Place | PK-5 | T | 793 | 51% 713/625-1499
5430 Hidalgo St, Houston 77056 | | | 10 | Fax 713/625-1481
Sean McClish

| | | | | | |
|---|---|---|---|---|---|
| Shadowbriar Elem Sch<br>2650 Shadowbriar Dr, Houston 77077<br>Mark Samuel | PK-5 | T | 596<br>45 | 72% | 281/368-2160<br>Fax 281/368-2170 |
| ⓜ Sharpstown International Acad<br>8330 Triola Ln, Houston 77036<br>Bryan Bordelon | 6-12 | TV | 1,179<br>80 | 95% | 713/778-3440<br>Fax 713/778-3444 |
| Sutton Elem Sch<br>7402 Albacore Dr, Houston 77074<br>Beatrice Akala | PK-5 | T | 1,121<br>70 | 91% | 713/778-3400<br>Fax 713/778-3407 |
| Sylvan Rodriguez Elem Sch<br>5858 Chimney Rock Rd, Houston 77081<br>Luz Deanda | PK-5 | T | 958 | 98% | 713/295-3870<br>Fax 713/295-3875 |
| Ⓐ T H Rogers Sch<br>5840 San Felipe St, Houston 77057<br>Tiffany Chenier | PK-12 | V | 979<br>50 | 25% | 713/917-3565<br>Fax 713/917-3534 |
| Tanglewood Middle Sch<br>5215 San Felipe St, Houston 77056<br>Gretchen Kasper-Hoffman | 6-8 | T | 846<br>45 | 59% | 713/625-1411<br>Fax 713/625-1415 🇫🇹 |
| Valley West Elem Sch<br>10707 S Gessner Rd, Houston 77071<br>**Brian VanNest** | PK-5 | T | 861<br>25 | 92% | 713/773-6151<br>Fax 713/773-6156 |
| Walnut Bend Elem Sch<br>10620 Briar Forest Dr, Houston 77042<br>Michele Dahlquist | PK-5 | T | 703<br>36 | 87% | 713/917-3540<br>Fax 713/917-3656 |
| West Briar Middle Sch<br>13733 Brimhurst Dr, Houston 77077<br>Gabriel Lopez | 6-8 | T | 1,114 | 61% | 281/368-2140<br>Fax 281/368-2194 |
| West University Elem Sch<br>3756 University Blvd, Houston 77005<br>Scott Disch | PK-5 | | 1,273<br>43 | 3% | 713/295-5215<br>Fax 713/667-8514 |
| Westside High Sch<br>14201 Briar Forest Dr, Houston 77077<br>**Peggi Stewart** | 9-12 | TV | 2,897 | 57% | 281/920-8000<br>Fax 281/920-8059 |
| Wharton Dual Language Academy<br>900 W Gray St, Houston 77019<br>Jennifer Day | PK-8 | T | 510<br>25 | 42% | 713/535-3771<br>Fax 713/535-3772 |
| ⓜ Wilson Montessori Elem Sch<br>2100 Yupon St, Houston 77006<br>Shameika Salvador | PK-8 | G | 600<br>20 | 29% | 713/942-1470<br>Fax 713/942-1472 |
| © Young Learners Elem Sch [293]<br>8432 Bissonnet St, Houston 77074<br>Lillan Conway | PK-PK | T | 1,344 | 99% | 713/772-7100<br>Fax 713/784-6345 |

## • Huffman Ind School Dist PID: 01026112
24302 FM 2100 Rd, Huffman 77336

281/324-1871
Fax 281/324-4319

Schools: 4 \ **Teachers:** 220 \ **Students:** 3,600 \ **Special Ed Students:** 358 \ **LEP Students:** 222 \ **College-Bound:** 75% \ **Ethnic:** African American 3%, Hispanic 24%, Caucasian 73% \ **Exp:** $515 (High) \ **Poverty:** 13% \ **Title I:** $480,129 \ **Special Education:** $667,000 \ **Open-Close:** 08/19 - 05/28 \ **DTBP:** $153 (High)

| | | | |
|---|---|---|---|
| Dr Benny Soileau | 1 | Tim Brittain | 2,11,19 |
| Joe Russo | 4 | Ernest Nelson | 5 |
| Mike McEachern | 6 | Dr Joel Nolte | 8,15 |
| Michelle Davenport | 34,57,58,77,88,271 | Kristin Breaux | 39,68,71,273 |
| Monica Dorcz | 45 | Matt Dutton | 67 |
| David Carpenter | 73,84,295 | Dena Bumgarner | 79 |
| Shannon Jones | 91* | Jim Dees | 285 |

| Public Schs..Principal | Grd | Prgm | Enr/#Cls | SN | |
|---|---|---|---|---|---|
| Falcon Ridge Elem Sch<br>26503 FM 2100 Rd, Huffman 77336<br>Amy Turner | K-5 | T | 749 | 42% | 281/324-7100<br>Fax 281/324-2076 |
| Huffman Elem Sch<br>24403 E Lake Houston Pkwy, Huffman 77336<br>Melissa Hutchinson | PK-5 | T | 918<br>33 | 44% | 281/324-1399<br>Fax 281/324-1646 |
| Huffman Middle Sch<br>3407 Huffman Eastgate Rd, Huffman 77336<br>Marybel Ruiz | 6-8 | TV | 838<br>35 | 32% | 281/324-2598<br>Fax 281/324-2710 |
| Willie J Hargrave High Sch<br>25400 Willy Ln, Huffman 77336<br>**Adam Skinner** | 9-12 | TV | 787<br>50 | 26% | 281/324-1845<br>Fax 281/324-3368 |

## • Humble Ind School Dist PID: 01026150
10203 Birchridge Dr, Humble 77338

281/641-1000
Fax 281/641-1050

Schools: 47 \ **Teachers:** 2,776 \ **Students:** 43,189 \ **Special Ed Students:** 3,543 \ **LEP Students:** 3,801 \ **College-Bound:** 60% \ **Ethnic:** Asian 3%, African American 22%, Hispanic 37%, Caucasian 37% \ **Exp:** $297 (Med) \ **Poverty:** 11% \ **Title I:** $5,625,265 \ **Special Education:** $5,153,000 \ **Open-Close:** 08/11 - 05/28 \ **DTBP:** $188 (High) \ 🇫🇹

| | | | |
|---|---|---|---|
| Dr Elizabeth Fagen | 1 | Billy Beattie | 2 |
| Deborah Connors | 2 | Ida Schultz | 2 |
| Janice Himpele | 2 | Robert Seale | 2,19 |
| Shelley Vineyard | 2 | Kenny Kendrick | 3 |
| Shirley Parker | 4 | Jerry Burd | 5 |
| Troy Kite | 6 | Dr Ann Johnson | 8,18 |
| Lisa McCorquodale | 8 | Stephanie Perry | 8,275 |
| Dr Jamie Bryson | 11,296 | Nolan Correa | 15,79 |
| Rick Gardner | 15,68,78,273 | Dr Roger Brown | 15 |
| Houston Hayes | 20 | Larkin Lesueur | 27,31* |
| Ellen Shimer | 34 | Helen Wagner | 35* |
| Matt Smith | 37 | Matthew Webb | 39 |
| Kathleen Goerner | 44 | Rachel Smith | 46* |
| Courtney Peterson | 47* | Myra Herbst | 49,51 |
| Dr Lumara Blanco-Lajara | 57 | Thelissa Edwards | 58 |
| Nancy Morrison | 67 | Jamie Tisdale | 68 |
| John Krippel | 68 | Kashonda Hurst | 68 |
| Kelly Gabrisch | 68 | Christina Trotter | 69 |
| Jamie Mount | 71 | Dustin Hardin | 73,76 |
| Deborah Perez | 74 | Elizabeth King | 74 |
| Reggie Boone | 76 | Dr Robert Meaux | 76 |
| Dr Charles Ned | 81 | Solomon Cook | 91 |
| Dr Warren Roane | 294 | Adrianne Holmes | 298 |

| Public Schs..Principal | Grd | Prgm | Enr/#Cls | SN | |
|---|---|---|---|---|---|
| Atascocita High Sch<br>13300 Will Clayton Pkwy, Humble 77346<br>Bill Daniels | 9-12 | V | 3,652 | 30% | 281/641-7500<br>Fax 281/641-7517 |
| Atascocita Middle Sch<br>18810 W Lake Houston Pkwy, Humble 77346<br>Karl Koehler | 6-8 | V | 1,226<br>70 | 35% | 281/641-4600<br>Fax 281/641-4617 |
| Atascocita Springs Elem Sch<br>13515 Valley Lodge Pkwy, Humble 77346<br>Cheryl Fennel | PK-5 | | 964 | 21% | 281/641-3600<br>Fax 281/641-3617 |
| Bear Branch Elem Sch<br>3500 Garden Lake Dr, Kingwood 77339<br>Katheryn Palmer | K-5 | | 617<br>28 | 14% | 281/641-1600<br>Fax 281/641-1617 |
| Ⓐ Cambridge Sch<br>18901 Timber Forest Dr, Humble 77346<br>Tammey Harlan | 2-12 | | 100 | | 281/641-7445<br>Fax 281/641-7399 |
| Career & Technical Ed Center<br>9155 Will Clayton Pkwy, Humble 77338<br>Dr Marley Morris | Voc | | 200<br>12 | | 281/641-7950<br>Fax 281/641-7967 🇹 |
| Centennial Elem Sch<br>15130 Timber Forest Dr, Houston 77044<br>**Alison Pierce** | PK-5 | | 575 | | 281/641-8800 |
| Ⓐ Community Learning Center<br>18901 Timber Forest Dr, Humble 77346<br>Tammy Alexander | 1-12 | GT | 50<br>52 | 65% | 281/641-7400<br>Fax 281/641-7417 |
| Creekwood Middle Sch<br>3603 W Lake Houston Pkwy, Kingwood 77339<br>Walter Winicki | 6-8 | V | 1,089<br>60 | 16% | 281/641-4400<br>Fax 281/641-4417 |

| | | | | | | | |
|---|---|---|---|---|---|---|---|
| 1 | Superintendent | 8 | Curric/Instruct K-12 | 19 | Chief Financial Officer | 29 | Family/Consumer Science |
| 2 | Bus/Finance/Purchasing | 9 | Curric/Instruct Elem | 20 | Art K-12 | 30 | Adult Education |
| 3 | Buildings And Grounds | 10 | Curric/Instruct Sec | 21 | Art Elem | 31 | Career/Sch-to-Work K-12 |
| 4 | Food Service | 11 | Federal Program | 22 | Art Sec | 32 | Career/Sch-to-Work Elem |
| 5 | Transportation | 12 | Title I | 23 | Music K-12 | 33 | Career/Sch-to-Work Sec |
| 6 | Athletic | 13 | Title V | 24 | Music Elem | 34 | Early Childhood Ed |
| 7 | Health Services | 15 | Asst Superintendent | 25 | Music Sec | 35 | Health/Phys Education |
| | | 16 | Instructional Media Svcs | 26 | Business Education | 36 | Guidance Services K-12 |
| | | 17 | Chief Operations Officer | 27 | Career & Tech Ed | 37 | Guidance Services Elem |
| | | 18 | Chief Academic Officer | 28 | Technology Education | 38 | Guidance Services Sec |

| | | | | | | | |
|---|---|---|---|---|---|---|---|
| 39 | Social Studies K-12 | 49 | English/Lang Arts Elem | 59 | Special Education Elem | 69 | Academic Assessment |
| 40 | Social Studies Elem | 50 | English/Lang Arts Sec | 60 | Special Education Sec | 70 | Research/Development |
| 41 | Social Studies Sec | 51 | Reading K-12 | 61 | Foreign/World Lang K-12 | 71 | Public Information |
| 42 | Science K-12 | 52 | Reading Elem | 62 | Foreign/World Lang Elem | 72 | Summer School |
| 43 | Science Elem | 53 | Reading Sec | 63 | Foreign/World Lang Sec | 73 | Instructional Tech |
| 44 | Science Sec | 54 | Remedial Reading K-12 | 64 | Religious Education K-12 | 74 | Inservice Training |
| 45 | Math K-12 | 55 | Remedial Reading Elem | 65 | Religious Education Elem | 75 | Marketing/Distributive |
| 46 | Math Elem | 56 | Remedial Reading Sec | 66 | Religious Education Sec | 76 | Info Systems |
| 47 | Math Sec | 57 | Bilingual/ELL | 67 | School Board President | 77 | Psychological Assess |
| 48 | English/Lang Arts K-12 | 58 | Special Education K-12 | 68 | Teacher Personnel | 78 | Affirmative Action |

| | | | | | | |
|---|---|---|---|---|---|---|
| Deerwood Elem Sch<br>2920 Forest Garden Dr, Kingwood 77345<br>MacAire Davies | PK-5 | | 603 | 13% | 281/641-2200<br>Fax 281/641-2217 |
| Eagle Springs Elem Sch<br>12500 Will Clayton Pkwy, Humble 77346<br>April Maldonado | K-5 | | 724 | 17% | 281/641-3100<br>Fax 281/641-3117 |
| Elm Grove Elem Sch<br>2815 Clear Ridge Dr, Kingwood 77339<br>**Cassie Pfeifer** | K-5 | T | 533<br>35 | 43% | 281/641-1700<br>Fax 281/641-1717 |
| Fall Creek Elem Sch<br>14435 Mesa Dr, Humble 77396<br>Christy Erb | K-5 | | 1,074 | 19% | 281/641-3400<br>Fax 281/641-3417 |
| Foster Elem Sch<br>1800 Trailwood Village Dr, Kingwood 77339<br>Diana Zelezinski | PK-5 | T | 539<br>36 | 41% | 281/641-1400<br>Fax 281/641-1417 |
| Greentree Elem Sch<br>3502 Brook Shadow Dr, Kingwood 77345<br>Denise Rodriguez | K-5 | | 710<br>35 | 17% | 281/641-1900<br>Fax 281/641-1917 |
| Groves Elem Sch<br>11902 Madera Run Pkwy, Humble 77346<br>Dr Brian Peters | K-5 | | 911 | 17% | 281/641-5000<br>Fax 281/641-5017 |
| Hidden Hollow Elem Sch<br>4104 Appalachian Trl, Kingwood 77345<br>Janice Wiederhold | K-5 | | 454<br>38 | 14% | 281/641-2400<br>Fax 281/641-2417 |
| Humble Elem Sch<br>20252 Fieldtree Dr, Humble 77338<br>Veronica Hernandez | PK-5 | T | 574<br>43 | 71% | 281/641-1100<br>Fax 281/641-1117 |
| Humble High Sch<br>1700 Wilson Rd, Humble 77338<br>Terri Osborne | 9-12 | TV | 2,385 | 68% | 281/641-6300<br>Fax 281/641-6517 |
| Humble Middle Sch<br>11207 Will Clayton Pkwy, Humble 77346<br>Sarahdia Johnson | 6-8 | TV | 1,219 | 70% | 281/641-4170<br>Fax 281/641-4188 |
| Jack M Fields Sr Elem Sch<br>2505 S Houston Ave, Humble 77396<br>Melissa Christensen | PK-5 | T | 547 | 78% | 281/641-2700<br>Fax 281/641-2717 |
| Kingwood High Sch<br>2701 Kingwood Dr, Kingwood 77339<br>Dr Michael Nasra | 9-12 | V | 2,742 | 12% | 281/641-6900<br>Fax 281/641-7217 |
| Kingwood Middle Sch<br>2407 Pine Terrace Dr, Kingwood 77339<br>Michael Curl | 6-8 | V | 1,026<br>100 | 31% | 281/641-4200<br>Fax 281/641-4217 |
| Kingwood Park High Sch<br>4015 Woodland Hills Dr, Kingwood 77339<br>Lisa Drabing | 9-12 | V | 1,848<br>50 | 25% | 281/641-6600<br>Fax 281/641-6617 |
| Lakeland Elem Sch<br>1500 Montgomery Ln, Humble 77338<br>Lucy Anderson | PK-5 | T | 809<br>47 | 86% | 281/641-1200<br>Fax 281/641-1217 |
| Lakeshore Elem Sch<br>13333 Breakwater Path Dr, Houston 77044<br>Annette Nevermann | PK-5 | | 990 | 25% | 281/641-3500<br>Fax 281/641-3517 |
| Maplebrook Elem Sch<br>7935 Farmingham Rd, Humble 77346<br>Tiffany Caseltine | PK-5 | | 708 | 34% | 281/641-2900<br>Fax 281/641-2917 |
| North Belt Elem Sch<br>8105 E North Belt, Humble 77396<br>Christina Morris | PK-5 | T | 740<br>28 | 88% | 281/641-1300<br>Fax 281/641-1317 |
| Oak Forest Elem Sch<br>6400 Kingwood Glen Dr, Humble 77346<br>Linda Schmidt | K-5 | T | 704<br>43 | 49% | 281/641-2800<br>Fax 281/641-2817 |
| Oaks Elem Sch<br>5858 Upper Lake Dr, Humble 77346<br>Kerri Smith | PK-5 | T | 580<br>36 | 63% | 281/641-1890<br>Fax 281/641-1817 |
| Park Lakes Elem Sch<br>4400 Wilson Rd, Humble 77396<br>Sarah Ballard | PK-5 | T | 731 | 67% | 281/641-3200<br>Fax 281/641-3217 |
| Pine Forest Elem Sch<br>19702 W Lake Houston Pkwy, Humble 77346<br>Sloan Simmons | PK-5 | | 623<br>40 | 33% | 281/641-2100<br>Fax 281/641-2117 |
| Quest Early College High Sch<br>1700 Wilson Rd Ste 3100, Humble 77338<br>Nachelle Scott | 9-12 | | 428 | 38% | 281/641-7300<br>Fax 281/641-7318 |
| Ridge Creek Elem Sch<br>15201 Woodland Hills Dr, Humble 77396<br>Stephanie Davis | PK-5 | T | 903 | 65% | 281/641-3700<br>Fax 281/641-3717 |
| River Pines Elem Sch<br>2400 Cold River Dr, Humble 77396<br>**Alicia Pearce** | PK-5 | T | 835 | 76% | 281/641-3300<br>Fax 281/641-3317 |
| Riverwood Middle Sch<br>2910 High Valley Dr, Kingwood 77345<br>Matthew Roser | 6-8 | V | 1,066<br>65 | 7% | 281/641-4800<br>Fax 281/641-4817 |
| Ross Sterling Middle Sch<br>1131 Wilson Rd, Humble 77338<br>Damico Bartley | 6-8 | TV | 931 | 78% | 281/641-6000<br>Fax 281/641-6017 |
| Shadow Forest Elem Sch<br>2300 Mills Branch Dr, Kingwood 77345<br>Lisa Lackey | PK-5 | | 577<br>30 | 8% | 281/641-2600<br>Fax 281/641-2617 |
| Summer Creek High Sch<br>14000 Weckford Blvd, Houston 77044<br>Brent McDonald | 9-12 | T | 2,385 | 40% | 281/641-5400<br>Fax 281/641-5417 |
| Summerwood Elem Sch<br>14000 Summerwood Lakes Dr, Houston 77044<br>Shannon Lalmansingh | PK-5 | | 743 | 23% | 281/641-3000<br>Fax 281/641-3017 |
| Timbers Elem Sch<br>6910 Lonesome Woods Trl, Humble 77346<br>Micah Bachemin | PK-5 | T | 651<br>25 | 51% | 281/641-2000<br>Fax 281/641-2017 |
| Timberwood Middle Sch<br>18450 Timber Forest Dr, Humble 77346<br>Kenneth Buck | 6-8 | | 1,151<br>65 | 41% | 281/641-3800<br>Fax 281/641-3817 |
| West Lake Middle Sch<br>11810 Madera Run Pkwy, Humble 77346<br>Dr Kenneth Hodgkinson | 6-8 | | 1,036 | 19% | 281/641-5800<br>Fax 281/641-5817 |
| Whispering Pines Elem Sch<br>17321 Woodland Hills Dr, Humble 77346<br>Wendy Anaya | K-5 | T | 603<br>42 | 59% | 281/641-2500<br>Fax 281/641-2517 |
| Willow Creek Elem Sch<br>2002 Willow Terrace Dr, Kingwood 77345<br>Scott Duncan | PK-5 | | 484<br>28 | 4% | 281/641-2300<br>Fax 281/641-2317 |
| Woodcreek Middle Sch<br>14600 Woodson Park Dr, Houston 77044<br>Alan Moye | 6-8 | | 1,538 | 38% | 281/641-5200<br>Fax 281/641-5217 |
| Woodland Hills Elem Sch<br>2222 Tree Ln, Kingwood 77339<br>Cindy Barker | K-5 | | 536<br>30 | 36% | 281/641-1500<br>Fax 281/641-1517 |

● **Klein Ind School Dist** PID: 01026289    832/249-4000
7200 Spring Cypress Rd, Klein 77379    Fax 832/249-4015

**Schools:** 49 \ **Teachers:** 3,519 \ **Students:** 53,292 \
**Special Ed Students:** 5,097 \ **LEP Students:** 7,600 \ **College-Bound:** 80%
\ **Ethnic:** Asian 9%, African American 16%, Hispanic 43%, Caucasian
32% \ **Exp:** $136 (Low) \ **Poverty:** 15% \ **Title I:** $11,590,492 \
**Special Education:** $7,559,000 \ **Open-Close:** 08/19 - 05/28 \ **DTBP:** $186
(High) \ 🇫 🇹

| | | | |
|---|---|---|---|
| Dr Jenny McGowan | 1,288 | Audrey Ambridge | 2 |
| Dan Schaefer | 2,19 | Jason Gossett | 2 |
| Robert Robertson | 3,15 | Scott Lazar | 3 |
| Doug Massey | 4 | John Rice | 5 |
| Darby Young | 6,35 | Yvonne Clark | 7 |
| Cheryl Gordy | 11 | Christopher Ruggerio | 11 |
| Dayna Hernandez | 15,71,79 | Kelly Schumacher | 15,68 |
| Larry Whitehead | 15,76 | Nicole Shepard | 16,71 |

| | |
|---|---|
| Joel Wren ..............................20,23 | Debra Broner Westerl ..........................27 |
| Kayla Shaw ...............................36,85 | Michele Thompson ..............................42 |
| Kathy Vegara .............................57,89 | Dr Kristen Allman ................................58 |
| Doug James ....................................67 | Stacy Kindsfather ..........................69,294 |
| Chris Cummings .........................73,84 | Kathleen Plott ....................................81 |
| Rick Stockton .............................83,88 | Brian Marr ......................................88* |
| David Kimberly ...............................91 | Dr Joffery Jones ................................91 |
| Ron Webster ...................................91 | Maria Ovalle Lopez ............................93 |
| Denise McLean ..............................297 | |

| Public Schs..Principal | Grd | Prgm | Enr/#Cls | SN |
|---|---|---|---|---|
| Benfer Elem Sch<br>18027 Kuykendahl Rd Ste B, Klein 77379<br>**Ashley Johnson** | PK-5 | T | 801<br>32 | 52% 832/484-6000<br>Fax 832/484-7850 |
| Benignus Elem Sch<br>7225 Alvin A Klein Dr, Klein 77379<br>Amanda O'Dowd | K-5 | | 708 | 23% 832/484-7750<br>Fax 832/484-7796 |
| Bernshausen Elem Sch<br>11116 Mahaffey Rd, Tomball 77375<br>Carrie Farmer | PK-5 | T | 875 | 60% 832/375-8000<br>Fax 832/375-8050 |
| Blackshear Elem Sch<br>11211 Lacey Rd, Tomball 77375<br>Meagan White | PK-5 | T | 1,067 | 45% 832/375-7600<br>Fax 832/375-7725 |
| Brill Elem Sch<br>9102 Herts Rd, Klein 77379<br>Sandra Speer | PK-5 | | 717<br>48 | 39% 832/484-6150<br>Fax 832/484-7851 |
| Doerre Intermediate Sch<br>18218 Theiss Mail Route Rd, Klein 77379<br>**Katherine Land** | 6-8 | | 1,361<br>86 | 19% 832/249-5700<br>Fax 832/249-4054 |
| Ehrhardt Elem Sch<br>6603 Rosebrook Ln, Klein 77379<br>Linda Galicia | PK-5 | T | 729<br>40 | 56% 832/484-6200<br>Fax 832/484-7853 |
| Eiland Elem Sch<br>6700 N Klein Circle Dr, Houston 77088<br>David Menendez | K-5 | T | 529<br>40 | 92% 832/484-6900<br>Fax 832/484-7854 |
| Epps Island Elem Sch<br>7403 Smiling Wood Ln, Houston 77086<br>Maribel Scarbrough | K-5 | T | 634<br>52 | 86% 832/484-5800<br>Fax 832/484-7856 |
| Frank Elem Sch<br>9225 Crescent Clover Dr, Klein 77379<br>Tyra Storie | PK-5 | | 658 | 10% 832/375-7000<br>Fax 832/375-7100 |
| French Elem Sch<br>5802 W Rayford Rd, Klein 77389<br>Holly Conroy | PK-5 | | 765 | 9% 832/375-8100<br>Fax 832/375-8175 |
| Ⓨ Grace England ECC<br>7535 Prairie Oak Dr, Houston 77086<br>Jaunee Perry | PK-PK | MT | 470 | 91% 832/375-7900<br>Fax 832/375-7925 |
| Greenwood Forest Elem Sch<br>12100 Misty Valley Dr, Houston 77066<br>Alisha Elrod | K-5 | T | 730<br>35 | 65% 832/484-5700<br>Fax 832/484-7858<br>🇫🇷 |
| Hassler Elem Sch<br>9325 Lochlea Ridge Dr, Klein 77379<br>Sarah Brown | PK-5 | | 855 | 17% 832/484-7100<br>Fax 832/484-7860 |
| Haude Elem Sch<br>3111 Louetta Rd, Spring 77388<br>Rachel Wall | PK-5 | | 721 | 27% 832/484-5600<br>Fax 832/484-7862 |
| Hildebrandt Intermediate Sch<br>22800 Hildebrandt Rd, Klein 77389<br>Lauren Marti | 6-8 | | 948<br>80 | 47% 832/249-5100<br>Fax 832/249-4068 |
| Hofius Intermediate Sch<br>8400 W Rayford Rd, Klein 77389<br>Christy Goforth | 6-8 | | 979 | 26% 832/375-8800<br>Fax 832/375-8835 |
| Kaiser Elem Sch<br>13430 Bammel North Houston Rd, Houston 77066<br>Betty Zavala | K-5 | T | 713 | 88% 832/484-6100<br>Fax 832/484-7864 |
| Kleb Intermediate Sch<br>7425 Louetta Rd, Klein 77379<br>**Ellen Hodge** | 6-8 | | 1,412<br>80 | 41% 832/249-5500<br>Fax 832/249-4053 |
| Ⓐ Klein Alternative Ed Center<br>7302 Kleingreen Ln, Klein 77379<br>Brian Marr | K-12 | | 100<br>25 | 70% 832/249-4801<br>Fax 832/249-4045 |
| Klein Cain High Sch<br>10201 Spring Cypress Rd, Houston 77070<br>Nicole Patin | 9-12 | | 1,400 | 34% 832/375-8400<br>Fax 832/375-8302 |
| Klein Collins High Sch<br>20811 Ella Blvd, Spring 77388<br>Randy Kirk | 9-12 | | 3,470<br>130 | 35% 832/484-5500<br>Fax 832/484-7811 |
| Klein Forest High Sch<br>11400 Misty Valley Dr, Houston 77066<br>Lance Alexander | 9-12 | TV | 3,566<br>120 | 74% 832/484-4500<br>Fax 832/484-4490 |
| Klein High Sch<br>16715 Stuebner Airline Rd, Klein 77379<br>Jessica Haddox | 9-12 | V | 3,433 | 32% 832/484-4000<br>Fax 832/484-7821 |
| Klein Intermediate Sch<br>4710 W Mount Houston Rd, Houston 77088<br>Charles Woods | 6-8 | T | 1,087 | 85% 832/249-4900<br>Fax 832/249-4046 |
| Klein Oak High Sch<br>22603 Northcrest Dr, Spring 77389<br>Thomas Hensley | 9-12 | V | 3,698 | 30% 832/484-5000<br>Fax 832/484-7831 |
| Klenk Elem Sch<br>6111 Bourgeois Rd, Houston 77066<br>Allie Martin | K-5 | T | 799<br>35 | 69% 832/484-6800<br>Fax 832/484-7866 |
| Kohrville Elem Sch<br>11600 Woodland Shore Dr, Tomball 77375<br>Kia Bowie | PK-5 | | 629<br>50 | 54% 832/484-7200<br>Fax 832/484-7890 |
| Krahn Elem Sch<br>9502 Eday Dr, Klein 77379<br>Leslie Kompelien | PK-5 | | 768 | 46% 832/484-6500<br>Fax 832/484-7868 |
| Kreinhop Elem Sch<br>20820 Ella Blvd, Spring 77388<br>Lauren Liesberger | PK-5 | T | 984 | 46% 832/484-7400<br>Fax 832/484-7404 |
| Krimmel Intermediate Sch<br>7070 FM 2920 Rd, Klein 77379<br>Prentiss Harper | 6-8 | | 1,377 | 34% 832/375-7200<br>Fax 832/375-7150 |
| Kuehnle Elem Sch<br>5510 Winding Ridge Dr, Klein 77379<br>Julia Funk | PK-5 | | 866<br>60 | 23% 832/484-6650<br>Fax 832/484-7870 |
| Lemm Elem Sch<br>19034 Joanleigh Dr, Spring 77388<br>**Adam Tietze** | PK-5 | | 708 | 32% 832/484-6300<br>Fax 832/484-7872 |
| Mahaffey Elem Sch<br>10255 Mahaffey Rd, Tomball 77375<br>Holly Mason \ **Sherri Davenport** | PK-5 | T | 851 | 42% 832/375-8300<br>Fax 832/375-8297 |
| McDougle Elem Sch<br>10410 Kansack Ln, Houston 77086<br>Kathy Rachal | K-5 | T | 555 | 83% 832/484-7550<br>Fax 832/484-7699 |
| Metzler Elem Sch<br>8500 W Rayford Rd, Klein 77389<br>Danis Boone | PK-5 | | 867 | 32% 832/484-7900<br>Fax 832/484-7999 |
| Mittelstadt Elem Sch<br>7525 Kleingreen Ln, Klein 77379<br>Julie Shumake | PK-5 | T | 904<br>38 | 56% 832/484-6700<br>Fax 832/484-7876 |
| Mueller Elem Sch<br>7074 FM 2920 Rd, Klein 77379<br>Kathryn Shealy | PK-5 | | 843 | 40% 832/375-7300<br>Fax 832/375-7425 |
| Nitsch Elem Sch<br>4702 W Mount Houston Rd, Houston 77088<br>Frank Ward | K-5 | T | 754 | 88% 832/484-6400<br>Fax 832/484-7878 |
| Northampton Elem Sch<br>6404 Root Rd, Klein 77389<br>Lisa Campbell | PK-5 | | 542<br>55 | 45% 832/484-5550<br>Fax 832/484-7880 |
| Roth Elem Sch<br>21623 Castlemont Ln, Spring 77388<br>Gail McGuire | PK-5 | T | 718<br>40 | 48% 832/484-6600<br>Fax 832/484-7882 |

| | | | | | | | | |
|---|---|---|---|---|---|---|---|---|
| 1 | Superintendent | 8 | Curric/Instruct K-12 | 19 | Chief Financial Officer | 29 | Family/Consumer Science | 39 Social Studies K-12 |
| 2 | Bus/Finance/Purchasing | 9 | Curric/Instruct Elem | 20 | Art K-12 | 30 | Adult Education | 40 Social Studies Elem |
| 3 | Buildings And Grounds | 10 | Curric/Instruct Sec | 21 | Art Elem | 31 | Career/Sch-to-Work K-12 | 41 Social Studies Sec |
| 4 | Food Service | 11 | Federal Program | 22 | Art Sec | 32 | Career/Sch-to-Work Elem | 42 Science K-12 |
| 5 | Transportation | 12 | Title V | 23 | Music K-12 | 33 | Career/Sch-to-Work Sec | 43 Science Elem |
| 6 | Athletic | 13 | Title V | 24 | Music Elem | 34 | Early Childhood Ed | 44 Science Sec |
| 7 | Health Services | 15 | Asst Superintendent | 25 | Music Sec | 35 | Health/Phys Education | 45 Math K-12 |
| | | 16 | Instructional Media Svcs | 26 | Business Education | 36 | Guidance Services K-12 | 46 Math Elem |
| | | 17 | Chief Operations Officer | 27 | Career & Tech Ed | 37 | Guidance Services Elem | 47 Math Sec |
| | | 18 | Chief Academic Officer | 28 | Technology Education | 38 | Guidance Services Sec | 48 English/Lang Arts K-12 |

| | | | |
|---|---|---|---|
| 49 English/Lang Arts Elem | 59 Special Education Elem | 69 Academic Assessment |
| 50 English/Lang Arts Sec | 60 Special Education Sec | 70 Research/Development |
| 51 Reading K-12 | 61 Foreign/World Lang K-12 | 71 Public Information |
| 52 Reading Elem | 62 Foreign/World Lang Elem | 72 Summer School |
| 53 Reading Sec | 63 Foreign/World Lang Sec | 73 Instructional Tech |
| 54 Remedial Reading K-12 | 64 Religious Education K-12 | 74 Inservice Training |
| 55 Remedial Reading Elem | 65 Religious Education Elem | 75 Marketing/Distributive |
| 56 Remedial Reading Sec | 66 Religious Education Sec | 76 Info Systems |
| 57 Bilingual/ELL | 67 School Board President | 77 Psychological Assess |
| 58 Special Education K-12 | 68 Teacher Personnel | 78 Affirmative Action |

| | Grd | Prgm | Enr/#Cls | SN | |
|---|---|---|---|---|---|
| Schindewolf Intermediate Sch<br>20903 Ella Blvd, Spring 77388<br>Dr Curtis Simmons | 6-8 | | 1,227 | 37% | 832/249-5900<br>Fax 832/249-4072 |
| Schultz Elem Sch<br>7920 Willow Forest Dr, Tomball 77375<br>Sherri Davenport | PK-5 | T | 644<br>70 | 50% | 832/484-7000<br>Fax 832/484-7884 |
| Strack Intermediate Sch<br>18027 Kuykendahl Rd Ste S, Klein 77379<br>Jason Ovalle | 6-8 | | 1,224 | 34% | 832/249-5400<br>Fax 832/249-4051 |
| Theiss Elem Sch<br>17510 Theiss Mail Route Rd, Klein 77379<br>Joann Keenan | PK-5 | | 678<br>32 | 22% | 832/484-5900<br>Fax 832/484-7886 |
| Ulrich Intermediate Sch<br>10103 Spring Cypress Rd, Houston 77070<br>Trevor Woolley | 6-8 | T | 1,331 | 46% | 832/375-7500<br>Fax 832/375-7599 |
| Ⓐ Vistas High Sch<br>12550 Bammel North Houston Rd, Houston 77066<br>**Bob Anderson** | 9-12 | | 75 | | 832/484-7650<br>Fax 832/484-7697 |
| Wunderlich Intermediate Sch<br>11800 Misty Valley Dr, Houston 77066<br>**Clay Huggins** | 6-8 | T | 1,525<br>85 | 75% | 832/249-5200<br>Fax 832/249-4050 |
| Zwink Elem Sch<br>22200 Frassati Way, Klein 77389<br>Stacey Vaglienty | PK-5 | T | 1,113 | 48% | 832/375-7800<br>Fax 832/375-7850 |

● **La Porte Ind School Dist** PID: 01026370     281/604-7000
1002 San Jacinto St, La Porte 77571     Fax 281/604-7010

**Schools:** 13 \ **Teachers:** 489 \ **Students:** 7,679 \ **Special Ed Students:** 808 \ **LEP Students:** 651 \ **Ethnic:** Asian 1%, African American 7%, Hispanic 50%, Native American: 1%, Caucasian 40% \ **Exp:** $269 (Med) \ **Poverty:** 12% \ **Title I:** $1,359,021 \ **Special Education:** $1,400,000 \ **Open-Close:** 08/19 - 05/27 \ **DTBP:** $183 (High)

| | | | |
|---|---|---|---|
| Dr Walter Jackson | 1 | Lynley Marlar | 2 |
| Sheila Cantu | 2 | Corey Marlar | 3,5,73 |
| Mike Clausen | 3,15,17,91 | Yvonne Bennett | 4 |
| Elisha Thompson | 6 | Carrie Rife | 7 |
| Dr Linda Wadleigh | 8,15 | Jewel Whitfield | 9 |
| Danette Tilley | 10 | Jennifer Green | 11,69,288,294,296,298 |
| Eddie Hill | 16,73,76,295 | Rhonda Cumbie | 19 |
| Matthew Burke | 20,23 | Cynthia Andersen | 58 |
| Lee Wallace | 67 | Angela Garza-Viator | 68,78* |
| Angela Garza-Viator | 68 | Adam Holland | 71 |

| Public Schs..Principal | Grd | Prgm | Enr/#Cls | SN | |
|---|---|---|---|---|---|
| Baker 6th Grade Campus<br>9800 Spencer Hwy, La Porte 77571<br>Alicia Upchurch | 6-6 | T | 590<br>50 | 50% | 281/604-6800<br>Fax 281/604-6885 |
| Bayshore Elem Sch<br>800 McCabe Rd, La Porte 77571<br>Donna Spaugh | PK-5 | T | 498<br>28 | 65% | 281/604-4600<br>Fax 281/604-4680 |
| College Park Elem Sch<br>4315 Luella Ave, Deer Park 77536<br>Camilla Whitlock | PK-5 | T | 331<br>35 | 72% | 281/604-4400<br>Fax 281/604-4460 |
| Ⓐ Daep Sch<br>732 S Broadway St, La Porte 77571<br>**Deborah Stewart** | 6-12 | | 20 | | 281/604-7350 |
| Heritage Elem Sch<br>4301 East Blvd, Deer Park 77536<br>Grisel Wallace | PK-5 | T | 408 | 52% | 281/604-2600<br>Fax 281/604-2605 |
| Jennie Reid Elem Sch<br>10001 W Fairmont Pkwy, La Porte 77571<br>Diane Weeden | PK-5 | T | 308<br>32 | 50% | 281/604-4500<br>Fax 281/604-4555 |
| La Porte Elem Sch<br>725 S Broadway, La Porte 77571<br>**Linda Hyde** | PK-5 | T | 518<br>30 | 77% | 281/604-4700<br>Fax 281/604-4787 |

| | Grd | Prgm | Enr/#Cls | SN | |
|---|---|---|---|---|---|
| La Porte High Sch<br>301 E Fairmont Pkwy, La Porte 77571<br>Carlin Grammer | 9-12 | GTV | 2,104 | 44% | 281/604-7500<br>Fax 281/604-7516 |
| La Porte Junior High Sch<br>401 S Broadway St, La Porte 77571<br>Earnest Brooks | 7-8 | T | 510<br>55 | 59% | 281/604-6600<br>Fax 281/604-6605  🅕 |
| Leo A Rizzuto Elem Sch<br>3201 Farrington Blvd, La Porte 77571<br>Deanna Narcisse | PK-5 | T | 489<br>32 | 53% | 281/604-6500<br>Fax 281/604-6555 |
| Lomax Elem Sch<br>10615 N Avenue L, La Porte 77571<br>**Tracy Greenwood** | PK-5 | T | 393<br>30 | 44% | 281/604-4300<br>Fax 281/604-4355 |
| Lomax Junior High Sch<br>9801 N Avenue L, La Porte 77571<br>Kade Griffin | 7-8 | T | 608 | 53% | 281/604-6700<br>Fax 281/604-6730 |
| Ⓐ Viola DeWalt High Sch<br>401 N 2nd St, La Porte 77571<br>Candace Pohl | 6-12 | T | 67<br>13 | 59% | 281/604-6900<br>Fax 281/604-6904 |

● **Pasadena Ind School Dist** PID: 01026631     713/740-0000
1515 Cherrybrook Ln, Pasadena 77502     Fax 713/740-4040

**Schools:** 68 \ **Teachers:** 3,822 \ **Students:** 53,157 \ **Special Ed Students:** 5,647 \ **LEP Students:** 14,328 \ **College-Bound:** 54% \ **Ethnic:** Asian 3%, African American 7%, Hispanic 84%, Caucasian 6% \ **Exp:** $312 (High) \ **Poverty:** 24% \ **Title I:** $23,168,160 \ **Special Education:** $9,259,000 \ **Open-Close:** 08/18 - 05/26 \ **DTBP:** $194 (High) 🅕 🆃

| | | | |
|---|---|---|---|
| Dr Deeann Powell | 1 | Bethany Jordan | 2 |
| Carla Merka | 2,15,19 | Kevin Fornof | 3,15 |
| Thomas Douglas | 3 | Mary Harryman | 4 |
| Robert Stock | 5* | Ruperto Jaso | 6 |
| Dr Karen Hickman | 8,15,288 | Rebecca Benner | 8 |
| Erin Comeaux | 11 | Gloria Gallegos | 11,15,57,271,274,296 |
| Alyta Harrell | 15,70* | Rhonda Parmer | 15 |
| Dr Troy McCarley | 15,70,71 | Linda Fletcher | 20,23 |
| Tanya Hagar | 27* | Jennifer Capra | 30* |
| Rebecca Terry | 34 | Pat Sermas | 36,69 |
| Debbie Barrett | 58 | Julie Reed | 58,294 |
| Marshall Kendrick | 67 | Cynthia Guerrero | 68,273* |
| Karen White | 69 | Donna Summers | 70 |
| Arthur Allen | 73,98,286 | Scott Harrell | 74 |
| Traci Goodwin | 74 | Allen Brown | 76 |
| Jamie Burt | 79 | Stewart Russell | 91 |
| Olivia Daugherty | 298 | | |

| Public Schs..Principal | Grd | Prgm | Enr/#Cls | SN | |
|---|---|---|---|---|---|
| Adella Young Elem Sch<br>4221 Fox Meadow Ln, Pasadena 77504<br>Amy McClellen | PK-4 | T | 620<br>38 | 93% | 713/740-0784<br>Fax 713/740-4151 |
| Atkinson Elem Sch<br>9602 Kingspoint Rd, Houston 77075<br>Lena Ortiz | K-4 | T | 449<br>36 | 80% | 713/740-0520<br>Fax 713/740-4128 |
| Bailey Elem Sch<br>2707 Lafferty Rd, Pasadena 77502<br>Karyn Johnson | PK-4 | T | 649<br>58 | 92% | 713/740-0528<br>Fax 713/740-4129 |
| Beverly Hills Intermediate Sch<br>11111 Beamer Rd, Houston 77089<br>Stacy Barber | 7-8 | T | 954<br>41 | 79% | 713/740-0420<br>Fax 713/740-4051 |
| Bobby Shaw Middle Sch<br>1201 Houston Ave, Pasadena 77502<br>Darby Hickman | 5-6 | T | 789 | 94% | 713/740-5268<br>Fax 713/740-5909 |
| Burnett Elem Sch<br>11825 Teaneck Dr, Houston 77089<br>Jae Lee | PK-4 | T | 431<br>44 | 93% | 713/740-0536<br>Fax 713/740-4130 |

Ⓐ Community Sch · 11-12 · 75 · 713/740-0298
1838A E Sam Houston Pkwy S, Pasadena 77503 · Fax 713/740-4048
Tom Swan

Dr Kirk Lewis Career & Tech HS · Voc · 500 · 81% 713/740-5320
1348 Genoa Red Bluff Rd, Houston 77034 · Fax 713/740-5910
Steve Fleming

Elmer Bondy Intermediate Sch · 7-8 · T · 942 55 · 73% 713/740-0430
5101 Keith Rd, Pasadena 77505 · Fax 713/740-4152
Roneka Lee

Felix Morales Elem Sch · PK-4 · T · 490 36 · 95% 713/740-0664
305 W Harris Ave, Pasadena 77506 · Fax 713/740-4104
Lisa Haws

Fisher Elem Sch · PK-5 · T · 748 · 88% 713/740-0552
2920 Watters Rd, Pasadena 77502 · Fax 713/740-4131
Norma Valenzuela

Frazier Elem Sch · PK-4 · T · 485 25 · 81% 713/740-0560
10503 Hughes Rd, Houston 77089 · Fax 713/740-4132
Wendy Wiseburn

Fred Roberts Middle Sch · 5-6 · T · 612 · 86% 713/740-5390
13402 Conklin Ln, Houston 77034
Jorly Thomas

Freeman Elem Sch · PK-4 · T · 502 35 · 95% 713/740-0568
2323 Theta St, Houston 77034 · Fax 713/740-4107
Michael Van Loenen

Gardens Elem Sch · PK-4 · T · 637 40 · 95% 713/740-0576
1107 Harris Ave, Pasadena 77506 · Fax 713/740-4133
Lindsey Lesniewski

Garfield Elem Sch · PK-4 · T · 660 40 · 88% 713/740-0584
10301 Hartsook St, Houston 77034 · Fax 713/740-4134
Courtney Merilatt

Genoa Elem Sch · PK-4 · T · 704 40 · 88% 713/740-0592
12900 Almeda Genoa Rd, Houston 77034 · Fax 713/740-4135
Tiffany Bennett

George A Thompson Interm Sch · 7-8 · T · 912 69 · 81% 713/740-0510
11309 Sagedowne Ln, Houston 77089 · Fax 713/740-4083
Tanis Griffin

Golden Acres Elem Sch · PK-4 · T · 471 37 · 86% 713/740-0600
5232 Sycamore Ave, Pasadena 77503 · Fax 713/740-4136
Lisa Davis

Ⓐ Guidance Center · 5-12 · 400 24 · 713/740-0792
3010 Bayshore Blvd, Pasadena 77502 · Fax 713/740-4108
Robert Sayavedra

Harvey Turner Elem Sch · PK-4 · T · 601 36 · 69% 713/740-0768
4333 Lily St, Pasadena 77505 · Fax 713/740-4149
Donna Duke

J Frank Dobie High Sch · 9-12 · TV · 3,782 125 · 75% 713/740-0370
10220 Blackhawk Blvd, Houston 77089 · Fax 713/740-4158
Franklin Moses

Jackson Intermediate Sch · 7-8 · T · 701 69 · 94% 713/740-0440
1020 Thomas Ave, Pasadena 77506 · Fax 713/740-4109
Paula Sword

Jensen Elem Sch · PK-5 · T · 675 31 · 86% 713/740-0608
3514 Tulip St, Pasadena 77504 · Fax 713/740-4137
Judy Diaz

Jessup Elem Sch · PK-4 · T · 639 40 · 97% 713/740-0616
9301 Almeda Genoa Rd, Houston 77075 · Fax 713/740-4112
Ryan Pavone

Keller Middle Sch · 5-6 · T · 717 · 93% 713/740-5284
1711 Magnolia Dr, Pasadena 77503 · Fax 713/740-5915
Daniel Eble

Kruse Elem Sch · PK-4 · T · 489 44 · 97% 713/740-0624
400 Park Lane, Pasadena 77506 · Fax 713/740-4138
Sandra Buckner

L F Smith Elem Sch · PK-5 · T · 688 42 · 93% 713/740-0720
2703 Perez Rd, Pasadena 77502 · Fax 713/740-4113
Cathy Danna

Laura Bush Elem Sch · PK-4 · T · 651 · 71% 713/740-0928
9100 Blackhawk Blvd, Houston 77075 · Fax 713/740-4126
Stephanie Miller

Lomax Middle Sch · 5-6 · T · 680 · 69% 713/740-5230
1519 Genoa Red Bluff Rd, Pasadena 77504 · Fax 713/740-4175
Norma Penny

Lorenzo Dezavala Middle Sch · 5-6 · T · 688 37 · 97% 713/740-0544
101 Jackson Ave, Pasadena 77506 · Fax 713/740-4159
Melissa Garza

Mae Smythe Elem Sch · PK-4 · T · 708 50 · 92% 713/740-0728
2424 Burke Rd, Pasadena 77502 · Fax 713/740-4114
Denise Moody

Marshall Kendricks Middle Sch · 5-6 · T · 821 · 91% 713/740-5380
3001 Watters Rd, Pasadena 77504 · Fax 713/740-5980
Melissa Messenger

McMasters Elem Sch · PK-4 · T · 430 30 · 91% 713/740-0640
1011 Bennett Dr, Pasadena 77503 · Fax 713/740-4079
Andrea Gilger

Meador Elem Sch · PK-4 · T · 569 37 · 87% 713/740-0648
10701 Seaford Dr, Houston 77089 · Fax 713/740-4105
Beverly Bolton

Melillo Middle Sch · 5-6 · T · 718 · 75% 713/740-5260
9220 Hughes Rd, Houston 77089 · Fax 713/740-5908
Diane Wheeler

Milstead Middle Sch · 5-6 · T · 828 38 · 92% 713/740-5238
338 Gilpin St, Houston 77034 · Fax 713/740-4176
Scott Pollack

Morris Middle Sch · 5-6 · T · 881 · 82% 713/740-0672
10415 Fuqua St, Houston 77089 · Fax 713/740-4047
Allison Lewallen

Nelda Sullivan Middle Sch · 5-6 · TV · 636 · 93% 713/740-5420
1112 Queens Rd, Pasadena 77502
Kelly Cook-Costley

Park View Intermediate Sch · 6-8 · TV · 659 45 · 90% 713/740-0460
3003 Dabney Dr, Pasadena 77502 · Fax 713/740-4115
Christina Serna

Parks Elem Sch · PK-4 · T · 455 32 · 96% 713/740-0680
3302 San Augustine Ave, Pasadena 77503 · Fax 713/740-4141
Frances Burley

Pasadena High Sch · 9-12 · GTV · 2,319 · 88% 713/740-0310
206 Shaver St, Pasadena 77506 · Fax 713/740-4085
Laura Gomez

Pasadena Memorial High Sch · 9-12 · 3,125 75 · 76% 713/740-0390
4410 Crenshaw Rd, Pasadena 77504 · Fax 713/740-4156
Jeremy Richardson

Pearl Hall Elem Sch · PK-4 · T · 589 43 · 94% 713/740-0688
1504 9th St, South Houston 77587 · Fax 713/740-4142
Allison Tamez

Pomeroy Elem Sch · PK-4 · T · 879 45 · 90% 713/740-0696
920 Burke Rd, Pasadena 77506 · Fax 713/740-4103
Stephen Harding

Queens Intermediate Sch · 6-8 · T · 646 50 · 91% 713/740-0470
1452 Queens St, Houston 77017 · Fax 713/740-4101
Cleveland Lee

Red Bluff Elem Sch · PK-4 · T · 435 53 · 95% 713/740-0704
416 Bearle St, Pasadena 77506 · Fax 713/740-4143
Tammie Hinton

Richard Moore Elem Sch · PK-4 · T · 382 30 · 74% 713/740-0656
8880 Southbluff Blvd, Houston 77089 · Fax 713/740-4140
Jill Lacamu

Richey Elem Sch · PK-4 · T · 680 48 · 95% 713/740-0712
610 Richey St, Pasadena 77506 · Fax 713/740-4098
Andrea Zapata

Rick Schneider Middle Sch · 5-6 · T · 761 44 · 93% 713/740-0920
8420 Easthaven Blvd, Houston 77075 · Fax 713/740-4125
Kristin Still

| | | | | | |
|---|---|---|---|---|---|
| 1 Superintendent | 8 Curric/Instruct K-12 | 19 Chief Financial Officer | 29 Family/Consumer Science | 39 Social Studies K-12 | 49 English/Lang Arts Elem | 59 Special Education Elem | 69 Academic Assessment |
| 2 Bus/Finance/Purchasing | 9 Curric/Instruct Elem | 20 Art K-12 | 30 Adult Education | 40 Social Studies Elem | 50 English/Lang Arts Sec | 60 Special Education Sec | 70 Research/Development |
| 3 Buildings And Grounds | 10 Curric/Instruct Sec | 21 Art Elem | 31 Career/Sch-to-Work K-12 | 41 Social Studies Sec | 51 Reading K-12 | 61 Foreign/World Lang K-12 | 71 Public Information |
| 4 Food Service | 11 Federal Program | 22 Art Sec | 32 Career/Sch-to-Work Elem | 42 Science K-12 | 52 Reading Elem | 62 Foreign/World Lang Elem | 72 Summer School |
| 5 Transportation | 12 Title I | 23 Music K-12 | 33 Career/Sch-to-Work Sec | 43 Science Elem | 53 Reading Sec | 63 Foreign/World Lang Sec | 73 Instructional Tech |
| 6 Athletic | 13 Title V | 24 Music Elem | 34 Early Childhood Ed | 44 Science Sec | 54 Remedial Reading K-12 | 64 Religious Education K-12 | 74 Inservice Training |
| 7 Health Services | 15 Asst Superintendent | 25 Music Sec | 35 Health/Phys Education | 45 Math K-12 | 55 Remedial Reading Elem | 65 Religious Education Elem | 75 Marketing/Distributive |
| | 16 Instructional Media Svcs | 26 Business Education | 36 Guidance Services K-12 | 46 Math Elem | 56 Remedial Reading Sec | 66 Religious Education Sec | 76 Info Systems |
| | 17 Chief Operations Officer | 27 Career & Tech Ed | 37 Guidance Services Elem | 47 Math Sec | 57 Bilingual/ELL | 67 School Board President | 77 Psychological Assess |
| | 18 Chief Academic Officer | 28 Technology Education | 38 Guidance Services Sec | 48 English/Lang Arts K-12 | 58 Special Education K-12 | 68 Teacher Personnel | 78 Affirmative Action |

| School | Grd | Prgm | Enr/#Cls | SN | Phone |
|---|---|---|---|---|---|
| Sam Rayburn High Sch<br>2121 Cherrybrook Ln, Pasadena 77502<br>Vanessa Reyes | 9-12 | TV | 2,681<br>140 | 89% | 713/740-0330<br>Fax 713/740-4157 |
| San Jacinto Intermediate Sch<br>3600 Red Bluff Rd, Pasadena 77503<br>Jennifer Phelan | 7-8 | T | 678<br>75 | 92% | 713/740-0480<br>Fax 713/740-4153 |
| South Belt Elem Sch<br>1801 Riverstone Ranch Rd, Houston 77089<br>Candy Howard | PK-4 | T | 583 | 61% | 713/740-5276<br>Fax 713/740-5924 |
| South Houston Elem Sch<br>900 Main St, South Houston 77587<br>Edna Zarzosa | PK-4 | T | 576<br>36 | 95% | 713/740-0736<br>Fax 713/740-4144 |
| South Houston High Sch<br>3820 S Shaver St, South Houston 77587<br>Andrea Wenke | 9-12 | TV | 2,369 | 89% | 713/740-0350<br>Fax 713/740-4155 |
| South Houston Intermediate Sch<br>900 College Ave, South Houston 77587<br>Jessica Swenson | 7-8 | T | 678<br>60 | 94% | 713/740-0490<br>Fax 713/740-4097 |
| South Shaver Elem Sch<br>200 West Ave, Pasadena 77502<br>Erica Lilly | PK-4 | T | 674<br>33 | 93% | 713/740-0842<br>Fax 713/740-4145 |
| Southmore Intermediate Sch<br>2000 Patricia Ln, Pasadena 77502<br>John Moody | 7-8 | T | 721<br>70 | 94% | 713/740-0500<br>Fax 713/740-4154 |
| Sparks Elem Sch<br>2503 Southmore Ave, Pasadena 77502<br>Sherri Means | PK-4 | T | 422<br>45 | 95% | 713/740-0744<br>Fax 713/740-4146 |
| Stuchbery Elem Sch<br>11210 Hughes Rd, Houston 77089<br>Jose Hernandez | PK-4 | T | 686<br>40 | 88% | 713/740-0752<br>Fax 713/740-4147 |
| Teague Elem Sch<br>4200 Crenshaw Rd, Pasadena 77504<br>Valorie Morris | PK-4 | T | 660<br>35 | 74% | 713/740-0760<br>Fax 713/740-4148 |
| Ⓐ Tegeler Career Center<br>4949 Burke Rd, Pasadena 77504<br>Jean Cain | 6-12 | GV | 215<br>10 | 91% | 713/740-0410<br>Fax 713/740-4077 |
| Ⓐ The Summit Sch<br>1838 E Sam Houston Pkwy S, Pasadena 77503<br>Robert De Wolfe | 6-12 | G | 156<br>21 | 88% | 713/740-0290<br>Fax 713/740-4049 |
| Thomas Hancock Elem Sch<br>9604 Minnesota St, Houston 77075<br>Veronica Sandoval | PK-4 | T | 438 | 91% | 713/740-5430 |
| Vincent W Miller Interm Sch<br>1002 Fairmont Pkwy, Pasadena 77504<br>Mikie Escamilla | 7-8 | T | 858<br>60 | 92% | 713/740-0450<br>Fax 713/740-4106 |
| Virtual Sch<br>1832 E Sam Houston Pkwy S, Pasadena 77503<br>Luci Weaver | 9-12 | | 1,000 | | 713/740-0124<br>Fax 713/740-4026 |
| Walter Matthys Elem Sch<br>1500 Main St, South Houston 77587<br>Becky Vargas | PK-4 | T | 627<br>55 | 93% | 713/740-0632<br>Fax 713/740-4139 |
| Williams Elem Sch<br>1522 Scarborough Ln, Pasadena 77502<br>Christine Coppedge | PK-5 | T | 599<br>40 | 92% | 713/740-0776<br>Fax 713/740-4150 |

## ● Sheldon Ind School Dist PID: 01027013

11411 C E King Pkwy, Houston 77044

281/727-2000
Fax 281/727-2085

---

**Schools:** 12 \ **Teachers:** 556 \ **Students:** 8,500 \ **Special Ed Students:** 750 \ **LEP Students:** 2,632 \ **College-Bound:** 54% \ **Ethnic:** African American 21%, Hispanic 72%, Caucasian 6% \ **Exp:** $341 (High) \ **Poverty:** 22% \ **Title I:** $2,300,033 \ **Special Education:** $1,121,000 \ **Open-Close:** 08/12 - 05/24 \ **DTBP:** $173 (High)

---

| | | | |
|---|---|---|---|
| King Davis ...................................... 1 | | Abraham George ................................ 2,19 | |
| Cristy Gates .............................. 3,17 | | Monica Tomas ................................ 4 | |

| | | | |
|---|---|---|---|
| Derek Fitzhenry ..................................6,35 | | Paula Patterson ................... 8,15,18 | |
| Juan Duenas ....................................9,288 | | Dr Keith Brooks ......................... 10 | |
| Dr Brenda DeArmon ....................... 11,298 | | Demetrius McCall ...................... 15 | |
| Susan Pansmith ...........................54,58 | | Quyen Tieu .................................. 58 | |
| Patricia Archie ................................. 67 | | Kristy Amarantos ......................... 68 | |
| Derik Moore ..................................... 71 | | Becky Zalefnik ............... 73,76,285,286 | |
| Marcie Herrera ................................ 76 | | James Webster ......................... 79,83 | |

| Public Schs..Principal | Grd | Prgm | Enr/#Cls | SN | |
|---|---|---|---|---|---|
| **C E King High Sch**<br>11433 E Sam Houston Pkwy N, Houston 77044<br>**Dr Raff Saeed** | 9-12 | T | 1,849<br>55 | 80% | 346/378-7000<br>Fax 281/459-7346 |
| **C E King Middle Sch**<br>8530 C E King Pkwy, Houston 77044<br>**Ashley Sampson** | 6-8 | T | 1,047<br>44 | 89% | 281/727-4300<br>Fax 281/459-7452 |
| **Carroll Elem Sch**<br>10210 C E King Pkwy, Houston 77044<br>Solmaria Benavides | 1-5 | T | 847 | 87% | 281/727-4100<br>Fax 281/727-4175 |
| **Cravens Early Childhood Acad**<br>13210 Tidwell Rd, Houston 77044<br>Denise Mustin | PK-K | T | 641<br>29 | 79% | 281/727-2100<br>Fax 281/727-2160 |
| **Garrett Elem Sch**<br>12017 Garrett Rd, Houston 77044<br>Tacarra Williams | 1-5 | T | 632 | 87% | 281/727-4200<br>Fax 281/727-4275 |
| **L E Monahan Elem Sch**<br>8901 Deep Valley Dr, Houston 77044<br>Cheri Dixon | 1-5 | T | 481<br>26 | 87% | 281/454-2900<br>Fax 281/459-7452 |
| **Michael R Null Middle Sch**<br>12117 Garrett Rd, Houston 77044<br>**Katrina White** | 6-8 | T | 779<br>32 | 87% | 281/436-2800<br>Fax 281/436-2875 |
| **Royalwood Elem Sch**<br>7715 Royalwood Dr, Houston 77049<br>**Jesus Altamirano** | 1-5 | T | 647<br>27 | 86% | 281/454-2700<br>Fax 281/454-2775 |
| **Sheldon Early Childhood Acad**<br>17010 Beaumont Hwy, Houston 77049<br>**Joel Leal** | PK-K | T | 574 | 62% | 281/456-6800<br>Fax 281/456-6875 |
| **Sheldon Early Clg High Sch**<br>8540 C E King Pkwy, Houston 77044<br>Robert Hernandez | 9-11 | A | 297 | | 281/727-3500 |
| **Sheldon Elem Sch**<br>17203 Hall Shepperd Rd, Houston 77049<br>Rachelle Ysquierdo | 1-5 | T | 724<br>40 | 80% | 281/456-6700<br>Fax 281/456-6775 |
| **Sheldon Lake Elem Sch**<br>13002 Sheldon Community Dr, Houston 77044<br>Christopher Dickson | 1-5 | T | 645 | | 281/727-1100 |

## ● Spring Branch Ind School Dist PID: 01027087

955 Campbell Rd, Houston 77024

713/464-1511
Fax 713/251-2215

---

**Schools:** 47 \ **Teachers:** 2,303 \ **Students:** 35,300 \ **Special Ed Students:** 2,859 \ **LEP Students:** 10,707 \ **College-Bound:** 62% \ **Ethnic:** Asian 7%, African American 5%, Hispanic 60%, Caucasian 28% \ **Exp:** $209 (Med) \ **Poverty:** 22% \ **Title I:** $12,801,092 \ **Special Education:** $5,782,000 \ **Open-Close:** 08/24 - 05/27 \ **DTBP:** $188 (High) \ 🅕 🅣

---

| | | |
|---|---|---|
| Dr Jennifer Blaine .................................... 1 | | Christine Porter ................................ 2,15 |
| Karen Wilson ..................................2,15 | | Richard Gay ..................................... 2 |
| Travis Stanford ...............................3,15 | | Christopher Kamradt ......................... 4 |
| Sherri Lawson .......................................5 | | Paige Hershey ..................................... 5 |
| Judith Christopherson ..................... 7* | | Kristen Craft ............................... 8,18 |
| Dr Rebecca Brown ......................... 8* | | Julie Hodson ............................ 11,298 |
| Lawanda Coffee ............................. 12 | | Bryan Williams .................................... 15 |
| Christina Masick ............. 15,71,73,76,97,295 | | Jennifer Parker ................................ 15 |
| Karen Heeth ................................ 15,68 | | Karen Liska ....................................... 15 |
| Linda Buchman ............................ 15,71 | | Jessica Lily Hughes ........................ 16 |
| Christina Rice-Imumwen ....................... 27 | | David Sablatura .............................. 27 |
| Joe Kolenda ..................................31* | | Michelle Burke ................................ 57 |

---

| | | |
|---|---|---|
| Joni Warren ........................ 58 | Pam Goodson ........................ 67 | |
| Dr Keith Haffey .............. 69,294 | Mike Thomas ....................... 70 | |
| Lance Stallworth .................. 79 | Randolph Adami ................... 91 | |
| Mary Uribe-Pizana ............. 273 | | |

| Public Schs..Principal | Grd | Prgm | Enr/#Cls | SN |
|---|---|---|---|---|
| Ⓐ Academy of Choice<br>9016 Westview Dr, Houston 77055<br>Angel Purdy | 6-12 | V | 77<br>30 | 713/251-1500<br>Fax 713/251-1515 |
| Bear Boulevard Pre-School<br>8860 Westview Dr, Houston 77055<br>Kimberly Hammer | PK-PK | T | 293 | 88% 713/251-7900<br>Fax 713/365-4106 |
| Bendwood Sch<br>12750 Kimberley Ln, Houston 77024<br>Jana Bassett | Spec | T | 100<br>6 | 57% 713/251-5200<br>Fax 713/365-4992 |
| Buffalo Creek Elem Sch<br>2801 Blalock Rd, Houston 77080<br>**Carrmilla Young** | K-5 | T | 507<br>35 | 94% 713/251-5300<br>Fax 713/392-6605<br>f t |
| Bunker Hill Elem Sch<br>11950 Taylorcrest Rd, Houston 77024<br>Dana Johnson | PK-5 | | 534<br>35 | 10% 713/251-5400<br>Fax 713/365-5059 |
| Cedar Brook Elem Sch<br>2121 Ojeman Rd, Houston 77080<br>Alejandra Perez | PK-5 | T | 726<br>34 | 81% 713/251-5500<br>Fax 713/365-5027<br>f t |
| © Cornerstone Academy<br>9016 C Westview Dr, Houston 77055<br>Angel Purdy | 6-8 | | 377<br>15 | 27% 713/251-1600<br>Fax 713/365-5787 |
| Edgewood Elem Sch<br>8757 Kempwood Dr, Houston 77080<br>Jessica Tejada | PK-5 | T | 583<br>39 | 85% 713/251-5600<br>Fax 713/365-4007<br>f t |
| Frostwood Elem Sch<br>12214 Memorial Dr, Houston 77024<br>Pamela Pennington | PK-5 | | 611<br>28 | 8% 713/251-5700<br>Fax 713/365-5086 |
| Guthrie Center<br>10660 Hammerly Blvd, Houston 77043<br>Joe Kolenda | Voc | | 181<br>20 | 713/251-1300<br>Fax 713/365-4621 |
| Hollibrook Elem Sch<br>3602 Hollister St, Houston 77080<br>Anabel Taylor | PK-5 | T | 743<br>30 | 99% 713/251-5800<br>Fax 713/329-6440<br>f t |
| Housman Elem Sch<br>6705 Housman St, Houston 77055<br>Lindy Robertson | PK-5 | T | 454<br>36 | 91% 713/251-5900<br>Fax 713/613-1706 |
| Hunters Creek Elem Sch<br>10650 Beinhorn Rd, Houston 77024<br>Robalyn Snyder | PK-5 | | 569<br>29 | 17% 713/251-6000<br>Fax 713/365-4937 |
| Landrum Middle Sch<br>2200 Ridgecrest Dr, Houston 77055<br>**Roy Moore** | 6-8 | T | 670 | 91% 713/251-3700<br>Fax 713/365-4040 |
| Lion Lane Sch<br>2210 Ridgecrest Dr, Houston 77055<br>Michele Gabriel | PK-PK | T | 304<br>16 | 90% 713/251-6100<br>Fax 713/365-4364 |
| Meadow Wood Elem Sch<br>14230 Memorial Dr, Houston 77079<br>Lynne Barry | PK-5 | T | 491<br>25 | 32% 713/251-6200<br>Fax 281/560-7409<br>f t |
| Memorial Drive Elem Sch<br>11202 Smithdale Rd, Houston 77024<br>Kathleen Jeremiassen \ **Thayer Hutcheson** | PK-5 | | 426<br>23 | 11% 713/251-6300<br>Fax 713/365-4967 |
| Memorial High Sch<br>935 Echo Ln, Houston 77024<br>Lisa Weir | 9-12 | V | 2,620<br>120 | 13% 713/251-2500<br>Fax 713/365-5138 |
| Memorial Middle Sch<br>12550 Vindon Dr, Houston 77024<br>Jane Green | 6-8 | | 1,336<br>75 | 7% 713/251-3900<br>Fax 713/365-5411 |
| Northbrook High Sch<br>1 Raider Cir S, Houston 77080<br>Randolph Adami | 9-12 | T | 2,578<br>75 | 91% 713/251-2800<br>Fax 713/365-4412 |
| Northbrook Middle Sch<br>3030 Rosefield Dr, Houston 77080<br>Sarah Guerrero | 6-8 | T | 885<br>66 | 97% 713/251-4100<br>Fax 713/329-6523 |
| Nottingham Elem Sch<br>570 Nottingham Oaks Trl, Houston 77079<br>Roy Moore | PK-5 | T | 471<br>26 | 35% 713/251-6400<br>Fax 281/560-7469 |
| Panda Path Sch<br>8575 Pitner Rd, Houston 77080<br>Amanda Ruiz | PK-PK | T | 211<br>6 | 99% 713/251-8000<br>Fax 713/329-6696<br>f t |
| Pine Shadows Elem Sch<br>9900 Neuens Rd, Houston 77080<br>Christina Winstead | PK-5 | T | 659<br>52 | 78% 713/251-6500<br>Fax 713/365-4274 |
| Ridgecrest Elem Sch<br>2015 Ridgecrest Dr, Houston 77055<br>Michelle Garcia | PK-5 | T | 673<br>50 | 98% 713/251-6600<br>Fax 713/365-4067 |
| Rummel Creek Elem Sch<br>625 Brittmoore Rd, Houston 77079<br>Nancy Harn \ **Dr Laura Sloan** | PK-5 | | 689<br>35 | 5% 713/251-6700<br>Fax 713/365-5462 |
| Shadow Oaks Elem Sch<br>1335 Shadowdale Dr, Houston 77043<br>Julie Baggerly | PK-5 | T | 585<br>46 | 95% 713/251-6800<br>Fax 713/365-4585 |
| Sherwood Elem Sch<br>1700 Sherwood Forest St, Houston 77043<br>Sarah Salas | PK-5 | T | 451<br>40 | 65% 713/251-6900<br>Fax 713/365-4806 |
| Spring Branch Academic Inst<br>8390 Westview Dr, Houston 77055<br>Patricia Kassir | K-9 | | 45 | 5% 713/251-1901 |
| Spring Branch Elem Sch<br>1700 Campbell Rd, Houston 77080<br>Lynn Austin | PK-5 | T | 506<br>50 | 97% 713/251-7000<br>Fax 713/251-7015 |
| Spring Branch Middle Sch<br>1000 Piney Point Rd, Houston 77024<br>Stefanie Spencer | 6-8 | T | 1,082<br>75 | 39% 713/251-4400<br>Fax 713/365-5515 |
| Spring Forest Middle Sch<br>14240 Memorial Dr, Houston 77079<br>Raymorris Barnes | 6-8 | T | 916 | 50% 713/251-4600<br>Fax 281/560-7509 |
| Spring Oaks Middle Sch<br>2150 Shadowdale Dr, Houston 77043<br>Maria Davalos | 6-8 | T | 717<br>65 | 74% 713/251-4800<br>Fax 713/365-4522 |
| Spring Shadows Elem Sch<br>9725 Kempwood Dr, Houston 77080<br>**Raymond Stubblefield** | K-5 | T | 614<br>35 | 91% 713/251-7100<br>Fax 713/329-6480 |
| Spring Woods High Sch<br>2045 Gessner Rd, Houston 77080<br>Jennifer Collier | 9-12 | TV | 2,150 | 76% 713/251-3100<br>Fax 713/365-4474 |
| Spring Woods Middle Sch<br>9810 Neuens Rd, Houston 77080<br>Cristian Delariva | 6-8 | T | 876<br>83 | 96% 713/251-5000<br>Fax 713/365-4115 |
| Stratford High Sch<br>14555 Fern Dr, Houston 77079<br>Chad Crowson | 9-12 | V | 2,137 | 29% 713/251-3400<br>Fax 281/560-7578 |
| Terrace Elem Sch<br>10400 Rothbury St, Houston 77043<br>April Blanco | PK-5 | T | 384<br>31 | 75% 713/251-7200<br>Fax 713/329-6406 |
| Thornwood Elem Sch<br>14400 Fern Dr, Houston 77079<br>Vicki Lullo | PK-5 | T | 407<br>22 | 88% 713/251-7300<br>Fax 281/560-7439 |
| Tiger Trail Sch<br>10406 Tiger Trl, Houston 77043<br>Vidal Garza | PK-PK | T | 305<br>15 | 90% 713/251-8100<br>Fax 713/365-4578 |
| Treasure Forest Elem Sch<br>7635 Amelia Rd, Houston 77055<br>Jerona Williams | K-5 | T | 498<br>40 | 97% 713/251-7400<br>Fax 713/613-1724 |
| Valley Oaks Elem Sch<br>8390 Westview Dr, Houston 77055<br>Kimberly Reynolds | PK-5 | | 671<br>70 | 14% 713/251-7500<br>Fax 713/365-4086 |

| © Westchester Acad Int'l Studies | 6-12 | GT | 1,014 | 61% | 713/251-1800 |
|---|---|---|---|---|---|
| 901 Yorkchester Dr, Houston 77079 | | | | | Fax 713/365-5686 |
| Valerie Muniz | | | | | |

| Westwood Elem Sch | PK-5 | T | 448 | 88% | 713/251-2100 |
|---|---|---|---|---|---|
| 10595 Hammerly Blvd, Houston 77043 | | | 40 | | Fax 713/365-4555 |
| Kay Kennard | | | | | |

| Wilchester Elem Sch | PK-5 | | 769 | 5% | 713/251-7700 |
|---|---|---|---|---|---|
| 13618 Saint Marys Ln, Houston 77079 | | | 24 | | Fax 713/365-4912 |
| Anna Goodman | | | | | |

| Wildcat Way Sch | PK-PK | T | 326 | 59% | 713/251-8200 |
|---|---|---|---|---|---|
| 12754 Kimberley Ln, Houston 77024 | | | 17 | | Fax 713/365-4745 |
| Morella Tapia | | | | | |

| Woodview Elem Sch | PK-5 | T | 564 | 97% | 713/251-7800 |
|---|---|---|---|---|---|
| 9749 Cedardale Dr, Houston 77055 | | | 50 | | Fax 713/365-4294 |
| Becky Hagan | | | | | |

## • Spring Ind School Dist PID: 01027465

16717 Ella Blvd, Houston 77090

281/891-6000
Fax 281/891-6006

**Schools:** 41 \ **Teachers:** 2,164 \ **Students:** 35,600 \
**Special Ed Students:** 3,157 \ **LEP Students:** 8,264 \ **College-Bound:** 55%
\ **Ethnic:** Asian 3%, African American 41%, Hispanic 47%, Native American:
2%, Caucasian 8% \ **Exp:** $186 (Low) \ **Poverty:** 27% \ **Title I:** $16,830,008 \
**Special Education:** $5,377,000 \ **Open-Close:** 08/17 - 05/28 \ **DTBP:** $184
(High) \ 🇫 🇹

| Dr Rodney Watson | 1,288 | Ann Westbrooks | 2,19 |
|---|---|---|---|
| Phillip Ellison | 2 | Susy Morales | 2 |
| Yvette Washington | 2 | Fred Sholmire | 3 |
| Dr Frederick Walker | 3 | Shelly Copeland | 4 |
| Keith Kaup | 5 | Willie Amendola | 6 |
| Jeanne Parker | 7 | Khechara Bradford | 8,280 |
| Matt Pariseau | 8,15 | Kelli Anderson | 9 |
| Kelly Cline | 11,15 | Luis Romero | 12 |
| Dr Efrain Oliva | 15 | Dr Jennifer Cobb | 15,69,70,294 |
| Julie Hill | 15,751 | Laquita Carter | 15,81 |
| Michelle Starr | 15 | Dr Miguel Perez | 15 |
| Dr Natasha Watson | 15 | Pam Farinas | 15 |
| Dr Tameka Bruce | 15,68 | Mark Miranda | 17 |
| Joe Clark | 20,23 | Cynthia Williams | 27,31 |
| Denise Zimmermann | 36 | Lettie Houck | 57 |
| Peg Sherwood | 58 | Rhonda Newhouse | 67 |
| Turkessa Taylor | 69,294 | Karen Garrison | 71 |
| Tiffany Dunne-Oldfield | 71,93 | Kevin Holiday | 73 |
| Laura Kelchner | 76 | Dr Lupita Hinojosa | 78,79 |
| Tiffany Williams | 81 | Darryl Simon | 91 |
| Kenneth Culbreath | 91 | Jeff Kohrman | 295 |

| Public Schs..Principal | Grd | Prgm | Enr/#Cls | SN | |
|---|---|---|---|---|---|
| Anderson Elem Sch | PK-5 | T | 608 | 71% | 281/891-8360 |
| 6218 Lynngate Dr, Spring 77373 | | | | | Fax 281/891-8361 |
| Kristin Falcon | | | | | |
| Andy Dekaney High Sch | 9-12 | ATV | 2,141 | 57% | 281/891-7260 |
| 22351 Imperial Valley Dr, Houston 77073 | | | | | Fax 281/891-7261 |
| Alonzo Reynolds | | | | | |
| B F Clark Primary Sch | PK-1 | T | 725 | 91% | 281/891-8600 |
| 12625 River Laurel Dr, Houston 77014 | | | | | Fax 281/880-6396 |
| Cynthia Gomez | | | | | |
| Bailey Sch for Performing Arts | 6-8 | T | 1,310 | 72% | 281/891-8000 |
| 3377 James C Leo Dr, Spring 77373 | | | | | Fax 281/528-8945 |
| Shundra Brown | | | | | |
| Bammel Elem Sch | PK-5 | T | 803 | 73% | 281/891-8150 |
| 17309 Red Oak Dr, Houston 77090 | | | 40 | | Fax 281/587-7167 |
| Dr Berky Owolabi | | | | | |
| Bammel Middle Sch | 6-8 | TV | 939 | 69% | 281/891-7900 |
| 16711 Ella Blvd, Houston 77090 | | | | | Fax 281/444-1447 |
| Dr H Hyder | | | | | |

| Beneke Elem Sch | PK-5 | T | 695 | 82% | 281/891-8450 |
|---|---|---|---|---|---|
| 3840 Briarchase Dr, Houston 77014 | | | | | Fax 281/891-8451 |
| Latracy Harris | | | | | |
| Carl Wunsche Sr High Sch | 9-12 | AGTV | 1,473 | 64% | 281/891-7650 |
| 900 Wunsche Loop, Spring 77373 | | | 60 | | Fax 281/891-7651 |
| **Alfred Jones** | | | | | |
| Carolee Booker Elem Sch | PK-5 | TV | 844 | 86% | 281/891-8750 |
| 22352 Imperial Valley Dr, Houston 77073 | | | | | Fax 281/891-8751 |
| Keisha Womack | | | | | |
| Chet Burchett Elem Sch | PK-5 | T | 802 | 69% | 281/891-8630 |
| 3366 James C Leo Dr, Spring 77373 | | | | | Fax 281/528-6351 |
| Yvette Casas | | | | | |
| Clark Intermediate Sch | 2-5 | T | 768 | 73% | 281/891-8540 |
| 1825 Rushworth Dr, Houston 77014 | | | | | Fax 281/891-8541 |
| Torrance Brooks | | | | | |
| Deloras E Thompson Elem Sch | PK-5 | T | 678 | 79% | 281/891-8480 |
| 12470 Walters Rd, Houston 77014 | | | | | Fax 281/891-8481 |
| De'Monica Amerson | | | | | |
| Donna Lewis Elem Sch | PK-5 | T | 670 | 86% | 281/891-8720 |
| 3230 Spears Rd, Houston 77067 | | | | | Fax 281/440-4088 |
| Grace Leal | | | | | |
| Dr Edward Roberson Middle Sch | 6-8 | T | 831 | 77% | 281/891-7700 |
| 1500 S Ridge Rd, Houston 77090 | | | | | Fax 281/891-7701 |
| Tracey Walker-Daniels | | | | | |
| Dueitt Middle Sch | 6-8 | T | 1,209 | 63% | 281/891-7800 |
| 1 Eagle Xing, Spring 77373 | | | 67 | | Fax 281/528-6611 |
| Stacy Rodgers | | | | | |
| Edwin M Wells Middle Sch | 6-8 | T | 1,132 | 67% | 281/891-7750 |
| 4033 Gladeridge Dr, Houston 77068 | | | | | Fax 281/891-7751 |
| Paolo Castagnoli | | | | | |
| Ginger McNabb Elm Sch | PK-5 | T | 731 | 79% | 281/891-8690 |
| 743 E Cypresswood Dr, Spring 77373 | | | | | Fax 281/528-5980 |
| Melissa Warford | | | | | |
| Gloria Marshall Elem Sch | PK-5 | T | 690 | 68% | 281/491-4900 |
| 24505 Birnam Wood Blvd, Spring 77373 | | | | | Fax 281/891-4901 |
| **Mike Walker** | | | | | |
| Helen Major Elm Sch | PK-5 | T | 717 | 85% | 281/891-8870 |
| 16855 Sugar Pine Dr, Houston 77090 | | | | | Fax 281/586-2049 |
| Shamethia Dillard | | | | | |
| Heritage Elem Sch | PK-5 | T | 667 | 81% | 281/891-8510 |
| 12255 T C Jester Blvd, Houston 77067 | | | 45 | | Fax 832/248-6934 |
| **Trenn Russell** | | | | | |
| Hoyland Elem Sch | PK-5 | T | 797 | 70% | 281/891-8810 |
| 2200 Wittershaw Dr, Houston 77090 | | | | | Fax 281/891-8811 |
| Elisa Cole | | | | | |
| Joan Link Elm Sch | PK-5 | T | 547 | 86% | 281/891-8390 |
| 2815 Ridge Hollow Dr, Houston 77067 | | | 40 | | Fax 281/891-8391 |
| **Tangy Stith** | | | | | |
| John Winship Elem Sch | PK-5 | T | 484 | 63% | 281/891-8210 |
| 2175 Spring Creek Dr, Spring 77373 | | | | | Fax 281/528-9158 |
| Todd Armelin | | | | | |
| Meyer Elem Sch | PK-5 | T | 736 | 81% | 281/891-8270 |
| 16330 Forest Way Dr, Houston 77090 | | | 50 | | Fax 281/895-0807 |
| C'Ne Dawkins | | | | | |
| Mildred Jenkins Elem Sch | PK-5 | T | 681 | 79% | 281/891-8300 |
| 4615 Reynaldo Dr, Spring 77373 | | | | | Fax 281/891-8301 |
| **Tiffany Weston** | | | | | |
| Milton Cooper Elem Sch | PK-5 | T | 791 | 82% | 281/891-8660 |
| 18655 Imperial Valley Dr, Houston 77073 | | | | | Fax 281/209-0035 |
| **Mayra Garcia** | | | | | |
| Northgate Crossing Elem Sch | PK-5 | T | 700 | 61% | 281/891-8780 |
| 23437 Northgate Crossing Blvd, Spring 77373 | | | | | Fax 281/891-8781 |
| **Kristi Brown** | | | | | |
| Pat Reynolds Elem Sch | PK-5 | T | 698 | 75% | 281/891-8240 |
| 3975 Gladeridge Dr, Houston 77068 | | | | | Fax 281/537-7603 |
| **Dr Angeles Perez** | | | | | |

| 79 | Student Personnel | 91 | Safety/Security | 275 | Response To Intervention | 298 | Grant Writer/Ptnrships | **School Programs** | | **Social Media** | |
|---|---|---|---|---|---|---|---|---|---|---|---|
| 80 | Driver Ed/Safety | 92 | Magnet School | 277 | Remedial Math K-12 | 750 | Chief Innovation Officer | A = Alternative Program | | | |
| 81 | Gifted/Talented | 93 | Parental Involvement | 280 | Literacy Coach | 751 | Chief of Staff | G = Adult Classes | | 🇫 = Facebook | |
| 82 | Video Services | 95 | Tech Prep Program | 285 | STEM | 752 | Social Emotional Learning | M = Magnet Program | | | |
| 83 | Substance Abuse Prev | 97 | Chief Information Officer | 286 | Digital Learning | | | T = Title I Schoolwide | | 🇹 = Twitter | |
| 84 | Erate | 98 | Chief Technology Officer | 288 | Common Core Standards | **Other School Types** | | V = Career & Tech Ed Programs | | | |
| 85 | AIDS Education | 270 | Character Education | 294 | Accountability | Ⓐ = Alternative School | | | | | |
| 88 | Alternative/At Risk | 271 | Migrant Education | 295 | Network System | Ⓒ = Charter School | | New Schools are shaded | | | |
| 89 | Multi-Cultural Curriculum | 273 | Teacher Mentor | 296 | Title II Programs | Ⓜ = Magnet School | | New Superintendents and Principals are bold | | | |
| 90 | Social Work | 274 | Before/After Sch | 297 | Webmaster | Ⓨ = Year-Round School | | Personnel with email addresses are underscored | | | |

## TX—207

| | | | | | | |
|---|---|---|---|---|---|---|
| Pearl M Hirsch Elem Sch<br>2633 Trailing Vine Rd, Spring 77373<br>Dr Clare Resilla | PK-5 | T | 738<br>34 | 74% | 281/891-8330<br>Fax 281/891-8331 | |
| Ponderosa Elem Sch<br>17202 Butte Creek Rd, Houston 77090<br>Shanna Swearingin | PK-5 | T | 714<br>36 | 77% | 281/891-8180<br>Fax 281/891-8181 | |
| Ralph Eickenroht Elem Sch<br>15252 Grand Point Rd, Houston 77090<br>Robert Green | PK-5 | T | 659 | 74% | 281/891-8840<br>Fax 281/891-8841 | |
| Salyers Elem Sch<br>25705 W Hardy Rd, Spring 77373<br>Sharon Carpenter \ **Asia Presswood** | PK-5 | T | 723<br>40 | 76% | 281/891-8570<br>Fax 281/907-6969 | |
| Smith Elem Sch<br>26000 Cypresswood Dr, Spring 77373<br>Shimona Eason | PK-5 | T | 620<br>62 | 69% | 281/891-8420<br>Fax 281/891-8421 | |
| Spring Early College Academy<br>2700 WW Thorne Blvd Ste A104, Houston 77073<br>Kristine Guidry | 9-12 | | 331 | 66% | 281/891-6880<br>Fax 281/891-6881 | |
| Spring High Sch<br>19428 I-45 N, Spring 77373<br>Diaka Melendez | 9-12 | TV | 3,075 | 60% | 281/891-7000<br>Fax 281/891-7001 | |
| Spring Leadership Acad Mid Sch<br>14450 T C Jester Blvd, Houston 77014<br>Kevin Banks | 6-8 | | 401 | | 281/891-8050 | |
| Ⓐ Spring Virtual Sch<br>22351 Imperial Valley Dr # 96, Houston 77073<br>Dr Rebecca Long | 9-12 | | 930 | | 281/891-6223<br>Fax 281/891-6176 | |
| Springwoods Village Mid Sch<br>1120 Crossgate Blvd, Spring 77373<br>Kimberly Culley | 6-8 | | 401 | | 281/891-8100<br>Fax 281/891-8101 | |
| Stelle Claughton Middle Sch<br>3000 Spears Rd, Houston 77067<br>Rodney Louis | 6-8 | T | 1,214 | 66% | 281/891-7950<br>Fax 281/891-7951 | |
| Twin Creeks Middle Sch<br>27100 Cypresswood Dr, Spring 77373<br>Kenisha Williams | 6-8 | T | 984<br>59 | 66% | 281/891-7850<br>Fax 281/891-7851 | |
| Westfield High Sch<br>16713 Ella Blvd, Houston 77090<br>David Mason | 9-12 | TV | 2,863 | 57% | 281/891-7130<br>Fax 281/891-7131 | |

- **Tomball Ind School Dist** PID: 01027568     281/357-3100
  310 S Cherry St, Tomball 77375     Fax 281/357-3128

---

**Schools:** 20 \ **Teachers:** 1,045 \ **Students:** 16,289 \
**Special Ed Students:** 1,386 \ **LEP Students:** 1,536 \ **College-Bound:** 64%
\ **Ethnic:** Asian 8%, African American 5%, Hispanic 32%, Caucasian
55% \ **Exp:** $186 (Low) \ **Poverty:** 7% \ **Title I:** $1,034,936 \
**Special Education:** $1,532,000 \ **Open-Close:** 08/18 - 05/27 \ **DTBP:** $188
(High) \ 🄵 🄴

---

| | | | |
|---|---|---|---|
| Dr Martha Salazar-Zamora | 1 | Zachery Boles | 2 |
| Aaron Wallace | 3 | Eric Saunders | 3 |
| Juan Trevino | 3 | Beth Hunt | 4 |
| Kevin White | 4 | Whitney Johnson | 4 |
| Beverly Beisert | 5 | Bullet Fenske | 5 |
| Deshaun Washington | 5 | Dyna Bigley | 5 |
| Vince Sebo | 6 | Cathy Pool | 7,35,85 |
| David Surdovel | 8,45 | Valerie Petrzelka | 9,15,69* |
| Dr Rick Fernandez | 10,15,69 | Mark White | 11,15,294 |
| Xochitl Salazar | 11 | Dr Michael Webb | 15,79 |
| Nefertari Mundy | 15,70,74 | Sharon Meanor | 15 |
| Dr Steven Gutierrez | 17 | Dr Amy Schindewolf | 18 |
| James Ross | 19 | J Janda | 20,23 |
| Karla Sandoval | 27 | James Watson | 28,76,95 |
| Jessica Perez | 34,57 | Crystal Romero-Mueller | 39,81 |
| Chris Scott | 42,45* | Jennifer Adams | 42 |
| Dr Katie Atkins | 48 | Keri Williams | 58 |
| Michael Pratt | 67 | Juan Santos | 68 |

| | | | |
|---|---|---|---|
| Juan Garza | 68 | Tricia Baldwin | 69 |
| Justin Warnasch | 71 | Jason Curry | 73 |
| Kenneth Cloud | 76 | Heather Nichols | 270 |
| Mary Beth Barr | 280 | Dianne Tidwell | 286 |
| Christopher Montgomery | 295 | Thomas Cranshaw | 295 |

| Public Schs..Principal | Grd | Prgm | Enr/#Cls | SN |
|---|---|---|---|---|
| Canyon Point Elem Sch<br>13002 Northpointe Blvd, Tomball 77377<br>Barbara Coleman | PK-4 | | 778 | 27% 281/357-3122<br>Fax 281/357-3147 |
| Creekside Forest Elem Sch<br>5949 Creekside Forest Dr, Spring 77389<br>Sherri Trammell | K-6 | | 576 | 3% 281/357-4526<br>Fax 281/357-4535 |
| Creekside Park Jr High Sch<br>8711 Creekside Green Dr, The Woodlands 77375<br>Dr Mindy Munoz | 6-8 | | 766 | 9% 281/357-3282<br>Fax 281/516-9606 |
| Creekview Elem Sch<br>8877 W New Harmony Trl, The Woodlands 77375<br>**Bianca Shaughnessy** | PK-5 | | 614 | 9% 281/357-3070<br>Fax 281/357-3071 |
| Decker Prairie Elem Sch<br>27427 Decker Prairie Rosehl Rd, Magnolia 77355<br>Brenda Blackmon | PK-4 | T | 705<br>38 | 46% 281/357-3134<br>Fax 281/357-3293<br>🄣 |
| Lakewood Elem Sch<br>15614 Gettysburg Dr, Tomball 77377<br>Deanna Porter | PK-4 | | 850 | 22% 281/357-3260<br>Fax 281/357-3271<br>🄣 |
| Northpointe Intermediate Sch<br>11855 Northpointe Blvd, Tomball 77377<br>Darrell McReynolds | 5-6 | | 752 | 21% 281/357-3020<br>Fax 281/357-3026 |
| Oakcrest Intermediate Sch<br>18202 Shaw Rd, Cypress 77429<br>George Flores | 5-6 | | 693 | 23% 281/357-3033<br>Fax 281/357-3034 |
| Rosehill Elem Sch<br>17950 Tomball Waller Rd, Tomball 77377<br>Gloria Vasquez | PK-4 | T | 369<br>20 | 39% 281/357-3075<br>Fax 281/357-3099<br>🄣 |
| Timber Creek Elem Sch<br>8455 Creekside Green Dr, The Woodlands 77389<br>Lauren Thompson | PK-6 | | 492 | 8% 281/357-3060<br>Fax 281/357-3061<br>🄣 |
| Ⓐ Tomball Connections Acadamy<br>1302 Keefer Rd Ste A, Tomball 77375<br>Bob Thompson | 5-12 | | 60<br>6 | 281/357-3281<br>Fax 281/357-3291 |
| Tomball Elem Sch<br>1110 Inwood St, Tomball 77375<br>Chad Schmidt | PK-4 | T | 700<br>35 | 55% 281/357-3280<br>Fax 281/357-3288 |
| Tomball High Sch<br>30330 Quinn Rd, Tomball 77375<br>Chris Scott | 9-12 | V | 2,055 | 27% 281/357-3220<br>Fax 281/357-3228<br>🄵🄣 |
| Tomball Intermediate Sch<br>723 W Main St, Tomball 77375<br>Samora Davis | 5-6 | T | 761<br>26 | 44% 281/357-3150<br>Fax 281/357-3148 |
| Tomball Junior High Sch<br>30403 Quinn Rd, Tomball 77375<br>Chad Allman | 7-8 | TV | 767 | 38% 281/357-3000<br>Fax 281/357-3027 |
| Tomball Memorial High Sch<br>19100 Northpointe Ridge Ln, Tomball 77377<br>Mike Metz | 9-12 | | 2,310 | 17% 281/357-3230<br>Fax 281/357-3240 |
| Tomball Star Academy<br>30330 Quinn Rd, Tomball 77375<br>Kimberle McKinney | 9-9 | | 104 | 21% 281/357-3222 |
| Wildwood Elem Sch<br>13802 Northpointe Blvd, Tomball 77377<br>**Beatriz Shaughnessy** | PK-4 | | 1,041 | 20% 281/357-3040<br>Fax 281/357-3041 |
| Willow Creek Elem Sch<br>18302 N Eldridge Pkwy, Tomball 77377<br>Teresa Sullivan | PK-4 | | 647<br>60 | 21% 281/357-3080<br>Fax 281/357-3092 |
| Willow Wood Junior High Sch<br>11770 Gregson Rd, Tomball 77377<br>Robert Frost | 7-8 | V | 1,353 | 18% 281/357-3030<br>Fax 281/357-3044 |

---

| | | | | | | | | |
|---|---|---|---|---|---|---|---|---|
| 1 | Superintendent | 8 | Curric/Instruct K-12 | 19 | Chief Financial Officer | 29 | Family/Consumer Science | |
| 2 | Bus/Finance/Purchasing | 9 | Curric/Instruct Elem | 20 | Art K-12 | 30 | Adult Education | |
| 3 | Buildings And Grounds | 10 | Curric/Instruct Sec | 21 | Art Elem | 31 | Career/Sch-to-Work K-12 | |
| 4 | Food Service | 11 | Federal Program | 22 | Art Sec | 32 | Career/Sch-to-Work Elem | |
| 5 | Transportation | 12 | Title I | 23 | Music K-12 | 33 | Career/Sch-to-Work Sec | |
| 6 | Athletic | 13 | Title V | 24 | Music Elem | 34 | Early Childhood Ed | |
| 7 | Health Services | 15 | Asst Superintendent | 25 | Music Sec | 35 | Health/Phys Education | |
| | | 16 | Instructional Media Svcs | 26 | Business Education | 36 | Guidance Services K-12 | |
| | | 17 | Chief Operations Officer | 27 | Career & Tech Ed | 37 | Guidance Services Elem | |
| | | 18 | Chief Academic Officer | 28 | Technology Education | 38 | Guidance Services Sec | |

| | | | | | | | |
|---|---|---|---|---|---|---|---|
| 39 | Social Studies K-12 | 49 | English/Lang Arts Elem | 59 | Special Education Elem | 69 | Academic Assessment |
| 40 | Social Studies Elem | 50 | English/Lang Arts Sec | 60 | Special Education Sec | 70 | Research/Development |
| 41 | Social Studies Sec | 51 | Reading K-12 | 61 | Foreign/World Lang K-12 | 71 | Public Information |
| 42 | Science K-12 | 52 | Reading Elem | 62 | Foreign/World Lang Elem | 72 | Summer School |
| 43 | Science Elem | 53 | Reading Sec | 63 | Foreign/World Lang Sec | 73 | Instructional Tech |
| 44 | Science Sec | 54 | Remedial Reading K-12 | 64 | Religious Education K-12 | 74 | Inservice Training |
| 45 | Math K-12 | 55 | Remedial Reading Elem | 65 | Religious Education Elem | 75 | Marketing/Distributive |
| 46 | Math Elem | 56 | Remedial Reading Sec | 66 | Religious Education Sec | 76 | Info Systems |
| 47 | Math Sec | 57 | Bilingual/ELL | 67 | School Board President | 77 | Psychological Assess |
| 48 | English/Lang Arts K-12 | 58 | Special Education K-12 | 68 | Teacher Personnel | 78 | Affirmative Action |

## HARRIS CATHOLIC SCHOOLS

● **Archdiocese Galveston-Houston** PID: 01027855   713/741-8704
2403 Holcombe Blvd, Houston 77021   Fax 713/741-7379

**Schools: 55 \ Students: 18,631**

Listing includes only schools located in this county. See District Index for location of Diocesan Offices.

| Catholic Schs..Principal | Grd | Prgm | Enr/#Cls | SN |
|---|---|---|---|---|
| Assumption Catholic Sch<br>801 Roselane St, Houston 77037<br>John Bates | PK-8 | | 257<br>14 | 281/447-2132<br>Fax 281/447-1825 |
| Christ the Redeemer Cath Sch<br>11511 Huffmeister Rd, Houston 77065<br>Dan Courtney | PK-8 | | 250 | 281/469-8440<br>Fax 281/984-9669 |
| Corpus Christi Catholic Sch<br>4005 Cheena Dr, Houston 77025<br>Dr Mazie McCoy | PK-8 | | 205<br>10 | 713/664-3351<br>Fax 713/664-6095 f |
| Duchesne Acad of Sacred Heart<br>10202 Memorial Dr, Houston 77024<br>Ginger Montalbano \ Amy Witten | PK-12 | | 700<br>65 | 713/468-8211<br>Fax 713/465-9809 |
| Epiphany of the Lord Cath Sch<br>20910 Highland Knolls Dr, Katy 77450<br>Dr Nicholas Morgan | K-6 | | 140 | 832/391-6500 |
| Frassati Catholic High Sch<br>22151 Frassati Way, Spring 77389<br>Sr John Paul | 9-12 | | 200 | 832/616-3217<br>Fax 281/907-0675 |
| Holy Ghost Catholic Sch<br>6920 Chimney Rock Rd, Houston 77081<br>Deborah Crowe | PK-8 | | 138<br>10 | 713/668-5327<br>Fax 713/667-4410 |
| Incarnate Word Academy<br>609 Crawford St, Houston 77002<br>Andrea Smith | 9-12 | | 273<br>30 | 713/227-3637<br>Fax 713/227-1014 |
| Our Lady of Fatima Sch<br>1702 9th St, Galena Park 77547<br>Miguel Sanchez | PK-6 | | 89<br>5 | 713/674-5832<br>Fax 713/674-3877 f |
| Our Lady of Guadalupe Sch<br>2405 Navigation Blvd, Houston 77003<br>Irazema Ortiz | PK-8 | | 218<br>13 | 713/224-6904<br>Fax 713/225-2122 |
| Regis Sch of the Sacred Heart<br>7330 Westview Dr, Houston 77055<br>Wendy Canales | PK-8 | | 200<br>20 | 713/682-8383<br>Fax 713/682-8388 f t |
| Resurrection Catholic Sch<br>916 Majestic St, Houston 77020<br>Dora Martinez | PK-8 | | 149<br>10 | 713/674-5545<br>Fax 713/674-2151 f t |
| Sacred Heart Sch<br>907 Runneburg Rd, Crosby 77532<br>Susan Harris | PK-8 | | 204<br>11 | 281/328-6561<br>Fax 281/462-0072 t |
| St Agnes Academy<br>9000 Bellaire Blvd, Houston 77036<br>Carleen Raymond | 9-12 | | 920<br>30 | 713/219-5400<br>Fax 713/219-5499 |
| St Ambrose Sch<br>4213 Mangum Rd, Houston 77092<br>Sarah MacDonald | PK-8 | | 281<br>24 | 713/686-6990 |
| St Anne Catholic Elem Sch<br>1111 S Cherry St, Tomball 77375<br>Joseph Noonan | PK-8 | | 350<br>20 | 281/351-0093<br>Fax 281/357-1905 |
| St Anne Sch<br>2120 Westheimer Rd, Houston 77098<br>Dawn Martinez | PK-8 | | 498<br>30 | 713/526-3279<br>Fax 713/526-8025 |
| St Augustine Catholic Sch<br>5500 Laurel Creek Way, Houston 77017<br>Denise Rios | PK-8 | | 202<br>15 | 713/946-9050<br>Fax 713/943-3444 f t |
| St Catherine's Montessori Sch<br>9821 Timberside Dr, Houston 77025<br>Susan Tracy | PK-9 | | 235<br>10 | 713/665-2195<br>Fax 713/665-1478 |
| St Cecilia Catholic Sch<br>11740 Joan of Arc Dr, Houston 77024<br>Jeff Matthews | PK-8 | | 590<br>13 | 713/468-9515<br>Fax 713/468-4698 |
| St Christopher Catholic Sch<br>8134 Park Place Blvd, Houston 77017<br>Claudia Cavazos | PK-8 | | 243<br>20 | 713/649-0009<br>Fax 713/649-1104 |
| St Clare of Assisi Sch<br>3131 El Dorado Blvd, Houston 77059<br>Dr Al Varisco | PK-8 | | 222<br>15 | 281/286-3395<br>Fax 281/286-1256 |
| St Edward Catholic Sch<br>2601 Spring Stuebner Rd, Spring 77389<br>Erin Makel | PK-8 | | 395<br>21 | 281/353-4570<br>Fax 281/353-8255 |
| St Elizabeth Seton Cath Sch<br>6646 Addicks Satsuma Rd, Houston 77084<br>Ignacio Aguilera | PK-8 | | 528<br>26 | 281/463-1444<br>Fax 281/463-8707 |
| St Francis DeSales Sch<br>8100 Roos Rd, Houston 77036<br>Anne Quatrini | PK-8 | | 470<br>19 | 713/774-4447<br>Fax 713/271-6744 |
| St Jerome Sch<br>8825 Kempwood Dr, Houston 77080<br>Jan Krametbauer | PK-8 | | 303<br>32 | 713/468-7946<br>Fax 713/464-0325 |
| St John Paul II Catholic Sch<br>1400 Parkway Plaza Dr, Houston 77077<br>Rebecca Bogard | PK-8 | | 712<br>40 | 281/496-1500<br>Fax 281/496-2943 |
| St John XXIII Preparatory HS<br>1800 W Grand Pkwy N, Katy 77449<br>Joseph Noonan | 9-12 | | 240 | 281/693-1000<br>Fax 281/693-1001 |
| St Joseph Sch<br>1811 Carolina St, Baytown 77520<br>Deborah Francis | PK-8 | | 115<br>15 | 281/422-9749<br>Fax 281/422-7001 |
| St Martha Catholic Sch<br>2411 Oak Shores Dr, Kingwood 77339<br>Jessica Munscher | PK-8 | | 250<br>21 | 281/358-5523<br>Fax 281/358-5526 |
| St Mary Magdalene Sch<br>530 Ferguson St, Humble 77338<br>Joshua Raab | PK-8 | | 300<br>19 | 281/446-8535<br>Fax 281/446-8527 |
| St Mary Purification Mont Sch<br>3006 Rosedale St, Houston 77004<br>Lois Goudeau | PK-5 | | 120<br>9 | 713/522-9276<br>Fax 713/522-1879 f |
| St Michael Catholic Sch<br>1833 Sage Rd, Houston 77056<br>Dr Kathleen Cox | PK-8 | | 500<br>20 | 713/621-6847<br>Fax 713/877-8812 |
| St Peter the Apostle Elem Sch<br>6220 La Salette St, Houston 77021<br>Toni Marshall | PK-8 | | 40<br>9 | 713/747-9484<br>Fax 713/842-7055 |
| St Pius X High Sch<br>811 W Donovan St, Houston 77091 | 9-12 | | 695<br>50 | 713/692-3581<br>Fax 713/692-5725 |
| St Rose of Lima Sch<br>3600 Brinkman St, Houston 77018<br>Bernadette Drabek | PK-8 | | 346<br>16 | 713/691-0104<br>Fax 713/692-8073 |
| St Theresa Sch<br>6623 Rodrigo St, Houston 77007<br>Melissa Ilski | PK-8 | | 275<br>8 | 713/864-4536<br>Fax 713/869-5184 |

| | Grd | | Enr/#Cls | SN | |
|---|---|---|---|---|---|
| St Thomas High Sch<br>4500 Memorial Dr, Houston 77007<br>Dr Aaron Dominguez | 9-12 | | 680<br>80 | | 713/864-6348<br>Fax 713/864-5750 |
| St Thomas More Sch<br>5927 Wigton Dr, Houston 77096<br>Kristen Thome | PK-8 | | 525<br>25 | | 713/729-3434<br>Fax 713/721-5644 |
| St Vincent De Paul Sch<br>6802 Buffalo Speedway, Houston 77025<br>Carolyn Sears | PK-8 | | 512<br>22 | | 713/666-2345<br>Fax 713/663-3562 |
| Strake Jesuit College Prep Sch<br>8900 Bellaire Blvd, Houston 77036<br>Ken Lojo | 9-12 | | 900<br>30 | | 713/774-7651<br>Fax 713/774-6427 |

## HARRIS PRIVATE SCHOOLS

| Private Schs..Principal | Grd | Prgm | Enr/#Cls | SN | |
|---|---|---|---|---|---|
| A Plus Unlimited Potential Sch<br>821 Chelsea Blvd, Houston 77002<br>Paul Castro | 6-8 | | 40 | | 713/658-1881 |
| Abiding Word Lutheran Sch<br>17123 Red Oak Dr, Houston 77090<br>Ben Carlovsky | K-8 | | 110<br>6 | | 281/895-7048<br>Fax 281/453-2920 |
| Al-Hadi Sch of Accel Lrng<br>14855 Richmond Ave, Houston 77082<br>Br Seyed Abedi | PK-12 | | 250 | | 832/617-8363<br>Fax 713/513-5315 |
| Alexander Smith Academy<br>10255 Richmond Ave Ste 100, Houston 77042<br>Pam Rameau | 9-12 | | 63<br>13 | | 713/266-0920<br>Fax 713/266-8857 |
| Annunciation Orthodox Sch<br>3600 Yoakum Blvd, Houston 77006<br>Sharon Corbett \ Heather Haas | PK-8 | | 710<br>40 | | 713/470-5630<br>Fax 713/470-5605 |
| Ⓐ Archway Academy<br>6221 Main St, Houston 77030<br>Tonya Sanders-Woods | 9-12 | | 20 | | 713/328-0780<br>Fax 713/328-0781 |
| Ascension Episcopal Sch<br>2525 Seagler Rd, Houston 77042<br>Nancy Clausey | PK-5 | | 125<br>16 | | 713/783-0260<br>Fax 713/787-9162 |
| Avondale House Sch<br>3737 Omeara Dr, Houston 77025<br>Becky Ingalls | Spec | | 60 | | 713/993-9544<br>Fax 713/993-0751 |
| Awty International Sch<br>7455 Awty School Ln, Houston 77055<br>Tim Long \ Tom Beuscher \ Sam Waugh | PK-12 | | 1,600 | | 713/686-4850<br>Fax 713/686-4956 |
| Banff Sch<br>13726 Cutten Rd, Houston 77069<br>Deborah Wasser | PK-12 | | 178<br>16 | | 281/444-9326 |
| Bay Area Montessori House<br>17222 Mercury Dr, Houston 77058<br>Tommie Jean Hebert | PK-6 | | 91<br>4 | | 281/480-7022<br>Fax 281/461-3597 |
| Baytown Christian Academy<br>5555 N Main St, Baytown 77521<br>James Twardowski | PK-12 | | 300<br>33 | | 281/421-4150<br>Fax 281/421-4038 |
| Beth Yeshurun Sch<br>4525 Beechnut St, Houston 77096<br>Cortney Hebert | PK-5 | | 196<br>30 | | 713/666-1884<br>Fax 713/666-2924 |
| Branch Sch<br>1424 Sherwood Forest St, Houston 77043<br>Emily Smith | PK-8 | | 120 | | 713/465-0288<br>Fax 713/465-0337 |
| Briarwood Sch<br>12207 Whittington Dr, Houston 77077<br>Amanda Jocz \ Lisa Landi | Spec | V | 320<br>50 | | 281/493-1070<br>Fax 281/493-1343 |
| British Int'l Sch of Houston<br>2203 N Westgreen Blvd, Katy 77449<br>Mark Wilson | PK-12 | | 1,090 | | 713/290-9025<br>Fax 713/290-9014 |
| Brookhollow Christian Academy<br>5725 Queenston Blvd, Houston 77084<br>Markena Kelley | PK-3 | | 401 | | 281/649-6813 |
| Center for Hearing & Speech<br>1417 Houston Ave, Houston 77007<br>Renee Davis | PK-1 | | 30<br>8 | | 713/523-3633<br>Fax 713/523-8399 |
| Central Christian Academy<br>2217 Bingle Rd, Houston 77055<br>Scott Jacobs | PK-12 | | 40<br>8 | | 713/468-3248<br>Fax 713/468-7322 |
| Centro Chrn Alpha Omega Acad<br>5621 North Fwy, Houston 77076<br>Gerardo Cardenas | PK-12 | | 76 | | 713/697-6726<br>Fax 713/697-1726 |
| Chinquapin Prep Sch<br>2615 E Wallisville Rd, Highlands 77562<br>Dorothy Scrutchin \ Dr Angela Postigo | 6-12 | | 150<br>10 | | 281/426-5551<br>Fax 281/426-5553 |
| Christian Life Center Academy<br>806 Russell Palmer Rd, Kingwood 77339<br>Dr Aaron Miller | K-12 | | 65<br>14 | | 281/319-4673<br>Fax 281/446-5501 |
| Concordia Lutheran High Sch<br>700 E Main St, Tomball 77375<br>Julie Kangas | 9-12 | | 580<br>24 | | 281/351-2547<br>Fax 281/255-8806 |
| Connection School of Houston<br>15815 House Hahl Rd, Cypress 77433<br>Kathleen Wrobleske | K-12 | | 200 | | 832/544-6031<br>Fax 855/286-3088 |
| Covenant Academy<br>11711 Telge Rd, Cypress 77429<br>Leslie Collins | K-12 | | 214<br>9 | | 281/373-2233<br>Fax 281/582-8227 |
| Covenant Preparatory Sch<br>1711 Hamblen Rd, Humble 77339<br>Erica Nevenglosky \ Claudiu Cimpean | PK-12 | | 300<br>20 | | 281/359-1090<br>Fax 281/359-5560 |
| Cristo Rey Jesuit Clg Prep HS<br>6700 Mount Carmel St, Houston 77087<br>Eileen Quinones | 9-12 | | 500 | | 281/501-1298<br>Fax 281/501-3485 |
| Crossroads Sch<br>5822 Dolores St, Houston 77057<br>Justin Adams | Spec | | 70<br>7 | | 713/977-1221<br>Fax 713/977-0010 |
| Cunae International Sch<br>5655 Creekside Forest Dr, Spring 77389<br>Anji Price | PK-12 | | 120 | | 281/516-3770 |
| Cypress Cmty Christian Sch<br>11123 Cypress N Houston Rd, Houston 77065<br>Joy Bezner \ Iva Nell Rhea \ Dr Ryan Berens | K-12 | | 600 | | 281/469-8829<br>Fax 281/469-6040 |
| Darul Arqam Sch<br>8830 Galveston Rd, Houston 77034<br>Zaheer Anwar | PK-6 | | 104<br>10 | | 713/948-0094<br>Fax 713/947-6294 |
| Darul Arqam School-North<br>11815 Adel Rd, Houston 77067<br>Saboohi Adhami | PK-12 | | 200 | | 281/583-1984<br>Fax 281/440-8024 |
| Emery Weiner Sch<br>9825 Stella Link Rd, Houston 77025<br>Kendall White \ Joseph Sears | 6-12 | | 450<br>50 | | 832/204-5900<br>Fax 832/204-5910 |
| Epiphany Lutheran Sch<br>14423 West Rd, Houston 77041<br>Jon Fraker | PK-8 | | 274 | | 713/896-1316 |
| Episcopal High Sch<br>4650 Bissonnet St, Bellaire 77401<br>Kim Randolph | 9-12 | | 676 | | 713/512-3400<br>Fax 713/512-3603 |
| Eternity Christian Sch<br>1122 West Rd, Houston 77038<br>Beth Bashinski | PK-8 | | 140 | | 281/999-5107 |
| Faith Christian Academy<br>3519 Burke Rd, Pasadena 77504<br>Rachel Mitchell | K-12 | | 70<br>13 | | 713/943-9978<br>Fax 713/944-4416 |
| Faith West Academy<br>2225 Porter Rd, Katy 77493<br>Mary Strickland | PK-12 | | 600 | | 281/391-5683<br>Fax 281/391-2606 |

| | | | |
|---|---|---|---|
| 1 Superintendent | 8 Curric/Instruct K-12 | 19 Chief Financial Officer | 29 Family/Consumer Science |
| 2 Bus/Finance/Purchasing | 9 Curric/Instruct Elem | 20 Art K-12 | 30 Adult Education |
| 3 Buildings And Grounds | 10 Curric/Instruct Sec | 21 Art Elem | 31 Career/Sch-to-Work K-12 |
| 4 Food Service | 11 Federal Program | 22 Art Sec | 32 Career/Sch-to-Work Elem |
| 5 Transportation | 12 Title I | 23 Music K-12 | 33 Career/Sch-to-Work Sec |
| 6 Athletic | 13 Title V | 24 Music Elem | 34 Early Childhood Ed |
| 7 Health Services | 15 Asst Superintendent | 25 Music Sec | 35 Health/Phys Education |
| | 16 Instructional Media Svcs | 26 Business Education | 36 Guidance Services K-12 |
| | 17 Chief Operations Officer | 27 Career & Tech Ed | 37 Guidance Services Elem |
| | 18 Chief Academic Officer | 28 Technology Education | 38 Guidance Services Sec |

| | | | |
|---|---|---|---|
| 39 Social Studies K-12 | 49 English/Lang Arts Elem | 59 Special Education Elem | 69 Academic Assessment |
| 40 Social Studies Elem | 50 English/Lang Arts Sec | 60 Special Education Sec | 70 Research/Development |
| 41 Social Studies Sec | 51 Reading K-12 | 61 Foreign/World Lang K-12 | 71 Public Information |
| 42 Science K-12 | 52 Reading Elem | 62 Foreign/World Lang Elem | 72 Summer School |
| 43 Science Elem | 53 Reading Sec | 63 Foreign/World Lang Sec | 73 Instructional Tech |
| 44 Science Sec | 54 Remedial Reading K-12 | 64 Religious Education K-12 | 74 Inservice Training |
| 45 Math K-12 | 55 Remedial Reading Elem | 65 Religious Education Elem | 75 Marketing/Distributive |
| 46 Math Elem | 56 Remedial Reading Sec | 66 Religious Education Sec | 76 Info Systems |
| 47 Math Sec | 57 Bilingual/ELL | 67 School Board President | 77 Psychological Assess |
| 48 English/Lang Arts K-12 | 58 Special Education K-12 | 68 Teacher Personnel | 78 Affirmative Action |

| School | Grades | Enrollment/Staff | Phone/Fax |
|---|---|---|---|
| Family Christian Academy<br>14718 Woodford Dr, Houston 77015<br>John Bohacek | PK-12 | 401 | 713/455-4483 |
| First Baptist Academy<br>7450 Memorial Woods Dr, Houston 77024<br>Dr Mary White \ Kelli Diers | K-8 | 450 | 713/290-2500<br>Fax 713/290-2508 |
| First Baptist Christian Acad<br>7500 Fairmont Pkwy, Pasadena 77505<br>Cindy McDonald \ Toni Shuman | PK-12 | 550<br>38 | 281/991-9191<br>Fax 281/991-7092 |
| Founders Christian Sch<br>24724 Aldine Westfield Rd, Spring 77373<br>Joe Jones | PK-12 | 105 | 281/602-8006 |
| Fusion Acad-Houston Galleria<br>5065 Westheimer Rd Ste 840, Houston 77056<br>Elizabeth Beguerie | 6-12 | 50 | 713/963-9096 |
| Gateway Academy<br>3721 Dacoma St, Houston 77092<br>Scott Adams | 7-12 | 36<br>13 | 713/659-7900<br>Fax 713/659-7901 |
| Generation One Academy<br>PO Box 8280, Houston 77288<br>Tori Dugar | PK-5 | 45 | 713/654-8008<br>Fax 832/767-1619 |
| Grace Christian Academy<br>14325 Crescent Landing Dr, Houston 77062<br>Ron McCallon | K-12 | 250 | 281/488-4883 |
| Grace Sch<br>10219 Ella Lee Ln, Houston 77042<br>Leigh Anne Shumate \ Robert Williford | PK-8 | 440<br>49 | 713/782-4421<br>Fax 713/267-5056 |
| Holy Spirit Episcopal Sch<br>12535 Perthshire Rd, Houston 77024<br>Karen Palividas \ Brian Smith | PK-8 | 250<br>30 | 713/468-5138<br>Fax 713/465-6972 |
| Holy Trinity Episcopal Sch<br>11810 Lockwood Rd, Houston 77044<br>Troy Roddy | PK-12 | 130<br>11 | 281/459-4323<br>Fax 281/459-4302<br>f |
| Houston Adventist Academy<br>11735 Grant Rd, Cypress 77429<br>Brenda Elms | K-12 | 150<br>7 | 713/896-0071 |
| Houston Christian High Sch<br>2700 W Sam Houston Pkwy N, Houston 77043<br>Dr Darren Price | 9-12 | 500<br>40 | 713/580-6000<br>Fax 713/580-6001 |
| Houston Learning Academy<br>6200 Winfield Rd, Houston 77050<br>Lesley Boyer | 9-12 | 30<br>6 | 281/449-1532<br>Fax 281/537-2361 |
| Humble Christian Sch<br>16202 Old Humble Rd, Humble 77396<br>Ted Howell | PK-12 | 330<br>22 | 281/441-1313<br>Fax 281/441-1329 |
| Ilm Academy<br>1209 Conrad Sauer Dr, Houston 77043<br>Zuhaira Razzack | PK-8 | 180 | 713/464-4720 |
| Iman Academy Southeast<br>825 Jetstream, Webster 77598<br>Aliyah Harris \ Ms Nikki | PK-11 | 295<br>15 | 281/204-8710<br>Fax 281/204-8717 |
| Iman Academy-Southwest<br>6240 Highway 6 S, Houston 77083<br>Baha Zaqat \ Abdullah Masias | PK-12 | 500 | 281/498-1345<br>Fax 281/498-5145 |
| Irvin M Shlenker Sch<br>5600 N Braeswood Blvd Ste A, Houston 77096<br>Dr Michelle Barton | PK-5 | 375<br>30 | 713/270-6127<br>Fax 713/270-6114 |
| Joy Sch<br>1 Chelsea Blvd, Houston 77006<br>Shara Bumgarner | Spec | 150<br>20 | 713/523-0660<br>Fax 713/523-5660<br>f |
| Kardia Christian Academy<br>10555 Spring Cypress Rd, Houston 77070<br>Joellis McCall | PK-6 | 57<br>7 | 281/378-4040<br>Fax 281/378-4081 |
| Katy Adventist Christian Sch<br>1913 East Ave, Katy 77493<br>Andrea Kiture | PK-8 | 40 | 281/392-5603 |
| Kingdom Academy<br>13334 Wallisville Rd, Houston 77049<br>Faith Coble | PK-6 | 53<br>4 | 713/450-0021<br>Fax 713/453-0855 |
| Living Word Christian Academy<br>6601 Antoine Dr, Houston 77091<br>Tina Armstrong | PK-PK | 55<br>25 | 713/686-5538<br>Fax 713/686-6840 |
| Lutheran High School North<br>1130 W 34th St, Houston 77018<br>Dana Gerard | 9-12 | 175<br>15 | 713/880-3131<br>Fax 713/880-5447 |
| Lutheran South Academy<br>12555 Ryewater Dr, Houston 77089<br>Debbie Baacke \ Jeremy Brumm \ Steve Garrabrant | PK-12 | 750<br>50 | 281/464-8299<br>Fax 281/464-6119 |
| Lycee International De Houston<br>15950 Park Row Dr, Houston 77084<br>Margaret Combs | PK-12 | 80 | 832/474-1013 |
| Memorial Chrn Academy<br>1315 S Dairy Ashford Rd Ste F, Houston 77077<br>Freda Spillman | K-5 | 75 | 281/493-3700<br>Fax 281/493-6233 |
| Memorial Hall High Sch<br>2501 Central Pkwy Ste A19, Houston 77092<br>George Aurich | 6-12 | 65<br>7 | 713/688-5566<br>Fax 713/956-9751 |
| Memorial Lutheran Sch<br>5800 Westheimer Rd, Houston 77057<br>Darrell Schepmann | PK-8 | 250<br>22 | 713/782-4022<br>Fax 713/782-1749 |
| Memorial Private High Sch<br>14333 Fern Dr, Houston 77079<br>Harry Camp | 7-12 | 44 | 281/759-2288 |
| Mirus Academy<br>5561 3rd St, Katy 77493<br>Laura Hogan | 3-12 | 100 | 281/392-4477<br>Fax 832/437-8273 |
| Mission Bend Christian Academy<br>3710 Highway 6 S, Houston 77082<br>Wendy Lewis | PK-6 | 94<br>7 | 281/497-4057<br>Fax 281/497-3395 |
| Monarch Sch<br>2815 Rosefield Dr, Houston 77080<br>Patti Pace | Spec | 130<br>14 | 713/479-0800<br>Fax 713/464-7499 |
| Montessori School Downtown<br>4510 Caroline St, Houston 77004<br>Theresa Devera | PK-5 | 200 | 713/520-6801<br>Fax 713/520-9731 |
| Mountaintop Learning Center<br>8420 Almeda Genoa Rd, Houston 77075<br>Latasha Siscer | PK-K | 40 | 713/808-9284<br>Fax 713/991-4210 |
| New Heights Christian Academy<br>1700 W 43rd St, Houston 77018<br>Victoria Grable | K-12 | 113<br>8 | 713/861-9101 |
| Northland Christian Sch<br>4363 Sylvanfield Dr, Houston 77014<br>Eric Wietstruck \ Monica Lewis | PK-12 | 650 | 281/440-1060<br>Fax 281/440-7572<br>f |
| Northwood Montessori Sch<br>14901 Welcome Ln, Houston 77014<br>Carita Goss | PK-1 | 79<br>3 | 281/444-9433 |
| Our Savior Lutheran Sch<br>5000 W Tidwell Rd, Houston 77091<br>Lance Gerard | PK-8 | 250<br>14 | 713/290-8277<br>Fax 713/290-0850 |
| Paratus Classical Academy<br>1610 Campbell Rd, Houston 77055<br>Pamela Dollins | PK-12 | 200 | 281/547-0060 |
| Parish Sch<br>11001 Hammerly Blvd, Houston 77043<br>Cheval Bryant | PK-5 | 140<br>20 | 713/467-4696<br>Fax 713/467-8341 |
| Pilgrim Lutheran Sch<br>8601 Chimney Rock Rd, Houston 77096<br>David Topp | PK-8 | 215<br>16 | 713/432-7082<br>Fax 713/666-6585 |
| Pines Montessori Sch<br>3535 Cedar Knolls Dr, Kingwood 77339<br>Patty Sobelman | PK-8 | 165<br>12 | 281/358-8933<br>Fax 281/358-3162 |

TX—211

| School | Grades | | Enroll/Staff | Phone/Fax |
|---|---|---|---|---|
| Post Oak Montessori Sch<br>4600 Bissonnet St, Bellaire 77401<br>Jeff Schneider | PK-6 | | 388<br>17 | 713/661-6688<br>Fax 713/661-4959 |
| Presbyterian Sch<br>40 Oakdale St, Houston 77006<br>Christy Heno \ Charles Gramtages | PK-8 | | 531 | 713/520-0284<br>Fax 713/620-6391 |
| Providence Classical Sch<br>18100 Stuebner Airline Rd, Spring 77379<br>Melissa Martin \ Vinodh Gunasekera | PK-12 | | 200 | 281/320-0500<br>Fax 281/379-2039 |
| Rainard School for the Gifted<br>11059 Timberline Rd, Houston 77043<br>Erin Chavez | PK-12 | | 65<br>7 | 713/647-7246<br>Fax 713/365-0372 |
| River Oaks Academy<br>10600 Richmond Ave, Houston 77042<br>Dr Louie Valdez | K-12 | | 30<br>6 | 713/783-7200<br>Fax 713/783-7286 |
| River Oaks Baptist Sch<br>2300 Willowick Rd, Houston 77027<br>Amy Womack \ Connor Cook | PK-8 | | 848<br>40 | 713/623-6938<br>Fax 713/621-8216 |
| Robert M Beren Academy<br>11333 Cliffwood Dr, Houston 77035<br>Dr Dawn McKernan \ Raquel Cedano | PK-12 | | 315<br>31 | 713/723-7170<br>Fax 713/723-8343 |
| Robindell Private Sch<br>6610 Alder Dr, Houston 77081<br>Chuck Wall | PK-1 | | 200 | 713/667-9895<br>Fax 713/669-9324 |
| Rosehill Christian Sch<br>19830 FM 2920 Rd, Tomball 77377<br>Christie Newell \ Catherine Davila \ Amber Hurst | PK-12 | | 360<br>27 | 281/351-8114<br>Fax 281/516-3418 |
| Saint Constantine Sch<br>6000 Dale Carnegie Ln, Houston 77036<br>Caitlin Gilbert | PK-12 | | 150 | 832/975-7075 |
| Salem Lutheran Sch<br>22601 Lutheran Church Rd, Tomball 77377<br>Amy Boatman | PK-8 | | 377<br>20 | 281/351-8223<br>Fax 281/290-1240 |
| School for Young Children<br>810 Sul Ross St, Houston 77006<br>Sheila McBrinn | Spec | | 36<br>6 | 713/520-8310<br>Fax 713/520-1109 |
| School of the Woods<br>1321 Wirt Rd, Houston 77055<br>Sherry Herron \ Betsy Coe | PK-12 | | 325<br>13 | 713/686-8811 |
| Second Baptist Sch<br>6410 Woodway Dr, Houston 77057<br>Evette Haberman \ Ellen Barrett | PK-12 | | 1,100 | 713/365-2310<br>Fax 713/365-2355 |
| Sherwood Forest Mont Sch<br>1331 Sherwood Forest St, Houston 77043<br>Sara Norton | PK-6 | | 112<br>4 | 713/464-5791<br>Fax 713/464-5810 |
| Southwest Christian Academy<br>7400 Eldridge Pkwy, Houston 77083<br>Paula Thurmond | K-12 | | 150 | 281/561-7400<br>Fax 281/561-9823 |
| Southwest Cmty Christian Acad<br>14880 Bellaire Blvd, Houston 77083<br>Trialica Heard | PK-1 | | 115<br>18 | 281/575-9400<br>Fax 281/575-1449 |
| Spring Baptist Academy<br>633 E Louetta Rd, Spring 77373<br>Dr Gloria Hammack | PK-8 | | 209 | 281/353-5448 |
| St Francis Episcopal Sch<br>335 Piney Point Rd, Houston 77024<br>Carol Christ \ Chris Bertha \ Cara Henderson | PK-10 | | 801 | 713/458-6100<br>Fax 713/782-4720 |
| St John Early Childhood Center<br>15237 Huffmeister Rd, Cypress 77429<br>Tiffany Bunker | PK-PK | | 257 | 281/304-5546 |
| St John's Sch<br>2401 Claremont Ln, Houston 77019<br>Thomas McLaughlin \ Chia-Chee Chiu \ Hollis Amley | K-12 | | 1,200 | 713/850-0222<br>Fax 713/622-2309 |
| St Mark Lutheran Sch<br>1515 Hillendahl Blvd, Houston 77055<br>Heidi Jerry | PK-8 | | 324<br>20 | 713/468-2623<br>Fax 713/468-6735 |
| St Mark's Episcopal Sch<br>3816 Bellaire Blvd, Houston 77025<br>Heather Williams \ Matthew Burgy | PK-8 | | 420<br>25 | 713/667-7030<br>Fax 713/349-0419 |
| St Michael's Learning Academy<br>6220 Westpark Dr Ste 180, Houston 77057<br>Christine Aboud | 9-12 | | 50 | 713/977-0566<br>Fax 713/977-0090 |
| St Nicholas Sch<br>1920 N Braeswood Blvd, Houston 77030<br>Margot Heard | PK-8 | | 100 | 713/791-9977<br>Fax 713/791-9594 |
| St Stephen's Episcopal Sch<br>1800 Sul Ross St, Houston 77098<br>Nahla Nasser | PK-8 | | 186<br>18 | 713/821-9100<br>Fax 713/821-9156 |
| St Thomas Apostle Episc Sch<br>18300 Upper Bay Rd, Houston 77058<br>C O'Neal | PK-5 | | 120<br>10 | 281/333-1340<br>Fax 281/333-9113 |
| St Thomas' Episcopal Sch<br>4900 Jackwood St, Houston 77096<br>Erica Maw \ Ryno Marais \ Dale King | PK-12 | | 630<br>30 | 713/666-3111<br>Fax 713/668-3887 |
| Step by Step Christian Sch<br>1119 S Cherry St, Tomball 77375<br>Pamela Collins | PK-8 | | 250 | 281/351-2888<br>Fax 281/516-0253 |
| Tenney Sch<br>3500 S Gessner Rd Ste 200, Houston 77063<br>Catherine DeLaRosa | 6-12 | | 65 | 713/783-6990<br>Fax 713/783-0786 |
| Texas Christian Sch<br>17810 Kieth Harrow Blvd, Houston 77084<br>Becky Soliz | PK-12 | | 270<br>20 | 281/550-6060 |
| The Bridge Sch<br>3333 Bering Dr, Houston 77057<br>Myah Aquil | 6-12 | | 250 | 713/974-2066 |
| The Fay Sch<br>105 N Post Oak Ln, Houston 77024<br>Melissa Sherman | PK-5 | | 340 | 713/681-8300<br>Fax 713/681-6826 |
| The Kinkaid Sch<br>201 Kinkaid School Dr, Houston 77024<br>Krista Babine \ Ann Haynes \ Peter Behr | PK-12 | G | 1,300 | 713/782-1640<br>Fax 713/782-3543 |
| Torah Day School of Houston<br>10900 Fondren Rd, Houston 77096<br>Chiena Lazaroff | PK-8 | | 130<br>12 | 713/777-2000<br>Fax 713/771-5770 |
| Torah Girls Academy<br>7811 Ludington Dr, Houston 77071<br>Ezra Sarna | 9-12 | | 20 | 713/936-0644 |
| Trafton Academy<br>4711 McDermed Dr, Houston 77035<br>Inez Hutchins | PK-8 | | 250 | 713/723-3732<br>Fax 713/723-1844 |
| Trinity Lutheran Chldrn's Ctr<br>1316 Washington Ave, Houston 77002<br>Darrell Schepmann | PK-8 | | 220<br>12 | 713/224-3207 |
| Trinity Lutheran Sch<br>18926 Klein Church Rd, Spring 77379<br>Keith Goedecke | PK-8 | | 600<br>19 | 281/376-5810<br>Fax 281/290-4950 |
| Veritas Christian Academy<br>7000 Ferris St, Bellaire 77401<br>Alecia Gallegos \ Lina DelGado | PK-8 | | 175 | 713/773-9605<br>Fax 713/773-9753 |
| Village Sch<br>13077 Westella Dr, Houston 77077<br>Aoi Carle \ Cindy Proske \ Carl Newman | PK-12 | | 750<br>40 | 281/496-7900<br>Fax 281/496-7799 |
| Waller Christian Academy<br>1208 Penick Rd, Waller 77484<br>Richard Keithley | PK-8 | | 99 | 936/372-0901<br>Fax 936/832-2022 |
| Wesley Academy<br>10570 Westpark Dr, Houston 77042<br>Heather Williams | PK-8 | | 133<br>30 | 713/266-3341<br>Fax 713/458-4766 |
| Westbury Christian Sch<br>10420 Hillcroft St, Houston 77096<br>Kaitlyn Ballard \ Amanda Archer \ Annette Turner | PK-12 | | 525<br>40 | 713/551-8100<br>Fax 713/551-8116 |

| | | | | | |
|---|---|---|---|---|---|
| Western Academy<br>1511 Butlercrest St, Houston 77080<br>Chris Carroll \ Alex Hoff | 3-8 | | 100 | | 713/461-7000<br>Fax 832/408-7861 |
| Westview Sch<br>1900 Kersten Dr, Houston 77043<br>Dr Carol Harrison \ Russell Avery | Spec | | 154 | | 713/973-1900<br>Fax 713/973-1970 |
| Wheeler Ave Christian Academy<br>3810 Ruth St, Houston 77004<br>Melanie Singleton | PK-1 | | 40 | | 713/579-2792<br>Fax 713/579-2790 |
| Woodlands Preparatory Sch<br>27440 Kuykendahl Rd, Tomball 77375<br>Erika Velez | K-12 | | 250 | | 281/561-0600<br>Fax 281/561-1155<br>f |
| Xavier Educational Academy<br>10042 Whiteside Ln, Houston 77080<br>Richard Delacuadra | 5-12 | | 140 | | 832/303-9638 |
| Yellowstone Academy<br>3000 Trulley St, Houston 77004<br>Deidra Lawson | PK-8 | | 309<br>16 | | 713/741-8000<br>Fax 713/741-8006<br>f |
| Yorkshire Academy<br>14120 Memorial Dr, Houston 77079<br>Janet Howard | PK-5 | | 160 | | 281/531-6088 |

## HARRIS REGIONAL CENTERS

- **Region 4 Ed Service Center** PID: 01027556          713/462-7708
  7145 W Tidwell Rd, Houston 77092          Fax 713/744-6514

| | | |
|---|---|---|
| Dr Pam Wells ....................................1 | Robert Zingelmann ......................2,3,19 |
| Kelly Ingram ................................8,15 | Dr Robby McGowen ...................15,79 |
| Dr Jennifer Brock .........34,39,48,51,57 | Dr Ginger Gates ................................58 |
| Dr Melody Goffney .............................68 | Kristi Hernandez ...............................71 |
| Pat Shear ......................................73,76 | Dr Rene Ruiz .....................................74 |
| Richard Armand ..............................286 | Ingrid Lee ........................................294 |

## HARRISON COUNTY

## HARRISON PUBLIC SCHOOLS

- **Elysian Fields Ind School Dist** PID: 01028433          903/633-2420
  2099 FM 451, Elysian Flds 75642          Fax 903/633-2498

**Schools:** 3 \ **Teachers:** 73 \ **Students:** 889 \ **Special Ed Students:** 127 \ **LEP Students:** 10 \ **College-Bound:** 70% \ **Ethnic:** Asian 1%, African American 14%, Hispanic 6%, Caucasian 79% \ **Exp:** $438 (High) \ **Poverty:** 21% \ **Title I:** $251,394 \ **Open-Close:** 08/12 - 05/14 \ **DTBP:** $357 (High)

| | | |
|---|---|---|
| Maynard Chapman ............................1 | Richard Hutsell .................................2 |
| Norman Barr ......................................3 | Scott Ford ..........................................6 |
| Monica Simmons .......................8,11,69 | Martha Lovaasen .............................9* |
| Katie Woodley ..............................36,83 | Emily Dickenson ..........................59,273 |
| Siera Bradshaw ................................60 | Harold Coburn ..................................67 |
| Bill Spencer ................................73,84 | |

| Public Schs..Principal | Grd | Prgm | Enr/#Cls | SN |
|---|---|---|---|---|
| Elysian Fields Elem Sch<br>565 FM 451, Elysian Flds 75642<br>Martha Lovaasen | PK-5 | T | 394<br>26 | 57% 903/633-2465<br>Fax 903/633-2187 |
| Elysian Fields High Sch<br>2400 FM 451, Elysian Flds 75642<br>Jackson Parker | 9-12 | TV | 278<br>40 | 45% 903/633-2455<br>Fax 903/633-8154 |
| Elysian Fields Middle Sch<br>2450 FM 451, Elysian Flds 75642<br>Brandon Goswick | 6-8 | TV | 217<br>20 | 45% 903/633-2306<br>Fax 903/633-2326 |

- **Hallsville Ind School Dist** PID: 01028483          903/668-5990
  311 Willow St, Hallsville 75650          Fax 903/688-5991

**Schools:** 5 \ **Teachers:** 363 \ **Students:** 5,000 \ **Special Ed Students:** 977 \ **LEP Students:** 322 \ **College-Bound:** 59% \ **Ethnic:** Asian 1%, African American 7%, Hispanic 16%, Caucasian 75% \ **Exp:** $366 (High) \ **Poverty:** 16% \ **Title I:** $811,371 \ **Open-Close:** 08/13 - 05/26 \ **DTBP:** $44 (Low)

| | | |
|---|---|---|
| Jeff Collum ..........................................1 | Mary Brown ...................................2,19 |
| Ben Avedikian ....................................3 | Roy Presley .......................................5 |
| Brian Farrell .......................................6 | Amy Whittle ...........7,11,35,57,77,83,88,275 |
| Shauna Hittel ............8,31,36,78,79,285 | John Martin ..............................15,68,74 |
| Mark Page ..........16,28,76,82,98,295,297* | Kathy Gaw ....................26,27,29,75,95* |
| Amy Collins .............................34,58,90 | Jay Nelson .........................................67 |
| Lacy Carter ..........................69,83,294 | Gwen Walker ................................71,93 |
| Jill Buchanan ...................................76 | Anda Juban .......................................81 |
| Kathy Bradford .................................84 | Christopher Miller ............................91 |

| Public Schs..Principal | Grd | Prgm | Enr/#Cls | SN |
|---|---|---|---|---|
| East Elem Sch<br>420 Galilee Rd, Hallsville 75650<br>Melissa Goulden | PK-3 | T | 799 | 53% 903/668-5984<br>Fax 903/668-5990 |
| Hallsville High Sch<br>616 Calyoung Rd, Hallsville 75650<br>Lindsay Slaten | 9-12 | AGV | 1,464<br>100 | 35% 903/668-5990 |
| Hallsville Intermediate Sch<br>401 Waldron Ferry Rd, Hallsville 75650<br>Karen Aikman | 4-5 | T | 756<br>50 | 44% 903/668-5989 |
| Hallsville Junior High Sch<br>1 Bobcat Ln, Hallsville 75650<br>James Gibson | 6-8 | ATV | 1,213<br>45 | 39% 903/668-5986<br>Fax 903/668-5990 |
| North Elem Sch<br>200 Billie Martin Pkwy, Hallsville 75650<br>Danieli Parker | K-3 | T | 682<br>45 | 41% 903/668-5981<br>Fax 903/668-5991 |

- **Harleton Ind School Dist** PID: 01028536          903/777-2372
  17000 State Highway 154, Harleton 75651          Fax 903/777-2406

**Schools:** 3 \ **Teachers:** 63 \ **Students:** 716 \ **Special Ed Students:** 78 \ **LEP Students:** 7 \ **College-Bound:** 63% \ **Ethnic:** African American 2%, Hispanic 7%, Caucasian 91% \ **Exp:** $402 (High) \ **Poverty:** 21% \ **Title I:** $165,693 \ **Open-Close:** 08/14 - 05/28 \ **DTBP:** $357 (High) \ f

| | | |
|---|---|---|
| Jay Ratcliff ..........................................1 | Tina Cox .............................................2 |
| Renay Stringfellow ............................3 | Connie Burrell ...................................4 |
| Mike Harper .......................................5 | Shannon Hearron ..............................7 |
| Liz Pendarvis .............8,11,57,58,69,81,93 | Kim Clynch .......................................16 |
| Pat McGill ..........................................67 | Cherly Shepherd ..............................68 |
| Kevin Jones ..................................73,76 | Traci Jones .....................................270* |
| Blake Brown ....................................295 | |

| Public Schs..Principal | Grd | Prgm | Enr/#Cls | SN |
|---|---|---|---|---|
| Harleton Elem Sch<br>17240 State Highway 154, Harleton 75651<br>Traci Jones | PK-5 | T | 318<br>25 | 50% 903/777-4092<br>Fax 903/777-2782 |
| Harleton High Sch<br>17000 State Highway 154, Harleton 75651<br>Crystal Brock | 9-12 | ATV | 219<br>12 | 39% 903/777-2711<br>Fax 903/777-2778 |

Harleton Junior High Sch | 6-8 | T | 179 | 45% 903/777-3010
17240 State Highway 154, Harleton 75651 | | | 15 | Fax 903/777-3009
Shane Wright

● **Karnack Ind School Dist** PID: 01028574 | 903/679-3117
655 Fason St, Karnack 75661 | Fax 903/679-4252

Schools: 1 \ **Teachers:** 13 \ **Students:** 145 \ **Special Ed Students:** 7
\ **LEP Students:** 9 \ **Ethnic:** African American 55%, Hispanic 10%,
Caucasian 35% \ **Exp:** $539 (High) \ **Poverty:** 19% \ **Title I:** $174,683 \
**Open-Close:** 08/17 - 05/21 \ **DTBP:** $350 (High)

Amy Dickson .................................1,11 | James Gholson ..........................................2
Cherie Franklin ...........................4 | Andy Hayes .............................................5
Louis Tennison ...........................6 | Ray Polk ................................................67
Janett McCray ..........................68 | Nicole Turner .........................................69
Madi Williams ...........................73

| Public Schs..Principal | Grd | Prgm | Enr/#Cls | SN |
|---|---|---|---|---|
| George Washington Carver ES<br>655 Fason St, Karnack 75661<br>Amy Dickson | PK-8 | T | 145<br>13 | 98% 903/679-3111 |

● **Marshall Ind School Dist** PID: 01028603 | 903/927-8700
1305 E Pinecrest Dr, Marshall 75670 | Fax 903/935-0203

Schools: 7 \ **Teachers:** 353 \ **Students:** 5,345 \ **Special Ed Students:** 373 \
**LEP Students:** 978 \ **Ethnic:** Asian 1%, African American 38%, Hispanic 38%,
Native American: 1%, Caucasian 24% \ **Exp:** $451 (High) \ **Poverty:** 26% \
**Title I:** $2,136,085 \ **Special Education:** $1,265,000 \ **Open-Close:** 08/26 -
05/28 \ **DTBP:** $165 (High)

Dr Jerry Gibson .........................................1 | Jessica Warner ..........................................2
Brad Ash ....................................................3 | Cindy Brandon ..........................................4
Joseph Brinker ...........................................5 | Jake Griedl ...............................................6
Jennifer Peters ...........................................7 | Anika Perkins ..........................8,27,34,57,81
Dr Melinda Jennings .......................11,296 | Beth Rowe .............................................. 15
Sharona Woolen .......................................58 | Kim Kalina .............................................. 60
Brad Burris ................................................67 | Tiffany Best ............................................ 68
David Weaver ...........................................71 | Ron Lehr ........................................73,84,295
Eddie Mulanax .........................................76 | Dayan Durrant ....................................... 285

| Public Schs..Principal | Grd | Prgm | Enr/#Cls | SN |
|---|---|---|---|---|
| David Crockett Elem Sch<br>700 Jasper Dr, Marshall 75672<br>Angela Fitzpatrick | K-5 | T | 693<br>45 | 80% 903/927-8880<br>Fax 903/927-8885 |
| Marshall High Sch<br>1900 Maverick Dr, Marshall 75670<br>**Matt Gregory** | 9-12 | TV | 1,413 | 68% 903/927-8800<br>Fax 903/938-7052 |
| Marshall Junior High Sch<br>2710 E Travis St, Marshall 75672<br>Nakeisha Adams Pegues | 6-8 | TV | 1,265<br>65 | 75% 903/927-8784<br>Fax 903/927-8837 |
| Price T Young Elem Sch<br>1501 Sanford St, Marshall 75670<br>Nakeisha Pegues | K-5 | T | 537<br>25 | 91% 903/927-8850<br>Fax 903/927-8858 |
| Sam Houston Elem Sch<br>2905 E Travis St, Marshall 75672<br>Jerry Hancock | K-5 | T | 520<br>30 | 65% 903/927-8860<br>Fax 903/927-8863 |
| Washington Early Childhood Ctr<br>1202 Evans St, Marshall 75670<br>Lesley Glanton | PK-PK | T | 282<br>16 | 98% 903/927-8790<br>Fax 903/927-8794 |
| William B Travis Elem Sch<br>300 W Carolanne Blvd, Marshall 75672<br>Tamekia Johnson | K-5 | T | 631<br>400 | 82% 903/927-8780<br>Fax 903/927-8782 |

● **Waskom Ind School Dist** PID: 01028744 | 903/687-3361
365 W School Ave, Waskom 75692 | Fax 903/687-3253

Schools: 3 \ **Teachers:** 76 \ **Students:** 850 \ **Special Ed Students:** 81
\ **LEP Students:** 81 \ **College-Bound:** 50% \ **Ethnic:** African American
17%, Hispanic 26%, Caucasian 56% \ **Exp:** $763 (High) \ **Poverty:** 28% \
**Title I:** $320,629 \ **Open-Close:** 08/12 - 05/21 \ **DTBP:** $350 (High)

Rae Ann Patty .........................................1 | Nancy Dillard ..........................................2
Ray Sudds ..................................3,5,91 | Joe Griffin ...............................................4
Whitney Keeling ............................6* | Jennifer Swank .....................................7,85*
Nicole Smith ............8,69,288,298 | Jennifer Troqville ...................11,271,296
Debrah Crisp ...................................37 | Melinda Bowben .................................. 38
Wendy Shelton ..............................57* | Staci Green .......................................... 58
Jacob Speight ..................................67 | La Vaughn Fields ..............................73,84
David Dulude ...................................83

| Public Schs..Principal | Grd | Prgm | Enr/#Cls | SN |
|---|---|---|---|---|
| Waskom Elem Sch<br>225 School Avenue, Waskom 75692<br>**Andrew Jones** | PK-5 | T | 373<br>19 | 69% 903/687-3361 |
| Waskom High Sch<br>980 School Ave, Waskom 75692<br>Kassie Watson | 9-12 | TV | 315<br>22 | 59% 903/687-3361<br>Fax 903/687-2897 |
| Waskom Middle Sch<br>255 School Ave, Waskom 75692<br>Bonita Cherry | 6-8 | T | 215<br>16 | 67% 903/687-3361<br>Fax 903/687-3224 |

## HARRISON PRIVATE SCHOOLS

| Private Schs..Principal | Grd | Prgm | Enr/#Cls | SN |
|---|---|---|---|---|
| Heartlight Boarding Sch<br>7345 E Highway 80, Hallsville 75650<br>Blake Nelson | 7-12 | | 56 | 903/668-2173<br>Fax 903/668-3453 |
| Trinity Episcopal Sch<br>2905 Rosborough Springs Rd, Marshall 75672<br>Carrie Hammack | PK-8 | | 155<br>33 | 903/938-3513<br>Fax 903/938-8725 |

# HARTLEY COUNTY

## HARTLEY PUBLIC SCHOOLS

● **Channing Ind School Dist** PID: 01028794 | 806/235-3432
900 Greenwood St, Channing 79018 | Fax 806/235-2609

Schools: 1 \ **Teachers:** 19 \ **Students:** 173 \ **Special Ed Students:** 23
\ **LEP Students:** 13 \ **Ethnic:** African American 1%, Hispanic 35%,
Caucasian 64% \ **Exp:** $537 (High) \ **Poverty:** 16% \ **Title I:** $41,365 \
**Open-Close:** 08/20 - 05/21 \ **DTBP:** $400 (High)

Robert McClain .....................1,11,57,288 | Anne Browning ..........................................2
Forrest Hebert ....................8,74,83* | Melissa Garcia ......................................58*
David Spinhirne .................................67 | Heather White ...................................73,295*

| Public Schs..Principal | Grd | Prgm | Enr/#Cls | SN |
|---|---|---|---|---|
| Channing Public Sch<br>900 Greenwood St, Channing 79018<br>Forrest Hebert | PK-12 | TV | 173<br>16 | 68% 806/235-3719 |

| | | | | | | | | | | |
|---|---|---|---|---|---|---|---|---|---|---|
| **1** Superintendent | **8** Curric/Instruct K-12 | **19** Chief Financial Officer | **29** Family/Consumer Science | **39** Social Studies K-12 | **49** English/Lang Arts Elem | **59** Special Education Elem | **69** Academic Assessment |
| **2** Bus/Finance/Purchasing | **9** Curric/Instruct Elem | **20** Art K-12 | **30** Adult Education | **40** Social Studies Elem | **50** English/Lang Arts Sec | **60** Special Education Sec | **70** Research/Development |
| **3** Buildings And Grounds | **10** Curric/Instruct Sec | **21** Art Elem | **31** Career/Sch-to-Work K-12 | **41** Social Studies Sec | **51** Reading K-12 | **61** Foreign/World Lang K-12 | **71** Public Information |
| **4** Food Service | **11** Federal Program | **22** Art Sec | **32** Career/Sch-to-Work Elem | **42** Science K-12 | **52** Reading Elem | **62** Foreign/World Lang Elem | **72** Summer School |
| **5** Transportation | **12** Title I | **23** Music K-12 | **33** Career/Sch-to-Work Sec | **43** Science Elem | **53** Reading Sec | **63** Foreign/World Lang Sec | **73** Instructional Tech |
| **6** Athletic | **13** Title V | **24** Music Elem | **34** Early Childhood Ed | **44** Science Sec | **54** Remedial Reading K-12 | **64** Religious Education K-12 | **74** Inservice Training |
| **7** Health Services | **15** Asst Superintendent | **25** Music Sec | **35** Health/Phys Education | **45** Math K-12 | **55** Remedial Reading Elem | **65** Religious Education Elem | **75** Marketing/Distributive |
| | **16** Instructional Media Svcs | **26** Business Education | **36** Guidance Services K-12 | **46** Math Elem | **56** Remedial Reading Sec | **66** Religious Education Sec | **76** Info Systems |
| | **17** Chief Operations Officer | **27** Career & Tech Ed | **37** Guidance Services Elem | **47** Math Sec | **57** Bilingual/ELL | **67** School Board President | **77** Psychological Assess |
| | **18** Chief Academic Officer | **28** Technology Education | **38** Guidance Services Sec | **48** English/Lang Arts K-12 | **58** Special Education K-12 | **68** Teacher Personnel | **78** Affirmative Action |

- **Hartley Ind School Dist** PID: 01028823     806/365-4458
9th & Johnson Street, Hartley 79044     Fax 806/365-4459

**Schools:** 1 \ **Teachers:** 21 \ **Students:** 205 \ **Special Ed Students:** 11
\ **LEP Students:** 52 \ **College-Bound:** 40% \ **Ethnic:** Hispanic 60%,
Caucasian 40% \ **Exp:** $492 (High) \ **Poverty:** 12% \ **Title I:** $26,519 \
**Open-Close:** 08/19 - 05/21 \ **DTBP:** $341 (High) \ 🗔 🗔

| | | |
|---|---|---|
| Scott Vincent | 1 | Anette Melius | 2 |
| Rebecca Zapata | 4 | Dedra Hill | 6* |
| Brandi Parker | 16,73 | Aaron Castanon | 58* |
| Wade Lenz | 67 | Juana Garcia | 271,273* |

| Public Schs..Principal | Grd | Prgm | Enr/#Cls | SN | |
|---|---|---|---|---|---|
| Hartley Sch<br>9th & Johnson Street, Hartley 79044<br>Kurtis Koepke | PK-12 | ATV | 205<br>14 | 70% | 806/365-4458 |

# HASKELL COUNTY

## HASKELL PUBLIC SCHOOLS

- **Haskell Cons Ind School Dist** PID: 01028873     940/864-2602
605 N Avenue E, Haskell 79521     Fax 940/864-8096

**Schools:** 3 \ **Teachers:** 66 \ **Students:** 550 \ **Special Ed Students:** 70 \
**LEP Students:** 11 \ **Ethnic:** Asian 1%, African American 3%, Hispanic 44%,
Native American: 1%, Caucasian 50% \ **Exp:** $495 (High) \ **Poverty:** 28% \
**Title I:** $254,314 \ **Open-Close:** 08/20 - 05/27 \ **DTBP:** $322 (High)

| | | | |
|---|---|---|---|
| Bill Alcorn | 1 | Brenda Turner | 2 |
| Bart Parhan | 3 | Edgwyna Flores | 4 |
| Daniel Turner | 5 | Brian Hodnett | 6* |
| Charistie Wheat | 7,35,83,85 | Michelle Thane | 8,11,57,88,273,296,298 |
| John Foster | 9 | Jacklyn Wheatley | 16,82* |
| Tara Hollingsworth | 58* | Paul Lenoard | 67 |
| Belinda Lytle | 69,288* | John Rutkowski | 73,84,286,295 |
| Tresa Martinez | 271 | Patsy Blakley | 275* |

| Public Schs..Principal | Grd | Prgm | Enr/#Cls | SN | |
|---|---|---|---|---|---|
| Haskell Elem Sch<br>306 S Avenue G, Haskell 79521<br>John Foster | PK-5 | AT | 258<br>30 | 78% | 940/864-2654<br>Fax 940/864-2369 |
| Haskell High Sch<br>600 N Avenue E, Haskell 79521<br>Jeff York | 9-12 | ATV | 165<br>30 | 57% | 940/864-8535<br>Fax 940/864-3977 |
| Haskell Junior High Sch<br>4th & Main Street, Rochester 79544<br>Kent Colley | 6-8 | ATV | 108<br>18 | 76% | 940/864-5981<br>Fax 940/864-5982 |

- **Paint Creek Ind School Dist** PID: 01028914     940/864-2471
4485 FM 600, Haskell 79521     Fax 940/864-8038

**Schools:** 1 \ **Teachers:** 16 \ **Students:** 108 \ **Special Ed Students:** 8 \
**College-Bound:** 70% \ **Ethnic:** Hispanic 41%, Caucasian 59% \ **Exp:** $376
(High) \ **Poverty:** 26% \ **Title I:** $18,220 \ **Open-Close:** 08/14 - 05/21 \
**DTBP:** $350 (High)

| | | | |
|---|---|---|---|
| Cheryl Floyd | 1 | Becky Thompson | 2 |
| Stain Terrell | 3 | Ken Wallace | 8* |

| | | |
|---|---|---|
| Molly Blankenship | 27* | Valine Bullinger | 36,69,83,85,88,270 |
| Samantha Carroll | 54,58,271* | Dana Pendegraft | 67 |
| Jennifer Prichard | 73,295 | | |

| Public Schs..Principal | Grd | Prgm | Enr/#Cls | SN | |
|---|---|---|---|---|---|
| Paint Creek Sch<br>4485 FM 600, Haskell 79521<br>Ken Wallace | PK-12 | TV | 108<br>18 | 85% | 940/864-2471 |

- **Rule Ind School Dist** PID: 01028964     940/997-2521
1100 Union Ave, Rule 79547     Fax 940/997-2446

**Schools:** 1 \ **Teachers:** 15 \ **Students:** 114 \ **Special Ed Students:** 15
\ **LEP Students:** 6 \ **College-Bound:** 90% \ **Ethnic:** African American
1%, Hispanic 51%, Caucasian 48% \ **Exp:** $636 (High) \ **Poverty:** 41% \
**Title I:** $87,120 \ **Open-Close:** 08/13 - 05/28 \ **DTBP:** $420 (High) \ 🗔 🗔

| | | | |
|---|---|---|---|
| Brad Jones | 1 | Sandy Flores | 2* |
| Lisa Saffel | 4* | Norma Rios | 4* |
| Ken Frazier | 11,83 | Leslie Kupatt | 31,69,270* |
| Linda Caddell | 57* | Jeffery Murray | 67 |
| Jerry Cannon | 73* | | |

| Public Schs..Principal | Grd | Prgm | Enr/#Cls | SN | |
|---|---|---|---|---|---|
| Rule Sch<br>1100 Union Ave, Rule 79547<br>Kenneth Frazier | PK-12 | TV | 114<br>30 | 86% | 940/997-2521<br>🗔 🗔 |

# HAYS COUNTY

## HAYS PUBLIC SCHOOLS

- **Dripping Springs Ind Sch Dist** PID: 01029011     512/858-3000
510 W Mercer St, Dripping Spgs 78620     Fax 512/858-3099

**Schools:** 7 \ **Teachers:** 450 \ **Students:** 6,400 \ **Special Ed Students:** 725
\ **LEP Students:** 287 \ **College-Bound:** 65% \ **Ethnic:** Asian 2%,
African American 1%, Hispanic 21%, Caucasian 75% \ **Exp:** $435 (High)
\ **Poverty:** 5% \ **Title I:** $376,172 \ **Special Education:** $907,000 \
**Open-Close:** 08/18 - 05/27 \ **DTBP:** $151 (High) \ 🗔 🗔

| | | | |
|---|---|---|---|
| Bruce Gearing | 1 | Elaine Cogburn | 2 |
| Clint Pruett | 3 | Mike Hruska | 3 |
| John Crowley | 4 | Nanci Freeborg | 4 |
| Pam Swanks | 5 | Galen Zimmerman | 6* |
| Diane Flaim | 8,15 | Nicole Poenitzsch | 15 |
| Kathy Leopold | 16,73,76,297 | Lucy Hansen | 30,31,274 |
| Rhonda Whitman | 57,69,74,79,271 | Jack Modgling | 58,275 |
| Carrie Kroll | 67 | Tiffany Duncan | 68 |
| Dale Whitaker | 71 | Cindi Wade | 84 |
| Kevin Haney | 295 | | |

| Public Schs..Principal | Grd | Prgm | Enr/#Cls | SN | |
|---|---|---|---|---|---|
| Dripping Springs Elem Sch<br>29400 Ranch Road 12, Dripping Spgs 78620<br>Kellie Raymond | PK-5 | T | 763 | 21% | 512/858-3700<br>Fax 512/858-3799 |
| Dripping Springs High Sch<br>940 W Highway 290, Dripping Spgs 78620<br>Angela Gamez | 9-12 | AV | 1,958 | 7% | 512/858-3100<br>Fax 512/858-3199 |

Dripping Springs Middle Sch | 6-8 | | 842 | 17% 512/858-3400
111 Tiger Ln, Dripping Spgs 78620 | | | 43 | Fax 512/858-3499
Jason Certain

Rooster Springs Elem Sch | PK-5 | | 770 | 3% 512/465-6200
1001 Belterra Dr, Austin 78737 | | | | Fax 512/465-6299
Steve Novickas

Sycamore Springs Elem Sch | PK-5 | | 824 | 3% 512/858-3900
14451 Sawyer Ranch Rd, Austin 78737 | | | | Fax 512/858-3999
Kristen Ray

Sycamore Springs Middle Sch | 6-8 | | 808 | 4% 512/858-3600
14451 Sawyer Ranch Rd, Austin 78737 | | | | Fax 512/858-3699
Daniel Diehl

Walnut Springs Elem Sch | PK-5 | T | 739 | 20% 512/858-3800
300 Sportsplex Dr, Dripping Spgs 78620 | | | 23 | Fax 512/858-3899
Melinda Gardner

---

● **Hays Cons Ind School Dist** PID: 01029059     512/268-2141
21003 Interstate 35, Kyle 78640     Fax 512/268-2147

**Schools:** 25 \ **Teachers:** 1,248 \ **Students:** 20,063 \
**Special Ed Students:** 2,365 \ **LEP Students:** 3,065 \ **College-Bound:** 55%
\ **Ethnic:** Asian 1%, African American 3%, Hispanic 65%, Caucasian
31% \ **Exp:** $291 (Med) \ **Poverty:** 10% \ **Title I:** $2,668,575 \
**Special Education:** $2,660,000 \ **Open-Close:** 09/08 - 05/28 \ **DTBP:** $195
(High) \ [f]

Dr Eric Wright ...........................1    Becka Palmer ..........................2
Michael Baker ............................3    Michael Thibodeaux ..............4
Filiberto Bonilla ........................5    Karrie Walker ..........................7
Sami Kinsey .............. 7,69,74,280,286,294    Sandra Dowdy ....................8,18
Mary Noale ..............................11    Max Cleaver ..........................17
Randall Rau .............................19    Suzi Mitchell .......................27,31
Dr Jennifer Edwardsen ....... 31,34,36,81,274    Patricia Santoyo .................34,274
Charlotte Winkelmann ...........36,270,752    Jesus Gomez ......................57,79
Patricia Melgar-Cook ...........57,89,271    Nadine Hogan .........................58
Esperanza Orosco ....................67    Marivel Sedillo .....................68,78
Kevin Malandruccolo ..............69,294    Tim Savoy ..............................71
Diane Borreson ......................73,98    Erica Garza ...........................74
Dana Braun ..............................76    Adrianna Price .......................79
Jeri Skrocki .............................91    Debbie Brown .......................275
Emily Herrin ...........................286    Alan Duerr ............................295
Linda Rosebrock .....................297

| Public Schs..Principal | Grd | Prgm | Enr/#Cls | SN |
|---|---|---|---|---|
| Barton Middle Sch<br>4950 Jack C Hays Trl, Buda 78610<br>Teri Eubank | 6-8 | | 683<br>60 | 32% 512/268-1472<br>Fax 512/268-1610 |
| Blanco Vista Elem Sch<br>2951 Blanco Vista Blvd, San Marcos 78666<br>Sean Fox | PK-5 | T | 627 | 62% 512/268-8506<br>Fax 512/268-7811 |
| Buda Elem Sch<br>1060 Old San Antonio Rd, Buda 78610<br>Timothy Robinson | PK-5 | T | 512<br>20 | 48% 512/268-8439<br>Fax 512/268-7369 |
| Camino Real Elem Sch<br>170 Las Brisas Blvd, Niederwald 78640<br>Yvette Soliz | PK-5 | T | 669 | 83% 512/268-8505<br>Fax 512/268-7813 |
| Carpenter Hill Elem Sch<br>4410 FM 967, Buda 78610<br>Ginger Bordeau | PK-5 | | 648 | 19% 512/268-8509<br>Fax 512/268-7374 |
| Chapa Middle Sch<br>3311 Dacy Ln, Kyle 78640<br>Lisa Walls \ Mr Chapa | 6-8 | T | 753 | 65% 512/268-8500<br>Fax 512/268-7812<br>[f] |
| Dahlstrom Middle Sch<br>3600 FM 967, Buda 78610<br>Dr Michael Watson | 6-8 | | 785<br>60 | 14% 512/268-8441<br>Fax 512/268-7628<br>[t] |
| Elm Grove Elem Sch<br>801 S FM 1626, Buda 78610<br>Kathryn Faulks | PK-5 | | 751<br>42 | 11% 512/268-8440<br>Fax 512/295-6809<br>[f][t] |

Hemphill Elem Sch | PK-5 | T | 99 | 82% 512/268-4688
3995 E FM 150, Kyle 78640 | | | | Fax 512/268-6208
Monica Salas

Ⓐ Impact Center | 6-12 | | 65 | 68% 512/268-8473
4125 FM 967, Buda 78610 | | | 5 | Fax 512/268-7376
Sylvia Villejo

Jack C Hays High Sch | 9-12 | AGV | 2,970 | 36% 512/268-2911
4800 Jack C Hays Trl, Buda 78610 | | | 100 | Fax 512/268-1394
David Pierce

Johnson High Sch | 9-12 | | 1,091 | 512/268-8512
4260 FM 967, Buda 78610 | | | | Fax 512/268-7370
Brett Miksch

Kyle Elem Sch | PK-5 | T | 591 | 53% 512/268-3311
500 W Blanco St, Kyle 78640 | | | 60 | Fax 512/268-7375
Karen Lucita | | | | [t]

Lehman High Sch | 9-12 | TV | 2,645 | 60% 512/268-8454
1700 Lehman Rd, Kyle 78640 | | | | Fax 512/268-5732
Karen Zuniga

Ⓐ Live Oak Academy | 10-12 | T | 200 | 47% 512/268-8462
4820 Jack C Hays Trl, Buda 78610 | | | 11 | Fax 512/268-7389
Doug Agnew

McCormick Middle Sch | 6-8 | | 899 | 512/268-8508
5700 Dacy Ln, Buda 78610 | | | | Fax 512/268-7377
James Cruz

Negley Elem Sch | PK-5 | | 807 | 30% 512/268-8501
5940 McNaughton, Kyle 78640 | | | | Fax 512/268-7823
Melody Crowther | | | | [f]

Ralph Pfluger Elem Sch | PK-5 | T | 596 | 51% 512/268-8510
4951 Marsh Ln, Buda 78610 | | | | Fax 512/268-7825
Kathy Noack | | | | [f]

Red Simon Middle Sch | 6-8 | T | 757 | 77% 512/268-8507
3839 E FM 150, Kyle 78640 | | | | Fax 512/268-4146
**Dr Michael Watson**

Science Hall Elem Sch | PK-5 | T | 505 | 73% 512/268-8502
1510 Bebee Rd, Kyle 78640 | | | | Fax 512/268-8784
Iric Ramos | | | | [f][t]

Susie T Fuentes Elem Sch | PK-5 | T | 541 | 62% 512/268-7827
901 Philomena Dr, Kyle 78640 | | | | Fax 512/268-5968
Regina Butcher

Ⓜ Tobias Elem Sch | PK-5 | T | 520 | 52% 512/268-8437
1005 E FM 150, Kyle 78640 | | | 27 | Fax 512/268-7885
Alisa DiPalma

Tom Green Elem Sch | PK-5 | T | 706 | 59% 512/268-8438
1301 Old Goforth Rd, Buda 78610 | | | 50 | Fax 512/295-4107
Jennifer Hanna

Uhland Elem Sch | PK-5 | T | 843 | 86% 512/268-8503
2331 High Rd, Uhland 78640 | | | | Fax 512/268-7364
Cynthia Vasquez

Wallace Middle Sch | 6-8 | T | 800 | 57% 512/268-2891
1500 W Center St, Kyle 78640 | | | 50 | Fax 512/268-7820
Sarah Hodges

---

● **San Marcos Cons Ind Sch Dist** PID: 01029114    512/393-6700
501 S Lbj Dr, San Marcos 78666    Fax 512/393-6787

**Schools:** 12 \ **Teachers:** 568 \ **Students:** 8,200 \ **Special Ed Students:** 972
\ **LEP Students:** 785 \ **College-Bound:** 70% \ **Ethnic:** Asian 1%,
African American 5%, Hispanic 73%, Caucasian 21% \ **Exp:** $439 (High)
\ **Poverty:** 19% \ **Title I:** $2,535,584 \ **Special Education:** $1,591,000 \
**Open-Close:** 08/26 - 05/28 \ **DTBP:** $181 (High)

Michael Cardona .....................1    Cindy Casparis .........................2
Denise Garcia ..........................2    Ulla Durham ..............................2
Jay Wesson .............................3    Robert Gutierrez ....................3,91
Mike Boone .............................4    Doug Wozniak ..........................5
Mark Soto ...............................6    Dyanna Eastwood ....................7*

---

| | | | | | | | |
|---|---|---|---|---|---|---|---|
| **1** Superintendent | **8** Curric/Instruct K-12 | **19** Chief Financial Officer | **29** Family/Consumer Science | **39** Social Studies K-12 | **49** English/Lang Arts Elem | **59** Special Education Elem | **69** Academic Assessment |
| **2** Bus/Finance/Purchasing | **9** Curric/Instruct Elem | **20** Art K-12 | **30** Adult Education | **40** Social Studies Elem | **50** English/Lang Arts Sec | **60** Special Education Sec | **70** Research/Development |
| **3** Buildings And Grounds | **10** Curric/Instruct Sec | **21** Art Elem | **31** Career/Sch-to-Work K-12 | **41** Social Studies Sec | **51** Reading K-12 | **61** Foreign/World Lang K-12 | **71** Public Information |
| **4** Food Service | **11** Federal Program | **22** Art Sec | **32** Career/Sch-to-Work Elem | **42** Science K-12 | **52** Reading Elem | **62** Foreign/World Lang Elem | **72** Summer School |
| **5** Transportation | **12** Title I | **23** Music K-12 | **33** Career/Sch-to-Work Sec | **43** Science Elem | **53** Reading Sec | **63** Foreign/World Lang Sec | **73** Instructional Tech |
| **6** Athletic | **13** Title V | **24** Music Elem | **34** Early Childhood Ed | **44** Science Sec | **54** Remedial Reading K-12 | **64** Religious Education K-12 | **74** Inservice Training |
| **7** Health Services | **14** Asst Superintendent | **25** Music Sec | **35** Health/Phys Education | **45** Math K-12 | **55** Remedial Reading Elem | **65** Religious Education Elem | **75** Marketing/Distributive |
| | **15** Asst Superintendent | **26** Business Education | **36** Guidance Services K-12 | **46** Math Elem | **56** Remedial Reading Sec | **66** Religious Education Sec | **76** Info Systems |
| | **16** Instructional Media Svcs | **27** Career & Tech Ed | **37** Guidance Services Elem | **47** Math Sec | **57** Bilingual/ELL | **67** School Board President | **77** Psychological Assess |
| | **17** Chief Operations Officer | **28** Technology Education | **38** Guidance Services Sec | **48** English/Lang Arts K-12 | **58** Special Education K-12 | **68** Teacher Personnel | **78** Affirmative Action |

| Personnel | Codes |
|---|---|
| Nicole Dray | 8,12,36,83,277,294 |
| Karen Griffith | 15 |
| Monica Ruiz Mills | 15,68,69 |
| Laura Zunker | 58 |
| Clementine Cantu | 67 |
| Andrew Fernandez | 71 |
| Jeremy Connell | 295 |
| Laura Lugo | 11,69,79,288 |
| Dr Marcella Vies | 15,68 |
| Clarissa Talbert | 58 |
| Tammy Maiorano | 58,77 |
| Stephanie Munoz | 68 |
| Greg Hubanek | 73,76,295 |
| James Bratton | 296* |

| Public Schs..Principal | Grd | Prgm | Enr/#Cls | SN | |
|---|---|---|---|---|---|
| Bonham Pre-Kindergarten Sch<br>1225 N State Highway 123, San Marcos 78666<br>Jennifer Gonzalez | PK-PK | T | 426 | 96% | 512/393-6031<br>Fax 512/353-0671 |
| Bowie Elem Sch<br>4020 Monterrey Oaks, San Marcos 78666<br>Pam Thomas | K-5 | T | 542<br>35 | 71% | 512/393-6200<br>Fax 512/393-6210 |
| Crockett Elem Sch<br>1300 Girard St, San Marcos 78666<br>Keith Cunningham | K-5 | T | 600<br>33 | 66% | 512/393-6400<br>Fax 512/353-3557 |
| De Zavala Elem Sch<br>150 E De Zavala Dr, San Marcos 78666<br>Elena Sanchezvillanu | K-5 | T | 567<br>34 | 82% | 512/393-6250<br>Fax 512/392-0620 |
| Doris Miller Middle Sch<br>301 Foxtail Run, San Marcos 78666<br>**Jessie Gipprich** | 6-8 | TV | 791<br>48 | 67% | 512/393-6660<br>Fax 512/393-6602 |
| Hernandez Elem Sch<br>333 Stagecoach Trl, San Marcos 78666<br>**Jennifer Gonzalez** | K-5 | T | 623<br>65 | 68% | 512/393-6100<br>Fax 512/393-6109 |
| Mendez Elem Sch<br>1805 Peter Garza Dr, San Marcos 78666<br>**Kristina Woody** | K-5 | T | 587 | 85% | 512/393-6060<br>Fax 512/393-6039 |
| Owen Goodnight Middle Sch<br>1301 N State Highway 123, San Marcos 78666<br>Rose Pearson | 6-8 | TV | 1,036<br>50 | 77% | 512/393-6550<br>Fax 512/393-6560 |
| Ⓐ Phoenix Learning Center<br>121 E De Zavala Dr, San Marcos 78666<br>Judy Mitchell | 10-12 | V | 95<br>5 | | 512/393-6864<br>Fax 512/393-6871 |
| Rodriguez Elem Sch<br>1481 Esplanade Pkwy, San Marcos 78666<br>Kash Greathouse | K-6 | | 480 | | 512/757-8490 |
| San Marcos High Sch<br>2601 Rattler Rd, San Marcos 78666<br>Denisha Presley | 9-12 | GTV | 2,310<br>150 | 68% | 512/393-6800<br>Fax 512/393-6893 |
| Travis Elem Sch<br>1437 Post Rd, San Marcos 78666<br>Scott Masini | K-5 | T | 615<br>35 | 84% | 512/393-6450<br>Fax 512/393-6976 |

- **Wimberley Ind School Dist** PID: 02903408    512/847-2414
  951 FM 2325, Wimberley 78676    Fax 512/847-2142

**Schools:** 4 \ **Teachers:** 176 \ **Students:** 2,500 \ **Special Ed Students:** 225 \ **LEP Students:** 139 \ **Ethnic:** African American 1%, Hispanic 25%, Native American: 1%, Caucasian 73% \ **Exp:** $455 (High) \ **Poverty:** 7% \ **Title I:** $221,834 \ **Special Education:** $392,000 \ **Open-Close:** 08/19 - 05/20

| Personnel | Codes |
|---|---|
| Dwain York | 1 |
| Darrell Rivera | 3 |
| Heather Baldwin | 4 |
| Doug Warren | 6* |
| Dee Howard | 8,11,15,286,288,296,298 |
| Misty Howard | 57 |
| Joe Malone | 67 |
| Ross Simmins | 91 |
| Moises Santiago | 2,19 |
| Eddie Campbell | 3 |
| Owen Baldwin | 5 |
| Darelle Jordan | 7,83,85* |
| Jason Grogan | 16,73,76,98,295 |
| Stephanie Norris | 58 |
| Tracey Ramsey | 68 |
| Jason Valentine | 285* |

| Public Schs..Principal | Grd | Prgm | Enr/#Cls | SN | |
|---|---|---|---|---|---|
| Blue Hole Primary Sch<br>15900 Winter Mills Pkwy, Wimberley 78676<br>Dara Richardson | PK-2 | | 423<br>21 | 42% | 512/847-3407<br>Fax 512/847-2738 |
| Danforth Junior High Sch<br>200 Texan Blvd, Wimberley 78676<br>Greg Howard | 6-8 | A | 590<br>30 | 26% | 512/847-2181<br>Fax 512/847-7897 |
| Jacobs Well Elem Sch<br>3470 FM 2325, Wimberley 78676<br>**Sueanna Thomas** | 3-5 | | 703<br>21 | 30% | 512/847-5558<br>Fax 512/847-6176 |
| Wimberley High Sch<br>100 Carney Ln, Wimberley 78676<br>Jason Valentine | 9-12 | AV | 785<br>40 | 21% | 512/847-5729<br>Fax 512/847-7269 |

---

## HAYS CATHOLIC SCHOOLS

- **Diocese of Austin Ed Office** PID: 01420568
  Listing includes only schools located in this county. See District Index for location of Diocesan Offices.

| Catholic Schs..Principal | Grd | Prgm | Enr/#Cls | SN | |
|---|---|---|---|---|---|
| Santa Cruz Elem Sch<br>1100 Main St, Buda 78610<br>Margaret McGettrick | PK-8 | | 187 | | 512/312-2137<br>Fax 512/312-2143 |

---

## HAYS PRIVATE SCHOOLS

| Private Schs..Principal | Grd | Prgm | Enr/#Cls | SN | |
|---|---|---|---|---|---|
| Advent Ridge Academy<br>1523 Old Ranch Road 12, San Marcos 78666<br>Carrie Suess | PK-10 | | 74<br>5 | | 512/392-9475<br>Fax 512/392-2693 |
| Aesa Preparatory Academy<br>14101 Canonade, Austin 78737<br>Barbara Garza | 5-12 | | 45 | | 512/560-5584<br>Fax 512/829-4461 |
| Austin Waldorf Sch<br>8700 South View Rd, Austin 78737<br>Marie-Helene Harlow \ Ryan Phillips | K-12 | G | 380<br>18 | | 512/288-5942<br>Fax 512/301-8997 |
| Dragonfly International Sch<br>610 W Highway 290, Dripping Spgs 78620<br>Robin McThompson | PK-6 | | 50<br>5 | | 512/858-9780 |
| Dripping Springs Christ Acad<br>800 W Highway 290 Bldg C, Dripping Spgs 78620<br>Becky Welborn | PK-10 | | 25 | | 512/858-9738 |
| Hill Country Christian Sch<br>1401 Davis Ln, San Marcos 78666<br>Joe Lunz | K-12 | | 145<br>11 | | 512/353-8976<br>Fax 512/396-3639<br>🅕 |
| Masters Sch<br>1664 Center Point Rd, San Marcos 78666<br>Tuck Blythe | K-8 | | 131<br>8 | | 512/392-4322<br>Fax 512/754-6017 |
| San Marcos Baptist Academy<br>2801 Ranch Road 12, San Marcos 78666<br>Steven McCray | 7-12 | | 300<br>36 | | 512/353-2400<br>Fax 512/753-8031 |
| St Stephen's Episcopal Sch<br>6000 FM 3237, Wimberley 78676<br>Amanda Ebner | PK-6 | | 58<br>12 | | 512/847-9857<br>Fax 512/847-5275 |
| The King's Academy<br>203 W Highway 290, Dripping Spgs 78620<br>Shelby Hubbard | PK-8 | | 50 | | 512/858-4700 |
| Wonderland Sch<br>302 Country Estates Dr, San Marcos 78666<br>Jim Fife | PK-6 | | 200<br>12 | | 512/392-9404<br>Fax 512/392-9048 |

---

# HEMPHILL COUNTY

## HEMPHILL PUBLIC SCHOOLS

● **Canadian Ind School Dist** PID: 01029205    806/323-5393
800 Hillside Ave, Canadian 79014    Fax 806/323-8143

**Schools:** 4 \ **Teachers:** 84 \ **Students:** 860 \ **Special Ed Students:** 70 \
**LEP Students:** 106 \ **Ethnic:** Hispanic 46%, Caucasian 53% \ **Exp:** $145
(Low) \ **Poverty:** 12% \ **Title I:** $108,054 \ **Open-Close:** 08/20 - 05/21 \
**DTBP:** $352 (High)

| | | |
|---|---|---|
| Lynn Pulliam ...........1 | Cindy Moore ...........2 | |
| Matt Dillon ...........3 | Lydia Nix ...........4 | |
| Shaffer Baxter ...........5 | Bruce Bryant ...........8* | |
| Lawana Pulliam ...........8,73 | Reagan Oles ...........9* | |
| Darlene Walker ...........38* | Larry Smith ...........67 | |
| David Calabrese ...........73,76,295 | | |

| Public Schs..Principal | Grd | Prgm | Enr/#Cls | SN |
|---|---|---|---|---|
| Baker Elem Sch | 3-5 | T | 203 | 47% 806/323-5386 |
| 723 Cheyenne Street, Canadian 79014 | | | 9 | Fax 806/323-9916 |
| Krista Daniel | | | | |
| Canadian Elem Sch | PK-2 | T | 175 | 49% 806/323-9331 |
| 500 Dogwood St, Canadian 79014 | | | 22 | Fax 806/323-6852 |
| Reagan Risley | | | | |
| Canadian High Sch | 9-12 | V | 267 | 33% 806/323-5373 |
| 621 S 5th Street, Canadian 79014 | | | 26 | Fax 806/323-9345 |
| James Bryant | | | | |
| Canadian Middle Sch | 6-8 | T | 221 | 43% 806/323-5351 |
| 404 S 6th St, Canadian 79014 | | | 30 | Fax 806/323-8791 |
| Drew Daniel | | | | |

# HENDERSON COUNTY

## HENDERSON PUBLIC SCHOOLS

● **Athens Ind School Dist** PID: 01029231    903/677-6900
104 Hawn St, Athens 75751    Fax 903/677-6908

**Schools:** 5 \ **Teachers:** 193 \ **Students:** 3,000 \ **Special Ed Students:** 314
\ **LEP Students:** 693 \ **Ethnic:** Asian 1%, African American 13%, Hispanic
51%, Caucasian 35% \ **Exp:** $465 (High) \ **Poverty:** 27% \ **Title I:** $1,422,993
\ **Special Education:** $605,000 \ **Open-Close:** 08/03 - 05/27 \ **DTBP:** $155
(High)

| | | |
|---|---|---|
| Dr Janie Sims ...........1 | Randy Jones ...........2,19 | |
| Barry Choate ...........3,4,5 | Erin Lopez ...........4 | |
| Zac Harrell ...........6 | Dr Cathy Kirkland ...........8,57,69,78,288 | |
| Jami Ivey ...........10,15 | Ginger Morrison ...........11,68,83,296,298 | |
| Edward Wilbanks ...........27* | Brooke Brock ...........58 | |
| Alicia Elliott ...........67 | Toni Clay ...........71 | |
| Tony Brooks ...........73,76,286 | Dana Dykes ...........91 | |

| Public Schs..Principal | Grd | Prgm | Enr/#Cls | SN |
|---|---|---|---|---|
| Athens High Sch | 9-12 | GTV | 899 | 67% 903/677-6920 |
| 708 E College St, Athens 75751 | | | 80 | Fax 903/677-6925 |
| Nicole Cornish | | | | |
| Athens Middle Sch | 6-8 | GT | 657 | 76% 903/677-3030 |
| 6800 State Highway 19 S, Athens 75751 | | | 45 | Fax 903/677-2111 |
| Jennifer Risinger | | | | |
| Bel Air Elem Sch | PK-5 | GT | 420 | 79% 903/677-6980 |
| 215 Willowbrook Dr, Athens 75751 | | | 29 | Fax 903/677-6986 |
| Lisa Howell | | | | |
| Central Athens Elem Sch | PK-5 | GT | 451 | 83% 903/677-6960 |
| 307 Madole St, Athens 75751 | | | 26 | Fax 903/677-6987 |
| Claudia Stiles | | | | |
| South Athens Elem Sch | PK-5 | GT | 435 | 82% 903/677-6970 |
| 718 Robbins Rd, Athens 75751 | | | 26 | Fax 903/677-3470 |
| Nicole Mason | | | | |

● **Brownsboro Ind School Dist** PID: 01029322    903/852-3701
14134 State Highway 31 E, Brownsboro 75756    Fax 903/852-3957

**Schools:** 7 \ **Teachers:** 190 \ **Students:** 2,800 \ **Special Ed Students:** 355
\ **LEP Students:** 121 \ **Ethnic:** African American 7%, Hispanic 16%,
Caucasian 76% \ **Exp:** $442 (High) \ **Poverty:** 23% \ **Title I:** $825,291 \
**Special Education:** $495,000 \ **Open-Close:** 08/17 - 05/27 \ **DTBP:** $152
(High) \

| | | |
|---|---|---|
| Dr Keri Hampton ...........1 | Jonathan Lundmark ...........2 | |
| Jeff Howard ...........3,5,91* | Gean Weinkaus ...........4 | |
| Greg Pearson ...........6,35* | Diana Williams ...........7 | |
| Rita Gray ...........11,57,69,88,271,274,275,752 | Jerry Feiner ...........28,73,76,295 | |
| Sandra Duke ...........34,58,77* | Steve Sanders ...........67 | |
| Carol Mayfield ...........68* | Bradley Robertson ...........79,270 | |

| Public Schs..Principal | Grd | Prgm | Enr/#Cls | SN |
|---|---|---|---|---|
| Ⓐ ACES Alternative | 9-12 | | 14 | 903/852-8021 |
| 14135 State Highway 31 E, Brownsboro 75756 | | | | Fax 903/852-6389 |
| Marion Jones | | | | |
| Brownsboro Elem Sch | PK-3 | T | 408 | 69% 903/852-6461 |
| 12331 State Highway 31 E, Brownsboro 75756 | | | 25 | Fax 903/852-2718 |
| Robbi McCarter | | | | |
| Brownsboro High Sch | 9-12 | T | 779 | 52% 903/852-2321 |
| 13942 State Highway 31 E, Brownsboro 75756 | | | 65 | Fax 903/852-5195 |
| Brent Cooper | | | | |
| Brownsboro Intermediate Sch | 4-6 | T | 343 | 59% 903/852-7325 |
| 13951 Saylors St, Brownsboro 75756 | | | 18 | Fax 903/852-6745 |
| Billy Beasley | | | | |
| Brownsboro Junior High Sch | 7-8 | T | 412 | 55% 903/852-6931 |
| 11233 Ingram St, Brownsboro 75756 | | | 30 | Fax 903/852-5238 |
| Jake Roach | | | | |
| Chandler Elem Sch | PK-3 | T | 389 | 69% 903/849-3400 |
| 615 N Broad St, Chandler 75758 | | | 22 | Fax 903/849-3628 |
| Ricky Daily | | | | |
| Chandler Intermediate Sch | 4-6 | T | 284 | 63% 903/849-6436 |
| 22250 Barron Rd, Chandler 75758 | | | 19 | Fax 903/849-3019 |
| Lisa Brown | | | | |

● **Cross Roads Ind School Dist** PID: 01029360    903/489-2001
14434 FM 59, Malakoff 75148    Fax 903/489-1103

**Schools:** 3 \ **Teachers:** 55 \ **Students:** 545 \ **Special Ed Students:** 63
\ **LEP Students:** 12 \ **College-Bound:** 61% \ **Ethnic:** African American
1%, Hispanic 11%, Caucasian 88% \ **Exp:** $848 (High) \ **Poverty:** 23% \
**Title I:** $176,166 \ **Open-Close:** 08/20 - 05/21 \ **DTBP:** $350 (High)

Richard Tedder ...........1,11    Ann Hornsby ...........2*

| | | | | |
|---|---|---|---|---|
| 1 Superintendent | 19 Chief Financial Officer | 39 Social Studies K-12 | 59 Special Education Elem | 69 Academic Assessment |
| 2 Bus/Finance/Purchasing | 20 Art K-12 | 40 Social Studies Elem | 60 Special Education Sec | 70 Research/Development |
| 3 Buildings And Grounds | 21 Art Elem | 41 Social Studies Sec | 61 Foreign/World Lang K-12 | 71 Public Information |
| 4 Food Service | 22 Art Sec | 42 Science K-12 | 62 Foreign/World Lang Elem | 72 Summer School |
| 5 Transportation | 23 Music K-12 | 43 Science Elem | 63 Foreign/World Lang Sec | 73 Instructional Tech |
| 6 Athletic | 24 Music Elem | 44 Science Sec | 64 Religious Education K-12 | 74 Inservice Training |
| 7 Health Services | 25 Music Sec | 45 Math K-12 | 65 Religious Education Elem | 75 Marketing/Distributive |
| 8 Curric/Instruct K-12 | 26 Business Education | 46 Math Elem | 66 Religious Education Sec | 76 Info Systems |
| 9 Curric/Instruct Elem | 27 Career & Tech Ed | 47 Math Sec | 67 School Board President | 77 Psychological Assess |
| 10 Curric/Instruct Sec | 28 Technology Education | 48 English/Lang Arts K-12 | 68 Teacher Personnel | 78 Affirmative Action |
| 11 Federal Program | 29 Family/Consumer Science | 49 English/Lang Arts Elem | | |
| 12 Title I | 30 Adult Education | 50 English/Lang Arts Sec | | |
| 13 Title V | 31 Career/Sch-to-Work K-12 | 51 Reading K-12 | | |
| 14 | 32 Career/Sch-to-Work Elem | 52 Reading Elem | | |
| 15 Asst Superintendent | 33 Career/Sch-to-Work Sec | 53 Reading Sec | | |
| 16 Instructional Media Svcs | 34 Early Childhood Ed | 54 Remedial Reading K-12 | | |
| 17 Chief Operations Officer | 35 Health/Phys Education | 55 Remedial Reading Elem | | |
| 18 Chief Academic Officer | 36 Guidance Services K-12 | 56 Remedial Reading Sec | | |
| | 37 Guidance Services Elem | 57 Bilingual/ELL | | |
| | 38 Guidance Services Sec | 58 Special Education K-12 | | |

| | | | | |
|---|---|---|---|---|
| Daniel Pierce ........... 6* | Gary Cahill ........... 16,73* |
| Kim Mattingly ........... 31,69,85* | Pam Taylor ........... 36* |
| Darren Himes ........... 67 | Gina Trammell ........... 68 |
| Kari Cahill ........... 270,271* | Dr Tammy Willis ........... 286 |

| Public Schs..Principal | Grd | Prgm | Enr/#Cls | SN | |
|---|---|---|---|---|---|
| Cross Roads Elem Sch<br>14434 FM 59, Malakoff 75148<br>Kari Cahill | PK-5 | T | 258<br>15 | 64% | 903/489-1774<br>Fax 903/489-1112 |
| Cross Roads High Sch<br>14434 FM 59, Malakoff 75148<br>John Miller | 9-12 | TV | 149<br>18 | 49% | 903/489-1275 |
| Cross Roads Junior High Sch<br>14434 FM 59, Malakoff 75148<br>Julie Koepp | 6-8 | T | 151<br>12 | 50% | 903/489-2667<br>Fax 903/489-1106 |

## ● Eustace Ind School Dist PID: 01029384
320 FM 316 S, Eustace 75124 — 903/425-5151 — Fax 903/425-5147

**Schools:** 4 \ **Teachers:** 123 \ **Students:** 1,566 \ **Special Ed Students:** 230 \ **LEP Students:** 22 \ **College-Bound:** 46% \ **Ethnic:** African American 1%, Hispanic 11%, Caucasian 87% \ **Exp:** $402 (High) \ **Poverty:** 27% \ **Title I:** $486,426 \ **Special Education:** $392,000 \ **Open-Close:** 08/21 - 05/21 \ **DTBP:** $357 (High) \ f t

| | | | | |
|---|---|---|---|---|
| Dr Coy Holcombe ........... 1,73 | Carol Warren ........... 2 |
| James Beverly ........... 3 | Carolyn Davis ........... 4 |
| Stan Sowers ........... 5,15* | Steven Smith ........... 6* |
| Deanna Haynes ........... 8,12,57 | Julie Gray ........... 34* |
| Kathryn Hendrickson ........... 58* | Ashley McKee ........... 67 |
| Phyllis Bice ........... 83,85,88* | Wade Morton ........... 91* |
| Rusty Meyners ........... 295 | |

| Public Schs..Principal | Grd | Prgm | Enr/#Cls | SN | |
|---|---|---|---|---|---|
| Eustace High Sch<br>318 FM 316 S, Eustace 75124<br>Christopher Whorton | 9-12 | ATV | 430<br>45 | 61% | 903/425-5161<br>Fax 903/425-5227 |
| Eustace Intermediate Sch<br>205 W Henderson St, Eustace 75124<br>Robert Reeve | 3-5 | T | 344<br>28 | 63% | 903/425-5181<br>Fax 903/425-5294 |
| Eustace Middle Sch<br>200 FM 316 S, Eustace 75124<br>Michael Rowland | 6-8 | T | 347<br>25 | 58% | 903/425-5171<br>Fax 903/425-5146<br>f t |
| Eustace Primary Sch<br>211 W Henderson St, Eustace 75124<br>Julie Gray | PK-2 | T | 445<br>30 | 75% | 903/425-5191<br>Fax 903/425-5148 |

## ● La Poynor Ind School Dist PID: 01029413
13155 US Highway 175 E, Larue 75770 — 903/876-4057 — Fax 903/876-4541

**Schools:** 1 \ **Teachers:** 35 \ **Students:** 470 \ **Special Ed Students:** 38 \ **LEP Students:** 6 \ **College-Bound:** 95% \ **Ethnic:** Asian 1%, African American 7%, Hispanic 11%, Caucasian 81% \ **Exp:** $322 (High) \ **Poverty:** 28% \ **Title I:** $180,791 \ **Open-Close:** 08/17 - 05/21 \ **DTBP:** $392 (High)

| | | | | |
|---|---|---|---|---|
| Dr James Young ........... 1 | Sherry Crawford ........... 2 |
| Ronnie Hambrick ........... 3,5,91* | Jessica Boyette ........... 4 |
| Dean Nuckolls ........... 6* | Pam Penney ........... 7,85* |
| Sandra Burch ........... 15 | Geneva Robinson ........... 31* |
| Ashley Fossett ........... 36,83,88 | Lori Griffith ........... 57* |
| Jacob Haynes ........... 67 | |

| Public Schs..Principal | Grd | Prgm | Enr/#Cls | SN | |
|---|---|---|---|---|---|
| La Poynor Sch<br>13155 US Highway 175 E, Larue 75770<br>Marsha Mills \ Crystal Woodard | PK-12 | ATV | 470<br>24 | 50% | 903/876-4057 |

## ● Malakoff Ind School Dist PID: 01029449
1308 FM 3062, Malakoff 75148 — 903/489-1152 — Fax 903/489-2566

**Schools:** 5 \ **Teachers:** 104 \ **Students:** 1,300 \ **Special Ed Students:** 156 \ **LEP Students:** 62 \ **Ethnic:** African American 13%, Hispanic 19%, Caucasian 68% \ **Exp:** $566 (High) \ **Poverty:** 27% \ **Title I:** $466,357 \ **Special Education:** $16,000 \ **Open-Close:** 08/19 - 05/27 \ **DTBP:** $340 (High)

| | | | | |
|---|---|---|---|---|
| Done Layton ........... 1 | Kim Spencer ........... 2 |
| Jennifer Gonzales ........... 4 | Tammy Baker ........... 5 |
| Jamie Driskell ........... 6* | Sybil Norris ........... 11,31,57,58,83,271,296,298 |
| Linda McMurtry ........... 16,82* | Laurie Holcombe ........... 58 |
| Rick Vieregge ........... 67 | Randy Webb ........... 73,95,295 |
| Stacy Hillhouse ........... 91 | |

| Public Schs..Principal | Grd | Prgm | Enr/#Cls | SN | |
|---|---|---|---|---|---|
| Ⓐ Leo Orr Sr Education Center<br>1209 W Royall Blvd, Malakoff 75148<br>Danielle Copeland | 6-12 | | 10<br>3 | | 903/489-4132<br>Fax 903/489-3239 |
| Malakoff Elem Sch<br>310 N Terry St, Malakoff 75148<br>**Chris Robinson** | PK-5 | T | 423<br>45 | 68% | 903/489-0313<br>Fax 903/489-1536 |
| Malakoff High Sch<br>15201 FM 3062, Malakoff 75148<br>Bill Morgan | 9-12 | GTV | 89<br>50 | 61% | 903/489-1527<br>Fax 903/489-0971 |
| Malakoff Middle Sch<br>106 N Cedar St, Malakoff 75148<br>Quintin Watkins | 6-8 | T | 320<br>26 | 56% | 903/489-0264<br>Fax 903/489-1812 |
| Tool Elem Sch<br>1201 S Tool Dr, Kemp 75143<br>**Brandi Sutton** | PK-5 | T | 200 | 72% | 903/432-2637<br>Fax 903/432-3666 |

## ● Murchison Ind Sch Dist PID: 01029487
9661 Bankhead St, Murchison 75778 — 903/469-3636 — Fax 903/469-3887

**Schools:** 1 \ **Teachers:** 16 \ **Students:** 200 \ **Special Ed Students:** 28 \ **LEP Students:** 12 \ **Ethnic:** African American 4%, Hispanic 18%, Caucasian 79% \ **Exp:** $204 (Med) \ **Poverty:** 35% \ **Title I:** $79,895 \ **Open-Close:** 09/08 - 05/21 \ **DTBP:** $303 (High)

| | | | | |
|---|---|---|---|---|
| Kimberly Followwell ........... 1,11,83 | Kerri Partridge ........... 2 |
| Jerid Heathman ........... 6* | Cindy Bailey ........... 57,88 |
| Lloyd Smith ........... 67 | Christy Wehrmann ........... 73,295 |

| Public Schs..Principal | Grd | Prgm | Enr/#Cls | SN | |
|---|---|---|---|---|---|
| Murchison Elem Sch<br>9661 Bankhead St, Murchison 75778<br>Susan Miller | PK-8 | T | 200<br>10 | 71% | 903/469-3636 |

## ● Trinidad Ind School Dist PID: 01029504
105 W Eaton St, Trinidad 75163 — 903/778-2673 — Fax 903/778-4120

**Schools:** 1 \ **Teachers:** 20 \ **Students:** 145 \ **Special Ed Students:** 16 \ **LEP Students:** 6 \ **College-Bound:** 75% \ **Ethnic:** African American 16%, Hispanic 20%, Caucasian 64% \ **Exp:** $313 (High) \ **Poverty:** 34% \ **Title I:** $79,043 \ **Open-Close:** 08/19 - 05/28 \ **DTBP:** $323 (High)

| | | | | |
|---|---|---|---|---|
| Corey Jenkins ........... 1 | Kristi Boggas ........... 4 |
| Matthew Mizell ........... 8,11,83,88,274,288* | Victrina Johnson ........... 58 |
| Eric Airheart ........... 67 | |

| Public Schs..Principal | Grd | Prgm | Enr/#Cls | SN | |
|---|---|---|---|---|---|
| Trinidad Sch<br>105 W Eaton St, Trinidad 75163<br>Matthew Mizell | PK-12 | TV | 145<br>30 | 74% | 903/778-2415<br>Fax 903/778-2663 |

## HENDERSON PRIVATE SCHOOLS

| Private Schs..Principal | Grd | Prgm | Enr/#Cls | SN | |
|---|---|---|---|---|---|
| Athens Christian Academy<br>105 S Carroll St, Athens 75751<br>Brent Williams | K-6 | | 64<br>14 | | 903/675-5135<br>Fax 903/675-4708 |
| Open Doors Christian Academy<br>202 Ranch Rd, Gun Barrel Cy 75156<br>Debra Turner | K-12 | | 42<br>9 | | 903/887-3621<br>Fax 903/713-0220 |

## HIDALGO COUNTY

## HIDALGO PUBLIC SCHOOLS

- **Donna Ind School Dist** PID: 01029554          956/464-1600
  116 N 10th St, Donna 78537          Fax 956/464-1752

**Schools:** 22 \ **Teachers:** 1,029 \
**Students:** 14,459 \ **Special Ed Students:** 1,319 \ **LEP Students:** 6,968
\ **College-Bound:** 54% \ **Ethnic:** Hispanic 100%, \ **Exp:** $334 (High) \
**Poverty:** 49% \ **Title I:** $14,309,718 \ **Special Education:** $2,076,000 \
**Open-Close:** 08/26 - 05/28 \ **DTBP:** $191 (High) \ [f]

| | | |
|---|---|---|
| Dr Hafedn Azaiez ........1 | Ludipina Cansino ........2,19 | |
| Olga Norriega ........2 | Rosa Campos ........7,85* | |
| Rebecca Castaneda ........11,271 | Dr Debra Aceves ........13,57,61,81 | |
| Juanita Rodriguez ........15,68,79,273 | David Chavez ........16,73,76,295* | |
| David Moreno ........27,33* | Stephanie Powelson ........39 | |
| Emily Anderson ........43 | Rashad Rana ........45 | |
| Diane Villanueva ........58,77,275 | Eva Watts ........67 | |
| John Mendoza ........88* | Daniel Walden ........91 | |
| Tomas Camez ........93 | | |

| Public Schs..Principal | Grd | Prgm | Enr/#Cls | SN | |
|---|---|---|---|---|---|
| ⓐ 3D Academy<br>2110 Hester Ave, Donna 78537<br>Jose Villanueva | 9-12 | T | 112 | 96% | 956/464-1254<br>Fax 956/464-2375 |
| A P Solis Middle Sch<br>700 South Ave, Donna 78537<br>Mary Lou Rodriguez | 6-8 | T | 850 | 88% | 956/464-1650<br>Fax 956/464-1786 |
| Antonio M Ochoa Elem Sch<br>424 S 11th St, Donna 78537<br>Melissa Smith | PK-5 | T | 423<br>26 | 91% | 956/464-1900<br>Fax 956/464-1918 |
| C Stainke Elem Sch<br>1309 South Ave, Donna 78537<br>Veronica Huerta | PK-5 | T | 464<br>30 | 95% | 956/464-1940<br>Fax 956/464-1790 |
| Capt D Salinas II Elem Sch<br>333 E Business Highway 83, Alamo 78516<br>Sanjuanito Franco | PK-5 | T | 526<br>38 | 95% | 956/783-1332<br>Fax 956/782-9175 |
| Daniel Singleterry Sr Elem Sch<br>9113 N Val Verde Rd, Donna 78537<br>Christopher Park | PK-5 | T | 542<br>39 | 97% | 956/464-1845<br>Fax 956/464-1849 |

| Public Schs..Principal | Grd | Prgm | Enr/#Cls | SN | |
|---|---|---|---|---|---|
| ⓐ Disciplinary Alt Ed Program<br>2006 Silver Ave, Donna 78537<br>John Mendoza | 1-12 | | 60<br>11 | | 956/464-1954<br>Fax 956/464-1951 |
| Donna High Sch<br>2301 E Wood Ave, Donna 78537<br>Nancy Castillo | 9-12 | GTV | 2,046 | 90% | 956/464-1700<br>Fax 956/464-1629 |
| Donna North High Sch<br>7250 N Val Verde Rd, Donna 78537<br>Bernadett Caceres | 9-12 | ATV | 2,180 | 96% | 956/464-4190 |
| Dora M Sauceda Middle Sch<br>520 N Valley View Rd, Donna 78537<br>Adela Troncoso \ **Karina Robledo** | 6-8 | T | 828<br>100 | 97% | 956/464-1360<br>Fax 956/464-1349 |
| Eloy Salazar Elem Sch<br>3207 N Goolie Rd, Donna 78537<br>Leticia Chavez | PK-5 | T | 522<br>37 | 92% | 956/464-1977<br>Fax 956/464-1983 |
| Guzman Elem Sch<br>510 S Salinas Blvd, Donna 78537<br>Emmy Delagarza | PK-5 | T | 331<br>25 | 98% | 956/464-1920<br>Fax 956/464-1926 |
| J S Adame Elem Sch<br>5001 N Farm Rd 493, Donna 78537<br>Maria Partida | PK-5 | T | 530<br>45 | 91% | 956/461-4010<br>Fax 956/461-4017 |
| Juan W Caceres Elem Sch<br>503 S Hutto Rd, Donna 78537<br>Celia Martinez | PK-5 | T | 325<br>29 | 94% | 956/464-1995<br>Fax 956/464-1743 |
| Le Noir Elem Sch<br>316 N Main St, Donna 78537<br>Karen Nieto | PK-5 | T | 405<br>35 | 92% | 956/464-1685<br>Fax 956/464-1877 |
| Magin Rivas Elem Sch<br>503 S Hutto Rd, Donna 78537<br>Rosalinda Navarro | PK-5 | T | 340<br>33 | 98% | 956/464-1990<br>Fax 956/464-1869 |
| Maria Alicia P Munoz Sch<br>1901 E Roosevelt Rd, Donna 78537<br>Nelda Calderon | PK-5 | T | 708<br>45 | 98% | 956/464-1310<br>Fax 956/464-1316 |
| Patricia S Garza Elem Sch<br>8801 W Alberta Rd, Donna 78537<br>Crystal Garza | PK-5 | T | 625<br>48 | 100% | 956/464-1886<br>Fax 956/464-1891 |
| Runn Elem Sch<br>1701 E Highway 281, Donna 78537<br>Maria Hinojosa | PK-5 | T | 267<br>22 | 93% | 956/464-1864<br>Fax 956/464-1934 |
| Truman Price Elem Sch<br>2906 E Roberts Ave, Donna 78537<br>Olga Cervantes | PK-5 | T | 418<br>26 | 97% | 956/464-1303<br>Fax 956/464-1676 |
| Veterans Middle Sch<br>2711 N Goolie Rd, Donna 78537<br>Claudia Guerrero | 6-8 | T | 890<br>35 | 92% | 956/464-1350<br>Fax 956/464-1356 |
| W A Todd Middle Sch<br>400 N Salinas Blvd, Donna 78537<br>Araceli Guerra | 6-8 | T | 722 | 93% | 956/464-1800 |

- **Edcouch Elsa Ind School Dist** PID: 01029621          956/262-6000
  301 N Yellow Jacket Dr, Edcouch 78538          Fax 956/262-6032

**Schools:** 8 \ **Teachers:** 320 \ **Students:** 5,450 \ **Special Ed Students:** 462
\ **LEP Students:** 1,199 \ **College-Bound:** 51% \ **Ethnic:** Hispanic 100%, \
**Exp:** $550 (High) \ **Poverty:** 47% \ **Title I:** $4,055,541 \ **Open-Close:** 08/26 -
05/21 \ **DTBP:** $189 (High)

| | |
|---|---|
| Dr Richard Riberou ........1 | Sylvia Garza ........2 |
| Elena Garza ........4 | Javier Romero ........4 |
| Martin Rodregez ........5 | Christian Navarro ........6,35 |
| Carmen Garcia ........8,11,15,296 | Maria Garcia ........8,15 |
| Denise Frando ........9,36* | Rosalinda DeLeon ........9* |
| Nehemias Cantu ........10 | Frances Rocha ........15 |
| Pete Vallejo ........16 | Joe Torres ........31,73,286 |
| Cynthia Brisero ........36,85* | Itza Flores ........58 |
| Fernando Torres ........67 | Virginio Gonzalez ........68 |
| Sandra Ochoa ........69,70 | Maria Gonzales ........81 |

| | | | | | | | | |
|---|---|---|---|---|---|---|---|---|
| 1 | Superintendent | 8 | Curric/Instruct K-12 | 19 | Chief Financial Officer | 29 | Family/Consumer Science | 39 | Social Studies K-12 | 49 | English/Lang Arts Elem | 59 | Special Education Elem | 69 | Academic Assessment |
| 2 | Bus/Finance/Purchasing | 9 | Curric/Instruct Elem | 20 | Art K-12 | 30 | Adult Education | 40 | Social Studies Elem | 50 | English/Lang Arts Sec | 60 | Special Education Sec | 70 | Research/Development |
| 3 | Buildings And Grounds | 10 | Curric/Instruct Sec | 21 | Art Elem | 31 | Career/Sch-to-Work K-12 | 41 | Social Studies Sec | 51 | Reading K-12 | 61 | Foreign/World Lang K-12 | 71 | Public Information |
| 4 | Food Service | 11 | Federal Program | 22 | Art Sec | 32 | Career/Sch-to-Work Elem | 42 | Science K-12 | 52 | Reading Elem | 62 | Foreign/World Lang Elem | 72 | Summer School |
| 5 | Transportation | 12 | Title I | 23 | Music K-12 | 33 | Career/Sch-to-Work Sec | 43 | Science Elem | 53 | Reading Sec | 63 | Foreign/World Lang Sec | 73 | Instructional Tech |
| 6 | Athletic | 13 | Title V | 24 | Music Elem | 34 | Early Childhood Ed | 44 | Science Sec | 54 | Remedial Reading K-12 | 64 | Religious Education K-12 | 74 | Inservice Training |
| 7 | Health Services | 14 | Asst Superintendent | 25 | Music Sec | 35 | Health/Phys Education | 45 | Math K-12 | 55 | Remedial Reading Elem | 65 | Religious Education Elem | 75 | Marketing/Distributive |
| | | 15 | Assistant Superintendent | 26 | Business Education | 36 | Guidance Services K-12 | 46 | Math Elem | 56 | Remedial Reading Sec | 66 | Religious Education Sec | 76 | Info Systems |
| | | 16 | Instructional Media Svcs | 27 | Career & Tech Ed | 37 | Guidance Services Elem | 47 | Math Sec | 57 | Bilingual/ELL | 67 | School Board President | 77 | Psychological Assess |
| | | 17 | Chief Operations Officer | 28 | Technology Education | 38 | Guidance Services Sec | 48 | English/Lang Arts K-12 | 58 | Special Education K-12 | 68 | Teacher Personnel | 78 | Affirmative Action |
| | | 18 | Chief Academic Officer | | | | | | | | | | | | |

Monica Vela ..... 93,271
Melinda Chapa ..... 298

| Public Schs..Principal | Grd | Prgm | Enr/#Cls | SN |
|---|---|---|---|---|
| Carlos Truan Jr High Sch<br>Mile 17 N & Mile 4 W, Edcouch 78538<br>Alfredo Aguilar | 6-8 | TV | 1,064<br>44 | 99% 956/262-5820<br>Fax 956/262-6079 |
| Early College High Sch<br>PO Box 127, Edcouch 78538<br>Jaime Garcia | 9-9 | V | 400 | 956/262-4731 |
| Edcouch Elsa High Sch<br>301 N Yellow Jacket Drive, Edcouch 78538<br>Janie Tijerina | 9-12 | ATV | 648 | 98% 956/262-6944<br>Fax 956/262-6060 |
| John F Kennedy Elem Sch<br>500 W 9th Street, Elsa 78543<br>Criselda Martinez | K-5 | T | 477<br>26 | 97% 956/262-6027<br>Fax 956/262-6029 |
| Jorge R Gutierrez ECC<br>1210 W Santa Rosa Ave, Edcouch 78538<br>Norma Hernandez | PK-PK | T | 420<br>28 | 95% 956/262-0040<br>Fax 956/262-0043 |
| Lyndon Baines Johnson Elem Sch<br>200 S Fannin Street, Elsa 78543<br>Aminta Limas | K-5 | T | 506<br>25 | 99% 956/262-2161<br>Fax 956/626-6012 |
| Ruben Rodriguez Elem Sch<br>1302 W Santa Rosa Rd, Edcouch 78538<br>Maricela Olivarez | K-5 | T | 434<br>15 | 96% 956/262-4712<br>Fax 956/262-6061 |
| Santiago Garcia Elem Sch<br>101 E Santa Rosa Ave, Edcouch 78538<br>Jesus Ramos | K-5 | T | 511<br>22 | 96% 956/262-4741<br>Fax 956/262-6004 |

## • Edinburg Cons Ind School Dist PID: 01029671

411 N 8th Ave, Edinburg 78541
956/289-2300
Fax 956/383-3576

**Schools:** 43 \ **Teachers:** 2,273 \ **Students:** 34,500 \ **Special Ed Students:** 2,147 \ **LEP Students:** 10,577 \ **College-Bound:** 61% \ **Ethnic:** Asian 1%, Hispanic 98%, Caucasian 1% \ **Exp:** $447 (High) \ **Poverty:** 37% \ **Title I:** $21,158,076 \ **Special Education:** $4,922,000 \ **Open-Close:** 08/31 - 06/11 \ **DTBP:** $191 (High) \ Facebook Twitter

Gilbert Garza ..... 1
Jaime Perez ..... 4*
Rogelio Garza ..... 6,35*
Dalia Guzman ..... 8,15
Irma Villareal ..... 12
Dr Edwardo Moreno ..... 15,28,73,84,297
Dora Estrada ..... 16,82
Arminda Lozano ..... 27,31
Azel Arredondo ..... 39
Vanessa Arrona ..... 44
Hugo Keal ..... 47
Alida Suarez ..... 58,77
Jorge Botello ..... 69
Noe Pena ..... 73,286
Sylvia Ledesna ..... 81
Rudy Jemenez ..... 90
Jenise Fuerte-Luna ..... 275
Alejandro Martinez ..... 297
Dr Rebecca Morrison ..... 2,15,72,274,296,298
Alonzo Barbosa ..... 5
Diana Davila ..... 7
Dr Anthony Garza ..... 10*
Melissa Rodriguez ..... 13
Dr Mario Salinas ..... 15
Nelinda Villarreal ..... 20,23
Sofia Hinojosa ..... 36,79,83,85,270
Mirella Garza ..... 43
Romero Leal ..... 46
Cynthia Saenz ..... 57,271
Oscar Saunas ..... 67
Romeo Cantu ..... 71
Mara Moats ..... 74,285
Ernestina Cano ..... 88*
Sandra Rodriguez ..... 93
Andy Rios ..... 295

| Public Schs..Principal | Grd | Prgm | Enr/#Cls | SN |
|---|---|---|---|---|
| A Villarreal Elem Sch<br>4014 N Doolittle Rd, Edinburg 78542<br>Odilia Villarreal | PK-5 | T | 589 | 93% 956/289-2377<br>Fax 956/381-4782 |
| Alfonso R Ramirez Elem Sch<br>1700 W Alberta Rd, Edinburg 78539<br>Clarisa Ramirez | PK-5 | T | 541 | 75% 956/289-2425<br>Fax 956/316-2355 |
| Anne L MaGee Elem Sch<br>3420 W Rogers Rd, Edinburg 78541<br>Marla Cavazos | PK-5 | T | 402 | 90% 956/289-2306<br>Fax 956/385-3320 |
| Austin Elem Sch<br>1023 E Kuhn St, Edinburg 78541<br>Homero Cano | PK-5 | T | 392<br>17 | 91% 956/289-2331<br>Fax 956/316-7560 |
| B L Garza Middle Sch<br>1202 N Monmack Rd, Edinburg 78541<br>Dale Ramos | 6-8 | T | 1,065<br>65 | 87% 956/289-2480<br>Fax 956/316-3109 |
| Betty Harwell Middle Sch<br>9207 N Avila Rd, Edinburg 78542<br>Marisa Garza | 6-8 | GTV | 1,394<br>76 | 97% 956/289-2440<br>Fax 956/316-7303 |
| Brewster Sch<br>22420 FM 1017, Edinburg 78541<br>**Zulema Garcia** | PK-8 | T | 171<br>18 | 82% 956/289-2334<br>Fax 956/316-7510 |
| Cano Gonzalez Elem Sch<br>1701 S Raul Longoria Rd, Edinburg 78542<br>Nelda Gaytan | PK-5 | T | 438<br>31 | 82% 956/289-2380<br>Fax 956/316-7457 |
| Canterbury Elem Sch<br>2821 W Canton Rd, Edinburg 78539<br>Ricardo Perez | PK-5 | T | 706<br>35 | 48% 956/289-2374<br>Fax 956/316-7606<br>Twitter |
| Carmen Avila Elem Sch<br>9205 Carmen Avila Rd, Edinburg 78542<br>**Ramiro Leal** | PK-5 | | 605<br>35 | 956/289-2307<br>Fax 956/385-3330 |
| Cavazos Elem Sch<br>1501 Freddy Gonzales Rd, McAllen 78504<br>Christine Gordon | PK-5 | T | 465<br>28 | 85% 956/289-2535<br>Fax 956/384-5147 |
| Crawford Elem Sch<br>1800 E Davis Rd, Edinburg 78542<br>**Denise Vega** | PK-5 | | 521 | 956/289-2410<br>Fax 956/287-0700 |
| De La Vina Elem Sch<br>1001 S Jackson Rd, Edinburg 78539<br>Erika Playle | PK-5 | T | 550 | 91% 956/289-2366<br>Fax 956/316-7782<br>Twitter |
| E B Guerra Elem Sch<br>10010 Via Fernandez, Edinburg 78541<br>Lisa Valdez | PK-5 | T | 507<br>45 | 94% 956/289-2530<br>Fax 956/384-5352 |
| Ⓐ Edinburg Alternative Academy<br>1301 E Schunior St, Edinburg 78541<br>Anibal Gorena | 6-12 | | 110<br>12 | 956/289-2598<br>Fax 956/316-7391 |
| Edinburg High Sch<br>2600 E Wisconsin Rd, Edinburg 78542<br>Yesena Molina | 9-12 | GTV | 2,541 | 88% 956/289-2400<br>Fax 956/386-1225 |
| Edinburg North High Sch<br>3101 N Closner Blvd, Edinburg 78541<br>Mark Micallef | 9-12 | TV | 2,738 | 88% 956/289-2500<br>Fax 956/316-7712 |
| Edinburg South Middle Sch<br>601 W Freddy Gonzalez Dr, Edinburg 78539<br>Mary Garza | 6-8 | TV | 1,370<br>61 | 71% 956/289-2415<br>Fax 956/316-8817 |
| Eisenhower Elem Sch<br>2901 E Mile 17 1/2 Rd, Edinburg 78542<br>S Faz | PK-5 | | 580<br>32 | 956/289-2540<br>Fax 956/316-7554 |
| Escandon Elem Sch<br>1100 E Trenton Rd, Edinburg 78542<br>Ruth Torres | PK-5 | T | 676<br>35 | 87% 956/289-2545<br>Fax 956/316-7647 |
| Esparza Elem Sch<br>2510 S Cesar Chavez Rd, Edinburg 78542<br>Mr Pesina | PK-5 | T | 427 | 89% 956/289-2308<br>Fax 956/385-3310 |
| Flores-Zapata Elem Sch<br>14000 N Rooth Rd, Edinburg 78541<br>Victoria Martinez | PK-5 | T | 485 | 91% 956/289-2445<br>Fax 956/383-0957 |
| Francisco Barrientes Mid Sch<br>1100 E Ebony Ln, Edinburg 78539<br>David Rivera | 6-8 | T | 1,314 | 88% 956/289-2430<br>Fax 956/316-7749 |
| Freddy Gonzalez Elem Sch<br>2401 S Sugar Rd, Edinburg 78539<br>Naida Torres | PK-5 | T | 430<br>29 | 71% 956/289-2520<br>Fax 956/316-7420<br>Twitter |
| Hargill Elem Sch<br>13394 4th St, Hargill 78549<br>Luisa Gonzalez | PK-5 | T | 392<br>24 | 96% 956/289-2338<br>Fax 956/845-6337 |

| School | Grd | Prgm | Enr/#Cls | SN |
|---|---|---|---|---|
| Jefferson Elem Sch<br>904 S 12th Ave, Edinburg 78539<br>Ana Salinas | PK-5 | T | 495<br>26 | 66% 956/289-2385<br>Fax 956/316-7427 |
| John F Kennedy Elem Sch<br>8610 Tex Mex Rd, Edinburg 78542<br>Gloria Alonzo | PK-5 | T | 478<br>36 | 97% 956/289-2390<br>Fax 956/384-5131 |
| Johnny Economedes High Sch<br>1414 N Alamo Rd, Edinburg 78542<br>Dr Raul D'Lorm | 9-12 | TV | 2,672<br>200 | 94% 956/289-2450<br>Fax 956/385-3050 |
| Lincoln Elem Sch<br>1319 E Lovett St, Edinburg 78541<br>Eva Sandoval | PK-5 | T | 459<br>25 | 95% 956/289-2525<br>Fax 956/384-5208 |
| Longoria Middle Sch<br>14101 N Rooth Rd, Edinburg 78541<br>Antonio Ballesteros | 6-8 | | 975 | 956/289-2486<br>Fax 956/381-6442 |
| Lorenzo De Zavala Elem Sch<br>3615 W Rogers Rd, Edinburg 78541<br>**Marisa Garza** | PK-5 | T | 438 | 89% 956/289-2350<br>Fax 956/316-7605<br>𝐭 |
| Lyndon B Johnson Elem Sch<br>1801 E Sprague St, Edinburg 78542<br>Enrique De La Cruz | PK-5 | T | 418<br>25 | 90% 956/289-2358<br>Fax 956/316-7630 |
| M D Betts Elem Sch<br>2720 S Cesar Chavez Rd, Edinburg 78542<br>**Ernestina Cano** | PK-5 | | 468<br>23 | 956/289-2560<br>Fax 956/384-5312 |
| MacAria Gorena Elem Sch<br>1801 E Freddy Gonzalez Dr, Edinburg 78542<br>Diane Willis | PK-5 | T | 508 | 88% 956/289-2460<br>Fax 956/316-6213 |
| Memorial Middle Sch<br>3105 N Doolittle Rd, Edinburg 78542<br>Fernin Gonzalez | 6-8 | TV | 1,232<br>69 | 94% 956/289-2470<br>Fax 956/316-7581 |
| Monte Cristo Elem Sch<br>4010 N Doolittle Rd, Edinburg 78542<br>Diana Smith | PK-5 | T | 661<br>40 | 96% 956/289-2362<br>Fax 956/316-7471 |
| N L Trevino Elem Sch<br>909 S Mon Mack Rd, Edinburg 78539<br>Brenda Alonzo | PK-5 | T | 576<br>35 | 56% 956/289-2550<br>Fax 956/384-5372 |
| Robert E Lee Elem Sch<br>1215 W Sprague St, Edinburg 78539<br>Alonda Navarro | PK-5 | T | 386<br>30 | 96% 956/289-2342<br>Fax 956/316-7596 |
| Robert Vela High Sch<br>801 E Canton Rd, Edinburg 78539<br>**Michele Pena** | 9-12 | TV | 1,194 | 69% 956/289-2650<br>Fax 956/316-7304 |
| San Carlos Elem Sch<br>505 S 83rd St, Edinburg 78542<br>Belinda De La Rosa | PK-5 | T | 490<br>29 | 97% 956/289-2370<br>Fax 956/316-7364 |
| Travis Elem Sch<br>1200 S 21st Ave, Edinburg 78539<br>Eliana Flores | PK-5 | T | 360<br>21 | 88% 956/289-2354<br>Fax 956/316-7637 |
| Truman Elem Sch<br>701 W Rogers Rd, Edinburg 78541<br>Leticia Duarte | PK-5 | T | 553<br>34 | 89% 956/289-2555<br>Fax 956/316-7527 |
| Ⓐ Vision Academy<br>1200 E Schunior Road, Edinburg 78541<br>Ernestina Cano | 9-12 | G | 315 | 956/289-2584<br>Fax 956/287-0812 |

● **Hidalgo Ind School Dist** PID: 01029827     956/843-4404
324 Flora Ave, Hidalgo 78557     Fax 956/843-3343

Schools: 7 \ **Teachers:** 221 \ **Students:** 2,600 \ **Special Ed Students:** 227
\ **LEP Students:** 1,714 \ **Ethnic:** Hispanic 100%, \ **Exp:** $359 (High) \
**Poverty:** 35% \ **Title I:** $1,466,863 \ **Special Education:** $544,000 \
**Open-Close:** 08/26 - 05/21 \ **DTBP:** $181 (High)

| | | | |
|---|---|---|---|
| Xavier Salinas | 1 | Guillermo Ramirez | 2,3,91 |
| Nancy Sanchez | 2,11,19 | Albert Guerra | 3,68 |
| Rosie Galvan | 4 | Roberto Guerrero | 5 |

| | | | |
|---|---|---|---|
| Monte Stumbaugh | 6 | Velma Molano | 7 |
| Angelica Guanzon | 8 | Martha Garza | 8 |
| Raquel Reyes | 8 | Sandra Cavazos | 8,69 |
| Jennifer Villarreal | 16 | Carmen Pacheco | 57,61,271 |
| Lenore Salinas | 58* | Blanca Lara | 67 |
| Jennifer Garza | 71 | Eloy Garcia | 73,84,295 |
| Mary Villegas | 76 | Arnulfo Ruiz | 271 |

| Public Schs..Principal | Grd | Prgm | Enr/#Cls | SN |
|---|---|---|---|---|
| Diaz Junior High Sch<br>1312 Pirate Dr, Hidalgo 78557<br>Jorge Guzman | 6-8 | T | 637<br>60 | 91% 956/843-4350<br>Fax 956/843-3198 |
| Dr Alejo Salinas Sch<br>411 Ebano St, Hidalgo 78557<br>Jose Esquivel | PK-5 | T | 355<br>30 | 85% 956/843-4250<br>Fax 956/843-3357 |
| Ⓐ Hidalgo Academy<br>310 E Esperanza St, Hidalgo 78557<br>Brenda De Hoyos | 9-12 | T | 15<br>2 | 88% 956/843-4390<br>Fax 956/843-3339 |
| Hidalgo Early College High Sch<br>910 E Pirate Dr, Hidalgo 78557<br>Judith Dimas | 9-12 | T | 221<br>75 | 91% 956/843-4300<br>Fax 956/843-3322 |
| Hidalgo Elem Sch<br>601 S 2nd Street, Hidalgo 78557<br>Rafael Tinoco | PK-5 | T | 259<br>30 | 92% 956/843-4225<br>Fax 956/843-3158 |
| Hidalgo Park Elem Sch<br>8700 S Veterans Blvd, Pharr 78577<br>Gregorio Solano | PK-5 | T | 274 | 90% 956/843-4275<br>Fax 956/781-4631 |
| Kelly Elem Sch<br>201 E Las Milpas Rd, Pharr 78577<br>Beatriz Solano | PK-5 | T | 376<br>35 | 94% 956/843-4200<br>Fax 956/781-5972 |

● **La Joya Ind School Dist** PID: 01029841     956/323-2000
200 W Expressway 83, La Joya 78560     Fax 956/323-2010

Schools: 41 \ **Teachers:** 1,885 \
**Students:** 27,000 \ **Special Ed Students:** 2,452 \ **LEP Students:** 14,394
\ **College-Bound:** 60% \ **Ethnic:** Hispanic 100%, \ **Exp:** $653 (High) \
**Poverty:** 49% \ **Title I:** $23,226,981 \ **Special Education:** $5,022,000 \
**Open-Close:** 09/08 - 06/04 \ **DTBP:** $181 (High)

| | | | |
|---|---|---|---|
| Dr Gisela Saenz | 1 | Joel Trevino | 2,15 |
| Sylvia Zapata | 2 | Arlando Nacianceno | 3,91 |
| Galina Reyes | 4 | Rolando Hernandez | 4 |
| Raul Gonzalez | 5* | Victor Garza | |
| Marissa Morales | 7 | Sebastian Duque | 8,69 |
| Linda Lopez | 9 | Marena Concres | 9 |
| Dr Ana Oliveira | 10 | Melinda Flores | 10 |
| Jose Flores | 11 | Martine Munoz | 15,68 |
| Ricardo Villareal | 15,79 | Jorge Flores | 27 |
| Myriam Tellez | 36 | Alejandro Carranza | 43 |
| David Cavazos | 44 | Rogelio Gomez | 44 |
| Lucy Munoz | 46 | Alfonso Rodriguez | 47 |
| Claudia Munoz | 49 | Leticia Martinez | 50 |
| Veronica Chavez | 50 | Irma Zuniga | 57 |
| Andrea Garza | 58,77 | Rosey Romo | 58 |
| Esperanza Ochoa | 67 | Blanca Cantu | |
| Clem Garza | 73,84 | Cynthia Solis | 74 |
| Aaron Lara | 76,295 | Sandra Ann Villiarreal | 81 |
| Bertha Perez | 88 | Velma Ochoa | 93 |
| Jose Luis Perez | 271 | Maria Leal | 298 |

| Public Schs..Principal | Grd | Prgm | Enr/#Cls | SN |
|---|---|---|---|---|
| Academy Health Sci Prof & STEM<br>801 College Dr, La Joya 78560<br>Leann Herrera | 9-12 | V | 200 | 956/323-2250<br>Fax 956/323-2251 |
| Ann Richards Middle Sch<br>7005 Ann Richards Rd, Mission 78572<br>Michael Ocana | 6-8 | T | 793<br>61 | 96% 956/323-2860<br>Fax 956/323-2861 |

| | | | | | | |
|---|---|---|---|---|---|---|
| 1 | Superintendent | 8 | Curric/Instruct K-12 | 19 | Chief Financial Officer | |
| 2 | Bus/Finance/Purchasing | 9 | Curric/Instruct Elem | 20 | Art K-12 | |
| 3 | Buildings And Grounds | 10 | Curric/Instruct Sec | 21 | Art Elem | |
| 4 | Food Service | 11 | Federal Program | 22 | Art Sec | |
| 5 | Transportation | 12 | Title I | 23 | Music K-12 | |
| 6 | Athletic | 13 | Title V | 24 | Music Elem | |
| 7 | Health Services | 14 | Asst Superintendent | 25 | Music Sec | |
| | | 15 | Instructional Media Svcs | 26 | Business Education | |
| | | 16 | Chief Operations Officer | 27 | Career & Tech Ed | |
| | | 17 | Chief Academic Officer | 28 | Technology Education | |

| | | | |
|---|---|---|---|
| 29 | Family/Consumer Science | 39 | Social Studies K-12 |
| 30 | Adult Education | 40 | Social Studies Elem |
| 31 | Career/Sch-to-Work K-12 | 41 | Social Studies Sec |
| 32 | Career/Sch-to-Work Elem | 42 | Science K-12 |
| 33 | Career/Sch-to-Work Sec | 43 | Science Elem |
| 34 | Early Childhood Ed | 44 | Science Sec |
| 35 | Health/Phys Education | 45 | Math K-12 |
| 36 | Guidance Services K-12 | 46 | Math Elem |
| 37 | Guidance Services Elem | 47 | Math Sec |
| 38 | Guidance Services Sec | 48 | English/Lang Arts K-12 |

| | | | |
|---|---|---|---|
| 49 | English/Lang Arts Elem | 59 | Special Education Elem |
| 50 | English/Lang Arts Sec | 60 | Special Education Sec |
| 51 | Reading K-12 | 61 | Foreign/World Lang K-12 |
| 52 | Reading Elem | 62 | Foreign/World Lang Elem |
| 53 | Reading Sec | 63 | Foreign/World Lang Sec |
| 54 | Remedial Reading K-12 | 64 | Religious Education K-12 |
| 55 | Remedial Reading Elem | 65 | Religious Education Elem |
| 56 | Remedial Reading Sec | 66 | Religious Education Sec |
| 57 | Bilingual/ELL | 67 | School Board President |
| 58 | Special Education K-12 | 68 | Teacher Personnel |

| | |
|---|---|
| 69 | Academic Assessment |
| 70 | Research/Development |
| 71 | Public Information |
| 72 | Summer School |
| 73 | Instructional Tech |
| 74 | Inservice Training |
| 75 | Marketing/Distributive |
| 76 | Info Systems |
| 77 | Psychological Assess |
| 78 | Affirmative Action |

| School | Grades | Prog | Enroll/Teachers | % | Phone/Fax |
|---|---|---|---|---|---|
| Cesar Chavez Middle Sch<br>1927 Showers Rd, Mission 78572<br>Rolando Rios | 6-8 | T | 830<br>58 | 86% | 956/323-2800<br>Fax 956/323-2801 |
| College & Career Center<br>603 N College Dr, La Joya 78560<br>Ronny Cabrera | 9-12 | V | 179<br>12 | | 956/323-2230<br>Fax 956/323-2231 |
| Corina Pena Elem Sch<br>4800 Liberty Blvd, Penitas 78576<br>Raul Luna | PK-5 | T | 696<br>35 | 93% | 956/323-2750<br>Fax 956/323-2751 |
| Diaz-Villarreal Elem Sch<br>5543 N La Homa Rd, Mission 78574<br>Yolanda Meave | PK-5 | T | 522<br>40 | 96% | 956/323-2470<br>Fax 956/323-2471 |
| Domingo Trevino Middle Sch<br>301 S Inspiration Blvd, Alton 78573<br>Jose Garcia | 6-8 | T | 755 | 98% | 956/323-2810<br>Fax 956/323-2811 |
| Dr Americo Paredes Elem Sch<br>5301 N Bentsen Palm Dr, Mission 78574<br>Erika Covarrubia | PK-5 | T | 446<br>40 | 95% | 956/323-2730<br>Fax 956/323-2731 |
| Dr Javier Saenz Middle Sch<br>39200 W Mile 7 Rd, Penitas 78576<br>Carlota Salinas | 6-8 | T | 788 | 98% | 956/323-2830<br>Fax 956/323-2831 |
| Dr Palmira Mendiola Elem Sch<br>6401 N Abram Rd, Mission 78574<br>Alicia Gutierrez | PK-5 | T | 634 | 97% | 956/323-2420<br>Fax 956/323-2421 |
| E B Reyna Elem Sch<br>707 E Veterans Blvd, Palmview 78572<br>Lucina Lara | PK-5 | T | 433<br>42 | 84% | 956/323-2390<br>Fax 956/323-2391 |
| Eligio Kika De La Garza Sch<br>5441 N La Homa Rd, Mission 78574<br>Irene Fernandez | PK-5 | T | 342<br>50 | 96% | 956/323-2380<br>Fax 956/323-2381 |
| Elodia R Chapa Elem Sch<br>5670 N Doffing Rd, Mission 78574<br>Linda Lopez | PK-5 | T | 455<br>42 | 94% | 956/323-2400<br>Fax 956/323-2401 |
| Emiliano Zapata Elem Sch<br>9100 N La Homa Rd, Mission 78574<br>Rosa Gonzalez Vela | PK-5 | T | 538 | 95% | 956/323-2700<br>Fax 956/323-2701 |
| Enrique Camarena Elem Sch<br>2612 N Moorefield Rd, Mission 78574<br>Mary Garza-Ibarra | PK-5 | T | 559 | 76% | 956/323-2720<br>Fax 956/323-2721 |
| Evangelina Garza Elem Sch<br>8731 N Doffing Rd, Mission 78574<br>Maria Flores-Guerra | PK-5 | T | 595 | 98% | 956/323-2350<br>Fax 956/323-2351 |
| Guillermo Flores Elem Sch<br>1913 Roque Salinas Rd, Mission 78572<br>Maria Flores | PK-5 | T | 339<br>50 | 86% | 956/323-2760<br>Fax 956/323-2761 |
| Henry B Gonzalez Elem Sch<br>3912 N FM 492, Mission 78574<br>**Sylvia Sandoval** | PK-5 | T | 496<br>57 | 88% | 956/323-2460<br>Fax 956/323-2461 |
| Ⓐ Hope Academy<br>101 E Expressway 83, La Joya 78560<br>Lindolfo Zamora | 6-12 | T | 83 | 93% | 956/323-2900<br>Fax 956/323-2901 |
| Irene Garcia Middle Sch<br>933 Paula St, Mission 78574<br>Santana Galvan | 6-8 | TV | 810 | 89% | 956/323-2840<br>Fax 956/323-2841 |
| J F Kennedy Elem Sch<br>1801 Diamond Ave, Penitas 78576<br>Maria Guerra | PK-5 | T | 728<br>46 | 76% | 956/323-2330<br>Fax 956/323-2339 |
| Jimmy Carter Early Clg HS<br>603 N College Dr, La Joya 78560<br>Claudia Gomez | 9-12 | T | 98 | 96% | 956/323-2200<br>Fax 956/323-2201 |
| Jose De Escandon Elem Sch<br>700 N Shuerbach Rd, Mission 78572<br>Mary Sepulveda | PK-5 | T | 524<br>42 | 84% | 956/323-2410<br>Fax 956/323-2411 |
| Juan D Salinas Middle Sch<br>6101 N Bentsen Palm Dr, Mission 78574<br>Nidia Ortiz | 6-8 | T | 847 | 99% | 956/323-2850<br>Fax 956/323-2851 |
| Juan N Seguin Elem Sch<br>8500 Western Rd, Mission 78574<br>Sandra Cerda | PK-5 | T | 519 | 97% | 956/323-2710<br>Fax 956/323-2711 |
| Juarez-Lincoln High Sch<br>7801 W Mile 7 Rd, Mission 78574<br>Ricardo Estrada | 9-12 | T | 2,430<br>100 | 98% | 956/323-2890<br>Fax 956/323-2891 |
| La Joya Early College HS<br>604 N Coyote Dr, La Joya 78560<br>Domingo Villarreal | 9-12 | T | 117 | 95% | 956/323-2930<br>Fax 956/323-2939 |
| La Joya Senior High Sch<br>604 N Coyote Dr, La Joya 78560<br>Antonio Cano | 9-12 | GV | 2,898 | | 956/323-2870<br>Fax 956/323-2871 |
| Ⓐ La Joya West Academy<br>215 E Expressway 83, La Joya 78560<br>Norma Garcia | 9-12 | G | 167<br>20 | | 956/323-2260<br>Fax 956/323-2221 |
| Leo J Leo Elem Sch<br>1625 Roque Salinas Rd, Mission 78572<br>Maria Jazinski | PK-5 | T | 408<br>40 | 90% | 956/323-2370<br>Fax 956/323-2371 |
| Lloyd M Bentsen Elem Sch<br>3301 W Mile 3 Rd, Mission 78574<br>Hilda Mendoza | PK-5 | T | 566 | 82% | 956/323-2480<br>Fax 956/323-2481 |
| Lorenzo De Zavala Middle Sch<br>603 Tabasco Rd, La Joya 78560<br>Antonio Uresti | 6-8 | T | 497<br>70 | 91% | 956/323-2770<br>Fax 956/323-2771 |
| Memorial Middle Sch<br>2610 N Moorefield Rd, Mission 78574<br>**Belen Martinez** | 6-8 | T | 489<br>80 | 90% | 956/323-2820<br>Fax 956/323-2821 |
| Narciso Cavazos Elem Sch<br>4563 N Minnesota Rd, Mission 78574<br>**Liz Longoria** | PK-5 | T | 443<br>40 | 96% | 956/323-2430<br>Fax 956/323-2431 |
| Palmview High Sch<br>3901 N La Homa Rd, Mission 78574<br>Yvonne Ayala | 9-12 | T | 2,191<br>85 | 93% | 956/323-2880<br>Fax 956/323-2881 |
| Patricio Perez Elem Sch<br>4431 N Minnesota Rd, Mission 78574<br>Myra Ramos | PK-5 | T | 457<br>50 | 96% | 956/323-2450<br>Fax 956/232-2451 |
| Rosendo Benavides Elem Sch<br>1885 El Pinto Rd, Sullivan City 78595<br>Dr Romeo Benavidez | PK-5 | T | 390<br>29 | 94% | 956/323-2360<br>Fax 956/323-2361 |
| Ⓜ Salinas STEM Early College Sch<br>801 College Dr, La Joya 78560<br>**Victor Rodriguez** | 9-12 | T | 408 | 93% | 956/323-2240<br>Fax 956/323-2241 |
| Sam Fordyce Elem Sch<br>801 FM 886, Sullivan City 78595<br>Roxanna Pena | PK-5 | T | 381<br>35 | 93% | 956/323-2490<br>Fax 956/323-2491 |
| Tabasco Elem Sch<br>223 S Leo Ave, La Joya 78560<br>Marena Contreras | PK-5 | T | 596<br>30 | 88% | 956/323-2440<br>Fax 956/323-2441 |
| William J Clinton Elem Sch<br>39202 W Mile 7 Rd, Penitas 78576<br>**Alma Perez** | PK-5 | T | 566<br>47 | 96% | 956/323-2740<br>Fax 956/323-2741 |

● **La Villa Ind School Dist** PID: 01029891 956/262-4755
500 E 9th Street, La Villa 78562 Fax 956/262-7323

**Schools:** 3 \ **Teachers:** 45 \ **Students:** 555 \ **Special Ed Students:** 37
\ **LEP Students:** 97 \ **Ethnic:** Hispanic 100%, \ **Exp:** $571 (High) \
**Poverty:** 36% \ **Title I:** $354,825 \ **Open-Close:** 08/28 - 06/01 \ **DTBP:** $539
(High)

| | | | | | |
|---|---|---|---|---|---|
| 79 Student Personnel | 91 Safety/Security | 275 Response To Intervention | 298 Grant Writer/Ptnrships | School Programs | Social Media |
| 80 Driver Ed/Safety | 92 Magnet School | 277 Remedial Math K-12 | 750 Chief Innovation Officer | A = Alternative Program | |
| 81 Gifted/Talented | 93 Parental Involvement | 280 Literacy Coach | 751 Chief of Staff | G = Adult Classes | 🟦 = Facebook |
| 82 Video Services | 95 Tech Prep Program | 285 STEM | 752 Social Emotional Learning | M = Magnet Program | |
| 83 Substance Abuse Prev | 97 Chief Information Officer | 286 Digital Learning | | T = Title I Schoolwide | 🟦 = Twitter |
| 84 Erate | 98 Chief Technology Officer | 288 Common Core Standards | Other School Types | V = Career & Tech Ed Programs | |
| 85 AIDS Education | 270 Character Education | 294 Accountability | Ⓐ = Alternative School | | |
| 88 Alternative/At Risk | 271 Migrant Education | 295 Network System | Ⓒ = Charter School | New Schools are shaded | |
| 89 Multi-Cultural Curriculum | 273 Teacher Mentor | 296 Title II Programs | Ⓜ = Magnet School | New Superintendents and Principals are bold | |
| 90 Social Work | 274 Before/After Sch | 297 Webmaster | Ⓨ = Year-Round School | Personnel with email addresses are underscored | |

| Public Schs..Principal | Grd | Prgm | Enr/#Cls | SN | |
|---|---|---|---|---|---|
| J B Munoz Elem Sch<br>810 N Cottonwood St, La Villa 78562<br>Edward Rivera | PK-5 | T | 256<br>15 | 95% | 956/262-9357<br>Fax 956/262-9452 |
| La Villa Early Clg High Sch<br>100 W Highway 107, La Villa 78562<br>Antonio Layton | 9-12 | TV | 178<br>25 | 90% | 956/262-4715<br>Fax 956/262-9798 |
| La Villa Middle Sch<br>500 E 9th St, La Villa 78562<br>**Paz Elizondo** | 6-8 | TV | 121<br>15 | 91% | 956/262-4760<br>Fax 956/262-5243 |

## ● McAllen Ind School Dist  PID: 01029918  956/618-6000
2000 N 23rd St, McAllen 78501

**Schools:** 31 \ **Teachers:** 1,564 \ **Students:** 24,000 \
**Special Ed Students:** 2,364 \ **LEP Students:** 6,962 \ **College-Bound:** 69%
\ **Ethnic:** Asian 1%, Hispanic 94%, Caucasian 4% \ **Exp:** $431 (High) \
**Poverty:** 36% \ **Title I:** $15,510,945 \ **Special Education:** $4,603,000 \
**Open-Close:** 08/24 - 05/28 \ **DTBP:** $194 (High) \ 🔲 🔲

| Public Schs..Principal | Grd | Prgm | Enr/#Cls | SN | |
|---|---|---|---|---|---|
| Achieve Early College High Sch<br>1601 N 27th St, McAllen 78501<br>Miguel Carmona | 9-12 | T | 483 | 73% | 956/872-1653<br>Fax 956/872-1650 |
| Alonzo De Leon Middle Sch<br>4201 N 29th Ln, McAllen 78504<br>Philip Grossweiler | 6-8 | TV | 1,019<br>65 | 79% | 956/632-8800<br>Fax 956/632-8805 |
| Andrew Jackson Elem Sch<br>501 W Harvey St, McAllen 78501<br>Miguel Herrera | PK-5 | T | 627<br>52 | 91% | 956/971-4277<br>Fax 956/632-5179 |
| Ben Milam Elem Sch<br>3800 N Main St, McAllen 78501<br>Christian Quintanilla | PK-5 | T | 793<br>43 | 59% | 956/971-4333<br>Fax 956/972-5649 |
| Blanca E Sanchez Elem Sch<br>2901 Incarnate Word Ave, McAllen 78504<br>Cynthia Rodriguez | PK-5 | T | 451<br>30 | 66% | 956/971-1100<br>Fax 956/618-9705 |
| Christa McAuliffe Elem Sch<br>3000 Daffodil Ave, McAllen 78501<br>Sandra Pitchford | PK-5 | T | 527<br>48 | 87% | 956/971-4400<br>Fax 956/971-4482 |
| Dorothea Brown Middle Sch<br>2700 S Ware Rd, McAllen 78503<br>Alfredo Gutierrez | 6-8 | TV | 746<br>40 | 89% | 956/632-8700<br>Fax 956/632-8709 |
| Dr Carlos Castaneda Elem Sch<br>4100 N 34th St, McAllen 78504<br>Jessica Rodriguez | PK-5 | T | 506<br>45 | 71% | 956/632-8882<br>Fax 956/632-3627 |
| Dr Pablo Perez Elem Sch<br>7801 N Main St, McAllen 78504<br>Albert Irlas | PK-5 | T | 507 | 51% | 956/971-1125<br>Fax 956/632-2880 |

| | Grd | Prgm | Enr/#Cls | SN | |
|---|---|---|---|---|---|
| Dr R D Cathey Middle Sch<br>1800 N Cynthia St, McAllen 78501<br>Melvin Benford | 6-8 | TV | 970<br>50 | 55% | 956/971-4300<br>Fax 956/632-2811 |
| Francisca Alvarez Elem Sch<br>2606 Gumwood Ave, McAllen 78501<br>Juan Montes | PK-5 | T | 403<br>27 | 91% | 956/971-4471<br>Fax 956/972-5668 |
| Homer J Morris Middle Sch<br>1400 Trenton Rd, McAllen 78504<br>Brian McClenny | 6-8 | TV | 906<br>48 | 54% | 956/618-7300<br>Fax 956/632-3666 |
| Ⓐ Instruction & Guidance Center<br>2604 Galveston Ave, McAllen 78501<br>Fernando Gutierrez | 6-12 | T | 26<br>13 | 82% | 956/971-4393<br>Fax 956/971-4294 |
| James Bonham Elem Sch<br>2501 Jordan Ave, McAllen 78503<br>Leticia Infante | PK-5 | T | 162<br>20 | 92% | 956/971-4440<br>Fax 956/971-4284<br>🔲🔲 |
| James Nikki Rowe High Sch<br>2101 N Ware Rd, McAllen 78501<br>Monica Kaufmann | 9-12 | TV | 2,138 | 65% | 956/632-5100<br>Fax 956/632-8850 |
| Jose De Escandon Elem Sch<br>2901 Colbath Ave, McAllen 78503<br>Carlos Mora | PK-5 | T | 428<br>24 | 83% | 956/971-4511<br>Fax 956/971-4508 |
| Juan Seguin Elem Sch<br>2200 N 29th St, McAllen 78501<br>Juan Nevarez | PK-5 | T | 568<br>45 | 93% | 956/971-4565<br>Fax 956/971-4589 |
| Ⓐ Lamar Academy<br>1009 N 10th St, McAllen 78501<br>Jeanette Nino | 9-12 | T | 41<br>23 | 76% | 956/632-3222<br>Fax 956/632-3662 |
| Leonelo H Gonzalez Elem Sch<br>201 E Martin Ave, McAllen 78504<br>Christina Hernandez | PK-5 | | 823<br>39 | 30% | 956/971-4577<br>Fax 956/971-4575 |
| Lucile M Hendricks Elem Sch<br>3900 Goldcrest Ave, McAllen 78504<br>Sandra Salinas | PK-5 | T | 433<br>6 | 68% | 956/971-1145<br>Fax 956/618-9726 |
| McAllen High Sch<br>2021 La Vista Ave, McAllen 78501<br>Albert Canales | 9-12 | GTV | 2,307<br>50 | 63% | 956/632-3100<br>Fax 956/632-3114 |
| Memorial High Sch<br>101 E Hackberry Ave, McAllen 78501<br>Pedro Alvarez | 9-12 | TV | 2,188<br>115 | 66% | 956/632-5201<br>Fax 956/632-5226 |
| Michael E Fossum Middle Sch<br>7800 N Ware Rd, McAllen 78504<br>Laura Williams | 6-8 | T | 808 | 52% | 956/971-1105<br>Fax 956/618-9718 |
| Reynaldo G Garza Elem Sch<br>6300 N 29th St, McAllen 78504<br>Nancy Valenzuela | PK-5 | T | 462<br>46 | 60% | 956/971-4554<br>Fax 956/971-4235 |
| Sam Houston Elem Sch<br>3221 Olga Ave, McAllen 78503<br>Debra Loya-Thomas | PK-5 | T | 437<br>32 | 86% | 956/971-4484<br>Fax 956/971-4295 |
| Sam Rayburn Elem Sch<br>7000 N Main St, McAllen 78504<br>Clarissa Partida | PK-5 | T | 416<br>39 | 70% | 956/971-4363<br>Fax 956/632-8453 |
| Theodore Roosevelt Elem Sch<br>4801 S 26th St, McAllen 78503<br>Gerardo Gonzalez | PK-5 | T | 474<br>40 | 94% | 956/971-4424<br>Fax 956/618-7362 |
| Thigpen-Zavala Elem Sch<br>2500 Galveston Ave, McAllen 78501<br>Sonia Casas | PK-5 | T | 467<br>26 | 95% | 956/971-4377<br>Fax 956/972-5660 |
| Victor Fields Elem Sch<br>500 Dallas Ave, McAllen 78501<br>Teresa Trdla | PK-5 | T | 431<br>21 | 91% | 956/971-4344<br>Fax 956/971-4351 |
| William B Travis Middle Sch<br>600 W Houston Ave, McAllen 78501<br>Efrain Amaya | 6-8 | TV | 445<br>55 | 95% | 956/971-4242<br>Fax 956/632-8454 |
| Woodrow Wilson Elem Sch<br>1200 W Hackberry Ave, McAllen 78501<br>Kristine Garza | PK-5 | T | 516<br>28 | 92% | 956/971-4525<br>Fax 956/971-4597 |

| | | | | | | | | |
|---|---|---|---|---|---|---|---|---|
| 1 | Superintendent | 8 | Curric/Instruct K-12 | 19 | Chief Financial Officer | 29 | Family/Consumer Science | 39 | Social Studies K-12 | 49 | English/Lang Arts Elem | 59 | Special Education Elem | 69 | Academic Assessment |
| 2 | Bus/Finance/Purchasing | 9 | Curric/Instruct Elem | 20 | Art K-12 | 30 | Adult Education | 40 | Social Studies Elem | 50 | English/Lang Arts Sec | 60 | Special Education Sec | 70 | Research/Development |
| 3 | Buildings And Grounds | 10 | Curric/Instruct Sec | 21 | Art Elem | 31 | Career/Sch-to-Work K-12 | 41 | Social Studies Sec | 51 | Reading K-12 | 61 | Foreign/World Lang K-12 | 71 | Public Information |
| 4 | Food Service | 11 | Federal Program | 22 | Art Sec | 32 | Career/Sch-to-Work Elem | 42 | Science K-12 | 52 | Reading Elem | 62 | Foreign/World Lang Elem | 72 | Summer School |
| 5 | Transportation | 12 | Title I | 23 | Music K-12 | 33 | Career/Sch-to-Work Sec | 43 | Science Elem | 53 | Reading Sec | 63 | Foreign/World Lang Sec | 73 | Instructional Tech |
| 6 | Athletic | 13 | Title V | 24 | Music Elem | 34 | Early Childhood Ed | 44 | Science Sec | 54 | Remedial Reading K-12 | 64 | Religious Education K-12 | 74 | Inservice Training |
| 7 | Health Services | 15 | Asst Superintendent | 25 | Music Sec | 35 | Health/Phys Education | 45 | Math K-12 | 55 | Remedial Reading Elem | 65 | Religious Education Elem | 75 | Marketing/Distributive |
| | | 16 | Instructional Media Svcs | 26 | Business Education | 36 | Guidance Services K-12 | 46 | Math Elem | 56 | Remedial Reading Sec | 66 | Religious Education Sec | 76 | Info Systems |
| | | 17 | Chief Operations Officer | 27 | Career & Tech Ed | 37 | Guidance Services Elem | 47 | Math Sec | 57 | Bilingual/ELL | 67 | School Board President | 77 | Psychological Assess |
| | | 18 | Chief Academic Officer | 28 | Technology Education | 38 | Guidance Services Sec | 48 | English/Lang Arts K-12 | 58 | Special Education K-12 | 68 | Teacher Personnel | 78 | Affirmative Action |

# TX—224

## Mercedes Ind School Dist  PID: 01030149

206 W 6th St, Mercedes 78570

956/514-2000
Fax 956/514-2033

**Schools:** 9 \ **Teachers:** 374 \ **Students:** 4,781 \ **Special Ed Students:** 407 \ **LEP Students:** 1,329 \ **College-Bound:** 80% \ **Ethnic:** Hispanic 99%, Caucasian 1% \ **Exp:** $492 (High) \ **Poverty:** 45% \ **Title I:** $4,329,252 \ **Open-Close:** 08/24 - 05/28 \ **DTBP:** $199 (High)

| | |
|---|---|
| Carolyn Mendiola .....................1 | Olga Hinds ...................................2,19 |
| Ralph Mendez .........................2 | Rolando Herrera .............................3 |
| Nancy Garza ...........................4 | Adan Vallejo .................................5 |
| Roger Adame .........................6* | Lisa Cantu-Reyes .........................11* |
| Dr Dana Yates .......................15 | Juanita Mariscal ...........................42 |
| Delia Castillo ........................58 | Oscar Riojas ................................67 |
| Daniel Runnels ......................69 | Rodolfo Canales ........................69,88 |
| Roland Handy ....................73,271 | Debbie Lee-Winslow ....................286 |

| Public Schs..Principal | Grd | Prgm | Enr/#Cls | SN |
|---|---|---|---|---|
| John F Kennedy Sch<br>801 Hidalgo St, Mercedes 78570<br>Elva Rivera | PK-5 | T | 552<br>30 | 95% 956/514-2300<br>Fax 956/514-2311 |
| Ⓐ Mercedes Academic Academy<br>720 S Mile 1 East, Mercedes 78570<br>Rafael Leal | 9-12 | T | 26 | 97% 956/825-5076<br>Fax 956/514-2171 |
| Ⓐ Mercedes Early College HS<br>837 S Ohio Ave, Mercedes 78570<br>Jeanne Venecia | 9-12 | TV | 182<br>13 | 77% 956/825-5180<br>Fax 956/514-2175 |
| Mercedes High Sch<br>1200 Florida St, Mercedes 78570<br>Orlando Rodriguez | 9-12 | TV | 1,096<br>105 | 89% 956/514-2100<br>Fax 956/514-2111 |
| Ruben Hinojosa Elem Sch<br>1551 S Georgia Ave, Mercedes 78570<br>Michelle Guajardo | PK-5 | T | 584<br>44 | 92% 956/514-2277<br>Fax 956/514-2292 |
| Sgt Manuel Chacon Middle Sch<br>801 S Mile 1 E, Mercedes 78570<br>Orlando Rodriguez | 6-8 | T | 669<br>38 | 85% 956/514-2200<br>Fax 956/514-2212 |
| Sgt William Harrell Middle Sch<br>2825 N FM 491, Mercedes 78570<br>Javier Deanda | 6-8 | T | 373 | 98% 956/825-5140<br>Fax 956/514-2323 |
| Taylor Elem Sch<br>900 Missouri St, Mercedes 78570<br>David Aguirre | PK-5 | T | 562<br>35 | 94% 956/514-2388<br>Fax 956/514-2377 |
| Travis Elem Sch<br>1551 S Georgia Ave, Mercedes 78570<br>Miguel Chacon | PK-5 | T | 558<br>33 | 91% 956/514-2366<br>Fax 956/514-2373 |

## Mission Cons Ind School Dist  PID: 01030228

1201 Bryce Dr, Mission 78572

956/323-5500
Fax 956/323-5523

**Schools:** 23 \ **Teachers:** 1,009 \ **Students:** 16,000 \ **Special Ed Students:** 1,132 \ **LEP Students:** 4,856 \ **College-Bound:** 69% \ **Ethnic:** Hispanic 99%, Caucasian 1% \ **Exp:** $567 (High) \ **Poverty:** 43% \ **Title I:** $11,062,405 \ **Special Education:** $2,201,000 \ **Open-Close:** 08/17 - 05/28 \ **DTBP:** $193 (High) \ 🅵 🆃

| | |
|---|---|
| Dr Carol Perez .........................1 | Ana Zuniga ...................................2* |
| Rumalda Ruiz ........................2,15 | Ricardo Rivera ............................3,15 |
| Maria Woodrum .......................4 | Carlos Lerma .................................5 |
| Laticia Ibarra ..........................6 | Jessie Trevino ...........................7,79 |
| Cynthia Wilson .......................10 | Kim Risica ..................................11 |
| Sharon Roberts ...................15,81 | Jorge Cabazos ...16,68,73,76,95,295,297 |
| Sergio Pena ......................27,31 | Faustino Cedillo ..........................39 |
| Jamie Shults .........................42 | Adelina Alaniz .............................45 |
| Jessica Reina-Garza .................49 | Diamond Tijerina ..........................50 |
| Edgar Ibarra ..........................57 | Tahnee Netro ...............................58 |
| Charlie Garcia .......................67 | Gerardo Gonzalez ......................69,77 |
| Craig Verley ..........................71 | Eduardo Alaniz ............................88* |

| | |
|---|---|
| Sylvia Cruz ...........................91 | Arminda Ramirez .............................271 |
| Dolores Reyna .....................298* | |

| Public Schs..Principal | Grd | Prgm | Enr/#Cls | SN |
|---|---|---|---|---|
| Alton Elem Sch<br>205 N Chicago St, Alton 78573<br>Araceli Escalona | PK-5 | T | 326<br>36 | 95% 956/323-7600<br>Fax 956/323-8181 |
| Alton Memorial Junior High Sch<br>521 S Los Ebanos Blvd, Alton 78573<br>Silvia Garcia | 6-8 | TV | 908<br>54 | 91% 956/323-5000<br>Fax 956/323-8196 |
| Bryan Elem Sch<br>1300 Elm Dr, Mission 78572<br>Linda Sanchez | PK-5 | T | 618<br>37 | 69% 956/323-4800<br>Fax 956/323-8182 |
| Cantu Elem Sch<br>920 W Main Ave, Alton 78573<br>Enrique Alvarez | PK-5 | T | 474<br>45 | 95% 956/323-7400<br>Fax 956/323-7415 |
| Carl Waitz Elem Sch<br>843 W Saint Francis Ave, Alton 78573<br>Jessica Reyna-Garza | PK-5 | T | 484<br>34 | 95% 956/323-6600<br>Fax 956/323-6618 |
| Castro Elem Sch<br>200 S Mayberry Rd, Mission 78572<br>Myra Garza | PK-5 | T | 392<br>35 | 94% 956/323-6800<br>Fax 956/323-6818 |
| Escobar-Rios Elem Sch<br>3505 N Trosper Rd, Mission 78573<br>Blanca Lopez | PK-5 | T | 420 | 89% 956/323-8400 |
| Hurla M Midkiff Elem Sch<br>4201 N Mayberry Rd, Palmhurst 78573<br>Dora Villalobos | PK-5 | T | 606 | 76% 956/323-7000<br>Fax 956/323-7025 |
| Kenneth White Jr High Sch<br>1101 W Griffin Pkwy, Mission 78572<br>Brenda Betancourt | 6-8 | TV | 895<br>180 | 91% 956/323-3600<br>Fax 956/323-3631 |
| Leal Elem Sch<br>318 S Los Ebanos Rd, Mission 78572<br>Trinidad Pena | PK-5 | T | 551<br>42 | 91% 956/323-4600<br>Fax 956/326-4615 |
| Marcell Elem Sch<br>1101 N Holland Ave, Mission 78572<br>Efrain Zamora | PK-5 | T | 398<br>26 | 85% 956/323-6400<br>Fax 956/323-6419 |
| Mims Elem Sch<br>200 E 2 Mile Rd, Mission 78574<br>Yvonne Zamora | PK-5 | T | 649<br>37 | 62% 956/323-4400<br>Fax 956/323-4418<br>🅵 🆃 |
| Mission Collegiate High Sch<br>605 S Los Ebanos Rd, Alton 78573<br>Ana Flores | 9-12 | T | 216 | 89% 956/323-6120 |
| Mission High Sch<br>1802 Cleo Dawson St, Mission 78572<br>Edilberto Flores | 9-12 | TV | 2,290 | 90% 956/323-5700<br>Fax 956/323-8203 |
| Mission Junior High Sch<br>415 E 14th St, Mission 78572<br>Adan Ramirez | 6-8 | TV | 861<br>53 | 77% 956/323-3300<br>Fax 956/323-3338 |
| Ⓐ Mission Options Academy<br>407 E 3rd St, Mission 78572<br>Dr Mary Aleman | 9-12 | | 150 | 956/323-3960<br>Fax 956/323-8223 |
| Ollie Ogrady Elem Sch<br>810 W Griffin Pkwy, Mission 78572<br>Angelina Garcia | PK-5 | T | 426<br>46 | 94% 956/323-4200<br>Fax 956/323-4220 |
| Pearson Elem Sch<br>315 N Holland Ave, Mission 78572<br>Melissa Davis | PK-5 | T | 441<br>35 | 93% 956/323-4000<br>Fax 956/323-4015 |
| Rafael Cantu Jr High Sch<br>5101 N Stewart Rd, Palmhurst 78573<br>Ana Flores | 6-8 | T | 229 | 89% 956/323-7800<br>Fax 956/323-7880 |
| Raquel Cavazos Elem Sch<br>803 S Los Ebanos Blvd, Mission 78574<br>Nelly Flores | PK-5 | T | 574<br>37 | 84% 956/323-7200<br>Fax 956/323-7225 |
| Ⓐ Roosevelt Alt Sch<br>407 E 3rd St, Mission 78572<br>Eduardo Alaniz | K-12 | T | 200<br>7 | 98% 956/323-3900<br>Fax 956/323-3925 |

| | | | | | |
|---|---|---|---|---|---|
| 79 Student Personnel | 91 Safety/Security | 275 Response To Intervention | 298 Grant Writer/Ptnrships | **School Programs** | **Social Media** |
| 80 Driver Ed/Safety | 92 Magnet School | 277 Remedial Math K-12 | 750 Chief Innovation Officer | **A** = Alternative Program | |
| 81 Gifted/Talented | 93 Parental Involvement | 280 Literacy Coach | 751 Chief of Staff | **G** = Adult Classes | 🅵 = Facebook |
| 82 Video Services | 95 Tech Prep Program | 285 STEM | 752 Social Emotional Learning | **M** = Magnet Program | |
| 83 Substance Abuse Prev | 97 Chief Information Officer | 286 Digital Learning | | **T** = Title I Schoolwide | 🆃 = Twitter |
| 84 Erate | 98 Chief Technology Officer | 288 Common Core Standards | **Other School Types** | **V** = Career & Tech Ed Programs | |
| 85 AIDS Education | 270 Character Education | 294 Accountability | Ⓐ = Alternative School | | |
| 88 Alternative/At Risk | 271 Migrant Education | 295 Network System | Ⓒ = Charter School | **New Schools are shaded** | |
| 89 Multi-Cultural Curriculum | 273 Teacher Mentor | 296 Title II Programs | Ⓜ = Magnet School | **New Superintendents and Principals are bold** | |
| 90 Social Work | 274 Before/After Sch | 297 Webmaster | Ⓨ = Year-Round School | Personnel with email addresses are underscored | |

## TX—225

| | | | | | |
|---|---|---|---|---|---|
| Salinas Elem Sch<br>10820 N Conway Ave, Alton 78573<br>Martina Garcia | PK-5 | T | 350<br>50 | 89% | 956/323-6200<br>Fax 956/323-6219 |
| Veterans Memorial High Sch<br>700 E Mile 2 Rd, Mission 78574<br>Fidel Garza | 9-12 | TV | 1,827<br>55 | 81% | 956/323-3000<br>Fax 956/323-3280 |

● **Monte Alto Ind School Dist** PID: 01030319    956/567-3100
25149 1st St, Monte Alto 78538    Fax 956/262-5535

**Schools:** 3 \ **Teachers:** 61 \ **Students:** 900 \ **Special Ed Students:** 67 \
**LEP Students:** 272 \ **Ethnic:** Hispanic 99%, Caucasian 1% \ **Exp:** $1,058
(High) \ **Poverty:** 34% \ **Title I:** $611,084 \ **Open-Close:** 09/10 - 05/27 \
**DTBP:** $452 (High)

| | |
|---|---|
| Dr Rosie Cobarrubias ...........................1 | Reynaldo Robles ..............................2,4,17 |
| Ana Zepeda ........................................ 8* | Barbara Cannon . 11,57,58,69,73,271,294,296 |
| Connie Villanueva ...............................67 | |

| Public Schs..Principal | Grd | Prgm | Enr/#Cls | SN | |
|---|---|---|---|---|---|
| Jose Borrego Middle Sch<br>25149 1st St, Monte Alto 78538<br>Perla Benavides | 6-8 | T | 231 | 93% | 956/262-1374<br>Fax 956/262-1377 |
| Monte Alto Ealry Clg High Sch<br>9000 Valdez St, Edcouch 78538<br>Jimmy Padilla | 9-12 | T | 256 | 95% | 956/262-6152<br>Fax 956/262-1011 |
| Monte Alto Elem Sch<br>25149 1st St, Monte Alto 78538<br>Alma Cerda | PK-5 | T | 407<br>35 | 94% | 956/262-6101<br>Fax 956/262-6112 |

● **Pharr-San Juan-Alamo Ind SD** PID: 01030333    956/354-2000
601 E Kelly Ave, Pharr 78577    Fax 956/354-3000

**Schools:** 42 \ **Teachers:** 2,148 \ **Students:** 32,000 \
**Special Ed Students:** 2,559 \ **LEP Students:** 11,751 \ **College-Bound:** 90%
\ **Ethnic:** Hispanic 99%, Caucasian 1% \ **Exp:** $531 (High) \ **Poverty:** 38% \
**Title I:** $19,020,283 \ **Special Education:** $5,074,000 \ **Open-Close:** 09/08 -
06/04 \ **DTBP:** $194 (High) \ 🅵 🅴

| | |
|---|---|
| Jorge Arrendondo ...............................1 | Emily Garza ........................................2 |
| Fernando Lopez ..................................3 | Aurora Palacios ..................................4 |
| Orlando Garcia ....................................6 | Sulema Solis ...........................7,35,85 |
| Dr James Curts .....................10,11,70,288 | Dr Nora Contu ...................................10 |
| Rebecca Sanchez ...............................12 | Orlando Noyola ............................15,79* |
| Rebecca Garza ...............................15,68* | Nora Galvan .......................................16 |
| Hestroverto Martinez ..........................17 | Rolando Trevino .................................18 |
| Janet Robles ......................................19 | Jon Taylor ..........................................20 |
| Adriana Garcia .............................27,31* | Yvette Mancillas .................................34 |
| Olivia Martinez .............................57,280 | Margarita Aguirre ...............................58 |
| Jorge Palacios ...................................67 | Melissa Aquero-Ramirez ....................68 |
| Arianna Hernandez .............................71 | Angela Salinas ............................74,273 |
| Debra Salinas ..............................77,275 | Laura Campos .............................79,294 |
| Noemi Serna ......................................81 | Romeo Garza .....................................91 |
| Yolanda Gomez ...............................271* | Marisela Zepeda ..............................285* |
| Santiago Zavala ................................297 | Georgia Montoya ..............................298 |
| Juan Alvarez ....................................751 | |

| Public Schs..Principal | Grd | Prgm | Enr/#Cls | SN | |
|---|---|---|---|---|---|
| Aida Escobar Elem Sch<br>901 W Kelly Ave, Pharr 78577<br>Catarina Espinoza | PK-5 | T | 795<br>35 | 90% | 956/354-2920<br>Fax 956/354-3288 |
| Alamo Middle Sch<br>1819 W US Highway 83, Alamo 78516<br>Cristina Esparza \ **Francisco Ortega** | 6-8 | T | 625<br>50 | 94% | 956/354-2550<br>Fax 956/354-3188 |
| Alfred Sorensen Elem Sch<br>701 E Sam Houston Blvd, San Juan 78589<br>Samuel Castillo | PK-5 | T | 670<br>22 | 84% | 956/354-2910<br>Fax 956/354-3282<br>🅵🅴 |

| | | | | | |
|---|---|---|---|---|---|
| Allen & William Arnold ES<br>615 W Eldora Rd, Pharr 78577<br>Pedro Trevino | PK-5 | T | 696<br>17 | 82% | 956/354-2710<br>Fax 956/354-3238 |
| Arnoldo Cantu Elem Sch<br>2900 N Raul Longoria Rd, San Juan 78589<br>Yvette Mancillas | PK-5 | T | 641<br>37 | 87% | 956/354-2850<br>Fax 956/354-3244 |
| Audie Murphy Middle Sch<br>924 Sioux Rd, Alamo 78516<br>Lizette Longoria | 6-8 | T | 870 | 96% | 956/354-2530<br>Fax 956/354-3224<br>🅵🅴 |
| Augusto Guerra Elem Sch<br>807 State Highway 495, Alamo 78516<br>**L Villarreal** | PK-5 | T | 622<br>35 | 96% | 956/354-2810<br>Fax 956/354-3264<br>🅵🅴 |
| Austin Middle Sch<br>804 S Stewart Rd, San Juan 78589<br>Larissa Saenz | 6-8 | T | 1,001<br>65 | 86% | 956/354-2570<br>Fax 956/354-3194 |
| Berta Palacios Elem Sch<br>801 E Thomas Rd, Pharr 78577<br>Michelle Cardoza | PK-5 | GT | 539<br>30 | 98% | 956/354-2930<br>Fax 956/354-3290 |
| Ⓐ Buell Central High Sch<br>218 E Juarez Ave, Pharr 78577<br>Mario Bracamontes | 6-12 | T | 76<br>21 | 100% | 956/354-2500<br>Fax 956/354-3110 |
| Carmen Anaya Elem Sch<br>1000 W Dicker Dr, Pharr 78577<br>Bertha Cantu | PK-5 | T | 421 | 97% | 956/784-8500<br>Fax 956/354-3284 |
| Cesar Chavez Elem Sch<br>401 E Thomas Rd, Pharr 78577<br>Roel Faz | PK-5 | T | 450<br>35 | 96% | 956/354-2720<br>Fax 956/354-3248 |
| Ⓐ College Career & Tech Academy<br>Ⓨ 1100 E US Highway 83, Pharr 78577<br>Darcia Cuellar | 12-12 | M | 173<br>10 | | 956/784-8515<br>Fax 956/354-3112 |
| Daniel Ramirez Elem Sch<br>1920 N Hibiscus St, Pharr 78577<br>Leonel Avila | PK-5 | T | 495<br>34 | 96% | 956/354-2880<br>Fax 956/354-3278 |
| Dr William Long Elem Sch<br>700 N Raiders Dr, Pharr 78577<br>Concepcion Ipina | PK-5 | T | 872<br>35 | 77% | 956/354-2750<br>Fax 956/354-3266 |
| Drs Reed & Mock Elem Sch<br>400 E Eldora Rd, San Juan 78589<br>**Dr Karla Montemayor** | PK-5 | T | 618<br>43 | 89% | 956/354-2890<br>Fax 956/354-3280<br>🅵🅴 |
| Edith & Ethel Carman Elem Sch<br>100 Ridge Rd, San Juan 78589<br>Adrian Karr | PK-5 | T | 600<br>33 | 75% | 956/354-2700<br>Fax 956/354-3246 |
| Farias Elem Sch<br>1100 W Acacia St, Alamo 78516<br>Leticia Rodriguez | PK-5 | GT | 600<br>32 | 95% | 956/354-2760<br>Fax 956/354-3254 |
| Garza-Pena Elem Sch<br>500 E FM 495, San Juan 78589<br>Judith Canales | PK-5 | T | 651<br>35 | 96% | 956/354-2800<br>Fax 956/354-3260 |
| Geraldine Palmer Elem Sch<br>1200 W Hall Acres Rd, Pharr 78577<br>Brisa Gonzalez | PK-5 | T | 611<br>25 | 90% | 956/354-2860<br>Fax 956/354-3272<br>🅵🅴 |
| Graciela Garcia Elem Sch<br>1002 W Juan Balli Rd, Pharr 78577<br>Sandra Garcia | PK-5 | T | 394<br>45 | 98% | 956/354-2790<br>Fax 956/354-3258 |
| Henry Ford Elem Sch<br>1110 E Polk Ave, Pharr 78577<br>Pricilla Salinas \ **Elizabeth Alaniz** | PK-5 | T | 679<br>29 | 91% | 956/354-2770<br>Fax 956/354-3256<br>🅵🅴 |
| Jaime Escalante Middle Schl<br>6123 S Cage Blvd, Pharr 78577<br>Raymundo Monrreal | 6-8 | T | 652 | 97% | 956/354-2670<br>Fax 956/354-3200 |
| John Doedyns Elem Sch<br>1401 N Raul Longoria Rd, San Juan 78589<br>Maria Guerrero | PK-5 | GT | 604<br>33 | 96% | 956/354-2740<br>Fax 956/354-3252<br>🅵🅴 |
| John McKeever Elem Sch<br>1310 Ridge Rd, Alamo 78516<br>Irma Gomez | PK-5 | T | 635 | 86% | 956/354-2860<br>Fax 956/354-3240<br>🅵🅴 |

| | | | | | |
|---|---|---|---|---|---|
| 1 | Superintendent | 8 | Curric/Instruct K-12 | 19 | Chief Financial Officer |
| 2 | Bus/Finance/Purchasing | 9 | Curric/Instruct Elem | 20 | Art K-12 |
| 3 | Buildings And Grounds | 10 | Curric/Instruct Sec | 21 | Art Elem |
| 4 | Food Service | 11 | Federal Program | 22 | Art Sec |
| 5 | Transportation | 12 | Title I | 23 | Music K-12 |
| 6 | Athletic | 13 | Title V | 24 | Music Elem |
| 7 | Health Services | 15 | Asst Superintendent | 25 | Music Sec |
| | | 16 | Instructional Media Svcs | 26 | Business Education |
| | | 17 | Chief Operations Officer | 27 | Career & Tech Ed |
| | | 18 | Chief Academic Officer | 28 | Technology Education |

| | | | | | |
|---|---|---|---|---|---|
| 29 | Family/Consumer Science | 39 | Social Studies K-12 | 49 | English/Lang Arts Elem |
| 30 | Adult Education | 40 | Social Studies Elem | 50 | English/Lang Arts Sec |
| 31 | Career/Sch-to-Work K-12 | 41 | Social Studies Sec | 51 | Reading K-12 |
| 32 | Career/Sch-to-Work Elem | 42 | Science K-12 | 52 | Reading Elem |
| 33 | Career/Sch-to-Work Sec | 43 | Science Elem | 53 | Reading Sec |
| 34 | Early Childhood Ed | 44 | Science Sec | 54 | Remedial Reading K-12 |
| 35 | Health/Phys Education | 45 | Math K-12 | 55 | Remedial Reading Elem |
| 36 | Guidance Services K-12 | 46 | Math Elem | 56 | Remedial Reading Sec |
| 37 | Guidance Services Elem | 47 | Math Sec | 57 | Bilingual/ELL |
| 38 | Guidance Services Sec | 48 | English/Lang Arts K-12 | 58 | Special Education K-12 |

| | | | | | |
|---|---|---|---|---|---|
| 59 | Special Education Elem | 69 | Academic Assessment |
| 60 | Special Education Sec | 70 | Research/Development |
| 61 | Foreign/World Lang K-12 | 71 | Public Information |
| 62 | Foreign/World Lang Elem | 72 | Summer School |
| 63 | Foreign/World Lang Sec | 73 | Instructional Tech |
| 64 | Religious Education K-12 | 74 | Inservice Training |
| 65 | Religious Education Elem | 75 | Marketing/Distributive |
| 66 | Religious Education Sec | 76 | Info Systems |
| 67 | School Board President | 77 | Psychological Assess |
| 68 | Teacher Personnel | 78 | Affirmative Action |

| | | | | | | |
|---|---|---|---|---|---|---|
| **Kelly-Pharr Elem Sch** | PK-5 | T | 758 | 88% | 956/354-2870 | |
| 500 E Sam Houston Blvd, Pharr 78577 | | | 35 | | Fax 956/354-3276 | |
| Lydia Trevino | | | | | | |
| **Kennedy Middle Sch** | 6-8 | T | 446 | 97% | 956/354-2650 | |
| 600 W Hall Acres Rd, Pharr 78577 | | | | | Fax 956/354-3206 | |
| Luis Villarreal | | | | | | |
| **Liberty Middle Sch** | 6-8 | TV | 877 | 91% | 956/354-2610 | |
| 1212 S Fir St, Pharr 78577 | | | 70 | | Fax 956/354-3218 | |
| Alfredo Carrillo | | | | | | |
| **Lyndon B Johnson Middle Sch** | 6-8 | ATV | 1,076 | 87% | 956/354-2590 | |
| 500 E Sioux Rd, Pharr 78577 | | | 77 | | Fax 956/354-3212 | |
| Linda Soto | | | | | | |
| **Marcia R Garza Elem Sch** | PK-5 | T | 625 | 98% | 956/354-2780 | |
| 810 El Gato Rd, Alamo 78516 | | | 21 | | Fax 956/354-3262 | |
| **Marisa Santoy** | | | | | | |
| **Pharr San Juan Alamo High Sch** | 9-12 | TV | 2,239 | 94% | 956/354-2300 | |
| 805 Ridge Rd, San Juan 78589 | | | 112 | | Fax 956/354-3156 | |
| Alejandro Elias | | | | | | |
| **Pharr San Juan Alamo North HS** | 9-12 | T | 2,162 | 87% | 956/354-2360 | |
| 500 E Nolana Loop, Pharr 78577 | | | 110 | | Fax 956/354-3140 | |
| Liza Diaz | | | | | | |
| Ⓐ **Psja Elvis J Ballew Echs** | 9-12 | | 353 | | 956/354-2520 | |
| 1100 US Business 83, Pharr 78577 | | | 20 | | Fax 956/354-3116 | |
| Darcia Cuellar | | | | | | |
| **Psja Memorial HS** | 9-12 | TV | 1,812 | 97% | 956/354-2420 | |
| 800 S Alamo Rd, Alamo 78516 | | | 100 | | Fax 956/354-3124 | |
| Dr Rowdy Vela | | | | | | |
| Ⓐ **Psja Sonia Sotomayer HS** | 8-12 | TV | 118 | 100% | 956/354-2510 | |
| 1200 E Polk Ave, Pharr 78577 | | | 10 | | Fax 956/354-3120 | |
| Rosa Rakay | | | | | | |
| **Psja Southwest EC High Sch** | 9-12 | T | 1,812 | 100% | 956/354-2480 | |
| 300 E Javelina Dr, Pharr 78577 | | | | | Fax 956/354-3172 | |
| Ranulfo Marquez | | | | | | |
| **Psja T Jefferson Echs** | 9-12 | T | 805 | 91% | 956/784-8525 | |
| 714 E US Highway 83, Pharr 78577 | | | | | Fax 956/354-3100 | |
| **Virna Maldonado** | | | | | | |
| **Raul Longoria Elem Sch** | PK-5 | T | 685 | 95% | 956/354-2820 | |
| 2500 N Cypress St, Pharr 78577 | | | 33 | | Fax 956/354-3268 | |
| Rosalina Borrego | | | | | | |
| **Raul Yzaguirre Middle Sch** | 6-8 | T | 813 | 95% | 956/354-2630 | |
| 605 E FM 495, San Juan 78589 | | | | | Fax 956/354-3230 | |
| Rebecca Luna | | | | | | |
| **Santos Livas Elem Sch** | PK-5 | T | 613 | 86% | 956/354-2840 | |
| 733 N Alamo Rd, Alamo 78516 | | | 43 | | Fax 956/354-3272 | |
| Rodrigo Hernandez | | | | | | |
| **Sgt Leonel Trevino Elem Sch** | PK-5 | T | 469 | 96% | 956/354-2900 | |
| 901 E Eldora Rd, San Juan 78589 | | | 34 | | Fax 956/354-3286 | |
| Dr Benito Carriaga | | | | | | |
| **Vida N Clover Elem Sch** | PK-5 | T | 566 | 95% | 956/354-2730 | |
| 800 Carroll Ln, San Juan 78589 | | | 42 | | Fax 956/354-3250 | |
| Guadalupe Garcia | | | | | | |

● **Progreso Ind School Dist** PID: 01030503      956/565-3002
600 N Business FM 1015, Progreso 78579      Fax 956/565-2128

**Schools:** 5 \ **Teachers:** 142 \ **Students:** 1,900 \ **Special Ed Students:** 132 \ **LEP Students:** 876 \ **College-Bound:** 50% \ **Ethnic:** Hispanic 99%, Caucasian 1% \ **Exp:** $327 (High) \ **Poverty:** 39% \ **Title I:** $1,293,071 \ **Special Education:** $339,000 \ **Open-Close:** 08/24 - 05/27 \ **DTBP:** $515 (High)

Sergio Coronado ........................................1      Guan Herenadez ...........................................2
Armando Cavazos ......................................3      Audrey Rocha ................................................4
Frank Quintero .......................................5,91      Margarito Jimenez .................................6*
Maribel Roriguez ..................................8,58      Zelda Rocha ...........................................57,88,93
Frank Alanis ............................................67      Maribel Rodriguez ...........................69,296

---

Gesus Pecina ............................................. 73   Jesus Pecina ....................................... 76

| Public Schs..Principal | Grd | Prgm | Enr/#Cls | SN |
|---|---|---|---|---|
| **Dorothy Thompson Middle Sch** | 6-8 | TV | 390 | 100% 956/565-1275 |
| 108 Business FM 1015 Rd, Progreso 78579 | | | | Fax 956/565-1718 |
| Yulia Molina | | | | |
| **Progreso Early Childhood Sch** | PK-2 | | 432 | 956/565-6473 |
| 1201 Business FM 1015, Progreso 78579 | | | | Fax 956/565-1103 |
| Edith Zuniga | | | | |
| **Progreso Early Clg Academy** | 9-12 | | 75 | 956/565-4142 |
| 700 N Business FM 1015, Progreso 78579 | | | | |
| Leticia Aquilar | | | | |
| **Progreso Elem Sch** | 3-5 | T | 376 | 99% 956/565-1335 |
| 1401 Business FM 1015, Progreso 78579 | | | | Fax 956/514-9503 |
| Marivel Garcia | | | | |
| **Progreso High Sch** | 9-12 | AGTV | 233 | 100% 956/565-4142 |
| 700 Business FM 1015, Progreso 78579 | | | 45 | Fax 956/565-6029 |
| Diana Aguilar | | | | |

● **Sharyland Ind School Dist** PID: 01030527      956/580-5200
1200 N Shary Rd, Mission 78572      Fax 956/580-2972

**Schools:** 14 \ **Teachers:** 637 \ **Students:** 10,295 \ **Special Ed Students:** 701 \ **LEP Students:** 2,703 \ **College-Bound:** 74% \ **Ethnic:** Asian 2%, African American 1%, Hispanic 93%, Caucasian 4% \ **Exp:** $414 (High) \ **Poverty:** 25% \ **Title I:** $3,595,631 \ **Special Education:** $1,387,000 \ **Open-Close:** 08/17 - 05/26 \ **DTBP:** $158 (High)

Dr Maria Vidaurri ......................................1      Ismael Gonzalez .............................2,15
Jamie Ortega ...........................................2      Mark Dougherty ..........................3,91
Cynthia Sanchez ......................................4      Enrique Mata ....................................5
Richard Thompson ...................................6      Jake Salcines ...................................8
Pamela Montalvo .................................8,15      Temoc Paz .........................................9
Teresa Gonzalez ..................................11,271      Belinda Gorene ................15,68,71,79
Carolyn Medola ..................15,68,71,79      Yoelia Nava ......................................27
Elizabeth Gongora .................................57      Lelia Torres .......................................58
Keith Padidilla .........................................67      Deborah Garza ................................68
Jennifer Martinez ................................69,81      Rocio Landin .....................................71
David Culberson ...............................84,98      Tisha Dahlberg ..............................295
Sergio Esquivel .................................. 297

| Public Schs..Principal | Grd | Prgm | Enr/#Cls | SN |
|---|---|---|---|---|
| **B L Gray Junior High Sch** | 7-8 | AT | 784 | 54% 956/580-5333 |
| 4400 S Glasscock Rd, Mission 78572 | | | 80 | Fax 956/580-5346 |
| Ericka Carranza | | | | |
| **Donna Wernecke Elem Sch** | PK-6 | T | 698 | 70% 956/928-1063 |
| 4500 Dove McAllen Rd, McAllen 78504 | | | | Fax 956/928-0221 |
| Lela Culberson | | | | |
| **Harry Shimotsu Elem Sch** | PK-6 | | 662 | 39% 956/583-5643 |
| 3101 San Mateo St, Mission 78572 | | | | Fax 936/519-1079 |
| Anthony Limon | | | | |
| **Hinojosa Elem Sch** | PK-6 | T | 378 | 58% 956/584-4990 |
| 4205 Los Indios Pkwy, Mission 78572 | | | | Fax 956/584-4998 |
| Lou Sarachene | | | | |
| **Jessie Jensen Elem Sch** | PK-6 | T | 588 | 92% 956/580-5252 |
| Glasscock Rd & 5 Mile Li, Mission 78572 | | | 40 | Fax 956/580-5266 |
| Niranda Flores | | | | |
| **John H Shary Elem Sch** | PK-6 | T | 717 | 62% 956/580-5282 |
| 2300 N Glasscock Rd, Mission 78574 | | | 51 | Fax 956/580-5294 |
| Rebekah Gerlach | | | | |
| **Lloyd & Dolly Bentsen Elem Sch** | PK-6 | T | 529 | 78% 956/686-0426 |
| 2101 S Taylor Rd, McAllen 78503 | | | 35 | Fax 956/668-0430 |
| Cecilia Boyd | | | | |
| **Olivero Garza Elem Sch** | PK-6 | T | 585 | 84% 956/580-5353 |
| 5 Mile Line & Taylor Rd, Mission 78572 | | | 45 | Fax 956/580-5363 |
| Veronica Rodriguez | | | | |

---

| | | | | | | |
|---|---|---|---|---|---|---|
| **79** Student Personnel | **91** Safety/Security | **275** Response To Intervention | **298** Grant Writer/Ptnrships | **School Programs** | **Social Media** |
| **80** Driver Ed/Safety | **92** Magnet School | **277** Remedial Math K-12 | **750** Chief Innovation Officer | **A = Alternative Program** | |
| **81** Gifted/Talented | **93** Parental Involvement | **280** Literacy Coach | **751** Chief of Staff | **G = Adult Classes** | = Facebook |
| **82** Video Services | **95** Tech Prep Program | **285** STEM | **752** Social Emotional Learning | **M = Magnet Program** | |
| **83** Substance Abuse Prev | **97** Chief Information Officer | **286** Digital Learning | | **T = Title I Schoolwide** | = Twitter |
| **84** Erate | **98** Chief Technology Officer | **288** Common Core Standards | **Other School Types** | **V = Career & Tech Ed Programs** | |
| **85** AIDS Education | **270** Character Education | **294** Accountability | Ⓐ = Alternative School | | |
| **88** Alternative/At Risk | **271** Migrant Education | **295** Network System | Ⓒ = Charter School | | |
| **89** Multi-Cultural Curriculum | **273** Teacher Mentor | **296** Title II Programs | Ⓜ = Magnet School | **New Schools are shaded** | |
| **90** Social Work | **274** Before/After Sch | **297** Webmaster | Ⓨ = Year-Round School | **New Superintendents and Principals are bold** | |
| | | | | **Personnel with email addresses are underscored** | |

| | | | | | | |
|---|---|---|---|---|---|---|
| Romulo Martinez Elem Sch<br>2571 E 4th St, Mission 78572<br>Nayeli Perez | PK-6 | T | 561<br>50 | 72% | 956/584-4900<br>Fax 956/584-4908 | |
| Sharyland Adv Academic Academy<br>1106 N Shary Rd, Mission 78572<br>Ivan Karr | 9-12 | T | 385 | 63% | 956/584-6467 | |
| Ⓐ Sharyland Alternative Ed Ctr<br>1501 N Taylor Rd, Mission 78572<br>Tizoc Silva | K-12 | | 24 | | 956/584-6407<br>Fax 956/213-8009 | |
| Sharyland High Sch<br>1216 N Shary Rd, Mission 78572<br>Lori Garza | 9-12 | ATV | 1,557<br>85 | 59% | 956/580-5300<br>Fax 956/580-5311 | |
| Sharyland North Jr High Sch<br>5100 W Dove Ave, McAllen 78504<br>Lorene Bazan | 7-8 | T | 836 | 67% | 956/686-1415<br>Fax 956/668-0425 | |
| Sharyland Pioneer High Sch<br>10001 N Shary Rd, Mission 78573<br>James Heath | 9-12 | T | 1,563 | 62% | 956/271-1600 | |

## ● Valley View Ind School Dist PID: 01030565

9701 S Jackson Rd, Pharr 78577 — 956/340-1000 — Fax 956/843-8688

**Schools:** 8 \ **Teachers:** 279 \ **Students:** 4,300 \ **Special Ed Students:** 306 \ **LEP Students:** 2,555 \ **Ethnic:** Hispanic 100%, \ **Exp:** $340 (High) \ **Poverty:** 36% \ **Title I:** $2,456,082 \ **Special Education:** $609,000 \ **Open-Close:** 08/31 - 05/27 \ **DTBP:** $158 (High) \ 🇫 🇹

| | | |
|---|---|---|
| Monica Luna ....................1 | Rolando Moreno ....................2 | |
| Alex Rodriguez ..............3,5 | Karla Rodriguez ....................4 | |
| Julio Martinez ....................6* | Camilo Martinez ..............11,93 | |
| Manuel Rodriguez ..........20,23 | Ramiro Balderas ....................27 | |
| Dr Matthew Meyers ........57,271 | Perla Deangel ....................58 | |
| Noe Pruneda ....................67 | Jorge Martinez ..............73,84 | |
| Gustavo Guzman ..............285* | | |

| Public Schs..Principal | Grd | Prgm | Enr/#Cls | SN | |
|---|---|---|---|---|---|
| Valley View 5th Grade Campus<br>9701 S Jackson Rd, Pharr 78577<br>Tomas Villagomez | 5-5 | T | 317 | 91% | 956/340-1400<br>Fax 956/843-3756<br>🇫 🇹 |
| Valley View Early College Sch<br>3000 E Dicker Rd, Hidalgo 78557<br>Isaias Vidal | 8-9 | | 623 | | 956/340-1200<br>Fax 956/213-8438<br>🇫 🇹 |
| Valley View Elem Sch<br>3804 E Anaya St, Hidalgo 78557<br>Jesus Cerda | PK-4 | | 392 | | 956/340-1450<br>Fax 956/843-8526<br>🇫 🇹 |
| Valley View High Sch<br>600 N Jackson Rd, Pharr 78577<br>Jesus Garza | 9-12 | AGTV | 1,162<br>45 | 92% | 956/340-1500<br>Fax 956/843-9368<br>🇫 🇹 |
| Valley View Junior High Sch<br>9601 S Jackson Rd, Pharr 78577<br>Antonio De La Cerda | 6-7 | T | 623<br>35 | 90% | 956/340-1300<br>Fax 956/843-3031 |
| Valley View North Elem Sch<br>1300 W Anaya Rd, Pharr 78577<br>Marina Leal | PK-4 | T | 478<br>30 | 97% | 956/340-1600<br>Fax 956/783-1163<br>🇫 🇹 |
| Valley View South Elem Sch<br>900 S McColl St, Hidalgo 78557<br>Elizabeth Reyes | PK-4 | T | 303 | 91% | 956/340-1650<br>Fax 956/843-7787 |
| Wilbur E Lucas Elem Sch<br>1300 N McColl St, Hidalgo 78557<br>Dr Rosemarie Gomez | PK-4 | T | 423<br>31 | 88% | 956/340-1700<br>Fax 956/843-3039 |

## ● Weslaco Ind School Dist PID: 01030589

319 W 4th St, Weslaco 78596 — 956/969-6500 — Fax 956/969-2664

**Schools:** 19 \ **Teachers:** 1,101 \ **Students:** 18,000 \ **Special Ed Students:** 1,468 \ **LEP Students:** 4,207 \ **College-Bound:** 57% \ **Ethnic:** Hispanic 99%, Caucasian 1% \ **Exp:** $279 (Med) \ **Poverty:** 37% \ **Title I:** $9,764,291 \ **Special Education:** $2,814,000 \ **Open-Close:** 08/20 - 05/21 \ **DTBP:** $172 (High)

| | |
|---|---|
| Dr Priscilla Canales ....................1 | Andres Sanchez ..............2,15 |
| Dora Pena ....................4 | Lupe Garcia ....................5 |
| Oscar Riojas ....................6 | Janie Pena ....................8 |
| Susan Peterson ..............8,15 | John Garlic ....................11 |
| Abel Aguilar ....................15 | Sergio Garcia ....................15 |
| Elias Trevino ....................57 | Neil Garza ....................58 |
| Isidoro Nieto ....................67 | Melva Segura ....................68 |
| Arminda Munoz ....................71 | Carlos Martinez ..............73,76,295 |
| Scott Amdahl ..............73,84 | Rick Flores ..............77,294 |
| Norma Brewer ....................79 | Michael De La Rosa ....................88 |
| Melissa Escalon ....................91 | Erica Garcia ....................93* |
| George Lopez ....................271 | |

| Public Schs..Principal | Grd | Prgm | Enr/#Cls | SN | |
|---|---|---|---|---|---|
| A N Rico Elem Sch<br>2202 N Intl Blvd, Weslaco 78596<br>Jacqueline Padilla | PK-5 | T | 846<br>38 | 93% | 956/969-6815<br>Fax 956/565-4676 |
| Airport Drive Elem Sch<br>410 N Airport Dr, Weslaco 78596<br>Ida Cuadra | PK-5 | T | 868<br>37 | 85% | 956/969-6770<br>Fax 956/968-4062 |
| B Garza Middle Sch<br>1111 W Sugarcane Dr, Weslaco 78599<br>Mr Rebolloso | 6-8 | T | 1,129<br>47 | 80% | 956/969-6774<br>Fax 956/447-0484 |
| Central Middle Sch<br>503 E 6th St, Weslaco 78596<br>Patricia Munoz | 6-8 | T | 903<br>70 | 77% | 956/969-6710<br>Fax 956/969-0779 |
| Cleckler-Heald Elem Sch<br>1601 W Sugarcane Dr, Weslaco 78599<br>Monica Vanderveer | PK-5 | T | 931<br>50 | 85% | 956/969-6888<br>Fax 956/968-6808 |
| Cte Early College High Sch<br>700 S Bridge St, Weslaco 78596<br>Marco Zamora | 9-9 | TV | 189 | 84% | 956/969-6742 |
| Ⓐ Disciplinary Alt Ed Program<br>104 S Iowa Ave, Weslaco 78596<br>**Roger Perez** | 6-12 | | 60<br>4 | | 956/969-6916<br>Fax 956/969-6782 |
| Dr Armando Cuellar Middle Sch<br>1201 S Bridge Ave, Weslaco 78596<br>D Rodriguez | 6-8 | T | 489<br>56 | 85% | 956/969-6720<br>Fax 956/973-9797 |
| Dr R E Margo Elem Sch<br>1701 S Bridge Ave, Weslaco 78596<br>Rubelina Martinez | PK-5 | T | 844<br>83 | 89% | 956/969-6800<br>Fax 956/969-8868 |
| Justice Raul A Gonzalez ES<br>3801 N Mile 5 1/2 W, Weslaco 78599<br>Rosa Garcia | PK-5 | T | 625<br>37 | 93% | 956/969-6760<br>Fax 956/969-9828 |
| Mary Hoge Middle Sch<br>2302 N Intl Blvd, Weslaco 78596<br>Vallejo Pablo | 6-8 | TV | 1,009<br>38 | 93% | 956/969-6730<br>Fax 956/514-0903 |
| Memorial Elem Sch<br>1700 S Border Ave, Weslaco 78596<br>Rhonda Sellman | PK-5 | T | 874<br>50 | 67% | 956/969-6780<br>Fax 956/968-5506 |
| North Bridge Elem Sch<br>2001 N Bridge Ave, Weslaco 78599<br>Daniel Budimir | PK-5 | | 631<br>43 | | 956/969-6810<br>Fax 956/968-1521 |
| Pfc Mario Ybarra Elem Sch<br>1800 E Mile 10 N, Weslaco 78599<br>Linda Hernandez | PK-5 | T | 551<br>30 | 94% | 956/969-6587<br>Fax 956/969-6518 |
| Rudy Silva Elem Sch<br>1001 W Mile 10 N, Weslaco 78599<br>Sonia Gonzalez | PK-5 | T | 589<br>40 | 80% | 956/969-6790<br>Fax 956/968-6937 |

| | | | | | | | | | |
|---|---|---|---|---|---|---|---|---|---|
| 1 | Superintendent | 8 | Curric/Instruct K-12 | 19 | Chief Financial Officer | 29 | Family/Consumer Science | 39 | Social Studies K-12 |
| 2 | Bus/Finance/Purchasing | 9 | Curric/Instruct Elem | 20 | Art K-12 | 30 | Adult Education | 40 | Social Studies Elem |
| 3 | Buildings And Grounds | 10 | Curric/Instruct Sec | 21 | Art Elem | 31 | Career/Sch-to-Work K-12 | 41 | Social Studies Sec |
| 4 | Food Service | 11 | Federal Program | 22 | Art Sec | 32 | Career/Sch-to-Work Elem | 42 | Science K-12 |
| 5 | Transportation | 12 | Title I | 23 | Music K-12 | 33 | Career/Sch-to-Work Sec | 43 | Science Elem |
| 6 | Athletic | 13 | Title V | 24 | Music Elem | 34 | Early Childhood Ed | 44 | Science Sec |
| 7 | Health Services | 14 | Title I | 25 | Music Sec | 35 | Health/Phys Education | 45 | Math K-12 |
| | | 15 | Asst Superintendent | 26 | Business Education | 36 | Guidance Services K-12 | 46 | Math Elem |
| | | 16 | Instructional Media Svcs | 27 | Career & Tech Ed | 37 | Guidance Services Elem | 47 | Math Sec |
| | | 17 | Chief Operations Officer | 28 | Technology Education | 38 | Guidance Services Sec | 48 | English/Lang Arts K-12 |
| | | 18 | Chief Academic Officer | | | | | | |

| | | | |
|---|---|---|---|
| 49 | English/Lang Arts Elem | 59 | Special Education Elem |
| 50 | English/Lang Arts Sec | 60 | Special Education Sec |
| 51 | Reading K-12 | 61 | Foreign/World Lang K-12 |
| 52 | Reading Elem | 62 | Foreign/World Lang Elem |
| 53 | Reading Sec | 63 | Foreign/World Lang Sec |
| 54 | Remedial Reading K-12 | 64 | Religious Education K-12 |
| 55 | Remedial Reading Elem | 65 | Religious Education Elem |
| 56 | Remedial Reading Sec | 66 | Religious Education Sec |
| 57 | Bilingual/ELL | 67 | School Board President |
| 58 | Special Education K-12 | 68 | Teacher Personnel |

| | | | |
|---|---|---|---|
| 69 | Academic Assessment | | |
| 70 | Research/Development | | |
| 71 | Public Information | | |
| 72 | Summer School | | |
| 73 | Instructional Tech | | |
| 74 | Inservice Training | | |
| 75 | Marketing/Distributive | | |
| 76 | Info Systems | | |
| 77 | Psychological Assess | | |
| 78 | Affirmative Action | | |

| | | | | | |
|---|---|---|---|---|---|
| Sam Houston Elem Sch<br>608 N Cantu St, Weslaco 78596<br>Selma Gutierrez | PK-5 | T | 752 | 87% | 956/969-6740<br>Fax 956/973-9404 |
| Ⓐ South Palm Gardens High Sch<br>3907 Camino Real Viejo, Weslaco 78596<br>Tina Wells | 10-12 | | 93 | | 956/969-6621<br>Fax 956/565-5994 |
| Weslaco East High Sch<br>810 S Pleasantview Dr, Weslaco 78596<br>David Gamboa | 9-12 | T | 2,051<br>110 | 89% | 956/969-6950<br>Fax 956/968-8693<br>🄣 |
| Weslaco High Sch<br>1005 W Pike Blvd, Weslaco 78596<br>Yvett Morales | 9-12 | GTV | 2,430 | 80% | 956/969-6700<br>Fax 956/968-8008 |

## HIDALGO CATHOLIC SCHOOLS

● **Diocese of Brownsville Ed Off** PID: 01004372    956/781-5323
700 Virgen De San Juan, San Juan 78589    Fax 956/784-5081

**Schools:** 12 \ **Students:** 2,831

Listing includes only schools located in this county. See District Index for location of Diocesan Offices.

| Catholic Schs..Principal | Grd | Prgm | Enr/#Cls | SN |
|---|---|---|---|---|
| Juan Diego Academy<br>5208 S FM 494, Mission 78572<br>Gerald Lugaresi | 9-12 | | 85 | 956/583-2752<br>Fax 956/583-3782 |
| Oratory Academy & Athenaeum<br>1407 W Moore Rd, Pharr 78577<br>Leo-Francis Daniels | PK-12 | | 440<br>15 | 956/781-3056<br>Fax 956/787-7729 |
| Our Lady of Sorrows Sch<br>1100 Gumwood Ave, McAllen 78501<br>Israel Martinez | PK-8 | | 520<br>22 | 956/686-3651<br>Fax 956/686-1996 |
| San Martin De Porres Sch<br>905 N Texas Blvd, Weslaco 78596<br>Reyna Ortega | PK-5 | | 90<br>9 | 956/973-8642<br>Fax 956/973-0522 |
| St Joseph Catholic Sch<br>119 W Fay St, Edinburg 78539<br>Angelina Karpinski | PK-8 | | 123<br>14 | 956/383-3957<br>Fax 956/318-0681 |

## HIDALGO PRIVATE SCHOOLS

| Private Schs..Principal | Grd | Prgm | Enr/#Cls | SN |
|---|---|---|---|---|
| Agape Christian Sch<br>1401 E 24th St, Mission 78574<br>Moises Gonzales | PK-7 | | 180<br>9 | 956/585-9773<br>Fax 956/585-9775 |
| Covenant Christian Academy<br>4201 N Ware Rd, McAllen 78504<br>Maria Bridwell | PK-8 | | 400<br>25 | 956/686-7886<br>Fax 956/686-9470 |
| Faith Christian Academy<br>4301 N Shary Rd, Palmhurst 78573<br>Robert Munne | PK-12 | | 140 | 956/581-1465<br>Fax 956/581-7786 |
| Grace Christian Sch<br>132 N Sugar Rd, Pharr 78577<br>Robert Logan | PK-12 | | 15<br>2 | 956/787-0701<br>Fax 956/787-5885 |

| | | | | |
|---|---|---|---|---|
| Harvest Christian Academy<br>1000 Las Alamedas, Edinburg 78541<br>Joe Cruz | PK-12 | | 300 | 956/383-8967 |
| Immanuel Lutheran Sch<br>703 W 3rd St, Mercedes 78570<br>Virginia Guzman | PK-5 | | 12<br>3 | 956/565-3208 |
| Mid-Valley Christian Sch<br>417 S Westgate Dr, Weslaco 78596<br>Nancy Mullins | PK-12 | | 135<br>10 | 956/968-6232<br>Fax 956/969-3517 |
| South Texas Christian Academy<br>7001 N Ware Rd, McAllen 78504<br>Federico Esquivel | PK-12 | | 317 | 956/682-1117<br>Fax 956/682-7398<br>🄵 |
| St John's Episcopal Day Sch<br>2500 N 10th St, McAllen 78501<br>Linda McGurk | PK-5 | | 250<br>21 | 956/686-0231<br>Fax 956/686-8779<br>🄵🄣 |
| St Matthew's Episcopal Sch<br>2620 Crestview Dr, Edinburg 78539<br>Laurie Cantu | PK-6 | | 135<br>14 | 956/383-4202<br>Fax 956/383-7846 |
| St Paul Lutheran Sch<br>300 Pecan Blvd, McAllen 78501<br>Nichole Perez | PK-8 | | 152<br>10 | 956/682-2345<br>Fax 956/682-7148 |
| Taylor Christian Sch<br>2021 W Jackson Ave, McAllen 78501<br>Andrea Cooper | PK-8 | | 39<br>9 | 956/686-7574<br>Fax 956/682-4945 |
| The Discovery Sch<br>1711 W Alberta Rd, Edinburg 78539<br>Leticia Sanchez | PK-6 | | 155<br>12 | 956/381-1117<br>Fax 956/381-1007 |
| Valley Christian Heritage Sch<br>932 N Alamo Rd, Alamo 78516<br>Mary Rydl | PK-12 | | 100<br>13 | 956/787-9743<br>Fax 956/787-1977 |

## HIDALGO REGIONAL CENTERS

● **Region 1 Ed Service Center** PID: 01030553    956/984-6000
1900 W Schunior St, Edinburg 78541    Fax 956/984-7655

## HILL COUNTY

## HILL PUBLIC SCHOOLS

● **Abbott Ind School Dist** PID: 01030709    254/582-3011
219 S 1st St, Abbott 76621    Fax 254/582-5430

**Schools:** 1 \ **Teachers:** 24 \ **Students:** 280 \ **Special Ed Students:** 33 \ **LEP Students:** 3 \ **College-Bound:** 90% \ **Ethnic:** African American 1%, Hispanic 13%, Caucasian 86% \ **Exp:** $793 (High) \ **Poverty:** 8% \ **Title I:** $22,774 \ **Open-Close:** 08/20 - 05/27 \ **DTBP:** $362 (High)

| | | |
|---|---|---|
| 79 Student Personnel | 91 Safety/Security | 275 Response To Intervention |
| 80 Driver Ed/Safety | 92 Magnet School | 277 Remedial Math K-12 |
| 81 Gifted/Talented | 93 Parental Involvement | 280 Literacy Coach |
| 82 Video Services | 95 Tech Prep Program | 285 STEM |
| 83 Substance Abuse Prev | 97 Chief Infomation Officer | 286 Digital Learning |
| 84 Erate | 98 Chief Technology Officer | 288 Common Core Standards |
| 85 AIDS Education | 270 Character Education | 294 Accountability |
| 88 Alternative/At Risk | 271 Migrant Education | 295 Network System |
| 89 Multi-Cultural Curriculum | 273 Teacher Mentor | 296 Title II Programs |
| 90 Social Work | 274 Before/After Sch | 297 Webmaster |

298 Grant Writer/Ptnrships
750 Chief Innovation Officer
751 Chief of Staff
752 Social Emotional Learning

**Other School Types**
Ⓐ = Alternative School
Ⓒ = Charter School
Ⓜ = Magnet School
Ⓨ = Year-Round School

**School Programs**
A = Alternative Program
G = Adult Classes
M = Magnet Program
T = Title I Schoolwide
V = Career & Tech Ed Programs

New Schools are shaded
New Superintendents and Principals are bold
Personnel with email addresses are underscored

**Social Media**
🄵 = Facebook
🄣 = Twitter

| Public Schs..Principal | Grd | Prgm | Enr/#Cls | SN | |
|---|---|---|---|---|---|
| Abbott Sch<br>219 S 1st St, Abbott 76621<br>Jon Coker | PK-12 | T | 280<br>25 | 25% | 254/582-3011 |

## ● Aquilla Ind School Dist PID: 01030735
404 N Richards, Aquilla 76622

254/694-3770
Fax 254/694-6237

**Schools:** 1 \ **Teachers:** 26 \ **Students:** 330 \ **Special Ed Students:** 33 \ **LEP Students:** 14 \ **Ethnic:** African American 2%, Hispanic 15%, Caucasian 83% \ **Exp:** $751 (High) \ **Poverty:** 10% \ **Title I:** $27,797 \ **Open-Close:** 08/26 - 05/28 \ **DTBP:** $353 (High)

| | | | |
|---|---|---|---|
| Dr David Edison .................1,11 | Andrew Christian ...............2,8,15,88 |
| Shaun Nugent ........................4* | Gregg Waddell ........................5 |
| Josh Ball .................................6* | Andrew Christian ...................8,88* |
| Keith Coffey ..........................12* | Kenneth Langdale ...............16,73* |
| Garla Montez ...............36,69,83* | Garla Montez ...............36,57,69 |
| Laura Hendrix ........................58* | David Snipes .........................67 |
| Pam Horton ............................70 | |

| Public Schs..Principal | Grd | Prgm | Enr/#Cls | SN | |
|---|---|---|---|---|---|
| Aquilla Sch<br>404 N Richards, Aquilla 76622<br>Keith Coffey \ Shari Page | PK-12 | TV | 330<br>19 | 59% | 254/694-3770 |

## ● Blum Ind School Dist PID: 01030761
310 S Avenue F, Blum 76627

254/874-5231
Fax 254/874-5233

**Schools:** 1 \ **Teachers:** 28 \ **Students:** 344 \ **Special Ed Students:** 49 \ **LEP Students:** 8 \ **College-Bound:** 60% \ **Ethnic:** African American 1%, Hispanic 12%, Caucasian 86% \ **Exp:** $435 (High) \ **Poverty:** 10% \ **Title I:** $41,250 \ **Open-Close:** 08/14 - 05/20 \ **DTBP:** $59 (Low) \ 🅵 🅣

| | |
|---|---|
| Jeff Sanders ........................1,11 | Dee Bellinger .........................2* |
| Kathy Haggerton ....................4* | Cooper Thornhill ....................6* |
| Tracy Bellomy ........................8* | Liuren McPherson ........31,69,83,88* |
| Chantele Hurt ........................57* | Julie Laverett ........................58 |
| Richard McPherson ................67 | Phillip Williams ......................73* |

| Public Schs..Principal | Grd | Prgm | Enr/#Cls | SN | |
|---|---|---|---|---|---|
| Blum Sch<br>310 S Avenue F, Blum 76627<br>Tracy Bellomy \ **Charles Brandenberger** | PK-12 | T | 344<br>28 | 60% | 254/874-5231 |

## ● Bynum Ind School Dist PID: 01030797
704 Toliver St, Bynum 76631

254/531-2341
Fax 254/531-2342

**Schools:** 1 \ **Teachers:** 17 \ **Students:** 195 \ **Special Ed Students:** 37 \ **LEP Students:** 6 \ **College-Bound:** 100% \ **Ethnic:** African American 5%, Hispanic 33%, Caucasian 63% \ **Exp:** $322 (High) \ **Poverty:** 10% \ **Title I:** $35,834 \ **Open-Close:** 08/14 - 05/20 \ **DTBP:** $357 (High) \ 🅵

| | |
|---|---|
| Larry Mynarcik ...............1,11,83 | Brandy Faulknor ....................2 |
| Josh Haws ............................3,5 | Shirley Horrice .......................4* |
| Lyndsey Pederson .....8,11,58,76,286,288* | Weldon Whalen .....................27* |
| Amy Haws ..............................36* | Grif Harris .............................67 |
| Shelia Beims .........................79* | |

| Public Schs..Principal | Grd | Prgm | Enr/#Cls | SN | |
|---|---|---|---|---|---|
| Bynum Sch<br>704 Toliver St, Bynum 76631<br>Lyndsey Pederson | PK-12 | TV | 195<br>25 | 62% | 254/623-4251 |

## ● Covington ISD School Dist PID: 01030826
501 N Main, Covington 76636

254/854-2215
Fax 254/854-2272

**Schools:** 1 \ **Teachers:** 23 \ **Students:** 390 \ **Special Ed Students:** 40 \ **LEP Students:** 4 \ **College-Bound:** 83% \ **Ethnic:** Hispanic 14%, Native American: 1%, Caucasian 85% \ **Exp:** $869 (High) \ **Poverty:** 11% \ **Title I:** $33,922 \ **Open-Close:** 08/13 - 05/19 \ **DTBP:** $354 (High)

| | |
|---|---|
| Dr Christopher Heskett ...................1 | Pam Frazier ...........................2 |
| Rhonda Kennedy .......................4* | Charles Steele .......................6* |
| Keri Heskett ...........36,88,270,271* | Andy Lopez ...........................67 |
| Kara Mackey ........................69,76* | Sonya Lanham .....................73,295* |

| Public Schs..Principal | Grd | Prgm | Enr/#Cls | SN | |
|---|---|---|---|---|---|
| Covington Sch<br>501 N Main, Covington 76636<br>Leslie Edens \ Joel Blalock | PK-12 | TV | 390<br>18 | 56% | 254/854-2215 |

## ● Hillsboro Ind School Dist PID: 01030852
121 E Franklin St, Hillsboro 76645

254/582-8585
Fax 254/582-4165

**Schools:** 5 \ **Teachers:** 163 \ **Students:** 2,000 \ **Special Ed Students:** 215 \ **LEP Students:** 252 \ **Ethnic:** Asian 1%, African American 13%, Hispanic 61%, Caucasian 25% \ **Exp:** $386 (High) \ **Poverty:** 21% \ **Title I:** $616,365 \ **Special Education:** $472,000 \ **Open-Close:** 08/13 - 05/28 \ **DTBP:** $340 (High) \ 🅵

| | |
|---|---|
| Vicky Adams ...........................1 | Dale Snyder ...........................2 |
| Raymond Nors .......................3,5 | Angela Boyd ..........................8 |
| Stephanie Tucker ........11,31,57,58,271 | Donald Gordon ...........16,73,76,97,295 |
| Dr Christopher Teague ...........67 | Keith Hannah .....................68,273 |

| Public Schs..Principal | Grd | Prgm | Enr/#Cls | SN | |
|---|---|---|---|---|---|
| Franklin Elem Sch<br>103 Country Club Rd, Hillsboro 76645<br>Cathy Patterson | PK-PK | T | 178<br>16 | 75% | 254/582-4130<br>Fax 254/582-4133 |
| Hillsboro Elem Sch<br>115 Jane Ln, Hillsboro 76645<br>Robin Ralston | K-2 | T | 429<br>34 | 76% | 254/582-4140<br>Fax 254/582-4145 |
| Hillsboro High Sch<br>1600 Abbott Ave, Hillsboro 76645<br>Keith Hannah | 9-12 | AGTV | 251<br>45 | 65% | 254/582-4100<br>Fax 254/582-4108 |
| Hillsboro Intermediate Sch<br>1000 Old Bynum Rd, Hillsboro 76645<br>Wendy Jones | 3-6 | T | 478 | 73% | 254/582-4170<br>Fax 254/582-4175<br>🅵 |
| Hillsboro Junior High Sch<br>210 E Walnut St, Hillsboro 76645<br>Patrick Harvell | 7-8 | TV | 437<br>25 | 75% | 254/582-4120<br>Fax 254/582-4122 |

## ● Hubbard Ind School Dist PID: 01030917
Highway 31 W, Hubbard 76648

254/576-2564
Fax 254/576-5019

**Schools:** 2 \ **Teachers:** 29 \ **Students:** 422 \ **Special Ed Students:** 58 \ **LEP Students:** 3 \ **Ethnic:** African American 14%, Hispanic 19%, Caucasian 67% \ **Exp:** $573 (High) \ **Poverty:** 19% \ **Title I:** $81,566 \ **Open-Close:** 08/14 - 05/28 \ **DTBP:** $349 (High)

| | |
|---|---|
| Tim Norman ...........................1,11 | Elizabeth Kaluzas ..................2 |
| Mike Saucke ...........................3 | Dianna Walter .......................4* |
| Russell Anderson ...................6 | Weldonna Vardeman ............8* |
| Summer Norman ..........12,31,69,83 | Shawn Gilham .......................67 |
| Kenny Carter ......................73,295* | |

| | | | | | |
|---|---|---|---|---|---|
| 1 Superintendent | 8 Curric/Instruct K-12 | 19 Chief Financial Officer | 29 Family/Consumer Science | 39 Social Studies K-12 | 49 English/Lang Arts Elem | 59 Special Education Elem | 69 Academic Assessment |
| 2 Bus/Finance/Purchasing | 9 Curric/Instruct Elem | 20 Art K-12 | 30 Adult Education | 40 Social Studies Elem | 50 English/Lang Arts Sec | 60 Special Education Sec | 70 Research/Development |
| 3 Buildings And Grounds | 10 Curric/Instruct Sec | 21 Art Elem | 31 Career/Sch-to-Work K-12 | 41 Social Studies Sec | 51 Reading K-12 | 61 Foreign/World Lang K-12 | 71 Public Information |
| 4 Food Service | 11 Federal Program | 22 Art Sec | 32 Career/Sch-to-Work Elem | 42 Science K-12 | 52 Reading Elem | 62 Foreign/World Lang Elem | 72 Summer School |
| 5 Transportation | 12 Title I | 23 Music K-12 | 33 Career/Sch-to-Work Sec | 43 Science Elem | 53 Reading Sec | 63 Foreign/World Lang Sec | 73 Instructional Tech |
| 6 Athletic | 13 Title V | 24 Music Elem | 34 Early Childhood Ed | 44 Science Sec | 54 Remedial Reading K-12 | 64 Religious Education K-12 | 74 Inservice Training |
| 7 Health Services | 15 Asst Superintendent | 25 Music Sec | 35 Health/Phys Education | 45 Math K-12 | 55 Remedial Reading Elem | 65 Religious Education Elem | 75 Marketing/Distributive |
| | 16 Instructional Media Svcs | 26 Business Education | 36 Guidance Services K-12 | 46 Math Elem | 56 Remedial Reading Sec | 66 Religious Education Sec | 76 Info Systems |
| | 17 Chief Operations Officer | 27 Career & Tech Ed | 37 Guidance Services Elem | 47 Math Sec | 57 Bilingual/ELL | 67 School Board President | 77 Psychological Assess |
| | 18 Chief Academic Officer | 28 Technology Education | 38 Guidance Services Sec | 48 English/Lang Arts K-12 | 58 Special Education K-12 | 68 Teacher Personnel | 78 Affirmative Action |

| Public Schs..Principal | Grd | Prgm | Enr/#Cls | SN |
|---|---|---|---|---|
| Hubbard Elem Sch<br>1801 NW 4th St, Hubbard 76648<br>**Sunny Beseda** | PK-5 | T | 208<br>14 | 62% 254/576-2359<br>Fax 254/576-5018 |
| Hubbard High Sch<br>1801 NW 4th St, Hubbard 76648<br>**Danny Dennie** | 6-12 | AGTV | 214<br>15 | 56% 254/576-2549<br>Fax 254/576-2477 |

● **Itasca Ind School Dist** PID: 01030955　　　254/687-2922
　123 N College St, Itasca 76055　　　　Fax 254/687-2637

**Schools:** 3 \ **Teachers:** 55 \ **Students:** 670 \ **Special Ed Students:** 76 \ **LEP Students:** 84 \ **College-Bound:** 73% \ **Ethnic:** Asian 1%, African American 8%, Hispanic 47%, Caucasian 44% \ **Exp:** $846 (High) \ **Poverty:** 22% \ **Title I:** $239,775 \ **Open-Close:** 08/19 - 05/28 \ **DTBP:** $440 (High)

| | | | |
|---|---|---|---|
| Mark Parsons ....................1 | Patty Miller ....................3,5 |
| Missey Montes ....................4 | Toni Daniels ....................4 |
| Obid Massey ....................5 | Amy Reyna ....................8,11* |
| Susan Bason ....................8,11,57,88 | Grace Hennig ....................36,83* |
| Allison Middleton ....................58,76,285,296 | Brian Basset ....................67 |
| Kristi Sargent ....................69* | Richard Wilson ....................73,295* |

| Public Schs..Principal | Grd | Prgm | Enr/#Cls | SN |
|---|---|---|---|---|
| Itasca Elem Sch<br>300 N Files St, Itasca 76055<br>Holli Merkel | PK-5 | T | 293<br>15 | 75% 254/687-2922 |
| Itasca High Sch<br>123 N College St, Itasca 76055<br>**Robert Webb** | 9-12 | ATV | 199<br>18 | 62% 254/687-2922 |
| Itasca Middle Sch<br>208 N Files St, Itasca 76055<br>Kristi Sargent | 6-8 | TV | 107<br>10 | 74% 254/687-2922 |

● **Malone Independent School Dist** PID: 01030981　254/533-2321
　202 W Hackberry, Malone 76660　　　　Fax 254/533-5660

**Schools:** 1 \ **Teachers:** 13 \ **Students:** 178 \ **Special Ed Students:** 22 \ **LEP Students:** 50 \ **Ethnic:** African American 7%, Hispanic 72%, Caucasian 21% \ **Exp:** $380 (High) \ **Poverty:** 11% \ **Title I:** $1,318 \ **Open-Close:** 08/21 - 05/21 \ **DTBP:** $333 (High)

| | |
|---|---|
| Linda Buffe ....................1,11,73,84,288 | Leonard Buffe ....................6,35* |
| Sharon Campbell ....................57* | Barbara Christian ....................58,270,273* |
| Larry Hancock ....................67 | Michael Johnson ....................76 |

| Public Schs..Principal | Grd | Prgm | Enr/#Cls | SN |
|---|---|---|---|---|
| Malone Elem Sch<br>262 W Hackberry St, Malone 76660<br>Lakeshia Johnson | PK-8 | T | 178<br>10 | 86% 254/533-2321 |

● **Mt Calm Ind School Dist** PID: 01031002　254/993-2611
　200 N Coates E, Mount Calm 76673　　　Fax 254/993-1022

**Schools:** 2 \ **Teachers:** 18 \ **Students:** 200 \ **Special Ed Students:** 25 \ **LEP Students:** 14 \ **College-Bound:** 65% \ **Ethnic:** African American 4%, Hispanic 29%, Native American: 1%, Caucasian 66% \ **Exp:** $865 (High) \ **Poverty:** 42% \ **Title I:** $109,698 \ **Open-Close:** 08/06 - 05/21 \ **DTBP:** $200 (High)

| | |
|---|---|
| James Wright ....................1,11 | Kristi Hawkins ....................2,11 |
| Rhonda Williams ....................4* | Christy Bailey ....................5,8,57,275,288 |
| Tom Duncan ....................6 | Brittney Coy ....................16,73,295,297* |
| Kaaron Cornish ....................58 | Brian Dunlap ....................67 |

| Public Schs..Principal | Grd | Prgm | Enr/#Cls | SN |
|---|---|---|---|---|
| Mt Calm Elem Sch<br>200 N Coates E, Mount Calm 76673<br>Pam Taylor | PK-8 | T | 141<br>12 | 83% 254/993-2611 |
| Mt Calm High Sch<br>100 N Coates E, Mount Calm 76673<br>Pam Taylor | 9-12 | V | 44 | 254/993-2611 |

● **Penelope ISD School Dist** PID: 01031026　254/533-2215
　309 Avenue D St, Penelope 76676　　　Fax 254/533-2262

**Schools:** 1 \ **Teachers:** 20 \ **Students:** 215 \ **Special Ed Students:** 32 \ **LEP Students:** 13 \ **Ethnic:** African American 1%, Hispanic 31%, Caucasian 68% \ **Exp:** $407 (High) \ **Poverty:** 12% \ **Title I:** $17,942 \ **Open-Close:** 08/13 - 05/03 \ **DTBP:** $350 (High) \ 🅕 🅣

| | |
|---|---|
| David Timmons ....................1 | Samantha Gutierrez ....................2,11 |
| Deborah Westmoreland ....................4* | Amanda Green ....................57* |
| David Kucera ....................67 | Traci Pustejovsky ....................73* |

| Public Schs..Principal | Grd | Prgm | Enr/#Cls | SN |
|---|---|---|---|---|
| Penelope Sch<br>309 Avenue D St, Penelope 76676<br>**Sherry Hueske** | PK-12 | ATV | 215<br>25 | 66% 254/533-2215 |

● **Whitney Ind School Dist** PID: 01031052　254/694-2254
　305 S San Jacinto St, Whitney 76692　　Fax 254/694-4001

**Schools:** 4 \ **Teachers:** 112 \ **Students:** 1,311 \ **Special Ed Students:** 188 \ **LEP Students:** 77 \ **Ethnic:** African American 4%, Hispanic 22%, Caucasian 73% \ **Exp:** $343 (High) \ **Poverty:** 19% \ **Title I:** $374,177 \ **Open-Close:** 08/19 - 05/21 \ **DTBP:** $385 (High) \ 🅕

| | |
|---|---|
| John McCullough ....................1 | Kim Martin ....................2 |
| Brian Caperton ....................3,5,91 | Judy Bailey ....................4 |
| Scott Sheffield ....................5 | Mark Byrd ....................6 |
| Jeanne Thompson ....................7 | Melissa Marbut ....................8,12,273 |
| Angie Rateike ....................9,36 | Jennifer Penney ....................10,31,36,69,83,85,88* |
| Melody Haley ....................11,15,58,271 | Kristy Smith ....................16,73,297 |
| Bradley Coffelt ....................27* | Maria Herrera ....................57 |
| Ray Mabry ....................67 | Laura Hunt ....................288,298 |

| Public Schs..Principal | Grd | Prgm | Enr/#Cls | SN |
|---|---|---|---|---|
| Whitney Elem Sch<br>308 S Bosque St, Whitney 76692<br>Amber Seely | PK-2 | T | 312<br>24 | 73% 254/694-3456<br>Fax 254/694-2059<br>🅕 |
| Whitney High Sch<br>1400 N Brazos St, Whitney 76692<br>Amy Leech | 9-12 | TV | 316<br>35 | 55% 254/694-3457<br>Fax 254/694-4206 |
| Whitney Intermediate Sch<br>301 S San Jacinto St, Whitney 76692<br>Russell Gauer | 3-5 | T | 339<br>18 | 66% 254/694-7303<br>Fax 254/694-7029<br>🅕 |
| Whitney Middle Sch<br>185 Hcr 1240, Whitney 76692<br>Paul Booth | 6-8 | T | 344<br>30 | 57% 254/946-6568<br>Fax 254/947-7913<br>🅕 |

**TX—231**

## HOCKLEY COUNTY

## HOCKLEY PUBLIC SCHOOLS

● **Anton Ind School Dist** PID: 01031090
100 E Ellwood Blvd, Anton 79313
806/997-2301
Fax 806/997-2062

**Schools:** 1 \ **Teachers:** 20 \ **Students:** 185 \ **Special Ed Students:** 29 \ **LEP Students:** 11 \ **Ethnic:** African American 4%, Hispanic 74%, Caucasian 22% \ **Exp:** $377 (High) \ **Poverty:** 43% \ **Title I:** $211,749 \ **Open-Close:** 08/24 - 05/28 \ **DTBP:** $350 (High)

Dwight Rice ...........................................1
Andrew Alcorta .....................................4*
Brian Reed ..........................................67
Nancy Webb ........................................2
Deeanne Betencourt ............................8*

| Public Schs..Principal | Grd | Prgm | Enr/#Cls | SN | |
|---|---|---|---|---|---|
| Anton Sch<br>100 Ellwood Boulevard, Anton 79313<br>David Cox \ **Deeanne Bentancourt** | PK-12 | TV | 185<br>25 | 83% | 806/997-5211<br>Fax 806/997-2312 |

● **Levelland Ind School Dist** PID: 01031129
704 11th St, Levelland 79336
806/894-9628
Fax 806/894-2583

**Schools:** 6 \ **Teachers:** 219 \ **Students:** 2,936 \ **Special Ed Students:** 425 \ **LEP Students:** 216 \ **Ethnic:** African American 3%, Hispanic 73%, Caucasian 23% \ **Exp:** $399 (High) \ **Poverty:** 28% \ **Title I:** $1,210,556 \ **Open-Close:** 08/19 - 05/27 \ **DTBP:** $154 (High)

Jeff Northern ........................................1
Steve Croyle .........................................4
Andrew Correll ...............................6,35
Heidi Blair ....8,16,36,69,275,285,288,294
Lyndsay Lucas ...................................10*
Kathy Hutchinson ...........................12,58
Tania Moody .......................................67
Rodney Caddell ............................91,751
Teresa Montemayor ........................2,19
Randi Bullard ......................................5
Judy Whisenant ...................................7
Christy Barnett ....................................9
Donna Pugh ......11,31,57,88,271,274,296,298
Sky Tucker ..........................................34*
Mike Sapia ............73,76,95,98,286,295,297

| Public Schs..Principal | Grd | Prgm | Enr/#Cls | SN | |
|---|---|---|---|---|---|
| Capitol Elem Sch<br>401 E Ellis St, Levelland 79336<br>Joanna Runkles | 1-3 | T | 369<br>17 | 73% | 806/894-4715<br>Fax 806/894-9860 |
| Levelland ABC<br>1412 E Ellis St, Levelland 79336<br>**Mrs Howad** | PK-1 | T | 428<br>22 | 77% | 806/894-6959<br>Fax 806/894-5512 |
| Levelland High Sch<br>1400 Hickory St, Levelland 79336<br>Robert Phillips | 9-12 | TV | 753<br>60 | 61% | 806/894-8515<br>Fax 806/894-6029 |
| Levelland Intermediate Sch<br>1100 Avenue D, Levelland 79336<br>Terri White | 4-5 | T | 468<br>25 | 72% | 806/894-3060<br>Fax 806/894-8957 |
| Levelland Middle Sch<br>1402 E Ellis St, Levelland 79336<br>Brad Clanton | 6-8 | T | 589<br>70 | 69% | 806/894-6355<br>Fax 806/894-8935 |
| South Elem Sch<br>1500 Avenue C, Levelland 79336<br>Shelbi Eugenis | 1-3 | T | 331<br>18 | 72% | 806/894-6255<br>Fax 806/894-1283 |

● **Ropes Ind School Dist** PID: 01031234
304 Ranch Rd, Ropesville 79358
806/562-4031
Fax 806/562-4059

**Schools:** 1 \ **Teachers:** 41 \ **Students:** 479 \ **Special Ed Students:** 32 \ **LEP Students:** 9 \ **College-Bound:** 85% \ **Ethnic:** African American 1%, Hispanic 35%, Caucasian 63% \ **Exp:** $796 (High) \ **Poverty:** 22% \ **Title I:** $73,159 \ **Open-Close:** 08/20 - 05/20 \ **DTBP:** $342 (High)

Joel Willmon .................................1,11
Jimmy Rascon ....................................3*
Wendee Rhoades .................................7*
Jay Sedberry ...................................16,73*
Melissa Bratcher .................................57*
Jean McNabb .......................................59*
Lindsay Luckie ................................69,83*
Delinda DelGado ...................................2
Lane Jackson .......................................6*
Tim Carter ...........................8,12,273*
Toyia Senter ......................................16*
Tami Hayes ........................................58*
Mike Metzig ........................................67

| Public Schs..Principal | Grd | Prgm | Enr/#Cls | SN | |
|---|---|---|---|---|---|
| Ropes Sch<br>304 Ranch Rd, Ropesville 79358<br>Dr Danny McNabb \ Dana Ketchersid | PK-12 | AT | 479<br>28 | 44% | 806/562-4031 |

● **Smyer Ind School Dist** PID: 01031272
4th & Lincoln St, Smyer 79367
806/234-2935
Fax 806/234-2411

**Schools:** 2 \ **Teachers:** 40 \ **Students:** 415 \ **Special Ed Students:** 58 \ **LEP Students:** 11 \ **Ethnic:** African American 3%, Hispanic 48%, Caucasian 50% \ **Exp:** $719 (High) \ **Poverty:** 22% \ **Title I:** $96,202 \ **Open-Close:** 08/19 - 05/20 \ **DTBP:** $340 (High)

**Chris Wade** ..................................1,83
Leo Martinez .....................................3,5*
Mike Schaap ......................................6*
Bill Black ...........................10,16,69,74*
Trevor Tucek ...................................73,295
Donna Robertson ................................2
Gene Sheets ......................................4
Tony Igo ........................9,11,57,271*
Juan Cavazos .....................................67
Shelly Bruster ..........................88,270,296

| Public Schs..Principal | Grd | Prgm | Enr/#Cls | SN | |
|---|---|---|---|---|---|
| Smyer Elem Sch<br>4th & Lincoln St, Smyer 79367<br>Tony Igo | PK-6 | T | 229<br>21 | 68% | 806/234-2935 |
| Smyer Jr Sr High Sch<br>4th & Lincoln St, Smyer 79367<br>Bill Black | 7-12 | TV | 207 | 53% | 806/234-2935 |

● **Sundown Ind School Dist** PID: 01031301
701 School Ave, Sundown 79372
806/229-3021
Fax 806/229-2004

**Schools:** 3 \ **Teachers:** 63 \ **Students:** 595 \ **Special Ed Students:** 46 \ **LEP Students:** 18 \ **College-Bound:** 82% \ **Ethnic:** Asian 1%, African American 2%, Hispanic 59%, Caucasian 39% \ **Exp:** $577 (High) \ **Poverty:** 19% \ **Title I:** $92,839 \ **Open-Close:** 08/18 - 05/20 \ **DTBP:** $333 (High)

Scott Marshall .....................................1
Riley Goodman ..................................3,5
Adam Cummings ..................................6*
Jeremy Griffith ..............................8,34,57
Randel Ramerez ......................16,82,295*
Delwin Britton .....................................67
Kris Thoms ............................2,11,298
Alicia Gonzales ....................................4
Brittany Huerta ....................................7
Mike Glaze .....................................16,73
Amanda Davis ................................37,270*
Ann Majors ...............69,83,85,88,273*

| Public Schs..Principal | Grd | Prgm | Enr/#Cls | SN | |
|---|---|---|---|---|---|
| Sundown Elem Sch<br>701 School Ave, Sundown 79372<br>Jason Powell | PK-5 | T | 287<br>30 | 42% | 806/229-5021 |
| Sundown High Sch<br>701 School Ave, Sundown 79372<br>Brent Evans | 9-12 | ATV | 95<br>24 | 31% | 806/229-5021 |

| | | | | | | | | | | |
|---|---|---|---|---|---|---|---|---|---|---|
| 1 | Superintendent | 8 | Curric/Instruct K-12 | 19 | Chief Financial Officer | 29 | Family/Consumer Science | 39 | Social Studies K-12 | 49 | English/Lang Arts Elem | 59 | Special Education Elem | 69 | Academic Assessment |

1 Superintendent
2 Bus/Finance/Purchasing
3 Buildings And Grounds
4 Food Service
5 Transportation
6 Athletic
7 Health Services
8 Curric/Instruct K-12
9 Curric/Instruct Elem
10 Curric/Instruct Sec
11 Federal Program
12 Title I
13 Title V
14 Asst Superintendent
15 Instructional Media Svcs
16 Chief Operations Officer
17 Chief Academic Officer
18 
19 Chief Financial Officer
20 Art K-12
21 Art Elem
22 Art Sec
23 Music K-12
24 Music Elem
25 Music Sec
26 Business Education
27 Career & Tech Ed
28 Technology Education
29 Family/Consumer Science
30 Adult Education
31 Career/Sch-to-Work K-12
32 Career/Sch-to-Work Elem
33 Career/Sch-to-Work Sec
34 Early Childhood Ed
35 Health/Phys Education
36 Guidance Services K-12
37 Guidance Services Elem
38 Guidance Services Sec
39 Social Studies K-12
40 Social Studies Elem
41 Social Studies Sec
42 Science K-12
43 Science Elem
44 Science Sec
45 Math K-12
46 Math Elem
47 Math Sec
48 English/Lang Arts K-12
49 English/Lang Arts Elem
50 English/Lang Arts Sec
51 Reading K-12
52 Reading Elem
53 Reading Sec
54 Remedial Reading K-12
55 Remedial Reading Elem
56 Remedial Reading Sec
57 Bilingual/ELL
58 Special Education K-12
59 Special Education Elem
60 Special Education Sec
61 Foreign/World Lang K-12
62 Foreign/World Lang Elem
63 Foreign/World Lang Sec
64 Religious Education K-12
65 Religious Education Elem
66 Religious Education Sec
67 School Board President
68 Teacher Personnel
69 Academic Assessment
70 Research/Development
71 Public Information
72 Summer School
73 Instructional Tech
74 Inservice Training
75 Marketing/Distributive
76 Info Systems
77 Psychological Assess
78 Affirmative Action

| Sundown Middle Sch | 6-8 | T | 134 | 36% | 806/229-5021 |
|---|---|---|---|---|---|
| 7th & School Ave, Sundown 79372 | | | 13 | | |
| Jeremy Griffith | | | | | |

● **Whitharral Ind School Dist** PID: 01031349    806/299-1184
201 2nd Street, Whitharral 79380    Fax 806/299-1257

**Schools:** 1 \ **Teachers:** 17 \ **Students:** 175 \ **Special Ed Students:** 15
\ **College-Bound:** 100% \ **Ethnic:** African American 2%, Hispanic 42%,
Caucasian 56% \ **Exp:** $598 (High) \ **Poverty:** 17% \ **Title I:** $35,286 \
**Open-Close:** 08/14 - 05/21 \ **DTBP:** $342 (High)

| Ed Sharp | 1,11,73 | Adrianna McCollister | 2 |
|---|---|---|---|
| Nick McCollister | 8,12,36,69,83,270* | Janay Crenshaw | 16* |
| Susan Pendergrass | 57* | Jamie Driver | 58* |
| Anthony Albus | 67 | | |

| Public Schs..Principal | Grd | Prgm | Enr/#Cls | SN | |
|---|---|---|---|---|---|
| Whitharral Sch | K-12 | TV | 175 | 49% | 806/299-1135 |
| 201 2nd Street, Whitharral 79380 | | | 50 | | |
| Alex McCollister | | | | | |

## HOCKLEY PRIVATE SCHOOLS

| Private Schs..Principal | Grd | Prgm | Enr/#Cls | SN | |
|---|---|---|---|---|---|
| Levelland Christian Sch | PK-8 | | 48 | | 806/894-6019 |
| 1905 Cactus Dr, Levelland 79336 | | | 7 | | |
| Alex Hoser | | | | | |

# HOOD COUNTY

## HOOD PUBLIC SCHOOLS

● **Granbury Ind School Dist** PID: 01031375    817/408-4000
217 N Jones St, Granbury 76048    Fax 817/408-4014

**Schools:** 11 \ **Teachers:** 467 \ **Students:** 6,971 \ **Special Ed Students:** 868
\ **LEP Students:** 586 \ **College-Bound:** 52% \ **Ethnic:** Asian 1%,
African American 2%, Hispanic 25%, Native American: 1%, Caucasian
72% \ **Exp:** $460 (High) \ **Poverty:** 14% \ **Title I:** $1,563,357 \
**Special Education:** $1,180,000 \ **Open-Close:** 08/12 - 05/27 \ **DTBP:** $167
(High) \ 🅕 🅣

| Dr Jeremy Glenn | 1 | Dobie Williams | 2 |
|---|---|---|---|
| Randy Leach | 3,91 | Amy Parker | 4 |
| Brian Caruthers | 5 | Dwight Butler | 6 |
| Latrisha Suitt | 7,27,35,70,75,83,88 | Sharon Williams | 8,11,36,57,273,296,298 |
| Ron Holmgreen | 15 | Amy Parsons | 16,28,73,76 |
| Jimmy Dawson | 27 | Becky Strain | 39,42,45 |
| Diane Fullerton | 58 | Nancy Alana | 67 |
| Wes Jones | 68 | Amy Gilbert | 69,77* |
| Jeff Meador | 71 | Rene Jackson | 88 |
| Curtis Starnes | 295 | | |

| Public Schs..Principal | Grd | Prgm | Enr/#Cls | SN | |
|---|---|---|---|---|---|
| Acton Elem Sch | PK-5 | T | 823 | 47% | 817/408-4200 |
| 3200 Acton School Rd, Granbury 76049 | | | | | Fax 817/408-4299 |
| Karla Willmeth | | | | | |

| Acton Middle Sch | 6-8 | | 942 | 42% | 817-408-4800 |
|---|---|---|---|---|---|
| 1300 James Rd, Granbury 76049 | | | 62 | | Fax 817-408-4849 |
| Jimmy Dawson | | | | | |
| Ⓐ Behavior Transition Center | 5-12 | | 50 | | 817/408-4400 |
| 301 N Hannaford St, Granbury 76048 | | | 2 | | Fax 817/408-4164 |
| Margaret Rodriquez | | | | | |
| Brawner Intermediate Sch | 3-5 | T | 391 | 68% | 817/408-4950 |
| 1520 S Meadows Dr, Granbury 76048 | | | 17 | | Fax 817/408-4999 |
| Jincy Ross | | | | | |
| Emma Roberson Elem Sch | PK-2 | T | 416 | 74% | 817/408-4500 |
| 1500 Misty Meadow Dr, Granbury 76048 | | | 35 | | Fax 817/408-4599 |
| Kellie Lambert | | | | | 🅕 🅣 |
| Granbury High Sch | 9-12 | ATV | 421 | 44% | 817/408-4600 |
| 2000 W Pearl St, Granbury 76048 | | | 110 | | Fax 817/408-4699 |
| Jeremy Ross | | | | | |
| Granbury Middle Sch | 6-8 | T | 775 | 62% | 817/408-4850 |
| 2000 Crossland Rd, Granbury 76048 | | | 35 | | Fax 817/408-4899 |
| Tammy Clark | | | | | |
| Nettie Baccus Elem Sch | PK-5 | T | 463 | 82% | 817/408-4300 |
| 901 Loop 567, Granbury 76048 | | | 29 | | Fax 817/408-4399 |
| Robert Herrera | | | | | |
| Oak Woods Sch | PK-5 | T | 573 | 46% | 817/408-4750 |
| 311 Davis Rd, Granbury 76049 | | | 52 | | Fax 817/408-4799 |
| Donnie Cody | | | | | |
| Ⓐ Stars Accelerated High Sch | 9-12 | T | 22 | 61% | 817/408-4450 |
| 301 N Hannaford St, Granbury 76048 | | | 5 | | Fax 817/408-4164 |
| Margaret Rodriquez | | | | | |
| The Steam Academy at Mambrino | PK-5 | T | 744 | 55% | 817/408-4900 |
| 3835 Mambrino Hwy, Granbury 76048 | | | 60 | | Fax 817/408-4949 |
| Stacie Brown | | | | | |

● **Lipan Ind School Dist** PID: 01031416    254/646-2266
211 N Kickapoo St, Lipan 76462    Fax 254/646-3499

**Schools:** 1 \ **Teachers:** 35 \ **Students:** 413 \ **Special Ed Students:** 29
\ **LEP Students:** 15 \ **College-Bound:** 50% \ **Ethnic:** Hispanic 15%,
Native American: 1%, Caucasian 85% \ **Exp:** $502 (High) \ **Poverty:** 17% \
**Title I:** $71,078 \ **Open-Close:** 08/14 - 05/28 \ **DTBP:** $346 (High) \ 🅕 🅣

| Ralph Carter | 1 | Clayton Long | 3 |
|---|---|---|---|
| Tony Phillips | 6,8* | Cindi Fields | 57* |
| John Cooper | 67 | Susan Taylor | 73* |
| Sandy Howard | 271 | | |

| Public Schs..Principal | Grd | Prgm | Enr/#Cls | SN | |
|---|---|---|---|---|---|
| Lipan Sch | PK-12 | TV | 413 | 50% | 254/646-2266 |
| 211 N Kickapoo St, Lipan 76462 | | | 30 | | |
| Jennifer Phillips \ Jodi Overton | | | | | |

● **Tolar Ind School Dist** PID: 01031430    254/835-4718
305 S Oak Ln, Tolar 76476    Fax 254/835-4704

**Schools:** 3 \ **Teachers:** 61 \ **Students:** 800 \ **Special Ed Students:** 42
\ **LEP Students:** 4 \ **College-Bound:** 75% \ **Ethnic:** Asian 1%, African
American 1%, Hispanic 7%, Caucasian 91% \ **Exp:** $517 (High) \
**Poverty:** 13% \ **Title I:** $94,952 \ **Open-Close:** 08/13 - 05/27 \ **DTBP:** $383
(High) \ 🅣

| Travis Stilwell | 1 | Vicki Carr | 2 |
|---|---|---|---|
| Jeremy Mullins | 6* | Lindsay Morgan | 11,58* |
| Dalton Nix | 67 | Kristin Carey | 73,295 |

| Public Schs..Principal | Grd | Prgm | Enr/#Cls | SN | |
|---|---|---|---|---|---|
| Tolar Elem Sch | PK-5 | | 344 | 40% | 254/835-4028 |
| 401 E 7th St, Tolar 76476 | | | 13 | | Fax 254/835-4319 |
| **Christal Hollinger** | | | | | |

| | | | | | |
|---|---|---|---|---|---|
| 79 Student Personnel | 91 Safety/Security | 275 Response To Intervention | 298 Grant Writer/Ptnrships | **School Programs** | **Social Media** |
| 80 Driver Ed/Safety | 92 Magnet School | 277 Remedial Math K-12 | 750 Chief Innovation Officer | **A** = Alternative Program | |
| 81 Gifted/Talented | 93 Parental Involvement | 280 Literacy Coach | 751 Chief of Staff | **G** = Adult Classes | 🅕 = Facebook |
| 82 Video Services | 95 Tech Prep Program | 285 STEM | 752 Social Emotional Learning | **M** = Magnet Program | |
| 83 Substance Abuse Prev | 97 Chief Information Officer | 286 Digital Learning | | **T** = Title I Schoolwide | 🅣 = Twitter |
| 84 Erate | 98 Chief Technology Officer | 288 Common Core Standards | **Other School Types** | **V** = Career & Tech Ed Programs | |
| 85 AIDS Education | 270 Character Education | 294 Accountability | Ⓐ = Alternative School | | |
| 88 Alternative/At Risk | 271 Migrant Education | 295 Network System | Ⓒ = Charter School | | |
| 89 Multi-Cultural Curriculum | 273 Teacher Mentor | 296 Title II Programs | Ⓜ = Magnet School | **New Schools are shaded** | |
| 90 Social Work | 274 Before/After Sch | 297 Webmaster | Ⓨ = Year-Round School | **New Superintendents and Principals are bold** | |
| | | | | **Personnel with email addresses are underscored** | |

| | | | | | |
|---|---|---|---|---|---|
| Tolar High Sch | 9-12 | V | 226 | 33% | 254/835-4316 |
| 301 Rock Church Hwy, Tolar 76476 | | | 26 | | Fax 254/835-4237 |
| Lindsay Morgan | | | | | |
| Tolar Junior High Sch | 6-8 | T | 186 | 42% | 254/835-5207 |
| 401 E 7th St, Tolar 76476 | | | | | Fax 254/835-5208 |
| **Jerrod Tidwell** | | | | | 🇫 🇹 |

## HOOD PRIVATE SCHOOLS

| Private Schs..Principal | Grd | Prgm | Enr/#Cls | SN | |
|---|---|---|---|---|---|
| Cornerstone Christian Academy | PK-12 | | 160 | | 817/910-8076 |
| 5150 N Gate Rd, Granbury 76049 | | | 19 | | Fax 817/573-7604 |
| Marci Martinez | | | | | 🇫 |
| Grace Classical Christian Acad | PK-9 | | 76 | | 817/771-4951 |
| 1851 Weatherford Hwy, Granbury 76048 | | | | | |
| Dr Preston Atwood | | | | | |
| North Central Texas Academy | K-12 | | 167 | | 254/897-4822 |
| 3846 N Highway 144, Granbury 76048 | | | 32 | | Fax 254/897-7650 |
| Jennifer Smith | | | | | 🇫 🇹 |

## HOPKINS COUNTY

## HOPKINS PUBLIC SCHOOLS

- **Como Pickton Cons Ind SD** PID: 01031466 — 903/488-3671
  13017 E Texas Highway 11, Como 75431 — Fax 903/488-3133

**Schools:** 1 \ **Teachers:** 64 \ **Students:** 700 \ **Special Ed Students:** 79 \ **LEP Students:** 186 \ **College-Bound:** 40% \ **Ethnic:** Asian 1%, African American 2%, Hispanic 44%, Native American: 1%, Caucasian 52% \ **Exp:** $542 (High) \ **Poverty:** 20% \ **Title I:** $223,201 \ **Special Education:** $127,000 \ **Open-Close:** 08/10 - 05/28 \ **DTBP:** $350 (High)

| | | | |
|---|---|---|---|
| Greg Bower | 1 | Lenise Boseman | 2* |
| Carlos Mejia | 4 | Mindy Friddle | 4 |
| Kelly Baird | 8* | Jenna Andrews | 11,58,298 |
| Lou Colvin | 38 | Amy Friddle | 57,73,76,271,286,288* |
| D Carr | 67 | | |

| Public Schs..Principal | Grd | Prgm | Enr/#Cls | SN | |
|---|---|---|---|---|---|
| Como Pickton Sch | PK-12 | TV | 700 | 71% | 903/488-3671 |
| 13017 E Texas Highway 11, Como 75431 | | | 65 | | |
| Linda Rankin \ Cassandra Bland \ Kelly Baird | | | | | |

- **Cumby Ind School Dist** PID: 01031492 — 903/994-2260
  303 Sayle St, Cumby 75433 — Fax 903/994-2399

**Schools:** 2 \ **Teachers:** 36 \ **Students:** 400 \ **Special Ed Students:** 53 \ **LEP Students:** 14 \ **College-Bound:** 47% \ **Ethnic:** African American 2%, Hispanic 14%, Native American: 2%, Caucasian 82% \ **Exp:** $492 (High) \ **Poverty:** 13% \ **Title I:** $68,486 \ **Open-Close:** 08/13 - 06/03 \ **DTBP:** $373 (High)

| | | | |
|---|---|---|---|
| Shelly Slaughter | 1,11 | Brenda Salinas | 2 |
| Mike Thorman | 3,5* | Charles Boles | 6 |
| Megan Petty | 8,36,69,270* | Jeremy Bain | 16,73,295 |
| Jason Hudson | 67 | | |

| Public Schs..Principal | Grd | Prgm | Enr/#Cls | SN | |
|---|---|---|---|---|---|
| Cumby Elem Sch | PK-5 | TV | 166 | 60% | 903/994-2260 |
| 303 Sayle St, Cumby 75433 | | | 16 | | Fax 903/994-2847 |
| Douglas Wicks | | | | | |
| Cumby High Sch | 6-12 | AT | 199 | 55% | 903/994-2260 |
| 303 Sayle St, Cumby 75433 | | | 24 | | Fax 903/994-2510 |
| Jennifer Dracos | | | | | |

- **Miller Grove Ind School Dist** PID: 01031521 — 903/459-3288
  7819 FM 275 S, Cumby 75433 — Fax 903/459-3744

**Schools:** 1 \ **Teachers:** 29 \ **Students:** 345 \ **Special Ed Students:** 36 \ **LEP Students:** 21 \ **College-Bound:** 55% \ **Ethnic:** Hispanic 18%, Caucasian 81% \ **Exp:** $545 (High) \ **Poverty:** 14% \ **Title I:** $38,632 \ **Open-Close:** 08/13 - 05/28 \ **DTBP:** $371 (High)

| | | | |
|---|---|---|---|
| Steve Johnson | 1,11,83 | Janet Teer | 2 |
| Robert Smith | 3 | Becky Brown | 4 |
| Gary Billingsley | 6,10* | Jaime Fox | 9,57,69,271* |
| Jeff Gatlin | 27* | Emma Hudson | 58,88 |
| Brandon Darrow | 67 | Davy Moseley | 73* |
| Jim Bayuk | 91 | | |

| Public Schs..Principal | Grd | Prgm | Enr/#Cls | SN | |
|---|---|---|---|---|---|
| Miller Grove Sch | PK-12 | T | 345 | 53% | 903/459-3288 |
| 7819 FM 275 S, Cumby 75433 | | | 24 | | |
| Jaime Fox \ Gary Billingsley | | | | | |

- **North Hopkins Ind School Dist** PID: 01031545 — 903/945-2192
  1994 Farm Road 71 W, Sulphur Spgs 75482 — Fax 903/945-2531

**Schools:** 1 \ **Teachers:** 44 \ **Students:** 550 \ **Special Ed Students:** 55 \ **LEP Students:** 48 \ **College-Bound:** 58% \ **Ethnic:** Hispanic 26%, Caucasian 73% \ **Exp:** $931 (High) \ **Poverty:** 22% \ **Title I:** $120,652 \ **Open-Close:** 08/19 - 05/27 \ **DTBP:** $393 (High)

| | | | |
|---|---|---|---|
| Dr Darin Jolly | 1 | Jan Vaughn | 2 |
| Cindy McPherson | 4* | Kenneth Cockrum | 5 |
| Carolyn Neal | 7* | Robert Stanley | 11 |
| David James | 67 | Daniel Caldwell | 73* |
| Cody Wright | 275* | | |

| Public Schs..Principal | Grd | Prgm | Enr/#Cls | SN | |
|---|---|---|---|---|---|
| North Hopkins Sch | PK-12 | ATV | 550 | 64% | 903/945-2192 |
| 1994 Farm Road 71 W, Sulphur Spgs 75482 | | | 28 | | |
| Kodi Wright \ Brian Lowe | | | | | |

- **Saltillo Ind School Dist** PID: 01031571 — 903/537-2386
  150 County Rd 3534, Saltillo 75478 — Fax 903/537-2191

**Schools:** 1 \ **Teachers:** 26 \ **Students:** 276 \ **Special Ed Students:** 27 \ **LEP Students:** 20 \ **College-Bound:** 65% \ **Ethnic:** African American 3%, Hispanic 26%, Caucasian 71% \ **Exp:** $478 (High) \ **Poverty:** 18% \ **Title I:** $56,761 \ **Open-Close:** 08/17 - 05/28 \ **DTBP:** $343 (High)

| | | | |
|---|---|---|---|
| David Stickels | 1,11 | Janice Teer | 2 |
| Timmy White | 3* | Susan Smith | 4* |
| Bill Gilse | 6 | Reta Eubanks | 58 |
| Mark Sustaire | 67 | Tim Lane | 73,286,288 |
| Dustin Ray | 83 | Geli Moroney | 752 |

| Public Schs..Principal | Grd | Prgm | Enr/#Cls | SN | |
|---|---|---|---|---|---|
| Saltillo Sch | PK-12 | ATV | 276 | 68% | 903/537-2386 |
| 150 County Rd 3534, Saltillo 75478 | | | 16 | | |
| Tim Lane \ David Stickels | | | | | |

| | | | | | | | |
|---|---|---|---|---|---|---|---|
| 1 | Superintendent | 8 | Curric/Instruct K-12 | 19 | Chief Financial Officer | 29 | Family/Consumer Science |
| 2 | Bus/Finance/Purchasing | 9 | Curric/Instruct Elem | 20 | Art K-12 | 30 | Adult Education |
| 3 | Buildings And Grounds | 10 | Curric/Instruct Sec | 21 | Art Elem | 31 | Career/Sch-to-Work K-12 |
| 4 | Food Service | 11 | Federal Program | 22 | Art Sec | 32 | Career/Sch-to-Work Elem |
| 5 | Transportation | 12 | Title I | 23 | Music K-12 | 33 | Career/Sch-to-Work Sec |
| 6 | Athletic | 13 | Title V | 24 | Music Elem | 34 | Early Childhood Ed |
| 7 | Health Services | 14 | Asst Superintendent | 25 | Music Sec | 35 | Health/Phys Education |
| | | 15 | Instructional Media Svcs | 26 | Business Education | 36 | Guidance Services K-12 |
| | | 16 | Chief Operations Officer | 27 | Career & Tech Ed | 37 | Guidance Services Elem |
| | | 17 | Chief Academic Officer | 28 | Technology Education | 38 | Guidance Services Sec |

| | | | | | |
|---|---|---|---|---|---|
| 39 | Social Studies K-12 | 49 | English/Lang Arts Elem | 59 | Special Education Elem |
| 40 | Social Studies Elem | 50 | English/Lang Arts Sec | 60 | Special Education Sec |
| 41 | Social Studies Sec | 51 | Reading K-12 | 61 | Foreign/World Lang K-12 |
| 42 | Science K-12 | 52 | Reading Elem | 62 | Foreign/World Lang Elem |
| 43 | Science Elem | 53 | Reading Sec | 63 | Foreign/World Lang Sec |
| 44 | Science Sec | 54 | Remedial Reading K-12 | 64 | Religious Education K-12 |
| 45 | Math K-12 | 55 | Remedial Reading Elem | 65 | Religious Education Elem |
| 46 | Math Elem | 56 | Remedial Reading Sec | 66 | Religious Education Sec |
| 47 | Math Sec | 57 | Bilingual/ELL | 67 | School Board President |
| 48 | English/Lang Arts K-12 | 58 | Special Education K-12 | 68 | Teacher Personnel |

| | |
|---|---|
| 69 | Academic Assessment |
| 70 | Research/Development |
| 71 | Public Information |
| 72 | Summer School |
| 73 | Instructional Tech |
| 74 | Inservice Training |
| 75 | Marketing/Distributive |
| 76 | Info Systems |
| 77 | Psychological Assess |
| 78 | Affirmative Action |

- **Sulphur Bluff Ind School Dist** PID: 01031595    903/945-2460
  1027 County Road 3550, Sulphur Bluff 75481    Fax 903/945-2459

**Schools:** 1 \ **Teachers:** 18 \ **Students:** 230 \ **Special Ed Students:** 32 \ **LEP Students:** 6 \ **College-Bound:** 50% \ **Ethnic:** African American 3%, Hispanic 12%, Caucasian 85% \ **Exp:** $360 (High) \ **Poverty:** 14% \ **Title I:** $31,551 \ **Open-Close:** 08/18 - 05/21 \ **DTBP:** $316 (High) \ **f**

| Dustin Carr | 1,11 | Troy Emerson | 5 |
| Amy Northcutt | 8,58,69,83,274,275* | Leah Gore | 31,36,294* |
| Donnie Powers | 67 | Jarret Wilson | 73* |

| Public Schs..Principal | Grd | Prgm | Enr/#Cls | SN | |
|---|---|---|---|---|---|
| Sulphur Bluff Sch | PK-12 | ATV | 230 | 57% | 903/945-2460 |
| 1027 County Road 3550, Sulphur Bluff 75481 | | | 15 | | |
| Marshall Moore | | | | | |

- **Sulphur Springs Ind Sch Dist** PID: 01031624    903/885-2153
  631 Connally St, Sulphur Spgs 75482    Fax 903/439-6162

**Schools:** 9 \ **Teachers:** 349 \ **Students:** 4,400 \ **Special Ed Students:** 501 \ **LEP Students:** 565 \ **College-Bound:** 64% \ **Ethnic:** Asian 1%, African American 11%, Hispanic 29%, Caucasian 58% \ **Exp:** $278 (Med) \ **Poverty:** 21% \ **Title I:** $1,111,404 \ **Special Education:** $711,000 \ **Open-Close:** 08/18 - 05/26 \ **DTBP:** $153 (High)

| Michael Lamb | 1 | Sherry McGraw | 2 |
| Dan Froneberger | 3* | Veronica Arnold | 4 |
| Greg Owens | 6* | Lisa Robinson | 8 |
| Kristin Monk | 9,15 | Josh Williams | 11,15,36,79,88,296 |
| Rusty Harden | 15,68 | Rodney White | 16,73,295 |
| Jenny Arledge | 26,27,31,75,95* | Anna Aguilar | 57,271 |
| Susan Johnston | 58 | Robert Cody | 67 |
| Jason Evans | 69,294 | John Bimmerle | 286* |
| Ben Scott | 295 | | |

| Public Schs..Principal | Grd | Prgm | Enr/#Cls | SN | |
|---|---|---|---|---|---|
| Ⓐ Austin Academic Center | 1-12 | | 90 | | 903/885-4942 |
| 808 Davis St S, Sulphur Spgs 75482 | | | | | Fax 903/439-6142 |
| Julie Ashmore | | | | | |
| Barbara Bush Primary Sch | K-1 | T | 164 | 73% | 903/439-6170 |
| 390 N Hillcrest Dr, Sulphur Spgs 75482 | | | 31 | | Fax 903/439-6177 |
| Ashanta Alexander | | | | | |
| Bowie Primary Sch | K-3 | T | 389 | 52% | 903/885-3772 |
| 1400 Mockingbird Ln, Sulphur Spgs 75482 | | | 19 | | Fax 903/885-5754 |
| Amanda Fenton | | | | | |
| Douglass ECLC | PK-K | T | 545 | 100% | 903/885-4516 |
| 600 Calvert St, Sulphur Spgs 75482 | | | 14 | | Fax 903/439-1181 |
| Angela Edwards | | | | | |
| Lamar Primary Sch | K-3 | T | 319 | 82% | 903/885-4550 |
| 825 Church St, Sulphur Spgs 75482 | | | 14 | | Fax 903/439-6144 |
| **Chandra Crawford** | | | | | |
| Sulphur Springs Elem Sch | 4-5 | T | 670 | 61% | 903/855-8466 |
| 829 Bell St, Sulphur Spgs 75482 | | | 14 | | Fax 903/885-5451 |
| Holly Folmar | | | | | |
| Sulphur Springs High Sch | 9-12 | TV | 1,270 | 53% | 903/885-2158 |
| 1200 Connally St, Sulphur Spgs 75482 | | | 75 | | Fax 903/885-6669 |
| Derek Driver | | | | | |
| Sulphur Springs Middle Sch | 6-8 | T | 962 | 58% | 903/885-7741 |
| 835 Wildcat Way, Sulphur Spgs 75482 | | | 70 | | Fax 903/439-6126 |
| Jena Williams | | | | | |
| Travis Primary Sch | K-3 | T | 385 | 81% | 903/885-5246 |
| 130 Garrison St, Sulphur Spgs 75482 | | | 25 | | Fax 903/438-2251 |
| Michelle Wallace | | | | | |

## HOPKINS PRIVATE SCHOOLS

| Private Schs..Principal | Grd | Prgm | Enr/#Cls | SN | |
|---|---|---|---|---|---|
| Water Oak Sch | K-5 | | 60 | | 903/439-3044 |
| 631 Davis St N, Sulphur Spgs 75482 | | | | | |
| Lesley Williams | | | | | |

## HOUSTON COUNTY

## HOUSTON PUBLIC SCHOOLS

- **Crockett Ind School Dist** PID: 01031715    936/544-2125
  1400 W Austin St, Crockett 75835    Fax 936/544-5727

**Schools:** 5 \ **Teachers:** 96 \ **Students:** 1,331 \ **Special Ed Students:** 144 \ **LEP Students:** 223 \ **Ethnic:** Asian 1%, African American 50%, Hispanic 35%, Caucasian 14% \ **Exp:** $466 (High) \ **Poverty:** 43% \ **Title I:** $1,096,651 \ **Special Education:** $374,000 \ **Open-Close:** 08/27 - 06/01 \ **DTBP:** $306 (High)

| John Emrich | 1 | Gail Hanson | 2,11,296 |
| Brian Fiolek | 3 | Louann Turner | 4 |
| Bruce Baker | 5 | Jimmy Thompson | 6 |
| Margaret Tuggle | 36 | Lela Wheeler | 67 |
| Rhonda Kendrick | 68 | Charlie Bobbitt | 73,297 |

| Public Schs..Principal | Grd | Prgm | Enr/#Cls | SN | |
|---|---|---|---|---|---|
| Ⓐ Crockett Aec-Pineywoods | 9-12 | G | 18 | | 936/546-5972 |
| 1400 W Austin St, Crockett 75835 | | | 3 | | Fax 936/546-0721 |
| Mecheal Abbs | | | | | |
| Crockett Elem Sch | 1-5 | T | 488 | 91% | 936/544-3758 |
| 1400 S Loop 304, Crockett 75835 | | | 29 | | Fax 936/544-2088 |
| **Crystal Montgomery** | | | | | |
| Crockett High Sch | 9-12 | TV | 364 | 79% | 936/544-2193 |
| 1600 SW Loop 304, Crockett 75835 | | | 34 | | Fax 936/546-0104 |
| Deborah Revels | | | | | |
| Crockett Junior High Sch | 6-8 | T | 306 | 92% | 936/544-2125 |
| 1500 SW Loop 304, Crockett 75835 | | | 30 | | Fax 936/544-4164 |
| **Johnny Gomez** | | | | | |
| Early Childhood Center | PK-K | T | 97 | 93% | 936/544-2125 |
| 1300 Mlk Blvd, Crockett 75835 | | | 12 | | Fax 936/544-9678 |
| Dylis Bobbitt | | | | | |

- **Grapeland Ind School Dist** PID: 01031753    936/687-4619
  116 W Myrtle Street, Grapeland 75844    Fax 936/687-4624

**Schools:** 3 \ **Teachers:** 46 \ **Students:** 600 \ **Special Ed Students:** 71 \ **LEP Students:** 6 \ **College-Bound:** 75% \ **Ethnic:** Asian 1%, African American 23%, Hispanic 9%, Caucasian 66% \ **Exp:** $453 (High) \ **Poverty:** 32% \ **Title I:** $285,938 \ **Open-Close:** 08/19 - 05/28 \ **DTBP:** $390 (High) \ **t**

| Don Jackson | 1,83 | Julie Martin | 2,11,296 |
| Terry Brown | 3 | Shamedria Gilmore | 4 |
| Paul Pick | 5 | Terry Ward | 6 |
| Cassie Satterwhite | 9,34,36,69* | Katie Doughty | 10 |
| Gary Graham | 27,298* | Amy Howard | 57,271* |
| Vicki Dial Branch | 58 | James Martin | 67 |
| Cidney Huff | 69,79 | John Norman | 76,295* |

---

| Public Schs..Principal | Grd | Prgm | Enr/#Cls | SN |
|---|---|---|---|---|
| Grapeland Elem Sch<br>796 N Olive St, Grapeland 75844<br>Cassie Satterwhite | PK-5 | TV | 281<br>17 | 71% 936/687-2317<br>Fax 936/687-2341 |
| Grapeland High Sch<br>318 N Olive St, Grapeland 75844<br>Rick Frauenberger | 9-12 | AGTV | 173<br>10 | 56% 936/687-4661<br>Fax 936/687-9739 |
| Grapeland Junior High Sch<br>116 West Myrtle St, Grapeland 75844<br>Rick Frauenberger | 6-8 | TV | 119<br>15 | 61% 936/687-2351<br>Fax 936/687-5285 |

● **Kennard Ind Sch Dist** PID: 01031791    936-655-2161
304 State Highway 7 E, Kennard 75847    Fax 936/655-2327

**Schools:** 1 \ **Teachers:** 24 \ **Students:** 256 \ **Special Ed Students:** 32 \
**LEP Students:** 3 \ **College-Bound:** 100% \ **Ethnic:** African American 11%, Hispanic 5%, Native American: 1%, Caucasian 83% \ **Exp:** $463 (High) \
**Poverty:** 43% \ **Title I:** $239,265 \ **Open-Close:** 08/13 - 05/19 \ **DTBP:** $530 (High)

Melinda Lindsey ........................ 1,11,73
Tracy Henderson ........................ 5
Cory Carden ........................ 6
Amy Gladden ........................ 31,69*
Cari Parrish ........................ 2
Corey Carden ........................ 6*
Debbie Pilkington ........................ 16,82*
Rebecca Parker ........................ 67

| Public Schs..Principal | Grd | Prgm | Enr/#Cls | SN |
|---|---|---|---|---|
| Kennard Sch<br>304 State Highway 7 E, Kennard 75847<br>Oscar Encarnacion | PK-12 | TV | 256<br>40 | 47% 936/655-2161 |

● **Latexo Ind School Dist** PID: 01031820    936/544-5664
298 FM 2663, Latexo 75849    Fax 936/544-5332

**Schools:** 2 \ **Teachers:** 35 \ **Students:** 475 \ **Special Ed Students:** 40
\ **LEP Students:** 8 \ **College-Bound:** 50% \ **Ethnic:** Asian 1%, African American 2%, Hispanic 10%, Caucasian 88% \ **Exp:** $443 (High) \
**Poverty:** 32% \ **Title I:** $150,909 \ **Open-Close:** 08/10 - 05/27 \ **DTBP:** $421 (High) \ 🅵 🆃

Michael Woodard ........................ 1
Logan Taylor ........................ 3,5*
Jessica Cutshall ........................ 6*
Lena Kelsey ........................ 28,73,286*
Kelly Nicol ........................ 67
Sandy Simpson ........................ 83,271,298
Jo Lane ........................ 2
Kim Brasher ........................ 4
Krystal Patterson ........................ 7*
Vicki Dial ........................ 58
Kimberly Watson ........................ 69*

| Public Schs..Principal | Grd | Prgm | Enr/#Cls | SN |
|---|---|---|---|---|
| Latexo Elem Sch<br>298 FM 2663, Latexo 75849<br>**Rachel Gallaway** | PK-6 | T | 214<br>22 | 54% 936/546-5630<br>Fax 936/546-2220 |
| Latexo High Sch<br>298 FM 2663, Latexo 75849<br>**Kimberly Watson** | 7-12 | T | 207<br>30 | 39% 936/544-5638<br>Fax 936/544-8456 |

● **Lovelady Ind School Dist** PID: 01031844    936/636-7616
11839 State Highway 19 S, Lovelady 75851    Fax 936/636-2212

**Schools:** 2 \ **Teachers:** 50 \ **Students:** 510 \ **Special Ed Students:** 58
\ **LEP Students:** 9 \ **College-Bound:** 80% \ **Ethnic:** Asian 1%, African American 11%, Hispanic 12%, Caucasian 77% \ **Exp:** $314 (High) \
**Poverty:** 22% \ **Title I:** $138,044 \ **Open-Close:** 08/19 - 05/28 \ **DTBP:** $357 (High) \ 🅵 🆃

Wendy Tullos ........................ 1
Cody Robinson ........................ 3,5,91
Rhonda Stone ........................ 2
Alisha Mosley ........................ 4

---

Johnny Zolman ........................ 4
Winnie McKnight ........................ 7*
Alice Ham ........................ 16,73,76,295
Jodi Carney ........................ 54
Dakota Ham ........................ 295
Will Kirchhoff ........................ 6
Ashley LaRue ........................ 8,11,57,58,270,298
Leslie Gilchrist ........................ 36,83,88,280*
Bruce Monk ........................ 67

| Public Schs..Principal | Grd | Prgm | Enr/#Cls | SN |
|---|---|---|---|---|
| Lovelady Elem Middle Sch<br>11839 Tx State Highway 19S, Lovelady 75851<br>Rhonda Lowery | PK-6 | T | 291<br>25 | 46% 936/636-7636<br>Fax 936/636-2529 |
| Lovelady Jr Sr High Sch<br>11839 Tx State Highway 19S, Lovelady 75851<br>Jobeth Martinez | 7-12 | TV | 243<br>28 | 41% 936/636-7636<br>Fax 936/636-2305 |

## HOWARD COUNTY

## HOWARD PUBLIC SCHOOLS

● **Big Spring Ind School Dist** PID: 01031870    432/264-3600
708 E 11th Pl, Big Spring 79720    Fax 432/264-3646

**Schools:** 9 \ **Teachers:** 258 \ **Students:** 4,000 \ **Special Ed Students:** 423 \
**LEP Students:** 182 \ **Ethnic:** Asian 1%, African American 6%, Hispanic 68%, Caucasian 25% \ **Exp:** $542 (High) \ **Poverty:** 26% \ **Title I:** $1,595,167 \
**Special Education:** $814,000 \ **Open-Close:** 08/19 - 05/20 \ **DTBP:** $157 (High)

Jay McWilliams ........................ 1
John Sparks ........................ 3,5*
Dennis Witt ........................ 5
Raemi Thompson ........................ 8,12,15,52
George Bancroft ........................ 15
Fabian Serrano ........................ 67
Debbie Park ........................ 70
Gina Slover ........................ 79
Brenda Mault ........................ 297
Susan Bryan ........................ 2
Judi Rodriguez ........................ 4
Mike Ritchey ........................ 6,51
Tyler Shepherd ........ 11,34,57,58,88,271,296,298
Vonnie Anderson ........................ 27,294
Gina Wells ........................ 68
Jamie Scott ........................ 73,286,295
Daniel Hoard ........................ 295

| Public Schs..Principal | Grd | Prgm | Enr/#Cls | SN |
|---|---|---|---|---|
| Ⓐ Anderson Accelerated High Sch<br>229 Airbase Rd, Big Spring 79720<br>Heidi Wagner | 7-12 | T | 15<br>3 | 85% 432/264-4115<br>Fax 432/264-3609 |
| Big Spring High Sch<br>707 E 11th Pl, Big Spring 79720<br>Michael Ritchey | 9-12 | TV | 540 | 61% 432/264-3641<br>Fax 432/264-4133 |
| Big Spring Interm Sch<br>2000 S Goliad St, Big Spring 79720<br>Patsy Sanchez | 5-6 | T | 625 | 75% 432/264-4121 |
| Big Spring Junior High Sch<br>624 E 6th St, Big Spring 79720<br>Rebecca Otto | 7-8 | ATV | 606<br>55 | 66% 432/264-4135<br>Fax 432/264-4196 |
| Goliad Elem Sch<br>1801 Goliad St, Big Spring 79720<br>Rosie Lain | 4-4 | T | 293<br>30 | 72% 432/264-4111<br>Fax 432/264-3618 |
| Kentwood Early Childhood Ctr<br>2500 Merrily Dr, Big Spring 79720<br>Jennifer Chesworth | PK-PK | T | 124 | 98% 432/264-4130<br>Fax 432/264-3612 |
| Marcy Elem Sch<br>2101 Wasson Rd, Big Spring 79720<br>Dana Pannell | K-2 | T | 426<br>25 | 74% 432/264-4144<br>Fax 432/264-3627 |
| Moss Elem Sch<br>3200 Fordham Ave, Big Spring 79720<br>Carman Wommack | K-2 | T | 475<br>18 | 74% 432/264-4148<br>Fax 432/264-3619 |

---

| | | | | | | | |
|---|---|---|---|---|---|---|---|
| 1 | Superintendent | 8 | Curric/Instruct K-12 | 19 | Chief Financial Officer | 29 | Family/Consumer Science |
| 2 | Bus/Finance/Purchasing | 9 | Curric/Instruct Elem | 20 | Art K-12 | 30 | Adult Education |
| 3 | Buildings And Grounds | 10 | Curric/Instruct Sec | 21 | Art Elem | 31 | Career/Sch-to-Work K-12 |
| 4 | Food Service | 11 | Federal Program | 22 | Art Sec | 32 | Career/Sch-to-Work Elem |
| 5 | Transportation | 12 | Title I | 23 | Music K-12 | 33 | Career/Sch-to-Work Sec |
| 6 | Athletic | 13 | Title V | 24 | Music Elem | 34 | Early Childhood Ed |
| 7 | Health Services | 15 | Asst Superintendent | 25 | Music Sec | 35 | Health/Phys Education |
| | | 16 | Instructional Media Svcs | 26 | Business Education | 36 | Guidance Services K-12 |
| | | 17 | Chief Operations Officer | 27 | Career & Tech Ed | 37 | Guidance Services Elem |
| | | 18 | Chief Academic Officer | 28 | Technology Education | 38 | Guidance Services Sec |

| | | | | | | | |
|---|---|---|---|---|---|---|---|
| 39 | Social Studies K-12 | 49 | English/Lang Arts Elem | 59 | Special Education Elem | 69 | Academic Assessment |
| 40 | Social Studies Elem | 50 | English/Lang Arts Sec | 60 | Special Education Sec | 70 | Research/Development |
| 41 | Social Studies Sec | 51 | Reading K-12 | 61 | Foreign/World Lang K-12 | 71 | Public Information |
| 42 | Science K-12 | 52 | Reading Elem | 62 | Foreign/World Lang Elem | 72 | Summer School |
| 43 | Science Elem | 53 | Reading Sec | 63 | Foreign/World Lang Sec | 73 | Instructional Tech |
| 44 | Science Sec | 54 | Remedial Reading K-12 | 64 | Religious Education K-12 | 74 | Inservice Training |
| 45 | Math K-12 | 55 | Remedial Reading Elem | 65 | Religious Education Elem | 75 | Marketing/Distributive |
| 46 | Math Elem | 56 | Remedial Reading Sec | 66 | Religious Education Sec | 76 | Info Systems |
| 47 | Math Sec | 57 | Bilingual/ELL | 67 | School Board President | 77 | Psychological Assess |
| 48 | English/Lang Arts K-12 | 58 | Special Education K-12 | 68 | Teacher Personnel | 78 | Affirmative Action |

| Washington Elem Sch<br>1201 Birdwell Ln, Big Spring 79720<br>Kaitlin Jeffrey | 3-3 | T | 316<br>23 | 74% 432/264-4126<br>Fax 432/264-3611 |

---

**● Coahoma Ind School Dist** PID: 01032056
600 Main St, Coahoma 79511

432/394-5000
Fax 432/394-4302

**Schools:** 3 \ **Teachers:** 79 \ **Students:** 1,061 \ **Special Ed Students:** 95 \ **LEP Students:** 23 \ **College-Bound:** 51% \ **Ethnic:** Hispanic 39%, Caucasian 60% \ **Exp:** $361 (High) \ **Poverty:** 18% \ **Title I:** $129,741 \ **Open-Close:** 08/13 - 05/20 \ **DTBP:** $341 (High)

| Brad Cox | .....1,73 | Stephanie Rameriz | .....4 |
| Chris Joslin | .....6 | Alison Alverez | .....9,11,16,34,57,271* |
| John Landin | .....23* | Carissa Hughes | .....35,83,85* |
| Christina Cox | .....58 | Kandy Alaman | .....67 |
| Megan Parrish | .....73,76,286,295 | | |

| Public Schs..Principal | Grd | Prgm | Enr/#Cls | SN |
|---|---|---|---|---|
| Coahoma Elem Sch<br>400 Ramsey Dr, Coahoma 79511<br>Alison Alverez | PK-5 | T | 540<br>23 | 37% 432/394-5000<br>Fax 432/394-4419 |
| Coahoma High Sch<br>606 N Main St, Coahoma 79511<br>Christina Cox | 9-12 | AV | 265<br>35 | 31% 432/394-5000 |
| Coahoma Junior High Sch<br>500 High School Dr, Coahoma 79511<br>Ashley Roberts | 6-8 | AT | 256<br>14 | 35% 432/394-5000<br>Fax 432/394-4052 |

---

**● Forsan Ind School Dist** PID: 01032094
411 W 6th St, Forsan 79733

432/457-2223
Fax 432/457-0008

**Schools:** 2 \ **Teachers:** 56 \ **Students:** 771 \ **Special Ed Students:** 54 \ **LEP Students:** 11 \ **College-Bound:** 67% \ **Ethnic:** Asian 2%, African American 2%, Hispanic 31%, Native American: 1%, Caucasian 65% \ **Exp:** $612 (High) \ **Poverty:** 14% \ **Title I:** $59,913 \ **Open-Close:** 08/10 - 05/27 \ **DTBP:** $350 (High)

| Randy Johnson | .....1 | Jason Mims | .....2 |
| Phillip Schuppert | .....3 | Sandra Sanchez | .....4 |
| Jason Phillips | .....6* | Hanna Carter | .....8,68,79,273* |
| Mysti Mims | .....8,57,69,88,271* | Lewis Boeker | .....67 |
| Shaun McVicars | .....73,286* | | |

| Public Schs..Principal | Grd | Prgm | Enr/#Cls | SN |
|---|---|---|---|---|
| Forsan Elem Sch<br>500 W Main St, Forsan 79733<br>Andrew Eudy | PK-5 | AT | 375<br>20 | 34% 432/457-0091<br>Fax 432/457-0040 |
| Forsan Jr Sr High Sch<br>411 W 6th Street, Forsan 79733<br>Hanna Carter | 6-12 | V | 396<br>33 | 28% 432/457-2223 |

---

## HUDSPETH PUBLIC SCHOOLS

**● Dell City Ind School Dist** PID: 01032147
110 N Main St, Dell City 79837

915/964-2663
Fax 915/964-2880

**Schools:** 1 \ **Teachers:** 11 \ **Students:** 61 \ **Special Ed Students:** 8 \ **LEP Students:** 18 \ **College-Bound:** 100% \ **Ethnic:** Hispanic 63%, Caucasian 38% \ **Exp:** $2,694 (High) \ **Poverty:** 15% \ **Title I:** $35,087 \ **Special Education:** $28,000 \ **Open-Close:** 08/27 - 06/01 \ **DTBP:** $416 (High)

| Ruben Cervantes | .....1 | Rita Archuleta | .....2,12 |
| Carlos Contreras | .....8,11,88,285,288,294* | Bernice Mora | .....57* |
| Steve Carpenter | .....67 | | |

| Public Schs..Principal | Grd | Prgm | Enr/#Cls | SN |
|---|---|---|---|---|
| Dell City Sch<br>110 N Main St, Dell City 79837<br>Carlos Contreras | PK-12 | TV | 61<br>17 | 83% 915/964-2663 |

---

**● Ft Hancock Ind School Dist** PID: 01032173
100 School Drive, Fort Hancock 79839

915/769-3811
Fax 915/769-3940

**Schools:** 3 \ **Teachers:** 37 \ **Students:** 377 \ **Special Ed Students:** 33 \ **LEP Students:** 219 \ **College-Bound:** 65% \ **Ethnic:** Hispanic 97%, Caucasian 2% \ **Exp:** $1,187 (High) \ **Poverty:** 28% \ **Title I:** $195,538 \ **Special Education:** $73,000 \ **Open-Close:** 08/10 - 05/27 \ **DTBP:** $347 (High)

| Jose Franco | .....1 | Victoria Gonzalez | .....2 |
| Norma Muniz | .....4 | Jorge Apodaca | .....5 |
| Frank Saldane | .....6 | Rosalia Arzate | .....7* |
| Yvonne Samaniego | .....11,57,285,288,296,298 | Joe Rodriguez | .....67 |
| Tomas Chavez | .....73 | | |

| Public Schs..Principal | Grd | Prgm | Enr/#Cls | SN |
|---|---|---|---|---|
| Benito Martinez Elem Sch<br>460 Knox Ave, Fort Hancock 79839<br>Yadira Munoz | PK-5 | T | 182<br>17 | 90% 915/769-1602<br>Fax 915/769-0043 |
| Ft Hancock High Sch<br>100 School Drive, Fort Hancock 79839<br>Lorena Molinar | 9-12 | T | 108<br>20 | 93% 915/769-1604<br>Fax 915/769-0044 |
| Ft Hancock Middle Sch<br>100 School Drive, Fort Hancock 79839<br>Danny Medina | 6-8 | T | 87 | 87% 915/769-1603<br>Fax 915/769-0045 |

---

**● Sierra Blanca Ind School Dist** PID: 01032202
500 Sierra Blanca Ave, Sierra Blanca 79851

915/369-3741
Fax 915/369-2605

**Schools:** 1 \ **Teachers:** 13 \ **Students:** 103 \ **Special Ed Students:** 14 \ **LEP Students:** 3 \ **College-Bound:** 70% \ **Ethnic:** Asian 2%, African American 2%, Hispanic 71%, Native American: 1%, Caucasian 25% \ **Exp:** $637 (High) \ **Poverty:** 19% \ **Title I:** $30,576 \ **Open-Close:** 08/26 - 05/21 \ **DTBP:** $257 (High)

| Evelyn Loeffler | .....1,11,73,83 | Ismael Ramirez | .....6* |
| Joel Sanchez | .....67 | | |

---

| Public Schs..Principal | Grd | Prgm | Enr/#Cls | SN |
|---|---|---|---|---|
| Sierra Blanca Sch<br>1111 Farm Rd, Sierra Blanca 79851<br>Beatriz Zavala | PK-12 | TV | 103<br>14 | 84% 915/369-2781 |

# HUNT COUNTY

## HUNT PUBLIC SCHOOLS

### ● Bland Ind School Dist PID: 01032238
2556 Lake Ave, Merit 75458

903/776-2239
Fax 903/776-2240

**Schools:** 3 \ **Teachers:** 55 \ **Students:** 700 \ **Special Ed Students:** 67 \
**LEP Students:** 106 \ **College-Bound:** 50% \ **Ethnic:** African American 1%,
Hispanic 40%, Native American: 1%, Caucasian 58% \ **Exp:** $397 (High) \
**Poverty:** 22% \ **Title I:** $220,042 \ **Open-Close:** 08/12 - 05/20 \ **DTBP:** $558
(High)

| | | | |
|---|---|---|---|
| Rick Tidwell ............................1,83 | Bryan Bymaster ....................... 2,15,88 |
| Jean Riley ...............................3,17 | Shelli Wendland ..........................8,58* |
| Rob Oconor ........................ 11,296 | Susan Douglas ................................ 16* |
| Jason Hammack ........................57* | Terry Hurst ....................................... 67 |
| Charity Morris ........................... 69 | Ted Capps ............................... 73,286* |

| Public Schs..Principal | Grd | Prgm | Enr/#Cls | SN |
|---|---|---|---|---|
| Bland Elem Sch<br>5123 FM 2194, Celeste 75423<br>**Cinda Owen** | PK-5 | T | 338<br>14 | 62% 903/527-5480<br>Fax 903/527-5481 |
| Bland High Sch<br>6164 FM 2194, Farmersville 75442<br>Dustin Evans | 9-12 | TV | 210<br>15 | 46% 903/776-2161<br>Fax 903/776-2426 |
| Bland Middle Sch<br>5123 FM 2194, Celeste 75423<br>Jason Hammack | 6-8 | T | 173<br>25 | 57% 903/527-5490<br>Fax 903/527-5491 |

### ● Boles Ind School Dist PID: 01032264
9777 FM 2101, Quinlan 75474

903/883-4464
Fax 903/883-4531

**Schools:** 3 \ **Teachers:** 48 \ **Students:** 545 \ **Special Ed Students:** 62
\ **LEP Students:** 10 \ **College-Bound:** 100% \ **Ethnic:** Asian 1%,
African American 2%, Hispanic 13%, Caucasian 84% \ **Exp:** $491 (High) \
**Poverty:** 20% \ **Title I:** $89,403 \ **Open-Close:** 08/17 - 05/27 \ **DTBP:** $376
(High)

| | | | |
|---|---|---|---|
| Micheal Goss ...........................1,83 | Mikayle Moreland ............. 2,11,74,296* |
| Cindy Mitchell .......................3,5,17 | Tim Dawson ...................................4* |
| Jeff Thomason ..............................6* | Irene Hearn ....................................... 7 |
| Amanda Scoggins ..................... 19 | Sheree Harris .............................36,83 |
| Linda Pitts ................................. 67 | David Hartford ....................... 73,76,295* |
| Shirley Duran ............................93* | |

| Public Schs..Principal | Grd | Prgm | Enr/#Cls | SN |
|---|---|---|---|---|
| Boles Elem Sch<br>9777 FM 2101, Quinlan 75474<br>Shirley Duran | PK-4 | T | 192<br>12 | 63% 903/883-2161<br>Fax 903/883-9094 |
| Boles High Sch<br>9777 FM 2101, Quinlan 75474<br>Jill Thomason | 9-12 | ATV | 177<br>20 | 50% 903/883-2918<br>Fax 903/883-5109 |

| Public Schs..Principal | Grd | Prgm | Enr/#Cls | SN |
|---|---|---|---|---|
| Boles Middle Sch<br>9777 FM 2101, Quinlan 75474<br>Gordon Jordan | 5-8 | T | 178<br>12 | 51% 903/883-4464<br>Fax 903/883-3097 |

### ● Caddo Mills Ind Sch Dist PID: 01032290
100 Fox Ln, Caddo Mills 75135

903/527-6056
Fax 903/527-4883

**Schools:** 5 \ **Teachers:** 136 \ **Students:** 2,000 \ **Special Ed Students:** 176
\ **LEP Students:** 61 \ **Ethnic:** African American 2%, Hispanic 18%, Native
American: 1%, Caucasian 79% \ **Exp:** $411 (High) \ **Poverty:** 11% \
**Title I:** $215,420 \ **Open-Close:** 08/20 - 05/27 \ 📘

| | | | |
|---|---|---|---|
| Luke Allison ...............................1 | Heidi Smith ......................................2 |
| Sam Day ....................................5 | Codi Crane .......................................6 |
| Julie Wiebersch ..........................8 | Kendra Moser ..................................9 |
| Robert Oconnor ....................11,84 | Kerri Allen ..................................... 15 |
| Rueben Terry ........................... 67 | Pete Rowe ..................................... 73 |
| Stefanie Duffer ......................... 73 | |

| Public Schs..Principal | Grd | Prgm | Enr/#Cls | SN |
|---|---|---|---|---|
| Ⓐ Caddo Mills Aep<br>100 Fox Ln, Caddo Mills 75135<br>Scott Hudspeth | 5-12 | | 30<br>3 | 903/527-2075<br>Fax 903/527-3313 |
| Caddo Mills High Sch<br>2710 Gilmer St, Caddo Mills 75135<br>Jana Everett | 9-12 | V | 488<br>20 | 31% 903/527-3164<br>Fax 903/527-4772 |
| Caddo Mills Middle Sch<br>2700 Gilmer St, Caddo Mills 75135<br>Anne Payne | 6-8 | | 437<br>32 | 33% 903/527-3161<br>Fax 903/527-2379 |
| Kathryn Griffis Elem Sch<br>3639 FM 1565, Caddo Mills 75135<br>Jennifer Brutonr | PK-5 | T | 444 | 38% 903/527-3525<br>Fax 903/527-3597 |
| Lee Elem Sch<br>2702 Gilmer St, Caddo Mills 75135<br>Vonda Farmer | PK-5 | T | 409<br>64 | 38% 903/527-3162<br>Fax 903/527-0166 |

### ● Campbell Ind School Dist PID: 01032329
480 N Patterson St, Campbell 75422

903/862-3259
Fax 903/862-2222

**Schools:** 1 \ **Teachers:** 28 \ **Students:** 300 \ **Special Ed Students:** 58
\ **LEP Students:** 15 \ **College-Bound:** 50% \ **Ethnic:** Asian 2%, African
American 1%, Hispanic 27%, Caucasian 70% \ **Exp:** $447 (High) \
**Poverty:** 23% \ **Title I:** $122,571 \ **Open-Close:** 08/11 - 05/20 \ **DTBP:** $350
(High)

| | | | |
|---|---|---|---|
| Dr Denise Morgan ........................1 | Hubert Bares ....................................2 |
| Justin Nicholson ..........................3 | Cynthia Long ....................................4 |
| Jason Crowe ...............................6 | Christy Sweeny ..............................7,35 |
| Karen Moore ........................16,286* | Sara Fields .....................................58* |
| Frank Owens ............................. 67 | James Osei ............................... 73,295 |

| Public Schs..Principal | Grd | Prgm | Enr/#Cls | SN |
|---|---|---|---|---|
| Campbell Sch<br>409 W North St, Campbell 75422<br>Jason Crow | PK-12 | ATV | 300<br>28 | 76% 903/862-3253<br>Fax 903/862-3547 |

### ● Celeste Ind School Dist PID: 01032355
207 S 5th St, Celeste 75423

903/568-4825
Fax 903/568-4495

**Schools:** 3 \ **Teachers:** 46 \ **Students:** 480 \ **Special Ed Students:** 68 \
**LEP Students:** 11 \ **College-Bound:** 49% \ **Ethnic:** African American 2%,
Hispanic 17%, Native American: 1%, Caucasian 80% \ **Exp:** $651 (High) \
**Poverty:** 12% \ **Title I:** $121,445 \ **Open-Close:** 08/19 - 05/21 \ **DTBP:** $251
(High)

| | | | | | | | |
|---|---|---|---|---|---|---|---|
| **1** Superintendent | **8** Curric/Instruct K-12 | **19** Chief Financial Officer | **29** Family/Consumer Science | **39** Social Studies K-12 | **49** English/Lang Arts Elem | **59** Special Education Elem | **69** Academic Assessment |
| **2** Bus/Finance/Purchasing | **9** Curric/Instruct Elem | **20** Art K-12 | **30** Adult Education | **40** Social Studies Elem | **50** English/Lang Arts Sec | **60** Special Education Sec | **70** Research/Development |
| **3** Buildings And Grounds | **10** Curric/Instruct Sec | **21** Art Elem | **31** Career/Sch-to-Work K-12 | **41** Social Studies Sec | **51** Reading K-12 | **61** Foreign/World Lang K-12 | **71** Public Information |
| **4** Food Service | **11** Federal Program | **22** Art Sec | **32** Career/Sch-to-Work Elem | **42** Science K-12 | **52** Reading Elem | **62** Foreign/World Lang Elem | **72** Summer School |
| **5** Transportation | **12** Title I | **23** Music K-12 | **33** Career/Sch-to-Work Sec | **43** Science Elem | **53** Reading Sec | **63** Foreign/World Lang Sec | **73** Instructional Tech |
| **6** Athletic | **13** Title V | **24** Music Elem | **34** Early Childhood Ed | **44** Science Sec | **54** Remedial Reading K-12 | **64** Religious Education K-12 | **74** Inservice Training |
| **7** Health Services | **14** Asst Superintendent | **25** Music Sec | **35** Health/Phys Education | **45** Math K-12 | **55** Remedial Reading Elem | **65** Religious Education Elem | **75** Marketing/Distributive |
| | **15** Instructional Media Svcs | **26** Business Education | **36** Guidance Services K-12 | **46** Math Elem | **56** Remedial Reading Sec | **66** Religious Education Sec | **76** Info Systems |
| | **16** Instructional Media Svcs | **27** Career & Tech Ed | **37** Guidance Services Elem | **47** Math Sec | **57** Bilingual/ELL | **67** School Board President | **77** Psychological Assess |
| | **17** Chief Operations Officer | **28** Technology Education | **38** Guidance Services Sec | **48** English/Lang Arts K-12 | **58** Special Education K-12 | **68** Teacher Personnel | **78** Affirmative Action |
| | **18** Chief Academic Officer | | | | | | |

Brad Connelly ............1  
Mark Harrison ............3,5*  
Jennifer Diles ............7,85*  
James Branam ............10*  
Chris Barnard ............67  

Tammy Shields ............2  
Demetrius Rictor ............6*  
Beth Ray ............9,34,271*  
Alice Dills ............12,36,69,83,88,273*  
Chris Johnston ............73*  

| Public Schs..Principal | Grd | Prgm | Enr/#Cls | SN |
|---|---|---|---|---|
| Celeste Elem Sch<br>605 Cockrell St, Celeste 75423<br>**Lindsay Walker** | PK-5 | T | 188<br>14 | 63% 903/568-4721<br>Fax 903/568-4651 |
| Celeste High Sch<br>609 FM 1562, Celeste 75423<br>James Branam | 9-12 | ATV | 179<br>16 | 50% 903/568-4721<br>Fax 903/568-4115 |
| Celeste Junior High Sch<br>200 S 5th St, Celeste 75423<br>Staci Beadles | 6-8 | T | 113<br>10 | 55% 903/568-4721<br>Fax 903/568-4277 |

• **Commerce Independent Sch Dist** PID: 01032381  903/886-3755  
3315 Washington St, Commerce 75428  Fax 903/886-6025

**Schools:** 4 \ **Teachers:** 113 \ **Students:** 1,442 \ **Special Ed Students:** 193 \ **LEP Students:** 129 \ **College-Bound:** 75% \ **Ethnic:** Asian 2%, African American 25%, Hispanic 22%, Native American: 1%, Caucasian 50% \ **Exp:** $294 (Med) \ **Poverty:** 22% \ **Title I:** $527,922 \ **Open-Close:** 08/12 - 05/27 \ **DTBP:** $561 (High) \ [facebook]

Charles Alderman ............1,57  
Dennis Yoakum ............3,5  
Jeff Davidson ............6*  
Patricia Tremmel ............15  
Rachel Myers ............58  
Ludonna Smithers ............68,71,297  

John Walker ............2  
Anika Whetstone ............4  
Mary Hendricks ............11,296  
Dr Andrea Ellis ............27,31  
Kathleen Hooten ............67  
Kathy Myers ............85*  

| Public Schs..Principal | Grd | Prgm | Enr/#Cls | SN |
|---|---|---|---|---|
| A C Williams Elem Sch<br>615 Culver St, Commerce 75428<br>Lisa Palazzetti | 3-5 | T | 335<br>19 | 72% 903/886-3758<br>Fax 903/468-8030 |
| Commerce Elem Sch<br>2900 FM 3218, Commerce 75428<br>Wanda Beane | PK-2 | T | 303<br>27 | 75% 903/886-3757<br>Fax 903/886-6112 |
| Commerce High Sch<br>3800 Sregit Dr, Commerce 75428<br>Steve Drummond | 9-12 | TV | 459<br>30 | 56% 903/886-3756<br>Fax 903/886-6209 |
| Commerce Middle Sch<br>606 Culver St, Commerce 75428<br>Shenequa Miller | 6-8 | T | 345<br>20 | 62% 903/886-3795<br>Fax 903/886-6102 |

• **Greenville Ind School Dist** PID: 01032446  903/457-2500  
4004 Moulton St, Greenville 75401  Fax 903/457-2575

**Schools:** 12 \ **Teachers:** 356 \ **Students:** 5,400 \ **Special Ed Students:** 637 \ **LEP Students:** 1,121 \ **Ethnic:** Asian 1%, African American 17%, Hispanic 48%, Caucasian 33% \ **Exp:** $334 (High) \ **Poverty:** 23% \ **Title I:** $1,816,926 \ **Special Education:** $961,000 \ **Open-Close:** 09/08 - 06/01 \ **DTBP:** $189 (High)

Dr Demetrus Liggins ............1  
Greg Anderson ............3  
Kellie Jones ............5  
Sharon Boothe ............8,15,74  
Samando Ortega ............57  
John Kelso ............67  
Shannon Fulp ............73,76,295  

Deidra Reeves ............2,15,19  
Sharee Osten ............4  
Noelle Bares ............7,83,88  
Dr Michelle Baird ............34  
Colleen Netterville ............58,68  
Rachael Driggers ............69,70,294  
David Stone ............295  

| Public Schs..Principal | Grd | Prgm | Enr/#Cls | SN |
|---|---|---|---|---|
| Bowie Elem Sch<br>6005 Stonewall St, Greenville 75402<br>Lauren Habluetzel | K-5 | | 637<br>22 | 903/457-2676<br>Fax 903/457-0725 |
| Carver Elem Sch<br>2110 College St, Greenville 75401<br>Stacie Wilson | K-5 | T | 549<br>27 | 95% 903/457-0777<br>Fax 903/457-0786 |
| Crockett Elem Sch<br>1316 Wolfe City Dr, Greenville 75401<br>Stacey Kluttz | K-5 | T | 209<br>19 | 88% 903/457-2684<br>Fax 903/457-0722 |
| Ⓐ Greenville Alt Center<br>3923 Henry St, Greenville 75401<br>Harold Gregory | 7-12 | | 13<br>4 | 903/457-2688<br>Fax 903/207-4641 |
| Greenville High Sch<br>3515 Lions Lair Rd, Greenville 75402<br>Heath Jarvis | 9-12 | GTV | 1,429<br>45 | 65% 903/457-2550<br>Fax 903/455-5158 |
| Greenville Middle Sch<br>3611 Texas St, Greenville 75401<br>Courtney Baker | 7-8 | TV | 741<br>60 | 71% 903/457-2620<br>Fax 903/457-2628 |
| Greenville Sixth Grade Center<br>3201 Stanford St, Greenville 75401<br>Lauren Habluetzel | 6-6 | | 370<br>50 | 903/457-2660<br>Fax 903/457-2533 |
| Katherine G Johnson STEM Acad<br>9315 Jack Finney Blvd, Greenville 75402<br>**Sebastian Bozas** | K-5 | T | 204 | 67% 903/454-5050<br>Fax 903/454-5070 |
| L P Waters Early Childhood Ctr<br>2504 Carver St, Greenville 75401<br>Sebastian Bozas | PK-PK | T | 412<br>13 | 90% 903/457-2680<br>Fax 903/457-0745 |
| Lamar Elem Sch<br>6321 Jack Finney Blvd, Greenville 75402<br>Lucretia Newton | K-5 | T | 581<br>28 | 60% 903/457-0765<br>Fax 903/457-0774 |
| Ⓐ New Horizons Learning Center<br>3923 Henry St, Greenville 75401<br>Harold Gregory | PK-12 | T | 66<br>8 | 74% 903/457-2688<br>Fax 903/457-2689 |
| Travis Elem Sch<br>3201 Stanford St, Greenville 75401<br>Vincent Dawes | K-6 | T | 625<br>18 | 84% 903/457-2660<br>Fax 903/457-2533 |

• **Lone Oak Ind School Dist** PID: 01032549  903/634-5247  
8162 US Highway 69 S, Lone Oak 75453  Fax 903/662-5290

**Schools:** 4 \ **Teachers:** 87 \ **Students:** 1,000 \ **Special Ed Students:** 139 \ **LEP Students:** 17 \ **Ethnic:** African American 2%, Hispanic 12%, Native American: 1%, Caucasian 85% \ **Exp:** $364 (High) \ **Poverty:** 11% \ **Title I:** $177,194 \ **Open-Close:** 08/10 - 05/27 \ **DTBP:** $352 (High)

Lance Campbell ............1  
Wayne Shepherd ............3  
Nate Compton ............6  
Justin Ramm ............67  
Isaiah Whitehead ............295  

Gary Sorrells ............2,5  
Brenda Standifer ............4  
Jeff Hicks ............8  
Cassie Pinkston ............73,76,297  

| Public Schs..Principal | Grd | Prgm | Enr/#Cls | SN |
|---|---|---|---|---|
| Ⓐ Lone Oak College St Campus<br>602 College St, Lone Oak 75453<br>Jared Smith | 6-12 | | 30 | 903/634-2071 |
| Lone Oak Elem Sch<br>8080 US Highway 69 S, Lone Oak 75453<br>Elizabeth Luhn | PK-5 | T | 436<br>40 | 44% 903/662-5151<br>Fax 903/662-0973 |
| Lone Oak High Sch<br>8204 Highway 69 S, Lone Oak 75453<br>Janee Carter | 9-12 | ATV | 345<br>30 | 42% 903/662-0980<br>Fax 903/662-0984 |
| Lone Oak Middle Sch<br>8160 Highway 69 S, Lone Oak 75453<br>Shannon Wilhite | 6-8 | T | 225<br>24 | 39% 903/662-5121<br>Fax 903/662-5017 |

| | | | |
|---|---|---|---|
| 79 Student Personnel | 91 Safety/Security | 275 Response To Intervention | 298 Grant Writer/Ptnrships |
| 80 Driver Ed/Safety | 92 Magnet School | 277 Remedial Math K-12 | 750 Chief Innovation Officer |
| 81 Gifted/Talented | 93 Parental Involvement | 280 Literacy Coach | 751 Chief of Staff |
| 82 Video Services | 95 Tech Prep Program | 285 STEM | 752 Social Emotional Learning |
| 83 Substance Abuse Prev | 97 Chief Information Officer | 286 Digital Learning | |
| 84 Erate | 98 Chief Technology Officer | 288 Common Core Standards | **Other School Types** |
| 85 AIDS Education | 270 Character Education | 294 Accountability | Ⓐ = Alternative School |
| 88 Alternative/At Risk | 271 Migrant Education | 295 Network System | Ⓒ = Charter School |
| 89 Multi-Cultural Curriculum | 273 Teacher Mentor | 296 Title II Programs | Ⓜ = Magnet School |
| 90 Social Work | 274 Before/After Sch | 297 Webmaster | Ⓨ = Year-Round School |

**School Programs**  
A = Alternative Program  
G = Adult Classes  
M = Magnet Program  
T = Title I Schoolwide  
V = Career & Tech Ed Programs  

**Social Media**  
[f] = Facebook  
[t] = Twitter  

New Schools are shaded  
New Superintendents and Principals are bold  
Personnel with email addresses are underscored

## Hutchinson County

• **Quinlan Ind School Dist** PID: 01032575
401 E Richmond, Quinlan 75474

903/356-1200
Fax 903/356-1201

**Schools:** 5 \ **Teachers:** 178 \ **Students:** 2,516 \ **Special Ed Students:** 329 \ **LEP Students:** 307 \ **Ethnic:** African American 2%, Hispanic 30%, Native American: 1%, Caucasian 67% \ **Exp:** $415 (High) \ **Poverty:** 19% \ **Title I:** $782,237 \ **Special Education:** $632,000 \ **Open-Close:** 08/20 - 05/27 \ **DTBP:** $158 (High)

| | | | |
|---|---|---|---|
| Jeff Irvin | 1 | Billie Miller | 2 |
| Tommy Underwood | 3,5,7,91 | Brenda Stone | 4 |
| Gary Overstreet | 5 | Todd Wallace | 6* |
| Alice Lafferty | 10 | Kathleen Witte | 11,57,74,271,285,294,298 |
| Michael Roberts | 16,73,295* | Jenifer Hogan | 36* |
| Lori Edwards | 57* | Sheila Jones | 58* |
| Kenny Stone | 67 | Sherry Reville | 68 |
| Tiffany Upchurch | 71 | Kathy Goleman | 75 |
| Anna Baker | 76 | Donna Hopson | 85* |
| Steve Walden | 91 | | |

| Public Schs..Principal | Grd | Prgm | Enr/#Cls | SN | |
|---|---|---|---|---|---|
| Butler Intermediate Sch<br>410 Clardy Dr, Quinlan 75474<br>Lindsay Walker | 3-5 | T | 575<br>29 | 73% | 903/356-1400<br>Fax 903/356-1499 |
| C B Thompson Middle Sch<br>423 Panther Path, Quinlan 75474<br>Brian Kinsworthy | 6-8 | T | 569<br>38 | 68% | 903/356-1500<br>Fax 903/356-1599 |
| D C Cannon Elem Sch<br>315 State Highway 34 S, Quinlan 75474<br>Angela House | PK-2 | T | 586<br>30 | 86% | 903/356-1300<br>Fax 903/356-1399 |
| Ⓐ Discipline Ed Alternative Sch<br>425 Panther Path, Quinlan 75474<br>Gary Pamplin | 6-12 | | 25<br>4 | | 903/356-1575<br>Fax 903/356-1598 |
| Ford High Sch<br>10064 State Highway Spur 264, Quinlan 75474<br>Jason Wallen | 9-12 | GTV | 786<br>50 | 59% | 903/356-1600<br>Fax 903/356-1699 |

• **Wolfe City Ind School Dist** PID: 01032616
505 W Dallas St, Wolfe City 75496

903/496-2283
Fax 903/496-7905

**Schools:** 3 \ **Teachers:** 58 \ **Students:** 646 \ **Special Ed Students:** 65 \ **LEP Students:** 33 \ **College-Bound:** 10% \ **Ethnic:** Asian 1%, African American 3%, Hispanic 19%, Native American: 1%, Caucasian 77% \ **Exp:** $604 (High) \ **Poverty:** 17% \ **Title I:** $124,341 \ **Special Education:** $159,000 \ **Open-Close:** 08/11 - 05/20 \ **DTBP:** $345 (High)

| | | | |
|---|---|---|---|
| Anthony Figueroa | 1,83 | Cindy McIlveene | 2 |
| Jessie Strayhorn | 3,5 | Marcie Duncan | 4 |
| Darren Anderson | 6 | Kimberly Johnson | 7 |
| Sheila Gardner | 8,73,286,288 | Mikayle Goss | 11,271,296 |
| Billy Eldridge | 31,69,77* | Sondra Northcutt | 57,58 |
| Ola Owens | 67 | Nancy Sanders | 76 |
| Donna Gazlick | 88 | Vick Lemieux | 295 |

| Public Schs..Principal | Grd | Prgm | Enr/#Cls | SN | |
|---|---|---|---|---|---|
| Wolfe City Elem Sch<br>501 W Dallas St, Wolfe City 75496<br>Ginger White | PK-5 | T | 287<br>17 | 67% | 903/496-2032<br>Fax 903/496-2233 |
| Wolfe City High Sch<br>8353 Highway 34 N, Wolfe City 75496<br>Rose Gardner | 9-12 | TV | 203<br>22 | 49% | 903/496-2891<br>Fax 903/496-7124 |
| Wolfe City Middle Sch<br>505 W Dallas St, Wolfe City 75496<br>Melanie Williams | 6-8 | T | 156<br>12 | 58% | 903/496-7333<br>Fax 903/496-2112 |

## HUNT PRIVATE SCHOOLS

| Private Schs..Principal | Grd | Prgm | Enr/#Cls | SN |
|---|---|---|---|---|
| Greenville Christian Sch<br>8420 Jack Finney Blvd, Greenville 75402<br>Mark Reisner | PK-12 | | 200<br>30 | 903/454-1111<br>Fax 903/455-8470 |

## HUTCHINSON COUNTY

## HUTCHINSON PUBLIC SCHOOLS

• **Borger Ind School Dist** PID: 01032642
200 E 9th St, Borger 79007

806/273-6481
Fax 806/273-1066

**Schools:** 6 \ **Teachers:** 192 \ **Students:** 2,700 \ **Special Ed Students:** 317 \ **LEP Students:** 242 \ **Ethnic:** Asian 1%, African American 2%, Hispanic 48%, Native American: 1%, Caucasian 48% \ **Exp:** $346 (High) \ **Poverty:** 18% \ **Title I:** $593,872 \ **Special Education:** $541,000 \ **Open-Close:** 08/17 - 06/01 \ **DTBP:** $173 (High)

| | | | |
|---|---|---|---|
| Chance Welch | 1 | Fay Hooper | 2 |
| Jeri Jett | 2 | Joy Howard | 4 |
| Robin Hudgens | 5 | Eric Wilson | 6 |
| Michael Cano | 7,8,15,68,74,78,79,83 | Amy Blansett | 11,15,38,57,273,296,298 |
| Rachel Ach | 16* | Danielle Watson | 38* |
| Patti Brown | 58,275 | Leslie Sharp | 67 |
| Barbie Schroader | 69,271,285 | Michael Bos | 73,84,295 |

| Public Schs..Principal | Grd | Prgm | Enr/#Cls | SN | |
|---|---|---|---|---|---|
| Ⓨ Borger High Sch<br>600 W 1st St, Borger 79007<br>Matt Ammerman | 9-12 | AMTV | 735<br>40 | 47% | 806/273-1029<br>Fax 806/273-1036 |
| Borger Intermediate Sch<br>1321 S Florida St, Borger 79007<br>Teresa Bodey | 5-6 | T | 392 | 57% | 806/273-4342<br>Fax 806/274-9752 |
| Borger Middle Sch<br>1321 S Florida St, Borger 79007<br>Michael Cano | 7-8 | TV | 407 | 61% | 806/273-1037<br>Fax 806/274-9731 |
| Crockett Elem Sch<br>400 Kaye St, Borger 79007<br>Randal Hatfield | 3-4 | T | 379<br>20 | 62% | 806/273-1054<br>Fax 806/273-1067 |
| Gateway Elem Sch<br>401 Tristram St, Borger 79007<br>James Russell | 1-2 | T | 349<br>25 | 66% | 806/273-1044<br>Fax 806/273-1071 |
| Paul Belton Early Chldhd Ctr<br>800 N McGee St, Borger 79007<br>Judy Cooper | PK-K | T | 239<br>16 | 64% | 806/273-1059<br>Fax 806/273-1070 |

• **Plemons-Stinnett-Phillips CISD** PID: 01032836
603 S Main St, Stinnett 79083

806/878-2858
Fax 806/878-3585

**Schools:** 3 \ **Teachers:** 70 \ **Students:** 731 \ **Special Ed Students:** 71 \ **LEP Students:** 6 \ **College-Bound:** 67% \ **Ethnic:** Hispanic 23%, Native American: 1%, Caucasian 76% \ **Exp:** $365 (High) \ **Poverty:** 19% \ **Title I:** $114,470 \ **Special Education:** $148,000 \ **Open-Close:** 08/21 - 05/20 \ **DTBP:** $347 (High)

| | | | |
|---|---|---|---|
| Bill Wiggins | 1 | Bettye Stevens | 2 |

| | | | | | |
|---|---|---|---|---|---|
| 1 Superintendent | 8 Curric/Instruct K-12 | 19 Chief Financial Officer | 29 Family/Consumer Science | 39 Social Studies K-12 | 49 English/Lang Arts Elem | 59 Special Education Elem | 69 Academic Assessment |
| 2 Bus/Finance/Purchasing | 9 Curric/Instruct Elem | 20 Art K-12 | 30 Adult Education | 40 Social Studies Elem | 50 English/Lang Arts Sec | 60 Special Education Sec | 70 Research/Development |
| 3 Buildings And Grounds | 10 Curric/Instruct Sec | 21 Art Elem | 31 Career/Sch-to-Work K-12 | 41 Social Studies Sec | 51 Reading K-12 | 61 Foreign/World Lang K-12 | 71 Public Information |
| 4 Food Service | 11 Federal Program | 22 Art Sec | 32 Career/Sch-to-Work Elem | 42 Science K-12 | 52 Reading Elem | 62 Foreign/World Lang Elem | 72 Summer School |
| 5 Transportation | 12 Title I | 23 Music K-12 | 33 Career/Sch-to-Work Sec | 43 Science Elem | 53 Reading Sec | 63 Foreign/World Lang Sec | 73 Instructional Tech |
| 6 Athletic | 13 Title V | 24 Music Elem | 34 Early Childhood Ed | 44 Science Sec | 54 Remedial Reading K-12 | 64 Religious Education K-12 | 74 Inservice Training |
| 7 Health Services | 14 Instructional Media Svcs | 25 Music Sec | 35 Health/Phys Education | 45 Math K-12 | 55 Remedial Reading Elem | 65 Religious Education Elem | 75 Marketing/Distributive |
| | 15 Asst Superintendent | 26 Business Education | 36 Guidance Services K-12 | 46 Math Elem | 56 Remedial Reading Sec | 66 Religious Education Sec | 76 Info Systems |
| | 16 Instructional Media Svcs | 27 Career & Tech Ed | 37 Guidance Services Elem | 47 Math Sec | 57 Bilingual/ELL | 67 School Board President | 77 Psychological Assess |
| | 17 Chief Operations Officer | 28 Technology Education | 38 Guidance Services Sec | 48 English/Lang Arts K-12 | 58 Special Education K-12 | 68 Teacher Personnel | 78 Affirmative Action |
| | 18 Chief Academic Officer | | | | | | |

**TX—240**

Greg Drennan ...................................... 3,5,91
Lori Williams .......................... 7,35,83,85*
Shawna Lamb .................................... 34
Tim Hall ................................................. 67

Pamela Shaw ........................................ 4
Jimmy Amaro ................... 8,11,15,69,288
Kendra Franklin ........................ 36,58,88*
Jill Knight .................................... 73,76

| Public Schs..Principal | Grd | Prgm | Enr/#Cls | SN | |
|---|---|---|---|---|---|
| West Texas Elem Sch<br>600 Stewart St, Stinnett 79083<br>Shawna Lamb | PK-5 | T | 303<br>26 | 37% | 806/878-2103<br>Fax 806/878-4213 |
| West Texas High Sch<br>600 Stewart Street, Stinnett 79083<br>Kent Torbert | 9-12 | T | 206<br>24 | 35% | 806/878-2456<br>Fax 806/878-4242 |
| West Texas Middle Sch<br>22 Farm Rd, Stinnett 79083<br>Rocky Ford | 6-8 | T | 163<br>18 | 36% | 806/878-2247<br>Fax 806/878-3434 |

• **Sanford-Fritch Ind School Dist** PID: 01032771
540 Eagle Blvd, Fritch 79036

806/397-0159
Fax 806/397-0629

**Schools:** 3 \ **Teachers:** 64 \ **Students:** 687 \ **Special Ed Students:** 102
\ **College-Bound:** 37% \ **Ethnic:** African American 1%, Hispanic 8%,
Native American: 1%, Caucasian 89% \ **Exp:** $303 (High) \ **Poverty:** 14% \
**Title I:** $120,807 \ **Special Education:** $206,000 \ **Open-Close:** 08/18 -
05/26 \ **DTBP:** $399 (High)

Jim McClellan ...................................... 1,83
Houston Moos ...................................... 6*
Stacey Boothe ........................................ 67
Noah Hernando ............................... 73,84

Richard Hein .................................... 2,11
Edie Allen ........................................ 8,15
Mike Leffew ......................................... 73

| Public Schs..Principal | Grd | Prgm | Enr/#Cls | SN | |
|---|---|---|---|---|---|
| Sanford Fritch Elem Sch<br>201 N Hoyne Ave, Fritch 79036<br>Kim Surles | PK-5 | T | 300<br>34 | 46% | 806/397-0159<br>Fax 806/397-0627 |
| Sanford Fritch High Sch<br>538 Eagle Blvd, Fritch 79036<br>Jason Garrison | 9-12 | GV | 209<br>28 | 31% | 806/359-0159<br>Fax 806/359-0625 |
| Sanford Fritch Jr High Sch<br>536 Eagle Blvd, Fritch 79036<br>Dixie Watson | 6-8 | T | 178<br>25 | 48% | 806/397-0159<br>Fax 806/397-0626 |

• **Spring Creek Ind School Dist** PID: 01032812
9849 FM 2171, Skellytown 79080

806/273-6791

**Schools:** 1 \ **Teachers:** 11 \ **Students:** 110 \ **Special Ed Students:** 4 \
**LEP Students:** 3 \ **Ethnic:** Asian 1%, Hispanic 18%, Caucasian 80% \
**Exp:** $758 (High) \ **Poverty:** 12% \ **Open-Close:** 08/04 - 05/21

Mandy Poer .............................. 1,11,73,83
Heather Weatherford ................. 57,58*

Danny Finch .............................................. 8
Bob Kasch ............................................. 67

| Public Schs..Principal | Grd | Prgm | Enr/#Cls | SN | |
|---|---|---|---|---|---|
| Spring Creek Sch<br>9849 FM 2171, Skellytown 79080<br>**Danny Finch** | K-12 | | 110<br>7 | 35% | 806/273-6791 |

## IRION PUBLIC SCHOOLS

• **Irion Co Ind School Dist** PID: 01032862
302 N 3rd St, Mertzon 76941

325/835-6111
Fax 325/835-2017

**Schools:** 2 \ **Teachers:** 28 \ **Students:** 300 \ **Special Ed Students:** 24
\ **LEP Students:** 3 \ **College-Bound:** 50% \ **Ethnic:** Hispanic 33%,
Caucasian 66% \ **Exp:** $1,545 (High) \ **Poverty:** 9% \ **Title I:** $28,947 \
**Open-Close:** 08/20 - 05/28 \ **DTBP:** $334 (High)

**Dr Ray Despain** .................................... 1
George McDowell .................................... 3
Brian Tillman ......................................... 5
Gina Feller .......................................... 7*
Kathy Settle ........................................ 60*
Raymond Flores .............................. 73,295*

Robert Helms ......................................... 2
Kristi Miller .......................... 4,10,11,296
Jacob Conner ........................................ 6*
Jessica Parker ......................................... 9
Vincinte Flores ...................................... 67
Leann Rutherford ................... 83,88,270*

| Public Schs..Principal | Grd | Prgm | Enr/#Cls | SN | |
|---|---|---|---|---|---|
| Irion County High Sch<br>309 N 3rd St, Mertzon 76941<br>Shannon Chapman | 7-12 | ATV | 126<br>15 | 28% | 325/835-2881<br>Fax 325/835-2298 |
| Irion Elem Sch<br>302 N 3rd St, Mertzon 76941<br>Jessica Parker | PK-6 | T | 122<br>20 | 30% | 325/835-3991<br>Fax 325/835-2281 |

## JACK PUBLIC SCHOOLS

• **Bryson Ind School Dist** PID: 01032898
300 N McCloud St, Bryson 76427

940/392-3281
Fax 940/392-2086

**Schools:** 1 \ **Teachers:** 22 \ **Students:** 241 \ **Special Ed Students:** 28 \
**LEP Students:** 8 \ **College-Bound:** 50% \ **Ethnic:** Hispanic 12%, Native
American: 1%, Caucasian 87% \ **Exp:** $582 (High) \ **Poverty:** 24% \
**Title I:** $88,607 \ **Open-Close:** 08/14 - 05/20 \ **DTBP:** $386 (High) \ 🇫 🇹

Greg London .................................... 1,11
Debbie Hearne ........................... 8,12,69*
Britney Hanks ..................................... 58*

Tina Register ......................................... 2
Ann Decker ................................... 16,28*
Bob Hauger ......................................... 67

| Public Schs..Principal | Grd | Prgm | Enr/#Cls | SN | |
|---|---|---|---|---|---|
| Bryson Sch<br>300 N McCloud St, Bryson 76427<br>Gary Kirby | PK-12 | TV | 241<br>24 | 52% | 940/392-2601<br>Fax 940/392-2238 |

## Jacksboro Ind Sch Dist PID: 01032927
750 W Belknap St, Jacksboro 76458
940/567-7203
Fax 940/567-2214

**Schools:** 3 \ **Teachers:** 79 \ **Students:** 1,023 \ **Special Ed Students:** 106 \
**LEP Students:** 147 \ **Ethnic:** Asian 1%, African American 1%, Hispanic 33%,
Native American: 1%, Caucasian 65% \ **Exp:** $833 (High) \ **Poverty:** 20% \
**Title I:** $230,229 \ **Open-Close:** 08/17 - 05/21 \ **DTBP:** $356 (High) \ 🅕 🆃

| | |
|---|---|
| Dwain Milam ........1 | Christy Thomas ........2,84 |
| Craig Adkins ........3,4,91 | Greg Sanders ........5* |
| Brannon Rodgers ........6,35* | Taylor Martin ........7* |
| Wade Wesley ........8,11,57,271,275,288,296,298 | Kevin Thomas ........27* |
| Dori Taylor ........36,69,83,85* | Brent Hackley ........67 |
| Carl Depew ........73,76,286 | |

| Public Schs..Principal | Grd | Prgm | Enr/#Cls | SN | |
|---|---|---|---|---|---|
| Jacksboro Elem Sch<br>1677 N Main St, Jacksboro 76458<br>**Michael Qualls** | PK-5 | T | 474<br>26 | 65% | 940/567-7206<br>Fax 940/567-2603 🅕🆃 |
| Jacksboro High Sch<br>1400 N Main St, Jacksboro 76458<br>Starla Sanders | 9-12 | GTV | 300<br>24 | 58% | 940/567-7204<br>Fax 940/567-6028 |
| Jacksboro Middle Sch<br>812 W Belknap St, Jacksboro 76458<br>Sara Mathis | 6-8 | TV | 249<br>25 | 70% | 940/567-7205<br>Fax 940/567-2681 |

## Perrin-Whitt Cons Ind Sch Dist PID: 01032965
216 N Benson St, Perrin 76486
940/798-3718
Fax 940/798-3071

**Schools:** 2 \ **Teachers:** 29 \ **Students:** 340 \ **Special Ed Students:** 43 \
**LEP Students:** 7 \ **Ethnic:** Hispanic 16%, Caucasian 84% \ **Exp:** $442 (High)
\ **Poverty:** 13% \ **Title I:** $55,002 \ **Open-Close:** 08/27 - 05/27 \ **DTBP:** $333
(High) \ 🅕

| | |
|---|---|
| Cliff Gilmore ........1 | Fran Self ........2 |
| Ben Staggs ........6* | Loren Sell ........10* |
| Dianna Gilmore ........36* | Chris Keeney ........67 |
| Bruce Martin ........73,84 | |

| Public Schs..Principal | Grd | Prgm | Enr/#Cls | SN | |
|---|---|---|---|---|---|
| Perrin-Whitt Elem Sch<br>216 N Benson St, Perrin 76486<br>Teresa Mathis | PK-6 | T | 179<br>16 | 58% | 940/798-2395 |
| Perrin-Whitt High Sch<br>216 N Benson St, Perrin 76486<br>Loren Sell | 7-12 | TV | 155<br>40 | 66% | 940/798-3718 |

## JACK PRIVATE SCHOOLS

| Private Schs..Principal | Grd | Prgm | Enr/#Cls | SN | |
|---|---|---|---|---|---|
| Grace Christian Academy-Main<br>1999 W FM 1885, Perrin 76486<br>Jody McGlothlin | PK-12 | | 401 | | 682/262-9288<br>🅕 |

## JACKSON PUBLIC SCHOOLS

## Edna Ind School Dist PID: 01032991
601 N Wells St, Edna 77957
361/782-3573
Fax 361/781-1002

**Schools:** 4 \ **Teachers:** 115 \ **Students:** 1,328 \ **Special Ed Students:** 167
\ **LEP Students:** 158 \ **College-Bound:** 48% \ **Ethnic:** Asian 2%,
African American 14%, Hispanic 45%, Caucasian 39% \ **Exp:** $629 (High)
\ **Poverty:** 20% \ **Title I:** $381,386 \ **Special Education:** $115,000 \
**Open-Close:** 07/30 - 05/21 \ **DTBP:** $364 (High)

| | |
|---|---|
| Robert Oconner ........1 | Daniel Harper ........2,19 |
| Sonny Strelec ........3,5,80,91 | Zach Norris ........4 |
| Jimmy Miytchell ........6 | Katie Fojtik ........7 |
| Brandie Roe ........8,57,73,83,285,286,288,296 | Madalyn Maresh ........11,298 |
| Andrew Wallace ........16* | Dustin Lambden ........16,76,295 |
| Amber Stansberry ........34,58,77 | April Cubriel ........36 |
| Patrick Brzozowski ........67 | |

| Public Schs..Principal | Grd | Prgm | Enr/#Cls | SN | |
|---|---|---|---|---|---|
| Ⓐ Edna Alternative Sch<br>112 W Ash St, Edna 77957<br>Sonya Proper | 6-12 | T | 50 | 77% | 361/782-9051 |
| Edna Elem Sch<br>400 Apollo Dr, Edna 77957<br>Katie Kucera | PK-5 | AT | 804 | 69% | 361/782-2953<br>Fax 361/781-1028 |
| Edna High Sch<br>1303 W Gayle St, Edna 77957<br>Scott Kana | 9-12 | ATV | 188 | 58% | 361/782-5255<br>Fax 361/781-1014 |
| Edna Junior High Sch<br>505 W Gayle St, Edna 77957<br>**Melissa Koop** | 6-8 | AT | 336<br>30 | 71% | 361/782-2351<br>Fax 361/781-1025 |

## Ganado Ind School Dist PID: 01033050
210 S 6th St, Ganado 77962
361/771-4200
Fax 361/771-2280

**Schools:** 3 \ **Teachers:** 61 \ **Students:** 700 \ **Special Ed Students:** 67
\ **LEP Students:** 75 \ **College-Bound:** 50% \ **Ethnic:** African American
3%, Hispanic 57%, Caucasian 41% \ **Exp:** $2,009 (High) \ **Poverty:** 18% \
**Title I:** $126,364 \ **Open-Close:** 08/19 - 05/21 \ **DTBP:** $343 (High) \ 🆃

| | |
|---|---|
| **Erin Fasel** ........1 | Wendy Nixon ........2 |
| Bert Skoruppa ........3 | Tracey Galetti ........4 |
| Tracey Galetti ........4* | Jack Turner ........5 |
| Brent Bennett ........6 | Diane Koop ........7 |
| Sarah Woodring ........8,288 | Jenny Nelson ........16,73,76,286,295,296* |
| Maria Vorajakkmol ........57 | Jamie Ramey ........58 |
| Clay Green ........67 | Kimberly Girndt ........68 |
| William Prats ........88 | Tina Gresham ........280 |
| Jenny Smiga ........298 | |

| Public Schs..Principal | Grd | Prgm | Enr/#Cls | SN | |
|---|---|---|---|---|---|
| Ganado Elem Sch<br>310 S 5th St, Ganado 77962<br>Jennifer Stephenson | PK-5 | T | 341 | 59% | 361/771-4250<br>Fax 361/771-3403 |
| Ganado High Sch<br>501 W Devers St, Ganado 77962<br>David Segers | 9-12 | ATV | 232<br>35 | 44% | 361/771-4300<br>Fax 361/771-3479 |

| | | | |
|---|---|---|---|
| 1 Superintendent | 19 Chief Financial Officer | 39 Social Studies K-12 | 59 Special Education Elem | 69 Academic Assessment |

(legend)
1 Superintendent | 8 Curric/Instruct K-12 | 19 Chief Financial Officer | 29 Family/Consumer Science | 39 Social Studies K-12 | 49 English/Lang Arts Elem | 59 Special Education Elem | 69 Academic Assessment
2 Bus/Finance/Purchasing | 9 Curric/Instruct Elem | 20 Art K-12 | 30 Adult Education | 40 Social Studies Elem | 50 English/Lang Arts Sec | 60 Special Education Sec | 70 Research/Development
3 Buildings And Grounds | 10 Curric/Instruct Sec | 21 Art Elem | 31 Career/Sch-to-Work K-12 | 41 Social Studies Sec | 51 Reading K-12 | 61 Foreign/World Lang K-12 | 71 Public Information
4 Food Service | 11 Federal Program | 22 Art Sec | 32 Career/Sch-to-Work Elem | 42 Science K-12 | 52 Reading Elem | 62 Foreign/World Lang Elem | 72 Summer School
5 Transportation | 12 Title I | 23 Music K-12 | 33 Career/Sch-to-Work Sec | 43 Science Elem | 53 Reading Sec | 63 Foreign/World Lang Sec | 73 Instructional Tech
6 Athletic | 13 Title V | 24 Music Elem | 34 Early Childhood Ed | 44 Science Sec | 54 Remedial Reading K-12 | 64 Religious Education K-12 | 74 Inservice Training
7 Health Services | 14 | 25 Music Sec | 35 Health/Phys Education | 45 Math K-12 | 55 Remedial Reading Elem | 65 Religious Education Elem | 75 Marketing/Distributive
| 15 Asst Superintendent | 26 Business Education | 36 Guidance Services K-12 | 46 Math Elem | 56 Remedial Reading Sec | 66 Religious Education Sec | 76 Info Systems
| 16 Instructional Media Svcs | 27 Career & Tech Ed | 37 Guidance Services Elem | 47 Math Sec | 57 Bilingual/ELL | 67 School Board President | 77 Psychological Assess
| 17 Chief Operations Officer | 28 Technology Education | 38 Guidance Services Sec | 48 English/Lang Arts K-12 | 58 Special Education K-12 | 68 Teacher Personnel | 78 Affirmative Action
| 18 Chief Academic Officer

| Ganado Junior High Sch | 6-8 | AT | 173 | 49% 361/771-4300 |
|---|---|---|---|---|
| 501 West Devers, Ganado 77962 | | | | Fax 361/771-4310 |
| Joey Rosalez | | | | |

## • Industrial Ind School Dist PID: 01033086
167 5th St, Vanderbilt 77991

361/284-3226
Fax 361/284-3349

Schools: 4 \ Teachers: 87 \ Students: 1,100 \ Special Ed Students: 123 \ LEP Students: 43 \ College-Bound: 66% \ Ethnic: African American 1%, Hispanic 29%, Caucasian 69% \ Exp: $584 (High) \ Poverty: 14% \ Title I: $159,929 \ Open-Close: 08/19 - 05/20 \ DTBP: $338 (High) \ [t]

| Dr Missy Klimitchek | 1,11 | Roxanne Rogers | 2 |
|---|---|---|---|
| Billy Barr | 3 | Barbara Thedford | 4 |
| James Dixon | 6 | Kathy Kuchler | 7 |
| Kristi Cope | 16 | Houston Cummings | 20,23* |
| Cynthia Adams | 58 | Dale Allen | 67 |
| Nathan Sappington | 73,84,295 | | |

| Public Schs..Principal | Grd | Prgm | Enr/#Cls | SN | |
|---|---|---|---|---|---|
| Industrial Elem Sch East | PK-5 | T | 210 | 49% | 361/284-3317 |
| 390 Main Street, Vanderbilt 77991 | | | 17 | | Fax 361/284-3377 |
| Lisa Baughman | | | | | |
| Industrial Elem Sch West | PK-5 | | 191 | 22% | 361/782-3325 |
| Farm Road 444, Inez 77968 | | | 15 | | Fax 361/782-0010 |
| **Stacey Bain** | | | | | |
| Industrial High Sch | 9-12 | AV | 351 | 29% | 361/284-3216 |
| 187 5th St, Vanderbilt 77991 | | | 30 | | Fax 361/284-3328 |
| Jim Green | | | | | |
| Industrial Junior High Sch | 6-8 | T | 306 | 35% | 361/284-3226 |
| Three 5th St, Vanderbilt 77991 | | | 17 | | Fax 361/284-3049 |
| Kim Schaefer | | | | | |

# JASPER COUNTY

## JASPER PUBLIC SCHOOLS

## • Brookeland Ind School Dist PID: 01033141
187 Wildcat Walk, Brookeland 75931

409/698-2677
Fax 409/698-2533

Schools: 1 \ Teachers: 39 \ Students: 380 \ Special Ed Students: 43 \ College-Bound: 50% \ Ethnic: African American 5%, Hispanic 6%, Caucasian 90% \ Exp: $545 (High) \ Poverty: 27% \ Title I: $135,249 \ Open-Close: 08/24 - 05/28

| Kevin McCugh | 1,83 | Tammi Haden | 2 |
|---|---|---|---|
| Donna Cooper | 3,5* | Kathryn Thomas | 4* |
| Dawn Moon | 7* | Charlotte Odom | 8,11,27,57,296,298* |
| Stacey Gillis | 8,31,36,69,88,92,271* | Carol MacLeod | 58* |
| Brett Holloway | 67 | Michael Defee | 73,295 |
| Tammy Gilbert | 81* | Deene McCland | 294 |
| Maranda Hightower | 294* | | |

| Public Schs..Principal | Grd | Prgm | Enr/#Cls | SN | |
|---|---|---|---|---|---|
| Brookeland Sch | PK-12 | TV | 380 | 64% | 409/698-2677 |
| Loop 149, Brookeland 75931 | | | 42 | | Fax 409/698-8974 |
| **Charlotte Odam** | | | | | |

## • Buna Ind School Dist PID: 01033177
1022 Tx State Highway 62, Buna 77612

409/994-5101
Fax 409/994-4808

Schools: 3 \ Teachers: 126 \ Students: 1,497 \ Special Ed Students: 177 \ LEP Students: 9 \ College-Bound: 55% \ Ethnic: African American 4%, Hispanic 3%, Caucasian 92% \ Exp: $319 (High) \ Poverty: 23% \ Title I: $421,442 \ Open-Close: 08/12 - 05/27

| Dr Donny Lee | 1 | Dr Sharon Mosely | 2,3,17 |
|---|---|---|---|
| Joe Menard | 3,5 | Bradley Morgan | 6* |
| Kelley Peck | 8,11,15,76,271 | Jerry Gore | 58 |
| Keith Mullins | 67 | Matt Ibanez | 295 |

| Public Schs..Principal | Grd | Prgm | Enr/#Cls | SN | |
|---|---|---|---|---|---|
| Buna Elem Sch | PK-5 | T | 713 | 50% | 409/994-4840 |
| 650 County Road 725, Buna 77612 | | | 40 | | Fax 409/994-5728 |
| Karen Hebert | | | | | |
| Buna High Sch | 9-12 | GV | 451 | 39% | 409/994-4811 |
| FM 177 253, Buna 77612 | | | 25 | | Fax 409/994-4818 |
| Mike Brewster | | | | | |
| Buna Junior High Sch | 6-8 | TV | 331 | 42% | 409/994-4860 |
| 420 County Rd 751 A, Buna 77612 | | | 40 | | Fax 409/994-4810 |
| Amber Flowers | | | | | |

## • Evadale Ind School Dist PID: 01033218
908 Hwy 105, Evadale 77615

409/276-1337
Fax 409/276-1908

Schools: 2 \ Teachers: 42 \ Students: 394 \ Special Ed Students: 50 \ LEP Students: 6 \ Ethnic: Hispanic 3%, Caucasian 97% \ Exp: $264 (Med) \ Poverty: 17% \ Title I: $67,652 \ Special Education: $119,000 \ Open-Close: 08/14 - 05/28 \ DTBP: $363 (High)

| Gary Fairchild | 1,11 | Brandy Black | 2 |
|---|---|---|---|
| Shannon Adams | 3,5,91 | Pam Cox | 4 |
| Mark Williams | 6* | Keisha Christian | 7,85* |
| Ashley Powell | 8 | Chris Fikes | 16,73,76,84,286,295 |
| Christie Sylvester | 16* | Piper Ayres | 57,58,88 |
| Jim Love | 67 | Margo Calhoun | 68,71 |
| Amy Haden | 69 | Rusty Minyard | 83,288* |

| Public Schs..Principal | Grd | Prgm | Enr/#Cls | SN | |
|---|---|---|---|---|---|
| Evadale Elem Jr High Sch | PK-8 | T | 287 | 30% | 409/276-1337 |
| Highway 105 S, Evadale 77615 | | | 20 | | Fax 409/276-1588 |
| Cheryl Jones | | | | | |
| Evadale High Sch | 9-12 | V | 107 | 31% | 409/276-1337 |
| Highway 105 S, Evadale 77615 | | | 15 | | Fax 409/276-1050 |
| Rusty Minyard | | | | | |

## • Jasper Ind School Dist PID: 01033244
128 Park Ln, Jasper 75951

409/384-2401
Fax 409/382-1084

Schools: 4 \ Teachers: 180 \ Students: 2,400 \ Special Ed Students: 287 \ LEP Students: 195 \ Ethnic: African American 41%, Hispanic 20%, Caucasian 39% \ Exp: $594 (High) \ Poverty: 30% \ Title I: $1,263,719 \ Special Education: $637,000 \ Open-Close: 08/24 - 05/27 \ DTBP: $168 (High) \ [f] [t]

| John Seybold | 1 | Paula Horton | 2,294 |
|---|---|---|---|
| Ronnie Bryan | 3 | Kimberly Dean | 4 |
| Donna Adams | 5 | Darrell Barbay | 6* |
| Stacey Woolems | 10,11,69,296 | Kim Parker | 58,77,88 |
| Mark Durand | 67 | Denitro Headnot | 73,76,295 |
| Jennifer White | 295 | | |

| Public Schs..Principal | Grd | Prgm | Enr/#Cls | SN | |
|---|---|---|---|---|---|
| Jasper High Sch<br>400 Bulldog Ave, Jasper 75951<br>Victor Williams | 9-12 | TV | 722 | 77% | 409/384-3242<br>Fax 409/382-1310<br>f |
| Jasper Junior High Sch<br>211 2nd St, Jasper 75951<br>David Burt | 6-8 | T | 604<br>60 | 79% | 409/384-3585<br>Fax 409/384-4585<br>f |
| Jean C Few Primary Sch<br>225 Bulldog Ave, Jasper 75951<br>**Wendi Stanley** | PK-3 | T | 677<br>65 | 89% | 409/489-9808<br>Fax 409/382-1399<br>f |
| Parnell Elem Sch<br>151 Park St, Jasper 75951<br>William Davis | 4-5 | T | 336<br>40 | 81% | 409/384-2212<br>Fax 409/382-1114<br>f t |

● **Kirbyville Cons Ind Sch Dist** PID: 01033282     409/423-2284
206 E Main St, Kirbyville 75956     Fax 409/423-2367

**Schools:** 3 \ **Teachers:** 105 \ **Students:** 1,500 \ **Special Ed Students:** 118 \ **LEP Students:** 36 \ **College-Bound:** 37% \ **Ethnic:** African American 9%, Hispanic 8%, Caucasian 82% \ **Exp:** $358 (High) \ **Poverty:** 31% \ **Title I:** $589,599 \ **Open-Close:** 08/14 - 05/27

Georgia Sayers .....................................1,11
Cindy Barlow .............................................4
James Gaspard .........................16,73,295*
Chad George .........................................67
James Dodson ..................................3
Craig Jones ......................................6
Cay Kent ........................................19

| Public Schs..Principal | Grd | Prgm | Enr/#Cls | SN | |
|---|---|---|---|---|---|
| Kirbyville Elem Sch<br>2100 S Margaret Ave, Kirbyville 75956<br>Kristi Gore | PK-5 | T | 733 | 68% | 409/423-8526<br>Fax 409/423-3753 |
| Kirbyville High Sch<br>1100 S Margaret Ave, Kirbyville 75956<br>Holli Farias | 9-12 | TV | 398<br>35 | 59% | 409/423-7500<br>Fax 409/423-5313 |
| Kirbyville Junior High Sch<br>2200 S Margaret Ave, Kirbyville 75956<br>**Chad Odom** \ **Ashley Powell** | 6-8 | T | 330<br>19 | 61% | 409/420-0692<br>Fax 409/423-6654 |

# JEFF DAVIS COUNTY

## JEFF DAVIS PUBLIC SCHOOLS

● **Fort Davis Ind School Dist** PID: 01033323     432/426-4440
400 W Webster Ave, Fort Davis 79734     Fax 432/426-3841

**Schools:** 2 \ **Teachers:** 25 \ **Students:** 225 \ **Special Ed Students:** 27 \ **LEP Students:** 30 \ **College-Bound:** 45% \ **Ethnic:** Hispanic 61%, Caucasian 39% \ **Exp:** $615 (High) \ **Poverty:** 18% \ **Title I:** $59,821 \ **Open-Close:** 08/24 - 05/20 \ **DTBP:** $350 (High)

Graydon Hicks ....................................1,11
Hortencia Aguilar ..................................13
Laticha Hartenett ...................................58
Laura Gonzalez ....................................73
Velvet Hardy ............................................2
Cyndi Wimberley .....................................37
David Whitesell .......................................67

| Public Schs..Principal | Grd | Prgm | Enr/#Cls | SN | |
|---|---|---|---|---|---|
| Dirks-Anderson Sch<br>Highway 17, Fort Davis 79734<br>**Cyndi Wimberly** | PK-5 | | 106<br>8 | | 432/426-4454<br>Fax 432/426-4456 |

| | | | | | |
|---|---|---|---|---|---|
| Fort Davis Jr Sr High Sch<br>401 W Webster Ave, Fort Davis 79734<br>Luane Porter | 6-12 | T | 125<br>17 | 49% | 432/426-4444<br>Fax 432/426-4449 |

● **Valentine Ind School Dist** PID: 01033359     432/467-2671
209 E Kentucky St, Valentine 79854     Fax 432/467-2004

**Schools:** 1 \ **Teachers:** 10 \ **Students:** 34 \ **Special Ed Students:** 4 \ **LEP Students:** 6 \ **College-Bound:** 100% \ **Ethnic:** Asian 3%, Hispanic 75%, Caucasian 22% \ **Exp:** $1,475 (High) \ **Poverty:** 23% \ **Title I:** $2,303 \ **Open-Close:** 08/21 - 05/28 \ **DTBP:** $394 (High)

Debbie Engle .............................1,11,57,83
Dawn Houy ............................8,36,288*
Brad Bernards .........................73,286,295*
Ernie Villarreal .....................................2
William Miller ........................................67

| Public Schs..Principal | Grd | Prgm | Enr/#Cls | SN | |
|---|---|---|---|---|---|
| Valentine Sch<br>209 E Kentucky St, Valentine 79854<br>William Cook | PK-12 | T | 34<br>11 | 61% | 432/467-2671<br>Fax 432/467-2114 |

# JEFFERSON COUNTY

## JEFFERSON COUNTY SCHOOLS

| County Schs..Principal | Grd | Prgm | Enr/#Cls | SN | |
|---|---|---|---|---|---|
| Ⓐ Jefferson Co Youth Academy<br>5030 Highway 69 S, Beaumont 77705<br>Steve Gatewood | 6-12 | | 42<br>5 | | 409/720-4078<br>Fax 409/720-4051 |

## JEFFERSON PUBLIC SCHOOLS

● **Beaumont Ind School Dist** PID: 01034092     409/617-5000
3395 Harrison Ave, Beaumont 77706     Fax 409/617-5184

**Schools:** 27 \ **Teachers:** 1,135 \ **Students:** 18,000 \ **Special Ed Students:** 1,484 \ **LEP Students:** 2,001 \ **Ethnic:** Asian 3%, African American 61%, Hispanic 26%, Caucasian 10% \ **Exp:** $480 (High) \ **Poverty:** 28% \ **Title I:** $8,848,938 \ **Special Education:** $4,229,000 \ **Open-Close:** 08/17 - 06/11 \ **DTBP:** $200 (High)

**Dr Shannon Allen** .................................1
Tracy Armstrong ..............3,12,34,88,295,750
Todd Coleman .......................................5
Dr Ardianne Lee ....................................16
Dr Donna Prudhomme .........................27,31*
Lyida Sylvester .....................................36,83
Monica Reynolds ...................................39,81
Sherri Wills ...........................................45
Laigh Langley ........................................58
Denise McLean ......................................71
Cindy Saveat .........................................79
Adam Thibodeaux ................................297
Cheryl Hernandez ...............................2,19
Tiffany Eckenrod .....................................4
Anita Frank ..........................................15
Raysield Lavan ...................................20,23
Rodney Saveat ......................................35
Rachel Guidry ....................................36,83
Patsy MaGee ........................................42
Blanca Jones ........................................57
Thomas Sigge ......................................67
Toni McPherson ....................................73
Veronica Redmon ..................................93

| Public Schs..Principal | Grd | Prgm | Enr/#Cls | SN | |
|---|---|---|---|---|---|
| Amelia Elem Sch<br>565 S Major Dr, Beaumont 77707<br>Yvonne DuPont \ **Dimitrise Haynes** | PK-5 | T | 710<br>27 | 89% | 409/617-6000<br>Fax 409/617-6024 |

| | | | | | | |
|---|---|---|---|---|---|---|
| Beaumont Early Clg High Sch<br>3410 Austin St, Beaumont 77706<br>Melanie Pharis | 9-12 | T | 127 | 79% | 409/617-6600 | |
| Ⓜ Beaumont United High Sch<br>3443 Fannett Rd, Beaumont 77705<br>Ron Jackson | 9-12 | GTV | 2,176 | 91% | 409/617-5400<br>Fax 409/617-5396 | |
| Bingham Head Start Ctr<br>5265 Kenneth Ave, Beaumont 77705<br>Carolyn Little \ **Lisa Bolton** | PK-PK | | 510<br>26 | 99% | 409/617-6200<br>Fax 409/617-6203 | |
| Blanchette Elem Sch<br>2550 Sarah St, Beaumont 77705<br>April Johnston | PK-5 | T | 610<br>25 | 97% | 409/617-6300<br>Fax 409/617-6203 | |
| Caldwood Elem Sch<br>102 Berkshire Ln, Beaumont 77707<br>Julie Corona | PK-5 | T | 537<br>33 | 89% | 409/617-6025<br>Fax 409/617-6048 | |
| Charlton-Pollard Elem Sch<br>1695 Irving St, Beaumont 77701<br>Valencia Greenwood | PK-5 | T | 426<br>24 | 97% | 409/617-6075<br>Fax 409/617-6098 | |
| Curtis Elem Sch<br>6225 N Circuit Dr, Beaumont 77706<br>Glenetta Henley | PK-5 | T | 496<br>25 | 52% | 409/617-6050<br>Fax 409/617-6073 | |
| Dishman Elem Sch<br>3475 Champions Dr, Beaumont 77707<br>Mellow Tatmon | PK-5 | T | 513<br>30 | 79% | 409/617-6250<br>Fax 409/617-6274 | |
| Dr Mae Jones-Clark Elem Sch<br>3525 Cleveland St, Beaumont 77703<br>Yvonne DuPont | PK-5 | T | 531<br>18 | 96% | 409/617-6350<br>Fax 409/617-6346 | |
| Fehl-Price Elem Sch<br>3350 Blanchette St, Beaumont 77701<br>Stephanie Ling | PK-5 | T | 564<br>20 | 96% | 409/617-6400<br>Fax 409/617-6421 | |
| Fletcher Elem Sch<br>1055 Avenue F, Beaumont 77701<br>Gloria Guillory | PK-5 | T | 341<br>35 | 97% | 409/617-6100<br>Fax 409/617-6123 | |
| Guess Elem Sch<br>8055 Voth Rd, Beaumont 77708<br>Debra Oge | K-5 | T | 567<br>45 | 79% | 409/617-6125<br>Fax 409/617-6148 | |
| Homer Drive Elem Sch<br>8950 Homer Dr, Beaumont 77708<br>Belinda George | PK-5 | T | 654<br>28 | 95% | 409/617-6225<br>Fax 409/617-6248 | |
| Lucas Pre-K Center<br>1750 E Lucas Dr, Beaumont 77703<br>**L Parker Langley** | PK-PK | T | 332<br>19 | 99% | 409/617-6450<br>Fax 409/617-6448 | |
| M L King Middle Sch<br>1400 Avenue A, Beaumont 77701<br>Julie Corona | 6-8 | TV | 627<br>35 | 95% | 409/617-5850<br>Fax 409/617-5873 | |
| Marshall Middle Sch<br>6455 Gladys Ave, Beaumont 77706<br>**Breaux Paul \ Charles Colvin** | 6-8 | TV | 910<br>48 | 61% | 409/617-5900<br>Fax 409/617-5924 | 🇫 🇹 |
| Martin Elem Sch<br>3500 Pine St, Beaumont 77703<br>Tamara Long | K-5 | T | 622<br>46 | 99% | 409/617-6425<br>Fax 409/617-6446 | |
| Ⓜ Odom Academy<br>2550 W Virginia St, Beaumont 77705<br>Lachandra Cobb-Eaglin | 6-8 | TV | 860<br>50 | 84% | 409/617-5925<br>Fax 409/617-5949 | |
| Ⓐ Pathways Alt Learning Center<br>3410 Austin St, Beaumont 77706<br>Charles Colvin | 6-12 | | 37<br>13 | 94% | 409/617-5206<br>Fax 409/617-5718 | |
| Ⓐ Paul A Brown Learning Center<br>88 Jaguar Dr, Beaumont 77702<br>**Dr Calvin Rice** | 9-12 | | 115<br>25 | | 409/617-5720<br>Fax 409/617-5738 | |
| Pietzsch-MacArthur Elem Sch<br>4301 Highland Ave, Beaumont 77705<br>Audrey Collins | PK-5 | T | 880<br>70 | 97% | 409/617-6475<br>Fax 409/617-6498 | |
| Regina-Howell Elem Sch<br>5850 Regina Ln, Beaumont 77706<br>Kimberly Janeaux | PK-5 | T | 625<br>35 | 50% | 409/617-6190<br>Fax 409/617-6199 | |

| | | | | | | |
|---|---|---|---|---|---|---|
| Ⓜ Smith Magnet Middle Sch<br>4415 Concord Rd, Beaumont 77703<br>**Andrea Renee Lee** | 6-8 | TV | 574<br>58 | 96% | 409/617-5825<br>Fax 409/617-5848 | |
| Taylor Career & Tech Ctr<br>2330 North St, Beaumont 77702<br>Michael Shelton | Voc | G | 500<br>30 | | 409/617-5740<br>Fax 409/617-5759 | |
| Vincent Middle Sch<br>350 Eldridge Dr, Beaumont 77707<br>Missy Gimble | 6-8 | TV | 553<br>89 | 85% | 409/617-5950<br>Fax 409/617-5974 | |
| West Brook High Sch<br>8750 Phelan Blvd, Beaumont 77706<br>Diana Valdez | 9-12 | GTV | 2,284<br>135 | 61% | 409/617-5500<br>Fax 409/617-5582 | |

---

● **Hamshire Fannett Ind Sch Dist** PID: 01033610    409/243-2133
12702 2nd St, Hamshire 77622    Fax 409/243-3437

**Schools:** 4 \ **Teachers:** 132 \ **Students:** 1,934 \ **Special Ed Students:** 186 \ **LEP Students:** 87 \ **College-Bound:** 59% \ **Ethnic:** Asian 2%, African American 8%, Hispanic 17%, Native American: 1%, Caucasian 73% \ **Exp:** $281 (Med) \ **Poverty:** 10% \ **Title I:** $186,613 \ **Open-Close:** 08/13 - 05/20 \ **DTBP:** $353 (High)

| | | | |
|---|---|---|---|
| Dr Dwaine Augustine | ...1 | Allison Byrd | 2,11,15 |
| Angel Wingate | ...4 | Mark Wagner | 6,35 |
| Jon Burris | 8,11,88,271,273,294 | Stephen Edwards | 15,73* |
| Erin Laughlin | 16 | Casey Hancock | 31* |
| Mandy Cormier | 34* | Marcy Bellenger | 36 |
| Bob Thuman | 67 | Rebecca Marshall | 69* |
| David Parker | 76,286,295 | | |

| Public Schs..Principal | Grd | Prgm | Enr/#Cls | SN |
|---|---|---|---|---|
| Hamshire Fannett Elem Sch<br>23395 Burrell Wingate Rd, Beaumont 77705<br>Byron Miller | PK-3 | T | 608<br>30 | 50% 409/794-1412<br>Fax 409/794-1049 |
| Hamshire Fannett High Sch<br>12552 2nd St, Hamshire 77622<br>Paul Shipman | 9-12 | AV | 557<br>38 | 46% 409/243-2131<br>Fax 409/243-2518 |
| Hamshire Fannett Interm Sch<br>11407 Dugat Rd, Beaumont 77705<br>Marla Gilmore | 4-6 | T | 463<br>34 | 52% 409/794-1558<br>Fax 409/794-1787 |
| Hamshire Fannett Middle Sch<br>11375 Dugat Rd, Beaumont 77705<br>Dr Cynthia Jackson | 7-8 | | 306<br>30 | 30% 409/794-1502<br>Fax 409/794-3042 |

---

● **Nederland Ind School Dist** PID: 01033660    409/724-2391
220 N 17th St, Nederland 77627    Fax 409/724-4280

**Schools:** 8 \ **Teachers:** 364 \ **Students:** 5,214 \ **Special Ed Students:** 587 \ **LEP Students:** 418 \ **College-Bound:** 66% \ **Ethnic:** Asian 7%, African American 9%, Hispanic 28%, Native American: 1%, Caucasian 56% \ **Exp:** $407 (High) \ **Poverty:** 13% \ **Title I:** $704,576 \ **Special Education:** $1,251,000 \ **Open-Close:** 08/17 - 05/26 \ **DTBP:** $181 (High) \ 🇫

| | | | |
|---|---|---|---|
| Melissa Wong | 2 | Kenny Litvik | 3,5 |
| Renee Bodden | 4 | Charles Polk | 5 |
| Monte Barrow | 6,35* | Heather Barrow | 9,81,89,271 |
| Mike Laird | 15,68,91 | Stuart Kieschnick | 15,57,88 |
| Deidre Powell | 34,36,54,58,77,79 | Cindi Bordelon | 38* |
| Micah Molsey | 67 | Darrell Evans | 69* |
| Jeff McKinnon | 69 | Cindy Laird | 73,84,95,297 |
| Curtis Randell | 76 | Adam Busby | 295 |

| Public Schs..Principal | Grd | Prgm | Enr/#Cls | SN |
|---|---|---|---|---|
| C O Wilson Middle Sch<br>2620 Helena Ave, Nederland 77627<br>Tina Oliver | 5-8 | TV | 814<br>40 | 42% 409/727-6224<br>Fax 409/726-2699 |

---

| | | | | | |
|---|---|---|---|---|---|
| Central Middle Sch<br>200 17th St, Nederland 77627<br>Natalie Gomez | 5-8 | T | 734 | 58% | 409/727-5765<br>Fax 409/724-4275 |
| Helena Park Elem Sch<br>2800 Helena Ave, Nederland 77627<br>Charlotte Junot | PK-4 | T | 644<br>30 | 36% | 409/722-0462<br>Fax 409/726-2698 **f** |
| Highland Park Elem Sch<br>200 S 6th St, Nederland 77627<br>Sissy Yeaman | PK-4 | T | 506<br>25 | 46% | 409/722-0236<br>Fax 409/726-2694 |
| Hillcrest Elem Sch<br>2611 Avenue H, Nederland 77627<br>Kevin Morrison | PK-4 | T | 505<br>35 | 63% | 409/722-3484<br>Fax 409/726-2690 |
| Langham Elem Sch<br>800 12th Street, Nederland 77627<br>Toby Latiolais | PK-4 | T | 405<br>50 | 52% | 409/722-4324<br>Fax 409/724-4286 |
| Nederland High Sch<br>2101 18th St, Nederland 77627<br>Steven Beagle | 9-12 | V | 1,521<br>100 | 38% | 409/727-2741<br>Fax 409/726-2679 |
| Ⓐ Netherland Alt Ed Sch<br>300 S 12th St, Nederland 77627<br>Jared Walker | 5-12 | | 12<br>3 | | 409/727-5241<br>Fax 409/724-4236 |

---

● **Port Arthur Ind School Dist** PID: 01033749     409/989-6222
4801 9th Ave, Port Arthur 77642     Fax 409/989-6229

> **Schools:** 16 \ **Teachers:** 609 \ **Students:** 9,000 \ **Special Ed Students:** 694
> \ **LEP Students:** 1,971 \ **College-Bound:** 51% \ **Ethnic:** Asian 3%,
> African American 42%, Hispanic 49%, Native American: 3%, Caucasian
> 3% \ **Exp:** $496 (High) \ **Poverty:** 32% \ **Title I:** $4,732,898 \
> **Special Education:** $1,997,000 \ **Open-Close:** 08/18 - 05/26 \ **DTBP:** $169
> (High)

| | | | |
|---|---|---|---|
| Dr Mark Porterie | 1 | Phyllis Geans | 2,15 |
| Stephanie Barth | 2 | Erika Sampson | 4 |
| Ester Chapman | 5 | Andre Boutte | 6 |
| Dr Kim Vine | 8 | Robin Beaty | 8,18,286 |
| Dr Melvin Getwood | 10,11,15,36,288,298 | Tuyen Tran | 16 |
| Freda Reynolds | 34 | Courtney Charles | 41 |
| Rita Leger | 43,285* | Melony Puz | 44,53 |
| Catherine Whitehead | 46 | Mekisha Bazile | 47* |
| Rhonda Calcoat | 52 | Dr Tatiana Owens | 57,271 |
| Debra Cartwright | 58,83,88 | Brandon Bartie | 67 |
| Kathy Londow | 68,79 | Kathy McEwen | 69 |
| Anthony Jackson | 73,76,294,295 | Kenneth Daigre | 73 |
| Dr Julie Sherman | 77 | Dr Lawanda Finney | 93,273 |
| Richard Tatar | 295 | Raul Picon | 297 |

| Public Schs..Principal | Grd | Prgm | Enr/#Cls | SN | |
|---|---|---|---|---|---|
| Abraham Lincoln Middle Sch<br>1023 Abe Lincoln Ave, Port Arthur 77640<br>Lasonya Baptiste | 6-8 | T | 436<br>55 | 77% | 409/984-8700<br>Fax 409/982-2847 |
| Dequeen Elem Sch<br>740 Dequeen Blvd, Port Arthur 77640<br>Jerry Gloston | 3-5 | T | 305<br>32 | 86% | 409/984-8900<br>Fax 409/982-1843 |
| Dowling Elem Sch<br>6301 Pat Ave, Port Arthur 77640<br>Amy Newcomb-Jordan | PK-5 | T | 430<br>21 | 81% | 409/984-4960<br>Fax 409/736-2406 |
| Lee Elem Sch<br>3900 10th St, Port Arthur 77642<br>Reuben Sampson | PK-5 | T | 748<br>42 | 85% | 409/984-8300<br>Fax 409/983-1649 |
| Lucian Adams Elem Sch<br>5701 9th Ave, Port Arthur 77642<br>Cheryl Tripplett | PK-5 | T | 542 | 89% | 409/984-4100<br>Fax 409/982-5564 |
| Memorial 9th Grade Academy<br>3505 Sgt Lucien Adams Blvd, Port Arthur 77642<br>Angel Murphy | 9-9 | V | 593<br>32 | | 409/984-4900<br>Fax 409/736-0267 |

| | | | | | |
|---|---|---|---|---|---|
| Memorial High Sch<br>3501 Sgt Lucien Adams Blvd, Port Arthur 77642<br>Dr Glenn Mitchell | 10-12 | TV | 1,538<br>60 | 69% | 409/984-4000<br>Fax 409/985-3376 |
| Memorial High School-Cate<br>3501 Sgt Lucien Adams Blvd, Port Arthur 77642<br>Raymond Polk | Voc | G | 300<br>14 | | 409/984-4750<br>Fax 409/983-2204 |
| Ⓐ Port Arthur Alternative Center<br>1030 Dunbar Ave, Port Arthur 77640<br>Luther Thompson | 6-12 | | 100<br>12 | | 409/984-8650<br>Fax 409/983-1108 |
| Sam Houston Elem Sch<br>3245 36th St, Port Arthur 77642<br>Marcia Sharp | PK-5 | T | 631<br>57 | 83% | 409/984-4800<br>Fax 409/984-4858 |
| Thomas Jefferson Middle Sch<br>2200 Jefferson Dr, Port Arthur 77642<br>Dr Melissa Oliva | 6-8 | GTV | 961<br>75 | 77% | 409/984-4860<br>Fax 409/960-6057 |
| Travis Elem Sch<br>1115 Lakeview Ave, Port Arthur 77642<br>Israel Taylor | PK-5 | T | 560<br>40 | 88% | 409/984-4700<br>Fax 409/984-4740 |
| Tyrrell Elem Sch<br>4401 Ferndale Dr, Port Arthur 77642<br>Dr Lisa Crochett | PK-5 | T | 821<br>39 | 81% | 409/984-4660<br>Fax 409/963-2765 |
| Washington Elem Sch<br>1300 Freeman Ave, Port Arthur 77640<br>Erica Seastrunt | PK-2 | T | 291<br>17 | 86% | 409/984-8600<br>Fax 409/984-9631 |
| Wheatley Sch Early Childhood<br>1100 Jefferson Dr, Port Arthur 77642<br>Fredia Reynolds | PK-PK | T | 424<br>28 | 99% | 409/984-8750<br>Fax 409/985-5487 |
| Wilson Early College High Sch<br>1500 Lakeshore Dr, Port Arthur 77640<br>Dr Gloria Dotson | 9-12 | | 300 | | 409/984-8960<br>Fax 409/984-8978 |

---

● **Port Neches-Groves Ind SD** PID: 01033957     409/722-4244
620 Avenue C, Port Neches 77651     Fax 409/724-7864

> **Schools:** 10 \ **Teachers:** 353 \ **Students:** 5,000 \ **Special Ed Students:** 497
> \ **LEP Students:** 265 \ **College-Bound:** 61% \ **Ethnic:** Asian 6%,
> African American 3%, Hispanic 27%, Caucasian 64% \ **Exp:** $381 (High)
> \ **Poverty:** 14% \ **Title I:** $715,898 \ **Special Education:** $1,339,000 \
> **Open-Close:** 08/19 - 05/27 \ **DTBP:** $182 (High)

| | | | |
|---|---|---|---|
| Dr Mike Gonzales | 1 | Sheri Drawhorn | 2 |
| Jeff Bergeron | 3 | Melissa Nunnelly | 4 |
| Kyle Segura | 5 | Dr Brenda Duhon | 8,15,69,73,74,288,294,298 |
| Roxanne Ferguson | 9 | Staci Gary | 9,57* |
| Misty Higgins | 11,58,88* | Julie Gauthier | 15,91,296 |
| Dr Scott Bartlett | 67 | Chrystal Werkheiser | 98 |
| Jon Deckert | 280* | Brett McThatter | 285 |

| Public Schs..Principal | Grd | Prgm | Enr/#Cls | SN | |
|---|---|---|---|---|---|
| Ⓐ Alternative Education Center<br>1810 Port Neches Ave, Port Neches 77651<br>Scott Ryan | 6-12 | | 20<br>3 | | 409/722-5924<br>Fax 409/724-1448 |
| Groves Elem Sch<br>3901 Cleveland Ave, Groves 77619<br>Mandie Champagne | 4-5 | T | 412<br>20 | 57% | 409/962-1531<br>Fax 409/963-2484 |
| Groves Middle Sch<br>5201 Wilson St, Groves 77619<br>Dr Paul Bryan | 6-8 | T | 647<br>50 | 51% | 409/962-0225<br>Fax 409/963-1898 |
| Port Neches Elem Sch<br>2101 Llano St, Port Neches 77651<br>Kimberly Carter | 4-5 | T | 383<br>15 | 44% | 409/722-2262<br>Fax 409/729-7003 |
| Port Neches Middle Sch<br>749 Central Dr, Port Neches 77651<br>Kyle Hooper | 6-8 | T | 426<br>34 | 42% | 409/722-8115<br>Fax 409/727-8342 |
| Port Neches-Groves High Sch<br>1401 Merriman St, Port Neches 77651<br>Dr Scott Ryan | 9-12 | AV | 714<br>60 | 41% | 409/729-7644<br>Fax 409/727-7217 |

| | | | | | | | | | |
|---|---|---|---|---|---|---|---|---|---|
| 1 | Superintendent | 8 | Curric/Instruct K-12 | 19 | Chief Financial Officer | 29 | Family/Consumer Science | 39 | Social Studies K-12 |
| 2 | Bus/Finance/Purchasing | 9 | Curric/Instruct Elem | 20 | Art K-12 | 30 | Adult Education | 40 | Social Studies Elem |
| 3 | Buildings And Grounds | 10 | Curric/Instruct Sec | 21 | Art Elem | 31 | Career/Sch-to-Work K-12 | 41 | Social Studies Sec |
| 4 | Food Service | 11 | Federal Program | 22 | Art Sec | 32 | Career/Sch-to-Work Elem | 42 | Science K-12 |
| 5 | Transportation | 12 | Title I | 23 | Music K-12 | 33 | Career/Sch-to-Work Sec | 43 | Science Elem |
| 6 | Athletic | 13 | Title V | 24 | Music Elem | 34 | Early Childhood Ed | 44 | Science Sec |
| 7 | Health Services | 14 | Title V | 25 | Music Sec | 35 | Health/Phys Education | 45 | Math K-12 |
| | | 15 | Asst Superintendent | 26 | Business Education | 36 | Guidance Services K-12 | 46 | Math Elem |
| | | 16 | Instructional Media Svcs | 27 | Career & Tech Ed | 37 | Guidance Services Elem | 47 | Math Sec |
| | | 17 | Chief Operations Officer | 28 | Technology Education | 38 | Guidance Services Sec | 48 | English/Lang Arts K-12 |
| | | 18 | Chief Academic Officer | | | | | | |

| | | | |
|---|---|---|---|
| 49 | English/Lang Arts Elem | 59 | Special Education Elem |
| 50 | English/Lang Arts Sec | 60 | Special Education Sec |
| 51 | Reading K-12 | 61 | Foreign/World Lang K-12 |
| 52 | Reading Elem | 62 | Foreign/World Lang Elem |
| 53 | Reading Sec | 63 | Foreign/World Lang Sec |
| 54 | Remedial Reading K-12 | 64 | Religious Education K-12 |
| 55 | Remedial Reading Elem | 65 | Religious Education Elem |
| 56 | Remedial Reading Sec | 66 | Religious Education Sec |
| 57 | Bilingual/ELL | 67 | School Board President |
| 58 | Special Education K-12 | 68 | Teacher Personnel |

| | |
|---|---|
| 69 | Academic Assessment |
| 70 | Research/Development |
| 71 | Public Information |
| 72 | Summer School |
| 73 | Instructional Tech |
| 74 | Inservice Training |
| 75 | Marketing/Distributive |
| 76 | Info Systems |
| 77 | Psychological Assess |
| 78 | Affirmative Action |

| | | | | | |
|---|---|---|---|---|---|
| Ridgewood Elem Sch<br>2820 Merriman St, Port Neches 77651<br>Kevin Schexnaider | K-3 | | 438<br>20 | 33% | 409/722-7641<br>Fax 409/721-9721 |
| Taft Elem Sch<br>2500 Taft Ave, Port Arthur 77642<br>Staci Gary | K-3 | T | 415<br>20 | 59% | 409/962-2262<br>Fax 409/963-1923 |
| Van Buren Elem Sch<br>6400 Van Buren St, Groves 77619<br>Joe Cegielski | K-3 | T | 343<br>18 | 46% | 409/962-6511<br>Fax 409/962-2043 |
| Woodcrest Elem Sch<br>1522 Heisler St, Port Neches 77651<br>Angela Abel | K-3 | T | 315<br>16 | 50% | 409/724-2309<br>Fax 409/729-9480 |

- **Sabine Pass Ind School Dist** PID: 01034066    409/971-2321
  5641 S Gulfway, Sabine Pass 77655    Fax 409/971-2120

**Schools:** 1 \ **Teachers:** 32 \ **Students:** 354 \ **Special Ed Students:** 10
\ **LEP Students:** 4 \ **College-Bound:** 95% \ **Ethnic:** Asian 2%, African
American 23%, Hispanic 39%, Caucasian 37% \ **Exp:** $653 (High)
\ **Poverty:** 54% \ **Title I:** $42,401 \ **Special Education:** $43,000 \
**Open-Close:** 08/21 - 05/25 \ **DTBP:** $417 (High)

| | | |
|---|---|---|
| Kristi Heid ..............1 | Duyen Blanton ................2,68 | |
| Tom Butler ..............3,5 | Chelsea Berg ................4* | |
| Jason Thibodeaux ..............6* | Mark Simmons ................16,73* | |
| Isabel Harvey ..............36,270* | Lane Plauche ................67 | |
| Scott Hagedorn ..............73 | | |

| Public Schs..Principal | Grd | Prgm | Enr/#Cls | SN | |
|---|---|---|---|---|---|
| Sabine Pass Sch<br>5641 S Gulfway, Sabine Pass 77655<br>Troy Gragg \ Andrew Bates | PK-12 | ATV | 354<br>25 | 66% | 409/971-2321 |

## JEFFERSON CATHOLIC SCHOOLS

- **Diocese of Beaumont Sch Office** PID: 01034339    409/924-4300
  710 Archie St, Beaumont 77701    Fax 409/838-4511

**Schools:** 5 \ **Students:** 1,500

Listing includes only schools located in this county. See District Index for
location of Diocesan Offices.

| | | |
|---|---|---|
| Marcia Stevens ..............1 | Sabrina Vrooman ................2,19 | |
| Elise Fulton ..............67 | Beverly Escamilla ................68 | |
| Karen Gilman ..............71 | | |

| Catholic Schs..Principal | Grd | Prgm | Enr/#Cls | SN | |
|---|---|---|---|---|---|
| Msgr Kelly Catholic HS<br>5950 Kelly Dr, Beaumont 77707<br>Teresa Shaffer | 9-12 | | 470<br>45 | | 409/866-2351<br>Fax 409/866-0917 |
| St Anne Catholic Sch<br>375 N 11th St, Beaumont 77702<br>Alison Kiker | PK-8 | | 600<br>33 | | 409/832-5939<br>Fax 409/832-4655 |
| St Anthony Cathedral Sch<br>850 Forsythe St, Beaumont 77701<br>Felicia Runnels | PK-8 | | 200<br>17 | | 409/832-3486<br>Fax 409/838-9051<br>f |
| St Catherine of Siena Sch<br>3840 Woodrow Dr, Port Arthur 77642<br>K Renee Tolin | PK-8 | | 183<br>17 | | 409/962-3011<br>Fax 409/962-5019 |

## JEFFERSON PRIVATE SCHOOLS

| Private Schs..Principal | Grd | Prgm | Enr/#Cls | SN | |
|---|---|---|---|---|---|
| All Saints Episcopal Sch<br>4108 Delaware St, Beaumont 77706<br>Scootie Clark | PK-8 | | 392<br>23 | | 409/892-1755<br>Fax 409/892-0166 |
| Friendship Pre-Sch & Chrn Acad<br>6750 Highway 105, Beaumont 77708<br>Casey Zimmerman | PK-12 | | 40 | | 409/898-0489 |
| Legacy Christian Academy<br>8200 Highway 105, Beaumont 77713<br>Brooke Moczygemba \ Dr Kevin Wharton | K-12 | | 184 | | 409/924-0500<br>Fax 409/924-0953 |
| Triangle Adventist Chrn Sch<br>2701 West Parkway, Groves 77619<br>Renee Leite | PK-8 | | 14<br>2 | | 409/963-3806 |
| Val Verde Christian Academy<br>3900 Cleveland Ave, Groves 77619<br>Nick Dignan | PK-12 | | 80 | | 409/962-8822<br>Fax 409/962-8464 |

## JEFFERSON REGIONAL CENTERS

- **Region 5 Ed Service Center** PID: 01034298    409/951-1700
  350 Pine St Ste 500, Beaumont 77701    Fax 409/951-1800

| | | |
|---|---|---|
| Dr Danny Lovett ..............1 | Denise Wallace ................2 | |
| Concetta Rollins ..............4 | Maris Peno ................7,298 | |
| Monica Mahfouz ..............8,27,31 | Brenda Schofield ................11,30 | |
| Dr Byron Terrier ..............15,16,73 | Dr Cindy Fussell ................58 | |
| Lynda Hoffpauir ..............76 | | |

## JIM HOGG COUNTY

## JIM HOGG PUBLIC SCHOOLS

- **Jim Hogg Co Ind School Dist** PID: 01034470    361/527-3203
  210 W Lucille St, Hebbronville 78361    Fax 361/527-4928

**Schools:** 3 \ **Teachers:** 86 \ **Students:** 1,100 \ **Special Ed Students:** 104
\ **LEP Students:** 80 \ **Ethnic:** Hispanic 97%, Caucasian 2% \ **Exp:** $520
(High) \ **Poverty:** 35% \ **Title I:** $635,817 \ **Special Education:** $267,000 \
**Open-Close:** 08/03 - 05/27 \ **DTBP:** $342 (High)

| | | |
|---|---|---|
| Dr Susana Garza ..............1 | Jennifer Benavides ................4 | |
| Roldan Montalvo ..............6* | Tiffany Forbes ................7* | |
| Gina Garza ..............8 | John Salinas ................58 | |
| Etna Ramirez ..............67 | Raquel Perez ................73* | |

| Public Schs..Principal | Grd | Prgm | Enr/#Cls | SN | |
|---|---|---|---|---|---|
| Hebbronville Elem Sch<br>210 W Lucille St, Hebbronville 78361<br>Leonor Hernandez | PK-5 | T | 510<br>45 | 87% | 361/527-3203<br>Fax 361/527-2133 |
| Hebbronville High Sch<br>210 Longhorn Ln, Hebbronville 78361<br>Joann Valderas | 9-12 | TV | 314<br>30 | 87% | 361/527-3203<br>Fax 361/527-3678 |
| Hebbronville Jr High Sch<br>910 N Wilhelma St, Hebbronville 78361<br>Anna Canales | 6-8 | T | 275<br>30 | 91% | 361/527-3203<br>Fax 361/527-3571 |

## JIM WELLS COUNTY

### JIM WELLS PUBLIC SCHOOLS

---

• **Alice Ind School Dist** PID: 01034511    361/664-0981
2 Coyote Trl, Alice 78332    Fax 361/660-2123

**Schools:** 9 \ **Teachers:** 302 \ **Students:** 4,784 \ **Special Ed Students:** 464
\ **LEP Students:** 123 \ **Ethnic:** African American 1%, Hispanic 93%,
Caucasian 6% \ **Exp:** $474 (High) \ **Poverty:** 33% \ **Title I:** $2,705,734 \
**Special Education:** $848,000 \ **Open-Close:** 08/24 - 06/04 \ **DTBP:** $158
(High)

| | | | |
|---|---|---|---|
| Dr Carl Scarbrough | 1 | David Flores | 2,19 |
| Willie Ruiz | 3,5,17,91 | Krystle Flores | 4 |
| Daniel Galvan | 5 | Kyle Atwood | 6* |
| Lisa Lozano | 7* | Dr Alma Garcia | 11,57,270,296 |
| Yolanda Abrigo | 16,73,76,82,286,295* | Arnold Garza | 23* |
| Erika Vasquez | 42 | Grace Garcia | 58 |
| Ben Salinas | 67 | Faustina Dominguez | 79 |
| Laurie Lerma | 81 | | |

| Public Schs..Principal | Grd | Prgm | Enr/#Cls | SN |
|---|---|---|---|---|
| Alice High Sch<br>1 Coyote Trl, Alice 78332<br>**Gianna Morales** \ Dr Marissa Kubala | 9-12 | AGTV | 1,290<br>100 | 74% 361/664-0126<br>Fax 361/660-2128<br>f |
| Dubose Intermediate Sch<br>1000 N Cameron St, Alice 78332<br>Lorie Orta | 5-6 | T | 416<br>25 | 89% 361/664-7512<br>Fax 361/660-2074 |
| Hillcrest Elem Sch<br>1400 Morningside Dr, Alice 78332<br>Elisa Carter | PK-4 | T | 289<br>10 | 78% 361/660-2095<br>Fax 361/660-2163<br>t |
| Memorial Intermediate Sch<br>900 W 3rd St, Alice 78332<br>Cristina Lopez | 5-6 | T | 371<br>26 | 87% 361/660-2080<br>Fax 361/660-2160 |
| Noonan Elem Sch<br>701 W 3rd St, Alice 78332<br>Monica Garcia | PK-4 | T | 417<br>21 | 91% 361/664-7591<br>Fax 361/660-2166 |
| Saenz Elem Sch<br>400 Palo Blanco St, Alice 78332<br>Marina Garza | PK-4 | T | 544<br>22 | 95% 361/664-4981<br>Fax 361/660-2167 |
| Salazar Elem Sch<br>1028 Pierce St, Alice 78332<br>**Vanessa Snyder** | PK-4 | T | 259<br>15 | 95% 361/664-6263<br>Fax 361/660-2168 |
| Schallert Elem Sch<br>1001 Jim Wells Dr, Alice 78332<br>Debra Guerra | PK-4 | T | 399<br>27 | 87% 361/664-6361<br>Fax 361/660-2169 |
| William Adams Middle Sch<br>901 E 3rd St, Alice 78332<br>Dr Judy Holmgreen | 7-8 | ATV | 761<br>45 | 85% 361/660-2055<br>Fax 361/660-2094 |

---

• **Ben Bolt-Palito Blanco ISD** PID: 01034638    361/664-9904
172 Badger Ln, Ben Bolt 78342    Fax 361/668-0446

**Schools:** 2 \ **Teachers:** 44 \ **Students:** 520 \ **Special Ed Students:** 43
\ **LEP Students:** 26 \ **College-Bound:** 90% \ **Ethnic:** Hispanic 94%,
Caucasian 6% \ **Exp:** $324 (High) \ **Poverty:** 17% \ **Title I:** $126,674 \
**Special Education:** $171,000 \ **Open-Close:** 08/24 - 05/27 \ **DTBP:** $350
(High)

| | | | |
|---|---|---|---|
| Dr Mike Barrera | 1 | Matthew Garza | 2 |
| Bobby Galvan | 8,11,76,296,298 | Zelda Saenz | 67 |

| Public Schs..Principal | Grd | Prgm | Enr/#Cls | SN |
|---|---|---|---|---|
| Ben Bolt-Palito Blanco ES<br>401 Whitney Dr, Ben Bolt 78342<br>Gloria Hamill | PK-6 | AT | 234<br>10 | 58% 361/664-9568<br>Fax 361/664-5235 |
| Ben Bolt-Palito Blanco HS<br>172 Badger Ln, Ben Bolt 78342<br>Gus Barrera | 7-12 | ATV | 257<br>18 | 63% 361/664-9822<br>Fax 361/664-5481 |

---

• **La Gloria Ind School Dist** PID: 01034664    361/325-2330
182 E County Road 401, Falfurrias 78355    Fax 361/325-2533

**Schools:** 1 \ **Teachers:** 8 \ **Students:** 108 \ **Special Ed Students:** 8 \
**LEP Students:** 3 \ **Ethnic:** Hispanic 98%, Caucasian 2% \ **Exp:** $626 (High) \
**Poverty:** 37% \ **Title I:** $25,491 \ **Open-Close:** 08/19 - 05/28 \ **DTBP:** $366
(High)

| | | | |
|---|---|---|---|
| David Braswell | 1,11,73,83,84,288 | Fidencio Madrigal | 6* |
| Melonie Miller | 16,57,59,273* | Martha Salazar | 67 |

| Public Schs..Principal | Grd | Prgm | Enr/#Cls | SN |
|---|---|---|---|---|
| La Gloria Elem Sch<br>182 E County Road 401, Falfurrias 78355<br>David Braswell | PK-6 | T | 108<br>7 | 63% 361/325-2330 |

---

• **Orange Grove Ind School Dist** PID: 01034688    361/384-2495
504 S Dibrell St, Orange Grove 78372    Fax 361/384-2148

**Schools:** 4 \ **Teachers:** 116 \ **Students:** 1,850 \ **Special Ed Students:** 195
\ **LEP Students:** 29 \ **College-Bound:** 51% \ **Ethnic:** Hispanic 60%,
Caucasian 39% \ **Exp:** $386 (High) \ **Poverty:** 32% \ **Title I:** $733,809 \
**Open-Close:** 08/20 - 05/28 \ **DTBP:** $322 (High)

| | | | |
|---|---|---|---|
| Dr Randy Hoyer | 1 | Jodi Schroedter | 2 |
| Gina Ochoa | 4 | Alton Goeztel | 5 |
| Mark Delpercio | 6 | Ernest Henderson | 8,11,57,69,74,275,294 |
| Lyn Perez | 9* | Lisa Jurecek | 16,82* |
| Sandy Clark | 36* | Will Klatt | 67 |
| Tracy Klatt | 73,295* | | |

| Public Schs..Principal | Grd | Prgm | Enr/#Cls | SN |
|---|---|---|---|---|
| Orange Grove Elem & Inter Sch<br>500 S Eugenia St, Orange Grove 78372<br>Jeanne Bridges | 2-5 | T | 559<br>18 | 61% 361/384-9358<br>Fax 361/384-2118 |
| Orange Grove High Sch<br>701 S Reynolds, Orange Grove 78372<br>Gildardo Salazar | 9-12 | ATV | 517<br>50 | 56% 361/384-2330<br>Fax 361/384-0206 |
| Orange Grove Jr High Sch<br>600 Thiel St, Orange Grove 78372<br>Kenneth Dykes | 6-8 | T | 440<br>40 | 58% 361/384-2323<br>Fax 361/384-9579 |
| Orange Grove Primary Sch<br>205 Dahme Ave, Orange Grove 78372<br>Lyn Perez | PK-1 | T | 244<br>20 | 68% 361/384-2316<br>Fax 361/384-9171 |

---

• **Premont Ind School Dist** PID: 01034717    361/348-3915
439 SW 4th St, Premont 78375    Fax 361/348-2882

**Schools:** 2 \ **Teachers:** 43 \ **Students:** 705 \ **Special Ed Students:** 70
\ **LEP Students:** 30 \ **College-Bound:** 80% \ **Ethnic:** Hispanic 97%,
Caucasian 2% \ **Exp:** $467 (High) \ **Poverty:** 30% \ **Title I:** $453,823 \
**Special Education:** $121,000 \ **Open-Close:** 08/24 - 05/25 \ **DTBP:** $351
(High)

---

| | | | | | |
|---|---|---|---|---|---|
| 1 Superintendent | 8 Curric/Instruct K-12 | 19 Chief Financial Officer | 29 Family/Consumer Science | 39 Social Studies K-12 | 49 English/Lang Arts Elem | 59 Special Education Elem | 69 Academic Assessment |
| 2 Bus/Finance/Purchasing | 9 Curric/Instruct Elem | 20 Art K-12 | 30 Adult Education | 40 Social Studies Elem | 50 English/Lang Arts Sec | 60 Special Education Sec | 70 Research/Development |
| 3 Buildings And Grounds | 10 Curric/Instruct Sec | 21 Art Elem | 31 Career/Sch-to-Work K-12 | 41 Social Studies Sec | 51 Reading K-12 | 61 Foreign/World Lang K-12 | 71 Public Information |
| 4 Food Service | 11 Federal Program | 22 Art Sec | 32 Career/Sch-to-Work Elem | 42 Science K-12 | 52 Reading Elem | 62 Foreign/World Lang Elem | 72 Summer School |
| 5 Transportation | 12 Title I | 23 Music K-12 | 33 Career/Sch-to-Work Sec | 43 Science Elem | 53 Reading Sec | 63 Foreign/World Lang Sec | 73 Instructional Tech |
| 6 Athletic | 13 Title V | 24 Music Elem | 34 Early Childhood Ed | 44 Science Sec | 54 Remedial Reading K-12 | 64 Religious Education K-12 | 74 Inservice Training |
| 7 Health Services | 15 Asst Superintendent | 25 Music Sec | 35 Health/Phys Education | 45 Math K-12 | 55 Remedial Reading Elem | 65 Religious Education Elem | 75 Marketing/Distributive |
| | 16 Instructional Media Svcs | 26 Business Education | 36 Guidance Services K-12 | 46 Math Elem | 56 Remedial Reading Sec | 66 Religious Education Sec | 76 Info Systems |
| | 17 Chief Operations Officer | 27 Career & Tech Ed | 37 Guidance Services Elem | 47 Math Sec | 57 Bilingual/ELL | 67 School Board President | 77 Psychological Assess |
| | 18 Chief Academic Officer | 28 Technology Education | 38 Guidance Services Sec | 48 English/Lang Arts K-12 | 58 Special Education K-12 | 68 Teacher Personnel | 78 Affirmative Action |

| | | | | |
|---|---|---|---|---|
| Stephen Vanmatre | ...............1,11 | Joanne Morano | ...................... | 2 |
| Annette Jaramillo | .........................4 | Dr Kristina Gonzalez | ............... | 12,15 |
| Ashley Cantu | ...........................58 | Frank Rios | ............................ | 67 |
| Donita Powell | .........................73* | Lilly Rodriguez | ................... | 83,752 |
| Lupe Cude | ..........................296 | | | |

| Public Schs..Principal | Grd | Prgm | Enr/#Cls | SN |
|---|---|---|---|---|
| Premont Collegiate High Sch<br>510 S Elaine St, Premont 78375<br>Claudette Garcia | 6-12<br> | ATV | 313<br>25 | 88% 361/348-3915<br>Fax 361/348-2914 |
| Premont Early College Academy<br>608 S Delores St, Premont 78375<br>Misty Benavides | PK-5 | T | 274 | 92% 361/348-3915<br>Fax 361/348-5010 |

## JIM WELLS CATHOLIC SCHOOLS

• **Diocese Corpus Christi Ed Off** PID: 01045170
Listing includes only schools located in this county. See District Index for location of Diocesan Offices.

| Catholic Schs..Principal | Grd | Prgm | Enr/#Cls | SN |
|---|---|---|---|---|
| St Elizabeth Sch<br>615 E 5th St, Alice 78332<br>Patricia Garcia | PK-6 | | 166<br>9 | 361/664-6271 |
| St Joseph Sch<br>311 Dewey Ave, Alice 78332<br>Katie Barrera | PK-8 | | 128<br>10 | 361/664-4642<br>Fax 361/664-5511 |

## JIM WELLS PRIVATE SCHOOLS

| Private Schs..Principal | Grd | Prgm | Enr/#Cls | SN |
|---|---|---|---|---|
| Alice Christian Sch<br>1200 N Stadium Rd, Alice 78332 | K-12 | | 25<br>3 | 361/668-6636<br>Fax 361/668-0840 |

## JOHNSON COUNTY

## JOHNSON PUBLIC SCHOOLS

• **Alvarado Ind School Dist** PID: 01034767      817/783-6800
102 Bill Jackson Dr, Alvarado 76009      Fax 817/783-3844

**Schools:** 6 \ **Teachers:** 229 \ **Students:** 3,500 \ **Special Ed Students:** 249 \ **LEP Students:** 602 \ **College-Bound:** 49% \ **Ethnic:** African American 3%, Hispanic 42%, Native American: 1%, Caucasian 54% \ **Exp:** $449 (High) \ **Poverty:** 17% \ **Title I:** $744,989 \ **Special Education:** $824,000 \ **Open-Close:** 08/19 - 05/27 \ **DTBP:** $190 (High) \ �facebook 🐦

| | | | |
|---|---|---|---|
| Dr Kenneth Estes | ...........................1 | Rodney Toon | ..........................2,19 |
| Mark Ratcliff | .........................3,15,91 | Jack Aspinall | ..............................4 |
| Jack Pruitt | ................................5 | Jeff Dixon | ..................................6 |
| Dr Lori Nunez | ....7,11,31,34,83,271,296,298 | Maribel Diaz | ..............8,18,57,286,288 |
| Julie Holland | .................16,73,295 | Micki McCrory | ......................42,285 |
| Junior Rayburne | ....................45,277 | Arlene Gallagher | ............................58 |
| Tom Head | ................................67 | Maryann Wood | .........................68,78 |
| Dandy Earley | ............................69 | Tommy Brown | ...............................71 |
| Andrea Wilbur | ...........................88 | Renee Warner | ...........................294 |

| Public Schs..Principal | Grd | Prgm | Enr/#Cls | SN |
|---|---|---|---|---|
| Alvarado Elem North Sch<br>1500 N Cummings Dr, Alvarado 76009<br>**Kristi Payne** | PK-3 | T | 328<br>23 | 63% 817/783-6863<br>Fax 817/783-6871<br>�facebook 🐦 |
| Alvarado Elem South Sch<br>1000 E Davis Ave, Alvarado 76009<br>**Jalynn Burnes** | PK-3 | T | 323<br>25 | 78% 817/783-6880<br>Fax 817/783-6889 |
| Alvarado High Sch<br>1301 S Parkway Dr, Alvarado 76009<br>Christopher MaGee | 9-12 | T | 1,105<br>45 | 54% 817/783-6940<br>Fax 817/783-6944 |
| Alvarado Intermediate Sch<br>1401 E Davis, Alvarado 76009<br>Kim Grant | 4-6 | T | 857<br>20 | 66% 817/783-6825<br>Fax 817/783-6837 |
| Alvarado Junior High Sch<br>1000 N Cummings Dr, Alvarado 76009<br>Melodye Brooks | 7-8 | T | 584<br>32 | 64% 817/783-6840<br>Fax 817/783-6844 |
| Lillian Elem Sch<br>5001 FM 2738, Alvarado 76009<br>**Tonya Kelley** | PK-3 | T | 335<br>30 | 80% 817/783-6815<br>Fax 817/783-6823 |

• **Burleson Ind School Dist** PID: 01034810      817/245-1000
1160 SW Wilshire Blvd, Burleson 76028      Fax 817/447-5737

**Schools:** 18 \ **Teachers:** 780 \ **Students:** 13,268 \ **Special Ed Students:** 1,124 \ **LEP Students:** 649 \ **College-Bound:** 57% \ **Ethnic:** Asian 1%, African American 7%, Hispanic 24%, Caucasian 67% \ **Exp:** $230 (Med) \ **Poverty:** 9% \ **Title I:** $1,255,362 \ **Special Education:** $1,807,000 \ **Open-Close:** 08/31 - 05/27 \ **DTBP:** $212 (High) \ 🐦

| | | | |
|---|---|---|---|
| Dr Bret Jimerson | ...........................1 | Brenda Mize | .........................2,19 |
| Regi Brackin | ................................3 | Emily Jones | ..............................4 |
| Courtney Peets | .............................7* | April Chiarelli | ........................9,18,34 |
| Leighanne Arthur | ..........................10 | Charles Osborne | .....................11,69 |
| Dr Eric Kibodeaux | ..........................27 | Stacy Sturlin | ........................36,81 |
| Joshua Hafford | .............................39 | Whitney Woody | ............................42 |
| Maria Jones | ...............................57 | Rachel Kistner | .............................58 |
| Pat Worrell | ................................67 | Tom Dyar | ..................................68 |
| Katelyn Tyler | ..............................71 | Stephen Logan | ....................76,98,295 |
| Dr Leslie Bender Jutzi | ..................750 | Theresa Paschall | ..........................752 |

| Public Schs..Principal | Grd | Prgm | Enr/#Cls | SN |
|---|---|---|---|---|
| Acad of Leadershp & Tech-Mound<br>205 SW Thomas St, Burleson 76028<br>Marla Bennette | K-5 | T | 434<br>36 | 51% 817/245-3100<br>Fax 817/447-5845 |
| Academy at Nola Dunn<br>201 S Dobson St, Burleson 76028<br>Lindsey Byrd | PK-5 | | 706<br>26 | 13% 817/245-3300<br>Fax 817/447-0523 |
| Academy of Arts at Branson<br>820 S Hurst Rd, Burleson 76028<br>Robert Balentine | PK-5 | | 502<br>25 | 34% 817/245-3600<br>Fax 817/447-5888 |
| Brock Elem Sch<br>12000 Oak Grove Rd S, Burleson 76028<br>Kim Kimberling | PK-5 | T | 630 | 53% 817/245-3800<br>Fax 817/293-0488 |
| Burleson Collegiate High Sch<br>201 S Hurst Rd, Burleson 76028<br>**Lindsey Byrd** | 9-12 | | 76 | 33% 817/245-1600<br>Fax 817/245-1606 |
| Burleson High Sch<br>100 Elk Dr, Burleson 76028<br>Allen Leek | 9-12 | V | 1,692 | 35% 817/245-0000<br>Fax 817/447-5796<br>�facebook |
| Centennial High Sch<br>201 S Hurst Rd, Burleson 76028<br>Ikie Holder | 9-12 | | 1,808 | 817/245-0250<br>Fax 817/447-2152 |
| Ⓐ Crossroads High Sch<br>505 Pleasant Manor Ave, Burleson 76028<br>Marcus Canonico | 9-12 | T | 53<br>7 | 56% 817/245-0500<br>Fax 817/447-5889 |

| | | | | | | |
|---|---|---|---|---|---|---|
| 79 | Student Personnel | 91 | Safety/Security | 275 | Response To Intervention | |
| 80 | Driver Ed/Safety | 92 | Magnet School | 277 | Remedial Math K-12 | |
| 81 | Gifted/Talented | 93 | Parental Involvement | 280 | Literacy Coach | |
| 82 | Video Services | 95 | Tech Prep Program | 285 | STEM | |
| 83 | Substance Abuse Prev | 97 | Chief Infomation Officer | 286 | Digital Learning | |
| 84 | Erate | 98 | Chief Technology Officer | 288 | Common Core Standards | |
| 85 | AIDS Education | 270 | Character Education | 294 | Accountability | |
| 88 | Alternative/At Risk | 271 | Migrant Education | 295 | Network System | |
| 89 | Multi-Cultural Curriculum | 273 | Teacher Mentor | 296 | Title II Programs | |
| 90 | Social Work | 274 | Before/After Sch | 297 | Webmaster | |

| | | | |
|---|---|---|---|
| 298 | Grant Writer/Ptnrships | | |
| 750 | Chief Innovation Officer | | |
| 751 | Chief of Staff | | |
| 752 | Social Emotional Learning | | |

**Other School Types**
Ⓐ = Alternative School
Ⓒ = Charter School
Ⓜ = Magnet School
Ⓨ = Year-Round School

**School Programs**
A = Alternative Program
G = Adult Classes
M = Magnet Program
T = Title I Schoolwide
V = Career & Tech Ed Programs

New Schools are shaded
New Superintendents and Principals are bold
Personnel with email addresses are underscored

**Social Media**
�facebook = Facebook
🐦 = Twitter

| School | Grd | Prgm | Enr/#Cls | SN | Phone |
|---|---|---|---|---|---|
| Frazier Elem Sch<br>1125 NW Summercrest Blvd, Burleson 76028<br>Tricia Lyday | PK-5 | T | 507<br>25 | 39% | 817/245-3000<br>Fax 817/447-4916 |
| Hughes Middle Sch<br>316 SW Thomas St, Burleson 76028<br>Dena Schimming | 6-8 | T | 1,047<br>70 | 40% | 817/245-0600<br>Fax 817/447-5748 🅣 |
| Irene Clinkscale Elem Sch<br>600 Blayke St, Burleson 76028<br>Lauri Allen | PK-5 | | 583 | 37% | 817/245-3900<br>Fax 817/295-4651 |
| Jack Taylor Elem Sch<br>400 NE Alsbury Blvd, Burleson 76028<br>Ana Ketchum | PK-5 | T | 419<br>28 | 72% | 817/245-3200<br>Fax 817/447-5841 |
| Judy Hajek Elem Sch<br>555 NE McAlister Rd, Burleson 76028<br>Lucretia Basham | K-5 | | 639 | 28% | 817/245-3700<br>Fax 817/447-4921 |
| Kerr Middle Sch<br>1320 E Hidden Creek Pkwy, Burleson 76028<br>Kalee McMullen | 6-8 | T | 1,211<br>53 | 39% | 817/245-0750<br>Fax 817/426-8386 🅕 🅣 |
| Norwood Elem Sch<br>619 Evelyn Ln, Burleson 76028<br>Christy Strayhorn | PK-5 | T | 311<br>20 | 64% | 817/245-3400<br>Fax 817/447-5831 🅣 |
| Realm Secondary Sch<br>517 SW Johnson Ave, Burleson 76028<br>Dr Jim Calvin | 9-12 | | 320 | | 817/245-1700 |
| Steam Academy at Stribling<br>1881 E Renfro St, Burleson 76028<br>Rebekah Hinkle | PK-5 | | 476<br>50 | 29% | 817/245-3500<br>Fax 817/447-5835 |
| Steam Middle Sch<br>900 SW Hillside Dr, Burleson 76028<br>**Noel Greenwood** | 6-8 | | 592 | 25% | 817/245-1500<br>Fax 817/245-1515 |

## • Cleburne Ind School Dist  PID: 01034872
505 N Ridgeway Dr Ste 100, Cleburne 76033

817/202-1100
Fax 817/202-1460

**Schools:** 12 \ **Teachers:** 472 \ **Students:** 6,749 \ **Special Ed Students:** 666 \ **LEP Students:** 1,262 \ **College-Bound:** 53% \ **Ethnic:** Asian 1%, African American 4%, Hispanic 45%, Native American: 1%, Caucasian 50% \ **Exp:** $389 (High) \ **Poverty:** 18% \ **Title I:** $1,778,362 \ **Special Education:** $957,000 \ **Open-Close:** 08/31 - 05/26 \ 🅕 🅣

| | | | |
|---|---|---|---|
| Dr Kyle Heath | 1 | Heidi Todd | 2 |
| Barry Hipp | 3 | Kim Chance | 4 |
| Chad Van Winkle | 5 | Alice Parker | 6 |
| Jeri Larson-Hall | 6 | Dr Kristi Rhone | 9 |
| Tammy Bright | 12,15,296 | Sarah Taylor | 19 |
| Ginger Tanem | 45 | Christy Burton | 57 |
| Cory Borden | 58 | John Finnell | 67 |
| Andrea Hensley | 68 | Janet Helmcamp | 69,81 |
| Dr Chris Jackson | 70 | Lisa Magers | 71,93 |
| Mike Wallace | 73 | Timothy Grijalva | 73 |
| Katie Cunningham | 285 | Jane Flynn | 286 |
| Tracy Shea | 286 | | |

| Public Schs..Principal | Grd | Prgm | Enr/#Cls | SN | |
|---|---|---|---|---|---|
| Adams Elem Sch<br>1492 Island Grove Rd, Cleburne 76031<br>Dawn Hitt | PK-5 | T | 388<br>28 | 71% | 817/202-2000<br>Fax 817/202-1482 |
| Cleburne High Sch<br>850 N Nolan River Rd, Cleburne 76033<br>Ben Renner | 9-12 | TV | 772<br>70 | 58% | 817/202-1200<br>Fax 817/202-1470 |
| Coleman Elem Sch<br>920 W Westhill Dr, Cleburne 76033<br>Marla Roth | PK-5 | T | 500<br>30 | 61% | 817/202-2030<br>Fax 817/202-1484 |
| Cooke Elem Sch<br>902 Phillips St, Cleburne 76033<br>Jacob Walker | PK-5 | T | 499<br>28 | 81% | 817/202-2060<br>Fax 817/202-1483 |

| School | Grd | Prgm | Enr/#Cls | SN | Phone |
|---|---|---|---|---|---|
| Gerard Elem Sch<br>1212 Hyde Park Blvd, Cleburne 76033<br>Tracy White | PK-5 | T | 508<br>20 | 43% | 817/202-2130<br>Fax 817/202-1485 🅕 🅣 |
| Irving Elem Sch<br>345 Hix Rd, Cleburne 76031<br>Sherqueena Jackson | PK-5 | T | 502<br>20 | 72% | 817/202-2100<br>Fax 817/202-1486 |
| Marti Elem Sch<br>2020 W Kilpatrick St, Cleburne 76033<br>Mary Boedeker | PK-5 | T | 432<br>30 | 65% | 817/202-1650<br>Fax 817/202-1487 |
| Ⓐ Phoenix Alt Campus 817<br>1005 S Anglin St, Cleburne 76031<br>Loyd Smith | 1-12 | | 250<br>7 | | 817/202-2160<br>Fax 817/202-1498 |
| Santa Fe Elem Sch<br>1601 E Henderson St, Cleburne 76031<br>Sabina Landeros | PK-5 | T | 356 | 87% | 817/202-2300<br>Fax 817/202-1497 |
| Smith Middle Sch<br>1710 Country Club Rd, Cleburne 76033<br>Amber White | 6-8 | TV | 831<br>78 | 60% | 817/202-1500<br>Fax 817/202-1475 |
| Ⓐ Team Sch<br>1005 S Anglin St, Cleburne 76031<br>Georgann Storm | 9-12 | GT | 17<br>14 | 71% | 817/202-2160<br>Fax 817/202-1489 |
| Wheat Middle Sch<br>810 N Colonial Dr, Cleburne 76033<br>Suzanne Keesee | 6-8 | T | 724<br>32 | 73% | 817/202-1300<br>Fax 817/202-1479 |

## • **Godley Ind School Dist**  PID: 01034963
313 N Pearson St, Godley 76044

817/389-2536
Fax 817/389-2543

**Schools:** 5 \ **Teachers:** 160 \ **Students:** 2,027 \ **Special Ed Students:** 242 \ **LEP Students:** 194 \ **Ethnic:** African American 1%, Hispanic 27%, Native American: 1%, Caucasian 70% \ **Exp:** $728 (High) \ **Poverty:** 14% \ **Title I:** $282,207 \ **Open-Close:** 08/12 - 05/27 \ **DTBP:** $342 (High)

| | | | |
|---|---|---|---|
| Dr Rich Dear | 1 | Bryan Myres | 2,11,296 |
| Bobby Reynolds | 3 | Mona Westerman | 3 |
| Lacey Manuel | 4 | Penny Reynolds | 4 |
| Richard Burciaga | 5 | Curtis Lowery | 6* |
| Mark Chauveaux | 6* | Dr Airemy Caudle | 9 |
| Keri Grimsley | 9* | Jason Karnes | 15 |
| Vicki Kattner | 16* | Joe Walker | 20,23 |
| Marty Oliver | 28,73,295 | Cheryl Villanueva | 31,57,69 |
| Angela Gonzalez | 58 | Matt McKittrick | 67 |
| David Williams | 68,79,91* | Kelly Hanna | 73* |
| Danna Allen | 76 | | |

| Public Schs..Principal | Grd | Prgm | Enr/#Cls | SN | |
|---|---|---|---|---|---|
| Godley Elem Sch<br>604 N Pearson St, Godley 76044<br>Keri Grimsley | PK-1 | T | 322<br>27 | 61% | 817/592-4410<br>Fax 817/389-3291 |
| Godley High Sch<br>9501 N Highway 171, Godley 76044<br>Kurtis Flood | 9-12 | AGTV | 537<br>22 | 49% | 817/592-4320<br>Fax 817/592-4294 |
| Godley Intermediate Sch<br>309 N Pearson St, Godley 76044<br>Melissa Block | 2-6 | T | 829<br>25 | 52% | 817/592-4380<br>Fax 817/592-4292 🅕 |
| Godley Middle Sch<br>9401 N Highway 171, Godley 76044<br>Leigh Brown | 7-8 | T | 157<br>40 | 53% | 817/592-4340<br>Fax 817/592-4293 |
| Ⓐ Links Academy<br>409 Bruce Rd, Godley 76044<br>Michelle Sveum | 9-12 | T | 40 | 50% | 817/592-4410<br>Fax 817/592-4291 |

| # | | # | | # | | # | | # | | # | | # | |
|---|---|---|---|---|---|---|---|---|---|---|---|---|---|
| 1 | Superintendent | 8 | Curric/Instruct K-12 | 19 | Chief Financial Officer | 29 | Family/Consumer Science | 39 | Social Studies K-12 | 49 | English/Lang Arts Elem | 59 | Special Education Elem | 69 | Academic Assessment |
| 2 | Bus/Finance/Purchasing | 9 | Curric/Instruct Elem | 20 | Art K-12 | 30 | Adult Education | 40 | Social Studies Elem | 50 | English/Lang Arts Sec | 60 | Special Education Sec | 70 | Research/Development |
| 3 | Buildings And Grounds | 10 | Curric/Instruct Sec | 21 | Art Elem | 31 | Career/Sch-to-Work K-12 | 41 | Social Studies Sec | 51 | Reading K-12 | 61 | Foreign/World Lang K-12 | 71 | Public Information |
| 4 | Food Service | 11 | Federal Program | 22 | Art Sec | 32 | Career/Sch-to-Work Elem | 42 | Science K-12 | 52 | Reading Elem | 62 | Foreign/World Lang Elem | 72 | Summer School |
| 5 | Transportation | 12 | Title I | 23 | Music K-12 | 33 | Career/Sch-to-Work Sec | 43 | Science Elem | 53 | Reading Sec | 63 | Foreign/World Lang Sec | 73 | Instructional Tech |
| 6 | Athletic | 13 | Title V | 24 | Music Elem | 34 | Early Childhood Ed | 44 | Science Sec | 54 | Remedial Reading K-12 | 64 | Religious Education K-12 | 74 | Inservice Training |
| 7 | Health Services | 14 | Title I | 25 | Music Sec | 35 | Health/Phys Education | 45 | Math K-12 | 55 | Remedial Reading Elem | 65 | Religious Education Elem | 75 | Marketing/Distributive |
| | | 15 | Asst Superintendent | 26 | Business Education | 36 | Guidance Services K-12 | 46 | Math Elem | 56 | Remedial Reading Sec | 66 | Religious Education Sec | 76 | Info Systems |
| | | 16 | Instructional Media Svcs | 27 | Career & Tech Ed | 37 | Guidance Services Elem | 47 | Math Sec | 57 | Bilingual/ELL | 67 | School Board President | 77 | Psychological Assess |
| | | 17 | Chief Operations Officer | 28 | Technology Education | 38 | Guidance Services Sec | 48 | English/Lang Arts K-12 | 58 | Special Education K-12 | 68 | Teacher Personnel | 78 | Affirmative Action |
| | | 18 | Chief Academic Officer | | | | | | | | | | | | |

## Grandview Ind School Dist  PID: 01034999
701 S 5th St, Grandview 76050

817/866-4500
Fax 817/866-3351

**Schools:** 3 \ **Teachers:** 94 \ **Students:** 1,365 \ **Special Ed Students:** 107 \ **LEP Students:** 43 \ **College-Bound:** 53% \ **Ethnic:** Asian 1%, African American 1%, Hispanic 17%, Native American: 1%, Caucasian 80% \ **Exp:** $611 (High) \ **Poverty:** 14% \ **Title I:** $179,791 \ **Open-Close:** 08/26 - 06/03 \ **DTBP:** $353 (High)

| | | |
|---|---|---|
| Joe Perrin .................................1 | Margie Fuller ...........................2,19 | |
| John King .................................3 | Lee Breton ...................................4 | |
| Odell Schronk ..........................5 | Brad Davis ...................................6 | |
| Lisa Davis ............................7,85* | Kristi Rhone ........ 8,11,76,88,285,288,296,298 | |
| Katherine Stewart ...................16* | Clint Jentsch ..............................37* | |
| Stephanie Davis .........38,69,83,270* | Clint Ishmael .............................67 | |
| John Clayton .................73,95,295* | | |

| Public Schs..Principal | Grd | Prgm | Enr/#Cls | SN | |
|---|---|---|---|---|---|
| Grandview Elem Sch<br>301 Zebra Pkwy, Grandview 76050<br>Katherine Stewart | PK-5 | T | 543<br>26 | 44% | 817/866-4600<br>Fax 817/866-2452 |
| Grandview High Sch<br>1009 Carroll Ln, Grandview 76050<br>Kirby Basham | 9-12 | V | 379<br>37 | 24% | 817/866-4520<br>Fax 817/866-2645 |
| Grandview Junior High Sch<br>705 S 5th St, Grandview 76050<br>Jeff Hudson | 6-8 | T | 306<br>22 | 36% | 817/866-4660<br>Fax 817/866-3912 |

## Joshua Ind School Dist  PID: 01035022
310 E 18th St, Joshua 76058

817/426-7500
Fax 817/641-2738

**Schools:** 10 \ **Teachers:** 404 \ **Students:** 5,626 \ **Special Ed Students:** 476 \ **LEP Students:** 530 \ **College-Bound:** 54% \ **Ethnic:** Asian 1%, African American 2%, Hispanic 30%, Native American: 1%, Caucasian 67% \ **Exp:** $447 (High) \ **Poverty:** 13% \ **Title I:** $815,089 \ **Special Education:** $834,000 \ **Open-Close:** 08/18 - 05/25 \ **DTBP:** $151 (High)

| | |
|---|---|
| Fran Marek ................................1 | Candace Fuchs ...........................2 |
| Rebecca Metzger ...................2,19 | Blake Bowman ............................3 |
| Kari Frederick ..........................4 | Gary Robinson ............................6 |
| Marcie Walker ..........................7* | Jo Lynn Augsburger .................8,294 |
| Julie Hampton ..........................9* | Michelle Snell ...........................10 |
| Rick Edwards ..........................15 | Brooklyn Shafer .........................30* |
| Faviola Arevalo ........................57 | Elizabeth Rosatelli .....................58* |
| Ronnie Galbreath .....................67 | Holly Stambaugh ........................68 |
| Tammy Riemenschneide ..........69 | Patty Webb ................................73 |
| Julie Hampton ..........................76 | Margaret Johnson .......................98 |
| Lindsey Elliott .........................274 | Jason Smith ..............................295 |
| Elizabeth Rosatelli .................296 | |

| Public Schs..Principal | Grd | Prgm | Enr/#Cls | SN | |
|---|---|---|---|---|---|
| A G Elder Elem Sch<br>513 Henderson St, Joshua 76058<br>Debra Brakel | PK-5 | T | 509<br>36 | 67% | 817/202-2500<br>Fax 817/641-2951 |
| Caddo Grove Elem Sch<br>7301 FM 1902, Joshua 76058<br>**Tanya Chernow** | PK-5 | T | 541 | 82% | 817/202-2500<br>Fax 817/645-6420 |
| H D Staples Elem Sch<br>505 S Main St, Joshua 76058<br>**Kate Howell** | PK-5 | T | 445<br>29 | 73% | 817/202-2500<br>Fax 817/556-0450 |
| Joshua 9th Grade Campus<br>1035 S Broadway St, Joshua 76058<br>**Toby Cox** | 9-9 | T | 408 | 45% | 817/202-2500<br>Fax 817/556-4640 |
| Joshua High Sch<br>909 S Broadway St, Joshua 76058<br>Celeste Neal | 10-12 | TV | 1,100<br>93 | 41% | 817/202-2500<br>Fax 817/556-3403 |

Ⓐ New Horizons High Sch — 9-12 — GTV — 19 / 5 — 47% — 817/202-2500 — Fax 817/202-8948
603 Plum St, Joshua 76058
**Toby Cox**

| Public Schs..Principal | Grd | Prgm | Enr/#Cls | SN | |
|---|---|---|---|---|---|
| Ⓐ New Horizons High Sch<br>603 Plum St, Joshua 76058<br>Toby Cox | 9-12 | GTV | 19<br>5 | 47% | 817/202-2500<br>Fax 817/202-8948 |
| North Joshua Elem Sch<br>100 Ranchway Dr, Burleson 76028<br>Tammy Watts | PK-5 | | 548<br>40 | 24% | 817/426-7500<br>Fax 817/295-9836 |
| Plum Creek Elem Sch<br>500 Plum St, Joshua 76058<br>Shelly Green | PK-5 | T | 460<br>30 | 56% | 817/202-2500<br>Fax 817/202-9133 |
| R C Loflin Middle Sch<br>6801 FM 1902, Joshua 76058<br>Damon Patterson | 7-8 | TV | 714<br>50 | 60% | 817/202-2500<br>Fax 817/202-9140 |
| Tom & Nita Nichols Middle Sch<br>2845 FM 731, Burleson 76028<br>Brian Rosatelli | 6-8 | T | 613 | 39% | 817/202-2500<br>Fax 817/202-2649 |

## Keene Ind School Dist  PID: 01035060
3625 E Highway 67 Bldg C, Keene 76059

817/774-5200
Fax 817/774-5400

**Schools:** 4 \ **Teachers:** 86 \ **Students:** 1,011 \ **Special Ed Students:** 90 \ **LEP Students:** 217 \ **Ethnic:** Asian 1%, African American 4%, Hispanic 46%, Caucasian 48% \ **Exp:** $521 (High) \ **Poverty:** 16% \ **Title I:** $242,463 \ **Open-Close:** 08/04 - 06/10 \ **DTBP:** $546 (High)

| | |
|---|---|
| Dr Ricky Stephens .....................1 | Sandra Denning ..............2,8,15,19,73 |
| Anthony Denning .......................3 | Ella Smith ...................................4 |
| John McFarlind ..........................6 | Sylvia Mora ...........................7,35,85 |
| Ted Oniel ...........................11,88,271 | Dana Stockton .....12,31,36,69,83,270 |
| Robert Hinerman ..................16,82 | Sasil Valdez ..........................16,82 |
| David Diaz ............................57,63* | Michele Kurmes ..........................58 |
| Donnie Beeson ........................67 | Tim Kosar ...................................91 |

| Public Schs..Principal | Grd | Prgm | Enr/#Cls | SN | |
|---|---|---|---|---|---|
| Ⓐ Keene Alternative Learning Ctr<br>36245 Highway 67 E, Keene 76059<br>Ted O'Neil | 9-12 | | 60<br>6 | | 817/774-5370<br>Fax 817/774-5405 |
| Keene Elem Sch<br>300 E Highway 67, Keene 76059<br>Kelly Turnage | PK-5 | T | 444<br>16 | 80% | 817/774-5323<br>Fax 817/774-5404 |
| Keene Junior High Sch<br>402 E 4th St, Keene 76059<br>Jamie Ingram | 6-8 | T | 241<br>15 | 73% | 817/774-5311<br>Fax 817/774-5402 |
| Keene Wanda R Smith High Sch<br>404 Charger Dr, Keene 76059<br>Christopher Taylor | 9-12 | TV | 186<br>20 | 59% | 817/774-5225<br>Fax 817/774-5401 |

## Rio Vista Ind School Dist  PID: 01035137
100 E Capps Street, Rio Vista 76093

817/373-2241
Fax 817/373-2076

**Schools:** 3 \ **Teachers:** 66 \ **Students:** 755 \ **Special Ed Students:** 70 \ **LEP Students:** 36 \ **College-Bound:** 55% \ **Ethnic:** Hispanic 18%, Caucasian 81% \ **Exp:** $561 (High) \ **Poverty:** 20% \ **Title I:** $282,633 \ **Open-Close:** 08/13 - 05/20 \ **DTBP:** $350 (High)

| | |
|---|---|
| Tony Martin ..............................1 | Billie Thornton ............................2 |
| Monie Bigham .........................3,5 | Angela Gonzales ........................58 |
| Chris Pinyan ............................67 | Charles Lister .......................73,295 |
| Lisa Collins ............................81* | |

| Public Schs..Principal | Grd | Prgm | Enr/#Cls | SN | |
|---|---|---|---|---|---|
| Rio Vista Elem Sch<br>501 S Cleburne Whitney Rd, Rio Vista 76093<br>**Michael Zook** | PK-5 | T | 355<br>35 | 58% | 817/373-2151<br>Fax 817/373-3042 |
| Rio Vista High Sch<br>100 Eagle Dr, Rio Vista 76093<br>Charles Mims | 9-12 | TV | 237<br>24 | 52% | 817/373-2009<br>Fax 469/405-1193 |

---

**TX—251**

| | | | | | |
|---|---|---|---|---|---|
| Rio Vista Middle Sch | 6-8 | TV | 163 | 59% | 817/760-0766 |
| 309 S Cleburne Whitney Rd, Rio Vista 76093 | | | 20 | | Fax 469/405-1192 |
| Brent Batch | | | | | |

| | | | | |
|---|---|---|---|---|
| Sycamore Academy | K-12 | | 100 | 817/645-0895 |
| 106 S Old Betsy Rd, Keene 76059 | | | | |
| Lorene Nicolas | | | | |

● **Venus Ind School Dist** PID: 01035163     972/366-3448
100 Student Dr, Venus 76084     Fax 972/232-2141

> **Schools:** 4 \ **Teachers:** 148 \ **Students:** 2,095 \ **Special Ed Students:** 187
> \ **LEP Students:** 484 \ **College-Bound:** 34% \ **Ethnic:** Asian 1%,
> African American 4%, Hispanic 58%, Native American: 1%, Caucasian
> 37% \ **Exp:** $656 (High) \ **Poverty:** 16% \ **Title I:** $387,155 \
> **Special Education:** $430,000 \ **Open-Close:** 08/13 - 05/26 \ **DTBP:** $321
> (High)

| | | | |
|---|---|---|---|
| James Hopper | 1 | Michelle Salazar | 2,19,84,288 |
| Ronnie Lisby | 3 | Tina McCormick | 4 |
| Kathy Windell | 5 | Steven Nazworth | 8,271* |
| Hollis Moore | 11,15,83 | Katherine Roberts | 16 |
| Gay Roden | 57 | Michelle Gidst-Barrow | 58 |
| Les Owens | 67 | Kelly Morris | 68 |
| Warren Hudson | 73 | Jacob Usery | 295 |

| Public Schs..Principal | Grd | Prgm | Enr/#Cls | SN | |
|---|---|---|---|---|---|
| Venus Elem Sch | 2-5 | T | 656 | 72% | 972/366-3748 |
| 20 Bulldog Dr, Venus 76084 | | | 27 | | Fax 972/366-8808 |
| Lori Box | | | | | |
| Venus High Sch | 9-12 | TV | 580 | 72% | 972/366-8815 |
| 12 Bulldog Dr, Venus 76084 | | | 44 | | Fax 972/366-8919 |
| Karen Woodworth | | | | | |
| Venus Middle Sch | 6-8 | T | 555 | 76% | 972/366-3358 |
| 1 Bulldog Dr, Venus 76084 | | | 40 | | Fax 972/366-1740 |
| Kim Buck | | | | | |
| Venus Primary Sch | PK-1 | T | 304 | 74% | 972/366-3268 |
| 102 Student Dr, Venus 76084 | | | 24 | | Fax 972/366-1826 |
| Steven Nazworth | | | | | 🅕🅣 |

## JOHNSON PRIVATE SCHOOLS

| Private Schs..Principal | Grd | Prgm | Enr/#Cls | SN | |
|---|---|---|---|---|---|
| Boulevard Baptist Chrstn Sch | PK-12 | | 50 | | 817/295-4342 |
| 315 N Burleson Blvd, Burleson 76028 | | | | | Fax 817/295-4364 |
| Jack Dunaway | | | | | |
| Burleson Adventist Sch | PK-8 | | 401 | | 817/295-6812 |
| 1635 Fox Ln, Burleson 76028 | | | | | Fax 817/295-8001 |
| Norman Rangel | | | | | |
| Chisholm Trail Academy | 9-12 | V | 148 | | 817/641-6626 |
| 401 S Old Betsy Rd, Keene 76059 | | | 12 | | Fax 817/556-2009 |
| Otto Keubler | | | | | |
| Cleburne Christian Academy | PK-8 | | 43 | | 817/641-2857 |
| 1410 Glenhaven Dr, Cleburne 76033 | | | 10 | | Fax 817/641-2863 |
| John Turner | | | | | |
| Holy Cross Christian Academy | K-8 | | 200 | | 817/295-7232 |
| 1233 Tarver Rd, Burleson 76028 | | | | | Fax 817/295-6307 |
| Karen Matejka | | | | | 🅕🅣 |
| Joshua Christian Academy | K-12 | | 101 | | 817/295-7377 |
| 510 N Broadway St, Joshua 76058 | | | 15 | | Fax 817/484-2415 |
| Brian Archer | | | | | |
| Joshua SDA Multi Grade Sch | PK-8 | | 60 | | 817/556-2109 |
| 1912 Conveyor Dr, Joshua 76058 | | | 4 | | Fax 817/556-0029 |
| Carol Schneider | | | | | |
| Keene Adventist Elem Sch | PK-8 | | 200 | | 817/645-9125 |
| 302 Pecan St, Keene 76059 | | | 13 | | Fax 817/645-9271 |
| Todd Coulter | | | | | |

# JONES COUNTY

## JONES PUBLIC SCHOOLS

● **Anson Ind School Dist** PID: 01035199     325/823-3671
1431 Commercial Ave, Anson 79501     Fax 325/823-4444

> **Schools:** 3 \ **Teachers:** 69 \ **Students:** 700 \ **Special Ed Students:** 92
> \ **LEP Students:** 10 \ **Ethnic:** African American 2%, Hispanic 52%,
> Caucasian 46% \ **Exp:** $854 (High) \ **Poverty:** 25% \ **Title I:** $211,669 \
> **Open-Close:** 08/18 - 05/20 \ **DTBP:** $371 (High)

| | | | |
|---|---|---|---|
| Jay Baccus | 1 | Marie Hargrove | 2 |
| Logan Vinson | 3,5 | Bobbi Lytle | 11,57,271,296* |
| Stephen Scitern | 27,31* | Sherry Meek | 38,83* |
| Phyllis Davis | 58* | Don Heller | 67 |
| Gary Westbrook | 73,76,98,295* | | |

| Public Schs..Principal | Grd | Prgm | Enr/#Cls | SN | |
|---|---|---|---|---|---|
| Anson Elem Sch | PK-5 | T | 373 | 73% | 325/823-3361 |
| 922 Avenue M, Anson 79501 | | | 45 | | Fax 325/823-3127 |
| Amy McIntire | | | | | |
| Anson High Sch | 9-12 | TV | 208 | 51% | 325/823-2404 |
| 1509 Commercial Ave, Anson 79501 | | | 26 | | Fax 325/823-2514 |
| Gina Overby | | | | | |
| Anson Middle Sch | 6-8 | T | 168 | 61% | 325/823-2771 |
| 1102 Ave M, Anson 79501 | | | 20 | | Fax 325/823-3667 |
| David Hagler | | | | | |

● **Hamlin Collegiate Ind Sch Dist** PID: 01035228     325/576-2722
250 SW Avenue F, Hamlin 79520     Fax 325/576-2152

> **Schools:** 2 \ **Teachers:** 31 \ **Students:** 430 \ **Special Ed Students:** 55
> \ **LEP Students:** 19 \ **College-Bound:** 90% \ **Ethnic:** Asian 1%, African
> American 3%, Hispanic 48%, Caucasian 48% \ **Exp:** $637 (High) \
> **Poverty:** 26% \ **Title I:** $191,618 \ **Open-Close:** 08/12 - 05/27 \ **DTBP:** $350
> (High)

| | | | |
|---|---|---|---|
| Dr Randy Burk | 1 | Becky Terry | 2,11 |
| Theresa Gholson | 3,5 | Russell Lucas | 6* |
| Laurie Pond | 8 | Cindy Hastings | 31,36,57,83,88,751* |
| Michelle Jones | 58* | Mason VanCleave | 67 |
| Katrina Bogle | 73,76,84,295 | | |

| Public Schs..Principal | Grd | Prgm | Enr/#Cls | SN | |
|---|---|---|---|---|---|
| © Hamlin Elem Sch | PK-6 | T | 211 | 71% | 325/576-3191 |
| 405 NW 5th St, Hamlin 79520 | | | 14 | | Fax 325/576-2358 |
| C Jones | | | | | |
| © Hamlin High Sch | 7-12 | T | 161 | 64% | 325/576-3624 |
| 450 SW Avenue F, Hamlin 79520 | | | 18 | | Fax 325/576-3926 |
| Matt Pond | | | | | |

| | | | | | |
|---|---|---|---|---|---|
| 1 Superintendent | 8 Curric/Instruct K-12 | 19 Chief Financial Officer | 29 Family/Consumer Science | 39 Social Studies K-12 | 49 English/Lang Arts Elem |
| 2 Bus/Finance/Purchasing | 9 Curric/Instruct Elem | 20 Art K-12 | 30 Adult Education | 40 Social Studies Elem | 50 English/Lang Arts Sec |
| 3 Buildings And Grounds | 10 Curric/Instruct Sec | 21 Art Elem | 31 Career/Sch-to-Work K-12 | 41 Social Studies Sec | 51 Reading K-12 |
| 4 Food Service | 11 Federal Program | 22 Art Sec | 32 Career/Sch-to-Work Elem | 42 Science K-12 | 52 Reading Elem |
| 5 Transportation | 12 Title I | 23 Music K-12 | 33 Career/Sch-to-Work Sec | 43 Science Elem | 53 Reading Sec |
| 6 Athletic | 13 Title V | 24 Music Elem | 34 Early Childhood Ed | 44 Science Sec | 54 Remedial Reading K-12 |
| 7 Health Services | 14 Asst Superintendent | 25 Music Sec | 35 Health/Phys Education | 45 Math K-12 | 55 Remedial Reading Elem |
| | 15 Asst Superintendent | 26 Business Education | 36 Guidance Services K-12 | 46 Math Elem | 56 Remedial Reading Sec |
| | 16 Instructional Media Svcs | 27 Career & Tech Ed | 37 Guidance Services Elem | 47 Math Sec | 57 Bilingual/ELL |
| | 17 Chief Operations Officer | 28 Technology Education | 38 Guidance Services Sec | 48 English/Lang Arts K-12 | 58 Special Education K-12 |
| | 18 Chief Academic Officer | | | | |

| | | |
|---|---|---|
| 59 Special Education Elem | 69 Academic Assessment | |
| 60 Special Education Sec | 70 Research/Development | |
| 61 Foreign/World Lang K-12 | 71 Public Information | |
| 62 Foreign/World Lang Elem | 72 Summer School | |
| 63 Foreign/World Lang Sec | 73 Instructional Tech | |
| 64 Religious Education K-12 | 74 Inservice Training | |
| 65 Religious Education Elem | 75 Marketing/Distributive | |
| 66 Religious Education Sec | 76 Info Systems | |
| 67 School Board President | 77 Psychological Assess | |
| 68 Teacher Personnel | 78 Affirmative Action | |

• **Hawley Ind School Dist** PID: 01035266
210 Ave E, Hawley 79525

325/537-2214
Fax 325/537-2265

**Schools:** 3 \ **Teachers:** 74 \ **Students:** 784 \ **Special Ed Students:** 70
\ **LEP Students:** 3 \ **College-Bound:** 51% \ **Ethnic:** African American
1%, Hispanic 20%, Caucasian 79% \ **Exp:** $488 (High) \ **Poverty:** 17% \
**Title I:** $121,338 \ **Open-Close:** 08/17 - 05/21 \ **DTBP:** $345 (High)

| | | | |
|---|---|---|---|
| Dr Cassidy McBrayer | 1 | Melody Collier | 2,8,11,57,288* |
| Matt Nixon | 3,5,91 | Wende McAndrew | 4* |
| Mitch Ables | 6 | Michelle Hussaker | 7 |
| Jacob Cox | 9 | Karrie Thompson | 16,82* |
| Kevin Stoker | 16,73,286* | Regina Siller | 27* |
| Nikki Grisham | 31,285* | Monty Vincet | 67 |
| Misty Heathington | 270,271,273 | | |

| Public Schs..Principal | Grd | Prgm | Enr/#Cls | SN |
|---|---|---|---|---|
| Hawley Elem Sch<br>210 Ave E, Hawley 79525<br>**Jacob Cox** | PK-5 | T | 378<br>20 | 56% 325/537-2721<br>Fax 325/537-9099 |
| Hawley High Sch<br>800 1st St, Hawley 79525<br>**Nikki Grisham** | 9-12 | TV | 212<br>20 | 44% 325/537-2722<br>Fax 325/537-4398 |
| Hawley Middle Sch<br>800 1st St, Hawley 79525<br>**Charles Hoffman** | 6-8 | T | 194<br>20 | 57% 325/537-2070<br>Fax 325/537-4399 |

• **Lueders-Avoca Ind School Dist** PID: 01035292
334 Vandeventer St, Lueders 79533

325/228-4211
Fax 325/228-4513

**Schools:** 2 \ **Teachers:** 16 \ **Students:** 100 \ **Special Ed Students:** 21
\ **College-Bound:** 75% \ **Ethnic:** African American 1%, Hispanic 32%,
Caucasian 67% \ **Exp:** $656 (High) \ **Poverty:** 27% \ **Title I:** $39,821 \
**Open-Close:** 08/10 - 05/27 \ **DTBP:** $350 (High)

| | | | |
|---|---|---|---|
| Bob Spikes | 1,84 | Mindy McCarter | 2 |
| Christopher Gasper | 6 | Christina Gasper | 8 |
| Robert Cummings | 8 | Pete Lopez | 67 |

| Public Schs..Principal | Grd | Prgm | Enr/#Cls | SN |
|---|---|---|---|---|
| Lueders-Avoca Elem Jr High Sch<br>334 Vandeventer St, Lueders 79533<br>**Chris Gaspar** \ **Robert Cummings** | PK-8 | T | 70<br>14 | 84% 325/228-4211 |
| Lueders-Avoca High Sch<br>8762 County Road 604, Avoca 79503<br>**Robert Cummings** | 9-12 | T | 37<br>8 | 70% 325/773-2785<br>Fax 325/773-3072 |

• **Stamford Ind School Dist** PID: 01035321
507 S Orient St, Stamford 79553

325/773-2705
Fax 325/773-5684

**Schools:** 3 \ **Teachers:** 59 \ **Students:** 630 \ **Special Ed Students:** 64 \
**LEP Students:** 21 \ **Ethnic:** Asian 1%, African American 10%, Hispanic 48%,
Native American: 1%, Caucasian 41% \ **Exp:** $710 (High) \ **Poverty:** 25% \
**Title I:** $197,136 \ **Open-Close:** 08/11 - 05/21 \ **DTBP:** $180 (High)

| | | | |
|---|---|---|---|
| Will Brewer | 1 | Staci Robertson | 2,15 |
| Joe Garcia | 3,91 | Ronnie Casey | 6* |
| Cindy Ford | 7,35,85* | Jennifer Hinds | 8,11,296 |
| Belinda Fernandez | 16,82* | Leann Mueller | 31,38* |
| Angie Gann | 58* | Jennifer Caddell | 67 |
| Julie Bryant | 69,83,88,270 | Michael Burfiend | 73* |

| Public Schs..Principal | Grd | Prgm | Enr/#Cls | SN |
|---|---|---|---|---|
| Oliver Elem Sch<br>400 Oliver Street, Stamford 79553<br>Kyle Chambers | PK-5 | T | 301<br>22 | 72% 325/773-5713<br>Fax 325/773-4077 |

| | 9-12 | TV | 182<br>22 | 64% 325/773-2701<br>Fax 325/773-4015 |
|---|---|---|---|---|
| Stamford High Sch<br>507 S Orient St, Stamford 79553<br>Chase Seelke | | | | |
| Stamford Middle Sch<br>800 E Reynolds Street, Stamford 79553<br>**Torrey Price** | 6-8 | T | 164<br>20 | 65% 325/773-2651<br>Fax 325/773-4052 |

## KARNES COUNTY

### KARNES PUBLIC SCHOOLS

• **Falls City Ind School Dist** PID: 01035369
700 N Nelson St, Falls City 78113

830/254-3551
Fax 830/254-3354

**Schools:** 2 \ **Teachers:** 33 \ **Students:** 340 \ **Special Ed Students:** 39
\ **LEP Students:** 10 \ **College-Bound:** 90% \ **Ethnic:** Hispanic 23%,
Caucasian 77% \ **Exp:** $562 (High) \ **Poverty:** 15% \ **Title I:** $63,966 \
**Open-Close:** 08/14 - 05/21

| | | | |
|---|---|---|---|
| Todd Pawelek | 1,11,83 | Kalyn Moczygemba | 2 |
| Mark Kirchoff | 6 | Elizabeth De Leon | 27,69* |
| Christy Blocker | 57,271* | Wayne Lyssy | 67 |
| Steve Stone | 73 | Patricia Startz | 295,298* |

| Public Schs..Principal | Grd | Prgm | Enr/#Cls | SN |
|---|---|---|---|---|
| Falls City Elem Sch<br>525 N Nelson St, Falls City 78113<br>**Jessica Ruple** | PK-6 | | 173<br>14 | 26% 830/254-3551 |
| Falls City High Sch<br>700 N Nelson St, Falls City 78113<br>Christy Blocker | 7-12 | V | 167<br>16 | 11% 830/254-3551 |

• **Karnes City Ind School Dist** PID: 01035395
404 N State Highway 123, Karnes City 78118

830/780-2321
Fax 830/780-3823

**Schools:** 5 \ **Teachers:** 94 \ **Students:** 1,062 \ **Special Ed Students:** 147
\ **LEP Students:** 57 \ **Ethnic:** African American 3%, Hispanic 74%,
Caucasian 23% \ **Exp:** $612 (High) \ **Poverty:** 25% \ **Title I:** $303,310 \
**Open-Close:** 08/10 - 05/27 \ **DTBP:** $326 (High)

| | | | |
|---|---|---|---|
| Hector Madrigal | 1 | Vanessa Pawelek | 2,17,68 |
| Jim Wood | 3,91 | Sidney Martin | 4 |
| Gloria Keller | 5 | Korey Graham | 5 |
| Daniel Oelsehlegel | 6,35 | Bernadette Bluhm | 7* |
| Gina Ortiz | 8,18,69,79,275,280,288,294 | Lisa Moczygemba | 11,57,88,271,296 |
| Holly Polasek | 16* | Micheal Kroll | 27,28* |
| Lyndall Wiatrek | 34 | Yolanda Solis | 36* |
| Jayma Wood | 58,77,752* | Terry Johnson | 67 |
| Kasey Newman | 73 | Jamie McKee | 84 |
| Frances Ehrlich | 274 | Alicia Wieding | 298 |

| Public Schs..Principal | Grd | Prgm | Enr/#Cls | SN |
|---|---|---|---|---|
| Karnes City Early Clg HS<br>400 N State Highway 123, Karnes City 78118<br>Raymond Robinson | 9-10 | | 45 | 830/780-2321 |
| Karnes City High Sch<br>400 N State Highway 123, Karnes City 78118<br>**Anthony Annis** | 9-12 | ATV | 160<br>25 | 59% 830/780-2321<br>Fax 830/780-4352 |
| Karnes City Junior High Sch<br>410 N State Highway 123, Karnes City 78118<br>**Theresa Molina** | 6-8 | ATV | 172<br>22 | 71% 830/780-2321<br>Fax 830/780-4382 |

Karnes City Primary Sch PK-1 T 149 80% 830/780-2321
203 E Mayfield St, Karnes City 78118 Fax 830/780-5376
Jennifer Foster

Roger E Sides Elem Sch PK-5 T 400 78% 830/780-2321
221 N Esplanade St, Karnes City 78118 30 Fax 830/780-4427
Jennifer Foster

- **Kenedy Ind School Dist** PID: 01035450 830/583-4100
  401 FM 719, Kenedy 78119 Fax 830/583-9950

**Schools:** 3 \ **Teachers:** 61 \ **Students:** 500 \ **Special Ed Students:** 102
\ **LEP Students:** 47 \ **College-Bound:** 57% \ **Ethnic:** African American
1%, Hispanic 88%, Caucasian 10% \ **Exp:** $428 (High) \ **Poverty:** 28% \
**Title I:** $315,566 \ **Open-Close:** 08/19 - 05/27 \ **DTBP:** $367 (High)

| | | | |
|---|---|---|---|
| Diana Ugarte | 1,11 | Stephanie Timms | 2 |
| Jerry Garcia | 3,91 | Johnnie Lopez | 5 |
| Shawn Alveraz | 6 | Kellie Kolodziej | 7* |
| Dimitrio Garica | 67 | Melanie Witte | 69 |
| Curtis Plant | 73,84 | Tim Cashner | 296 |

| Public Schs..Principal | Grd | Prgm | Enr/#Cls | SN | |
|---|---|---|---|---|---|
| Kenedy Elem Sch | PK-5 | T | 323 | 80% | 830/583-4100 |
| 401 FM 719, Kenedy 78119 | | | 23 | | Fax 830/583-3973 |
| **Katy Wiatrek** | | | | | |
| Kenedy High Sch | 9-12 | T | 84 | 56% | 830/583-4100 |
| 401 FM 719, Kenedy 78119 | | | 35 | | Fax 830/583-9126 |
| Deborah Del Bosque | | | | | |
| Kenedy Middle Sch | 6-8 | T | 113 | 55% | 830/583-4100 |
| 401 FM 719, Kenedy 78119 | | | 22 | | Fax 830/583-9519 |
| Richard Cardin | | | | | |

- **Runge Ind School Dist** PID: 01035503 830/239-4315
  600 N Reiffert, Runge 78151 Fax 830/239-4816

**Schools:** 1 \ **Teachers:** 23 \ **Students:** 238 \ **Special Ed Students:** 36
\ **LEP Students:** 3 \ **College-Bound:** 50% \ **Ethnic:** Hispanic 87%,
Caucasian 13% \ **Exp:** $1,234 (High) \ **Poverty:** 16% \ **Title I:** $94,735 \
**Open-Close:** 08/31 - 05/28 \ **DTBP:** $26 (Low) \ 📘 🇪

| | | | |
|---|---|---|---|
| **Linda Bettin** | 1,11 | Randy Ramirez | 2 |
| Pete Ybarra | 3 | Steven Davis | 6 |
| Linda Martin | 7 | Aiden Everett | 28,73,286* |
| Heather Dubose | 36,69,83,88 | Gloria Donaubauer | 58* |
| Sandy Villarrell | 67 | Aiden Everett | 84 |

| Public Schs..Principal | Grd | Prgm | Enr/#Cls | SN | |
|---|---|---|---|---|---|
| Runge Sch | PK-12 | ATV | 238 | 74% | 830/239-4315 |
| 600 N Reiffert, Runge 78151 | | | 30 | | |
| Brenda DeLaRosa | | | | | |

**KAUFMAN COUNTY**

## KAUFMAN PUBLIC SCHOOLS

- **Crandall Ind School Dist** PID: 01035539 972/427-6000
  400 W Lewis Street, Crandall 75114 Fax 972/427-6036

**Schools:** 8 \ **Teachers:** 277 \ **Students:** 4,700 \ **Special Ed Students:** 454
\ **LEP Students:** 484 \ **College-Bound:** 60% \ **Ethnic:** Asian 1%,
African American 18%, Hispanic 31%, Caucasian 50% \ **Exp:** $544 (High)
\ **Poverty:** 10% \ **Title I:** $349,654 \ **Special Education:** $536,000 \
**Open-Close:** 08/18 - 05/25 \ **DTBP:** $350 (High)

| | | | |
|---|---|---|---|
| Dr Wendy Eldredge | 1 | Larry Guerry | 2,19 |
| Pete DelGado | 3 | Amy Mitchell | 4 |
| Scott Stewart | 5 | Kyle Harden | 6 |
| Dr Anjanette Murry | 8,11,15,288 | Christy Starrett | 15,68 |
| Sharlene Gonzalez | 57 | Candice Burke | 58 |
| Rick Harrell | 67 | Monica Aspegren | 69 |
| Chris Moore | 71 | Scott Phipps | 73,76,98,286 |
| Emily Christianson | 294 | | |

| Public Schs..Principal | Grd | Prgm | Enr/#Cls | SN | |
|---|---|---|---|---|---|
| Barbara Walker Elem Sch | PK-5 | T | 675 | 52% | 972/427-6030 |
| 4060 Abbey Rd, Heartland 75126 | | | | | Fax 972/427-6031 |
| **Abby Baker** | | | | | |
| Crandall Compass Academy | 3-12 | T | 65 | 70% | 972/427-6100 |
| 400 W Lewis St, Crandall 75114 | | | 5 | | Fax 972/427-8239 |
| Jennifer Coward | | | | | |
| Crandall High Sch | 9-12 | T | 522 | 45% | 972/427-6150 |
| 13385 FM 3039, Crandall 75114 | | | 30 | | Fax 972/427-6130 |
| **Jared Miller** | | | | | |
| Crandall Middle Sch | 6-8 | T | 877 | 51% | 972/427-6080 |
| 500 W Lewis St, Crandall 75114 | | | 50 | | Fax 972/427-6129 |
| **Amy McAfee** | | | | | |
| Hollis T Dietz Elem Sch | PK-6 | T | 563 | 54% | 972/427-6050 |
| 2080 Sunnybrook Dr, Heartland 75126 | | | | | Fax 972/427-6052 |
| **Jennifer Baker** | | | | | |
| Noble-Reed Elem Sch | K-6 | | 160 | | 972/427-6060 |
| 2020 Wildcat Tr, Crandall 75114 | | | | | |
| Paige Hopkins | | | | | |
| Nola Kathryn Wilson Elem Sch | PK-5 | T | 553 | 44% | 972/427-6040 |
| 300 Meadowcreek Dr, Crandall 75114 | | | 30 | | Fax 972/472-8111 |
| **Ginger Sikes** | | | | | |
| W A Martin Elem Sch | PK-5 | T | 615 | 63% | 972/427-6020 |
| 1160 W Highway 175, Crandall 75114 | | | 30 | | Fax 972/427-6039 |
| Dave Christensen | | | | | |

- **Forney Ind School Dist** PID: 01035565 972/564-4055
  600 S Bois D Arc St, Forney 75126 Fax 972/552-3038

**Schools:** 14 \ **Teachers:** 652 \ **Students:** 9,681 \ **Special Ed Students:** 1,072
\ **LEP Students:** 798 \ **College-Bound:** 55% \ **Ethnic:** Asian 2%,
African American 20%, Hispanic 28%, Caucasian 50% \ **Exp:** $464 (High)
\ **Poverty:** 7% \ **Title I:** $700,129 \ **Special Education:** $1,025,000 \
**Open-Close:** 08/17 - 05/25 \ **DTBP:** $155 (High) \ 📘

| | | | |
|---|---|---|---|
| Dr Justin Terry | 1 | John Chase | 2,19 |
| Christopher Gibbs | 3 | Tracy Money | 4 |
| Mickey Krone | 5 | Neal Weaver | 6 |
| Richard Geer | 7,88,270 | Judy Webber | 8,18,27,30,34,69 |

| | | | | | | | | | | | |
|---|---|---|---|---|---|---|---|---|---|---|---|
| 1 | Superintendent | 8 | Curric/Instruct K-12 | 19 | Chief Financial Officer | 29 | Family/Consumer Science | 39 | Social Studies K-12 | 49 | English/Lang Arts Elem | 59 | Special Education Elem | 69 | Academic Assessment |
| 2 | Bus/Finance/Purchasing | 9 | Curric/Instruct Elem | 20 | Art K-12 | 30 | Adult Education | 40 | Social Studies Elem | 50 | English/Lang Arts Sec | 60 | Special Education Sec | 70 | Research/Development |
| 3 | Buildings And Grounds | 10 | Curric/Instruct Sec | 21 | Art Elem | 31 | Career/Sch-to-Work K-12 | 41 | Social Studies Sec | 51 | Reading K-12 | 61 | Foreign/World Lang K-12 | 71 | Public Information |
| 4 | Food Service | 11 | Federal Program | 22 | Art Sec | 32 | Career/Sch-to-Work Elem | 42 | Science K-12 | 52 | Reading Elem | 62 | Foreign/World Lang Elem | 72 | Summer School |
| 5 | Transportation | 12 | Title I | 23 | Music K-12 | 33 | Career/Sch-to-Work Sec | 43 | Science Elem | 53 | Reading Sec | 63 | Foreign/World Lang Sec | 73 | Instructional Tech |
| 6 | Athletic | 14 | Title V | 24 | Music Elem | 34 | Early Childhood Ed | 44 | Science Sec | 54 | Remedial Reading K-12 | 64 | Religious Education K-12 | 74 | Inservice Training |
| 7 | Health Services | 15 | Asst Superintendent | 25 | Music Sec | 35 | Health/Phys Education | 45 | Math K-12 | 55 | Remedial Reading Elem | 65 | Religious Education Elem | 75 | Marketing/Distributive |
| | | 16 | Instructional Media Svcs | 26 | Business Education | 36 | Guidance Services K-12 | 46 | Math Elem | 56 | Remedial Reading Sec | 66 | Religious Education Sec | 76 | Info Systems |
| | | 17 | Chief Operations Officer | 27 | Career & Tech Ed | 37 | Guidance Services Elem | 47 | Math Sec | 57 | Bilingual/ELL | 67 | School Board President | 77 | Psychological Assess |
| | | 18 | Chief Academic Officer | 28 | Technology Education | 38 | Guidance Services Sec | 48 | English/Lang Arts K-12 | 58 | Special Education K-12 | 68 | Teacher Personnel | 78 | Affirmative Action |

| Public Schs..Principal | Grd | Prgm | Enr/#Cls | SN |
|---|---|---|---|---|
| Blackburn Elem Sch<br>2401 Concord St, Forney 75126<br>Courtney Parker | PK-6 | T | 718<br>36 | 59% 469/762-4300<br>Fax 469/762-4301 |
| Brown Middle Sch<br>1050 Windmill Farms Blvd, Forney 75126<br>Dr Pamelia Luttrull | 7-8 | T | 995<br>30 | 35% 469/762-4260<br>Fax 469/762-4261 |
| Claybon Elem Sch<br>1011 FM 741, Forney 75126<br>Kristi Crabtree | PK-6 | | 595<br>30 | 26% 469/762-4305<br>Fax 469/762-4306 |
| Criswell Elem Sch<br>401 FM 740 N, Forney 75126<br>Rachel Bonner | PK-6 | | 564<br>30 | 29% 469/762-4310<br>Fax 469/762-4311 |
| Crosby Elem Sch<br>495 Diamond Creek Dr, Forney 75126<br>Leslie Rader | PK-6 | | 590 | 30% 469/762-4315<br>Fax 469/762-4316 |
| Ⓐ Forney Academic Center<br>309 S Bois D Arc St, Forney 75126<br>Steve Whiffen | 4-12 | | 50<br>5 | 469/762-4350<br>Fax 469/762-4351 |
| Forney High Sch<br>1800 College Ave, Forney 75126<br>Dr Jonathan Campbell | 9-12 | GV | 1,511 | 18% 469/762-4200<br>Fax 469/762-4201 |
| Henderson Elem Sch<br>12755 FM 1641, Forney 75126<br>Laurie Branch | PK-6 | | 537<br>34 | 17% 469/762-4320<br>Fax 469/762-4321 |
| Johnson Elem Sch<br>701 S Bois D Arc St, Forney 75126<br>Nancy McElroy | K-6 | | 506<br>25 | 18% 469/762-4325<br>Fax 469/762-4326 |
| Lewis Elem Sch<br>1309 Luckenbach Dr, Forney 75126<br>Jenny Harstrom | PK-6 | | 608 | 29% 469/762-4330<br>Fax 469/762-4331 |
| North Forney High Sch<br>6170 Falcon Way, Forney 75126<br>Michael Jung | 9-12 | | 1,785 | 29% 469/762-4210<br>Fax 469/762-4211 |
| Rhea Elem Sch<br>250 Monitor Dr, Forney 75126<br>Barbi Donehoo | PK-6 | T | 635 | 26% 469/762-4360<br>Fax 469/762-4361 |
| Smith Elem Sch<br>1750 Iron Gate Blvd, Forney 75126<br>Courtney Rodriguez | PK-6 | T | 618<br>30 | 42% 469/762-4365<br>Fax 469/762-4366 |
| Warren Middle Sch<br>811 S Bois D Arc St, Forney 75126<br>Joshua Garcia | 7-8 | | 807 | 19% 469/762-4250<br>Fax 469/762-4251 |

● **Kaufman Ind School Dist**  PID: 01035606
1000 S Houston St, Kaufman 75142

972/932-2622
Fax 972/932-3325

**Schools:** 7 \ **Teachers:** 269 \ **Students:** 3,500 \ **Special Ed Students:** 383 \ **LEP Students:** 677 \ **College-Bound:** 67% \ **Ethnic:** African American 5%, Hispanic 49%, Native American: 1%, Caucasian 45% \ **Exp:** $492 (High) \ **Poverty:** 17% \ **Title I:** $917,221 \ **Special Education:** $912,000 \ **Open-Close:** 08/17 - 05/20 \ **DTBP:** $175 (High)

| Public Schs..Principal | Grd | Prgm | Enr/#Cls | SN |
|---|---|---|---|---|
| Ⓐ Gary W Campbell High Sch<br>4814 County Road 151, Kaufman 75142<br>**Cindy Fowler** | 6-12 | T | 40<br>8 | 65% 972/932-8789<br>Fax 972/932-2278 |
| Helen Edwards Early Chldhd Ctr<br>1605 Rand Rd, Kaufman 75142<br>Melanie Bowers | PK-K | T | 485 | 81% 972/932-0800<br>Fax 972/932-6850 |
| J W Monday Elem Sch<br>905 S Madison St, Kaufman 75142<br>Kathy Allen | 1-5 | | 461<br>28 | 972/932-3513<br>Fax 972/932-2758 |
| Kaufman High Sch<br>3205 S Houston St, Kaufman 75142<br>Gavin Eastep | 9-12 | TV | 553<br>66 | 60% 972/932-2811<br>Fax 972/932-1948 |
| Lucille Nash Elem Sch<br>1002 S Houston St, Kaufman 75142<br>Alicia Thurston | 1-5 | | 501<br>25 | 972/932-6415<br>Fax 972/932-4028 |
| O P Norman Junior High Sch<br>3701 S Houston St, Kaufman 75142<br>**Meagan McNeely** | 6-8 | T | 935<br>50 | 72% 972/932-2410<br>Fax 972/932-7771 |
| Phillips Elem Sch<br>1501 Royal Dr, Kaufman 75142<br>Kara Holley | 1-5 | | 458<br>30 | 972/932-4500<br>Fax 972/932-7633 |

● **Kemp Ind School Dist**  PID: 01035656
905 S Main St, Kemp 75143

903/498-1314
Fax 903/498-1315

**Schools:** 4 \ **Teachers:** 120 \ **Students:** 1,236 \ **Special Ed Students:** 236 \ **LEP Students:** 164 \ **Ethnic:** African American 2%, Hispanic 28%, Caucasian 70% \ **Exp:** $484 (High) \ **Poverty:** 20% \ **Title I:** $458,857 \ **Special Education:** $257,000 \ **Open-Close:** 08/21 - 05/21 \ **DTBP:** $340 (High)

| Public Schs..Principal | Grd | Prgm | Enr/#Cls | SN |
|---|---|---|---|---|
| Kemp High Sch<br>220 State Highway 274, Kemp 75143<br>Jim Lamb | 9-12 | ATV | 128<br>25 | 61% 903/498-1401<br>Fax 903/498-1452 |
| Kemp Intermediate Sch<br>101 Old State Highway 40 Rd, Kemp 75143<br>**Shelby Adams** | 3-5 | T | 391<br>26 | 73% 903/498-1403<br>Fax 903/498-1454 |
| Kemp Junior High Sch<br>1000 Tolosa Rd, Kemp 75143<br>Kyle Hutchings | 6-8 | AT | 393<br>20 | 70% 903/498-1402<br>Fax 903/498-1453 |
| Kemp Primary Sch<br>601 E 8th St, Kemp 75143<br>Jennifer Welch | PK-2 | T | 324<br>28 | 79% 903/498-1404<br>Fax 903/498-1455 |

● **Mabank Ind School Dist**  PID: 01035682
310 E Market St, Mabank 75147

903/880-1300
Fax 903/880-1303

**Schools:** 8 \ **Teachers:** 249 \ **Students:** 3,664 \ **Special Ed Students:** 418 \ **LEP Students:** 130 \ **Ethnic:** Asian 1%, African American 2%, Hispanic 20%, Native American: 1%, Caucasian 77% \ **Exp:** $445 (High) \ **Poverty:** 26% \ **Title I:** $1,229,684 \ **Special Education:** $727,000 \ **Open-Close:** 08/19 - 05/28 \ **DTBP:** $175 (High)

| | | | |
|---|---|---|---|
| Brad Koskelin | .....1 | Brenda Rodriguez | .....2 |
| Steve Templin | .....3,91 | Kim LeGrande | .....4* |
| Randy Welch | .....5 | Zach Hudson | .....6 |
| Pam Odom | .....7,35,85 | Rebecca Stephens | .....8,11,57,69,83,88,294 |
| Henry Tracy | .....15,68 | James Pate | .....16 |
| Shela Koskelin | .....31* | Timbra Yoakem | .....58 |
| Kenneth Odom | .....67 | Jk Hyde | .....73,295,297 |

| Public Schs..Principal | Grd | Prgm | Enr/#Cls | SN | |
|---|---|---|---|---|---|
| Ⓐ Academy<br>822 W Mason St, Mabank 75147<br>Ray Duncan | 9-12 | | 58 | | 903/880-1600 |
| Central Elem Sch<br>19119 E US Highway 175, Mabank 75147<br>Chelsea Capehart | PK-4 | T | 543<br>25 | 64% | 903/880-1380<br>Fax 903/880-1383 |
| Lakeview Elem Sch<br>306 Harbor Point Rd, Mabank 75156<br>Melanie McAllister | K-4 | T | 286<br>22 | 71% | 903/880-1361<br>Fax 903/880-1363 |
| Ⓐ Mabank Daep<br>349 E Market St, Mabank 75147<br>Edna Duncan | K-12 | | 22<br>4 | | 903/880-1320<br>Fax 903/880-1323 |
| Mabank High Sch<br>18786 E US Highway 175, Mabank 75147<br>**Charity Groom** | 9-12 | GTV | 1,018 | 57% | 903/880-1600<br>Fax 903/880-1603 |
| Mabank Intermediate Sch<br>513 N 3rd St, Mabank 75147<br>Debra DeRosa | 5-6 | T | 592<br>21 | 59% | 903/880-1640<br>Fax 903/880-1643 |
| Mabank Junior High Sch<br>822 W Mason St, Mabank 75147<br>Barbie Conrad | 7-8 | T | 531 | 62% | 903/880-1670<br>Fax 903/880-1673 |
| Southside Elem Sch<br>109 Paschall Blvd, Mabank 75147<br>Brandi Dyer | PK-4 | T | 438<br>26 | 77% | 903/880-1340<br>Fax 903/880-1343 |

---

● **Scurry Rosser Ind School Dist** PID: 01035723    972/452-8823
10705 S State Highway 34, Scurry 75158    Fax 972/452-8586

**Schools:** 3 \ **Teachers:** 81 \ **Students:** 1,037 \ **Special Ed Students:** 111 \ **LEP Students:** 50 \ **College-Bound:** 50% \ **Ethnic:** African American 2%, Hispanic 18%, Caucasian 79% \ **Exp:** $359 (High) \ **Poverty:** 21% \ **Title I:** $271,304 \ **Special Education:** $213,000 \ **Open-Close:** 08/13 - 05/20 \ **DTBP:** $349 (High)

| | | | |
|---|---|---|---|
| James Sanders | .....1,11,83 | Cindy Wiedemann | .....2 |
| Chandra Babovec | .....4 | Jess Cleveland | .....6 |
| Rebecca Rowe | .....7,85* | Gail Crow | .....8 |
| Kandy Shirey | .....9,34* | Chad Collins | .....15 |
| David Crawford | .....27* | Heather Jestis | .....58 |
| Chris Taliaferro | .....67 | Mark Sampson | .....73* |
| Erik Scott | .....91 | | |

| Public Schs..Principal | Grd | Prgm | Enr/#Cls | SN | |
|---|---|---|---|---|---|
| Scurry Rosser Elem Sch<br>9511 Silver Creek Dr, Scurry 75158<br>Kandy Shirey | PK-3 | T | 312<br>20 | 53% | 972/452-8823<br>Fax 972/452-3434 |
| Scurry Rosser High Sch<br>8321 S State Highway 34, Scurry 75158<br>**Adan Casas** | 9-12 | GV | 316<br>25 | 43% | 972/452-8823<br>Fax 972/452-3694 |
| Scurry Rosser Middle Sch<br>10729 S State Highway 34, Scurry 75158<br>Grant Miller | 4-8 | V | 409<br>20 | 47% | 972/452-8823<br>Fax 972/452-8902 |

---

● **Terrell Ind School Dist** PID: 01035759    972/563-7504
700 N Catherine St, Terrell 75160    Fax 972/563-1406

**Schools:** 10 \ **Teachers:** 297 \ **Students:** 4,711 \ **Special Ed Students:** 446 \ **LEP Students:** 891 \ **Ethnic:** African American 23%, Hispanic 52%, Caucasian 24% \ **Exp:** $425 (High) \ **Poverty:** 20% \ **Title I:** $1,327,223 \ **Special Education:** $881,000 \ **Bilingual Education:** $420,000 \ **Open-Close:** 08/19 - 05/27 \ **DTBP:** $185 (High) \ f

| | | | |
|---|---|---|---|
| Georgeanne Warnock | .....1 | Crystal Shirley | .....2 |
| Dasha McIver | .....2 | Dianna Tidwell | .....4 |
| Stan Heisel | .....5,73,76,295 | Buster Leaf | .....6 |
| Melody Stowe | .....7* | Julie Fisher | .....11,36,69,275,288,296 |
| Dr Jason Gomez | .....15 | Dr Larry Polk | .....15,298 |
| John Young | .....20,23 | Peggy Bridges | .....27,31* |
| Debi Rogers | .....58 | Dena Risinger | .....67 |
| Stacey Ellis | .....68,79,273 | Micah Taylor | .....70 |
| Aimy Martinez | .....71 | Olivia Rice | .....71 |
| Juan Solis | .....79 | Shuck Wieland | .....79 |
| Pam Chamberlain | .....286 | David Osinski | .....295 |

| Public Schs..Principal | Grd | Prgm | Enr/#Cls | SN | |
|---|---|---|---|---|---|
| Dr Bruce Wood Elem Sch<br>121 Poetry Rd, Terrell 75160<br>Tracie Pritchett | K-5 | T | 622<br>55 | 78% | 972/563-3750<br>Fax 972/563-4774<br>f |
| Gilbert Willie Sr Elem Sch<br>1400 S Rockwall Ave, Terrell 75160<br>Raquel Villarreal | K-5 | T | 729<br>55 | 85% | 972/563-1443<br>Fax 972/563-4783 |
| Global Leadership Academy<br>305 W College St, Terrell 75160<br>Tiffany Swain | K-5 | | 170 | | 972/551-5796 |
| Herman Furlough Jr Middle Sch<br>1351 Colquitt Rd, Terrell 75160<br>Brenda Navaja | 6-8 | TV | 1,032<br>50 | 78% | 972/563-7501<br>Fax 972/563-5721 |
| J W Long Elem Sch<br>300 Creekside Dr, Terrell 75160<br>Magda Carrero-Diaz | K-5 | T | 712<br>17 | 76% | 972/563-1448<br>Fax 972/563-4780 |
| Ⓐ Phoenix Center<br>103 9th Street, Terrell 75160<br>Renae Jones | 9-12 | T | 8<br>2 | | 972/563-6319<br>Fax 972/563-4786 |
| Ⓐ Terrell Alternative Ed Center<br>103 9th Street, Terrell 75160<br>Renee Jones | K-12 | | 45<br>4 | | 972/563-6319<br>Fax 972/563-4786 |
| Terrell High Sch<br>701 Town North Dr, Terrell 75160<br>Jay Thompson | 9-12 | TV | 1,202<br>40 | 67% | 972/563-7525<br>Fax 972/563-6318 |
| Tisd Child & Adolescent Ctr<br>1200 E Brin St, Terrell 75160<br>Dwight Malone | 1-12 | | 23<br>4 | 12% | 972/551-8960<br>Fax 972/551-8848 |
| W H Burnett Early Chldhd Ctr<br>921 S Rockwall Ave, Terrell 75160<br>Melissa Nichols | PK-PK | T | 568<br>31 | 94% | 972/563-1452<br>Fax 972/563-4782 |

## KAUFMAN PRIVATE SCHOOLS

| Private Schs..Principal | Grd | Prgm | Enr/#Cls | SN | |
|---|---|---|---|---|---|
| Kaufman Christian Sch<br>401 N Shannon St, Kaufman 75142<br>Christy Butler | PK-6 | | 80<br>12 | | 972/932-4672<br>Fax 972/962-0531 |
| Poetry Community Christian Sch<br>18688 FM 986, Terrell 75160<br>Ann Horan | K-12 | | 250 | | 972/563-7227<br>Fax 972/563-0025 |

---

| | | | | | | | | | | |
|---|---|---|---|---|---|---|---|---|---|---|
| 1 | Superintendent | 8 | Curric/Instruct K-12 | 19 | Chief Financial Officer | 29 | Family/Consumer Science | 39 | Social Studies K-12 | 49 | English/Lang Arts Elem | 59 | Special Education Elem | 69 | Academic Assessment |
| 2 | Bus/Finance/Purchasing | 9 | Curric/Instruct Elem | 20 | Art K-12 | 30 | Adult Education | 40 | Social Studies Elem | 50 | English/Lang Arts Sec | 60 | Special Education Sec | 70 | Research/Development |
| 3 | Buildings And Grounds | 10 | Curric/Instruct Sec | 21 | Art Elem | 31 | Career/Sch-to-Work K-12 | 41 | Social Studies Sec | 51 | Reading K-12 | 61 | Foreign/World Lang K-12 | 71 | Public Information |
| 4 | Food Service | 11 | Federal Program | 22 | Art Sec | 32 | Career/Sch-to-Work Elem | 42 | Science K-12 | 52 | Reading Elem | 62 | Foreign/World Lang Elem | 72 | Summer School |
| 5 | Transportation | 12 | Title I | 23 | Music K-12 | 33 | Career/Sch-to-Work Sec | 43 | Science Elem | 53 | Reading Sec | 63 | Foreign/World Lang Sec | 73 | Instructional Tech |
| 6 | Athletic | 13 | Title V | 24 | Music Elem | 34 | Early Childhood Ed | 44 | Science Sec | 54 | Remedial Reading K-12 | 64 | Religious Education K-12 | 74 | Inservice Training |
| 7 | Health Services | 15 | Asst Superintendent | 25 | Music Sec | 35 | Health/Phys Education | 45 | Math K-12 | 55 | Remedial Reading Elem | 65 | Religious Education Elem | 75 | Marketing/Distributive |
| | | 16 | Instructional Media Svcs | 26 | Business Education | 36 | Guidance Services K-12 | 46 | Math Elem | 56 | Remedial Reading Sec | 66 | Religious Education Sec | 76 | Info Systems |
| | | 17 | Chief Operations Officer | 27 | Career & Tech Ed | 37 | Guidance Services Elem | 47 | Math Sec | 57 | Bilingual/ELL | 67 | School Board President | 77 | Psychological Assess |
| | | 18 | Chief Academic Officer | 28 | Technology Education | 38 | Guidance Services Sec | 48 | English/Lang Arts K-12 | 58 | Special Education K-12 | 68 | Teacher Personnel | 78 | Affirmative Action |

# KENDALL COUNTY

## KENDALL PUBLIC SCHOOLS

- **Boerne Ind School Dist** PID: 01035814          830/357-2000
  235 Johns Rd, Boerne 78006          Fax 830/357-2009

> **Schools:** 12 \ **Teachers:** 566 \ **Students:** 9,000 \ **Special Ed Students:** 940
> \ **LEP Students:** 402 \ **College-Bound:** 59% \ **Ethnic:** Asian 1%,
> African American 1%, Hispanic 32%, Caucasian 66% \ **Exp:** $200 (Med)
> \ **Poverty:** 7% \ **Title I:** $738,256 \ **Special Education:** $1,119,000 \
> **Open-Close:** 08/12 - 05/26 \ **DTBP:** $198 (High)

| | | |
|---|---|---|
| Thomas Price ....................................1 | Tish Grill ..........................................2,15 | |
| Mark Stahl .......................................3 | Cheryl Rayburg .....................................4 | |
| Paul Spencer ....................................5 | Stan Leech .......................................6,35 | |
| Carole Gish .......................................7* | Jodi Spoor ............8,15,36,74,81,88,273* | |
| Bibi Bermudez ............11,83,270,271 | Ashley Stewart ..................................15 | |
| Ken Peach .......................................20 | Sandie Ford .......................................27 | |
| Bret Bunker .....................................39 | Chris Ormiston ..................................42 | |
| Linda Gann ......................................45 | Jayne Burton .................................48,51 | |
| Daphne Morris ..............................49,52 | Francis Garcia ...................................54 | |
| Bibiana Stosberg ..............................57 | Annie Seiter ......................................58 | |
| Carlin Friar ......................................67 | Elaine Howard ...............................68,79 | |
| Jocelyn Durand ................................71 | Jason Essig ..................................73,286 | |
| Shana Dillon ....................................81 | Hector Hernandez ...............................91 | |

| Public Schs..Principal | Grd | Prgm | Enr/#Cls | SN |
|---|---|---|---|---|
| Ⓐ Boerne Academy<br>210 Live Oak St, Boerne 78006<br>Cory Bell | 6-12 | | 20<br>4 | 830/572-2600<br>Fax 830/357-2919 |
| Boerne High Sch<br>1 Greyhound Ln, Boerne 78006<br>Ross Sproul | 9-12 | AV | 1,136<br>72 | 19% 830/357-2200<br>Fax 830/357-2208 |
| Boerne Middle School North<br>240 Johns Rd, Boerne 78006<br>Thomas Hungate | 6-8 | | 871<br>40 | 26% 830/357-3100<br>Fax 830/357-3199 |
| Boerne Middle School South<br>10 Cascade Caverns Rd, Boerne 78015<br>Dr Angelia Watson | 6-8 | | 1,277<br>50 | 13% 830/357-3300<br>Fax 830/357-3399 |
| Champion High Sch<br>210 Charger Blvd, Boerne 78006<br>Eddie Ashley | 9-12 | AV | 1,739 | 9% 830/357-2600<br>Fax 830/357-2699 |
| Cibolo Creek Elem Sch<br>300 Herff Ranch Blvd, Boerne 78006<br>Krista Nail | PK-5 | | 747 | 13% 830/357-4400<br>Fax 830/357-4499 |
| Curington Elem Sch<br>601 Adler St, Boerne 78006<br>Tanya Tate | PK-5 | | 702<br>41 | 33% 830/357-4000<br>Fax 830/357-4099 |
| Fabra Elem Sch<br>723 Johns Rd, Boerne 78006<br>Troy Latiolais | PK-5 | T | 551<br>32 | 43% 830/357-4200<br>Fax 830/357-4299 |
| Fair Oaks Ranch Elem Sch<br>29085 Ralph Fair Rd, Fair Oaks 78015<br>Lauren Walch | PK-5 | | 590<br>60 | 7% 830/357-4800<br>Fax 830/357-4899 |
| Kendall Elem Sch<br>141 Old San Antonio Rd, Boerne 78006<br>Shanda Wolff | PK-5 | | 688<br>42 | 30% 830/357-4600<br>Fax 830/357-4699 |
| Mark T Voss Middle Sch<br>917 State Highway 46, Boerne 78006<br>Dr Beto Hinojosa | 6-8 | | 800 | 830/357-3500 |

| | | | | |
|---|---|---|---|---|
| Van Raub Elem Sch<br>8776 Dietz Elkhorn Rd, Boerne 78015<br>Jamie Robinson | PK-5 | | 768 | 9% 830/357-4100 |

- **Comfort Ind School Dist** PID: 01035864          830/995-6400
  327 High St, Comfort 78013          Fax 830/995-2236

> **Schools:** 3 \ **Teachers:** 92 \ **Students:** 1,052 \ **Special Ed Students:** 145
> \ **LEP Students:** 125 \ **College-Bound:** 25% \ **Ethnic:** Hispanic 57%,
> Native American: 1%, Caucasian 42% \ **Exp:** $358 (High) \ **Poverty:** 17% \
> **Title I:** $360,084 \ **Open-Close:** 08/17 - 05/27 \ **DTBP:** $102 (High)

| | | |
|---|---|---|
| Dr Tanya Monroe ....................................1 | Barbara Flores ....................................2,11 | |
| Josh Limmer ...............................3,5,91 | Kenny Webb .......................................5 | |
| Brandon Easterly .................................6 | Dayna Gwaltney .............................7,85* | |
| Dr Jerry Adam ..........8,12,57,74,83,288 | Jodi Klemstein ..................................16* | |
| Deanna Brummett .............................38* | Brad Spenrath ...................................67 | |
| Amanda Rust ....................................68 | Susan Lantz .............................73,82,295* | |

| Public Schs..Principal | Grd | Prgm | Enr/#Cls | SN |
|---|---|---|---|---|
| Comfort Elem Sch<br>605 3rd Street, Comfort 78013<br>Angela Westerfield | PK-5 | GT | 441<br>30 | 69% 830/995-6410<br>Fax 830/995-4153 |
| Comfort High Sch<br>143 Highway 87 N, Comfort 78013<br>Darren Williams | 9-12 | ATV | 343<br>23 | 48% 830/995-6430<br>Fax 830/995-2261 |
| Comfort Middle Sch<br>216 High St, Comfort 78013<br>Michael Colvin | 6-8 | AT | 268<br>30 | 54% 830/995-6420<br>Fax 830/995-2248 |

## KENDALL PRIVATE SCHOOLS

| Private Schs..Principal | Grd | Prgm | Enr/#Cls | SN |
|---|---|---|---|---|
| Crestmont Christian Prep Sch<br>631 S School St, Boerne 78006<br>Susan Maias | K-12 | | 50 | 210/254-4534 |
| Crestmont Prep Sch<br>631 S School St, Boerne 78006<br>Stacey Baxter | K-11 | | 87 | 210/254-4534<br>Fax 210/247-9607 |
| Geneva School of Boerne<br>113 Cascade Caverns Rd, Boerne 78015<br>Jessica Gombert \ Jeff Jones \ Rob Shelton | K-12 | | 581 | 830/755-6101<br>Fax 830/755-6102 |
| Hill Country Montessori Sch<br>50 Stone Wall Dr, Boerne 78006<br>Joanna Balzer | PK-8 | | 110 | 830/229-5377<br>Fax 830/229-5378 |

# KENEDY COUNTY

## KENEDY COUNTY SCHOOLS

- **Kenedy Co Schools** PID: 02091342          361/294-5381
  150 E La Para St, Sarita 78385          Fax 361/294-5718

| | | |
|---|---|---|
| Kristen Tinsley ....................................1 | Felix Serna ........................................67 | |
| Becky Hagemen ..................................73 | | |

## KENEDY PUBLIC SCHOOLS

- **Kenedy Co Wide Common Sch Dist** PID: 01035905    361/294-5381
  150 E La Parra St, Sarita 78385                     Fax 361/294-5718

**Schools:** 1 \ **Teachers:** 11 \ **Students:** 80 \ **Special Ed Students:** 13
\ **LEP Students:** 3 \ **Ethnic:** African American 6%, Hispanic 81%,
Caucasian 13% \ **Exp:** $1,518 (High) \ **Poverty:** 15% \ **Title I:** $17,944 \
**Open-Close:** 08/24 - 05/21 \ **DTBP:** $371 (High)

| | | |
|---|---|---|
| Kristen Tinsley | ............................ 1,11,57 | Jerry Rosa ............................................6* |
| Felix Serna | ........................................ 67 | Becky Hageman ..........................73,97,98* |
| Michelle DuPont | .................................... 81 | |

| Public Schs..Principal | Grd | Prgm | Enr/#Cls | SN | |
|---|---|---|---|---|---|
| Sarita Elem Sch<br>150 E La Parra St, Sarita 78385<br>Kristen Tinsley | PK-6 | G | 80<br>11 | 61% | 361/294-5381 |

## KENT COUNTY

## KENT PUBLIC SCHOOLS

- **Jayton-Girard Ind School Dist** PID: 01035931    806/237-2991
  700 Madison Ave, Jayton 79528                     Fax 806/237-2670

**Schools:** 1 \ **Teachers:** 20 \ **Students:** 143 \ **Special Ed Students:** 21 \
**College-Bound:** 100% \ **Ethnic:** Hispanic 21%, Caucasian 79% \ **Exp:** $808
(High) \ **Poverty:** 17% \ **Title I:** $21,942 \ **Open-Close:** 08/14 - 05/21 \
**DTBP:** $378 (High) \ 

| | | |
|---|---|---|
| Trig Overbo | ............................................1 | Laci Scogin ..............................................2* |
| Lyle Lackey | ............................. 6,8,11,16,36* | Roger Smetak ...........................11,73,295* |
| Darla Harrison | ......................... 31,69,83,88* | Justin Gibson ........................................ 58 |
| Kathy Owen | .......................................... 67 | |

| Public Schs..Principal | Grd | Prgm | Enr/#Cls | SN | |
|---|---|---|---|---|---|
| Jayton-Girard Sch<br>700 Madison Ave, Jayton 79528<br>Jon Lackey | PK-12 | TV | 143<br>25 | 34% | 806/237-2991 |

## KERR COUNTY

## KERR PUBLIC SCHOOLS

- **Center Point Ind School Dist** PID: 01035979    830/634-2171
  215 China St, Center Point 78010                   Fax 830/634-2254

**Schools:** 3 \ **Teachers:** 41 \ **Students:** 569 \ **Special Ed Students:** 65
\ **LEP Students:** 95 \ **Ethnic:** African American 1%, Hispanic 56%,
Caucasian 42% \ **Exp:** $566 (High) \ **Poverty:** 18% \ **Title I:** $246,342 \
**Special Education:** $124,000 \ **Open-Close:** 08/20 - 05/21 \ **DTBP:** $342
(High) \ 

| | | |
|---|---|---|
| Cody Newcomb | ...................................1,83 | Kim Bishop ..........................................2,11 |
| Sam McLarty | ..................................... 4,5 | Guy Walters .........................................6* |
| Janet Wolf | ........................................7,85 | Casey Johnson ..............8,12,16,73,79,286* |
| Beverly Newcomb | ..............................31* | Kim Bolin .............................................58* |
| Michael Butler | ..................................... 67 | |

| Public Schs..Principal | Grd | Prgm | Enr/#Cls | SN | |
|---|---|---|---|---|---|
| Center Point Elem Sch<br>215 China St, Center Point 78010<br>Jennifer George | PK-5 | T | 265<br>17 | 73% | 830/634-2257<br>Fax 830/634-2119 |
| Center Point High Sch<br>207 China St, Center Point 78010<br>Keith Mills | 9-12 | ATV | 168<br>25 | 61% | 830/353-8100<br>Fax 830/634-7430 |
| Center Point Middle Sch<br>207 China St, Center Point 78010<br>Keith Mills | 6-8 | ATV | 136<br>9 | 72% | 830/634-2244<br>Fax 830/634-7430 |

- **Divide ISD School Dist** PID: 01036014    830/640-3322
  120 Divide School Rd, Mountain Home 78058          Fax 830/640-3323

**Schools:** 1 \ **Teachers:** 2 \ **Students:** 23 \ **Special Ed Students:** 5 \
**LEP Students:** 3 \ **Ethnic:** Hispanic 14%, Caucasian 86% \ **Exp:** $264 (Med) \
**Poverty:** 26% \ **Open-Close:** 08/24 - 05/27 \ **DTBP:** $320 (High)

| | |
|---|---|
| William Bacon ........................... 1,57,73,83 | Dana Beatchge ......................................2 |

| Public Schs..Principal | Grd | Prgm | Enr/#Cls | SN | |
|---|---|---|---|---|---|
| Divide Elem Sch<br>120 Divide School Rd, Mountain Home 78058<br>William Bacon | PK-6 | | 23<br>3 | | 830/640-3322 |

- **Hunt Ind School Dist** PID: 01036038    830/238-4893
  115 School Rd, Hunt 78024                          Fax 830/238-4691

**Schools:** 1 \ **Teachers:** 15 \ **Students:** 204 \ **Special Ed Students:** 18 \
**LEP Students:** 34 \ **Ethnic:** Asian 1%, African American 1%, Hispanic 35%,
Caucasian 65% \ **Exp:** $596 (High) \ **Poverty:** 15% \ **Title I:** $59,447 \
**Special Education:** $33,000 \ **Open-Close:** 08/26 - 05/21 \ **DTBP:** $436
(High)

| | | |
|---|---|---|
| Lucy Harman | ................................. 1,11,73 | Gina Walker ......................................... 2,4 |
| Marybel Walker | .......................................3 | Lee Poole ..............................................6* |
| Jane Furbush | .............................. 7,83,85* | Cindy Lambert ...........................11,59,275* |
| Sally West | ........................................ 16 | Sarah Nichols ..................................16,297* |
| Verlene Wallace | ................... 36,69,88,271* | Linda Pipkin ......................................... 67 |
| Tammy Brown | .......................... 273,288* | |

| | | | | | |
|---|---|---|---|---|---|
| 1 Superintendent | 8 Curric/Instruct K-12 | 19 Chief Financial Officer | 29 Family/Consumer Science | 39 Social Studies K-12 | 49 English/Lang Arts Elem | 59 Special Education Elem | 69 Academic Assessment |
| 2 Bus/Finance/Purchasing | 9 Curric/Instruct Elem | 20 Art K-12 | 30 Adult Education | 40 Social Studies Elem | 50 English/Lang Arts Sec | 60 Special Education Sec | 70 Research/Development |
| 3 Buildings And Grounds | 10 Curric/Instruct Sec | 21 Art Elem | 31 Career/Sch-to-Work K-12 | 41 Social Studies Sec | 51 Reading K-12 | 61 Foreign/World Lang K-12 | 71 Public Information |
| 4 Food Service | 11 Federal Program | 22 Art Sec | 32 Career/Sch-to-Work Elem | 42 Science K-12 | 52 Reading Elem | 62 Foreign/World Lang Elem | 72 Summer School |
| 5 Transportation | 12 Title I | 23 Music K-12 | 33 Career/Sch-to-Work Sec | 43 Science Elem | 53 Reading Sec | 63 Foreign/World Lang Sec | 73 Instructional Tech |
| 6 Athletic | 13 Title V | 24 Music Elem | 34 Early Childhood Ed | 44 Science Sec | 54 Remedial Reading K-12 | 64 Religious Education K-12 | 74 Inservice Training |
| 7 Health Services | 15 Asst Superintendent | 25 Music Sec | 35 Health/Phys Education | 45 Math K-12 | 55 Remedial Reading Elem | 65 Religious Education Elem | 75 Marketing/Distributive |
| | 16 Instructional Media Svcs | 26 Business Education | 36 Guidance Services K-12 | 46 Math Elem | 56 Remedial Reading Sec | 66 Religious Education Sec | 76 Info Systems |
| | 17 Chief Operations Officer | 27 Career & Tech Ed | 37 Guidance Services Elem | 47 Math Sec | 57 Bilingual/ELL | 67 School Board President | 77 Psychological Assess |
| | 18 Chief Academic Officer | 28 Technology Education | 38 Guidance Services Sec | 48 English/Lang Arts K-12 | 58 Special Education K-12 | 68 Teacher Personnel | 78 Affirmative Action |

| Public Schs..Principal | Grd | Prgm | Enr/#Cls | SN | |
|---|---|---|---|---|---|
| Hunt Sch<br>115 School Rd, Hunt 78024<br>Tammy Brown | PK-8 | GT | 204<br>15 | 50% | 830/238-4893 |

● **Ingram Ind School Dist** PID: 01036052    830/367-5517
510 College St, Ingram 78025    Fax 830/367-4869

**Schools:** 3 \ **Teachers:** 81 \ **Students:** 1,100 \ **Special Ed Students:** 110
\ **LEP Students:** 156 \ **Ethnic:** African American 1%, Hispanic 47%,
Caucasian 52% \ **Exp:** $483 (High) \ **Poverty:** 20% \ **Title I:** $380,340 \
**Special Education:** $267,000 \ **Open-Close:** 08/17 - 05/20 \ **DTBP:** $404
(High)

| | | | |
|---|---|---|---|
| Dr Robert Templeton ...........1 | Bill Orr ...........2,19 |
| Trey Whitten ...........3,5 | April Steele ...........4 |
| Duane Kroeker ...........6 | Catherine Kern ...........7 |
| Mindy Curran ........8,11,57,83,88,288,296,298 | Holly Lambert ...........58 |
| Jack Fairchild ...........67 | Juan DeLeon ...........73,76,84,295 |
| Karen Bordousky ...........83,275,294 | Rodney Robins ...........91 |

| Public Schs..Principal | Grd | Prgm | Enr/#Cls | SN | |
|---|---|---|---|---|---|
| Ingram Elem Sch<br>125 Brave Run, Ingram 78025<br>Donna Jenschke | PK-5 | AT | 568<br>30 | 86% | 830/367-5751<br>Fax 830/367-7333 |
| Ingram Middle Sch<br>700 Highway 39, Ingram 78025<br>Karenrose Vela | 6-8 | T | 273 | 77% | 830/367-4012<br>Fax 830/367-7335 |
| Ingram Tom Moore High Sch<br>700 Highway 39, Ingram 78025<br>Justin Crittenden | 9-12 | ATV | 327<br>60 | 66% | 830/367-4111<br>Fax 830/367-7332 |

● **Kerrville Ind School Dist** PID: 01036076    830/257-2200
1009 Barnett St, Kerrville 78028    Fax 830/257-2249

**Schools:** 10 \ **Teachers:** 328 \ **Students:** 4,800 \ **Special Ed Students:** 462
\ **LEP Students:** 342 \ **Ethnic:** Asian 1%, African American 2%, Hispanic 46%,
Caucasian 50% \ **Exp:** $404 (High) \ **Poverty:** 22% \ **Title I:** $1,487,940 \
**Special Education:** $1,016,000 \ **Open-Close:** 08/24 - 06/04 \ **DTBP:** $154
(High)

| | | | |
|---|---|---|---|
| Dr Mark Foust ...........1 | Brenda Taylor ...........2 |
| Jarrett Jachade .........2,15,16,19,73,76,295* | Carolina Hurtado ...........3,91 |
| Scott Anglesee ...........4 | Brad Harvey ...........5 |
| Sue Hendrick ...........5 | David Jones ...........6 |
| Katie Jachade ...........7,35,85* | Heather Engstrom ...........8,15,288 |
| Lynn Pluao ...........11,58,83,88,275,298 | Wade Ivy ...........15,68,78,79 |
| Sylvia Flannery ...........27,31,57,81,271 | Kendall Young ...........36* |
| Dr David Sprouse ...........67 | Charli Stehling ...........68 |
| Jimmy Grmela ...........69 | Holly Bogt ...........71 |
| Laurie Rees ...........273 | Andrea Dixon ...........286* |

| Public Schs..Principal | Grd | Prgm | Enr/#Cls | SN | |
|---|---|---|---|---|---|
| B T Wilson 6th Grade Sch<br>605 Tivy St, Kerrville 78028<br>Harper Stewart | 6-6 | T | 362<br>25 | 60% | 830/257-2207<br>Fax 830/257-1316 |
| Daniels Elem Sch<br>2002 Singing Wind Dr, Kerrville 78028<br>Amy Billieter | K-5 | T | 609<br>32 | 66% | 830/257-2208<br>Fax 830/257-1310 |
| Early Childhood Campus<br>1011 3rd St, Kerrville 78028<br>Susana Alejandro | PK-PK | T | 250<br>11 | 94% | 830/257-1335<br>Fax 830/257-7885 |
| Fred H Tally Elem Sch<br>1840 Goat Creek Pkwy, Kerrville 78028<br>Gena Robertson | K-5 | T | 522<br>24 | 43% | 830/257-2222<br>Fax 830/257-2288 |

| Public Schs..Principal | Grd | Prgm | Enr/#Cls | SN | |
|---|---|---|---|---|---|
| Ⓐ Hill Country High Sch<br>1200 Sidney Baker St, Kerrville 78028<br>Steve Schwarz | 11-12 | TV | 43<br>2 | 74% | 830/257-2232<br>Fax 830/792-5020 |
| Ⓐ Kerrville Discipline Alt Sch<br>1010 Barnett St, Kerrville 78028<br>Steve Schwarz | 7-12 | | 40<br>3 | | 830/257-1332<br>Fax 830/895-1481 |
| Nimitz Elem Sch<br>100 Valley View Dr, Kerrville 78028<br>Julie Johnson | K-5 | T | 482<br>26 | 66% | 830/257-2209<br>Fax 830/895-7905 |
| Peterson Middle Sch<br>1607 Sidney Baker St, Kerrville 78028<br>Tamela Crawford | 7-8 | TV | 737<br>54 | 55% | 830/257-2204<br>Fax 830/257-1300 |
| Starkey Elem Sch<br>1030 W Main St, Kerrville 78028<br>Jenna Wentrcek | K-5 | T | 537<br>29 | 61% | 830/257-2210<br>Fax 830/792-3727 |
| Tivy High Sch<br>3250 Loop 534, Kerrville 78028<br>Shelby Balser | 9-12 | TV | 340<br>80 | 44% | 830/257-2212<br>Fax 830/895-0411 |

## KERR CATHOLIC SCHOOLS

● **Archdiocese San Antonio Ed Off** PID: 00999724
Listing includes only schools located in this county. See District Index for
location of Diocesan Offices.

| Catholic Schs..Principal | Grd | Prgm | Enr/#Cls | SN | |
|---|---|---|---|---|---|
| Notre Dame Sch<br>907 Main St, Kerrville 78028<br>Sandi Killo | PK-8 | | 130<br>17 | | 830/257-6707<br>Fax 830/792-4370 |
| Our Lady of the Hills Cath HS<br>235 Peterson Farm Rd, Kerrville 78028<br>Therese Schwarz | 9-12 | | 109<br>5 | | 830/895-0501<br>Fax 830/895-3470 |

## KERR PRIVATE SCHOOLS

| Private Schs..Principal | Grd | Prgm | Enr/#Cls | SN | |
|---|---|---|---|---|---|
| Hill Country Adventist Sch<br>611 Harper Rd, Kerrville 78028<br>Brendia Bennett | 1-8 | | 17<br>2 | | 830/257-3903 |

## KIMBLE COUNTY

## KIMBLE PUBLIC SCHOOLS

● **Junction Ind School Dist** PID: 01036155    325/446-3510
1700 College St, Junction 76849    Fax 325/446-4413

**Schools:** 3 \ **Teachers:** 58 \ **Students:** 605 \ **Special Ed Students:** 78
\ **LEP Students:** 20 \ **College-Bound:** 80% \ **Ethnic:** Hispanic 39%,
Caucasian 61% \ **Exp:** $728 (High) \ **Poverty:** 35% \ **Title I:** $278,220 \
**Open-Close:** 08/20 - 05/27 \ **DTBP:** $389 (High)

| | | | |
|---|---|---|---|
| Mike Carter ...........1 | Cheryl Herring ...........2,84 |
| Mary Condarco ...........4 | John Contrucci ...........6 |
| Renee Schulze ...........11 | Jennifer Martinez ...........16,82* |

Robin Gardner ...................... 38,83,85,270*    Renee Braswell ...................................... 57*
Lainey Simon ....................................... 58    Luke Levien ......................................... 67
Kaycie Sullivan .................................73,295*

| Public Schs..Principal | Grd | Prgm | Enr/#Cls | SN |
|---|---|---|---|---|
| Junction Elem Sch<br>1700 College St, Junction 76849<br>**Janel Murff** | PK-5 | T | 296<br>24 | 74% 325/446-2055<br>Fax 325/446-4569 |
| Junction High Sch<br>1700 College St, Junction 76849<br>Dana Davis | 9-12 | T | 173<br>22 | 51% 325/446-3326<br>Fax 325/446-8206 |
| Junction Middle Sch<br>1700 College St, Junction 76849<br>Joe Jones | 6-8 | T | 136<br>20 | 63% 325/446-2464<br>Fax 325/446-2255 |

## KING COUNTY

## KING PUBLIC SCHOOLS

● **Guthrie Common School Dist** PID: 01036193        806/596-4466
301 Jaguar Ln, Guthrie 79236                          Fax 806/596-4519

**Schools:** 1 \ **Teachers:** 20 \ **Students:** 95 \ **Special Ed Students:** 6
\ **LEP Students:** 4 \ **College-Bound:** 92% \ **Ethnic:** Hispanic 8%,
Caucasian 92% \ **Exp:** $1,178 (High) \ **Poverty:** 13% \ **Title I:** $1,494 \
**Open-Close:** 08/21 - 05/18 \ **DTBP:** $407 (High) \ 🅕 🅣

Kevin Chisum .................................1,83    Cynthia Fox ........................................2
James Gilbert ...................................... 3*    Jodi Tarver ..........................................7*
Jodie Reel ......................................8,31*    Lynn Hill ............................12,69,88,294
McKenzie Chisum ..........................57,271*    Sharrmie Bergvall ......................58,275*
Travis Adams ...................................... 67    Trent Van Meter ........................73,295*

| Public Schs..Principal | Grd | Prgm | Enr/#Cls | SN |
|---|---|---|---|---|
| Guthrie Sch<br>301 Jaguar Ln, Guthrie 79236<br>Lynn Hill | PK-12 | V | 95<br>16 | 24% 806/596-4466 |

## KINNEY COUNTY

## KINNEY PUBLIC SCHOOLS

● **Brackett Ind School Dist** PID: 01036222          830/563-2491
201 N Ann St, Brackettville 78832                     Fax 830/563-9264

**Schools:** 3 \ **Teachers:** 58 \ **Students:** 570 \ **Special Ed Students:** 69
\ **LEP Students:** 24 \ **College-Bound:** 80% \ **Ethnic:** Hispanic 70%,
Caucasian 29% \ **Exp:** $452 (High) \ **Poverty:** 23% \ **Title I:** $173,640 \
**Open-Close:** 08/20 - 05/27 \ **DTBP:** $408 (High)

Guillermo Mancha ...................................1    Marla Madrid ...............................2,11,84
Fernando Quiraz .....................................3    Honey Bee Meyers ..............................4
Isauro Rivas ...........................................5    Gary Griffin .........................................6*
Savannah Molinar ..................................7    Cindy Welch .......................................31

---

Jeannie Moulton ...............................37,69    Dario Gonzalez ................................... 57*
Michael Paxon ..................................... 67    Susan Esparza ................................... 68
Michael Munoz ..................................... 73*    Christine Hutchison ......................77,88*

| Public Schs..Principal | Grd | Prgm | Enr/#Cls | SN |
|---|---|---|---|---|
| Brackett High Sch<br>400 N Ann St, Brackettville 78832<br>Christy Price | 9-12 | ATV | 169<br>40 | 52% 830/563-2480<br>Fax 830/563-3213 |
| Brackett Junior High Sch<br>400 N Ann St, Brackettville 78832<br>Daron Worrell | 6-8 | AT | 133<br>8 | 58% 830/563-2480<br>Fax 830/563-3213 |
| Jones Elem Sch<br>400 N Ann St, Brackettville 78832<br>**Eliza Diaz** | PK-5 | T | 233<br>15 | 60% 830/563-2492<br>Fax 830/563-9355 |

## KLEBERG COUNTY

## KLEBERG PUBLIC SCHOOLS

● **Kingsville Ind School Dist** PID: 01036258        361/592-3387
207 N 3rd St, Kingsville 78363                        Fax 361/595-7805

**Schools:** 8 \ **Teachers:** 207 \ **Students:** 3,050 \ **Special Ed Students:** 420
\ **LEP Students:** 98 \ **College-Bound:** 50% \ **Ethnic:** Asian 1%, African
American 4%, Hispanic 86%, Caucasian 10% \ **Exp:** $562 (High) \
**Poverty:** 34% \ **Title I:** $2,181,644 \ **Special Education:** $729,000 \
**Open-Close:** 08/24 - 06/04 \ **DTBP:** $169 (High) \ 🅕 🅣

Dr Cecilia Reynolds-Perez .................1    Peter Pitts .....................................2,68
Michelle Butler ...................................... 4    Michael Davila .....................................6
Lou Wilson .......................................7,85*    Kamara Adams .................................8,15
Porfirio Mendez .................................23*    Joe Martinez ................................28,73
Brian Coufal ........................................ 67    Rolando Bazan ................................ 295

| Public Schs..Principal | Grd | Prgm | Enr/#Cls | SN |
|---|---|---|---|---|
| Gillett Intermediate Sch<br>1007 N 17th St, Kingsville 78363<br>Belinda Gamez \ **Adriana Gutierrez** | 5-6 | T | 453<br>40 | 81% 361/595-8200<br>Fax 361/595-9008<br>🅕 🅣 |
| Ⓐ H M K Care Academy<br>2210 S Brahma Blvd, Kingsville 78363<br>Ismael Maldonado | 9-12 | | 17 | 361/595-8600 |
| H M King High Sch<br>2210 S Brahma Blvd, Kingsville 78363<br>Gregory Mihleder | 9-12 | TV | 960<br>89 | 64% 361/595-8600<br>Fax 361/595-9170 |
| Harvey Elem Sch<br>1301 E Kenedy Ave, Kingsville 78363<br>Abigayle Barton | PK-4 | T | 441<br>26 | 84% 361/592-4327<br>Fax 361/595-9130 |
| Kleberg Elem Sch<br>900 N 6th St, Kingsville 78363<br>Ode Moreno | PK-4 | T | 270<br>23 | 95% 361/592-2615<br>Fax 361/595-9145 |
| Memorial Middle Sch<br>915 S Armstrong Ave, Kingsville 78363<br>Dr Alys Williams | 7-8 | T | 404<br>45 | 82% 361/595-8675<br>Fax 361/595-4198<br>🅕 🅣 |
| N M Harrel Elem Sch<br>925 W Johnston Ave, Kingsville 78363<br>John Trevino | PK-4 | T | 261<br>13 | 100% 361/592-9305<br>Fax 361/516-1313 |
| Perez Elem Sch<br>1111 E Ailsie Ave, Kingsville 78363<br>**Analese Tennyson** | PK-4 | T | 445<br>22 | 73% 361/592-8511<br>Fax 361/516-1468 |

---

| | | | | | | | | | | | | | |
|---|---|---|---|---|---|---|---|---|---|---|---|---|---|
| 1 | Superintendent | 8 | Curric/Instruct K-12 | 19 | Chief Financial Officer | 29 | Family/Consumer Science | 39 | Social Studies K-12 | 49 | English/Lang Arts Elem | 59 | Special Education Elem | 69 | Academic Assessment |
| 2 | Bus/Finance/Purchasing | 9 | Curric/Instruct Elem | 20 | Art K-12 | 30 | Adult Education | 40 | Social Studies Elem | 50 | English/Lang Arts Sec | 60 | Special Education Sec | 70 | Research/Development |
| 3 | Buildings And Grounds | 10 | Curric/Instruct Sec | 21 | Art Elem | 31 | Career/Sch-to-Work K-12 | 41 | Social Studies Sec | 51 | Reading K-12 | 61 | Foreign/World Lang K-12 | 71 | Public Information |
| 4 | Food Service | 11 | Federal Program | 22 | Art Sec | 32 | Career/Sch-to-Work Elem | 42 | Science K-12 | 52 | Reading Elem | 62 | Foreign/World Lang Elem | 72 | Summer School |
| 5 | Transportation | 12 | Title I | 23 | Music K-12 | 33 | Career/Sch-to-Work Sec | 43 | Science Elem | 53 | Reading Sec | 63 | Foreign/World Lang Sec | 73 | Instructional Tech |
| 6 | Athletic | 13 | Title V | 24 | Music Elem | 34 | Early Childhood Ed | 44 | Science Sec | 54 | Remedial Reading K-12 | 64 | Religious Education K-12 | 74 | Inservice Training |
| 7 | Health Services | 14 | Instructional Media Svcs | 25 | Music Sec | 35 | Health/Phys Education | 45 | Math K-12 | 55 | Remedial Reading Elem | 65 | Religious Education Elem | 75 | Marketing/Distributive |
| | | 15 | Asst Superintendent | 26 | Business Education | 36 | Guidance Services K-12 | 46 | Math Elem | 56 | Remedial Reading Sec | 66 | Religious Education Sec | 76 | Info Systems |
| | | 16 | Instructional Media Svcs | 27 | Career & Tech Ed | 37 | Guidance Services Elem | 47 | Math Sec | 57 | Bilingual/ELL | 67 | School Board President | 77 | Psychological Assess |
| | | 17 | Chief Operations Officer | 28 | Technology Education | 38 | Guidance Services Sec | 48 | English/Lang Arts K-12 | 58 | Special Education K-12 | 68 | Teacher Personnel | 78 | Affirmative Action |
| | | 18 | Chief Academic Officer | | | | | | | | | | | | |

## • Ricardo Ind School Dist PID: 01036375
138 W County Road 2160, Kingsville 78363

361/593-0703
Fax 361/592-3101

Schools: 1 \ Teachers: 45 \ Students: 670 \ Special Ed Students: 50 \ LEP Students: 16 \ Ethnic: African American 2%, Hispanic 81%, Caucasian 17% \ Exp: $198 (Low) \ Poverty: 24% \ Title I: $262,035 \ Open-Close: 08/17 - 05/26 \ DTBP: $334 (High) \ 🇹

| | | |
|---|---|---|
| Dr Sam Bueno ...................................1 | Andrew Smith ...............................2,11,296 | |
| Alfredo Olivarez .......................3,16,83 | Noemie Garza ...............................4* | |
| Frank Lopez .....................................6 | Suzie Howard ...............................7,85 | |
| Dr Marci Braswell ......................9,57* | Charles Saverline ...............................67 | |
| Monika Garza ...............69,88,270 | Tim Etzler ...............................73,84 | |
| Gina Viches ...............................288* | | |

| Public Schs..Principal | Grd | Prgm | Enr/#Cls | SN | |
|---|---|---|---|---|---|
| Ricardo Elem Middle Sch<br>138 W County Road 2160, Kingsville 78363<br>Dr Marci Braswell \ Gina Vilches | PK-8 | T | 670<br>45 | 48% | 361/592-6465 |

## • Riviera Ind School Dist PID: 01036399
203 Seahawk Dr, Riviera 78379

361/296-3101
Fax 361/296-3108

Schools: 2 \ Teachers: 39 \ Students: 440 \ Special Ed Students: 35 \ LEP Students: 18 \ Ethnic: Hispanic 76%, Caucasian 24% \ Exp: $393 (High) \ Poverty: 16% \ Title I: $53,940 \ Special Education: $75,000 \ Open-Close: 08/13 - 05/27 \ DTBP: $350 (High)

| | | |
|---|---|---|
| Karen Unterbrink ...................................1 | Jose Betancourt ...............2,4,5,11,91 | |
| Virginia Pena ...................................2 | Toby Yaklin ...............................3 | |
| Nathan Borden ...................................6* | Brooke Hicky ...............12,31,69,92 | |
| Mable Pippin ...................................16 | Burt Bull ...............................67 | |
| Rick Gonzalez ...............................73,84 | | |

| Public Schs..Principal | Grd | Prgm | Enr/#Cls | SN | |
|---|---|---|---|---|---|
| Kaufer High Sch<br>203 Seahawk Dr, Riviera 78379<br>Dawn Schuenemann | 7-12 | ATV | 248<br>20 | 66% | 361/296-3607<br>Fax 361/296-3845 |
| Nanny Elem Sch<br>203 Seahawk Dr, Riviera 78379<br>Tarrah Dobson | PK-6 | T | 178<br>13 | 66% | 361/296-2446<br>Fax 361/296-3461 |

## • Santa Gertrudis Ind Sch Dist PID: 01809536
Highway 141 King Ranch, Kingsville 78363

361/384-5087
Fax 361/592-7736

Schools: 2 \ Teachers: 52 \ Students: 800 \ Special Ed Students: 21 \ LEP Students: 7 \ College-Bound: 80% \ Ethnic: Asian 4%, African American 1%, Hispanic 72%, Caucasian 22% \ Poverty: 33% \ Special Education: $99,000 \ Open-Close: 07/29 - 05/24 \ DTBP: $349 (High)

| | | |
|---|---|---|
| Veronica Alfaro ...................................1 | Amanda Ramirez ...............................2 | |
| Norma Carrales ...................................4* | Marissa Flores ...............................7* | |
| Nicole Rodriguez ...........11,58,271,275,296 | Susan Rutherford ...............16,69,82,294* | |
| Leonor De Los Santos ...........................31 | Carrie DeLaney ...............................67 | |
| Gerry Lopez ...................................73 | Julie Greenwood ...............................83,85* | |

| Public Schs..Principal | Grd | Prgm | Enr/#Cls | SN | |
|---|---|---|---|---|---|
| Ⓨ Academy High Sch<br>1055 W Santa Gertrudis, Kingsville 78363<br>**Charles Odom** | 9-12 | M | 355<br>18 | | 361/384-5041<br>Fax 361/592-5335 |
| Ⓨ Santa Gertrudis Elem MS<br>803 Santa Rosa, Kingsville 78364<br>**Fatima Garcia** | PK-8 | MT | 449<br>10 | 44% | 361/384-5046<br>Fax 361/592-3128 |

## KLEBERG PRIVATE SCHOOLS

| Private Schs..Principal | Grd | Prgm | Enr/#Cls | SN | |
|---|---|---|---|---|---|
| Epiphany Montessori Sch<br>206 N 3rd St, Kingsville 78363<br>Peggy DeRouen | PK-K | | 25<br>10 | | 361/592-2871<br>Fax 361/592-2105 |
| Presbyterian Pan American Sch<br>223 N FM 772, Kingsville 78363<br>Ellie Perez | 9-12 | | 140<br>20 | | 361/592-4307<br>Fax 361/592-6126 |

# KNOX COUNTY

## KNOX PUBLIC SCHOOLS

## • Benjamin Ind School Dist PID: 01036442
300 Hayes St, Benjamin 79505

940/459-2231
Fax 940/459-2007

Schools: 1 \ Teachers: 15 \ Students: 108 \ Special Ed Students: 12 \ LEP Students: 3 \ College-Bound: 75% \ Ethnic: Asian 1%, Hispanic 44%, Caucasian 55% \ Exp: $1,792 (High) \ Poverty: 20% \ Title I: $18,735 \ Open-Close: 08/19 - 05/21 \ DTBP: $319 (High) \ 🇫 🇹

| | | |
|---|---|---|
| Olivia Gloria ...............................1,11,83,288 | Stacia Propps ...............................2,84 | |
| Shawn Donham ...............................3* | Gracie Homstead ...............................4 | |
| James Jackson ...............................6* | Rebecca Clark ...............................7* | |
| Melissa Everson ...............57,58,271,286* | Stephen Keeler ...............................67 | |

| Public Schs..Principal | Grd | Prgm | Enr/#Cls | SN | |
|---|---|---|---|---|---|
| Benjamin Sch<br>300 Hayes St, Benjamin 79505<br>Olivia Gloria | PK-12 | | 108<br>10 | 69% | 940/459-2231 |

## • Knox City-O'Brien Cons Ind SD PID: 01036507
606 E Main St, Knox City 79529

940/657-3521
Fax 940/657-3379

Schools: 3 \ Teachers: 30 \ Students: 280 \ Special Ed Students: 38 \ LEP Students: 15 \ Ethnic: Asian 1%, African American 3%, Hispanic 54%, Caucasian 41% \ Exp: $1,027 (High) \ Poverty: 23% \ Title I: $83,156 \ Open-Close: 08/18 - 05/21 \ DTBP: $350 (High) \ 🇫 🇹

| | | |
|---|---|---|
| Colin Howeth ...................................1,84 | Tammy Gonzales ...............................2,4,11,19 | |
| Terry Butler ...................................3 | Caleb Calloway ...............................6 | |
| Mandi Perry ...................................7 | Marsha Quade ...............................9,57,271* | |
| Mark Tucker ...............10,83,88,275 | Christie Howeth ...............34,69,270* | |
| Jennifer Caddell ...............................58 | Joe Albus ...............................67 | |
| Sharon Wainscott ...............................68 | Stony Krusemark ...............73,88,98,286* | |
| Jordan Carter ...................................298 | | |

| Public Schs..Principal | Grd | Prgm | Enr/#Cls | SN | |
|---|---|---|---|---|---|
| Knox City Elem Sch<br>300 N 4th Street, Knox City 79529<br>Marsha Quade | PK-4 | T | 99<br>13 | 76% | 940/657-3147 |
| Knox City High Sch<br>400 N 4th Street, Knox City 79529<br>**Mark Tucker** | 9-12 | AGTV | 82<br>20 | 65% | 940/657-3565 |
| O'Brien Middle Sch<br>711 9th St, O Brien 79539<br>**Jordan Carter** | 5-8 | T | 72<br>14 | 74% | 940/657-3731 |

| | | | | |
|---|---|---|---|---|
| 79 Student Personnel | 91 Safety/Security | 275 Response To Intervention | 298 Grant Writer/Ptnrships | School Programs |
| 80 Driver Ed/Safety | 92 Magnet School | 277 Remedial Math K-12 | 750 Chief Innovation Officer | A = Alternative Program |
| 81 Gifted/Talented | 93 Parental Involvement | 280 Literacy Coach | 751 Chief of Staff | G = Adult Classes |
| 82 Video Services | 95 Tech Prep Program | 285 STEM | 752 Social Emotional Learning | M = Magnet Program |
| 83 Substance Abuse Prev | 97 Chief Information Officer | 286 Digital Learning | | T = Title I Schoolwide |
| 84 Erate | 98 Chief Technology Officer | 288 Common Core Standards | Other School Types | V = Career & Tech Ed Programs |
| 85 AIDS Education | 270 Character Education | 294 Accountability | Ⓐ = Alternative School | |
| 88 Alternative/At Risk | 271 Migrant Education | 295 Network System | Ⓒ = Charter School | Social Media |
| 89 Multi-Cultural Curriculum | 273 Teacher Mentor | 296 Title II Programs | Ⓜ = Magnet School | 🇫 = Facebook |
| 90 Social Work | 274 Before/After Sch | 297 Webmaster | Ⓨ = Year-Round School | 🇹 = Twitter |

New Schools are shaded
New Superintendents and Principals are bold
Personnel with email addresses are underscored

### TX—261

## Munday Consolidated Ind SD PID: 01036533
811 W D Street, Munday 76371

940/422-4241
Fax 940/422-5331

**Schools:** 2 \ **Teachers:** 36 \ **Students:** 392 \ **Special Ed Students:** 58 \ **LEP Students:** 19 \ **College-Bound:** 85% \ **Ethnic:** Asian 1%, African American 6%, Hispanic 50%, Caucasian 43% \ **Exp:** $800 (High) \ **Poverty:** 36% \ **Title I:** $207,285 \ **Open-Close:** 08/19 - 05/20 \ **DTBP:** $378 (High)

| | | | |
|---|---|---|---|
| Troy Parton | 1,11 | Cheryl Berryhill | 2,68,79 |
| Terry Hendricks | 3* | Bob Bowen | 5 |
| Patrick Corcoran | 6,35* | Mandi Perry | 7* |
| Kristi Bufkin | 9,12,57,288,296* | Christel Shahan | 27,36,69,77,88,294* |
| Jenni Redwine | 34* | Jennifer Caddell | 58 |
| Sam Hunter | 67 | Kimberly Bowman | 73,273,286,295* |
| Zann Messer | 81* | Leanne Tidwell | 271* |

| Public Schs..Principal | Grd | Prgm | Enr/#Cls | SN | |
|---|---|---|---|---|---|
| Munday Elem Sch<br>1111 W Main Street, Munday 76371<br>Kristi Bufkin | PK-6 | T | 266<br>19 | 60% | 940/422-4321 |
| Munday High Sch<br>911 W D Street, Munday 76371<br>Brent Drury | 7-12 | T | 126<br>23 | 56% | 940/422-4321 |

## LA SALLE COUNTY

## LA SALLE PUBLIC SCHOOLS

## Cotulla Ind School Dist PID: 01037197
310 N Main St, Cotulla 78014

830/879-3073
Fax 830/879-3609

**Schools:** 4 \ **Teachers:** 110 \ **Students:** 1,180 \ **Special Ed Students:** 186 \ **LEP Students:** 94 \ **College-Bound:** 85% \ **Ethnic:** Hispanic 95%, Caucasian 5% \ **Exp:** $519 (High) \ **Poverty:** 35% \ **Title I:** $545,539 \ **Open-Close:** 08/10 - 05/28 \ **DTBP:** $350 (High)

| | | | |
|---|---|---|---|
| Dr Jack Seals | 1 | Alfredo Vela | 2,5 |
| Marcena Martinez | 4 | David Filda | 6 |
| Heather Ramirez | 8,11,288,296,298,752 | Marlene Maldonado | 38* |
| Alecia Rumfield | 58 | Deonicio Ramirez | 67 |
| Joseph Yanez | 73 | Sayna Rodriguez | 294 |

| Public Schs..Principal | Grd | Prgm | Enr/#Cls | SN | |
|---|---|---|---|---|---|
| Cotulla High Sch<br>1034 Highway Highway 97, Cotulla 78014<br>Scott Norris | 9-12 | T | 375<br>36 | 88% | 830/879-2374<br>Fax 830/879-4302 |
| Encinal Elem Sch<br>503 Encinal Blvd, Encinal 78019<br>Louisa Franklin | PK-5 | T | 89<br>7 | 83% | 956/948-5324<br>Fax 956/948-5534 |
| Frank Newman Middle Sch<br>608 Carrizo St, Cotulla 78014<br>Dr Brenda Jirasek | 6-8 | T | 302<br>30 | 92% | 830/879-4376<br>Fax 830/879-4357 |
| Ramirez-Burks Elem Sch<br>604 Tilden St, Cotulla 78014<br>Cynthia Perkins | PK-5 | T | 422<br>29 | 89% | 830/879-2511<br>Fax 830/879-4361 |

## LAMAR COUNTY

## LAMAR PUBLIC SCHOOLS

## Chisum Ind School Dist PID: 01036600
3250 S Church St, Paris 75462

903/737-2830
Fax 903/737-2831

**Schools:** 3 \ **Teachers:** 78 \ **Students:** 1,020 \ **Special Ed Students:** 95 \ **LEP Students:** 43 \ **College-Bound:** 59% \ **Ethnic:** African American 3%, Hispanic 8%, Native American: 1%, Caucasian 87% \ **Exp:** $453 (High) \ **Poverty:** 29% \ **Title I:** $337,086 \ **Open-Close:** 08/13 - 05/21 \ **DTBP:** $360 (High)

| | | | |
|---|---|---|---|
| Tommy Chalaire | 1,11 | Kim Williams | 2,11 |
| Lynn Williams | 3,5 | Wanda Armstrong | 4 |
| Darren Pevey | 6 | Dusty Felts | 38,88 |
| Travis Ball | 67 | April North | 71,76 |
| Sherri Gribble | 294 | | |

| Public Schs..Principal | Grd | Prgm | Enr/#Cls | SN | |
|---|---|---|---|---|---|
| Chisum Elem Sch<br>3250 S Church St, Paris 75462<br>Wendy Ruthart | PK-5 | TV | 440<br>38 | 60% | 903/737-2820 |
| Chisum High Sch<br>3250 S Church St, Paris 75462<br>Clint Miller | 9-12 | T | 293<br>47% | | 903/737-2800 |
| Chisum Middle Sch<br>3250 S Church St, Paris 75462<br>Aaron Bridges | 6-8 | T | 221<br>54% | | 903/737-2806 |

## Paris Ind School Dist PID: 01036698
1920 Clarksville St, Paris 75460

903/737-7473
Fax 903/737-7484

**Schools:** 8 \ **Teachers:** 312 \ **Students:** 3,900 \ **Special Ed Students:** 484 \ **LEP Students:** 377 \ **College-Bound:** 66% \ **Ethnic:** Asian 1%, African American 34%, Hispanic 25%, Native American: 1%, Caucasian 39% \ **Exp:** $496 (High) \ **Poverty:** 27% \ **Title I:** $1,448,274 \ **Special Education:** $742,000 \ **Open-Close:** 08/19 - 05/27 \ **DTBP:** $224 (High)

| | | | |
|---|---|---|---|
| Paul Jones | 1 | Tish Holleman | 2 |
| Terry Anderson | 3 | Lori McEntyre | 4 |
| Joseph Justiss | 5 | Steven Hohenberger | 6 |
| Althea Dixon | 8,15,294 | Jennifer Ray | 9,81 |
| Caleb Tindel | 10,27 | Karol Ackley | 11 |
| Gary Preston | 15,68,273 | Eva Williams | 34* |
| Yesica Munguia | 57 | Joi Roberts | 58 |
| Lisa Malone | 58 | George Fisher | 67 |
| Jeanne Kraft | 71 | Dale Loughmiller | 73 |
| Jennifer Simmons | 73 | Kay Grubb | 85* |
| Brad Ruthart | 91 | Eddie LaRue | 295 |

| Public Schs..Principal | Grd | Prgm | Enr/#Cls | SN | |
|---|---|---|---|---|---|
| A M Aikin Elem Sch<br>3100 Pine Mill Rd, Paris 75460<br>Kimberly Donnan | K-4 | T | 895<br>49 | 73% | 903/737-7443<br>Fax 903/737-7517 |
| Crockett Intermediate Sch<br>655 S Collegiate Dr, Paris 75460<br>Brock Blassingame | 5-6 | T | 589<br>35 | 79% | 903/737-7450<br>Fax 903/737-7526 |

| | | | | | | | | | | | |
|---|---|---|---|---|---|---|---|---|---|---|---|
| 1 | Superintendent | 8 | Curric/Instruct K-12 | 19 | Chief Financial Officer | 29 | Family/Consumer Science | 39 | Social Studies K-12 | 49 | English/Lang Arts Elem | 59 | Special Education Elem | 69 | Academic Assessment |
| 2 | Bus/Finance/Purchasing | 9 | Curric/Instruct Elem | 20 | Art K-12 | 30 | Adult Education | 40 | Social Studies Elem | 50 | English/Lang Arts Sec | 60 | Special Education Sec | 70 | Research/Development |
| 3 | Buildings And Grounds | 10 | Curric/Instruct Sec | 21 | Art Elem | 31 | Career/Sch-to-Work K-12 | 41 | Social Studies Sec | 51 | Reading K-12 | 61 | Foreign/World Lang K-12 | 71 | Public Information |
| 4 | Food Service | 11 | Federal Program | 22 | Art Sec | 32 | Career/Sch-to-Work Elem | 42 | Science K-12 | 52 | Reading Elem | 62 | Foreign/World Lang Elem | 72 | Summer School |
| 5 | Transportation | 12 | Title I | 23 | Music K-12 | 33 | Career/Sch-to-Work Sec | 43 | Science Elem | 53 | Reading Sec | 63 | Foreign/World Lang Sec | 73 | Instructional Tech |
| 6 | Athletic | 13 | Title V | 24 | Music Elem | 34 | Early Childhood Ed | 44 | Science Sec | 54 | Remedial Reading K-12 | 64 | Religious Education K-12 | 74 | Inservice Training |
| 7 | Health Services | 15 | Asst Superintendent | 25 | Music Sec | 35 | Health/Phys Education | 45 | Math K-12 | 55 | Remedial Reading Elem | 65 | Religious Education Elem | 75 | Marketing/Distributive |
| | | 16 | Instructional Media Svcs | 26 | Business Education | 36 | Guidance Services K-12 | 46 | Math Elem | 56 | Remedial Reading Sec | 66 | Religious Education Sec | 76 | Info Systems |
| | | 17 | Chief Operations Officer | 27 | Career & Tech Ed | 37 | Guidance Services Elem | 47 | Math Sec | 57 | Bilingual/ELL | 67 | School Board President | 77 | Psychological Assess |
| | | 18 | Chief Academic Officer | 28 | Technology Education | 38 | Guidance Services Sec | 48 | English/Lang Arts K-12 | 58 | Special Education K-12 | 68 | Teacher Personnel | 78 | Affirmative Action |

| | Grd | Prgm | Enr/#Cls | SN | |
|---|---|---|---|---|---|
| Givens Early Childhood Center | PK-PK | T | 127 | 93% | 903/737-7466 |
| 655 Martin Luther King Jr Dr, Paris 75460 | | | 28 | | Fax 903/737-7531 |
| Sheila Ensey | | | | | |
| Lamar Co Head Start Center | PK-PK | T | 193 | 100% | 903/737-7469 |
| 1350 6th St NE, Paris 75460 | | | | | Fax 903/737-7514 |
| Eva Williams | | | | | |
| Paris High Sch | 9-12 | TV | 405 | 68% | 903/737-7400 |
| 2255 S Collegiate Dr, Paris 75460 | | | 80 | | Fax 903/737-7515 |
| Chris Vaughn | | | | | |
| Paris Junior High Sch | 7-8 | TV | 543 | 73% | 903/737-7434 |
| 2400 Jefferson Rd, Paris 75460 | | | 26 | | Fax 903/737-7534 |
| Kristi Callihan | | | | | |
| Thomas Justiss Elem Sch | K-4 | T | 559 | 92% | 903/737-7458 |
| 401 18th St NW, Paris 75460 | | | 28 | | Fax 903/737-7530 |
| Renee Elmore | | | | | |
| Ⓐ Travis High School of Choice | 1-12 | T | 90 | 76% | 903/737-7560 |
| 3270 Graham St, Paris 75460 | | | 13 | | Fax 903/737-7574 |
| Stephen Long | | | | | |

• **Prairiland Ind School Dist** PID: 01036789
466 FM 196 S, Pattonville 75468
903/652-6476
Fax 903/652-3738

**Schools:** 4 \ **Teachers:** 87 \ **Students:** 1,088 \ **Special Ed Students:** 99 \ **LEP Students:** 26 \ **Ethnic:** Hispanic 9%, Native American: 1%, Caucasian 90% \ **Exp:** $378 (High) \ **Poverty:** 14% \ **Title I:** $162,976 \ **Open-Close:** 08/13 - 05/20 \ **DTBP:** $345 (High) \ 🅕 🅣

| | | | |
|---|---|---|---|
| Jeff Ballard | 1 | Ronda Weatherford | 2,296,298 |
| Randell Bridges | 3 | Lesa Clarkson | 4 |
| Steven Weddle | 6 | Christal Pilip | 7* |
| Dana Stowell | 8,16,73 | Jennifer Clark | 11,38,69,83,88,270,752* |
| Michael Sessums | 67 | | |

| Public Schs..Principal | Grd | Prgm | Enr/#Cls | SN | |
|---|---|---|---|---|---|
| Blossom Elem Sch | PK-5 | T | 376 | 56% | 903/982-5230 |
| 310 High St, Blossom 75416 | | | 18 | | Fax 903/982-5260 |
| Leslie Martin | | | | | |
| Deport Elem Sch | PK-5 | T | 131 | 71% | 903/652-3325 |
| 247 Church St, Deport 75435 | | | 15 | | Fax 903/652-2212 |
| Lanny Mathews | | | | | |
| Prairiland High Sch | 9-12 | TV | 319 | 43% | 903/652-5681 |
| 466 FM 196 S, Pattonville 75468 | | | 18 | | Fax 903/652-6400 |
| Jason Hostetler | | | | | |
| Prairiland Junior High Sch | 6-8 | TV | 262 | 51% | 903/652-5681 |
| 466 FM 196 S, Pattonville 75468 | | | 20 | | Fax 903/652-3232 |
| Brad Bassano | | | | | |

# LAMB COUNTY

# LAMB PUBLIC SCHOOLS

• **Amherst Ind School Dist** PID: 01036882
100 Main St, Amherst 79312
806/246-7729
Fax 806/246-3265

**Schools:** 1 \ **Teachers:** 19 \ **Students:** 130 \ **Special Ed Students:** 16 \ **LEP Students:** 60 \ **Ethnic:** African American 4%, Hispanic 89%, Caucasian 6% \ **Exp:** $642 (High) \ **Poverty:** 24% \ **Title I:** $64,999 \ **Open-Close:** 08/24 - 05/21

| | | | |
|---|---|---|---|
| Joel Rodgers | 1,11,83 | Susan Meier | 2 |

| | | | |
|---|---|---|---|
| Richard Rinegeart | 3,5,91 | Julie Gonzales | 4 |
| Daniel Hinojosa | 6 | Ronnie Schroeder | 67 |
| Ashley Hanlin | 69,77* | Michael Nace | 84,295* |

| Public Schs..Principal | Grd | Prgm | Enr/#Cls | SN | |
|---|---|---|---|---|---|
| Amherst Sch | PK-12 | ATV | 130 | 82% | 806/246-3221 |
| 100 Main St, Amherst 79312 | | | 24 | | Fax 806/246-3494 |
| Jose Gonzales | | | | | |

• **Littlefield Ind School Dist** PID: 01036911
1207 E 14th St, Littlefield 79339
806/385-3844
Fax 806/385-4195

**Schools:** 4 \ **Teachers:** 96 \ **Students:** 1,300 \ **Special Ed Students:** 147 \ **LEP Students:** 82 \ **Ethnic:** African American 6%, Hispanic 74%, Caucasian 20% \ **Exp:** $408 (High) \ **Poverty:** 31% \ **Title I:** $573,685 \ **Open-Close:** 08/17 - 05/21 \ **DTBP:** $350 (High)

| | | | |
|---|---|---|---|
| Robert Dillard | 1 | Rick Richards | 2,5,8,11,79,88,92,298 |
| Mark Warsing | 3 | Brent Green | 6 |
| Amber Hays | 12,34,57* | Brett Southard | 58 |
| Lance Broadhurst | 67 | Tim Gau | 73,84,295 |

| Public Schs..Principal | Grd | Prgm | Enr/#Cls | SN | |
|---|---|---|---|---|---|
| Littlefield Elem Sch | 3-5 | T | 303 | 74% | 806/385-6217 |
| 120 N Westside Ave, Littlefield 79339 | | | 17 | | Fax 806/385-4193 |
| Tom Whistler | | | | | |
| Littlefield High Sch | 9-12 | TV | 373 | 71% | 806/385-5683 |
| 1100 W Waylon Jennings Blvd, Littlefield 79339 | | | 25 | | Fax 806/385-4191 |
| **Mike Read** | | | | | |
| Littlefield Junior High Sch | 6-8 | T | 302 | 73% | 806/385-3922 |
| 105 N Lake Ave, Littlefield 79339 | | | 20 | | Fax 806/385-4192 |
| Mitch McNeese | | | | | |
| Littlefield Primary Sch | PK-2 | T | 291 | 84% | 806/385-3922 |
| 815 W 2nd St, Littlefield 79339 | | | 25 | | Fax 806/385-4194 |
| Jan Richards | | | | | |

• **Olton Ind School Dist** PID: 01036973
701 6th Street, Olton 79064
806/285-2641
Fax 806/285-2724

**Schools:** 3 \ **Teachers:** 56 \ **Students:** 600 \ **Special Ed Students:** 50 \ **LEP Students:** 95 \ **College-Bound:** 52% \ **Ethnic:** African American 1%, Hispanic 77%, Caucasian 22% \ **Exp:** $395 (High) \ **Poverty:** 27% \ **Title I:** $225,191 \ **Open-Close:** 08/13 - 05/21 \ **DTBP:** $350 (High)

| | | | |
|---|---|---|---|
| Kevin McCasland | 1 | Fran Trotter | 2 |
| Joe Villanueva | 3 | Manuel Jimenez | 5 |
| Ross Lassiter | 6* | Cathi Freeman | 7,85* |
| Kelly Smith | 8,31,58 | Terri Sandoval | 11,69,294* |
| Kelli Smith | 16,82* | Tara Ford | 34 |
| Connie Maxwell | 67 | Angela Martin | 83 |
| Blanca Pedroza | 271 | Stephen Miller | 295* |

| Public Schs..Principal | Grd | Prgm | Enr/#Cls | SN | |
|---|---|---|---|---|---|
| Olton High Sch | 9-12 | TV | 191 | 76% | 806/285-2691 |
| 800 Avenue G, Olton 79064 | | | 20 | | Fax 806/285-3316 |
| Gregg Ammons | | | | | |
| Olton Junior High Sch | 6-8 | TV | 128 | 80% | 806/285-2681 |
| 800 Avenue G, Olton 79064 | | | 20 | | Fax 806/285-3348 |
| **Colby Huseman** | | | | | |
| Webb Elem Sch | PK-5 | TV | 255 | 71% | 806/285-2657 |
| 801 Avenue G, Olton 79064 | | | 31 | | Fax 806/285-2438 |
| Stacie Ramage | | | | | |

## Springlake-Earth Ind Sch Dist PID: 01037044
Highway 2901, Earth 79031
806/257-3310
Fax 806/257-3927

**Schools:** 2 \ **Teachers:** 34 \ **Students:** 370 \ **Special Ed Students:** 51 \ **LEP Students:** 54 \ **College-Bound:** 80% \ **Ethnic:** African American 1%, Hispanic 70%, Caucasian 29% \ **Exp:** $1,007 (High) \ **Poverty:** 15% \ **Title I:** $60,359 \ **Open-Close:** 08/13 - 05/20 \ **DTBP:** $372 (High)

| | | | | |
|---|---|---|---|---|
| Denver Crum | 1 | Rosie Davis | | 2* |
| Israel DeLeon | 6* | Cindy Furr | | 10,69,270* |
| Cathy Bean | 59* | Mark Parrish | | 67 |

| Public Schs..Principal | Grd | Prgm | Enr/#Cls | SN |
|---|---|---|---|---|
| Springlake-Earth Elem Mid Sch<br>Highway 2901, Earth 79031<br>Jimmi Johnson | PK-8 | T | 380<br>18 | 74% 806/257-3310 |
| Springlake-Earth High Sch<br>472 FM 302, Earth 79031<br>Cindy Furr | 8-12 | ATV | 109<br>18 | 65% 806/257-3819<br>Fax 806/257-3370 |

## Sudan Ind School Dist PID: 01037082
107 Highway 303, Sudan 79371
806/227-2431
Fax 806/227-2146

**Schools:** 2 \ **Teachers:** 44 \ **Students:** 424 \ **Special Ed Students:** 46 \ **LEP Students:** 31 \ **College-Bound:** 80% \ **Ethnic:** African American 1%, Hispanic 55%, Caucasian 44% \ **Exp:** $504 (High) \ **Poverty:** 21% \ **Title I:** $91,544 \ **Open-Close:** 08/19 - 05/21 \ **DTBP:** $341 (High)

| | | | | |
|---|---|---|---|---|
| Scott Harrell | 1,11 | Tonjua Scisson | | 2 |
| Mark Scisson | 3* | Brianna Lashbrook | | 4 |
| Carroll Legg | 5 | John Cornelius | | 6 |
| Wendy Swarb | 7,85* | Chanda Schovajsa | | 16,82* |
| Angela Shultz | 57* | Daniel Guterrez | | 58* |
| Tim Rich | 67 | Kayela Harrell | | 69,288* |
| Jonathan Robertson | 73,286,298* | D Provence | | 295 |

| Public Schs..Principal | Grd | Prgm | Enr/#Cls | SN |
|---|---|---|---|---|
| Sudan Elem Sch<br>107 Highway 303, Sudan 79371<br>Deann Wilson | PK-7 | T | 325<br>19 | 58% 806/227-2431 |
| Sudan High Sch<br>Highway 303, Sudan 79371<br>Gordon Martin | 8-12 | T | 99<br>25 | 43% 806/227-2431<br>Fax 806/227-2121 |

# LAMPASAS COUNTY

## LAMPASAS PUBLIC SCHOOLS

## Lampasas Ind School Dist PID: 01037111
207 W 8th St, Lampasas 76550
512/556-6224
Fax 512/556-8711

**Schools:** 5 \ **Teachers:** 228 \ **Students:** 3,400 \ **Special Ed Students:** 449 \ **LEP Students:** 118 \ **College-Bound:** 47% \ **Ethnic:** Asian 1%, African American 3%, Hispanic 28%, Native American: 1%, Caucasian 68% \ **Exp:** $369 (High) \ **Poverty:** 17% \ **Title I:** $757,886 \ **Special Education:** $619,000 \ **Open-Close:** 08/10 - 05/20 \ **DTBP:** $178 (High)

| | | | |
|---|---|---|---|
| Dr Chane Rascoe | 1 | Shane Jones | 2,19 |
| David Edgar | 3 | Calvin Pittman | 4 |

| | | | |
|---|---|---|---|
| Beverley Spencer | 5 | Troy Rogers | 6* |
| Kevin Bott | 8,11,57,83,286,288,296,298 | Karen Turner | 58 |
| Sam Walker | 67 | Ron Poage | 73,295 |
| Whitney Walker | 79 | Julie Salvato | 285 |

| Public Schs..Principal | Grd | Prgm | Enr/#Cls | SN |
|---|---|---|---|---|
| Hanna Springs Elem Sch<br>604 E Avenue F, Lampasas 76550<br>Lindsay Duhon | PK-5 | T | 549<br>60 | 60% 512/556-2152<br>Fax 512/556-0225 |
| Kline Whitis Elem Sch<br>500 S Willis St, Lampasas 76550<br>Wes Graham | PK-5 | T | 315<br>40 | 58% 512/556-8291<br>Fax 512/556-8285 |
| Lampasas High Sch<br>2716 S Highway 281, Lampasas 76550<br>Joey McQueen | 9-12 | ATV | 995 | 44% 512/564-2310<br>Fax 512/564-2406 |
| Lampasas Middle Sch<br>902 S Broad St, Lampasas 76550<br>Dana Holcomb | 6-8 | ATV | 762<br>60 | 49% 512/556-3101<br>Fax 512/556-0245 |
| Taylor Creek Elem Sch<br>2096 Big Divide Rd, Copperas Cove 76522<br>Renee Cummings | PK-5 | T | 503 | 55% 512/564-2585<br>Fax 512/564-2606 |

## Lometa Ind School Dist PID: 01037161
100 N 8th St, Lometa 76853
512/752-3384
Fax 512/752-3424

**Schools:** 1 \ **Teachers:** 25 \ **Students:** 300 \ **Special Ed Students:** 43 \ **LEP Students:** 35 \ **College-Bound:** 50% \ **Ethnic:** Asian 1%, African American 1%, Hispanic 56%, Native American: 1%, Caucasian 41% \ **Exp:** $554 (High) \ **Poverty:** 21% \ **Title I:** $205,229 \ **Open-Close:** 08/19 - 05/21 \ **DTBP:** $292 (High)

| | | | | |
|---|---|---|---|---|
| David Fisher | 1,11 | Ronda Bridges | | 2 |
| Tim Williams | 3* | B J Burnett | | 4* |
| Michael Sibberson | 5,51* | D T Torres | | 6* |
| Rob Moore | 8,16,31,73,273,286* | Heather Oliver | | 57,271* |
| Renee Young | 58* | Matt Molter | | 67 |
| Elizabeth Dickison | 69,83,88* | | | |

| Public Schs..Principal | Grd | Prgm | Enr/#Cls | SN |
|---|---|---|---|---|
| Ⓨ Lometa Sch<br>100 N 8th St, Lometa 76853<br>Michael Sibberson | PK-12 | MTV | 300<br>20 | 79% 512/752-3384 |

# LAVACA COUNTY

## LAVACA PUBLIC SCHOOLS

## Ezzell Ind School Dist PID: 01037264
20500 FM 531, Hallettsville 77964
361/798-4448
Fax 361/798-9331

**Schools:** 1 \ **Teachers:** 9 \ **Students:** 85 \ **Special Ed Students:** 4 \ **Ethnic:** African American 2%, Hispanic 7%, Caucasian 91% \ **Exp:** $578 (High) \ **Poverty:** 15% \ **Title I:** $23,551 \ **Open-Close:** 08/13 - 05/20

| | | | |
|---|---|---|---|
| Lisa Berckenhoff | 1,11 | Jackie Goranson | 2 |
| Henri McCord | 67 | | |

| Public Schs..Principal | Grd | Prgm | Enr/#Cls | SN | |
|---|---|---|---|---|---|
| Ezzell Elem Sch | PK-8 | T | 85 | 47% | 361/798-4448 |
| 20500 FM 531, Hallettsville 77964 | | | 9 | | |
| Lisa Berckenhoff | | | | | |

● **Hallettsville Ind Sch Dist** PID: 01037288     361/798-2242
302 N Ridge St, Hallettsville 77964     Fax 361/798-5902

> Schools: 3 \ Teachers: 80 \ Students: 1,100 \ Special Ed Students: 111
> \ LEP Students: 24 \ College-Bound: 59% \ Ethnic: African American
> 10%, Hispanic 22%, Caucasian 68% \ Exp: $679 (High) \ Poverty: 16% \
> Title I: $221,245 \ Open-Close: 08/20 - 05/27 \ DTBP: $360 (High) \ 🅕 🅣

| | | | |
|---|---|---|---|
| Joann Bludau | 1 | Kristin Marak | 2 |
| Johnny Densman | 3 | Thomas Psencik | 6 |
| Mandy Bucek | 8* | Renae Phillips | 16* |
| Stephanie Grahmann | 34 | Michele Etzler | 35,83,85 |
| Robert Lundy | 67 | Farrah Jernegen | 73,295* |
| Trina Patek | 79 | | |

| Public Schs..Principal | Grd | Prgm | Enr/#Cls | SN | |
|---|---|---|---|---|---|
| Hallettsville Elem Sch | PK-4 | T | 354 | 49% | 361/798-2242 |
| 308 N Ridge St, Hallettsville 77964 | | | 20 | | Fax 361/798-4349 |
| **Stephanie Grahmann \ Trina Patek** | | | | | |
| Hallettsville High Sch | 9-12 | ATV | 364 | 38% | 361/798-2242 |
| 200 N Ridge St, Hallettsville 77964 | | | 40 | | Fax 361/798-9297 |
| Darrin Bickham | | | | | |
| Hallettsville Jr High Sch | 5-8 | TV | 286 | 48% | 361/798-2242 |
| 410 S Russell St, Hallettsville 77964 | | | 35 | | Fax 361/798-3573 |
| Sophie Teltschik | | | | | |

● **Moulton Ind School Dist** PID: 01037329     361/596-4609
500 N Pecan St, Moulton 77975     Fax 361/596-7578

> Schools: 2 \ Teachers: 28 \ Students: 300 \ Special Ed Students: 42
> \ LEP Students: 26 \ College-Bound: 85% \ Ethnic: Hispanic 45%,
> Native American: 1%, Caucasian 53% \ Exp: $589 (High) \ Poverty: 22% \
> Title I: $98,773 \ Open-Close: 08/17 - 05/14 \ DTBP: $315 (High) \ 🅕 🅣

| | | | |
|---|---|---|---|
| **Chris Ulcak** | 1 | Johnna Jasek | 2 |
| Rose Bartos | 4* | Kevin Fishbeck | 6* |
| Deborah Rother | 7* | Laura Kusack | 36,69 |
| Daniel Beyer | 67 | | |

| Public Schs..Principal | Grd | Prgm | Enr/#Cls | SN | |
|---|---|---|---|---|---|
| Moulton Elem Sch | PK-6 | T | 140 | 68% | 361/596-4605 |
| 202 W Bobkat, Moulton 77975 | | | 12 | | Fax 361/596-4894 |
| **April Simper** | | | | | |
| Moulton High Sch | 7-12 | TV | 124 | 47% | 361/596-4691 |
| 502 N Pecan St, Moulton 77975 | | | 10 | | |
| Jamie Dornak | | | | | |

● **Shiner Ind School Dist** PID: 01037355     361/594-3121
510 County Road 348, Shiner 77984     Fax 361/594-3925

> Schools: 2 \ Teachers: 51 \ Students: 650 \ Special Ed Students: 84
> \ LEP Students: 10 \ College-Bound: 70% \ Ethnic: Asian 1%, African
> American 6%, Hispanic 18%, Caucasian 75% \ Exp: $438 (High) \
> Poverty: 13% \ Title I: $100,182 \ Open-Close: 08/19 - 05/28 \ DTBP: $333
> (High)

| | | | |
|---|---|---|---|
| Alex Remschel | 1 | Dawn Winkenwerder | 2,68 |
| Sherri Vincik | 2,11 | Melvin Brooks | 3 |
| Libby Hornacky | 7* | Andrew Schacherl | 67 |
| Janette Berkovsky | 73,295* | | |

| Public Schs..Principal | Grd | Prgm | Enr/#Cls | SN | |
|---|---|---|---|---|---|
| Shiner Elem Sch | PK-6 | T | 325 | 36% | 361/594-3131 |
| 510 County Road 348, Shiner 77984 | | | 18 | | Fax 361/594-8106 |
| Greg Murrile | | | | | |
| Shiner High Sch | 7-12 | TV | 303 | 31% | 361/594-3251 |
| 510 County Road 348, Shiner 77984 | | | 17 | | Fax 361/594-4295 |
| Caleb McCain | | | | | |

● **Sweet Home Ind School Dist** PID: 01037381     361/293-3221
7508 FM 531, Sweet Home 77987     Fax 361/741-2499

> Schools: 1 \ Teachers: 12 \ Students: 140 \ Special Ed Students: 6 \
> Ethnic: Hispanic 14%, Caucasian 86% \ Exp: $478 (High) \ Poverty: 20% \
> Title I: $34,633 \ Open-Close: 08/13 - 05/26 \ 🅕

| | | | |
|---|---|---|---|
| Shane Wagner | 1,11,73,83,84 | Candice Hilt | 4 |
| Jolene Janka | 7 | Jenny Pohler | 59,752 |
| Ricky Raz | 67 | | |

| Public Schs..Principal | Grd | Prgm | Enr/#Cls | SN | |
|---|---|---|---|---|---|
| Sweet Home Elem Sch | PK-8 | | 140 | 17% | 361/293-3221 |
| 7508 FM 531, Sweet Home 77987 | | | 12 | | |
| Shane Wagner | | | | | |

● **Vysehrad Ind School Dist** PID: 01037408     361/798-4118
595 County Road 182, Hallettsville 77964     Fax 361/798-3131

> Schools: 1 \ Teachers: 11 \ Students: 115 \ Special Ed Students: 6
> \ LEP Students: 3 \ Ethnic: Asian 2%, African American 15%, Hispanic
> 9%, Caucasian 75% \ Exp: $291 (Med) \ Poverty: 8% \ Title I: $9,822 \
> Open-Close: 08/13 - 05/20 \ 🅕 🅣

| | | | |
|---|---|---|---|
| Jason Appelt | 1,11,83,84 | Leann Migl | 59,275* |
| Alice Janak | 67 | Claudia Baker | 73,286* |

| Public Schs..Principal | Grd | Prgm | Enr/#Cls | SN | |
|---|---|---|---|---|---|
| Vysehrad Elem Sch | PK-8 | | 115 | 44% | 361/798-4118 |
| 595 County Road 182, Hallettsville 77964 | | | 10 | | |
| Jason Appelt | | | | | 🅕🅣 |

## LAVACA CATHOLIC SCHOOLS

● **Diocese of Victoria Ed Office** PID: 02181727
Listing includes only schools located in this county. See District Index for
location of Diocesan Offices.

| Catholic Schs..Principal | Grd | Prgm | Enr/#Cls | SN | |
|---|---|---|---|---|---|
| Sacred Heart Catholic Sch | PK-12 | | 310 | | 361/798-5349 |
| 313 S Texana St, Hallettsville 77964 | | | 14 | | Fax 361/798-4970 |
| Kevin Haas | | | | | |
| Shiner Catholic School-St Paul | PK-12 | | 277 | | 361/594-2313 |
| 424 S Saint Ludmila St, Shiner 77984 | | | 14 | | Fax 361/594-8599 |
| Neely Yackel | | | | | |
| St Joseph Catholic Sch | PK-8 | | 125 | | 361/293-9000 |
| 310 Orth St, Yoakum 77995 | | | 12 | | Fax 361/293-3004 |
| Sean Mooney | | | | | 🅕🅣 |

| | | | | | School Programs | Social Media |
|---|---|---|---|---|---|---|
| 79 Student Personnel | 91 Safety/Security | 275 Response To Intervention | 298 Grant Writer/Ptnrships | | A = Alternative Program | |
| 80 Driver Ed/Safety | 92 Magnet School | 277 Remedial Math K-12 | 750 Chief Innovation Officer | | G = Adult Classes | 🅕 = Facebook |
| 81 Gifted/Talented | 93 Parental Involvement | 280 Literacy Coach | 751 Chief of Staff | | M = Magnet Program | |
| 82 Video Services | 95 Tech Prep Program | 285 STEM | 752 Social Emotional Learning | | T = Title I Schoolwide | 🅣 = Twitter |
| 83 Substance Abuse Prev | 97 Chief Information Officer | 286 Digital Learning | | | V = Career & Tech Ed Programs | |
| 84 Erate | 98 Chief Technology Officer | 288 Common Core Standards | Other School Types | | | |
| 85 AIDS Education | 270 Character Education | 294 Accountability | Ⓐ = Alternative School | | | |
| 88 Alternative/At Risk | 271 Migrant Education | 295 Network System | Ⓒ = Charter School | | New Schools are shaded | |
| 89 Multi-Cultural Curriculum | 273 Teacher Mentor | 296 Title II Programs | Ⓜ = Magnet School | | New Superintendents and Principals are bold | |
| 90 Social Work | 274 Before/After Sch | 297 Webmaster | Ⓨ = Year-Round School | | Personnel with email addresses are underscored | |

**TX—265**

# LEE COUNTY

## LEE PUBLIC SCHOOLS

● **Dime Box Ind School Dist** PID: 01037422     979/884-2324
1079 Stephen F Austin Blvd, Dime Box 77853     Fax 979/884-0106

**Schools:** 1 \ **Teachers:** 17 \ **Students:** 160 \ **Special Ed Students:** 25
\ **LEP Students:** 18 \ **College-Bound:** 50% \ **Ethnic:** African American
38%, Hispanic 38%, Caucasian 24% \ **Exp:** $904 (High) \ **Poverty:** 12% \
**Title I:** $23,712 \ **Open-Close:** 08/06 - 05/28 \ **DTBP:** $350 (High)

| | | |
|---|---|---|
| Nicholas West | 1,11,84 | Stephanie Kieschnick | 2,4 |
| Jay Smith | 8,73* | Zach Zgabay | 35 |
| Charles Fritsche | 67 | | |

| Public Schs..Principal | Grd | Prgm | Enr/#Cls | SN | |
|---|---|---|---|---|---|
| Dime Box Sch
1079 Stephen F Austin Blvd, Dime Box 77853
Jay Smith | PK-12 | ATV | 160
25 | 75% | 979/884-3366 |

● **Giddings Ind School Dist** PID: 01037458     979/542-2854
2337 N Main St, Giddings 78942     Fax 979/542-9264

**Schools:** 4 \ **Teachers:** 140 \ **Students:** 1,900 \ **Special Ed Students:** 219
\ **LEP Students:** 362 \ **Ethnic:** Asian 1%, African American 8%, Hispanic
58%, Caucasian 33% \ **Exp:** $279 (Med) \ **Poverty:** 18% \ **Title I:** $411,145
\ **Special Education:** $369,000 \ **Open-Close:** 08/31 - 05/27 \ **DTBP:** $356
(High)

| | | | |
|---|---|---|---|
| Roger Dees | 1 | Angie Bloodworth | 2,19 |
| Andy Masek | 3,5 | Traci Campbell | 4 |
| Curtis Krause | 5 | Shane Holman | 8,11,57,58,83,88,288,296 |
| Ashton Booth | 58 | Mark Johnson | 67 |
| Todd Walsh | 73,295 | | |

| Public Schs..Principal | Grd | Prgm | Enr/#Cls | SN | |
|---|---|---|---|---|---|
| Giddings Elem Sch
1402 E Industry St, Giddings 78942
Alisa Niemeyer | PK-3 | T | 482
30 | 71% | 979/542-2886
Fax 979/542-1153 |
| Giddings High Sch
2335 N Main St, Giddings 78942
Chad Rood | 9-12 | ATV | 591
55 | 57% | 979/542-3351
Fax 979/542-5312 |
| Giddings Intermediate Sch
2337 N Main St, Giddings 78942
**Michael Mahoney** | 4-5 | T | 283
20 | 65% | 979/542-4403
Fax 979/542-4327 |
| Giddings Middle Sch
2335 N Main St, Giddings 78942
Charlotte Penn | 6-8 | T | 437
20 | 70% | 979/542-2057
Fax 979/542-3941 |

● **Lexington Ind School Dist** PID: 01037496     979/773-2254
8731 N Highway 77, Lexington 78947     Fax 979/773-4455

**Schools:** 3 \ **Teachers:** 83 \ **Students:** 1,066 \ **Special Ed Students:** 98
\ **LEP Students:** 22 \ **College-Bound:** 50% \ **Ethnic:** African American
8%, Hispanic 18%, Native American: 1%, Caucasian 74% \ **Exp:** $460
(High) \ **Poverty:** 11% \ **Title I:** $98,217 \ **Special Education:** $251,000 \
**Open-Close:** 08/19 - 05/26 \ **DTBP:** $354 (High)

| | | | |
|---|---|---|---|
| Tonya Knowlton | 1 | Kathy Dube | 2 |
| Allen Retzlaff | 3 | Kathleen Lamb | 4* |
| James Marburger | 5 | Kirk Muhl | 6 |
| Dusty Mathews | 7* | Rebecca French | 8,11,74,271 |
| Debbie Johnson | 16,82* | Curtis Patschke | 17,18,19,73,286,295,298,750 |
| Nancy Stobaugh | 58 | Scott Sanders | 67 |
| Rebecca French | 273,288,296* | | |

| Public Schs..Principal | Grd | Prgm | Enr/#Cls | SN | |
|---|---|---|---|---|---|
| Lexington Elem Sch
222 5th St, Lexington 78947
Bryan Ladd | PK-5 | T | 453
30 | 41% | 979/773-2525 |
| Lexington High Sch
8783 N Highway 77, Lexington 78947
Sarah Garrison | 9-12 | ATV | 305 | 37% | 979/773-2255 |
| Lexington Middle Sch
121 3rd St, Lexington 78947
Andre Johnson | 6-8 | T | 238
16 | 37% | 979/773-2254 |

## LEE PRIVATE SCHOOLS

| Private Schs..Principal | Grd | Prgm | Enr/#Cls | SN | |
|---|---|---|---|---|---|
| Immanuel Lutheran Sch
382 N Grimes St, Giddings 78942
Dale Wolfgram | K-8 | | 140
9 | | 979/542-3319
Fax 979/542-9084 |
| St Paul Lutheran Sch
1578 County Road 211, Giddings 78942
James House | K-8 | | 93
9 | | 979/366-2218
Fax 979/366-2200 |

# LEON COUNTY

## LEON PUBLIC SCHOOLS

● **Buffalo Ind School Dist** PID: 01037551     903/322-3765
708 Cedar Creek Rd, Buffalo 75831     Fax 903/322-3091

**Schools:** 4 \ **Teachers:** 78 \ **Students:** 900 \ **Special Ed Students:** 76 \
**LEP Students:** 142 \ **Ethnic:** Asian 1%, African American 4%, Hispanic 42%,
Caucasian 53% \ **Exp:** $612 (High) \ **Poverty:** 27% \ **Title I:** $338,392 \
**Open-Close:** 08/11 - 05/27 \ **DTBP:** $332 (High)

| | | | |
|---|---|---|---|
| Lacy Freeman | 1,83 | Courtney Rodell | 2,11 |
| Rick Frazee | 3 | Sarah Corbin | 4* |
| Lee George | 5 | Brandon Houston | 6,35* |
| Stacy Gaskin | 7 | Georgeanna Adams-Molina | 11,73,271,286* |
| Leslie Morman | 57,274* | Jack Helmcamp | 67 |
| Becky Poole | 68,71 | Melonie Menefee | 82* |
| John Clements | 83 | Melissa Smith | 88* |

| Public Schs..Principal | Grd | Prgm | Enr/#Cls | SN | |
|---|---|---|---|---|---|
| Buffalo Elem Sch
1700 E Commerce St, Buffalo 75831
Tina Rayborn | PK-2 | GT | 198
27 | 69% | 903/322-2473
Fax 903/322-4077 |
| Buffalo High Sch
1724 N Buffalo Ave, Buffalo 75831
Corey Hickerson | 9-12 | ATV | 278
15 | 58% | 903/322-2473
Fax 903/322-5806 |
| Buffalo Lower Junior High Sch
335 Bison Trl, Buffalo 75831
Kelli Moore | 3-5 | A | 210
12 | | 903/322-2473
Fax 903/322-4803 |

| | | | | | | | | |
|---|---|---|---|---|---|---|---|---|
| 1 | Superintendent | 8 | Curric/Instruct K-12 | 19 | Chief Financial Officer | 29 | Family/Consumer Science | 39 | Social Studies K-12 | 49 | English/Lang Arts Elem | 59 | Special Education Elem | 69 | Academic Assessment |
| 2 | Bus/Finance/Purchasing | 9 | Curric/Instruct Elem | 20 | Art K-12 | 30 | Adult Education | 40 | Social Studies Elem | 50 | English/Lang Arts Sec | 60 | Special Education Sec | 70 | Research/Development |
| 3 | Buildings And Grounds | 10 | Curric/Instruct Sec | 21 | Art Elem | 31 | Career/Sch-to-Work K-12 | 41 | Social Studies Sec | 51 | Reading K-12 | 61 | Foreign/World Lang K-12 | 71 | Public Information |
| 4 | Food Service | 11 | Federal Program | 22 | Art Sec | 32 | Career/Sch-to-Work Elem | 42 | Science K-12 | 52 | Reading Elem | 62 | Foreign/World Lang Elem | 72 | Summer School |
| 5 | Transportation | 12 | Title I | 23 | Music K-12 | 33 | Career/Sch-to-Work Sec | 43 | Science Elem | 53 | Reading Sec | 63 | Foreign/World Lang Sec | 73 | Instructional Tech |
| 6 | Athletic | 13 | Title V | 24 | Music Elem | 34 | Early Childhood Ed | 44 | Science Sec | 54 | Remedial Reading K-12 | 64 | Religious Education K-12 | 74 | Inservice Training |
| 7 | Health Services | 14 | Instructional Media Svcs | 25 | Music Sec | 35 | Health/Phys Education | 45 | Math K-12 | 55 | Remedial Reading Elem | 65 | Religious Education Elem | 75 | Marketing/Distributive |
| | | 15 | Asst Superintendent | 26 | Business Education | 36 | Guidance Services K-12 | 46 | Math Elem | 56 | Remedial Reading Sec | 66 | Religious Education Sec | 76 | Info Systems |
| | | 16 | Instructional Media Svcs | 27 | Career & Tech Ed | 37 | Guidance Services Elem | 47 | Math Sec | 57 | Bilingual/ELL | 67 | School Board President | 77 | Psychological Assess |
| | | 17 | Chief Operations Officer | 28 | Technology Education | 38 | Guidance Services Sec | 48 | English/Lang Arts K-12 | 58 | Special Education K-12 | 68 | Teacher Personnel | 78 | Affirmative Action |
| | | 18 | Chief Academic Officer | | | | | | | | | | | | |

| Buffalo Upper Junior High Sch | 6-8 | T | 210 | 69% | 903/322-2473 |
| 145 Bison Trl, Buffalo 75831 | | | | | Fax 903/322-3862 |
| Greg Kennedy | | | | | |

## ● Centerville Ind School Dist PID: 01037587
813 S Commerce St, Centerville 75833

903/536-7812
Fax 903/536-3133

**Schools:** 2 \ **Teachers:** 58 \ **Students:** 700 \ **Special Ed Students:** 60 \ **LEP Students:** 17 \ **College-Bound:** 75% \ **Ethnic:** African American 10%, Hispanic 11%, Caucasian 78% \ **Exp:** $617 (High) \ **Poverty:** 32% \ **Title I:** $305,812 \ **Open-Close:** 08/12 - 05/21 \ **DTBP:** $322 (High)

| | | |
|---|---|---|
| Jason Jeitz ..................1 | Carole Dickey ..............2,4,15,298 | |
| Nathan Gilber ...............3 | Gary Bladen ................5 | |
| Kyle Hardee ...............6* | Cara Dudley ..............8,11,285,286 | |
| Angela Rodell ...........16,73* | Dotty Sullivan ...........57 | |
| Sandra Welker ............58 | Charles Nash .............67 | |
| Layne Gregson ..........76,295 | Rebecca Moutray .........83 | |

| Public Schs..Principal | Grd | Prgm | Enr/#Cls | SN | |
|---|---|---|---|---|---|
| Centerville Elem Sch | PK-6 | T | 338 | 54% | 903/536-2235 |
| 346 W Church St, Centerville 75833 | | | 22 | | Fax 903/536-3525 |
| Dottie Sullivan | | | | | |
| Centerville Jr Sr High Sch | 7-12 | TV | 300 | 42% | 903/536-2625 |
| 813 S Commerce St, Centerville 75833 | | | 50 | | |
| Claudia Mordecai | | | | | |

## ● Leon Ind School Dist PID: 01037628
12168 US Highway 79, Jewett 75846

903/626-1400
Fax 903/626-1420

**Schools:** 2 \ **Teachers:** 62 \ **Students:** 700 \ **Special Ed Students:** 61 \ **LEP Students:** 105 \ **College-Bound:** 75% \ **Ethnic:** Asian 2%, Hispanic 31%, Caucasian 66% \ **Exp:** $527 (High) \ **Poverty:** 14% \ **Title I:** $161,587 \ **Open-Close:** 08/10 - 05/28 \ **DTBP:** $292 (High)

| | |
|---|---|
| David Raines ..................1 | Jamie Watson ...............2,298 |
| Britney Taylor .................3,5 | Jeremy Colvert ............6* |
| Jessica Turner ................6 | Julie Noey ...............7,35,83 |
| Geoffery Bowdoin .........8,11,274,296* | Elise Watson .............31,36,69* |
| Shelly Charlton ..............54* | Pam Jensen ..............58 |
| Collin Robertson ............67 | Jerrod Hartioz ...........73 |

| Public Schs..Principal | Grd | Prgm | Enr/#Cls | SN | |
|---|---|---|---|---|---|
| Leon Elem Sch | PK-6 | T | 425 | 55% | 903/626-1425 |
| 12168 US Highway 79, Jewett 75846 | | | 35 | | Fax 903/626-1440 |
| **Nan Grisham** | | | | | |
| Leon High Sch | 7-12 | ATV | 275 | 47% | 903/626-1476 |
| 12168 US Highway 79, Jewett 75846 | | | 22 | | Fax 903/626-1490 |
| Jay Winn | | | | | |

## ● Normangee Ind School Dist PID: 01037654
35078 Osr St, Normangee 77871

936/396-3111
Fax 936/396-3112

**Schools:** 3 \ **Teachers:** 46 \ **Students:** 605 \ **Special Ed Students:** 57 \ **LEP Students:** 17 \ **Ethnic:** Asian 1%, African American 7%, Hispanic 14%, Native American: 1%, Caucasian 76% \ **Exp:** $345 (High) \ **Poverty:** 15% \ **Title I:** $105,545 \ **Open-Close:** 08/13 - 05/26 \ **DTBP:** $365 (High)

| | |
|---|---|
| Mark Ruffin ..................1 | Jaimie Bell ...............2 |
| Joel Tedder ..................3,91* | Tara Green ...............4* |
| Brad Hipple ..................5 | Keith Sitton ..............6 |
| Erica Sorters .................7* | Tera Phillips .........9,57,83,270,271,296* |
| Cara Phillips ...............10,31* | Kim Tesch ..............36,69,88* |
| Phyllis Rogers ...............58* | Andres Dela-Garza ........67 |
| Brian Furbee ..............73,82,286 | |

| Public Schs..Principal | Grd | Prgm | Enr/#Cls | SN | |
|---|---|---|---|---|---|
| Normangee Elem Sch | PK-5 | T | 269 | 63% | 936/396-9999 |
| 116 Spur 3, Normangee 77871 | | | 40 | | Fax 936/396-2609 |
| Cody Gore | | | | | |
| Normangee Middle Sch | 6-8 | TV | 128 | 46% | 936/396-3111 |
| 116 Spur 3, Normangee 77871 | | | | | Fax 936/396-6879 |
| Jake George | | | | | |
| Normangee Senior High Sch | 9-12 | TV | 208 | 46% | 936/396-6111 |
| 116 Spur 3, Normangee 77871 | | | | | Fax 936/396-6879 |
| Trae Davis | | | | | |

## ● Oakwood Ind School Dist PID: 01037680
631 N Holly St, Oakwood 75855

903/545-2666
Fax 903/545-2310

**Schools:** 2 \ **Teachers:** 20 \ **Students:** 199 \ **Special Ed Students:** 17 \ **LEP Students:** 3 \ **College-Bound:** 80% \ **Ethnic:** African American 21%, Hispanic 18%, Caucasian 61% \ **Exp:** $535 (High) \ **Poverty:** 31% \ **Title I:** $80,905 \ **Open-Close:** 08/21 - 05/25 \ **DTBP:** $350 (High)

| | |
|---|---|
| Russell Holden ..................1 | Diana Neel ...............2,11,296 |
| Ray Cunningham ...............3,5 | Melissa Barnett ..........4 |
| Tommy Tritz ..................6 | Lori Olive ..............8,69* |
| Mack Botard ..................67 | Lane Gregson ...........73 |
| Dr Donny Lee ................288 | |

| Public Schs..Principal | Grd | Prgm | Enr/#Cls | SN | |
|---|---|---|---|---|---|
| Oakwood Elem Sch | PK-6 | T | 118 | 90% | 903/545-2106 |
| 631 N Holly St, Oakwood 75855 | | | 7 | | Fax 903/545-1130 |
| Greg Branch | | | | | |
| Oakwood Jr Sr High Sch | 7-12 | TV | 81 | 77% | 903/545-2140 |
| 631 N Holly St, Oakwood 75855 | | | 17 | | Fax 903/545-1820 |
| Dr Sharon Ragland | | | | | |

# LIBERTY COUNTY

# LIBERTY PUBLIC SCHOOLS

## ● Cleveland Ind School Dist PID: 01037719
316 E Dallas St, Cleveland 77327

281/592-8717
Fax 281/592-8283

**Schools:** 7 \ **Teachers:** 422 \ **Students:** 6,338 \ **Special Ed Students:** 493 \ **LEP Students:** 2,634 \ **College-Bound:** 45% \ **Ethnic:** African American 5%, Hispanic 76%, Caucasian 18% \ **Exp:** $679 (High) \ **Poverty:** 28% \ **Title I:** $1,806,879 \ **Open-Close:** 08/19 - 05/27 \ **DTBP:** $180 (High) \ [f]

| | |
|---|---|
| Chris Trotter ..................1 | Karen Billingsley .........2,19 |
| Gerald Lee ..................3 | Jennifer Leos ...........4 |
| Larry Smith ..................5 | Jason Fiaaco ............6,35 |
| Valerie Murphy ...............7* | Maria Silva ........8,11,16,57,69,285,294,296 |
| Dr Nathan Boughton ..........15 | Chris Wood ............67 |
| Dawn O'Connor ............69,294 | Susan Ard .............71 |
| James Gonzalez ...........73,295 | |

| Public Schs..Principal | Grd | Prgm | Enr/#Cls | SN | |
|---|---|---|---|---|---|
| Cleveland High Sch | 9-12 | ATV | 1,674 | 81% | 281/592-8752 |
| 1600 E Houston St, Cleveland 77327 | | | 80 | | Fax 281/592-7485 |
| Glenn Barnes | | | | | |
| Cleveland Middle Sch | 6-8 | T | 722 | 87% | 281/593-1148 |
| 2000 E Houston St, Cleveland 77327 | | | 45 | | Fax 281/593-3400 |
| Shelia Stephens | | | | | |

| | | | |
|---|---|---|---|
| 79 Student Personnel | 91 Safety/Security | 275 Response To Intervention | 298 Grant Writer/Ptnrships |
| 80 Driver Ed/Safety | 92 Magnet School | 277 Remedial Math K-12 | 750 Chief Innovation Officer |
| 81 Gifted/Talented | 93 Parental Involvement | 280 Literacy Coach | 751 Chief of Staff |
| 82 Video Services | 95 Tech Prep Program | 285 STEM | 752 Social Emotional Learning |
| 83 Substance Abuse Prev | 97 Chief Infomation Officer | 286 Digital Learning | |
| 84 Erate | 98 Chief Technology Officer | 288 Common Core Standards | Other School Types |
| 85 AIDS Education | 270 Character Education | 294 Accountability | Ⓐ = Alternative School |
| 88 Alternative/At Risk | 271 Migrant Education | 295 Network System | Ⓒ = Charter School |
| 89 Multi-Cultural Curriculum | 273 Teacher Mentor | 296 Title II Programs | Ⓜ = Magnet School |
| 90 Social Work | 274 Before/After Sch | 297 Webmaster | Ⓨ = Year-Round School |

**School Programs**
A = Alternative Program
G = Adult Classes
M = Magnet Program
T = Title I Schoolwide
V = Career & Tech Ed Programs

**Social Media**
[f] = Facebook
[t] = Twitter

New Schools are shaded
New Superintendents and Principals are bold
Personnel with email addresses are underscored

# TX—267

| Cottonwood Elem Sch | PK-5 | | 200 | | 281/761-7540 |
|---|---|---|---|---|---|
| 1922 County Road 3549, Cleveland 77327 | | | | | |
| **Richard Pena** | | | | | |

| Eastside Elem Sch | PK-5 | T | 1,098 | 90% | 281/592-0125 |
|---|---|---|---|---|---|
| 1602 Shell Ave, Cleveland 77327 | | | 28 | | Fax 281/592-0277 |
| Rebecca Smith | | | | | |

Ⓐ Frederick A Douglass Lrng Acad    9-12   T   33   89% 281/592-7595
900 Sam Wiley Dr, Cleveland 77327       Fax 281/432-2754
John Fritts

| Northside Elem Sch | PK-5 | T | 506 | 85% | 281/592-4628 |
|---|---|---|---|---|---|
| 1522 N Blair Ave, Cleveland 77327 | | | 27 | | Fax 281/592-9678 |
| Edward Husk | | | | | |

| Southside Elem Sch | PK-5 | T | 1,279 | 89% | 281/592-0594 |
|---|---|---|---|---|---|
| 303 E Fort Worth St, Cleveland 77327 | | | 40 | | Fax 281/592-2185 |
| Janie Snyder | | | | | �f |

● **Dayton Ind School Dist** PID: 01037771    936/258-2667
100 Cherry Creek Rd, Dayton 77535      Fax 936/258-5616

> **Schools:** 7 \ **Teachers:** 339 \ **Students:** 5,400 \ **Special Ed Students:** 527
> \ **LEP Students:** 951 \ **College-Bound:** 50% \ **Ethnic:** African American
> 7%, Hispanic 43%, Native American: 1%, Caucasian 48% \ **Exp:** $291 (Med)
> \ **Poverty:** 16% \ **Title I:** $1,159,543 \ **Special Education:** $837,000 \
> **Open-Close:** 08/14 - 05/21 \ **DTBP:** $178 (High)

| | | | |
|---|---|---|---|
| Dr Jessica Johnson | 1 | Melissa Vandeventer | 2 |
| Tami Pierce | 2,15,19 | Steve Bell | 3 |
| Marcy Rutland | 4 | Paci Cantu | 5 |
| Kay Stratmann | 7* | Allen Painter | 8,12,13,36,79,88,288 |
| Shanna McCracken | 8 | Michael Dyer | 11,80,296 |
| Abigail Cumbie | 57 | Michaelene Morrison | 58* |
| Linda Harris | 67 | Maryellen Conner | 68,273 |
| Jenny Gunter | 69,294* | Travis Young | 71,83* |
| Nathan Davis | 76,295 | Suzanne Chachere | 84,286 |
| Hector Herrera | 91 | Julie Chachere | 275 |

| Public Schs..Principal | Grd | Prgm | Enr/#Cls | SN | |
|---|---|---|---|---|---|
| Colbert Elem Sch | PK-PK | T | 230 | 71% | 936/258-2727 |
| 231 S Colbert, Dayton 77535 | | | 5 | | Fax 936/257-4151 |
| Jennifer Narvaez | | | | | |
| Dayton High Sch | 9-12 | ATV | 1,511 | 60% | 936/258-2510 |
| 3200 N Cleveland St, Dayton 77535 | | | 80 | | Fax 936/257-4047 |
| Geoff McCracken | | | | | |
| Dr E R Richter Elem Sch | K-5 | T | 725 | 62% | 936/258-7126 |
| 90 Cherry Creek Rd, Dayton 77535 | | | 50 | | Fax 936/257-4179 |
| Kristie Kelley | | | | | |
| Ⓐ Fredda Nottingham Alt Educ Ctr | 9-12 | | 3 | 70% | 936/257-4100 |
| 302 S Cleveland St, Dayton 77535 | | | | | Fax 936/257-4110 |
| Stacie Lott | | | | | |
| Kimmie M Brown Elem Sch | K-5 | T | 783 | 71% | 936/257-2796 |
| 151 Brown Rd, Dayton 77535 | | | 22 | | Fax 936/257-4154 |
| Jessica Ott | | | | | |
| Stephen F Austin Elem Sch | K-5 | T | 930 | 74% | 936/258-2535 |
| 701 W Houston St, Dayton 77535 | | | 44 | | Fax 936/257-4138 |
| Atiya Wortham | | | | | |
| Woodrow Wilson Jr High Sch | 6-8 | T | 1,260 | 68% | 936/258-2309 |
| 309 Highway 146, Dayton 77535 | | | 90 | | Fax 936/257-4109 |
| Matt Barnett | | | | | |

● **Devers Ind School Dist** PID: 01037824    936/549-7591
201 S Chism, Devers 77538      Fax 936/549-7595

> **Schools:** 1 \ **Teachers:** 14 \ **Students:** 176 \ **Special Ed Students:** 17
> \ **LEP Students:** 28 \ **Ethnic:** African American 7%, Hispanic 27%,
> Caucasian 66% \ **Exp:** $493 (High) \ **Poverty:** 14% \ **Title I:** $35,388 \
> **Open-Close:** 08/10 - 05/27 \ **DTBP:** $354 (High)

| | | | |
|---|---|---|---|
| Elizabeth Harris | 1,11,57,288 | Melissa Jordan | 2,295 |
| Deidra Hargrave | 4* | Libby Smith | 6 |
| Elizabeth Harris | 12,57,83* | Missy Horelica | 16,69* |
| Michael Rimarez | 67 | Penny Gilliland | 73 |

| Public Schs..Principal | Grd | Prgm | Enr/#Cls | SN | |
|---|---|---|---|---|---|
| Devers Elem Sch | PK-8 | TV | 176 | 49% | 936/549-7591 |
| 201 S Chism St, Devers 77538 | | | 20 | | Fax 936/549-7085 |
| Elizabeth Harris | | | | | |

● **Hardin Ind School Dist** PID: 01037848    936/298-2112
209 County Rd 2003 N, Hardin 77561      Fax 936/298-9161

> **Schools:** 3 \ **Teachers:** 103 \ **Students:** 1,700 \ **Special Ed Students:** 108
> \ **LEP Students:** 30 \ **College-Bound:** 75% \ **Ethnic:** African American
> 4%, Hispanic 14%, Native American: 1%, Caucasian 81% \ **Exp:** $510
> (High) \ **Poverty:** 26% \ **Title I:** $518,149 \ **Special Education:** $50,000 \
> **Open-Close:** 09/01 - 05/20 \ **DTBP:** $343 (High)

| | | | |
|---|---|---|---|
| Gerald Nixson | 1 | Chris Contreras | 2,19 |
| Keith Carpenter | 3 | Nathan Barrier | 6 |
| Karen Ivey | 8 | Cami Jones | 11,57,296* |
| Ronald Scott | 34 | Cody Parrish | 67 |
| Todd English | 73,286* | | |

| Public Schs..Principal | Grd | Prgm | Enr/#Cls | SN | |
|---|---|---|---|---|---|
| Hardin Elem Sch | PK-5 | T | 701 | 59% | 936/298-2114 |
| 11285 Highway 146 North, Hardin 77561 | | | | | Fax 936/298-9153 |
| **Ronald Scott** | | | | | |
| Hardin High Sch | 9-12 | ATV | 353 | 46% | 936/298-2118 |
| 501 FM 834, Liberty 77575 | | | 25 | | Fax 936/298-3612 |
| **Stacy Tucker** | | | | | |
| Hardin Junior High Sch | 6-8 | T | 322 | 58% | 936/298-2054 |
| 395 FM 834 E, Hardin 77561 | | | | | Fax 936/298-3264 |
| Jennifer Stein | | | | | |

● **Hull Daisetta Ind School Dist** PID: 01037886    936/536-6321
117 N Main St FM 770, Daisetta 77533      Fax 936/536-6251

> **Schools:** 3 \ **Teachers:** 48 \ **Students:** 453 \ **Special Ed Students:** 53
> \ **LEP Students:** 13 \ **College-Bound:** 37% \ **Ethnic:** African American
> 10%, Hispanic 11%, Caucasian 79% \ **Exp:** $573 (High) \ **Poverty:** 10% \
> **Title I:** $72,881 \ **Special Education:** $15,000 \ **Open-Close:** 08/13 - 05/28 \
> **DTBP:** $424 (High)

| | | | |
|---|---|---|---|
| Timothy Bartram | 1 | Erin Stephens | 2 |
| Brenda Brown | 4 | Cindy Davie | 5 |
| Stan Hodges | 6* | Caroline Potetz | 7,83,85 |
| Lacey Brelove | 9 | Justin Anderson | 10,13 |
| Kerry Dillard | 31* | Kelley Berry | 67 |
| Justus Cook | 73,295* | Rhonda Ritter | 286* |

| Public Schs..Principal | Grd | Prgm | Enr/#Cls | SN | |
|---|---|---|---|---|---|
| Hull Daisetta Elem Sch | PK-6 | T | 227 | 77% | 936/536-6321 |
| 7243 FM 834 E, Hull 77564 | | | | | Fax 936/536-3800 |
| Kevin Frauenberger | | | | | |

| | | | | | | | |
|---|---|---|---|---|---|---|---|
| 1 Superintendent | 8 Curric/Instruct K-12 | 19 Chief Financial Officer | 29 Family/Consumer Science | 39 Social Studies K-12 | 49 English/Lang Arts Elem | 59 Special Education Elem | 69 Academic Assessment |
| 2 Bus/Finance/Purchasing | 9 Curric/Instruct Elem | 20 Art K-12 | 30 Adult Education | 40 Social Studies Elem | 50 English/Lang Arts Sec | 60 Special Education Sec | 70 Research/Development |
| 3 Buildings And Grounds | 10 Curric/Instruct Sec | 21 Art Elem | 31 Career/Sch-to-Work K-12 | 41 Social Studies Sec | 51 Reading K-12 | 61 Foreign/World Lang K-12 | 71 Public Information |
| 4 Food Service | 11 Federal Program | 22 Art Sec | 32 Career/Sch-to-Work Elem | 42 Science K-12 | 52 Reading Elem | 62 Foreign/World Lang Elem | 72 Summer School |
| 5 Transportation | 12 Title I | 23 Music K-12 | 33 Career/Sch-to-Work Sec | 43 Science Elem | 53 Reading Sec | 63 Foreign/World Lang Sec | 73 Instructional Tech |
| 6 Athletic | 13 Title V | 24 Music Elem | 34 Early Childhood Ed | 44 Science Sec | 54 Remedial Reading K-12 | 64 Religious Education K-12 | 74 Inservice Training |
| 7 Health Services | 15 Asst Superintendent | 25 Music Sec | 35 Health/Phys Education | 45 Math K-12 | 55 Remedial Reading Elem | 65 Religious Education Elem | 75 Marketing/Distributive |
| | 16 Instructional Media Svcs | 26 Business Education | 36 Guidance Services K-12 | 46 Math Elem | 56 Remedial Reading Sec | 66 Religious Education Sec | 76 Info Systems |
| | 17 Chief Operations Officer | 27 Career & Tech Ed | 37 Guidance Services Elem | 47 Math Sec | 57 Bilingual/ELL | 67 School Board President | 77 Psychological Assess |
| | 18 Chief Academic Officer | 28 Technology Education | 38 Guidance Services Sec | 48 English/Lang Arts K-12 | 58 Special Education K-12 | 68 Teacher Personnel | 78 Affirmative Action |

| Hull Daisetta High Sch | 9-12 | ATV | 155 | 66% | 936/536-6321 |
|---|---|---|---|---|---|
| 117 N Main St, Daisetta 77533 | | | 14 | | Fax 936/536-3839 |
| Quinn Godwin | | | | | |

| Hull Daisetta Junior High Sch | 7-8 | AT | 71 | 65% | 936/536-6321 |
|---|---|---|---|---|---|
| 117 N Main St, Daisetta 77533 | | | 14 | | Fax 936/536-3839 |
| Quinn Godwin | | | | | |

● **Liberty Ind School Dist** PID: 01037927 — 936/336-7213
1600 Grand Ave, Liberty 77575 — Fax 936/336-2283

> **Schools:** 4 \ **Teachers:** 137 \ **Students:** 2,227 \ **Special Ed Students:** 272 \ **LEP Students:** 367 \ **College-Bound:** 58% \ **Ethnic:** Asian 1%, African American 16%, Hispanic 41%, Caucasian 42% \ **Exp:** $453 (High) \ **Poverty:** 25% \ **Title I:** $790,917 \ **Open-Close:** 08/12 - 05/26 \ **DTBP:** $510 (High)

| | | | |
|---|---|---|---|
| Cody Abshier | 1 | Annette Taylor | 2 |
| Ginger Ramer | 2,19 | Robert Ward | 3,5* |
| Sandy Sizemore | 4 | Chad Taylor | 6 |
| Margaret Gardzina | 8,11 | Dustin McGee | 15 |
| Susan Baker | 16* | Keith Ming | 33 |
| Tonya Freeman | 37* | Bruce Bell | 67 |
| Stephanie Smith | 68 | Yvonne Lawrence | 69 |
| Angela Kriegel | 76 | Angela Walker | 79 |
| Leslie Waller | 295 | | |

| Public Schs..Principal | Grd | Prgm | Enr/#Cls | SN | |
|---|---|---|---|---|---|
| Liberty Elem Sch | 2-5 | T | 703 | 68% | 936/336-3603 |
| 1002 Bowie St, Liberty 77575 | | | 48 | | Fax 936/336-6077 |
| Stephanie Cox | | | | | |
| Liberty High Sch | 9-12 | GTV | 582 | 50% | 936/336-6483 |
| 2615 Jefferson Dr, Liberty 77575 | | | 65 | | Fax 936/336-7914 |
| Benicia Bendele | | | | | |
| Liberty Middle Sch | 6-8 | T | 479 | 62% | 936/336-3582 |
| 2515 Jefferson Dr, Liberty 77575 | | | 36 | | Fax 936/336-1021 |
| Rhonda Smith | | | | | |
| San Jacinto Elem Sch | PK-1 | T | 463 | 74% | 936/336-3161 |
| 1629 Grand Ave, Liberty 77575 | | | 35 | | Fax 936/336-5751 |
| Tom Connelly | | | | | |

● **Tarkington Ind School Dist** PID: 01037977 — 281/592-8781
2770 FM 163 Rd, Cleveland 77327 — Fax 281/592-3969

> **Schools:** 4 \ **Teachers:** 127 \ **Students:** 1,810 \ **Special Ed Students:** 219 \ **LEP Students:** 60 \ **College-Bound:** 41% \ **Ethnic:** African American 1%, Hispanic 12%, Caucasian 87% \ **Exp:** $230 (Med) \ **Poverty:** 23% \ **Title I:** $640,243 \ **Open-Close:** 08/21 - 05/28 \ **DTBP:** $553 (High)

| | | | |
|---|---|---|---|
| Dr Marc Keith | 1 | Dennis Shew | 2,15 |
| Ronnie Yancey | 3 | Karen Blum | 4* |
| Melanie Owens | 5 | Mary-Jane Moore | 8,11,57,76,85,88,296,298 |
| Angie Thomas | 34* | Jackie Owens | 37* |
| Grant Cook | 67 | Renee Padgett | 69 |
| Crystal Dean | 73,286,295* | Pam Williams | 73 |

| Public Schs..Principal | Grd | Prgm | Enr/#Cls | SN | |
|---|---|---|---|---|---|
| Tarkington High Sch | 9-12 | TV | 520 | 42% | 281/592-7739 |
| 2770 FM 163 Rd, Cleveland 77327 | | | 48 | | Fax 281/592-0693 |
| **Jennifer Fierro** | | | | | |
| Tarkington Intermediate Sch | 4-5 | T | 277 | 53% | 281/592-6134 |
| 2770 FM 163 Rd, Cleveland 77327 | | | 25 | | Fax 281/592-2453 |
| Calesta House | | | | | |
| Tarkington Middle Sch | 6-8 | T | 445 | 49% | 281/592-7737 |
| 2770 FM 163 Rd, Cleveland 77327 | | | | | Fax 281/592-5241 |
| **Sean McCabe** | | | | | |

| Tarkington Primary Sch | PK-3 | T | 568 | 54% | 281/592-7736 |
|---|---|---|---|---|---|
| 2770 FM 163 Rd, Cleveland 77327 | | | 34 | | Fax 281/592-2361 |
| **Calesta House** \ **Sean McCabe** | | | | | |

## LIMESTONE COUNTY

## LIMESTONE PUBLIC SCHOOLS

● **Coolidge Ind School Dist** PID: 01038012 — 254/786-2206
1002 Kirvan St, Coolidge 76635 — Fax 254/786-4835

> **Schools:** 2 \ **Teachers:** 29 \ **Students:** 295 \ **Special Ed Students:** 49 \ **LEP Students:** 36 \ **Ethnic:** African American 17%, Hispanic 54%, Caucasian 29% \ **Exp:** $655 (High) \ **Poverty:** 35% \ **Title I:** $148,541 \ **Special Education:** $66,000 \ **Open-Close:** 07/30 - 05/27 \ **DTBP:** $347 (High)

| | | | |
|---|---|---|---|
| Dr Robert Lowry | 1 | Danielle Bateman | 2 |
| Donald Erwin | 3,5* | Tonya Barnett | 4* |
| Danny Baker | 6* | Christina Smiley | 12 |
| Erin Cox | 58 | Danny Finley | 67 |
| Tennie Sumrall | 73,95 | | |

| Public Schs..Principal | Grd | Prgm | Enr/#Cls | SN | |
|---|---|---|---|---|---|
| Coolidge Elem Sch | PK-5 | T | 143 | 81% | 254/786-2206 |
| 1000 Kirvan St, Coolidge 76635 | | | 14 | | Fax 254/786-2130 |
| Laci Lowry | | | | | |
| Coolidge Jr Sr High Sch | 6-12 | T | 144 | 77% | 254/786-4612 |
| 1002 Kirvan St, Coolidge 76635 | | | 14 | | Fax 254/786-2038 |
| Justin Cox | | | | | |

● **Groesbeck Ind School Dist** PID: 01038048 — 254/729-4100
1202 N Ellis St, Groesbeck 76642 — Fax 254/729-5167

> **Schools:** 4 \ **Teachers:** 124 \ **Students:** 1,500 \ **Special Ed Students:** 197 \ **LEP Students:** 74 \ **College-Bound:** 65% \ **Ethnic:** Asian 1%, African American 11%, Hispanic 30%, Caucasian 57% \ **Exp:** $230 (Med) \ **Poverty:** 26% \ **Title I:** $498,781 \ **Special Education:** $333,000 \ **Open-Close:** 08/12 - 05/27 \ **DTBP:** $355 (High)

| | | | |
|---|---|---|---|
| James Cowley | 1,73 | Dayne Duncan | 2,4,5,91 |
| Jackie Ancelet | 3 | Jerry Bomar | 6 |
| Jenny Flower | 7 | Dr Diana Freeman | 8,11,83,88,288,296,298 |
| Melody Sadler | 11,58* | Tracy Smith | 37 |
| Susan Swick | 38* | Tom Sutton | 67 |
| Don Waller | 295 | | |

| Public Schs..Principal | Grd | Prgm | Enr/#Cls | SN | |
|---|---|---|---|---|---|
| Enge-Washington Interm Sch | 3-6 | T | 586 | 73% | 254/729-4103 |
| 803 S Ellis St, Groesbeck 76642 | | | 16 | | Fax 254/729-5309 |
| Beth Westhoff | | | | | |
| Groesbeck High Sch | 9-12 | T | 334 | 64% | 254/729-4101 |
| 1202 N Ellis St, Groesbeck 76642 | | | 50 | | Fax 254/729-5458 |
| Dr Bonnie Bomar | | | | | |
| Groesbeck Middle Sch | 7-8 | T | 123 | 69% | 254/729-4102 |
| 410 Elwood Enge Dr, Groesbeck 76642 | | | 42 | | Fax 254/729-8763 |
| Dayne Duncan | | | | | |
| H O Whitehurst Elem Sch | PK-5 | T | 600 | 77% | 254/729-4104 |
| 801 S Ellis St, Groesbeck 76642 | | | 24 | | Fax 254/729-2798 |
| Kimberly Carter | | | | | |

---

| | | | | |
|---|---|---|---|---|
| 79 Student Personnel | 91 Safety/Security | 275 Response To Intervention | 298 Grant Writer/Ptnrships | **School Programs** |
| 80 Driver Ed/Safety | 92 Magnet School | 277 Remedial Math K-12 | 750 Chief Innovation Officer | A = Alternative Program |
| 81 Gifted/Talented | 93 Parental Involvement | 280 Literacy Coach | 751 Chief of Staff | G = Adult Classes |
| 82 Video Services | 95 Tech Prep Program | 285 STEM | 752 Social Emotional Learning | M = Magnet Program |
| 83 Substance Abuse Prev | 97 Chief Infomation Officer | 286 Digital Learning | | T = Title I Schoolwide |
| 84 Erate | 98 Chief Technology Officer | 288 Common Core Standards | **Other School Types** | V = Career & Tech Ed Programs |
| 85 AIDS Education | 270 Character Education | 294 Accountability | Ⓐ = Alternative School | |
| 88 Alternative/At Risk | 271 Migrant Education | 295 Network System | Ⓒ = Charter School | |
| 89 Multi-Cultural Curriculum | 273 Teacher Mentor | 296 Title II Programs | Ⓜ = Magnet School | |
| 90 Social Work | 274 Before/After Sch | 297 Webmaster | Ⓨ = Year-Round School | |

**Social Media**
f = Facebook
t = Twitter

New Schools are shaded
New Superintendents and Principals are bold
Personnel with email addresses are underscored

● **Mexia Ind School Dist** PID: 01038086     254/562-4000
616 N Red River St, Mexia 76667     Fax 254/562-5508

**Schools:** 5 \ **Teachers:** 147 \ **Students:** 1,800 \ **Special Ed Students:** 210
\ **LEP Students:** 320 \ **College-Bound:** 69% \ **Ethnic:** Asian 1%,
African American 27%, Hispanic 47%, Caucasian 25% \ **Exp:** $470 (High)
\ **Poverty:** 32% \ **Title I:** $952,647 \ **Special Education:** $508,000 \
**Open-Close:** 08/13 - 05/21 \ **DTBP:** $350 (High) \ 🅕

| | | |
|---|---|---|
| Dr Lyle Debus ............1 | Dr Brian Ziener .............2,12 |
| Alvis Minter ...........3,5 | Craig Hempel ...............4 |
| Frank Sandoval ..........6* | Dr Celia Drews ...........8,11,15 |
| Dr Celia Drews ......13,296* | Donna Scott ................37* |
| Wendy Dunn ............38* | Shelli Killingsworth .........57,68 |
| Darcy Tyus ............58 | Benji Reed ................67 |
| Cherilyn Zimmer .........73 | Randal Dobson ............83,91* |
| Tracy Porter ..........286 | Anthony Brooks .............295 |
| William Belees .........295 | |

| Public Schs..Principal | Grd | Prgm | Enr/#Cls | SN | |
|---|---|---|---|---|---|
| A B McBay Elem Sch<br>1000 N Ross Ave, Mexia 76667<br>Josh Hollingsworth | PK-2 | T | 535<br>38 | 76% | 254/562-4030<br>Fax 254/562-0074 |
| Mexia High Sch<br>1120 N Ross Ave, Mexia 76667<br>Robert White | 9-12 | T | 506<br>55 | 60% | 254/562-4010<br>Fax 254/562-7072 |
| Mexia Junior High Sch<br>1 Blackcat Dr, Mexia 76667<br>Brian Bartlett | 6-8 | T | 403<br>45 | 67% | 254/562-4020<br>Fax 254/562-5053 |
| Misd Developmental Center<br>616 N Red River St, Mexia 76667<br>Galen Remmers | Spec | AT | 31 | 100% | 254/562-4023<br>Fax 254/562-4024 |
| R Q Sims Intermediate Sch<br>1010 N Ross Ave, Mexia 76667<br>Kelli Fortner | 3-5 | T | 415<br>30 | 71% | 254/562-4025<br>Fax 254/562-4028 |

## LIPSCOMB COUNTY

## LIPSCOMB PUBLIC SCHOOLS

● **Booker Ind School Dist** PID: 01038139     806/658-4501
600 S Main St, Booker 79005     Fax 806/658-4503

**Schools:** 2 \ **Teachers:** 38 \ **Students:** 371 \ **Special Ed Students:** 36
\ **LEP Students:** 101 \ **College-Bound:** 33% \ **Ethnic:** Hispanic 74%,
Native American: 1%, Caucasian 25% \ **Exp:** $662 (High) \ **Poverty:** 12% \
**Title I:** $46,162 \ **Open-Close:** 08/20 - 05/21 \ **DTBP:** $355 (High)

| | | |
|---|---|---|
| Dr Brian Holt ............1 | Debbie Babitzke .............2 |
| Griselda Desantiago .......4* | Brent Lile ................6* |
| Susie Wynn ..........10,16,69* | Jenifer Davis ..............58* |
| Creed Hoover ...........67 | Susy Wynn ................69* |
| Leah Terrell ..........73* | Debbie Dempsay .............84 |

| Public Schs..Principal | Grd | Prgm | Enr/#Cls | SN | |
|---|---|---|---|---|---|
| Bob L Kirksey Elem Sch<br>600 S Main, Booker 79005<br>Kelli Cates | PK-5 | T | 185<br>20 | 67% | 806/658-4559<br>Fax 806/658-9279 |
| Booker High Sch<br>600 S Main St, Booker 79005<br>Howard Barton | 6-12 | TV | 186<br>34 | 66% | 806/658-4521<br>Fax 806/658-9530 |

● **Darrouzett Ind School Dist** PID: 01038165     806/624-2221
102 W Kansas Ave, Darrouzett 79024     Fax 806/624-4361

**Schools:** 1 \ **Teachers:** 13 \ **Students:** 105 \ **Special Ed Students:** 12 \
\ **LEP Students:** 3 \ **College-Bound:** 50% \ **Ethnic:** Hispanic 49%, Native
American: 1%, Caucasian 50% \ **Exp:** $567 (High) \ **Poverty:** 20% \
**Title I:** $26,297 \ **Open-Close:** 08/17 - 05/21 \ **DTBP:** $280 (High)

| | | |
|---|---|---|
| Deidre Parish ............1,11 | Kim Duke ..................2 |
| Brandi Howell ............4 | Donavan Ferguson .............11 |
| Joyce Coppock .......36,275,288* | Kelley White ...............58* |
| Randy Miller ............67 | Nieda Schoenhals .........73,286,295* |
| Tracy Meier ............273* | |

| Public Schs..Principal | Grd | Prgm | Enr/#Cls | SN | |
|---|---|---|---|---|---|
| Darrouzett Sch<br>102 W Kansas Ave, Darrouzett 79024<br>Donavan Ferguson | PK-12 | TV | 105<br>10 | 69% | 806/624-3001 |

● **Follett Ind School Dist** PID: 01038191     806/653-2301
205 E Ivanhoe Ave, Follett 79034     Fax 806/653-2036

**Schools:** 1 \ **Teachers:** 19 \ **Students:** 165 \ **Special Ed Students:** 9
\ **LEP Students:** 14 \ **Ethnic:** Hispanic 32%, Native American: 1%,
Caucasian 67% \ **Exp:** $757 (High) \ **Poverty:** 16% \ **Title I:** $25,604 \
**Open-Close:** 08/19 - 05/21 \ **DTBP:** $331 (High)

| | | |
|---|---|---|
| **Jamie Copley** ............1,11 | Trudy Ashpaugh .............2 |
| Sharon Chadwick ..........4* | Teresa Robison .........8,88,752* |
| Nichole Fraizer ..........58 | Kenton Laubhan .............67 |
| Arlen Barnes ..........73,76* | Teresa Robison ............752 |

| Public Schs..Principal | Grd | Prgm | Enr/#Cls | SN | |
|---|---|---|---|---|---|
| Follett Sch<br>205 E Ivanhoe Ave, Follett 79034<br>Megan Robertson | PK-12 | TV | 165<br>16 | 49% | 806/653-2301 |

● **Higgins Ind School Dist** PID: 01038220     806/852-2171
406 N Main Street, Higgins 79046     Fax 806/852-3502

**Schools:** 1 \ **Teachers:** 16 \ **Students:** 96 \ **Special Ed Students:** 14 \
**LEP Students:** 9 \ **College-Bound:** 50% \ **Ethnic:** African American 2%,
Hispanic 26%, Native American: 2%, Caucasian 70% \ **Exp:** $1,078 (High) \
**Poverty:** 28% \ **Title I:** $30,985 \ **Open-Close:** 08/12 - 05/21 \ **DTBP:** $277
(High)

| | | |
|---|---|---|
| Kristy White ............1,11,83 | Amy Woods .................2 |
| James McGinley ...........3 | Nic Tarr ...............6,80* |
| Javon Hassler .........16,73,286* | Jody Wiederstein .............58* |
| Jay Barbee ............67 | Mavonteine Slavin ............85 |
| Nancy Habekutt ..........270* | |

| Public Schs..Principal | Grd | Prgm | Enr/#Cls | SN | |
|---|---|---|---|---|---|
| Higgins Sch<br>406 N Main Street, Higgins 79046<br>Becky Suthers | PK-12 | T | 96<br>15 | 66% | 806/852-2631 |

| | | | | | | |
|---|---|---|---|---|---|---|
| 1 | Superintendent | 8 | Curric/Instruct K-12 | 19 | Chief Financial Officer | 29 Family/Consumer Science |
| 2 | Bus/Finance/Purchasing | 9 | Curric/Instruct Elem | 20 | Art K-12 | 30 Adult Education |
| 3 | Buildings And Grounds | 10 | Curric/Instruct Sec | 21 | Art Elem | 31 Career/Sch-to-Work K-12 |
| 4 | Food Service | 11 | Federal Program | 22 | Art Sec | 32 Career/Sch-to-Work Elem |
| 5 | Transportation | 12 | Title I | 23 | Music K-12 | 33 Career/Sch-to-Work Sec |
| 6 | Athletic | 13 | Title V | 24 | Music Elem | 34 Early Childhood Ed |
| 7 | Health Services | 14 | Instructional Media Svcs | 25 | Music Sec | 35 Health/Phys Education |
| | | 15 | Asst Superintendent | 26 | Business Education | 36 Guidance Services K-12 |
| | | 16 | Instructional Media Svcs | 27 | Career & Tech Ed | 37 Guidance Services Elem |
| | | 17 | Chief Operations Officer | 28 | Technology Education | 38 Guidance Services Sec |
| | | 18 | Chief Academic Officer | | | |

| | | | |
|---|---|---|---|
| 39 Social Studies K-12 | 49 English/Lang Arts Elem | 59 Special Education Elem | 69 Academic Assessment |
| 40 Social Studies Elem | 50 English/Lang Arts Sec | 60 Special Education Sec | 70 Research/Development |
| 41 Social Studies Sec | 51 Reading K-12 | 61 Foreign/World Lang K-12 | 71 Public Information |
| 42 Science K-12 | 52 Reading Elem | 62 Foreign/World Lang Elem | 72 Summer School |
| 43 Science Elem | 53 Reading Sec | 63 Foreign/World Lang Sec | 73 Instructional Tech |
| 44 Science Sec | 54 Remedial Reading K-12 | 64 Religious Education K-12 | 74 Inservice Training |
| 45 Math K-12 | 55 Remedial Reading Elem | 65 Religious Education Elem | 75 Marketing/Distributive |
| 46 Math Elem | 56 Remedial Reading Sec | 66 Religious Education Sec | 76 Info Systems |
| 47 Math Sec | 57 Bilingual/ELL | 67 School Board President | 77 Psychological Assess |
| 48 English/Lang Arts K-12 | 58 Special Education K-12 | 68 Teacher Personnel | 78 Affirmative Action |

| LIVE OAK COUNTY | LLANO COUNTY |
|---|---|

## LIVE OAK PUBLIC SCHOOLS

● **George West Ind School Dist** PID: 01038256
913 Houston St, George West 78022

361/449-1914
Fax 361/449-1426

**Schools:** 4 \ **Teachers:** 79 \ **Students:** 1,100 \ **Special Ed Students:** 117 \ **LEP Students:** 30 \ **College-Bound:** 60% \ **Ethnic:** Hispanic 59%, Caucasian 40% \ **Exp:** $377 (High) \ **Poverty:** 23% \ **Title I:** $322,746 \ **Open-Close:** 08/13 - 05/27 \ **DTBP:** $350 (High) \ 🇫 🇪

| | | | |
|---|---|---|---|
| Dr Roland Quesada | 1 | Nita Peck | 2 |
| Joe Chappa | 3 | Rena Cuevas | 4 |
| Sharon Clifton | 4 | Margaret Yarborough | 5 |
| Brent Kornegay | 6,35 | Raachelle Clayton | 7 |
| Kristy Keach | 11,69 | Deanna Blackwell | 16,73,84 |
| Elda Buenteo | 16* | Jay Jamesison | 27 |
| Heather Lee | 31 | Ethel Murphy | 58 |
| Cheri Moore | 67 | Laurl Jones | 76 |

| Public Schs..Principal | Grd | Prgm | Enr/#Cls | SN |
|---|---|---|---|---|
| George West Elem Sch<br>910 Houston St, George West 78022<br>Omar De La Rosa | 4-6 | T | 254<br>35 | 69% 361/449-1914<br>Fax 361/449-2177 |
| George West High Sch<br>1013 Houston St, George West 78022<br>**Richard Waterhouse** | 9-12 | ATV | 318<br>35 | 48% 361/449-1914<br>Fax 361/449-3128 |
| George West Junior High Sch<br>900 Houston St, George West 78022<br>Ashley Lowe | 7-8 | TV | 159<br>15 | 67% 361/449-1914<br>Fax 361/449-3909 |
| George West Primary Sch<br>405 Travis St, George West 78022<br>Christina Cortez | PK-3 | T | 336<br>20 | 66% 361/449-1914<br>Fax 361/449-8921 |

● **Three Rivers Ind School Dist** PID: 01038309
351 S School Rd, Three Rivers 78071

361/786-3626
Fax 361/786-2555

**Schools:** 2 \ **Teachers:** 54 \ **Students:** 628 \ **Special Ed Students:** 76 \ **LEP Students:** 31 \ **College-Bound:** 80% \ **Ethnic:** African American 1%, Hispanic 61%, Caucasian 38% \ **Exp:** $548 (High) \ **Poverty:** 21% \ **Title I:** $160,782 \ **Open-Close:** 08/13 - 05/21 \ **DTBP:** $180 (High)

| | | | |
|---|---|---|---|
| Les Dragon | 1 | Stephanie Timms | 2 |
| Whitney Means | 4 | Arturo Lozano | 6,85* |
| Audra Huff | 11,52,58,286,296 | Robin Curbello | 16* |
| Karl Arnst | 67 | Daniel Fernandez | 73,84 |

| Public Schs..Principal | Grd | Prgm | Enr/#Cls | SN |
|---|---|---|---|---|
| Three Rivers Elem Sch<br>351 S School Rd, Three Rivers 78071<br>Cindy Miller | PK-6 | T | 328<br>24 | 64% 361/786-3592<br>Fax 361/786-3594 |
| Three Rivers Jr Sr High Sch<br>351 S School Rd, Three Rivers 78071<br>Sandy Villarreal | 7-12 | ATV | 300<br>20 | 56% 361/786-3531<br>Fax 361/786-3533 |

## LLANO PUBLIC SCHOOLS

● **Llano Ind School Dist** PID: 01038347
1400 Oatman St, Llano 78643

325/247-4747
Fax 325/247-5623

**Schools:** 4 \ **Teachers:** 135 \ **Students:** 1,701 \ **Special Ed Students:** 216 \ **LEP Students:** 119 \ **College-Bound:** 45% \ **Ethnic:** Asian 1%, African American 1%, Hispanic 27%, Caucasian 71% \ **Exp:** $532 (High) \ **Poverty:** 22% \ **Title I:** $616,544 \ **Special Education:** $358,000 \ **Open-Close:** 08/13 - 05/28 \ **DTBP:** $136 (High)

| | | | |
|---|---|---|---|
| Mac Edwards | 1 | Ryan Turner | 2,19,270 |
| Sue Ann Clandenen | 2 | Keith Nelson | 3 |
| Kayla Earnshaw | 4 | Melissa Pike | 5 |
| Matthew Green | 6 | James Paine | 8,11,280,285,286,288,294,298 |
| Kim Stubblefiled | 9,11,34,51,54,271 | Jill Dillard | 16,82* |
| Scott Patrick | 31,83,88 | Toby Fletcher | 31,83,88 |
| Jennifer Watkins | 37 | Courtney Edwards | 38 |
| Shelly Schuessler | 58* | Rick Tisdale | 67 |
| Jim Beasley | 73,76,95,295,297 | Eliabeth Kloepper | 85 |

| Public Schs..Principal | Grd | Prgm | Enr/#Cls | SN |
|---|---|---|---|---|
| Llano Elem Sch<br>1600 Oatman St, Llano 78643<br>Douglas Debord | PK-5 | T | 359<br>28 | 60% 325/247-5718<br>Fax 325/247-5731 |
| Llano High Sch<br>2509 S State Highway 16, Llano 78643<br>**Scott Patrick** | 9-12 | TV | 505<br>45 | 59% 325/248-2200<br>Fax 325/247-2122 |
| Llano Junior High Sch<br>400 E State Highway 71, Llano 78643<br>Jennifer Caropepe | 6-8 | T | 407<br>50 | 61% 325/247-4659<br>Fax 325/247-5821 |
| Packsaddle Elem Sch<br>150 Pioneer Ln, Kingsland 78639<br>Ryan Turner | PK-5 | T | 430<br>36 | 82% 325/388-8129<br>Fax 325/388-7000 |

## LLANO PRIVATE SCHOOLS

| Private Schs..Principal | Grd | Prgm | Enr/#Cls | SN |
|---|---|---|---|---|
| Llano Christian Academy<br>507 E Green St, Llano 78643<br>Dr Alice Smith | PK-12 | | 76 | 325/247-4942 |

| | | | | | |
|---|---|---|---|---|---|
| 79 Student Personnel | 91 Safety/Security | 275 Response To Intervention | 298 Grant Writer/Ptnrships | **School Programs** | **Social Media** |
| 80 Driver Ed/Safety | 92 Magnet School | 277 Remedial Math K-12 | 750 Chief Innovation Officer | A = Alternative Program | |
| 81 Gifted/Talented | 93 Parental Involvement | 280 Literacy Coach | 751 Chief of Staff | G = Adult Classes | 🇫 = Facebook |
| 82 Video Services | 95 Tech Prep Program | 285 STEM | 752 Social Emotional Learning | M = Magnet Program | |
| 83 Substance Abuse Prev | 97 Chief Infomation Officer | 286 Digital Learning | | T = Title I Schoolwide | 🇪 = Twitter |
| 84 Erate | 98 Chief Technology Officer | 288 Common Core Standards | **Other School Types** | V = Career & Tech Ed Programs | |
| 85 AIDS Education | 270 Character Education | 294 Accountability | Ⓐ = Alternative School | | |
| 88 Alternative/At Risk | 271 Migrant Education | 295 Network System | Ⓒ = Charter School | **New Schools are shaded** | |
| 89 Multi-Cultural Curriculum | 273 Teacher Mentor | 296 Title II Programs | Ⓜ = Magnet School | **New Superintendents and Principals are bold** | |
| 90 Social Work | 274 Before/After Sch | 297 Webmaster | Ⓨ = Year-Round School | Personnel with email addresses are underscored | |

**TX—271**

| | | | | | |
|---|---|---|---|---|---|
| Westwind Elem Sch | PK-5 | T | 514 | 63% | 806/799-3731 |
| 6401 43rd St, Lubbock 79407 | | | 30 | | |
| Todd Newberry | | | | | |
| Willow Bend Elem Sch | PK-5 | T | 548 | 80% | 806/796-0090 |
| 8816 13 St, Lubbock 79416 | | | | | Fax 806/796-1517 |
| Vivian Fisher | | | | | |

## LUBBOCK COUNTY

## LUBBOCK PUBLIC SCHOOLS

● **Frenship Ind School Dist** PID: 01038402    806/866-9541
501 7th St, Wolfforth 79382    Fax 806/866-4135

**Schools:** 13 \ **Teachers:** 660 \ **Students:** 9,900 \ **Special Ed Students:** 919 \ **LEP Students:** 388 \ **College-Bound:** 57% \ **Ethnic:** Asian 3%, African American 4%, Hispanic 46%, Caucasian 47% \ **Exp:** $435 (High) \ **Poverty:** 12% \ **Title I:** $1,285,284 \ **Special Education:** $1,691,000 \ **Open-Close:** 08/12 - 05/20 \ **DTBP:** $137 (High) \ 🅵 🆃

| | | | |
|---|---|---|---|
| Dr Michelle McCord | 1 | Farley Reeves | 2,15 |
| Tim Williams | 2,15 | Allen Tanner | 3 |
| Derek Cobb | 3 | Joyce Trevino | 4 |
| Michael Brooks | 5* | Kenneth Catney | 6 |
| Cassandra Slayton | 8 | Cindy Cobb | 8,15,74,273 |
| Melissa Wade | 11,85 | Amy Baker | 27 |
| Regan Lamberson | 39* | Julie Rogers | 48 |
| Senon Cruz | 57 | Doug Smith | 58 |
| Brad Draper | 67 | Rhonda Dillard | 68,78 |
| Emily Solis | 71 | Joe Barnett | 73,98,297 |
| Laurie Davis | 73* | Michelle Traylor | 73 |
| Richard Dean | 91 | Leanne Fisher | 288 |

| Public Schs..Principal | Grd | Prgm | Enr/#Cls | SN | |
|---|---|---|---|---|---|
| Bennett Elem Sch | PK-5 | | 670 | 37% | 806/866-4443 |
| 101 Donald Preston Dr, Wolfforth 79382 | | | 25 | | Fax 806/866-4715 |
| Chera Bessire | | | | | |
| Crestview Elem Sch | PK-5 | | 550 | 25% | 806/794-3661 |
| 6020 81st St, Lubbock 79424 | | | 29 | | Fax 806/798-2373 |
| Stacy Davis | | | | | |
| Frenship High Sch | 9-12 | V | 1,975 | 33% | 806/866-4440 |
| 902 N Dowden Rd, Wolfforth 79382 | | | 115 | | Fax 806/866-9370 |
| Gregory Hernandez | | | | | |
| Frenship Middle Sch | 6-8 | | 290 | 37% | 806/866-4464 |
| 500 Main St, Wolfforth 79382 | | | 40 | | Fax 806/866-9137 |
| Casey Loafman | | | | | |
| Heritage Middle Sch | 6-8 | | 484 | 36% | 806/794-9400 |
| 6110 73rd St, Lubbock 79424 | | | | | Fax 806/783-8958 |
| Chelsey Campbell | | | | | |
| Legacy Elem Sch | PK-3 | T | 484 | 54% | 806/792-3800 |
| 6424 Kemper Ave, Lubbock 79416 | | | | | Fax 806/792-3801 |
| Carole Kidd | | | | | |
| North Ridge Elem Sch | PK-5 | T | 605 | 49% | 806/793-6686 |
| 6302 11th Pl, Lubbock 79416 | | | 39 | | Fax 806/792-3798 |
| **Aimee Stroope** | | | | | |
| Oak Ridge Elem Sch | PK-5 | T | 572 | 36% | 806/794-5200 |
| 6514 68th St, Lubbock 79424 | | | | | Fax 806/698-0440 |
| Shane Langen | | | | | |
| Ⓐ Reese Education Center | 6-12 | T | 75 | 61% | 806/885-4910 |
| 9421 W 4th St, Lubbock 79416 | | | 12 | | Fax 806/885-2442 |
| Stephanie Spear | | | | | |
| Terra Vista Middle Sch | 6-8 | T | 811 | 58% | 806/796-0076 |
| 1111 Upland Ave, Lubbock 79416 | | | | | Fax 806/796-1540 |
| Jill Jaquess | | | | | |
| Upland Heights Elem Sch | PK-5 | | 653 | 36% | 806/698-6611 |
| 10020 Upland Ave, Lubbock 79424 | | | | | |
| Denise Stewart | | | | | |

● **Idalou Ind School Dist** PID: 01038452    806/892-1900
601 Walnut St, Idalou 79329    Fax 806/892-3204

**Schools:** 3 \ **Teachers:** 78 \ **Students:** 984 \ **Special Ed Students:** 83 \ **LEP Students:** 27 \ **College-Bound:** 70% \ **Ethnic:** Hispanic 42%, Caucasian 57% \ **Exp:** $634 (High) \ **Poverty:** 9% \ **Title I:** $82,503 \ **Open-Close:** 08/19 - 05/21 \ **DTBP:** $350 (High)

| | | | |
|---|---|---|---|
| **Robert Gibson** | 1 | Shelly Tubbs | 2,11,19,71 |
| Shelly Kirkendall | 2 | Adam Oliva | 3 |
| Jeff Lofton | 6* | Steve Gunter | 8,11,274* |
| Karen Carroll | 10,31* | Landon Jackson | 16,73 |
| Lori Irwin | 57,69,270,271* | Amy Estrada | 58 |
| Dustan Moyers | 67 | | |

| Public Schs..Principal | Grd | Prgm | Enr/#Cls | SN | |
|---|---|---|---|---|---|
| Idalou Elem Sch | PK-4 | T | 372 | 43% | 806/892-2524 |
| 601 Walnut St, Idalou 79329 | | | 19 | | Fax 806/892-2666 |
| Steve Gunter | | | | | |
| Idalou High Sch | 9-12 | V | 294 | 23% | 806/892-2123 |
| 601 Walnut St, Idalou 79329 | | | 25 | | Fax 806/892-2690 |
| **Jerry Estrada** | | | | | |
| Idalou Middle Sch | 5-8 | | 318 | 34% | 806/892-2133 |
| 403 W 7th St, Idalou 79329 | | | 18 | | Fax 806/892-2388 |
| Josh Damron | | | | | |

● **Lubbock Ind School Dist** PID: 01038490    806/766-1000
1628 19th St, Lubbock 79401    Fax 806/219-0000

**Schools:** 48 \ **Teachers:** 1,970 \ **Students:** 26,000 \ **Special Ed Students:** 3,171 \ **LEP Students:** 1,208 \ **Ethnic:** Asian 2%, African American 14%, Hispanic 60%, Caucasian 23% \ **Exp:** $516 (High) \ **Poverty:** 22% \ **Title I:** $11,105,196 \ **Special Education:** $5,835,000 \ **Open-Close:** 08/17 - 05/28 \ **DTBP:** $186 (High) \ 🆃

| | | | |
|---|---|---|---|
| Kathryn Reno-Rollo | 1 | Kelley Lewis | 2 |
| Nina Waller | 2 | Shane Jennigs | 2 |
| Bill Craft | 3 | Lauren Johnson | 4* |
| Mike Meeks | 6 | Paulett Rozneck | 7,83,85 |
| Misty Rieber | 8,15,288 | Doyle Volger | 9,15 |
| Johnna Weatherbee | 12,93 | Doug Rodriguez | 15,68,78,751 |
| Jenny Flores | 16* | Ricardo Rodriguez | 17 |
| Andrew Babcock | 20,23 | Jill Berset | 27,31 |
| Bryan Sessom | 34 | Charlotte Sessom | 36 |
| Joni Rodela | 39 | Michael Sizemore | 42,285 |
| Amador Vasquez | 45 | Lori Greaves | 48,51 |
| Melissa Hernandez | 57 | Kami Finger | 58 |
| Dr Shelly Bratcher | 58 | Laura Cook | 61* |
| Zack Brady | 67 | Doug Bawcom | 68 |
| Wonderful Loud | 68 | Pam Leftwich | 69,70,294 |
| Jeffrey Klopzman | 71 | Carri Fulgham | 73,286 |
| Damon Jackson | 73,98 | Anna Jackson | 74* |
| Dathan Mullins | 76,295 | Dana King | 78,90,275 |
| Lynn Akin | 79,88 | Chad Haskins | 81,92,286 |
| Dr Gail Smith | 81 | Jody Scifres | 91 |
| Maria Patino | 271 | | |

| Public Schs..Principal | Grd | Prgm | Enr/#Cls | SN | |
|---|---|---|---|---|---|
| Alderson Elem Sch | PK-5 | T | 448 | 98% | 806/219-8000 |
| 219 Walnut Ave, Lubbock 79403 | | | 22 | | Fax 806/766-1490 |
| Drue Coleman | | | | | |

| | | | | | | |
|---|---|---|---|---|---|---|
| 1 Superintendent | 8 Curric/Instruct K-12 | 19 Chief Financial Officer | 29 Family/Consumer Science | 39 Social Studies K-12 | 49 English/Lang Arts Elem | 59 Special Education Elem | 69 Academic Assessment |
| 2 Bus/Finance/Purchasing | 9 Curric/Instruct Elem | 20 Art K-12 | 30 Adult Education | 40 Social Studies Elem | 50 English/Lang Arts Sec | 60 Special Education Sec | 70 Research/Development |
| 3 Buildings And Grounds | 10 Curric/Instruct Sec | 21 Art Elem | 31 Career/Sch-to-Work K-12 | 41 Social Studies Sec | 51 Reading K-12 | 61 Foreign/World Lang K-12 | 71 Public Information |
| 4 Food Service | 11 Federal Program | 22 Art Sec | 32 Career/Sch-to-Work Elem | 42 Science K-12 | 52 Reading Elem | 62 Foreign/World Lang Elem | 72 Summer School |
| 5 Transportation | 12 Title I | 23 Music K-12 | 33 Career/Sch-to-Work Sec | 43 Science Elem | 53 Reading Sec | 63 Foreign/World Lang Sec | 73 Instructional Tech |
| 6 Athletic | 13 Title V | 24 Music Elem | 34 Early Childhood Ed | 44 Science Sec | 54 Remedial Reading K-12 | 64 Religious Education K-12 | 74 Inservice Training |
| 7 Health Services | 15 Asst Superintendent | 25 Music Sec | 35 Health/Phys Education | 45 Math K-12 | 55 Remedial Reading Elem | 65 Religious Education Elem | 75 Marketing/Distributive |
| | 16 Instructional Media Svcs | 26 Business Education | 36 Guidance Services K-12 | 46 Math Elem | 56 Remedial Reading Sec | 66 Religious Education Sec | 76 Info Systems |
| | 17 Chief Operations Officer | 27 Career & Tech Ed | 37 Guidance Services Elem | 47 Math Sec | 57 Bilingual/ELL | 67 School Board President | 77 Psychological Assess |
| | 18 Chief Academic Officer | 28 Technology Education | 38 Guidance Services Sec | 48 English/Lang Arts K-12 | 58 Special Education K-12 | 68 Teacher Personnel | 78 Affirmative Action |

| School | Grades | Media | Enrollment | % | Phone |
|---|---|---|---|---|---|
| Atkins Middle Sch<br>5401 Avenue U, Lubbock 79412<br>Chris Huber | 6-8 | TV | 611<br>50 | 88% | 806/219-3000<br>Fax 806/766-2226 |
| Bayless Elem Sch<br>2115 58th St, Lubbock 79412<br>Brandi McKinney | PK-5 | T | 527<br>38 | 93% | 806/219-5000<br>Fax 806/766-1651 |
| Bean Elem Sch<br>3001 Avenue N, Lubbock 79411<br>Tom Thomas | PK-5 | T | 455<br>31 | 97% | 806/219-5100<br>Fax 806/766-1671 |
| Brown Elem Sch<br>2315 36th St, Lubbock 79412<br>Staci Sumners | PK-5 | T | 348<br>25 | 96% | 806/219-5300<br>Fax 806/766-0831 |
| Byron Martin Advanced Tech Ctr<br>3201 Avenue Q, Lubbock 79411<br>Charlotte Sessom | Voc | | 200 | | 806/219-2800 |
| Cavazos Middle Sch<br>210 N University Ave, Lubbock 79415<br>Marti Makuta | 6-8 | TV | 541<br>50 | 99% | 806/219-3200<br>Fax 806/766-6627 |
| Centennial Elem Sch<br>1301 N Utica Ave, Lubbock 79416<br>Davida Burks | PK-5 | T | 648<br>31 | 76% | 806/219-7800<br>Fax 806/766-1982 |
| Coronado High Sch<br>4910 29th Dr, Lubbock 79410<br>Julia Stephen | 9-12 | TV | 2,137<br>90 | 61% | 806/219-1100<br>Fax 806/766-0560 |
| Dunbar College Prep Academy<br>2010 E 26th St, Lubbock 79404<br>Gabe Gillespie | 6-8 | TV | 583<br>50 | 97% | 806/219-3400<br>Fax 806/766-1320 |
| Dupre Elem Sch<br>2008 Avenue T, Lubbock 79411<br>Robin Conkwright | PK-5 | T | 234<br>17 | 96% | 806/219-5400<br>Fax 806/766-1691 |
| Estacado High Sch<br>1504 E Itasca St, Lubbock 79403<br>Angelica Wilbanks | 9-12 | TV | 754<br>53 | 92% | 806/766-1400<br>Fax 806/766-1952 |
| Evans Middle Sch<br>4211 58th St, Lubbock 79413<br>Justin Newman | 6-8 | TV | 882 | 51% | 806/219-3600<br>Fax 806/766-0570 |
| Guadalupe Elem Sch<br>101 N Avenue P, Lubbock 79401<br>Alma Cunningtubby | PK-5 | T | 184<br>21 | 95% | 806/219-5500<br>Fax 806/766-1702 |
| Hardwick Elem Sch<br>1420 Chicago Ave, Lubbock 79416<br>Kimberly Callison | PK-5 | T | 373<br>21 | 79% | 806/219-5600<br>Fax 806/766-0842 |
| Harwell Elem Sch<br>4101 Avenue D, Lubbock 79404<br>Jorge Sanchez | PK-5 | T | 418<br>30 | 90% | 806/219-5700<br>Fax 806/766-1713 |
| Hodges Elem Sch<br>5001 Avenue P, Lubbock 79412<br>Dora Jimenez | PK-5 | T | 333<br>25 | 96% | 806/219-5800<br>Fax 806/766-1730 |
| Honey Elem Sch<br>3615 86th St, Lubbock 79423<br>Phillip Neeb | PK-5 | | 372<br>24 | 45% | 806/219-5900<br>Fax 806/766-0864 |
| Hutchinson Middle Sch<br>3102 Canton Ave, Lubbock 79410<br>Heidi Dye | 6-8 | TV | 866<br>45 | 40% | 806/219-3800<br>Fax 806/766-0538 |
| Irons Middle Sch<br>5214 79th St, Lubbock 79424<br>Philip Riewe | 6-8 | ATV | 608<br>58 | 40% | 806/219-4000<br>Fax 806/766-2070 |
| Jackson Elem Sch<br>201 Vernon Ave, Lubbock 79415<br>Alma Cunningtubby | PK-5 | T | 181<br>19 | 96% | 806/219-6000<br>Fax 806/766-1765 |
| Jayne Ann Miller Elem Sch<br>6705 Joliet Dr, Lubbock 79413<br>Kevin Booe | PK-5 | T | 623<br>22 | 39% | 806/219-8100<br>Fax 806/766-0557 |
| Joan Y Ervin Elem Sch<br>1802 E 28th St, Lubbock 79404<br>Joshlyn Cotton | PK-5 | T | 388<br>30 | 98% | 806/219-8200<br>Fax 806/766-1875 |
| Lubbock Senior High Sch<br>2004 19th St, Lubbock 79401<br>Douglas Young | 9-12 | TV | 1,923 | 59% | 806/219-1600<br>Fax 806/766-1469 |
| MacKenzie Middle Sch<br>5402 12th St, Lubbock 79416<br>John Martinez | 6-8 | TV | 655<br>45 | 78% | 806/219-4200<br>Fax 806/766-0510 |
| Maedgen Elem Sch<br>4401 Nashville Ave, Lubbock 79413<br>Ofelia Mendez | PK-5 | T | 323<br>24 | 90% | 806/219-6200<br>Fax 806/766-0990 |
| Ⓐ Matthews Alt HS/New Directions<br>417 N Akron Ave, Lubbock 79415<br>Carolyn Thompson-Conwr | 6-12 | GTV | 156<br>19 | 98% | 806/219-2600<br>Fax 806/766-1532 |
| McWhorter Elem Sch<br>2711 1st St, Lubbock 79415<br>Karla Mann | PK-5 | T | 591<br>26 | 94% | 806/219-6100<br>Fax 806/766-1797 |
| Monterey Senior High Sch<br>3211 47th St, Lubbock 79413<br>Les Purkeypile | 9-12 | ATV | 2,134<br>70 | 68% | 806/219-1900<br>Fax 806/766-0509 |
| O L Slaton Middle Sch<br>1602 32nd St, Lubbock 79411<br>Kris Blodgett | 6-8 | TV | 527<br>45 | 93% | 806/219-4400<br>Fax 806/766-1571 |
| Overton Elem Sch<br>2902 Louisville Ave, Lubbock 79410<br>Ann Archer | PK-5 | T | 341<br>21 | 91% | 806/219-6300<br>Fax 806/766-0895 |
| Parsons Elem Sch<br>2811 58th St, Lubbock 79413<br>Yvonne Avey | PK-5 | T | 457<br>32 | 81% | 806/219-6400<br>Fax 806/766-0902 |
| Ⓐ Priority Intervention Academy<br>1324 E 24th St, Lubbock 79404<br>David Johnson | 6-12 | V | 77<br>30 | 85% | 806/219-2400<br>Fax 806/766-1964 |
| Ⓒ Ramirez Charter Sch<br>702 Avenue T, Lubbock 79401<br>Melissa Serenil | PK-5 | T | 427<br>26 | 57% | 806/219-6500<br>Fax 806/766-1825 |
| Roscoe Wilson Elem Sch<br>2807 25th St, Lubbock 79410<br>Paula January | PK-5 | | 559<br>26 | 23% | 806/219-7500<br>Fax 806/766-0525 |
| Roy Roberts Elem Sch<br>7901 Avenue P, Lubbock 79423<br>Anissa Briseno | PK-5 | T | 581 | 77% | 806/219-7900<br>Fax 806/766-6222 |
| Rush Elem Sch<br>4702 15th St, Lubbock 79416<br>Mary McGann | PK-5 | T | 322<br>29 | 76% | 806/219-6700<br>Fax 806/766-0929 |
| Smith Elem Sch<br>8707 Dover Ave, Lubbock 79424<br>Gale Latimer | PK-5 | T | 663<br>35 | 40% | 806/219-6800<br>Fax 806/766-2035 |
| Smylie Wilson Middle Sch<br>4402 31st St, Lubbock 79410<br>Kelly Brownfield | 6-8 | TV | 516<br>20 | 89% | 806/219-4600<br>Fax 806/766-0814 |
| Stewart Elem Sch<br>4815 46th St, Lubbock 79414<br>Jaci Underwood | PK-5 | T | 455<br>23 | 91% | 806/219-6900<br>Fax 806/766-0943 |
| Talkington Sch Young Women<br>415 N Ivory Ave, Lubbock 79403<br>Julie Wyatt | 6-12 | T | 466 | 45% | 806/219-2200<br>Fax 806/766-1738 |
| Waters Elem Sch<br>3006 78th St, Lubbock 79423<br>**Melissa Portwood** | PK-5 | T | 541<br>32 | 67% | 806/219-7000<br>Fax 806/766-6209 |
| Wester Elem Sch<br>4602 Chicago Ave, Lubbock 79414<br>Amelia Kimbley | PK-5 | T | 385<br>19 | 92% | 806/219-7100<br>Fax 806/766-0962 |
| Wheelock Elem Sch<br>3008 42nd St, Lubbock 79413<br>Elizabeth Berridge | PK-5 | T | 347<br>18 | 91% | 806/219-7200<br>Fax 806/766-0976 |
| Whiteside Elem Sch<br>7508 Albany Ave, Lubbock 79424<br>Brandi Lay | PK-5 | T | 518<br>37 | 47% | 806/219-7300<br>Fax 806/766-2081 |

| | | | | | |
|---|---|---|---|---|---|
| Williams Elem Sch<br>4812 58th St, Lubbock 79414<br>Denise Neeb | PK-5 | T | 372<br>22 | 78% | 806/219-7400<br>Fax 806/766-0989 |
| Wolffarth Elem Sch<br>3202 Erskine St, Lubbock 79415<br>Catherine Gillespie | PK-5 | T | 341<br>17 | 96% | 806/219-7600<br>Fax 806/766-1893 |
| Wright Elem Sch<br>1302 Adrian St, Lubbock 79403<br>Stacy Hurst | PK-5 | AT | 203<br>6 | 92% | 806/219-7700<br>Fax 806/766-1906 |

## ● Lubbock-Cooper Ind Sch Dist PID: 01039030

13807 Indiana Ave, Lubbock 79423

806/863-7100
Fax 806/863-3130

**Schools:** 9 \ **Teachers:** 501 \ **Students:** 6,000 \ **Special Ed Students:** 611 \ **LEP Students:** 179 \ **Ethnic:** Asian 2%, African American 2%, Hispanic 38%, Caucasian 57% \ **Exp:** $332 (High) \ **Poverty:** 10% \ **Title I:** $502,873 \ **Special Education:** $1,150,000 \ **Open-Close:** 08/19 - 05/27 \ **DTBP:** $150 (High)

| | | |
|---|---|---|
| Keith Bryant | 1 | |
| John Windham | 3 | |
| Trevor Edgemon | 5 | |
| Sandra Beilue | 8,294 | |
| Betsy Adams Taylor | 13,296 | |
| Macy Satterwhite | 15 | |
| Pam Brown | 36,69 | |
| Tracy Fogerson | 58 | |
| Britt Spears | 68 | |
| Jaque Fewin | 73,84 | |
| Jay Whitefield | 79* | |
| Shay Troutman | 280 | |
| Ann Ferris | 2 | |
| Rudy Luna | 4* | |
| Katt Winkel | 6 | |
| Darla Heinrich | 11 | |
| Danny Davis | 15 | |
| Deborah Smith | 27* | |
| Sandra Jimenez | 57,271* | |
| Paul Ehlers | 67 | |
| Sadie Alderson | 71 | |
| Donna Hanfeld | 76* | |
| Maggie McNab | 88* | |
| Jeremy Wagner | 285 | |

| Public Schs..Principal | Grd | Prgm | Enr/#Cls | SN | |
|---|---|---|---|---|---|
| Central Elem Sch<br>4020 135th St, Lubbock 79423<br>Colter Cox | PK-5 | T | 673 | 26% | 806/776-2150<br>Fax 806/776-2151 |
| East Elem Sch<br>2727 134th St, Lubbock 79423<br>Candice Cross | PK-5 | T | 366 | 54% | 806/776-2109<br>Fax 806/776-2110 |
| Laura Bush Middle Sch<br>3425 118th St, Lubbock 79423<br>Edna Parr | 6-8 | | 914 | 30% | 806/776-0750<br>Fax 806/776-0751 |
| Lubbock-Cooper High Sch<br>910 Woodrow Rd, Lubbock 79423<br>Angie Inklebarger | 9-12 | V | 1,643<br>25 | 29% | 806/863-7105<br>Fax 806/863-7196 |
| Lubbock-Cooper Middle Sch<br>Highway 87 S, Lubbock 79423<br>Tamara Gunset | 6-8 | GT | 619<br>35 | 36% | 806/863-7104<br>Fax 806/863-7163 |
| Ⓐ New Hope Academy<br>16302 Loop 493, Lubbock 79423<br>Phillip Saffel | 11-12 | T | 48 | 63% | 806/863-7109 |
| North Elem Sch<br>3202 108th St, Lubbock 79423<br>Andrea Crawford | PK-5 | T | 857<br>28 | 45% | 806/776-2700<br>Fax 806/687-2714 |
| South Elem Sch<br>Highway 87 S, Lubbock 79423<br>Frances Alonzo | PK-5 | T | 649<br>56 | 43% | 806/863-7102<br>Fax 806/863-7120 |
| West Elem Sch<br>10101 Fulton Ave, Lubbock 79424<br>Sasha Bennett | PK-5 | | 700 | 25% | 806/776-0700<br>Fax 806/771-9970 |

## ● New Deal Ind School Dist PID: 01039080

401 S Auburn Ave, New Deal 79350

806/746-5833
Fax 806/746-5707

**Schools:** 3 \ **Teachers:** 58 \ **Students:** 750 \ **Special Ed Students:** 58 \ **LEP Students:** 20 \ **Ethnic:** African American 2%, Hispanic 50%, Caucasian 48% \ **Exp:** $476 (High) \ **Poverty:** 22% \ **Title I:** $236,682 \ **Open-Close:** 08/17 - 05/20 \ **DTBP:** $342 (High) \ Ⓣ

| | | |
|---|---|---|
| Matt Reed | 1,11 | |
| John Salter | 4 | |
| Matt Hill | 6* | |
| Shelley Carver | 8,69 | |
| Hannah McCorkle | 16* | |
| Sandra Gowens | 67 | |
| Eric Gosett | 2,19 | |
| Derek Copeland | 5 | |
| Patti Hensley | 7,85* | |
| Rebbeca Cooper | 12,57 | |
| Tricia Williams | 38,83,88,270* | |
| Phillip Goodgion | 73* | |

| Public Schs..Principal | Grd | Prgm | Enr/#Cls | SN | |
|---|---|---|---|---|---|
| New Deal Elem Sch<br>312 S Monroe Ave, New Deal 79350<br>Rebecca Cooper | PK-4 | T | 260<br>18 | 70% | 806/746-5849<br>Fax 806/746-5142 Ⓣ |
| New Deal High Sch<br>209 S Auburn Ave, New Deal 79350<br>Jeff Quisenberry | 9-12 | T | 229<br>17 | 57% | 806/746-5933<br>Fax 806/746-5544 |
| New Deal Middle Sch<br>312 S Monroe Ave, New Deal 79350<br>Jesus Arenas | 5-8 | T | 258<br>17 | 65% | 806/746-6633<br>Fax 806/746-5244 |

## ● Roosevelt Ind School Dist PID: 01039119

1406 County Road 3300, Lubbock 79403

806/842-3282
Fax 806/842-3266

**Schools:** 3 \ **Teachers:** 94 \ **Students:** 1,012 \ **Special Ed Students:** 124 \ **LEP Students:** 35 \ **Ethnic:** African American 4%, Hispanic 58%, Caucasian 38% \ **Exp:** $630 (High) \ **Poverty:** 16% \ **Title I:** $479,525 \ **Open-Close:** 08/20 - 05/19 \ **DTBP:** $350 (High) \ Ⓣ

| | | |
|---|---|---|
| Dallas Grimes | 1 | |
| Roy Turner | 3 | |
| Jimmy Miller | 6 | |
| Linda Hernandez | 8,11,69,83,273,274,286,296 | |
| Jim Warnock | 67 | |
| Kyle Hammock | 2 | |
| Darryl Driver | 5 | |
| Carla Patchke | 7 | |
| Shannon Bohlken | 37 | |
| James Crawford | 73,295* | |

| Public Schs..Principal | Grd | Prgm | Enr/#Cls | SN | |
|---|---|---|---|---|---|
| Roosevelt Elem Sch<br>1406 County Road 3300, Lubbock 79403<br>DeLynn Wheeler | PK-5 | T | 442<br>34 | 79% | 806/842-3284<br>Fax 806/842-3930 |
| Roosevelt High Sch<br>1406 County Road 3300, Lubbock 79403<br>**Tim Crane** | 9-12 | ATV | 300<br>50 | 70% | 806/842-3283<br>Fax 806/842-3931 |
| Roosevelt Junior High Sch<br>1406 County Road 3300, Lubbock 79403<br>**Stacy Franklin** | 6-8 | T | 270<br>30 | 75% | 806/842-3218<br>Fax 806/842-3337 |

## ● Shallowater Ind School Dist PID: 01039157

1100 Avenue K, Shallowater 79363

806/832-4531
Fax 806/832-4350

**Schools:** 4 \ **Teachers:** 135 \ **Students:** 1,351 \ **Special Ed Students:** 126 \ **LEP Students:** 43 \ **College-Bound:** 80% \ **Ethnic:** African American 1%, Hispanic 32%, Caucasian 67% \ **Exp:** $427 (High) \ **Poverty:** 13% \ **Title I:** $188,577 \ **Open-Close:** 08/24 - 05/20 \ **DTBP:** $534 (High) \ Ⓣ

| | | |
|---|---|---|
| **Anita Hebert** | 1 | |
| Greg Couch | 3 | |
| Brett Holder | 5 | |
| Tammy Blackburn | 8* | |
| Kamber Smith | 38* | |
| Barbie Priest | 58 | |
| Stacey Barber | 73,84,297 | |
| Marcie Romos | 2,19 | |
| Pat Kerin | 4 | |
| Mary Hughes | 7,12,15,69,275,295* | |
| J'Rae Tineda | 16 | |
| Tiffany Fisher | 57 | |
| Garrett Nelson | 67 | |
| Cindy Couch | 298 | |

| | | | | | | | |
|---|---|---|---|---|---|---|---|
| 1 | Superintendent | 8 | Curric/Instruct K-12 | 19 | Chief Financial Officer | 29 | Family/Consumer Science |
| 2 | Bus/Finance/Purchasing | 9 | Curric/Instruct Elem | 20 | Art K-12 | 30 | Adult Education |
| 3 | Buildings And Grounds | 10 | Curric/Instruct Sec | 21 | Art Elem | 31 | Career/Sch-to-Work K-12 |
| 4 | Food Service | 11 | Federal Program | 22 | Art Sec | 32 | Career/Sch-to-Work Elem |
| 5 | Transportation | 12 | Title I | 23 | Music K-12 | 33 | Career/Sch-to-Work Sec |
| 6 | Athletic | 13 | Title V | 24 | Music Elem | 34 | Early Childhood Ed |
| 7 | Health Services | 15 | Asst Superintendent | 25 | Music Sec | 35 | Health/Phys Education |
| | | 16 | Instructional Media Svcs | 26 | Business Education | 36 | Guidance Services K-12 |
| | | 17 | Chief Operations Officer | 27 | Career & Tech Ed | 37 | Guidance Services Elem |
| | | 18 | Chief Academic Officer | 28 | Technology Education | 38 | Guidance Services Sec |

| | | | | | | | |
|---|---|---|---|---|---|---|---|
| 39 | Social Studies K-12 | 49 | English/Lang Arts Elem | 59 | Special Education Elem | 69 | Academic Assessment |
| 40 | Social Studies Elem | 50 | English/Lang Arts Sec | 60 | Special Education Sec | 70 | Research/Development |
| 41 | Social Studies Sec | 51 | Reading K-12 | 61 | Foreign/World Lang K-12 | 71 | Public Information |
| 42 | Science K-12 | 52 | Reading Elem | 62 | Foreign/World Lang Elem | 72 | Summer School |
| 43 | Science Elem | 53 | Reading Sec | 63 | Foreign/World Lang Sec | 73 | Instructional Tech |
| 44 | Science Sec | 54 | Remedial Reading K-12 | 64 | Religious Education K-12 | 74 | Inservice Training |
| 45 | Math K-12 | 55 | Remedial Reading Elem | 65 | Religious Education Elem | 75 | Marketing/Distributive |
| 46 | Math Elem | 56 | Remedial Reading Sec | 66 | Religious Education Sec | 76 | Info Systems |
| 47 | Math Sec | 57 | Bilingual/ELL | 67 | School Board President | 77 | Psychological Assess |
| 48 | English/Lang Arts K-12 | 58 | Special Education K-12 | 68 | Teacher Personnel | 78 | Affirmative Action |

| Public Schs..Principal | Grd | Prgm | Enr/#Cls | SN |
|---|---|---|---|---|
| Shallowater Elem Sch<br>1009 Avenue L, Shallowater 79363<br>Sherry Oliver | PK-1 | T | 263<br>20 | 46% 806/832-4531<br>Fax 806/832-4534 |
| Shallowater High Sch<br>1009 Avenue L, Shallowater 79363<br>**Craig Nell** | 9-12 | V | 323<br>30 | 36% 806/832-4531<br>Fax 806/832-4523 |
| Shallowater Intermediate Sch<br>1201 Avenue N, Shallowater 79363<br>Michelle Southard | 2-4 | T | 373<br>15 | 42% 806/832-4531<br>Fax 806/832-1884 |
| Shallowater Middle Sch<br>1009 Avenue L, Shallowater 79363<br>Aron Strickland | 5-8 | | 392<br>18 | 42% 806/832-4531<br>Fax 806/832-5543 |

---

• **Slaton Ind School Dist** PID: 01039195    806/828-6591
140 E Panhandle St, Slaton 79364    Fax 806/828-5506

**Schools:** 4 \ **Teachers:** 106 \ **Students:** 950 \ **Special Ed Students:** 201 \ **LEP Students:** 49 \ **College-Bound:** 26% \ **Ethnic:** African American 6%, Hispanic 65%, Caucasian 29% \ **Exp:** $682 (High) \ **Poverty:** 26% \ **Title I:** $667,364 \ **Open-Close:** 08/21 - 05/20 \ **DTBP:** $572 (High)

| | | | |
|---|---|---|---|
| Julee Broscoss ...........1 | | Art Martin ...........2 | |
| Mike Hernandez ...........3,5 | | Paula Garcia ...........4* | |
| Jeffrey Cassey ...........6 | | James Andrus ...........8,11,15,74,88,275,294* | |
| Felicia Boyd ...........34* | | David Martinez ...........57* | |
| Denise Kirby ...........58 | | Carlos Bentancourt ...........67 | |
| Christian Shute ...........81* | | | |

| Public Schs..Principal | Grd | Prgm | Enr/#Cls | SN |
|---|---|---|---|---|
| Cathelene Thomas Elem Sch<br>615 W Lubbock St, Slaton 79364<br>**Margaret Francis** | 1-5 | T | 461<br>30 | 82% 806/828-5805<br>Fax 806/828-2046 |
| Slaton High Sch<br>105 N 20th St, Slaton 79364<br>Tiffany Potts | 9-12 | TV | 91<br>30 | 73% 806/828-5833<br>Fax 806/828-1229 |
| Slaton Junior High Sch<br>300 W Jean St, Slaton 79364<br>Kimberly Perry | 6-8 | T | 205<br>40 | 83% 806/828-6583<br>Fax 806/828-2080 |
| Stephen F Austin Primary<br>740 S 7th St, Slaton 79364<br>Felicia Boyd \ **Sammi Johnson** | PK-K | T | 193<br>10 | 74% 806/828-5813<br>Fax 806/828-2079 |

## LUBBOCK CATHOLIC SCHOOLS

• **Diocese of Lubbock Ed Office** PID: 02204290    806/795-8283
4620 4th St, Lubbock 79416    Fax 806/792-8109

**Schools:** 1 \ **Students:** 360

Listing includes only schools located in this county. See District Index for location of Diocesan Offices.

| | | | |
|---|---|---|---|
| Christine Wanjura ...........1 | | Christy Duran ...........2 | |
| Claudia Riney ...........8 | | | |

| Catholic Schs..Principal | Grd | Prgm | Enr/#Cls | SN |
|---|---|---|---|---|
| Christ the King Cathedral Sch<br>4011 54th St, Lubbock 79413<br>Gail Ambrose | PK-12 | | 300<br>19 | 806/795-8283<br>Fax 806/795-9715 |

## LUBBOCK PRIVATE SCHOOLS

| Private Schs..Principal | Grd | Prgm | Enr/#Cls | SN |
|---|---|---|---|---|
| All Saints Episcopal Sch<br>3222 103rd St, Lubbock 79423<br>Bruce Latta | PK-12 | | 315<br>27 | 806/745-7701<br>Fax 806/748-0454 |
| Kingdom Preparatory Academy<br>PO Box 64028, Lubbock 79464<br>Jared Squires | PK-12 | | 180<br>25 | 806/767-9334<br>Fax 806/767-9342 |
| Lubbock Christian Sch<br>2604 Dover Ave, Lubbock 79407<br>Jerry Lawrence | PK-12 | | 430<br>28 | 806/796-8700<br>Fax 806/791-3569<br>fb |
| Lubbock Junior Academy<br>5302 Elgin Ave, Lubbock 79413<br>Marybel Orellana | K-8 | | 10 | 806/793-8614<br>Fax 806/799-5136 |
| New Life Academy<br>2102 5th St, Lubbock 79401<br>Jeff McCreight | K-12 | G | 104 | 806/763-0117 |
| Southcrest Christian Sch<br>3801 S Loop 289, Lubbock 79423<br>Shonda Mayer \ Susie Driscoll | PK-12 | | 237<br>7 | 806/797-7400<br>Fax 806/797-5100 |
| Trinity Christian Elem Sch<br>7002 Canton Ave, Lubbock 79413<br>Jill Roberts | PK-5 | | 350<br>30 | 806/791-6581 |
| Trinity Christian Jr Sr HS<br>6701 University Ave, Lubbock 79413<br>Tyler Neal | 6-12 | | 272<br>40 | 806/791-6583<br>fb |

## LUBBOCK REGIONAL CENTERS

• **Region 17 Ed Service Center** PID: 01039248    806/792-4000
1111 W Loop 289, Lubbock 79416    Fax 806/792-1523

| | | | |
|---|---|---|---|
| Kyle Wargo ...........1,11 | | Kerry Wright ...........2 | |
| Wayne Blount ...........2,3,4,15,76 | | Syd Sexton ...........8 | |
| Chris Gossett ...........16,73 | | Alicia Holligan ...........36,77 | |
| Anna Phillips ...........58 | | | |

## LYNN COUNTY

## LYNN PUBLIC SCHOOLS

• **New Home Ind School Dist** PID: 01039274    806/924-7543
225 N Main St, New Home 79381    Fax 806/924-7520

**Schools:** 1 \ **Teachers:** 40 \ **Students:** 580 \ **Special Ed Students:** 29 \ **LEP Students:** 9 \ **College-Bound:** 80% \ **Ethnic:** Hispanic 25%, Caucasian 75% \ **Exp:** $509 (High) \ **Poverty:** 17% \ **Title I:** $30,438 \ **Open-Close:** 08/17 - 05/20 \ **DTBP:** $345 (High)

| | | | |
|---|---|---|---|
| Shane Fiedler ...........1,11 | | Monica Maeker ...........2 | |
| Dale Clem ...........3* | | Lisa Alvarado ...........4* | |
| Ara Sanders ...........7* | | Kodi Chapman ...........58* | |
| Travis Smith ...........67 | | Shane Moore ...........69,73 | |
| Stina Nieman ...........76 | | | |

**TX—275**

| Public Schs..Principal | Grd | Prgm | Enr/#Cls | SN |
|---|---|---|---|---|
| New Home Sch<br>225 N Main St, New Home 79381<br>Kelly Baum \ **Brady Webb** | PK-12 | TV | 580<br>20 | 18% 806/924-7543 |

• **O'Donnell Ind School Dist** PID: 01039315    806/428-3241
400 Small St, Odonnell 79351    Fax 806/428-3395

**Schools:** 2 \ **Teachers:** 33 \ **Students:** 300 \ **Special Ed Students:** 41 \ **LEP Students:** 20 \ **College-Bound:** 90% \ **Ethnic:** Hispanic 67%, Caucasian 33% \ **Exp:** $674 (High) \ **Poverty:** 22% \ **Title I:** $85,320 \ **Open-Close:** 08/24 - 05/20 \ **DTBP:** $355 (High)

| | | | |
|---|---|---|---|
| Dr Cathy Palmer ....................1,11 | Melissa Clark ...........................2 |
| Joseph Luera .........................3,5 | Eva Belossanton ......................4 |
| Blake Nichols ...........................6* | Tonya Graham ..........8,42,57,58,69,81* |
| Mandy Stidham .........................67 | Pam Wilson ...........................73* |
| Cody White ...............83,88,298* | |

| Public Schs..Principal | Grd | Prgm | Enr/#Cls | SN |
|---|---|---|---|---|
| O'Donnell Elem Sch<br>300 Small St, Odonnell 79351<br>Sharla Edwards | PK-5 | | 148<br>14 | 806/428-3244<br>Fax 806/428-3277 |
| O'Donnell Jr Sr High Sch<br>400 Small St, Odonnell 79351<br>Cody White | 6-12 | TV | 140<br>15 | 73% 806/428-3247<br>Fax 806/428-3759 |

• **Tahoka Ind School Dist** PID: 01039341    806/561-4105
2129 Main St, Tahoka 79373    Fax 806/561-4160

**Schools:** 3 \ **Teachers:** 65 \ **Students:** 600 \ **Special Ed Students:** 51 \ **LEP Students:** 19 \ **College-Bound:** 80% \ **Ethnic:** African American 2%, Hispanic 64%, Caucasian 33% \ **Exp:** $684 (High) \ **Poverty:** 26% \ **Title I:** $209,853 \ **Open-Close:** 08/18 - 05/18 \ **DTBP:** $376 (High)

| | |
|---|---|
| Dick Van Hoose ..........................1 | Lisa Jones ..................2,4,12,19 |
| Joey Earrientes ...........................3* | Sam Monsizias ......................5,91 |
| Stephen Overstreet .....................6* | Lana Martinez ..........8,83,88,270,280,752* |
| Angelica Aguirre ...........16,73,98,286,295* | Cynthia Jolly ...........................16* |
| Kaci May .................................57* | Paige Rivas .....................58,275* |
| Clay Taylor ................................67 | Angelica Aguirre ...............73,98,286 |

| Public Schs..Principal | Grd | Prgm | Enr/#Cls | SN |
|---|---|---|---|---|
| Tahoka Elem Sch<br>1925 Avenue O, Tahoka 79373<br>Donald Scott | PK-5 | T | 266<br>24 | 73% 806/561-4350<br>Fax 806/561-5334 |
| Tahoka High Sch<br>1925 Avenue P, Tahoka 79373<br>Donald Worth | 9-12 | T | 159<br>25 | 69% 806/561-4538<br>Fax 806/561-6082 |
| Tahoka Middle Sch<br>1925 Avenue P, Tahoka 79373<br>Kelly Kieth | 6-8 | T | 159<br>12 | 65% 806/561-4539<br>Fax 806/561-6082 |

• **Wilson Ind School Dist** PID: 01039391    806/628-6261
1411 Green Ave, Wilson 79381    Fax 806/628-6441

**Schools:** 1 \ **Teachers:** 18 \ **Students:** 94 \ **Special Ed Students:** 15 \ **LEP Students:** 17 \ **College-Bound:** 70% \ **Ethnic:** Hispanic 76%, Caucasian 24% \ **Exp:** $595 (High) \ **Poverty:** 36% \ **Title I:** $91,502 \ **Open-Close:** 08/24 - 05/19 \ **DTBP:** $379 (High) \ 🇫 🇹

| | |
|---|---|
| Jerry Burger ..........................1,83 | Vondi Braddock .......................2 |
| Gary Reed .................................3 | Kris Foust ...............................6 |
| Keith Church ...........................16* | Juvencio Portillo .............31,36,69* |
| Stefanie Cortez .......................58* | Doug Boylard .........................67 |

Katelyn Church .........................73    Elvira Mendez ........................271*

| Public Schs..Principal | Grd | Prgm | Enr/#Cls | SN |
|---|---|---|---|---|
| Wilson Sch<br>1411 Green Ave, Wilson 79381<br>Jp Portillo | PK-12 | TV | 94<br>16 | 78% 806/628-6261 |

## MADISON COUNTY

## MADISON PUBLIC SCHOOLS

• **Madisonville Cons ISD** PID: 01040596    936/348-2797
718 Bacon St, Madisonville 77864    Fax 936/348-2751

**Schools:** 4 \ **Teachers:** 168 \ **Students:** 2,233 \ **Special Ed Students:** 208 \ **LEP Students:** 306 \ **Ethnic:** Asian 1%, African American 19%, Hispanic 36%, Caucasian 44% \ **Exp:** $483 (High) \ **Poverty:** 25% \ **Title I:** $744,741 \ **Special Education:** $481,000 \ **Open-Close:** 08/24 - 05/27 \ **DTBP:** $350 (High) \ 🇫 🇹

| | |
|---|---|
| Keith Smith ................................1 | Scott Singletary .......................2 |
| Frank Kelly ............................3,91 | Kelley Terry ............................4 |
| Nelly Vega ................................4 | Rusty Nail ...............................6* |
| Raelyn Williamson ...................7,85* | C Keith Smith ........11,15,31,36,57,58,88,271 |
| Dr Keith West ...........................15 | Joyce Singletary .....................16* |
| Shelli Sheppard .........27,38,69,75* | Dr Mark Bennett ....................67 |
| Laney Smith ............................73 | |

| Public Schs..Principal | Grd | Prgm | Enr/#Cls | SN |
|---|---|---|---|---|
| Madisonville Elem Sch<br>1000 Raney Ln, Madisonville 77864<br>Rhodena Brooks | PK-2 | T | 514<br>36 | 81% 936/348-2261<br>Fax 936/349-8028<br>🇫 🇹 |
| Madisonville High Sch<br>811 S May St A, Madisonville 77864<br>Heath Brown | 9-12 | TV | 664<br>50 | 62% 936/348-2721<br>Fax 936/348-5753<br>🇫 🇹 |
| Madisonville Intermediate Sch<br>926 Raney Ln, Madisonville 77864<br>Tawnya Nail | 3-5 | T | 526<br>40 | 74% 936/348-2921<br>Fax 936/348-2249 |
| Madisonville Jr High Sch<br>724 Raney Ln, Madisonville 77864<br>Rhonda Morgan | 6-8 | T | 529<br>30 | 70% 936/348-3587<br>Fax 936/348-5603<br>🇫 🇹 |

• **North Zulch Ind School Dist** PID: 01040637    936/241-7100
11390 5th St, North Zulch 77872    Fax 936/241-7093

**Schools:** 1 \ **Teachers:** 31 \ **Students:** 310 \ **Special Ed Students:** 29 \ **LEP Students:** 11 \ **Ethnic:** Asian 2%, African American 1%, Hispanic 19%, Caucasian 78% \ **Exp:** $408 (High) \ **Poverty:** 21% \ **Title I:** $88,205 \ **Open-Close:** 08/19 - 05/28 \ **DTBP:** $360 (High)

| | |
|---|---|
| Alan Andrus ...........................1,11 | Dawn Brenner .........................2* |
| Brenda Andrews .........................4* | Clay Todd ...........................6,60 |
| Lea-Ann Andrus ...................8,288 | Autumn Nauling .......................16* |
| Kori Batten .........................36,752* | Brian Baker ............................67 |
| Denise Dacus ...........73,76,286,295 | Jane Dill ...............................83* |
| Jennifer Andrus ......................285 | |

| | | |
|---|---|---|
| 1 Superintendent | 8 Curric/Instruct K-12 | 19 Chief Financial Officer |
| 2 Bus/Finance/Purchasing | 9 Curric/Instruct Elem | 20 Art K-12 |
| 3 Buildings And Grounds | 10 Curric/Instruct Sec | 21 Art Elem |
| 4 Food Service | 11 Federal Program | 22 Art Sec |
| 5 Transportation | 12 Title I | 23 Music K-12 |
| 6 Athletic | 13 Title V | 24 Music Elem |
| 7 Health Services | 15 Asst Superintendent | 25 Music Sec |
| | 16 Instructional Media Svcs | 26 Business Education |
| | 17 Chief Operations Officer | 27 Career & Tech Ed |
| | 18 Chief Academic Officer | 28 Technology Education |

| | | |
|---|---|---|
| 29 Family/Consumer Science | 39 Social Studies K-12 | 49 English/Lang Arts Elem |
| 30 Adult Education | 40 Social Studies Elem | 50 English/Lang Arts Sec |
| 31 Career/Sch-to-Work K-12 | 41 Social Studies Sec | 51 Reading K-12 |
| 32 Career/Sch-to-Work Elem | 42 Science K-12 | 52 Reading Elem |
| 33 Career/Sch-to-Work Sec | 43 Science Elem | 53 Reading Sec |
| 34 Early Childhood Ed | 44 Science Sec | 54 Remedial Reading K-12 |
| 35 Health/Phys Education | 45 Math K-12 | 55 Remedial Reading Elem |
| 36 Business Education | 46 Math Elem | 56 Remedial Reading Sec |
| 37 Guidance Services Elem | 47 Math Sec | 57 Bilingual/ELL |
| 38 Guidance Services Sec | 48 English/Lang Arts K-12 | 58 Special Education K-12 |

| | |
|---|---|
| 59 Special Education Elem | 69 Academic Assessment |
| 60 Special Education Sec | 70 Research/Development |
| 61 Foreign/World Lang K-12 | 71 Public Information |
| 62 Foreign/World Lang Elem | 72 Summer School |
| 63 Foreign/World Lang Sec | 73 Instructional Tech |
| 64 Religious Education K-12 | 74 Inservice Training |
| 65 Religious Education Elem | 75 Marketing/Distributive |
| 66 Religious Education Sec | 76 Info Systems |
| 67 School Board President | 77 Psychological Assess |
| 68 Teacher Personnel | 78 Affirmative Action |

| Public Schs..Principal | Grd | Prgm | Enr/#Cls | SN | |
|---|---|---|---|---|---|
| North Zulch Sch<br>11390 5th St, North Zulch 77872<br>Janie Pope | PK-12 | TV | 310<br>30 | 54% | 936/241-7100 |

# MARION COUNTY

## MARION PUBLIC SCHOOLS

● **Jefferson Ind School Dist**  PID: 01040687        903/665-2461
1600 Martin Luther King Dr, Jefferson 75657        Fax 903/665-7367

**Schools:** 4 \ **Teachers:** 102 \ **Students:** 1,324 \ **Special Ed Students:** 169 \ **LEP Students:** 18 \ **College-Bound:** 49% \ **Ethnic:** Asian 1%, African American 32%, Hispanic 6%, Caucasian 61% \ **Exp:** $697 (High) \ **Poverty:** 32% \ **Title I:** $609,528 \ **Special Education:** $231,000 \ **Open-Close:** 08/17 - 05/21 \ **DTBP:** $327 (High)

| | | | |
|---|---|---|---|
| Rob Barnwell ...............................1 | Mike Wood ...................................2 |
| Terry Moore ................................4* | Jack Smith ...................................5 |
| Antwain Jimmerson .....................6 | Debbie Hall ..................................7 |
| Debbie Hall ................................7* | Lynn Fratangelo .............8,31,288 |
| Clinton Coyne ...........11,34,57,58,61,88,296* | Linda Scott .................................37* |
| Jason Bonner .............................67 | Jay Patrick ...........................73,295 |
| Terence Jimerson .......................88 | |

| Public Schs..Principal | Grd | Prgm | Enr/#Cls | SN | |
|---|---|---|---|---|---|
| Jefferson Elem Sch<br>301 W Harrison St, Jefferson 75657<br>Lindsey Whitaker | 1-4 | T | 391<br>20 | 77% | 903/665-2461<br>Fax 903/665-6401 |
| Jefferson High Sch<br>1 Bulldog Dr, Jefferson 75657<br>Michael Walker | 9-12 | T | 374<br>30 | 71% | 903/665-2461<br>Fax 903/665-2146 |
| Jefferson Junior High Sch<br>804 N Alley St, Jefferson 75657<br>Tim Phy | 5-8 | T | 393<br>57 | 71% | 903/665-2461<br>Fax 903/665-7149 |
| Jefferson Primary Sch<br>304 W Broadway St, Jefferson 75657<br>Lindsey Whitaker | PK-K | T | 166 | 80% | 903/665-2461<br>Fax 903/665-7092 |

## MARION PRIVATE SCHOOLS

| Private Schs..Principal | Grd | Prgm | Enr/#Cls | SN | |
|---|---|---|---|---|---|
| Cypress Bendadventist ES<br>2997 FM 728, Jefferson 75657<br>Peggy Dyke | PK-8 | | 29<br>3 | | 903/665-7402 |
| Jefferson Christian Academy<br>3060 FM 728, Jefferson 75657<br>Lyne Ho | 9-12 | V | 40<br>7 | | 903/665-3973<br>Fax 903/665-5987<br>[f] |

## MARTIN COUNTY

## MARTIN PUBLIC SCHOOLS

● **Grady Ind School Dist**  PID: 01040730        432/459-2444
3500 FM 829, Lenorah 79749        Fax 432/459-2729

**Schools:** 1 \ **Teachers:** 21 \ **Students:** 233 \ **Special Ed Students:** 12 \ **LEP Students:** 9 \ **College-Bound:** 75% \ **Ethnic:** Asian 1%, Hispanic 34%, Caucasian 65% \ **Exp:** $548 (High) \ **Poverty:** 30% \ **Title I:** $65,597 \ **Open-Close:** 08/12 - 05/19 \ **DTBP:** $333 (High)

| | | | |
|---|---|---|---|
| Leandro Gonzales ..............................1,83 | Bonnie Lucas ..............................2,11,296* |
| Belen Rodriquez ..................................4* | Sherra Harrell .............................58* |
| David Matthews .....................................67 | |

| Public Schs..Principal | Grd | Prgm | Enr/#Cls | SN | |
|---|---|---|---|---|---|
| Grady Sch<br>3500 FM 829, Lenorah 79749<br>Gary Jones | PK-12 | T | 233<br>22 | 36% | 432/459-2445 |

● **Stanton Ind School Dist**  PID: 01040754        432/607-3700
200 N College St, Stanton 79782        Fax 432/756-2052

**Schools:** 3 \ **Teachers:** 81 \ **Students:** 1,053 \ **Special Ed Students:** 79 \ **LEP Students:** 90 \ **College-Bound:** 52% \ **Ethnic:** African American 1%, Hispanic 68%, Caucasian 30% \ **Exp:** $798 (High) \ **Poverty:** 17% \ **Title I:** $206,039 \ **Open-Close:** 08/17 - 05/21 \ **DTBP:** $346 (High)

| | | | |
|---|---|---|---|
| Dr Merl Brandon .....................................1 | Brad Holland ..........................2,19 |
| Pam Shaffer ...........................................2 | Dennis Simpson ..........................3 |
| George Ramirez .....................................5 | Cody Hogan ...................................6 |
| Jan McCown .......................................8,15 | Shasta Brian ..........................11,271 |
| Robna Anderson ...................................58 | Jermey Louder .............................67 |
| Jay Baker .......................................73,295 | |

| Public Schs..Principal | Grd | Prgm | Enr/#Cls | SN | |
|---|---|---|---|---|---|
| Stanton Elem Sch<br>911 W Broadway St, Stanton 79782<br>Leah Mitchell | PK-5 | T | 530<br>21 | 62% | 432/756-2285<br>Fax 432/756-2151 |
| Stanton High Sch<br>705 Koonce St, Stanton 79782<br>Matt Turney | 9-12 | T | 280<br>24 | 48% | 432/756-3326<br>Fax 432/756-2248 |
| Stanton Middle Sch<br>200 N Gray St, Stanton 79782<br>Jennifer Ruiz | 6-8 | T | 243<br>25 | 56% | 432/756-2544<br>Fax 432/756-2702 |

---

| | | | | |
|---|---|---|---|---|
| 79 Student Personnel | 91 Safety/Security | 275 Response To Intervention | 298 Grant Writer/Ptnrships | **School Programs** |
| 80 Driver Ed/Safety | 92 Magnet School | 277 Remedial Math K-12 | 750 Chief Innovation Officer | **A** = Alternative Program |
| 81 Gifted/Talented | 93 Parental Involvement | 280 Literacy Coach | 751 Chief of Staff | **G** = Adult Classes |
| 82 Video Services | 95 Tech Prep Program | 285 STEM | 752 Social Emotional Learning | **M** = Magnet Program |
| 83 Substance Abuse Prev | 97 Chief Infomation Officer | 286 Digital Learning | | **T** = Title I Schoolwide |
| 84 Erate | 98 Chief Technology Officer | 288 Common Core Standards | **Other School Types** | **V** = Career & Tech Ed Programs |
| 85 AIDS Education | 270 Character Education | 294 Accountability | (A) = Alternative School | |
| 88 Alternative/At Risk | 271 Migrant Education | 295 Network System | (C) = Charter School | **New Schools are shaded** |
| 89 Multi-Cultural Curriculum | 273 Teacher Mentor | 296 Title II Programs | (M) = Magnet School | **New Superintendents and Principals are bold** |
| 90 Social Work | 274 Before/After Sch | 297 Webmaster | (Y) = Year-Round School | **Personnel with email addresses are underscored** |

**Social Media**
[f] = Facebook
[t] = Twitter

**TX—277**

# MASON COUNTY

## MASON PUBLIC SCHOOLS

● **Mason Ind School Dist** PID: 01040780
200 Ft McKavitt St, Mason 76856

325/347-1144
Fax 325/294-4412

**Schools:** 3 \ **Teachers:** 71 \ **Students:** 674 \ **Special Ed Students:** 67 \ **LEP Students:** 55 \ **College-Bound:** 57% \ **Ethnic:** Asian 1%, Hispanic 34%, Caucasian 65% \ **Exp:** $759 (High) \ **Poverty:** 23% \ **Title I:** $190,718 \ **Special Education:** $140,000 \ **Open-Close:** 08/18 - 05/26 \ **DTBP:** $350 (High)

| | | |
|---|---|---|
| Stan Whittle ............1 | Teri Price .............2 | |
| Julie Parker ............4 | Larry Smith ............5,88 | |
| Michael McLeod ............6 | Jennifer Moneyhon ............7,35* | |
| Holly Whittle ............11,57,69,271,298 | Shannon Hofmann ............58,752* | |
| Jim Smith ............67 | Cathy Felts ............68 | |
| Merlina Gamel ............73 | Vondell Jordan ............280 | |
| Kade Burns ............285 | | |

| Public Schs..Principal | Grd | Prgm | Enr/#Cls | SN | |
|---|---|---|---|---|---|
| Mason Elem Sch<br>807 W College Ave, Mason 76856<br>Ryan Holbrook | PK-4 | T | 280<br>23 | 53% | 325/347-1122<br>Fax 325/347-5461 |
| Mason High Sch<br>1105 W College Ave, Mason 76856<br>Kade Burns | 9-12 | TV | 216<br>15 | 41% | 325/347-1122<br>Fax 325/347-8247 |
| Mason Junior High Sch<br>807 W College Ave, Mason 76856<br>Ryan Holbrook | 5-8 | T | 219 | 46% | 325/347-1122 |

# MATAGORDA COUNTY

## MATAGORDA PUBLIC SCHOOLS

● **Bay City Ind School Dist** PID: 01040819
520 7th St, Bay City 77414

979/401-1000
Fax 979/245-3175

**Schools:** 5 \ **Teachers:** 237 \ **Students:** 3,670 \ **Special Ed Students:** 343 \ **LEP Students:** 504 \ **College-Bound:** 53% \ **Ethnic:** Asian 1%, African American 16%, Hispanic 65%, Caucasian 19% \ **Exp:** $567 (High) \ **Poverty:** 31% \ **Title I:** $1,660,759 \ **Open-Close:** 08/26 - 05/28 \ **DTBP:** $172 (High) \ ▪

| | |
|---|---|
| Marshall Scott ............1 | Richard Johnson ............2,19 |
| Stewart Crouch ............3 | Mildred Hawkins ............4 |
| Lynette Cooper ............7* | Lisa Moya ............8,18,57,69,88,285,288,294 |
| Lisa Volkmer ............11,57,271,273,296 | Sonya Sonia ............34,58 |
| Robert Klepac ............67 | Allison Silva ............71 |
| Joshua Solis ............73,76,98,295 | Leroy Cunningham ............91* |

| Public Schs..Principal | Grd | Prgm | Enr/#Cls | SN | |
|---|---|---|---|---|---|
| Bay City High Sch<br>400 7th St, Bay City 77414<br>Estela Reyes | 9-12 | ATV | 968 | 78% | 979/401-1100<br>Fax 979/245-1220 |
| Bay City Junior High Sch<br>1507 Sycamore Ave, Bay City 77414<br>Rosemarie Cumings | 6-8 | AT | 802<br>46 | 74% | 979/401-1600<br>Fax 979/245-1419 |
| Cherry Elem Sch<br>2619 8th St, Bay City 77414<br>Merideth Dodd \ **Jana White** | PK-5 | T | 705<br>20 | 76% | 979/401-1300<br>Fax 979/245-1702 |
| Roberts Elem Sch<br>1212 Whitson St, Bay City 77414<br>**Marissa Wendel** | K-5 | T | 487<br>28 | 86% | 979/401-1500<br>Fax 979/245-1573 |
| Tenie Holmes Elem Sch<br>3200 5th St, Bay City 77414<br>**Ashley Hagg** | K-5 | T | 708<br>31 | 76% | 979/401-1400<br>Fax 979/245-1645 |

● **Matagorda Ind School Dist** PID: 01040895
717 Wightman Street, Matagorda 77457

979/863-7693
Fax 979/863-2230

**Schools:** 1 \ **Teachers:** 11 \ **Students:** 120 \ **Special Ed Students:** 17 \ **LEP Students:** 11 \ **Ethnic:** Hispanic 45%, Caucasian 55% \ **Exp:** $620 (High) \ **Poverty:** 28% \ **Title I:** $38,545 \ **Open-Close:** 08/24 - 05/26 \ **DTBP:** $335 (High)

| | |
|---|---|
| Susan Phillips ............1,11,57,83,288 | Tara Simons ............2,76,84,98,271,752 |
| Dennis Chambers ............3,5* | Jackie Rawlings ............4 |
| Kyle Thurmon ............6* | Michelle Ottis ............35 |
| Ronda Thompson ............59* | Tim Meador ............73,295,297 |

| Public Schs..Principal | Grd | Prgm | Enr/#Cls | SN | |
|---|---|---|---|---|---|
| Matagorda Sch<br>717 Wightman St, Matagorda 77457<br>Susan Phillips \ Kyle Thurmon | PK-8 | T | 120<br>11 | 65% | 979/863-7693 |

● **Palacios Ind School Dist** PID: 01040912
1209 12th St, Palacios 77465

361/972-5491
Fax 361/972-3567

**Schools:** 4 \ **Teachers:** 104 \ **Students:** 1,506 \ **Special Ed Students:** 144 \ **LEP Students:** 186 \ **Ethnic:** Asian 7%, African American 2%, Hispanic 70%, Caucasian 22% \ **Exp:** $284 (Med) \ **Poverty:** 25% \ **Title I:** $447,981 \ **Open-Close:** 08/12 - 05/20 \ **DTBP:** $350 (High) \ ▪

| | |
|---|---|
| Dr Missy Glenn ............1 | Christy Miller ............2 |
| Santos Perez ............3,5* | Candy Gifford ............4 |
| Lisa Harper ............7 | Dr Julia McMains ..8,11,16,57,58,271,273,274 |
| Steven Stuhrenberg ............67 | Dr Brian Williams ............68,69,83,294,296,298 |
| Robert Fiorini ............73,295* | Becky Aguilera ............91 |

| Public Schs..Principal | Grd | Prgm | Enr/#Cls | SN | |
|---|---|---|---|---|---|
| Central Elem Sch<br>1001 5th St, Palacios 77465<br>Nancy Flores | PK-3 | T | 420<br>42 | 74% | 361/972-2911<br>Fax 361/972-5539 |
| East Side Intermediate Sch<br>901 2nd St, Palacios 77465<br>Brandon Karl | 4-6 | T | 329<br>20 | 75% | 361/972-2544<br>Fax 361/972-2695 |
| Palacios High Sch<br>100 Shark Dr, Palacios 77465<br>Stephanie Garcia | 9-12 | TV | 406<br>65 | 66% | 361/972-2571<br>Fax 361/972-6287 |
| Palacios Junior High Sch<br>200 Shark Dr, Palacios 77465<br>Buddy Kelley | 7-8 | TV | 198<br>20 | 74% | 361/972-2417<br>Fax 361/972-6372 |

| | | | | | | | |
|---|---|---|---|---|---|---|---|
| 1 Superintendent | 8 Curric/Instruct K-12 | 19 Chief Financial Officer | 29 Family/Consumer Science | 39 Social Studies K-12 | 49 English/Lang Arts Elem | 59 Special Education Elem | 69 Academic Assessment |
| 2 Bus/Finance/Purchasing | 9 Curric/Instruct Elem | 20 Art K-12 | 30 Adult Education | 40 Social Studies Elem | 50 English/Lang Arts Sec | 60 Special Education Sec | 70 Research/Development |
| 3 Buildings And Grounds | 10 Curric/Instruct Sec | 21 Art Elem | 31 Career/Sch-to-Work K-12 | 41 Social Studies Sec | 51 Reading K-12 | 61 Foreign/World Lang K-12 | 71 Public Information |
| 4 Food Service | 11 Federal Program | 22 Art Sec | 32 Career/Sch-to-Work Elem | 42 Science K-12 | 52 Reading Elem | 62 Foreign/World Lang Elem | 72 Summer School |
| 5 Transportation | 12 Title I | 23 Music K-12 | 33 Career/Sch-to-Work Sec | 43 Science Elem | 53 Reading Sec | 63 Foreign/World Lang Sec | 73 Instructional Tech |
| 6 Athletic | 13 Title V | 24 Music Elem | 34 Early Childhood Ed | 44 Science Sec | 54 Remedial Reading K-12 | 64 Religious Education K-12 | 74 Inservice Training |
| 7 Health Services | 15 Asst Superintendent | 25 Music Sec | 35 Health/Phys Education | 45 Math K-12 | 55 Remedial Reading Elem | 65 Religious Education Elem | 75 Marketing/Distributive |
| | 16 Instructional Media Svcs | 26 Business Education | 36 Guidance Services K-12 | 46 Math Elem | 56 Remedial Reading Sec | 66 Religious Education Sec | 76 Info Systems |
| | 17 Chief Operations Officer | 27 Career & Tech Ed | 37 Guidance Services Elem | 47 Math Sec | 57 Bilingual/ELL | 67 School Board President | 77 Psychological Assess |
| | 18 Chief Academic Officer | 28 Technology Education | 38 Guidance Services Sec | 48 English/Lang Arts K-12 | 58 Special Education K-12 | 68 Teacher Personnel | 78 Affirmative Action |

- **Tidehaven Ind School Dist** PID: 01040962          979/843-4300
  47 County Road 427, Elmaton 77440                    Fax 979/843-4309

---

**Schools:** 4 \ **Teachers:** 68 \ **Students:** 980 \ **Special Ed Students:** 75 \ **LEP Students:** 84 \ **College-Bound:** 64% \ **Ethnic:** African American 3%, Hispanic 53%, Caucasian 45% \ **Exp:** $591 (High) \ **Poverty:** 26% \ **Title I:** $273,471 \ **Open-Close:** 08/13 - 05/20 \ **DTBP:** $354 (High) \ 🄵 🅃

---

| | | | |
|---|---|---|---|
| Dr Andrew Seigrist ......................1 | Mariah Langston ..........................2 |
| Ryan Cobb .................................3 | Karen Black ...............................4 |
| Debra Taska ........5,9,11,69,285,296,298 | Galvan Migel ..............................5 |
| Mike Galvan ..............................5 | David Lucio ...............................6* |
| Kathy Boyett ..........................8,288* | Tamara Davant ......................31,36,85 |
| Maria Enoch .........................57,271* | Stephen Crow .............................67 |
| Zachary Daugherty ..................73,295* | Jamie Buis .............................83,91* |

| Public Schs..Principal | Grd | Prgm | Enr/#Cls | SN |
|---|---|---|---|---|
| Blessing Elem Sch<br>231 FM 616, Blessing 77419<br>Selena Garcia | PK-5 | GT | 236<br>15 | 64% 979/843-4330<br>Fax 361/588-1150<br>🄵🅃 |
| Markham Elem Sch<br>299 Ave I North, Markham 77456<br>Stacie Murry | PK-5 | GT | 197<br>16 | 61% 979/843-4340<br>Fax 979/843-5018<br>🄵🅃 |
| Tidehaven High Sch<br>205 FM 1095, Elmaton 77440<br>Patrick Talbert | 9-12 | ATV | 287<br>25 | 47% 979/843-4310<br>Fax 361/588-6696<br>🄵🅃 |
| Tidehaven Intermediate Sch<br>205 FM 1059, Elmaton 77440<br>Patrick Talbert | 6-8 | T | 215<br>20 | 54% 361/843-4320<br>Fax 361/588-6965<br>🄵🅃 |

- **Van Vleck Ind School Dist** PID: 01041019          979/323-5000
  142 S Ford St, Van Vleck 77482                       Fax 979/245-1214

---

**Schools:** 4 \ **Teachers:** 77 \ **Students:** 1,027 \ **Special Ed Students:** 95 \ **LEP Students:** 17 \ **College-Bound:** 48% \ **Ethnic:** African American 11%, Hispanic 31%, Caucasian 58% \ **Exp:** $544 (High) \ **Poverty:** 15% \ **Title I:** $149,944 \ **Special Education:** $108,000 \ **Open-Close:** 08/24 - 05/27 \ 🅃

---

| | | | |
|---|---|---|---|
| John O'Brien ..............................1 | Gayle Blackmon ..........................2 |
| Louis Ryman ..............................3 | Connie Brown ............................4 |
| Robert Blackmon ........................6* | Kim Wied .................................7 |
| Christie Dement ......................11,27 | Amy Matchett .............................37* |
| Tony Kucera ..............................67 | Randy Keys ............................73,84 |

| Public Schs..Principal | Grd | Prgm | Enr/#Cls | SN |
|---|---|---|---|---|
| E Rudd Intermediate Sch<br>128 5th St, Van Vleck 77482<br>Sarah Roper | 4-5 | T | 147<br>12 | 57% 979/245-6561<br>Fax 979/245-3624 |
| O H Herman Middle Sch<br>719 1st St, Van Vleck 77482<br>Brandon Hood | 6-8 | ATV | 264<br>16 | 57% 979/245-6401<br>Fax 979/245-8538 |
| Van Vleck Elem Sch<br>178 S 4th St, Van Vleck 77482<br>Sarah Roper | PK-3 | T | 298<br>17 | 61% 979/245-8681<br>Fax 979/323-0479 |
| Van Vleck High Sch<br>133 S 4th St, Van Vleck 77482<br>Chris Townsend | 9-12 | ATV | 318<br>20 | 50% 979/245-4664<br>Fax 979/244-3485 |

---

## MATAGORDA CATHOLIC SCHOOLS

- **Diocese of Victoria Ed Office** PID: 02181727
  Listing includes only schools located in this county. See District Index for location of Diocesan Offices.

| Catholic Schs..Principal | Grd | Prgm | Enr/#Cls | SN |
|---|---|---|---|---|
| Holy Cross Catholic Sch<br>2001 Katy Ave, Bay City 77414<br>Angela Kupcho | PK-6 | | 110<br>9 | 979/245-5632<br>Fax 979/245-6120 |

## MAVERICK COUNTY

## MAVERICK PUBLIC SCHOOLS

- **Eagle Pass Ind School Dist** PID: 01041057          830/773-5181
  876 Madison St, Eagle Pass 78852                      Fax 830/773-7252

---

**Schools:** 23 \ **Teachers:** 853 \ **Students:** 15,000 \ **Special Ed Students:** 1,472 \ **LEP Students:** 4,892 \ **College-Bound:** 58% \ **Ethnic:** Hispanic 97%, Native American: 2%, Caucasian 1% \ **Exp:** $299 (Med) \ **Poverty:** 35% \ **Title I:** $6,634,503 \ **Special Education:** $2,300,000 \ **Open-Close:** 08/26 - 06/03 \ **DTBP:** $166 (High)

---

| | | | |
|---|---|---|---|
| Gilberto Gonzalez ........................1 | Ismael Mijares ........................2,15 |
| Luis Velez .................................2 | Pedro Felan ...........................3,91 |
| Mario Garcia ..............................4* | Humberto Araiza .........................5 |
| Edward Graf ............................6,35 | David Camarillo .......................8,294 |
| Samuel Mijares .............8,15,81,288 | Norma Serna .........11,72,271,296,298 |
| Rolando Salinas .............15,78,275 | Diana Saucedo ..........................16* |
| Gilbert Sanchez ......................20,57 | Carlos Martinez .........................23* |
| Ana Castillon ...............26,27,28,31 | Lana Harper ......30,74,83,90,93,273,274 |
| Francis Vilema ..........................39,42* | Rita Carreon ........................46,277 |
| Rodolfo Musquiz ....48,51,54,61,280,298* | Elizabeth Torres ..........................58 |
| Jorge Barrera ............................67 | Jesus Costilla ........................68,77 |
| Denniella Bryne ..........................71 | Jose Munoz ..........73,82,98,295* |
| Patrick Salines ......................73,95 | Timito Chares ...........................271 |
| Umberto Duran ..........................297 | |

| Public Schs..Principal | Grd | Prgm | Enr/#Cls | SN |
|---|---|---|---|---|
| Armando Cerna Elem Sch<br>2268 Mondragon Blvd, Eagle Pass 78852<br>Sandra Lopez | 1-6 | T | 491<br>13 | 67% 830/758-7004<br>Fax 830/773-2731 |
| Benavides Heights Elem Sch<br>1750 Mesa Dr, Eagle Pass 78852<br>Olivia Garcia | 1-6 | T | 320<br>26 | 89% 830/758-7006<br>Fax 830/758-0216 |
| C C Winn High Sch<br>265 Foster Maldonado Blvd, Eagle Pass 78852<br>Jesus Diaz-Wever | 9-12 | TV | 1,133<br>58 | 84% 830/757-0828<br>Fax 830/757-3268 |
| Eagle Pass High Sch<br>2020 2nd St, Eagle Pass 78852<br>John Cox | 9-12 | TV | 2,322<br>105 | 73% 830/773-2381<br>Fax 830/758-1795 |
| Eagle Pass Junior High Sch<br>1750 N Bibb Ave, Eagle Pass 78852<br>Mario Escobar | 7-8 | TV | 1,081<br>50 | 74% 830/758-7037 |
| Early Childhood Center<br>636 Kelso Dr, Eagle Pass 78852<br>Letty Sandoval | PK-K | T | 485<br>25 | 79% 830/758-7027<br>Fax 830/757-1153 |

---

| | | | | | |
|---|---|---|---|---|---|
| Glass Elem Sch<br>1501 Boehmer Ave, Eagle Pass 78852<br>Laura Telles | 1-6 | T | 537<br>28 | 75% | 830/758-7042<br>Fax 830/773-5989 |
| Graves Elem Sch<br>720 Kelso Dr, Eagle Pass 78852<br>Veronica Gonzalez | 1-6 | T | 502<br>30 | 79% | 830/758-7043<br>Fax 830/758-0342 |
| Henry B Gonzalez Elem Sch<br>400 Balcones Blvd, Eagle Pass 78852<br>Carmen Garcia | 1-6 | T | 404<br>27 | 94% | 830/758-7099<br>Fax 830/757-3274 |
| Kennedy Elem Sch<br>1610B Del Rio Blvd, Eagle Pass 78852<br>Lisa Ruiz | PK-K | T | 398<br>17 | 76% | 830/758-7189<br>Fax 830/758-7192 |
| Kirchner Elem Sch<br>Crockett St, Quemado 78877<br>Rosanna Rios | PK-6 | | 114<br>8 | | 830/758-7045<br>Fax 830/758-0328 |
| Language Development Center<br>1681 S Veterans Blvd, Eagle Pass 78852<br>Rosella Even | PK-K | T | 483<br>23 | 82% | 830/758-7047<br>Fax 830/757-1528 |
| Liberty Elem Sch<br>1850 Flowers, Eagle Pass 78852<br>Rosalinda Barcena | 1-6 | T | 514<br>35 | 65% | 830/758-7156<br>Fax 830/757-3237 |
| Memorial Junior High Sch<br>1800 Lewis St, Eagle Pass 78852<br>Jose Hernandez | 7-8 | TV | 1,093<br>70 | 87% | 830/758-7053<br>Fax 830/773-8900 |
| Perfecto Mancha Elem Sch<br>3269 Fletcher Rd, Eagle Pass 78852<br>Sandra Koenig | 1-6 | T | 523 | 84% | 830/758-7216<br>Fax 830/758-7201 |
| Pete Gallego Elem Sch<br>300 Azucena St, Eagle Pass 78852<br>Jose Villalobos | 1-6 | T | 393<br>23 | 83% | 830/758-7130<br>Fax 830/757-5795 |
| Ray Darr Elem Sch<br>1420 Eidson Rd, Eagle Pass 78852<br>Veronica Chacon | 1-6 | T | 442<br>26 | 92% | 830/758-7060<br>Fax 830/758-0090 |
| Robert E Lee Elem Sch<br>300 S Monroe St, Eagle Pass 78852<br>Blanca Muzquiz | 1-6 | T | 292<br>30 | 92% | 830/758-7062<br>Fax 830/773-3471 |
| Rosita Valley Elem Sch<br>587 Madison St, Eagle Pass 78852<br>Cynthia Guedea | 1-6 | T | 473<br>25 | 91% | 830/758-7065<br>Fax 830/757-2098 |
| Rosita Valley Literacy Academy<br>Highnoon Rd, Eagle Pass 78852<br>Aida Pang-Villa | PK-1 | T | 377<br>10 | 89% | 830/758-7067<br>Fax 830/773-8859 |
| Sam Houston Elem Sch<br>2789 FM 1021, Eagle Pass 78852<br>Amalia Riojas | 2-6 | T | 465<br>26 | 94% | 830/758-7069<br>Fax 830/757-6639 |
| San Luis Elem Sch<br>2090 Williams St, Eagle Pass 78852<br>Sylvia Saucedo | 1-6 | T | 422<br>30 | 86% | 830/758-7071<br>Fax 830/773-1632 |
| Seco Mines Elem Sch<br>1654 S Veterans Blvd, Eagle Pass 78852<br>Maribel Martinez | 1-6 | T | 327<br>24 | 92% | 830/758-7073<br>Fax 830/773-8725 |

## MAVERICK CATHOLIC SCHOOLS

• **Diocese of Laredo Ed Office** PID: 04938095
Listing includes only schools located in this county. See District Index for location of Diocesan Offices.

| Catholic Schs..Principal | Grd | Prgm | Enr/#Cls | SN |
|---|---|---|---|---|
| Our Lady of Refuge Sch<br>577 Washington St, Eagle Pass 78852<br>Ana Bermea | PK-8 | | 200<br>13 | 830/773-3531<br>Fax 830/773-7310 |

## MAVERICK PRIVATE SCHOOLS

| Private Schs..Principal | Grd | Prgm | Enr/#Cls | SN |
|---|---|---|---|---|
| Redeemer Episcopal Sch<br>648 Madison St, Eagle Pass 78852<br>Jeanette Edwards | PK-6 | | 80<br>7 | 830/773-5122<br>Fax 830/773-3525 |

## MCCULLOCH COUNTY

## MCCULLOCH PUBLIC SCHOOLS

• **Brady Ind School Dist** PID: 01039420     325/597-2301
1003 W 11th St, Brady 76825     Fax 325/597-3984

**Schools:** 4 \ **Teachers:** 99 \ **Students:** 1,050 \ **Special Ed Students:** 173 \ **LEP Students:** 43 \ **College-Bound:** 61% \ **Ethnic:** Asian 1%, African American 2%, Hispanic 48%, Caucasian 49% \ **Exp:** $459 (High) \ **Poverty:** 25% \ **Title I:** $417,457 \ **Open-Close:** 08/24 - 05/27 \ **DTBP:** $435 (High)

| | | | |
|---|---|---|---|
| Hector Martinez | 1 | Barbara Landry | 2 |
| Roy Smith | 3 | Mike Hagan | 5 |
| Shay Easterwood | 6 | Richard Sweeeney | 11,296 |
| Shana Baronet | 37* | Sonia Cain | 58 |
| Michael Probst | 67 | Judy Fincher | 73,84 |
| Michael Tarr | 98 | | |

| Public Schs..Principal | Grd | Prgm | Enr/#Cls | SN |
|---|---|---|---|---|
| Ⓐ Brady Alternative Sch<br>601 W 11th St, Brady 76825<br>Hollis Moore | 6-12 | | 25<br>2 | 325/597-2170<br>Fax 325/597-7396 |
| Brady Elem Sch<br>205 W China St, Brady 76825<br>Christy Finn | PK-5 | T | 496<br>45 | 70% 325/597-2590<br>Fax 325/597-0490 |
| Brady High Sch<br>2301 Highway 190, Brady 76825<br>Kevin White | 9-12 | TV | 326<br>35 | 56% 325/597-2491<br>Fax 325/597-2147 |
| Brady Middle Sch<br>2309 Hwy 190, Brady 76825<br>Shona Moore | 6-8 | T | 260<br>25 | 63% 325/597-8110<br>Fax 325/597-4166 |

• **Lohn Ind School Dist** PID: 01039482     325/344-5749
1112 FM 504, Lohn 76852     Fax 325/344-5790

**Schools:** 1 \ **Teachers:** 13 \ **Students:** 100 \ **Special Ed Students:** 13 \ **College-Bound:** 25% \ **Ethnic:** Hispanic 42%, Caucasian 58% \ **Exp:** $1,013 (High) \ **Poverty:** 16% \ **Open-Close:** 08/17 - 05/21 \ **DTBP:** $344 (High)

| | | | |
|---|---|---|---|
| Leon Freeman | 1,83,84 | Christie Snodgrass | 11,73* |
| Robert Swenson | 67 | Dottie DeLeon | 271 |

| Public Schs..Principal | Grd | Prgm | Enr/#Cls | SN |
|---|---|---|---|---|
| Lohn Sch<br>1112 FM 504, Lohn 76852<br>Dottie De Leon | PK-12 | ATV | 100<br>16 | 87% 325/344-5749 |

| | | | |
|---|---|---|---|
| 1 Superintendent | 19 Chief Financial Officer | 39 Social Studies K-12 | 59 Special Education Elem | 69 Academic Assessment |
| 2 Bus/Finance/Purchasing | 20 Art K-12 | 40 Social Studies Elem | 60 Special Education Sec | 70 Research/Development |
| 3 Buildings And Grounds | 21 Art Elem | 41 Social Studies Sec | 61 Foreign/World Lang K-12 | 71 Public Information |
| 4 Food Service | 22 Art Sec | 31 Career/Sch-to-Work K-12 | 62 Foreign/World Lang Elem | 72 Summer School |
| 5 Transportation | 23 Music K-12 | 32 Career/Sch-to-Work Elem | 63 Foreign/World Lang Sec | 73 Instructional Tech |
| 6 Athletic | 24 Music Elem | 33 Career/Sch-to-Work Sec | 64 Religious Education K-12 | 74 Inservice Training |
| 7 Health Services | 25 Music Sec | 34 Early Childhood Ed | 65 Religious Education Elem | 75 Marketing/Distributive |
| 8 Curric/Instruct K-12 | 26 Business Education | 35 Health/Phys Education | 66 Religious Education Sec | 76 Info Systems |
| 9 Curric/Instruct Elem | 27 Career & Tech Ed | 36 Guidance Services K-12 | 67 School Board President | 77 Psychological Assess |
| 10 Curric/Instruct Sec | 28 Technology Education | 37 Guidance Services Elem | 68 Teacher Personnel | 78 Affirmative Action |

1 Superintendent · 2 Bus/Finance/Purchasing · 3 Buildings And Grounds · 4 Food Service · 5 Transportation · 6 Athletic · 7 Health Services · 8 Curric/Instruct K-12 · 9 Curric/Instruct Elem · 10 Curric/Instruct Sec · 11 Federal Program · 12 Title I · 13 Title V · 14 ... · 15 Asst Superintendent · 16 Instructional Media Svcs · 17 Chief Operations Officer · 18 Chief Academic Officer · 19 Chief Financial Officer · 20 Art K-12 · 21 Art Elem · 22 Art Sec · 23 Music K-12 · 24 Music Elem · 25 Music Sec · 26 Business Education · 27 Career & Tech Ed · 28 Technology Education · 29 Family/Consumer Science · 30 Adult Education · 31 Career/Sch-to-Work K-12 · 32 Career/Sch-to-Work Elem · 33 Career/Sch-to-Work Sec · 34 Early Childhood Ed · 35 Health/Phys Education · 36 Guidance Services K-12 · 37 Guidance Services Elem · 38 Guidance Services Sec · 39 Social Studies K-12 · 40 Social Studies Elem · 41 Social Studies Sec · 42 Science K-12 · 43 Science Elem · 44 Science Sec · 45 Math K-12 · 46 Math Elem · 47 Math Sec · 48 English/Lang Arts K-12 · 49 English/Lang Arts Elem · 50 English/Lang Arts Sec · 51 Reading K-12 · 52 Reading Elem · 53 Reading Sec · 54 Remedial Reading K-12 · 55 Remedial Reading Elem · 56 Remedial Reading Sec · 57 Bilingual/ELL · 58 Special Education K-12 · 59 Special Education Elem · 60 Special Education Sec · 61 Foreign/World Lang K-12 · 62 Foreign/World Lang Elem · 63 Foreign/World Lang Sec · 64 Religious Education K-12 · 65 Religious Education Elem · 66 Religious Education Sec · 67 School Board President · 68 Teacher Personnel · 69 Academic Assessment · 70 Research/Development · 71 Public Information · 72 Summer School · 73 Instructional Tech · 74 Inservice Training · 75 Marketing/Distributive · 76 Info Systems · 77 Psychological Assess · 78 Affirmative Action

## • Rochelle Ind School Dist PID: 01039509
5902 Lafayette Ave, Rochelle 76872

325/243-5224
Fax 325/243-5216

**Schools:** 1 \ **Teachers:** 24 \ **Students:** 179 \ **Special Ed Students:** 27
\ **College-Bound:** 30% \ **Ethnic:** African American 2%, Hispanic 25%,
Caucasian 73% \ **Exp:** $603 (High) \ **Poverty:** 18% \ **Title I:** $34,463 \
**Open-Close:** 08/03 - 05/27 \ **DTBP:** $358 (High) \ [f]

| Dave Lewis | 1,11 | Claylene Gossett | 2 |
| David Baker | 3,5 | Anna Wolfe | 4 |
| Jeff Corean | 6,9,74,288* | Matthew Fields | 8* |
| Tammy Parrish | 11,36,69* | Cody Houlbec | 27* |
| Connie Humphreys | 58 | Mike Wolf | 67 |

| Public Schs..Principal | Grd | Prgm | Enr/#Cls | SN | |
|---|---|---|---|---|---|
| Rochelle Sch<br>5902 Lafayette Ave, Rochelle 76872<br>Matthew Fields | PK-12 | TV | 179<br>17 | 45%<br>[f] | 325/243-5224<br>Fax 325/243-5283 |

## MCLENNAN COUNTY

## MCLENNAN PUBLIC SCHOOLS

## • Axtell Ind School Dist PID: 01039535
308 Ottawa, Axtell 76624

254/863-5301
Fax 254/863-5608

**Schools:** 2 \ **Teachers:** 76 \ **Students:** 580 \ **Special Ed Students:** 140
\ **LEP Students:** 8 \ **Ethnic:** African American 1%, Hispanic 18%,
Caucasian 80% \ **Exp:** $586 (High) \ **Poverty:** 24% \ **Title I:** $362,183 \
**Special Education:** $224,000 \ **Open-Close:** 08/19 - 05/27 \ **DTBP:** $343
(High) \ [f] [t]

| Dr J R Proctor | 1 | Penny Kocian | 2,10,11,35,57,88* |
| Ronnie Fedro | 3 | Janice Hornsby | 31,73,83,286,298* |
| Lacey Hollingsworth | 58* | Brian Frankum | 67 |
| Ashley Hardin | 69* | Brandon Dieterich | 76,751 |

| Public Schs..Principal | Grd | Prgm | Enr/#Cls | SN | |
|---|---|---|---|---|---|
| Axtell Elem Sch<br>1178 Longhorn Pkwy, Axtell 76624<br>Danette Stranacher | PK-5 | T | 336<br>30 | 54% | 254/863-5419<br>Fax 254/863-5944 |
| Axtell High Sch<br>308 Ottawa, Axtell 76624<br>Sunny Beseda | 6-12 | AV | 244<br>36 | 51% | 254/863-5301<br>Fax 254/863-5651 |

## • Bosqueville Ind School Dist PID: 01039561
7636 Rock Creek Rd, Waco 76708

254/757-3113
Fax 254/752-4909

**Schools:** 3 \ **Teachers:** 58 \ **Students:** 699 \ **Special Ed Students:** 87
\ **LEP Students:** 18 \ **College-Bound:** 60% \ **Ethnic:** African American
4%, Hispanic 24%, Caucasian 72% \ **Exp:** $690 (High) \ **Poverty:** 13% \
**Title I:** $66,549 \ **Special Education:** $133,000 \ **Open-Close:** 08/13 - 05/25
\ **DTBP:** $219 (High)

| James Skeeler | 1 | Catherine Boren | 2 |
| Steve Meyer | 3* | Mary Mynar | 4 |
| Michael Lamere | 5 | Clint Zander | 6 |
| Eary Penny | 7 | Kelly Bray | 8,11,271,274* |
| Cliff Heath | 10* | Kim Schwarz | 16* |
| Judy Nunn | 36,69,83,88,275,285,288,294 | Elicia Krunnow | 57 |

| Jennifer Riggs | 58* | Debbie Wrighthood | 67 |
| Rachel Carter | 73,286,295* | Jason Hancock | 295 |

| Public Schs..Principal | Grd | Prgm | Enr/#Cls | SN | |
|---|---|---|---|---|---|
| Bosqueville Elem Sch<br>1000 Washington Ln, Waco 76708<br>Kelly Bray | PK-5 | T | 324<br>32 | 42% | 254/752-6006<br>Fax 254/759-7065 |
| Bosqueville Middle Sch<br>7636 Rock Creek Rd, Waco 76708<br>Cliff Heath | 6-8 | T | 177 | 34% | 254/759-7077<br>Fax 254/752-5459<br>[f] |
| Bosqueville Secondary Sch<br>7636 Rock Creek Rd, Waco 76708<br>Cliff Heath | 9-12 | TV | 198 | 35% | 254/752-8513<br>Fax 254/752-0326 |

## • Bruceville-Eddy Ind Sch Dist PID: 01039585
1 Eagle Dr, Eddy 76524

254/859-5525
Fax 254/859-4023

**Schools:** 4 \ **Teachers:** 70 \ **Students:** 630 \ **Special Ed Students:** 92
\ **LEP Students:** 9 \ **College-Bound:** 49% \ **Ethnic:** African American
1%, Hispanic 32%, Caucasian 66% \ **Exp:** $408 (High) \ **Poverty:** 17% \
**Title I:** $164,016 \ **Special Education:** $240,000 \ **Open-Close:** 08/25 -
05/28 \ **DTBP:** $360 (High)

| Richard Kilgore | 1 | Sheryl Robbins | 2,68 |
| Lowell Hill | 3 | Patricia Novian | 4 |
| Mike Hawkins | 5* | Kyle Shoppach | 6 |
| Lisa Moon | 7,85 | Joe Woodard | 8,288* |
| Sharon Johnson | 9* | Marie Brockett | 11,69,294,296,298* |
| Linda Hargis | 16,82* | Stephanie Burkett | 31,36,83,88,271* |
| David Duty | 67 | Leah Price | 73,76,84,98,286,295 |

| Public Schs..Principal | Grd | Prgm | Enr/#Cls | SN | |
|---|---|---|---|---|---|
| Bruceville-Eddy Elem Sch<br>1 Eagle Dr, Eddy 76524<br>Sharon Johnson | K-3 | AT | 167<br>26 | 66% | 254/859-5525<br>Fax 254/859-5179 |
| Bruceville-Eddy High Sch<br>1 Eagle Dr, Eddy 76524<br>Joe Woodard | 9-12 | ATV | 213<br>25 | 52% | 254/859-5525<br>Fax 254/859-5001 |
| Bruceville-Eddy Interm Sch<br>1 Eagle Dr, Eddy 76524<br>Sharon Johnson | 4-6 | AT | 179<br>18 | 62% | 254/859-5525<br>Fax 254/859-5638 |
| Bruceville-Eddy Jr High Sch<br>1 Eagle Dr, Eddy 76524<br>Mike Hawkins | 7-8 | ATV | 159<br>16 | 62% | 254/859-5525<br>Fax 254/859-3207 |

## • China Spring Ind School Dist PID: 01039614
12166 Yankie Rd, China Spring 76633

254/836-1115
Fax 254/836-0559

**Schools:** 5 \ **Teachers:** 195 \ **Students:** 2,748 \ **Special Ed Students:** 296
\ **LEP Students:** 44 \ **Ethnic:** Asian 1%, African American 6%, Hispanic
19%, Caucasian 73% \ **Exp:** $466 (High) \ **Poverty:** 9% \ **Title I:** $233,757
\ **Special Education:** $451,000 \ **Open-Close:** 08/19 - 05/27 \ **DTBP:** $55
(Low)

| Dr Marc Faulkner | 1 | Brenda Poteet | 2 |
| Jim Ditto | 3,5 | Mark Bell | 6* |
| Jennifer Crook | 8,15,288 | Lesley Smith | 8 |
| Lisa Howard | 11,58 | Dr Kevin Pitts | 15 |
| Rick Hines | 67 | Raymond Medina | 73,295 |
| Scott Tyner | 295 | | |

| Public Schs..Principal | Grd | Prgm | Enr/#Cls | SN | |
|---|---|---|---|---|---|
| China Spring Elem Sch<br>200 Bob Johnson Rd, China Spring 76633<br>**Kristen Dutschmann \ Kim Coe** | PK-3 | T | 900<br>42 | 32% | 254/836-4635<br>Fax 254/836-4637 |

| | | | | | |
|---|---|---|---|---|---|
| China Spring High Sch | 9-12 | V | 182 | 20% | 254/836-1771 |
| 7301 N River Xing, China Spring 76633 | | | 40 | | Fax 254/836-1416 |
| Max Rutherford | | | | | |
| China Spring Intermediate Sch | 4-6 | | 639 | 30% | 254/759-1200 |
| 4001 Flat Rock Rd, Waco 76708 | | | 19 | | Fax 254/759-1208 |
| Heather Jenkins | | | | | |
| China Spring Middle Sch | 7-8 | | 427 | 27% | 254/836-4611 |
| 7201 N River Xing, China Spring 76633 | | | 27 | | Fax 254/836-4777 |
| Kristen Dutschmann \ **Lath Boykin** | | | | | |
| Ⓐ Daep | 3-12 | | 40 | | 254/836-0676 |
| 412 E Cougar Ln, China Spring 76633 | | | | | |
| Miranda Brown | | | | | |

---

● **Connally Ind School Dist** PID: 01039640    254/296-6460
200 Cadet Way, Waco 76705        Fax 254/412-5530

> **Schools:** 6 \ **Teachers:** 176 \ **Students:** 2,300 \ **Special Ed Students:** 189
> \ **LEP Students:** 229 \ **College-Bound:** 61% \ **Ethnic:** Asian 1%,
> African American 35%, Hispanic 33%, Native American: 1%, Caucasian
> 30% \ **Exp:** $418 (High) \ **Poverty:** 28% \ **Title I:** $1,201,361 \
> **Special Education:** $532,000 \ **Open-Close:** 08/14 - 05/21 \ **DTBP:** $189
> (High)

| | | | |
|---|---|---|---|
| Wesley Holt | 1 | James Slater | 2,15 |
| Janes Flater | 2,15 | Jennifer Moss | 2 |
| Jeremy Richard | 3 | Amanda Bailey | 4 |
| Terry McHam | 5 | Shane Anderson | 6* |
| Pam White | 7 | Sandra Hancock | 8,15 |
| Thurman Brown | 8* | David Wimberly | 11 |
| Laurie Tresl | 34,58 | Chris Howard | 57,69,294 |
| Greg Davis | 67 | Larry Cumby | 68 |
| Kevin Tye | 73 | Ronnie Price | 83,91 |
| Nona King | 274 | | |

| Public Schs..Principal | Grd | Prgm | Enr/#Cls | SN | |
|---|---|---|---|---|---|
| Connally Early Childhood Ctr | PK-K | T | 311 | 89% | 254/750-7160 |
| 100 B B Brown Dr, Waco 76705 | | | | | |
| Misty Gerik | | | | | |
| Connally Early Clg Career Tech | 10-12 | | 115 | | 254/296-6700 |
| 200 Cadet Way, Waco 76705 | | | | | |
| Herman Pereira | | | | | |
| Connally Elem Sch | 3-5 | T | 360 | 82% | 254/750-7100 |
| 300 Cadet Way, Waco 76705 | | | 25 | | Fax 254/412-5525 |
| Eric Cantu | | | | | |
| Connally High Sch | 9-12 | TV | 617 | 71% | 254/296-6700 |
| 901 N Lacy Dr, Waco 76705 | | | 50 | | Fax 254/412-5549 |
| Jill Talamantez | | | | | |
| Connally Junior High Sch | 6-8 | TV | 329 | 82% | 254/296-7700 |
| 100 Hancock Dr, Elm Mott 76640 | | | 34 | | Fax 254/829-2354 |
| Thurman Brown | | | | | |
| Connally Primary Sch | PK-2 | T | 600 | 85% | 254/296-7600 |
| 100 Little Cadet Ln, Elm Mott 76640 | | | 32 | | Fax 254/829-1273 |
| Marlo Moore | | | | | |

---

● **Crawford Ind School Dist** PID: 01039705    254/486-2381
200 Pirate Dr, Crawford 76638        Fax 254/486-2198

> **Schools:** 2 \ **Teachers:** 51 \ **Students:** 560 \ **Special Ed Students:** 59
> \ **LEP Students:** 7 \ **College-Bound:** 93% \ **Ethnic:** Asian 1%, African
> American 1%, Hispanic 8%, Caucasian 90% \ **Exp:** $577 (High) \
> **Poverty:** 11% \ **Title I:** $67,770 \ **Open-Close:** 08/19 - 05/21 \ **DTBP:** $339
> (High) \ 🄵 🅃

| | | | |
|---|---|---|---|
| Dr Kenneth Hall | 1,11 | Billy Lynch | 2,286,296 |
| Cody Gibson | 3 | Stephanie Howe | 4 |
| Greg Jacobs | 6 | Monty Prichard | 8,73,88 |

---

| | | | |
|---|---|---|---|
| Linda Stout | 9,57,83,85* | Christine Wilkins | 16* |
| Joy Allovio | 36,69,270 | Mary Claxon | 38 |
| Kevin Harrington | 58 | Ricky Steinkamp | 67 |
| Tami Burch | 295* | | |

| Public Schs..Principal | Grd | Prgm | Enr/#Cls | SN | |
|---|---|---|---|---|---|
| Crawford Elem Sch | PK-6 | T | 264 | 26% | 254/486-9083 |
| 100 Leonard Love Dr, Crawford 76638 | | | 18 | | Fax 254/486-9085 |
| Linda Stout | | | | | |
| Crawford High Sch | 7-12 | T | 281 | 18% | 254/486-2381 |
| 200 Pirate Dr, Crawford 76638 | | | 20 | | |
| Monte Pritchett | | | | | |

---

● **Gholson Ind School Dist** PID: 01039731    254/829-1528
137 Hamilton Dr, Waco 76705        Fax 254/829-0054

> **Schools:** 1 \ **Teachers:** 17 \ **Students:** 246 \ **Special Ed Students:** 29
> \ **LEP Students:** 10 \ **College-Bound:** 33% \ **Ethnic:** African American
> 3%, Hispanic 26%, Caucasian 71% \ **Exp:** $416 (High) \ **Poverty:** 28% \
> **Title I:** $99,873 \ **Open-Close:** 08/19 - 05/27 \ **DTBP:** $560 (High)

| | | | |
|---|---|---|---|
| Heather McCartney | 1,11,83,84 | Carmen Moore | 2,13,296 |
| Carson Moore | 3* | Tina McComb | 4 |
| Stephanie Taylor | 8,285,286,288,752* | Rebecca Lane | 37 |
| Laura Reed | 59* | David Walker | 67 |
| Ana Mercado | 73 | | |

| Public Schs..Principal | Grd | Prgm | Enr/#Cls | SN | |
|---|---|---|---|---|---|
| Gholson Sch | PK-12 | T | 246 | 74% | 254/829-1528 |
| 137 Hamilton Dr, Waco 76705 | | | 10 | | |
| Stephanie Taylor | | | | | |

---

● **Hallsburg Ind School Dist** PID: 01039755    254/875-2331
2313 Hallsburg Rd, Waco 76705        Fax 254/875-2436

> **Schools:** 1 \ **Teachers:** 11 \ **Students:** 170 \ **Special Ed Students:** 13
> \ **LEP Students:** 9 \ **Ethnic:** African American 5%, Hispanic 22%,
> Caucasian 73% \ **Exp:** $546 (High) \ **Poverty:** 13% \ **Title I:** $31,535 \
> **Open-Close:** 08/19 - 05/26 \ **DTBP:** $437 (High)

| | | | |
|---|---|---|---|
| Dr Kent Reynolds | 1,11,83 | Jewell Armstrong | 2 |
| Carol Lewis | 4* | Jonathan Eggerton | 15,280,285,294,296,298 |
| Elzene Barton | 57,59* | Norman Huddleston | 67 |
| Michael Johnson | 73,286* | Gary Parady | 752 |

| Public Schs..Principal | Grd | Prgm | Enr/#Cls | SN | |
|---|---|---|---|---|---|
| Hallsburg Elem Sch | PK-6 | T | 170 | 56% | 254/875-2331 |
| 2313 Hallsburg Rd, Waco 76705 | | | 7 | | |
| Kent Reynolds | | | | | |

---

● **La Vega Ind School Dist** PID: 01039779    254/299-6700
400 E Loop 340, Waco 76705        Fax 254/799-8642

> **Schools:** 5 \ **Teachers:** 210 \ **Students:** 3,140 \ **Special Ed Students:** 255
> \ **LEP Students:** 652 \ **Ethnic:** African American 28%, Hispanic 57%,
> Caucasian 15% \ **Exp:** $523 (High) \ **Poverty:** 28% \ **Title I:** $1,090,646 \
> **Special Education:** $623,000 \ **Open-Close:** 08/14 - 05/21 \ **DTBP:** $210
> (High) \ 🄵

| | | | |
|---|---|---|---|
| Dr Sharon Shields | 1 | Diane Roepke | 2 |
| James Langlotz | 3,91 | David Thiel | 4 |
| Mandi Livingston | 5 | Willie Williams | 6,35* |
| Dr Charla Rudd | 8,15 | Dr Peggy Johnson | 9,11,294,296,298 |
| Todd Gooden | 15,68,74,78,273 | Diane Dietiker | 16* |
| Angela Ward | 58 | Henry Jennings | 67 |
| Lori Mynarcik | 71 | Justin Peebles | 73,84,295 |

---

| | | | | | | | |
|---|---|---|---|---|---|---|---|
| 1 | Superintendent | 8 | Curric/Instruct K-12 | 19 | Chief Financial Officer | 29 | Family/Consumer Science |
| 2 | Bus/Finance/Purchasing | 9 | Curric/Instruct Elem | 20 | Art K-12 | 30 | Adult Education |
| 3 | Buildings And Grounds | 10 | Curric/Instruct Sec | 21 | Art Elem | 31 | Career/Sch-to-Work K-12 |
| 4 | Food Service | 11 | Federal Program | 22 | Art Sec | 32 | Career/Sch-to-Work Elem |
| 5 | Transportation | 12 | Title I | 23 | Music K-12 | 33 | Career/Sch-to-Work Sec |
| 6 | Athletic | 13 | Title V | 24 | Music Elem | 34 | Early Childhood Ed |
| 7 | Health Services | 14 | Asst Superintendent | 25 | Music Sec | 35 | Health/Phys Education |
| | | 15 | Instructional Media Svcs | 26 | Business Education | 36 | Guidance Services K-12 |
| | | 16 | Chief Operations Officer | 27 | Career & Tech Ed | 37 | Guidance Services Elem |
| | | 17 | Chief Academic Officer | 28 | Technology Education | 38 | Guidance Services Sec |

| | | | | | | | |
|---|---|---|---|---|---|---|---|
| 39 | Social Studies K-12 | 49 | English/Lang Arts Elem | 59 | Special Education Elem | 69 | Academic Assessment |
| 40 | Social Studies Elem | 50 | English/Lang Arts Sec | 60 | Special Education Sec | 70 | Research/Development |
| 41 | Social Studies Sec | 51 | Reading K-12 | 61 | Foreign/World Lang K-12 | 71 | Public Information |
| 42 | Science K-12 | 52 | Reading Elem | 62 | Foreign/World Lang Elem | 72 | Summer School |
| 43 | Science Elem | 53 | Reading Sec | 63 | Foreign/World Lang Sec | 73 | Instructional Tech |
| 44 | Science Sec | 54 | Remedial Reading K-12 | 64 | Religious Education K-12 | 74 | Inservice Training |
| 45 | Math K-12 | 55 | Remedial Reading Elem | 65 | Religious Education Elem | 75 | Marketing/Distributive |
| 46 | Math Elem | 56 | Remedial Reading Sec | 66 | Religious Education Sec | 76 | Info Systems |
| 47 | Math Sec | 57 | Bilingual/ELL | 67 | School Board President | 77 | Psychological Assess |
| 48 | English/Lang Arts K-12 | 58 | Special Education K-12 | 68 | Teacher Personnel | 78 | Affirmative Action |

| Public Schs..Principal | Grd | Prgm | Enr/#Cls SN | | |
|---|---|---|---|---|---|
| La Vega Elem Sch<br>3100 Wheeler St, Waco 76705<br>Shaunte Stewart | 1-3 | AT | 655<br>35 | 87% | 254/299-6755<br>Fax 254/799-4453 |
| La Vega High Sch<br>555 N Loop 340, Waco 76705<br>Sandra Gibson | 9-12 | ATV | 895 | 90% | 254/299-6820<br>Fax 254/799-0720 |
| La Vega IS-H P Miles Campus<br>4201 Williams Rd, Bellmead 76705<br>Kristy Rizo | 4-6 | T | 673<br>19 | 90% | 254/299-6770<br>Fax 254/799-9738 |
| La Vega Junior High Sch<br>4401 Orchard Ln, Waco 76705<br>Virginia Ellis | 7-8 | T | 491<br>45 | 94% | 254/299-6790<br>Fax 254/799-8943 |
| La Vega Primary Center<br>4400 Harrison St, Waco 76705<br>Lisa Seawright | PK-K | T | 426<br>29 | 90% | 254/299-6730<br>Fax 254/799-1369 |

## ● Lorena Ind School Dist PID: 01039822
308 N Frontage Rd, Lorena 76655

254/857-3616
Fax 254/857-4533

**Schools:** 4 \ **Teachers:** 122 \ **Students:** 1,673 \ **Special Ed Students:** 150 \ **LEP Students:** 25 \ **College-Bound:** 80% \ **Ethnic:** African American 2%, Hispanic 17%, Caucasian 81% \ **Exp:** $383 (High) \ **Poverty:** 8% \ **Title I:** $152,237 \ **Special Education:** $344,000 \ **Open-Close:** 08/13 - 05/21 \ **DTBP:** $350 (High) \

| | | | |
|---|---|---|---|
| Dr Joe Kucera | 1 | Jeff Linnstaedter | 2,19 |
| Gary Sutherland | 3 | Shirley Oliver | 4 |
| Elaine George | 5 | Rusty Grimm | 5,79,83,91,294 |
| Ray Biles | 6 | Cheri Borchardt | 8,11,57,76,286,288,296,751 |
| Mary Timmons | 67 | Jennifer Grimm | 73,295 |
| David Payne | 295 | | |

| Public Schs..Principal | Grd | Prgm | Enr/#Cls SN | | |
|---|---|---|---|---|---|
| Lorena Elem Sch<br>420 N Houston St, Lorena 76655<br>Liza Cunningham | 3-5 | T | 408<br>25 | 29% | 254/857-4613<br>Fax 254/857-9019 |
| Lorena High Sch<br>1 Leopard Ln, Lorena 76655<br>Kevin Johnson | 9-12 | AV | 544<br>40 | 20% | 254/857-4604<br>Fax 254/857-3883 |
| Lorena Middle Sch<br>500 Leopard Ln, Lorena 76655<br>Jennifer Allison | 6-8 | | 378<br>33 | 26% | 254/857-4621<br>Fax 254/857-3419 |
| Lorena Primary Sch<br>1191 Old Lorena Rd, Lorena 76655<br>April Jewell | PK-2 | T | 343 | 32% | 254/857-8909<br>Fax 254/857-8815 |

## ● Mart Ind School Dist PID: 01039858
700 E Navarro Ave, Mart 76664

254/876-2523
Fax 254/876-3028

**Schools:** 2 \ **Teachers:** 43 \ **Students:** 426 \ **Special Ed Students:** 62 \ **LEP Students:** 16 \ **College-Bound:** 60% \ **Ethnic:** African American 25%, Hispanic 23%, Native American: 1%, Caucasian 51% \ **Exp:** $512 (High) \ **Poverty:** 22% \ **Title I:** $241,406 \ **Open-Close:** 08/19 - 05/21 \ **DTBP:** $339 (High) \

| | | | |
|---|---|---|---|
| Leonard Williams | 1 | Rena Graves | 2 |
| Darrell Wolf | 3 | Paula Abbott | 4 |
| Kevin Hoffman | 6* | John Luedke | 16,73,82,297* |
| Pete Rowe | 67 | | |

| Public Schs..Principal | Grd | Prgm | Enr/#Cls SN | | |
|---|---|---|---|---|---|
| Mart Elem Sch<br>1400 E Kensington St, Mart 76664<br>Amy Stone | PK-6 | T | 280<br>13 | 83% | 254/876-2762<br>Fax 254/876-2317 |

| Public Schs..Principal | Grd | Prgm | Enr/#Cls SN | | |
|---|---|---|---|---|---|
| Mart High Sch<br>700 E Navarro Ave, Mart 76664<br>**Beau Sanchez \ Betsy Burnett** | 7-12 | ATV | 146<br>20 | 71% | 254/876-2574<br>Fax 254/876-2576 |

## ● McGregor Ind School Dist PID: 01039896
525 Bluebonnet Pkwy, Mc Gregor 76657

254/840-2828
Fax 254/840-4077

**Schools:** 4 \ **Teachers:** 120 \ **Students:** 1,342 \ **Special Ed Students:** 123 \ **LEP Students:** 161 \ **College-Bound:** 58% \ **Ethnic:** African American 6%, Hispanic 49%, Native American: 3%, Caucasian 42% \ **Exp:** $301 (High) \ **Poverty:** 20% \ **Title I:** $324,159 \ **Open-Close:** 08/12 - 05/26 \

| | | | |
|---|---|---|---|
| James Lenamon | 1 | Theresa Kinnear | 2 |
| Richard Schwake | 3,5 | John Carpenter | 4 |
| Mike Sheilds | 6 | Paul Miller | 7,15,91 |
| David Everett | 8,11,15,83 | Tonya Burgess | 9,31* |
| Kelly Tharpe | 10* | Michelle Lenamon | 16 |
| Kevin Harrington | 58,275 | Kyle Paschall | 67 |
| Melissa Seward | 73,76,286,295 | Lisa Rainey | 294 |

| Public Schs..Principal | Grd | Prgm | Enr/#Cls SN | | |
|---|---|---|---|---|---|
| H G Isbill Junior High Sch<br>305 S Van Buren St, Mc Gregor 76657<br>Kelly Tharpe | 6-8 | T | 313<br>36 | 59% | 254/840-3251<br>Fax 254/840-3572 |
| McGregor Elem Sch<br>913 Bluebonnet Pkwy, Mc Gregor 76657<br>Tonya Burgess | 2-5 | T | 422<br>27 | 64% | 254/840-3204<br>Fax 254/840-3540 |
| McGregor High Sch<br>903 Bluebonnet Pkwy, Mc Gregor 76657<br>Seth Fortenberry | 9-12 | ATV | 396<br>29 | 52% | 254/840-2853<br>Fax 254/840-2489 |
| McGregor Primary Sch<br>923 Bluebonnet Pkwy, Mc Gregor 76657<br>Cheri Zacharias | PK-1 | T | 211 | 64% | 254/840-2973<br>Fax 254/840-3345 |

## ● Midway Ind School Dist PID: 01039937
13885 Woodway Dr, Woodway 76712

254/761-5600
Fax 254/761-5789

**Schools:** 10 \ **Teachers:** 506 \ **Students:** 8,100 \ **Special Ed Students:** 792 \ **LEP Students:** 232 \ **College-Bound:** 75% \ **Ethnic:** Asian 5%, African American 12%, Hispanic 25%, Caucasian 57% \ **Exp:** $320 (High) \ **Poverty:** 8% \ **Title I:** $708,469 \ **Special Education:** $1,227,000 \ **Open-Close:** 08/18 - 05/26 \ **DTBP:** $147 (High) \

| | | | |
|---|---|---|---|
| Dr George Kazanas | 1 | Wesley Brooks | 2,15 |
| Buddy Freeman | 3 | Thomas Yourman | 3 |
| Colton Lawrence | 4 | Robert Anderson | 5 |
| Brad Shelton | 6* | Dr Aaron Pena | 8,15,288 |
| Sharon Blanchard | 12,58,77 | Dr Jeanie Johnson | 15,79,91 |
| Mary-Lou Glaesmann | 15,68 | Darrell Umhoefer | 20,23 |
| Dr Ashley Canuteson | 27,31 | Melissa Sulak | 34 |
| Kimberly Johnson | 46 | Lisa Cochran | 58 |
| Pete Rusek | 67 | Lorri Sapp | 69 |
| Traci Marlin | 71 | Dr Becky Odajima | 73,286 |
| Russell Seiler | 76,295 | Tammy Smith | 79 |
| Dr Beth Brabham | 81,271,280 | Ginger Rowe | 81 |
| Brooke Baker | 83 | Jesse Garn | 98 |
| Debbie Perry | 273 | Mindy Huime | 274 |

| Public Schs..Principal | Grd | Prgm | Enr/#Cls SN | | |
|---|---|---|---|---|---|
| Castleman Creek Elem Sch<br>755 S Hewitt Dr, Hewitt 76643<br>Amanda Johnson | PK-4 | T | 631 | 43% | 254/761-5755<br>Fax 254/761-5759 |
| Hewitt Elem Sch<br>900 W Panther Way, Hewitt 76643<br>Christy Watley | PK-4 | T | 502<br>30 | 57% | 254/761-5750<br>Fax 254/666-7540 |

| | | | | | |
|---|---|---|---|---|---|
| **Midway High Sch**<br>8200 Mars Dr, Waco 76712<br>Alison Smith | 9-12 | AV | 1,230<br>85 | 28% | 254/761-5650<br>Fax 254/761-5770 |
| **Midway Middle Sch**<br>800 N Hewitt Dr, Hewitt 76643<br>Dr Herb Cox | 7-8 | AV | 1,281<br>45 | 34% | 254/761-5680<br>Fax 254/761-5775 |
| **River Valley Intermediate Sch**<br>4750 Speegleville Rd, Mc Gregor 76657<br>Paul Offill | 5-6 | | 612 | | 254/761-5699<br>Fax 254/761-5698 |
| **South Bosque Elem Sch**<br>1 Wickson Rd, Waco 76712<br>Stacey Voigt | PK-4 | | 661<br>25 | 17% | 254/761-5720<br>Fax 254/776-2493 |
| **Speegleville Elem Sch**<br>101 Maywood Dr, Waco 76712<br>Mandi Bronstad | PK-4 | T | 277<br>25 | 55% | 254/761-5730<br>Fax 254/320-0070 |
| **Spring Valley Elem Sch**<br>610 W Spring Valley Rd, Hewitt 76643<br>Jay Fischer | PK-4 | | 520<br>30 | 39% | 254/761-5710<br>Fax 254/666-4654 |
| **Woodgate Intermediate Sch**<br>9400 Chapel Rd, Waco 76712<br>Wes Kanawyer | 5-6 | AT | 673<br>38 | 45% | 254/761-5690<br>Fax 254/666-0928 |
| **Woodway Elem Sch**<br>325 Estates Dr, Waco 76712<br>Angela Kirkpatrick | PK-4 | | 587<br>25 | 38% | 254/761-5740<br>Fax 254/772-5765 |

● **Moody Ind School Dist** PID: 01039975    254/853-2172
    12084 S Lone Star Pkwy Unit A, Moody 76557    Fax 254/853-2886

**Schools:** 3 \ **Teachers:** 60 \ **Students:** 660 \ **Special Ed Students:** 81 \ **LEP Students:** 53 \ **College-Bound:** 80% \ **Ethnic:** African American 5%, Hispanic 33%, Caucasian 62% \ **Exp:** $727 (High) \ **Poverty:** 18% \ **Title I:** $197,212 \ **Open-Close:** 08/18 - 05/21 \ **DTBP:** $332 (High)

| | | | |
|---|---|---|---|
| Gary Martel | 1,11,83 | Susan Landua | 2 |
| Marty Garcia | 6 | Belinda Brand | 8,12,57,69,286,298 |
| Nancy Molina | 16,69,73,286 | Kevin Harrington | 58 |
| Staci Evins | 67 | Andrew Miller | 285 |

| Public Schs..Principal | Grd | Prgm | Enr/#Cls | SN | |
|---|---|---|---|---|---|
| **Moody Elem Sch**<br>200 Ave D, Moody 76557<br>**Tina Stansel** | K-4 | T | 237<br>12 | 66% | 254/853-2155<br>Fax 254/853-3009 |
| **Moody High Sch**<br>11862 S Lone Star Pkwy, Moody 76557<br>Andrew Miller | 9-12 | ATV | 203<br>26 | 58% | 254/853-3622<br>Fax 254/853-3822 |
| **Moody Middle Sch**<br>107 Coralee Ln, Moody 76557<br>Eric Cox | 5-8 | AT | 213<br>19 | 67% | 254/853-2181<br>Fax 254/853-9128 |

● **Riesel Ind School Dist** PID: 01040003    254/896-6411
    600 E Frederick St, Riesel 76682    Fax 254/896-2981

**Schools:** 2 \ **Teachers:** 51 \ **Students:** 660 \ **Special Ed Students:** 75 \ **LEP Students:** 9 \ **College-Bound:** 75% \ **Ethnic:** Asian 1%, African American 2%, Hispanic 24%, Caucasian 72% \ **Exp:** $277 (Med) \ **Poverty:** 13% \ **Title I:** $68,300 \ **Open-Close:** 08/19 - 05/26 \ **DTBP:** $350 (High) \ 

| | | | |
|---|---|---|---|
| Brandon Cope | 1 | Toni Petrich | 2 |
| Jamie Glenn | 8,11,73,288,296* | Lisa Jackson | 58 |
| Tom McClimtok | 67 | | |

| Public Schs..Principal | Grd | Prgm | Enr/#Cls | SN | |
|---|---|---|---|---|---|
| **Dr James D Foster Elem Sch**<br>200 Williams, Riesel 76682<br>Brittni Summers | PK-6 | T | 304<br>23 | 50% | 254/896-2297<br>Fax 254/896-2319 |

| | | | | | |
|---|---|---|---|---|---|
| **Riesel High Sch**<br>600 E Frederick St, Riesel 76682<br>Jody Wood \ Krystal Wilson | 7-12 | ATV | 356<br>30 | 49% | 254/896-3171 |

● **Robinson Ind School Dist** PID: 01040039    254/662-0194
    500 W Lyndale Ave, Robinson 76706    Fax 254/662-0215

**Schools:** 5 \ **Teachers:** 181 \ **Students:** 2,200 \ **Special Ed Students:** 229 \ **LEP Students:** 43 \ **Ethnic:** Asian 1%, African American 3%, Hispanic 29%, Caucasian 67% \ **Exp:** $247 (Med) \ **Poverty:** 13% \ **Title I:** $317,197 \ **Special Education:** $509,000 \ **Open-Close:** 09/09 - 05/26 \ **DTBP:** $204 (High) \ 

| | | | |
|---|---|---|---|
| Michael Hope | 1 | Stacey Proctor | 2,19 |
| Dennis Ferguson | 3 | Alma Ramirz | 4 |
| Jay Zeller | 6* | Colette Pledger | 8,18 |
| Tim VanCleave | 11,15 | Dr Amy Perez | 12,58 |
| Willie Thomas | 16 | Dawn Griffin | 27,31 |
| Danielle Hughes | 57* | Laura Crawford | 67 |
| Bryan Fuqua | 73,84 | Justin Brink | 295 |

| Public Schs..Principal | Grd | Prgm | Enr/#Cls | SN | |
|---|---|---|---|---|---|
| **Robinson Elem Sch**<br>151 Peplow Dr, Robinson 76706<br>Shelly Chudej | 2-3 | T | 365<br>19 | 37% | 254/662-5000<br>Fax 254/662-3140 |
| **Robinson High Sch**<br>700 W Tate St, Robinson 76706<br>Kati Dietzman | 9-12 | T | 350<br>32 | 26% | 254/662-3840<br>Fax 254/662-4007 |
| **Robinson Intermediate Sch**<br>500 W Lyndale Ave, Robinson 76706<br>Sara Laughlin | 4-5 | T | 499<br>16 | 38% | 254/662-6113<br>Fax 254/662-6183 |
| **Robinson Junior High Sch**<br>410 W Lyndale Ave, Robinson 76706<br>Cynthia McCoy | 6-8 | T | 371<br>40 | 34% | 254/662-3843<br>Fax 254/662-1845 |
| **Robinson Primary Sch**<br>541 N Old Robinson Rd, Robinson 76706<br>Melissa Zacharias | PK-1 | T | 380<br>17 | 46% | 254/662-0251<br>Fax 254/662-3361 |

● **Waco Ind School Dist** PID: 01040132    254/755-9473
    501 Franklin Ave Ofc, Waco 76701    Fax 254/755-9690

**Schools:** 24 \ **Teachers:** 982 \ **Students:** 15,050 \ **Special Ed Students:** 1,194 \ **LEP Students:** 2,609 \ **College-Bound:** 53% \ **Ethnic:** African American 29%, Hispanic 62%, Caucasian 9% \ **Exp:** $483 (High) \ **Poverty:** 31% \ **Title I:** $8,305,280 \ **Special Education:** $2,855,000 \ **Open-Close:** 08/18 - 05/27 \ **DTBP:** $200 (High) \ 

| | | | |
|---|---|---|---|
| Susan Kincannon | 1 | Sheryl Davis | 2,19 |
| Israel Carrera | 3,15 | Rolando Gomez | 3 |
| Cliff Reece | 4 | David Gray | 5 |
| Johnny Tusa | 6 | Rhiannon Settles | 7 |
| Kim Ellis | 8,15 | Dr Robin McDurham | 10 |
| Dr Robin Wilson | 11 | Elaine Botello | 15 |
| Grace Benson | 15,57 | Sherry Trotts | 15 |
| Yolanda Williams | 15 | Larry Carpenter | 20,23 |
| Donna McKethan | 27,31 | Tiffany Sommerfeld | 36 |
| Robert Glinski | 39 | Suzanne Hamilton | 58* |
| Angela Tekell | 67 | Sue Pfleging | 68 |
| Kyle DeBeer | 71 | Darvis Griffin | 73,98 |
| Paul Mach | 73 | Patrick Uptmore | 74,273 |
| Cecelia Boswell | 81 | Scott McClanahan | 81 |
| David Williams | 91 | Pennie Graeber | 275 |
| Matt Wolfe | 295 | Sharla Garcia | 298 |

| Public Schs..Principal | Grd | Prgm | Enr/#Cls | SN | |
|---|---|---|---|---|---|
| **Alta Vista Elem Sch**<br>3637 Alta Vista Dr, Waco 76706<br>Lindsey Helton | PK-5 | T | 502<br>24 | 89% | 254/662-3050<br>Fax 254/662-7353 |

| | | | | | | | | | | |
|---|---|---|---|---|---|---|---|---|---|---|
| 1 | Superintendent | 8 | Curric/Instruct K-12 | 19 | Chief Financial Officer | 29 | Family/Consumer Science | 39 | Social Studies K-12 | 49 English/Lang Arts Elem · 59 Special Education Elem · 69 Academic Assessment |
| 2 | Bus/Finance/Purchasing | 9 | Curric/Instruct Elem | 20 | Art K-12 | 30 | Adult Education | 40 | Social Studies Elem | 50 English/Lang Arts Sec · 60 Special Education Sec · 70 Research/Development |
| 3 | Buildings And Grounds | 10 | Curric/Instruct Sec | 21 | Art Elem | 31 | Career/Sch-to-Work K-12 | 41 | Social Studies Sec | 51 Reading K-12 · 61 Foreign/World Lang K-12 · 71 Public Information |
| 4 | Food Service | 11 | Federal Program | 22 | Art Sec | 32 | Career/Sch-to-Work Elem | 42 | Science K-12 | 52 Reading Elem · 62 Foreign/World Lang Elem · 72 Summer School |
| 5 | Transportation | 12 | Title I | 23 | Music K-12 | 33 | Career/Sch-to-Work Sec | 43 | Science Elem | 53 Reading Sec · 63 Foreign/World Lang Sec · 73 Instructional Tech |
| 6 | Athletic | 13 | Title V | 24 | Music Elem | 34 | Early Childhood Ed | 44 | Science Sec | 54 Remedial Reading K-12 · 64 Religious Education K-12 · 74 Inservice Training |
| 7 | Health Services | 14 | | 25 | Music Sec | 35 | Health/Phys Education | 45 | Math K-12 | 55 Remedial Reading Elem · 65 Religious Education Elem · 75 Marketing/Distributive |
| | | 15 | Asst Superintendent | 26 | Business Education | 36 | Guidance Services K-12 | 46 | Math Elem | 56 Remedial Reading Sec · 66 Religious Education Sec · 76 Info Systems |
| | | 16 | Instructional Media Svcs | 27 | Career & Tech Ed | 37 | Guidance Services Elem | 47 | Math Sec | 57 Bilingual/ELL · 67 School Board President · 77 Psychological Assess |
| | | 17 | Chief Operations Officer | 28 | Technology Education | 38 | Guidance Services Sec | 48 | English/Lang Arts K-12 | 58 Special Education K-12 · 68 Teacher Personnel · 78 Affirmative Action |
| | | 18 | Chief Academic Officer | | | | | | | |

| School | Grade | Prgm | Enr/#Cls | SN | Phone |
|---|---|---|---|---|---|
| Bell's Hill Elem Sch<br>2100 Ross Ave, Waco 76706<br>Rebekah Mechell | PK-5 | T | 680<br>30 | 94% | 254/754-4171<br>Fax 254/750-3559 |
| Ⓐ Brazos Credit Recovery HS<br>3005 Edna Ave, Waco 76708<br>Daphanie Latchison | 7-12 | T | 250<br>4 | 81% | 254/754-9422 |
| Brook Ave Elem Sch<br>720 Brook Ave, Waco 76708<br>Julie Sapaugh | PK-5 | T | 371<br>20 | 97% | 254/750-3562<br>Fax 254/750-3545 🔵🔵 |
| Cedar Ridge Elem Sch<br>2115 Meridian Ave, Waco 76708<br>Helen Smith | PK-5 | T | 481<br>40 | 93% | 254/756-1241<br>Fax 254/750-3531 |
| Cesar Chavez Middle Sch<br>700 S 15th St, Waco 76706<br>Alonzo McAdoo | 6-8 | T | 865 | 64% | 254/750-3736<br>Fax 254/750-3739 |
| Crestview Elem Sch<br>1120 N New Rd, Waco 76710<br>Samantha Craytor | PK-5 | T | 470<br>37 | 77% | 254/776-1704<br>Fax 254/741-4910 |
| Dean Highland Elem Sch<br>3300 Maple Ave, Waco 76707<br>Thia Allen | PK-5 | T | 641<br>19 | 88% | 254/752-3751<br>Fax 254/750-3458 |
| Ⓐ G L Wiley Opportunity Center<br>1030 E Live Oak St, Waco 76704<br>Larryl Curtis | 6-12 | T | 77<br>11 | 75% | 254/757-3829<br>Fax 254/750-3772 |
| G W Carver Middle Sch<br>1601 J J Flewellen Rd, Waco 76704<br>Dr Isaac Carrier | 6-8 | T | 488<br>39 | 72% | 254/757-0787<br>Fax 254/750-3442 🔵🔵 |
| Ⓜ Hillcrest Prof Dev Sch<br>4225 Pine Ave, Waco 76710<br>Jennifer Lundquist | PK-5 | T | 441<br>13 | 45% | 254/772-4286<br>Fax 254/741-4938 |
| Indian Spring Middle Sch<br>500 N University Parks Dr, Waco 76701<br>Joseph Alexander | 6-8 | T | 519 | 97% | 254/757-6200<br>Fax 254/757-6299 |
| J H Hines Elem Sch<br>301 Garrison St, Waco 76704<br>Everette Taylor | PK-5 | T | 452<br>35 | 98% | 254/753-1362<br>Fax 254/750-3799 |
| Kendrick Elem Sch<br>1801 Kendrick Ln, Waco 76711<br>Isabel Lozano | PK-5 | T | 501<br>21 | 95% | 254/752-3316<br>Fax 254/750-3472 |
| Ⓜ Lake Air Mont Magnet Sch<br>4601 Cobbs Dr, Waco 76710<br>Stephanie Tankersley | PK-8 | T | 775<br>25 | | 254/772-1910<br>Fax 254/741-4945 |
| Ⓐ McLennan Co Challenge Academy<br>2015 Alexander Ave, Waco 76708<br>Christopher Rankin | 6-12 | | 50<br>8 | 72% | 254/754-0803<br>Fax 254/754-6029 |
| Mountainview Elem Sch<br>5901 Bishop Dr, Waco 76710<br>Melissa Pritchard | PK-5 | T | 375<br>22 | 72% | 254/772-2520<br>Fax 254/741-4961 |
| Parkdale Elem Sch<br>6400 Edmond Ave, Waco 76710<br>Lena Ortiz | PK-5 | T | 669<br>20 | 97% | 254/772-2170<br>Fax 254/741-4979 |
| Provident Heights Elem Sch<br>2415 Bosque Blvd, Waco 76707<br>Debbie Sims | PK-5 | T | 367<br>27 | 83% | 254/750-3930<br>Fax 254/750-3934 |
| South Waco Elem Sch<br>2104 Gurley Ln, Waco 76706<br>Twana Lee | PK-5 | T | 441<br>29 | 98% | 254/753-6802<br>Fax 254/750-3527 |
| Tennyson Middle Sch<br>6100 Tennyson Dr, Waco 76710<br>Matt Rambo | 6-8 | T | 921<br>50 | 69% | 254/772-1440<br>Fax 254/741-4970 🔵🔵 |
| University High Sch<br>3201 S New Rd, Waco 76706<br>Richard Edison | 9-12 | TV | 1,652 | | 254/756-1843<br>Fax 254/750-3709 |
| Waco High Sch<br>2020 N 42nd St, Waco 76710<br>James Stewart | 9-12 | TV | 2,053 | 73% | 254/776-1150<br>Fax 254/741-4815 |

| West Ave Elem Sch<br>1101 N 15th St, Waco 76707<br>John Weeks | PK-5 | T | 295<br>13 | 91% | 254/750-3900<br>Fax 254/750-3904 |

● **West Ind School Dist** PID: 01040481     254/981-2050
801 N Reagan St, West 76691

> **Schools:** 4 \ **Teachers:** 88 \ **Students:** 826 \ **Special Ed Students:** 117 \ **LEP Students:** 43 \ **College-Bound:** 70% \ **Ethnic:** African American 3%, Hispanic 18%, Caucasian 78% \ **Exp:** $320 (High) \ **Poverty:** 10% \ **Title I:** $193,021 \ **Special Education:** $453,000 \ **Open-Close:** 08/19 - 05/21 \ **DTBP:** $582 (High) \ 🔵 🔵

| | | | | |
|---|---|---|---|---|
| David Truitt | 1,11,73,83 | Charles Mikeska | 2,3,91 |
| Kevin Maler | 5 | David Woodard | 6* |
| Amanda Adams | 8 | Becky Kersh | 8 |
| Tory Dobecka | 8 | Carla Sykora | 58 |
| Larry Sparks | 67 | | |

| Public Schs..Principal | Grd | Prgm | Enr/#Cls | SN | |
|---|---|---|---|---|---|
| Ⓐ Brookhaven Sch<br>5467 Rogers Hill Rd, West 76691<br>Theresa Soukup | 6-12 | T | 75 | 91% | 254/981-2240<br>Fax 254/829-1522 |
| West Elem Sch<br>209 N Harrison St, West 76691<br>Carrie Kazda | PK-5 | T | 498<br>35 | 39% | 254/981-2000<br>Fax 254/826-3342 |
| West High Sch<br>1008 Jerry Mashek Dr, West 76691<br>Charles Klander | 9-12 | T | 119 | 28% | 254/981-2050<br>Fax 254/826-3342 |
| West Middle Sch<br>1008 Jerry Mashek Dr, West 76691<br>Charles Klander | 6-8 | T | 209<br>12 | 40% | 254/981-2120<br>Fax 254/826-3342 |

# MCLENNAN CATHOLIC SCHOOLS

● **Diocese of Austin Ed Office** PID: 01420568
Listing includes only schools located in this county. See District Index for location of Diocesan Offices.

| Catholic Schs..Principal | Grd | Prgm | Enr/#Cls | SN | |
|---|---|---|---|---|---|
| Louis Reicher Catholic Sch<br>2208 N 23rd St, Waco 76708<br>Rob Whitworth | PK-12 | | 314<br>27 | | 254/754-2041<br>Fax 254/754-2091 |
| Reicher Catholic High Sch<br>2102 N 23rd St, Waco 76708<br>Blake Evans | 9-12 | | 177<br>15 | | 254/752-8349<br>Fax 254/752-8408 |
| St Mary Catholic Sch<br>507 W Spruce St, West 76691<br>Ericka Sammon | PK-8 | | 141<br>11 | | 254/826-5991<br>Fax 254/826-7047 |

# MCLENNAN PRIVATE SCHOOLS

| Private Schs..Principal | Grd | Prgm | Enr/#Cls | SN | |
|---|---|---|---|---|---|
| Eagle Christian Academy<br>6125 Bosque Blvd, Waco 76710<br>Dr Kahrin Wessel \ Tracy Jimenez | PK-12 | | 115<br>20 | | 254/772-2122 |
| Live Oak Classical Sch<br>420 S 5th St, Waco 76706<br>Alison Moffatt | PK-12 | | 275 | | 254/714-1007<br>Fax 254/714-1150 |

| | | | |
|---|---|---|---|
| Parkview Christian Academy<br>1100 E Lake Shore Dr, Waco 76708<br>Amy Landers | K-12 | 95<br>40 | 254/753-0159<br>Fax 254/753-0271 |
| St Paul's Episcopal Sch<br>517 Columbus Ave, Waco 76701<br>M'Lissa Howen | PK-6 | 70<br>10 | 254/753-0246<br>Fax 254/755-7488 |
| Valor Preparatory Academy<br>4600 Sanger Ave, Waco 76710<br>Jared Nazarian | PK-10 | 215 | 254/235-0575 |
| Vanguard College Prepatory Sch<br>2517 Mount Carmel Dr, Waco 76710<br>Bill Borg | 7-12 | 215<br>29 | 254/772-8111<br>Fax 254/772-8263 |
| Waco Montessori Sch<br>1920 Columbus Ave, Waco 76701<br>Shirley Jansing | PK-6 | 250 | 254/754-3966<br>Fax 254/752-2922 |

## MCLENNAN REGIONAL CENTERS

● **Region 12 Ed Service Center** PID: 01040120  254/297-1212
2101 W Loop 340, Waco 76712  Fax 254/666-0823

| | | | |
|---|---|---|---|
| Jerry Maze | 1 | Terry Marak | 2,19 |
| Tammy Becker | 8 | Linda Roper | 12 |
| Dwan Pickens | 57 | Chris Griffin | 58 |
| Larry Robinson | 68 | Lisa McCray | 73 |
| Ed Newman | 76 | Michelle Butler | 77 |
| David McKamie | 79 | Yolanda Rollins | 271 |

# MCMULLEN COUNTY

## MCMULLEN PUBLIC SCHOOLS

● **McMullen Co Ind Sch Dist** PID: 01040560  361/274-2000
901 River St, Tilden 78072  Fax 361/274-3665

**Schools:** 1 \ **Teachers:** 26 \ **Students:** 289 \ **Special Ed Students:** 24 \
**LEP Students:** 3 \ **College-Bound:** 100% \ **Ethnic:** Asian 1%, Hispanic
37%, Caucasian 61% \ **Exp:** $1,406 (High) \ **Poverty:** 14% \ **Title I:** $19,169 \
**Open-Close:** 08/14 - 05/21 \ **DTBP:** $299 (High)

| | | | |
|---|---|---|---|
| Jason Jones | 1 | Krystal Huschke | 2 |
| Larry Garcia | 3,5 | Tracie Rios | 4* |
| Shannon Taylor | 6 | Joe Timms | 8,31,57,85,273* |
| Joel Trudeau | 11* | Holly Schorch | 58,83,88,270* |
| Walt Franklin | 67 | Kelly James | 69,83,88,270* |
| Mary Pate | 73,76* | | |

| Public Schs..Principal | Grd | Prgm | Enr/#Cls | SN | |
|---|---|---|---|---|---|
| McMullen Co Sch<br>901 River St, Tilden 78072<br>Joe Timms | PK-12 | V | 289<br>20 | 25% | 361/274-2000<br>Fax 361/274-3580 |

## MEDINA PUBLIC SCHOOLS

● **D'Hanis Ind School Dist** PID: 01041162  830/363-7216
6751 County Rd 5216, D Hanis 78850  Fax 830/363-7390

**Schools:** 1 \ **Teachers:** 35 \ **Students:** 368 \ **Special Ed Students:** 30
\ **LEP Students:** 3 \ **College-Bound:** 90% \ **Ethnic:** Hispanic 48%,
Caucasian 52% \ **Exp:** $702 (High) \ **Poverty:** 19% \ **Title I:** $65,791 \
**Open-Close:** 08/26 - 05/21 \ **DTBP:** $353 (High) \ [f]

| | | | |
|---|---|---|---|
| Vickie Whorton | 2,4 | Ray Garza | 3* |
| Todd Craft | 6* | Sandra Sexton | 16,73* |
| Annaliza Pieratt | 57* | Clay Bell | 67 |
| Bunny Voigt | 76 | | |

| Public Schs..Principal | Grd | Prgm | Enr/#Cls | SN | |
|---|---|---|---|---|---|
| D'Hanis Sch<br>6751 Cr 5216, D Hanis 78850<br>Miranda Santos \ Kurt Schumaker | PK-12 | T | 368<br>30 | 42% | 830/363-7216 |

● **Devine Ind School Dist** PID: 01041198  830/851-0795
605 W Hondo Ave, Devine 78016  Fax 830/663-6706

**Schools:** 4 \ **Teachers:** 138 \ **Students:** 1,900 \ **Special Ed Students:** 245
\ **LEP Students:** 67 \ **College-Bound:** 43% \ **Ethnic:** Hispanic 65%,
Caucasian 35% \ **Exp:** $324 (High) \ **Poverty:** 16% \ **Title I:** $372,346 \
**Special Education:** $381,000 \ **Open-Close:** 08/24 - 05/27 \ **DTBP:** $517
(High)

| | | | |
|---|---|---|---|
| Todd Grandjean | 1 | Shannon Ramirez | 2 |
| Darren Van Fussen | 3 | David Cardenas | 3 |
| Ruben Ramirez | 3 | Joseph Yates | 4 |
| Jon Eichman | 5 | Chad Quisenberry | 6* |
| Daryl Wendel | 8,15,68 | Lysandra Saldana | 9* |
| Abigail Beadle | 11 | Roland Cadena | 38* |
| Valerie Dykstra | 58 | Nancy Pepper | 67 |
| Daniel Garza | 73* | Dawn Schneider | 79 |
| Dan Garcia | 84 | | |

| Public Schs..Principal | Grd | Prgm | Enr/#Cls | SN | |
|---|---|---|---|---|---|
| Devine High Sch<br>1225 W Highway 173, Devine 78016<br>Derrick Byrd | 9-12 | AGTV | 268<br>65 | 49% | 830/851-0895<br>Fax 830/663-6792 |
| Devine Intermediate Sch<br>900 Atkins Ave, Devine 78016<br>Blain Martin | 3-5 | T | 448<br>25 | 58% | 830/851-0495<br>Fax 830/663-6746 |
| Devine Middle Sch<br>400 Cardinal Dr, Devine 78016<br>Kandi Darnell | 6-8 | TV | 137<br>45 | 59% | 830/851-0695<br>Fax 830/663-6769 |
| John J Ciavarra Elem Sch<br>112 Bentson Dr, Devine 78016<br>Brenda Gardner | PK-2 | T | 411<br>29 | 68% | 830/851-0395<br>Fax 830/663-6730 |

| | | | | | |
|---|---|---|---|---|---|
| **1** Superintendent | **8** Curric/Instruct K-12 | **19** Chief Financial Officer | **29** Family/Consumer Science | **39** Social Studies K-12 | **49** English/Lang Arts Elem | **59** Special Education Elem | **69** Academic Assessment |
| **2** Bus/Finance/Purchasing | **9** Curric/Instruct Elem | **20** Art K-12 | **30** Adult Education | **40** Social Studies Elem | **50** English/Lang Arts Sec | **60** Special Education Sec | **70** Research/Development |
| **3** Buildings And Grounds | **10** Curric/Instruct Sec | **21** Art Elem | **31** Career/Sch-to-Work K-12 | **41** Social Studies Sec | **51** Reading K-12 | **61** Foreign/World Lang K-12 | **71** Public Information |
| **4** Food Service | **11** Federal Program | **22** Art Sec | **32** Career/Sch-to-Work Elem | **42** Science K-12 | **52** Reading Elem | **62** Foreign/World Lang Elem | **72** Summer School |
| **5** Transportation | **12** Title I | **23** Music K-12 | **33** Career/Sch-to-Work Sec | **43** Science Elem | **53** Reading Sec | **63** Foreign/World Lang Sec | **73** Instructional Tech |
| **6** Athletic | **13** Title V | **24** Music Elem | **34** Early Childhood Ed | **44** Science Sec | **54** Remedial Reading K-12 | **64** Religious Education K-12 | **74** Inservice Training |
| **7** Health Services | **15** Asst Superintendent | **25** Music Sec | **35** Health/Phys Education | **45** Math K-12 | **55** Remedial Reading Elem | **65** Religious Education Elem | **75** Marketing/Distributive |
| | **16** Instructional Media Svcs | **26** Business Education | **36** Guidance Services K-12 | **46** Math Elem | **56** Remedial Reading Sec | **66** Religious Education Sec | **76** Info Systems |
| **TX—286** | **17** Chief Operations Officer | **27** Career & Tech Ed | **37** Guidance Services Elem | **47** Math Sec | **57** Bilingual/ELL | **67** School Board President | **77** Psychological Assess |
| | **18** Chief Academic Officer | **28** Technology Education | **38** Guidance Services Sec | **48** English/Lang Arts K-12 | **58** Special Education K-12 | **68** Teacher Personnel | **78** Affirmative Action |

- **Hondo Ind School Dist** PID: 01041239       830/426-3027
2604 Avenue E, Hondo 78861       Fax 830/426-7683

**Schools:** 4 \ **Teachers:** 150 \ **Students:** 1,838 \ **Special Ed Students:** 206 \ **LEP Students:** 47 \ **Ethnic:** African American 1%, Hispanic 71%, Caucasian 28% \ **Exp:** $257 (Med) \ **Poverty:** 16% \ **Title I:** $438,830 \ **Special Education:** $357,000 \ **Open-Close:** 08/14 - 05/28 \ **DTBP:** $553 (High)

| | | | |
|---|---|---|---|
| Dr Alann Truelock | 1 | Patricia Gonzales | 2 |
| Chuck Beard | 3 | Michelle Thacker | 4 |
| Jessie Baez | 6* | Chesney Brown | 7* |
| Misty Ptasnik | 9* | Robert Knight | 10,31* |
| Stephanie Laughinghouse | 11,54,57,83,271,273,275,296 | Rosemary Mares | 15,69,74,91 |
| Kami Neuman | 16,82* | Vanessa Alvarado | 30,38* |
| Cynthia Gann | 58,77 | Jay Gardenhire | 67 |
| Mary Peters | 73,286,295* | James White | 79 |
| Flint Huey | 88* | | |

| Public Schs..Principal | Grd | Prgm | Enr/#Cls | SN | |
|---|---|---|---|---|---|
| Hondo High Sch<br>2603 Avenue H, Hondo 78861<br>Robert Knight | 9-12 | ATV | 619<br>50 | 47% | 830/426-3341<br>Fax 830/426-7691 |
| McDowell Middle Sch<br>1602 27th St S, Hondo 78861<br>Scott Backus | 6-8 | AT | 416 | 47% | 830/426-2261<br>Fax 830/426-7624 |
| Meyer Elem Sch<br>2502 Avenue Q, Hondo 78861<br>Misty Ptasnik | PK-2 | AT | 382<br>32 | 74% | 830/426-3161<br>Fax 830/426-7679 |
| Newell E Woolls Interm Sch<br>2802 Avenue Q, Hondo 78861<br>Steve Ayers | 3-5 | AT | 421<br>25 | 66% | 830/426-7666<br>Fax 830/426-7669 |

- **Medina Valley Ind School Dist** PID: 01041277     830/931-2243
8449 FM 471 S, Castroville 78009     Fax 830/931-4050

**Schools:** 7 \ **Teachers:** 332 \ **Students:** 5,087 \ **Special Ed Students:** 629 \ **LEP Students:** 300 \ **College-Bound:** 53% \ **Ethnic:** Asian 1%, African American 3%, Hispanic 62%, Caucasian 34% \ **Exp:** $492 (High) \ **Poverty:** 18% \ **Title I:** $823,365 \ **Special Education:** $1,503,000 \ **Open-Close:** 08/25 - 06/03 \ **DTBP:** $178 (High)

| | | | |
|---|---|---|---|
| Dr Kenneth Rohrbach | 1 | Michael Homann | 2,15 |
| Paul Holzhaus | 2,5,15 | Sylvia Morales | 2 |
| Tommy Ellison | 3 | Vicki Beck | 4 |
| Richard Broome | 5 | Todd Tschirhart | 5 |
| Lee Crisp | 6 | Patricia Mechler | 7* |
| Tina Schmelzer | 7 | Andrea Moreno-Hewitt | 8,57,69 |
| Arcelia Leon | 8,69 | Michael Nesbit | 8,15,69 |
| Gabriel Cary | 11 | Thomas Galvez | 20 |
| Leah Graves | 45 | Stephine Keller Perkins | 58 |
| Shannon Beasley | 67 | Jason Migura | 68 |
| Bridget Ayala | 69 | Samuel Alaniz | 71 |
| Carl Lyles | 73,295,297 | Julie Oppelt | 81 |
| Kenneth Englehart | 84,98 | Holly Havey | 88* |
| Christine Orozco | 93 | Nathan Harper | 295 |

| Public Schs..Principal | Grd | Prgm | Enr/#Cls | SN | |
|---|---|---|---|---|---|
| Castroville Elem Sch<br>1000 Madrid St, Castroville 78009<br>Ken Center | PK-5 | T | 637<br>32 | 54% | 830/931-2243<br>Fax 830/931-3973 |
| Loma Alta Middle Sch<br>266 Cr 361, San Antonio 78253<br>Julie Center | 6-8 | | 692 | | 830/931-2243 |
| Luckey Ranch Elem Sch<br>12045 Luckey River, San Antonio 78252<br>Georgia Neuman | PK-5 | T | 735 | 63% | 830/931-2243 |

| | | | | | |
|---|---|---|---|---|---|
| Medina Valley High Sch<br>8365 FM 471 S, Castroville 78009<br>Tanner Lange | 9-12 | GTV | 1,127 | 44% | 830/931-2243<br>Fax 830/931-0371 |
| Medina Valley Lacoste ES<br>16069 Uvalde St, La Coste 78039<br>Elizabeth Vera | PK-5 | T | 487<br>20 | 62% | 830/931-2243<br>Fax 830/985-3732 |
| Medina Valley Middle Sch<br>8395 FM 471 S, Castroville 78009<br>Lesli Solis | 6-8 | T | 609<br>38 | 55% | 830/931-2243<br>Fax 830/931-3258 |
| Potranco Elem Sch<br>190 County Road 381 S, San Antonio 78253<br>Sandy Bermea | PK-5 | T | 634 | 43% | 830/931-2243<br>Fax 210/579-1083 |

- **Natalia Ind School Dist** PID: 01041320     830/663-4416
805 Pearson St, Natalia 78059     Fax 830/663-4186

**Schools:** 4 \ **Teachers:** 77 \ **Students:** 1,000 \ **Special Ed Students:** 93 \ **LEP Students:** 82 \ **College-Bound:** 48% \ **Ethnic:** Hispanic 84%, Caucasian 16% \ **Exp:** $494 (High) \ **Poverty:** 15% \ **Title I:** $245,961 \ **Special Education:** $114,000 \ **Open-Close:** 08/24 - 06/04 \ **DTBP:** $350 (High) \ **t**

| | | | |
|---|---|---|---|
| Lana Collavo | 1 | Aida Ramos | 2 |
| Norma Sriddle | 2 | Philip Riddle | 3 |
| Tonya Rodriguez | 4 | Ilyan Martinez | 6 |
| Lori Robinson | 8,271,285 | Carmen Maglievaz | 9* |
| Dr Andrea Moreno Hewitt | 10 | Edgar Camacho | 10* |
| Laticia Buenrostro | 11,58,288,296,298,752 | Eric Smith | 67 |
| Jennett Roberts | 73,286,295,297 | | |

| Public Schs..Principal | Grd | Prgm | Enr/#Cls | SN | |
|---|---|---|---|---|---|
| Early Childhood Center<br>8th & Pearson Streets, Natalia 78059<br>Carmen Maglievaz | PK-1 | | 167<br>17 | | 830/663-9739 |
| Natalia Elem Sch<br>8th & Pearson Streets, Natalia 78059<br>Carmen Maglievaz | 2-5 | T | 306<br>17 | 79% | 830/663-2837<br>Fax 830/663-9693 |
| Natalia High Sch<br>8th & Kearny St, Natalia 78059<br>Dr Andrea Moreno-Hewitt | 9-12 | ATV | 305<br>36 | 73% | 830/663-4417<br>Fax 830/663-6410 |
| Natalia Junior High Sch<br>8th & Pearson Streets, Natalia 78059<br>Edgar Camacho | 6-8 | T | 247<br>22 | 75% | 830/663-4027<br>Fax 830/663-2347 |

## MEDINA CATHOLIC SCHOOLS

- **Archdiocese San Antonio Ed Off** PID: 00999724
Listing includes only schools located in this county. See District Index for location of Diocesan Offices.

| Catholic Schs..Principal | Grd | Prgm | Enr/#Cls | SN | |
|---|---|---|---|---|---|
| St Louis Sch<br>607 Madrid St, Castroville 78009<br>Dr Jimmy Gouard | PK-5 | | 125<br>15 | | 830/931-3544<br>Fax 830/931-9016 |

## MEDINA PRIVATE SCHOOLS

| Private Schs..Principal | Grd | Prgm | Enr/#Cls | SN | |
|---|---|---|---|---|---|
| DayStar Academy<br>8406 FM 471 S, Castroville 78009<br>Jan Carnley | PK-1 | | 20 | | 830/931-0808 |

## MENARD COUNTY

### MENARD PUBLIC SCHOOLS

● **Menard Ind School Dist** PID: 01041368      325/396-2404
221 E San Saba St, Menard 76859      Fax 325/396-2143

**Schools:** 2 \ **Teachers:** 28 \ **Students:** 305 \ **Special Ed Students:** 26
\ **LEP Students:** 13 \ **College-Bound:** 94% \ **Ethnic:** African American
1%, Hispanic 48%, Caucasian 51% \ **Exp:** $782 (High) \ **Poverty:** 40% \
**Title I:** $175,709 \ **Open-Close:** 08/19 - 05/21 \ **DTBP:** $350 (High)

| | | |
|---|---|---|
| Amy Bannowsky ................................1 | Holly Bryan .................................2,68 | |
| Beau Tipton .................................3,5 | Johnny Whitson ...................16,73,295* | |
| Felicia Laxson ..............36,83,88,275* | Myghan Meadow ........................58 | |
| Arnold Saucedo .............................67 | | |

| Public Schs..Principal | Grd | Prgm | Enr/#Cls | SN | |
|---|---|---|---|---|---|
| Menard Elem Middle Sch<br>300 Gay St, Menard 76859<br>Amy Bannowsky | PK-8 | T | 223<br>17 | 73% 325/396-2348<br>Fax 325/396-2761 | |
| Menard High Sch<br>401 W Travis, Menard 76859<br>**Jacob Hand** | 9-12 | TV | 82<br>13 | 72% 325/396-2513<br>Fax 325/396-2053 | |

## MIDLAND COUNTY

### MIDLAND PUBLIC SCHOOLS

● **Greenwood Ind School Dist** PID: 01041394      432/683-6461
2700 FM 1379, Midland 79706      Fax 432/685-7804

**Schools:** 4 \ **Teachers:** 171 \ **Students:** 2,831 \ **Special Ed Students:** 199
\ **LEP Students:** 221 \ **College-Bound:** 66% \ **Ethnic:** African American
1%, Hispanic 50%, Caucasian 49% \ **Exp:** $454 (High) \ **Poverty:** 21% \
**Title I:** $557,648 \ **Open-Close:** 08/14 - 05/21 \ **DTBP:** $317 (High)

| | |
|---|---|
| Ariel Elliott ....................................1 | Byron Moreland .........................2,11,15 |
| Darrell Dodds ..............................2,15 | Brian Cooper ...............................3,15* |
| Sandra Smith .................................4* | Rusty Purser ...................................6* |
| Madelaine Gully ......................7,83,85* | Debra Kiehl ......................................8 |
| Mary Aldarado ........................57,271* | Heidi Delk ......................................59 |
| Justin Brooks ................................67 | Debbie Dodds ...........................73,295* |

| Public Schs..Principal | Grd | Prgm | Enr/#Cls | SN |
|---|---|---|---|---|
| Greenwood Elem Sch<br>2700 FM 1379, Midland 79706<br>Leslie Goodrum | PK-2 | T | 600<br>22 | 46% 432/685-7821<br>Fax 432/685-7822 |
| Greenwood High Sch<br>2700 FM 1379, Midland 79706<br>Stacy Jones | 9-12 | AV | 718<br>40 | 29% 432/685-7806<br>Fax 432/685-7814 |
| Greenwood Interm Sch<br>2700 FM 1379, Midland 79706<br>Crysten Hopkins | 3-5 | | 522 | 432/685-7819 |

| | | | | |
|---|---|---|---|---|
| James R Brooks Middle Sch<br>2700 FM 1379, Midland 79706<br>Kristi Brown-Griffin | 6-8 | | 846<br>30 | 40% 432/685-7837<br>Fax 432/253-6731 |

● **Midland Ind School Dist** PID: 01041423      432/689-1000
615 W Missouri Ave, Midland 79701      Fax 432/689-1932

**Schools:** 40 \ **Teachers:** 1,569 \ **Students:** 26,000 \
**Special Ed Students:** 1,892 \ **LEP Students:** 3,092 \ **College-Bound:** 58%
\ **Ethnic:** Asian 2%, African American 8%, Hispanic 64%, Caucasian
25% \ **Exp:** $205 (Med) \ **Poverty:** 13% \ **Title I:** $5,318,489 \
**Special Education:** $3,546,000 \ **Open-Close:** 08/19 - 05/28 \ **DTBP:** $197
(High)

| | |
|---|---|
| Orlando Riddick ...................................1 | Darla Moss ...................................2,19 |
| James Riggen .........................3,17,70,91 | Willie Tarleton .....................................5 |
| John Feldt .............................................6 | Imo Douglas ........................................7 |
| Patrick Jones ..................................8,18 | Diane Lopez .........................................9 |
| Lisa Neighbors .....................................9 | Jeff Horner ........................................10 |
| Teresa Moore ......................................11 | Debbie Shaw ................................20,23 |
| Kim Evans .....................................27,31* | Della Frye .........................................34 |
| Ron Moss ...........................................36 | Chris Hightower .................................39 |
| Rob Pena ...........................................42 | Wendy DeVault ..................................46 |
| Linda Hill ...........................................47 | Sylvia Bernal .....................................51 |
| Leticia Amaya ....................................57 | Dawn Miller ...................................58,77 |
| Debbie Oliver .....................................61 | Rick Davis .........................................67 |
| Tony DeLaRosa ..................................68 | Elaina Ladd .......................................71 |
| Michael Lloyd .....................................73 | Tom Holly .....................73,76,295,297 |
| Jill Rivera ..........................................74 | Tonia Hale .........................................76 |
| Judy Bridges .....................................81 | Claudia Alanis .................................294 |
| Josh Tipton ......................................297 | |

| Public Schs..Principal | Grd | Prgm | Enr/#Cls | SN |
|---|---|---|---|---|
| Abell Junior High Sch<br>3201 Heritage Blvd, Midland 79707<br>Cyndi Pyles | 7-8 | TV | 1,077<br>50 | 41% 432/689-6200<br>Fax 432/689-6217 |
| Alamo Junior High Sch<br>3800 Storey Ave, Midland 79703<br>Paul Hidalgo | 7-8 | TV | 841<br>50 | 51% 432/689-1700<br>Fax 432/689-1712 |
| Bonham Elem Sch<br>909 Bonham St, Midland 79703<br>Tricia Teran | PK-6 | T | 624<br>36 | 56% 432/240-6000<br>Fax 432/240-6001 |
| ⊛ Bowie Fine Arts Academy<br>805 Elk Ave, Midland 79701<br>Melissa Horner | K-6 | | 507<br>24 | 24% 432/240-6100<br>Fax 432/689-5121 |
| Bunche Elem Sch<br>700 S Jackson St, Midland 79701<br>Sha Burdsal | PK-6 | T | 768 | 77% 432/240-8600 |
| Burnet Elem Sch<br>900 Raymond Rd, Midland 79703<br>**Maribel Hernandez** | PK-6 | T | 471<br>29 | 71% 432/240-6200<br>Fax 432/689-1783 |
| Bush Elem Sch<br>5001 Preston Dr, Midland 79707<br>Aaron Fong | PK-6 | T | 479<br>23 | 51% 432/240-6300<br>Fax 432/689-1879 |
| Carver Center<br>1300 E Wall St, Midland 79701<br>Stephanie Carnett | Spec | | 511<br>20 | 11% 432/240-6400<br>Fax 432/689-1426 |
| Dezavala Elem Sch<br>705 N Lee St, Midland 79701<br>Julie Sims | PK-6 | T | 647<br>28 | 80% 432/240-6600<br>Fax 432/240-6601 |
| Early College High Sch-Midland<br>3600 N Garfield St, Midland 79705<br>Renee Aldrin | 9-12 | T | 352 | 47% 432/685-4641<br>Fax 432/685-4669 |
| Emerson Elem Sch<br>2800 Moss Ave, Midland 79705<br>Christine Reeves | PK-6 | T | 480<br>22 | 46% 432/240-6700<br>Fax 432/689-6271 |

| | | | | | | |
|---|---|---|---|---|---|---|
| 1 | Superintendent | 8 | Curric/Instruct K-12 | 19 | Chief Financial Officer | 29 | Family/Consumer Science | 39 | Social Studies K-12 | 49 | English/Lang Arts Elem | 59 | Special Education Elem | 69 | Academic Assessment |
| 2 | Bus/Finance/Purchasing | 9 | Curric/Instruct Elem | 20 | Art K-12 | 30 | Adult Education | 40 | Social Studies Elem | 50 | English/Lang Arts Sec | 60 | Special Education Sec | 70 | Research/Development |
| 3 | Buildings And Grounds | 10 | Curric/Instruct Sec | 21 | Art Elem | 31 | Career/Sch-to-Work K-12 | 41 | Social Studies Sec | 51 | Reading K-12 | 61 | Foreign/World Lang K-12 | 71 | Public Information |
| 4 | Food Service | 11 | Federal Program | 22 | Art Sec | 32 | Career/Sch-to-Work Elem | 42 | Science K-12 | 52 | Reading Elem | 62 | Foreign/World Lang Elem | 72 | Summer School |
| 5 | Transportation | 12 | Title I | 23 | Music K-12 | 33 | Career/Sch-to-Work Sec | 43 | Science Elem | 53 | Reading Sec | 63 | Foreign/World Lang Sec | 73 | Instructional Tech |
| 6 | Athletic | 13 | Title V | 24 | Music Elem | 34 | Early Childhood Ed | 44 | Science Sec | 54 | Remedial Reading K-12 | 64 | Religious Education K-12 | 74 | Inservice Training |
| 7 | Health Services | 15 | Asst Superintendent | 25 | Music Sec | 35 | Health/Phys Education | 45 | Math K-12 | 55 | Remedial Reading Elem | 65 | Religious Education Elem | 75 | Marketing/Distributive |
| | | 16 | Instructional Media Svcs | 26 | Business Education | 36 | Guidance Services K-12 | 46 | Math Elem | 56 | Remedial Reading Sec | 66 | Religious Education Sec | 76 | Info Systems |
| | | 17 | Chief Operations Officer | 27 | Career & Tech Ed | 37 | Guidance Services Elem | 47 | Math Sec | 57 | Bilingual/ELL | 67 | School Board President | 77 | Psychological Assess |
| | | 18 | Chief Academic Officer | 28 | Technology Education | 38 | Guidance Services Sec | 48 | English/Lang Arts K-12 | 58 | Special Education K-12 | 68 | Teacher Personnel | 78 | Affirmative Action |

| School | Grd | Prgm | Enr/#Cls | SN | Phone |
|--------|-----|------|----------|-----|-------|
| Fannin Elem Sch<br>2400 Fannin Ave, Midland 79705<br>**Lisa Cisneros** | PK-6 | | 525<br>35 | 34% | 432/240-6800<br>Fax 432/689-1346 |
| Fasken Elem Sch<br>5806 Val Verde Dr, Midland 79707<br>Dr Joshua Gamboa | PK-6 | | 749 | 39% | 432/240-8400 |
| Gen Tommy Franks Elem Sch<br>401 E Parker Ave, Midland 79701<br>Andra Jones | PK-6 | | 404<br>26 | 29% | 432/240-6500<br>Fax 432/689-1429 |
| Goddard Junior High Sch<br>2500 Haynes Dr, Midland 79705<br>Brandy Copeland | 7-8 | TV | 1,046<br>30 | 51% | 432/689-1300<br>Fax 432/689-1321 |
| Greathouse Elem Sch<br>5107 Greathouse Ave, Midland 79707<br>Tonya Sanchez | PK-6 | | 830<br>33 | 27% | 432/240-6900<br>Fax 432/689-6901 |
| Henderson Elem Sch<br>4800 Graceland Dr, Midland 79703<br>Ray Portillo | PK-6 | T | 386<br>40 | 55% | 432/240-7000<br>Fax 432/689-1807 |
| Jones Elem Sch<br>4919 Shadylane Dr, Midland 79703<br>**Amber Harmon** | PK-6 | T | 298<br>24 | 47% | 432/240-7200<br>Fax 432/240-7201 |
| Lamar Elem Sch<br>3200 Kessler Ave, Midland 79701<br>Amy Clark | PK-6 | T | 457<br>25 | 71% | 432/240-7300<br>Fax 432/689-1893 |
| Long Elem Sch<br>4200 Cedar Spring Dr, Midland 79703<br>Terri Rimer | PK-6 | T | 557<br>28 | 70% | 432/240-7400<br>Fax 432/689-1836 |
| Ⓐ Midland Alternative Program<br>2101 W Missouri Ave, Midland 79701<br>Angelina Buck | 7-12 | | 12 | 61% | 432/240-4700<br>Fax 432/240-4701 |
| Midland Freshman High Sch<br>101 E Gist Ave, Midland 79701<br>Shannon Torres | 9-9 | AT | 803 | 45% | 432/689-1200<br>Fax 432/689-1209 |
| Midland Senior High Sch<br>906 W Illinois Ave, Midland 79701<br>Leslie Sparacello | 9-12 | AV | 2,365<br>100 | 34% | 432/689-1100<br>Fax 432/689-1116 |
| Milam Elem Sch<br>301 E Dormard Ave, Midland 79705<br>Iliana Bermea | PK-6 | T | 439<br>30 | 77% | 432/240-7500<br>Fax 432/240-7501 |
| Parker Elem Sch<br>3800 Norwood St, Midland 79707<br>Tracie Burrow | PK-6 | T | 523<br>20 | 39% | 432/240-7600<br>Fax 432/240-7601 |
| Ⓜ Pease Communication/Tech Acad<br>1700 Magnolia Ave, Midland 79705<br>Gabriel Moya | K-6 | T | 583<br>26 | 57% | 432/240-7700<br>Fax 432/240-7701 |
| Ⓒ Pre-K Academy at Midland Clg<br>3600 N Garfield St, Midland 79705<br>Lori Smith | PK-PK | | 401 | | 432/685-4500 |
| Robert E Lee Freshman High Sch<br>1400 E Oak Ave, Midland 79705<br>**Judi Tarlton** | 9-9 | TV | 853<br>52 | 36% | 432/689-1250<br>Fax 432/689-1253 |
| Robert E Lee Sr High Sch<br>3500 Neely Ave, Midland 79707<br>Stan Vanhoozer | 9-12 | AV | 2,288<br>100 | 30% | 432/689-1600<br>Fax 432/689-1647 |
| Rusk Elem Sch<br>2601 Wedgwood St, Midland 79707<br>Dora Flores | PK-6 | T | 379<br>22 | 50% | 432/240-7800<br>Fax 432/240-7801 |
| Sam Houston Elem Sch<br>2000 W Louisiana Ave, Midland 79701<br>Stephanie Ramos | PK-6 | T | 464<br>31 | 54% | 432/240-7100<br>Fax 432/689-5026 |
| San Jacinto Junior High Sch<br>1400 N N St, Midland 79701<br>**Jessica Gore** | 6-8 | TV | 528 | 48% | 432/689-1350<br>Fax 432/689-1385 |
| Santa Rita Elem Sch<br>5306 Whitman Dr, Midland 79705<br>Debra Alba | PK-6 | | 515<br>27 | 35% | 432/240-7900<br>Fax 432/689-5094 |

| School | Grd | Prgm | Enr/#Cls | SN | Phone |
|--------|-----|------|----------|-----|-------|
| Scharbauer Elem Sch<br>2115 Hereford Blvd, Midland 79707<br>Sharla Butler | PK-6 | T | 758<br>27 | 49% | 432/240-8000<br>Fax 432/689-6286 |
| South Elem Sch<br>200 W Dakota Ave, Midland 79701<br>Juan Dominguez | PK-6 | T | 598<br>26 | 81% | 432/240-8100<br>Fax 432/689-1539 |
| Travis Elem Sch<br>900 E Gist Ave, Midland 79701<br>Terri Matthews | PK-6 | T | 679<br>32 | 81% | 432/240-8200<br>Fax 432/689-5054 |
| Ⓐ Viola M Coleman High Sch<br>1600 E Golf Course Rd, Midland 79701<br>David Moore | 9-12 | T | 107<br>10 | 62% | 432/689-5000<br>Fax 432/689-5016 |
| Ⓜ Washington STEM Academy<br>1800 E Wall St, Midland 79701<br>Ann Newton | K-6 | T | 474<br>23 | 45% | 432/240-8300<br>Fax 432/689-1593 |
| Yarbrough Elem Sch<br>6000 Riverfront Dr, Midland 79706<br>Jill Arthur | PK-6 | T | 714 | 42% | 432/240-8500<br>Fax 432/240-8501 |
| Young Women's Leadership Acad<br>126 Thornridge Dr, Midland 79703<br>Jennifer Seybert | 6-7 | | 100 | | 432/240-8700 |

## MIDLAND CATHOLIC SCHOOLS

- **Diocese of San Angelo Ed Off** PID: 01055929
  Listing includes only schools located in this county. See District Index for location of Diocesan Offices.

| Catholic Schs..Principal | Grd | Prgm | Enr/#Cls | SN | Phone |
|--------------------------|-----|------|----------|-----|-------|
| St Ann's Sch<br>2000 W Texas Ave, Midland 79701<br>Joan Wilmes | PK-8 | G | 363<br>30 | | 432/684-4563<br>Fax 432/687-2468<br>f |

## MIDLAND PRIVATE SCHOOLS

| Private Schs..Principal | Grd | Prgm | Enr/#Cls | SN | Phone |
|-------------------------|-----|------|----------|-----|-------|
| Ⓨ Bynum Sch<br>8404 W County Road 60, Midland 79707<br>Keri St John | PK-12 | M | 45 | | 432/520-0075 |
| Hillander Sch<br>1600 W Wadley Ave, Midland 79705<br>Buffy Meadore | PK-6 | | 300<br>20 | | 432/684-8681<br>Fax 432/684-3863 |
| Hillcrest Sch<br>2800 N A St, Midland 79705<br>Betty Starnes | Spec | | 112<br>8 | | 432/570-7444<br>Fax 432/684-9675<br>f |
| Midland Christian Sch<br>2001 Culver Dr, Midland 79705<br>Cristin Coulter \ Laura Eves \ Dana Ellis \ Jumon Hailey | PK-12 | | 1,250 | | 432/694-1661<br>Fax 432/694-5281 |
| Midland Classical Academy<br>5711 Whitman Dr, Midland 79705<br>Amy Avampato | K-12 | | 500 | | 432/694-0995<br>Fax 432/694-0978 |
| Trinity School of Midland<br>3500 W Wadley Ave, Midland 79707<br>Chrystal Myers \ Tim Jones | K-12 | | 620<br>70 | | 432/697-3281<br>Fax 432/697-7403 |

| | | | | |
|---|---|---|---|---|
| 79 Student Personnel | 91 Safety/Security | 275 Response To Intervention | 298 Grant Writer/Ptnrships | **School Programs** |
| 80 Driver Ed/Safety | 92 Magnet School | 277 Remedial Math K-12 | 750 Chief Innovation Officer | **A** = Alternative Program |
| 81 Gifted/Talented | 93 Parental Involvement | 280 Literacy Coach | 751 Chief of Staff | **G** = Adult Classes |
| 82 Video Services | 95 Tech Prep Program | 285 STEM | 752 Social Emotional Learning | **M** = Magnet Program |
| 83 Substance Abuse Prev | 97 Chief Information Officer | 286 Digital Learning | | **T** = Title I Schoolwide |
| 84 Erate | 98 Chief Technology Officer | 288 Common Core Standards | **Other School Types** | **V** = Career & Tech Ed Programs |
| 85 AIDS Education | 270 Character Education | 294 Accountability | Ⓐ = Alternative School | |
| 88 Alternative/At Risk | 271 Migrant Education | 295 Network System | Ⓒ = Charter School | **New Schools are shaded** |
| 89 Multi-Cultural Curriculum | 273 Teacher Mentor | 296 Title II Programs | Ⓜ = Magnet School | **New Superintendents and Principals are bold** |
| 90 Social Work | 274 Before/After Sch | 297 Webmaster | Ⓨ = Year-Round School | **Personnel with email addresses are underscored** |

**Social Media**

f = Facebook

t = Twitter

## MIDLAND REGIONAL CENTERS

- **Region 18 Ed Service Center** PID: 01041693　　432/563-2380
  2811 La Force Blvd, Midland 79706　　　　　　Fax 432/567-3290

DeWitt Smith .............................................1 　Britt Hayes ........................................................2
Nicole Gabriel .........................7,8,73,74,85 　Kirsty Hall ......................................................16
Linda Jolly ..............................................58 　Nancy Dunnam ..............................................76

## MILAM COUNTY

## MILAM PUBLIC SCHOOLS

- **Buckholts Ind School Dist** PID: 01041722　　254/593-3011
  203 S 10th St, Buckholts 76518　　　　　　　Fax 254/593-2270

**Schools:** 1 \ **Teachers:** 14 \ **Students:** 132 \ **Special Ed Students:** 20
\ **LEP Students:** 3 \ **College-Bound:** 50% \ **Ethnic:** Hispanic 59%,
Caucasian 41% \ **Exp:** $527 (High) \ **Poverty:** 28% \ **Title I:** $89,779 \
**Open-Close:** 08/17 - 05/21 \ **DTBP:** $338 (High)

**Joe Oliver** ......................................1,11 　Sherry Lopez .............................................2,68
Cindy Hernandez .......................................4 　Kyle Hauk ........................................................6
Adam Losoya ...........................................67 　Marcus Lee ....................................................73
Dr Remy Godfrey ....................................752

| Public Schs..Principal | Grd | Prgm | Enr/#Cls | SN | |
|---|---|---|---|---|---|
| Buckholts Sch | PK-12 | TV | 132 | 73% | 254/593-2744 |
| 203 S 10th St, Buckholts 76518 | | | 25 | | |
| Kris Shaver | | | | | |

- **Cameron Ind School Dist** PID: 01041758　　254/697-3512
  304 E 12th St, Cameron 76520　　　　　　　Fax 254/697-2448

**Schools:** 4 \ **Teachers:** 130 \ **Students:** 1,684 \ **Special Ed Students:** 147
\ **LEP Students:** 159 \ **College-Bound:** 56% \ **Ethnic:** African American
17%, Hispanic 50%, Caucasian 33% \ **Exp:** $681 (High) \ **Poverty:** 29% \
**Title I:** $876,486 \ **Open-Close:** 08/19 - 05/27 \ **DTBP:** $350 (High) \ f

Kevin Sprinkles ........................................1 　Missi Giesenschlag .........................................2
Abbie Hanke .............................................4 　Tommy Brashear ..............................................6
Mistie Dakroub ........................................15 　Jason Dohnalik ...............................................67
Jerrica Mendoza ......................................68

| Public Schs..Principal | Grd | Prgm | Enr/#Cls | SN | |
|---|---|---|---|---|---|
| Ben Milam Elem Sch | PK-2 | T | 413 | 83% | 254/697-3641 |
| 1100 E 21st St, Cameron 76520 | | | 25 | | Fax 254/605-0354 |
| Tracey Jordan | | | | | |
| C H Yoe High Sch | 9-12 | ATV | 494 | 71% | 254/697-3902 |
| 303 E 12th St, Cameron 76520 | | | | | Fax 254/605-0413 |
| Brian Stork | | | | | |
| Cameron Elem Sch | 3-5 | T | 400 | 76% | 254/697-2381 |
| 404 E 22nd St, Cameron 76520 | | | 23 | | Fax 254/605-0356 |
| Wendy Mahan | | | | | f |
| Cameron Junior High Sch | 6-8 | ATV | 377 | 75% | 254/697-2131 |
| 404 E 22nd St, Cameron 76520 | | | 27 | | Fax 254/605-0379 |
| Wendy Mahan | | | | | |

- **Gause Ind School Dist** PID: 01041801　　979/279-5891
  400 College St, Gause 77857　　　　　　　Fax 979/279-5142

**Schools:** 1 \ **Teachers:** 15 \ **Students:** 170 \ **Special Ed Students:** 14
\ **LEP Students:** 21 \ **Ethnic:** Asian 2%, African American 10%, Hispanic
42%, Caucasian 46% \ **Exp:** $791 (High) \ **Poverty:** 24% \ **Title I:** $70,184 \
**Open-Close:** 08/13 - 05/21 \ **DTBP:** $150 (High)

Brad Jones ...........................................1,11 　Diane Lazrine ...................................................2
Sondra Sheppard ......................................4 　Lynnette Taylor ...................................16,73,295*
Theresa Russell ......................................57 　Samantha Russell .................................59,275*
Bill Jones ...............................................67

| Public Schs..Principal | Grd | Prgm | Enr/#Cls | SN | |
|---|---|---|---|---|---|
| Gause Elem Sch | PK-8 | TV | 170 | 72% | 979/279-5891 |
| 400 College St, Gause 77857 | | | 17 | | |
| Brad Jones | | | | | |

- **Milano Ind School Dist** PID: 01041825　　512/455-2533
  500 N 5th, Milano 76556　　　　　　　　Fax 512/455-9311

**Schools:** 3 \ **Teachers:** 43 \ **Students:** 419 \ **Special Ed Students:** 40
\ **LEP Students:** 23 \ **College-Bound:** 75% \ **Ethnic:** Asian 1%, African
American 5%, Hispanic 28%, Caucasian 66% \ **Exp:** $615 (High) \
**Poverty:** 22% \ **Title I:** $123,698 \ **Open-Close:** 08/20 - 05/27 \ **DTBP:** $368
(High)

Robert Westbrook ......................................1 　Stephanie Gage ..........................................2,11
Brad Hobson .............................................3 　Dana Gage .....................................................4*
Joey Gage .................................................5 　Wendy King ....................................................6*
Courtney Todd ............................12,57,296 　Catrina Steinbecker ..........36,69,79,83,85,88
Angie Brashear ........................................58 　John Yakesch ................................................67
Kevin Terry ........................................73,295* 　Charlotte Jones .............................................76

| Public Schs..Principal | Grd | Prgm | Enr/#Cls | SN | |
|---|---|---|---|---|---|
| Milano Elem Sch | PK-5 | T | 163 | 63% | 512/455-2062 |
| 500 N 5th, Milano 76556 | | | 13 | | Fax 512/455-1204 |
| Courtney Todd | | | | | |
| Milano High Sch | 9-12 | TV | 173 | 50% | 512/455-9333 |
| 600 N 6th St, Milano 76556 | | | 14 | | Fax 512/455-1202 |
| Catrina Steinbecker | | | | | f t |
| Milano Junior High Sch | 6-8 | T | 110 | 57% | 512/455-6701 |
| 600 N 6th St, Milano 76556 | | | 10 | | Fax 512/455-1203 |
| Clint Mc Mahon | | | | | |

- **Rockdale Ind School Dist** PID: 01041851　　512/430-6000
  520 Davilla Street, Rockdale 76567　　　　Fax 512/446-3460

**Schools:** 4 \ **Teachers:** 115 \ **Students:** 1,432 \ **Special Ed Students:** 135
\ **LEP Students:** 77 \ **College-Bound:** 49% \ **Ethnic:** Asian 1%, African
American 9%, Hispanic 50%, Caucasian 40% \ **Exp:** $356 (High) \
**Poverty:** 21% \ **Title I:** $508,606 \ **Open-Close:** 08/14 - 05/28 \ **DTBP:** $350
(High) \ f t

Dr Denise Monzingo ..................................1 　Genelle Korenek ..............................................2
Lance Weidler ...........................................3 　Sheri Wheeler ..................................................4
Robert Hunter ...........................................5 　Jeff Miller .........................................................6
Keari Spence .............................................7* 　Pam Kaufmann .........8,11,15,58,288,296,298
Rebecca King ...............................16,73,286 　Bretina Pesak ................................................27
Kelly Windham .........................................38* 　Micki Daniels .................................................57
Troy Zinn .................................................67 　Keely Reisner ..........................................69,77*
Ken Sweich ...............................73,76,295 　Allen Sanders ................................................83

| 1 | Superintendent | 8 | Curric/Instruct K-12 | 19 | Chief Financial Officer | 29 | Family/Consumer Science | 39 | Social Studies K-12 | 49 | English/Lang Arts Elem | 59 | Special Education Elem | 69 | Academic Assessment |
|---|---|---|---|---|---|---|---|---|---|---|---|---|---|---|---|
| 2 | Bus/Finance/Purchasing | 9 | Curric/Instruct Elem | 20 | Art K-12 | 30 | Adult Education | 40 | Social Studies Elem | 50 | English/Lang Arts Sec | 60 | Special Education Sec | 70 | Research/Development |
| 3 | Buildings And Grounds | 10 | Curric/Instruct Sec | 21 | Art Elem | 31 | Career/Sch-to-Work K-12 | 41 | Social Studies Sec | 51 | Reading K-12 | 61 | Foreign/World Lang K-12 | 71 | Public Information |
| 4 | Food Service | 11 | Federal Program | 22 | Art Sec | 32 | Career/Sch-to-Work Elem | 42 | Science K-12 | 52 | Reading Elem | 62 | Foreign/World Lang Elem | 72 | Summer School |
| 5 | Transportation | 12 | Title I | 23 | Music K-12 | 33 | Career/Sch-to-Work Sec | 43 | Science Elem | 53 | Reading Sec | 63 | Foreign/World Lang Sec | 73 | Instructional Tech |
| 6 | Athletic | 13 | Title V | 24 | Music Elem | 34 | Early Childhood Ed | 44 | Science Sec | 54 | Remedial Reading K-12 | 64 | Religious Education K-12 | 74 | Inservice Training |
| 7 | Health Services | 15 | Asst Superintendent | 25 | Music Sec | 35 | Health/Phys Education | 45 | Math K-12 | 55 | Remedial Reading Elem | 65 | Religious Education Elem | 75 | Marketing/Distributive |
| | | 16 | Instructional Media Svcs | 26 | Business Education | 36 | Guidance Services K-12 | 46 | Math Elem | 56 | Remedial Reading Sec | 66 | Religious Education Sec | 76 | Info Systems |
| | | 17 | Chief Operations Officer | 27 | Career & Tech Ed | 37 | Guidance Services Elem | 47 | Math Sec | 57 | Bilingual/ELL | 67 | School Board President | 77 | Psychological Assess |
| | | 18 | Chief Academic Officer | 28 | Technology Education | 38 | Guidance Services Sec | 48 | English/Lang Arts K-12 | 58 | Special Education K-12 | 68 | Teacher Personnel | 78 | Affirmative Action |

| Public Schs..Principal | Grd | Prgm | Enr/#Cls | SN | |
|---|---|---|---|---|---|
| Rockdale Elem Sch<br>625 W Belton Ave, Rockdale 76567<br>Alesha Eoff | PK-2 | T | 311<br>65 | 83% | 512/430-6030<br>Fax 512/446-5229 |
| Rockdale High Sch<br>500 Childress Dr, Rockdale 76567<br>Brent Hasselbach | 9-12 | TV | 434<br>30 | 65% | 512/430-6140<br>Fax 512/446-3512<br>f t |
| Rockdale Intermediate Sch<br>1338 W US Highway 79, Rockdale 76567<br>Kathy Pelzel | 3-5 | T | 334<br>21 | 74% | 512/430-6200<br>Fax 512/446-3682 |
| Rockdale Junior High Sch<br>814 Bushdale Rd, Rockdale 76567<br>Kelly Blair | 6-8 | T | 353<br>28 | 68% | 512/430-6100<br>Fax 512/446-2597<br>f t |

• **Thorndale Ind School Dist** PID: 01041904    512/898-2538
300 N Main St, Thorndale 76577    Fax 512/898-5356

**Schools:** 3 \ **Teachers:** 52 \ **Students:** 650 \ **Special Ed Students:** 54 \ **LEP Students:** 36 \ **College-Bound:** 50% \ **Ethnic:** African American 2%, Hispanic 26%, Caucasian 72% \ **Exp:** $355 (High) \ **Poverty:** 14% \ **Title I:** $91,141 \ **Open-Close:** 08/17 - 05/28 \ **DTBP:** $375 (High)

| | | | |
|---|---|---|---|
| Adam Ivy ......................1,11 | | Rebecca Peel .................................2 | |
| Russell Ellington ..............3 | | Bradley Dickerson ..........................6* | |
| Scott Hawkins ..............6* | | John Kovar ...............................11,83* | |
| Tricia Cabrera ..............36,88 | | Susan Sekaqattewa ......................57 | |
| David Hall ....................67 | | Lisa Todd .................................68 | |
| Jennifer Parnum ...........69* | | Deby Leschber ...............73,286,295 | |

| Public Schs..Principal | Grd | Prgm | Enr/#Cls | SN | |
|---|---|---|---|---|---|
| Thorndale Elem Sch<br>300 N Main St, Thorndale 76577<br>Michael Young | PK-5 | T | 192<br>10 | 63% | 512/898-2912<br>Fax 512/898-5541 |
| Thorndale High Sch<br>300 N Main St, Thorndale 76577<br>Jennifer Parnum | 9-12 | V | 226<br>30 | 41% | 512/898-2321<br>Fax 512/898-5090 |
| Thorndale Middle Sch<br>300 N Main St, Thorndale 76577<br>Scott Frei | 6-8 | TV | 115<br>9 | 51% | 512/898-2670<br>Fax 512/898-5505 |

## MILAM PRIVATE SCHOOLS

| Private Schs..Principal | Grd | Prgm | Enr/#Cls | SN | |
|---|---|---|---|---|---|
| St Paul Lutheran Sch<br>101 N 3rd St, Thorndale 76577<br>David Mueller | PK-8 | | 97<br>6 | | 512/898-2711<br>Fax 512/898-5298 |

## MILAM REGIONAL CENTERS

• **Burleson Milam Spec Serv Co-op** PID: 11551771    512/455-7801
400 E Park St, Milano 76556    Fax 512/455-9681

Angie Brashear ..........................................1

## MILLS COUNTY

## MILLS PUBLIC SCHOOLS

• **Goldthwaite Consolidated ISD** PID: 01041942    325/648-3531
1509 Hanna Valley Rd, Goldthwaite 76844    Fax 325/648-2456

**Schools:** 3 \ **Teachers:** 62 \ **Students:** 555 \ **Special Ed Students:** 68 \ **LEP Students:** 32 \ **Ethnic:** Asian 1%, Hispanic 28%, Caucasian 71% \ **Exp:** $1,039 (High) \ **Poverty:** 16% \ **Title I:** $322,128 \ **Open-Close:** 08/10 - 05/20 \ **DTBP:** $338 (High)

| | | | |
|---|---|---|---|
| Ronny Wright ..............................1,11,83 | | Glenn Benningfield .................................2 | |
| Erik Edwards .............................3 | | Becky Stewart .................................4 | |
| Becky Stewart ...........................4* | | Angie Hermesmeyer .....................6,285* | |
| Keith Virdell ............................6* | | Leslie Watson ...............................7,85 | |
| Cheryl Wright ..........36,69,88,270,271* | | Rosalinda Martinez ......................57* | |
| Donna Sanders .........................58 | | Keri Roberts .................................67 | |
| Jenice Benningfield .............73,84,298 | | Annette Watson ..........................286* | |

| Public Schs..Principal | Grd | Prgm | Enr/#Cls | SN | |
|---|---|---|---|---|---|
| Goldthwaite Elem Sch<br>1501 Campbell Street, Goldthwaite 76844<br>Arla Wright | PK-5 | T | 226<br>20 | 50% | 325/648-3055<br>Fax 325/648-3528 |
| Goldthwaite High Sch<br>1509 Hanna Valley Rd, Goldthwaite 76844<br>Rusty Hollingsworth | 9-12 | TV | 176<br>20 | 36% | 325/648-3081<br>Fax 325/648-2325 |
| Goldthwaite Middle Sch<br>1507 Trent St, Goldthwaite 76844<br>Michael Sanderson | 6-8 | T | 140<br>14 | 43% | 325/648-3630<br>Fax 325/648-3571 |

• **Mullin Ind School Dist** PID: 01041978    855/467-0030
403 W Bulldog Dr, Mullin 76864    Fax 855/467-0776

**Schools:** 6 \ **Teachers:** 36 \ **Students:** 294 \ **Special Ed Students:** 95 \ **LEP Students:** 17 \ **College-Bound:** 70% \ **Ethnic:** Asian 1%, African American 23%, Hispanic 33%, Native American: 1%, Caucasian 42% \ **Exp:** $1,639 (High) \ **Poverty:** 31% \ **Title I:** $122,297 \ **Special Education:** $83,000 \ **Open-Close:** 08/28 - 06/25 \ **DTBP:** $392 (High)

| | | | |
|---|---|---|---|
| Kristi Mickelson ...........................1,73 | | Jesse Griffin .................................2* | |
| Patricia Eldridge .........................4* | | Kristi Mickelson ..........8,11,83,271,294* | |
| Justin Hopkins ...........................42* | | Becky Nelson ...............................57* | |
| Marion Ferguson .........................67 | | Thomas Gravey .............................273 | |

| Public Schs..Principal | Grd | Prgm | Enr/#Cls | SN | |
|---|---|---|---|---|---|
| Mullin Elem Sch<br>403 W Bulldog Dr, Mullin 76864<br>Bryndan Wright | PK-6 | T | 34 | 80% | 325/985-3374<br>Fax 325/985-3372 |
| Mullin Middle High Sch<br>403 W Bulldog Dr, Mullin 76864<br>Chayden Feist | 7-12 | ATV | 37<br>24 | 84% | 855/467-0030 |
| Ⓐ Mullin Oaks Sch<br>800 FM 3254, Brownwood 76801<br>**Chayden Feist** | 9-12 | T | 91 | 97% | 325/203-5315<br>Fax 325/203-5316 |
| Ⓐ Parkview School-Levelland<br>1515 5th St, Levelland 79336<br>Jesse Jalomo | K-12 | | 20 | | 806/568-1420<br>Fax 806/568-1431 |

---

| | |
|---|---|
| 79 Student Personnel | 91 Safety/Security |
| 80 Driver Ed/Safety | 92 Magnet School |
| 81 Gifted/Talented | 93 Parental Involvement |
| 82 Video Services | 95 Tech Prep Program |
| 83 Substance Abuse Prev | 97 Chief Infomation Officer |
| 84 Erate | 98 Chief Technology Officer |
| 85 AIDS Education | 270 Character Education |
| 88 Alternative/At Risk | 271 Migrant Education |
| 89 Multi-Cultural Curriculum | 273 Teacher Mentor |
| 90 Social Work | 274 Before/After Sch |

| | |
|---|---|
| 275 Response To Intervention | 298 Grant Writer/Ptnrships |
| 277 Remedial Math K-12 | 750 Chief Innovation Officer |
| 280 Literacy Coach | 751 Chief of Staff |
| 285 STEM | 752 Social Emotional Learning |
| 286 Digital Learning | |
| 288 Common Core Standards | **Other School Types** |
| 294 Accountability | Ⓐ = Alternative School |
| 295 Network System | Ⓒ = Charter School |
| 296 Title II Programs | Ⓜ = Magnet School |
| 297 Webmaster | Ⓨ = Year-Round School |

**School Programs**
A = Alternative Program
G = Adult Classes
M = Magnet Program
T = Title I Schoolwide
V = Career & Tech Ed Programs

New Schools are shaded
New Superintendents and Principals are bold
Personnel with email addresses are underscored

**Social Media**
f = Facebook
t = Twitter

# TX—291

| | | | | | |
|---|---|---|---|---|---|
| Parkview School-Lubbock<br>2402 Canyon Lake Dr, Lubbock 79415<br>Dr Jesse Jalomo | K-12 | T | 17 | 92% | 806/568-1420<br>Fax 806/568-1072 |
| Ⓐ Pecan Ridge High Sch<br>206 S Wallace Creek Rd, San Saba 76877<br>Sara McDowell | 9-12 | T | 94 | 97% | 325/372-4092 |

● **Priddy Ind School Dist** PID: 01042001
1375 Highway 16, Priddy 76870

325/966-3323
Fax 325/966-3380

---

**Schools:** 1 \ **Teachers:** 14 \ **Students:** 115 \ **Special Ed Students:** 15 \
**College-Bound:** 25% \ **Ethnic:** Hispanic 28%, Caucasian 72% \ **Exp:** $628
(High) \ **Poverty:** 20% \ **Title I:** $20,725 \ **Open-Close:** 08/14 - 05/20 \
**DTBP:** $346 (High) \ 🅕

---

| | | |
|---|---|---|
| Dr Adrianne Burden ........1,11,57,73,83,84 | Melanie Connally ..................2 | |
| Curtis Hurst ........6 | Landon Buffe ........27* | |
| Stephanie Smith ........58* | Dean Cagle ........67 | |
| Rachel Dudley ........71 | Tani Menchaca ........271 | |
| John Smith ........286* | | |

| Public Schs..Principal | Grd | Prgm | Enr/#Cls | SN | |
|---|---|---|---|---|---|
| Priddy Sch<br>1375 Highway 16, Priddy 76870<br>Carl Spruell | PK-12 | TV | 115<br>13 | 60% | 325/966-3323 |

---

# MITCHELL COUNTY

---

## MITCHELL PUBLIC SCHOOLS

● **Colorado Ind School Dist** PID: 01042063
534 E 11th St, Colorado City 79512

325/728-5312
Fax 325/728-1015

---

**Schools:** 4 \ **Teachers:** 65 \ **Students:** 900 \ **Special Ed Students:** 114
\ **LEP Students:** 32 \ **College-Bound:** 51% \ **Ethnic:** Asian 1%, African
American 9%, Hispanic 46%, Caucasian 43% \ **Exp:** $718 (High) \
**Poverty:** 24% \ **Title I:** $302,997 \ **Open-Close:** 08/13 - 05/19 \ **DTBP:** $341
(High)

---

| | | |
|---|---|---|
| Reggy Spencer ........1 | Shelia Redwine ........2,11 | |
| Becky Sanford ........4 | Robert Oliver ........5 | |
| Dan Gainey ........6* | Kelsee Graham ........7,85* | |
| Denise Farmer ........8,12,15,83,88,296 | Jody Womack ........37* | |
| Kaci Griffith ........38* | Sally Neff ........67 | |
| Bradley Graham ........73,295 | | |

| Public Schs..Principal | Grd | Prgm | Enr/#Cls | SN | |
|---|---|---|---|---|---|
| Colorado Elem Sch<br>1244 E 10th St, Colorado City 79512<br>Melinda Alexander | PK-2 | | 284<br>19 | | 325/728-3471<br>Fax 325/728-1036 |
| Colorado High Sch<br>1500 Lone Wolf Blvd, Colorado City 79512<br>Rebecca Russell | 9-12 | T | 129<br>30 | 57% | 325/728-3424<br>Fax 325/728-1068 |
| Colorado Middle Sch<br>1244 E 10th St, Colorado City 79512<br>Robby Russell | 3-8 | T | 426<br>20 | 65% | 325/728-2673<br>Fax 325/728-1051 |
| Wallace Accelerated High Sch<br>149 S Highway 208, Colorado City 79512<br>Steven Reese | 9-12 | T | 13 | | 325/728-2392<br>Fax 325/728-1025 |

● **Loraine Ind School Dist** PID: 01042128
800 S Lightfoot St, Loraine 79532

325/737-2225
Fax 325/737-2701

---

**Schools:** 1 \ **Teachers:** 18 \ **Students:** 142 \ **Special Ed Students:** 25 \
**LEP Students:** 5 \ **College-Bound:** 50% \ **Ethnic:** African American 7%,
Hispanic 59%, Native American: 1%, Caucasian 32% \ **Exp:** $549 (High) \
**Poverty:** 21% \ **Title I:** $85,922 \ **Open-Close:** 08/19 - 05/21 \ **DTBP:** $408
(High)

---

| | | |
|---|---|---|
| Dustin Anders ........1 | Debbie Finley ........2 | |
| Teresa Bruton ........4* | Jacob Popham ........6* | |
| Michael Barrientez ........31* | Jana Edmonds ........58* | |
| Ron Gibson ........67 | John Rawlings ........73,295 | |

| Public Schs..Principal | Grd | Prgm | Enr/#Cls | SN | |
|---|---|---|---|---|---|
| Loraine Sch<br>800 S Lightfoot St, Loraine 79532<br>Dustin Anders | PK-12 | TV | 142<br>21 | 78% | 325/737-2225 |

● **Westbrook Ind School Dist** PID: 01042154
102 Bertner St, Westbrook 79565

325/644-2311
Fax 325/644-5101

---

**Schools:** 1 \ **Teachers:** 25 \ **Students:** 272 \ **Special Ed Students:** 27 \
**LEP Students:** 3 \ **College-Bound:** 50% \ **Ethnic:** Hispanic 33%, Native
American: 1%, Caucasian 65% \ **Exp:** $1,503 (High) \ **Poverty:** 36% \
**Title I:** $74,198 \ **Open-Close:** 08/14 - 05/21 \ **DTBP:** $374 (High)

---

| | | |
|---|---|---|
| Todd Burleson ........1 | Leslie Moody ........2 | |
| Nick Lopez ........3,5* | Jackie Waldrep ........4* | |
| Jim Hill ........6* | Sherry Rowden ........8* | |
| Peggy Hill ........12,57* | Carolyn Redwine ........16,82* | |
| Hayden Walters ........58* | Tina Miles ........59* | |
| Renee Dawson ........67 | Jackie White ........73* | |

| Public Schs..Principal | Grd | Prgm | Enr/#Cls | SN | |
|---|---|---|---|---|---|
| Westbrook Sch<br>102 Bertner St, Westbrook 79565<br>Sherry Rowden | PK-12 | T | 272<br>16 | 24% | 325/644-2311<br>Fax 325/644-5501 |

---

# MONTAGUE COUNTY

---

## MONTAGUE PUBLIC SCHOOLS

● **Bowie Ind School Dist** PID: 01042180
100 W Wichita St, Bowie 76230

940/872-1151
Fax 940/872-5979

---

**Schools:** 4 \ **Teachers:** 122 \ **Students:** 1,720 \ **Special Ed Students:** 198
\ **LEP Students:** 94 \ **Ethnic:** Asian 1%, African American 1%, Hispanic 18%,
Native American: 1%, Caucasian 80% \ **Exp:** $418 (High) \ **Poverty:** 20% \
**Title I:** $416,428 \ **Special Education:** $4,000 \ **Open-Close:** 08/21 - 05/21 \
**DTBP:** $369 (High)

---

| | | |
|---|---|---|
| Blake Enlow ........1 | John Meek ........3 | |
| Lauri Crescenzo ........5 | Christie Walker ........8,11,57,58,77,88,288,294 | |
| Brant Farris ........16,286,297 | Jacky Betts ........67 | |
| Jim Britt ........73,84,295 | Brad Costello ........88 | |

---

| | | | | | | | | | |
|---|---|---|---|---|---|---|---|---|---|
| 1 | Superintendent | 8 | Curric/Instruct K-12 | 19 | Chief Financial Officer | 29 | Family/Consumer Science | 39 | Social Studies K-12 |
| 2 | Bus/Finance/Purchasing | 9 | Curric/Instruct Elem | 20 | Art K-12 | 30 | Adult Education | 40 | Social Studies Elem |
| 3 | Buildings And Grounds | 10 | Curric/Instruct Sec | 21 | Art Elem | 31 | Career/Sch-to-Work K-12 | 41 | Social Studies Sec |
| 4 | Food Service | 11 | Federal Program | 22 | Art Sec | 32 | Career/Sch-to-Work Elem | 42 | Science K-12 |
| 5 | Transportation | 12 | Title I | 23 | Music K-12 | 33 | Career/Sch-to-Work Sec | 43 | Science Elem |
| 6 | Athletic | 13 | Title V | 24 | Music Elem | 34 | Early Childhood Ed | 44 | Science Sec |
| 7 | Health Services | 14 | Instructional Media Svcs | 25 | Music Sec | 35 | Health/Phys Education | 45 | Math K-12 |
| | | 15 | Asst Superintendent | 26 | Business Education | 36 | Guidance Services K-12 | 46 | Math Elem |
| | | 16 | Instructional Media Svcs | 27 | Career & Tech Ed | 37 | Guidance Services Elem | 47 | Math Sec |
| | | 17 | Chief Operations Officer | 28 | Technology Education | 38 | Guidance Services Sec | 48 | English/Lang Arts K-12 |

| | | | | | |
|---|---|---|---|---|---|
| 49 | English/Lang Arts Elem | 59 | Special Education Elem | 69 | Academic Assessment |
| 50 | English/Lang Arts Sec | 60 | Special Education Sec | 70 | Research/Development |
| 51 | Reading K-12 | 61 | Foreign/World Lang K-12 | 71 | Public Information |
| 52 | Reading Elem | 62 | Foreign/World Lang Elem | 72 | Summer School |
| 53 | Reading Sec | 63 | Foreign/World Lang Sec | 73 | Instructional Tech |
| 54 | Remedial Reading K-12 | 64 | Religious Education K-12 | 74 | Inservice Training |
| 55 | Remedial Reading Elem | 65 | Religious Education Elem | 75 | Marketing/Distributive |
| 56 | Remedial Reading Sec | 66 | Religious Education Sec | 76 | Info Systems |
| 57 | Bilingual/ELL | 67 | School Board President | 77 | Psychological Assess |
| 58 | Special Education K-12 | 68 | Teacher Personnel | 78 | Affirmative Action |

| Public Schs..Principal | Grd | Prgm | Enr/#Cls | SN | |
|---|---|---|---|---|---|
| Bowie Elem Sch<br>405 Lovers Ln, Bowie 76230<br>Kathy Green | PK-2 | | 458<br>28 | | 940/689-2950<br>Fax 940/872-3041 |
| Bowie High Sch<br>341 US Highway 287 N Access Rd, Bowie 76230<br>Sergio Menchaca | 9-12 | TV | 507<br>50 | 44% | 940/689-2840<br>Fax 940/689-2922 |
| Bowie Intermediate Sch<br>800 N Mill St, Bowie 76230<br>Lee Farris | 3-5 | T | 382<br>40 | 57% | 940/689-2895<br>Fax 940/872-1299 |
| Bowie Junior High Sch<br>501 E Tarrant St, Bowie 76230<br>Jeneanne Fleming | 6-8 | T | 391<br>28 | 50% | 940/689-2975<br>Fax 940/872-8921 |

## ● Forestburg Ind School Dist PID: 01042257
16346 Highway 455 W, Forestburg 76239 — 940/964-2323 Fax 940/964-2531

**Schools:** 1 \ **Teachers:** 20 \ **Students:** 173 \ **Special Ed Students:** 29 \ **College-Bound:** 95% \ **Ethnic:** Hispanic 16%, Caucasian 84% \ **Exp:** $654 (High) \ **Poverty:** 17% \ **Title I:** $33,948 \ **Open-Close:** 08/14 - 05/21 \ **DTBP:** $350 (High) \ 🅵 🅴

John Metzler .............1  Cori Hayes .............6*
Candi Raney .............11*  Karen Wiley .............51,54,270*
Julie Sandusky .............58*  Jimmy Raney .............67
Rich Lewis .............73,286*

| Public Schs..Principal | Grd | Prgm | Enr/#Cls | SN | |
|---|---|---|---|---|---|
| Forestburg Sch<br>10346 Highway 455 W, Forestburg 76239<br>Karen Wiley | PK-12 | GTV | 173<br>25 | 54% | 940/964-2323 |

## ● Gold-Burg Ind School Dist PID: 01042283
468 Prater Rd, Bowie 76230 — 940/872-3562 Fax 940/872-5933

**Schools:** 1 \ **Teachers:** 15 \ **Students:** 127 \ **Special Ed Students:** 12 \ **LEP Students:** 5 \ **College-Bound:** 82% \ **Ethnic:** African American 3%, Hispanic 15%, Native American: 1%, Caucasian 81% \ **Exp:** $839 (High) \ **Poverty:** 20% \ **Title I:** $31,452 \ **Open-Close:** 08/17 - 05/21

Roger Ellis .............1  Carla Karl .............3*
Leo Murguia .............6  Thomas Flinchum .............8,11,36,69,83,88*
Charlotte Haley .............16,73,286*  David Winingham .............41*
Pam Demoss .............58*  Becky Case .............67

| Public Schs..Principal | Grd | Prgm | Enr/#Cls | SN | |
|---|---|---|---|---|---|
| Gold-Burg Sch<br>468 Prater Rd, Bowie 76230<br>**Chad Tallon** | PK-12 | TV | 127<br>18 | 67% | 940/872-3562 |

## ● Montague Ind School Dist PID: 01042312
8020 Highway 175, Montague 76251 — 940/894-2811 Fax 940/894-6605

**Schools:** 1 \ **Teachers:** 12 \ **Students:** 166 \ **Special Ed Students:** 13 \ **Ethnic:** Hispanic 7%, Caucasian 93% \ **Exp:** $490 (High) \ **Poverty:** 34% \ **Title I:** $45,645 \ **Open-Close:** 08/19 - 05/21 \ **DTBP:** $350 (High)

Carla Hennessey .............1,11,83  T Thompson .............2
Todd Minor .............3,5  Kelly Travis .............4
Angela Kleinhans .............16,73*  Taygon Jones .............67

| Public Schs..Principal | Grd | Prgm | Enr/#Cls | SN | |
|---|---|---|---|---|---|
| Montague Elem Sch<br>8020 Highway 175, Montague 76251<br>Angela Kleinhans | PK-8 | T | 166<br>8 | 42% | 940/894-2811 |

## ● Nocona Ind School Dist PID: 01042336
220 Clay St, Nocona 76255 — 940/825-3267 Fax 940/825-4945

**Schools:** 3 \ **Teachers:** 70 \ **Students:** 725 \ **Special Ed Students:** 104 \ **LEP Students:** 103 \ **College-Bound:** 63% \ **Ethnic:** Asian 1%, African American 1%, Hispanic 35%, Native American: 1%, Caucasian 64% \ **Exp:** $564 (High) \ **Poverty:** 19% \ **Title I:** $238,368 \ **Open-Close:** 08/14 - 05/28 \ **DTBP:** $358 (High)

David Waters .............1  Paula Peterson .............2
Jimmy Hill .............3  Norman Waters .............4
Walter Waters .............4  Mike Poore .............5
Guy Hill .............67  Malissa Swofford .............73,76,84

| Public Schs..Principal | Grd | Prgm | Enr/#Cls | SN | |
|---|---|---|---|---|---|
| Nocona Elem Sch<br>300 Montague St, Nocona 76255<br>Rod Bailey | PK-5 | T | 294<br>29 | 75% | 940/825-3151<br>Fax 940/825-4253 |
| Nocona High Sch<br>1012 Clay St, Nocona 76255<br>Stephanie Wright | 9-12 | TV | 264<br>34 | 51% | 940/825-3264<br>Fax 940/825-7270 |
| Nocona Middle Sch<br>220 Clay St, Nocona 76255<br>Amy Murphey | 6-8 | T | 167<br>12 | 66% | 940/825-3121<br>Fax 940/825-6151 |

## ● Prairie Valley Ind School Dist PID: 01042374
12920 FM 103, Nocona 76255 — 940/825-4425 Fax 940/825-4650

**Schools:** 1 \ **Teachers:** 16 \ **Students:** 167 \ **Special Ed Students:** 25 \ **College-Bound:** 75% \ **Ethnic:** Hispanic 9%, Caucasian 91% \ **Exp:** $288 (Med) \ **Poverty:** 17% \ **Title I:** $21,795 \ **Open-Close:** 08/14 - 05/21 \ **DTBP:** $181 (High)

Tim West .............1,84  Brittany Womack .............27*
Krysta Woods .............29*  Lisa Sadler .............58*
Jesse Kincy .............60*  Scott Carpenter .............67
Carol Luton .............69*  Stacey Ward .............73*
Cathy Harris .............79

| Public Schs..Principal | Grd | Prgm | Enr/#Cls | SN | |
|---|---|---|---|---|---|
| Prairie Valley Sch<br>12920 FM 103, Nocona 76255<br>Lisa Sadler | PK-12 | T | 167<br>18 | 58% | 940/825-4425 |

## ● St Jo Ind School Dist PID: 01042403
206 W Evans St, Saint Jo 76265 — 940/995-2668 Fax 940/995-2026

**Schools:** 2 \ **Teachers:** 29 \ **Students:** 330 \ **Special Ed Students:** 39 \ **LEP Students:** 3 \ **Ethnic:** Hispanic 10%, Native American: 1%, Caucasian 89% \ **Exp:** $472 (High) \ **Poverty:** 13% \ **Title I:** $45,536 \ **Open-Close:** 08/12 - 05/21 \ **DTBP:** $356 (High) \ 🅵 🅴

Curtis Elridge .............1  Andy Maas .............3,5
Kelly Durham .............36,69*  Leeton Phillips .............67
Julie Kline .............73,76,82*  Denise Thurman .............83*

| Public Schs..Principal | Grd | Prgm | Enr/#Cls | SN | |
|---|---|---|---|---|---|
| St Jo Elem Sch<br>206 W Evans St, Saint Jo 76265<br>Denise Thurman | PK-6 | T | 152<br>11 | 53% | 940/995-2541 |
| St Jo High Sch<br>206 W Evans St, Saint Jo 76265<br>Katie Morman | 7-12 | TV | 128<br>13 | 49% | 940/995-2532<br>Fax 940/995-2087 |

---

## MONTGOMERY COUNTY

## MONTGOMERY PUBLIC SCHOOLS

● **Conroe Ind School Dist** PID: 01042439          936/709-7752
  3205 W Davis St, Conroe 77304                    Fax 936/709-9701

**Schools:** 65 \ **Teachers:** 3,820 \ **Students:** 64,500 \
**Special Ed Students:** 5,312 \ **LEP Students:** 8,252 \ **College-Bound:** 58% \
**Ethnic:** Asian 5%, African American 8%, Hispanic 38%, Native American: 1%,
Caucasian 49% \ **Exp:** $283 (Med) \ **Poverty:** 10% \ **Title I:** $9,726,799 \
**Special Education:** $9,577,000 \ **Open-Close:** 08/12 - 05/26 \ **DTBP:** $181
(High)

| | |
|---|---|
| Dr Curtis Null ...............................1 | Darrin Rice ...........................................2,19 |
| Rick Reeves ...............................2 | Chris McCord ...........................................3 |
| Marshall Schroeder ....................3 | Robyn Hughes ...........................................4 |
| Sam Davila ................................5 | Danny Long ...........................................6 |
| Barbara Robertson ......................7 | Rodrigo Chaves ..................7,30,88,93,271 |
| Wade Haymark ........................7,35 | Dr Hedith Sauceda-Upshaw ..........8,74,273 |
| Shawn Creswell ...........................8 | Dr Pamela Zoda ...........................11,298 |
| Dr Chris Hines ..........................15 | Krissy Calhoun .........................16,73 |
| Dr Robert Horton ....................20,23 | Greg Shipp ...........................27,31 |
| Tammy Zunker .......................34,46 | Denise Cipolla ...........................36 |
| Manuel Texidor .....................36,83 | Richard Woodruff ...........................39 |
| Sheryl Hime ............................42 | Carlos Barron ...........................47 |
| Dr Sharon Henry .......................49 | Debra McNeely .........................50,63 |
| Dayren Carlisle ..........................57 | Dr Kendra Wiggins ...........................58 |
| Datren Williams .........................67 | Paula Green ...........................68 |
| Dana Boyer ............................69 | Dr Tamika Taylor .........................69,294 |
| Sarah Blakelock .........................71 | Teri Ross ...........................76 |
| Kim Earthman ...........................79 | Christine Reichelt ...........................81 |
| Bill Harness ............................91 | Terry McClaugherty .........................295 |

| Public Schs..Principal | Grd | Prgm | Enr/#Cls | SN | |
|---|---|---|---|---|---|
| Academy Careers Engr Science<br>27330 Oak Ridge School Rd, Conroe 77385<br>Dr Michael Papadimitriou | 9-9 | | 77 | | 832/482-6700<br>Fax 832/482-6706 |
| Academy of Science & Tech<br>3701 College Park Dr, The Woodlands 77384<br>Dr Susan Caffery | 9-12 | | 285<br>8 | | 936/709-3250<br>Fax 936/709-3299 |
| ⓜ Academy-Science & Health Prof<br>3200 W Davis St, Conroe 77304<br>Terri Benson | 9-12 | | 385 | | 936/709-5731<br>Fax 936/709-5842 |
| Anderson Elem Sch<br>1414 E Dallas St, Conroe 77301<br>**Laura Quinonesaceved** | PK-4 | T | 543<br>50 | 83% | 936/709-5300<br>Fax 936/709-5312 |
| Armstrong Elem Sch<br>110 Gladstell St, Conroe 77301<br>**Theresa Waller** | PK-4 | T | 444<br>25 | 94% | 936/709-3400<br>Fax 936/709-3415 |
| Austin Elem Sch<br>14796 Highway 105 E, Conroe 77306<br>Dr Serena Pierson | PK-4 | T | 926<br>30 | 81% | 936/709-8400<br>Fax 936/709-8403 |
| Birnham Woods Elem Sch<br>31150 Birnham Woods Dr, Spring 77386<br>Natalie Buckley | PK-4 | | 1,040 | 20% | 832/663-4200<br>Fax 832/663-4299 |
| Bozman Intermediate Sch<br>800 Beach Airport Rd, Conroe 77301<br>Amber Debeaumont | 5-6 | T | 865 | 63% | 936/709-1800<br>Fax 936/709-1899 |
| Bradley Elem Sch<br>4200 Falls Lake Dr, Spring 77386<br>Dr Christine Butler | PK-4 | | 838 | 34% | 832/482-6800<br>Fax 832/482-6899 |

| | | | | | |
|---|---|---|---|---|---|
| Buckalew Elem Sch<br>4909 Alden Bridge Dr, The Woodlands 77382<br>Jill Price | PK-4 | | 554<br>48 | 9% | 281/465-3400<br>Fax 281/465-3499 |
| Bush Elem Sch<br>7420 Crownridge Dr, The Woodlands 77382<br>Dr Jarod Lambert | PK-4 | | 608<br>55 | 13% | 936/709-1600<br>Fax 936/709-1699 |
| Caney Creek High Sch<br>13470 FM 1485 Rd, Conroe 77306<br>Jeffrey Stichler | 9-12 | TV | 2,094<br>65 | 74% | 936/709-2000<br>Fax 936/709-2099 |
| Clark Intermediate Sch<br>4182 Trench Ln, Spring 77386<br>Lindsay Ardoin | 5-6 | | 820 | 21% | 281/939-0600<br>Fax 281/939-0699 |
| Colin Powell Elem Sch<br>7332 Cochrans Crossing Dr, The Woodlands 77381<br>**Erin Mathe** | PK-4 | | 871<br>45 | 24% | 936/709-1700<br>Fax 936/709-1799<br>🅵🅣 |
| Collins Intermediate Sch<br>6020 Shadow Bend Pl, The Woodlands 77381<br>Shelli LeBlanc | 5-6 | | 754<br>24 | 13% | 281/298-3800<br>Fax 281/298-3803 |
| Conroe 9th Grade High Sch<br>400 Sgt Ed Holcomb Blvd N, Conroe 77304<br>**Bryan Gorka** | 9-9 | A | 1,000 | | 936/709-4000<br>Fax 936/709-4099 |
| Conroe High Sch<br>3200 W Davis St, Conroe 77304<br>Rotasha Smith | 10-12 | TV | 2,600 | 59% | 936/709-5700<br>Fax 936/709-5772 |
| Coulson Tough Elem Sch<br>11660 Cranebrook Dr, Spring 77382<br>Shawn Creswell \ **Christina Julien** | PK-6 | | 791 | 7% | 281/465-5900<br>Fax 281/465-5959 |
| Creighton Elem Sch<br>12089 FM 1485 Rd, Conroe 77306<br>**Patricia Thacker** | PK-4 | T | 745<br>45 | 79% | 936/709-2900<br>Fax 936/709-2999 |
| Cryar Intermediate Sch<br>2375 Montgomery Park Blvd, Conroe 77304<br>Bethany Medford | 5-6 | T | 793 | 57% | 936/709-7300<br>Fax 936/709-7313 |
| David Elem Sch<br>5301 Shadow Bend Pl, The Woodlands 77381<br>Lee Allen | PK-4 | | 537 | 9% | 281/298-4700<br>Fax 281/298-4703 |
| Deretchin Elem Sch<br>11000 Merit Oaks Dr, The Woodlands 77382<br>Alicia Reeves | PK-6 | | 808 | 9% | 832/592-8700<br>Fax 832/592-8780 |
| Dolly F Vogel Intermediate Sch<br>27125 Geffert Wright Rd, Spring 77386<br>Christa Haymark | 5-6 | T | 1,088 | 44% | 832/663-4300<br>Fax 832/663-4399 |
| Ford Elem Sch<br>25460 Richards Rd, Spring 77386<br>Paola Gorman | PK-4 | T | 824 | 66% | 832/592-5700<br>Fax 832/592-5709 |
| Galatas Elem Sch<br>9001 Cochrans Crossing Dr, The Woodlands 77381<br>Denae Wilker | PK-4 | | 515<br>40 | 7% | 936/709-5000<br>Fax 936/709-5003 |
| Giesinger Elem Sch<br>2323 White Oak Blvd, Conroe 77304<br>Melissa Ralston | PK-4 | T | 719<br>44 | 41% | 936/709-2600<br>Fax 936/709-2699 |
| Glen Loch Elem Sch<br>27505 Glen Loch Dr, The Woodlands 77381<br>Cassie Hertzenberg | PK-4 | T | 702<br>40 | 59% | 281/298-4900<br>Fax 281/298-4903 |
| Grand Oaks High Sch<br>4800 Riley Fuzzel Rd, Spring 77386<br>Dr Christopher Povich | 9-10 | | 1,241 | | 281/939-0000<br>Fax 281/939-0099 |
| Grangerland Interm Sch<br>16283 FM 3083 Rd, Conroe 77302<br>Karen Jones | 5-6 | T | 1,172<br>45 | 80% | 936/709-3500<br>Fax 936/709-3565 |
| Hailey Elem Sch<br>12051 Sawmill Rd, The Woodlands 77380<br>Tracy Horne | PK-4 | T | 718<br>34 | 51% | 832/663-4100<br>Fax 832/663-4199 |
| Ⓐ Hauke Academic Alt High Sch<br>701 N 3rd St, Conroe 77301<br>John Williams | 8-12 | TV | 50<br>22 | 57% | 936/709-3420<br>Fax 936/709-3499 |

| | | | | |
|---|---|---|---|---|
| 1 | Superintendent | 8 | Curric/Instruct K-12 | 19 Chief Financial Officer |
| 2 | Bus/Finance/Purchasing | 9 | Curric/Instruct Elem | 20 Art K-12 |
| 3 | Buildings And Grounds | 10 | Curric/Instruct Sec | 21 Art Elem |
| 4 | Food Service | 11 | Federal Program | 22 Art Sec |
| 5 | Transportation | 12 | Title I | 23 Music K-12 |
| 6 | Athletic | 13 | Title V | 24 Music Elem |
| 7 | Health Services | 15 | Asst Superintendent | 25 Music Sec |
| | | 16 | Instructional Media Svcs | 26 Business Education |
| | | 17 | Chief Operations Officer | 27 Career & Tech Ed |
| | | 18 | Chief Academic Officer | 28 Technology Education |

| | | |
|---|---|---|
| 29 Family/Consumer Science | 39 Social Studies K-12 | 49 English/Lang Arts Elem |
| 30 Adult Education | 40 Social Studies Elem | 50 English/Lang Arts Sec |
| 31 Career/Sch-to-Work K-12 | 41 Social Studies Sec | 51 Reading K-12 |
| 32 Career/Sch-to-Work Elem | 42 Science K-12 | 52 Reading Elem |
| 33 Career/Sch-to-Work Sec | 43 Science Elem | 53 Reading Sec |
| 34 Early Childhood Ed | 44 Science Sec | 54 Remedial Reading K-12 |
| 35 Health/Phys Education | 45 Math K-12 | 55 Remedial Reading Elem |
| 36 Guidance Services K-12 | 46 Math Elem | 56 Remedial Reading Sec |
| 37 Guidance Services Elem | 47 Math Sec | 57 Bilingual/ELL |
| 38 Guidance Services Sec | 48 English/Lang Arts K-12 | 58 Special Education K-12 |

| | | |
|---|---|---|
| 59 Special Education Elem | 69 Academic Assessment |
| 60 Special Education Sec | 70 Research/Development |
| 61 Foreign/World Lang K-12 | 71 Public Information |
| 62 Foreign/World Lang Elem | 72 Summer School |
| 63 Foreign/World Lang Sec | 73 Instructional Tech |
| 64 Religious Education K-12 | 74 Inservice Training |
| 65 Religious Education Elem | 75 Marketing/Distributive |
| 66 Religious Education Sec | 76 Info Systems |
| 67 School Board President | 77 Psychological Assess |
| 68 Teacher Personnel | 78 Affirmative Action |

| School | Grd | Prgm | Enr | % | Phone |
|---|---|---|---|---|---|
| Houser Elem Sch<br>27370 Oak Ridge School Rd, Conroe 77385<br>Angela Lozano | PK-4 | T | 815<br>50 | 62% | 832/663-4000<br>Fax 832/663-4076 |
| Houston Elem Sch<br>1000 N Thompson St, Conroe 77301<br>Viviana Harris | PK-4 | T | 551<br>35 | 93% | 936/709-5100<br>Fax 936/709-5103 |
| Irons Junior High Sch<br>16780 Needham Rd, Conroe 77385<br>**Robert MacFarlane** | 7-8 | V | 1,152 | 42% | 936/709-8500<br>Fax 936/709-8599 |
| Jean E Stewart Elem Sch<br>680 Fish Creek Thoroughfare, Montgomery 77316<br>**Julie English** | PK-6 | | 711 | 26% | 936/709-4200<br>Fax 936/709-4299 |
| Kaufman Elem Sch<br>2760 Northridge Forest Dr D, Spring 77386<br>Tina Oliver | PK-4 | | 713 | 22% | 832/592-5600<br>Fax 832/592-5617 |
| Knox Junior High Sch<br>12104 Sawmill Rd, The Woodlands 77380<br>Donny Daw | 7-8 | V | 1,200<br>80 | 27% | 832/592-8400<br>Fax 832/592-8410 |
| Lamar Elem Sch<br>1300 Many Pines Rd, The Woodlands 77380<br>Kristen Belcher | PK-4 | T | 777<br>36 | 44% | 832/592-5800<br>Fax 832/592-5810 |
| McCullough Junior High Sch<br>3800 S Panther Creek Dr, Spring 77381<br>**Jill Hooser** | 7-8 | V | 1,800 | 10% | 832/592-5100<br>Fax 832/592-5116 |
| Milam Elem Sch<br>16415 FM 3083 Rd, Conroe 77302<br>Gilberto Lozano | PK-4 | T | 745<br>43 | 81% | 936/709-5200<br>Fax 936/709-5203 |
| Mitchell Intermediate Sch<br>6800 Alden Bridge Dr, The Woodlands 77382<br>Paula Klapesky | 5-6 | | 1,195<br>40 | 9% | 832/592-8500<br>Fax 832/592-8518 |
| Moorhead Junior High Sch<br>13475 FM 1485 Rd, Conroe 77306<br>Roberto Garcia | 7-8 | TV | 1,152<br>60 | 77% | 936/709-2400<br>Fax 936/709-2499 |
| Oak Ridge Elem Sch<br>19675 Interstate 45 S, Conroe 77385<br>Tami Eldridge | PK-4 | T | 722<br>24 | 50% | 832/592-5900<br>Fax 832/592-5968 |
| Oak Ridge High Sch<br>27330 Oak Ridge School Rd, Conroe 77385<br>Anthony Livecchi | 10-12 | V | 2,839<br>125 | 30% | 832/592-5300<br>Fax 832/592-5544 ⓕⓣ |
| Oak Ridge HS 9th Grade Campus<br>27310 Oak Ridge School Rd, Conroe 77385<br>Melanie Bujnoch | 9-9 | V | 1,179 | | 281/465-5000<br>Fax 281/465-5099 |
| Patterson Elem Sch<br>670 Beach Airport Rd, Conroe 77301<br>Julie Miller | PK-4 | T | 849 | 70% | 936/709-4300<br>Fax 936/709-4399 |
| Peet Junior High Sch<br>1895 Longmire Rd, Conroe 77304<br>Christopher Kuempel | 7-8 | TV | 1,200 | 55% | 936/709-3700<br>Fax 936/709-3828 |
| Reaves Elem Sch<br>1717 N Loop 336 W, Conroe 77304<br>Nicole Walker | PK-4 | T | 683<br>38 | 79% | 936/709-5400<br>Fax 936/709-5407 |
| Rice Elem Sch<br>904 Gladstell Rd, Conroe 77304<br>**Melissa Sciba** | PK-4 | T | 441<br>26 | 67% | 936/709-2700<br>Fax 936/709-2799 |
| Runyan Elem Sch<br>1101 Foster Dr, Conroe 77301<br>Tracy Voelker | PK-4 | T | 417<br>40 | 87% | 936/709-2800<br>Fax 936/709-2899 |
| Sally K Ride Elem Sch<br>4920 W Panther Creek Dr, The Woodlands 77381<br>Megan Burnham | PK-4 | | 581 | 12% | 281/465-2800<br>Fax 281/465-2803 |
| San Jacinto Elem Sch<br>17601 FM 1314 Rd, Conroe 77302<br>**Jamie Almond** | PK-4 | T | 591<br>41 | 80% | 281/465-7700<br>Fax 281/465-7799 |
| Snyder Elem Sch<br>28601 Birnham Woods Dr, Spring 77386<br>Crystal Poncho | PK-4 | | 1,039 | 14% | 832/663-4400<br>Fax 832/663-4499 |
| Stockton Junior High Sch<br>2750 Excellence Ave, Conroe 77301<br>**Bryan Gorka** | 7-8 | V | 1,000 | | 936/709-4500<br>Fax 936/709-4599 |
| Suchma Elementary<br>10261 Harpers School Rd, Conroe 77385<br>Dr Tara Vandermark | PK-6 | | 897 | | 936/709-4400<br>Fax 936/709-4499 |
| Sue Park Broadway Elem Sch<br>2855 Spring Trails Bnd, Spring 77386<br>Shannon Conley | PK-4 | | 977 | 12% | 281/465-2900<br>Fax 281/465-2903 |
| The Woodlands High Sch<br>6101 Research Forest Dr, The Woodlands 77381<br>Ted Landry | 10-12 | V | 3,234 | 7% | 936/709-1200<br>Fax 936/709-1299 |
| The Woodlands HS-9th GR Campus<br>10010 Branch Crossing Dr, The Woodlands 77382<br>Jill Houser | 9-9 | V | 1,108 | | 832/592-8200<br>Fax 832/592-8299 |
| The Woodlands-College Park HS<br>3701 College Park Dr, The Woodlands 77384<br>Dr Mark Murrell | 9-12 | | 3,127 | 19% | 936/709-3000<br>Fax 936/709-3019 ⓕⓣ |
| Tom Cox Intermediate Sch<br>3333 Waterbend Cv, Spring 77386<br>Deborah Spoon | 5-6 | | 849 | 20% | 281/465-3200<br>Fax 281/465-3299 |
| Travis Intermediate Sch<br>1100 N Thompson St, Conroe 77301<br>Charita Smith | 5-6 | T | 672<br>30 | 91% | 936/709-7000<br>Fax 936/709-7019 |
| Washington Junior High Sch<br>507 Dr Mlk Pl N, Conroe 77301<br>Hartwell Brown | 7-8 | TV | 821<br>65 | 84% | 936/709-7400<br>Fax 936/709-7492 |
| Wilkerson Intermediate Sch<br>12312 Sawmill Rd, The Woodlands 77380<br>Jennifer Daw | 5-6 | T | 743<br>45 | 45% | 832/592-8900<br>Fax 832/592-8910 |
| Wilkinson Elem Sch<br>2575 Ed Kharbat Dr, Conroe 77301<br>**Malinda Stewart** | PK-4 | T | 676 | 46% | 936/709-1500<br>Fax 936/709-1599 |
| York Junior High Sch<br>3515 Waterbend Cv, Spring 77386<br>Brian Lee | 7-8 | V | 1,200<br>68 | 19% | 832/592-8600<br>Fax 832/592-8684 |

● **Magnolia Ind School Dist** PID: 01042582
31141 Nichols Sawmill Rd, Magnolia 77355
281/356-3571
Fax 281/252-2235

**Schools:** 16 \ **Teachers:** 819 \ **Students:** 13,100 \
**Special Ed Students:** 1,300 \ **LEP Students:** 1,796 \ **Ethnic:** Asian 1%, African American 3%, Hispanic 36%, Caucasian 60% \ **Exp:** $379 (High) \ **Poverty:** 16% \ **Title I:** $3,139,760 \ **Special Education:** $1,922,000 \
**Open-Close:** 08/12 - 05/26 \ **DTBP:** $169 (High) \ ⓣ

| | | | |
|---|---|---|---|
| Dr Todd Stephens ...................................1 | Adam Stearns .............................................2 |
| Dr Erich Morris ...............................2,15 | Allen Meeks ..............................................3 |
| Kimberly Ohlendorf .................................4 | Cindy Mooneyham .........................................5 |
| JD Berna ..............................................6 | Amy Locker ..........................................8,69 |
| Suzy McKinny ..........................................9 | Brandon Garza .................... 11,36,275,294 |
| Dr Benjamin Petty .............................13,58 | Dr Jason Bullock .......................................15 |
| Dr Foy Cambell ............................20,23,27 | Jerry Krusleski .........................27,31,39,73 |
| Tammy Haley ..........................................34 | Sherry Galamore .......................................42 |
| Susan Johnson .......................................45 | Shay Garland ...........................................48 |
| Nancy Rodriguez .....................................57 | Gary Blizzard .........................................67 |
| Sam Bell ..............................................68 | Denise Meyer ...........................................71 |
| Rob Stewart .......................................79,91 | Sarah Etter ...........................................286 |

| Public Schs..Principal | Grd | Prgm | Enr/#Cls | SN | Phone |
|---|---|---|---|---|---|
| Ⓐ Alpha Academy<br>919 Cloyd Dr, Magnolia 77355<br>Bryan Cooper | 9-12 | | 26<br>10 | | 281/252-2265<br>Fax 281/252-2268 |
| Ⓐ Alternative Education Ctr<br>919 Cloyd Dr, Magnolia 77355<br>Fowler Robert | 9-12 | | 120 | | 281/252-2275<br>Fax 281/252-2278 |

---

| | | | | |
|---|---|---|---|---|
| 79 Student Personnel | 91 Safety/Security | 275 Response To Intervention | 298 Grant Writer/Ptnrships | **School Programs** | **Social Media** |
| 80 Driver Ed/Safety | 92 Magnet School | 277 Remedial Math K-12 | 750 Chief Innovation Officer | **A** = Alternative Program | |
| 81 Gifted/Talented | 93 Parental Involvement | 280 Literacy Coach | 751 Chief of Staff | **G** = Adult Classes | ⓕ = Facebook |
| 82 Video Services | 95 Tech Prep Program | 285 STEM | 752 Social Emotional Learning | **M** = Magnet Program | |
| 83 Substance Abuse Prev | 97 Chief Infomation Officer | 286 Digital Learning | | **T** = Title I Schoolwide | ⓣ = Twitter |
| 84 Erate | 98 Chief Technology Officer | 288 Common Core Standards | **Other School Types** | **V** = Career & Tech Ed Programs | |
| 85 AIDS Education | 270 Character Education | 294 Accountability | Ⓐ = Alternative School | | |
| 88 Alternative/At Risk | 271 Migrant Education | 295 Network System | Ⓒ = Charter School | **New Schools are shaded** | |
| 89 Multi-Cultural Curriculum | 273 Teacher Mentor | 296 Title II Programs | Ⓜ = Magnet School | **New Superintendents and Principals are bold** | |
| 90 Social Work | 274 Before/After Sch | 297 Webmaster | Ⓨ = Year-Round School | **Personnel with email addresses are underscored** | |

| | | | | | |
|---|---|---|---|---|---|
| Bear Branch Elem Sch<br>8909 FM 1488 Rd, Magnolia 77354<br>Jim Gassaway | PK-4 | | 447<br>38 | 25% | 281/356-4771<br>Fax 281/252-2074 |
| Bear Branch Intermediate Sch<br>8040 Ken Lake Dr, Magnolia 77354<br>Tommy Burns | 5-6 | | 510 | 38% | 281/252-2031<br>Fax 281/252-2032 |
| Bear Branch Junior High Sch<br>31310 FM 2978 Rd, Magnolia 77354<br>**Julia Venghaus** | 7-8 | V | 984<br>56 | 35% | 281/356-6088<br>Fax 281/252-2060 |
| Cedric C Smith Elem Sch<br>28747 Hardin Store Rd, Magnolia 77354<br>Dion Rivera | PK-5 | T | 804<br>30 | 63% | 281/252-2300<br>Fax 281/252-2304 |
| J L Lyons Elem Sch<br>27035 Nichols Sawmill Rd, Magnolia 77355<br>Erin Vance | PK-5 | T | 819<br>50 | 73% | 281/356-8115<br>Fax 281/252-2170 |
| Magnolia Elem Sch<br>31900 Nichols Sawmill Rd, Magnolia 77355<br>**Donna Covarrubias** | PK-5 | T | 844<br>50 | 63% | 281/356-6434<br>Fax 281/252-2150 |
| Magnolia High Sch<br>14350 FM 1488 Rd, Magnolia 77354<br>Greg Quinn | 9-12 | V | 2,005<br>80 | 28% | 281/356-3572<br>Fax 281/252-2092 |
| Magnolia Intermediate Sch<br>110 S Magnolia Blvd, Magnolia 77355<br>Lisa Bertrand | 5-6 | T | 1,072<br>35 | 59% | 281/252-2033<br>Fax 281/252-2024 |
| Magnolia Junior High Sch<br>31138 Nichols Sawmill Rd, Magnolia 77355<br>David Slater | 7-8 | TV | 1,056<br>45 | 52% | 281/356-1327<br>Fax 281/252-2125 |
| Magnolia Parkway Elem Sch<br>11745 FM 1488 Rd, Magnolia 77354<br>Megan Baker | PK-5 | T | 713 | 48% | 281/252-7440<br>Fax 281/252-7446 |
| Magnolia West High Sch<br>42202 FM 1774 Rd, Magnolia 77354<br>Ben King | 9-12 | TV | 2,041 | 47% | 281/252-2550<br>Fax 281/252-2560 |
| Nichols-Saw Mill Elem Sch<br>28750 Nichols Sawmill Rd, Magnolia 77355<br>Carrie Quinn | PK-5 | T | 626<br>45 | 46% | 281/252-2133<br>Fax 281/252-2138 |
| Tom R Ellisor Elem Sch<br>33040 Egypt Ln, Magnolia 77354<br>Kristin Boyd | PK-5 | | 752 | 41% | 281/252-7400<br>Fax 281/252-7401 |
| Willie E Williams Elem Sch<br>18101 FM 1488 Rd, Magnolia 77354<br>Claudia Dominguez | PK-5 | T | 719<br>34 | 79% | 281/356-6866<br>Fax 281/252-2204 |

● **Montgomery Ind School Dist** PID: 01042623　　936/276-2000
20774 Eva St, Montgomery 77356　　　　　　　　Fax 936/276-2009

**Schools:** 10 \ **Teachers:** 588 \ **Students:** 9,048 \ **Special Ed Students:** 669 \ **LEP Students:** 186 \ **College-Bound:** 57% \ **Ethnic:** Asian 1%, African American 3%, Hispanic 16%, Caucasian 80% \ **Exp:** $227 (Med) \ **Poverty:** 7% \ **Title I:** $655,110 \ **Special Education:** $1,017,000 \ **Open-Close:** 08/13 - 05/21 \ **DTBP:** $158 (High)

| | | |
|---|---|---|
| **Dr Heath Morrison** ...... 1 | Kristopher Lynn ...... 2,19 |
| Bobby Morris ...... 3,17 | Joe Kinard ...... 3 |
| Lena Neugebauer ...... 4 | Mike Foster ...... 5 |
| Clint Heard ...... 6,35 | Dr Sonja Lopez ...... 7,15,68,71,273 |
| Wendy Graves ...... 9,11,15,16,34,57,270,274 | Duane McFadden ...... 10,15 |
| Meredith Burg ...... 58,79 | Jim Dossey ...... 67 |
| Dr Amy Busby ...... 73,76,79,286,295 | |

| Public Schs..Principal | Grd | Prgm | Enr/#Cls | SN | |
|---|---|---|---|---|---|
| Keenan Elem Sch<br>19180 Keenan Cut Off Rd, Montgomery 77316<br>Mallory Kirby | PK-5 | | 770<br>45 | 21% | 936/276-5500<br>Fax 936/276-5501 |
| Lake Creek High Sch<br>20639 FM 2854 Rd, Montgomery 77316<br>Phil Eaton | 9-12 | | 331 | 22% | 936/276-4000 |

| | | | | | |
|---|---|---|---|---|---|
| Lincoln Elem Sch<br>700 Dr Martin Luther King Dr, Montgomery 77356<br>Courtney Dyer | PK-5 | T | 495 | 38% | 936/276-4700<br>Fax 936/276-4701 |
| Lone Star Elem Sch<br>16600 FM 2854 Rd, Montgomery 77316<br>Dr Catherine Bartlett | PK-5 | | 769 | 17% | 936/276-4500<br>Fax 936/276-4501 |
| Madeley Ranch Elem Sch<br>3500 Madeley Ranch Rd, Montgomery 77356<br>Shelby Smith | PK-5 | | 736 | 21% | 936/276-4600<br>Fax 936/276-4601 |
| Montgomery Elem Sch<br>13755 Liberty St, Montgomery 77316<br>Carrie Fitzpatrick | PK-5 | T | 384<br>30 | 36% | 936/276-3600<br>Fax 936/276-3601 |
| Montgomery High Sch<br>22825 Highway 105 W, Montgomery 77356<br>**Dr Andria Schur** | 9-12 | V | 1,775 | 21% | 936/276-3000<br>Fax 936/276-3001 |
| Montgomery Junior High Sch<br>19000 Stuart Creek Rd, Montgomery 77356<br>Angela Chapman | 6-8 | | 1,151<br>45 | 24% | 936/276-3300<br>Fax 936/276-3301 |
| Oak Hills Junior High Sch<br>19190 Keenan Cut Off Rd, Montgomery 77316<br>Tim Williams | 6-8 | | 1,081<br>34 | 23% | 936/276-4300<br>Fax 936/276-4301 |
| Stewart Creek Elem Sch<br>18990 Stewart Creek Rd, Montgomery 77356<br>Michele Salter | PK-5 | T | 780 | 46% | 936/276-3500<br>Fax 936/276-3501 |

● **New Caney Ind School Dist** PID: 01042661　　281/577-8600
21580 Loop 494, New Caney 77357　　　　　　　Fax 281/354-2639

**Schools:** 19 \ **Teachers:** 1,030 \ **Students:** 15,000 \ **Special Ed Students:** 1,288 \ **LEP Students:** 4,580 \ **Ethnic:** Asian 2%, African American 4%, Hispanic 61%, Caucasian 33% \ **Exp:** $286 (Med) \ **Poverty:** 17% \ **Title I:** $2,744,518 \ **Special Education:** $2,051,000 \ **Open-Close:** 09/08 - 05/21 \ **DTBP:** $141 (High)

| | | |
|---|---|---|
| Kenn Franklin ...... 1 | Brandy Fain ...... 2 |
| Michelle Marable ...... 3 | Paul Batchelder ...... 3 |
| Tim Battenfield ...... 3 | Debbie Needham ...... 4 |
| Richard Ressler ...... 5 | Brent Sipe ...... 6 |
| Christina Nunez ...... 7* | Kristi Shofner ...... 8 |
| Holly Hanks ...... 9 | Dr Mark Weatherly ...... 10 |
| Brande Bass ...... 11,83,88,296 | Brande Bass ...... 11,83,88,296* |
| Blake Carrol ...... 15 | Matt Calvert ...... 15 |
| Warren Stripling ...... 27 | Yolanda Rios ...... 57,271 |
| Lori Waldrop ...... 58 | Chad Turner ...... 67 |
| Steve Freeman ...... 68 | Dr Scott Powers ...... 71 |
| Ben Rice ...... 73 | Dan Casteel ...... 76 |
| Laura Sunosky ...... 79 | Scott Castleberry ...... 79 |
| Loree Munro ...... 81 | Troy Wooten ...... 91 |
| Jeanie Reed ...... 286 | Crosby Doug ...... 295 |

| Public Schs..Principal | Grd | Prgm | Enr/#Cls | SN | |
|---|---|---|---|---|---|
| Bens Branch Elem Sch<br>24160 Briar Berry Ln, Porter 77365<br>Catherine Olano | PK-5 | T | 590 | 48% | 281/577-8700<br>Fax 281/354-4296 |
| Brookwood Forest Elem Sch<br>25545 Sorters Rd, Porter 77365<br>Ericka Gutierrez | PK-5 | T | 742 | 82% | 281/577-8820 |
| Dogwood Elem Sch<br>600 Dogwood, New Caney 77357<br>**Sheri Lowe** | PK-5 | T | 696 | 88% | 281/577-2960<br>Fax 281/399-8920 |
| Infinity Early College HS<br>26751 Sorters Rd, Porter 77365<br>Patricia Beal | 9-12 | T | 341 | 65% | 281/577-2890 |
| Keefer Crossing Middle Sch<br>20350 FM 1485 Rd, New Caney 77357<br>**Jonathan Powell** | 6-8 | TV | 867<br>35 | 75% | 281/577-8840<br>Fax 281/399-9859 |

| | | | |
|---|---|---|---|
| 1 Superintendent | 8 Curric/Instruct K-12 | 19 Chief Financial Officer | 29 Family/Consumer Science |
| 2 Bus/Finance/Purchasing | 9 Curric/Instruct Elem | 20 Art K-12 | 30 Adult Education |
| 3 Buildings And Grounds | 10 Curric/Instruct Sec | 21 Art Elem | 31 Career/Sch-to-Work K-12 |
| 4 Food Service | 11 Federal Program | 22 Art Sec | 32 Career/Sch-to-Work Elem |
| 5 Transportation | 12 Title I | 23 Music K-12 | 33 Career/Sch-to-Work Sec |
| 6 Athletic | 13 Title V | 24 Music Elem | 34 Early Childhood Ed |
| 7 Health Services | 15 Asst Superintendent | 25 Music Sec | 35 Health/Phys Education |
| | 16 Instructional Media Svcs | 26 Business Education | 36 Guidance Services K-12 |
| | 17 Chief Operations Officer | 27 Career & Tech Ed | 37 Guidance Services Elem |
| | 18 Chief Academic Officer | 28 Technology Education | 38 Guidance Services Sec |

| | | |
|---|---|---|
| 39 Social Studies K-12 | 49 English/Lang Arts Elem | 59 Special Education Elem | 69 Academic Assessment |
| 40 Social Studies Elem | 50 English/Lang Arts Sec | 60 Special Education Sec | 70 Research/Development |
| 41 Social Studies Sec | 51 Reading K-12 | 61 Foreign/World Lang K-12 | 71 Public Information |
| 42 Science K-12 | 52 Reading Elem | 62 Foreign/World Lang Elem | 72 Summer School |
| 43 Science Elem | 53 Reading Sec | 63 Foreign/World Lang Sec | 73 Instructional Tech |
| 44 Science Sec | 54 Remedial Reading K-12 | 64 Religious Education K-12 | 74 Inservice Training |
| 45 Math K-12 | 55 Remedial Reading Elem | 65 Religious Education Elem | 75 Marketing/Distributive |
| 46 Math Elem | 56 Remedial Reading Sec | 66 Religious Education Sec | 76 Info Systems |
| 47 Math Sec | 57 Bilingual/ELL | 67 School Board President | 77 Psychological Assess |
| 48 English/Lang Arts K-12 | 58 Special Education K-12 | 68 Teacher Personnel | 78 Affirmative Action |

| School | Grd | Prgm | Enr/#Cls | SN | Phone |
|---|---|---|---|---|---|
| Kings Manor Elem Sch<br>21111 Royal Crossing Dr, Kingwood 77339<br>Stacey Paine | PK-5 | | 645<br>41 | 41% | 281/577-2940<br>Fax 281/359-6391 |
| New Caney Elem Sch<br>20501 FM 1485 Rd, New Caney 77357<br>Jennifer Andjelic | PK-5 | T | 488<br>48 | 84% | 281/577-8720<br>Fax 281/399-2174 |
| New Caney High Sch<br>21650 Loop 494, New Caney 77357<br>Eric Holton | 9-12 | TV | 1,893<br>100 | 71% | 281/577-2800<br>Fax 281/354-0186 |
| New Caney Middle Sch<br>22784 Highway 59, Porter 77365<br>Holly Ray | 6-8 | T | 836 | 73% | 281/577-8860<br>Fax 281/577-8870 |
| Oakley Elem Sch<br>22320 Loop 494, New Caney 77357<br>Erica Gruber | PK-5 | T | 846 | 84% | 281/577-5970<br>Fax 281/577-0026 |
| Porter Elem Sch<br>22256 Ford Rd, Porter 77365<br>**Nicole Land** | PK-5 | T | 640<br>35 | 83% | 281/577-2920<br>Fax 281/354-7583 |
| Porter High Sch<br>22625 Sandy Ln, Porter 77365<br>**Cesar Condarco** | 9-12 | T | 2,017 | 55% | 281/577-5900<br>Fax 281/577-9175 |
| Robert L Crippen Elem Sch<br>18690 Cumberland Blvd, Porter 77365<br>Crystal Mayes | PK-5 | T | 550<br>61 | 76% | 281/577-8740<br>Fax 281/354-6823 |
| Sorters Mill Elem Sch<br>23300 Sorters Rd, Porter 77365<br>Kindy Tomhave | PK-5 | T | 715 | 71% | 281/577-8780<br>Fax 281/354-0914 |
| Tavola Elem Sch<br>18885 Winding Summit Dr, New Caney 77357<br>**Kimberly Felts** | PK-5 | T | 594<br>35 | 65% | 281/577-2900<br>Fax 281/399-9946 |
| Ⓐ The Learning Center<br>20419 FM 1485 Rd, New Caney 77357<br>Jack Dumesnil | 5-12 | | 50<br>12 | 67% | 281/577-2850<br>Fax 281/399-4005 |
| Valley Ranch Elem Sch<br>21700 Valley Ranch Crossing Dr, Porter 77365<br>**Stephanie Coronado** | PK-5 | T | 728 | 61% | 281/577-8760<br>Fax 281/577-9209 |
| White Oak Middle Sch<br>24161 Briar Berry Ln, Porter 77365<br>Everett Simons | 6-8 | TV | 918<br>60 | 63% | 281/577-8800<br>Fax 281/354-5186 |
| Woodridge Forest Middle Sch<br>4540 Woodridge Pkwy, Porter 77365<br>Bridgett Heine | 6-8 | TV | 888 | 59% | 281/577-8880<br>Fax 281/359-1364 |

• **Splendora Ind School Dist** PID: 01042726    281/689-3128
23419 FM 2090 Rd, Splendora 77372    Fax 281/689-7509

**Schools:** 6 \ **Teachers:** 272 \ **Students:** 4,200 \ **Special Ed Students:** 430 \ **LEP Students:** 665 \ **College-Bound:** 43% \ **Ethnic:** Hispanic 42%, Caucasian 57% \ **Exp:** $467 (High) \ **Poverty:** 13% \ **Title I:** $627,149 \ **Open-Close:** 08/12 - 05/26 \ **DTBP:** $142 (High)

| Public Schs..Principal | Grd | Prgm | Enr/#Cls | SN | Phone |
|---|---|---|---|---|---|
| Greenleaf Elem Sch<br>26275 FM 2090 Rd, Splendora 77372<br>Dr Carolyn King | K-5 | T | 789<br>33 | 82% | 281/689-8020<br>Fax 281/689-3213 |
| Peach Creek Elem Sch<br>14455 Cox St, Splendora 77372<br>Duana Brashear | K-5 | T | 424 | 67% | 281/689-3114<br>Fax 281/689-7128 |
| Piney Woods Elem Sch<br>23395 FM 2090 Rd, Splendora 77372<br>Heath Lucas | PK-5 | T | 780 | 60% | 281/689-3073<br>Fax 281/689-7975 |
| Splendora High Sch<br>23747 FM 2090 Rd, Splendora 77372<br>Dianna Archer | 9-12 | TV | 1,206<br>55 | 56% | 281/689-8008<br>Fax 281/689-8675 |
| Splendora Junior High Sch<br>23411 FM 2090 Rd, Splendora 77372<br>Kent Broussard | 6-8 | TV | 909<br>33 | 66% | 281/689-6343<br>Fax 281/689-5198 |
| Timber Lakes Elem Sch<br>5450 Herrington Dr, New Caney 77357<br>**Carrie Garza** | PK-6 | | 500 | | 281/689-4375 |

• **Willis Ind School Dist** PID: 01042764    936/856-1200
204 W Rogers St, Willis 77378    Fax 936/856-5182

**Schools:** 9 \ **Teachers:** 435 \ **Students:** 6,709 \ **Special Ed Students:** 650 \ **LEP Students:** 1,033 \ **College-Bound:** 51% \ **Ethnic:** Asian 1%, African American 7%, Hispanic 38%, Caucasian 54% \ **Exp:** $190 (Low) \ **Poverty:** 13% \ **Title I:** $1,402,035 \ **Special Education:** $1,220,000 \ **Open-Close:** 08/12 - 05/21 \ **DTBP:** $177 (High) \ 

| Public Schs..Principal | Grd | Prgm | Enr/#Cls | SN | Phone |
|---|---|---|---|---|---|
| A R Turner Elem Sch<br>10575 Hwy 75 N, Willis 77378<br>Kameron Wilder | K-5 | T | 779<br>38 | 37% | 936/856-1289<br>Fax 936/856-1677 |
| C C Hardy Elem Sch<br>701 Gerald St, Willis 77378<br>**Jason Bond** | K-5 | T | 518 | 78% | 936/856-1241<br>Fax 936/856-1242 |
| Edward B Cannan Elem Sch<br>7639 County Line Rd, Willis 77378<br>**Kent Copley** | K-5 | T | 660<br>40 | 72% | 936/890-8660<br>Fax 936/890-2616 |
| Lynn Lucas Middle Sch<br>1304 N Campbell St, Willis 77378<br>Kim Sprayberry \ Eric Burns | 6-8 | TV | 271<br>45 | 70% | 936/856-1274<br>Fax 936/856-1065 |
| Meador Elem Sch<br>10020 FM 830 Rd, Willis 77318<br>**Tamara Good** | K-5 | T | 733 | 61% | 936/890-7550<br>Fax 936/890-7540 |
| Mel Parmley Elem Sch<br>600 N Campbell St, Willis 77378<br>Kelley Moore | K-5 | T | 640<br>25 | 71% | 936/856-1231<br>Fax 936/856-1239 |
| Robert Brabham Middle Sch<br>10000 FM 830 Rd, Willis 77318<br>Richard Ray | 6-8 | T | 889 | 52% | 936/890-2312<br>Fax 936/856-2910 |
| Ⓐ Stubblefield Alternative Acad<br>207 Philpot St, Willis 77378<br>Tanya Maddin | 1-12 | | 22<br>9 | 88% | 936/856-1302<br>Fax 936/890-0312 |
| Willis High Sch<br>10005 Highway 75 N, Willis 77378<br>Stephanie Hodgins | 9-12 | TV | 1,174<br>100 | 54% | 936/856-1250<br>Fax 936/856-3391 |

| | | | | |
|---|---|---|---|---|
| 79 Student Personnel | 91 Safety/Security | 275 Response To Intervention | 298 Grant Writer/Ptnrships | **School Programs** |
| 80 Driver Ed/Safety | 92 Magnet School | 277 Remedial Math K-12 | 750 Chief Innovation Officer | A = Alternative Program |
| 81 Gifted/Talented | 93 Parental Involvement | 280 Literacy Coach | 751 Chief of Staff | G = Adult Classes |
| 82 Video Services | 95 Tech Prep Program | 285 STEM | 752 Social Emotional Learning | M = Magnet Program |
| 83 Substance Abuse Prev | 97 Chief Information Officer | 286 Digital Learning | | T = Title I Schoolwide |
| 84 Erate | 98 Chief Technology Officer | 288 Common Core Standards | **Other School Types** | V = Career & Tech Ed Programs |
| 85 AIDS Education | 270 Character Education | 294 Accountability | Ⓐ = Alternative School | |
| 88 Alternative/At Risk | 271 Migrant Education | 295 Network System | Ⓒ = Charter School | New Schools are shaded |
| 89 Multi-Cultural Curriculum | 273 Teacher Mentor | 296 Title II Programs | Ⓜ = Magnet School | New Superintendents and Principals are bold |
| 90 Social Work | 274 Before/After Sch | 297 Webmaster | Ⓨ = Year-Round School | Personnel with email addresses are underscored |

**Social Media**
f = Facebook
t = Twitter

**TX—297**

## MONTGOMERY CATHOLIC SCHOOLS

• **Archdiocese Galveston-Houston** PID: 01027855
Listing includes only schools located in this county. See District Index for location of Diocesan Offices.

| Catholic Schs..Principal | Grd | Prgm | Enr/#Cls | SN | |
|---|---|---|---|---|---|
| Sacred Heart Sch<br>615 McDade St, Conroe 77301<br>Deb Brown | PK-8 | | 318<br>18 | | 936/756-3848<br>Fax 936/756-4097 |
| St Anthony of Padua Sch<br>7901 Bay Branch Dr, The Woodlands 77382<br>Veronica Tucker | PK-8 | | 458<br>20 | | 281/296-0300<br>Fax 281/296-7236 |

## MONTGOMERY PRIVATE SCHOOLS

| Private Schs..Principal | Grd | Prgm | Enr/#Cls | SN | |
|---|---|---|---|---|---|
| Academy at World Champions Ctr<br>28865 Birnham Dr, Spring 77386<br>Dr Amelia Robinson | K-12 | | 25 | | 281/292-6284 |
| Calvary Baptist Sch<br>3401 N Frazier St, Conroe 77303<br>Becky Burchett | PK-12 | | 199<br>13 | | 936/756-0743<br>Fax 936/756-0764 |
| Central Baptist Academy<br>37135 FM 1774 Rd, Magnolia 77355<br>Jason Messer | PK-12 | | 52<br>6 | | 281/356-2861<br>Fax 281/259-5120 |
| Christ Community Sch<br>1488 Wellman Rd, Shenandoah 77384<br>Jessica Pierrel | PK-6 | | 140<br>16 | | 936/321-6300<br>Fax 936/460-3096 |
| Conroe Adventist Academy<br>3601 S Loop 336 E, Conroe 77301<br>Michelle Battistone | PK-12 | | 102<br>6 | | 936/756-5078 |
| Covenant Christian Sch<br>4503 Interstate 45 N, Conroe 77304<br>Sara Cummins \ Dathan Petruccio | PK-12 | GV | 300<br>30 | | 936/890-8080<br>Fax 936/890-5343 |
| Esprit International Sch<br>4890 W Panther Creek Dr, The Woodlands 77381<br>Rosemary Brumbelow | PK-12 | | 150 | | 281/298-9200<br>Fax 832/415-0486 |
| Fusion Academy-the Woodlands<br>1201 Lake Woodlands Dr #4000, The Woodlands 77380 | 6-12 | | 50 | | 281/419-1436 |
| Glenwood Private Sch<br>912 W Lewis St, Conroe 77301<br>Abbey Brawner | PK-2 | | 120<br>11 | | 936/756-1223 |
| John Cooper Sch<br>1 John Cooper Dr, The Woodlands 77381<br>Teresa Robson \ Charles Williams | PK-12 | | 1,000<br>50 | | 281/367-0900<br>Fax 281/292-9201 |
| Legacy Preparatory Chrn Acad<br>9768 Research Forest Dr, Magnolia 77354<br>Shannon Jones \ Lisa Bontrager | K-12 | | 140 | | 936/337-2000 |
| Lifestyle Christian Sch<br>3993 Interstate 45 N, Conroe 77304<br>Dr Nimmy Zachariah | K-12 | | 192<br>15 | | 936/756-9383<br>Fax 936/760-3003 |
| Montgomery Christian Academy<br>12681 FM 149 Rd, Montgomery 77316<br>Stacy Grant | PK-6 | | 72 | | 936/622-4598 |
| Rubicon Academy<br>14211 Horseshoe Bnd, The Woodlands 77384<br>Franci Roberts | PK-8 | | 40<br>7 | | 936/273-9111 |
| Sojourn Academy<br>27420 Robinson Rd, Conroe 77385<br>Becky Staggs | PK-12 | | 160 | | 281/298-5800<br>Fax 281/292-2818 |

| | | | | |
|---|---|---|---|---|
| The Woodlands Methodist Sch<br>1915 Lake Front Cir, Spring 77380<br>Tim Patton | K-8 | 325 | | 281/882-8220 |
| Woodlands Christian Academy<br>5800 Academy Way, The Woodlands 77384<br>Patty Bruha \ Julie Ambler | PK-12 | 550 | | 936/273-2555<br>Fax 936/271-3115 |

## MOORE COUNTY

## MOORE PUBLIC SCHOOLS

• **Dumas Ind School Dist** PID: 01042817
421 W 4th St, Dumas 79029

806/935-6461
Fax 806/935-6275

**Schools:** 9 \ **Teachers:** 320 \ **Students:** 4,300 \ **Special Ed Students:** 419 \ **LEP Students:** 1,207 \ **Ethnic:** Asian 7%, African American 2%, Hispanic 74%, Native American: 1%, Caucasian 17% \ **Exp:** $347 (High) \ **Poverty:** 16% \ **Title I:** $825,287 \ **Special Education:** $792,000 \ **Open-Close:** 08/11 - 05/28 \ **DTBP:** $154 (High) \

| | | | |
|---|---|---|---|
| Monty Hysinger | 1 | Daniel West | 2,19 |
| Eddie Crossland | 3,5,91 | Patty Woods | 4 |
| Stan Stroebel | 6,35 | Kelly Legg | 8,11,15,88,296 |
| Lisa Hatley | 9,34 | Nikole Soote | 10,280 |
| Brett Beesley | 15 | Frankie Blue | 58,275 |
| Patty Willis | 67 | Larry Payne | 71,83* |
| Jake Aragon | 73,76,95,295 | Cindy Rhoades | 79,294 |
| Kim Schnucker | 274 | Rhonda Artho | 286 |

| Public Schs..Principal | Grd | Prgm | Enr/#Cls | SN | |
|---|---|---|---|---|---|
| Cactus Elem Sch<br>100 South Drive, Cactus 79013<br>Thomas Funderburg | PK-4 | T | 367<br>35 | 94% | 806/966-5102<br>Fax 806/966-5561 |
| Dumas Intermediate Sch<br>400 Texas Ave, Dumas 79029<br>Philip Rhodes | 5-6 | T | 643 | 72% | 806/935-6474<br>Fax 806/935-6484 |
| Dumas Junior High Sch<br>700 E 5th St, Dumas 79029<br>Kurt Baxter | 7-8 | T | 644<br>50 | 61% | 806/935-4155<br>Fax 806/934-1434 |
| Ⓐ Dumas Senior High Sch<br>300 S Klein Ave, Dumas 79029<br>**Carl Clements** | 9-12 | TV | 535<br>60 | 54% | 806/935-4151<br>Fax 806/934-1433 |
| Green Acres Elem Sch<br>300 Oak Ave, Dumas 79029<br>Andrea Cox | PK-4 | T | 393<br>27 | 74% | 806/935-4157<br>Fax 806/934-1444 |
| Hillcrest Elem Sch<br>514 Pear Ave, Dumas 79029<br>Stephanie Schilling | PK-4 | T | 252<br>23 | 46% | 806/935-5629<br>Fax 806/934-1439 |
| Morningside Elem Sch<br>623 Powell Ave, Dumas 79029<br>Erin Pingelton | PK-4 | T | 343<br>23 | 69% | 806/935-4153<br>Fax 806/934-1438 |
| Ⓐ North Plains Opportunity Ctr<br>1015 N Maddox Ave, Dumas 79029<br>**Stan Williams** | 9-12 | | 35 | 76% | 806/935-8774<br>Fax 806/935-6376 |
| Sunset Elem Sch<br>401 W 14th St, Dumas 79029<br>Caynon Strickland | PK-4 | T | 201<br>37 | 83% | 806/935-2127<br>Fax 806/934-1441 |

| # | | # | | # | | # | | # | | # | | # | |
|---|---|---|---|---|---|---|---|---|---|---|---|---|---|
| 1 | Superintendent | 8 | Curric/Instruct K-12 | 19 | Chief Financial Officer | 29 | Family/Consumer Science | 39 | Social Studies K-12 | 49 | English/Lang Arts Elem | 59 | Special Education Elem | 69 | Academic Assessment |
| 2 | Bus/Finance/Purchasing | 9 | Curric/Instruct Elem | 20 | Art K-12 | 30 | Adult Education | 40 | Social Studies Elem | 50 | English/Lang Arts Sec | 60 | Special Education Sec | 70 | Research/Development |
| 3 | Buildings And Grounds | 10 | Curric/Instruct Sec | 21 | Art Elem | 31 | Career/Sch-to-Work K-12 | 41 | Social Studies Sec | 51 | Reading K-12 | 61 | Foreign/World Lang K-12 | 71 | Public Information |
| 4 | Food Service | 11 | Federal Program | 22 | Art Sec | 32 | Career/Sch-to-Work Elem | 42 | Science K-12 | 52 | Reading Elem | 62 | Foreign/World Lang Elem | 72 | Summer School |
| 5 | Transportation | 12 | Title I | 23 | Music K-12 | 33 | Career/Sch-to-Work Sec | 43 | Science Elem | 53 | Reading Sec | 63 | Foreign/World Lang Sec | 73 | Instructional Tech |
| 6 | Athletic | 13 | Title V | 24 | Music Elem | 34 | Early Childhood Ed | 44 | Science Sec | 54 | Remedial Reading K-12 | 64 | Religious Education K-12 | 74 | Inservice Training |
| 7 | Health Services | 15 | Asst Superintendent | 25 | Music Sec | 35 | Health/Phys Education | 45 | Math K-12 | 55 | Remedial Reading Elem | 65 | Religious Education Elem | 75 | Marketing/Distributive |
| | | 16 | Instructional Media Svcs | 26 | Business Education | 36 | Guidance Services K-12 | 46 | Math Elem | 56 | Remedial Reading Sec | 66 | Religious Education Sec | 76 | Info Systems |
| | | 17 | Chief Operations Officer | 27 | Career & Tech Ed | 37 | Guidance Services Elem | 47 | Math Sec | 57 | Bilingual/ELL | 67 | School Board President | 77 | Psychological Assess |
| | | 18 | Chief Academic Officer | 28 | Technology Education | 38 | Guidance Services Sec | 48 | English/Lang Arts K-12 | 58 | Special Education K-12 | 68 | Teacher Personnel | 78 | Affirmative Action |

● **Sunray Ind School Dist** PID: 01042910
400 E 7th, Sunray 79086

806/948-4411
Fax 806/948-5274

Schools: 3 \ Teachers: 56 \ Students: 556 \ Special Ed Students: 58
\ LEP Students: 70 \ Ethnic: Hispanic 57%, Native American: 1%,
Caucasian 42% \ Exp: $562 (High) \ Poverty: 10% \ Title I: $54,549 \
Open-Close: 08/13 - 05/28 \ DTBP: $339 (High) \ 🇹

| | | | |
|---|---|---|---|
| Marshall Harrison | 1,11,57 | Chad Ely | 3,5 |
| Misty Lowman | 4* | Matt Stricklen | 6,35* |
| Marybeth Jones | 35,36,69,83* | Scott Peeples | 67 |
| Mandy Trailor | 88,285 | Mary Jones | 275* |

| Public Schs..Principal | Grd | Prgm | Enr/#Cls | SN | |
|---|---|---|---|---|---|
| Sunray Elem Sch<br>509 Ave Q, Sunray 79086<br>Cody McDowell | PK-4 | T | 236<br>18 | 48% | 806/948-4222<br>Fax 806/948-4180 |
| Sunray High Sch<br>900 Ave Q, Sunray 79086<br>Mandy Traylor | 9-12 | ATV | 143<br>35 | 31% | 806/948-5515<br>Fax 806/948-5399 |
| Sunray Middle Sch<br>400 E 7th, Sunray 79086<br>Pam Kiesling | 5-8 | T | 177<br>15 | 47% | 806/948-4444<br>Fax 806/948-4208 |

## MORRIS COUNTY

## MORRIS PUBLIC SCHOOLS

● **Daingerfield-Lone Star Ind SD** PID: 01042946
200 Tiger Dr, Daingerfield 75638

903/645-2239
Fax 903/645-2137

Schools: 4 \ Teachers: 84 \ Students: 970 \ Special Ed Students: 159
\ LEP Students: 93 \ College-Bound: 64% \ Ethnic: Asian 1%, African
American 41%, Hispanic 20%, Caucasian 38% \ Exp: $340 (High) \
Poverty: 33% \ Title I: $692,321 \ Open-Close: 08/17 - 05/21 \ DTBP: $343
(High)

| | | | |
|---|---|---|---|
| Sandra Quarles | 1 | Daniel Pritchett | 2,11 |
| Jamie Bess | 4 | Davin Nelson | 6* |
| Martha Campbell | 8,11,69,74,79,273,294,296 | Jason Johnson | 16,73,295 |
| Vickie Lilley | 34,58,275 | Neil Roney | 67 |
| Ben Rameriz | 270 | | |

| Public Schs..Principal | Grd | Prgm | Enr/#Cls | SN | |
|---|---|---|---|---|---|
| Daingerfield High Sch<br>202 Tiger Dr, Daingerfield 75638<br>Tommy Stewart | 9-12 | ATV | 296<br>45 | 82% | 903/645-3968<br>Fax 903/645-7662 |
| Daingerfield Jr High Sch<br>200 Texas St, Daingerfield 75638<br>Amy Billingslea | 6-8 | T | 211<br>35 | 86% | 903/645-2261<br>Fax 903/645-4010 |
| South Elem Sch<br>1301 Linda Dr, Daingerfield 75638<br>Angie Reeder | 3-5 | T | 234<br>12 | 91% | 903/645-3501<br>Fax 903/645-2295 |
| West Elem Sch<br>1305 W Watson Blvd, Daingerfield 75638<br>Lesia Lewis | PK-2 | T | 231<br>18 | 89% | 903/645-2901<br>Fax 903/645-7178 |

● **Pewitt Cons Ind School Dist** PID: 01043005
1330 US Highway 67 W, Omaha 75571

903/884-2136
Fax 903/884-2866

Schools: 3 \ Teachers: 71 \ Students: 870 \ Special Ed Students: 122
\ LEP Students: 57 \ Ethnic: African American 16%, Hispanic 15%,
Caucasian 69% \ Exp: $672 (High) \ Poverty: 21% \ Title I: $253,899 \
Open-Close: 08/18 - 05/28 \ DTBP: $214 (High)

| | | | |
|---|---|---|---|
| Melissa Reid | 1 | Chris Cobb | 2,19* |
| Steve Litton | 3,17 | Monica Buford | 4 |
| Tim Coleman | 5 | Richard Strickland | 6 |
| Kristie Jones | 11,288 | Vickie Lilley | 58 |
| Michael Jarvis | 67 | Stephen Belk | 73,98,295 |
| Monica Kiefer | 76 | | |

| Public Schs..Principal | Grd | Prgm | Enr/#Cls | SN | |
|---|---|---|---|---|---|
| Pewitt Elem Sch<br>374 County Rd 4108, Omaha 75571<br>Amy Barron | PK-5 | T | 388<br>24 | 76% | 903/884-2404<br>Fax 903/884-3076 |
| Pewitt High Sch<br>1216 US Highway 67 W, Omaha 75571<br>Jay Wylie | 9-12 | TV | 238<br>29 | 54% | 903/884-2293<br>Fax 903/884-3111 |
| Pewitt Junior High Sch<br>US Highway 67 West, Omaha 75571<br>**James Cartwright** | 6-8 | T | 185<br>20 | 69% | 903/884-2505<br>Fax 903/884-3111 |

## MOTLEY COUNTY

## MOTLEY PUBLIC SCHOOLS

● **Motley Co Ind School Dist** PID: 01043043
1600 Bundy St, Matador 79244

806/347-2676
Fax 806/347-2871

Schools: 1 \ Teachers: 17 \ Students: 162 \ Special Ed Students: 13
\ LEP Students: 3 \ College-Bound: 80% \ Ethnic: African American
1%, Hispanic 26%, Caucasian 73% \ Exp: $636 (High) \ Poverty: 28% \
Title I: $70,709 \ Open-Close: 08/17 - 05/26 \ DTBP: $359 (High)

| | | | |
|---|---|---|---|
| William Cochran | 1 | Darlene Thomas | 2 |
| Jimmy Erickson | 2 | Chuck Ream | 5* |
| Mike Bigham | 6* | Becky Decker | 11 |
| Licey Rankin | 57* | Tanya Givins | 58* |
| Lewis Drum | 67 | Kathy Gillespie | 69* |
| Shelley Cox | 73* | | |

| Public Schs..Principal | Grd | Prgm | Enr/#Cls | SN | |
|---|---|---|---|---|---|
| Motley Co Sch<br>1600 Bundy St, Matador 79244<br>James Richards | PK-12 | TV | 162<br>27 | 71% | 806/347-2676 |

## NACOGDOCHES COUNTY

## NACOGDOCHES PUBLIC SCHOOLS

• **Central Heights Ind Sch Dist** PID: 01043079     936/564-2681
10317 US Highway 259, Nacogdoches 75965     Fax 936/569-6889

**Schools:** 3 \ **Teachers:** 84 \ **Students:** 1,100 \ **Special Ed Students:** 77
\ **LEP Students:** 53 \ **College-Bound:** 48% \ **Ethnic:** Asian 1%, African
American 5%, Hispanic 18%, Caucasian 76% \ **Exp:** $479 (High) \
**Poverty:** 22% \ **Title I:** $214,731 \ **Open-Close:** 08/24 - 05/20 \ **DTBP:** $395
(High) \ f

| | | | |
|---|---|---|---|
| David Russell | 1 | Sidney Dees | 2 |
| Tanya Bryant | 4 | Kevin Matheny | 5 |
| Kevin Herron | 6* | Kathryn Engle | 8,16,57,271,274* |
| Andy Binford | 10* | Martha Labbit | 11,76,296,298* |
| Julie Feasel | 13,37* | Sharon Duke | 27,31 |
| Lauren Tyler | 38,69,83,85,88,285 | Deborah Jones | 58 |
| Don Shoemaker | 67 | Jeffery Hightower | 73* |
| Martha Labbit | 84 | | |

| Public Schs..Principal | Grd | Prgm | Enr/#Cls | SN |
|---|---|---|---|---|
| Central Heights Elem Sch<br>10317 US Highway 259, Nacogdoches 75965<br>**Kathryn Engle** | PK-5 | T | 497<br>30 | 46% 936/552-3424<br>Fax 936/560-2099 |
| Central Heights High Sch<br>10471 US Highway 259, Nacogdoches 75965<br>Jonathan Vick | 9-12 | | 345<br>35 | 33% 936/552-3408<br>Fax 936/560-2016 |
| Central Heights Middle Sch<br>1471 Highway 259N, Nacogdoches 75965<br>Andy Binford | 6-8 | | 304 | 37% 936/552-3441<br>Fax 936/560-2016 |

• **Chireno ISD School Dist** PID: 01043108     936/362-2132
901 Main St, Chireno 75937     Fax 936/362-2490

**Schools:** 1 \ **Teachers:** 29 \ **Students:** 400 \ **Special Ed Students:** 52
\ **LEP Students:** 30 \ **College-Bound:** 88% \ **Ethnic:** African American
4%, Hispanic 23%, Caucasian 73% \ **Exp:** $1,035 (High) \ **Poverty:** 23% \
**Title I:** $151,934 \ **Open-Close:** 08/19 - 05/27 \ **DTBP:** $345 (High)

| | | | |
|---|---|---|---|
| Michael Skinner | 1 | Jeanne Holloway | 2,11 |
| Kirk Turner | 3* | Amber Evans | 4* |
| Heather Hagle | 8,11,79,275,286,294,296* | Micheal Skinner | 8,273* |
| Kevin Helmer | 16,73,295* | Sam Thomas | 27* |
| Sandy Pinner | 36,57,69,83,88,93,271* | Crystal Zienko | 58 |
| Michael Sanford | 67 | Brian King | 273 |

| Public Schs..Principal | Grd | Prgm | Enr/#Cls | SN |
|---|---|---|---|---|
| Chireno Sch<br>901 Main St, Chireno 75937<br>Brandy Gray | PK-12 | TV | 400<br>23 | 57% 936/362-2132 |

• **Cushing Ind School Dist** PID: 01043134     936/326-4890
1088 Bearcat Dr, Cushing 75760     Fax 936/326-4115

**Schools:** 2 \ **Teachers:** 39 \ **Students:** 524 \ **Special Ed Students:** 69
\ **LEP Students:** 19 \ **College-Bound:** 40% \ **Ethnic:** Asian 1%, African
American 7%, Hispanic 15%, Native American: 1%, Caucasian 76% \
**Exp:** $503 (High) \ **Poverty:** 21% \ **Title I:** $166,171 \ **Open-Close:** 08/26 -
05/21 \ **DTBP:** $340 (High)

| | | | |
|---|---|---|---|
| Michael Davis | 1 | Martha Lee | 2 |
| Casey Copelan | 3,73 | Brenda Marshall | 4 |
| Shane Johnson | 5,83,91 | Shane Smelley | 6* |
| Dee Cruz | 7,11,57,69,271,296* | Lynda Langham | 67 |
| Tammy Smith | 79 | Shane Johnson | 83,91* |

| Public Schs..Principal | Grd | Prgm | Enr/#Cls | SN |
|---|---|---|---|---|
| Cushing Elem Sch<br>1165 Bearcat Dr, Cushing 75760<br>Stefani Jackson | PK-5 | T | 246<br>14 | 65% 936/326-4234<br>Fax 936/326-4265 |
| Cushing Jr Sr High Sch<br>1088 Bearcat Dr, Cushing 75760<br>Andy Gresham | 6-12 | AGTV | 278<br>20 | 59% 936/326-4890<br>Fax 936/326-4131 |

• **Douglass Ind School Dist** PID: 01043160     936/569-9804
20712 S FM 225, Douglass 75943     Fax 936/569-9446

**Schools:** 1 \ **Teachers:** 38 \ **Students:** 440 \ **Special Ed Students:** 46 \
**LEP Students:** 32 \ **College-Bound:** 100% \ **Ethnic:** Asian 1%, African
American 5%, Hispanic 15%, Native American: 1%, Caucasian 78% \
**Exp:** $550 (High) \ **Poverty:** 19% \ **Title I:** $108,782 \ **Open-Close:** 08/19 -
05/21 \ **DTBP:** $341 (High)

| | | | |
|---|---|---|---|
| Justin Keeling | 1 | Casey Watson | 2 |
| Brian Gandy | 8,57,271,273 | Sue Paul | 36,69,83,88,270 |
| Craig Matson | 58* | Bobby Hobson | 67 |
| Ty Porterfield | 73,76,286 | | |

| Public Schs..Principal | Grd | Prgm | Enr/#Cls | SN |
|---|---|---|---|---|
| Douglass Sch<br>20712 S FM 225, Douglass 75943<br>Phil Gersback \ Jason Purke | PK-12 | AV | 440<br>25 | 41% 936/569-9804 |

• **Etoile Ind School Dist** PID: 01043196     936/465-9404
16039 FM 226, Etoile 75944     Fax 936/854-2241

**Schools:** 1 \ **Teachers:** 14 \ **Students:** 100 \ **Special Ed Students:** 24
\ **Ethnic:** African American 1%, Hispanic 2%, Native American: 1%,
Caucasian 96% \ **Exp:** $673 (High) \ **Poverty:** 21% \ **Title I:** $97,938 \
**Open-Close:** 08/20 - 06/11 \ **DTBP:** $365 (High) \ f

| | | | |
|---|---|---|---|
| Sarah Hottman | 1,11 | Rose Pate | 2,28 |
| Skipper Eberlan | 3,5 | Delayne Di Donato | 6 |
| Stephenie Ellisor | 7 | Mark Whitehead | 59,69 |
| Gayle Riley | 67 | Adam Craft | 73,286 |

| Public Schs..Principal | Grd | Prgm | Enr/#Cls | SN |
|---|---|---|---|---|
| Etoile Elem Sch<br>16039 FM 226, Etoile 75944<br>Adam Craft | PK-8 | T | 100<br>12 | 83% 936/465-9404<br>f |

| | | | | | | | | |
|---|---|---|---|---|---|---|---|---|
| 1 | Superintendent | 8 | Curric/Instruct K-12 | 19 | Chief Financial Officer | 29 | Family/Consumer Science | 39 | Social Studies K-12 | 49 | English/Lang Arts Elem | 59 | Special Education Elem | 69 | Academic Assessment |
| 2 | Bus/Finance/Purchasing | 9 | Curric/Instruct Elem | 20 | Art K-12 | 30 | Adult Education | 40 | Social Studies Elem | 50 | English/Lang Arts Sec | 60 | Special Education Sec | 70 | Research/Development |
| 3 | Buildings And Grounds | 10 | Curric/Instruct Sec | 21 | Art Elem | 31 | Career/Sch-to-Work K-12 | 41 | Social Studies Sec | 51 | Reading K-12 | 61 | Foreign/World Lang K-12 | 71 | Public Information |
| 4 | Food Service | 11 | Federal Program | 22 | Art Sec | 32 | Career/Sch-to-Work Elem | 42 | Science K-12 | 52 | Reading Elem | 62 | Foreign/World Lang Elem | 72 | Summer School |
| 5 | Transportation | 12 | Title I | 23 | Music K-12 | 33 | Career/Sch-to-Work Sec | 43 | Science Elem | 53 | Reading Sec | 63 | Foreign/World Lang Sec | 73 | Instructional Tech |
| 6 | Athletic | 13 | Title V | 24 | Music Elem | 34 | Early Childhood Ed | 44 | Science Sec | 54 | Remedial Reading K-12 | 64 | Religious Education K-12 | 74 | Inservice Training |
| 7 | Health Services | 14 | Asst Superintendent | 25 | Music Sec | 35 | Health/Phys Education | 45 | Math K-12 | 55 | Remedial Reading Elem | 65 | Religious Education Elem | 75 | Marketing/Distributive |
| | | 15 | Asst Superintendent | 26 | Business Education | 36 | Guidance Services K-12 | 46 | Math Elem | 56 | Remedial Reading Sec | 66 | Religious Education Sec | 76 | Info Systems |
| | | 16 | Instructional Media Svcs | 27 | Career & Tech Ed | 37 | Guidance Services Elem | 47 | Math Sec | 57 | Bilingual/ELL | 67 | School Board President | 77 | Psychological Assess |
| | | 17 | Chief Operations Officer | 28 | Technology Education | 38 | Guidance Services Sec | 48 | English/Lang Arts K-12 | 58 | Special Education K-12 | 68 | Teacher Personnel | 78 | Affirmative Action |
| | | 18 | Chief Academic Officer | | | | | | | | | | | | |

- ## Garrison Ind School Dist PID: 01043213
459 N US Highway 59, Garrison 75946

936/347-7000
Fax 936/347-2529

**Schools:** 3 \ **Teachers:** 62 \ **Students:** 682 \ **Special Ed Students:** 72 \ **LEP Students:** 16 \ **College-Bound:** 70% \ **Ethnic:** Asian 2%, African American 17%, Hispanic 13%, Caucasian 68% \ **Exp:** $328 (High) \ **Poverty:** 19% \ **Title I:** $153,983 \ **Open-Close:** 08/19 - 05/21 \ **DTBP:** $294 (High)

| | | | |
|---|---|---|---|
| Reid Spivey | 1 | Patterson Hill | 2 |
| Andrew Schmidt | 3 | Denise Derby | 4 |
| Christopher Lee | 5 | Brandon Alverez | 6 |
| Amie Adkison | 7 | Colleen Hill | 11* |
| William Weeks | 16,73,84 | Eugenia Uribe | 36,57,85* |
| Joya Konderla | 37 | Leslie McFadden | 58* |
| Bart Reneau | 67 | Joel Barton | 83* |

| Public Schs..Principal | Grd | Prgm | Enr/#Cls | SN |
|---|---|---|---|---|
| Garrison Elem Sch<br>459 N US Highway 59, Garrison 75946<br>Colleen Hill | PK-5 | T | 298<br>28 | 59% 936/347-7010<br>Fax 936/347-7004 |
| Garrison Middle Sch<br>459 N US Highway 59, Garrison 75946<br>**Larry Prince** | 6-8 | T | 110<br>14 | 52% 936/347-7020<br>Fax 936/347-7004 |
| Garrison Senior High Sch<br>459 N US Highway 59, Garrison 75946<br>Clark Barnett | 9-12 | T | 108<br>28 | 43% 936/347-7030<br>Fax 936/347-7059 |

- ## Martinsville Ind School Dist PID: 01043249
12952 E State Highway 7, Nacogdoches 75961

936/564-3455
Fax 936/569-0498

**Schools:** 1 \ **Teachers:** 33 \ **Students:** 400 \ **Special Ed Students:** 47 \ **LEP Students:** 24 \ **College-Bound:** 52% \ **Ethnic:** African American 6%, Hispanic 16%, Caucasian 78% \ **Exp:** $720 (High) \ **Poverty:** 26% \ **Title I:** $117,515 \ **Open-Close:** 08/17 - 05/28 \ **DTBP:** $320 (High)

| | | | |
|---|---|---|---|
| Dr David Simmons | 1 | Samantha Cobb | 2 |
| Will Cauphen | 8,57,69,74,92,271 | Keith Kimbrough | 9,12,58,275,296 |
| Roni Waller | 11,36,83,752* | Teresa Weaver | 67 |
| Chad Huckaby | 73,76 | | |

| Public Schs..Principal | Grd | Prgm | Enr/#Cls | SN |
|---|---|---|---|---|
| Martinsville Sch<br>12952 E State Highway 7, Nacogdoches 75961<br>Shelia Cobb \ Will Cauthen | PK-12 | TV | 400<br>22 | 52% 936/564-3455 |

- ## Nacogdoches Ind School Dist PID: 01043275
420 S Shawnee St, Nacogdoches 75961

936/569-5000
Fax 936/569-5798

**Schools:** 10 \ **Teachers:** 422 \ **Students:** 6,400 \ **Special Ed Students:** 640 \ **LEP Students:** 1,636 \ **College-Bound:** 58% \ **Ethnic:** Asian 1%, African American 31%, Hispanic 49%, Caucasian 19% \ **Exp:** $450 (High) \ **Poverty:** 28% \ **Title I:** $3,658,483 \ **Special Education:** $1,160,000 \ **Open-Close:** 08/31 - 05/27 \ **DTBP:** $158 (High) 🔲 🔲

| | | | |
|---|---|---|---|
| **Dr Gabriel Trujillo** | 1,83 | Lisa Barbarick | 2,19 |
| Ralph LaRue | 3 | Robin Thacker | 4 |
| Stacy Lampkin | 5 | Darren Allman | 6 |
| Dr Daya Hill | 8,18,285 | Dr Jolynn Corley | 11,294 |
| Harold Whitaker | 15,68 | Michael Martin | 15 |
| Kirstin Morris | 16,73,76,295,297 | Donald Hasley | 27* |
| Jacob Lusk | 27 | Cindy Ivy | 36,69 |
| Evelyn Sauceda | 57,271 | Dr Audrey Young | 58,752 |
| Pam Fitch | 67 | Les Linebarger | 71 |
| Eddie Harwell | 90 | | |

| Public Schs..Principal | Grd | Prgm | Enr/#Cls | SN |
|---|---|---|---|---|
| Brooks-Quinn Jones Elem Sch<br>907 N Sanders St, Nacogdoches 75964<br>Tom Miller \ **Gerald Fonzie** | PK-5 | T | 778<br>26 | 90% 936/569-5040<br>Fax 936/569-5796<br>🔲🔲 |
| Carpenter Elem Sch<br>1005 Leroy St, Nacogdoches 75961<br>Lola Moore | PK-5 | T | 454<br>24 | 96% 936/569-5070<br>Fax 936/569-3165 |
| Fredonia Elem Sch<br>1326 S Fredonia St, Nacogdoches 75964<br>Melinda Wiebold | PK-5 | T | 396<br>26 | 91% 936/569-5080<br>Fax 936/569-3168 |
| Ⓐ Malcolm Rector Technical HS<br>6003 North St, Nacogdoches 75965<br>James Adams | 9-12 | T | 50<br>14 | 87% 936/205-1000 |
| McMichael Middle Sch<br>4330 SE Stallings Dr, Nacogdoches 75961<br>Tim Mullican | 6-8 | T | 721 | 84% 936/552-0519<br>Fax 936/552-0523 |
| Mike Moses Middle Sch<br>2801 Park St, Nacogdoches 75961<br>Stephen Autrey | 6-8 | T | 653<br>50 | 76% 936/569-5001<br>Fax 936/569-5031<br>🔲 |
| Nacogdoches High Sch<br>4310 Appleby Sand Rd, Nacogdoches 75965<br>Romulo Crespo | 9-12 | TV | 760<br>60 | 63% 936/564-2466<br>Fax 936/560-8162 |
| Nettie Marshall Elem Sch<br>422 W Cox St, Nacogdoches 75964<br>Joseph Rodriguez | K-5 | T | 355<br>16 | 85% 936/569-5062<br>Fax 936/569-5038 |
| Raguet Elem Sch<br>2708 Raguet St, Nacogdoches 75965<br>Julia Wells | K-5 | T | 559<br>26 | 78% 936/569-5052<br>Fax 936/569-5060 |
| Thomas J Rusk Elem Sch<br>411 N Mound St, Nacogdoches 75961<br>Paula Harshbarger | PK-5 | T | 583<br>36 | 93% 936/569-3100<br>Fax 936/569-5759 |

- ## Woden Ind School Dist PID: 01043354
5263 Farm Rd 226, Nacogdoches 75961

936/564-2073
Fax 936/564-1250

**Schools:** 3 \ **Teachers:** 64 \ **Students:** 780 \ **Special Ed Students:** 52 \ **LEP Students:** 64 \ **Ethnic:** Asian 1%, African American 1%, Hispanic 22%, Caucasian 76% \ **Exp:** $468 (High) \ **Poverty:** 16% \ **Title I:** $213,914 \ **Special Education:** $121,000 \ **Open-Close:** 08/13 - 05/20 \ **DTBP:** $356 (High)

| | | | |
|---|---|---|---|
| Brady Taylor | 1 | Lindsay Lunsford | 2 |
| Jodee Woodcock | 8,11,294,296,298 | Susan Harrison | 16* |
| Brandi Bentley | 58 | Perry Grimes | 67 |
| Malinda Holzapfel | 73,76 | | |

| Public Schs..Principal | Grd | Prgm | Enr/#Cls | SN |
|---|---|---|---|---|
| Woden Elem Sch<br>5263 FM 226, Nacogdoches 75961<br>John Donihoo | PK-5 | T | 364<br>45 | 63% 936/564-2386<br>Fax 936/564-3322 |
| Woden High Sch<br>5263 FM 226, Nacogdoches 75961<br>Jesse Stroud | 9-12 | TV | 220 | 51% 936/564-7903<br>Fax 936/462-4962 |
| Woden Junior High Sch<br>5263 FM 226, Nacogdoches 75961<br>Dr Jerry Meador | 6-8 | T | 179<br>12 | 60% 936/564-7903<br>Fax 936/622-0566 |

## NACOGDOCHES PRIVATE SCHOOLS

| Private Schs..Principal | Grd | Prgm | Enr/#Cls | SN |
|---|---|---|---|---|
| Christ Episcopal Sch<br>1430 N Mound St, Nacogdoches 75961<br>Catherine Oliver | PK-6 | | 114<br>11 | 936/564-0621<br>Fax 936/552-7120 |

| | | | | |
|---|---|---|---|---|
| Fredonia Hill Baptist Academy<br>1711 South St, Nacogdoches 75964<br>Jason Boyd | PK-6 | 130<br>14 | | 936/564-4472<br>Fax 936/564-0518 ▪ |
| Nacogdoches Christian Academy<br>211 SE Stallings Dr, Nacogdoches 75964<br>Donna Baker | PK-K | 54 | | 936/462-1021<br>Fax 936/462-1176 |
| Regents Academy<br>200 NE Stallings Dr, Nacogdoches 75961<br>Shannon Henry \ Lance Vermillion | K-12 | 158 | | 936/559-7343<br>Fax 936/559-7344 ▪ |

## NAVARRO COUNTY

## NAVARRO PUBLIC SCHOOLS

● **Blooming Grove Ind School Dist** PID: 01043392     903/695-2541
212 W Grady St, Blooming GRV 76626     Fax 903/695-2594

**Schools:** 3 \ **Teachers:** 72 \ **Students:** 950 \ **Special Ed Students:** 77 \ **LEP Students:** 123 \ **College-Bound:** 66% \ **Ethnic:** African American 3%, Hispanic 33%, Caucasian 64% \ **Exp:** $498 (High) \ **Poverty:** 15% \ **Title I:** $170,131 \ **Open-Close:** 08/18 - 05/28 \ **DTBP:** $382 (High) \ ▪

| | | | |
|---|---|---|---|
| Rick Hartley | 1 | Amy Nicholason | 2 |
| Kenneth Hutchison | 3,5 | Sharen Lewis | 4* |
| Ervin Chandler | 6 | Chyrl Hollingsworth | 7 |
| Ashley Crabtree | 8,11,69,285,288,298 | Denise Clifton | 37 |
| Lori Kirby | 37 | Jon Southard | 67 |
| Dennis Williams | 73,76,295* | | |

| Public Schs..Principal | Grd | Prgm | Enr/#Cls | SN | |
|---|---|---|---|---|---|
| Blooming Grove Elem Sch<br>601 N Elm St, Blooming GRV 76626<br>**Allyson King** | PK-5 | AT | 378<br>24 | 64% | 903/695-2541<br>Fax 903/695-2009 |
| Blooming Grove High Sch<br>212 W Grady St, Blooming GRV 76626<br>John Gillen | 9-12 | ATV | 291<br>27 | 51% | 903/695-2541 |
| Blooming Grove Junior High Sch<br>604 Ramsey St, Blooming GRV 76626<br>Doyle Bell | 6-8 | AT | 218<br>15 | 63% | 903/695-2541<br>Fax 903/695-4601 |

● **Corsicana Ind School Dist** PID: 01043421     903/874-7441
2200 W 4th Ave, Corsicana 75110     Fax 903/602-8515

**Schools:** 9 \ **Teachers:** 416 \ **Students:** 6,000 \ **Special Ed Students:** 609 \ **LEP Students:** 1,331 \ **College-Bound:** 67% \ **Ethnic:** Asian 1%, African American 17%, Hispanic 55%, Caucasian 27% \ **Exp:** $276 (Med) \ **Poverty:** 25% \ **Title I:** $1,927,840 \ **Special Education:** $998,000 \ **Open-Close:** 08/13 - 05/27 \ **DTBP:** $104 (High) \ ▪ ▪

| | | | |
|---|---|---|---|
| Dr Diane Frost | 1 | Richie Cutrer | 3,5,83,91 |
| Shirrell Jessie | 4 | Carla Whitt | 7,85* |
| Kim Holcomb | 8,15,34,39 | Elmer Avellaneda | 11,58,77 |
| Rhonda Dulworth | 31* | Danzel Lee | 36,79,294 |
| Debbie Cottar | 57,88 | Leah Blackard | 67 |
| Paula Simpson | 69* | Susan Johnson | 71,76,93,297 |
| Austin Contreras | 73,295 | Carla Stanford | 288 |

| Public Schs..Principal | Grd | Prgm | Enr/#Cls | SN | |
|---|---|---|---|---|---|
| Bowie Elem Sch<br>1800 Bowie Dr, Corsicana 75110<br>Hollye Usery | K-4 | T | 534<br>35 | 61% | 903/872-6541<br>Fax 903/872-6298 |

| Public Schs..Principal | Grd | Prgm | Enr/#Cls | SN | |
|---|---|---|---|---|---|
| Carroll Elem Sch<br>1101 E 13th Ave, Corsicana 75110<br>Cheryl Murdock | K-4 | T | 381<br>36 | 95% | 903/872-3074<br>Fax 903/641-4153 |
| Collins Intermediate Sch<br>1500 Dobbins Rd, Corsicana 75110<br>Scott Doring | 5-6 | T | 952<br>40 | 81% | 903/872-3979<br>Fax 903/874-1423 ▪▪ |
| Corsicana High Sch<br>3701 W State Highway 22, Corsicana 75110<br>Sean Kays | 9-12 | T | 1,700<br>55 | 69% | 903/874-8211<br>Fax 903/874-7403 ▪▪ |
| Corsicana Middle Sch<br>4101 FM 744, Corsicana 75110<br>Janice Johnson | 7-8 | T | 826<br>45 | 79% | 430/775-6200<br>Fax 903/874-1423 |
| Drane Learning Center<br>110 S 18th St, Corsicana 75110<br>Mickey White | PK-PK | T | 282 | 90% | 903/874-8281<br>Fax 903/641-4130 |
| Fannin Elem Sch<br>3201 N Beaton St, Corsicana 75110<br>Dallas Horne | K-4 | T | 444<br>35 | 88% | 903/874-3728<br>Fax 903/874-0758 ▪▪ |
| Jose Antonio Navarro Elem Sch<br>601 S 45th St, Corsicana 75110<br>Tim Betts | K-4 | T | 523<br>44 | 88% | 903/874-1011<br>Fax 903/874-3874 ▪ |
| Sam Houston Elem Sch<br>1213 W 4th Ave, Corsicana 75110<br>Molly Corrington | K-4 | T | 362 | 78% | 903/874-6971<br>Fax 903/641-4114 ▪▪ |

● **Dawson Ind School Dist** PID: 01043524     254/578-1031
199 N School Ave, Dawson 76639     Fax 254/578-1721

**Schools:** 1 \ **Teachers:** 38 \ **Students:** 512 \ **Special Ed Students:** 47 \ **LEP Students:** 28 \ **College-Bound:** 50% \ **Ethnic:** African American 11%, Hispanic 17%, Native American: 1%, Caucasian 71% \ **Exp:** $717 (High) \ **Poverty:** 19% \ **Title I:** $175,973 \ **Open-Close:** 08/17 - 05/27 \ **DTBP:** $335 (High)

| | | | |
|---|---|---|---|
| Stacy Henderson | 1 | Kelly Miller | 2 |
| Aaron Hogue | 3,5* | Lori James | 4* |
| Ronnie Striplin | 6* | Sheryl Bragg | 8,13,31,38,69,286,288* |
| Andrea Farish | 9,12,57* | Robert Bray | 11,83,88,271* |
| Lisa Murray | 58* | David Mathews | 67 |
| Cameron Shaw | 73,76,295* | | |

| Public Schs..Principal | Grd | Prgm | Enr/#Cls | SN | |
|---|---|---|---|---|---|
| Dawson Sch<br>199 N School Ave, Dawson 76639<br>Robert Bray \ Andrea Farish | PK-12 | ATV | 512<br>24 | 67% | 254/578-1031 |

● **Frost Ind School Dist** PID: 01043550     903/682-2711
208 N Wyrick St, Frost 76641     Fax 903/682-2107

**Schools:** 2 \ **Teachers:** 38 \ **Students:** 368 \ **Special Ed Students:** 32 \ **LEP Students:** 52 \ **College-Bound:** 75% \ **Ethnic:** African American 2%, Hispanic 32%, Caucasian 67% \ **Exp:** $371 (High) \ **Poverty:** 22% \ **Title I:** $98,062 \ **Open-Close:** 08/19 - 05/27 \ **DTBP:** $350 (High)

| | | | |
|---|---|---|---|
| Mickie Jackson | 1,11,83 | Deanna Harrington | 2* |
| Larry Kern | 3,5 | Aubrey May | 4 |
| Randy Fulton | 6 | Dan Lunsford | 10,74* |
| Precia Woodall | 16,73,76,295 | Lisa Bland | 51,54* |
| Jason Curl | 67 | | |

| Public Schs..Principal | Grd | Prgm | Enr/#Cls | SN | |
|---|---|---|---|---|---|
| Frost Elem Sch<br>208 N Wyrick St, Frost 76641<br>Natalie Rose | PK-5 | ATV | 190 | 58% | 903/682-2541 |

| | | | | | |
|---|---|---|---|---|---|
| 1 Superintendent | 8 Curric/Instruct K-12 | 19 Chief Financial Officer | 29 Family/Consumer Science | 39 Social Studies K-12 | 49 English/Lang Arts Elem | 59 Special Education Elem | 69 Academic Assessment |
| 2 Bus/Finance/Purchasing | 9 Curric/Instruct Elem | 20 Art K-12 | 30 Adult Education | 40 Social Studies Elem | 50 English/Lang Arts Sec | 60 Special Education Sec | 70 Research/Development |
| 3 Buildings And Grounds | 10 Curric/Instruct Sec | 21 Art Elem | 31 Career/Sch-to-Work K-12 | 41 Social Studies Sec | 51 Reading K-12 | 61 Foreign/World Lang K-12 | 71 Public Information |
| 4 Food Service | 11 Federal Program | 22 Art Sec | 32 Career/Sch-to-Work Elem | 42 Science K-12 | 52 Reading Elem | 62 Foreign/World Lang Elem | 72 Summer School |
| 5 Transportation | 12 Title I | 23 Music K-12 | 33 Career/Sch-to-Work Sec | 43 Science Elem | 53 Reading Sec | 63 Foreign/World Lang Sec | 73 Instructional Tech |
| 6 Athletic | 13 Title V | 24 Music Elem | 34 Early Childhood Ed | 44 Science Sec | 54 Remedial Reading K-12 | 64 Religious Education K-12 | 74 Inservice Training |
| 7 Health Services | 14 Instructional Media Svcs | 25 Music Sec | 35 Health/Phys Education | 45 Math K-12 | 55 Remedial Reading Elem | 65 Religious Education Elem | 75 Marketing/Distributive |
| | 15 Asst Superintendent | 26 Business Education | 36 Guidance Services K-12 | 46 Math Elem | 56 Remedial Reading Sec | 66 Religious Education Sec | 76 Info Systems |
| | 16 Instructional Media Svcs | 27 Career & Tech Ed | 37 Guidance Services Elem | 47 Math Sec | 57 Bilingual/ELL | 67 School Board President | 77 Psychological Assess |
| **TX—302** | 17 Chief Operations Officer | 28 Technology Education | 38 Guidance Services Sec | 48 English/Lang Arts K-12 | 58 Special Education K-12 | 68 Teacher Personnel | 78 Affirmative Action |

Frost High Sch | 6-12 | ATV | 178 | 46% | 903/682-2541
208 N Wyrick St, Frost 76641 | | | 45 | |
Dan Lunsford

• **Kerens Ind School Dist** PID: 01043586     903/396-2924
200 Bobcat Ln, Kerens 75144     Fax 903/396-2334

---

**Schools:** 3 \ **Teachers:** 48 \ **Students:** 600 \ **Special Ed Students:** 55 \ **LEP Students:** 27 \ **College-Bound:** 75% \ **Ethnic:** African American 24%, Hispanic 25%, Caucasian 50% \ **Exp:** $493 (High) \ **Poverty:** 49% \ **Title I:** $574,911 \ **Open-Close:** 08/14 - 05/21 \ **DTBP:** $461 (High) \ 🅕

---

Martin Brumit ....................................... 1,11,83
Cliff Davis ....................................................3
Terrell Harris ..............................................6*
Janice Quinn .............................................. 16
Robin Williams ........................................38,69
Teresa Jennings ......................................... 67
Jim Kendall .................................................2
Kayla Duncan .............................................. 4
Cindy Sattewhite ......................................... 9
Misty Blue ..............................................37,57*
Kayce Bonner .............................................. 58

| Public Schs..Principal | Grd | Prgm | Enr/#Cls | SN | |
| --- | --- | --- | --- | --- | --- |
| Kerens Elem Sch<br>200 Bobcat Ln, Kerens 75144<br>**Cindy Satterwhite** | PK-4 | | 229<br>25 | | 903/396-7941 |
| Kerens High Sch<br>200 Bobcat Ln, Kerens 75144<br>Greg Priddy | 9-12 | T | 180<br>21 | 76% | 903/396-2931 |
| Kerens Middle Sch<br>200 Bobcat Ln, Kerens 75144<br>Greg Priddy | 6-8 | | 198<br>19 | | 903/396-2570 |

• **Mildred Ind School Dist** PID: 01043615     903/872-6505
5475 S US Highway 287, Corsicana 75109     Fax 903/872-1341

---

**Schools:** 1 \ **Teachers:** 59 \ **Students:** 730 \ **Special Ed Students:** 57 \ **LEP Students:** 20 \ **Ethnic:** African American 3%, Hispanic 18%, Native American: 1%, Caucasian 78% \ **Exp:** $304 (High) \ **Poverty:** 13% \ **Title I:** $82,507 \ **Open-Close:** 08/12 - 05/27

---

Shannon Baker ....................................1,11
Tim Gorden ...............................................3,5
Daphany Garrett ................ 36,69,83,85,270
Justin Barham ............................................ 73
Beverly McQuary .........................................2
Duke Dalton ............................................... 6
Bradley Boyte ............................................ 67
Corrine Thompson ...................................... 81

| Public Schs..Principal | Grd | Prgm | Enr/#Cls | SN | |
| --- | --- | --- | --- | --- | --- |
| Mildred Sch<br>5475 S US Highway 287, Corsicana 75109<br>Michelle Coker \ Aaron Tidwell | K-12 | ATV | 730<br>50 | 43% | 903/872-6505 |

• **Rice Ind School Dist** PID: 01043641     903/326-4287
1302 SW McKinney St, Rice 75155     Fax 903/326-4164

---

**Schools:** 4 \ **Teachers:** 70 \ **Students:** 975 \ **Special Ed Students:** 72 \ **LEP Students:** 178 \ **College-Bound:** 30% \ **Ethnic:** African American 3%, Hispanic 66%, Caucasian 31% \ **Exp:** $385 (High) \ **Poverty:** 25% \ **Title I:** $236,954 \ **Open-Close:** 08/12 - 05/20 \ **DTBP:** $342 (High) \ 🅕

---

Amy Harvell ...............................................1
Robert Allen ......................................3,4,5,8
Rachel Tidwell ............................................7*
Justin Bruton ............... 16,76,97,98,286,295
Shannna Lopez ........................................... 67
Robert Gray .............................................. 91
Julie Obanon ..........................2,11,58,68,88
Andy Mills ................................................. 6
Cindy Black .............................................9,57
Casey Sellers ............................................ 31
Reagan Greer ........................................69,270

| Public Schs..Principal | Grd | Prgm | Enr/#Cls | SN | |
| --- | --- | --- | --- | --- | --- |
| Ⓐ Navarro Co Alt Educ Ctr<br>705 N Beaton St, Corsicana 75110<br>Melinda Richardson | K-12 | | 75 | | 903/872-4502 |
| Rice Elem Sch<br>1500 SW McKinney St, Rice 75155<br>Kelly Walters | PK-2 | T | 164<br>19 | 86% | 903/326-4151<br>Fax 903/326-4900 |
| Rice High Sch<br>1400 SW McKinney St, Rice 75155<br>Robert Allen | 9-12 | TV | 269<br>20 | 68% | 903/326-4502<br>Fax 903/326-5042 |
| Rice Intermediate Middle Sch<br>1402 SW McKinney St, Rice 75155<br>Monnie Metcalfe | 3-8 | T | 433 | 74% | 903/326-4190<br>Fax 903/326-4620 |

## NAVARRO CATHOLIC SCHOOLS

• **Diocese of Dallas Ed Office** PID: 01012367
Listing includes only schools located in this county. See District Index for location of Diocesan Offices.

| Catholic Schs..Principal | Grd | Prgm | Enr/#Cls | SN | |
| --- | --- | --- | --- | --- | --- |
| James L Collins Catholic Sch<br>3000 W State Highway 22, Corsicana 75110<br>Vicky Morrison | PK-8 | | 160<br>10 | | 903/872-1751<br>Fax 903/872-1186 |

## NAVARRO PRIVATE SCHOOLS

| Private Schs..Principal | Grd | Prgm | Enr/#Cls | SN | |
| --- | --- | --- | --- | --- | --- |
| Agape Christian Academy<br>3116 W State Highway 22, Corsicana 75110<br>Kathi McMullan | PK-12 | | 120 | | 903/641-0900<br>Fax 903/641-0905 |
| Park Meadows Academy<br>3401 Country Club Rd, Corsicana 75110<br>Paul Davis | PK-12 | | 60 | | 903/872-2391 |

## NEWTON COUNTY

## NEWTON PUBLIC SCHOOLS

• **Burkeville Ind School Dist** PID: 01043677     409/565-2201
231 County Road 2099, Burkeville 75932     Fax 409/565-2012

---

**Schools:** 2 \ **Teachers:** 23 \ **Students:** 250 \ **Special Ed Students:** 35 \ **College-Bound:** 25% \ **Ethnic:** African American 25%, Hispanic 2%, Caucasian 73% \ **Exp:** $544 (High) \ **Poverty:** 22% \ **Title I:** $117,431 \ **Special Education:** $80,000 \ **Open-Close:** 08/13 - 05/14 \ **DTBP:** $402 (High)

---

Dr Brant Graham ...............................1,11
Donnie Dickerson ........................3,5*
Phylis Stephens .......... 8,31,57,83,88,275,294
Ronald Graham .................................... 67
Pam Dickerson ....................................2,286
Betty Jennings .........................................4*
Donna Graham ...................................... 58

---

| Public Schs..Principal | Grd | Prgm | Enr/#Cls | SN |
|---|---|---|---|---|
| Burkeville Elem Sch<br>231 County Road 2099, Burkeville 75932<br>**Kevin Day** | PK-6 | | 144<br>30 | 409/565-4284<br>Fax 409/565-4558 |
| Burkeville Jr Sr High Sch<br>231 County Road 2099, Burkeville 75932<br>Kimberly Urie | 7-12 | T | 99<br>18 | 82% 409/565-4284<br>Fax 409/565-4558 |

● **Newton Ind School Dist** PID: 01043744　　　409/420-6600
720 Rusk St, Newton 75966　　　　　　　　　Fax 409/379-2189

**Schools:** 3 \ **Teachers:** 92 \ **Students:** 1,041 \ **Special Ed Students:** 154 \ **College-Bound:** 51% \ **Ethnic:** African American 38%, Hispanic 5%, Caucasian 56% \ **Exp:** $526 (High) \ **Poverty:** 27% \ **Title I:** $419,295 \ **Special Education:** $287,000 \ **Open-Close:** 09/08 - 05/28 \ **DTBP:** $363 (High)

| | | | |
|---|---|---|---|
| Michelle Barrow ........................1,11 | Kristi Lee ..............................................2 |
| Kathy Morrow ...............................4 | Drew Johnston ...................................6 |
| Debbie Johnston ......................8,69 | Johnny Metz ......................................15 |
| Bill Gobblin ............................58,88 | Donnie Meek .....................................67 |
| Connie Richardson ......................84 | |

| Public Schs..Principal | Grd | Prgm | Enr/#Cls | SN |
|---|---|---|---|---|
| Newton Elem Sch<br>414 Main St, Newton 75966<br>Bonetha Christopher | PK-5 | T | 537<br>37 | 77% 409/420-6600<br>Fax 409/379-2801 |
| Newton High Sch<br>2812 US Highway 190 E, Newton 75966<br>Lydia Bean | 9-12 | TV | 283<br>30 | 57% 409/420-6600<br>Fax 409/379-3321 |
| Newton Middle Sch<br>2814 US Highway 190 E, Newton 75966<br>Cathy Marshall | 6-8 | T | 221<br>27 | 67% 409/420-6600<br>Fax 409/379-5082 |

## NEWTON PRIVATE SCHOOLS

| Private Schs..Principal | Grd | Prgm | Enr/#Cls | SN |
|---|---|---|---|---|
| Agape Christian Academy<br>216 Glover Dr, Newton 75966<br>Holly Hopson | K-12 | | 20 | 409/379-4611 |

## NOLAN COUNTY

## NOLAN PUBLIC SCHOOLS

● **Blackwell Cons Ind Sch Dist** PID: 01043794　　325/282-2311
610 N Alamo St, Blackwell 79506　　　　　　　　Fax 325/282-2027

**Schools:** 1 \ **Teachers:** 22 \ **Students:** 150 \ **Special Ed Students:** 26 \ **LEP Students:** 3 \ **College-Bound:** 98% \ **Ethnic:** Hispanic 21%, Native American: 1%, Caucasian 78% \ **Exp:** $1,229 (High) \ **Poverty:** 28% \ **Title I:** $62,579 \ **Open-Close:** 08/12 - 05/14 \ **DTBP:** $373 (High)

| | | | |
|---|---|---|---|
| Abe Gott ...........................................1 | Jill Jones ...........................................2* |
| Ronnie Harris ...............................3,5* | Beverly Williams .................................4 |
| Clint Lowry ......................................6* | Bryan Shipman .............8,11,31,36,58,69,83* |
| Cassie Olivas ................................16* | Bryce Barnett ...................................27* |
| Jason Jones ...................................67 | |

| Public Schs..Principal | Grd | Prgm | Enr/#Cls | SN |
|---|---|---|---|---|
| Blackwell Sch<br>610 N Alamo St, Blackwell 79506<br>Jason Powers \ Bryan Shipman | PK-12 | AV | 150<br>30 | 38% 325/282-2311<br>Fax 325/282-4384 |

● **Highland Ind School Dist** PID: 01043859　　　325/766-3652
6625 FM 608, Roscoe 79545　　　　　　　　　　Fax 325/766-2281

**Schools:** 1 \ **Teachers:** 21 \ **Students:** 239 \ **Special Ed Students:** 18 \ **College-Bound:** 98% \ **Ethnic:** Hispanic 18%, Caucasian 81% \ **Exp:** $739 (High) \ **Poverty:** 24% \ **Title I:** $22,981 \ **Open-Close:** 08/20 - 05/25 \ **DTBP:** $342 (High)

| | | | |
|---|---|---|---|
| Duane Hyde ................................1,11 | Lynn Duniven .....................................2 |
| Bradley Hall ................................3,5 | Kyle Jeffrey .......................................6* |
| Shahala Hoelscher .................36,69* | Leigh Petty ........................................57 |
| Brent Allen ...................................67 | Brooke Sanford ...............................73* |

| Public Schs..Principal | Grd | Prgm | Enr/#Cls | SN |
|---|---|---|---|---|
| Highland Sch<br>6625 FM 608, Roscoe 79545<br>Brittany Lloyd \ Shane Mallory | PK-12 | TV | 239<br>17 | 33% 325/766-3651 |

● **Roscoe Collegiate Ind Sch Dist** PID: 01043885　325/766-3629
1101 W 7th St, Roscoe 79545　　　　　　　　　　　Fax 325/766-3138

**Schools:** 3 \ **Teachers:** 46 \ **Students:** 593 \ **Special Ed Students:** 48 \ **LEP Students:** 57 \ **College-Bound:** 90% \ **Ethnic:** African American 1%, Hispanic 55%, Caucasian 44% \ **Exp:** $858 (High) \ **Poverty:** 22% \ **Title I:** $99,812 \ **Open-Close:** 08/07 - 05/14 \ **DTBP:** $365 (High)

| | | | |
|---|---|---|---|
| Dr Kim Alexander ...............................1 | Rita Fried ............................................2 |
| Joe Smith ......................................3,5 | Jake Freeman ...................................6* |
| Gregory Althof ................................8* | Crystal Althof ...................................11* |
| Jared Seals .......................16,73,84 | Marsha Alexander ...36,83,88,271,273* |
| Lindsey Freeman .........................57 | Janie Abrigo .....................................58 |
| Wes Williams ...............................67 | Andrew Wilson ...............................285* |

| Public Schs..Principal | Grd | Prgm | Enr/#Cls | SN |
|---|---|---|---|---|
| Roscoe Collegiate High Sch<br>700 Elm St, Roscoe 79545<br>Gregory Althof | 6-12 | TV | 292<br>12 | 46% 325/766-3327<br>Fax 325/766-3419 |
| Roscoe Collegiate Mont ECC<br>1006 Main St, Roscoe 79545<br>Crystal Althof | PK-K | | 80 | 40% 325/766-3323<br>Fax 325/766-3605 |
| Roscoe Elem Sch<br>800 Elm St, Roscoe 79545<br>Crystal Althof | 1-5 | T | 221<br>10 | 46% 325/766-3323<br>Fax 325/766-3605 |

● **Sweetwater ISD School Dist** PID: 01043914　　325/235-8601
207 Musgrove St, Sweetwater 79556　　　　　　　Fax 325/235-5561

**Schools:** 7 \ **Teachers:** 146 \ **Students:** 1,888 \ **Special Ed Students:** 317 \ **LEP Students:** 46 \ **Ethnic:** Asian 1%, African American 6%, Hispanic 55%, Caucasian 38% \ **Exp:** $677 (High) \ **Poverty:** 25% \ **Title I:** $751,688 \ **Open-Close:** 08/10 - 05/27 \ **DTBP:** $328 (High) \ 🅕

| | | | |
|---|---|---|---|
| Dr Drew Howard ................................1 | Tim Hampton ..................................3,91 |
| Hunter Deming ...............................4 | Angela Duran ......................................5 |
| Ben McGeehee .........................6,35 | Nancy Soles ...................................7,85 |
| Dr Jared Duncum ......11,15,18,57,61,288 | Casey Bills .......................................19 |
| Rebecca Duncan ..........................27* | Amy Clark ............................31,38,88* |
| Kirk Stroman .................................58 | Jeff Allen ..........................................67 |
| Tammi Stafford .............................69 | Nick Rutherford .......76,84,95,286 |

| | | | |
|---|---|---|---|
| 1 Superintendent | 8 Curric/Instruct K-12 | 19 Chief Financial Officer | 29 Family/Consumer Science | 39 Social Studies K-12 | 49 English/Lang Arts Elem | 59 Special Education Elem | 69 Academic Assessment |
| 2 Bus/Finance/Purchasing | 9 Curric/Instruct Elem | 20 Art K-12 | 30 Adult Education | 40 Social Studies Elem | 50 English/Lang Arts Sec | 60 Special Education Sec | 70 Research/Development |
| 3 Buildings And Grounds | 10 Curric/Instruct Sec | 21 Art Elem | 31 Career/Sch-to-Work K-12 | 41 Social Studies Sec | 51 Reading K-12 | 61 Foreign/World Lang K-12 | 71 Public Information |
| 4 Food Service | 11 Federal Program | 22 Art Sec | 32 Career/Sch-to-Work Elem | 42 Science K-12 | 52 Reading Elem | 62 Foreign/World Lang Elem | 72 Summer School |
| 5 Transportation | 12 Title I | 23 Music K-12 | 33 Career/Sch-to-Work Sec | 43 Science Elem | 53 Reading Sec | 63 Foreign/World Lang Sec | 73 Instructional Tech |
| 6 Athletic | 13 Title V | 24 Music Elem | 34 Early Childhood Ed | 44 Science Sec | 54 Remedial Reading K-12 | 64 Religious Education K-12 | 74 Inservice Training |
| 7 Health Services | 15 Asst Superintendent | 25 Music Sec | 35 Health/Phys Education | 45 Math K-12 | 55 Remedial Reading Elem | 65 Religious Education Elem | 75 Marketing/Distributive |
| | 16 Instructional Media Svcs | 26 Business Education | 36 Guidance Services K-12 | 46 Math Elem | 56 Remedial Reading Sec | 66 Religious Education Sec | 76 Info Systems |
| | 17 Chief Operations Officer | 27 Career & Tech Ed | 37 Guidance Services Elem | 47 Math Sec | 57 Bilingual/ELL | 67 School Board President | 77 Psychological Assess |
| | 18 Chief Academic Officer | 28 Technology Education | 38 Guidance Services Sec | 48 English/Lang Arts K-12 | 58 Special Education K-12 | 68 Teacher Personnel | 78 Affirmative Action |

| Public Schs..Principal | Grd | Prgm | Enr/#Cls | SN |
|---|---|---|---|---|
| East Ridge Elem Sch<br>1700 E 12th St, Sweetwater 79556<br>Dawn Cornutt | 2-3 | T | 304<br>15 | 74% 325/235-5282<br>Fax 325/235-3740 |
| J P Cowan Achievement Center<br>700 W 4th St, Sweetwater 79556<br>**Betsy Stanaland** | 4-12 | A | 36 | 325/235-7850 |
| Southeast Early Childhood Ctr<br>1202 Corral St, Sweetwater 79556<br>**David Hargrove** | PK-PK | | 157 | 325/235-3482<br>Fax 325/235-2771 |
| Southeast Elem Sch<br>1201 Mustang Dr, Sweetwater 79556<br>Peggy Elliott | PK-1 | T | 264 | 78% 325/235-9222<br>Fax 325/235-0260 |
| Sweetwater High Sch<br>1205 Ragland St, Sweetwater 79556<br>Jeff Perez | 9-12 | ATV | 288 | 58% 325/235-4371<br>Fax 325/235-4861 |
| Sweetwater Intermediate Sch<br>705 E 3rd St, Sweetwater 79556<br>Mandy Welch | 4-5 | T | 325<br>17 | 67% 325/235-3491<br>Fax 325/235-8016 |
| Sweetwater Middle Sch<br>305 Lamar St, Sweetwater 79556<br>Jeff Withrow | 6-8 | T | 514<br>47 | 72% 325/236-6303<br>Fax 325/236-6941 |

# NUECES COUNTY

## NUECES PUBLIC SCHOOLS

● **Agua Dulce Ind School Dist** PID: 01043988      361/998-2542
1 Longhorn Drive, Agua Dulce 78330      Fax 361/998-2816

**Schools:** 2 \ **Teachers:** 33 \ **Students:** 374 \ **Special Ed Students:** 26 \ **LEP Students:** 3 \ **College-Bound:** 44% \ **Ethnic:** African American 1%, Hispanic 77%, Caucasian 22% \ **Exp:** $500 (High) \ **Poverty:** 22% \ **Title I:** $93,314 \ **Special Education:** $11,000 \ **Open-Close:** 08/18 - 05/27 \ **DTBP:** $368 (High)

**Richard Wright** ........................1  Dena Riley ................................2
Rachel Vardeman ............8,11,57,58,69,270*  Noel Estrada ..........................67
Tom Sorrell ...................73,76,84,286  Eugene Velleas ...................83,88
Dee Scott ...........................752

| Public Schs..Principal | Grd | Prgm | Enr/#Cls | SN |
|---|---|---|---|---|
| Agua Dulce Elem Sch<br>1 Longhorn Drive, Agua Dulce 78330<br>Nora Lopez | PK-5 | T | 149<br>16 | 95% 361/998-2335<br>Fax 361/998-2333 |
| Agua Dulce Secondary Sch<br>1 Longhorn Drive, Agua Dulce 78330<br>Dr Christopher Daniels | 6-12 | T | 197<br>18 | 80% 361/998-2214<br>Fax 361/998-2994 |

● **Banquete Ind School Dist** PID: 01044011      361/387-2551
4339 4th St, Banquete 78339      Fax 361/387-7188

**Schools:** 3 \ **Teachers:** 81 \ **Students:** 900 \ **Special Ed Students:** 92 \ **LEP Students:** 24 \ **Ethnic:** Hispanic 85%, Caucasian 15% \ **Exp:** $608 (High) \ **Poverty:** 18% \ **Title I:** $184,520 \ **Open-Close:** 08/19 - 05/28 \ **DTBP:** $385 (High)

Dr Max Thompson .....................1,11,84  Adrian Pena .............................2
Leah Civis ......................4*  Kevin Hermes ........................6*

Kerry Thompson ...........................8  Roel Garza ........................27*
Denise Blanchard .....................33,285*  Amy Jackson ...................58,77
Tracy Wright ........................67

| Public Schs..Principal | Grd | Prgm | Enr/#Cls | SN |
|---|---|---|---|---|
| Banquete Elem Sch<br>5436 Bulldog Ln, Banquete 78339<br>Adriana Tagle | PK-5 | T | 367<br>34 | 80% 361/387-4329<br>Fax 361/767-8105 |
| Banquete High Sch<br>5519 E Highway 44, Banquete 78339<br>Denise Blanchard | 9-12 | TV | 264<br>18 | 77% 361/387-8588<br>Fax 361/767-6504 |
| Banquete Junior High Sch<br>4339 4th St, Banquete 78339<br>Ramiro Pena | 6-8 | T | 210<br>15 | 75% 361/387-2551<br>Fax 361/387-7051 |

● **Bishop Cons Ind School Dist** PID: 01044059      361/584-3591
719 E 6th St, Bishop 78343      Fax 361/584-3147

**Schools:** 5 \ **Teachers:** 105 \ **Students:** 1,380 \ **Special Ed Students:** 192 \ **LEP Students:** 74 \ **College-Bound:** 64% \ **Ethnic:** Asian 1%, African American 1%, Hispanic 85%, Caucasian 13% \ **Exp:** $437 (High) \ **Poverty:** 22% \ **Title I:** $310,567 \ **Special Education:** $234,000 \ **Open-Close:** 08/24 - 05/24 \ **DTBP:** $553 (High)

Christina Gutierrez .....................1  Manuel Tamez ..........................2
Charles Farek ...........................3,5  Rachel DelGado .......................4
George Luna ...........................6*  Dr Eden Hernandez ... 8,11,34,58,69,73,81,83
Dr Andrea Kuyatt ...................11,57,296*  Sheri Hayes ...................16,82,84
Tracy Smith ...........................39,48*  Shirley Barrington ...................42,45
Marc Morales ........................67

| Public Schs..Principal | Grd | Prgm | Enr/#Cls | SN |
|---|---|---|---|---|
| Bishop Elem Sch<br>200 S Fir Ave, Bishop 78343<br>**Rosalinda Trevino** | 3-5 | T | 190<br>14 | 66% 361/584-3571 |
| Bishop High Sch<br>100 Badger Ln, Bishop 78343<br>Dr Andrea Kuyatt | 9-12 | ATV | 521<br>50 | 60% 361/584-2547<br>Fax 361/584-3593 |
| Bishop Primary Sch<br>705 W Main St, Bishop 78343<br>Emily Salazar | PK-2 | T | 226<br>21 | 71% 361/584-2434<br>Fax 361/584-7600 |
| Lillion E Luehrs Jr High Sch<br>717 E 6th St, Bishop 78343<br>Ray Garza | 6-8 | AT | 357<br>20 | 59% 361/584-3576<br>Fax 361/584-3592 |
| Petronila Elem Sch<br>2391 County Road 67, Robstown 78380<br>Rick Gutierrez | PK-5 | T | 86<br>7 | 79% 361/387-2834<br>Fax 361/584-3880 |

● **Calallen Ind School Dist** PID: 01044114      361/242-5600
4205 Wildcat Dr, Corp Christi 78410      Fax 361/242-5620

**Schools:** 5 \ **Teachers:** 289 \ **Students:** 3,914 \ **Special Ed Students:** 477 \ **LEP Students:** 117 \ **College-Bound:** 54% \ **Ethnic:** Asian 1%, African American 1%, Hispanic 63%, Caucasian 35% \ **Exp:** $422 (High) \ **Poverty:** 11% \ **Title I:** $536,740 \ **Special Education:** $698,000 \ **Open-Close:** 08/17 - 05/27 \ **DTBP:** $96 (Med) \ 🇹

Dr Arturo Almendarez .....................1  Kelsey Ramos ..........................2
Randall Curtis ...........................3,91  Leticia Gracia .......................4
Carol Barnhart ...........................5  Phil Danaher .......................6*
Teresa Shaw ...........................7,85*  Dr Anita Danaher ...................8,11,16,296
Rosanne Meyer ...........................9,57  Blare McLear .......................10,69
Melana Silva ...........................10  Emily Lorenz ...................15,68,83
Sonya Durrwachter ... 34,57,58,72,88,271  Jason Floyd .......................67
Candy Morris ........................69  Kevin Beatty .......................73*

| Public Schs..Principal | Grd | Prgm | Enr/#Cls | SN |
|---|---|---|---|---|
| Calallen High Sch<br>4001 Wildcat Dr, Corp Christi 78410<br>Yvonne Marquez-Neth | 9-12 | ATV | 1,175<br>105 | 43% 361/242-5626<br>Fax 361/242-5632 |
| Calallen Middle Sch<br>4602 Cornett Dr, Corp Christi 78410<br>Rey Saenz | 6-8 | T | 971<br>65 | 51% 361/242-5672<br>Fax 361/242-0628 |
| East Elem Sch<br>3709 Lott Ave, Corp Christi 78410<br>Kimberly Rodriguez | PK-3 | T | 560<br>18 | 66% 361/242-5938<br>Fax 361/242-5944 |
| MaGee Elem Sch<br>4201 Calallen Dr, Corp Christi 78410<br>Melissa Cardona | 4-5 | T | 623<br>38 | 50% 361/242-5900<br>Fax 361/242-5913 |
| Wood River Elem Sch<br>15118 Dry Creek Dr, Corp Christi 78410<br>Dr Debbie Litton | PK-3 | T | 585<br>28 | 45% 361/242-7560<br>Fax 361/387-3114 |

● **Corpus Christi Ind Sch Dist** PID: 01044176    361/695-7200
801 Leopard St, Corp Christi 78401    Fax 361/886-9209

---

Schools: 58 \ **Teachers:** 2,239 \ **Students:** 37,000 \
**Special Ed Students:** 3,592 \ **LEP Students:** 2,186 \ **College-Bound:** 50%
\ **Ethnic:** Asian 2%, African American 4%, Hispanic 81%, Caucasian
14% \ **Exp:** $381 (High) \ **Poverty:** 20% \ **Title I:** $13,462,373 \
**Special Education:** $7,329,000 \ **Open-Close:** 08/13 - 06/03 \ **DTBP:** $190
(High) \ 🅵 🅣

---

| | | | |
|---|---|---|---|
| Dr Roland Hernandez | 1 | Karen Griffth | 2,15 |
| Deborah Meader | 4 | Kyle Pelichet | 5 |
| Brenda Marshall | 6 | Angie Guerrero | 7* |
| Dr James Rosebrock | 8,18 | Maria Luisa Guerra | 8,15 |
| Dr Kelli Powell | 10,15 | Dr Laura Stout | 10,273 |
| Victor Hernandez | 10,16 | Valarie Buhidar | 12,40 |
| Jennifer Arismendi | 13,58,77 | Elizabeth Ortega Ruiz | 20 |
| Orlando Salazar | 27,36,79,90,285 | Iris Estrada | 34 |
| Dr Ada Besiniaz | 36,83 | Ruben Rocha | 41 |
| Luci Sosa | 43 | Wendy DeVoe | 44 |
| Cindy Perez | 46 | Dr Shere Salinas | 47 |
| Jane Bell | 67 | Debbie Nunez | 68 |
| Dr Elda Garcia | 69,294 | Leanne Libby | 71 |
| Laura Perales | 73 | Sean Babcock | 73,295 |
| Marilyn Doughty | 76,295 | Kirby Warnke | 91 |
| Angie Ramirez | 273 | Dr Ralph Silva | 273 |
| Cynthia Hernandez | 280 | Kimberley James | 751 |

| Public Schs..Principal | Grd | Prgm | Enr/#Cls | SN |
|---|---|---|---|---|
| Berlanga Elem Sch<br>4120 Carroll Ln, Corp Christi 78411<br>**Cynthia Winchester** | PK-5 | T | 521 | 86% 361/878-2160<br>Fax 361/878-2303 |
| Blanche Moore Elem Sch<br>6121 Durant Dr, Corp Christi 78414<br>Christine Marroquin | PK-5 | T | 534<br>40 | 85% 361/878-2660<br>Fax 361/994-3619 |
| C P Yeager Elem Sch<br>5414 Tripoli Dr, Corp Christi 78411<br>Tammy Gathright | PK-5 | T | 271<br>25 | 70% 361/878-2920<br>Fax 361/878-1832 |
| Calk-Wilson Elem Sch<br>3925 Fort Worth St, Corp Christi 78411<br>Sheila Thomas | PK-5 | T | 765<br>26 | 75% 361/878-2860<br>Fax 361/878-1831 |
| Carl O Hamlin Middle Sch<br>3900 Hamlin Dr, Corp Christi 78411<br>Prudence Farrell | 6-8 | ATV | 641<br>45 | 69% 361/878-4210<br>Fax 361/878-1839 |
| Claude Cunningham Middle Sch<br>2901 McArdle Rd, Corp Christi 78415<br>**Sandy Salinas-DeLeon** | 6-8 | V | 557<br>56 | 361/878-4720<br>Fax 361/878-1844 |
| Club Estates Elem Sch<br>5222 Merganser Dr, Corp Christi 78413<br>Anita Bircher | PK-5 | T | 363<br>24 | 62% 361/878-3780<br>Fax 361/994-3615 |

| Public Schs..Principal | Grd | Prgm | Enr/#Cls | SN |
|---|---|---|---|---|
| Ⓐ Coles High Sch & Ed Center<br>924 Winnebago St, Corp Christi 78401<br>Monica Bayarena | 9-12 | TV | 250<br>14 | 89% 361/878-7380<br>Fax 361/844-0436 |
| Collegiate High Sch<br>101 Baldwin Blvd - St, Corp Christi 78404<br>Tracie Rodriguez | 9-12 | | 411<br>13 | 361/698-2425<br>Fax 361/698-2427 |
| David Crockett Elem Sch<br>2625 Belton St, Corp Christi 78416<br>Dr Olivia Ballesteros | PK-5 | T | 377<br>25 | 94% 361/878-2220<br>Fax 361/878-2366 |
| Dawson Elem Sch<br>6821 Sanders Dr, Corp Christi 78413<br>Roberto Arredondo | PK-5 | T | 535<br>34 | 49% 361/878-0140<br>Fax 361/878-4805<br>🅵 🅣 |
| Dorothy Adkins Middle Sch<br>2402 Ennis Joslin Rd, Corp Christi 78414<br>Norma Cullum | 6-8 | T | 676 | 44% 361/878-3800<br>Fax 361/878-3828 |
| Driscoll Middle Sch<br>3501 Kenwood Dr, Corp Christi 78408<br>Werner Hartman | 6-8 | TV | 722<br>60 | 92% 361/878-4660<br>Fax 361/886-9890 |
| E E & Jovita Mireles Elem Sch<br>7658 Cimarron Blvd, Corp Christi 78414<br>Carolyn Bence | PK-5 | T | 651<br>40 | 34% 361/878-0120<br>Fax 361/994-6970 |
| Early Childhood Dev Center<br>6300 Ocean Dr Unit 5834, Corp Christi 78412<br>Kellye Loving | PK-6 | T | 187<br>8 | 41% 361/825-3366<br>Fax 361/825-3301 |
| Ella Barnes Elem Sch<br>2829 Oso Pkwy, Corp Christi 78414<br>Katherine Gorman | PK-5 | T | 660<br>30 | 52% 361/878-7330<br>Fax 361/994-0860 |
| Elliot Grant Middle Sch<br>4350 Aaron Dr, Corp Christi 78413<br>Carla Villarreal | 6-8 | T | 948<br>125 | 45% 361/878-3740<br>Fax 361/878-1865 |
| Evans Elem Sch<br>1315 Comanche St, Corp Christi 78401<br>**Molli Martinez** | PK-5 | T | 305<br>23 | 96% 361/878-2240<br>Fax 361/886-9877 |
| Faye Webb Elem Sch<br>6953 Boardwalk Ave, Corp Christi 78414<br>Kristina Kahil | PK-5 | T | 764 | 35% 361/878-2740<br>Fax 361/991-2167 |
| Foy H Moody High Sch<br>1818 Trojan Dr, Corp Christi 78416<br>Enrique Vela | 9-12 | TV | 1,661 | 83% 361/878-7340<br>Fax 361/857-8253 |
| Fred R Sanders Elem Sch<br>4102 Republic Dr, Corp Christi 78413<br>Criselda Castillo | PK-5 | T | 425<br>25 | 75% 361/878-2820<br>Fax 361/878-1829 |
| Harold Branch Acad Career/Tech<br>3902 Morgan Ave, Corp Christi 78405<br>Dr Tracie Rodriguez | Voc | AGT | 222 | 62% 361/878-4780<br>Fax 361/885-7797 |
| Harold C Kaffie Middle Sch<br>5922 Brockhampton St, Corp Christi 78414<br>Alexis Soulas | 6-8 | TV | 1,173<br>40 | 33% 361/878-3700<br>Fax 361/994-3604 |
| Hicks Elem Sch<br>3602 McArdle Rd, Corp Christi 78415<br>Alicia Garza | PK-5 | T | 622<br>21 | 83% 361/878-2200<br>Fax 361/806-0578 |
| J A Garcia Elem Sch<br>1945 Gollihar Rd, Corp Christi 78416<br>Norma DeLeon \ **Daniel Noyola** | PK-5 | T | 595<br>23 | 91% 361/878-2280<br>Fax 361/878-2367 |
| James W Fannin Elem Sch<br>2730 Gollihar Rd, Corp Christi 78415<br>Analisa Farah | PK-5 | T | 339<br>40 | 91% 361/878-2260<br>Fax 361/878-1820 |
| Kolda Elem Sch<br>3730 Rodd Field Rd, Corp Christi 78414<br>Josie Alvarez | PK-5 | T | 627 | 22% 361/878-2980<br>Fax 361/980-1136 |
| Kostoryz Elem Sch<br>3602 Panama Dr, Corp Christi 78415<br>Kelsie Morris | PK-5 | T | 408<br>35 | 87% 361/878-2540<br>Fax 361/878-2329 |
| Lorenzo De Zavala Spec Emp Sch<br>3125 Ruth St, Corp Christi 78405<br>Judith Hinojosa | PK-5 | T | 616<br>32 | 98% 361/878-2720<br>Fax 361/886-9884 |

---

| | | | | | |
|---|---|---|---|---|---|
| 1 | Superintendent | 8 | Curric/Instruct K-12 | 19 | Chief Financial Officer |
| 2 | Bus/Finance/Purchasing | 9 | Curric/Instruct Elem | 20 | Art K-12 |
| 3 | Buildings And Grounds | 10 | Curric/Instruct Sec | 21 | Art Elem |
| 4 | Food Service | 11 | Federal Program | 22 | Art Sec |
| 5 | Transportation | 12 | Title I | 23 | Music K-12 |
| 6 | Athletic | 13 | Title V | 24 | Music Elem |
| 7 | Health Services | 15 | Asst Superintendent | 25 | Music Sec |
| | | 16 | Instructional Media Svcs | 26 | Business Education |
| | | 17 | Chief Operations Officer | 27 | Career & Tech Ed |
| | | 18 | Chief Academic Officer | 28 | Technology Education |

| | | | | | |
|---|---|---|---|---|---|
| 29 | Family/Consumer Science | 39 | Social Studies K-12 | 49 | English/Lang Arts Elem |
| 30 | Adult Education | 40 | Social Studies Elem | 50 | English/Lang Arts Sec |
| 31 | Career/Sch-to-Work K-12 | 41 | Social Studies Sec | 51 | Reading K-12 |
| 32 | Career/Sch-to-Work Elem | 42 | Science K-12 | 52 | Reading Elem |
| 33 | Career/Sch-to-Work Sec | 43 | Science Elem | 53 | Reading Sec |
| 34 | Early Childhood Ed | 44 | Science Sec | 54 | Remedial Reading K-12 |
| 35 | Health/Phys Education | 45 | Math K-12 | 55 | Remedial Reading Elem |
| 36 | Guidance Services K-12 | 46 | Math Elem | 56 | Remedial Reading Sec |
| 37 | Guidance Services Elem | 47 | Math Sec | 57 | Bilingual/ELL |
| 38 | Guidance Services Sec | 48 | English/Lang Arts K-12 | 58 | Special Education K-12 |

| | | | | | |
|---|---|---|---|---|---|
| 59 | Special Education Elem | 69 | Academic Assessment |
| 60 | Special Education Sec | 70 | Research/Development |
| 61 | Foreign/World Lang K-12 | 71 | Public Information |
| 62 | Foreign/World Lang Elem | 72 | Summer School |
| 63 | Foreign/World Lang Sec | 73 | Instructional Tech |
| 64 | Religious Education K-12 | 74 | Inservice Training |
| 65 | Religious Education Elem | 75 | Marketing/Distributive |
| 66 | Religious Education Sec | 76 | Info Systems |
| 67 | School Board President | 77 | Psychological Assess |
| 68 | Teacher Personnel | 78 | Affirmative Action |

| School | Grd | Prgm | Enr/#Cls | % | Phone |
|---|---|---|---|---|---|
| Los Encinos Ses Elem Sch<br>1826 Frio St, Corp Christi 78417<br>Christine Sierra | PK-5 | T | 345<br>22 | 79% | 361/878-2600<br>Fax 361/878-1826 |
| Luther Jones Elem Sch<br>7533 Lipes Blvd, Corp Christi 78413<br>Lisa Bowers | PK-5 | T | 550<br>30 | 38% | 361/878-0100<br>Fax 361/994-3616 |
| Martin Middle Sch<br>3502 Greenwood Dr, Corp Christi 78416<br>John Prezas | 6-8 | TV | 657<br>45 | 95% | 361/878-4690<br>Fax 361/878-2455 |
| Marvin P Baker Middle Sch<br>3445 Pecan St, Corp Christi 78411<br>John Dobbins | 6-8 | TV | 971<br>40 | 64% | 361/878-4600<br>Fax 361/878-1834 |
| Mary Carroll High Sch<br>5301 Weber Rd, Corp Christi 78411<br>Jamie Copeland | 9-12 | TV | 1,416<br>140 | 54% | 361/878-5140<br>Fax 361/878-2403 |
| Mary Grett Sch<br>4402 Castenon St, Corp Christi 78416<br>Dr Debra Stanley | Spec | T | 82<br>16 | 35% | 361/878-1738<br>Fax 361/878-2301 |
| Meadowbrook Elem Sch<br>901 Meadowbrook Dr, Corp Christi 78412<br>Dr Latricia Johnson | PK-5 | T | 444<br>32 | 81% | 361/878-2620<br>Fax 361/994-3650 |
| Metro Elem School of Design<br>1707 Ayers St, Corp Christi 78404<br>Cori Gilbert | K-6 | TV | 513<br>100 | 65% | 361/878-2780<br>Fax 361/878-1818 |
| Miller HS-Metro Sch of Design<br>1 Battlin Buc Blvd, Corp Christi 78408<br>Bruce Wilson | 7-12 | TV | 1,225<br>85 | 80% | 361/878-5100<br>Fax 361/883-1928 |
| Montclair Elem Sch<br>5241 Kentner St, Corp Christi 78412<br>Steve Barrera | PK-5 | T | 275<br>29 | 72% | 361/878-0160<br>Fax 361/994-6940 |
| Moses Menger Elem Sch<br>2401 S Alameda St, Corp Christi 78404<br>Christina Barrera | PK-5 | T | 281<br>25 | 85% | 361/878-2640<br>Fax 361/886-9880 |
| Oak Park Special Emphasis Sch<br>3801 Leopard St, Corp Christi 78408<br>Laura Perales | PK-5 | T | 615<br>29 | 93% | 361/878-2120<br>Fax 361/886-2139 |
| Paul R Haas Middle Sch<br>6630 McArdle Rd, Corp Christi 78412<br>Anna Fuentes | 6-8 | TV | 729<br>40 | 74% | 361/878-4240<br>Fax 361/994-3626 |
| Rafael Galvan Elem Sch<br>3126 Masterson Dr, Corp Christi 78415<br>Diana Ybarra | PK-5 | T | 603<br>37 | 69% | 361/878-2800<br>Fax 361/878-1821 |
| Richard King High Sch<br>5225 Gollihar Rd, Corp Christi 78412<br>Elizabeth Perez | 9-12 | TV | 1,545<br>80 | 56% | 361/906-3400<br>Fax 361/994-6918 |
| Sam Houston Elem Sch<br>363 Norton St, Corp Christi 78415<br>Zonia Lopez | PK-5 | T | 396<br>35 | 91% | 361/878-2520<br>Fax 361/878-1823 |
| Schanen Estates Elem Sch<br>5717 Killarnet Dr, Corp Christi 78413<br>David Crabtree | PK-5 | T | 405<br>32 | 80% | 361/878-2940<br>Fax 361/878-1830 |
| Shaw Spec Emphasis Sch<br>2920 Soledad St, Corp Christi 78405<br>Rebecca Casas | PK-5 | T | 408<br>39 | 93% | 361/878-2100<br>Fax 361/878-2109 |
| South Park Middle Sch<br>2901 McArdle Rd, Corp Christi 78415<br>Irosema Salinas-DeLeon | 6-8 | TV | 449<br>33 | 87% | 361/878-4720<br>Fax 361/878-1844 |
| Ⓐ Student Support Center<br>4401 Greenwood Dr, Corp Christi 78416<br>Jessica Albert | 1-12 | TV | 22 | 92% | 361/878-2840<br>Fax 361/878-1437 |
| T G Allen Elem Sch<br>1414 18th St, Corp Christi 78404<br>Elodia Gutierrez | PK-5 | T | 297<br>28 | 97% | 361/878-2140<br>Fax 361/886-9874 |
| Tom Browne Middle Sch<br>4301 Schanen Blvd, Corp Christi 78413<br>George Lerma | 6-8 | TV | 555<br>50 | 62% | 361/878-4270<br>Fax 361/878-1836 |
| Veterans Memorial High Sch<br>3750 Cimarron Blvd, Corp Christi 78414<br>Scott Walker | 9-12 | T | 2,280 | 26% | 361/878-7900<br>Fax 361/878-7910 |
| W B Ray High Sch<br>1002 Texan Trl, Corp Christi 78411<br>Roxanne Cuevas | 9-12 | TV | 1,976 | 64% | 361/878-7300<br>Fax 361/852-6528 |
| Weldon Gibson Elem Sch<br>5723 Hampshire Rd, Corp Christi 78408<br>Julissa Segovia | PK-5 | T | 371<br>25 | 91% | 361/878-2500<br>Fax 361/289-7406 |
| Weldon Smith Elem Sch<br>6902 Williams Dr, Corp Christi 78412<br>Rebecca Raesz | PK-5 | T | 457<br>29 | 75% | 361/878-2760<br>Fax 361/994-3681 |
| William B Travis Elem Sch<br>3210 Churchill Dr, Corp Christi 78415<br>Laura Quiroz-Colunga | PK-5 | T | 475<br>20 | 98% | 361/878-2700<br>Fax 361/884-0341 |
| Windsor Park Elem Sch<br>4525 S Alameda St, Corp Christi 78412<br>Dr Kimberly Bissell | 1-5 | T | 581<br>31 | 25% | 361/878-3770<br>Fax 361/994-3621 |
| Woodlawn Elem Sch<br>1110 Woodlawn Dr, Corp Christi 78412<br>Kathryn Ortiz | PK-5 | T | 287<br>24 | 76% | 361/878-2900<br>Fax 361/994-3622 |

---

## • Driscoll Ind School Dist  PID: 01044798                361/387-7349
310 W Dragon St, Driscoll 78351

**Schools:** 1 \ **Teachers:** 25 \ **Students:** 281 \ **Special Ed Students:** 29 \ **LEP Students:** 9 \ **Ethnic:** African American 1%, Hispanic 91%, Caucasian 8% \ **Exp:** $530 (High) \ **Poverty:** 26% \ **Title I:** $118,608 \ **Special Education:** $51,000 \ **Open-Close:** 07/22 - 05/20 \ **DTBP:** $348 (High)

| | | | |
|---|---|---|---|
| Dr Cindy Garcia ...................................1 | Annette Vasquez ...............................2,11 |
| Mark Gonzalez ...................................3* | Minerva Zapata ......................................4 |
| Danny Vasquez ...................................6* | Lynn Landenberger ..............................8* |
| Monica Morin ............ 9,37,57,69,88,93,270* | Letty Garza .......................................... 59 |
| Veronica Ramon ................................. 67 | Patricia Myers .....................................73* |

| Public Schs..Principal | Grd | Prgm | Enr/#Cls | SN | |
|---|---|---|---|---|---|
| Driscoll Sch<br>310 W Dragon St, Driscoll 78351<br>Lynn Landenberger | PK-8 | T | 281<br>26 | 85% | 361/387-7349 |

---

## • Flour Bluff Ind School Dist  PID: 01044815                361/694-9000
2505 Waldron Rd, Corp Christi 78418                Fax 361/694-9800

**Schools:** 7 \ **Teachers:** 370 \ **Students:** 5,750 \ **Special Ed Students:** 639 \ **LEP Students:** 170 \ **College-Bound:** 59% \ **Ethnic:** Asian 2%, African American 3%, Hispanic 48%, Caucasian 47% \ **Exp:** $380 (High) \ **Poverty:** 12% \ **Title I:** $800,954 \ **Special Education:** $990,000 \ **Open-Close:** 08/13 - 05/26 \ **DTBP:** $147 (High) \ 🇫 🇪

| | | | |
|---|---|---|---|
| Dr David Freeman ...................................1 | Emily Youngblood .....................................2 |
| Clayton Pocius ...................................3,5 | Gina Valdez .............................................4 |
| Christopher Steinbruck ...........................6 | Allison Schaum ........................8,12,13,15* |
| Dr Linda Barganski ....................11,83,298 | Louise Day ............................................ 15 |
| Victor Lara ..........................................23* | Edgar Van Geem ............................58,77* |
| Shirley Thornton ................................. 67 | Jeanette Revels ................................... 68 |
| Kimberly Sneed .................................. 71 | Alex Puente ..........................73,76,84,295 |
| Ron Fisher ........................................... 91 | |

| Public Schs..Principal | Grd | Prgm | Enr/#Cls | SN | |
|---|---|---|---|---|---|
| Early Childhood Center<br>2505 Waldron Rd, Corp Christi 78418<br>Amy Seeds | PK-K | T | 551<br>24 | 57% | 361/694-9036<br>Fax 361/694-9810<br>🇫🇪 |

---

| | | | |
|---|---|---|---|
| **79** Student Personnel | **91** Safety/Security | **275** Response To Intervention | **298** Grant Writer/Ptnrships |
| **80** Driver Ed/Safety | **92** Magnet School | **277** Remedial Math K-12 | **750** Chief Innovation Officer |
| **81** Gifted/Talented | **93** Parental Involvement | **280** Literacy Coach | **751** Chief of Staff |
| **82** Video Services | **95** Tech Prep Program | **285** STEM | **752** Social Emotional Learning |
| **83** Substance Abuse Prev | **97** Chief Infomation Officer | **286** Digital Learning | |
| **84** Erate | **98** Chief Technology Officer | **288** Common Core Standards | **Other School Types** |
| **85** AIDS Education | **270** Character Education | **294** Accountability | Ⓐ = Alternative School |
| **88** Alternative/At Risk | **271** Migrant Education | **295** Network System | Ⓒ = Charter School |
| **89** Multi-Cultural Curriculum | **273** Teacher Mentor | **296** Title II Programs | Ⓜ = Magnet School |
| **90** Social Work | **274** Before/After Sch | **297** Webmaster | Ⓨ = Year-Round School |

**School Programs**
A = Alternative Program
G = Adult Classes
M = Magnet Program
T = Title I Schoolwide
V = Career & Tech Ed Programs

**Social Media**
🇫 = Facebook
🇪 = Twitter

New Schools are shaded
New Superintendents and Principals are bold
Personnel with email addresses are underscored

Flour Bluff Elem Sch | 3-4 | T | 796 | 53% 361/694-9500
2505 Waldron Rd, Corp Christi 78418 | | | | Fax 361/694-9805
Dr Nikol Youngberg  [f][t]

Flour Bluff High Sch | 9-12 | ATV | 1,320 | 38% 361/694-9100
2505 Waldron Rd, Corp Christi 78418 | | | 90 | Fax 361/694-9802
James Crenshaw

Flour Bluff Interm Sch | 5-6 | T | 843 | 51% 361/694-9400
2505 Waldron Rd, Corp Christi 78418 | | | 33 | Fax 361/694-9804
Sal Alvarado

Flour Bluff Junior High Sch | 7-8 | T | 463 | 48% 361/694-9300
2505 Waldron Rd, Corp Christi 78418 | | | 25 | Fax 361/694-9803
Brodie Wallace

Flour Bluff Primary Sch | 1-2 | T | 754 | 54% 361/694-9400
2505 Waldron Rd, Corp Christi 78418 | | | 40 | Fax 361/694-9806
Shea Hernanadez

University Preparatory HS | 9-12 | | 302 | 361/694-9780
2505 Waldron Rd, Corp Christi 78418 | | | 8 | Fax 361/694-9814
**Kathy Kellar**

## • London Ind School Dist PID: 01044865

361/855-0183
1306 FM 43, Corp Christi 78415
Fax 361/855-0198

**Schools:** 1 \ **Teachers:** 70 \ **Students:** 900 \ **Special Ed Students:** 62 \
**LEP Students:** 5 \ **Ethnic:** Asian 3%, African American 2%, Hispanic 46%,
Caucasian 49% \ **Exp:** $385 (High) \ **Poverty:** 6% \ **Title I:** $27,763 \
**Special Education:** $103,000 \ **Open-Close:** 07/17 - 05/25 \ **DTBP:** $169
(High)

Dr David Freeman .....................................1 | Victoria Boge ......................................... 2
Carlos Vargas ......................................3,5 | Roxanne Bright ..................................... 4
Vickie George ....................................4,19 | Cassie Freeman .................................. 11
Jessica Gutierrez ..........................12,271* | Linda Bartlett .................................. 16,73*
Marcella Lockett ....................................57* | Holly Salazar ........................................ 58
Scott Frasier ...........................................67 | Rebecca Hitchcock ........................ 74,88*
Mariano Cervantes ................................91 | Ron Lawver .......................................... 91
Margo Glover ........................................93*

| Public Schs..Principal | Grd | Prgm | Enr/#Cls | SN | |
|---|---|---|---|---|---|
| ⓥ London Sch | PK-12 | M | 900 | 18% | 361/855-0092 |
| 1306 FM 43, Corp Christi 78415 | | | 23 | | |
| Jessica Gutierrez \ Amanda Barmore \ Rebecca Hitchcock | | | | | |

## • Port Aransas Ind School Dist PID: 01044889

361/749-1200
100 S Station St, Port Aransas 78373
Fax 361/749-1215

**Schools:** 3 \ **Teachers:** 48 \ **Students:** 480 \ **Special Ed Students:** 45 \
**LEP Students:** 7 \ **College-Bound:** 85% \ **Ethnic:** Asian 1%, Hispanic 16%,
Native American: 1%, Caucasian 82% \ **Exp:** $320 (High) \ **Poverty:** 8% \
**Title I:** $56,943 \ **Special Education:** $132,000 \ **Open-Close:** 08/10 - 05/27
\ **DTBP:** $553 (High)

Sharon McKinney .....................................1 | Carolsue Hipp ....................................... 2
Steve Reaves ..........................................6* | Kelye Garcie .......................................... 9
Tisha Piwetz ...................................11,298 | Meghan Zigmond ................................ 16*
Laura Cazalis ..........................................58 | Marnie Pate .......................................... 67
Tom Driver ..............................................73*

| Public Schs..Principal | Grd | Prgm | Enr/#Cls | SN | |
|---|---|---|---|---|---|
| Brundreet Middle Sch | 6-8 | T | 114 | 37% | 361/749-1209 |
| 100 S Station St, Port Aransas 78373 | | | 14 | | Fax 361/749-1218 |
| James Garrett | | | | | |
| Olsen Elem Sch | PK-5 | T | 179 | 44% | 361/749-1212 |
| 100 S Station St, Port Aransas 78373 | | | 20 | | Fax 361/749-1219 |
| Kelye Garcie | | | | | |

Port Aransas High Sch | 9-12 | TV | 187 | 18% 361/749-1206
100 S Station St, Port Aransas 78373 | | | 25 | Fax 361/749-1226
Jim Potts  [f][t]

## • Robstown Ind School Dist PID: 01044906

361/767-6600
801 N 1st St, Robstown 78380
Fax 361/387-6311

**Schools:** 7 \ **Teachers:** 177 \ **Students:** 2,000 \ **Special Ed Students:** 291
\ **LEP Students:** 104 \ **College-Bound:** 36% \ **Ethnic:** African American
1%, Hispanic 98%, Caucasian 2% \ **Exp:** $636 (High) \ **Poverty:** 33% \
**Title I:** $1,757,107 \ **Special Education:** $667,000 \ **Open-Close:** 08/13 -
05/26 \ **DTBP:** $200 (High)

Dr Jose Moreno ......................................1 | Nina Conway ....................................2,19
Lee Gonzalez ..........................................3 | Lisa Mendoza ........................................ 4
Richard Gonzalez .............5,27,73,76,84,286 | Arturo Garcia ........................................ 6
Rosi Moreno ............................................7* | Diana Silvas .................8,15,36,68,285,288
Lornea Ceballos .....................................8 | Yolanda Reyna ..........................11,57,83*
Dr Daniel Ceballos ..............................15 | Charles Cabrera .................................. 23*
Maricela Pena .....................................30* | Pamela Kiawatski .............................. 58
Oscar Lopez ..........................................67 | Kelsey Picou ........................................ 71
Delma Salinas .......................................81 | Eric Gonzalez .............................. 88,275
Michelle Delapena .................................93

| Public Schs..Principal | Grd | Prgm | Enr/#Cls | SN | |
|---|---|---|---|---|---|
| Lotspeich Elem Sch | PK-3 | T | 301 | 92% | 361/767-6655 |
| 1100 Ruben Chavez Rd, Robstown 78380 | | | 24 | | Fax 361/387-6019 |
| Angelita Lopez \ **Vanessa Perez-Peterson** | | | | | |
| Robert Driscoll Jr Elem Sch | PK-3 | T | 552 | 94% | 361/767-6641 |
| 122 W Avenue H, Robstown 78380 | | | 29 | | Fax 361/767-6610 |
| Manuel Lunoff | | | | | |
| Robstown High Sch | 9-12 | AGTV | 304 | 85% | 361/387-5999 |
| 609 Highway 44, Robstown 78380 | | | 50 | | Fax 361/767-6629 |
| Sylvia Romero | | | | | |
| ⓐ Salazar Crossroads Academy | 9-12 | T | 33 | 96% | 361/767-6600 |
| 701 N 1st St, Robstown 78380 | | | 9 | | |
| Belinda Alaniz | | | | | |
| San Pedro Elem Sch | PK-3 | T | 199 | 94% | 361/767-6648 |
| 800 W Avenue D, Robstown 78380 | | | 21 | | Fax 361/767-2243 |
| Laura Cueva | | | | | |
| Seale Junior High Sch | 6-8 | T | 606 | 85% | 361/767-6631 |
| 401 E Avenue G, Robstown 78380 | | | 43 | | Fax 361/767-2272 |
| Maribel Trevino | | | | | |
| Solomon P Ortiz Interm Sch | 4-5 | T | 384 | 88% | 361/767-6662 |
| 208 E Avenue H, Robstown 78380 | | | 24 | | Fax 361/767-2651 |
| Anisa Chavera | | | | | |

## • Tuloso-Midway Ind School Dist PID: 01045015

361/903-6400
9760 La Branch Dr, Corp Christi 78410
Fax 361/241-5836

**Schools:** 5 \ **Teachers:** 284 \ **Students:** 3,043 \ **Special Ed Students:** 358
\ **LEP Students:** 254 \ **College-Bound:** 52% \ **Ethnic:** African American
1%, Hispanic 80%, Caucasian 18% \ **Exp:** $557 (High) \ **Poverty:** 20% \
**Title I:** $697,014 \ **Special Education:** $703,000 \ **Open-Close:** 07/15 -
05/27 \ **DTBP:** $144 (High) \ [t]

Rodney Sumner ......................................1 | Philip Carroll ...............................2,19,75
Patrick Hernandez ...............................3,5 | Stephanie Gallegos ............................. 4
Wade Miller .............................................6 | Holly Alderson ...............8,11,57,92,296
Christopher Casarez ..........................15,91 | Yolanda Alvaro .................................. 58
Paul Mostella ........................................67 | Anna Elizando .............................. 68,78
David Wiltshire ....................................295 | Robin Murray ...................................... 298

| Public Schs..Principal | Grd | Prgm | Enr/#Cls | SN | |
|---|---|---|---|---|---|
| ⓐ Academic Career Center | 9-12 | TV | 23 | 81% | 361/903-6450 |
| 7601 Leopard St, Corp Christi 78409 | | | 7 | | Fax 361/289-5642 |
| Melodie McClarren | | | | | |

| | | | | | | | | | | | |
|---|---|---|---|---|---|---|---|---|---|---|---|
| 1 | Superintendent | 8 | Curric/Instruct K-12 | 19 | Chief Financial Officer | 29 | Family/Consumer Science | 39 | Social Studies K-12 | 49 | English/Lang Arts Elem | 59 | Special Education Elem | 69 | Academic Assessment |
| 2 | Bus/Finance/Purchasing | 9 | Curric/Instruct Elem | 20 | Art K-12 | 30 | Adult Education | 40 | Social Studies Elem | 50 | English/Lang Arts Sec | 60 | Special Education Sec | 70 | Research/Development |
| 3 | Buildings And Grounds | 10 | Curric/Instruct Sec | 21 | Art Elem | 31 | Career/Sch-to-Work K-12 | 41 | Social Studies Sec | 51 | Reading K-12 | 61 | Foreign/World Lang K-12 | 71 | Public Information |
| 4 | Food Service | 11 | Federal Program | 22 | Art Sec | 32 | Career/Sch-to-Work Elem | 42 | Science K-12 | 52 | Reading Elem | 62 | Foreign/World Lang Elem | 72 | Summer School |
| 5 | Transportation | 12 | Title I | 23 | Music K-12 | 33 | Career/Sch-to-Work Sec | 43 | Science Elem | 53 | Reading Sec | 63 | Foreign/World Lang Sec | 73 | Instructional Tech |
| 6 | Athletic | 13 | Title V | 24 | Music Elem | 34 | Early Childhood Ed | 44 | Science Sec | 54 | Remedial Reading K-12 | 64 | Religious Education K-12 | 74 | Inservice Training |
| 7 | Health Services | 15 | Asst Superintendent | 25 | Music Sec | 35 | Health/Phys Education | 45 | Math K-12 | 55 | Remedial Reading Elem | 65 | Religious Education Elem | 75 | Marketing/Distributive |
| | | 16 | Instructional Media Svcs | 26 | Business Education | 36 | Guidance Services K-12 | 46 | Math Elem | 56 | Remedial Reading Sec | 66 | Religious Education Sec | 76 | Info Systems |
| | | 17 | Chief Operations Officer | 27 | Career & Tech Ed | 37 | Guidance Services Elem | 47 | Math Sec | 57 | Bilingual/ELL | 67 | School Board President | 77 | Psychological Assess |
| | | 18 | Chief Academic Officer | 28 | Technology Education | 38 | Guidance Services Sec | 48 | English/Lang Arts K-12 | 58 | Special Education K-12 | 68 | Teacher Personnel | 78 | Affirmative Action |

| | Grd | Prgm | Enr/#Cls | SN | |
|---|---|---|---|---|---|
| Tuloso-Midway High Sch | 9-12 | ATV | 578 | 50% | 361/903-6700 |
| 2653 McKinzie Rd, Corp Christi 78410 | | | 85 | | Fax 361/241-4258 |
| **Benito Portillo** | | | | | |
| Tuloso-Midway Intermediate Sch | 3-5 | T | 898 | 59% | 361/903-6550 |
| 1921 Overland Trl, Corp Christi 78410 | | | 34 | | Fax 361/903-6572 |
| David Calk | | | | | |
| Tuloso-Midway Middle Sch | 6-8 | T | 590 | 53% | 361/903-6600 |
| 9768 La Branch Dr, Corp Christi 78410 | | | 35 | | Fax 361/242-9829 |
| Tuloso-Midway Primary Sch | PK-2 | T | 954 | 66% | 361/903-6500 |
| 3125 Dear Run Dr, Corp Christi 78410 | | | | | Fax 361/241-5617 |

- **West Oso Ind School Dist** PID: 01045065    361/806-5900
  5050 Rockford Dr, Corp Christi 78416    Fax 361/225-8308

**Schools:** 4 \ **Teachers:** 149 \ **Students:** 1,946 \ **Special Ed Students:** 245 \ **LEP Students:** 153 \ **College-Bound:** 40% \ **Ethnic:** African American 8%, Hispanic 89%, Caucasian 3% \ **Exp:** $441 (High) \ **Poverty:** 26% \ **Title I:** $696,414 \ **Special Education:** $462,000 \ **Open-Close:** 08/06 - 05/28 \ **DTBP:** $214 (High)

Conrado Garcia ........................................1
Denise Hernandez ............................3,5
Cheryl Fillmore ......................................6
Christopher Summers .........................11
R Alvarado ......................................58,79
Isabel Olivarez ..............................69,294
Amanda Chavarria ...............................76
Andrew Martinez .............................. 295
David Palacios ...............................2,3,15
Ray Williams ........................................4*
Dr Cissy Reynolds-Perez ............ 8,15,68
Kimberly Moore ............................27,285
Cella Boyd ........................................... 67
Lindie Hagdorn ............................. 73,297
Monica Vidal ........................................ 93

| Public Schs..Principal | Grd | Prgm | Enr/#Cls | SN | |
|---|---|---|---|---|---|
| Kennedy Elem Sch | PK-2 | T | 559 | 94% | 361/806-5920 |
| 1102 Villarreal Dr, Corp Christi 78416 | | | 25 | | Fax 361/806-5969 |
| Marcella Davis | | | | | |
| West Oso Elem Sch | 3-5 | T | 458 | 91% | 361/806-5930 |
| 1526 Cliff Maus Dr, Corp Christi 78416 | | | 40 | | Fax 361/225-8956 |
| Fernando Gonzalez | | | | | |
| West Oso High Sch | 9-12 | TV | 461 | 88% | 361/806-5960 |
| 754 Flato Rd, Corp Christi 78405 | | | 50 | | Fax 361/806-5961 |
| Terry Avery | | | | | |
| West Oso Junior High Sch | 6-8 | AT | 468 | 91% | 361/806-5950 |
| 5202 Bear Ln, Corp Christi 78405 | | | 40 | | Fax 361/299-3111 |
| Margaret Evans | | | | | |

## NUECES CATHOLIC SCHOOLS

- **Diocese Corpus Christi Ed Off** PID: 01045170    361/882-6191
  555 N Carancahua St Ste 750, Corp Christi 78401    Fax 361/693-6798

**Schools:** 16 \ **Students:** 3,300

Listing includes only schools located in this county. See District Index for location of Diocesan Offices.

Dr Rosemary Henry ...........................1,11
Nannette Hatch ....................................... 15
April Esparza ........................................ 7
Monica Maldonado ............................... 73

| Catholic Schs..Principal | Grd | Prgm | Enr/#Cls | SN | |
|---|---|---|---|---|---|
| Bishop Garriga Middle Sch | 6-8 | | 86 | | 361/851-0853 |
| 3114 Saratoga Blvd, Corp Christi 78415 | | | 9 | | Fax 361/853-5145 |
| Norma Castaneda | | | | | |
| Holy Family Catholic Sch | PK-5 | | 120 | | 361/884-9142 |
| 2526 Soledad St, Corp Christi 78416 | | | 15 | | Fax 361/884-1750 |
| Sr Marilyn Springs | | | | | |

| | Grd | Prgm | Enr/#Cls | SN | |
|---|---|---|---|---|---|
| Incarnate Word Academy | 9-12 | | 245 | | 361/883-0857 |
| 2910 S Alameda St, Corp Christi 78404 | | | 32 | | Fax 361/881-8742 |
| Jose Torres | | | | | |
| Incarnate Word Elem Sch | PK-5 | | 245 | | 361/883-0857 |
| 450 Chamberlain St, Corp Christi 78404 | | | 15 | | Fax 361/881-9519 |
| Pamela Carrillo | | | | | |
| Incarnate Word Middle Sch | 6-8 | | 199 | | 361/883-0857 |
| 2917 Austin St, Corp Christi 78404 | | | 24 | | Fax 361/882-9193 |
| Marci Levings | | | | | |
| Most Precious Catholic Sch | PK-5 | | 204 | | 361/852-4800 |
| 3502 Saratoga Blvd, Corp Christi 78415 | | | 12 | | Fax 361/855-8707 |
| Nelda Bazan | | | | | |
| Our Lady of Perpetual Help Sch | PK-8 | | 206 | | 361/991-3305 |
| 5814 Williams Dr, Corp Christi 78412 | | | 13 | | Fax 361/994-3305 |
| Diane Martinez | | | | | |
| Our Lady of the Rosary Sch | PK-1 | | 15 | | 361/939-9847 |
| 2237 Waldron Rd, Corp Christi 78418 | | | | | Fax 361/937-0890 |
| Sr Claudia | | | | | |
| SS Cyril & Methodius Sch | PK-5 | | 140 | | 361/853-9392 |
| 5002 Kostoryz Rd, Corp Christi 78415 | | | 15 | | Fax 361/853-0280 |
| Lilly Samaniego | | | | | |
| St Anthony Sch | PK-8 | | 136 | | 361/387-3814 |
| 203 Dunne Ave, Robstown 78380 | | | 11 | | Fax 361/387-3842 |
| Anna Gonzalez | | | | | |
| St John Paul II High Sch | 9-12 | | 314 | | 361/855-5744 |
| 3036 Saratoga Blvd, Corp Christi 78415 | | | | | Fax 361/855-1343 |
| Michael Edghill | | | | | |
| St Patrick Sch | PK-6 | | 316 | | 361/852-1211 |
| 3340 S Alameda St, Corp Christi 78411 | | | 21 | | Fax 361/852-4855 |
| Evelyn Burton | | | | | 🅕 |
| St Pius X Sch | PK-6 | | 190 | | 361/992-1343 |
| 737 Saint Pius Dr, Corp Christi 78412 | | | 9 | | Fax 361/992-0329 |
| Beth Hinojosa | | | | | |

## NUECES PRIVATE SCHOOLS

| Private Schs..Principal | Grd | Prgm | Enr/#Cls | SN | |
|---|---|---|---|---|---|
| Annapolis Christian Academy | PK-12 | | 280 | | 361/991-6004 |
| 3875 S Staples St Ste A, Corp Christi 78411 | | | 40 | | Fax 361/232-5629 |
| Travis Lockyer | | | | | |
| Arlington Heights Chrn Sch | PK-12 | | 140 | | 361/241-0090 |
| 9550 Leopard St, Corp Christi 78410 | | | | | Fax 361/242-9284 |
| Leanne Isom | | | | | 🅕 |
| Cogin Memorial Elem Sch | PK-8 | | 23 | | 361/991-6968 |
| 6645 Downing St, Corp Christi 78414 | | | 3 | | |
| Ana Luna | | | | | |
| St James Episcopal Sch | PK-8 | | 200 | | 361/883-0835 |
| 602 S Carancahua St, Corp Christi 78401 | | | 24 | | Fax 361/883-0837 |
| Galen Hoffstadt | | | | | |
| St Paul Lutheran Sch | PK-4 | | 32 | | 361/584-2778 |
| 801 E Main St, Bishop 78343 | | | 4 | | |
| Tawnya Denkeler | | | | | |
| Yorktown Christian Academy | PK-12 | | 202 | | 361/985-9960 |
| 5025A Yorktown Blvd, Corp Christi 78413 | | | | | Fax 361/985-9821 |
| John Gilbert | | | | | |

## NUECES REGIONAL CENTERS

- **Region 2 Ed Service Center** PID: 01045003    361/561-8400
  209 N Water St, Corp Christi 78401    Fax 361/883-3442

Rick Alvarado ...........................................1,11
Randy Purdy ................................. 8,16,73
Ryan Johnston ..................................2,76
Sonia Zyla ............................................. 58

| OCHILTREE COUNTY | OLDHAM COUNTY |
|---|---|

## OCHILTREE PUBLIC SCHOOLS

## OLDHAM PUBLIC SCHOOLS

● **Perryton Ind School Dist** PID: 01045455          806/435-5478
821 SW 17th Ave, Perryton 79070                       Fax 806/435-4689

**Schools:** 6 \ **Teachers:** 186 \ **Students:** 2,217 \ **Special Ed Students:** 167 \ **LEP Students:** 624 \ **College-Bound:** 46% \ **Ethnic:** Hispanic 73%, Caucasian 26% \ **Exp:** $526 (High) \ **Poverty:** 14% \ **Title I:** $398,192 \ **Open-Close:** 08/17 - 05/20 \ **DTBP:** $338 (High)

| | | | |
|---|---|---|---|
| James Mireles | 1 | Doug Kile | 2,19 |
| Allen Kemp | 3 | Shelli Walker | 4 |
| Dustin Klaska | 6* | Todd White | 8,11,57,88,271,298 |
| Kelly Vernon | 11 | Cindy Boxwell | 16* |
| Stacy Tanner | 29* | Valerie Merkel | 36* |
| Paige Waide | 38* | Mary Nine | 58 |
| Monty Kinnard | 67 | Darin Clark | 71 |
| Rodney Throgmorton | 73,295 | Danny Finch | 83 |

| Public Schs..Principal | Grd | Prgm | Enr/#Cls | SN | |
|---|---|---|---|---|---|
| Edwin F Williams Interm Sch<br>902 SW 19th Ave, Perryton 79070<br>Read Cates | 4-5 | T | 346<br>17 | 67% | 806/435-3436<br>Fax 806/435-9231 |
| James L Wright Elem Sch<br>1702 S Grinnell St, Perryton 79070<br>Tiffany Bietz | 1-3 | T | 475 | 58% | 806/435-2371<br>Fax 806/434-8844 |
| Ludi Pena Martin Accel Ed Ctr<br>605 N Main St, Perryton 79070<br>Ludi Martin | 9-12 | T | 10<br>6 | 83% | 806/434-0389<br>Fax 806/434-0402 |
| Perryton High Sch<br>1200 S Jefferson St, Perryton 79070<br>Danny Finch | 9-12 | T | 304<br>40 | 45% | 806/435-3633<br>Fax 806/435-2602 |
| Perryton Junior High Sch<br>510 S Eton St, Perryton 79070<br>Dimitri Garcia | 6-8 | T | 512<br>30 | 60% | 806/435-3601<br>Fax 806/435-3624 |
| Perryton Kindergarten<br>410 S Eton St, Perryton 79070<br>Dent Felix | PK-K | T | 149<br>22 | 72% | 806/435-2463<br>Fax 806/435-6093 |

## OCHILTREE PRIVATE SCHOOLS

| Private Schs..Principal | Grd | Prgm | Enr/#Cls | SN | |
|---|---|---|---|---|---|
| Victory Christian Academy<br>2322 S Main St, Perryton 79070<br>Kathy Sparks | PK-6 | | 42<br>6 | | 806/435-3476<br>Fax 806/435-9256 |

● **Adrian Ind School Dist** PID: 01045522          806/538-6203
301 Matador Dr, Adrian 79001                          Fax 806/538-6291

**Schools:** 1 \ **Teachers:** 18 \ **Students:** 120 \ **Special Ed Students:** 14 \ **LEP Students:** 3 \ **Ethnic:** Hispanic 61%, Caucasian 39% \ **Exp:** $887 (High) \ **Poverty:** 15% \ **Special Education:** $16,000 \ **Open-Close:** 08/13 - 05/21

| | | | |
|---|---|---|---|
| Steve Reynolds | 1,11 | Stephanie Green | 2 |
| Debra Jones | 7* | Dawn Brooks | 8,288* |
| Thresa Vines | 58* | Morris Blackenship | 67 |
| Monty Hale | 73,286,295* | | |

| Public Schs..Principal | Grd | Prgm | Enr/#Cls | SN | |
|---|---|---|---|---|---|
| Adrian Sch<br>301 Matador Dr, Adrian 79001<br>Dawn Brooks | PK-12 | TV | 120<br>20 | 67% | 806/538-6203 |

● **Boys Ranch Ind School Dist** PID: 01484461          806/534-2221
163 River Rd, Boys Ranch 79010                         Fax 806/534-2384

**Schools:** 3 \ **Teachers:** 55 \ **Students:** 240 \ **Special Ed Students:** 51 \ **LEP Students:** 6 \ **College-Bound:** 50% \ **Ethnic:** African American 11%, Hispanic 21%, Native American: 1%, Caucasian 67% \ **Exp:** $1,512 (High) \ **Poverty:** 8% \ **Title I:** $547,812 \ **Special Education:** $24,000 \ **Open-Close:** 08/24 - 05/21 \ **DTBP:** $335 (High)

| | | | |
|---|---|---|---|
| Kenneth Brown | 1 | Meleta Bailey | 2 |
| Paul Jones | 6,15,275 | Kaylia Thomas | 8,16 |
| Maggie Taylor | 11,15,57,83,298 | Kelli Boydstun | 27,31,36* |
| Mark Strother | 67 | Randy Carter | 73,295 |

| Public Schs..Principal | Grd | Prgm | Enr/#Cls | SN | |
|---|---|---|---|---|---|
| Blakemore Middle Sch<br>30 Julian Bivins Blvd, Boys Ranch 79010<br>Brandon Sanders | 6-8 | AT | 78<br>14 | 74% | 806/534-2361<br>Fax 806/534-0041 |
| Boys Ranch High Sch<br>163 River Rd, Boys Ranch 79010<br>Shawn Read | 9-12 | ATV | 178<br>40 | 92% | 806/534-0032<br>Fax 806/534-0033 |
| Mimi Farley Elem Sch<br>29 Ag Lane, Boys Ranch 79010<br>Joanna Martinez | PK-5 | T | 47<br>12 | 32% | 806/534-2248<br>Fax 806/534-0111 |

● **Vega Ind School Dist** PID: 01045558          806/267-2123
200 Longhorn Dr, Vega 79092                      Fax 806/267-2146

**Schools:** 2 \ **Teachers:** 40 \ **Students:** 370 \ **Special Ed Students:** 23 \ **LEP Students:** 19 \ **College-Bound:** 95% \ **Ethnic:** Hispanic 20%, Caucasian 80% \ **Exp:** $698 (High) \ **Poverty:** 11% \ **Title I:** $28,868 \ **Open-Close:** 08/19 - 05/21 \ **DTBP:** $318 (High)

| | | | |
|---|---|---|---|
| Jody Johnson | 1,11 | Haylie Galvan | 2 |
| Jason Porton | 6* | Tammie Cook | 8,31,36,69,83,270* |
| Amy Kirkland | 16,73* | Mehgan Graves | 58* |
| Tj Barclay | 67 | Terri Richardson | 286* |

| | | | | | | |
|---|---|---|---|---|---|---|
| 1 | Superintendent | 8 | Curric/Instruct K-12 | 19 | Chief Financial Officer | 29 Family/Consumer Science |
| 2 | Bus/Finance/Purchasing | 9 | Curric/Instruct Elem | 20 | Art K-12 | 30 Adult Education |
| 3 | Buildings And Grounds | 10 | Curric/Instruct Sec | 21 | Art Elem | 31 Career/Sch-to-Work K-12 |
| 4 | Food Service | 11 | Federal Program | 22 | Art Sec | 32 Career/Sch-to-Work Elem |
| 5 | Transportation | 12 | Title I | 23 | Music K-12 | 33 Career/Sch-to-Work Sec |
| 6 | Athletic | 13 | Title V | 24 | Music Elem | 34 Early Childhood Ed |
| 7 | Health Services | 15 | Asst Superintendent | 25 | Music Sec | 35 Health/Phys Education |
| | | 16 | Instructional Media Svcs | 26 | Business Education | 36 Guidance Services K-12 |
| | | 17 | Chief Operations Officer | 27 | Career & Tech Ed | 37 Guidance Services Elem |
| | | 18 | Chief Academic Officer | 28 | Technology Education | 38 Guidance Services Sec |

| | | | | | | |
|---|---|---|---|---|---|---|
| 39 Social Studies K-12 | 49 | English/Lang Arts Elem | 59 | Special Education Elem | 69 | Academic Assessment |
| 40 Social Studies Elem | 50 | English/Lang Arts Sec | 60 | Special Education Sec | 70 | Research/Development |
| 41 Social Studies Sec | 51 | Reading K-12 | 61 | Foreign/World Lang K-12 | 71 | Public Information |
| 42 Science K-12 | 52 | Reading Elem | 62 | Foreign/World Lang Elem | 72 | Summer School |
| 43 Science Elem | 53 | Reading Sec | 63 | Foreign/World Lang Sec | 73 | Instructional Tech |
| 44 Science Sec | 54 | Remedial Reading K-12 | 64 | Religious Education K-12 | 74 | Inservice Training |
| 45 Math K-12 | 55 | Remedial Reading Elem | 65 | Religious Education Elem | 75 | Marketing/Distributive |
| 46 Math Elem | 56 | Remedial Reading Sec | 66 | Religious Education Sec | 76 | Info Systems |
| 47 Math Sec | 57 | Bilingual/ELL | 67 | School Board President | 77 | Psychological Assess |
| 48 English/Lang Arts K-12 | 58 | Special Education K-12 | 68 | Teacher Personnel | 78 | Affirmative Action |

| Public Schs..Principal | Grd | Prgm | Enr/#Cls | SN |
|---|---|---|---|---|
| Vega Elem Sch<br>200 Longhorn Dr, Vega 79092<br>Johnett Stribling | PK-4 | T | 140<br>20 | 31% 806/267-2126 |
| Vega Jr Sr High Sch<br>200 Longhorn Dr, Vega 79092<br>Tracey Bell \ Kassidy Rosas | 5-12 | TV | 240<br>20 | 21% 806/267-2126 |

● **Wildorado Ind Sch Dist** PID: 01045584  806/426-3317
1523 S Locust St, Wildorado 79098  Fax 806/426-3523

Schools: 1 \ Teachers: 15 \ Students: 210 \ Special Ed Students: 15 \
Ethnic: Hispanic 17%, Caucasian 83% \ Exp: $563 (High) \ Poverty: 22% \
Title I: $19,401 \ Open-Close: 08/19 - 05/21 \ DTBP: $337 (High)

| | | | | |
|---|---|---|---|---|
| Troy Duck ................... 1,11,73 | Shan Allen ................... 2,271 |
| Loretta Gouldy ................... 7* | Sherry Clark ................... 12 |
| Robin Welch ................... 57* | Lane Mason ................... 67 |
| Jill Rankin ................... 296 | |

| Public Schs..Principal | Grd | Prgm | Enr/#Cls | SN |
|---|---|---|---|---|
| Wildorado Sch<br>1523 S Locust St, Wildorado 79098<br>Mike Cheverzer | PK-11 | T | 210<br>8 | 23% 806/426-3317 |

## ORANGE COUNTY

## ORANGE PUBLIC SCHOOLS

● **Bridge City Ind School Dist** PID: 01045601  409/735-1501
1031 W Round Bunch Rd, Bridge City 77611  Fax 409/735-1512

Schools: 4 \ Teachers: 193 \ Students: 3,057 \ Special Ed Students: 242
\ LEP Students: 142 \ College-Bound: 51% \ Ethnic: Asian 3%,
African American 1%, Hispanic 17%, Caucasian 79% \ Exp: $373 (High)
\ Poverty: 12% \ Title I: $283,848 \ Special Education: $738,000 \
Open-Close: 08/19 - 05/27 \ DTBP: $178 (High) \ f t

| | |
|---|---|
| Todd Lintzen ................... 1 | Melinda James ................... 2 |
| Maggie Joubert ................... 4 | Allen DeShazo ................... 6 |
| Terra Fountain ................... 8,16,88,288,296 | Gina Mannino ................... 11,15,271,274,294 |
| Arron Conner ................... 27* | Nichole Harris ................... 36* |
| Johnna Smith ................... 37* | Jennifer Rumsey ................... 38* |
| Corrin Gonzales ................... 58 | Judy Cole ................... 67 |
| Natasha Ray ................... 73 | Steve Brinson ................... 83,91 |
| Shane Preston ................... 295 | |

| Public Schs..Principal | Grd | Prgm | Enr/#Cls | SN |
|---|---|---|---|---|
| Bridge City Elem Sch<br>1035 W Round Bunch Rd, Bridge City 77611<br>Melanie Toups | PK-2 | T | 823<br>17 | 47% 409/735-0900<br>Fax 409/735-0906 |
| Bridge City High Sch<br>2690 Texas Ave, Bridge City 77611<br>Tim Woolley | 9-12 | TV | 811<br>75 | 31% 409/735-1600<br>Fax 409/735-1606 |
| Bridge City Intermediate Sch<br>1029 W Round Bunch Rd, Bridge City 77611<br>Julie Motomura | 3-5 | T | 737<br>30 | 42% 409/792-8800<br>Fax 409/792-8806 |
| Bridge City Middle Sch<br>300 Bower Dr, Bridge City 77611<br>Amanda Hoffman | 6-8 | T | 686<br>50 | 38% 409/735-1700<br>Fax 409/735-1706 |

● **Deweyville Ind School Dist** PID: 01043718  409/746-2731
43200 State Highway 87 S, Orange 77632  Fax 409/349-9338

Schools: 2 \ Teachers: 50 \ Students: 575 \ Special Ed Students: 92
\ College-Bound: 44% \ Ethnic: African American 2%, Hispanic 5%,
Native American: 1%, Caucasian 92% \ Exp: $387 (High) \ Poverty: 24% \
Title I: $173,073 \ Special Education: $186,000 \ Open-Close: 08/17 -
05/21 \ DTBP: $358 (High) \ f t

| | |
|---|---|
| Dr Keith Jones ................... 1,11 | Janae Welch ................... 2 |
| Sharlene Hryhorchuk ................... 4 | Michael Richarb ................... 5 |
| Brandon Prouse ................... 6 | Lisa Brinson ................... 7,85* |
| Jennifer Parkhurst ................... 12 | Cheryl Inboden ................... 16* |
| Carmen Purgahn ................... 58* | Luke Smith ................... 67 |

| Public Schs..Principal | Grd | Prgm | Enr/#Cls | SN |
|---|---|---|---|---|
| Deweyville Elem Sch<br>43200 State Highway 87 S, Orange 77632<br>Lajuan Addison | PK-5 | T | 244<br>30 | 65% 409/746-2731<br>Fax 409/206-2697 |
| Deweyville Jr Sr High Sch<br>171 State Highway 12 W, Orange 77632<br>Brian East | 6-12 | TV | 305<br>25 | 52% 409/746-2685 |

● **Little Cypress Mauriceville SD** PID: 01045651  409/883-2232
6586 FM 1130, Orange 77632  Fax 409/883-3509

Schools: 6 \ Teachers: 229 \ Students: 3,100 \ Special Ed Students: 395
\ LEP Students: 66 \ College-Bound: 62% \ Ethnic: Asian 1%, African
American 6%, Hispanic 11%, Caucasian 81% \ Exp: $641 (High) \
Poverty: 15% \ Title I: $656,066 \ Special Education: $1,299,000 \
Open-Close: 08/14 - 05/20 \ DTBP: $168 (High)

| | |
|---|---|
| Dr Pauline Hargrove ................... 1 | Greg Perry ................... 2,15 |
| Phillip Matthews ................... 3,91 | Sheri Tregre ................... 3 |
| Suzanne MaGee ................... 4 | Michele Leblew ................... 5 |
| Randall Crouch ................... 6* | Kelly Meadows ................... 7* |
| Julia Dickerson ................... 9,57,81,271,288* | Todd Loupe ................... 10,30,36,69,85,88* |
| Laurie Gordon ................... 11 | Roy Mazzagate ................... 16,297 |
| Sandy Reynolds ................... 16 | Hollie Fregia ................... 19 |
| Kristine Brown ................... 35,75* | Beverly Knight ................... 58,72,270 |
| Marlene Courmier ................... 67 | Beth Sonnier ................... 68 |
| Kim Allen ................... 73,84 | |

| Public Schs..Principal | Grd | Prgm | Enr/#Cls | SN |
|---|---|---|---|---|
| Little Cypress Elem Sch<br>5723 Meeks Dr, Orange 77632<br>Kayla Casey | PK-3 | T | 513<br>35 | 48% 409/886-2838<br>Fax 409/886-8172 |
| Little Cypress Interm Sch<br>2300 Allie Payne Rd, Orange 77632<br>Michael Ridout | 4-5 | T | 320<br>18 | 38% 409/886-4245<br>Fax 409/886-1828 |
| Little Cypress Jr High Sch<br>6765 FM 1130, Orange 77632<br>Jason Yeaman | 6-8 | T | 461<br>36 | 31% 409/883-2317<br>Fax 409/670-4626 |
| Little Cypress-Mauriceville HS<br>7327 Highway 87 N, Orange 77632<br>Ryan Dubose | 9-12 | ATV | 980<br>95 | 31% 409/886-5821<br>Fax 409/886-5762 |
| Mauriceville Elem Sch<br>20040 FM 1130, Orange 77632<br>Carie Broussard | PK-5 | T | 562<br>38 | 43% 409/745-1615<br>Fax 409/670-4641 |
| Mauriceville Middle Sch<br>19952 FM 1130, Orange 77632<br>Kim Cox | 6-8 | T | 276<br>25 | 44% 409/745-3970<br>Fax 409/670-4636 |

- **Orangefield Ind School Dist** PID: 01045704
  9974 FM 105, Orange 77630

  409/735-5337
  Fax 409/735-2080

  **Schools:** 3 \ **Teachers:** 127 \ **Students:** 1,785 \ **Special Ed Students:** 181 \ **LEP Students:** 35 \ **College-Bound:** 65% \ **Ethnic:** Asian 2%, Hispanic 10%, Caucasian 88% \ **Exp:** $674 (High) \ **Poverty:** 10% \ **Title I:** $255,128 \ **Special Education:** $402,000 \ **Open-Close:** 08/12 - 05/27 \ **DTBP:** $6 (Low)

| | | |
|---|---|---|
| Dr Stephen Patterson | 1 | |
| Brian Ousley | 4 | |
| Beena Vanpelt | 8 | |
| Dr Dayna Smith | 11,34,57,58,88,271,275,296 | |
| Candi Patterson | 31,36,69,83,93* | |
| Jennifer Gauthier | 73,76,84,295 | |
| Shaun McAlpin | 2,15,298 | |
| Josh Smalley | 6 | |
| Kim Smalley | 8,273,286,288 | |
| Sunshine Copeland | 16* | |
| Dr Ronald Risinger | 67 | |
| Matthew Lanier | 295 | |

| Public Schs..Principal | Grd | Prgm | Enr/#Cls | SN | |
|---|---|---|---|---|---|
| Orangefield Elem Sch<br>10288 FM 105, Orange 77630<br>Amanda Jenkins | PK-5 | TV | 728<br>32 | 40%<br>Fax | 409/735-5346<br>409/735-3940 |
| Orangefield High Sch<br>10058 FM 105, Orange 77630<br>Zach Quinn | 9-12 | TV | 543<br>45 | 42%<br>Fax | 409/735-3851<br>409/697-2301 |
| Orangefield Junior High Sch<br>7745 Sand Bar Rd, Orange 77630<br>Rea Wrinkle | 6-8 | T | 436<br>50 | 49%<br>Fax | 409/735-6737<br>409/792-9605 |

- **Vidor Ind School Dist** PID: 01045754
  120 E Bolivar St, Vidor 77662

  409/951-8700
  Fax 409/769-0093

  **Schools:** 7 \ **Teachers:** 332 \ **Students:** 4,400 \ **Special Ed Students:** 577 \ **LEP Students:** 67 \ **Ethnic:** Asian 1%, Hispanic 7%, Caucasian 92% \ **Exp:** $387 (High) \ **Poverty:** 18% \ **Title I:** $1,048,834 \ **Special Education:** $1,221,000 \ **Open-Close:** 08/12 - 05/27 \ **DTBP:** $177 (High)

| | | |
|---|---|---|
| Dr Jay Killgo | 1,84 | |
| Sheila Schoen | 2 | |
| Mary Ellen Vivreet | 4 | |
| Jeff Matthews | 6,35* | |
| Heather Watson | 8,39,48 | |
| Travis Maines | 15,68 | |
| Kana Philips | 23* | |
| Karrie Clark | 34,57,58,77 | |
| Sally Andrews | 71 | |
| Barbara Silver | 76 | |
| Mike Sanchez | 91 | |
| David Croak | 2 | |
| Tommy Gilcrease | 3 | |
| Jeanne Taylor | 5 | |
| Deena Bunting | 7 | |
| Kelly Waters | 9,11,93,286,288,296,298 | |
| Jana Cash | 16 | |
| Penny Singleton | 27,31* | |
| David Camp | 67 | |
| Jim Gordon | 73 | |
| Janet Bradley | 76 | |
| Jaime Hagler | 93 | |

| Public Schs..Principal | Grd | Prgm | Enr/#Cls | SN | |
|---|---|---|---|---|---|
| Ⓐ Aim Center High Sch<br>690 Orange St, Vidor 77662<br>Brandy Antill | 10-12 | GT | 35<br>6 | 53%<br>Fax | 409/951-8780<br>409/769-0443 |
| Oak Forest Elem Sch<br>2400 Highway 12, Vidor 77662<br>Carolyn Wedgeworth | PK-4 | T | 564<br>39 | 63%<br>Fax | 409/951-8860<br>409/769-2678 |
| Pine Forest Elem Sch<br>4150 N Main St, Vidor 77662<br>Preston Clark | PK-4 | T | 547<br>36 | 58%<br>Fax | 409/951-8800<br>409/786-1728 |
| Vidor Elem Sch<br>400 Old Highway 90 E, Vidor 77662<br>**Brandy Antill** | PK-4 | T | 643<br>48 | 71%<br>Fax | 409/951-8830<br>409/769-0211 |
| Vidor High Sch<br>500 Orange St, Vidor 77662<br>James McDowell | 9-12 | T | 630<br>60 | 46%<br>Fax | 409/951-8900<br>409/769-6767 |
| Vidor Junior High Sch<br>945 N Tram Rd, Vidor 77662<br>Aaron Herrington | 7-8 | T | 676<br>50 | 51%<br>Fax | 409/951-8970<br>409/769-6754 |

| | | | | | | |
|---|---|---|---|---|---|---|
| Vidor Middle Sch<br>2500 Highway 12, Vidor 77662<br>Kerri Pierce | 5-6 | T | 694<br>36 | 56%<br>Fax | 409/951-8880<br>409/783-0309 |

- **West Orange-Cove Cons ISD** PID: 01045819
  902 W Park Ave, Orange 77630

  409/882-5437
  Fax 409/882-5467

  **Schools:** 4 \ **Teachers:** 171 \ **Students:** 2,485 \ **Special Ed Students:** 249 \ **LEP Students:** 158 \ **Ethnic:** Asian 1%, African American 62%, Hispanic 20%, Caucasian 18% \ **Exp:** $499 (High) \ **Poverty:** 32% \ **Title I:** $1,299,392 \ **Special Education:** $704,000 \ **Open-Close:** 08/12 - 06/04 \ **DTBP:** $183 (High) \ 🇫

| | | |
|---|---|---|
| Rickie Harris | 1 | |
| Greg Willis | 3 | |
| Manuel Vera | 5 | |
| Ashton Knox | 8,296 | |
| Larry Haynes | 11 | |
| Heather Knox | 58,90,91 | |
| Dawn Martin | 71 | |
| Robin Hathaway | 2 | |
| Danielle Robinson | 4 | |
| Cornel Thompson | 6* | |
| Dr Nina LeBlanc | 8,11,17,57,58,91,273,288 | |
| Elvis Rushing | 16,73,82* | |
| Linda Platt-Bryant | 67 | |
| Alicia Sigee | 79 | |

| Public Schs..Principal | Grd | Prgm | Enr/#Cls | SN | |
|---|---|---|---|---|---|
| North Early Learning Center<br>801 Cordrey St, Orange 77630<br>Vickie Oceguera | PK-PK | T | 296<br>18 | 99%<br>Fax | 409/882-5434<br>409/882-5449 |
| West Orange-Stark Elem Sch<br>2605 Martin Luther King Jr Dr, Orange 77630<br>Troy Bethley | K-5 | T | 1,059<br>29 | 68%<br>Fax | 409/882-5630<br>409/882-5644 |
| West Orange-Stark High Sch<br>1400 Newton St, Orange 77630<br>Rolanda Holifield | 9-12 | ATV | 633<br>40 | 75%<br>Fax | 409/882-5570<br>409/882-5573 |
| West Orange-Stark Middle Sch<br>1402 Green Ave, Orange 77630<br>Brodrick McGrew | 6-8 | ATV | 497 | 69%<br>Fax | 409/882-5520<br>409/882-5545 |

## ORANGE CATHOLIC SCHOOLS

- **Diocese of Beaumont Sch Office** PID: 01034339
  Listing includes only schools located in this county. See District Index for location of Diocesan Offices.

| Catholic Schs..Principal | Grd | Prgm | Enr/#Cls | SN | |
|---|---|---|---|---|---|
| St Mary Catholic Sch<br>2600 Bob Hall Rd, Orange 77630<br>Katie Sanders | PK-8 | | 200<br>14 | | 409/883-8913<br>Fax 409/883-0827 |

## ORANGE PRIVATE SCHOOLS

| Private Schs..Principal | Grd | Prgm | Enr/#Cls | SN | |
|---|---|---|---|---|---|
| Community Christian Sch<br>3400 M L King Dr, Orange 77632<br>Macey Jackson | PK-12 | | 325<br>30 | | 409/883-4531<br>Fax 409/883-8855 |

| | | | | |
|---|---|---|---|---|
| 1 | Superintendent | 8 | Curric/Instruct K-12 | 19 Chief Financial Officer |
| 2 | Bus/Finance/Purchasing | 9 | Curric/Instruct Elem | 20 Art K-12 |
| 3 | Buildings And Grounds | 10 | Curric/Instruct Sec | 21 Art Elem |
| 4 | Food Service | 11 | Federal Program | 22 Art Sec |
| 5 | Transportation | 12 | Title I | 23 Music K-12 |
| 6 | Athletic | 13 | Title V | 24 Music Elem |
| 7 | Health Services | 15 | Asst Superintendent | 25 Music Sec |
| | | 16 | Instructional Media Svcs | 26 Business Education |
| | | 17 | Chief Operations Officer | 27 Career & Tech Ed |
| | | 18 | Chief Academic Officer | 28 Technology Education |

| | | | |
|---|---|---|---|
| 29 Family/Consumer Science | 39 Social Studies K-12 | 49 English/Lang Arts Elem | 59 Special Education Elem | 69 Academic Assessment |
| 30 Adult Education | 40 Social Studies Elem | 50 English/Lang Arts Sec | 60 Special Education Sec | 70 Research/Development |
| 31 Career/Sch-to-Work K-12 | 41 Social Studies Sec | 51 Reading K-12 | 61 Foreign/World Lang K-12 | 71 Public Information |
| 32 Career/Sch-to-Work Elem | 42 Science K-12 | 52 Reading Elem | 62 Foreign/World Lang Elem | 72 Summer School |
| 33 Career/Sch-to-Work Sec | 43 Science Elem | 53 Reading Sec | 63 Foreign/World Lang Sec | 73 Instructional Tech |
| 34 Early Childhood Ed | 44 Science Sec | 54 Remedial Reading K-12 | 64 Religious Education K-12 | 74 Inservice Training |
| 35 Health/Phys Education | 45 Math K-12 | 55 Remedial Reading Elem | 65 Religious Education Elem | 75 Marketing/Distributive |
| 36 Guidance Services K-12 | 46 Math Elem | 56 Remedial Reading Sec | 66 Religious Education Sec | 76 Info Systems |
| 37 Guidance Services Elem | 47 Math Sec | 57 Bilingual/ELL | 67 School Board President | 77 Psychological Assess |
| 38 Guidance Services Sec | 48 English/Lang Arts K-12 | 58 Special Education K-12 | 68 Teacher Personnel | 78 Affirmative Action |

## PALO PINTO COUNTY

### PALO PINTO PUBLIC SCHOOLS

• **Gordon Ind School Dist** PID: 01045950 — 254/693-5582
112-116 Rusk Street, Gordon 76453 — Fax 254/693-5503

> **Schools:** 1 \ **Teachers:** 17 \ **Students:** 210 \ **Special Ed Students:** 15
> \ **LEP Students:** 3 \ **College-Bound:** 98% \ **Ethnic:** Hispanic 18%,
> Caucasian 82% \ **Exp:** $823 (High) \ **Poverty:** 17% \ **Title I:** $39,805 \
> **Open-Close:** 08/04 - 05/27 \ **DTBP:** $323 (High) \ 🅕

Holly Campbell ...........................1   Jessica Hendrickson ............................2,19
Patty Hopkins ............................4   Mike Reed ..................................................6*
Katie Elrod .....................8,16,36,74*   Michael Rouse ........................................ 67
Rick Spear ..........................73,295

| Public Schs..Principal | Grd | Prgm | Enr/#Cls | SN | |
|---|---|---|---|---|---|
| Gordon Sch<br>112-116 Rusk Street, Gordon 76453<br>Holly Campbell | PK-12 | T | 210<br>20 | 53% | 254/693-5342 |

• **Graford Ind School Dist** PID: 01045986 — 940/664-3101
400 W Division St, Graford 76449 — Fax 940/664-2123

> **Schools:** 2 \ **Teachers:** 33 \ **Students:** 340 \ **Special Ed Students:** 27 \
> **LEP Students:** 15 \ **Ethnic:** Hispanic 13%, Caucasian 86% \ **Exp:** $373 (High)
> \ **Poverty:** 17% \ **Title I:** $72,317 \ **Open-Close:** 08/20 - 05/26 \ **DTBP:** $331
> (High)

Dennis Holt ...............................1   Michelle Davis ............................................2
David Taylor ..............................3   Rodney Hall .........................................5,83*
Tina Alvarado .............12,59,79,296*   Heather Thompson ...............................57*
Jeff Lemley .............................67   Chris Thompson .........................73,84,295

| Public Schs..Principal | Grd | Prgm | Enr/#Cls | SN | |
|---|---|---|---|---|---|
| Graford Elem Sch<br>400 W Division St, Graford 76449<br>**Tina Alvarado** | PK-5 | T | 174<br>11 | 62% | 940/664-3101<br>Fax 940/664-2765 |
| Graford Jr Sr High Sch<br>400 W Division St, Graford 76449<br>Clifton Womack | 6-12 | TV | 173<br>20 | 55% | 940/664-3101 |

• **Mineral Wells Ind School Dist** PID: 01046019 — 940/325-6404
906 SW 5th Ave, Mineral Wells 76067 — Fax 940/325-6378

> **Schools:** 6 \ **Teachers:** 228 \ **Students:** 3,200 \ **Special Ed Students:** 329
> \ **LEP Students:** 330 \ **College-Bound:** 45% \ **Ethnic:** Asian 1%,
> African American 4%, Hispanic 41%, Caucasian 54% \ **Exp:** $517 (High) \
> **Poverty:** 23% \ **Title I:** $1,122,239 \ **Open-Close:** 08/18 - 05/26 \ **DTBP:** $93
> (Med)

Dr John Kuhn ............................1   Paul Hearn ..........................................2,19
James Bradford ......................3,91   Carrie Martin ............................................. 4
Brett Barrick ..............................5   Brett Barrick .............................................5*
Gerald Perry ..............................6*   Wanda Voelcker .................................7,35,85*
Carey Carter ........8,16,54,69,74,273,294   Natalie Griffin ....................11,57,81,271,298
David Tarver ........................15,68   Deeann Hampton .....................................31*
Parisa Lerma ......................58,275   Maria Jones .............................................67
Karyn Bullock .........................71   Janna Lee Martin ....................................73

| Public Schs..Principal | Grd | Prgm | Enr/#Cls | SN | |
|---|---|---|---|---|---|
| Houston Elem Sch<br>300 SW 13th St, Mineral Wells 76067<br>Amy Salazar | 2-3 | | 487<br>27 | | 940/325-3427<br>Fax 940/325-7683 |
| Lamar Elem Sch<br>2012 SE 12th St, Mineral Wells 76067<br>Kendra Fowler | PK-1 | | 707<br>45 | | 940/325-5303<br>Fax 940/328-0152 |
| Ⓐ Mineral Wells Academy<br>3810 Ram Blvd, Mineral Wells 76067<br>Jeffery Smith | 9-12 | T | 32<br>3 | 68% | 940/325-3033<br>Fax 940/325-6044 |
| Mineral Wells High Sch<br>3801 Ram Blvd, Mineral Wells 76067<br>Dr Doug Funk | 9-12 | TV | 247<br>39 | 68% | 940/325-4408<br>Fax 940/325-7623 |
| Mineral Wells Jr High Sch<br>1301 SE 14th Ave, Mineral Wells 76067<br>**Shanna Spillers** | 7-8 | T | 493<br>44 | 75% | 940/325-0711<br>Fax 940/328-0450 |
| Travis Elem Sch<br>1001 SE M L King Jr St, Mineral Wells 76067<br>David Wells | 4-6 | T | 745 | 81% | 940/325-7801<br>Fax 940/328-0972 |

• **Palo Pinto Ind Sch Dist 906** PID: 01046100 — 940/659-2745
821 Oak St, Palo Pinto 76484 — Fax 940/659-2936

> **Schools:** 1 \ **Teachers:** 10 \ **Students:** 100 \ **Special Ed Students:** 5 \
> **LEP Students:** 3 \ **Ethnic:** Asian 1%, Hispanic 10%, Caucasian 89% \
> **Exp:** $222 (Med) \ **Poverty:** 12% \ **Title I:** $37,774 \ **Open-Close:** 08/17 -
> 05/21 \ **DTBP:** $304 (High) \ 🅕

Wendell Barker ........................1,84   Natalie Rogers ...............9,57,69,88,271,273
Wendell Barker ..................11,36,73,83*   Bud Price ................................................67
Amanda Hinojos .......................85

| Public Schs..Principal | Grd | Prgm | Enr/#Cls | SN | |
|---|---|---|---|---|---|
| Palo Pinto Elem Sch<br>821 Oak St, Palo Pinto 76484<br>Natalie Rogers | PK-6 | T | 100<br>8 | 65% | 940/659-2745 |

• **Santo Ind School Dist** PID: 01046124 — 940/769-2835
406 S FM 2201, Santo 76472 — Fax 940/769-3116

> **Schools:** 2 \ **Teachers:** 39 \ **Students:** 451 \ **Special Ed Students:** 34
> \ **LEP Students:** 21 \ **College-Bound:** 67% \ **Ethnic:** Hispanic 20%,
> Caucasian 80% \ **Exp:** $544 (High) \ **Poverty:** 25% \ **Title I:** $185,895 \
> **Open-Close:** 08/14 - 05/21

Greg Gilbert ..............................1   Karen Mori ...........................................2,84
Stacy Finley ..............................4   Cathy Longley ......................................12,57*
Amy Bryan ...............................67   Shauna Bradshaw .................................752

| Public Schs..Principal | Grd | Prgm | Enr/#Cls | SN | |
|---|---|---|---|---|---|
| Santo Elem Sch<br>Farm Road 2201, Santo 76472<br>Cathy Longley | PK-5 | T | 193<br>15 | 49% | 940/769-3215 |
| Santo Jr Sr High Sch<br>406 S FM 2201, Santo 76472<br>Darla Henry | 6-12 | TV | 258<br>30 | 38% | 940/769-3847<br>Fax 940/769-2796 |

---

| | | | | |
|---|---|---|---|---|
| 79 Student Personnel | 91 Safety/Security | 275 Response To Intervention | 298 Grant Writer/Ptnrships | **School Programs** |
| 80 Driver Ed/Safety | 92 Magnet School | 277 Remedial Math K-12 | 750 Chief Innovation Officer | A = Alternative Program |
| 81 Gifted/Talented | 93 Parental Involvement | 280 Literacy Coach | 751 Chief of Staff | G = Adult Classes |
| 82 Video Services | 95 Tech Prep Program | 285 STEM | 752 Social Emotional Learning | M = Magnet Program |
| 83 Substance Abuse Prev | 97 Chief Information Officer | 286 Digital Learning | | T = Title I Schoolwide |
| 84 Erate | 98 Chief Technology Officer | 288 Common Core Standards | **Other School Types** | V = Career & Tech Ed Programs |
| 85 AIDS Education | 270 Character Education | 294 Accountability | Ⓐ = Alternative School | |
| 88 Alternative/At Risk | 271 Migrant Education | 295 Network System | Ⓒ = Charter School | |
| 89 Multi-Cultural Curriculum | 273 Teacher Mentor | 296 Title II Programs | Ⓜ = Magnet School | |
| 90 Social Work | 274 Before/After Sch | 297 Webmaster | Ⓨ = Year-Round School | |

**Social Media**
🅕 = Facebook
🅣 = Twitter

New Schools are shaded
New Superintendents and Principals are bold
Personnel with email addresses are underscored

• **Strawn Ind School Dist** PID: 01046150      254/672-5313
224 E Walnut Street, Strawn 76475      Fax 254/672-5662

**Schools:** 1 \ **Teachers:** 19 \ **Students:** 160 \ **Special Ed Students:** 16
\ **LEP Students:** 23 \ **College-Bound:** 60% \ **Ethnic:** Hispanic 43%,
Native American: 1%, Caucasian 57% \ **Exp:** $744 (High) \ **Poverty:** 23% \
**Title I:** $44,992 \ **Open-Close:** 08/24 - 05/28 \ 🅵 🅣

| | | | |
|---|---|---|---|
| Richard Mitchell | 1,11 | Kathryn Lynn | 2 |
| Darryl Atkins | 3,5 | Nancy Montgomery | 4 |
| Dewaine Lee | 6 | Joyce Gray | 57* |
| Melaine McCormack | 58,296 | Tina Spakes | 67 |
| Shan Nowak | 73* | Jessica Mallory | 288* |

| Public Schs..Principal | Grd | Prgm | Enr/#Cls | SN | |
|---|---|---|---|---|---|
| Strawn Sch<br>224 E Walnut St, Strawn 76475<br>Melanie Cormack | PK-12 | TV | 160<br>12 | 65% | 254/672-5313 |

## PALO PINTO PRIVATE SCHOOLS

| Private Schs..Principal | Grd | Prgm | Enr/#Cls | SN | |
|---|---|---|---|---|---|
| Community Christian Sch<br>2501 Garrett Morris Pkwy, Mineral Wells 76067<br>William Jefferson | PK-12 | | 72<br>13 | | 940/328-1333<br>Fax 940/328-1277 |

## PANOLA COUNTY

## PANOLA PUBLIC SCHOOLS

• **Beckville Ind School Dist** PID: 01046186      903/678-3311
4398 State Highway 149, Beckville 75631      Fax 903/678-2157

**Schools:** 2 \ **Teachers:** 64 \ **Students:** 700 \ **Special Ed Students:** 71
\ **LEP Students:** 15 \ **College-Bound:** 99% \ **Ethnic:** African American
5%, Hispanic 12%, Caucasian 83% \ **Exp:** $294 (Med) \ **Poverty:** 20% \
**Title I:** $128,988 \ **Special Education:** $128,000 \ **Open-Close:** 08/13 -
05/28 \ **DTBP:** $347 (High)

| | | | |
|---|---|---|---|
| Devin Tate | 1 | Charmaine Chappell | 2 |
| Gay Harris | 3,5 | Jaime Swanson | 4 |
| Cody Ross | 6 | Dr Georgia King | 8,11,58,83,286,296,298* |
| Amy English | 57* | Casey Travis | 67 |
| Trecia Woodall | 73* | | |

| Public Schs..Principal | Grd | Prgm | Enr/#Cls | SN | |
|---|---|---|---|---|---|
| Beckville Jr Sr High Sch<br>169 N Washington St, Beckville 75631<br>**Brandon Kruebbe** | 6-12 | TV | 364<br>25 | 39% | 903/678-3851<br>Fax 903/678-3827 |
| Beckville Sunset Elem Sch<br>4378 State Highway 149, Beckville 75631<br>Brandon Kruebbe | PK-5 | T | 296<br>24 | 43% | 903/678-3601<br>Fax 903/678-2257 |

• **Carthage Ind School Dist** PID: 01046215      903/693-3806
1 Bulldog Dr, Carthage 75633      Fax 903/693-2511

**Schools:** 6 \ **Teachers:** 185 \ **Students:** 2,600 \ **Special Ed Students:** 304
\ **LEP Students:** 225 \ **College-Bound:** 52% \ **Ethnic:** Asian 1%, African
American 22%, Hispanic 20%, Caucasian 57% \ **Exp:** $476 (High) \
**Poverty:** 21% \ **Title I:** $728,153 \ **Open-Close:** 08/12 - 05/21 \ **DTBP:** $153
(High)

| | | | |
|---|---|---|---|
| John Wink | 1 | Kathy Ballard | 2 |
| Renee Reysinger | 3,4,5,15 | Llyod Williams | 4 |
| Scott Surratt | 6,35* | Bonnie McMillian | 7* |
| Allen Koch | 8,69,294 | Mike Baysinger | 8 |
| Donna Porter | 11,57,88,285,288,296,298* | Bonnie Pope | 16* |
| Shannon Royce | 38,270 | Angie Bishop | 58 |
| Dr Ben Donald | 67 | Jean Thomas | 71 |
| Richard Sullivan | 73,76,95,295 | | |

| Public Schs..Principal | Grd | Prgm | Enr/#Cls | SN | |
|---|---|---|---|---|---|
| Baker Koonce Intermediate Sch<br>320 N Daniels St, Carthage 75633<br>Clarinda Collins | 4-6 | T | 633<br>49 | 56% | 903/693-8611<br>Fax 903/693-5948 |
| Carthage High Sch<br>1600 West Panola, Carthage 75633<br>**Justin Smith** | 9-12 | T | 798<br>60 | 48% | 903/693-2552<br>Fax 903/693-9752 |
| Carthage Junior High Sch<br>616 Holly St, Carthage 75633<br>Wade Watson | 7-8 | T | 409<br>35 | 56% | 903/693-2751<br>Fax 903/694-9582 |
| Carthage Primary Sch<br>510 N Adams St, Carthage 75633<br>Kiley Schumacher | PK-1 | T | 500<br>33 | 66% | 903/693-2254<br>Fax 903/693-3287 |
| Libby Elem Sch<br>419 Davis St, Carthage 75633<br>Staci Davis | 2-3 | T | 368<br>22 | 61% | 903/693-8862<br>Fax 903/693-4696 |
| Ⓐ Pace Academy<br>320 W College St, Carthage 75633<br>Mike Baysinger | 6-12 | | 30 | | 903/694-7554 |

• **Gary Ind School Dist** PID: 01046277      903/685-2291
132 Bobcat Trl, Gary 75643      Fax 903/685-2639

**Schools:** 1 \ **Teachers:** 40 \ **Students:** 443 \ **Special Ed Students:** 53
\ **LEP Students:** 15 \ **Ethnic:** Hispanic 7%, Native American: 1%,
Caucasian 92% \ **Exp:** $419 (High) \ **Poverty:** 30% \ **Title I:** $138,170 \
**Special Education:** $94,000 \ **Open-Close:** 08/17 - 05/21 \ **DTBP:** $329
(High)

| | | | |
|---|---|---|---|
| Todd Greer | 1 | Jason Woodfin | 2,3,5,11,88 |
| Mark Brown | 6* | Janie Thomas | 7* |
| Dr Richard Ballenger | 8,15,58,69* | Tiffany Brown | 57* |
| Stacy Cransord | 67 | Mark Baisden | 73* |
| Tonja Coleman | 81 | | |

| Public Schs..Principal | Grd | Prgm | Enr/#Cls | SN | |
|---|---|---|---|---|---|
| Gary Sch<br>132 Bobcat Trl, Gary 75643<br>**Chris Price** \ Brittney Davis | PK-12 | ATV | 443<br>30 | 50% | 903/685-2291 |

## PANOLA PRIVATE SCHOOLS

| Private Schs..Principal | Grd | Prgm | Enr/#Cls | SN | |
|---|---|---|---|---|---|
| Northside Christian Academy<br>108 E Ash St, Carthage 75633<br>Scott Dragoo | PK-12 | | 90<br>5 | | 903/693-7700<br>Fax 903/694-9272 |

| | | | | | |
|---|---|---|---|---|---|
| 1 Superintendent | 8 Curric/Instruct K-12 | 19 Chief Financial Officer | 29 Family/Consumer Science | 39 Social Studies K-12 | 49 English/Lang Arts Elem | 59 Special Education Elem | 69 Academic Assessment |
| 2 Bus/Finance/Purchasing | 9 Curric/Instruct Elem | 20 Art K-12 | 30 Adult Education | 40 Social Studies Sec | 50 English/Lang Arts Sec | 60 Special Education Sec | 70 Research/Development |
| 3 Buildings And Grounds | 10 Curric/Instruct Sec | 21 Art Elem | 31 Career/Sch-to-Work K-12 | 41 Social Studies Sec | 51 Reading K-12 | 61 Foreign/World Lang K-12 | 71 Public Information |
| 4 Food Service | 11 Federal Program | 22 Art Sec | 32 Career/Sch-to-Work Elem | 42 Science K-12 | 52 Reading Elem | 62 Foreign/World Lang Elem | 72 Summer School |
| 5 Transportation | 12 Title I | 23 Music K-12 | 33 Career/Sch-to-Work Sec | 43 Science Elem | 53 Reading Sec | 63 Foreign/World Lang Sec | 73 Instructional Tech |
| 6 Athletic | 13 Title V | 24 Music Elem | 34 Early Childhood Ed | 44 Science Sec | 54 Remedial Reading K-12 | 64 Religious Education K-12 | 74 Inservice Training |
| 7 Health Services | 15 Asst Superintendent | 25 Music Sec | 35 Health/Phys Education | 45 Math K-12 | 55 Remedial Reading Elem | 65 Religious Education Elem | 75 Marketing/Distributive |
| | 16 Instructional Media Svcs | 26 Business Education | 36 Guidance Services K-12 | 46 Math Elem | 56 Remedial Reading Sec | 66 Religious Education Sec | 76 Info Systems |
| | 17 Chief Operations Officer | 27 Career & Tech Ed | 37 Guidance Services Elem | 47 Math Sec | 57 Bilingual/ELL | 67 School Board President | 77 Psychological Assess |
| | 18 Chief Academic Officer | 28 Technology Education | 38 Guidance Services Sec | 48 English/Lang Arts K-12 | 58 Special Education K-12 | 68 Teacher Personnel | 78 Affirmative Action |

## PARKER COUNTY

## PARKER PUBLIC SCHOOLS

● **Aledo Ind School Dist** PID: 01046306 817/441-8327
1008 Bailey Ranch Rd, Aledo 76008 Fax 817/441-4845

**Schools:** 10 \ **Teachers:** 355 \ **Students:** 6,000 \ **Special Ed Students:** 490
\ **LEP Students:** 158 \ **College-Bound:** 61% \ **Ethnic:** Asian 1%,
African American 1%, Hispanic 15%, Caucasian 82% \ **Exp:** $383 (High)
\ **Poverty:** 5% \ **Title I:** $307,420 \ **Special Education:** $669,000 \
**Open-Close:** 08/19 - 05/27 \ **DTBP:** $151 (High) \ [f] [t]

| | | | |
|---|---|---|---|
| Dr Susan Bohn | 1 | Buffy Hanson | 2 |
| Earl Husfeld | 2,19 | Randy Campbell | 3 |
| Patty Willhite | 4 | Ken Burns | 5 |
| Steve Wood | 6 | Amber Crissey | 8 |
| Lynn McKinney | 11,15,296 | Julie Baker | 16,82* |
| Mary Smith | 27 | Candace Summerhill | 57,74,273,294 |
| Cheryl Wooten | 58 | Hoyt Harris | 67 |
| Sherry Taylor | 68 | Rick Herrin | 71 |
| Brooks Moore | 73,98,295 | Melissa Quisenberry | 73 |
| Scott Kessel | 88* | | |

| Public Schs..Principal | Grd | Prgm | Enr/#Cls | SN | |
|---|---|---|---|---|---|
| Aledo High Sch<br>1000 Bailey Ranch Rd, Aledo 76008<br>Dan Peterson | 9-12 | V | 1,321<br>55 | 10% | 817/441-8711<br>Fax 817/441-5136 |
| Ⓐ Aledo Learning Center<br>1016 Bailey Ranch Rd, Aledo 76008<br>Cheryl Jones | 9-12 | G | 25<br>5 | | 817/441-5176<br>Fax 817/441-9488 |
| Aledo Middle Sch<br>416 S FM 1187, Aledo 76008<br>Mandy Musselwhite | 7-8 | | 943<br>45 | 14% | 817/441-5198<br>Fax 817/441-5133 |
| Coder Elem Sch<br>12 Vernon Rd, Aledo 76008<br>Amy Sadler | PK-4 | T | 541<br>22 | 35% | 817/441-6095<br>Fax 817/441-5135 |
| Don R Daniel 9th Grade Campus<br>990 Bailey Ranch Rd, Aledo 76008<br>Angela Tims | 9-9 | | 466 | 12% | 817/441-4504<br>Fax 817/441-2146 |
| McAnally Intermediate Sch<br>151 S FM 5, Aledo 76008<br>**Joshua Jenkins** | 5-6 | | 834 | 17% | 817/441-8347<br>Fax 817/441-5177 |
| McCall Elem Sch<br>400 Scenic Trl, Willow Park 76087<br>Julie Choate | PK-4 | T | 423 | 16% | 817/441-4500<br>Fax 817/441-4535 |
| Stuard Elem Sch<br>200 Thunder Head Ln, Aledo 76008<br>Ron Shelton | PK-4 | | 579<br>23 | 5% | 817/441-5103<br>Fax 817/441-5116 |
| Vandagriff Elem Sch<br>408 S FM 1187, Aledo 76008<br>Stephanie Covington | PK-4 | | 541<br>20 | 9% | 817/441-8771<br>Fax 817/441-5150 |
| Walsh Elem Sch<br>1 Dean Dr, Aledo 76008<br>Kerry Cooper | PK-5 | | 334 | 20% | 817/207-3355 |

● **Brock Ind School Dist** PID: 01046344 817/594-7642
410 Eagle Spirit Ln, Brock 76087 Fax 817/599-3246

**Schools:** 4 \ **Teachers:** 107 \ **Students:** 1,476 \ **Special Ed Students:** 108
\ **LEP Students:** 23 \ **Ethnic:** Hispanic 10%, Native American: 1%,
Caucasian 89% \ **Exp:** $421 (High) \ **Poverty:** 5% \ **Title I:** $55,984 \
**Open-Close:** 08/13 - 05/20 \ **DTBP:** $329 (High) \ [t]

| | | | |
|---|---|---|---|
| Dr Cade Smith | 1 | Mike McSwain | 2,19 |
| Burt Green | 3 | Mere Marcus | 4* |
| Jeff Fulmer | 5 | Chad Massey | 6* |
| Dee Ann Mills | 12,298 | Dr Martin Ivey | 67 |
| Ingia Saxton | 79 | | |

| Public Schs..Principal | Grd | Prgm | Enr/#Cls | SN | |
|---|---|---|---|---|---|
| Brock Elem Sch<br>3000 FM 1189, Brock 76087<br>Erin Griffith | PK-2 | T | 349<br>18 | 10% | 817/592-6555<br>Fax 817/592-6559 |
| Brock High Sch<br>400 Eagle Spirit Ln, Weatherford 76087<br>Bobby Atchley | 9-12 | V | 435<br>20 | 7% | 817/596-7425<br>Fax 817/594-2509 |
| Brock Intermediate Sch<br>100 Grindstone Rd, Brock 76087<br>**Ranae Lane** | 3-6 | | 467 | 10% | 817/594-8017<br>Fax 817/599-5117 |
| Brock Junior High Sch<br>300 Grindstone Rd, Brock 76087<br>Andy Hudson | 7-8 | | 225<br>25 | 12% | 817/594-3195<br>Fax 817/594-3191 |

● **Garner Ind School Dist** PID: 01046370 940/682-4251
2222 Garner School Rd, Weatherford 76088 Fax 940/682-4141

**Schools:** 1 \ **Teachers:** 14 \ **Students:** 212 \ **Special Ed Students:** 18
\ **LEP Students:** 8 \ **Ethnic:** African American 1%, Hispanic 22%,
Caucasian 78% \ **Exp:** $384 (High) \ **Poverty:** 9% \ **Title I:** $30,447 \
**Open-Close:** 08/20 - 05/20 \ **DTBP:** $362 (High) \ [f]

| | | | |
|---|---|---|---|
| Rebecca Hallmark | 1 | Carolyn Jones | 2,13 |
| B Carlton | 3,5 | Vicki McBride | 4 |
| Tony Smith | 6* | Diane Shaw | 7,11,16,34,69* |
| Clay Yougblood | 67 | Jimmy Autry | 73* |

| Public Schs..Principal | Grd | Prgm | Enr/#Cls | SN | |
|---|---|---|---|---|---|
| Garner Elem Sch<br>2222 Garner School Rd, Weatherford 76088<br>Diane Shaw | PK-8 | T | 212<br>15 | 56% | 940/682-4251 |

● **Millsap Ind School Dist** PID: 01046394 940/682-4994
201 E Brazos St, Millsap 76066 Fax 940/682-4476

**Schools:** 3 \ **Teachers:** 77 \ **Students:** 989 \ **Special Ed Students:** 93
\ **LEP Students:** 24 \ **College-Bound:** 43% \ **Ethnic:** African American
1%, Hispanic 14%, Caucasian 84% \ **Exp:** $736 (High) \ **Poverty:** 11% \
**Title I:** $82,503 \ **Open-Close:** 08/20 - 05/21 \ **DTBP:** $347 (High) \ [f] [t]

| | | | |
|---|---|---|---|
| Deann Lee | 1,11 | Kim Alexander | 2 |
| Deborah Wright | 3 | Norman Adkins | 3 |
| Tina Stevens | 4 | Brad Littlefields | 5 |
| Stephanie Gast | 7* | Edi Martin | 15,296 |
| Pam Davis | 34* | Dr Dene Herbel | 67 |
| John Briese | 73 | Zach Greer | 73* |

| Public Schs..Principal | Grd | Prgm | Enr/#Cls | SN | |
|---|---|---|---|---|---|
| Millsap Elem Sch<br>101 Wilson Bend Rd, Millsap 76066<br>Cathy Bradshaw | PK-5 | T | 465<br>23 | 48% | 940/682-3121 |

| | | | | |
|---|---|---|---|---|
| 79 Student Personnel | 91 Safety/Security | 275 Response To Intervention | 298 Grant Writer/Ptnrships | **School Programs** |
| 80 Driver Ed/Safety | 92 Magnet School | 277 Remedial Math K-12 | 750 Chief Innovation Officer | **A =** Alternative Program |
| 81 Gifted/Talented | 93 Parental Involvement | 280 Literacy Coach | 751 Chief of Staff | **G =** Adult Classes |
| 82 Video Services | 95 Tech Prep Program | 285 STEM | 752 Social Emotional Learning | **M =** Magnet Program |
| 83 Substance Abuse Prev | 97 Chief Information Officer | 286 Digital Learning | | **T =** Title I Schoolwide |
| 84 Erate | 98 Chief Technology Officer | 288 Common Core Standards | **Other School Types** | **V =** Career & Tech Ed Programs |
| 85 AIDS Education | 270 Character Education | 294 Accountability | Ⓐ = Alternative School | |
| 88 Alternative/At Risk | 271 Migrant Education | 295 Network System | Ⓒ = Charter School | **Social Media** |
| 89 Multi-Cultural Curriculum | 273 Teacher Mentor | 296 Title II Programs | Ⓜ = Magnet School | [f] = Facebook |
| 90 Social Work | 274 Before/After Sch | 297 Webmaster | Ⓨ = Year-Round School | [t] = Twitter |

New Schools are shaded
New Superintendents and Principals are bold
Personnel with email addresses are underscored

| | | | | | |
|---|---|---|---|---|---|
| Millsap High Sch | 9-12 | AV | 301 | 45% | 940/682-3182 |
| 600 Bulldog Dr, Millsap 76066 | | | 30 | | Fax 940/682-4035 |
| Tammy Addison | | | | | |
| Millsap Middle Sch | 6-8 | TV | 223 | 43% | 940/682-4489 |
| 301 E Brazos St, Millsap 76066 | | | | | |
| Jeffrey Clark | | | | | |

● **Peaster Ind School Dist** PID: 01046423    817/341-5000
3602 Harwell Lake Rd, Weatherford 76088    Fax 817/341-5003

**Schools:** 3 \ **Teachers:** 116 \ **Students:** 1,210 \ **Special Ed Students:** 99 \ **LEP Students:** 41 \ **Ethnic:** Hispanic 15%, Caucasian 84% \ **Exp:** $529 (High) \ **Poverty:** 9% \ **Title I:** $102,146 \ **Special Education:** $24,000 \ **Open-Close:** 08/19 - 05/27 \ **DTBP:** $353 (High)

| | | | |
|---|---|---|---|
| Matt Adams | 1 | Sarah Kirk | 2 |
| Jay Lionberger | 3 | Paula Melton | 4 |
| Michael Rudock | 5,8,11,68,69,78,83,298* | Michelle Madison | 9,57,88* |
| Kim Hubbard | 12,271* | Melinda Cofper | 16 |
| Kathy Gilbert | 58* | Mike Bowling | 67 |
| Nicole Elliott | 73,76,286,295 | Nick Rudolph | 288 |

| Public Schs..Principal | Grd | Prgm | Enr/#Cls | SN | |
|---|---|---|---|---|---|
| Peaster Elem Sch | PK-6 | T | 653 | 34% | 817/341-5000 |
| 3400 Harwell Lake Rd, Weatherford 76088 | | | 26 | | Fax 817/594-1890 |
| Michelle Madison | | | | | 🅵 |
| Peaster High Sch | 9-12 | AV | 356 | 28% | 817/341-5000 |
| 3600 Harwell Lake Rd, Weatherford 76088 | | | 40 | | Fax 817/341-5027 |
| Chris Pennington | | | | | |
| Peaster Middle Sch | 6-8 | | 201 | 28% | 817/341-5000 |
| 8512 FM 920, Weatherford 76088 | | | 23 | | Fax 817/341-5052 |
| **Jimmy Steen** | | | | | |

● **Poolville Ind School Dist** PID: 01046459    817/594-4452
16025 FM 920, Poolville 76487    Fax 817/594-2651

**Schools:** 3 \ **Teachers:** 48 \ **Students:** 550 \ **Special Ed Students:** 61 \ **LEP Students:** 34 \ **College-Bound:** 60% \ **Ethnic:** Hispanic 21%, Caucasian 78% \ **Exp:** $520 (High) \ **Poverty:** 13% \ **Title I:** $105,569 \ **Open-Close:** 08/19 - 05/20 \ **DTBP:** $333 (High)

| | | | |
|---|---|---|---|
| Jeff Kirby | 1 | Paula Hall | 2 |
| Cathy Pennington | 8,11,57,58,69,271,296,298 | Doug Martella | 8,16,73 |
| Jason Cheslock | 9,59 | Lindsay Back | 36,83,270* |
| Lynn DuVall | 67 | | |

| Public Schs..Principal | Grd | Prgm | Enr/#Cls | SN | |
|---|---|---|---|---|---|
| Poolville Elem Sch | PK-5 | T | 260 | 66% | 817/599-3308 |
| 16025 FM 920, Poolville 76487 | | | 25 | | Fax 817/599-6593 |
| Jason Cheslock | | | | | |
| Poolville High Sch | 9-12 | T | 161 | 48% | 817/599-5134 |
| 1001 Lone Star Rd, Poolville 76487 | | | 40 | | Fax 817/599-5171 |
| Jennifer Shifflett | | | | | |
| Poolville Junior High Sch | 6-8 | T | 91 | 57% | 817/594-4539 |
| 16025 FM 920, Poolville 76487 | | | 12 | | Fax 817/594-0081 |
| Jamie Dunnam | | | | | |

● **Springtown Ind School Dist** PID: 01046514    817/220-7243
301 E 5th St, Springtown 76082    Fax 817/523-5766

**Schools:** 6 \ **Teachers:** 259 \ **Students:** 3,470 \ **Special Ed Students:** 310 \ **LEP Students:** 177 \ **Ethnic:** African American 1%, Hispanic 20%, Native American: 1%, Caucasian 78% \ **Exp:** $418 (High) \ **Poverty:** 12% \ **Title I:** $557,423 \ **Special Education:** $648,000 \ **Open-Close:** 08/17 - 05/27 \ **DTBP:** $163 (High)

| | | | |
|---|---|---|---|
| Mike Kelley | 1 | Gary Shaw | 2,19 |
| Jerrell Rutherford | 3 | Kim Nash | 4 |
| Micheal Chavez | 5,79* | Brian Hulett | 6* |
| Tiffany Cano | 9 | Michelle Bateman | 10 |
| Dr Lisa Kirkpatrick | 11,31,57,83,88,271,296,298 | Shane Strickland | 15,68,273 |
| Stacy Johnson | 34,58 | Amy Walker | |
| Wesley Thomas | 69 | Robert McHenry | 73,98,286,295 |
| Sheila Schram | 76 | | |

| Public Schs..Principal | Grd | Prgm | Enr/#Cls | SN | |
|---|---|---|---|---|---|
| Goshen Creek Elem Sch | PK-4 | T | 395 | 52% | 817/220-0272 |
| 401 S PO Jo Dr, Springtown 76082 | | | 14 | | Fax 817/220-0471 |
| Kelly Jones | | | | | |
| Reno Elem Sch | PK-4 | T | 245 | 75% | 817/221-5001 |
| 172 W Reno Rd, Azle 76020 | | | 21 | | Fax 817/677-1214 |
| Jenna Showers | | | | | |
| Springtown Elem Sch | PK-4 | T | 474 | 70% | 817/220-2498 |
| 416 E 3rd St, Springtown 76082 | | | 35 | | Fax 817/523-4094 |
| Pearl Russell | | | | | |
| Springtown High Sch | 9-12 | TV | 992 | 50% | 817/220-3888 |
| 915 W Highway 199, Springtown 76082 | | | 64 | | Fax 817/523-5290 |
| Mrs Hutchison | | | | | |
| Springtown Intermediate Sch | 5-6 | T | 561 | 56% | 817/220-1219 |
| 300 PO Jo Dr, Springtown 76082 | | | 25 | | Fax 817/220-0889 |
| Joe Brown | | | | | |
| Springtown Middle Sch | 7-8 | T | 517 | 54% | 817/220-7455 |
| 500 PO Jo Dr, Springtown 76082 | | | 28 | | Fax 817/220-0279 |
| Mark Wilson | | | | | |

● **Weatherford Ind School Dist** PID: 01046564    817/598-2800
1100 Longhorn Dr, Weatherford 76086    Fax 817/598-2951

**Schools:** 12 \ **Teachers:** 522 \ **Students:** 8,000 \ **Special Ed Students:** 852 \ **LEP Students:** 650 \ **College-Bound:** 58% \ **Ethnic:** Asian 1%, African American 3%, Hispanic 28%, Native American: 1%, Caucasian 68% \ **Exp:** $577 (High) \ **Poverty:** 11% \ **Title I:** $1,281,810 \ **Special Education:** $1,306,000 \ **Open-Close:** 08/20 - 05/27 \ **DTBP:** $180 (High) \ 🅵 🆃

| | | | |
|---|---|---|---|
| Dr Jeffrey Hanks | 1 | Patricia Melendez | 2,298 |
| Sharon Landrum | 2 | Bob Bridges | 3 |
| J P Kechnie | 3 | Alicia Hernandez | 4 |
| Monte Chapman | 5,15,68,78 | Richard Scoggin | 6 |
| Shaelee Mitchell | 7,83* | Rachel Rife | 8,74,273,285,288* |
| Racheal Rife | 9,69,74,81,752 | Marie Hernandez | 10,280* |
| Janet McNeely | 11 | John Tarrant | 16,82* |
| Andy Donaghey | 23,27 | James Buckner | 23* |
| Kady Donaghey | 27,31,75* | Donnie McGowen | 30 |
| Jennie Morris | 30 | Linda Bourland | 42 |
| Melanie Gonzalez | 46 | Amy Cribbs | 47 |
| Amy Hall | 48 | Amanda McCown | 50 |
| Marie Hernandez | 57 | Leslie Ackmann | 58,275 |
| Mike Guest | 67 | Rhiannon Montgomery | 73 |
| Rhiannon Montgomery | 73* | Rebecca Nelson | 74 |
| Cody Lee | 76,286 | Lynn Pool | 78,79 |
| Grant Priess | 88* | Bruno Diaz | 91 |
| Luis Duenez | 91 | Charlette LaGrone | 93 |
| Jennifer Holcomb | 274* | Tracy Montgomery | 295 |

| | | | | | | | | |
|---|---|---|---|---|---|---|---|---|
| 1 | Superintendent | 8 | Curric/Instruct K-12 | 19 | Chief Financial Officer | 29 | Family/Consumer Science | |
| 2 | Bus/Finance/Purchasing | 9 | Curric/Instruct Elem | 20 | Art K-12 | 30 | Adult Education | |
| 3 | Buildings And Grounds | 10 | Curric/Instruct Sec | 21 | Art Elem | 31 | Career/Sch-to-Work K-12 | |
| 4 | Food Service | 11 | Federal Program | 22 | Art Sec | 32 | Career/Sch-to-Work Elem | |
| 5 | Transportation | 12 | Title I | 23 | Music K-12 | 33 | Career/Sch-to-Work Sec | |
| 6 | Athletic | 13 | Title V | 24 | Music Elem | 34 | Early Childhood Ed | |
| 7 | Health Services | 14 | Asst Superintendent | 25 | Music Sec | 35 | Health/Phys Education | |
| | | 15 | Asst Superintendent | 26 | Business Education | 36 | Guidance Services K-12 | |
| | | 16 | Instructional Media Svcs | 27 | Career & Tech Ed | 37 | Guidance Services Elem | |
| | | 17 | Chief Operations Officer | 28 | Technology Education | 38 | Guidance Services Sec | |
| | | 18 | Chief Academic Officer | | | | | |

| | | | | | |
|---|---|---|---|---|---|
| 39 | Social Studies K-12 | 49 | English/Lang Arts Elem | 59 | Special Education Elem |
| 40 | Social Studies Elem | 50 | English/Lang Arts Sec | 60 | Special Education Sec |
| 41 | Social Studies Sec | 51 | Reading K-12 | 61 | Foreign/World Lang K-12 |
| 42 | Science K-12 | 52 | Reading Elem | 62 | Foreign/World Lang Elem |
| 43 | Science Elem | 53 | Reading Sec | 63 | Foreign/World Lang Sec |
| 44 | Science Sec | 54 | Remedial Reading K-12 | 64 | Religious Education K-12 |
| 45 | Math K-12 | 55 | Remedial Reading Elem | 65 | Religious Education Elem |
| 46 | Math Elem | 56 | Remedial Reading Sec | 66 | Religious Education Sec |
| 47 | Math Sec | 57 | Bilingual/ELL | 67 | School Board President |
| 48 | English/Lang Arts K-12 | 58 | Special Education K-12 | 68 | Teacher Personnel |

| | | | | |
|---|---|---|---|---|
| 69 | Academic Assessment | | | |
| 70 | Research/Development | | | |
| 71 | Public Information | | | |
| 72 | Summer School | | | |
| 73 | Instructional Tech | | | |
| 74 | Inservice Training | | | |
| 75 | Marketing/Distributive | | | |
| 76 | Info Systems | | | |
| 77 | Psychological Assess | | | |
| 78 | Affirmative Action | | | |

| Public Schs..Principal | Grd | Prgm | Enr/#Cls | SN | |
|---|---|---|---|---|---|
| Austin Elem Sch<br>1776 Texas Dr, Weatherford 76086<br>Kelsey Smith | PK-6 | | 658<br>50 | 35% | 817/598-2848<br>Fax 817/598-2978 |
| Bill W Wright Elem Sch<br>1309 Charles St, Weatherford 76086<br>Tra Hall | PK-6 | T | 644 | 61% | 817/598-2828<br>Fax 817/598-2830 |
| Bose Ikard Elem Sch<br>100 Ikard Ln, Weatherford 76086<br>Christy Burton | PK-6 | T | 647<br>22 | 63% | 817/598-2818<br>Fax 817/598-2805 |
| Ⓐ Bridge Academy<br>1007 S Main St, Weatherford 76086<br>Ben Schoonover | 10-12 | | 50 | | 817/598-2847<br>Fax 817/598-2928 |
| Crockett Elem Sch<br>1015 Jameson St, Weatherford 76086<br>Marilisa Moore | PK-6 | T | 524<br>27 | 48% | 817/598-2811<br>Fax 817/598-2813 |
| Curtis Elem Sch<br>501 W Russell St, Weatherford 76086<br>Lorie Bratcher | PK-6 | T | 741<br>34 | 48% | 817/598-2838<br>Fax 817/598-2840 |
| Joe Tison Middle Sch<br>102 Meadowview Rd Ste 100, Weatherford 76087<br>Renee Treat | 7-8 | TV | 597<br>65 | 40% | 817/598-2960<br>Fax 817/598-2963 |
| Juan Seguin Elem Sch<br>499 E 8th St, Weatherford 76086<br>Jessica Shugart | PK-6 | T | 602<br>34 | 68% | 817/598-2814<br>Fax 817/598-2826 |
| Mary Martin Elem Sch<br>719 N Oakridge Dr, Weatherford 76087<br>Amy Crippen | PK-6 | | 658<br>28 | 21% | 817/598-2910<br>Fax 817/598-2912 |
| Shirley Hall Middle Sch<br>902 Charles St, Weatherford 76086<br>Stephanie Wynne | 7-8 | TV | 633<br>40 | 42% | 817/598-2822<br>Fax 817/598-2854 |
| Weatherford 9th Grade Center<br>1007 S Main St, Weatherford 76086<br>Brannon Kidd | 9-9 | V | 618 | | 817/598-2847<br>Fax 817/598-2928 |
| Weatherford High Sch<br>2121 Bethel Rd, Weatherford 76087<br>Brannon Kidd | 10-12 | AV | 1,700 | 34% | 817/598-2858<br>Fax 817/598-2881 |

## PARKER PRIVATE SCHOOLS

| Private Schs..Principal | Grd | Prgm | Enr/#Cls | SN | |
|---|---|---|---|---|---|
| Aledo Christian Sch<br>400 Queen St, Aledo 76008<br>Kay Ross | PK-12 | | 150<br>9 | | 817/441-7357<br>Fax 817/441-2713 |
| Grace Christian Academy-Brock<br>127 Lazy Bend Rd, Brock 76087<br>Jody McGlothlin | K-8 | | 901 | | 682/262-9288 |
| Trinity Christian Academy<br>4954 E I-20 Service Rd S, Willow Park 76087<br>Dr Steve Newby \ Ken Nobles | PK-12 | | 400<br>31 | | 817/441-7901<br>Fax 817/441-7912 |
| Victory Baptist Academy<br>1311 E Bankhead Dr, Weatherford 76086<br>Patti Catuto | PK-12 | | 100 | | 817/596-2711<br>Fax 817/550-6207 |
| Weatherford Christian Sch<br>2300 Ranger Hwy, Weatherford 76088<br>Amy Butler \ Karen Mooney | PK-12 | | 230 | | 817/596-7807<br>Fax 817/596-0529 |

## PARMER COUNTY

## PARMER PUBLIC SCHOOLS

● **Bovina Ind School Dist** PID: 01046655
500 Halsell Street, Bovina 79009
806/251-1336
Fax 806/251-1578

**Schools:** 3 \ **Teachers:** 45 \ **Students:** 460 \ **Special Ed Students:** 37 \ **LEP Students:** 113 \ **College-Bound:** 67% \ **Ethnic:** Hispanic 96%, Caucasian 4% \ **Exp:** $428 (High) \ **Poverty:** 16% \ **Title I:** $102,728 \ **Open-Close:** 08/13 - 05/20 \ **DTBP:** $350 (High)

| | | | |
|---|---|---|---|
| Denise Anderson ...................1 | Darlene Miller ...........................2 |
| Richard Villarreal .................3,5 | Beverly Felan .......................7,85 |
| Darla Sealey .........................8,11 | Joanne Belcher .........................58 |
| George Villarreal ......................67 | Stan Miller ...............73,84,295 |
| Roseo Monto .............................88 | Lory Saenz ...........................271 |

| Public Schs..Principal | Grd | Prgm | Enr/#Cls | SN | |
|---|---|---|---|---|---|
| Bovina Elem Sch<br>500 Halsell Street, Bovina 79009<br>Kaylene Davis | PK-5 | T | 227<br>24 | 89% | 806/251-1336 |
| Bovina High Sch<br>500 Halsell St, Bovina 79009<br>Dan Castillo | 9-12 | TV | 134 | 84% | 806/251-1336 |
| Bovina Middle Sch<br>500 Halsell St, Bovina 79009<br>Mark Barnes | 6-8 | T | 110 | 85% | 806/251-1336 |

● **Farwell Ind School Dist** PID: 01046693
705 6th St, Farwell 79325
806/481-3371
Fax 806/481-9275

**Schools:** 3 \ **Teachers:** 56 \ **Students:** 539 \ **Special Ed Students:** 61 \ **LEP Students:** 92 \ **College-Bound:** 43% \ **Ethnic:** Hispanic 52%, Caucasian 47% \ **Poverty:** 15% \ **Title I:** $80,296 \ **Open-Close:** 08/19 - 05/26 \ **DTBP:** $231 (High) | **Exp:** $526 (High)

| | | | |
|---|---|---|---|
| Colby Waldrop ..........................1 | Edie Kalbas ........................2,11 |
| Tim Kasel .............................3,5,91 | Leticia Olmos ............................4 |
| Shane Perkins ..........................6* | Michelle Jaime ......................7,83* |
| Hayley Christian ...........36,88,270* | Deirdre Guthals ......................57* |
| Jay Be Barrett ...........................67 | Karen Schilling .........................69* |
| Kathy Curtis ...............73,76,295* | Yvonne Ortega ........................93* |

| Public Schs..Principal | Grd | Prgm | Enr/#Cls | SN | |
|---|---|---|---|---|---|
| Farwell Elem Sch<br>602 Avenue G, Farwell 79325<br>Tonya O'Neill | PK-5 | T | 255<br>17 | 62% | 806/481-9131<br>Fax 806/481-3255 |
| Farwell High Sch<br>801 Avenue G, Farwell 79325<br>Coby Norman | 9-12 | TV | 151<br>15 | 54% | 806/481-3351<br>Fax 806/481-3531 |
| Farwell Junior High Sch<br>701 Avenue G, Farwell 79325<br>Kristy White | 6-8 | T | 133<br>12 | 56% | 806/481-9260<br>Fax 806/481-9258 |

| | | | |
|---|---|---|---|
| 79 Student Personnel | 91 Safety/Security | 275 Response To Intervention | 298 Grant Writer/Ptnrships |
| 80 Driver Ed/Safety | 92 Magnet School | 277 Remedial Math K-12 | 750 Chief Innovation Officer |
| 81 Gifted/Talented | 93 Parental Involvement | 280 Literacy Coach | 751 Chief of Staff |
| 82 Video Services | 95 Tech Prep Program | 285 STEM | 752 Social Emotional Learning |
| 83 Substance Abuse Prev | 97 Chief Infomation Officer | 286 Digital Learning | |
| 84 Erate | 98 Chief Technology Officer | 288 Common Core Standards | Other School Types |
| 85 AIDS Education | 270 Character Education | 294 Accountability | Ⓐ = Alternative School |
| 88 Alternative/At Risk | 271 Migrant Education | 295 Network System | Ⓒ = Charter School |
| 89 Multi-Cultural Curriculum | 273 Teacher Mentor | 296 Title II Programs | Ⓜ = Magnet School |
| 90 Social Work | 274 Before/After Sch | 297 Webmaster | Ⓨ = Year-Round School |

**School Programs**
A = Alternative Program
G = Adult Classes
M = Magnet Program
T = Title I Schoolwide
V = Career & Tech Ed Programs

**Social Media**
🅵 = Facebook
🆃 = Twitter

New Schools are shaded
New Superintendents and Principals are bold
Personnel with email addresses are underscored

# TX–317

● **Friona Ind School Dist** PID: 01046734     806/250-2747
909 E 11th St, Friona 79035     Fax 806/250-3805

**Schools:** 4 \ **Teachers:** 100 \ **Students:** 1,045 \ **Special Ed Students:** 100 \ **LEP Students:** 323 \ **Ethnic:** Hispanic 90%, Caucasian 9% \ **Exp:** $307 (High) \ **Poverty:** 22% \ **Title I:** $278,310 \ **Open-Close:** 08/19 - 05/27 \ **DTBP:** $350 (High)

| | | | |
|---|---|---|---|
| Jimmy Burns | 1 | Dianna Wright | 2* |
| Daniel Hidalgo | 3 | Serapio Cabavule | 5 |
| Jimmy Arias | 6* | Teresa Echavaria | 7 |
| Ashley Smith | 8 | Amy Cook | 16* |
| Carrie Arias | 34,58 | Antonio Rocha | 67 |
| Trisha Steelman | 73,76,286,295 | | |

| Public Schs..Principal | Grd | Prgm | Enr/#Cls | SN |
|---|---|---|---|---|
| Friona Elem Sch<br>200 W 8th St, Friona 79035<br>M'Kell Jeter | 2-5 | T | 337<br>29 | 70% 806/250-2240<br>Fax 806/250-5078 |
| Friona High Sch<br>810 Chieftain Way, Friona 79035<br>Erika Montana | 9-12 | TV | 310<br>50 | 61% 806/250-3951<br>Fax 806/250-2188 |
| Friona Junior High Sch<br>1001 Euclid St, Friona 79035<br>**Daniel Rosales** | 6-8 | T | 217<br>30 | 70% 806/250-2788<br>Fax 806/250-8155 |
| Friona Primary Sch<br>802 Euclid Ave, Friona 79035<br>Deirdre Osborn | PK-1 | T | 181<br>16 | 72% 806/250-3935<br>Fax 806/250-3937 |

● **Lazbuddie Ind School Dist** PID: 01046772     806/965-2156
675 FM 1172, Lazbuddie 79053     Fax 806/965-2892

**Schools:** 1 \ **Teachers:** 18 \ **Students:** 168 \ **Special Ed Students:** 20 \ **LEP Students:** 17 \ **College-Bound:** 89% \ **Ethnic:** African American 1%, Hispanic 39%, Native American: 2%, Caucasian 58% \ **Exp:** $559 (High) \ **Poverty:** 16% \ **Title I:** $25,270 \ **Open-Close:** 08/14 - 05/21 \ **DTBP:** $307 (High)

| | | | |
|---|---|---|---|
| Steve Wolf | 1,73 | Carolyn Scott | 2 |
| Lyneldon Randolph | 3,5* | Lareta Barber | 7* |
| Staci Buie | 57,69,81 | Candice Weaver | 67 |
| Pat Randolph | 275 | Ken Hoskins | 285* |

| Public Schs..Principal | Grd | Prgm | Enr/#Cls | SN |
|---|---|---|---|---|
| Ⓐ Lazbuddie Sch<br>675 FM 1172, Lazbuddie 79053<br>**Gina Chambers** | PK-12 | TV | 168<br>22 | 76% 806/965-2153 |

# PECOS COUNTY

## PECOS PUBLIC SCHOOLS

● **Buena Vista Ind School Dist** PID: 01046801     432/536-2225
404 W State Highway 11, Imperial 79743     Fax 432/536-2469

**Schools:** 1 \ **Teachers:** 18 \ **Students:** 250 \ **Special Ed Students:** 8 \ **LEP Students:** 14 \ **College-Bound:** 36% \ **Ethnic:** African American 2%, Hispanic 70%, Caucasian 27% \ **Exp:** $582 (High) \ **Poverty:** 26% \ **Title I:** $58,114 \ **Open-Close:** 08/19 - 05/27 \ **DTBP:** $408 (High)

| | | | |
|---|---|---|---|
| Mark Dominguez | 1,11,83 | Julian Castillo | 2,11,57* |
| Dale Pustejovsky | 6 | Cruz Gomez | 67 |
| Jacob Benavidez | 73 | | |

| Public Schs..Principal | Grd | Prgm | Enr/#Cls | SN |
|---|---|---|---|---|
| Buena Vista Sch<br>404 W State Highway 11, Imperial 79743<br>Adelina Alcala | PK-12 | TV | 250<br>21 | 42% 432/536-2336<br><br>🅕 |

● **Ft Stockton Ind School Dist** PID: 01046837     432/336-4000
101 W Division St, Fort Stockton 79735     Fax 432/336-4008

**Schools:** 5 \ **Teachers:** 175 \ **Students:** 2,469 \ **Special Ed Students:** 176 \ **LEP Students:** 240 \ **College-Bound:** 43% \ **Ethnic:** Asian 1%, African American 1%, Hispanic 86%, Caucasian 12% \ **Exp:** $477 (High) \ **Poverty:** 24% \ **Title I:** $753,072 \ **Special Education:** $672,000 \ **Open-Close:** 08/19 - 05/21 \ **DTBP:** $374 (High) \ 🅕 🆃

| | | | |
|---|---|---|---|
| Ralph Traynham | 1 | Maria Gomez | 2 |
| Robert Stallard | 3* | Paul Casias | 4 |
| Cecil Bradshaw | 5 | Mike Peters | 6 |
| Cynthia Milan | 7 | Robin Derington | 8 |
| Gil Madrid | 15 | Sylvia Ogas | 57 |
| Dr Zana Hanson | 58 | Billy Espino | 67 |
| Debra Ezell | 73,76 | Omar Sanchez | 73 |
| Robert Knight | 83* | Irene Vargas | 271 |
| Amy Porras | 274 | Chris Terry | 295 |
| Gabriel Cyfton | 295 | Reba Subia | 297 |

| Public Schs..Principal | Grd | Prgm | Enr/#Cls | SN |
|---|---|---|---|---|
| Alamo Elem Sch<br>804 S US Highway 385, Fort Stockton 79735<br>Adrienne Horton | PK-3 | T | 458<br>32 | 71% 432/336-4016<br>Fax 432/336-4028 |
| Apache Elem Sch<br>208 W 18th St, Fort Stockton 79735<br>Betty McCallister | K-3 | T | 288<br>14 | 72% 432/336-4161<br>Fax 432/336-4167 |
| Ft Stockton High Sch<br>1200 W 17th St, Fort Stockton 79735<br>Roy Alvarado | 9-12 | ATV | 704<br>60 | 58% 432/336-4101<br>Fax 432/336-4113 |
| Ft Stockton Intermediate Sch<br>1100 W 2nd St, Fort Stockton 79735<br>Amanda Urias | 4-5 | AT | 432<br>21 | 69% 432/336-4141<br>Fax 432/336-4147 |
| Ft Stockton Middle Sch<br>2400 W 5th St, Fort Stockton 79735<br>Linda Chavez | 6-8 | AT | 587<br>32 | 71% 432/336-4131<br>Fax 432/336-4136 |

● **Iraan-Sheffield Ind Sch Dist** PID: 01046904     432/639-2512
100 S Farr Street, Iraan 79744     Fax 432/639-2501

**Schools:** 3 \ **Teachers:** 41 \ **Students:** 375 \ **Special Ed Students:** 35 \ **LEP Students:** 48 \ **College-Bound:** 80% \ **Ethnic:** Asian 1%, African American 1%, Hispanic 69%, Native American: 1%, Caucasian 29% \ **Exp:** $451 (High) \ **Poverty:** 19% \ **Title I:** $78,059 \ **Open-Close:** 08/12 - 05/18 \ **DTBP:** $342 (High)

| | | | |
|---|---|---|---|
| **Dr Tracy Canter** | 1,11 | Melissa Hanna | 2 |
| Kurt Hannah | 3,73,76,286,295 | Katrina Kent | 4* |
| Matthew Luddeke | 6 | Monica Lopez | 7,83,85* |
| Carrie Holmes | 16 | Norma Whaley | 58 |
| Steve Garlock | 67 | Amy Fraizer | 274 |

| Public Schs..Principal | Grd | Prgm | Enr/#Cls | SN |
|---|---|---|---|---|
| Iraan Elem Sch<br>100 S Farr Street, Iraan 79744<br>Amy Frazier | PK-5 | T | 198<br>14 | 58% 432/639-2524<br>Fax 432/639-2201 |

| | | | | | | | |
|---|---|---|---|---|---|---|---|
| **1** | Superintendent | **8** | Curric/Instruct K-12 | **19** | Chief Financial Officer | **29** | Family/Consumer Science |
| **2** | Bus/Finance/Purchasing | **9** | Curric/Instruct Elem | **20** | Art K-12 | **30** | Adult Education |
| **3** | Buildings And Grounds | **10** | Curric/Instruct Sec | **21** | Art Elem | **31** | Career/Sch-to-Work K-12 |
| **4** | Food Service | **11** | Federal Program | **22** | Art Sec | **32** | Career/Sch-to-Work Elem |
| **5** | Transportation | **12** | Title I | **23** | Music K-12 | **33** | Career/Sch-to-Work Sec |
| **6** | Athletic | **13** | Title V | **24** | Music Elem | **34** | Early Childhood Ed |
| **7** | Health Services | **15** | Asst Superintendent | **25** | Music Sec | **35** | Health/Phys Education |
| | | **16** | Instructional Media Svcs | **26** | Business Education | **36** | Guidance Services K-12 |
| | | **17** | Chief Operations Officer | **27** | Career & Tech Ed | **37** | Guidance Services Elem |
| | | **18** | Chief Academic Officer | **28** | Technology Education | **38** | Guidance Services Sec |

| | | | | | | | |
|---|---|---|---|---|---|---|---|
| **39** | Social Studies K-12 | **49** | English/Lang Arts Elem | **59** | Special Education Elem | **69** | Academic Assessment |
| **40** | Social Studies Elem | **50** | English/Lang Arts Sec | **60** | Special Education Sec | **70** | Research/Development |
| **41** | Social Studies Sec | **51** | Reading K-12 | **61** | Foreign/World Lang K-12 | **71** | Public Information |
| **42** | Science K-12 | **52** | Reading Elem | **62** | Foreign/World Lang Elem | **72** | Summer School |
| **43** | Science Elem | **53** | Reading Sec | **63** | Foreign/World Lang Sec | **73** | Instructional Tech |
| **44** | Science Sec | **54** | Remedial Reading K-12 | **64** | Religious Education K-12 | **74** | Inservice Training |
| **45** | Math K-12 | **55** | Remedial Reading Elem | **65** | Religious Education Elem | **75** | Marketing/Distributive |
| **46** | Math Elem | **56** | Remedial Reading Sec | **66** | Religious Education Sec | **76** | Info Systems |
| **47** | Math Sec | **57** | Bilingual/ELL | **67** | School Board President | **77** | Psychological Assess |
| **48** | English/Lang Arts K-12 | **58** | Special Education K-12 | **68** | Teacher Personnel | **78** | Affirmative Action |

| | | | | | | |
|---|---|---|---|---|---|---|
| Iraan High Sch | 9-12 | GV | 101 | 37% | 432/639-2512 | |
| 100 S Farr Street, Iraan 79744 | | | 15 | | Fax 432/639-2272 | |
| Blake Andrews | | | | | | |
| Iraan Junior High Sch | 6-8 | T | 76 | 47% | 432/639-2512 | |
| 100 S Farr Street, Iraan 79744 | | | 10 | | Fax 432/639-2381 | |
| Amy Frazier | | | | | | |

## POLK COUNTY

## POLK PUBLIC SCHOOLS

● **Big Sandy Ind School Dist** PID: 01046954    936/563-1000
9180 FM 1276, Livingston 77351    Fax 936/563-1010

> **Schools:** 1 \ **Teachers:** 41 \ **Students:** 484 \ **Special Ed Students:** 53 \ **College-Bound:** 45% \ **Ethnic:** Asian 1%, African American 1%, Hispanic 8%, Native American: 21%, Caucasian 70% \ **Exp:** $368 (High) \ **Poverty:** 22% \ **Title I:** $144,344 \ **Open-Close:** 08/14 - 05/21 \ **DTBP:** $397 (High)

| | | | |
|---|---|---|---|
| Eric Carpenter | 1,11 | Linda Kidd | 2 |
| Kimberley Moore | 4 | Kevin Foster | 6* |
| Sally Elester | 8,31,69,83,88* | Jan Slack | 58* |
| Glen Goodwin | 67 | Susan Crawford | 73,295* |

| Public Schs..Principal | Grd | Prgm | Enr/#Cls | SN |
|---|---|---|---|---|
| Big Sandy Sch | PK-12 | ATV | 484 | 53% 936/563-1000 |
| 9180 FM 1276, Dallardsville 77332 | | | 50 | |
| Shelby Tillery \ Diane Houston \ Stephanie Hendrix | | | | |

● **Corrigan-Camden Ind Sch Dist** PID: 01046980    936/398-2341
504 S Home St, Corrigan 75939    Fax 936/398-4616

> **Schools:** 3 \ **Teachers:** 71 \ **Students:** 830 \ **Special Ed Students:** 75 \ **LEP Students:** 117 \ **Ethnic:** African American 26%, Hispanic 41%, Caucasian 32% \ **Exp:** $569 (High) \ **Poverty:** 29% \ **Title I:** $432,563 \ **Open-Close:** 08/04 - 05/27 \ **DTBP:** $300 (High)

| | | | |
|---|---|---|---|
| Richard Cooper | 1 | Cindy Owens | 2 |
| James Kemper | 3,5 | Debbie Hueske | 4 |
| Brette Ritliff | 6 | Paula Martin | 8,11,16,57,286,288,296,298 |
| Sage Taylor | 38 | Tracy Cobb | 58 |
| Sean Burks | 67 | Susan Torrez | 73* |

| Public Schs..Principal | Grd | Prgm | Enr/#Cls | SN |
|---|---|---|---|---|
| Corrigan-Camden Elem Sch | PK-5 | T | 373 | 85% 936/398-2501 |
| 1664 US Highway 287 W, Corrigan 75939 | | | 13 | Fax 936/398-5042 |
| Larry Cupit | | | | |
| Corrigan-Camden High Sch | 9-12 | T | 239 | 77% 936/398-2543 |
| 504 S Home St, Corrigan 75939 | | | 30 | Fax 936/398-2685 |
| Javier Perez \ **Diana Locke** | | | | |
| Corrigan-Camden Jr High Sch | 6-8 | T | 210 | 69% 936/398-2962 |
| 502 S Mathews St, Corrigan 75939 | | | 20 | Fax 936/398-4608 |
| Robert Elliott | | | | |

● **Goodrich Ind School Dist** PID: 01047025    936/365-1100
234 Katie Simpson Ave, Goodrich 77335    Fax 936/365-3518

> **Schools:** 2 \ **Teachers:** 18 \ **Students:** 218 \ **Special Ed Students:** 21 \ **LEP Students:** 42 \ **College-Bound:** 83% \ **Ethnic:** African American 13%, Hispanic 40%, Caucasian 47% \ **Exp:** $941 (High) \ **Poverty:** 17% \ **Title I:** $119,202 \ **Open-Close:** 08/19 - 05/27 \ **DTBP:** $327 (High)

| | | | |
|---|---|---|---|
| Bryan Taulton | 1,11,83 | Gwen Messiner | 2 |
| Climet Hutchins | 3,5 | Lester King | 6* |
| Caloby Isaacs | 8,288 | Brenda Bennett | 67 |
| Walter Risner | 295 | | |

| Public Schs..Principal | Grd | Prgm | Enr/#Cls | SN |
|---|---|---|---|---|
| Goodrich Elem Sch | PK-5 | T | 108 | 88% 936/365-1100 |
| 234 Katie Simpson Ave, Goodrich 77335 | | | 25 | Fax 936/365-2375 |
| Nikki Henderson | | | | |
| Goodrich Middle High Sch | 6-12 | T | 110 | 81% 936/365-1100 |
| 234 Katie Simpson Ave, Goodrich 77335 | | | 15 | Fax 936/365-2371 |
| Calobe Isaacs | | | | |

● **Leggett Ind School Dist** PID: 01047051    936/398-2804
254 E FM 942, Leggett 77350    Fax 936/398-9109

> **Schools:** 1 \ **Teachers:** 17 \ **Students:** 167 \ **Special Ed Students:** 14 \ **LEP Students:** 8 \ **College-Bound:** 85% \ **Ethnic:** African American 21%, Hispanic 30%, Native American: 2%, Caucasian 46% \ **Exp:** $1,064 (High) \ **Poverty:** 16% \ **Title I:** $79,337 \ **Open-Close:** 08/26 - 05/28 \ **DTBP:** $362 (High)

| | | | |
|---|---|---|---|
| Jana Lowe | 1,11,73 | Cathy Leloux | 2,4,11 |
| Mike Watts | 3,5 | Robin Lee | 16 |
| Amanda Lawson | 36,69,88* | Curtis Jefferson | 67 |
| Chrystal Tinker | 83 | | |

| Public Schs..Principal | Grd | Prgm | Enr/#Cls | SN |
|---|---|---|---|---|
| Leggett Sch | PK-12 | GTV | 167 | 100% 936/398-2412 |
| 254 E FM 942, Leggett 77350 | | | 25 | Fax 936/398-0889 |
| Jana Lowe | | | | |

● **Livingston Ind School Dist** PID: 01047075    936/328-2100
1412 S Houston Ave, Livingston 77351    Fax 936/967-8603

> **Schools:** 7 \ **Teachers:** 271 \ **Students:** 3,963 \ **Special Ed Students:** 395 \ **LEP Students:** 315 \ **College-Bound:** 27% \ **Ethnic:** Asian 1%, African American 10%, Hispanic 24%, Caucasian 65% \ **Exp:** $409 (High) \ **Poverty:** 22% \ **Title I:** $1,334,985 \ **Special Education:** $688,000 \ **Open-Close:** 08/12 - 05/28 \ **DTBP:** $196 (High) \ 

| | | | |
|---|---|---|---|
| Dr Brent Hawkins | 1 | Ben Davidson | 2,19 |
| Lisa Pearson | 2 | Stewart Russell | 3,91 |
| Mark Young | 4 | Donna Soto | 5 |
| Finis Vanover | 6 | Janan Moore | 8,18,69,74 |
| Lana Smith | 9,11,57,68,79,83,88,751 | Jennifer Birdwell | 16 |
| Tracey Ludwig | 37 | Christine Jackson | 42,45 |
| Pamela Mitchell | 58 | Ben Ogletree | 67 |
| Ben Wilroy | 68 | Emily Williamson | 73 |
| Lily Hopson | 294 | Mike Wallace | 295 |

| Public Schs..Principal | Grd | Prgm | Enr/#Cls | SN |
|---|---|---|---|---|
| Cedar Grove Elem Sch | PK-1 | T | 485 | 74% 936/328-2240 |
| 819 W Church St, Livingston 77351 | | | | Fax 936/328-2259 |
| Erin Barnes | | | | |
| Creekside Elem Sch | 1-5 | | 645 | 936/328-2150 |
| 1 Lions Ave, Livingston 77351 | | | 27 | Fax 936/328-2149 |
| Elisha Bell | | | | |

| Public Schs..Principal | Grd | Prgm | Enr/#Cls | SN |
|---|---|---|---|---|
| Ⓐ Livingston High Sch Academy<br>400 FM 350 S, Livingston 77351<br>Dr Lynn Cummins | 9-12 | T | 14 | 59% 936/328-8600<br>Fax 936/328-2199 |
| Livingston High Sch<br>400 FM 350 S, Livingston 77351<br>Paul Drake | 9-12 | AGTV | 203<br>55 | 64% 936/328-8600 |
| Livingston Junior High Sch<br>1801 Highway 59 Loop N, Livingston 77351<br>Jared Nettles | 6-8 | TV | 940<br>35 | 72% 936/328-2120<br>Fax 936/328-2139 |
| Pine Ridge Elem Sch<br>1200 Mill Rdg, Livingston 77351<br>Mary Hill | PK-3 | T | 379<br>66 | 82% 936/328-2160<br>Fax 936/328-2179 |
| Timber Creek Elem Sch<br>701 N Willis Ave, Livingston 77351<br>Sheri Murphy | PK-3 | T | 381<br>28 | 85% 936/328-2180<br>Fax 936/328-2199 |

● **Onalaska Ind School Dist** PID: 01809809　　　936/646-1000
134 N FM 356, Onalaska 77360　　　　　　　　　Fax 936/646-2605

---

**Schools:** 2 \ **Teachers:** 78 \ **Students:** 1,056 \ **Special Ed Students:** 130
\ **LEP Students:** 14 \ **College-Bound:** 20% \ **Ethnic:** Asian 1%, African
American 3%, Hispanic 8%, Native American: 1%, Caucasian 88% \ **Exp:** $583
(High) \ **Poverty:** 24% \ **Title I:** $417,924 \ **Open-Close:** 08/26 - 05/28 \
**DTBP:** $349 (High) \ 🄵 🄴

---

Anthony Roberts .......................................1
James Ard ..............................................3,4
Nicholas Tyerman ....................................6*
Ted Wiggins ...........................................67

Angela Foster ...........................................2
Mike Skaggs ............................................5
Robyn Thornton ........... 8,11,16,57,58,69,88*
Charles Boyce ...........................73,84,286

| Public Schs..Principal | Grd | Prgm | Enr/#Cls | SN |
|---|---|---|---|---|
| Onalaska Elem Sch<br>391 Old Trinity S, Onalaska 77360<br>David Murphy | PK-6 | T | 589<br>21 | 75% 936/646-1010<br>Fax 936/646-1019 |
| Onalaska Jr Sr High Sch<br>1885 FM 3459, Onalaska 77360<br>Robyn Thornton | 7-12 | T | 467<br>41 | 74% 936/646-1020<br>Fax 936/646-1022 |

## POTTER COUNTY

## POTTER PUBLIC SCHOOLS

● **Amarillo Ind School Dist** PID: 01047128　　　806/326-1000
7200 W Interstate 40, Amarillo 79106　　　　　Fax 806/354-4378

---

**Schools:** 55 \ **Teachers:** 2,194 \ **Students:** 33,311 \
**Special Ed Students:** 3,717 \ **LEP Students:** 4,401 \ **College-Bound:** 50%
\ **Ethnic:** Asian 6%, African American 11%, Hispanic 48%, Caucasian
35% \ **Exp:** $334 (High) \ **Poverty:** 22% \ **Title I:** $11,055,912 \
**Special Education:** $5,892,000 \ **Open-Close:** 09/01 - 05/28 \ **DTBP:** $203
(High)

---

Doug Loomis .............................................1
Pati Buchenau ......................................2,19
Brad Thiessen ...........................................6
Debbie Chapman .......................................8
Sandy Whitlow .....................................8,18
Karyn Pierce .......................................27,31
Tracey Morman ................................36,270
Cayla Cielencki .......................................42
Shannon Davis ....................................57,93

Gary Elliott ..............................................2
Tim Loan ................................................3
Patricia Miranda ...................................7,85
Kyle Hallett .............................................8
Dr Christopher Reidlinger .......................23
Jeff Roller .........................28,73,76,84,98
Devia Cearlock .......................................39
Laura Ramos ...........................................54
Sylvia Hughes .................................57,271

Dr Maria Garcia ...............................58
Robin Malone ..................................67
Holly Shelton ..................................71
Maria Chrzanowski ..........................81

Todd Bigham ....................................58
Chris Tatum .....................................68
Keitha Ivey ......................................76
Denise Blanchard .............................93

| Public Schs..Principal | Grd | Prgm | Enr/#Cls | SN |
|---|---|---|---|---|
| Alice Landergin Elem Sch<br>3209 S Taylor St, Amarillo 79110<br>Ramon Garcia | PK-5 | T | 249<br>25 | 88% 806/326-4650<br>Fax 806/371-6035 |
| Allen 6th Grade Campus<br>700 N Lincoln St, Amarillo 79107<br>Dalea Tatum | 6-6 | T | 236 | 94% 806/326-3770<br>Fax 806/371-5829 |
| Amarillo Area Ctr Advance Lrng<br>1100 N Forest St, Amarillo 79106<br>Jay Barrett | 9-12 | V | 18<br>18 | 17% 806/326-2800<br>Fax 806/371-6100 |
| Amarillo High Sch<br>4225 Danbury Dr, Amarillo 79109<br>**Andrea Pfeifer** | 9-12 | V | 2,090<br>106 | 24% 806/326-2000<br>Fax 806/354-5092 |
| Avondale Elem Sch<br>1500 S Avondale St, Amarillo 79106<br>Randalyn Huyck | PK-5 | T | 583<br>25 | 78% 806/326-4000<br>Fax 806/354-4498 |
| Belmar Elem Sch<br>6342 Adirondack Trl, Amarillo 79106<br>Nicki Roush | PK-5 | T | 371<br>20 | 39% 806/326-4050<br>Fax 806/354-5081 |
| Bivins Elem Sch<br>1500 S Fannin St, Amarillo 79102<br>**R Soleyjacks** | PK-5 | T | 501<br>25 | 72% 806/326-4100<br>Fax 806/371-6133 |
| CapRock High Sch<br>3001 SE 34th Ave, Amarillo 79103<br>Chad Huseman | 9-12 | TV | 2,074<br>120 | 74% 806/326-2200<br>Fax 806/371-6042 |
| Ⓜ Carver Academy Elem Sch<br>1905 NW 12th Ave, Amarillo 79107<br>Melody Fox | 2-5 | T | 327<br>23 | 66% 806/326-4150<br>Fax 806/371-6081<br>🄵 🄴 |
| Carver Early Childhood Academy<br>1800 N Travis St, Amarillo 79107<br>Mitzi Malcolm | PK-1 | T | 243<br>21 | 56% 806/326-4200<br>Fax 806/371-6178 |
| Coronado Elem Sch<br>3210 Wimberly Rd, Amarillo 79109<br>**Ramon Garcia** | PK-5 | T | 509<br>24 | 63% 806/326-4250<br>Fax 806/356-4821 |
| David Crockett Middle Sch<br>4720 Floyd Ave, Amarillo 79106<br>Lisa Loan | 6-8 | V | 892<br>60 | 38% 806/326-3300<br>Fax 806/356-4873 |
| Eastridge Elem Sch<br>1314 Evergreen St, Amarillo 79107<br>Genie Baca | PK-5 | T | 759<br>39 | 94% 806/326-4300<br>Fax 806/381-7333 |
| Emerson Elem Sch<br>600 N Cleveland St, Amarillo 79107<br>Amanda Bales | PK-5 | T | 454<br>21 | 97% 806/326-4350<br>Fax 806/371-6055 |
| Forest Hill Elem Sch<br>3515 E Amarillo Blvd, Amarillo 79107<br>Bethany Rose | PK-5 | T | 475<br>34 | 96% 806/326-4400<br>Fax 806/381-7221 |
| Glenwood Elem Sch<br>2407 S Houston St, Amarillo 79103<br>Holly Holder | PK-5 | T | 433<br>27 | 95% 806/326-4450<br>Fax 806/371-5848 |
| Hamlet Elem Sch<br>705 Sycamore St, Amarillo 79104<br>Victor Favela | PK-5 | T | 344<br>30 | 98% 806/326-4500<br>Fax 806/381-7366<br>🄵 |
| Horace Mann Middle Sch<br>610 N Buchanan St, Amarillo 79107<br>Tammie Villarreal | 7-8 | TV | 450<br>40 | 93% 806/326-3700<br>Fax 806/371-5617 |
| Humphrey's Highland Elem Sch<br>3901 SE 15th Ave, Amarillo 79104<br>Erin Prickett | PK-5 | T | 593<br>39 | 92% 806/326-4550<br>Fax 806/371-5822 |
| James Bonham Middle Sch<br>5600 SW 49th Ave, Amarillo 79109<br>Andrea Pfeifer | 6-8 | V | 861 | 33% 806/326-3100<br>Fax 806/356-4865 |

| # | | # | | # | | # | | # | | # | | # | |
|---|---|---|---|---|---|---|---|---|---|---|---|---|---|
| 1 | Superintendent | 8 | Curric/Instruct K-12 | 19 | Chief Financial Officer | 29 | Family/Consumer Science | 39 | Social Studies K-12 | 49 | English/Lang Arts Elem | 59 | Special Education Elem | 69 | Academic Assessment |
| 2 | Bus/Finance/Purchasing | 9 | Curric/Instruct Elem | 20 | Art K-12 | 30 | Adult Education | 40 | Social Studies Elem | 50 | English/Lang Arts Sec | 60 | Special Education Sec | 70 | Research/Development |
| 3 | Buildings And Grounds | 10 | Curric/Instruct Sec | 21 | Art Elem | 31 | Career/Sch-to-Work K-12 | 41 | Social Studies Sec | 51 | Reading K-12 | 61 | Foreign/World Lang K-12 | 71 | Public Information |
| 4 | Food Service | 11 | Federal Program | 22 | Art Sec | 32 | Career/Sch-to-Work Elem | 42 | Science K-12 | 52 | Reading Elem | 62 | Foreign/World Lang Elem | 72 | Summer School |
| 5 | Transportation | 12 | Title I | 23 | Music K-12 | 33 | Career/Sch-to-Work Sec | 43 | Science Elem | 53 | Reading Sec | 63 | Foreign/World Lang Sec | 73 | Instructional Tech |
| 6 | Athletic | 13 | Title V | 24 | Music Elem | 34 | Early Childhood Ed | 44 | Science Sec | 54 | Remedial Reading K-12 | 64 | Religious Education K-12 | 74 | Inservice Training |
| 7 | Health Services | 14 | Asst Superintendent | 25 | Music Sec | 35 | Health/Phys Education | 45 | Math K-12 | 55 | Remedial Reading Elem | 65 | Religious Education Elem | 75 | Marketing/Distributive |
| | | 15 | Asst Superintendent | 26 | Business Education | 36 | Guidance Services K-12 | 46 | Math Elem | 56 | Remedial Reading Sec | 66 | Religious Education Sec | 76 | Info Systems |
| | | 16 | Instructional Media Svcs | 27 | Career & Tech Ed | 37 | Guidance Services Elem | 47 | Math Sec | 57 | Bilingual/ELL | 67 | School Board President | 77 | Psychological Assess |
| | | 17 | Chief Operations Officer | 28 | Technology Education | 38 | Guidance Services Sec | 48 | English/Lang Arts K-12 | 58 | Special Education K-12 | 68 | Teacher Personnel | 78 | Affirmative Action |

| School | Grd | Prgm | Enr/#Cls | SN | Phone |
|--------|-----|------|----------|-----|-------|
| James Bowie 6th Grade Campus<br>2905 Tee Anchor Blvd, Amarillo 79104<br>Derek Davis | 6-6 | T | 397 | 86% | 806/326-3270<br>Fax 806/322-3687 |
| James Bowie Middle Sch<br>2901 Tee Anchor Blvd, Amarillo 79104<br>Joann Ramirez | 7-8 | TV | 730<br>80 | 87% | 806/326-3200<br>Fax 806/371-5719 |
| James W Fannin Middle Sch<br>4627 S Rusk St, Amarillo 79110<br>Nathan Culwell | 6-8 | TV | 677<br>36 | 74% | 806/326-3500<br>Fax 806/354-4588 |
| Lamar Elem Sch<br>3800 S Lipscomb St, Amarillo 79110<br>Ginny Smith | PK-5 | T | 323<br>36 | 80% | 806/326-4600<br>Fax 806/356-4871 |
| Lawndale Elem Sch<br>2215 S Bivins St, Amarillo 79103<br>Jana Toliver | PK-5 | T | 337<br>30 | 86% | 806/326-4700<br>Fax 806/371-5687 |
| Lorenzo De Zavala Middle Sch<br>2801 N Coulter St, Amarillo 79124<br>Mike Manchee | 5-8 | | 422<br>30 | 29% | 806/326-3400<br>Fax 806/354-4286 |
| Margaret Wills Elem Sch<br>3500 SW 11th Ave, Amarillo 79106<br>**Lindsay Elliott** | PK-5 | T | 562<br>22 | 89% | 806/326-5650<br>Fax 806/371-5842 |
| Mesa Verde Elem Sch<br>4011 Beaver Dr, Amarillo 79107<br>**Charla Cobb** | PK-5 | T | 468<br>17 | 94% | 806/326-4800<br>Fax 806/381-7323 |
| Ⓐ North Heights Alt Sch<br>607 N Hughes St, Amarillo 79107<br>**Mark Leach** | 7-12 | | 429<br>15 | 45% | 806/326-2850<br>Fax 806/371-5715 |
| Oak Dale Elem Sch<br>2711 S Hill St, Amarillo 79103<br>Amy Barragan | PK-5 | T | 417<br>26 | 81% | 806/326-4850<br>Fax 806/371-6106 |
| Olsen Park Elem Sch<br>2409 Anna St, Amarillo 79106<br>Kris Schellhamer | PK-5 | T | 370<br>18 | 48% | 806/326-4900<br>Fax 806/356-4944 |
| Palo Duro High Sch<br>1400 N Grant St, Amarillo 79107<br>Amy Dorris | 9-12 | TV | 1,993<br>60 | 79% | 806/326-2400<br>Fax 806/381-7166 |
| Paramount Terrace Elem Sch<br>3906 Cougar Dr, Amarillo 79109<br>Lisa Greenhouse | PK-5 | T | 329<br>17 | 64% | 806/326-4950<br>Fax 806/354-4623 |
| Park Hills Elem Sch<br>119 NE 15th Ave, Amarillo 79107<br>Margarita Ogden | PK-5 | T | 272<br>32 | 94% | 806/326-4750<br>Fax 806/371-6046 |
| Pleasant Valley Elem Sch<br>4413 River Rd, Amarillo 79108<br>**Nick Cardenas** | PK-5 | T | 238<br>19 | 86% | 806/326-5000<br>Fax 806/381-7372 |
| Puckett Elem Sch<br>6700 Oakhurst Dr, Amarillo 79109<br>Cheri Hess | PK-5 | | 328<br>19 | 28% | 806/326-5050<br>Fax 806/356-4833 |
| Ridgecrest Elem Sch<br>5306 SW 37th Ave, Amarillo 79109<br>Lesley McCoy | K-5 | T | 417<br>25 | 49% | 806/326-5100<br>Fax 806/356-4835 |
| Sam Houston Middle Sch<br>815 S Independence St, Amarillo 79106<br>Melody Stephenson | 6-8 | TV | 671<br>59 | 86% | 806/326-3600<br>Fax 806/371-5577 |
| San Jacinto Elem Sch<br>3400 SW 4th Ave, Amarillo 79106<br>Justin Ruiz | PK-5 | T | 597<br>27 | 93% | 806/326-5200<br>Fax 806/371-5843 |
| Sanborn Elem Sch<br>700 S Roberts St, Amarillo 79102<br>Sandra Tudon | PK-5 | T | 416<br>27 | 94% | 806/326-5250<br>Fax 806/371-6171 |
| Sleepy Hollow Elem Sch<br>3435 Reeder Dr, Amarillo 79121<br>Amy Krieger | PK-5 | T | 476<br>20 | 18% | 806/326-5300<br>Fax 806/354-5079 🟦 |
| South Georgia Elem Sch<br>5018 Susan Dr, Amarillo 79110<br>Heather Newman | PK-5 | T | 452<br>24 | 65% | 806/326-5350<br>Fax 806/356-4959 |
| South Lawn Elem Sch<br>4719 Bowie St, Amarillo 79110<br>Donna Harris | PK-5 | T | 423<br>25 | 80% | 806/326-5400<br>Fax 806/356-4879 |
| Stephen F Austin Middle Sch<br>1808 Wimberly Rd, Amarillo 79109<br>**Brandy Self** | 6-8 | TV | 793<br>45 | 67% | 806/326-3000<br>Fax 806/356-4802 |
| Sunrise Elem Sch<br>5123 SE 14th Ave, Amarillo 79104<br>Sonia Castaneda | PK-5 | T | 267<br>24 | 91% | 806/326-5450<br>Fax 806/371-5841 |
| Tascosa High Sch<br>3921 Westlawn St, Amarillo 79102<br>John Smith | 9-12 | TV | 2,339<br>110 | 53% | 806/326-2600<br>Fax 806/354-4702 |
| Tradewind Elem Sch<br>4300 S Williams St, Amarillo 79118<br>Kim Bentley | PK-5 | T | 589 | 75% | 806/326-5500<br>Fax 806/371-6535 |
| Western Plateau Elem Sch<br>4927 Shawnee Trl, Amarillo 79109<br>Lori Berryman | K-5 | T | 424<br>23 | 54% | 806/326-5550<br>Fax 806/356-4872 🟦 |
| Whittier Elem Sch<br>2004 N Marrs St, Amarillo 79107<br>Linda Rangel | PK-5 | T | 538<br>60 | 94% | 806/326-5600<br>Fax 806/381-7322 |
| Will Rogers Elem Sch<br>920 N Mirror St, Amarillo 79107<br>Terri Huseman | PK-5 | T | 555<br>38 | 94% | 806/326-5150<br>Fax 806/371-5718 |
| William B Travis 6th GR Campus<br>2801 NE 24th Ave, Amarillo 79107<br>Casey Newman | 6-6 | T | 384 | 94% | 806/326-3870<br>Fax 806/322-3690 |
| William B Travis Middle Sch<br>2815 Martin Rd, Amarillo 79107<br>Jennifer Wilkerson | 7-8 | GTV | 687<br>65 | 93% | 806/326-3800<br>Fax 806/381-7207 |
| Windsor Elem Sch<br>6700 Hyde Pkwy, Amarillo 79109<br>Allison Woodington | PK-5 | | 526<br>25 | 25% | 806/326-5700<br>Fax 806/356-4999 |
| Wolflin Elem Sch<br>2026 S Hughes St, Amarillo 79109<br>Stephanie Chew | PK-5 | T | 367<br>22 | 68% | 806/326-5750<br>Fax 806/371-6101 |
| Woodlands Elem Sch<br>2501 N Coulter St, Amarillo 79124<br>Traci Gabel | PK-4 | | 340<br>14 | 24% | 806/326-5800<br>Fax 806/356-4926 |

● **Bushland Ind School Dist** PID: 01047568    806/359-6683
2400 Wells St, Amarillo 79124    Fax 806/359-6769

**Schools:** 3 \ **Teachers:** 121 \ **Students:** 1,400 \ **Special Ed Students:** 181 \ **LEP Students:** 13 \ **Ethnic:** African American 1%, Hispanic 16%, Native American: 1%, Caucasian 83% \ **Exp:** $394 (High) \ **Poverty:** 10% \ **Title I:** $118,843 \ **Special Education:** $155,000 \ **Open-Close:** 08/13 - 05/27 \ **DTBP:** $331 (High)

| | | | |
|---|---|---|---|
| Chris Wigington | 1 | Karen Grantham | 2* |
| James Folkerts | 3,5 | Billy Maples | 4 |
| Josh Reynolds | 6 | Tom Giles | 8,11,15,74,296 |
| Paula Schwertner | 16* | Michelle Lancaster | 31* |
| Stephanie Donnell | 37,83,85* | Tiffany Fisk | 38,83* |
| Angella Noel | 57,271,294 | Terri Moss | 58* |
| Holly Jefferys | 67 | Ivan Lopez | 73,286,295,297 |
| Randy Tinsley | 91 | Kristin Lavender | 752 |

| Public Schs..Principal | Grd | Prgm | Enr/#Cls | SN | Phone |
|------------------------|-----|------|----------|-----|-------|
| Bushland Elem Sch<br>2400 Wells St, Amarillo 79124<br>Brandi Rankin | PK-4 | T | 489<br>30 | 21% | 806/359-5410<br>Fax 806/322-1166 |
| Bushland High Sch<br>1201 S FM 2381, Amarillo 79124<br>Kristi Culpepper | 9-12 | V | 465 | 11% | 806/359-6683<br>Fax 806/322-1180 🟦🟦 |

Bushland Middle Sch    5-8    V    473    20%   806/359-5418
20101 25th St, Bushland 79012     Fax 806/355-2841
Jessica Garrett

---

- **Highland Park Ind School Dist** PID: 01047582    806/335-2823
15300 E Amarillo Blvd, Amarillo 79108    Fax 806/335-3547

> **Schools:** 3 \ **Teachers:** 66 \ **Students:** 864 \ **Special Ed Students:** 107
> \ **LEP Students:** 63 \ **College-Bound:** 51% \ **Ethnic:** Asian 7%,
> African American 3%, Hispanic 42%, Native American: 1%, Caucasian
> 48% \ **Exp:** $491 (High) \ **Poverty:** 28% \ **Title I:** $277,757 \
> **Special Education:** $154,000 \ **Open-Close:** 08/21 - 05/21 \ **DTBP:** $223
> (High)

| | | |
|---|---|---|
| Jimmy Hannon ...........1 | Lisa Messner ...........2 | |
| Garry Leafloor ...........3* | Garon Newton ...........4 | |
| Wade Wilson ...........6 | Rala Underwood ...........38* | |
| Kristi Waters ...........58* | Tonya Detten ...........67 | |
| Susan Looney ...........73* | Mark Glick ...........83,91 | |

| Public Schs..Principal | Grd | Prgm | Enr/#Cls | SN |
|---|---|---|---|---|
| Highland Park Elem Sch | PK-5 | T | 424 | 72% 806/335-1334 |
| 15300 E Amarillo Blvd, Amarillo 79108 | | | 23 | Fax 806/335-3184 |
| **Shannon Woodward** | | | | 📘 |
| Highland Park High Sch | 9-12 | ATV | 212 | 55% 806/335-2821 |
| 15300 E Amarillo Blvd, Amarillo 79108 | | | 16 | Fax 806/335-3215 |
| Dixie Shettel | | | | |
| Highland Park Middle Sch | 6-8 | TV | 228 | 68% 806/335-2821 |
| 15300 E Amarillo Blvd, Amarillo 79108 | | | | Fax 806/335-3215 |
| Dixie Shettel | | | | |

- **River Road Ind School Dist** PID: 01047609    806/381-7800
9500 N US Highway 287, Amarillo 79108    Fax 806/381-1357

> **Schools:** 4 \ **Teachers:** 104 \ **Students:** 1,278 \ **Special Ed Students:** 157
> \ **LEP Students:** 28 \ **Ethnic:** African American 2%, Hispanic 24%, Native
> American: 1%, Caucasian 73% \ **Exp:** $371 (High) \ **Poverty:** 17% \
> **Title I:** $283,071 \ **Special Education:** $277,000 \ **Open-Close:** 08/20 -
> 05/28 \ **DTBP:** $348 (High)

| | |
|---|---|
| Richard Kelley ...........1 | Andy Nies ...........2,8,11,74,88,270,294,296 |
| David Perry ...........3 | Kim Terry ...........4* |
| Bryan Perryman ...........5 | Bryan Welps ...........6* |
| Kim Franks ...........7* | Robin Wood ...........34,57,58,69,271 |
| Amanda Brown ...........67 | Gina Montgomery ...........73,295* |
| Gina Montgomery ...........84 | |

| Public Schs..Principal | Grd | Prgm | Enr/#Cls | SN |
|---|---|---|---|---|
| River Road High Sch | 9-12 | T | 388 | 51% 806/383-8867 |
| 101 W Mobley St, Amarillo 79108 | | | 45 | Fax 806/381-7818 |
| Dean Birkes | | | | |
| River Road Middle Sch | 7-8 | | 206 | 806/383-8721 |
| 9500 N US Highway 287, Amarillo 79108 | | | 12 | Fax 806/381-7815 |
| Penny Rosson | | | | 📘 |
| Rolling Hills Elem Sch | PK-4 | T | 479 | 63% 806/383-8621 |
| 2800 W Cherry Ave, Amarillo 79108 | | | 70 | Fax 806/381-7814 |
| Erin Brandstatt | | | | 📘 |
| Willow Vista Intermediate Sch | 5-6 | T | 201 | 71% 806/383-8820 |
| 7600 Pavillard Dr, Amarillo 79108 | | | 10 | Fax 806/381-7827 |
| Mike Cheverier | | | | |

---

# POTTER CATHOLIC SCHOOLS

- **Diocese of Amarillo Ed Office** PID: 01047659    806/383-2243
4512 NE 24th Ave, Amarillo 79107    Fax 806/383-8452

> **Schools:** 5 \ **Students:** 850

Listing includes only schools located in this county. See District Index for
location of Diocesan Offices.

Christina Wanjura ...........1    Phil Whitson ...........2

| Catholic Schs..Principal | Grd | Prgm | Enr/#Cls | SN |
|---|---|---|---|---|
| St Maryis Cathedral Sch | PK-5 | | 175 | 806/376-9112 |
| 1200 S Washington St, Amarillo 79102 | | | 10 | Fax 806/376-4314 |
| Lydia O'Rear | | | | |

---

# POTTER PRIVATE SCHOOLS

| Private Schs..Principal | Grd | Prgm | Enr/#Cls | SN |
|---|---|---|---|---|
| Mosaic Academy | PK-12 | | 100 | 817/204-0300 |
| 1400 College Ave, Amarillo 79104 | | | | |
| Kristen Bray | | | | |
| San Jacinto Christian Academy | PK-12 | | 475 | 806/372-2285 |
| 501 S Carolina St, Amarillo 79106 | | | 50 | Fax 806/376-6712 |
| Amy Sternenberg \ Chandra Barnes \ Ed Thomas | | | | 📘 |
| St Andrew's Episcopal Day Sch | PK-8 | | 300 | 806/376-9501 |
| 1515 S Georgia St, Amarillo 79102 | | | | Fax 806/376-8421 |
| Laura Gabel \ Kurt Grawunder | | | | |
| Trinity Lutheran Sch | PK-6 | | 75 | 806/352-5620 |
| 5005 W Interstate 40, Amarillo 79106 | | | 8 | Fax 806/353-7785 |
| Rick Ryan | | | | 📘 |

---

# PRESIDIO COUNTY

---

# PRESIDIO PUBLIC SCHOOLS

- **Marfa Ind School Dist** PID: 01047829    432/729-4252
400 W Lincoln St, Marfa 79843    Fax 432/729-4310

> **Schools:** 2 \ **Teachers:** 33 \ **Students:** 342 \ **Special Ed Students:** 28
> \ **LEP Students:** 80 \ **College-Bound:** 42% \ **Ethnic:** African American
> 3%, Hispanic 83%, Caucasian 14% \ **Exp:** $920 (High) \ **Poverty:** 30% \
> **Title I:** $156,771 \ **Open-Close:** 09/08 - 05/28 \ **DTBP:** $292 (High)

| | |
|---|---|
| Oscar Aguero ...........1 | Linda Ojeda ...........6* |
| Mesinda Llanez ...........58 | Katie Fowlkes ...........67 |
| Brian Salcido ...........73 | Valerie Valerio ...........76 |

| Public Schs..Principal | Grd | Prgm | Enr/#Cls | SN |
|---|---|---|---|---|
| Marfa Elem Sch | PK-5 | | 202 | 432/729-4252 |
| 413 W Columbia St, Marfa 79843 | | | 23 | Fax 432/729-3417 |
| Amy White | | | | |
| Marfa Jr Sr High Sch | 6-12 | TV | 151 | 79% 432/729-4252 |
| 300 N Gonzales St, Marfa 79843 | | | 30 | Fax 432/729-4053 |
| John Sherrill | | | | |

| | | | | | |
|---|---|---|---|---|---|
| 1 Superintendent | 19 Chief Financial Officer | 29 Family/Consumer Science | 39 Social Studies K-12 | 49 English/Lang Arts Elem | 69 Academic Assessment |
| 2 Bus/Finance/Purchasing | 20 Art K-12 | 30 Adult Education | 40 Social Studies Elem | 50 English/Lang Arts Sec | 70 Research/Development |
| 3 Buildings And Grounds | 21 Art Elem | 31 Career/Sch-to-Work K-12 | 41 Social Studies Sec | 51 Reading K-12 | 71 Public Information |
| 4 Food Service | 22 Art Sec | 32 Career/Sch-to-Work Elem | 42 Science K-12 | 52 Reading Elem | 72 Summer School |
| 5 Transportation | 23 Music K-12 | 33 Career/Sch-to-Work Sec | 43 Science Elem | 53 Reading Sec | 73 Instructional Tech |
| 6 Athletic | 24 Music Elem | 34 Early Childhood Ed | 44 Science Sec | 54 Remedial Reading K-12 | 74 Inservice Training |
| 7 Health Services | 25 Music Sec | 35 Health/Phys Education | 45 Math K-12 | 55 Remedial Reading Elem | 75 Marketing/Distributive |
| 8 Curric/Instruct K-12 | 26 Business Education | 36 Guidance Services K-12 | 46 Math Elem | 56 Remedial Reading Sec | 76 Info Systems |
| 9 Curric/Instruct Elem | 27 Career & Tech Ed | 37 Guidance Services Elem | 47 Math Sec | 57 Bilingual/ELL | 77 Psychological Assess |
| 10 Curric/Instruct Sec | 28 Technology Education | 38 Guidance Services Sec | 48 English/Lang Arts K-12 | 58 Special Education K-12 | 78 Affirmative Action |
| 11 Federal Program | | | | 59 Special Education Elem | |
| 12 Title I | | | | 60 Special Education Sec | |
| 13 Title V | | | | 61 Foreign/World Lang K-12 | |
| 14 | | | | 62 Foreign/World Lang Elem | |
| 15 Asst Superintendent | | | | 63 Foreign/World Lang Sec | |
| 16 Instructional Media Svcs | | | | 64 Religious Education K-12 | |
| 17 Chief Operations Officer | | | | 65 Religious Education Elem | |
| 18 Chief Academic Officer | | | | 66 Religious Education Sec | |
| | | | | 67 School Board President | |
| | | | | 68 Teacher Personnel | |

## Presidio Ind School Dist PID: 01047867
701 E Market St, Presidio 79845

432/229-3275
Fax 432/229-4228

**Schools:** 3 \ **Teachers:** 96 \ **Students:** 1,162 \ **Special Ed Students:** 71 \ **LEP Students:** 593 \ **College-Bound:** 50% \ **Ethnic:** Asian 1%, Hispanic 98%, Caucasian 1% \ **Exp:** $843 (High) \ **Poverty:** 41% \ **Title I:** $634,025 \ **Open-Close:** 08/12 - 05/28 \ **DTBP:** $371 (High)

| | | | |
|---|---|---|---|
| Ray Vasquez | 1 | Raquel Baeza | 2 |
| Ruben Armendariz | 3,5 | Hezila Ramos | 6 |
| Dr Laura Postillo | 8,11,57,58,271,298 | Samuel Carrasco | 30,69 |
| Ethel Barriga | 67 | Larry Quintna | 73 |
| Jaime Sanchez | 295 | | |

| Public Schs..Principal | Grd | Prgm | Enr/#Cls | SN | |
|---|---|---|---|---|---|
| Lucy Rede Franco Middle Sch<br>1515 E Highland St, Presidio 79845<br>**Yvette Deanda** | 7-9 | AT | 332<br>29 | 90% | 432/229-3113<br>Fax 432/229-4087 |
| Presidio Elem Sch<br>701 E Market Street, Presidio 79845<br>**Dr Edgar Tibayan** | PK-6 | T | 565<br>50 | 94% | 432/229-3200<br>Fax 432/229-4267 |
| Presidio High Sch<br>701 Highway 170 E, Presidio 79845<br>**Hevila Ramos** | 10-12 | AT | 440<br>34 | 93% | 432/229-3365<br>Fax 432/229-4625 |

# RAINS COUNTY

## RAINS PUBLIC SCHOOLS

## Rains Ind School Dist PID: 01047893
1759 W US Highway 69, Emory 75440

903/473-2222
Fax 903/473-3053

**Schools:** 4 \ **Teachers:** 130 \ **Students:** 1,500 \ **Special Ed Students:** 231 \ **LEP Students:** 105 \ **College-Bound:** 54% \ **Ethnic:** African American 3%, Hispanic 17%, Native American: 1%, Caucasian 79% \ **Exp:** $388 (High) \ **Poverty:** 21% \ **Title I:** $479,793 \ **Special Education:** $481,000 \ **Open-Close:** 08/13 - 05/28 \ **DTBP:** $340 (High)

| | | | |
|---|---|---|---|
| Jennifer Johnson | 1,11 | Jeff Fisher | 2,15 |
| Jesse Brubaker | 3 | Jennifer Melancon | 16 |
| Bill Morgan | 34 | Jennifer Melton | 58 |
| Phillip Alexander | 67 | Lisa Clark | 73,295* |
| Lauri Evans | 76 | | |

| Public Schs..Principal | Grd | Prgm | Enr/#Cls | SN | |
|---|---|---|---|---|---|
| Rains Elem Sch<br>372 FM 3299, Mumford 77867<br>Angie Trull | PK-2 | T | 397<br>28 | 68% | 903/473-2222<br>Fax 903/473-7259 |
| Rains High Sch<br>1651 W US Highway 69, Emory 75440<br>Randell Wellman | 9-12 | ATV | 461<br>46 | 57% | 903/473-2222<br>Fax 903/473-5584 |
| Rains Intermediate Sch<br>409 FM 3299, Emory 75440<br>J Vance | 3-5 | T | 410<br>20 | 67% | 903/473-2222<br>Fax 903/473-5162 |
| Rains Junior High Sch<br>1755 W US Highway 69, Emory 75440<br>Gina Hildebrandt | 6-8 | T | 371<br>30 | 59% | 903/473-2222<br>Fax 903/473-5162 |

# RANDALL COUNTY

## RANDALL PUBLIC SCHOOLS

## Canyon Ind School Dist PID: 01047934
3301 N 23rd St, Canyon 79015

806/677-2600
Fax 806/677-2659

**Schools:** 16 \ **Teachers:** 626 \ **Students:** 11,000 \ **Special Ed Students:** 1,153 \ **LEP Students:** 178 \ **College-Bound:** 55% \ **Ethnic:** Asian 1%, African American 3%, Hispanic 26%, Native American: 1%, Caucasian 70% \ **Exp:** $385 (High) \ **Poverty:** 8% \ **Title I:** $1,012,298 \ **Special Education:** $1,590,000 \ **Open-Close:** 08/19 - 05/28 \ **DTBP:** $181 (High)

| | | | |
|---|---|---|---|
| Darryl Flusche | 1 | Bryon McCafferty | 2 |
| Heather Wilson | 2,15 | Jeff Millner | 3 |
| Mike Schnitger | 4 | Caleb Hidalgo | 5,91 |
| Toby Tucker | 6 | Cameron Rosser | 8,273 |
| Yolanda DeLaney | 9 | Marc Hamil | 10,27,31 |
| Robyn Cranmer | 11,57,93,270,271 | Bridget Johnson | 58 |
| Bruce Cobb | 67 | Paul Kimbrough | 68 |
| April McDaniel | 71 | Chris Norton | 73,285,286 |
| Michael Keough | 76,98 | Montess Callahan | 79 |
| Lisa Hill | 280 | Kenneth Boehs | 295 |

| Public Schs..Principal | Grd | Prgm | Enr/#Cls | SN | |
|---|---|---|---|---|---|
| Arden Road Elem Sch<br>6801 Learning Tree Ln, Amarillo 79119<br>Travis Willard | PK-4 | | 377<br>25 | 22% | 806/677-2360<br>Fax 806/677-2379 |
| Canyon High Sch<br>1701 23rd St, Canyon 79015<br>Jennifer Boren | 9-12 | V | 1,149<br>60 | 29% | 806/677-2740<br>Fax 806/677-2779 |
| Canyon Intermediate Sch<br>506 8th St, Canyon 79015<br>Tricia Cook | 5-6 | T | 647<br>50 | 32% | 806/677-2800<br>Fax 806/677-2829 |
| Canyon Junior High Sch<br>910 9th Ave, Canyon 79015<br>Kirk Kear | 7-8 | | 640<br>33 | 37% | 806/677-2700<br>Fax 806/677-2739 🅣 |
| City View Elem Sch<br>3400 Knoll Dr, Amarillo 79118<br>Andrew Burgoon | PK-4 | | 448 | 27% | 806/677-2500<br>Fax 806/677-2519 |
| Crestview Elem Sch<br>80 Hunsley Rd, Canyon 79015<br>Amy Meek | PK-4 | | 376<br>23 | 17% | 806/677-2780<br>Fax 806/677-2799 |
| Gene Howe Elem Sch<br>5108 Pico Blvd, Amarillo 79110<br>Kandi Kempf | PK-4 | T | 308<br>26 | 39% | 806/677-2380<br>Fax 806/677-2399 🅣 |
| Greenways Intermediate Sch<br>8100 Pineridge Dr, Amarillo 79119<br>Toby King | 5-6 | | 204<br>60 | 23% | 806/677-2460<br>Fax 806/677-2499 |
| Hillside Elem Sch<br>9600 Perry Ave, Amarillo 79119<br>**Adam Kerns** | PK-4 | | 563 | 24% | 806/677-2520<br>Fax 806/677-2539 |
| Lakeview Elem Sch<br>6407 Lair Rd, Amarillo 79118<br>Krystal Hare | PK-4 | T | 491<br>24 | 66% | 806/677-2830<br>Fax 806/677-2849 |
| Ⓐ Midway Alternative High Sch<br>1403 23rd St, Canyon 79015<br>Shawn Neeley | 11-12 | T | 23 | 59% | 806/677-2455<br>Fax 806/677-2459 |
| Pinnacle Intermediate Sch<br>4545 Meadow Ridge Dr, Amarillo 79118<br>Kimberly Lackey | 5-6 | T | 613 | 39% | 806/677-2570 |

---

| | | | | |
|---|---|---|---|---|
| 79 Student Personnel | 91 Safety/Security | 275 Response To Intervention | 298 Grant Writer/Ptnrships | **School Programs** |
| 80 Driver Ed/Safety | 92 Magnet School | 277 Remedial Math K-12 | 750 Chief Innovation Officer | **A** = Alternative Program |
| 81 Gifted/Talented | 93 Parental Involvement | 280 Literacy Coach | 751 Chief of Staff | **G** = Adult Classes |
| 82 Video Services | 95 Tech Prep Program | 285 STEM | 752 Social Emotional Learning | **M** = Magnet Program |
| 83 Substance Abuse Prev | 97 Chief Information Officer | 286 Digital Learning | | **T** = Title I Schoolwide |
| 84 Erate | 98 Chief Technology Officer | 288 Common Core Standards | **Other School Types** | **V** = Career & Tech Ed Programs |
| 85 AIDS Education | 270 Character Education | 294 Accountability | Ⓐ = Alternative School | |
| 88 Alternative/At Risk | 271 Migrant Education | 295 Network System | Ⓒ = Charter School | **Social Media** |
| 89 Multi-Cultural Curriculum | 273 Teacher Mentor | 296 Title II Programs | Ⓜ = Magnet School | 🅕 = Facebook |
| 90 Social Work | 274 Before/After Sch | 297 Webmaster | Ⓨ = Year-Round School | 🅣 = Twitter |

New Schools are shaded
New Superintendents and Principals are bold
Personnel with email addresses are underscored

| | | | | | | |
|---|---|---|---|---|---|---|
| Randall High Sch | 9-12 | V | 1,684 | 29% | 806/677-2333 | |
| 5800 Attebury Dr, Amarillo 79118 | | | 85 | | Fax 806/677-2329 | |
| Steven Singleton | | | | | | |
| Reeves Hinger Elem Sch | PK-4 | T | 771 | 42% | 806/677-2870 | |
| 1005 21st St, Canyon 79015 | | | | | Fax 806/677-2889 | |
| Nicole Johnston | | | | | | |
| Sundown Lane Elem Sch | PK-4 | T | 170 | 52% | 806/677-2400 | |
| 4546 W Sundown Ln, Amarillo 79118 | | | 12 | | Fax 806/677-2419 | |
| Noe Renteria | | | | | | |
| Westover Park Jr High Sch | 7-8 | | 923 | | 806/677-2420 | |
| 7200 Pinnacle Dr, Amarillo 79119 | | | 40 | | Fax 806/356-2439 | |
| Doug Voran | | | | | | |

## RANDALL CATHOLIC SCHOOLS

- **Diocese of Amarillo Ed Office** PID: 01047659
  Listing includes only schools located in this county. See District Index for location of Diocesan Offices.

| Catholic Schs..Principal | Grd | Prgm | Enr/#Cls | SN | |
|---|---|---|---|---|---|
| Holy Cross Catholic Academy | 6-12 | | 102 | | 806/355-9637 |
| 4110 S Bonham St, Amarillo 79110 | | | 13 | | Fax 806/353-9520 |
| Angela Seidenberger | | | | | |
| St Joseph Elem Sch | PK-5 | | 124 | | 806/359-1604 |
| 4118 S Bonham St, Amarillo 79110 | | | 10 | | Fax 806/359-1605 |
| David Hernandez | | | | | |

## RANDALL PRIVATE SCHOOLS

| Private Schs..Principal | Grd | Prgm | Enr/#Cls | SN | |
|---|---|---|---|---|---|
| Ascension Academy | 6-12 | | 200 | | 806/342-0515 |
| 9301 Ascension Pkwy, Amarillo 79119 | | | 15 | | Fax 806/342-0535 |
| William Summerhill | | | | | |

## RANDALL REGIONAL CENTERS

- **Region 16 Ed Service Center** PID: 01047984    806/677-5000
  5800 Bell St, Amarillo 79109    Fax 806/677-5001

| | | |
|---|---|---|
| Ray Cogburn .............................1 | Cole Cordell ..................................2 | |
| Melissa Shaver .........................34 | Kelisa Nelson .........................58,77 | |
| Michelle Wilson ........................68 | Greg Stockstill ...........................73 | |

## REAGAN PUBLIC SCHOOLS

- **Reagan Co Ind School Dist** PID: 01048017    325/884-3705
  1111 E 12th St, Big Lake 76932    Fax 325/884-3021

**Schools:** 3 \ **Teachers:** 80 \ **Students:** 850 \ **Special Ed Students:** 67 \ **LEP Students:** 111 \ **College-Bound:** 59% \ **Ethnic:** Asian 1%, African American 1%, Hispanic 83%, Caucasian 16% \ **Exp:** $1,112 (High) \ **Poverty:** 13% \ **Title I:** $141,426 \ **Special Education:** $225,000 \ **Open-Close:** 08/21 - 05/28 \ **DTBP:** $690 (High) \ **f**

| | | |
|---|---|---|
| Bobby Fryar .............................1 | Susan Gunnels ..........................2,79 | |
| Jamal Rivers .........................3,5 | April Martinez .............................4 | |
| Blake Weston ...........................6* | Eric Hallmark ...............8,11,15,57* | |
| Kent Coker ..........................60,752 | Jed Hruska ................................67 | |
| Teressa Tekell .........................69* | Tracey McPhaul ....................73,295 | |
| Kyle Brown ...........................83,88 | | |

| Public Schs..Principal | Grd | Prgm | Enr/#Cls | SN | |
|---|---|---|---|---|---|
| Reagan Co Elem Sch | PK-5 | T | 386 | 62% | 325/884-3741 |
| 501 N Texas Ave, Big Lake 76932 | | | 29 | | Fax 325/884-2194 |
| **Trish Soto** | | | | | |
| Reagan Co High Sch | 9-12 | | 238 | 58% | 325/884-3714 |
| 1111 E 12th St, Big Lake 76932 | | | 26 | | Fax 325/884-5759 |
| **Kyle Brown** | | | | | |
| Reagan Co Middle Sch | 6-8 | T | 197 | 68% | 325/884-3728 |
| 500 N Pennsylvania Ave, Big Lake 76932 | | | 20 | | Fax 325/884-2327 |
| **Kalum McKay** | | | | | |

## REAL PUBLIC SCHOOLS

- **Leakey Ind School Dist** PID: 01048055    830/232-5595
  429 N US Highway 83, Leakey 78873    Fax 830/232-5535

**Schools:** 1 \ **Teachers:** 27 \ **Students:** 279 \ **Special Ed Students:** 38 \ **LEP Students:** 12 \ **College-Bound:** 60% \ **Ethnic:** Hispanic 38%, Caucasian 62% \ **Exp:** $535 (High) \ **Poverty:** 30% \ **Title I:** $121,779 \ **Open-Close:** 08/26 - 05/21 \ **DTBP:** $389 (High)

| | | |
|---|---|---|
| Chris Yeschke ...........................1 | Kathy Antes ...........................2,297 | |
| Jim Couvillion ...........................3 | Leann Waligura ..........................4 | |
| Carolyn Jones ...........................5 | Donnie Dutton ...........................6* | |
| Patrish Sewell ...........8,36,83,88,275* | Deanna Lanton .......9,11,58,69,271,294* | |
| Rick Davis ...................16,73,295* | Esmarelda Ruiz ..........................57* | |
| Brandi Pichardo .........................67 | | |

| Public Schs..Principal | Grd | Prgm | Enr/#Cls | SN | |
|---|---|---|---|---|---|
| Leakey Sch | PK-12 | TV | 279 | 61% | 830/232-5595 |
| 429 N US Highway 83, Leakey 78873 | | | 20 | | |
| Vicki Goebel | | | | | f t |

| | | | | | | | | |
|---|---|---|---|---|---|---|---|---|
| 1 | Superintendent | 8 | Curric/Instruct K-12 | 19 | Chief Financial Officer | 29 | Family/Consumer Science | 39 Social Studies K-12 |
| 2 | Bus/Finance/Purchasing | 9 | Curric/Instruct Elem | 20 | Art K-12 | 30 | Adult Education | 40 Social Studies Elem |
| 3 | Buildings And Grounds | 10 | Curric/Instruct Sec | 21 | Art Elem | 31 | Career/Sch-to-Work K-12 | 41 Social Studies Sec |
| 4 | Food Service | 11 | Federal Program | 22 | Art Sec | 32 | Career/Sch-to-Work Elem | 42 Science K-12 |
| 5 | Transportation | 12 | Title I | 23 | Music K-12 | 33 | Career/Sch-to-Work Sec | 43 Science Elem |
| 6 | Athletic | 13 | Title V | 24 | Music Elem | 34 | Early Childhood Ed | 44 Science Sec |
| 7 | Health Services | 15 | Asst Superintendent | 25 | Music Sec | 35 | Health/Phys Education | 45 Math K-12 |
| | | 16 | Instructional Media Svcs | 26 | Business Education | 36 | Guidance Services K-12 | 46 Math Elem |
| | | 17 | Chief Operations Officer | 27 | Career & Tech Ed | 37 | Guidance Services Elem | 47 Math Sec |
| | | 18 | Chief Academic Officer | 28 | Technology Education | 38 | Guidance Services Sec | 48 English/Lang Arts K-12 |

| | | | |
|---|---|---|---|
| 49 English/Lang Arts Elem | 59 Special Education Elem | 69 Academic Assessment |
| 50 English/Lang Arts Sec | 60 Special Education Sec | 70 Research/Development |
| 51 Reading K-12 | 61 Foreign/World Lang K-12 | 71 Public Information |
| 52 Reading Elem | 62 Foreign/World Lang Elem | 72 Summer School |
| 53 Reading Sec | 63 Foreign/World Lang Sec | 73 Instructional Tech |
| 54 Remedial Reading K-12 | 64 Religious Education K-12 | 74 Inservice Training |
| 55 Remedial Reading Elem | 65 Religious Education Elem | 75 Marketing/Distributive |
| 56 Remedial Reading Sec | 66 Religious Education Sec | 76 Info Systems |
| 57 Bilingual/ELL | 67 School Board President | 77 Psychological Assess |
| 58 Special Education K-12 | 68 Teacher Personnel | 78 Affirmative Action |

## RED RIVER COUNTY

### RED RIVER PUBLIC SCHOOLS

● **Avery Ind School Dist** PID: 01048081     903/684-3460
150 San Antonio St, Avery 75554     Fax 903/684-3294

**Schools:** 2 \ **Teachers:** 32 \ **Students:** 323 \ **Special Ed Students:** 42 \
**LEP Students:** 11 \ **College-Bound:** 54% \ **Ethnic:** African American 2%,
Hispanic 10%, Native American: 2%, Caucasian 86% \ **Exp:** $551 (High) \
**Poverty:** 18% \ **Title I:** $53,851 \ **Open-Close:** 08/24 - 05/28 \ **DTBP:** $333
(High) \ 🇫 🇹

| | | |
|---|---|---|
| Debbie Drew ...........1 | Kelli House ...........2 | |
| Judy Peeks ...........4 | Bret Harp ...........6 | |
| Jullia Lennon ...........7* | Jill Maham ...........11 | |
| Karen Downs ...........11,296* | Jeannie Beaman ...........16,73,286,295* | |
| Ann Stephenson ...........59* | Stacie Moore ...........67 | |

| Public Schs..Principal | Grd | Prgm | Enr/#Cls | SN |
|---|---|---|---|---|
| Avery Elem Sch<br>150 San Antonio St, Avery 75554<br>Karen Downs | PK-5 | T | 157<br>9 | 72% 903/684-3116<br>Fax 903/684-3093 |
| Avery Secondary Sch<br>150 San Antonio St, Avery 75554<br>Jill Mahan | 6-12 | TV | 166<br>13 | 51% 903/684-3431<br>Fax 903/684-3059 |

● **Clarksville Ind School Dist** PID: 01048110     903/427-3891
1500 W Main St, Clarksville 75426     Fax 903/427-5071

**Schools:** 2 \ **Teachers:** 37 \ **Students:** 534 \ **Special Ed Students:** 65
\ **LEP Students:** 46 \ **College-Bound:** 40% \ **Ethnic:** African American
53%, Hispanic 27%, Caucasian 19% \ **Exp:** $527 (High) \ **Poverty:** 33% \
**Title I:** $392,536 \ **Special Education:** $181,000 \ **Open-Close:** 08/17 -
05/27 \ **DTBP:** $361 (High)

| | | |
|---|---|---|
| Kermit Ward ...........1 | Melissa Darrow ...........2 | |
| Pamela Vandeaver ...........2,3 | Sheryl Scott ...........4 | |
| Lonnie Rushing ...........5 | Henry Sharp ...........11 | |
| Mikki Perry ...........11,58 | Robert Beaty ...........67 | |
| Howard Taylor ...........73* | | |

| Public Schs..Principal | Grd | Prgm | Enr/#Cls | SN |
|---|---|---|---|---|
| Cheatham Elem Sch<br>1500 W Main St, Clarksville 75426<br>Marianne Whitehouse | PK-5 | T | 281<br>35 | 93% 903/427-3891<br>Fax 903/427-4118 |
| Clarksville Middle High Sch<br>202 S Donoho St, Clarksville 75426<br>James Johnson | 6-12 | T | 253<br>20 | 87% 903/427-3891<br>Fax 903/427-1344 |

● **Detroit Ind School Dist** PID: 01048172     903/674-6131
110 E Garner St, Detroit 75436     Fax 903/674-2478

**Schools:** 3 \ **Teachers:** 53 \ **Students:** 530 \ **Special Ed Students:** 63
\ **LEP Students:** 3 \ **Ethnic:** African American 8%, Hispanic 3%, Native
American: 1%, Caucasian 87% \ **Exp:** $527 (High) \ **Poverty:** 23% \
**Title I:** $102,035 \ **Open-Close:** 08/21 - 05/27 \ **DTBP:** $353 (High)

| | | |
|---|---|---|
| Kathy Thompson ...........1 | Greg Jones ...........2,11 | |
| Sandra Galley ...........4,79* | Bobby George ...........5 | |

| | | |
|---|---|---|
| Jeff Allensworth ...........6* | Christie Welch ...........36* | |
| Cheryl Marquez ...........57* | Carrie Gray ...........58 | |
| Doug Miller ...........67 | David Williams ...........73* | |

| Public Schs..Principal | Grd | Prgm | Enr/#Cls | SN |
|---|---|---|---|---|
| Detroit Elem Sch<br>110 E Garner St, Detroit 75436<br>Henry Sharp | PK-5 | T | 232<br>14 | 65% 903/674-3137<br>Fax 903/674-2407 |
| Detroit High Sch<br>110 E Garner St, Detroit 75436<br>Jonathan Lloyd | 9-12 | ATV | 168<br>14 | 49% 903/674-2646<br>Fax 903/674-2815 |
| Detroit Middle Sch<br>110 E Garner St, Detroit 75436<br>Amanda Tidwell | 6-8 | T | 104<br>15 | 63% 903/674-2646<br>Fax 903/674-2815 |

● **Rivercrest Ind School Dist** PID: 01048213     903/632-5203
4100 US Highway 271 S, Bogata 75417     Fax 903/632-4691

**Schools:** 3 \ **Teachers:** 62 \ **Students:** 700 \ **Special Ed Students:** 75
\ **LEP Students:** 35 \ **College-Bound:** 77% \ **Ethnic:** African American
5%, Hispanic 17%, Caucasian 78% \ **Exp:** $516 (High) \ **Poverty:** 27% \
**Title I:** $212,431 \ **Open-Close:** 08/28 - 05/27 \ **DTBP:** $363 (High) \ 🇫 🇹

| | | |
|---|---|---|
| Stanley Jessee ...........1 | Tiffany Mabe ...........2,8,11,288,294,296,298 | |
| Lisa Roach ...........4* | Ricky Moore ...........5 | |
| Lance Connot ...........6* | Kelly Tietjan ...........16,82* | |
| Tasha Blagg ...........36,83,85,88* | Latrishia English ...........57 | |
| Joseph Rose ...........67 | Stephen Reese ...........73,295 | |

| Public Schs..Principal | Grd | Prgm | Enr/#Cls | SN |
|---|---|---|---|---|
| Rivercrest Elem Sch<br>4220 US Highway 271 S, Bogata 75417<br>Tonya Gifford | PK-5 | T | 301<br>25 | 63% 903/632-5214<br>Fax 903/632-2424<br>🇫🇹 |
| Rivercrest High Sch<br>4126 US Highway 271 S, Bogata 75417<br>Ronny Alsup | 9-12 | ATV | 219<br>20 | 45% 903/632-5204<br>Fax 903/632-5231 |
| Rivercrest Junior High Sch<br>4100 US Highway 271 S, Bogata 75417<br>Lee Wilson | 6-8 | AT | 160<br>15 | 61% 903/632-5204 |

## REEVES COUNTY

### REEVES PUBLIC SCHOOLS

● **Balmorhea Ind School Dist** PID: 01048251     432/375-2223
608 W 1st St, Balmorhea 79718     Fax 432/375-2511

**Schools:** 1 \ **Teachers:** 20 \ **Students:** 165 \ **Special Ed Students:** 19
\ **LEP Students:** 13 \ **College-Bound:** 20% \ **Ethnic:** African American
1%, Hispanic 85%, Caucasian 14% \ **Exp:** $874 (High) \ **Poverty:** 11% \
**Title I:** $40,752 \ **Open-Close:** 08/24 - 05/28 \ **DTBP:** $339 (High)

| | | |
|---|---|---|
| John Massey ...........1,11 | Rosela Rivera ...........2 | |
| Robert Jones ...........6* | Gary Laramore ...........8,13,74,271,296 | |
| Able Garcia ...........57 | Brandi Massey ...........58,286 | |
| Tommy Dominguez ...........67 | Stacie Laramore ...........69 | |
| Richard Galindo ...........73* | | |

| Public Schs..Principal | Grd | Prgm | Enr/#Cls | SN |
|---|---|---|---|---|
| Balmorhea Sch<br>608 W 1st St, Balmorhea 79718<br>**Gary Laramore** | PK-12 | TV | 165<br>36 | 84% 432/375-2224 |

● **Pecos-Barstow-Toyah Ind SD** PID: 01048304　　　432/447-7201
　1302 S Park St, Pecos 79772　　　　　　　　　　　Fax 432/447-2690

**Schools:** 5 \ **Teachers:** 177 \ **Students:** 2,700 \ **Special Ed Students:** 277
\ **LEP Students:** 365 \ **College-Bound:** 37% \ **Ethnic:** Asian 1%,
African American 1%, Hispanic 91%, Caucasian 8% \ **Exp:** $666 (High)
\ **Poverty:** 22% \ **Title I:** $794,441 \ **Special Education:** $362,000 \
**Open-Close:** 08/17 - 05/27 \ **DTBP:** $350 (High)

| | | | |
|---|---|---|---|
| Brent Jaco ...........1 | | Scott Tipton ...........2,19 | |
| Tim Gilbert ...........3 | | Wayne North ...........3 | |
| Joy Peters ...........4 | | Lee Serrano ...........5 | |
| Chad Olson ...........6,35 | | Simona Acosta ...........7* | |
| Rosie Salcido ...........37* | | Donna Davis ...........58 | |
| Sam Contreras ...........67 | | Cynthia Fields ...........69 | |
| Dr Faith Ann Cheek ...........271 | | | |

| Public Schs..Principal | Grd | Prgm | Enr/#Cls | SN |
|---|---|---|---|---|
| Austin Elem Sch<br>1501 W Normandy, Pecos 79772<br>Leeann McGraw | 1-3 | T | 671<br>32 | 72% 432/447-7541<br>Fax 432/447-4248 |
| Bessie Haynes Elem Sch<br>800 E 11th St, Pecos 79772<br>**Chris Henson** | 4-5 | T | 513<br>28 | 73% 432/447-7497<br>Fax 432/445-1612 |
| Crockett Middle Sch<br>1801 S Missouri St, Pecos 79772<br>Cindy Duke | 6-8 | T | 594<br>18 | 73% 432/447-7461<br>Fax 432/447-4853 |
| Pecos High Sch<br>1201 S Park St, Pecos 79772<br>Latanya Sadler | 9-12 | TV | 696<br>60 | 66% 432/447-7400<br>Fax 432/447-9055 |
| Pecos Kindergarten<br>300 W 10th St, Pecos 79772<br>**Paul Abundez** | PK-K | T | 207<br>17 | 77% 432/447-7596<br>Fax 432/445-4203 |

## REFUGIO COUNTY

## REFUGIO PUBLIC SCHOOLS

● **Austwell Tivoli Ind SD** PID: 01048419　　　　361/286-3212
　207 Redfish St, Tivoli 77990　　　　　　　　　Fax 361/286-3637

**Schools:** 2 \ **Teachers:** 17 \ **Students:** 140 \ **Special Ed Students:** 24
\ **LEP Students:** 3 \ **College-Bound:** 50% \ **Ethnic:** African American
1%, Hispanic 76%, Caucasian 22% \ **Exp:** $542 (High) \ **Poverty:** 36% \
**Title I:** $94,467 \ **Open-Close:** 08/10 - 06/01 \ 🅵 🅴

| | | | |
|---|---|---|---|
| Dolores Vela ...........1 | | Becky Carter ...........4* | |
| Eric Cortez ...........11,57,88 | | Melanie Wright ...........16* | |
| William Lumpkins ...........36,83,752* | | Linda Duenez ...........60* | |
| Carlton Hopper ...........67 | | Armand Gonzalez ...........73,285* | |

| Public Schs..Principal | Grd | Prgm | Enr/#Cls | SN |
|---|---|---|---|---|
| Austwell Tivoli Elem Sch<br>207 Redfish St, Tivoli 77990<br>Eric Cortez | PK-5 | T | 74<br>9 | 49% 361/286-3222 |

| Public Schs..Principal | Grd | Prgm | Enr/#Cls | SN |
|---|---|---|---|---|
| Austwell Tivoli Jr Sr High Sch<br>207 Redfish St, Tivoli 77990<br>John Cortez | 6-12 | T | 66<br>10 | 39% 361/286-3212<br>Fax 361/214-1231<br>🅵 |

● **Refugio Ind School Dist** PID: 01048457　　　361/526-2325
　212 W Vance St, Refugio 78377　　　　　　　Fax 361/526-2326

**Schools:** 3 \ **Teachers:** 63 \ **Students:** 654 \ **Special Ed Students:** 75
\ **LEP Students:** 32 \ **Ethnic:** African American 11%, Hispanic 66%,
Caucasian 23% \ **Exp:** $508 (High) \ **Poverty:** 23% \ **Title I:** $188,809 \
**Open-Close:** 08/24 - 05/27 \ **DTBP:** $365 (High)

| | | | |
|---|---|---|---|
| Melissa Gonzalez ...........1 | | Lisa Herring ...........2,11,57,69,74,270,294,298 | |
| Albert Van Ness ...........3* | | Jason Herring ...........6* | |
| Emilee Cox ...........7,85* | | Anna Garcia ...........16,82* | |
| Lori Homeyer ...........58 | | Andy Rocha ...........67 | |
| Cliff Smith ...........73,295 | | | |

| Public Schs..Principal | Grd | Prgm | Enr/#Cls | SN |
|---|---|---|---|---|
| Refugio Elem Sch<br>601 Crockett St, Refugio 78377<br>Twyla Thomas | PK-6 | T | 353<br>32 | 78% 361/526-4844<br>Fax 361/526-1053<br>🅵 🆃 |
| Refugio High Sch<br>212 W Vance St, Refugio 78377<br>Brandon Duncan | 9-12 | ATV | 210<br>23 | 66% 361/526-2344<br>Fax 361/526-1075 |
| Refugio Junior High Sch<br>212 W Vance St, Refugio 78377<br>Melissa Gonzales | 7-8 | T | 91 | 74% 361/526-2434<br>Fax 361/526-1054 |

● **Woodsboro Ind School Dist** PID: 01048495　　361/543-4518
　408 South Kasten, Woodsboro 78393　　　　　Fax 361/543-4856

**Schools:** 2 \ **Teachers:** 34 \ **Students:** 441 \ **Special Ed Students:** 58
\ **College-Bound:** 80% \ **Ethnic:** African American 4%, Hispanic 54%,
Caucasian 42% \ **Exp:** $1,729 (High) \ **Poverty:** 23% \ **Title I:** $126,872 \
**Open-Close:** 08/19 - 05/28 \ **DTBP:** $387 (High)

| | | | |
|---|---|---|---|
| Janice Sykora ...........1,11 | | Angela Carrasco ...........2 | |
| Mary Alice Ortega ...........4 | | Gary Carpenter ...........6 | |
| Carolyn Baker ...........7* | | Chantel Schulz ...........8,27,31,36,69,83,88,288 | |
| Leslie Garza ...........9,11* | | Tom Diles ...........10,273 | |
| Lori Homeyer ...........58 | | Robert Thomas ...........73 | |
| Casey Newman ...........73,91 | | Christina Grey ...........73,79,295 | |
| Sharon Musich ...........275 | | | |

| Public Schs..Principal | Grd | Prgm | Enr/#Cls | SN |
|---|---|---|---|---|
| Woodsboro Elem Sch<br>105 Myrtle St, Woodsboro 78393<br>Leslie Garza | PK-6 | T | 251<br>22 | 100% 361/543-4518<br>Fax 361/543-5478 |
| Woodsboro Jr Sr High Sch<br>508 Kasten Ave, Woodsboro 78393<br>**Dr David Segers** | 7-12 | ATV | 190<br>18 | 100% 361/543-4622<br>Fax 361/543-5140 |

| | | | | | | | | |
|---|---|---|---|---|---|---|---|
| 1 | Superintendent | 8 | Curric/Instruct K-12 | 19 | Chief Financial Officer | 29 | Family/Consumer Science |
| 2 | Bus/Finance/Purchasing | 9 | Curric/Instruct Elem | 20 | Art K-12 | 30 | Adult Education |
| 3 | Buildings And Grounds | 10 | Curric/Instruct Sec | 21 | Art Elem | 31 | Career/Sch-to-Work K-12 |
| 4 | Food Service | 11 | Federal Program | 22 | Art Sec | 32 | Career/Sch-to-Work Elem |
| 5 | Transportation | 12 | Title I | 23 | Music K-12 | 33 | Career/Sch-to-Work Sec |
| 6 | Athletic | 13 | Title V | 24 | Music Elem | 34 | Early Childhood Ed |
| 7 | Health Services | 14 | Asst Superintendent | 25 | Music Sec | 35 | Health/Phys Education |
| | | 15 | Instructional Media Svcs | 26 | Business Education | 36 | Guidance Services K-12 |
| | | 16 | Chief Operations Officer | 27 | Career & Tech Ed | 37 | Guidance Services Elem |
| | | 17 | Chief Academic Officer | 28 | Technology Education | 38 | Guidance Services Sec |

| | | | | | | | |
|---|---|---|---|---|---|---|
| 39 | Social Studies K-12 | 49 | English/Lang Arts Elem | 59 | Special Education Elem | 69 | Academic Assessment |
| 40 | Social Studies Elem | 50 | English/Lang Arts Sec | 60 | Special Education Sec | 70 | Research/Development |
| 41 | Social Studies Sec | 51 | Reading K-12 | 61 | Foreign/World Lang K-12 | 71 | Public Information |
| 42 | Science K-12 | 52 | Reading Elem | 62 | Foreign/World Lang Elem | 72 | Summer School |
| 43 | Science Elem | 53 | Reading Sec | 63 | Foreign/World Lang Sec | 73 | Instructional Tech |
| 44 | Science Sec | 54 | Remedial Reading K-12 | 64 | Religious Education K-12 | 74 | Inservice Training |
| 45 | Math K-12 | 55 | Remedial Reading Elem | 65 | Religious Education Elem | 75 | Marketing/Distributive |
| 46 | Math Elem | 56 | Remedial Reading Sec | 66 | Religious Education Sec | 76 | Info Systems |
| 47 | Math Sec | 57 | Bilingual/ELL | 67 | School Board President | 77 | Psychological Assess |
| 48 | English/Lang Arts K-12 | 58 | Special Education K-12 | 68 | Teacher Personnel | 78 | Affirmative Action |

## ROBERTS COUNTY

### ROBERTS PUBLIC SCHOOLS

● **Miami Ind School Dist** PID: 01048536      806/868-3971
800 Warrior Way, Miami 79059      Fax 806/868-3171

**Schools:** 1 \ **Teachers:** 22 \ **Students:** 190 \ **Special Ed Students:** 16
\ **LEP Students:** 3 \ **College-Bound:** 80% \ **Ethnic:** Hispanic 14%,
Caucasian 85% \ **Exp:** $749 (High) \ **Poverty:** 10% \ **Title I:** $14,733 \
**Open-Close:** 08/20 - 05/26 \ **DTBP:** $302 (High) \ [f] [t]

| | | | |
|---|---|---|---|
| Donna Hale | 1,11 | Teresa Manor | 2 |
| Ron Carr | 3,5 | Joanne Ginn | 7 |
| Tommy Tritz | 12,88 | Dann Gonzales | 16 |
| Tara Royal | 16,73,295 | Shelly Brooks | 57 |
| Tealer Wilkes | 58* | Logan Hudson | 67 |
| Karen Alston | 275 | | |

| Public Schs..Principal | Grd | Prgm | Enr/#Cls | SN | |
|---|---|---|---|---|---|
| Miami Sch | PK-12 | TV | 190 | 29% | 806/868-3971 |
| 800 Warrior Way, Miami 79059 | | | 20 | | |
| **Tommy Tritz** | | | | | |

## ROBERTSON COUNTY

### ROBERTSON PUBLIC SCHOOLS

● **Bremond Ind School Dist** PID: 01048550      254/746-7145
601 W Collins St, Bremond 76629      Fax 254/746-7726

**Schools:** 3 \ **Teachers:** 40 \ **Students:** 500 \ **Special Ed Students:** 49 \
**LEP Students:** 16 \ **Ethnic:** Asian 1%, African American 14%, Hispanic 14%,
Caucasian 71% \ **Exp:** $293 (Med) \ **Poverty:** 20% \ **Title I:** $118,273 \
**Open-Close:** 08/19 - 05/21 \ **DTBP:** $350 (High)

| | | | |
|---|---|---|---|
| Daryl Stuard | 1 | Rachel Bell | 2 |
| Victor Boudreaux | 3 | Margaret Smith | 4 |
| Kenney Growlaski | 5,10,83,88 | Lynn Pruett | 7* |
| Shelli McNutt | 9 | Rose Kujawa | 16* |
| Theresa Martin | 27 | John Burnett | 57,271* |
| Randy Yanowski | 67 | Lynn Drews | 69,270 |
| Josh Hymer | 73,76* | Bev Swick | 286* |

| Public Schs..Principal | Grd | Prgm | Enr/#Cls | SN | |
|---|---|---|---|---|---|
| Bremond Elem Sch | PK-5 | T | 246 | 65% | 254/746-7145 |
| 601 W Collins St, Bremond 76629 | | | 30 | | |
| Shelli McNutt | | | | | [f] [t] |
| Bremond High Sch | 9-12 | T | 133 | 53% | 254/746-7061 |
| 601 W Collins St, Bremond 76629 | | | | | |
| Dr Kenneth Groholski | | | | | |
| Bremond Middle Sch | 6-8 | T | 108 | 53% | 254/746-5022 |
| 601 W Collins St, Bremond 76629 | | | 11 | | |
| John Burnett | | | | | |

● **Calvert Ind School Dist** PID: 01048586      979/364-2824
310 Hickory St, Calvert 77837      Fax 979/364-2468

**Schools:** 1 \ **Teachers:** 16 \ **Students:** 166 \ **Special Ed Students:** 23
\ **LEP Students:** 3 \ **Ethnic:** African American 80%, Hispanic 16%,
Caucasian 4% \ **Exp:** $471 (High) \ **Poverty:** 46% \ **Title I:** $221,258 \
**Open-Close:** 08/21 - 06/01 \ **DTBP:** $350 (High) \ [t]

| | | | |
|---|---|---|---|
| Dr Thyrun Hurst | 1 | James Whitaker | 67 |
| Daniel Arnold | 73* | Maxie Morgan | 84 |

| Public Schs..Principal | Grd | Prgm | Enr/#Cls | SN | |
|---|---|---|---|---|---|
| Calvert Sch | PK-12 | GTV | 166 | 94% | 979/364-2845 |
| 310 Hickory St, Calvert 77837 | | | 9 | | Fax 979/364-2043 |
| Dr Lori Schneider | | | | | |

● **Franklin Ind School Dist** PID: 01048615      979/828-7000
1216 FM 1644, Franklin 77856      Fax 979/828-1910

**Schools:** 3 \ **Teachers:** 105 \ **Students:** 1,100 \ **Special Ed Students:** 145
\ **LEP Students:** 31 \ **Ethnic:** Asian 1%, African American 7%, Hispanic 18%,
Caucasian 73% \ **Exp:** $322 (High) \ **Poverty:** 14% \ **Title I:** $181,422 \
**Open-Close:** 08/19 - 05/28 \ **DTBP:** $350 (High)

| | | | |
|---|---|---|---|
| Bret Lowry | 1 | Michelle Mathews | 2 |
| Harold Rowan | 3,5 | Bridgette Young | 4 |
| Stacy Ely | 8,11,74,294,296* | Susan Nelson | 16,28,73,297 |
| Deanna May | 57 | Leslee Falco | 58 |
| Scott Phillips | 67 | Martha Barnett | 69 |
| Becky Permann | 295* | | |

| Public Schs..Principal | Grd | Prgm | Enr/#Cls | SN | |
|---|---|---|---|---|---|
| Franklin High Sch | 9-12 | AV | 340 | 34% | 979/828-7100 |
| 1252 FM 1644, Franklin 77856 | | | 50 | | Fax 979/828-3364 |
| Russell White | | | | | |
| Franklin Middle Sch | 5-8 | ATV | 396 | 40% | 979/828-7200 |
| 1098 W Decherd St, Franklin 77856 | | | 20 | | Fax 979/828-7207 |
| Susan Nelson | | | | | [f] [t] |
| Roland Reynolds Elem Sch | PK-4 | T | 433 | 42% | 979/828-7300 |
| 317 N Owensville, Franklin 77856 | | | 26 | | Fax 979/828-5048 |
| Christie Smitherman | | | | | |

● **Hearne Ind School Dist** PID: 01048641      979/279-3200
900 Wheelock St, Hearne 77859      Fax 979/279-3631

**Schools:** 3 \ **Teachers:** 68 \ **Students:** 766 \ **Special Ed Students:** 142
\ **LEP Students:** 141 \ **College-Bound:** 35% \ **Ethnic:** African American
48%, Hispanic 44%, Caucasian 9% \ **Exp:** $647 (High) \ **Poverty:** 28% \
**Title I:** $536,018 \ **Open-Close:** 08/19 - 05/28 \ **DTBP:** $350 (High) \ [f] [t]

| | | | |
|---|---|---|---|
| Dr Adrian Johnson | 1 | Erica Duplechain | 2 |
| Joe Taylor | 3 | Rhonda Cloud | 4 |
| Ricky Sargent | 6 | Jeremy Gaston | 16,73,82,295* |
| Leslee Falco | 58 | Maryjane Rameriz | 67 |
| Jay Davis | 79 | | |

| Public Schs..Principal | Grd | Prgm | Enr/#Cls | SN | |
|---|---|---|---|---|---|
| Hearne Elem Sch | PK-6 | T | 412 | 98% | 979/279-3341 |
| 1210 Hackberry St, Hearne 77859 | | | 42 | | Fax 979/279-8011 |
| Stephanie Heinchon | | | | | |
| Hearne High Sch | 9-12 | ATV | 231 | 91% | 979/279-2332 |
| 1201 W Brown St, Hearne 77859 | | | 25 | | Fax 979/279-8006 |
| Bruce Hill | | | | | |
| Hearne Junior High Sch | 7-8 | T | 123 | 100% | 979/279-2449 |
| 1201B W Brown St, Hearne 77859 | | | 20 | | Fax 979/279-8033 |
| Lucinda McDaniel | | | | | [f] [t] |

## ROCKWALL COUNTY

### ROCKWALL PUBLIC SCHOOLS

• **Rockwall Ind School Dist** PID: 01048718          972/771-0605
1050 Williams St, Rockwall 75087                     Fax 972/771-2637

**Schools:** 22 \ **Teachers:** 1,014 \ **Students:** 17,078 \
**Special Ed Students:** 1,676 \ **LEP Students:** 1,109 \ **College-Bound:** 80%
\ **Ethnic:** Asian 3%, African American 9%, Hispanic 23%, Native American:
1%, Caucasian 64% \ **Exp:** $253 (Med) \ **Poverty:** 6% \ **Title I:** $1,098,085 \
**Special Education:** $2,000,000 \ **Open-Close:** 08/26 - 06/03 \ **DTBP:** $194
(High) \ ◉ ◉

| | | | |
|---|---|---|---|
| Dr John Villarreal | 1 | David Carter | 2,19 |
| Jamie Tomalin | 2 | Will Salee | 3 |
| Kim Pugsley | 4 | Terry Penn | 5 |
| Russ Reeves | 6 | Adrienne Hergert | 7,35* |
| Dr Amy Ellis | 8 | Dr Mary Johnston | 9,18 |
| Sonya Carpenter | 11,34,88,298 | Luann Hughes | 16,73,76,82,295 |
| Ben Sumrak | 20,23 | Alison Belliveau | 27,285 |
| Bart Walters | 27,31 | Jennifer Penton | 40,280 |
| Dr Matthew Redman | 41 | Katie Braden | 43 |
| Joey Belgard | 44 | Megan Humphrey | 46 |
| Jennifer Johnson | 47 | Doug Frank | 57 |
| Patricia Martinez | 57 | Melissa Melton | 58 |
| Jon Bailey | 67 | Joey Byrum | 68 |
| Mark Speck | 68,74,79 | Linda Reid | 69,77,294 |
| Renae Murphy | 71 | Dr Kelvin Stroy | 79 |
| Jennifer Leal | 81 | Missy Wall | 90 |
| Marsha Welsh | 280 | | |

| Public Schs..Principal | Grd | Prgm | Enr/#Cls | SN |
|---|---|---|---|---|
| Amanda Rochell Elem Sch<br>899 Rochell Ct, Rockwall 75032<br>Kelli Crossland | PK-6 | T | 561<br>30 | 65% 972/771-2112<br>Fax 972/772-0829 |
| Amy Parks-Heath Elem Sch<br>330 Laurence Dr, Heath 75032<br>Lindy Lewis | PK-6 | | 445<br>26 | 3% 972/772-4300<br>Fax 972/772-2098 |
| Billie Stevenson Elem Sch<br>636 Stevenson Dr, Rockwall 75087<br>Mike Pitcher | PK-6 | | 643 | 15% 469/698-7474 |
| Celia Hays Elem Sch<br>1880 Tannerson Dr, Rockwall 75087<br>Tammi Schmitt | PK-6 | | 856<br>19 | 11% 469/698-2800<br>Fax 469/698-2809 ◉◉ |
| Doris Cullins-Lake Pointe ES<br>5701 Scenic Dr, Rowlett 75088<br>Dr Mary Pugh | PK-6 | T | 633<br>45 | 45% 972/412-3070<br>Fax 972/475-7920 |
| Dorothy Smith Pullen Elem Sch<br>6492 FM 3097, Rockwall 75032<br>Michael Stuart | K-6 | | 558<br>36 | 20% 972/772-1177<br>Fax 972/772-2424 |
| Dorris Jones Elem Sch<br>2051 Trail Gln, Rockwall 75032<br>Teresa Twedell | PK-6 | T | 624<br>44 | 59% 972/772-1070<br>Fax 972/772-5789 ◉◉ |
| Dr Gene Burton C & C Academy<br>2301 John King Blvd, Rockwall 75032<br>Alison Belliveau | Voc | | 800 | 469/698-0660 |
| Grace Hartman Elem Sch<br>1325 Petaluma Dr, Rockwall 75087<br>Rebecca Reidling | PK-6 | | 570 | 9% 972/772-2080<br>Fax 972/772-5794 |

| School | Grd | Prgm | Enr/#Cls | SN |
|---|---|---|---|---|
| Herman E Utley Middle Sch<br>1201 T L Townsend Dr, Rockwall 75087<br>Dane Steinberger | 7-8 | | 896 | 28% 972/771-5281<br>Fax 972/772-1164 |
| Howard Dobbs Elem Sch<br>901 E Interurban St, Rockwall 75087<br>**Laura Mejia** | PK-6 | T | 569<br>33 | 58% 972/771-5232<br>Fax 972/772-1145 ◉ |
| J W Williams Middle Sch<br>625 E FM 552, Rockwall 75087<br>David Blake | 7-8 | | 824<br>56 | 18% 972/771-8313<br>Fax 972/772-2033 |
| Linda Lyon Elem Sch<br>2186 Trophy Dr, Heath 75126<br>Megan Gist | PK-6 | | 439 | 20% 214/771-4910 |
| Maurine Cain Middle Sch<br>6620 FM 3097, Rockwall 75032<br>Derrice Randle | 7-8 | | 996<br>60 | 27% 972/772-1170<br>Fax 972/772-2414 ◉◉ |
| Nebbie Williams Elem Sch<br>350 Dalton Rd, Rockwall 75087<br>Paige White | PK-6 | | 438<br>22 | 12% 972/772-0502<br>Fax 972/772-2046 ◉◉ |
| Ouida Springer Elem Sch<br>3025 Limestone Hill Ln, Rockwall 75032<br>Sara Reeves | PK-6 | T | 713 | 32% 972/772-7160<br>Fax 972/772-2464 |
| Rockwall High Sch<br>901 W Yellowjacket Ln, Rockwall 75087<br>Kevin Samples | 9-12 | V | 2,684<br>65 | 17% 972/771-7339<br>Fax 972/772-2099 ◉◉ |
| ⒶRockwall Quest Academy<br>1050 Williams St, Rockwall 75087<br>**Christina Bradford** | 7-12 | GTV | 59<br>7 | 41% 972/772-2077<br>Fax 972/772-1055 |
| Rockwall-Heath High Sch<br>801 Laurence Dr, Heath 75032<br>Todd Bradford | 9-12 | | 1,208 | 25% 972/772-2474<br>Fax 469/698-2608 ◉◉ |
| Sharon Shannon Elem Sch<br>3130 Fontana Blvd, Rockwall 75032<br>Steven Pesek | K-6 | | 738 | 25% 469/698-2900<br>Fax 469/698-2909 |
| Sherry & Paul Hamm Elem Sch<br>2911 Greenway Dr, Rockwall 75087<br>**Megan Smith** | K-6 | | 500 | 469/698-2854 |
| Virginia Reinhardt Elem Sch<br>615 Highland Dr, Rockwall 75087<br>Amanda Payne | K-6 | | 572<br>19 | 25% 972/771-5247<br>Fax 972/772-2097 ◉ |

• **Royse City Ind School Dist** PID: 01048770          972/636-2413
810 E Old Greenville Rd, Royse City 75189            Fax 972/635-7037

**Schools:** 9 \ **Teachers:** 403 \ **Students:** 6,300 \ **Special Ed Students:** 649
\ **LEP Students:** 602 \ **College-Bound:** 45% \ **Ethnic:** Asian 1%,
African American 8%, Hispanic 34%, Caucasian 57% \ **Exp:** $595 (High)
\ **Poverty:** 7% \ **Title I:** $425,281 \ **Special Education:** $812,000 \
**Open-Close:** 08/13 - 05/21 \ **DTBP:** $161 (High)

| | | | |
|---|---|---|---|
| Kevin Worthy | 1 | Angel McCrary | 2 |
| Byron Bryant | 2,19 | Jim Lawson | 3 |
| Cohnie Harris | 4 | Tammy Loveless | 5 |
| David Petroff | 6 | Deborah Summers | 7* |
| Julia Robinson | 8 | Kenny Hudson | 11,15,296 |
| Jeff Webb | 15,68,273 | Zach Snow | 27,73,285,286 |
| Linda Taylor | 38 | Dana Grieb | 39,50 |
| Valerie James | 46 | Kristen Weichel | 49 |
| Shannon Hayes | 58,79* | Scott Muckensturm | 67 |
| Kathy Milton | 69,294 | Adi Bryant | 71,298 |
| Zach Allen | 73,98,295 | Jere Craighead | 88,275* |
| Lloyd Blaine | 91 | Mike Medlin | 274 |

| Public Schs..Principal | Grd | Prgm | Enr/#Cls | SN |
|---|---|---|---|---|
| Anita Scott Elem Sch<br>1401 Erby Campbell Blvd, Royse City 75189<br>Teresa Atkins | PK-4 | T | 492 | 52% 972/636-3300<br>Fax 972/635-6503 |

| | | | | | | |
|---|---|---|---|---|---|
| 1 | Superintendent | 8 | Curric/Instruct K-12 | 19 | Chief Financial Officer |
| 2 | Bus/Finance/Purchasing | 9 | Curric/Instruct Elem | 20 | Art K-12 |
| 3 | Buildings And Grounds | 10 | Curric/Instruct Sec | 21 | Art Elem |
| 4 | Food Service | 11 | Federal Program | 22 | Art Sec |
| 5 | Transportation | 12 | Title I | 23 | Music K-12 |
| 6 | Athletic | 13 | Title V | 24 | Music Elem |
| 7 | Health Services | 15 | Asst Superintendent | 25 | Music Sec |
| | | 16 | Instructional Media Svcs | 26 | Business Education |
| | | 17 | Chief Operations Officer | 27 | Career & Tech Ed |
| | | 18 | Chief Academic Officer | 28 | Technology Education |

| | | | | | | |
|---|---|---|---|---|---|
| 29 | Family/Consumer Science | 39 | Social Studies K-12 | 49 | English/Lang Arts Elem |
| 30 | Adult Education | 40 | Social Studies Elem | 50 | English/Lang Arts Sec |
| 31 | Career/Sch-to-Work K-12 | 41 | Social Studies Sec | 51 | Reading K-12 |
| 32 | Career/Sch-to-Work Elem | 42 | Science K-12 | 52 | Reading Elem |
| 33 | Career/Sch-to-Work Sec | 43 | Science Elem | 53 | Reading Sec |
| 34 | Early Childhood Ed | 44 | Science Sec | 54 | Remedial Reading K-12 |
| 35 | Health/Phys Education | 45 | Math K-12 | 55 | Remedial Reading Elem |
| 36 | Guidance Services K-12 | 46 | Math Elem | 56 | Remedial Reading Sec |
| 37 | Guidance Services Elem | 47 | Math Sec | 57 | Bilingual/ELL |
| 38 | Guidance Services Sec | 48 | English/Lang Arts K-12 | 58 | Special Education K-12 |

| | | | |
|---|---|---|---|
| 59 | Special Education Elem | 69 | Academic Assessment |
| 60 | Special Education Sec | 70 | Research/Development |
| 61 | Foreign/World Lang K-12 | 71 | Public Information |
| 62 | Foreign/World Lang Elem | 72 | Summer School |
| 63 | Foreign/World Lang Sec | 73 | Instructional Tech |
| 64 | Religious Education K-12 | 74 | Inservice Training |
| 65 | Religious Education Elem | 75 | Marketing/Distributive |
| 66 | Religious Education Sec | 76 | Info Systems |
| 67 | School Board President | 77 | Psychological Assess |
| 68 | Teacher Personnel | 78 | Affirmative Action |

Ⓐ Browning Learning Center    9-12    16    972/635-5077
810 E Old Greenville Rd, Royse City 75189    4    Fax 972/635-2504
Jere Craighead

Davis Elem Sch    PK-4   T    573    45% 972/636-9549
1500 FM 1777, Royse City 75189    28    Fax 972/635-2535
Cynthia Pense

Harry H Herndon Interm Sch    5-6   T    549    42% 469/721-8101
300 Blackland Rd, Fate 75132    Fax 469/874-2186
Shanna Brown    🅵🅣

Miss May Vernon Elem Sch    PK-4   T    732    38% 972/635-5006
100 Miss May Drive, Fate 75132    Fax 972/722-8577
Brittany Lancaster

Royse City High Sch    9-12   V    1,752    34% 972/636-9991
700 S FM 2642, Royse City 75189    50    Fax 972/635-2906
Dr Sean Walker \ **Jere Craighead**

Royse City Middle Sch    7-8    932    37% 972/636-9544
1310 E Highway 66, Royse City 75189    40    Fax 972/635-5093
Angelee Morales    🅵

Ruth Cherry Interm Sch    5-6    489    39% 972/636-3301
1400 FM 1777, Royse City 75189    16    Fax 972/635-5008
Kara Onken

W R Fort Elem Sch    PK-4   T    569    39% 972/636-3304
2801 Epps Rd, Royse City 75189    Fax 469/874-4050
Wendy Prater

## ROCKWALL PRIVATE SCHOOLS

| Private Schs..Principal | Grd | Prgm | Enr/#Cls | SN |
|---|---|---|---|---|
| Heritage Christian Academy<br>1408 S Goliad St, Rockwall 75087<br>Dr Leslie Minter \ Jeff Bassett | K-12 | | 352<br>30 | 972/772-3003<br>Fax 972/772-3770 |
| The Fulton Sch<br>1626 Smirl Dr, Heath 75032<br>Tracy Ross | PK-3 | | 50<br>🅵 | 972/772-4445 |

## RUNNELS COUNTY

## RUNNELS PUBLIC SCHOOLS

● **Ballinger Ind School Dist** PID: 01048809    325/365-3588
802 Conda Ave, Ballinger 76821    Fax 325/365-5920

**Schools:** 3 \ **Teachers:** 78 \ **Students:** 798 \ **Special Ed Students:** 88 \ **LEP Students:** 12 \ **College-Bound:** 85% \ **Ethnic:** Asian 1%, African American 1%, Hispanic 48%, Caucasian 50% \ **Exp:** $575 (High) \ **Poverty:** 21% \ **Title I:** $268,660 \ **Open-Close:** 08/19 - 05/20 \ **DTBP:** $348 (High)

| | | | |
|---|---|---|---|
| Jeff Butts ...........1 | Liz Garza ...........2 |
| Tony Harral ...........3,5 | Caroline Toliver ...........8,11,286,288,296,298 |
| Tessa Knickerbocker ...........38 | Brian Arrott ...........58* |
| Manuel Galvan ...........67 | Billy Mobley ...........73 |

| Public Schs..Principal | Grd | Prgm | Enr/#Cls | SN |
|---|---|---|---|---|
| Ballinger Elem Sch<br>800 Broad Ave, Ballinger 76821<br>Jamie Dudley | PK-5 | T | 371<br>26 | 61% 325/365-3527<br>Fax 325/365-2943 |

Ballinger High Sch    9-12   ATV   203    45% 325/365-3547
2107 N Broadway St, Ballinger 76821    40    Fax 325/365-5366
Ryan Knickerbocker

Ballinger Junior High Sch    6-8   T    224    63% 325/365-3537
1006 Conda Ave, Ballinger 76821    20    Fax 325/365-3102
Leslie Griffis

● **Miles Ind School Dist** PID: 01048847    325/468-2861
1001 Robinson St, Miles 76861    Fax 325/468-2179

**Schools:** 1 \ **Teachers:** 42 \ **Students:** 480 \ **Special Ed Students:** 27 \ **LEP Students:** 32 \ **College-Bound:** 53% \ **Ethnic:** African American 1%, Hispanic 38%, Caucasian 61% \ **Exp:** $713 (High) \ **Poverty:** 16% \ **Title I:** $60,475 \ **Special Education:** $9,000 \ **Open-Close:** 08/19 - 05/26 \ **DTBP:** $350 (High)

| | | | |
|---|---|---|---|
| Clint Askins ...........1 | Debra Blackwell ...........2 |
| Bud Hunt ...........3,5 | Jason Wilhelm ...........6 |
| Curt McNelly ...........9 | Lela Taubert ...........10,36,88 |
| Joan McCleery ...........11,45,57,83,270,271,273 | Sarah Crouch ...........12,51* |
| Paige Ernhart ...........31* | Mark Sklenarik ...........67 |
| Janna Rouse ...........73* | |

| Public Schs..Principal | Grd | Prgm | Enr/#Cls | SN |
|---|---|---|---|---|
| Miles Sch<br>1001 Robinson St, Miles 76861<br>Curt McKneely \ **Lela Taubert** | PK-12 | V | 480 | 30% 325/468-2861 |

● **Olfen Ind School Dist** PID: 01048873    325/442-4301
1122 PR 2562, Rowena 76875    Fax 325/442-2133

**Schools:** 1 \ **Teachers:** 10 \ **Students:** 205 \ **Special Ed Students:** 10 \ **LEP Students:** 3 \ **College-Bound:** 100% \ **Ethnic:** Asian 2%, African American 3%, Hispanic 48%, Caucasian 48% \ **Exp:** $1,797 (High) \ **Poverty:** 13% \ **Open-Close:** 08/10 - 05/18 \ **DTBP:** $300 (High)

| | | | |
|---|---|---|---|
| Gabe Zamora ...........1,11,57 | Brenda Blake ...........2 |
| Debbie Fisher ...........4 | Travis Tennison ...........6* |
| Lizette Pacely ...........8 | Marisa Dannheim ...........58 |
| Tracy Grimes ...........67 | Russell Hoelscher ...........73,286,295* |

| Public Schs..Principal | Grd | Prgm | Enr/#Cls | SN |
|---|---|---|---|---|
| Olfen Sch<br>1122 Private Road 2562, Rowena 76875<br>Lizette Paceley | K-12 | T | 205<br>8 | 74% 325/442-4301 |

● **Winters Ind School Dist** PID: 01048914    325/754-5574
603 N Heights St, Winters 79567    Fax 325/754-5374

**Schools:** 3 \ **Teachers:** 52 \ **Students:** 525 \ **Special Ed Students:** 65 \ **LEP Students:** 20 \ **Ethnic:** African American 1%, Hispanic 60%, Caucasian 38% \ **Exp:** $990 (High) \ **Poverty:** 26% \ **Title I:** $210,233 \ **Special Education:** $108,000 \ **Open-Close:** 08/21 - 05/21 \ **DTBP:** $339 (High) \ 🅵

| | | | |
|---|---|---|---|
| **Sean Leamon** ...........1 | Rhonda Neal ...........2,11 |
| Gordon Fenwick ...........3 | June Watson ...........4 |
| Mark Bridgman ...........5 | Mike Morath ...........7 |
| Kari Callcoat ...........58 | Dan Killough ...........67 |
| Michelle Alexander ...........68 | Matthew Howard ...........73,295 |

| Public Schs..Principal | Grd | Prgm | Enr/#Cls | SN |
|---|---|---|---|---|
| Winters Elem Sch<br>702 N Heights St, Winters 79567<br>Edward Garcia | PK-5 | T | 228<br>21 | 68% 325/754-5577<br>Fax 325/754-4686 |

| | | | | | |
|---|---|---|---|---|---|
| Winters High Sch<br>205 Jones St, Winters 79567<br>Randy Gartman | 9-12 | TV | 175<br>17 | 56% | 325/754-5516<br>Fax 325/754-5085 📵 |
| Winters Junior High Sch<br>705 Rogers Rd, Winters 79567<br>Terry Payne | 6-8 | T | 122<br>11 | 78% | 325/754-5518<br>Fax 325/754-5085 |

## RUSK COUNTY

## RUSK PUBLIC SCHOOLS

● **Carlisle Ind School Dist** PID: 01048940          903/861-3801
8960 FM 13 W, Henderson 75654                    Fax 903/861-3932

---

**Schools:** 1 \ **Teachers:** 55 \ **Students:** 587 \ **Special Ed Students:** 56 \
**LEP Students:** 184 \ **College-Bound:** 61% \ **Ethnic:** African American 4%,
Hispanic 52%, Native American: 1%, Caucasian 43% \ **Exp:** $641 (High) \
**Poverty:** 17% \ **Title I:** $124,227 \ **Open-Close:** 08/14 - 05/21 \ **DTBP:** $527
(High)

---

| | | |
|---|---|---|
| Michael Payne | 1,11,83 | Marcy Honzell ..........2 |
| Andy Hodkinson | 3,5* | Margaret Wilson ..........4* |
| Rocky Baker | 6* | Connie Barton ..........7* |
| Jennifer Hale | 8,31,69,270* | Andrea Loyola ..........16* |
| Lisha Smith | 31,36* | Stephanie Rowan ..........57,274* |
| Drew Bennett | 58* | Kevin Curvo ..........67 |
| Brian Jennings | 73,74,76,295* | |

| Public Schs..Principal | Grd | Prgm | Enr/#Cls | SN | |
|---|---|---|---|---|---|
| Carlisle Sch<br>8960 FM 13 W, Henderson 75654<br>Stephanie Rowan \ Norman Carter \ Sarah Baker | PK-12 | T | 587<br>150 | 74% | 903/861-3801<br>Fax 903/861-0100 |

● **Henderson Ind School Dist** PID: 01048976          903/655-5000
300 Crosby Dr, Henderson 75652                    Fax 903/657-9271

---

**Schools:** 6 \ **Teachers:** 234 \ **Students:** 3,400 \ **Special Ed Students:** 356
\ **LEP Students:** 436 \ **College-Bound:** 54% \ **Ethnic:** Asian 1%,
African American 19%, Hispanic 32%, Caucasian 47% \ **Exp:** $465 (High)
\ **Poverty:** 18% \ **Title I:** $784,036 \ **Special Education:** $915,000 \
**Open-Close:** 08/05 - 05/27 \ **DTBP:** $193 (High) \ 📘

---

| | | |
|---|---|---|
| Dr Thurston Lamb | 1 | Christen Byrd ..........2 |
| Shannon Bennett | 3,91 | Tonya Davis ..........4 |
| Kyle Gatlin | 5 | Phil Castles ..........6,35 |
| Leandrea Cally | 7,85 | Stephanie Boonau 8,11,57,88,286,288,296,298 |
| Terry Everett | 8,39,42,48,51,54,61 | Craig Haney ..........23 |
| Lisa McReery | 27,31 | Mindy Rucker ..........45,72,277 |
| Eileen Johnson | 58,77 | Drew Butler ..........67 |
| Amanda Wallace | 68,79 | David Shenault ..........71,97 |
| Kevin Bryan | 73,98,295 | Kim Free ..........76 |
| Chad Bradley | 83* | Gray Young ..........295 |

| Public Schs..Principal | Grd | Prgm | Enr/#Cls | SN | |
|---|---|---|---|---|---|
| Henderson High Sch<br>1900 State Highway 64 W, Henderson 75652<br>Terry Everitt | 9-12 | ATV | 913 | 56% | 903/655-5000<br>Fax 903/657-7604 |
| Henderson Middle Sch<br>501 Richardson Dr, Henderson 75654<br>Shannon Dickerson | 6-8 | AT | 828<br>70 | 65% | 903/655-5400<br>Fax 903/657-6499 |

| | | | | | |
|---|---|---|---|---|---|
| Ⓐ Montgomery Achievement Center<br>308 Smith St, Henderson 75654<br>Clay Freeman | 11-12 | | 25 | | 903/655-5552<br>Fax 903/657-3510 |
| Northside Interm Sch<br>800 N Van Buren St, Henderson 75652<br>Dea Henry | 4-5 | T | 516<br>24 | 65% | 903/655-5300<br>Fax 903/657-5238 |
| Wylie Elem Sch<br>1735 US Highway 259 S, Henderson 75654<br>Deidra Sutton | 1-3 | T | 785<br>14 | 70% | 903/655-5200<br>Fax 903/657-5299 |
| Wylie Primary Sch<br>1735 US Highway 259 S, Henderson 75654<br>Angela Dowling | PK-K | T | 228<br>29 | 83% | 903/655-5100<br>Fax 903/655-5199 |

● **Laneville Ind School Dist** PID: 01049061          903/863-5353
7415 FM 1798 W, Laneville 75667                    Fax 903/863-5319

---

**Schools:** 1 \ **Teachers:** 17 \ **Students:** 157 \ **Special Ed Students:** 20 \
**LEP Students:** 18 \ **College-Bound:** 50% \ **Ethnic:** African American 53%,
Hispanic 29%, Native American: 1%, Caucasian 17% \ **Exp:** $559 (High) \
**Poverty:** 17% \ **Title I:** $55,304 \ **Open-Close:** 08/21 - 05/21 \ **DTBP:** $350
(High) \ 📘 📵

---

| | | |
|---|---|---|
| Theresa Shelton | 1,11 | Sandra Upshaw ..........2 |
| Gay Harper | 4 | Tracy Kincade ..........6 |
| Susie Davis | 7,85* | Nathan Templeton .....8,34,74,83,88,271,273* |
| Cynthia Thurmond | 16* | Shirley McDaniel ..........36,58,69,83* |
| Jean Kelly | 50 | Robert Loftis ..........67 |
| Jason Rich | 73,295* | Julia Faye Anderson ..........92,93,270* |
| Susie Owens | 294 | |

| Public Schs..Principal | Grd | Prgm | Enr/#Cls | SN | |
|---|---|---|---|---|---|
| Laneville Sch<br>7415 FM 1798 W, Laneville 75667<br>Joshua Tremont | PK-12 | TV | 157<br>25 | 82% | 903/863-5353<br>Fax 903/863-2736 📵 |

● **Leveretts Chapel Ind Sch Dist** PID: 01049097          903/834-6675
8956 State Highway 42 N, Overton 75684                    Fax 903/834-6602

---

**Schools:** 1 \ **Teachers:** 25 \ **Students:** 240 \ **Special Ed Students:** 25
\ **LEP Students:** 58 \ **College-Bound:** 90% \ **Ethnic:** African American
6%, Hispanic 29%, Caucasian 65% \ **Exp:** $638 (High) \ **Poverty:** 21% \
**Title I:** $53,132 \ **Open-Close:** 08/17 - 05/25 \ **DTBP:** $330 (High)

---

| | | |
|---|---|---|
| Josh Johnson | 1 | Jill Spearman ..........2 |
| Jennifer Gough | 4,73 | Nikki Saxton ..........12 |
| Jimmie Waller | 67 | |

| Public Schs..Principal | Grd | Prgm | Enr/#Cls | SN | |
|---|---|---|---|---|---|
| Leveretts Chapel Sch<br>8956 Highway 42/135 N, Overton 75684<br>Matt Everett \ Nikki Saxton | PK-12 | ATV | 240<br>14 | 94% | 903/834-3181 |

● **Mt Enterprise Ind School Dist** PID: 01049126          903/822-3575
301 NW 3rd St, Mt Enterprise 75681                    Fax 903/822-3633

---

**Schools:** 1 \ **Teachers:** 40 \ **Students:** 398 \ **Special Ed Students:** 48
\ **LEP Students:** 16 \ **College-Bound:** 60% \ **Ethnic:** Asian 1%, African
American 9%, Hispanic 9%, Native American: 1%, Caucasian 81% \ **Exp:** $526
(High) \ **Poverty:** 14% \ **Title I:** $45,584 \ **Open-Close:** 08/19 - 05/21 \
**DTBP:** $380 (High)

---

| | | |
|---|---|---|
| Byron Jordan | 1,11 | Andy Lee ..........2,68,73,76* |
| Jeremy Jenkins | 6 | Dr Chance Mays ..........10* |
| Michelle Lee | 16,270* | Tiffanie Jones ..........36,69,83,88* |
| Kimberly Fryman | 57* | Akiko Jones ..........58 |

Don Rogers .......................................... 67   Andy Lee .................................................. 84

| Public Schs..Principal | Grd | Prgm | Enr/#Cls | SN | |
|---|---|---|---|---|---|
| Mt Enterprise Sch<br>301 NW 3rd St, Mt Enterprise 75681<br>Dr Chance Mays \ Lawren McDermand | PK-12 | ATV | 398<br>24 | 66% | 903/822-3545 |

● **Overton Ind School Dist** PID: 01049152   903/834-6145
111 E McKay St, Overton 75684   Fax 903/834-6755

Schools: 2 \ **Teachers:** 48 \ **Students:** 500 \ **Special Ed Students:** 60 \
**LEP Students:** 5 \ **Ethnic:** Asian 1%, African American 14%, Hispanic 9%,
Native American: 1%, Caucasian 76% \ **Exp:** $633 (High) \ **Poverty:** 21% \
**Title I:** $157,748 \ **Open-Close:** 08/18 - 05/21 \ **DTBP:** $318 (High)

Steven Dubose .................................. 1,11   Matthew Blake ........................................ 2
Jerry Thornton .................................... 3,5   Justin Arnold .......................................... 6*
Wendy Jackson ...................... 8,36,69,85   Nikki Senter ......................................... 12*
Irana Hendrick ...................................... 16   Jeff Hogg ............................................... 27
Akiko Jones ......................................... 58   Shane McCasland ................................. 67
William Mansfield ................................. 73   Courtney Mosley ................................. 275

| Public Schs..Principal | Grd | Prgm | Enr/#Cls | SN | |
|---|---|---|---|---|---|
| Overton Elem Sch<br>501 E Henderson St, Overton 75684<br>Nichole Fenter | PK-5 | T | 236<br>13 | 76% | 903/834-6144<br>Fax 903/834-3913 |
| Overton Secondary Sch<br>501 E Henderson St, Overton 75684<br>**Jeff Hogg** | 6-12 | ATV | 234<br>13 | 59% | 903/834-6143<br>Fax 903/834-3256 |

● **Tatum Ind School Dist** PID: 01049188   903/947-6482
510 Crystal Farms Rd, Tatum 75691   Fax 903/947-3295

Schools: 4 \ **Teachers:** 105 \ **Students:** 1,461 \ **Special Ed Students:** 124 \
**LEP Students:** 195 \ **College-Bound:** 52% \ **Ethnic:** African American 21%,
Hispanic 32%, Native American: 1%, Caucasian 46% \ **Exp:** $342 (High) \
**Poverty:** 21% \ **Title I:** $292,059 \ **Open-Close:** 08/14 - 05/21 \ **DTBP:** $331
(High) \ 🔲 🔲

Dr J Richardson ...................................... 1   Brandon Milam ....................................... 2
Kathy Goodwin ...................................... 4*   Jason Holman ......................................... 6
Drenon Fite ..................................... 15,68   Wes Boyd ........................... 16,73,84,295
Matt Crawford ...................................... 67   Jennifer Malone .................................... 69

| Public Schs..Principal | Grd | Prgm | Enr/#Cls | SN | |
|---|---|---|---|---|---|
| Tatum Elem Sch<br>1525 N Hill St, Tatum 75691<br>**Jennifer Malone** | 3-5 | T | 314<br>14 | 62% | 903/947-0352<br>Fax 903/947-3299 |
| Tatum High Sch<br>600 Crystal Farms Rd, Tatum 75691<br>**Matthew Quick** | 9-12 | TV | 472<br>45 | 53% | 903/947-6482<br>Fax 903/765-7816 |
| Tatum Middle Sch<br>410 N Hill St, Tatum 75691<br>Kin Bryan | 6-8 | TV | 369<br>19<br>🔲 | 55% | 903/947-6482<br>Fax 903/765-7782 |
| Tatum Primary Sch<br>1200 N Hill St, Tatum 75691<br>Tamara Fite | PK-2 | T | 306<br>20 | 69% | 903/947-6485<br>Fax 903/765-7376 |

● **West Rusk Co Cons Ind Sch Dist** PID: 01049217   903/392-7850
10705 S Main St, New London 75682   Fax 903/392-7866

Schools: 4 \ **Teachers:** 82 \ **Students:** 980 \ **Special Ed Students:** 121 \
**LEP Students:** 126 \ **College-Bound:** 53% \ **Ethnic:** African American 14%,
Hispanic 28%, Native American: 2%, Caucasian 57% \ **Exp:** $375 (High) \
**Poverty:** 22% \ **Title I:** $301,609 \ **Open-Close:** 08/24 - 05/28 \ **DTBP:** $350
(High) \ 🔲

Lawrence Coleman .................................. 1   Belinda Walker ....................................... 2
James Masinger .................................... 3   Steve Alexander .................................... 4
Bruce Mason ......................................... 5   Nick Harrison ........................................ 6
Megan Wriggle ..................................... 7*   Leah Bobbitt ............................... 8,15,288
Gwen Gilliam ............. 11,16,69,271,296,298   Judy Chapman ...................................... 57*
Sandra Smith ...................................... 67   Cody Walker ................................... 73,295
Vivian Sharp ........................................ 73   Paul Thompson ..................................... 91

| Public Schs..Principal | Grd | Prgm | Enr/#Cls | SN | |
|---|---|---|---|---|---|
| West Rusk Elem Sch<br>10705 S Main St, New London 75682<br>Carlette Mills | PK-2 | T | 205<br>23 | 73% | 903/392-7857 |
| West Rusk High Sch<br>10705 S Main, New London 75682<br>Jake Jackson | 9-12 | TV | 347<br>40 | 69% | 903/392-7857 |
| West Rusk Intermediate Sch<br>10705 S Main, New London 75682<br>Dulce Savala \ Burt Langley | 3-5 | T | 226 | 71% | 903/392-7856 |
| West Rusk Junior High Sch<br>10705 S Main, New London 75682<br>Brian Keith | 6-8 | T | 187<br>15 | 72% | 903/392-7855 |

## RUSK PRIVATE SCHOOLS

| Private Schs..Principal | Grd | Prgm | Enr/#Cls | SN | |
|---|---|---|---|---|---|
| Full Armor Christian Academy<br>2324 FM 3135 E, Henderson 75652<br>Chris Ford | K-12 | | 135<br>12 | | 903/655-8489<br>Fax 903/657-8267 |

## SABINE COUNTY

## SABINE PUBLIC SCHOOLS

● **Hemphill Ind School Dist** PID: 01049267   409/787-3371
1000 Milam St, Hemphill 75948   Fax 409/787-4005

Schools: 3 \ **Teachers:** 73 \ **Students:** 906 \ **Special Ed Students:** 96
\ **LEP Students:** 19 \ **College-Bound:** 50% \ **Ethnic:** Asian 1%, African
American 11%, Hispanic 10%, Native American: 1%, Caucasian 78% \
**Exp:** $620 (High) \ **Poverty:** 25% \ **Title I:** $331,760 \ **Open-Close:** 08/17 -
05/27 \ **DTBP:** $359 (High)

Reese Briggs ........................................ 1   Sally Butler ....................................... 2,11
Josh Bennett ...................................... 3,5   Kathleen Henson .................................... 4
Gary Vanya ....................................... 6,35*   Cecily Bridges .................................. 7,85*
Monica Butler .................................. 9,273*   Shelly Starr ......................................... 16*
Cassie Whitsit ..................................... 58   Kim Scales ........................................... 67
Eric Heslip .................................... 73,295   Marc Griffin ......................................... 88*

| 79 Student Personnel | 91 Safety/Security | 275 Response To Intervention | 298 Grant Writer/Ptnrships | **School Programs** | **Social Media** |
| 80 Driver Ed/Safety | 92 Magnet School | 277 Remedial Math K-12 | 750 Chief Innovation Officer | **A** = Alternative Program | |
| 81 Gifted/Talented | 93 Parental Involvement | 280 Literacy Coach | 751 Chief of Staff | **G** = Adult Classes | 🔲 = Facebook |
| 82 Video Services | 95 Tech Prep Program | 285 STEM | 752 Social Emotional Learning | **M** = Magnet Program | |
| 83 Substance Abuse Prev | 97 Chief Information Officer | 286 Digital Learning | | **T** = Title I Schoolwide | 🔲 = Twitter |
| 84 Erate | 98 Chief Technology Officer | 288 Common Core Standards | **Other School Types** | **V** = Career & Tech Ed Programs | |
| 85 AIDS Education | 270 Character Education | 294 Accountability | Ⓐ = Alternative School | | |
| 88 Alternative/At Risk | 271 Migrant Education | 295 Network System | Ⓒ = Charter School | **New Schools are shaded** | |
| 89 Multi-Cultural Curriculum | 273 Teacher Mentor | 296 Title II Programs | Ⓜ = Magnet School | **New Superintendents and Principals are bold** | |
| 90 Social Work | 274 Before/After Sch | 297 Webmaster | Ⓨ = Year-Round School | Personnel with email addresses are underscored | **TX—331** |

| Public Schs..Principal | Grd | Prgm | Enr/#Cls | SN |
|---|---|---|---|---|
| Hemphill Elem Sch<br>1000 Milam St, Hemphill 75948<br>**Monica Butler** | PK-4 | T | 313<br>30 | 73% 409/787-3371<br>Fax 409/787-4137 |
| Hemphill Middle Sch<br>1000 Milam St, Hemphill 75948<br>**Jeremy McDaniel** | 5-8 | T | 278<br>18 | 62% 409/787-3371<br>Fax 409/787-2252 |
| Hemphill Senior High Sch<br>1000 Milam St, Hemphill 75948<br>**Marc Griffin** | 9-12 | TV | 253<br>35 | 55% 409/787-3371<br>Fax 409/787-1259 |

● **West Sabine Ind Sch Dist** PID: 01049293     409/584-2655
101 Timberland Hwy, Pineland 75968     Fax 409/584-2139

**Schools:** 2 \ **Teachers:** 50 \ **Students:** 578 \ **Special Ed Students:** 66 \ **LEP Students:** 3 \ **College-Bound:** 50% \ **Ethnic:** African American 8%, Hispanic 6%, Native American: 1%, Caucasian 86% \ **Exp:** $347 (High) \ **Poverty:** 29% \ **Title I:** $202,299 \ **Open-Close:** 08/12 - 05/21 \ **DTBP:** $397 (High)

| | | | |
|---|---|---|---|
| Cristal Joslin ............................1 | Natasha McClelland ....................2,296 |
| Tammy Rogers ...........................4 | Jerred Wallace .............................6* |
| Carnelaus Gilder .......................8 | Daniel Havard .................16,73,295* |
| Marie Smith ............................57* | Carla Williams ...........................67 |
| Patricia Jacks .......................69,83* | |

| Public Schs..Principal | Grd | Prgm | Enr/#Cls | SN |
|---|---|---|---|---|
| West Sabine Elem Sch<br>459 Temple Rd N, Pineland 75968<br>**Deborah Lane** | PK-5 | T | 266<br>22 | 85% 409/584-2205<br>Fax 409/584-3096 |
| West Sabine Jr Sr High Sch<br>109 Timberland Hwy, Pineland 75968<br>**Colleen Conn** | 6-12 | ATV | 312<br>23 | 71% 409/584-2525<br>Fax 409/584-2695 |

## SAN AUGUSTINE COUNTY

## SAN AUGUSTINE PUBLIC SCHOOLS

● **Broaddus Ind School Dist** PID: 01049334     936/872-3041
1 Bulldog Plaza, Broaddus 75929     Fax 936/872-3699

**Schools:** 2 \ **Teachers:** 37 \ **Students:** 400 \ **Special Ed Students:** 50 \ **LEP Students:** 18 \ **College-Bound:** 75% \ **Ethnic:** African American 1%, Hispanic 11%, Native American: 1%, Caucasian 87% \ **Exp:** $420 (High) \ **Poverty:** 35% \ **Title I:** $216,257 \ **Open-Close:** 08/12 - 05/21 \ **DTBP:** $255 (High)

| | |
|---|---|
| Lucas Hollway ............................1,83 | Leah Hollway .............................2,11 |
| Brandon Weatherford .........................3 | Sheila Williams ...........................4* |
| Henry Hoya ...............................5 | Murray Wall ...............................5 |
| Zach Crawford ............................6 | Amanda Sowell .........................7,85* |
| Natile Hand ..........8,11,36,69,88,275,294,752 | Gary Mitchell .....................16,73,295 |
| Faith Kilmer ............................57* | Travis Elizalde ...........................67 |
| Leigh Stewart .............................76 | |

| Public Schs..Principal | Grd | Prgm | Enr/#Cls | SN |
|---|---|---|---|---|
| Broaddus Elem Sch<br>215 Buchanan St, Broaddus 75929<br>**Karianna Grant** | PK-5 | T | 180<br>17 | 85% 936/872-3315<br>Fax 936/872-3439 |

| Public Schs..Principal | Grd | Prgm | Enr/#Cls | SN |
|---|---|---|---|---|
| Broaddus High Sch<br>16405 Highway 147 S, Broaddus 75929<br>**Zach Crawford** | 6-12 | AGTV | 216<br>30 | 77% 936/872-3610<br>Fax 936/872-9020 |

● **San Augustine Ind School Dist** PID: 01049360     936/275-2306
1002 Barrett St, San Augustine 75972     Fax 936/275-9776

**Schools:** 2 \ **Teachers:** 68 \ **Students:** 720 \ **Special Ed Students:** 106 \ **LEP Students:** 80 \ **Ethnic:** African American 53%, Hispanic 24%, Caucasian 23% \ **Exp:** $620 (High) \ **Poverty:** 30% \ **Title I:** $343,557 \ **Special Education:** $179,000 \ **Open-Close:** 08/19 - 05/28 \ **DTBP:** $341 (High)

| | |
|---|---|
| Virginia Liepman ............................1 | Patti McLerran ...........................2 |
| Allen Eberlan ............................3,91 | Sharon Taylor .............................4 |
| Rick Russell ...............................5 | Marty Murr .................................6 |
| Jason Mixon ..................8,11,15,69 | Ryan Ham .........................16,31,73 |
| Anna Sharp ...............................58 | Charles Boyette ...........................67 |
| Veronica Porter ..........................294 | |

| Public Schs..Principal | Grd | Prgm | Enr/#Cls | SN |
|---|---|---|---|---|
| San Augustine Elem Sch<br>101 S Milam St, San Augustine 75972<br>**Rebecca Whitton** | PK-5 | TV | 348 | 90% 936/275-3424<br>Fax 936/275-9719 |
| San Augustine Mid High Sch<br>702 N Clark St, San Augustine 75972<br>**Hugh Perkins** | 6-12 | TV | 370<br>20 | 87% 936/275-9603<br>Fax 936/275-9829 |

## SAN JACINTO COUNTY

## SAN JACINTO PUBLIC SCHOOLS

● **Coldspring-Oakhurst Cons ISD** PID: 01049401     936/653-1115
125 FM 1514 Rd, Coldspring 77331     Fax 936/653-2197

**Schools:** 4 \ **Teachers:** 109 \ **Students:** 1,465 \ **Special Ed Students:** 198 \ **LEP Students:** 15 \ **College-Bound:** 42% \ **Ethnic:** African American 19%, Hispanic 9%, Caucasian 71% \ **Exp:** $451 (High) \ **Poverty:** 27% \ **Title I:** $696,449 \ **Special Education:** $285,000 \ **Open-Close:** 08/26 - 05/28 \ **DTBP:** $394 (High) \ 🅕

| | |
|---|---|
| Dr Leland Moore ............................1 | Adam Jenke ...............................2 |
| Charles Cotton ...........................3,5 | Dawn Smith ...............................4 |
| Ken Stanley ............................6,35 | Kristi Benastante ............................ |
| Vikki Curry ..................8,15,288 | Jeff Eichman .............................11 |
| Mary Seago ..............................16 | Sheri Wilson ..............................58 |
| Tony Sewell ..............................67 | Candy Yager ..............................68 |
| Charles Camden ....................73,295 | Missy Eichman .....................73,286 |
| Roosevelt Joseph .........................91 | |

| Public Schs..Principal | Grd | Prgm | Enr/#Cls | SN |
|---|---|---|---|---|
| Coldspring Intermediate Sch<br>1510 Hwy 150, Coldspring 77331<br>Paula McClendon | 3-5 | T | 350<br>30 | 64% 936/653-1152<br>Fax 936/653-3689 |
| Coldspring-Oakhurst High Sch<br>14100 State Highway 150 W, Coldspring 77331<br>**Donna Thompson** | 9-12 | ATV | 439<br>58 | 56% 936/653-1140<br>Fax 936/653-3687 |
| James Street Elem Sch<br>125 Jones Ave, Coldspring 77331<br>Paula McClendon | PK-2 | T | 310<br>19 | 67% 936/653-1187<br>Fax 936/653-3690 |

| | | | | | | | |
|---|---|---|---|---|---|---|---|
| 1 | Superintendent | 8 | Curric/Instruct K-12 | 19 | Chief Financial Officer | 29 | Family/Consumer Science |
| 2 | Bus/Finance/Purchasing | 9 | Curric/Instruct Elem | 20 | Art K-12 | 30 | Adult Education |
| 3 | Buildings And Grounds | 10 | Curric/Instruct Sec | 21 | Art Elem | 31 | Career/Sch-to-Work K-12 |
| 4 | Food Service | 11 | Federal Program | 22 | Art Sec | 32 | Career/Sch-to-Work Elem |
| 5 | Transportation | 12 | Title I | 23 | Music K-12 | 33 | Career/Sch-to-Work Sec |
| 6 | Athletic | 13 | Title V | 24 | Music Elem | 34 | Early Childhood Ed |
| 7 | Health Services | 15 | Asst Superintendent | 25 | Music Sec | 35 | Health/Phys Education |
| | | 16 | Instructional Media Svcs | 26 | Business Education | 36 | Guidance Services K-12 |
| | | 17 | Chief Operations Officer | 27 | Career & Tech Ed | 37 | Guidance Services Elem |
| | | 18 | Chief Academic Officer | 28 | Technology Education | 38 | Guidance Services Sec |

| | | | | | |
|---|---|---|---|---|---|
| 39 | Social Studies K-12 | 49 | English/Lang Arts Elem | 59 | Special Education Elem |
| 40 | Social Studies Elem | 50 | English/Lang Arts Sec | 60 | Special Education Sec |
| 41 | Social Studies Sec | 51 | Reading K-12 | 61 | Foreign/World Lang K-12 |
| 42 | Science K-12 | 52 | Reading Elem | 62 | Foreign/World Lang Elem |
| 43 | Science Elem | 53 | Reading Sec | 63 | Foreign/World Lang Sec |
| 44 | Science Sec | 54 | Remedial Reading K-12 | 64 | Religious Education K-12 |
| 45 | Math K-12 | 55 | Remedial Reading Elem | 65 | Religious Education Elem |
| 46 | Math Elem | 56 | Remedial Reading Sec | 66 | Religious Education Sec |
| 47 | Math Sec | 57 | Bilingual/ELL | 67 | School Board President |
| 48 | English/Lang Arts K-12 | 58 | Special Education K-12 | 68 | Teacher Personnel |

| | |
|---|---|
| 69 | Academic Assessment |
| 70 | Research/Development |
| 71 | Public Information |
| 72 | Summer School |
| 73 | Instructional Tech |
| 74 | Inservice Training |
| 75 | Marketing/Distributive |
| 76 | Info Systems |
| 77 | Psychological Assess |
| 78 | Affirmative Action |

| Lincoln Junior High Sch | 6-8 | ATV | 366 | 66% 936/653-1166 |
|---|---|---|---|---|
| 13605 Sh 156, Coldspring 77331 | | | 60 | Fax 936/653-3688 |
| Frank Brown | | | | |

● **Shepherd Ind School Dist** PID: 01049449                936/628-3396
1401 S Byrd Ave, Shepherd 77371                Fax 936/628-3841

> **Schools:** 4 \ **Teachers:** 132 \ **Students:** 2,041 \ **Special Ed Students:** 179
> \ **LEP Students:** 313 \ **College-Bound:** 43% \ **Ethnic:** African American
> 6%, Hispanic 35%, Caucasian 59% \ **Exp:** $529 (High) \ **Poverty:** 25% \
> **Title I:** $631,557 \ **Open-Close:** 08/13 - 05/27 \ **DTBP:** $350 (High) \ 🅔

| | | | |
|---|---|---|---|
| Jason Hewitt ...........1 | Deanna Clavell ...........2 | | |
| Brandon Barrow ...........3,5 | Randy Milton ...........4 | | |
| Miles Robison ...........6* | Holly Oliphant ...........7 | | |
| Holly Oliphant ...........7* | Dr Elizabeth Torres .......11,57,88,271,288,298 | | |
| Rebecca Bany ...........16* | Shannon Wallace ...........58 | | |
| Yvonne Johnson ...........67 | Brenda Cronin ...........68,74 | | |
| Tommy Hues ...........73,84 | | | |

| Public Schs..Principal | Grd | Prgm | Enr/#Cls SN |
|---|---|---|---|
| Shepherd High Sch | 9-12 | T | 563   66% 936/628-3371 |
| 1 Pirate Ln, Shepherd 77371 | | | 55   Fax 936/628-6986 |
| **Daniel Barton** | | | |
| Shepherd Intermediate Sch | 3-5 | T | 456   78% 936/628-6764 |
| 420 S Railroad Ave, Shepherd 77371 | | | 23   Fax 936/628-6507 |
| **Jennifer Stein** | | | |
| Shepherd Middle Sch | 6-8 | T | 452   71% 936/628-3377 |
| 1401 S Byrd Ave, Shepherd 77371 | | | 30   Fax 936/628-6749 |
| **Heather Gore** | | | |
| Shepherd Primary Sch | PK-2 | T | 570   77% 936/628-3302 |
| 10300 Highway 150, Shepherd 77371 | | | 29   Fax 936/628-6459 |
| **Alisa Lott** | | | |

# SAN PATRICIO COUNTY

## SAN PATRICIO PUBLIC SCHOOLS

● **Aransas Pass Ind School Dist** PID: 01049487           361/758-3466
2300 McMullen Ln Ste 600, Aransas Pass 78336           Fax 361/758-2962

> **Schools:** 5 \ **Teachers:** 114 \ **Students:** 1,484 \ **Special Ed Students:** 142
> \ **LEP Students:** 129 \ **College-Bound:** 45% \ **Ethnic:** Asian 1%,
> African American 2%, Hispanic 65%, Caucasian 32% \ **Exp:** $608 (High)
> \ **Poverty:** 26% \ **Title I:** $694,419 \ **Special Education:** $425,000 \
> **Open-Close:** 08/26 - 05/28 \ **DTBP:** $615 (High)

| | | | |
|---|---|---|---|
| Mrs Cooke ...........1 | Cheryle Stansberry ...........2 | | |
| Charlie Ochoa ...........3,5 | Lanell Jones ...........4 | | |
| Ryan Knostman ...........6* | Sally McCutchan ...........7* | | |
| Shelly Dominqueze 8,16,57,88,271,273,286,288 | Mark Kemp ...........11 | | |
| Wayne Bennett ...........15,31* | Susan Coleman ...........16* | | |
| Carla Dees ...........37* | Christine Johnson ...........58 | | |
| Victor Galvan ...........67 | Jason Brou ...........73 | | |
| Diane Genovese ...........76 | Tammy Shedd ...........295 | | |

| Public Schs..Principal | Grd | Prgm | Enr/#Cls SN |
|---|---|---|---|
| A C Blunt Middle Sch | 6-8 | T | 318   81% 361/758-2711 |
| 2103 Demory Ln, Aransas Pass 78336 | | | 40   Fax 361/758-4690 |
| Derick King | | | |

| Aransas Pass High Sch | 9-12 | ATV | 469 | 79% 361/758-3248 |
|---|---|---|---|---|
| 450 S Avenue A, Aransas Pass 78336 | | | 34 | Fax 361/758-3251 |
| Michelle Hale | | | | |
| Charlie Marshall Elem Sch | 4-5 | T | 232 | 81% 361/758-3455 |
| 2300 McMullen Ln, Aransas Pass 78336 | | | 18 | Fax 361/758-3046 |
| Jeremy Saegert | | | | |
| Faulk Early Childhood Center | PK-1 | T | 230 | 76% 361/758-3141 |
| 430 S 8th St, Aransas Pass 78336 | | | 26 | Fax 361/758-5493 |
| Jason Mansfield | | | | |
| Kieberger Elem Sch | 2-3 | T | 235 | 78% 361/758-3113 |
| 748 W Goodnight Ave, Aransas Pass 78336 | | | 18 | Fax 361/758-3605 |
| Jason Mansfield | | | | |

● **Gregory-Portland Ind Sch Dist** PID: 01049530           361/777-1091
608 College St, Portland 78374           Fax 361/777-1093

> **Schools:** 7 \ **Teachers:** 318 \ **Students:** 4,600 \ **Special Ed Students:** 438
> \ **LEP Students:** 183 \ **College-Bound:** 60% \ **Ethnic:** Asian 2%,
> African American 2%, Hispanic 58%, Caucasian 38% \ **Exp:** $368 (High)
> \ **Poverty:** 15% \ **Title I:** $702,742 \ **Special Education:** $950,000 \
> **Open-Close:** 08/13 - 05/27 \ **DTBP:** $181 (High)

| | | | |
|---|---|---|---|
| **Michelle Cazazos** ...........1 | Alberto Silguero ...........2 | | |
| Bridget Clark ...........2,19 | Ernesto Polomo ...........3 | | |
| Jeff Atkinson ...........4 | Alton Coleman ...........5 | | |
| Rick Rhodes ...........6* | Velma Soliz-Garcia ...........8,15,68 | | |
| Sharon Reckaway .......10,69,88,270,271,273 | Dr Leslie Faught ...........15 | | |
| Andrew Guerra ...........16,73,84,295 | Barbie Ezell ...........34,58 | | |
| Geoffrey Rickerhauser ...........42,45 | Victor Hernandez ...........67 | | |
| Michael Thieme ...........91 | | | |

| Public Schs..Principal | Grd | Prgm | Enr/#Cls SN |
|---|---|---|---|
| East Cliff Elem Sch | PK-5 | T | 468   34% 361/777-4255 |
| 1140 Broadway Blvd, Portland 78374 | | | 20   Fax 361/777-4256 |
| Penny Armstrong | | | |
| Gregory-Portland High Sch | 9-12 | TV | 1,351   37% 361/777-4251 |
| 4601 Wildcat Dr, Portland 78374 | | | 93   Fax 361/777-4272 |
| Kyde Eddleman | | | |
| Gregory-Portland Mid Sch | 6-8 | T | 1,059   45% 361/777-4042 |
| 4600 Wildcat Dr, Portland 78374 | | | 50   Fax 361/643-3187 |
| Gabe Alvarado | | | |
| Stephen F Austin Elem Sch | PK-5 | T | 332   61% 361/777-4252 |
| 308 N Gregory Ave, Gregory 78359 | | | Fax 361/777-4261 |
| Brenda Brinkman | | | |
| T M Clark Elem Sch | PK-5 | T | 593   60% 361/777-4045 |
| 2250 Memorial Pkwy, Portland 78374 | | | 35   Fax 361/777-4046 |
| Bobby Rister | | | |
| W C Andrews Elem Sch | PK-5 | T | 451   52% 361/777-4048 |
| 4015 Moore Ave, Portland 78374 | | | 25   Fax 361/643-0775 |
| Julie Verstuyft | | | |
| Ⓐ Wildcat Learning Alt Center | 9-12 | | 50   361/777-4051 |
| 1100 Lang Rd, Portland 78374 | | | Fax 361/777-4052 |
| **Kyde Eddleman** | | | |

● **Ingleside Ind School Dist** PID: 01049592           361/776-7631
2664 San Angelo Ave, Ingleside 78362           Fax 361/776-0267

> **Schools:** 5 \ **Teachers:** 139 \ **Students:** 2,046 \ **Special Ed Students:** 192
> \ **LEP Students:** 160 \ **College-Bound:** 60% \ **Ethnic:** Asian 1%,
> African American 1%, Hispanic 56%, Native American: 1%, Caucasian
> 41% \ **Exp:** $429 (High) \ **Poverty:** 19% \ **Title I:** $494,227 \
> **Special Education:** $234,000 \ **Open-Close:** 08/17 - 05/26 \ **DTBP:** $540
> (High) \ 🅕 🅔

| | | | |
|---|---|---|---|
| Troy Mircovich ...........1 | Ronald Robles ...........3,5,92 | | |
| Ross Schonhoeft ...........4 | Lynne Porter ...........8,15 | | |

Karen Mircovich ...................... 11,57,69,83
Camille Burger .................................58
Steven Snyder ...................................71
Danny Glover ....................................79

Selena Villaneda ..............................16*
Julio Salinas ......................................67
Delana Lightfoot ..........................73,286

| Public Schs..Principal | Grd | Prgm | Enr/#Cls | SN |
|---|---|---|---|---|
| Blaschke-Sheldon Elem Sch<br>2624 Mustang Dr, Ingleside 78362<br>Stephanie McNew | 5-6 | T | 331<br>20 | 68% 361/776-3050<br>Fax 361/776-7912 |
| Gilbert Mircovich Elem Sch<br>2720 Big Oak Ln, Ingleside 78362<br>**Suzy Ponton** | 2-4 | T | 478<br>31 | 68% 361/776-1683<br>Fax 361/775-0509 |
| Ingleside High Sch<br>2807 Mustang Dr, Ingleside 78362<br>**Steven Edlin** | 9-12 | ATV | 609<br>54 | 67% 361/776-2712<br>Fax 361/776-5200 |
| Ingleside Primary Sch<br>2100 Achievement Blvd, Ingleside 78362<br>Stephanie Dotson | PK-1 | T | 275<br>23 | 69% 361/776-3060<br>Fax 361/775-2070 |
| Leon Taylor Junior High Sch<br>2739 Mustang Dr, Ingleside 78362<br>Heather Waugh-Freeze | 7-8 | AT | 353<br>27 | 68% 361/776-2232<br>Fax 361/776-2192 |

● **Mathis Ind School Dist** PID: 01049645
602 E San Patricio Ave, Mathis 78368

361/547-3378
Fax 361/547-9474

Schools: 4 \ Teachers: 117 \ Students: 1,600 \ Special Ed Students: 165 \ LEP Students: 42 \ College-Bound: 31% \ Ethnic: African American 1%, Hispanic 89%, Caucasian 10% \ Exp: $581 (High) \ Poverty: 42% \ Title I: $1,121,306 \ Special Education: $319,000 \ Open-Close: 08/03 - 06/23 \ DTBP: $490 (High)

Benny Hernandez ......................... 1,57,83
Suanne Martinez ................................4
Trae Stevens ....................................6*
Jose Avila .............................16,73,84
Dr Veronica Gutierrez ......................45
Veronica Garza ................................58
Jennifer Encinia ...............................68

Gail Shepler ......................................2
Rosie Huerta .....................................5
Christina Alvarado .....................11,36,69
Dr Jesse Riojas ...............................27*
Lacy Brauchle ..............................48,51
Melinda Barajas ...............................67
Leobardo Cano ...............................88*

| Public Schs..Principal | Grd | Prgm | Enr/#Cls | SN |
|---|---|---|---|---|
| Mathis Elem Sch<br>315 S Duval St, Mathis 78368<br>Patricia Pittman | PK-2 | T | 362<br>37 | 89% 361/547-4106<br>Fax 361/547-4162 |
| Mathis High Sch<br>1615 E San Patricio Ave, Mathis 78368<br>Dr Jesse Riojas | 9-12 | AGTV | 441<br>42 | 80% 361/547-4131<br>Fax 361/547-4139 |
| Mathis Intermediate Sch<br>550 E San Patricio Ave, Mathis 78368<br>Cynthia Westbrook | 3-5 | T | 358<br>24 | 84% 361/547-2472<br>Fax 361/547-4119 |
| Mathis Middle Sch<br>1627 E San Patricio Ave, Mathis 78368<br>Randy Tiemann | 6-8 | T | 392<br>24 | 84% 361/547-2381<br>Fax 361/547-4156 |

● **Odem-Edroy Ind School Dist** PID: 01049700
1 Owl Sq, Odem 78370

361/368-8121
Fax 361/368-2879

Schools: 4 \ Teachers: 65 \ Students: 900 \ Special Ed Students: 76 \ LEP Students: 22 \ College-Bound: 90% \ Ethnic: African American 1%, Hispanic 87%, Caucasian 12% \ Exp: $488 (High) \ Poverty: 30% \ Title I: $492,811 \ Special Education: $193,000 \ Open-Close: 08/21 - 05/19 \ DTBP: $606 (High)

Yolanda Carr .....................................1
Arnold Maldonado .............................3*
Armando Huerta .................................6*
Esmeralda Martinez ........................34*

Tonya Romero ....................................2
Janie Luna .........................................4
Lori Schulze ...........................10,11,285
Jana Kieshhnick ...........................57,58

Jacob Romero ..................................67
Lisa Perez ...................................83,85*

Joey Avila .................................73,286
Lupita Carrizales ...........................274*

| Public Schs..Principal | Grd | Prgm | Enr/#Cls | SN |
|---|---|---|---|---|
| Odem Elem Sch<br>1 Owl Sq, Odem 78370<br>Esmeralda Martinez | PK-2 | T | 276<br>31 | 67% 361/368-3881<br>Fax 361/368-2317 |
| Odem High Sch<br>1 Owl Sq Ste A, Odem 78370<br>Calvin Bowers | 9-12 | ATV | 284<br>31 | 58% 361/368-8121<br>Fax 361/368-3781 |
| Odem Intermediate Sch<br>1 Owl Sq, Odem 78370<br>Erica Tapia | 3-5 | T | 201 | 65% 361/368-8121 |
| Odem Junior High Sch<br>1 Owl Sq, Odem 78370<br>Joe Vela | 6-8 | T | 217<br>16 | 61% 361/368-8121<br>Fax 361/368-2398 |

● **Sinton Ind School Dist** PID: 01049762
322 S Archer St, Sinton 78387

361/364-6800
Fax 361/364-6905

Schools: 4 \ Teachers: 146 \ Students: 1,339 \ Special Ed Students: 279 \ LEP Students: 20 \ Ethnic: Asian 1%, African American 1%, Hispanic 83%, Caucasian 15% \ Exp: $468 (High) \ Poverty: 32% \ Title I: $871,102 \ Special Education: $384,000 \ Open-Close: 08/13 - 05/26 \ DTBP: $558 (High)

Chad Jones .......................................1
Donald Mercier ..................................3
Joseph Buffa .............5,73,76,97,98,295
Gina Guajardo ......................11,83,296
Michelle Wendel ...............................16
Carol Reagan ...................................67
Rosie Salinas ...............................73,84
Mary Lankford ...............................285*

Melissa Villarreal ..........................2,15
Filke West ........................................4
Lori Soliz ..........................................7*
Dana Allen ..................................15,68
Michael Elbert ..................................58
Eileen Troup ....................................71
Heidi Menchaca ..............................271

| Public Schs..Principal | Grd | Prgm | Enr/#Cls | SN |
|---|---|---|---|---|
| E Merle Smith Middle Sch<br>900 S San Patricio St, Sinton 78387<br>Jennifer Davis | 6-8 | T | 336<br>26 | 64% 361/364-6840<br>Fax 361/364-6856 |
| Sinton Elem Sch<br>200 S Bowie St, Sinton 78387<br>Lori Trevino | 3-5 | T | 304<br>25 | 77% 361/364-6900<br>Fax 361/364-6914 |
| Sinton High Sch<br>400 N Pirate Blvd, Sinton 78387<br>Albert Byrom | 9-12 | TV | 141<br>60 | 66% 361/364-6650<br>Fax 361/364-6668 |
| Welder Elem Sch<br>901 Hamilton St, Sinton 78387<br>Luci Rodriguez | PK-2 | T | 558<br>24 | 67% 361/364-6600<br>Fax 361/364-6608 |

● **Taft Ind School Dist** PID: 01049827
400 College St, Taft 78390

361/528-2636
Fax 361/528-2223

Schools: 3 \ Teachers: 90 \ Students: 1,154 \ Special Ed Students: 117 \ LEP Students: 26 \ College-Bound: 85% \ Ethnic: African American 1%, Hispanic 90%, Caucasian 9% \ Exp: $421 (High) \ Poverty: 28% \ Title I: $416,124 \ Special Education: $234,000 \ Open-Close: 08/12 - 05/28 \ DTBP: $613 (High)

**Ricardo Trevino** ...............................1
Ismael Olivares .................................3
Joe Richard Castellano .......................6
Lamar Galindo ..................................58
Bernon Phillips .................................73
Vangie Lopez ..................................271

Ivonne Banda ....................................2
Margie Longoria .................................4
Angel Lopez ..............................8,11,57
Jimmy Adame ....................................67
Tony Arsuaga ...............................83,91

| | | | | | | | |
|---|---|---|---|---|---|---|---|
| 1 | Superintendent | 8 | Curric/Instruct K-12 | 19 | Chief Financial Officer | 29 | Family/Consumer Science |
| 2 | Bus/Finance/Purchasing | 9 | Curric/Instruct Elem | 20 | Art K-12 | 30 | Adult Education |
| 3 | Buildings And Grounds | 10 | Curric/Instruct Sec | 21 | Art Elem | 31 | Career/Sch-to-Work K-12 |
| 4 | Food Service | 11 | Federal Program | 22 | Art Sec | 32 | Career/Sch-to-Work Elem |
| 5 | Transportation | 12 | Title I | 23 | Music K-12 | 33 | Career/Sch-to-Work Sec |
| 6 | Athletic | 13 | Title V | 24 | Music Elem | 34 | Early Childhood Ed |
| 7 | Health Services | 14 | Asst Superintendent | 25 | Music Sec | 35 | Health/Phys Education |
| | | 15 | Instructional Media Svcs | 26 | Business Education | 36 | Guidance Services K-12 |
| | | 16 | Chief Operations Officer | 27 | Career & Tech Ed | 37 | Guidance Services Elem |
| | | 17 | Chief Academic Officer | 28 | Technology Education | 38 | Guidance Services Sec |

| | | | | | |
|---|---|---|---|---|---|
| 39 | Social Studies K-12 | 49 | English/Lang Arts Elem | 59 | Special Education Elem |
| 40 | Social Studies Elem | 50 | English/Lang Arts Sec | 60 | Special Education Sec |
| 41 | Social Studies Sec | 51 | Reading K-12 | 61 | Foreign/World Lang K-12 |
| 42 | Science K-12 | 52 | Reading Elem | 62 | Foreign/World Lang Elem |
| 43 | Science Elem | 53 | Reading Sec | 63 | Foreign/World Lang Sec |
| 44 | Science Sec | 54 | Remedial Reading K-12 | 64 | Religious Education K-12 |
| 45 | Math K-12 | 55 | Remedial Reading Elem | 65 | Religious Education Elem |
| 46 | Math Elem | 56 | Remedial Reading Sec | 66 | Religious Education Sec |
| 47 | Math Sec | 57 | Bilingual/ELL | 67 | School Board President |
| 48 | English/Lang Arts K-12 | 58 | Special Education K-12 | 68 | Teacher Personnel |

| | |
|---|---|
| 69 | Academic Assessment |
| 70 | Research/Development |
| 71 | Public Information |
| 72 | Summer School |
| 73 | Instructional Tech |
| 74 | Inservice Training |
| 75 | Marketing/Distributive |
| 76 | Info Systems |
| 77 | Psychological Assess |
| 78 | Affirmative Action |

| Public Schs..Principal | Grd | Prgm | Enr/#Cls | SN |
|---|---|---|---|---|
| Taft High Sch<br>502 Rincon Rd, Taft 78390<br>Matthew Lohse | 9-12 | GTV | 277<br>26 | 91% 361/528-2636<br>Fax 361/528-3918 |
| Taft Junior High Sch<br>1150 Gregory St, Taft 78390<br>Christine Acosta | 6-8 | GTV | 232<br>30 | 94% 361/528-2636<br>Fax 361/528-5477 |
| Woodroe Petty Elem Sch<br>401 Peach St, Taft 78390<br>Joshua Rombs | PK-5 | T | 476<br>17 | 94% 361/528-2636<br>Fax 361/528-3570 |

## SAN SABA COUNTY

## SAN SABA PUBLIC SCHOOLS

### ● Cherokee Ind School Dist PID: 01049889
305 S Indian Ave, Cherokee 76832 — 325/622-4298 — Fax 325/622-4430

Schools: 1 \ Teachers: 18 \ Students: 112 \ Special Ed Students: 12 \
College-Bound: 75% \ Ethnic: African American 4%, Hispanic 21%, Native
American: 1%, Caucasian 74% \ Exp: $1,103 (High) \ Poverty: 16% \
Title I: $71,804 \ Open-Close: 08/12 - 05/27 \ DTBP: $356 (High)

Jennifer Bordner ....................................1  Denise Woolsey .........................................2
Tommy Morrison ...................................67  Eldon Franco ...........................................84

| Public Schs..Principal | Grd | Prgm | Enr/#Cls | SN |
|---|---|---|---|---|
| Cherokee Sch<br>305 S Indian Ave, Cherokee 76832<br>Rick Panter | PK-12 | TV | 112<br>8 | 54% 325/622-4298 |

### ● Richland Springs Ind Sch Dist PID: 01049918
700 W Coyote Trl, Richland Spgs 76871 — 325/452-3524 — Fax 325/452-3230

Schools: 1 \ Teachers: 14 \ Students: 123 \ Special Ed Students: 22 \
LEP Students: 3 \ College-Bound: 90% \ Ethnic: African American 2%,
Hispanic 22%, Native American: 1%, Caucasian 76% \ Exp: $961 (High) \
Poverty: 15% \ Title I: $35,055 \ Open-Close: 08/07 - 05/28 \ DTBP: $438
(High)

Don Fowler ...................................... 1,11,84  Linda Morris ............................................2
Shannon Sutherland .................................4  Jerry Burkhart .........................................6
Rhonda Wyatt .........................................8*  Rhonda Wyatt .........................................8
Shawn Rogers .......................................58*  Jason Lewis ...........................................67
Pamela Starr ..........................................73*

| Public Schs..Principal | Grd | Prgm | Enr/#Cls | SN |
|---|---|---|---|---|
| Richland Springs Sch<br>700 W Coyote Trl, Richland Spgs 76871<br>Rhonda Wyatt | K-12 | ATV | 123<br>16 | 66% 325/452-3427<br>Fax 325/452-3580 |

### ● San Saba Ind School Dist PID: 01049944
808 W Wallace St, San Saba 76877 — 325/372-3771 — Fax 325/372-5977

Schools: 3 \ Teachers: 71 \ Students: 717 \ Special Ed Students: 89 \
LEP Students: 125 \ College-Bound: 40% \ Ethnic: Asian 1%, Hispanic
56%, Caucasian 42% \ Exp: $471 (High) \ Poverty: 29% \ Title I: $263,387 \
Special Education: $7,000 \ Open-Close: 08/20 - 05/27 \ DTBP: $333 (High)
\ 🈁

Wayne Kelly .............................1,83  Buck Martin .............................................2
Kenneth Groomes ....................................3  Dianna Wood ..........................................4*
Alton Tinney .........................................5  Andreas Aguirre .......................................6
Brenda Martinez ......... 8,11,15,57,88,288,296  Deanne Cromer ......................................16*
Kevin Shahan .........................................67  Tim Cooper ...........................73,286,295

| Public Schs..Principal | Grd | Prgm | Enr/#Cls | SN |
|---|---|---|---|---|
| San Saba Elem Sch<br>808 W Wallace St, San Saba 76877<br>Denise Deckard | PK-4 | T | 298<br>20 | 79% 325/372-3019<br>Fax 325/372-6187 |
| San Saba High Sch<br>S 8th St, San Saba 76877<br>Dr Scott Snyder | 9-12 | T | 206<br>19 | 61% 325/372-3786<br>Fax 325/372-3478 |
| San Saba Middle Sch<br>10th St, San Saba 76877<br>Joshua Ham | 5-8 | T | 213<br>22 | 74% 325/372-3200<br>Fax 325/372-5228 |

## SCHLEICHER COUNTY

## SCHLEICHER PUBLIC SCHOOLS

### ● Schleicher Co Ind Sch Dist PID: 01049982
205 Fields Ave, Eldorado 76936 — 325/853-2514 — Fax 325/853-2695

Schools: 3 \ Teachers: 55 \ Students: 540 \ Special Ed Students: 32 \
LEP Students: 44 \ Ethnic: Hispanic 75%, Caucasian 25% \ Exp: $497
(High) \ Poverty: 20% \ Title I: $153,246 \ Special Education: $8,000 \
Open-Close: 08/19 - 05/20 \ DTBP: $367 (High)

Robert Gibson ....................................1,11  Ray Ballew .............................................2
Oscar Martinez .......................................3  Vikki Cathey ...........................................4
Joey Jones ...........................................5  Jon Long ................................................6
Lu Ann Shipman ....................................16*  Kriss Griffin ...........................................67
Sandra Robledo .....................................68  Lyndi Oneil ...............69,83,85,88,270,288*
JD Doyle ...........................73,76,286,295*  Sharon Spinks .............................285,298

| Public Schs..Principal | Grd | Prgm | Enr/#Cls | SN |
|---|---|---|---|---|
| Eldorado Elem Sch<br>205 W Fields Ave, Eldorado 76936<br>Michael Rudewick | PK-4 | T | 197<br>20 | 60% 325/853-2514<br>Fax 325/853-2177 |
| Eldorado High Sch<br>205 W Fields Ave, Eldorado 76936<br>Perry Graves | 9-12 | T | 154<br>27 | 52% 325/853-2514<br>Fax 325/853-2710 🈁 |
| Eldorado Middle Sch<br>205 W Fields Ave, Eldorado 76936<br>Ezra Walling | 5-8 | T | 164<br>25 | 59% 325/853-2514<br>Fax 325/853-2895 🈁 |

| | | | | | |
|---|---|---|---|---|---|
| 79 Student Personnel | 91 Safety/Security | 275 Response To Intervention | 298 Grant Writer/Ptnrships | School Programs | Social Media |
| 80 Driver Ed/Safety | 92 Magnet School | 277 Remedial Math K-12 | 750 Chief Innovation Officer | A = Alternative Program | |
| 81 Gifted/Talented | 93 Parental Involvement | 280 Literacy Coach | 751 Chief of Staff | G = Adult Classes | 🈁 = Facebook |
| 82 Video Services | 95 Tech Prep Program | 285 STEM | 752 Social Emotional Learning | M = Magnet Program | |
| 83 Substance Abuse Prev | 97 Chief Information Officer | 286 Digital Learning | | T = Title I Schoolwide | 🈁 = Twitter |
| 84 Erate | 98 Chief Technology Officer | 288 Common Core Standards | Other School Types | V = Career & Tech Ed Programs | |
| 85 AIDS Education | 270 Character Education | 294 Accountability | Ⓐ = Alternative School | | |
| 88 Alternative/At Risk | 271 Migrant Education | 295 Network System | Ⓒ = Charter School | New Schools are shaded | |
| 89 Multi-Cultural Curriculum | 273 Teacher Mentor | 296 Title II Programs | Ⓜ = Magnet School | New Superintendents and Principals are bold | |
| 90 Social Work | 274 Before/After Sch | 297 Webmaster | Ⓨ = Year-Round School | Personnel with email addresses are underscored | |

# TX—335

## SCURRY COUNTY

### SCURRY PUBLIC SCHOOLS

● **Hermleigh Ind School Dist** PID: 01050046    325/863-2451
8010 Business 84 H, Hermleigh 79526    Fax 325/863-2713

**Schools:** 1 \ **Teachers:** 20 \ **Students:** 275 \ **Special Ed Students:** 16
\ **LEP Students:** 14 \ **College-Bound:** 75% \ **Ethnic:** African American
2%, Hispanic 40%, Caucasian 58% \ **Exp:** $636 (High) \ **Poverty:** 10% \
**Title I:** $31,159 \ **Open-Close:** 08/20 - 05/27 \ **DTBP:** $358 (High)

| | | | |
|---|---|---|---|
| Cathy Petty | 1 | Marci Beard | 2 |
| Belinda Lara | 4 | Nathan Pettigrew | 8 |
| Christina Espinoza | 60* | Larry Nachlinger | 67 |
| Heath Gibson | 73 | | |

| Public Schs..Principal | Grd | Prgm | Enr/#Cls | SN |
|---|---|---|---|---|
| Hermleigh Sch | PK-12 | TV | 275 | 45% 325/863-2451 |
| 8010 Business 84 H, Hermleigh 79526 | | | 16 | |
| Amber Palmer | | | | |

● **Ira Ind School Dist** PID: 01050072    325/573-2628
6190 W FM 1606, Ira 79527    Fax 325/573-0705

**Schools:** 1 \ **Teachers:** 22 \ **Students:** 275 \ **Special Ed Students:** 21
\ **LEP Students:** 9 \ **College-Bound:** 95% \ **Ethnic:** African American
1%, Hispanic 27%, Caucasian 72% \ **Exp:** $527 (High) \ **Poverty:** 10% \
**Title I:** $11,786 \ **Open-Close:** 08/19 - 05/21 \ **DTBP:** $350 (High)

| | | | |
|---|---|---|---|
| Brian Patterson | 1 | Keeli Hines | 2 |
| Brittney Lomax | 4 | Brian Patterson | 6* |
| Kati Patrick | 7* | Bobbie Hale | 8,11,57,69,270,273,752* |
| Dale Jones | 13* | Dave Hanes | 16,73,286,295* |
| Leo Sellers | 27* | Dirk Dunn | 67 |
| Lacee Cox | 88* | | |

| Public Schs..Principal | Grd | Prgm | Enr/#Cls | SN |
|---|---|---|---|---|
| Ira Sch | PK-12 | V | 275 | 23% 325/573-2628 |
| 6190 W FM 1606, Ira 79527 | | | 18 | |
| Dale Jones | | | | |

● **Snyder Ind School Dist** PID: 01050101    325/574-8900
2901 37th St, Snyder 79549    Fax 325/573-9025

**Schools:** 4 \ **Teachers:** 195 \ **Students:** 2,700 \ **Special Ed Students:** 293 \
**LEP Students:** 253 \ **Ethnic:** Asian 1%, African American 2%, Hispanic 66%,
Native American: 1%, Caucasian 31% \ **Exp:** $595 (High) \ **Poverty:** 20% \
**Title I:** $773,800 \ **Special Education:** $678,000 \ **Open-Close:** 08/12 -
05/28 \ **DTBP:** $158 (High)

| | | | |
|---|---|---|---|
| Eddie Bland | 1 | Morgan Preston | 2 |
| Clay Cade | 3 | Wes Wood | 6 |
| Rachael McClain | 8* | Kathy Scott | 11,79 |
| Rosie Lopez | 57 | Matthew Nelson | 58 |
| Ralph Ramon | 67 | Jeff McGinnis | 73* |

| Public Schs..Principal | Grd | Prgm | Enr/#Cls | SN |
|---|---|---|---|---|
| Snyder High Sch | 9-12 | TV | 715 | 58% 325/574-8800 |
| 3801 Austin Ave, Snyder 79549 | | | 45 | Fax 325/573-9500 |
| **Shaye Murphy** | | | | |
| Snyder Intermediate Sch | 4-5 | T | 407 | 69% 325/574-8650 |
| 3301 El Paso Ave, Snyder 79549 | | | | Fax 325/574-6024 |
| Jerry Russell | | | | |
| Snyder Junior High Sch | 6-8 | TV | 588 | 71% 325/574-8700 |
| 3806 37th St, Snyder 79549 | | | 30 | Fax 325/574-8708 |
| Rebecca Mebane | | | | |
| Snyder Primary Sch | 1-3 | T | 1,051 | 71% 325/574-8600 |
| 3601 El Paso Ave, Snyder 79549 | | | 26 | Fax 325/573-0342 |
| Canita Rhodes | | | | |

## SHACKELFORD COUNTY

### SHACKELFORD PUBLIC SCHOOLS

● **Albany Ind School Dist** PID: 01050216    325/762-2823
501 E S 1st St, Albany 76430    Fax 325/762-3876

**Schools:** 2 \ **Teachers:** 45 \ **Students:** 512 \ **Special Ed Students:** 47
\ **LEP Students:** 9 \ **College-Bound:** 99% \ **Ethnic:** African American
2%, Hispanic 16%, Caucasian 81% \ **Exp:** $726 (High) \ **Poverty:** 14% \
**Title I:** $89,180 \ **Open-Close:** 08/19 - 05/27 \ **DTBP:** $350 (High) \ 📱

| | | | |
|---|---|---|---|
| Jonathan Scott | 1 | Angelyn Faith | 2 |
| Debra Boyett | 4* | Ryder Peacock | 6* |
| Glen Hill | 10 | Jenny Scott | 16,38* |
| Robert Montgomery | 67 | Dan Key | 73* |

| Public Schs..Principal | Grd | Prgm | Enr/#Cls | SN |
|---|---|---|---|---|
| Albany Jr Sr High Sch | 7-12 | TV | 221 | 28% 325/762-3974 |
| 501 E S 1st St, Albany 76430 | | | 50 | Fax 325/762-3850 |
| Edward Morales | | | | |
| Nancy Smith Elem Sch | PK-6 | T | 248 | 42% 325/762-3384 |
| 741 Griffin Rd, Albany 76430 | | | 27 | Fax 325/762-3070 |
| John Gallagher | | | | 📱 |

● **Moran Ind School Dist** PID: 01050242    325/945-3101
900 Main St, Moran 76464    Fax 325/945-2741

**Schools:** 1 \ **Teachers:** 17 \ **Students:** 105 \ **Special Ed Students:** 17
\ **College-Bound:** 50% \ **Ethnic:** African American 1%, Hispanic 9%,
Native American: 1%, Caucasian 89% \ **Exp:** $350 (High) \ **Poverty:** 46% \
**Title I:** $54,425 \ **Special Education:** $1,000 \ **Open-Close:** 08/26 - 05/28 \
**DTBP:** $327 (High)

| | | | |
|---|---|---|---|
| Danny Freeman | 1,11 | Diedre Cauble | 2 |
| Charles Russek | 3,5* | Tiffany Cambell | 4 |
| Lee Lewis | 6* | Kim Holland | 8,69,288* |
| Elizabeth Walls | 58,83* | Jimmie Roller | 67 |
| Anita Wheat | 73,295* | Jeannie Tencate | 271* |

| Public Schs..Principal | Grd | Prgm | Enr/#Cls | SN |
|---|---|---|---|---|
| Moran Sch | PK-12 | TV | 105 | 90% 325/945-3101 |
| 900 Main St, Moran 76464 | | | 12 | |
| Danny Freeman | | | | |

| | | | | | | | |
|---|---|---|---|---|---|---|---|
| 1 | Superintendent | 8 | Curric/Instruct K-12 | 19 | Chief Financial Officer | 29 | Family/Consumer Science |
| 2 | Bus/Finance/Purchasing | 9 | Curric/Instruct Elem | 20 | Art K-12 | 30 | Adult Education |
| 3 | Buildings And Grounds | 10 | Curric/Instruct Sec | 21 | Art Elem | 31 | Career/Sch-to-Work K-12 |
| 4 | Food Service | 11 | Federal Program | 22 | Art Sec | 32 | Career/Sch-to-Work Elem |
| 5 | Transportation | 12 | Title I | 23 | Music K-12 | 33 | Career/Sch-to-Work Sec |
| 6 | Athletic | 13 | Title V | 24 | Music Elem | 34 | Early Childhood Ed |
| 7 | Health Services | 14 | Asst Superintendent | 25 | Music Sec | 35 | Health/Phys Education |
| | | 15 | Instructional Media Svcs | 26 | Business Education | 36 | Guidance Services K-12 |
| | | 16 | Chief Operations Officer | 27 | Career & Tech Ed | 37 | Guidance Services Elem |
| | | 17 | Chief Academic Officer | 28 | Technology Education | 38 | Guidance Services Sec |

| | | | | | |
|---|---|---|---|---|---|
| 39 | Social Studies K-12 | 49 | English/Lang Arts Elem | 59 | Special Education Elem |
| 40 | Social Studies Elem | 50 | English/Lang Arts Sec | 60 | Special Education Sec |
| 41 | Social Studies Sec | 51 | Reading K-12 | 61 | Foreign/World Lang K-12 |
| 42 | Science K-12 | 52 | Reading Elem | 62 | Foreign/World Lang Elem |
| 43 | Science Elem | 53 | Reading Sec | 63 | Foreign/World Lang Sec |
| 44 | Science Sec | 54 | Remedial Reading K-12 | 64 | Religious Education K-12 |
| 45 | Math K-12 | 55 | Remedial Reading Elem | 65 | Religious Education Elem |
| 46 | Math Elem | 56 | Remedial Reading Sec | 66 | Religious Education Sec |
| 47 | Math Sec | 57 | Bilingual/ELL | 67 | School Board President |
| 48 | English/Lang Arts K-12 | 58 | Special Education K-12 | 68 | Teacher Personnel |

| | |
|---|---|
| 69 | Academic Assessment |
| 70 | Research/Development |
| 71 | Public Information |
| 72 | Summer School |
| 73 | Instructional Tech |
| 74 | Inservice Training |
| 75 | Marketing/Distributive |
| 76 | Info Systems |
| 77 | Psychological Assess |
| 78 | Affirmative Action |

## SHELBY PUBLIC SCHOOLS

- **Center Ind School Dist** PID: 01050278    936/598-5642
  107 PR 605, Center 75935    Fax 936/598-1515

**Schools:** 6 \ **Teachers:** 204 \ **Students:** 2,600 \ **Special Ed Students:** 304 \ **LEP Students:** 689 \ **College-Bound:** 56% \ **Ethnic:** Asian 3%, African American 20%, Hispanic 45%, Caucasian 33% \ **Exp:** $405 (High) \ **Poverty:** 30% \ **Title I:** $923,858 \ **Special Education:** $539,000 \ **Open-Close:** 08/12 - 05/21 \ **DTBP:** $158 (High)

| | | | |
|---|---|---|---|
| Dr Brian Morris | 1 | Betty McDaniel | 2,19 |
| Rick Baker | 3,5 | Tina Byrnes | 4 |
| Scott Ponder | 6 | Jennifer Guillory | 11,37,57,271* |
| Carey Herew | 34,58 | Sommer Herndon | 38,69* |
| Matthew Mettauer | 67 | Holly Mikesh | 68 |
| Richard Miller | 73,76 | Jeremy Wallace | 88 |
| Teresa Richard | 275 | | |

| Public Schs..Principal | Grd | Prgm | Enr/#Cls | SN | |
|---|---|---|---|---|---|
| Center Elem Sch 621 Rough Rider Dr, Center 75935 Lana Whitworth | 1-3 | T | 553 19 | 82% | 936/598-3625 Fax 936/598-1507 |
| Center High Sch 658 Rough Rider Dr, Center 75935 Matthew Gregory | 9-12 | ATV | 640 70 | 72% | 936/598-6173 Fax 936/598-1527 |
| Center Intermediate Sch 624 Malone Dr, Center 75935 Lee Masterson | 4-5 | T | 372 20 | 82% | 936/598-6148 Fax 936/598-1555 |
| Center Middle Sch 302 Kennedy St, Center 75935 Jake Henson | 6-8 | TV | 583 65 | 81% | 936/598-5619 Fax 936/598-1534 |
| Ⓐ Center Roughrider Academy 658 Rough Rider Dr, Center 75935 Jill Gaston | 6-12 | T | 61 | 78% | 936/598-1540 Fax 936/591-8374 |
| F L Moffett Primary Sch 294 Stadium Dr, Center 75935 Inez Hughes | PK-K | T | 238 36 | 91% | 936/598-6266 Fax 936/598-1545 |

- **Excelsior Ind School Dist** PID: 01050321    936/598-5866
  11270 State Highway 7W, Center 75935    Fax 936/598-2076

**Schools:** 1 \ **Teachers:** 11 \ **Students:** 80 \ **Special Ed Students:** 22 \ **LEP Students:** 3 \ **Ethnic:** African American 1%, Hispanic 10%, Native American: 1%, Caucasian 88% \ **Exp:** $533 (High) \ **Poverty:** 26% \ **Title I:** $37,336 \ **Open-Close:** 08/24 - 05/26 \ **DTBP:** $335 (High)

| | | | |
|---|---|---|---|
| Wayne Mason | 1 | Terre Noble | 2 |
| Sonya Nutt | 6,83* | Judy Andrews | 11,57,76,88,286,288,296,298 |
| Barbara Scates | 16,73,295,297* | Rebecca Adkinson | 34* |
| Benny Russell | 67 | | |

| Public Schs..Principal | Grd | Prgm | Enr/#Cls | SN | |
|---|---|---|---|---|---|
| Excelsior Elem Sch 11270 State Highway 7W, Center 75935 Johnny Lewis | PK-8 | T | 80 10 | 75% | 936/598-5866 |

- **Joaquin Ind School Dist** PID: 01050357    936/269-3128
  11109 US Highway 84 E, Joaquin 75954    Fax 936/269-3615

**Schools:** 3 \ **Teachers:** 54 \ **Students:** 680 \ **Special Ed Students:** 123 \ **LEP Students:** 46 \ **College-Bound:** 56% \ **Ethnic:** African American 5%, Hispanic 16%, Caucasian 78% \ **Exp:** $457 (High) \ **Poverty:** 31% \ **Title I:** $290,224 \ **Special Education:** $159,000 \ **Open-Close:** 08/10 - 05/21 \ **DTBP:** $344 (High)

| | | | |
|---|---|---|---|
| Ryan Fuller | 1 | Joel Bumback | 2,12 |
| Mark Bonner | 3* | Judy Strong | 4* |
| Rodney Prnka | 5* | Steven McCann | 6* |
| Sherri Scruggs | 8* | Kathy Carrington | 11,58* |
| Justin Wilburn | 16,73,76,295 | Lisa Barton | 16* |
| Ashley Rambin | 36,57,271* | Chrisco Bragg | 67 |
| Donna Vergo | 68 | | |

| Public Schs..Principal | Grd | Prgm | Enr/#Cls | SN | |
|---|---|---|---|---|---|
| Joaquin Elem Sch 120 Southern St, Joaquin 75954 Sherry Scruggs | PK-5 | T | 276 26 | 66% | 936/269-3128 Fax 936/269-3324 |
| Joaquin High Sch 10901 US Highway 84 E, Joaquin 75954 Rodney Prnka | 9-12 | TV | 193 50 | 62% | 936/269-3128 Fax 936/269-9123 |
| Joaquin Junior High Sch 10901 US Highway 84 E, Joaquin 75954 Terri Gray | 6-8 | TV | 172 15 | 62% | 936/269-3128 Fax 936/269-9123 |

- **Shelbyville Ind School Dist** PID: 01050395    936/598-2641
  5322 State Highway 87 S, Shelbyville 75973    Fax 936/598-6842

**Schools:** 3 \ **Teachers:** 68 \ **Students:** 790 \ **Special Ed Students:** 81 \ **LEP Students:** 42 \ **Ethnic:** African American 19%, Hispanic 13%, Native American: 1%, Caucasian 67% \ **Exp:** $424 (High) \ **Poverty:** 32% \ **Title I:** $283,729 \ **Special Education:** $172,000 \ **Open-Close:** 08/20 - 05/20 \ **DTBP:** $339 (High)

| | | | |
|---|---|---|---|
| Dr Ray West | 1 | Joyce Dean | 2 |
| Terry Walton | 3* | Brenda Hogue | 4* |
| Thomas Swearengen | 5,8,83,85,88* | David Bendon | 6 |
| Jeane Taylor | 7* | Jill Baty | 11,15,270,271,274 |
| Catherine Duvon | 13,57,58* | Kaelee Fallin | 27 |
| Patricia Bays | 31* | Sonya Parker | 39* |
| Etola Jones | 67 | Mike Furlow | 69,273* |
| Scott Gilchrist | 73* | | |

| Public Schs..Principal | Grd | Prgm | Enr/#Cls | SN | |
|---|---|---|---|---|---|
| S W Carter Elem Sch 343 Farm Rd 417 W, Shelbyville 75973 Mike Furlow | PK-5 | | 390 25 | | 936/598-7363 Fax 936/598-6843 |
| Shelbyville High Sch 5322 State Highway 87 S, Shelbyville 75973 Mario Osby | 9-12 | V | 228 7 | | 936/598-7323 Fax 936/598-3868 |
| Shelbyville Middle Sch 343 Farm Rd 417 W, Shelbyville 75973 Thomas Swearengen | 6-8 | TV | 177 14 | 63% | 936/598-5146 Fax 936/598-3830 |

- **Tenaha Ind School Dist** PID: 01050424    936/248-5000
  138 College St, Tenaha 75974    Fax 936/248-3902

**Schools:** 1 \ **Teachers:** 41 \ **Students:** 542 \ **Special Ed Students:** 81 \ **LEP Students:** 96 \ **College-Bound:** 66% \ **Ethnic:** African American 25%, Hispanic 44%, Caucasian 31% \ **Exp:** $659 (High) \ **Poverty:** 30% \ **Title I:** $196,356 \ **Special Education:** $155,000 \ **Open-Close:** 08/19 - 05/28 \ **DTBP:** $311 (High) \ f

Scott Tyner ....................................................1
Joshua Campbell ............................................3*
Terry Bowlin ...................................5,17,298*
Stella Baker ...................................................7*
Martha Boren .................................8,11,69*
Ray Jackson ..............................16,73,295*
Judy Monroe ...............................................58*
Emily Bowlin ................................................68

Emily LeMoine ...................................2,294*
Melanie Duncan ...........................................4*
Greg Jenkins ................................................6*
Karen Fallin ...................8,13,36,83,88,270*
Linda Jacobs-Worrell ...................................9*
Laurie Sisk ........................................57,271
Aaron Roland ...............................................67

| Public Schs..Principal | Grd | Prgm | Enr/#Cls | SN | |
|---|---|---|---|---|---|
| Tenaha Sch<br>1 Tiger Drive, Tenaha 75974<br>Linda Jacobs-Worrell | PK-12 | TV | 542<br>18 | 87% | 936/248-5000 |

## ● Timpson Ind School Dist PID: 01050450

836 Bear Dr, Timpson 75975

936/254-2463  
Fax 936/254-3878

Schools: 3 \ Teachers: 55 \ Students: 628 \ Special Ed Students: 80 \ LEP Students: 23 \ College-Bound: 90% \ Ethnic: African American 24%, Hispanic 14%, Caucasian 63% \ Exp: $680 (High) \ Poverty: 25% \ Title I: $348,798 \ Special Education: $143,000 \ Open-Close: 08/19 - 05/27 \ DTBP: $347 (High) \ 🅕 🅣

Dr Mid Johnson ...............................................1
Ginger Lee .......................................................4
Kerry Therwhanger .........................................6
Dana Evans ....................................................58
Annette Johnson ...............................73,76
Calvin Smith ...............................................285*

Raily Daniels ..................................................2
Fred Wilcox .....................................................5
Lynette Alford .................................................7
Brinson Stewart ............................................67
Kim Graham ...................................................91

| Public Schs..Principal | Grd | Prgm | Enr/#Cls | SN | |
|---|---|---|---|---|---|
| Timpson Elem Sch<br>836 Bear Dr, Timpson 75975<br>DeWayne Carrington | PK-5 | | 304<br>20 | | 936/254-2462<br>Fax 936/254-3261 |
| Timpson High Sch<br>836 Bear Dr, Timpson 75975<br>Ronald Lindgren | 9-12 | TV | 182<br>20 | 71% | 936/254-3125<br>Fax 936/254-3263 |
| Timpson Middle Sch<br>836 Bear Dr, Timpson 75975<br>Calvin Smith | 6-8 | | 142 | | 936/254-2078<br>Fax 936/254-2355 |

## SHELBY PRIVATE SCHOOLS

| Private Schs..Principal | Grd | Prgm | Enr/#Cls | SN | |
|---|---|---|---|---|---|
| Central Baptist Christian Sch<br>909 Cora St, Center 75935<br>Danny Dodson | PK-12 | | 42<br>9 | | 936/598-3642<br>Fax 936/598-9175 |

## SHERMAN PUBLIC SCHOOLS

## ● Stratford Ind School Dist PID: 01050486

503 8th St, Stratford 79084

806/366-3300  
Fax 806/366-3304

Schools: 3 \ Teachers: 57 \ Students: 560 \ Special Ed Students: 44 \ LEP Students: 94 \ College-Bound: 80% \ Ethnic: African American 1%, Hispanic 67%, Caucasian 32% \ Exp: $436 (High) \ Poverty: 14% \ Title I: $84,870 \ Open-Close: 08/17 - 05/27 \ DTBP: $345 (High)

Mike Dominguez ...........................1,73,83
Frank Castaneda ............................................3
Jeff Kautz .......................................................5
Doug Rawlins ..........................................8,15
Misti McBryde ...........36,57,58,69,79,85
Beatrice Coreo ...........................................271

Lynette Kautz ............................2,11,84,296
Tina Brooks .....................................................4
Matt Lovrn .......................................................6*
Ashley Lavake ...............................................12
Jo Hinds ........................................................67

| Public Schs..Principal | Grd | Prgm | Enr/#Cls | SN | |
|---|---|---|---|---|---|
| Mary Allen Elem Sch<br>501 N Shirley Ave, Stratford 79084<br>**Doug Rawlins** | PK-4 | T | 204<br>25 | 67% | 806/366-3340<br>Fax 806/366-3343 |
| Stratford High Sch<br>503 8th St, Stratford 79084<br>Phillip Hanna | 9-12 | AGTV | 154<br>30 | 62% | 806/366-3330 |
| Stratford Junior High Sch<br>503 8th St, Stratford 79084<br>Clint Seward | 5-8 | T | 185<br>30 | 62% | 806/366-3320<br>Fax 806/366-3307 |

## ● Texhoma Ind School Dist PID: 01050527

402 W Denver St, Texhoma 73960

806/827-7400  
Fax 806/827-7657

Schools: 1 \ Teachers: 12 \ Students: 130 \ Special Ed Students: 19 \ LEP Students: 62 \ Ethnic: Hispanic 59%, Native American: 1%, Caucasian 40% \ Exp: $214 (Med) \ Poverty: 14% \ Title I: $17,679 \ Open-Close: 08/13 - 05/21 \ DTBP: $367 (High)

Kayla Yates ........................1,11,73,83,288
Alejo Ortega ....................................................3
Kayla Yates ...........11,73,83,275,286,288,296*
Cody Cartwright ...........................................67
Jim Pierce ...................................................295

Danielle Harland ................................2,71
Macy Burrow ...................................................4
Missy Cartwright ..........11,73,83,275,286,288
Crystal Seymure ........................................271

| Public Schs..Principal | Grd | Prgm | Enr/#Cls | SN | |
|---|---|---|---|---|---|
| Texhoma Elem Sch<br>402 W Denver St, Texhoma 73960<br>Kayla Yates | PK-4 | T | 130<br>16 | 66% | 806/827-7400 |

| | | | | | | | | | |
|---|---|---|---|---|---|---|---|---|---|
| 1 | Superintendent | 8 | Curric/Instruct K-12 | 19 | Chief Financial Officer | 29 | Family/Consumer Science | 39 | Social Studies K-12 |
| 2 | Bus/Finance/Purchasing | 9 | Curric/Instruct Elem | 20 | Art K-12 | 30 | Adult Education | 40 | Social Studies Elem |
| 3 | Buildings And Grounds | 10 | Curric/Instruct Sec | 21 | Art Elem | 31 | Career/Sch-to-Work K-12 | 41 | Social Studies Sec |
| 4 | Food Service | 11 | Federal Program | 22 | Art Sec | 32 | Career/Sch-to-Work Elem | 42 | Science K-12 |
| 5 | Transportation | 12 | Title I | 23 | Music K-12 | 33 | Career/Sch-to-Work Sec | 43 | Science Elem |
| 6 | Athletic | 13 | Title V | 24 | Music Elem | 34 | Early Childhood Ed | 44 | Science Sec |
| 7 | Health Services | 15 | Asst Superintendent | 25 | Music Sec | 35 | Health/Phys Education | 45 | Math K-12 |
| | | 16 | Instructional Media Svcs | 26 | Business Education | 36 | Guidance Services K-12 | 46 | Math Elem |
| | | 17 | Chief Operations Officer | 27 | Career & Tech Ed | 37 | Guidance Services Elem | 47 | Math Sec |
| | | 18 | Chief Academic Officer | 28 | Technology Education | 38 | Guidance Services Sec | 48 | English/Lang Arts K-12 |

| | | | | | |
|---|---|---|---|---|---|
| 49 | English/Lang Arts Elem | 59 | Special Education Elem | 69 | Academic Assessment |
| 50 | English/Lang Arts Sec | 60 | Special Education Sec | 70 | Research/Development |
| 51 | Reading K-12 | 61 | Foreign/World Lang K-12 | 71 | Public Information |
| 52 | Reading Elem | 62 | Foreign/World Lang Elem | 72 | Summer School |
| 53 | Reading Sec | 63 | Foreign/World Lang Sec | 73 | Instructional Tech |
| 54 | Remedial Reading K-12 | 64 | Religious Education K-12 | 74 | Inservice Training |
| 55 | Remedial Reading Elem | 65 | Religious Education Elem | 75 | Marketing/Distributive |
| 56 | Remedial Reading Sec | 66 | Religious Education Sec | 76 | Info Systems |
| 57 | Bilingual/ELL | 67 | School Board President | 77 | Psychological Assess |
| 58 | Special Education K-12 | 68 | Teacher Personnel | 78 | Affirmative Action |

# SMITH COUNTY

## SMITH PUBLIC SCHOOLS

### • Arp Ind School Dist PID: 01050541
101 Toney Dr, Arp 75750      903/859-8482   Fax 903/859-2621

Schools: 3 \ Teachers: 75 \ Students: 870 \ Special Ed Students: 80 \ LEP Students: 26 \ College-Bound: 52% \ Ethnic: Asian 1%, African American 15%, Hispanic 12%, Caucasian 71% \ Exp: $515 (High) \ Poverty: 14% \ Title I: $189,421 \ Open-Close: 08/19 - 05/20 \ DTBP: $341 (High)

| | | | |
|---|---|---|---|
| John Arrington | 1 | Daniella Sanders | 2,19 |
| Randal Wilson | 3,5 | Kim Wood | 4 |
| Dale Irwin | 6 | Shelby Brown | 7,85 |
| Lana Brady | 8,11,74,273 | Dr Joy Rousseau | 16,73,270,286,295,298* |
| Monica Johnson | 37 | Donna Lowery | 38* |
| Lara Parker | 38,57,81* | Sanya Burnette | 58 |
| Ernest Stroupe | 67 | Craig Sanders | 275 |

| Public Schs..Principal | Grd | Prgm | Enr/#Cls | SN | |
|---|---|---|---|---|---|
| Arp Elem Sch<br>16438 Co Rd 294, Arp 75750<br>Stephanie Schminkey | PK-5 | T | 390<br>21 | 57% | 903/859-4650<br>Fax 903/859-3683 |
| Arp High Sch<br>101 Toney Dr, Arp 75750<br>Bryan Hurst | 9-12 | TV | 249<br>25 | 53% | 903/859-4917<br>Fax 903/859-1541 |
| Arp Junior High Sch<br>105 School St, Arp 75750<br>Mike Miller | 6-8 | T | 196<br>20 | 57% | 903/859-4936<br>Fax 903/859-3980 |

### • Bullard Ind School Dist PID: 01050577
1426B S Houston St, Bullard 75757      903/894-6639   Fax 903/894-9291

Schools: 6 \ Teachers: 201 \ Students: 2,700 \ Special Ed Students: 281 \ LEP Students: 59 \ Ethnic: African American 4%, Hispanic 7%, Caucasian 88% \ Exp: $436 (High) \ Poverty: 15% \ Title I: $380,182 \ Special Education: $26,000 \ Open-Close: 08/18 - 05/21 \ DTBP: $341 (High)

| | | | |
|---|---|---|---|
| Dr Jack Lee | 1 | Dalton Smith | 3,5,73 |
| Stephanie Hayes | 4 | Dalton Smith | 5* |
| Scott Callaway | 6 | Cheryl Hindricks | 8,11,88,271 |
| Carol Martin | 16* | Lisa Williams | 58 |
| Jason Campbell | 67 | Jodie Albritton | 69* |
| Kory Prince | 73 | | |

| Public Schs..Principal | Grd | Prgm | Enr/#Cls | SN | |
|---|---|---|---|---|---|
| Bullard Early Childhood Center<br>318 Schoolhouse Rd, Bullard 75757<br>Amanda Goode | PK-K | T | 177 | 60% | 903/894-6389<br>Fax 903/894-5937 |
| Bullard Elem Sch<br>2008 Panther Crossing, Bullard 75757<br>Jenny Kasson | 3-4 | T | 396<br>41 | 35% | 903/894-2930<br>Fax 903/894-2931 |
| Bullard High Sch<br>1426 S Houston St, Bullard 75757<br>Mr Blain | 9-12 | | 808<br>37 | 27% | 903/894-3272<br>Fax 903/894-3051 |
| Bullard Intermediate Sch<br>218 Schoolhouse Rd, Bullard 75757<br>Jodie Albritton | 5-6 | T | 387<br>13 | 31% | 903/894-6793<br>Fax 903/894-3982 |

| Bullard Middle Sch<br>909 W Main St, Bullard 75757<br>**Mark McDonald** | 7-8 | | 385<br>32 | 31% | 903/894-6533<br>Fax 903/894-7592 |
|---|---|---|---|---|---|
| Bullard Primary Sch<br>2016 Panther Crossing, Bullard 75757<br>Kim Murphy | 1-2 | T | 383 | 34% | 903/894-2890<br>Fax 903/894-2893 |

### • Chapel Hill Ind School Dist PID: 01050606
11134 County Road 2249, Tyler 75707      903/566-2441   Fax 903/566-8935

Schools: 5 \ Teachers: 249 \ Students: 3,513 \ Special Ed Students: 387 \ LEP Students: 736 \ College-Bound: 23% \ Ethnic: Asian 1%, African American 18%, Hispanic 50%, Caucasian 31% \ Exp: $629 (High) \ Poverty: 21% \ Title I: $1,058,908 \ Special Education: $604,000 \ Open-Close: 08/19 - 05/28 \ DTBP: $222 (High)

| | | | |
|---|---|---|---|
| LaMond Dean | 1 | Lisa Lemon | 2 |
| Jason Godbolt | 3,4,5 | Steven Lenz | 3,4,5,91 |
| Jeffrey Riordan | 6 | Lisa Krumm | 9,69* |
| Deidra Sutton | 11 | Dr Rebecca Roos | 34,58,90 |
| April Munoz | 57 | Martin Ibarra | 67 |
| Elizabeth Rowe | 68 | Benjamin Wood | 73,95 |
| Dr Josh Tremont | 76 | Chuck Munoz | 84 |
| Tony Gibbs | 295 | | |

| Public Schs..Principal | Grd | Prgm | Enr/#Cls | SN | |
|---|---|---|---|---|---|
| Chapel Hill High Sch<br>13172 State Highway 64 E, Tyler 75707<br>**Jason Caldwell** | 9-12 | ATV | 1,013<br>90 | 75% | 903/566-2311<br>Fax 903/565-5155 |
| Chapel Hill Middle Sch<br>13174 State Highway 64 E, Tyler 75707<br>Matt Strode | 6-8 | AT | 822<br>55 | 81% | 903/566-1491<br>Fax 903/565-5125 |
| Jackson Elem Sch<br>16406 FM 2767, Tyler 75705<br>Jill Clay | PK-4 | T | 411<br>24 | 92% | 903/566-3411<br>Fax 903/565-5185 |
| Kissam Elem Sch<br>12800 State Highway 64 E, Tyler 75707<br>Keith Collins | PK-5 | T | 635<br>30 | 84% | 903/566-8334<br>Fax 903/565-5195 |
| Ⓜ Wise Elem Fine Arts Magnet Sch<br>10659 State Highway 64 E, Tyler 75707<br>Cyndy Reagan | PK-5 | T | 473<br>30 | 77% | 903/566-2271<br>Fax 903/565-5135 |

### • Lindale Ind School Dist PID: 01050656
505 Pierce St, Lindale 75771      903/881-4000   Fax 903/881-4004

Schools: 6 \ Teachers: 284 \ Students: 4,200 \ Special Ed Students: 424 \ LEP Students: 148 \ College-Bound: 80% \ Ethnic: Asian 1%, African American 5%, Hispanic 18%, Caucasian 75% \ Exp: $435 (High) \ Poverty: 18% \ Title I: $889,160 \ Special Education: $660,000 \ Open-Close: 08/19 - 05/28 \ DTBP: $181 (High)

| | | | |
|---|---|---|---|
| Stan Surratt | 1 | Michelle Tate | 2 |
| Ed Rhinehart | 3 | Jamie Holder | 3,15,76 |
| Cindy McClenny | 4 | Pete Ridge | 5* |
| Mike Maddox | 6,35,83 | Traci Fountain | 7* |
| Jane Silvey | 8,74,273 | Macie Thompson | 8 |
| Lori Anderson | 11 | Rhonda Walker | 16* |
| Brent Berryman | 27 | David Ramsey | 36,69* |
| Deb Kellas | 57* | Christy Clouse | 58 |
| Mike Combs | 67 | Courtney Sanguinetti | 71 |
| Randy Anderson | 73,84,295 | Joey King | 91 |

| Public Schs..Principal | Grd | Prgm | Enr/#Cls | SN | |
|---|---|---|---|---|---|
| College Street Elem Sch<br>106 N College St, Lindale 75771<br>Ashley Smith | 1-3 | T | 444<br>23 | 47% | 903/881-4350<br>Fax 903/881-4351 |

---

| | | | | | | | |
|---|---|---|---|---|---|---|---|
| 79 | Student Personnel | 91 | Safety/Security | 275 | Response To Intervention | 298 | Grant Writer/Ptnrships |
| 80 | Driver Ed/Safety | 92 | Magnet School | 277 | Remedial Math K-12 | 750 | Chief Innovation Officer |
| 81 | Gifted/Talented | 93 | Parental Involvement | 280 | Literacy Coach | 751 | Chief of Staff |
| 82 | Video Services | 95 | Tech Prep Program | 285 | STEM | 752 | Social Emotional Learning |
| 83 | Substance Abuse Prev | 97 | Chief Infomation Officer | 286 | Digital Learning | | |
| 84 | Erate | 98 | Chief Technology Officer | 288 | Common Core Standards | | Other School Types |
| 85 | AIDS Education | 270 | Character Education | 294 | Accountability | Ⓐ | = Alternative School |
| 88 | Alternative/At Risk | 271 | Migrant Education | 295 | Network System | Ⓒ | = Charter School |
| 89 | Multi-Cultural Curriculum | 273 | Teacher Mentor | 296 | Title II Programs | Ⓜ | = Magnet School |
| 90 | Social Work | 274 | Before/After Sch | 297 | Webmaster | Ⓨ | = Year-Round School |

| School Programs | Social Media |
|---|---|
| A = Alternative Program | |
| G = Adult Classes | 🄵 = Facebook |
| M = Magnet Program | |
| T = Title I Schoolwide | 🅃 = Twitter |
| V = Career & Tech Ed Programs | |

New Schools are shaded
New Superintendents and Principals are bold
Personnel with email addresses are underscored

| | Grd | Prgm | Enr/#Cls | SN |
|---|---|---|---|---|
| E J Moss Intermediate Sch<br>411 Eagle Spirit Dr, Lindale 75771<br>**Candace Widemon** | 4-6 | T | 970<br>24 | 44% 903/881-4200<br>Fax 903/881-4201 |
| Early Childhood Center<br>201 Stadium Dr, Lindale 75771<br>Kaela Deslatte | PK-K | T | 447<br>21 | 63% 903/881-4400<br>Fax 903/881-4401 |
| Lindale High Sch<br>920 E Hubbard St, Lindale 75771<br>Jeremy Chilek | 9-12 | TV | 1,144<br>80 | 37% 903/881-4050<br>Fax 903/882-2813 [f] |
| Lindale Junior High Sch<br>15000 County Rd 463, Lindale 75771<br>Tracie Rand | 7-8 | T | 641<br>40 | 39% 903/881-4150<br>Fax 903/882-2842 |
| Velma Penny Elem Sch<br>1000 Mt Silvan Hwy, Lindale 75771<br>Monica Moore | 1-3 | T | 469<br>26 | 50% 903/881-4250<br>Fax 903/881-4251 |

• **Troup Ind School Dist** PID: 01050709     903/842-3067
201 N Carolina St, Troup 75789     Fax 903/842-4563

**Schools:** 3 \ **Teachers:** 81 \ **Students:** 1,100 \ **Special Ed Students:** 78 \
**LEP Students:** 47 \ **Ethnic:** Asian 1%, African American 11%, Hispanic 13%,
Caucasian 75% \ **Exp:** $636 (High) \ **Poverty:** 21% \ **Title I:** $271,499 \
**Open-Close:** 08/12 - 05/26 \ **DTBP:** $99 (Med) \ [f]

| | | | |
|---|---|---|---|
| Tammy Jones ............1 | Lisa White ............2,68 |
| Teresa Gillespie ............4 | Preston Lindsey ............5 |
| John Eastman ............6* | Laurie Larison ............7* |
| David Smith ............8,11,57,69,83,88,273 | Reginald Gossett ............16,73 |
| Tracy Martin ............38 | Shane Jasper ............67 |
| Kim Shockner ............274 | |

| Public Schs..Principal | Grd | Prgm | Enr/#Cls | SN |
|---|---|---|---|---|
| Troup Elem Sch<br>201 E Bryant St, Troup 75789<br>Amy Ledford | PK-5 | T | 481<br>40 | 61% 903/842-3071<br>Fax 903/842-3197 |
| Troup High Sch<br>927 Arp Dr, Troup 75789<br>Bobby Dyess | 9-12 | ATV | 328<br>25 | 48% 903/842-3065<br>Fax 903/842-5199 |
| Troup Middle Sch<br>817 Arp Dr, Troup 75789<br>Stephen Cooksey | 6-8 | T | 252<br>30 | 51% 903/842-3081<br>Fax 903/842-5198 |

• **Tyler Ind School Dist** PID: 01050747     903/262-1000
1319 Earl Campbell Pkwy, Tyler 75701     Fax 903/262-1174

**Schools:** 29 \ **Teachers:** 1,210 \ **Students:** 18,000 \
**Special Ed Students:** 1,450 \ **LEP Students:** 3,766 \ **College-Bound:** 63%
\ **Ethnic:** Asian 1%, African American 28%, Hispanic 48%, Caucasian
22% \ **Exp:** $409 (High) \ **Poverty:** 22% \ **Title I:** $7,362,734 \
**Special Education:** $3,250,000 \ **Open-Close:** 08/19 - 05/26 \ **DTBP:** $184
(High) \ [f] [t]

| | | | |
|---|---|---|---|
| Dr Marty Crawford ............1 | Tosha Bjork ............2,19 |
| Tim Loper ............3 | Victor Olivares ............4 |
| John Bagert ............5 | Greg Priest ............6,85 |
| Rachel Barber ............7 | Dr Christy Hanson ............8,15 |
| Jennifer Jones ............9,36 | Brandy Holland ............11 |
| Vernora Jones ............12 | Ron Jones ............15,68,751 |
| Sandra Newton ............20,23 | Jeannia Dykman ............34,58 |
| Anna Sgulin ............57 | Wade Watsmen ............67 |
| Sheri Taylor ............68 | Johnita Ward ............69,294 |
| Joseph Jacks ............73 | John Johnson ............79 |
| Nicole Schumer ............81 | Danny Brown ............83,91 |

| Public Schs..Principal | Grd | Prgm | Enr/#Cls | SN |
|---|---|---|---|---|
| Austin Elem Sch<br>1105 W Franklin St, Tyler 75702<br>**Joshua Currie** | K-5 | T | 420<br>30 | 97% 903/262-1765<br>Fax 903/262-1767 |
| Bell Elem Sch<br>1409 E Hankerson St, Tyler 75701<br>Tamara Johnson | K-5 | T | 392<br>28 | 82% 903/262-1820<br>Fax 903/262-1821 |
| Birdwell Elem Sch<br>2010 S Talley Ave, Tyler 75701<br>**Bethany Moody** | PK-5 | T | 546<br>30 | 88% 903/262-1870<br>Fax 903/262-1871 [f] [t] |
| Bonner Elem Sch<br>235 S Saunders Ave, Tyler 75702<br>Stephanie Burns | PK-5 | T | 441<br>31 | 94% 903/262-1920<br>Fax 903/262-1921 [f] [t] |
| Ⓜ Boulter Middle Sch<br>2926 Garden Valley Rd, Tyler 75702<br>**Vanessa Holmes** | 6-8 | TV | 957<br>50 | 93% 903/262-1390<br>Fax 903/262-1392 |
| Caldwell Arts Academy<br>331 S College Ave, Tyler 75702<br>Bobby Markle | PK-5 | T | 649<br>25 | 53% 903/262-2250<br>Fax 903/262-2252 |
| Ⓨ Clarkston Elem Sch<br>2915 Williamsburg Dr, Tyler 75701<br>Gretchen Nabi | PK-5 | MT | 408<br>30 | 69% 903/262-1980<br>Fax 903/262-1981 [f] [t] |
| Dixie Elem Sch<br>213 Patton Ln, Tyler 75704<br>**Kimberly Simmons** | PK-5 | T | 567<br>35 | 88% 903/262-2040<br>Fax 903/262-2041 |
| Douglas Elem Sch<br>1525 N Carlyle Ave, Tyler 75702<br>Christy Roach | PK-5 | T | 575<br>33 | 95% 903/262-2100<br>Fax 903/262-2101 |
| Dr Bryan C Jack Elem Sch<br>1900 Balsam Gap, Tyler 75703<br>Brett Shelby | K-5 | | 671<br>30 | 37% 903/262-3260<br>Fax 903/262-3329 |
| Griffin Elem Sch<br>2650 N Broadway Ave, Tyler 75702<br>Steven Ladd | PK-5 | T | 691<br>35 | 96% 903/262-2310<br>Fax 903/262-2311 |
| Hubbard Middle Sch<br>1300 Hubbard Dr, Tyler 75703<br>Geoffrey Sherman | 6-8 | TV | 721<br>58 | 56% 903/262-1560<br>Fax 903/262-1566 [f] [t] |
| James S Hogg Middle Sch<br>920 S Broadway Ave, Tyler 75701<br>**Kristen Walls** | 6-8 | TV | 366<br>47 | 95% 903/262-1500<br>Fax 903/262-1501 |
| Jones Elem Sch<br>3450 Chandler Hwy, Tyler 75702<br>Natasha Crain | PK-5 | T | 348<br>14 | 90% 903/262-2360<br>Fax 903/262-2362 |
| Legacy High Sch<br>4500 Red Raider Dr, Tyler 75703<br>Daniel Crawford | 9-12 | GTV | 2,240 | 56% 903/262-2625<br>Fax 903/262-2630 |
| Ⓜ Moore Mst Magnet Sch<br>2101 E Devine St, Tyler 75701<br>**Aubrey Ballard** | 6-8 | TV | 1,131<br>55 | 83% 903/262-1640<br>Fax 903/262-1648 |
| Orr Elem Sch<br>3350 Pine Haven Rd, Tyler 75703<br>Steve Young | K-5 | T | 695<br>38 | 93% 903/262-2400<br>Fax 903/262-2401 |
| Owens Elem Sch<br>11780 County Road 168, Tyler 75703<br>Rachel Sherman | PK-5 | | 656<br>44 | 37% 903/262-2175<br>Fax 903/262-2176 [f] [t] |
| Peete Elem Sch<br>1511 Bellwood Rd, Tyler 75701<br>**Cassandra Chapa** | K-5 | T | 363<br>25 | 94% 903/262-2460<br>Fax 903/262-2461 [f] [t] |
| Ramey Elem Sch<br>2000 N Forest Ave, Tyler 75702<br>Guillermina Naranjo | K-5 | T | 502<br>35 | 95% 903/262-2505<br>Fax 903/262-2506 [f] [t] |
| Rice Elem Sch<br>5215 Old Bullard Rd, Tyler 75703<br>Shelly Bosley | PK-5 | T | 656<br>38 | 56% 903/262-2555<br>Fax 903/262-2556 |
| Ⓐ Rise Academy<br>2800 W Shaw St, Tyler 75701<br>Dexter Floyd | 9-12 | | 142<br>8 | 903/262-3040<br>Fax 903/262-3041 |

| School | Grd | Prgm | Enr/#Cls | SN | Phone |
|---|---|---|---|---|---|
| Ⓨ St Louis Early Childhood Ctr<br>2800 Walton Rd, Tyler 75701<br>Gloria Bell | PK-PK | MT | 98<br>18 | 98% | 903/262-1180<br>Fax 903/262-1351 |
| Ⓨ Three Lakes Middle Sch<br>2445 Three Lakes Pkwy, Tyler 75703<br>Christopher Blake | 6-8 | MTV | 893<br>50 | 56% | 903/952-4400<br>Fax 903/534-2871 🖪 🔳 |
| Tyler Career & Technology Ctr<br>3013 Earl Campbell Pkwy, Tyler 75701<br>Vanessa Holmes | Voc | | 300 | | 903/262-1024<br>Fax 903/526-0889 |
| Tyler Early College High Sch<br>2800 W Shaw St, Tyler 75701<br>Delsena Frazier | 9-12 | T | 381 | 81% | 903/262-3040<br>Fax 903/262-3041 |
| Tyler High Sch<br>1120 N Northwest Loop 323, Tyler 75702<br>**Claude Lane** | 9-12 | TV | 2,097 | 89% | 903/262-2850<br>Fax 903/593-8655 |
| Wayne D Boshears Center<br>3450 Chandler Hwy, Tyler 75702<br>Lora King | Spec | | 80 | | 903/262-1350<br>Fax 903/262-1351 |
| Woods Elem Sch<br>3131 Fry Ave, Tyler 75701<br>Georgeanna Jones | PK-5 | T | 671<br>33 | 51% | 903/262-1280<br>Fax 903/262-1281 |

● **UT Tyler University Acad Dist** PID: 12317047  903/730-3988
3900 University Blvd, Tyler 75799  Fax 903/705-4330

> **Schools:** 3 \ **Teachers:** 54 \ **Students:** 400 \ **Special Ed Students:** 49 \
> **LEP Students:** 13 \ **College-Bound:** 100% \ **Ethnic:** Asian 4%, African
> American 10%, Hispanic 17%, Native American: 2%, Caucasian 66% \
> **Open-Close:** 08/18 - 05/28

| | | | |
|---|---|---|---|
| Dr Joann Simmons | 1 | Christian Chesnut | 2 |
| Juan Cabrera | 3 | J'Ann Sartain | 4 |
| Jaclyn Pedersen | 8,298 | Kathy Parker | 8,18 |
| Katie Adams | 27 | Chelsea Nardozza | 58 |
| Dr Yanira Oliveras-Ortiz | 67 | Brian Weaver | 69 |
| Dalton Abrams | 73 | | |

| Public Schs..Principal | Grd | Prgm | Enr/#Cls | SN | Phone |
|---|---|---|---|---|---|
| Ⓒ UT Tyler Univ Acad-Longview<br>3201 N Eastman Rd, Longview 75605<br>Rachel Hawkins | 2-11 | | 218 | | 903/663-8219 |
| Ⓒ UT Tyler Univ Acad-Palestine<br>1820 W Spring St, Palestine 75803<br>Dr Becky Rutlage | 2-11 | | 201 | | 903/705-4330 |
| Ⓒ UT Tyler Univ Acad-Tyler<br>3900 University Blvd, Tyler 75799<br>Aimee Dennis | K-12 | | 313 | 14% | 903/705-4330 |

● **Whitehouse Ind School Dist** PID: 01050993  903/839-5500
104 State Highway 110 N, Whitehouse 75791  Fax 903/839-5515

> **Schools:** 8 \ **Teachers:** 314 \ **Students:** 4,800 \ **Special Ed Students:** 504
> \ **LEP Students:** 167 \ **College-Bound:** 59% \ **Ethnic:** Asian 3%,
> African American 13%, Hispanic 15%, Caucasian 68% \ **Exp:** $292 (Med)
> \ **Poverty:** 14% \ **Title I:** $918,751 \ **Special Education:** $825,000 \
> **Open-Close:** 08/19 - 05/27 \ **DTBP:** $176 (High)

| | | | |
|---|---|---|---|
| Chris Moran | 1 | Clint Ray | 2,19 |
| Duane Barber | 4,5,15 | Theresa Wilson | 4 |
| Kevin Whitman | 5 | Betty Lough | 8,11,57,74,85,273,274,296 |
| Susanna Campbell | 8 | Jackie Vigtema | 11,58,271 |
| Travis Bass | 15,88,285,286 | Sonya Johnston | 36,69,83 |
| Kathryn Pratt | 39 | Ann Butler | 42,81 |
| Mary Skinner | 47 | Denise Martin | 50,53 |
| Jaculyn Zigtema | 58 | Greg Hood | 67 |
| Kelley Vannatta | 68 | Monet Brown | 68 |
| Scott Starkey | 73 | Tony Black | 73,84,95,297 |

| Public Schs..Principal | Grd | Prgm | Enr/#Cls | SN | Phone |
|---|---|---|---|---|---|
| Ⓐ Aim Center<br>110 Wildcat Dr, Whitehouse 75791<br>Gary Jacobs | K-12 | | 150<br>8 | | 903/839-5556<br>Fax 903/839-5384 |
| Gus Winston Cain Elem Sch<br>801 State Highway 110 S, Whitehouse 75791<br>Laurie Blain | PK-5 | T | 515<br>32 | 47% | 903/839-5600<br>Fax 903/839-5604 |
| Higgins Elem Sch<br>306 Bascom Rd, Whitehouse 75791<br>**Joanne Saul** | PK-5 | T | 523<br>37 | 55% | 903/839-5580<br>Fax 903/839-5584 |
| Hollaway Sixth Grade Sch<br>701 E Main St, Whitehouse 75791<br>Stacy Pineda | 6-6 | T | 396<br>35 | 42% | 903/839-5656<br>Fax 903/839-1568 |
| Mozelle Brown Elem Sch<br>14600 County Road 2191, Whitehouse 75791<br>Lisa Schwartz | PK-5 | T | 581<br>16 | 58% | 903/839-5610<br>Fax 903/839-5607 |
| Stanton-Smith Elem Sch<br>500 Zavala Trl, Whitehouse 75791<br>Sterling Haskell | PK-5 | T | 475<br>30 | 50% | 903/839-5730<br>Fax 903/839-5744 |
| Whitehouse High Sch<br>901 E Main St, Whitehouse 75791<br>Josh Garred | 9-12 | V | 1,426<br>70 | 37% | 903/839-5551<br>Fax 903/839-5530 |
| Whitehouse Junior High Sch<br>108 Wildcat Dr, Whitehouse 75791<br>William Ripley | 7-8 | T | 754<br>50 | 42% | 903/839-5590<br>Fax 903/839-5518 |

● **Winona Ind School Dist** PID: 01051038  903/939-4000
611 Wildcat Dr, Winona 75792  Fax 903/877-9387

> **Schools:** 4 \ **Teachers:** 87 \ **Students:** 1,050 \ **Special Ed Students:** 135
> \ **LEP Students:** 128 \ **College-Bound:** 52% \ **Ethnic:** African American
> 19%, Hispanic 33%, Caucasian 48% \ **Exp:** $405 (High) \ **Poverty:** 47% \
> **Title I:** $840,509 \ **Special Education:** $192,000 \ **Open-Close:** 08/12 -
> 05/19 \ **DTBP:** $361 (High)

| | | | |
|---|---|---|---|
| **Damenion Miller** | 1 | Sheila Bowie | 2,298 |
| Ronnie Marsh | 3 | Terry Gibbs | 3 |
| Angela Nick | 4 | Carla Davis | 5 |
| Keylon Kincade | 6 | Amanda Marsh | 8 |
| Heather Carnes | 11,271* | Josh Groves | 12,296 |
| Angela Adams | 13,58 | Jamie McNutt | 16,82* |
| Natasha Martinez | 57* | Randy Hawkins | 67 |
| Kyle Pugh | 73,84 | Keith Sparkman | 88* |
| Fabian Arteaga | 91 | Joshua Snook | 91* |
| Wanda Hensley | 271* | | |

| Public Schs..Principal | Grd | Prgm | Enr/#Cls | SN | Phone |
|---|---|---|---|---|---|
| Winona Elem Sch<br>605 Wildcat Dr, Winona 75792<br>Jason Caldwell | PK-3 | T | 387<br>25 | 73% | 903/939-4800<br>Fax 903/877-2457 |
| Winona High Sch<br>102 Wildcat Dr, Winona 75792<br>**Keith Sparkman** | 9-12 | TV | 318<br>40 | 62% | 903/939-4100<br>Fax 903/877-2451 |
| Winona Intermediate Sch<br>611 Wildcat Dr, Winona 75792<br>Jason Caldwell | 4-5 | | 160 | | 903/939-4800<br>Fax 903/877-2457 |
| Winona Middle Sch<br>611 Wildcat Dr, Winona 75792<br>Mark McDonald | 6-8 | T | 247<br>13 | 70% | 903/939-4040<br>Fax 903/877-9150 |

---

| 79 Student Personnel | 91 Safety/Security | 275 Response To Intervention | 298 Grant Writer/Ptnrships | **School Programs** | **Social Media** |
|---|---|---|---|---|---|

79 Student Personnel
80 Driver Ed/Safety
81 Gifted/Talented
82 Video Services
83 Substance Abuse Prev
84 Erate
85 AIDS Education
88 Alternative/At Risk
89 Multi-Cultural Curriculum
90 Social Work

91 Safety/Security
92 Magnet School
93 Parental Involvement
95 Tech Prep Program
97 Chief Infomation Officer
98 Chief Technology Officer
270 Character Education
271 Migrant Education
273 Teacher Mentor
274 Before/After Sch

275 Response To Intervention
277 Remedial Math K-12
280 Literacy Coach
285 STEM
286 Digital Learning
288 Common Core Standards
294 Accountability
295 Network System
296 Title II Programs
297 Webmaster

298 Grant Writer/Ptnrships
750 Chief Innovation Officer
751 Chief of Staff
752 Social Emotional Learning

**Other School Types**
Ⓐ = Alternative School
Ⓒ = Charter School
Ⓜ = Magnet School
Ⓨ = Year-Round School

**School Programs**
A = Alternative Program
G = Adult Classes
M = Magnet Program
T = Title I Schoolwide
V = Career & Tech Ed Programs

New Schools are shaded
New Superintendents and Principals are bold
Personnel with email addresses are underscored

**Social Media**
🖪 = Facebook
🔳 = Twitter

# TX—341

## SMITH CATHOLIC SCHOOLS

• **Diocese of Tyler Ed Office** PID: 03014660    903/534-1077
1015 E Southeast Loop 323, Tyler 75701    Fax 903/534-1370

| Schools: 4 \ Students: 1,300 |
| --- |

Listing includes only schools located in this county. See District Index for location of Diocesan Offices.

Robin Perry ..........................................1,11

| Catholic Schs..Principal | Grd | Prgm | Enr/#Cls | SN |
| --- | --- | --- | --- | --- |
| Bishop T K Gorman Cath Sch | 6-12 | | 365 | 903/561-2424 |
| 1405 E Southeast Loop 323, Tyler 75701 | | | 30 | Fax 903/561-2645 |
| Zachary Allen | | | | |
| St Gregory Cathedral Sch | PK-5 | | 170 | 903/595-4109 |
| 500 S College Ave, Tyler 75702 | | | 17 | Fax 903/592-8626 |
| Robin Perry | | | | |

## SMITH PRIVATE SCHOOLS

| Private Schs..Principal | Grd | Prgm | Enr/#Cls | SN |
| --- | --- | --- | --- | --- |
| All Saints Episcopal Sch | PK-12 | | 700 | 903/579-6000 |
| 2695 S Southwest Loop 323, Tyler 75701 | | | 40 | Fax 903/579-6002 |
| Karla Long | | | | 🅕 🅣 |
| Bridgemark Center for Learning | Spec | | 77 | 903/939-3511 |
| 6704 Old Jacksonville Hwy, Tyler 75703 | | | | |
| Jaime Warren | | | | |
| Brook Hill Sch | PK-12 | | 605 | 903/894-5000 |
| 1051 N Houston St, Bullard 75757 | | | | Fax 903/894-6332 |
| Kris Shustella \ Michelle Rozell | | | | |
| Brook Hills Lower Sch | K-5 | | 240 | 903/894-4164 |
| 1010 N Rather St, Bullard 75757 | | | | Fax 903/894-4674 |
| Jonathan Kegler | | | | |
| Christian Heritage Sch | K-12 | | 100 | 903/593-2702 |
| 961 County Road 1143, Tyler 75704 | | | 15 | Fax 903/531-2226 |
| Jeff Schapansky | | | | |
| East Texas Christian Academy | PK-12 | | 215 | 903/561-8642 |
| 2448 Roy Rd, Tyler 75707 | | | 23 | Fax 903/561-9620 |
| Curtis Williams | | | | |
| Good Shepherd Sch | PK-12 | | 200 | 903/592-4045 |
| 2525 Old Jacksonville Rd, Tyler 75701 | | | | Fax 903/596-7149 |
| Mark Hoyt | | | | |
| Grace Community Jr Sr High Sch | 6-12 | | 582 | 903/566-5661 |
| 3001 University Blvd, Tyler 75701 | | | 30 | Fax 903/566-5639 |
| Karla Flournoy \ Lanny Witt | | | | |
| Grace Community Sch | PK-5 | | 427 | 903/593-1977 |
| 3001 University Blvd, Tyler 75701 | | | 27 | Fax 903/593-2897 |
| Jennifer Dozier | | | | |
| Kingdom Life Academy | 8-12 | | 401 | 903/283-3444 |
| 7330 S Broadway Ave, Tyler 75703 | | | | |
| Joel Enge | | | | |
| Kings Academy Chrn Sch | K-12 | | 77 | 903/534-9992 |
| 7330 S Broadway Ave, Tyler 75703 | | | 13 | Fax 903/526-7929 |
| Erin Baggs | | | | |
| Promise Academy | K-2 | | 36 | 903/630-7369 |
| 504 W 32nd St, Tyler 75702 | | | | |
| Sarah Cumming | | | | |
| Tyler Adventist Sch | K-8 | | 13 | 903/595-6706 |
| 2931 S Southeast Loop 323, Tyler 75701 | | | 2 | |
| Dorothy Sauder | | | | |

## SOMERVELL PUBLIC SCHOOLS

• **Glen Rose Ind School Dist** PID: 01051088    254/898-3900
1102 Stadium Dr, Glen Rose 76043    Fax 254/897-3651

| **Schools:** 4 \ **Teachers:** 137 \ **Students:** 1,970 \ **Special Ed Students:** 137 \ **LEP Students:** 163 \ **College-Bound:** 80% \ **Ethnic:** Asian 1%, African American 1%, Hispanic 30%, Native American: 1%, Caucasian 67% \ **Exp:** $551 (High) \ **Poverty:** 12% \ **Title I:** $229,096 \ **Open-Close:** 08/12 - 05/28 \ **DTBP:** $342 (High) |
| --- |

| | | | |
| --- | --- | --- | --- |
| Wayne Rotan ...........................1 | Kayla O'Quinn ..........................2 |
| Tommy Corcan ........3,5,15,17,68,83,91 | Jill Lawson .............................4 |
| Cliff Watkins ...........................6,35 | Janon Stephenson .....................7 |
| Susan Wright .......8,11,18,57,58,88,296,298 | Shelly Statler ............................16* |
| Kelley Snodgrass ......................67 | Courtney Cordova .................69,288 |
| Terri Taff ..............................69 | Doug McClure ............73,76,98,295 |
| Patty Flanary ..........................286 | |

| Public Schs..Principal | Grd | Prgm | Enr/#Cls | SN |
| --- | --- | --- | --- | --- |
| Glen Rose Elem Sch | PK-2 | T | 412 | 54% 254/898-3503 |
| 601 Stadium Dr, Glen Rose 76043 | | | 30 | Fax 254/897-3086 |
| Debbie Morris | | | | |
| Glen Rose High Sch | 9-12 | AV | 536 | 33% 254/898-3800 |
| 900 Stadium Dr, Glen Rose 76043 | | | 46 | Fax 254/898-3866 |
| Kelly Shackelford | | | | |
| Glen Rose Intermediate Sch | 3-5 | T | 400 | 42% 254/898-3600 |
| 201 Allen Dr, Glen Rose 76043 | | | 31 | Fax 254/898-3645 |
| Lauri Mapes | | | | |
| Glen Rose Junior High Sch | 6-8 | TV | 435 | 38% 254/898-3700 |
| 805 College St, Glen Rose 76043 | | | 50 | Fax 254/898-3771 |
| Lance Cathey | | | | |

## STARR PUBLIC SCHOOLS

• **Rio Grande City Ind Sch Dist** PID: 01051117    956/716-6700
1 S Fort Ringgold St, Rio Grande Cy 78582    Fax 956/487-8506

| **Schools:** 18 \ **Teachers:** 799 \ **Students:** 10,175 \ **Special Ed Students:** 1,031 \ **LEP Students:** 6,765 \ **Ethnic:** Hispanic 100%, \ **Exp:** $285 (Med) \ **Poverty:** 42% \ **Title I:** $6,114,183 \ **Special Education:** $2,054,000 \ **Open-Close:** 08/17 - 05/27 \ **DTBP:** $171 (High) |
| --- |

| | | |
| --- | --- | --- |
| Vilma Garza ...........................1 | Deanna Robles Mendez .............2,19 |
| Marin Lopez ...........................3 | Patsy Ramirez .......................4 |
| Ricardo Solis ..........................5 | Leonel Mierles ......................6 |
| Rolando Barrera .......................7* | Eddie Saenz ..............8,16,73,76,82 |
| Dr Leticia Trevino ..........10,15,36,69 | Gina Gonzalez ....................11,296 |
| Adolfo Pena ...........................15 | Cynthia Bazan ......................18 |
| Rogerio Olivarez ......................23 | Adelina Villarreal ...................27 |

---

| | | | | | | | |
| --- | --- | --- | --- | --- | --- | --- | --- |
| 1 | Superintendent | 8 | Curric/Instruct K-12 | 19 | Chief Financial Officer | 29 | Family/Consumer Science | 39 | Social Studies K-12 | 49 | English/Lang Arts Elem | 59 | Special Education Elem | 69 | Academic Assessment |
| 2 | Bus/Finance/Purchasing | 9 | Curric/Instruct Elem | 20 | Art K-12 | 30 | Adult Education | 40 | Social Studies Elem | 50 | English/Lang Arts Sec | 60 | Special Education Sec | 70 | Research/Development |
| 3 | Buildings And Grounds | 10 | Curric/Instruct Sec | 21 | Art Elem | 31 | Career/Sch-to-Work K-12 | 41 | Social Studies Sec | 51 | Reading K-12 | 61 | Foreign/World Lang K-12 | 71 | Public Information |
| 4 | Food Service | 11 | Federal Program | 22 | Art Sec | 32 | Career/Sch-to-Work Elem | 42 | Science K-12 | 52 | Reading Elem | 62 | Foreign/World Lang Elem | 72 | Summer School |
| 5 | Transportation | 12 | Title I | 23 | Music K-12 | 33 | Career/Sch-to-Work Sec | 43 | Science Elem | 53 | Reading Sec | 63 | Foreign/World Lang Sec | 73 | Instructional Tech |
| 6 | Athletic | 13 | Title V | 24 | Music Elem | 34 | Early Childhood Ed | 44 | Science Sec | 54 | Remedial Reading K-12 | 64 | Religious Education K-12 | 74 | Inservice Training |
| 7 | Health Services | 15 | Asst Superintendent | 25 | Music Sec | 35 | Health/Phys Education | 45 | Math K-12 | 55 | Remedial Reading Elem | 65 | Religious Education Elem | 75 | Marketing/Distributive |
| | | 16 | Instructional Media Svcs | 26 | Business Education | 36 | Guidance Services K-12 | 46 | Math Elem | 56 | Remedial Reading Sec | 66 | Religious Education Sec | 76 | Info Systems |
| | | 17 | Chief Operations Officer | 27 | Career & Tech Ed | 37 | Guidance Services Elem | 47 | Math Sec | 57 | Bilingual/ELL | 67 | School Board President | 77 | Psychological Assess |
| | | 18 | Chief Academic Officer | 28 | Technology Education | 38 | Guidance Services Sec | 48 | English/Lang Arts K-12 | 58 | Special Education K-12 | 68 | Teacher Personnel | 78 | Affirmative Action |

| | | | |
|---|---|---|---|
| Serapio Trillayes | 34 | Guadalupe Garza | 39* |
| Jesus Martinez | 57 | Maricela Garcia | 58 |
| Eleazar Velasquez | 67 | Elsa Villareal-Morr | 69,294 |
| Omar Riojas | 71 | Mariselda Tanguna | 79 |
| Javier Garcia | 91* | Norma McKee | 93 |
| Veronica Garcia | 271 | Dr Paul Doyno | 298 |

| Public Schs..Principal | Grd | Prgm | Enr/#Cls | SN |
|---|---|---|---|---|
| Ⓜ Academy Academic Enhancemnt-ES<br>1 S Fort Ringgold St, Rio Grande Cy 78582<br>Pedro Pena | 1-5 | | 415 | 956/716-6941<br>Fax 956/716-6797 |
| Ⓜ Academy Academic Enhancemnt-MS<br>144 FM Rd 3167, Rio Grande Cy 78582<br>**Lillian Jones** | 6-8 | | 267 | 956/352-6324<br>Fax 956/488-6063 |
| Alberto & Celia Barrera ES<br>1400 N Lopez St, Rio Grande Cy 78582<br>Nora Rivera | PK-5 | | 460<br>26 | 956/716-6618<br>Fax 956/716-8634 |
| Alto Bonito Elem Sch<br>753 N FM 2360, Rio Grande Cy 78582<br>Yvette Pena | PK-5 | T | 478<br>35 | 95% 956/487-6295<br>Fax 956/487-5755 |
| Daep/Seas Center<br>6667 FM 1430, Garciasville 78547<br>Julio Eugia | 1-12 | | 60<br>6 | 956/488-0014<br>Fax 956/487-7311 |
| Dr Mario Ramirez Elem Sch<br>8001 Trophy St, Rio Grande Cy 78582<br>Daniel Ramirez | PK-5 | T | 436<br>23 | 93% 956/487-4457<br>Fax 956/487-4415 |
| General Ricardo Sanchez ES<br>2801 W Eisenhower Rd, Rio Grande Cy 78582<br>Teresa Garcia | PK-5 | T | 604<br>32 | 91% 956/487-7043<br>Fax 956/487-7133 |
| Grulla Elem Sch<br>599 Old Military Rd, Rio Grande Cy 78582<br>Epigmenio Gonzalez | PK-5 | T | 464<br>32 | 84% 956/487-3306<br>Fax 956/716-8615 |
| Grulla High Sch<br>6884 E Highway 83, Rio Grande Cy 78582<br>Adolfo Pena | 9-12 | | 859 | 956/487-7278<br>Fax 956/487-4312 |
| Grulla Middle Sch<br>FM 2360, Grulla 78548<br>Rene Pena | 6-8 | T | 677<br>56 | 91% 956/487-5558<br>Fax 956/487-5633 |
| John & Olive Hinojosa Elem Sch<br>2448 Embassy St, Rio Grande Cy 78582<br>**Mark Olivarez** | PK-5 | T | 406<br>35 | 96% 956/487-3710<br>Fax 956/487-4942 |
| La Union Elem Sch<br>6300 NE Highway 83, Rio Grande Cy 78582<br>Lorena Trevino | PK-5 | T | 317<br>25 | 97% 956/487-3404<br>Fax 956/487-4076 |
| Prep for Early College HS<br>144 FM 3167, Rio Grande Cy 78582<br>Tina Gorena | 9-12 | T | 503 | 86% 956/352-6349<br>Fax 956/352-6387 |
| Ringgold Elem Sch<br>1 S Fort Ringgold St, Rio Grande Cy 78582<br>Idani Salinas | PK-5 | T | 412<br>27 | 95% 956/716-6929<br>Fax 956/716-6930 |
| Ringgold Middle Sch<br>144 FM 3167, Rio Grande Cy 78582<br>Lillian Jones | 6-8 | T | 706<br>120 | 93% 956/716-6851<br>Fax 956/716-6807 |
| Rio Grande City High Sch<br>5726 N FM 755, Rio Grande Cy 78582<br>Jorge Pena | 9-12 | T | 1,783 | 80% 956/488-6000<br>Fax 956/488-6050 |
| Roque Guerra Jr Elem Sch<br>1600 W Main St, Rio Grande Cy 78582<br>Laura Barrera | PK-5 | T | 628<br>41 | 90% 956/716-6982<br>Fax 956/487-1046 |
| Veterans Middle Sch<br>2700 W Eisenhower St, Rio Grande Cy 78582<br>Enrique Cantu | 6-8 | T | 889 | 87% 956/488-0252<br>Fax 956/488-0261 |

## ● Roma Ind School Dist PID: 01051222

608 N Garcia St, Roma 78584

956/849-1377
Fax 956/849-3118

> **Schools:** 10 \ **Teachers:** 448 \ **Students:** 6,000 \ **Special Ed Students:** 455 \ **LEP Students:** 4,264 \ **College-Bound:** 70% \ **Ethnic:** Hispanic 100%, \ **Exp:** $329 (High) \ **Poverty:** 51% \ **Title I:** $5,091,810 \ **Special Education:** $1,068,000 \ **Open-Close:** 08/26 - 05/28 \ **DTBP:** $158 (High)

| | | | |
|---|---|---|---|
| Carlos Guzman | 1 | Alfonso Perez | 2 |
| Juan Trevino | 4* | Ricardo Esparza | 5 |
| Jaime Escobar | 6,35* | Rosa Nelda Flores | 7 |
| Yadira Diaz | 8,51 | Mary Lou Cruz | 11,88,270,271,296,298 |
| Luis Garza | 15,68,83,273 | Leticia Cadena | 16,73,84,89,297 |
| Noe Muniz | 27,31,83,88* | Marissa Belmontes | 57,81* |
| Hartadelia Barrera | 58 | Raul Moreno | 67 |
| Helen Escobar | 71 | Manuel Garcia | 76 |
| Francisco Rodriguez | 286 | | |

| Public Schs..Principal | Grd | Prgm | Enr/#Cls | SN |
|---|---|---|---|---|
| Delia Gonzalez Garcia ES<br>4186 W US Highway 83, Rio Grande Cy 78582<br>Edgar Garza | PK-5 | T | 464<br>33 | 88% 956/849-8450<br>Fax 956/849-4566 |
| Emma Vera Elem Sch<br>2015 N Hwy 83, Roma 78584<br>Yvonne Guerrero | PK-5 | T | 321<br>33 | 87% 956/849-4552<br>Fax 956/849-1118 |
| Florence J Scott Elem Sch<br>800 Pfc Angel J Moreno St, Roma 78584<br>Diana Salinas | PK-5 | T | 493<br>30 | 86% 956/849-1175<br>Fax 956/849-7274 |
| Rafaela T Barrera Elem Sch<br>126 N FM 649, Roma 78584<br>**Marissa Garcia** | PK-5 | T | 244<br>38 | 90% 956/486-2475<br>Fax 956/486-2474 |
| Ramiro Barrera Middle Sch<br>2 1/2 Miles N FM 649, Roma 78584<br>Rodrigo Bazan | 6-8 | GTV | 622 | 89% 956/486-2670<br>Fax 956/486-2607 |
| Roel & Celia Saenz Elem Sch<br>310 S Gate Rd, Roma 78584<br>Odette Garcia | PK-5 | T | 484 | 93% 956/849-7230<br>Fax 956/849-7250 |
| Roma High Sch<br>2021 N US Highway 83, Roma 78584<br>Ildefonso Saldivar | 9-12 | TV | 450<br>110 | 82% 956/849-1333<br>Fax 956/849-7503 |
| Ⓐ Roma Instructional Sch<br>807 N Raucon St, Roma 78584<br>Maria Ramirez | 6-12 | | 35<br>5 | 956/849-2803<br>Fax 956/849-4421 |
| Roma Middle Sch<br>2047 N Hwy 83, Roma 78584<br>Danelo Gonzalez | 6-8 | TV | 784<br>60 | 86% 956/849-1434<br>Fax 956/849-1895 |
| Veterans Memorial Elem Sch<br>4772 E Highway 83, Roma 78584<br>Leida Reyez | PK-5 | T | 485 | 93% 956/849-1717<br>Fax 956/849-3854 |

## ● San Isidro Ind School Dist PID: 01051296

5175 FM 1017, San Isidro 78588

956/481-3100
Fax 956/481-3597

> **Schools:** 1 \ **Teachers:** 22 \ **Students:** 200 \ **Special Ed Students:** 37 \ **LEP Students:** 31 \ **College-Bound:** 80% \ **Ethnic:** Hispanic 100%, \ **Exp:** $532 (High) \ **Poverty:** 42% \ **Title I:** $132,035 \ **Special Education:** $52,000 \ **Open-Close:** 09/01 - 05/31 \ **DTBP:** $367 (High)

| | | | |
|---|---|---|---|
| Mario Alvarado | 1,73,83,84 | Leonel Olivarez | 2,4 |
| Luis Alvardo | 3 | Jesse Rodriquez | 8,11,16,57,273,280,285* |
| Marisa Garza | 36,88* | Diolia Hinjosa | 58 |
| Velinda Reyes | 67 | | |

| Public Schs..Principal | Grd | Prgm | Enr/#Cls | SN |
|---|---|---|---|---|
| San Isidro Sch<br>5175 FM 1017, San Isidro 78588<br>**Jesse Rodriquez** | PK-12 | TV | 200<br>25 | 64% 956/481-3100<br>Fax 956/481-3224 |

## STARR CATHOLIC SCHOOLS

- **Diocese of Brownsville Ed Off** PID: 01004372
  Listing includes only schools located in this county. See District Index for location of Diocesan Offices.

| Catholic Schs..Principal | Grd | Prgm | Enr/#Cls | SN |
|---|---|---|---|---|
| Immaculate Conception Sch<br>305 N Britton Ave, Rio Grande Cy 78582<br>Maria Olivarez | PK-8 | | 94<br>12 | 956/487-2558<br>Fax 956/487-6478 |

## STEPHENS COUNTY

## STEPHENS PUBLIC SCHOOLS

- **Breckenridge Ind School Dist** PID: 01051325      254/559-2278
  208 N Miller St, Breckenridge 76424                            Fax 254/559-3180

**Schools:** 5 \ **Teachers:** 110 \ **Students:** 1,413 \ **Special Ed Students:** 164 \ **LEP Students:** 114 \ **College-Bound:** 70% \ **Ethnic:** Asian 1%, African American 1%, Hispanic 34%, Native American: 2%, Caucasian 63% \ **Exp:** $501 (High) \ **Poverty:** 29% \ **Title I:** $617,511 \ **Special Education:** $340,000 \ **Open-Close:** 08/19 - 05/27 \ **DTBP:** $349 (High) \ 📘

| | | | |
|---|---|---|---|
| Bryan Allen ........................................1 | Lou Simmons ...............................2 |
| Bryan Dieterich ...............................3* | Mark Nelson ................................4 |
| Casey Hubble ..................................6* | Tonya McKenzie ..........................7* |
| Molly Johnson ..........8,11,69,88,273,296 | Beth Hand ...................................16* |
| Dwayne Dove .........................28,73,297* | Marjorie Thompson ....................57* |
| Susan Britting ...............................58* | Graham Reaugh .........................67 |

| Public Schs..Principal | Grd | Prgm | Enr/#Cls | SN |
|---|---|---|---|---|
| Breckenridge High Sch<br>500 W Lindsey St, Breckenridge 76424<br>William Paul | 9-12 | ATV | 426<br>50 | 54% 254/559-2231<br>Fax 254/559-7485 |
| Breckenridge Jr High Sch<br>502 W Lindsey St, Breckenridge 76424<br>Mary Perkins | 7-8 | AT | 230<br>33 | 57% 254/559-6581<br>Fax 254/212-4311 |
| East Elem Sch<br>1310 E Elm St, Breckenridge 76424<br>Barbara Collinsworth | PK-1 | T | 204<br>19 | 76% 254/559-6531<br>Fax 254/212-4627 |
| North Elem Sch<br>300 W 7th St, Breckenridge 76424<br>Prairie Freeman | 2-3 | T | 211<br>13 | 65% 254/559-6511<br>Fax 254/212-4661 |
| South Elem Sch<br>1001 W Elliott St, Breckenridge 76424<br>Kenna Rainey | 4-6 | T | 342<br>20 | 64% 254/559-6554<br>Fax 254/212-4691 |

## STERLING COUNTY

## STERLING PUBLIC SCHOOLS

- **Sterling City Ind School Dist** PID: 01051387      325/378-4781
  700 7th St, Sterling City 76951                            Fax 325/378-2283

**Schools:** 2 \ **Teachers:** 27 \ **Students:** 320 \ **Special Ed Students:** 51 \ **LEP Students:** 24 \ **Ethnic:** African American 1%, Hispanic 45%, Caucasian 54% \ **Exp:** $905 (High) \ **Poverty:** 17% \ **Title I:** $57,423 \ **Open-Close:** 08/20 - 05/21 \ **DTBP:** $304 (High)

| | | | |
|---|---|---|---|
| Bob Rauch .......................................1 | Danetta Ferguson .......................2 |
| Brent Harmon .................................3 | Carol Spindler .............................4* |
| Trey Sisco ......................................6 | Michelle Guetersloh ...........11,298 |
| Stephanie Stafford ...........36,69,83,85* | Sarah Miller .........................57,58 |
| Jason Cox .......................................67 | Shelli Long ..................................68 |
| Dow Ferguson ...........................73,286 | Ty Stevens ...............................285* |

| Public Schs..Principal | Grd | Prgm | Enr/#Cls | SN |
|---|---|---|---|---|
| Sterling Elem Sch<br>700 7th St, Sterling City 76951<br>Jami Keele | PK-5 | | 141<br>17 | 325/378-5821<br>Fax 325/378-2087 |
| Sterling Middle High Sch<br>700 7th St, Sterling City 76951<br>Ty Stevens | 6-12 | ATV | 150 | 43% 325/378-5821<br>Fax 325/378-2087 |

## STONEWALL COUNTY

## STONEWALL PUBLIC SCHOOLS

- **Aspermont Ind School Dist** PID: 01051416      940/989-3355
  528 E 7th St, Aspermont 79502                            Fax 940/989-3353

**Schools:** 2 \ **Teachers:** 19 \ **Students:** 214 \ **Special Ed Students:** 20 \ **LEP Students:** 4 \ **College-Bound:** 90% \ **Ethnic:** Asian 3%, African American 2%, Hispanic 29%, Caucasian 66% \ **Exp:** $385 (High) \ **Poverty:** 15% \ **Title I:** $42,974 \ **Open-Close:** 08/19 - 05/27 \ **DTBP:** $357 (High)

| | | | |
|---|---|---|---|
| Zack Morris ....................................1 | Charla Leonard ..........................2 |
| James Albright ............................3,91 | Kristin Marsh ..............4,11,296,298 |
| Mark Weaver ..................................6 | Teddye Myers ......8,36,69,83,88,270,271,275* |
| Terry White ...................................58 | Lacy English ...............................67 |
| Cesioy Hecks .................................73 | Allison Martin .............................273 |

| Public Schs..Principal | Grd | Prgm | Enr/#Cls | SN |
|---|---|---|---|---|
| Aspermont Elem Sch<br>528 E 7th St, Aspermont 79502<br>**Trent Van Meter** | PK-5 | T | 93<br>9 | 53% 940/989-3323<br>Fax 940/989-2954 |
| Aspermont High Sch<br>528 E 7th St, Aspermont 79502<br>**Ronnie Garcia** | 6-12 | | 120<br>15 | 38% 940/989-2707<br>Fax 940/989-3486 |

| | | | | | | | |
|---|---|---|---|---|---|---|---|
| 1 Superintendent | 8 Curric/Instruct K-12 | 19 Chief Financial Officer | 29 Family/Consumer Science | 39 Social Studies K-12 | 49 English/Lang Arts Elem | 59 Special Education Elem | 69 Academic Assessment |
| 2 Bus/Finance/Purchasing | 9 Curric/Instruct Elem | 20 Art K-12 | 30 Adult Education | 40 Social Studies Elem | 50 English/Lang Arts Sec | 60 Special Education Sec | 70 Research/Development |
| 3 Buildings And Grounds | 10 Curric/Instruct Sec | 21 Art Elem | 31 Career/Sch-to-Work K-12 | 41 Social Studies Sec | 51 Reading K-12 | 61 Foreign/World Lang K-12 | 71 Public Information |
| 4 Food Service | 11 Federal Program | 22 Art Sec | 32 Career/Sch-to-Work Elem | 42 Science K-12 | 52 Reading Elem | 62 Foreign/World Lang Elem | 72 Summer School |
| 5 Transportation | 12 Title I | 23 Music K-12 | 33 Career/Sch-to-Work Sec | 43 Science Elem | 53 Reading Sec | 63 Foreign/World Lang Sec | 73 Instructional Tech |
| 6 Athletic | 13 Title V | 24 Music Elem | 34 Early Childhood Ed | 44 Science Sec | 54 Remedial Reading K-12 | 64 Religious Education K-12 | 74 Inservice Training |
| 7 Health Services | 14 Asst Superintendent | 25 Music Sec | 35 Health/Phys Education | 45 Math K 12 | 55 Remedial Reading Elem | 65 Religious Education Elem | 75 Marketing/Distributive |
| | 15 Asst Superintendent | 26 Business Education | 36 Business Education | 46 Math Elem | 56 Remedial Reading Sec | 66 Religious Education Sec | 76 Info Systems |
| | 16 Instructional Media Svcs | 27 Career & Tech Ed | 37 Guidance Services Elem | 47 Math Sec | 57 Bilingual/ELL | 67 School Board President | 77 Psychological Assess |
| | 17 Chief Operations Officer | 28 Technology Education | 38 Guidance Services Sec | 48 English/Lang Arts K-12 | 58 Special Education K-12 | 68 Teacher Personnel | 78 Affirmative Action |
| | 18 Chief Academic Officer | | | | | | |

## SUTTON COUNTY

### SUTTON PUBLIC SCHOOLS

• **Sonora Ind School Dist** PID: 01051478          325/387-6940
807 S Concho Ave, Sonora 76950          Fax 325/387-5090

Schools: 3 \ **Teachers:** 71 \ **Students:** 767 \ **Special Ed Students:** 79
\ **LEP Students:** 93 \ **College-Bound:** 64% \ **Ethnic:** Hispanic 72%,
Caucasian 27% \ **Exp:** $710 (High) \ **Poverty:** 22% \ **Title I:** $184,785 \
**Special Education:** $190,000 \ **Open-Close:** 08/17 - 05/27 \ **DTBP:** $355
(High)

| | | |
|---|---|---|
| Ross Aschenbeck ...........................1 | Greta Ramsdell ...........................................2 | |
| Josie Torres ...................................4 | Kevin Sherrill ...............................................6 | |
| Pennie Latterell ..............................7,83,85 | Stephanie Taylor ....................8,11,27,58,88* | |
| Lindsey Geske ...............................16* | Kay Friess ...................................................38* | |
| Laura Valeriano .............................54 | Shanna Petty-Castro ..................................67 | |
| Karen Evans ...................................73,98,286 | Terisa Jones .......................................90,752 | |

| Public Schs..Principal | Grd | Prgm | Enr/#Cls | SN |
|---|---|---|---|---|
| Sonora Elemementary Sch<br>907 S Concho Ave, Sonora 76950<br>Michael Kissire | PK-6 | T | 387<br>26 | 63% 325/387-6940<br>Fax 325/387-9604 |
| Sonora High Sch<br>1717 Tayloe Ave, Sonora 76950<br>**Rene Valeriano** | 9-12 | ATV | 257<br>35 | 51% 325/387-6940<br>Fax 325/387-5348 |
| Sonora Middle Sch<br>408 E 1st St, Sonora 76950<br>**Rene Valeriano** | 7-8 | T | 181<br>20 | 60% 325/387-6940<br>Fax 325/387-2007 |

## SWISHER COUNTY

### SWISHER PUBLIC SCHOOLS

• **Happy Ind School Dist** PID: 01051519          806/558-5331
500 NW 3rd St, Happy 79042          Fax 806/209-0077

Schools: 2 \ **Teachers:** 25 \ **Students:** 248 \ **Special Ed Students:** 25
\ **LEP Students:** 12 \ **Ethnic:** African American 2%, Hispanic 18%,
Caucasian 80% \ **Exp:** $920 (High) \ **Poverty:** 17% \ **Title I:** $43,932 \
**Open-Close:** 08/19 - 05/19 \ **DTBP:** $372 (High)

| | |
|---|---|
| Ray Keith ........................................1 | Shannon Bressler ...................2,11,296,298 |
| Ike Lawson ....................................3,5 | Diane McPherson .....................................4 |
| Glenda Birkenfeild ........................7 | Julie Dempsey ......................................8,16 |
| Krista Ellison ...............9,45,48,51,85,274,288 | Sara Reinart ...................................27,30,31* |
| Staci Wyatt ...................................36,752 | Cindy Givens ............................................58* |
| Mace Middleton .............................67 | Rowdy Bryan .......................73,286,295,297 |

| Public Schs..Principal | Grd | Prgm | Enr/#Cls | SN |
|---|---|---|---|---|
| Happy Elem Sch<br>400 NW 3rd St, Happy 79042<br>Toni Waldo | PK-6 | T | 133<br>13 | 44% 806/558-2561<br>Fax 806/558-2484 |

| Public Schs..Principal | Grd | Prgm | Enr/#Cls | SN |
|---|---|---|---|---|
| Happy Middle High Sch<br>401 NW 3rd St, Happy 79042<br>**Jennifer Sperry** | 7-12 | ATV | 115<br>16 | 35% 806/558-5311<br>Fax 806/558-4301 |

• **Kress Ind School Dist** PID: 01051545          806/684-2652
200 E 5th St, Kress 79052          Fax 806/684-2687

Schools: 2 \ **Teachers:** 23 \ **Students:** 242 \ **Special Ed Students:** 20
\ **LEP Students:** 15 \ **College-Bound:** 75% \ **Ethnic:** African American
6%, Hispanic 56%, Caucasian 38% \ **Exp:** $503 (High) \ **Poverty:** 18% \
**Title I:** $61,337 \ **Open-Close:** 08/21 - 05/21 \ **DTBP:** $316 (High)

| | |
|---|---|
| Leah Zeigler ...........................1,11,73,84 | Laura Reyes ...........................................4* |
| Mickey Bye ...........................................5* | Mark Earhart ...........................................6 |
| Shawn Langston ..................................9* | Phil Zolman ...............11,73,286,294,295,298* |
| Kimberley Couch ................................57* | Sheri Warren ............................................58* |
| Tiffany Reed .......................................67 | Clemente Rodriguez ...............................76 |
| Yvonne Hernandez ............................285 | |

| Public Schs..Principal | Grd | Prgm | Enr/#Cls | SN |
|---|---|---|---|---|
| Kress Elem Sch<br>401 Ripley Ave, Kress 79052<br>Robert Langston | PK-6 | T | 138<br>15 | 71% 806/684-2326<br>Fax 806/684-2778 |
| Kress Jr Sr High Sch<br>500 Ripley St, Kress 79052<br>Phil Zolman | 7-12 | T | 104<br>20 | 65% 806/684-2651 |

• **Tulia Ind School Dist** PID: 01051571          806/995-4591
702 NW 8th St, Tulia 79088          Fax 806/995-3169

Schools: 3 \ **Teachers:** 98 \ **Students:** 1,040 \ **Special Ed Students:** 112
\ **LEP Students:** 76 \ **Ethnic:** African American 10%, Hispanic 64%,
Caucasian 26% \ **Exp:** $681 (High) \ **Poverty:** 29% \ **Title I:** $430,628 \
**Open-Close:** 08/19 - 05/27 \ **DTBP:** $338 (High)

| | |
|---|---|
| Tim Glover ...........................................1 | Mike Huseman ........................................2 |
| Dusty George ......................................3 | Debbie Earl .............................................4* |
| Tim Gibbons ........................................5 | Steven Coursey ......................................6 |
| Jaclyn Street ...................................7,85* | Daniel Keith ..............8,11,57,285,286,288,298 |
| Dixie Johnson .......................34,58,275 | Terry Murrell ...........................................67 |
| Johnny McCasland .................73,76,295 | Kris Friel ...........................................84,295 |
| Mary Verver .......................................271 | |

| Public Schs..Principal | Grd | Prgm | Enr/#Cls | SN |
|---|---|---|---|---|
| Tulia Elem Sch<br>800 NW 9th St, Tulia 79088<br>Pam Miner | PK-5 | T | 475<br>46 | 85% 806/995-4141<br>Fax 806/995-2265 |
| Tulia High Sch<br>501 Hornet Pl, Tulia 79088<br>**Dixie Johnson** | 9-12 | TV | 302<br>42 | 70% 806/995-2759<br>Fax 806/995-4413 |
| Tulia Junior High Sch<br>421 NE 3rd St, Tulia 79088<br>Casey McBroom | 6-8 | T | 246<br>26 | 80% 806/995-4842<br>Fax 806/995-4498 |

## TARRANT COUNTY

## TARRANT PUBLIC SCHOOLS

• **Arlington Ind School Dist** PID: 01051624
1203 W Pioneer Pkwy, Arlington 76013

682/867-4611
Fax 817/459-7286

**Schools:** 78 \ **Teachers:** 4,101 \ **Students:** 59,500 \
**Special Ed Students:** 5,332 \ **LEP Students:** 15,057 \ **College-Bound:** 73%
\ **Ethnic:** Asian 6%, African American 25%, Hispanic 48%, Caucasian
20% \ **Exp:** $202 (Med) \ **Poverty:** 17% \ **Title I:** $20,419,820 \
**Special Education:** $10,030,000 \ **Open-Close:** 08/17 - 05/26 \ **DTBP:** $192
(High) \ 🆕 🅴

| | |
|---|---|
| Dr Marcelo Cavazos ..............1 | Cindy Powell .............2,19 |
| Tammy Craig .....................3 | Tony Drollinger ...........2 |
| Kelly Horn .......................3 | David Lewis ...............4 |
| Tim Collins ......................5 | Eric White ................6 |
| Connie Wallace ..................8 | Dr Steven Wurtz ........8,18 |
| Dr Tamela Horton ...............8 | Julie McGuire ............11 |
| A Tracie Brown .................15 | Dr Christi Buell ..........15 |
| Eric Upchurch ...............15,73 | Dr Michael Hill ..........15 |
| Scott Kahl ................15,68,79 | Dr Theodore Jarchow .....15 |
| Dr Christopher Anderson .......20 | Susan Patterson .........27 |
| Telisa Brown ...................36 | Kandi Hunter ............45 |
| Cassandra Perez .............57,61 | Lori Thurston ...........58 |
| Kecia Mays ....................67 | Dr Peggy Porterfield .....69 |
| Dr Kevin Barlow ............70,294 | Elita Driskill ............73 |
| Barry Fox ......................76 | Mark Murray ............76* |
| Patty Bustamante ..............79 | Dr Karen Zeske ..........81 |
| Wendy Carrington ..............88 | David Stevens ...........91 |
| Aaron Perales .................93 | Dwight Goodwin .........95 |
| Steve Simpson ................286 | John Atchison ..........295 |
| Frank Sack ...................297 | Luis Valdespino ........752 |

| Public Schs..Principal | Grd | Prgm | Enr/#Cls | SN | |
|---|---|---|---|---|---|
| **Adams Elem Sch**<br>2220 Sherry St, Arlington 76010<br>Lesley Rhodes | PK-6 | T | 805 | 92% | 682/867-2130 |
| **Agriculture Science Center**<br>2101 Browning Dr, Arlington 76010<br>Ginger Polster | Voc | | 700 | | 682/867-9500<br>Fax 682/867-9505 |
| **Amos Elem Sch**<br>3100 Daniel Dr, Arlington 76014<br>Carin Tufts | PK-6 | AT | 453<br>30 | 90% | 682/867-4700<br>Fax 817/419-4705 |
| **Anderson Elem Sch**<br>1101 Timberlake Dr, Arlington 76010<br>Angela Peragine | PK-6 | AT | 554 | 97% | 682/867-7750<br>Fax 682/867-7773 |
| **Arlington College & Career HS**<br>4900 W Arkansas Ln, Arlington 76016<br>Dr Ben Bholan | 9-12 | | 500 | | 682/867-9600 |
| **Arlington Collegiate High Sch**<br>2224 Southeast Pkwy, Arlington 76018<br>Jeff Krieger | 9-12 | T | 407 | 86% | 817/515-3550<br>Fax 817/515-3540 |
| **Arlington High Sch**<br>818 W Park Row Dr, Arlington 76013<br>Shahveer Dhalla | 9-12 | TV | 2,694<br>120 | 58% | 682/867-8100<br>Fax 682/867-8119 |
| **Ashworth Elem Sch**<br>6700 Silo Rd, Arlington 76002<br>Stacey Maddoux | PK-6 | AT | 437<br>38 | 67% | 682/867-4800<br>Fax 682/867-4808 |
| **Atherton Elem Sch**<br>2101 Overbrook Dr, Arlington 76014<br>Bianca Gholston | PK-6 | AT | 570<br>70 | 90% | 682/867-4900<br>Fax 682/867-4916 |

| | Grd | Prgm | Enr/#Cls | SN | |
|---|---|---|---|---|---|
| **Bailey Junior High Sch**<br>2411 Winewood Ln, Arlington 76013<br>**Jason Davis** | 7-8 | T | 827<br>40 | 58% | 682/867-0700<br>Fax 682/867-0708 |
| **Barnett Junior High Sch**<br>2101 E Sublett Rd, Arlington 76018<br>Stephanie Hawthorne | 7-8 | TV | 800<br>25 | 70% | 682/867-5000<br>Fax 682/867-5096 |
| **Bebensee Elem Sch**<br>5900 Inks Lake Dr, Arlington 76018<br>Charlotte Carter | PK-6 | AT | 633<br>65 | 82% | 682/867-5100<br>Fax 817/419-5105 |
| **Beckham Elem Sch**<br>1700 Southeast Pkwy, Arlington 76018<br>**Karen Hicks** | PK-6 | AT | 552<br>25 | 68% | 682/867-6600<br>Fax 817/375-6605 |
| **Berry Elem Sch**<br>1800 Joyce St, Arlington 76010<br>**Carlos Lopez** | PK-6 | AT | 611<br>37 | 98% | 682/867-0850<br>Fax 817/801-0905 |
| **Blanton Elem Sch**<br>1900 S Collins St, Arlington 76010<br>Joshua Leonard | PK-6 | AT | 532<br>49 | 94% | 682/867-1000<br>Fax 817/801-0955 |
| **Boles Junior High Sch**<br>3900 SW Green Oaks Blvd, Arlington 76017<br>Dr Angela Smith | 7-8 | V | 693<br>55 | 42% | 682/867-8000<br>Fax 682/867-8067 |
| **Bryant Elem Sch**<br>2201 Havenwood Dr, Arlington 76018<br>Randi Smith | PK-6 | AT | 499 | 73% | 682/867-5200<br>Fax 817/419-5205 |
| **Burgin Elem Sch**<br>401 E Mayfield Rd, Arlington 76014<br>Christi Wilks | PK-6 | AT | 521<br>60 | 91% | 682/867-1300<br>Fax 817/419-1416 |
| **Butler Elem Sch**<br>2121 Margaret Dr, Arlington 76012<br>Jennifer Bohannon | PK-6 | A | 521<br>36 | 21% | 682/867-1010<br>Fax 817/801-1015 |
| **Carter Junior High Sch**<br>701 Tharp St, Arlington 76010<br>Claudia Herrera | 7-8 | TV | 1,118<br>50 | 93% | 682/867-1700<br>Fax 682/867-1721 |
| **Corey Acad Fine Arts**<br>5200 Kelly Elliott Rd, Arlington 76017<br>Nidia Zaravar | K-6 | A | 606<br>60 | 32% | 682/867-3900<br>Fax 682/867-3904 |
| **Crouch Elem Sch**<br>2810 Prairie Hill Dr, Grand Prairie 75051<br>Jaime Stephens | K-6 | AT | 611 | 94% | 682/867-0200<br>Fax 972/595-0205 |
| **Crow Leadership Academy**<br>1201 Coke Dr, Arlington 76010<br>Jamie MacDougall | K-6 | AT | 398<br>46 | 92% | 682/867-1850<br>Fax 817/801-1855 |
| **Dan Dipert Career & Tech Ctr**<br>2101 Browning Dr, Arlington 76010<br>Ginger Polster | Voc | | 1,000 | | 682/867-9500 |
| ⓥ **Diane Patrick Elem Sch**<br>755 Timber Oaks Ln, Grand Prairie 75051<br>Ena Meyers | PK-6 | MT | 683 | 92% | 682/867-0600 |
| **Ditto Elem Sch**<br>3001 Quail Ln, Arlington 76016<br>Bel Williams | PK-6 | A | 625<br>75 | 33% | 682/867-3100<br>Fax 682/867-3176 |
| **Duff Elem Sch**<br>3100 Lynnwood Dr, Arlington 76013<br>Cynthia Harbison | PK-6 | AT | 612 | 43% | 682/867-2000<br>Fax 817/801-2005 |
| **Dunn Elem Sch**<br>2201 Woodside Dr, Arlington 76013<br>Mary Helen Burnett | PK-6 | AT | 556<br>45 | 69% | 682/867-3200<br>Fax 817/492-3205 |
| **Eddy & Debbie Peach Elem Sch**<br>2020 Baird Farm Rd, Arlington 76006<br>Dr Stephanie Lee | PK-6 | T | 836 | 82% | 682/867-6100 |
| **Ellis Elem Sch**<br>2601 Shadow Ridge Dr, Arlington 76006<br>Keith Boyd | PK-6 | AT | 766<br>40 | 79% | 682/867-7900<br>Fax 817/652-7905 |
| **Emma Ousley Jr HS**<br>950 Southeast Pkwy, Arlington 76018<br>Grayson Toperzer | 7-8 | TV | 999<br>50 | 74% | 682/867-5700<br>Fax 682/867-5775 |

| | | | |
|---|---|---|---|
| 1 Superintendent | 8 Curric/Instruct K-12 | 19 Chief Financial Officer | 29 Family/Consumer Science |
| 2 Bus/Finance/Purchasing | 9 Curric/Instruct Elem | 20 Art K-12 | 30 Adult Education |
| 3 Buildings And Grounds | 10 Curric/Instruct Sec | 21 Art Elem | 31 Career/Sch-to-Work K-12 |
| 4 Food Service | 11 Federal Program | 22 Art Sec | 32 Career/Sch-to-Work Elem |
| 5 Transportation | 12 Title I | 23 Music K-12 | 33 Career/Sch-to-Work Sec |
| 6 Athletic | 13 Title V | 24 Music Elem | 34 Early Childhood Ed |
| 7 Health Services | 15 Asst Superintendent | 25 Music Sec | 35 Health/Phys Education |
| | 16 Instructional Media Svcs | 26 Business Education | 36 Guidance Services K-12 |
| | 17 Chief Operations Officer | 27 Career & Tech Ed | 37 Guidance Services Elem |
| | 18 Chief Academic Officer | 28 Technology Education | 38 Guidance Services Sec |

| | | |
|---|---|---|
| 39 Social Studies K-12 | 49 English/Lang Arts Elem | 59 Special Education Elem | 69 Academic Assessment |
| 40 Social Studies Elem | 50 English/Lang Arts Sec | 60 Special Education Sec | 70 Research/Development |
| 41 Social Studies Sec | 51 Reading K-12 | 61 Foreign/World Lang K-12 | 71 Public Information |
| 42 Science K-12 | 52 Reading Elem | 62 Foreign/World Lang Elem | 72 Summer School |
| 43 Science Elem | 53 Reading Sec | 63 Foreign/World Lang Sec | 73 Instructional Tech |
| 44 Science Sec | 54 Remedial Reading K-12 | 64 Religious Education K-12 | 74 Inservice Training |
| 45 Math K-12 | 55 Remedial Reading Elem | 65 Religious Education Elem | 75 Marketing/Distributive |
| 46 Math Elem | 56 Remedial Reading Sec | 66 Religious Education Sec | 76 Info Systems |
| 47 Math Sec | 57 Bilingual/ELL | 67 School Board President | 77 Psychological Assess |
| 48 English/Lang Arts K-12 | 58 Special Education K-12 | 68 Teacher Personnel | 78 Affirmative Action |

| School | Grades | Type | Enroll | % | Phone |
|---|---|---|---|---|---|
| Farrell Elem Sch<br>3410 Paladium Dr, Grand Prairie 75052<br>Glen Brunk | PK-6 | AT | 630<br>50 | 76% | 682/867-0300<br>Fax 682/867-0370 |
| Fitzgerald Elem Sch<br>5201 Creek Valley Dr, Arlington 76018<br>Cindy Brown | PK-6 | AT | 540<br>47 | 80% | 682/867-5300<br>Fax 817/419-5305 |
| Foster Elem Sch<br>1025 High Point Rd, Arlington 76015<br>Jacquelyn Burden | PK-6 | AT | 526<br>38 | 89% | 682/867-5350<br>Fax 817/419-5355 |
| Goodman Elem Sch<br>1400 Rebecca Ln, Arlington 76014<br>Stephanie Savala | PK-6 | AT | 552<br>40 | 91% | 682/867-2200<br>Fax 817/801-2205 |
| Gunn Junior High Sch<br>3000 S Fielder Rd, Arlington 76015<br>Dr Matt Varnell | 7-8 | T | 469<br>40 | 80% | 682/867-5400<br>Fax 817/419-5405 |
| Hale Elem Sch<br>2400 E Mayfield Rd, Arlington 76014<br>Natasha Harris | PK-6 | AT | 424<br>43 | 93% | 682/867-1530<br>Fax 817/419-1535 |
| Hill Elem Sch<br>2020 W Tucker Blvd, Arlington 76013<br>Kasie Longonia | PK-6 | A | 503<br>34 | 39% | 682/867-2300<br>Fax 682/867-2375 |
| James Bowie High Sch<br>2101 Highbank Dr, Arlington 76018<br>Reny Lizardo | 9-12 | TV | 2,653 | 65% | 682/867-4400<br>Fax 682/867-4406 |
| James Martin High Sch<br>4501 W Pleasant Ridge Rd, Arlington 76016<br>Mary Roddy | 9-12 | V | 3,459<br>185 | 32% | 682/867-8600<br>Fax 682/867-8609 |
| Johns Elem Sch<br>1900 Sherry St, Arlington 76010<br>Dawn Zdrojewski | PK-6 | AT | 609<br>38 | 97% | 682/867-2500<br>Fax 682/867-2502 |
| Jones Aca of Fine Arts & Dual<br>2001 Van Buren Dr, Arlington 76011<br>Katiuska Herrador | K-6 | AT | 504<br>40 | 65% | 682/867-3580<br>Fax 817/801-3505 |
| Juan Seguin High Sch<br>7001 Silo Rd, Arlington 76002<br>Ray Borden | 9-12 | T | 1,564 | 64% | 682/867-6700<br>Fax 817/375-6705 |
| Key Elem Sch<br>3621 Roosevelt Dr, Arlington 76016<br>Hallema Jackson | K-6 | AT | 465<br>30 | 63% | 682/867-5500<br>Fax 817/419-5505 |
| Kooken Educational Center<br>423 N Center St, Arlington 76011<br>Dr Connie Spence | PK-PK | T | 344<br>13 | 99% | 682/867-7152<br>Fax 817/459-7155 |
| Larson Elem Sch<br>2620 E Avenue K, Grand Prairie 75050<br>Teri Conely | PK-6 | AT | 562<br>50 | 78% | 682/867-0000<br>Fax 682/867-0079 |
| Little Elem Sch<br>3721 Little Rd, Arlington 76016<br>Beth Woodward | PK-6 | A | 726<br>43 | 47% | 682/867-3300<br>Fax 817/492-3305 |
| M B Lamar High Sch<br>1400 W Lamar Blvd, Arlington 76012<br>Andy Hagman | 9-12 | TV | 2,814<br>120 | 66% | 682/867-8300<br>Fax 682/867-6959 |
| Mary Moore Elem Sch<br>5500 Park Springs Blvd, Arlington 76017<br>Nathan Prange | PK-6 | A | 828<br>45 | 49% | 682/867-8900<br>Fax 817/561-8905 |
| Miller Elem Sch<br>6401 W Pleasant Ridge Rd, Arlington 76016<br>Shelly Osten | PK-6 | AT | 640<br>48 | 68% | 682/867-8400<br>Fax 817/561-8405 |
| Morton Elem Sch<br>2900 Barrington Pl, Arlington 76014<br>Leigh Adams | PK-6 | T | 544<br>53 | 92% | 682/867-5600<br>Fax 682/867-5679 |
| Ⓐ Newcomer Center<br>600 SE Green Oaks Blvd, Arlington 76018<br>Greg Meeks | 7-12 | TV | 247<br>18 | 92% | 682/867-7100<br>Fax 682/867-7146 |
| Nichols Junior High Sch<br>2201 Ascension Blvd, Arlington 76006<br>Catherine Claiborne | 7-8 | T | 737<br>30 | 84% | 682/867-2600<br>Fax 682/867-2649 |
| Pearcy STEM Academy<br>601 E Harris Rd, Arlington 76002<br>Codi Van Duzee | PK-6 | AT | 451<br>45 | 67% | 682/867-5555<br>Fax 817/419-5554 |
| Pope Elem Sch<br>901 Chestnut Dr, Arlington 76012<br>Celina Kilgore | PK-6 | AT | 511<br>27 | 79% | 682/867-2750<br>Fax 682/867-2795 |
| Rankin Elem Sch<br>1900 Oleander St, Arlington 76010<br>Lori Mosley | PK-6 | AT | 556<br>32 | 96% | 682/867-2800<br>Fax 817/801-2805 |
| Remynse Elem Sch<br>2720 Fall Dr, Grand Prairie 75052<br>Selina Ozuna | PK-6 | AT | 497<br>25 | 90% | 682/867-0500<br>Fax 972/595-0505 |
| Roark Elem Sch<br>2401 Roberts Cir, Arlington 76010<br>Dr Angela Eaton | PK-6 | AT | 407<br>44 | 92% | 682/867-2900<br>Fax 817/801-2905 |
| Sam Houston High Sch<br>2000 Sam Houston Dr, Arlington 76014<br>Juan Villarreal | 9-12 | TV | 3,687 | 88% | 682/867-8200<br>Fax 682/867-6290 |
| Sandy McNutt Elem Sch<br>3609 S Center St, Arlington 76014<br>Ginger Cole-Leffel | PK-6 | T | 723 | 85% | 682/867-9100 |
| Shackelford Junior High Sch<br>2000 N Fielder Rd, Arlington 76012<br>Kelli Smith | 7-8 | TV | 649 | 69% | 682/867-3600<br>Fax 682/867-3603 |
| Sherrod Elem Sch<br>2626 Lincoln Dr, Arlington 76006<br>Dr Michelle Cummings | PK-6 | AT | 704<br>48 | 84% | 682/867-3700<br>Fax 817/801-3705 |
| Short Elem Sch<br>2000 California Ln, Arlington 76015<br>Katina Martinez | PK-6 | AT | 440<br>32 | 85% | 682/867-5850<br>Fax 817/419-5855 |
| South Davis Elem Sch<br>2001 S Davis Dr, Arlington 76013<br>Debra Wall | PK-6 | AT | 607<br>34 | 93% | 682/867-3800<br>Fax 817/801-3805 |
| Speer Elem Sch<br>811 Fuller St, Arlington 76012<br>Tashalon McDonald | PK-6 | AT | 655 | 96% | 682/867-4000<br>Fax 817/801-4005 |
| Starrett Elem Sch<br>2675 Fairmont Dr, Grand Prairie 75052<br>Allison Gilmore | PK-6 | AT | 508<br>40 | 72% | 682/867-0400<br>Fax 972/595-0405 |
| Swift Elem Sch<br>1101 S Fielder Rd, Arlington 76013<br>Bailey Morris | PK-6 | AT | 398<br>33 | 81% | 682/867-4100<br>Fax 817/801-4105 |
| Thornton Elem Sch<br>2301 E Park Row Dr, Arlington 76010<br>Alicia Rodriguez | PK-6 | AT | 770<br>65 | 97% | 682/867-4200<br>Fax 817/801-4205 |
| Ⓐ Turning Point Secondary Sch<br>2209 N Davis Dr, Arlington 76012<br>Jeanne Muldrew | 7-12 | V | 200<br>26 | 81% | 682/867-3050<br>Fax 682/867-3045 |
| Veda Knox Elem Sch<br>2315 Stonegate St, Arlington 76010<br>Rose Ravin | PK-6 | AT | 554 | 96% | 682/867-2051<br>Fax 817/801-2056 |
| Ⓐ Venture High Sch<br>600 SE Green Oaks Blvd, Arlington 76018<br>Greg Meeks | 9-12 | GTV | 303<br>30 | 67% | 682/867-6400<br>Fax 682/867-6441 |
| Webb Elem Sch<br>1200 N Cooper St, Arlington 76011<br>Elena Lopez | PK-6 | AT | 641<br>50 | 94% | 682/867-4300<br>Fax 817/801-4305 |
| West Elem Sch<br>2911 Kingswood Blvd, Grand Prairie 75052<br>Wendy Britton | PK-6 | AT | 616<br>37 | 63% | 682/867-0100<br>Fax 682/867-0190 |
| Williams Elem Sch<br>4915 Red Birch Dr, Arlington 76018<br>Mark Kammlah | PK-6 | AT | 666<br>60 | 79% | 682/867-5900<br>Fax 817/419-5905 |
| Wimbish World Language Academy<br>1601 Wright St, Arlington 76012<br>Delisse Hardy | PK-6 | AT | 463<br>35 | 91% | 682/867-6000<br>Fax 817/801-6005 |

Wood Elem Sch | PK-6 | A | 758 | 51% 682/867-1100
3300 Pimlico Dr, Arlington 76017 | | | 50 | Fax 817/419-1105
David Dillard

Workman Junior High Sch | 7-8 | TV | 1,481 | 92% 682/867-1200
701 E Arbrook Blvd, Arlington 76014 | | | | Fax 682/867-1218
Jacquelyn McClendon

Young Junior High Sch | 7-8 | | 804 | 42% 682/867-3400
3200 Woodside Dr, Arlington 76016 | | | 60 | Fax 817/492-3405
Stacie Humbles 🇹

---

● **Azle Ind School Dist** PID: 01051973 | 817/444-3235
300 Roe St, Azle 76020 | Fax 817/444-6866

**Schools:** 12 \ **Teachers:** 415 \ **Students:** 5,900 \ **Special Ed Students:** 646 \ **LEP Students:** 319 \ **College-Bound:** 50% \ **Ethnic:** African American 1%, Hispanic 23%, Caucasian 74% \ **Exp:** $509 (High) \ **Poverty:** 13% \ **Title I:** $1,132,161 \ **Special Education:** $1,073,000 \ **Open-Close:** 08/18 - 05/27 \ **DTBP:** $169 (High)

Tanya Anderson ............................ 1 | Matt Adams ............................ 2,11
Hunter Aaron ............................... 4 | Becky Spurlock ............................ 6
Amanda Wimpee ......... 8,30,88,286,296,298 | Jordan Siem ............................ 11
Todd Smith ................................ 15 | Eddie Alford ............... 16,73,297
Suzanne Murr ............................. 27 | Gwen Gordon ............................ 58
Bill Lane ................................. 67 | Mark Kehoe ............................ 68
Jaime Westbrook .......................... 90 | Gwen Sheldon ............................ 752

| Public Schs..Principal | Grd | Prgm | Enr/#Cls | SN |
|---|---|---|---|---|
| Ⓐ Alt Edu Program Phoenix Campus | 4-12 | | 80 | 817/444-4564 |
| 1010 Boyd Rd, Azle 76020 | | | 7 | Fax 817/270-0830 |
| Diane Boone | | | | |
| Azle Elem Sch | 5-6 | T | 595 | 42% 817/444-1312 |
| 1200 Lakeview Dr, Azle 76020 | | | 20 | Fax 817/444-6934 |
| Gina Lee | | | | |
| Azle High Sch | 9-12 | TV | 923 | 36% 817/444-5555 |
| 1200 Boyd Rd, Azle 76020 | | | | Fax 817/444-8884 |
| Randy Cobb | | | | |
| Azle Hornet Academy | 9-12 | T | 44 | 37% 817/444-4564 |
| 1010 Boyd Rd, Azle 76020 | | | | |
| Dianne Boone | | | | |
| Azle Junior High Sch | 7-8 | T | 545 | 36% 817/444-2564 |
| 201 School St, Azle 76020 | | | 25 | Fax 817/270-0880 |
| Brian Roberts | | | | |
| Cross Timbers Elem Sch | PK-4 | T | 564 | 52% 817/444-3802 |
| 831 Jackson Trl, Azle 76020 | | | 24 | Fax 817/444-0730 |
| Shelly Wynns | | | | |
| Eagle Heights Elem Sch | K-4 | T | 404 | 60% 817/237-4161 |
| 6505 Lucerne Dr, Fort Worth 76135 | | | 32 | Fax 817/237-0656 |
| Amy Rollman | | | | |
| Hoover Elem Sch | 5-6 | T | 446 | 56% 817/444-7766 |
| 484 Sandy Beach Rd, Azle 76020 | | | 18 | Fax 817/270-1425 |
| Joni Bettis | | | | |
| Liberty Elem Sch | PK-4 | T | 502 | 70% 817/444-1317 |
| 11450 Liberty School Rd, Azle 76020 | | | 22 | Fax 817/444-1937 |
| Lisa Koehler | | | | |
| Santo J Forte Jr High Sch | 7-8 | T | 467 | 51% 817/270-1133 |
| 479 Sandy Beach Rd, Azle 76020 | | | 47 | Fax 817/270-5973 |
| William Manley | | | | |
| Silver Creek Elem Sch | PK-4 | T | 596 | 40% 817/444-0257 |
| 10300 S FM 730, Azle 76020 | | | 33 | Fax 817/270-2383 |
| Heidi Nelson | | | | |
| Walnut Creek Elem Sch | K-4 | T | 575 | 46% 817/444-4045 |
| 500 Stribling Dr, Azle 76020 | | | 21 | Fax 817/270-2576 |
| Jessica Hanson | | | | |

---

● **Birdville Ind School Dist** PID: 01052032 | 817/547-5700
6125 E Belknap St, Haltom City 76117 | Fax 817/547-5530

**Schools:** 33 \ **Teachers:** 1,540 \ **Students:** 23,513 \
**Special Ed Students:** 2,387 \ **LEP Students:** 4,600 \ **College-Bound:** 57% \
**Ethnic:** Asian 5%, African American 9%, Hispanic 44%, Native American: 1%, Caucasian 41% \ **Exp:** $280 (Med) \ **Poverty:** 16% \ **Title I:** $5,964,317 \
**Special Education:** $4,296,000 \ **Open-Close:** 08/17 - 05/26 \ **DTBP:** $184 (High) \ 🇫 🇹

Dr Darrell Brown ............................ 1 | Katie Bowman ............................ 2
Sharay Boynton ............................ 2 | Shelley Freeman ............................ 2
John Hughes ............................... 3 | Judy Sargent ............................ 4
Dave Powers ............................... 5 | Chris Feris ............................ 6
Michelle Province ......................... 7* | Donna Solley ............................ 8*
Dr Elizabeth Clark ....................... 8,15 | Clarence Simmons ............................ 9
James Smith .............................. 9,34* | Lorene Ownby ............................ 9
Adrienne Walker ..................... 11,296,298 | Dr Laura Holt ............................ 12,58
Skip Baskerville ......................... 15,68 | Kelli Montgomery ............................ 16,286
Danny Detrick ............................ 20,23 | Allison Vinson ............... 27,30,31,73*
Leann Carroll ............... 36,77,83,85,88 | Jennifer Miller ............................ 39,59
Dawna Schweitzer ......................... 42 | Brenda Mesa ............................ 45
Jack McCarty ............................. 67 | Paige Curry ............................ 68
David Holland ......................... 69,294* | Mark Thomas ............................ 71
Dave Lambson ............... 73,76,295,297 | Joseph Showell ............... 79,93
Chris Reese .............................. 91

| Public Schs..Principal | Grd | Prgm | Enr/#Cls | SN |
|---|---|---|---|---|
| Academy at Carrie F Thomas | PK-5 | T | 589 | 74% 817/547-3000 |
| 8200 O Brian Way, N Richlnd Hls 76180 | | | 27 | Fax 817/581-5490 |
| Dr Sabrina Lindsey | | | | 🇫 |
| Alliene Mullendore Elem Sch | PK-5 | T | 327 | 65% 817/547-1900 |
| 4100 Flory St, N Richlnd Hls 76180 | | | 21 | Fax 817/581-5326 |
| **Merritt Dobecka** | | | | 🇫🇹 |
| Birdville Elem Sch of Fine Art | PK-5 | T | 418 | 81% 817/547-1500 |
| 3111 Carson St, Haltom City 76117 | | | 23 | Fax 817/831-5736 |
| Tammy Pope | | | | 🇫🇹 |
| Birdville High Sch | 9-12 | GV | 2,077 | 38% 817/547-8000 |
| 9100 Mid Cities Blvd, N Richlnd Hls 76180 | | | | Fax 817/547-8009 |
| Jason Wells | | | | |
| Bisd Ctr Tech & Advanced Lrng | Voc | | 300 | 817/547-3800 |
| 7020 Mid Cities Blvd, N Richlnd Hls 76180 | | | | Fax 817/503-8965 |
| Carol Adcocok | | | | |
| David E Smith Elem Sch | PK-5 | T | 487 | 78% 817/547-1600 |
| 3701 Haltom Rd, Haltom City 76117 | | | 25 | Fax 817/831-5817 |
| Jennifer Martin | | | | 🇫🇹 |
| Foster Village Elem Sch | PK-5 | T | 440 | 58% 817/547-3100 |
| 6800 Springdale Ln, N Richlnd Hls 76182 | | | 28 | Fax 817/581-5832 |
| Sherri Gamble | | | | |
| Grace E Hardeman Elem Sch | PK-5 | T | 590 | 56% 817/547-2800 |
| 6100 Whispering Ln, Watauga 76148 | | | 36 | Fax 817/581-5496 |
| Katie Moran | | | | |
| Green Valley Elem Sch | PK-5 | | 484 | 18% 817/547-3400 |
| 7900 Smithfield Rd, N Richlnd Hls 76182 | | | 26 | Fax 817/581-5477 |
| **Dr Jim Calvin** | | | | |
| Haltom High Sch | 9-12 | TV | 2,691 | 68% 817/547-6000 |
| 5501 Haltom Rd, Haltom City 76137 | | | 170 | Fax 817/581-5385 |
| Dion Varnado | | | | |
| Haltom Middle Sch | 6-8 | TV | 925 | 85% 817/547-4000 |
| 5000 Hires Ln, Haltom City 76117 | | | 50 | Fax 817/831-5778 |
| Tim Drysdale | | | | 🇫🇹 |
| Holiday Heights Elem Sch | PK-5 | T | 586 | 57% 817/547-2600 |
| 5221 Susan Lee Ln, N Richlnd Hls 76180 | | | 40 | Fax 817/581-5396 |
| Lisa Walker | | | | |
| Jack C Binion Elem Sch | PK-5 | T | 712 | 71% 817/547-1800 |
| 7400 Glenview Dr, Richland Hls 76180 | | | 33 | Fax 817/595-5111 |
| **Donald Bartlett** | | | | 🇫🇹 |

---

| | | | | | | | |
|---|---|---|---|---|---|---|---|
| **1** Superintendent | **8** Curric/Instruct K-12 | **19** Chief Financial Officer | **29** Family/Consumer Science | **39** Social Studies K-12 | **49** English/Lang Arts Elem | **59** Special Education Elem | **69** Academic Assessment |
| **2** Bus/Finance/Purchasing | **9** Curric/Instruct Elem | **20** Art K-12 | **30** Adult Education | **40** Social Studies Elem | **50** English/Lang Arts Sec | **60** Special Education Sec | **70** Research/Development |
| **3** Buildings And Grounds | **10** Curric/Instruct Sec | **21** Art Elem | **31** Career/Sch-to-Work K-12 | **41** Social Studies Sec | **51** Reading K-12 | **61** Foreign/World Lang K-12 | **71** Public Information |
| **4** Food Service | **11** Federal Program | **22** Art Sec | **32** Career/Sch-to-Work Elem | **42** Science K-12 | **52** Reading Elem | **62** Foreign/World Lang Elem | **72** Summer School |
| **5** Transportation | **12** Title I | **23** Music K-12 | **33** Career/Sch-to-Work Sec | **43** Science Elem | **53** Reading Sec | **63** Foreign/World Lang Sec | **73** Instructional Tech |
| **6** Athletic | **13** Title V | **24** Music Elem | **34** Early Childhood Ed | **44** Science Sec | **54** Remedial Reading K-12 | **64** Religious Education K-12 | **74** Inservice Training |
| **7** Health Services | **15** Asst Superintendent | **25** Music Sec | **35** Health/Phys Education | **45** Math K-12 | **55** Remedial Reading Elem | **65** Religious Education Elem | **75** Marketing/Distributive |
| | **16** Instructional Media Svcs | **26** Business Education | **36** Guidance Services K-12 | **46** Math Elem | **56** Remedial Reading Sec | **66** Religious Education Sec | **76** Info Systems |
| **TX—348** | **17** Chief Operations Officer | **27** Career & Tech Ed | **37** Guidance Services Elem | **47** Math Sec | **57** Bilingual/ELL | **67** School Board President | **77** Psychological Assess |
| | **18** Chief Academic Officer | **28** Technology Education | **38** Guidance Services Sec | **48** English/Lang Arts K-12 | **58** Special Education K-12 | **68** Teacher Personnel | **78** Affirmative Action |

| | | | | | | |
|---|---|---|---|---|---|---|
| John D Spicer Elem Sch<br>4300 Estes Park Rd, Haltom City 76137<br>Dr Cheryl Waddell | PK-5 | T | 432 | 63% | 817/547-3300<br>Fax 817/581-5497 | |
| Major Cheney ES-S Birdville<br>2600 Solona St, Haltom City 76117<br>**Shane Conklin** | PK-5 | T | 394<br>21 | 84% | 817/547-2300<br>Fax 817/831-5798 | f t |
| North Oaks Middle Sch<br>4800 Jordan Park Dr, Haltom City 76117<br>Dr Jennifer Klaerner | 6-8 | TV | 372<br>60 | 75% | 817/547-4600<br>Fax 817/581-5352 | |
| North Richland Middle Sch<br>4801 Redondo St, N Richlnd Hls 76180<br>Stephen Ellis | 6-8 | TV | 912<br>50 | 66% | 817/547-4200<br>Fax 817/581-5372 | |
| North Ridge Elem Sch<br>7331 Holiday Ln, N Richlnd Hls 76182<br>Deborah Coulson | PK-5 | | 419<br>35 | 37% | 817/547-3200<br>Fax 817/581-5440 | |
| North Ridge Middle Sch<br>7332 Douglas Ln, N Richlnd Hls 76182<br>John Davis | 6-8 | V | 737<br>49 | 37% | 817/547-5200<br>Fax 817/581-5460 | f t |
| O H Stowe Elem Sch<br>4201 Rita Ln, Haltom City 76117<br>Nathan Frymark | PK-5 | T | 567<br>39 | 77% | 817/547-2400<br>Fax 817/581-5328 | f t |
| Richland Elem Sch<br>3250 Scruggs Park Dr, Richland Hls 76118<br>Kerri Sands | PK-5 | T | 164<br>22 | 73% | 817/547-2000<br>Fax 817/595-5110 | |
| Richland High Sch<br>5201 Holiday Ln, N Richlnd Hls 76180<br>Mark McCanlies | 9-12 | TV | 2,114<br>110 | 45% | 817/547-7000<br>Fax 817/581-5454 | |
| Richland Middle Sch<br>7400 Hovenkamp Ave, Richland Hls 76118<br>Jody Fadely | 6-8 | TV | 709<br>40 | 73% | 817/547-4400<br>Fax 817/595-5139 | |
| Ⓐ Shannon High Sch<br>6010 Walker St, Haltom City 76117<br>David Williams | 9-12 | GTV | 50<br>15 | 63% | 817/547-5400<br>Fax 817/831-5847 | |
| Smithfield Elem Sch<br>6724 Smithfield Rd, N Richlnd Hls 76182<br>Melissa Minix | PK-5 | T | 451<br>30 | 43% | 817/547-2100<br>Fax 817/581-5377 | f t |
| Smithfield Middle Sch<br>8400 Main St, N Richlnd Hls 76182<br>Kyle Pekurney | 6-8 | V | 808<br>50 | 23% | 817/547-5000<br>Fax 817/581-5480 | |
| Snow Heights Elem Sch<br>4801 Vance Rd, N Richlnd Hls 76180<br>Susan Nall | PK-5 | T | 318<br>15 | 44% | 817/547-2200<br>Fax 817/581-5323 | |
| W A Porter Elem Sch<br>2750 Prestondale Dr, Hurst 76054<br>Chad Paris | PK-5 | | 548<br>35 | 20% | 817/547-2900<br>Fax 817/581-5381 | f t |
| W T Francisco Elem Sch<br>3701 Layton Ave, Haltom City 76117<br>Angela Limon | PK-5 | T | 326<br>19 | 76% | 817/547-1700<br>Fax 817/831-5724 | |
| Walker Creek Elem Sch<br>8780 Bridge St, N Richlnd Hls 76180<br>Marsha Perry | PK-5 | | 562<br>33 | 26% | 817/547-3500<br>Fax 817/581-2932 | f t |
| Watauga Elem Sch<br>5937 Whitley Rd, Watauga 76148<br>Sara Uppchurch | PK-5 | T | 663<br>48 | 78% | 817/547-2700<br>Fax 817/581-5425 | f t |
| Watauga Middle Sch<br>6300 Maurie Dr, Watauga 76148<br>Shannon Shedd | 6-8 | T | 706<br>75 | 66% | 817/547-4800<br>Fax 817/581-5369 | |
| West Birdville Elementary<br>3001 Layton Ave, Haltom City 76117<br>Vanessa Sutton | PK-5 | T | 752<br>50 | 84% | 817/547-2500<br>Fax 817/831-5795 | f t |

---

● **Carroll Independent Sch Dist** PID: 01052252
2400 N Carroll Ave, Southlake 76092

817/949-8222
Fax 817/949-8228

**Schools:** 11 \ **Teachers:** 539 \ **Students:** 8,000 \ **Special Ed Students:** 642 \ **LEP Students:** 164 \ **College-Bound:** 75% \ **Ethnic:** Asian 19%, African American 2%, Hispanic 10%, Caucasian 68% \ **Exp:** $232 (Med) \ **Poverty:** 3% \ **Title I:** $152,158 \ **Special Education:** $1,169,000 \ **Open-Close:** 08/17 - 05/27 \ **DTBP:** $184 (High) \ f t

| | | | |
|---|---|---|---|
| Dr David Faltys | 1 | Scott Wrehe | 2,15 |
| Bob Carabajal | 3 | Suzanne Teal | 3 |
| Susan Wilson | 4 | Ranjan George | 5 |
| Steve Keasler | 6 | Gina Peddy | 8,61,81 |
| Tyisha Nelson | 11,27,57,58,88 | Julie Thannum | 15,71,297 |
| Matt Miller | 15,68 | Julie Stephens | 16,43,46 |
| Jaclyn Hemmila | 22,44,47 | Melanie Ringman | 35,41,50 |
| Angela Hammond | 40,49 | Michelle Moore | 67 |
| Carie Barthelemess | 69,294 | Randy Stuart | 73 |
| Janet McDade | 79 | | |

| Public Schs..Principal | Grd | Prgm | Enr/#Cls | SN | |
|---|---|---|---|---|---|
| Carroll Elem Sch<br>1705 W Continental Blvd, Southlake 76092<br>Stacy Wagnon | PK-4 | | 546<br>33 | 1% | 817/949-4300<br>Fax 817/949-4343<br>f t |
| Carroll High Sch<br>800 N White Chapel Blvd, Southlake 76092<br>Pj Giamanco | 9-10 | | 1,370 | 1% | 817/949-5600<br>Fax 817/949-5656 |
| Carroll Middle Sch<br>1800 Kirkwood Blvd, Southlake 76092<br>Stephanie Mangels | 7-8 | | 723<br>60 | 1% | 817/949-5400<br>Fax 817/949-5454<br>f t |
| Carroll Senior High Sch<br>1501 W Southlake Blvd, Southlake 76092<br>Shawn Duhon | 11-12 | A | 1,342<br>80 | 1% | 817/949-5800<br>Fax 817/949-5858<br>f t |
| Cleburn Eubanks Interm Sch<br>500 S Kimball Ave, Southlake 76092<br>Mary Stockton | 5-6 | | 569<br>27 | 1% | 817/949-5200<br>Fax 817/949-5252 |
| Don Durham Intermediate Sch<br>801 Shady Oaks Dr, Southlake 76092<br>Mike Wyrick | 5-6 | | 749<br>23 | 1% | 817/949-5300<br>Fax 817/949-5353 |
| George Dawson Middle Sch<br>400 S Kimball Ave, Southlake 76092<br>Ryan Wilson | 7-8 | | 651<br>150 | 1% | 817/949-5500<br>Fax 817/949-5555 |
| Jack D Johnson Elem Sch<br>1301 N Carroll Ave, Southlake 76092<br>Rene Moses | PK-4 | | 669<br>30 | 2% | 817/949-4500<br>Fax 817/949-4545 |
| Old Union Elem Sch<br>1050 S Carroll Ave, Southlake 76092<br>Jon Fike | PK-4 | | 348<br>30 | 3% | 817/949-4600<br>Fax 817/949-4646 |
| Rockenbaugh Elem Sch<br>301 Byron Nelson Pkwy, Southlake 76092<br>Janet Blackwell | PK-4 | | 453<br>30 | 1% | 817/949-4700<br>Fax 817/949-4747 |
| Walnut Grove Elem Sch<br>2520 N White Chapel Blvd, Southlake 76092<br>Mike Landers | K-4 | | 701<br>24 | 1% | 817/949-4400<br>Fax 817/949-4444<br>f t |

---

● **Castleberry Ind School Dist** PID: 01052290
5228 Ohio Garden Rd, Fort Worth 76114

817/252-2000
Fax 817/252-2099

**Schools:** 7 \ **Teachers:** 243 \ **Students:** 3,574 \ **Special Ed Students:** 368 \ **LEP Students:** 1,165 \ **Ethnic:** African American 2%, Hispanic 82%, Caucasian 16% \ **Exp:** $516 (High) \ **Poverty:** 20% \ **Title I:** $1,105,585 \ **Special Education:** $530,000 \ **Open-Close:** 08/12 - 05/27 \ **DTBP:** $181 (High) \ f

| | | | |
|---|---|---|---|
| John Ramos | 1 | Deanne Page | 2 |
| Kayla Lynn | 4 | Chris Page | 5 |
| Lenny Lasher | 6,7,35 | Kenneth Casarez | 10 |

---

| | | | | |
|---|---|---|---|---|
| 79 Student Personnel | 91 Safety/Security | 275 Response To Intervention | 298 Grant Writer/Ptnrships | **School Programs** |
| 80 Driver Ed/Safety | 92 Magnet School | 277 Remedial Math K-12 | 750 Chief Innovation Officer | **A** = Alternative Program |
| 81 Gifted/Talented | 93 Parental Involvement | 280 Literacy Coach | 751 Chief of Staff | **G** = Adult Classes |
| 82 Video Services | 95 Tech Prep Program | 285 STEM | 752 Social Emotional Learning | **M** = Magnet Program |
| 83 Substance Abuse Prev | 97 Chief Infomation Officer | 286 Digital Learning | | **T** = Title I Schoolwide |
| 84 Erate | 98 Chief Technology Officer | 288 Common Core Standards | **Other School Types** | **V** = Career & Tech Ed Programs |
| 85 AIDS Education | 270 Character Education | 294 Accountability | Ⓐ = Alternative School | |
| 88 Alternative/At Risk | 271 Migrant Education | 295 Network System | Ⓒ = Charter School | **Social Media** |
| 89 Multi-Cultural Curriculum | 273 Teacher Mentor | 296 Title II Programs | Ⓜ = Magnet School | f = Facebook |
| 90 Social Work | 274 Before/After Sch | 297 Webmaster | Ⓨ = Year-Round School | t = Twitter |

New Schools are shaded
New Superintendents and Principals are bold
Personnel with email addresses are underscored

| | |
|---|---|
| Kelli Kelsoe ............................................. 16* | Abigail Crawford ................................. 20,23 |
| Denise Fisher ........................................... 42 | Tyler Neal .............................................. 48 |
| Lynn Jamison ........................................... 58 | David Holder .......................................... 67 |
| Renee Smith-Faulkner ............. 71,73,95,286 | Heather Mayfield ................................... 76 |
| Jacob Bowser ........................................... 76 | Brian Huff ....................................... 84,295 |
| Samiel Cervantez ..................................... 91 | Laura Little .......................................... 294 |

### Public Schs..Principal

| Public Schs..Principal | Grd | Prgm | Enr/#Cls | SN | |
|---|---|---|---|---|---|
| A V Cato Elem Sch<br>4501 Barbara Rd, Fort Worth 76114<br>Meredith Strambler | PK-5 | T | 598<br>18 | 87% | 817/252-2400<br>Fax 817/252-2499 |
| Castleberry Elem Sch<br>1100 Roberts Cut Off Rd, Fort Worth 76114<br>Michelle Stapp | PK-5 | T | 664<br>50 | 80% | 817/252-2300<br>Fax 817/625-1884 |
| Castleberry High Sch<br>215 Churchill Rd, Fort Worth 76114<br>**Catherine Ridley** | 9-12 | GTV | 768<br>70 | 77% | 817/252-2100<br>Fax 817/252-2575 🛐🅣 |
| Irma Marsh Middle Sch<br>415 Hagg Dr, Fort Worth 76114<br>Mareka Austin | 6-8 | TV | 571<br>60 | 85% | 817/252-2200<br>Fax 817/738-3454 |
| Joy James Elem Sch<br>5300 Buchanan St, Fort Worth 76114<br>Leighann Turner | PK-5 | T | 416<br>24 | 89% | 817/252-2500<br>Fax 817/252-2599 |
| Reach High Sch<br>1101 Merritt St, Fort Worth 76114<br>Wanda Byther | 9-12 | AGTV | 12<br>4 | 77% | 817/252-2390<br>Fax 817/252-2398 🛐🅣 |
| Ⓐ Truce Learning Center<br>1101 Merritt St, Fort Worth 76114<br>Wanda Byther | 6-12 | T | 25<br>2 | 70% | 817/252-2490<br>Fax 817/252-2499 |

---

● **Crowley Ind School Dist** PID: 01052355　　817/297-5800
512 Peach St, Crowley 76036　　　　　　　　Fax 817/297-5805

> **Schools:** 25 \ **Teachers:** 1,065 \ **Students:** 15,215 \
> **Special Ed Students:** 1,546 \ **LEP Students:** 2,332 \ **College-Bound:** 52%
> \ **Ethnic:** Asian 5%, African American 47%, Hispanic 34%, Caucasian
> 14% \ **Exp:** $331 (High) \ **Poverty:** 14% \ **Title I:** $3,787,647 \
> **Special Education:** $2,490,000 \ **Open-Close:** 08/13 - 05/27 \ **DTBP:** $175
> (High) \ 🛐 🅣

| | |
|---|---|
| Dr Michael McFarland ............................... 1 | Dwayne Jones .......................................... 2 |
| Stacy Adrian ...................................... 2,19 | Randy Reaves ........................................... 3 |
| Jason Lowery ........................................... 5 | Charles Lincoln ........................................ 6 |
| Paige Williams ......................................... 7* | Maryann Middleton .................................... 8 |
| Ted Kretchmar ....................... 11,294,296 | Billy Johnson ........................... 15,79,83,85 |
| Theresa Paschall ..................................... 36 | Maria Anguiano ....................................... 57 |
| Ruby Batiste ............................................ 58 | Mia Hall ................................................. 67 |
| Dr Theresa Kohler ................................... 68 | Anthony Kirchner ..................................... 71 |
| Jerald Allen .................................. 73,95,98* | Jaretha Jordan ........................................ 74 |
| Stan Swann ............................................. 79 | Dr John Hamlett ...................................... 88 |
| Pat Panek ............................................... 91 | Bradley Parker ....................................... 286 |
| Matt Hoover ........................................... 297 | Crystel Polk ........................................... 298* |
| Veronica Kunschik .................................. 750 | Stefani Allen .......................................... 752 |

### Public Schs..Principal

| Public Schs..Principal | Grd | Prgm | Enr/#Cls | SN | |
|---|---|---|---|---|---|
| Bess Race Elem Sch<br>537 S Heights Dr, Crowley 76036<br>Holly Anderson | PK-4 | T | 527<br>33 | 63% | 817/297-5080<br>Fax 817/297-5084 |
| Bill R Johnson Cte Center<br>1033 McCart Ave, Crowley 76036<br>Markeba Warfield | Voc | G | 610 | | 817/297-3018<br>Fax 817/297-1839 |
| Crowley High Sch<br>1005 W Main St, Crowley 76036<br>Daryle Moffett | 10-12 | TV | 1,500 | 63% | 817/297-5810<br>Fax 817/297-5854 🛐🅣 |
| Crowley HS 9th Grade Campus<br>1016 FM 1187 W, Crowley 76036<br>Christopher White | 9-9 | V | 540<br>50 | | 817/297-5845<br>Fax 817/297-5847 |

| Public Schs..Principal | Grd | Prgm | Enr/#Cls | SN | |
|---|---|---|---|---|---|
| Ⓐ Crowley Learning Center<br>1008 FM 1187 W, Crowley 76036<br>Rashad Muhammad | 3-12 | | 150<br>11 | | 817/297-6992<br>Fax 817/297-4087 |
| Crowley Middle Sch<br>3800 W Risinger Rd, Fort Worth 76123<br>Omarian Brown | 7-8 | TV | 659<br>45 | 78% | 817/370-5650<br>Fax 817/370-5656 🅣 |
| Dallas Park Elem Sch<br>8700 Viridian Ln, Fort Worth 76123<br>Veronica DelGado | PK-4 | T | 732<br>37 | 56% | 817/370-5620<br>Fax 817/370-5624 |
| David L Walker Interm Sch<br>9901 Hemphill St, Fort Worth 76134<br>Melanie Randall | 5-6 | T | 631 | 86% | 817/568-2745<br>Fax 817/568-2209 |
| Deer Creek Elem Sch<br>805 S Crowley Rd, Crowley 76036<br>Anna Roe | PK-4 | T | 448<br>30 | 61% | 817/297-5880<br>Fax 817/297-5884 |
| Ⓐ Global Prep Academy<br>1033 McCart Ave, Crowley 76036<br>Dr Markeba Warfield | 7-12 | | 56 | | 817/297-3018<br>Fax 817/297-8139 |
| H F Stevens Middle Sch<br>940 N Crowley Rd, Crowley 76036<br>Kimberly Buckhalton | 7-8 | TV | 881<br>35 | 74% | 817/297-5840<br>Fax 817/297-5850 |
| J A Hargrave Elem Sch<br>9200 Poynter St, Fort Worth 76123<br>Rolanda McKenzie | PK-4 | T | 592 | 78% | 817/370-5630<br>Fax 817/370-5635 |
| Jackie Carden Elem Sch<br>3701 Garden Springs Dr, Fort Worth 76123<br>Paula Brooks | PK-4 | T | 374<br>32 | 77% | 817/370-5600<br>Fax 817/370-5604 |
| June W Davis Elem Sch<br>6301 Rockrose Trl, Fort Worth 76123<br>Kevin Hunt | PK-5 | | 550 | | 817/885-5700<br>Fax 817/885-8720 |
| Mary Harris Intermediate Sch<br>8400 W Cleburne Rd, Fort Worth 76123<br>Clarence Williams | 5-6 | T | 587 | 81% | 817/370-7571<br>Fax 817/294-1594 |
| Meadowcreek Elem Sch<br>2801 Country Creek Ln, Fort Worth 76123<br>Tonya Coleman | PK-4 | T | 561<br>30 | 78% | 817/370-5690<br>Fax 817/370-5694 |
| North Crowley 9th Grade Campus<br>4630 McPherson Blvd, Fort Worth 76123<br>Camcea Stapinski | 9-9 | V | 656 | | 817/297-5896<br>Fax 817/297-5878 |
| North Crowley High Sch<br>9100 S Hulen St, Fort Worth 76123<br>**Camcea Stapinski** | 10-12 | TV | 1,759<br>100 | 58% | 817/263-1250<br>Fax 817/263-1282 |
| Oakmont Elem Sch<br>6651 Oakmont Trl, Fort Worth 76132<br>Kimberly Scoggins | PK-4 | T | 655<br>40 | 65% | 817/370-5610<br>Fax 817/370-5615 |
| Parkway Elem Sch<br>1320 W Everman Pkwy, Fort Worth 76134<br>Roslyn Bell | PK-4 | T | 629<br>34 | 84% | 817/568-5710<br>Fax 817/568-5714 |
| S H Crowley Intermediate Sch<br>10525 McCart Ave, Crowley 76036<br>Deidra Castro | 5-6 | | 537 | | 817/297-5960<br>Fax 817/297-5964 |
| Sidney Poynter Elem Sch<br>521 Ashdale Dr, Fort Worth 76140<br>Shaketa Traylor | PK-4 | T | 389<br>40 | 73% | 817/568-5730<br>Fax 817/568-5734 |
| Sue Crouch Intermediate Sch<br>8036 Cedar Lake Ln, Fort Worth 76123<br>Arthurlyn Morgan | 5-6 | T | 639 | 56% | 817/370-5670<br>Fax 817/370-5676 |
| Summer Creek Middle Sch<br>10236 Summercreek Dr, Crowley 76036<br>Cayla Grossman | 7-8 | TV | 800 | 64% | 817/297-5090<br>Fax 817/297-5094 🛐🅣 |
| Sycamore Elem Sch<br>1601 Country Manor Rd, Fort Worth 76134<br>Rebekah Hunt | PK-4 | T | 498<br>28 | 80% | 817/568-5700<br>Fax 817/568-5704 |

---

| | | | | | | | | | | | | |
|---|---|---|---|---|---|---|---|---|---|---|---|---|
| 1 | Superintendent | 8 | Curric/Instruct K-12 | 19 | Chief Financial Officer | 29 | Family/Consumer Science | 39 | Social Studies K-12 | 49 | English/Lang Arts Elem | 59 | Special Education Elem |
| 2 | Bus/Finance/Purchasing | 9 | Curric/Instruct Elem | 20 | Art K-12 | 30 | Adult Education | 40 | Social Studies Elem | 50 | English/Lang Arts Sec | 60 | Special Education Sec |
| 3 | Buildings And Grounds | 10 | Curric/Instruct Sec | 21 | Art Elem | 31 | Career/Sch-to-Work K-12 | 41 | Social Studies Sec | 51 | Reading K-12 | 61 | Foreign/World Lang K-12 |
| 4 | Food Service | 11 | Federal Program | 22 | Art Sec | 32 | Career/Sch-to-Work Elem | 42 | Science K-12 | 52 | Reading Elem | 62 | Foreign/World Lang Elem |
| 5 | Transportation | 12 | Title I | 23 | Music K-12 | 33 | Career/Sch-to-Work Sec | 43 | Science Elem | 53 | Reading Sec | 63 | Foreign/World Lang Sec |
| 6 | Athletic | 13 | Title V | 24 | Music Elem | 34 | Early Childhood Ed | 44 | Science Sec | 54 | Remedial Reading K-12 | 64 | Religious Education K-12 |
| 7 | Health Services | 15 | Asst Superintendent | 25 | Music Sec | 35 | Health/Phys Education | 45 | Math K-12 | 55 | Remedial Reading Elem | 65 | Religious Education Elem |
| | | 16 | Instructional Media Svcs | 26 | Business Education | 36 | Guidance Services K-12 | 46 | Math Elem | 56 | Remedial Reading Sec | 66 | Religious Education Sec |
| | | 17 | Chief Operations Officer | 27 | Career & Tech Ed | 37 | Guidance Services Elem | 47 | Math Sec | 57 | Bilingual/ELL | 67 | School Board President |
| | | 18 | Chief Academic Officer | 28 | Technology Education | 38 | Guidance Services Sec | 48 | English/Lang Arts K-12 | 58 | Special Education K-12 | 68 | Teacher Personnel |

| | |
|---|---|
| 69 | Academic Assessment |
| 70 | Research/Development |
| 71 | Public Information |
| 72 | Summer School |
| 73 | Instructional Tech |
| 74 | Inservice Training |
| 75 | Marketing/Distributive |
| 76 | Info Systems |
| 77 | Psychological Assess |
| 78 | Affirmative Action |

● **Eagle Mtn-Saginaw Ind Sch Dist** PID: 01052408    817/232-0880
1200 Old Decatur Rd, Saginaw 76179    Fax 817/847-6124

**Schools:** 27 \ **Teachers:** 1,225 \ **Students:** 21,000 \
**Special Ed Students:** 1,901 \ **LEP Students:** 2,010 \ **College-Bound:** 54%
\ **Ethnic:** Asian 5%, African American 12%, Hispanic 40%, Caucasian
42% \ **Exp:** $303 (High) \ **Poverty:** 9% \ **Title I:** $1,953,573 \
**Special Education:** $2,229,000 \ **Open-Close:** 08/18 - 05/28 \ **DTBP:** $187
(High) \ 🇫 🇹

| | | | |
|---|---|---|---|
| Dr Jim Chadwell | 1 | Jane Valdez | 2 |
| Jim Schiele | 2,19 | Lucia Cieszlak | 2 |
| Charles Hamilton | 3 | Clete Welch | 3,5,17 |
| Aaron Wylie | 4 | Brent Barker | 6 |
| Cheryl Phalen | 7 | Dr Linda Parker | 8,15,34,74,294 |
| Stacy Summerhill | 8 | Dr Mary Jones | 11,69,88,271,296 |
| Shawn Bell | 20,23 | Dr Dana Barnes | 27,30,31* |
| Dana Eldredge | 27* | Mariella Alvarado | 36 |
| Dr Heather Hughes | 58,77 | Steven Newcom | 67 |
| Dr Deborah Dockens | 68,79 | Dr Maria Gamell | 68 |
| Dr Philo Waters | 68 | Megan Overman | 71 |
| Kirk Murdock | 73,295 | Karen Miller | 74,273 |
| Belinda Newman | 76 | Dr Barry Baker | 91 |
| Ally Surface | 298 | | |

| Public Schs..Principal | Grd | Prgm | Enr/#Cls | SN | |
|---|---|---|---|---|---|
| Bryson Elem Sch<br>8601 Old Decatur Rd, Fort Worth 76179<br>Jennifer Gillard | PK-5 | T | 464<br>35 | 49% | 817/237-8306<br>Fax 817/238-8991 |
| Chisholm Ridge Elem Sch<br>8301 Running River Ln, Fort Worth 76131<br>Krystle Green | PK-5 | T | 565 | 47% | 817/232-0715<br>Fax 817/306-4391 |
| Chisholm Trail High Sch<br>3100 NW College Dr, Fort Worth 76179<br>**Winston McCowan** | 9-12 | TV | 2,019 | 44% | 817/232-7112<br>Fax 817/306-1327 |
| Comanche Springs Elem Sch<br>8100 Comanche Springs Dr, Fort Worth 76131<br>Melissa Davis | PK-5 | | 617<br>26 | 27% | 817/847-8700<br>Fax 817/847-0941 |
| Creekview Middle Sch<br>6716 Bob Hanger St, Fort Worth 76179<br>Anthe Anagnostis | 6-8 | TV | 993 | 42% | 817/237-4261<br>Fax 817/237-2387 |
| Dozier Elem Sch<br>6201 Redeagle Creek Dr, Fort Worth 76179<br>Rachel Bradley | PK-5 | T | 616 | 53% | 817/847-6340<br>Fax 817/237-8015 |
| Eagle Mountain Elem Sch<br>9700 Morris Dido Newark Rd, Fort Worth 76179<br>Jason Beaty | PK-5 | T | 552<br>31 | 20% | 817/236-7191<br>Fax 817/236-1461<br>🇫🇹 |
| Ed Willkie Middle Sch<br>6129 Texas Shiner Dr, Fort Worth 76179<br>Brian Booker | 6-8 | T | 1,045 | 48% | 817/237-9631<br>Fax 817/237-9643 |
| Elkins Elem Sch<br>7259 Elkins School Rd, Fort Worth 76179<br>Randiann Cowden | PK-5 | T | 310<br>36 | 45% | 817/237-0805<br>Fax 817/237-0948 |
| Ⓐ Elmer C Watson High Sch<br>5900 Hereford Dr, Fort Worth 76179<br>Melanie Stitt | 9-12 | GT | 62<br>25 | 53% | 817/238-7925<br>Fax 817/237-0753 |
| Greenfield Elem Sch<br>6020 Ten Mile Bridge Rd, Fort Worth 76135<br>Kelly Ramsey | PK-5 | T | 635<br>38 | 43% | 817/237-0357<br>Fax 817/237-5809 |
| Hafley Development Center<br>616 W McLeroy Blvd, Fort Worth 76179<br>Stacey De Hoyos | PK-PK | GT | 468<br>18 | 76% | 817/232-2071<br>Fax 817/232-5126 |
| High Country Elem Sch<br>1301 High Country Trl, Fort Worth 76131<br>Elizabeth Sanders | K-5 | T | 550<br>35 | 44% | 817/306-8007<br>Fax 817/306-5852 |
| Highland Middle Sch<br>1001 E Bailey Boswell Rd, Fort Worth 76131<br>David Coker | 6-8 | TV | 596<br>50 | 47% | 817/847-5143<br>Fax 817/847-1922 |

| | Voc/Grd | Prgm | Enr/#Cls | SN | |
|---|---|---|---|---|---|
| Hollenstein Career & Tech Ctr<br>5501 Marine Creek Pkwy, Fort Worth 76179<br>Dr Dana Barnes | Voc | | 1,600 | | 817/306-1925<br>Fax 817/306-1327 |
| L A Gililland Elem Sch<br>701 Waggoman Rd, Fort Worth 76131<br>Christina Fehler | PK-5 | T | 438<br>39 | 76% | 817/232-0331<br>Fax 817/232-8822 |
| Lake Pointe Elem Sch<br>5501 Park Dr, Fort Worth 76179<br>Audrey Arnold | PK-5 | | 614 | 27% | 817/236-8801<br>Fax 817/236-8805 |
| Marine Creek Middle Sch<br>5825 Marine Creek Pkwy, Fort Worth 76179<br>**Ron Gatlin** | 6-8 | | 1,000 | | 817/847-2945 |
| Northbrook Elem Sch<br>2500 Cantrell Sansom Rd, Fort Worth 76131<br>Magdalena Highlen | PK-5 | T | 478 | 68% | 817/232-0086<br>Fax 817/232-9861 |
| Parkview Elem Sch<br>6225 Crystal Lake Dr, Fort Worth 76179<br>Mindy Miller | PK-5 | T | 519 | 48% | 817/237-5121<br>Fax 817/237-5187 |
| Prairie Vista Middle Sch<br>8000 Comanche Springs Dr, Fort Worth 76131<br>Dr Anna King | 6-8 | T | 311 | 51% | 817/847-9210<br>Fax 817/847-4255 |
| Remington Point Elem Sch<br>6000 Old Decatur Rd, Fort Worth 76179<br>Chaney Curran | PK-5 | T | 421<br>37 | 53% | 817/232-1342<br>Fax 817/232-2594 |
| Saginaw Elem Sch<br>301 W McLeroy Blvd, Fort Worth 76179<br>**Melissa Curtis** | PK-5 | T | 238<br>50 | 61% | 817/232-0631<br>Fax 817/232-3357 |
| Saginaw High Sch<br>800 N Blue Mound Rd, Fort Worth 76131<br>Karen Pressley | 9-12 | TV | 1,886 | 44% | 817/306-0914<br>Fax 817/306-1344 |
| W E Boswell High Sch<br>5805 W Bailey Boswell Rd, Fort Worth 76179<br>Nika Davis | 9-12 | GV | 2,032<br>100 | 31% | 817/237-3314<br>Fax 817/238-8706 |
| Wayside Middle Sch<br>1300 Old Decatur Rd, Fort Worth 76179<br>Raymond Fahey | 6-8 | V | 965<br>60 | 34% | 817/232-0541<br>Fax 817/232-2391 |
| Willow Creek Elem Sch<br>1100 W McLeroy Blvd, Saginaw 76179<br>**Stacie Witt** | PK-5 | T | 520 | 46% | 817/232-2845<br>Fax 817/847-1859 |

● **Everman Ind School Dist** PID: 01052460    817/568-3500
1520 Everman Pkwy, Fort Worth 76140    Fax 817/568-3508

**Schools:** 11 \ **Teachers:** 371 \ **Students:** 6,345 \ **Special Ed Students:** 542
\ **LEP Students:** 1,622 \ **College-Bound:** 56% \ **Ethnic:** Asian 1%,
African American 38%, Hispanic 58%, Caucasian 4% \ **Exp:** $655 (High)
\ **Poverty:** 22% \ **Title I:** $1,822,241 \ **Special Education:** $1,056,000 \
**Open-Close:** 08/13 - 05/25 \ **DTBP:** $171 (High)

| | | | |
|---|---|---|---|
| Dr Curtis Amos | 1 | Joee Gainer | 2,19 |
| Glenn Brown | 3 | Rebecca Noon | 4,34 |
| Felicia Donaldson | 5,7,15,36,68,78,80,298 | Jason Gillis | 5 |
| Dale Matlock | 6* | Kentrell Phillips | 8,73 |
| Jennifer Samuel | 9,69,288,294 | Colette Kotula | 11 |
| Susan Geye | 16,73,286,295 | Susan Alvey | 27 |
| Pam McCoy | 34 | Melissa Sigler | 47* |
| Monica Plowman | 57 | Ginna Marks | 58 |
| Rickey Burgess | 67 | Gina Sanderson | 68 |
| Dr Nikita Russell | 71 | Hubert Pickett | 79 |
| James King | 79,91 | | |

| Public Schs..Principal | Grd | Prgm | Enr/#Cls | SN | |
|---|---|---|---|---|---|
| Baxter Junior High Sch<br>3038 Shelby Rd, Fort Worth 76140<br>**Tanisha Boone** | 7-8 | AT | 1,027<br>30 | 93% | 817/568-3530<br>Fax 817/568-3594 |

| | | | | |
|---|---|---|---|---|
| 79 Student Personnel | 91 Safety/Security | 275 Response To Intervention | 298 Grant Writer/Ptnrships | **School Programs** |
| 80 Driver Ed/Safety | 92 Magnet School | 277 Remedial Math K-12 | 750 Chief Innovation Officer | A = Alternative Program |
| 81 Gifted/Talented | 93 Parental Involvement | 280 Literacy Coach | 751 Chief of Staff | G = Adult Classes |
| 82 Video Services | 95 Tech Prep Program | 285 STEM | 752 Social Emotional Learning | M = Magnet Program |
| 83 Substance Abuse Prev | 97 Chief Infomation Officer | 286 Digital Learning | | T = Title I Schoolwide |
| 84 Erate | 98 Chief Technology Officer | 288 Common Core Standards | **Other School Types** | V = Career & Tech Ed Programs |
| 85 AIDS Education | 270 Character Education | 294 Accountability | Ⓐ = Alternative School | |
| 88 Alternative/At Risk | 271 Migrant Education | 295 Network System | Ⓒ = Charter School | |
| 89 Multi-Cultural Curriculum | 273 Teacher Mentor | 296 Title II Programs | Ⓜ = Magnet School | New Schools are shaded |
| 90 Social Work | 274 Before/After Sch | 297 Webmaster | Ⓨ = Year-Round School | New Superintendents and Principals are bold |
| | | | | Personnel with email addresses are underscored |

**Social Media**
🇫 = Facebook
🇹 = Twitter

**TX—351**

| School | Grd | Prgm | Enr/#Cls | SN | Phone |
|--------|-----|------|----------|-----|-------|
| Dan Powell Intermediate Sch<br>8875 Oak Grove Rd, Fort Worth 76140<br>Tanisha Boone | 5-5 | T | 449<br>36 | 92% | 817/568-3523<br>Fax 817/568-3533 |
| Davis 9th Grade Center<br>615 Townley Dr, Everman 76140<br>Patrick Lamers | 9-9 | AGV | 433 | | 817/568-5280<br>Fax 817/568-3538 |
| E Ray Elem Sch<br>7309 Sheridan Rd, Fort Worth 76134<br>Eva Quinonez | PK-4 | T | 424<br>25 | 91% | 817/568-3545<br>Fax 817/568-3544 |
| Ⓐ Everman Academy High Sch<br>300 Shelby Rd, Everman 76140<br>Cherie Pace | 9-12 | T | 67 | 95% | 817/568-3520<br>Fax 817/568-3516 |
| Everman Joe C Bean High Sch<br>1000 S Race St, Everman 76140<br>Mario Layne | 9-12 | AGT | 887<br>125 | 87% | 817/568-5200<br>Fax 817/568-5219 |
| Hommel Elem Sch<br>308 W Enon Ave, Everman 76140<br>Martin DeHoyos | PK-4 | T | 409<br>25 | 95% | 817/568-3540<br>Fax 817/568-3543 |
| J W Bishop Elem Sch<br>501 Vaughn Ave, Everman 76140<br>Ollie Clark | PK-4 | T | 453<br>37 | 93% | 817/568-3575<br>Fax 817/568-3572 |
| Ray Johnson 6th Grade Ctr<br>8901 Oak Grove Rd, Fort Worth 76140<br>Mary Preston | 6-6 | T | 511 | 91% | 817/615-3670<br>Fax 817/615-3675 |
| Souder Elem Sch<br>201 N Forest Hill Dr, Everman 76140<br>**Kimberly Little** | PK-4 | T | 467<br>30 | 93% | 817/568-3580<br>Fax 817/568-3589 |
| Townley Elem Sch<br>2200 McPherson Rd, Fort Worth 76140<br>Tarnika Dees | PK-4 | T | 391 | 94% | 817/568-3560<br>Fax 817/568-5177 |

● **Ft Worth Ind School Dist** PID: 01052525     817/871-2000
100 N University Dr, Fort Worth 76107     Fax 817/814-1935

**Schools:** 134 \ **Teachers:** 5,778 \ **Students:** 89,000 \
**Special Ed Students:** 7,776 \ **LEP Students:** 25,661 \ **College-Bound:** 57%
\ **Ethnic:** Asian 2%, African American 22%, Hispanic 64%, Caucasian
11% \ **Exp:** $343 (High) \ **Poverty:** 24% \ **Title I:** $39,602,221 \
**Special Education:** $13,702,000 \ **Open-Close:** 08/17 - 05/27 \ **DTBP:** $129
(High) \ 🅵 🅴

| | | | |
|---|---|---|---|
| Dr Kent Scribner | 1 | Jonathan Bey | 2 |
| Arturo Cavazos | 3,15 | Glenn Headlee | 4 |
| Bill Ray | 5 | Todd Vesely | 6 |
| Alice Turner Jackson | 7 | Charles Carroll | 8,18 |
| Mirgitt Crespo | 11 | Dr Becky Navarre | 15,95 |
| Dr Cherie Washington | 15 | Dr Maria Sheffield | 15,58 |
| Michael Steinert | 15,79,83 | Sara Arispe | 15,294 |
| Sherry Breed | 15,79 | Carter Cook | 16 |
| Elsie Schiro | 19 | Beverly Fletcher | 20 |
| Dick Clardy | 23 | Dinah Menger | 24 |
| Nyda Lewis | 30 | Cheryl Mixon | 34 |
| Georgiann Roberts | 35 | Kathryn Everest | 36 |
| Joseph Niedziela | 39 | Dr Herman Jackson | 42 |
| Shannon Hernandez | 45 | Stacy Parker | 46 |
| Cherron Ukpaka | 52,280 | Michelle McCone | 53,280 |
| Suann Claunch | 57 | Elda Rojas | 61 |
| Jacinto Ramos | 67 | Ken Torres | 69 |
| Tracy Marshall | 70,298 | Barbara Griffith | 71 |
| Dr Karla Lester | 73 | Dr Lezley Lewis | 74 |
| Dr Carlos Antoline | 77 | Danny Garcia | 91 |
| Miguel Garcia | 274 | Patricia Sutton | 275 |
| John Cope | 297 | Karen Molinar | 751 |

| Public Schs..Principal | Grd | Prgm | Enr/#Cls | SN | Phone |
|------------------------|-----|------|----------|-----|-------|
| Ⓨ A M Pate Elem Sch<br>3800 Anglin Dr, Fort Worth 76119<br>Rochelle Horton | PK-5 | MT | 449<br>35 | 98% | 817/815-3800<br>Fax 817/815-3850 🅵🅴 |
| Adult Education Center<br>5701 Meadowbrook Dr Bldg 1, Fort Worth 76112<br>Sofia Zamarripa | Adult | V | 500<br>5 | | 817/492-7960<br>Fax 817/492-7977 |
| Ⓨ Alice Carlson Applied Lrng Ctr<br>3320 W Cantey St, Fort Worth 76109<br>Janis Harris | K-5 | M | 387<br>17 | 24% | 817/815-5700<br>Fax 817/815-5750 |
| Alice Contreras Elem Sch<br>4100 Lubbock Ave, Fort Worth 76115<br>Amelia Cortes-Rangel | PK-5 | T | 620 | 93% | 817/814-7800<br>Fax 817/814-7850 🅵🅴 |
| Amon Carter-Riverside High Sch<br>3301 Yucca Ave, Fort Worth 76111<br>Greg Ruthart | 9-12 | TV | 1,155 | 94% | 817/814-9000<br>Fax 817/814-9050 🅵🅴 |
| Ⓨ Applied Learning Academy<br>7060 Camp Bowie Blvd, Fort Worth 76116<br>Alice Buckley | 6-8 | MT | 318<br>20 | 64% | 817/815-5500<br>Fax 817/815-5550 |
| Arlington Heights High Sch<br>4501 West Fwy, Fort Worth 76107<br>Sarah Weeks | 9-12 | TV | 1,866<br>75 | 70% | 817/815-1000<br>Fax 817/815-1050 |
| Atwood McDonald Elem Sch<br>1850 Barron Ln, Fort Worth 76112<br>Nkosi Geary-Smith | PK-5 | T | 441 | 91% | 817/815-4800<br>Fax 817/815-4850 🅵🅴 |
| Benbrook Elem Sch<br>800 Mercedes St, Fort Worth 76126<br>Shelly Mayer | PK-5 | | 526<br>25 | 52% | 817/815-6400<br>Fax 817/815-6450 |
| Benbrook Middle High Sch<br>201 Overcrest Dr, Fort Worth 76126<br>Richard Penland | 6-12 | T | 1,745 | 56% | 817/815-7100<br>Fax 817/815-7150 |
| Bill J Elliott Elem Sch<br>2501 Cooks Ln, Fort Worth 76120<br>Latonya Ordaz | PK-5 | T | 388<br>38 | 87% | 817/815-4600<br>Fax 817/815-4650 |
| Bonnie Brae Elem Sch<br>3504 Kimbo Rd, Fort Worth 76111<br>Samantha Gonzalez | PK-5 | T | 402<br>22 | 93% | 817/814-3700<br>Fax 817/814-3750 |
| Boulevard Heights Sch<br>5100 El Campo Ave, Fort Worth 76107<br>Dr Terry Guthrie | Spec | | 50<br>9 | 76% | 817/814-6400<br>Fax 817/814-6450 🅵🅴 |
| Bruce Shulkey Elem Sch<br>5533 Whitman Ave, Fort Worth 76133<br>Vanessa Tritten | PK-5 | T | 446<br>28 | 85% | 817/814-8400<br>Fax 817/814-8450 |
| Burton Hill Elem Sch<br>519 Burton Hill Rd, Fort Worth 76114<br>Dr Tm Bigley | PK-5 | T | 451<br>25 | 60% | 817/815-1400<br>Fax 817/815-1450 🅵🅴 |
| Carroll Peak Elem Sch<br>1201 E Jefferson Ave, Fort Worth 76104<br>Kalyn Sanjacinto | PK-5 | T | 491<br>24 | 95% | 817/814-0700<br>Fax 817/814-0750 🅵🅴 |
| Carter Park Elem Sch<br>1204 E Broadus Ave, Fort Worth 76115<br>**Cassandra McCalister** | PK-5 | T | 631<br>25 | 97% | 817/815-8600<br>Fax 817/815-8650 🅵🅴 |
| Cesar Chavez Elem Sch<br>3710 Deen Rd, Fort Worth 76106<br>Monica Ordaz | PK-5 | T | 448 | 95% | 817/815-0300<br>Fax 817/815-0350 |
| Charles E Nash Elem Sch<br>401 Samuels Ave, Fort Worth 76102<br>Blanca Galindo | PK-5 | T | 261<br>12 | 85% | 817/814-9400<br>Fax 817/814-9450 🅵🅴 |
| Christene Moss Elem Sch<br>4108 Eastland St, Fort Worth 76119<br>Charla Staten | PK-5 | T | 433<br>31 | 96% | 817/815-3600<br>Fax 817/815-3650 |
| Clifford Davis Elem Sch<br>4300 Campus Dr, Fort Worth 76119<br>Pamela Henderson | PK-5 | T | 685<br>24 | 97% | 817/815-8700<br>Fax 817/815-8750 |
| Ⓜ Como Montessori Sch<br>4001 Littlepage St, Fort Worth 76107<br>**Daniel McAlister** | K-8 | T | 313<br>19 | 76% | 817/815-7200<br>Fax 817/815-7250 |
| Ⓨ D McRae Elem Sch<br>3316 Avenue N, Fort Worth 76105<br>Aura Angel | PK-5 | MT | 532<br>32 | 95% | 817/814-0500<br>Fax 817/814-0550 |

| # | | # | | # | | # | |
|---|---|---|---|---|---|---|---|
| 1 | Superintendent | 8 | Curric/Instruct K-12 | 19 | Chief Financial Officer | 29 | Family/Consumer Science |
| 2 | Bus/Finance/Purchasing | 9 | Curric/Instruct Elem | 20 | Art K-12 | 30 | Adult Education |
| 3 | Buildings And Grounds | 10 | Curric/Instruct Sec | 21 | Art Elem | 31 | Career/Sch-to-Work K-12 |
| 4 | Food Service | 11 | Federal Program | 22 | Art Sec | 32 | Career/Sch-to-Work Elem |
| 5 | Transportation | 12 | Title I | 23 | Music K-12 | 33 | Career/Sch-to-Work Sec |
| 6 | Athletic | 13 | Title V | 24 | Music Elem | 34 | Early Childhood Ed |
| 7 | Health Services | 15 | Asst Superintendent | 25 | Music Sec | 35 | Health/Phys Education |
| | | 16 | Instructional Media Svcs | 26 | Business Education | 36 | Guidance Services K-12 |
| | | 17 | Chief Operations Officer | 27 | Career & Tech Ed | 37 | Guidance Services Elem |
| | | 18 | Chief Academic Officer | 28 | Technology Education | 38 | Guidance Services Sec |

| # | | # | | # | | # | |
|---|---|---|---|---|---|---|---|
| 39 | Social Studies K-12 | 49 | English/Lang Arts Elem | 59 | Special Education Elem | 69 | Academic Assessment |
| 40 | Social Studies Elem | 50 | English/Lang Arts Sec | 60 | Special Education Sec | 70 | Research/Development |
| 41 | Social Studies Sec | 51 | Reading K-12 | 61 | Foreign/World Lang K-12 | 71 | Public Information |
| 42 | Science K-12 | 52 | Reading Elem | 62 | Foreign/World Lang Elem | 72 | Summer School |
| 43 | Science Elem | 53 | Reading Sec | 63 | Foreign/World Lang Sec | 73 | Instructional Tech |
| 44 | Science Sec | 54 | Remedial Reading K-12 | 64 | Religious Education K-12 | 74 | Inservice Training |
| 45 | Math K-12 | 55 | Remedial Reading Elem | 65 | Religious Education Elem | 75 | Marketing/Distributive |
| 46 | Math Elem | 56 | Remedial Reading Sec | 66 | Religious Education Sec | 76 | Info Systems |
| 47 | Math Sec | 57 | Bilingual/ELL | 67 | School Board President | 77 | Psychological Assess |
| 48 | English/Lang Arts K-12 | 58 | Special Education K-12 | 68 | Teacher Personnel | 78 | Affirmative Action |

| School | Grades | Prog | Enroll | % | Phone |
|---|---|---|---|---|---|
| Daggett Montessori Elem Sch<br>801 W Jessamine St, Fort Worth 76110<br>Victorius Eugenio | K-8 | T | 497 | 47% | 817/814-6300<br>Fax 817/814-6350 |
| David K Sellars Elem Sch<br>4200 Dorsey St, Fort Worth 76119<br>Steven Mattic | PK-5 | T | 535<br>28 | 95% | 817/815-9200<br>Fax 817/815-9250 |
| Ⓨ De Zavala Elem Sch<br>1419 College Ave, Fort Worth 76104<br>Marlette Martinez | PK-5 | MT | 267<br>30 | 84% | 817/814-5600<br>Fax 817/814-5650 |
| Diamond Hill Elem Sch<br>2000 Dewey St, Fort Worth 76106<br>Maryln Martinez | PK-5 | T | 574<br>32 | 95% | 817/815-0400<br>Fax 817/815-0450 |
| Diamond Hill-Jarvis High Sch<br>1411 Maydell St, Fort Worth 76106<br>James Garcia | 9-12 | TV | 983 | 96% | 817/815-0000<br>Fax 817/815-0050 |
| Dolores Huerta Elem Sch<br>3309 W Long Ave, Fort Worth 76106<br>Carla Coscia | PK-5 | T | 501 | 96% | 817/814-4400<br>Fax 817/814-4450 |
| E M Daggett Elem Sch<br>958 Page Ave, Fort Worth 76110<br>Kendall Miller | PK-5 | T | 585<br>35 | 89% | 817/814-5500<br>Fax 817/814-5550 |
| E M Daggett Middle Sch<br>1108 Carlock St, Fort Worth 76110<br>Monica Garrett | 6-8 | TV | 383<br>35 | 93% | 817/814-5200<br>Fax 817/814-5250 |
| East Handley Elem Sch<br>2617 Mims St, Fort Worth 76112<br>Tiffany Hayes | PK-5 | T | 359<br>19 | 94% | 817/815-4400<br>Fax 817/815-4450 |
| Eastern Hills Elem Sch<br>5917 Shelton St, Fort Worth 76112<br>Whitney Scott | PK-5 | T | 557<br>30 | 91% | 817/815-4500<br>Fax 817/815-4550 |
| Eastern Hills High Sch<br>5701 Shelton St, Fort Worth 76112<br>Katrina Smith | 9-12 | GTV | 1,123 | 90% | 817/815-4000<br>Fax 817/815-4050 |
| Ⓨ Edward J Briscoe Elem Sch<br>2751 Yuma Ave, Fort Worth 76104<br>**Devona Burgess** | PK-5 | MT | 430<br>25 | 97% | 817/814-0300<br>Fax 817/814-0350 |
| Ⓨ Forest Oak Middle Sch<br>3221 Pecos St, Fort Worth 76119<br>Seretha Lofton | 6-8 | MTV | 868<br>50 | 96% | 817/815-8200<br>Fax 817/815-8250 |
| George Clarke Elem Sch<br>3300 S Henderson St, Fort Worth 76110<br>Kimberly Benavides | PK-5 | T | 419<br>38 | 94% | 817/814-6100<br>Fax 817/814-6150 |
| Glen Park Elem Sch<br>3601 Pecos St, Fort Worth 76119<br>**Hilda Herrera** | PK-5 | T | 496<br>37 | 96% | 817/815-8800<br>Fax 817/815-8850 |
| Glencrest 6th Grade Middle Sch<br>4801 Eastline Dr, Fort Worth 76119<br>Cassandra McCalister | 6-6 | T | 406<br>50 | 97% | 817/815-8400<br>Fax 817/815-8450 |
| Green B Trimble Tech High Sch<br>1003 W Cannon St, Fort Worth 76104<br>E Omar Ramos | 9-12 | TV | 1,698<br>100 | 91% | 817/815-2500<br>Fax 817/815-2550 |
| Greenbriar Elem Sch<br>1605 Grady Lee St, Fort Worth 76134<br>**Staros Guajardo** | PK-5 | T | 513<br>39 | 93% | 817/814-7400<br>Fax 817/814-7450 |
| H V Helbing Elem Sch<br>3524 N Crump St, Fort Worth 76106<br>Ana Morales | PK-5 | TV | 394<br>29 | 92% | 817/815-0500<br>Fax 817/815-0550 |
| Handley Middle Sch<br>2801 Patino Rd, Fort Worth 76112<br>Reginald Terrell | 6-8 | TV | 452<br>30 | 88% | 817/815-4200<br>Fax 817/815-4250 |
| Harlean Beal Elem Sch<br>5615 Forest Hill Dr, Fort Worth 76119<br>**Jodie Adair** | PK-5 | T | 359<br>25 | 93% | 817/815-8500<br>Fax 817/531-7738 |
| Hazel Harvey Peace Elem Sch<br>7555 Trail Lake Dr, Fort Worth 76133<br>Anthony Avery | PK-5 | T | 470 | 87% | 817/814-8800<br>Fax 817/814-8850 |
| Ⓨ Hubbard Heights Elem Sch<br>1333 W Spurgeon St, Fort Worth 76115<br>Amparo Martinez | PK-5 | MT | 517<br>35 | 93% | 817/814-7500<br>Fax 817/814-7550 |
| I M Terrell Elem Sch<br>1411 I M Terrell Cir S, Fort Worth 76102<br>Baldwin Brown | PK-5 | | 244<br>12 | | 817/815-1900<br>Fax 817/871-1950 |
| Ⓨ International Newcomer Academy<br>7060 Camp Bowie Blvd, Fort Worth 76116<br>Angelia Ross | 6-9 | AMT | 348<br>44 | 97% | 817/815-5600<br>Fax 817/815-5650 |
| J Martin Jacquet Middle Sch<br>2501 Stalcup Rd, Fort Worth 76119<br>**Kristin Foreman** | 6-8 | TV | 729<br>38 | 95% | 817/815-3500<br>Fax 817/815-3550 |
| J P Elder Middle Sch<br>709 NW 21st St, Fort Worth 76164<br>Dr David Trimble | 6-8 | TV | 1,230<br>58 | 92% | 817/814-4100<br>Fax 817/814-4150 |
| J T Stevens Elem Sch<br>6161 Wrigley Way, Fort Worth 76133<br>Jessica Johnson | PK-5 | T | 448<br>25 | 70% | 817/814-8500<br>Fax 817/814-8550 |
| Jean McClung Middle Sch<br>3000 Forest Ave, Fort Worth 76112<br>**Tremayna Thomas** | 6-8 | T | 716 | 92% | 817/815-5300<br>Fax 817/815-5350 |
| Ⓨ Jo Kelly Sch<br>201 N Bailey Ave, Fort Worth 76107<br>**Amelia McMillen** | Spec | M | 43<br>13 | 82% | 817/815-5900<br>Fax 817/815-5950 |
| John T White Elem Sch<br>7300 John T White Rd, Fort Worth 76120<br>Nikita Moye | PK-5 | T | 462 | 95% | 817/814-7900<br>Fax 817/814-7950 |
| Ⓨ Kirkpatrick Middle Sch<br>3201 Refugio Ave, Fort Worth 76106<br>Jeffrey Bartolotta | 6-8 | MT | 508 | 97% | 817/814-4200<br>Fax 817/814-4250 |
| Leadership Acad Como ES<br>4000 Horne St, Fort Worth 76107<br>Valencia Rhines | PK-5 | T | 415 | 94% | 817/815-6500<br>Fax 817/815-6550 |
| Ⓨ Leadership Acad Mitchell Blvd<br>3601 Mitchell Blvd, Fort Worth 76105<br>**Danny Fracassi** | PK-5 | MT | 370<br>30 | 96% | 817/815-9000<br>Fax 817/815-9050 |
| Leonard Middle Sch<br>8900 Chapin Rd, Fort Worth 76116<br>**Cathy Ridley \ Mandi Murphy** | 6-8 | TV | 831<br>65 | 89% | 817/815-6200<br>Fax 817/815-6250 |
| Lily B Clayton Elem Sch<br>2000 Park Place Ave, Fort Worth 76110<br>Stephanie Hughes | PK-5 | | 548<br>25 | 44% | 817/815-5400<br>Fax 817/815-5450 |
| Lowery Road Elem Sch<br>7600 Lowery Rd, Fort Worth 76120<br>Debra Williamson | PK-5 | T | 701<br>43 | 86% | 817/815-4700<br>Fax 817/815-4750 |
| Luella Merrett Elem Sch<br>7325 Kermit Ave, Fort Worth 76116<br>**Delain Sandifer** | PK-5 | T | 564 | 95% | 817/815-6600<br>Fax 817/815-6650 |
| M G Ellis Primary Sch<br>215 NE 14th St, Fort Worth 76164<br>Deborah Carrasquillo | PK-K | T | 374<br>22 | 90% | 817/814-3800<br>Fax 817/814-3850 |
| M H Moore Elem Sch<br>1809 NE 36th St, Fort Worth 76106<br>Elizabeth Yoder | PK-5 | T | 574<br>16 | 94% | 817/815-0600<br>Fax 817/815-0650 |
| Manuel Jara Elem Sch<br>2100 Lincoln Ave, Fort Worth 76164<br>Marta Plata | 1-5 | T | 540<br>45 | 95% | 817/814-4500<br>Fax 817/814-4550 |
| Marine Creek Collegiate HS<br>4801 Marine Creek Pkwy, Fort Worth 76179<br>Thomas Fraire | 9-12 | T | 370 | 86% | 817/515-7784<br>Fax 817/515-7094 |
| Mary Louise Phillips Elem Sch<br>3020 Bigham Blvd, Fort Worth 76116<br>Laura Hill | PK-5 | T | 486<br>35 | 87% | 817/815-1600<br>Fax 817/815-1650 |
| Ⓨ Maude I Logan Elem Sch<br>2300 Dillard St, Fort Worth 76105<br>Steven Moore | PK-5 | MT | 451<br>21 | 98% | 817/815-3700<br>Fax 817/815-3750 |

| School | Grades | Code | Enroll | Staff | % | Phone | Fax |
|---|---|---|---|---|---|---|---|
| Maudrie M Walton Elem Sch — 5816 Rickenbacker Pl, Fort Worth 76112 — Dr Christina Hanson | PK-5 | T | 342 | 24 | 97% | 817/815-3300 | Fax 817/815-3350 |
| McLean Sixth Grade Sch — 3201 South Hills Ave, Fort Worth 76109 — Karen Brown | 6-6 | T | 503 | 21 | 67% | 817/814-5700 | Fax 817/814-5750 |
| Meadowbrook Elem Sch — 4330 Meadowbrook Dr, Fort Worth 76103 — Suzelle Birkmire | PK-5 | T | 497 | 40 | 95% | 817/815-4900 | Fax 817/815-4950 |
| Meadowbrook Middle Sch — 2001 Ederville Rd S, Fort Worth 76103 — **Crystal Culton** | 6-8 | TV | 776 | 40 | 90% | 817/815-4300 | Fax 817/815-4350 |
| Ⓐ Metro Opportunity Sch — 2720 Cullen St, Fort Worth 76107 — Aundra Bohanon | 9-12 | V | 39 | 30 | 96% | 817/814-6700 | Fax 817/814-6750 |
| Ⓐ Ⓨ Middle Level Learning Center — 3813 Valentine St, Fort Worth 76107 — Aundra Bohanon | 6-8 | MV | 24 | 11 | | 817/814-6800 | Fax 817/814-6850 |
| Ⓨ Milton L Kirkpatrick Elem Sch — 3229 Lincoln Ave, Fort Worth 76106 — Christine Renteria | PK-5 | MT | 332 | 20 | 98% | 817/814-4600 | Fax 817/814-4650 |
| Morningside Elem Sch — 2601 Evans Ave, Fort Worth 76104 — Vanessa Cuarenta | PK-5 | T | 520 | 60 | 91% | 817/814-0600 | Fax 817/814-0650 |
| Morningside Middle Sch — 2751 Mississippi Ave, Fort Worth 76104 — Justin Edwards | 6-8 | T | 692 | 28 | 97% | 817/815-8300 | Fax 817/815-8350 |
| Nathan Howell Elem Sch — 1324 Kings Hwy, Haltom City 76117 — Monica Granados | PK-5 | T | 455 | 25 | 95% | 817/814-9300 | Fax 817/814-9350 |
| Ⓨ North Hi Mount Elem Sch — 3801 W 7th St, Fort Worth 76107 — Myrna Blanchard | PK-5 | MT | 363 | 13 | 51% | 817/815-1500 | Fax 817/815-1550 |
| North Side High Sch — 2211 McKinley Ave, Fort Worth 76164 — Antonio Martinez | 9-12 | TV | 1,765 | 87 | 93% | 817/814-4000 | Fax 817/814-4050 |
| O D Wyatt High Sch — 2400 E Seminary Dr, Fort Worth 76119 — Howard Robinson | 9-12 | TV | 1,425 | | 95% | 817/815-8000 | Fax 817/815-8050 |
| Oakhurst Elem Sch — 2700 Yucca Ave, Fort Worth 76111 — Guadalupe Cortez | PK-5 | T | 522 | 32 | 93% | 817/814-9500 | Fax 817/814-9550 |
| Oaklawn Elem Sch — 3220 Hardeman St, Fort Worth 76119 — Nanedra Golding | PK-5 | T | 490 | 26 | 97% | 817/815-9100 | Fax 817/815-9150 |
| Paul Laurence Dunbar High Sch — 5700 Ramey Ave, Fort Worth 76112 — Oscar Adams | 9-12 | TV | 918 | | 91% | 817/815-3000 | Fax 817/815-3050 |
| Polytechnic High Sch — 1300 Conner Ave, Fort Worth 76105 — Nick Torrez | 9-12 | TV | 1,230 | 74 | 94% | 817/814-0000 | Fax 817/814-0050 |
| R L Paschal High Sch — 3001 Forest Park Blvd, Fort Worth 76110 — Troy Langston | 9-12 | TV | 2,536 | 120 | 65% | 817/814-5000 | Fax 817/814-5050 |
| Richard J Wilson Elem Sch — 900 W Fogg St, Fort Worth 76110 — Irma Ayala | PK-5 | T | 513 | 34 | 96% | 817/814-7700 | Fax 817/814-7750 |
| Ridglea Hills Elem Sch — 6817 Cumberland Rd, Fort Worth 76116 — Crenesha Cotton | PK-5 | T | 769 | 36 | 45% | 817/815-1700 | Fax 817/815-1750 |
| Ⓨ Riverside Applied Lrng Center — 3600 Fossil Dr, Fort Worth 76111 — Jennifer Kennedy | Spec | MT | 284 | | 82% | 817/815-5800 | Fax 817/815-5850 |
| Ⓨ Riverside Middle Sch — 1600 Bolton St, Fort Worth 76111 — Victor Alfaro | 6-8 | MTV | 974 | | 97% | 817/814-9200 | Fax 817/814-9250 |
| Rosemont 6th Grade Center — 3908 McCart Ave, Fort Worth 76110 — Kathrina Andersen | 6-6 | T | 505 | 25 | 98% | 817/814-7300 | Fax 817/814-7350 |
| Rosemont Elem Sch — 1401 W Seminary Dr, Fort Worth 76115 — Rodolfo Valdez | PK-5 | T | 582 | | 96% | 817/815-5200 | Fax 817/815-5250 |
| Rosemont Middle Sch — 1501 W Seminary Dr, Fort Worth 76115 — **Xavier Sanchez** | 7-8 | GTV | 950 | 36 | 97% | 817/814-7200 | Fax 817/814-7250 |
| Rufino Mendoza Elem Sch — 1412 Denver Ave, Fort Worth 76164 — Jennifer Sanchez | 1-5 | T | 400 | 23 | 96% | 817/814-4700 | Fax 817/814-4750 |
| S S Dillow Elem Sch — 4000 Avenue N, Fort Worth 76105 — Duvaughn Flagler | PK-5 | T | 461 | 50 | 98% | 817/814-0400 | Fax 817/814-0450 |
| Ⓨ Sagamore Hill Elem Sch — 701 S Hughes Ave, Fort Worth 76103 — Dirrick Butler | PK-5 | MT | 595 | | 93% | 817/815-5000 | Fax 817/815-5050 |
| Sam Rosen Elem Sch — 2613 Roosevelt Ave, Fort Worth 76164 — Alberto Herrera | PK-5 | T | 447 | 26 | 94% | 817/814-4800 | Fax 817/814-4850 |
| Seminary Hills Park Elem Sch — 5037 Townsend Dr, Fort Worth 76115 — Lorena Ferrales | PK-5 | T | 360 | | 94% | 817/814-7600 | Fax 817/814-7650 |
| South Hi Mount Elem Sch — 4101 Birchman Ave, Fort Worth 76107 — Melissa Bryan | PK-5 | T | 465 | 35 | 82% | 817/815-1800 | Fax 817/815-1850 |
| South Hills Elem Sch — 3009 Bilglade Rd, Fort Worth 76133 — Melissa Russell | PK-5 | T | 750 | 46 | 89% | 817/814-5800 | Fax 817/814-5850 |
| South Hills High Sch — 6101 McCart Ave, Fort Worth 76133 — Rodrigo Durbin | 9-12 | TV | 2,076 | 78 | 94% | 817/814-7000 | Fax 817/814-7050 |
| Southwest High Sch — 4100 Altamesa Blvd, Fort Worth 76133 — John Engel | 9-12 | GTV | 1,334 | 86 | 80% | 817/814-8000 | Fax 817/814-8050 |
| Springdale Elem Sch — 3207 Hollis St, Fort Worth 76111 — Leann Moreno | PK-5 | GT | 483 | 25 | 97% | 817/814-9600 | Fax 817/814-9650 |
| Ⓐ Success High Sch — 1003 W Cannon St, Fort Worth 76104 — Ingrid Williams | 9-12 | T | 175 | | 96% | 817/815-2700 | Fax 817/815-2750 |
| Sunrise-McMillian Elem Sch — 3409 Stalcup Rd, Fort Worth 76119 — Latres Cole | PK-5 | T | 369 | 35 | 98% | 817/815-3900 | Fax 817/815-3950 |
| T A Sims Elem Sch — 3500 Crenshaw Ave, Fort Worth 76105 — Andrea Harper | PK-5 | T | 656 | 50 | 98% | 817/814-0800 | Fax 817/814-0850 |
| Tanglewood Elem Sch — 3060 Overton Park Dr W, Fort Worth 76109 — Dana McKenzie | PK-5 | | 885 | 28 | 9% | 817/814-5900 | Fax 817/814-5950 |
| TCC South-Fwisd Collegiate HS — 5301 Campus Dr, Fort Worth 76119 — Quanda Collins | 9-10 | | 75 | | | 817/515-4402 | Fax 817/515-4208 |
| ⓦ Texas Academy of Biomed Sci — 300 Trinity Campus Cir, Fort Worth 76102 — Jack Henson | 9-12 | TV | 397 | | 74% | 817/515-1660 | Fax 817/815-2350 |
| Transition Center — 5100 El Campo Ave, Fort Worth 76107 — Terry Guthrie | Spec | | 61 | | 82% | 817/814-6418 | Fax 817/814-6451 |
| Ⓨ Van Zandt-Guinn Elem Sch — 600 S Kentucky Ave, Fort Worth 76104 — Debora Fuentes | PK-5 | MT | 521 | 15 | 97% | 817/815-2000 | Fax 817/815-2050 |
| Ⓨ Versia L Williams Elem Sch — 901 Baurline St, Fort Worth 76111 — Angela Wright | PK-5 | MT | 363 | 22 | 96% | 817/814-9700 | Fax 817/814-9750 |

---

| # | | # | | # | | # | | # | | # | | # | |
|---|---|---|---|---|---|---|---|---|---|---|---|---|---|
| 1 | Superintendent | 8 | Curric/Instruct K-12 | 19 | Chief Financial Officer | 29 | Family/Consumer Science | 39 | Social Studies K-12 | 49 | English/Lang Arts Elem | 59 | Special Education Elem | 69 | Academic Assessment |
| 2 | Bus/Finance/Purchasing | 9 | Curric/Instruct Elem | 20 | Art K-12 | 30 | Adult Education | 40 | Social Studies Elem | 50 | English/Lang Arts Sec | 60 | Special Education Sec | 70 | Research/Development |
| 3 | Buildings And Grounds | 10 | Curric/Instruct Sec | 21 | Art Elem | 31 | Career/Sch-to-Work K-12 | 41 | Social Studies Sec | 51 | Reading K-12 | 61 | Foreign/World Lang K-12 | 71 | Public Information |
| 4 | Food Service | 11 | Federal Program | 22 | Art Sec | 32 | Career/Sch-to-Work Elem | 42 | Science K-12 | 52 | Reading Elem | 62 | Foreign/World Lang Elem | 72 | Summer School |
| 5 | Transportation | 12 | Title I | 23 | Music K-12 | 33 | Career/Sch-to-Work Sec | 43 | Science Elem | 53 | Reading Sec | 63 | Foreign/World Lang Sec | 73 | Instructional Tech |
| 6 | Athletic | 13 | Title V | 24 | Music Elem | 34 | Early Childhood Ed | 44 | Science Sec | 54 | Remedial Reading K-12 | 64 | Religious Education K-12 | 74 | Inservice Training |
| 7 | Health Services | 14 | Asst Superintendent | 25 | Music Sec | 35 | Health/Phys Education | 45 | Math K-12 | 55 | Remedial Reading Elem | 65 | Religious Education Elem | 75 | Marketing/Distributive |
| | | 15 | | 26 | Business Education | 36 | Guidance Services K-12 | 46 | Math Elem | 56 | Remedial Reading Sec | 66 | Religious Education Sec | 76 | Info Systems |
| | | 16 | Instructional Media Svcs | 27 | Career & Tech Ed | 37 | Guidance Services Elem | 47 | Math Sec | 57 | Bilingual/ELL | 67 | School Board President | 77 | Psychological Assess |
| | | 17 | Chief Operations Officer | 28 | Technology Education | 38 | Guidance Services Sec | 48 | English/Lang Arts K-12 | 58 | Special Education K-12 | 68 | Teacher Personnel | 78 | Affirmative Action |
| | | 18 | Chief Academic Officer | | | | | | | | | | | | |

| School | Grd | Prgm | Enr/#Cls | SN | Phone |
|---|---|---|---|---|---|
| W A Meacham Middle Sch<br>3600 Weber St, Fort Worth 76106<br>Oscar Martinez | 6-8 | TV | 859<br>55 | 93% | 817/815-0200<br>Fax 817/815-0250 |
| Ⓨ W C Stripling Middle Sch<br>2100 Clover Ln, Fort Worth 76107<br>Amy Chritian | 6-8 | AMTV | 741<br>47 | 73% | 817/815-1300<br>Fax 817/815-1350 🇫 |
| Ⓨ W J Turner Elem Sch<br>3000 NW 26th St, Fort Worth 76106<br>Elida Gonzales | PK-5 | MT | 381<br>39 | 97% | 817/814-4900<br>Fax 817/814-4950 |
| W M Green Elem Sch<br>4612 David Strickland Rd, Fort Worth 76119<br>Edra Bailey | PK-5 | T | 662<br>80 | 96% | 817/815-8900<br>Fax 817/815-8950 |
| W P McLean Middle Sch<br>3816 Stadium Dr, Fort Worth 76109<br>Barbara Ozuna | 6-8 | TV | 1,077<br>50 | 66% | 817/814-5300 |
| Washington Heights Elem Sch<br>3124 Clinton Ave, Fort Worth 76106<br>Maryjane Cantu | PK-5 | T | 333<br>18 | 97% | 817/815-0700<br>Fax 817/815-0750 |
| Waverly Park Elem Sch<br>3604 Cimmaron Trl, Fort Worth 76116<br>Roberto Gutierrez | PK-5 | T | 749<br>35 | 80% | 817/815-6700<br>Fax 817/815-6750 |
| Wedgwood 6th Grade Middle Sch<br>4212 Belden Ave, Fort Worth 76132<br>**Dr Cheryl Johnson** | 6-6 | T | 443<br>40 | 89% | 817/814-8300<br>Fax 817/814-8350 |
| Wedgwood Middle Sch<br>3909 Wilkie Way, Fort Worth 76133<br>Robert Burrell | 7-8 | TV | 956<br>62 | 89% | 817/814-8200<br>Fax 817/814-8250 🇫🇹 |
| West Handley Elem Sch<br>2749 Putnam St, Fort Worth 76112<br>Julie Moynihan | PK-5 | T | 505<br>25 | 97% | 817/815-5100<br>Fax 817/815-5150 |
| Westcliff Elem Sch<br>4300 Clay Ave, Fort Worth 76109<br>Sara Gillaspie | PK-5 | T | 580<br>22 | 76% | 817/814-6000<br>Fax 817/814-6050 |
| Ⓨ Westcreek Elem Sch<br>3401 Walton Ave, Fort Worth 76133<br>Julia Cortina | PK-5 | MT | 518<br>45 | 94% | 817/814-8600<br>Fax 817/814-8650 🇫🇹 |
| Western Hills Elem Sch<br>2805 Laredo Dr, Fort Worth 76116<br>Alexandra Montes | 2-5 | T | 798<br>42 | 98% | 817/815-6800<br>Fax 817/815-6850 |
| Western Hills High Sch<br>3600 Boston Ave, Benbrook 76116<br>Keri Flores | 9-12 | TV | 865<br>75 | 84% | 817/815-6000<br>Fax 817/815-6050 🇫🇹 |
| Western Hills Primary Sch<br>8300 Mojave Trl, Fort Worth 76116<br>Sonya Kelly | PK-1 | T | 418 | 94% | 817/815-6900<br>Fax 817/815-6950 |
| Westpark Elem Sch<br>10202 Jerry Dunn Pkwy, Fort Worth 76126<br>Kendall Condit | PK-5 | | 692<br>19 | 34% | 817/815-7000<br>Fax 817/815-7050 |
| William James Middle Sch<br>1101 Nashville Ave, Fort Worth 76105<br>**Melissa Rincon** | 6-8 | TV | 895<br>68 | 92% | 817/814-0200<br>Fax 817/814-0250 🇫🇹 |
| William Monnig Middle Sch<br>3136 Bigham Blvd, Fort Worth 76116<br>Kellye Kirkpatrick | 6-8 | TV | 678<br>47 | 77% | 817/815-1200<br>Fax 817/815-1250 🇫🇹 |
| Ⓨ Woodway Elem Sch<br>6701 Woodway Dr, Fort Worth 76133<br>Bryan Johnson | PK-5 | MT | 566<br>36 | 91% | 817/814-8700<br>Fax 817/814-8750 |
| World Languages Institute<br>4921 Benbrook Hwy, Fort Worth 76116<br>Guadalupe Barreto | 6-8 | T | 221 | 88% | 817/815-2200<br>Fax 817/815-2250 |
| Ⓨ Worth Heights Elem Sch<br>519 E Butler St, Fort Worth 76110<br>Andrea Lange | PK-5 | MT | 531<br>44 | 95% | 817/814-6200<br>Fax 817/814-6250 |
| Young Men's Leadership Academy<br>5100 Willie St, Fort Worth 76105<br>Rodney White | 6-10 | T | 308 | 79% | 817/815-3400<br>Fax 817/815-3450 |
| Young Women's Leadership Acad<br>401 E 8th St, Fort Worth 76102<br>Tamara Albury | 6-12 | T | 416 | 78% | 817/815-2400<br>Fax 817/815-2450 🇫 |

## ● Grapevine-Colleyville Ind SD PID: 01053672
3051 Ira E Woods Ave, Grapevine 76051

817/251-5200
Fax 817/251-5375

> **Schools:** 21 \ **Teachers:** 962 \ **Students:** 14,000 \
> **Special Ed Students:** 1,191 \ **LEP Students:** 1,200 \ **Ethnic:** Asian 11%,
> African American 6%, Hispanic 25%, Caucasian 58% \ **Exp:** $223 (Med)
> \ **Poverty:** 5% \ **Title I:** $1,216,031 \ **Special Education:** $1,656,000 \
> **Open-Close:** 08/17 - 05/27 \ **DTBP:** $188 (High) \ 🇫 🇹

| | | | |
|---|---|---|---|
| Dr Robin Ryan | 1 | Christi Drilling | 2 |
| Daiann Mooney | 2,19 | Paula Barbaroux | 3,17 |
| Ramon Castanuela | 3 | Julie Telesca | 4 |
| Manny Rubio | 5 | Bryan Gerlich | 6 |
| Amy Taldo | 7,35 | Lani Norman | 8,11,16,20,27,36 |
| Dr Brad Schnautz | 15 | Jessica Ramos Jones | 30 |
| Rick Bracy | 31 | Khristie Brown | 34 |
| Emberly Hill | 36 | Jodi Cox | 57,61 |
| Dr Joann Wiechmann | 58 | Lisa Pardo | 67 |
| Gema Padgett | 68 | Shannon Kovar | 69,294 |
| Kyle Berger | 73,98 | Marina Flores | 79 |
| Robin Davis | 83* | Alan Smith | 91 |
| Megan Scarbourgh | 274 | Tony Zahn | 285 |

| Public Schs..Principal | Grd | Prgm | Enr/#Cls | SN | Phone |
|---|---|---|---|---|---|
| Bear Creek Elem Sch<br>401 Bear Creek Dr, Euless 76039<br>Bryan Calvert | PK-5 | T | 638<br>31 | 34% | 817/305-4860<br>Fax 817/267-3863 |
| Bransford Elem Sch<br>601 Glade Rd, Colleyville 76034<br>**Erin Gerdes** | PK-5 | | 461<br>36 | 14% | 817/305-4920<br>Fax 817/428-1203 |
| ⒶBridges Accel Lrng Ctr<br>5800 Colleyville Blvd, Colleyville 76034<br>**Jessica Ramos** | 9-12 | GV | 21<br>5 | 48% | 817/251-5474<br>Fax 817/581-4893 |
| Cannon Elem Sch<br>1300 W College St, Grapevine 76051<br>Tina Garrett | PK-5 | T | 469<br>26 | 37% | 817/251-5680<br>Fax 817/421-0982 |
| Collegiate Acad Tarrant Clg<br>828 W Harwood Rd, Hurst 76054<br>Bobbe Knutz | 9-12 | T | 317 | 44% | 817/515-6775<br>Fax 817/515-6766 |
| Colleyville Elem Sch<br>5911 Pleasant Run Rd, Colleyville 76034<br>**Tracey Lafara** | PK-5 | | 475<br>25 | 6% | 817/305-4940<br>Fax 817/498-2062 |
| Colleyville Heritage High Sch<br>5401 Heritage Ave, Colleyville 76034<br>Lance Groppel | 9-12 | V | 1,974<br>120 | 17% | 817/305-4700<br>Fax 817/358-4765 |
| Colleyville Middle Sch<br>1100 Bogart Dr, Colleyville 76034<br>David Arencibia | 6-8 | V | 630<br>54 | 7% | 817/305-4900<br>Fax 817/498-9764 |
| Cross Timbers Middle Sch<br>2301 Pool Rd, Grapevine 76051<br>**Dr Jamie Halliburton** | 6-8 | TV | 853<br>51 | 32% | 817/251-5320<br>Fax 817/305-4958 |
| Dove Elem Sch<br>1932 Dove Rd, Grapevine 76051<br>Heather Landrum | PK-5 | T | 382<br>26 | 33% | 817/251-5700<br>Fax 817/481-6730 |
| Glenhope Elem Sch<br>6600 Glenhope Cir N, Colleyville 76034<br>Wynette Griffin | PK-5 | | 426<br>22 | 11% | 817/251-5720<br>Fax 817/329-5618 |
| Grapevine Elem Sch<br>1801 Hall Johnson Rd, Grapevine 76051<br>Nancy Hale | PK-5 | | 526<br>32 | 16% | 817/251-5735<br>Fax 817/481-6451 |
| Grapevine High Sch<br>3223 Mustang Dr, Grapevine 76051<br>David Denning | 9-12 | GV | 1,923<br>110 | 20% | 817/251-5210<br>Fax 817/481-5957 |

| | | | | | |
|---|---|---|---|---|---|
| Grapevine Middle Sch<br>301 Pony Pkwy, Grapevine 76051<br>Laura Koehler | 6-8 | TV | 744<br>60 | 38% | 817/251-5660<br>Fax 817/424-1626 |
| Heritage Elem Sch<br>4500 Heritage Ave, Grapevine 76051<br>Jill Hemme | PK-5 | | 466<br>31 | 9% | 817/305-4820<br>Fax 817/540-2892 |
| Heritage Middle Sch<br>5300 Heritage Ave, Colleyville 76034<br>James Whitfield | 6-8 | V | 784<br>60 | 23% | 817/305-4790<br>Fax 817/267-9929 |
| Iuniversity Prep Virtual Acad<br>3051 Ira E Woods Ave, Grapevine 76051<br>Klinetta Rogers | 4-12 | | 427 | 6% | 855/779-7357<br>Fax 888/342-4927 🖪 |
| O C Taylor Elem Sch<br>5300 Pool Rd, Colleyville 76034<br>Lisa Pedevilla | PK-5 | | 471<br>27 | 11% | 817/305-4870<br>Fax 817/540-3940 |
| Silver Lake Elem Sch<br>1301 N Dooley St, Grapevine 76051<br>Nicole Whiteside | PK-5 | T | 477<br>25 | 54% | 817/251-5750<br>Fax 817/329-4536 |
| Timberline Elem Sch<br>3220 Timberline Dr, Grapevine 76051<br>Liz Hilcher | PK-5 | T | 597<br>35 | 78% | 817/251-5770<br>Fax 817/329-5666 |
| Ⓐ Vista Alt Learning Center<br>5800 Colleyville Blvd, Colleyville 76034<br>Roger Alzamora | K-12 | | 60<br>5 | | 817/251-5466<br>Fax 817/581-9140 |

---

● **Hurst-Euless-Bedford ISD** PID: 01053737　　817/283-4461
1849 Central Dr, Bedford 76022　　Fax 817/354-3311

---

**Schools:** 31 \ **Teachers:** 1,403 \ **Students:** 23,000 \
**Special Ed Students:** 2,337 \ **LEP Students:** 3,336 \ **College-Bound:** 61%
\ **Ethnic:** Asian 8%, African American 22%, Hispanic 33%, Caucasian
37% \ **Exp:** $377 (High) \ **Poverty:** 13% \ **Title I:** $4,468,896 \
**Special Education:** $3,793,000 \ **Open-Close:** 08/18 - 05/27 \ **DTBP:** $188
(High) \ 🖪 🖪

---

| | | |
|---|---|---|
| Steve Chapman | ........ | 1 |
| Josh Minor | ........ | 3 |
| Brian Merchant | ........ | 5 |
| Holly Norgaard | ........ | 8,15 |
| Darla Clark | ........ | 9,15 |
| Mary Morris | ........ | 11,298 |
| Scott Forester | ........ | 15,73,295 |
| Mark Chandler | ........ | 20,23 |
| Carla Docken | ........ | 36,88,270 |
| Wade Carrington | ........ | 42 |
| Kristen Manning | ........ | 47 |
| Terri Smith | ........ | 50 |
| Julie Cole | ........ | 67 |
| Deanne Hullender | ........ | 71 |
| John Sellgren | ........ | 76 |
| David Nielsen | ........ | 297 |
| David Garcia | ........ | 2,15 |
| Mariella Naugher | ........ | 4 |
| Mike Fielder | ........ | 6 |
| Dr Joe Harrington | ........ | 8,15 |
| Conrad Streeter | ........ | 10,15 |
| Cicely Tuttle | ........ | 15,68 |
| Kiera Elledge | ........ | 16,285 |
| Lisa Karr | ........ | 27,28* |
| Marci Deal | ........ | 39,89 |
| Garri Adcox | ........ | 46 |
| Ladonna Schwobell | ........ | 49 |
| Rene Riek | ........ | 58* |
| Gail Long | ........ | 69 |
| Ann Rodriguez | ........ | 74 |
| Marianne White | ........ | 274 |

| Public Schs..Principal | Grd | Prgm | Enr/#Cls | SN | |
|---|---|---|---|---|---|
| Ⓐ Alternative Education Program<br>1100 Raider Dr, Euless 76040<br>Dr June Jacoby | 6-12 | T | 175<br>9 | 79% | 817/354-3398<br>Fax 817/358-5001 |
| Bedford Heights Elem Sch<br>1000 Cummings Dr, Bedford 76021<br>**Kathleen Harrell** | PK-6 | | 670<br>36 | 25% | 817/788-3150<br>Fax 817/788-3112 |
| Bedford Junior High Sch<br>325 Carolyn Dr, Bedford 76021<br>Michael Martinak | 7-9 | V | 285<br>60 | 42% | 817/788-3101<br>Fax 817/788-3105 🖪 |
| Bell Manor Elem Sch<br>1300 Winchester Way, Bedford 76022<br>Keri McCarty | PK-6 | T | 751<br>35 | 71% | 817/354-3370<br>Fax 817/354-3374 |
| Bellaire Elem Sch<br>501 Bellaire Dr, Hurst 76053<br>Katina Rhodes | PK-6 | T | 681<br>32 | 91% | 817/285-3230<br>Fax 817/285-3203 🖪 |

| | | | | | |
|---|---|---|---|---|---|
| Central Junior High Sch<br>3191 W Pipeline Rd, Euless 76040<br>Randy Belcher | 7-9 | TV | 1,182<br>55 | 61% | 817/354-3350<br>Fax 817/354-3357 |
| Donna Park Elem Sch<br>1125 Scott Dr, Hurst 76053<br>Julie McAvoy | PK-6 | T | 450<br>24 | 67% | 817/285-3285<br>Fax 817/285-3289 |
| Euless Junior High Sch<br>306 Airport Fwy, Euless 76039<br>Sonya Stanton | 7-9 | TV | 1,105<br>44 | 67% | 817/354-3340<br>Fax 817/354-3345 🖪 |
| Gene A Buinger Cte Academy<br>1849 Central Dr Bldg E, Bedford 76022<br>Lisa Karr | Voc | | 600<br>12 | | 817/354-3542<br>Fax 817/354-3546 |
| Harrison Lane Elem Sch<br>1000 Harrison Ln, Hurst 76053<br>**Shannon Huber** | PK-6 | T | 686<br>25 | 79% | 817/285-3270<br>Fax 817/285-3207 |
| Harwood Junior High Sch<br>3000 Martin Dr, Bedford 76021<br>Dr Toby Givens | 7-9 | V | 994 | 42% | 817/354-3360<br>Fax 817/354-3365 |
| Hurst Hills Elem Sch<br>525 Billie Ruth Ln, Hurst 76053<br>Misty Donaho | K-6 | T | 442<br>38 | 49% | 817/285-3295<br>Fax 817/285-3208 |
| Hurst Junior High Sch<br>500 Harmon Rd, Hurst 76053<br>Michael Smith | 7-9 | TV | 1,117 | 62% | 817/285-3220<br>Fax 817/285-3225 🖪 |
| Ⓐ Keys High Sch<br>1100 Raider Dr, Euless 76040<br>John Adkins | 9-12 | T | 100<br>15 | 65% | 817/354-3580<br>Fax 817/354-3586 |
| Lakewood Elem Sch<br>1600 Donley Dr, Euless 76039<br>Cameron Ramirez | PK-6 | T | 672<br>36 | 51% | 817/354-3375<br>Fax 817/354-3525 🖪🖪 |
| Lawrence D Bell High Sch<br>1601 Brown Trl, Hurst 76054<br>Jim Bannister | 10-12 | TV | 2,320 | 45% | 817/282-2551<br>Fax 817/285-3200 |
| Meadow Creek Elem Sch<br>3001 Harwood Rd, Bedford 76021<br>**Ann Rodriguez** | PK-6 | | 738<br>36 | 26% | 817/354-3500<br>Fax 817/354-3329 🖪 |
| Midway Park Elem Sch<br>409 N Ector Dr, Euless 76039<br>Liesl James | PK-6 | T | 776<br>35 | 73% | 817/354-3380<br>Fax 817/354-3332 🖪🖪 |
| North Euless Elem Sch<br>1101 Denton Dr, Euless 76039<br>Melissa Meadows | PK-6 | T | 673<br>27 | 71% | 817/354-3505<br>Fax 817/354-3334 🖪 |
| Oakwood Terrace Elem Sch<br>700 Ranger St, Euless 76040<br>Anmarie Garcia | PK-6 | T | 629<br>45 | 84% | 817/354-3386<br>Fax 817/354-3335 🖪🖪 |
| River Trails Elem Sch<br>8850 Elbe Trl, Fort Worth 76118<br>Tammy Daggs | PK-6 | T | 585<br>41 | 45% | 817/285-3235<br>Fax 817/285-3238 |
| Shady Brook Elem Sch<br>2601 Shady Brook Dr, Bedford 76021<br>Shannon Gauntt | PK-6 | T | 534<br>26 | 55% | 817/354-3513<br>Fax 817/354-3336 🖪🖪 |
| Shady Oaks Elem Sch<br>1400 Cavender Dr, Hurst 76053<br>Darla Clark | PK-6 | T | 551<br>28 | 69% | 817/285-3240<br>Fax 817/285-3209 🖪🖪 |
| South Euless Elem Sch<br>605 S Main St, Euless 76040<br>Maureen Sterling | PK-6 | T | 596<br>65 | 66% | 817/354-3521<br>Fax 817/354-3523 🖪 |
| Spring Garden Elem Sch<br>2400 Cummings Dr, Bedford 76021<br>Sarah Williams | PK-6 | T | 650<br>40 | 46% | 817/354-3395<br>Fax 817/354-3337 |
| Stonegate Elem Sch<br>900 Bedford Rd, Bedford 76022<br>Talana Bean | PK-6 | T | 428<br>26 | 70% | 817/285-3250<br>Fax 817/285-3210 |
| Transition Center<br>1849 Central Dr, Bedford 76022<br>Rene Riek | Spec | | 44<br>1 | | 817/354-3537<br>Fax 817/354-3540 |

---

| | | | | | |
|---|---|---|---|---|---|
| 1 | Superintendent | 8 | Curric/Instruct K-12 | 19 | Chief Financial Officer |
| 2 | Bus/Finance/Purchasing | 9 | Curric/Instruct Elem | 20 | Art K-12 |
| 3 | Buildings And Grounds | 10 | Curric/Instruct Sec | 21 | Art Elem |
| 4 | Food Service | 11 | Federal Program | 22 | Art Sec |
| 5 | Transportation | 12 | Title I | 23 | Music K-12 |
| 6 | Athletic | 13 | Title V | 24 | Music Elem |
| 7 | Health Services | 15 | Asst Superintendent | 25 | Music Sec |
| | | 16 | Instructional Media Svcs | 26 | Business Education |
| | | 17 | Chief Operations Officer | 27 | Career & Tech Ed |
| | | 18 | Chief Academic Officer | 28 | Technology Education |

| | | | | | |
|---|---|---|---|---|---|
| 29 | Family/Consumer Science | 39 | Social Studies K-12 | 49 | English/Lang Arts Elem | 59 | Special Education Elem | 69 | Academic Assessment |
| 30 | Adult Education | 40 | Social Studies Elem | 50 | English/Lang Arts Sec | 60 | Special Education Sec | 70 | Research/Development |
| 31 | Career/Sch-to-Work K-12 | 41 | Social Studies Sec | 51 | Reading K-12 | 61 | Foreign/World Lang K-12 | 71 | Public Information |
| 32 | Career/Sch-to-Work Elem | 42 | Science K-12 | 52 | Reading Elem | 62 | Foreign/World Lang Elem | 72 | Summer School |
| 33 | Career/Sch-to-Work Sec | 43 | Science Elem | 53 | Reading Sec | 63 | Foreign/World Lang Sec | 73 | Instructional Tech |
| 34 | Early Childhood Ed | 44 | Science Sec | 54 | Remedial Reading K-12 | 64 | Religious Education K-12 | 74 | Inservice Training |
| 35 | Health/Phys Education | 45 | Math K-12 | 55 | Remedial Reading Elem | 65 | Religious Education Elem | 75 | Marketing/Distributive |
| 36 | Guidance Services K-12 | 46 | Math Elem | 56 | Remedial Reading Sec | 66 | Religious Education Sec | 76 | Info Systems |
| 37 | Guidance Services Elem | 47 | Math Sec | 57 | Bilingual/ELL | 67 | School Board President | 77 | Psychological Assess |
| 38 | Guidance Services Sec | 48 | English/Lang Arts K-12 | 58 | Special Education K-12 | 68 | Teacher Personnel | 78 | Affirmative Action |

| School..Principal | Grd | Prgm | Enr/#Cls | SN | Phone |
|---|---|---|---|---|---|
| Trinity High Sch<br>500 N Industrial Blvd, Euless 76039<br>Mike Harris | 10-12 | TV | 2,583<br>100 | 49% | 817/571-0271<br>Fax 817/354-3322 |
| Viridian Elem Sch<br>4001 Cascade Sky Dr, Arlington 76005<br>Dr Aungelique Brading | PK-6 | | 869 | 29% | 817/864-0550<br>Fax 817/354-3280 |
| West Hurst Elem Sch<br>501 Precinct Line Rd, Hurst 76053<br>Debra Day | PK-6 | T | 482<br>40 | 70% | 817/285-3290<br>Fax 817/285-3212 [f][t] |
| Wilshire Elem Sch<br>420 Wilshire Dr, Euless 76040<br>Jodie Ramos | PK-6 | T | 718 | 62% | 817/354-3529<br>Fax 817/354-3338 [f][t] |

● **Keller Ind School Dist**  PID: 01053983          817/744-1000
350 Keller Pkwy, Keller 76248          Fax 817/337-3261

---

**Schools:** 42 \ **Teachers:** 2,338 \ **Students:** 35,352 \
**Special Ed Students:** 3,617 \ **LEP Students:** 2,910 \ **Ethnic:** Asian 8%,
African American 9%, Hispanic 22%, Native American: 1%, Caucasian
61% \ **Exp:** $380 (High) \ **Poverty:** 5% \ **Title I:** $2,602,337 \
**Special Education:** $4,454,000 \ **Open-Close:** 08/19 - 05/27 \ **DTBP:** $67
(Low) \ [f] [t]

---

| | | | |
|---|---|---|---|
| Dr Rick Westfall | 1 | Kristin Williams | 2 |
| Hudson Huff | 3 | David Smith | 4* |
| Jim Koons | 5 | Eric Persyn | 6* |
| Cindy Parsons | 7,83,85 | Lindsay Anderson | 8,15 |
| Sara Kopowski | 8,275,296 | Leigh Cook | 11,298 |
| Tracy Johnson | 15,68 | Lepaula Smith | 17 |
| Cecil McDaniel | 18 | Scott Wreke | 19 |
| Kim Blann | 20,23 | Leslee Shepherd | 27* |
| Dr Robert Wright | 27,31,286* | Carrie Pearson | 34 |
| Jennifer Fleming | 36 | Suzanne McGahey | 39 |
| Tracy Hosek | 42* | Chrissy Greeling | 46 |
| Shannon Bryant | 47 | Sheree Felan | 50* |
| Dawn Bailey | 52,286 | Marie Coker | 57 |
| Dr Gena Koster | 58 | Brandy Crow | 61* |
| Ruthie Keyes | 67 | Jennifer Price | 69,294 |
| Shellie Johnson | 71 | Joe Griffin | 73,76,98,295 |
| Donna Hodge | 81* | Marcene Weatherall | 83 |
| Kevin Kinley | 91 | | |

| Public Schs..Principal | Grd | Prgm | Enr/#Cls | SN | Phone |
|---|---|---|---|---|---|
| Basswood Elem Sch<br>3100 Clay Mountain Trl, Fort Worth 76137<br>Tony Johnson | K-4 | T | 371 | 62% | 817/744-6500<br>Fax 817/744-6538 |
| Bear Creek Intermediate Sch<br>801 Bear Creek Pkwy, Keller 76248<br>Brenda Riebkes | 5-6 | | 989<br>34 | 8% | 817/744-3650<br>Fax 817/744-3738 [f][t] |
| Bette Perot Elem Sch<br>9345 General Worth Dr, Keller 76244<br>Lisa Young | K-4 | | 607<br>42 | 20% | 817/744-4600<br>Fax 817/744-4638 |
| Bluebonnet Elem Sch<br>7000 Teal Dr, Fort Worth 76137<br>Rhonda McGee | K-4 | T | 537<br>65 | 42% | 817/744-4500<br>Fax 817/744-4538 |
| CapRock Elem Sch<br>12301 Grey Twig Dr, Keller 76244<br>Amy Erb | K-4 | T | 645 | 49% | 817/744-6400<br>Fax 817/744-6438 |
| Central High Sch<br>9450 Ray White Rd, Fort Worth 76244<br>Liz Russo | 9-12 | G | 2,541 | 25% | 817/744-2000<br>Fax 817/744-2038 |
| Chisholm Trail Interm Sch<br>3901 Summerfields Blvd, Fort Worth 76137<br>Trish McKeel | 5-6 | T | 889 | 57% | 817/744-3800<br>Fax 817/744-3838 |
| Eagle Ridge Elem Sch<br>4600 Alta Vista Rd, Keller 76244<br>Stacy Blevins | K-4 | | 613<br>31 | 14% | 817/744-6300<br>Fax 817/744-6338 |

| School..Principal | Grd | Prgm | Enr/#Cls | SN | Phone |
|---|---|---|---|---|---|
| Early Learning Ctr North<br>10310 N Riverside Dr, Fort Worth 76244<br>David Rische | PK-PK | T | 314 | 72% | 817/744-6700 |
| Early Learning Ctr South<br>3975 Summerfields Blvd, Fort Worth 76137<br>Christy Johnson | PK-PK | T | 383 | 80% | 817/743-8300 |
| Florence Elem Sch<br>3095 Johnson Rd, Southlake 76092<br>Jacqueline Hughes | K-4 | | 470<br>32 | 8% | 817/744-4700<br>Fax 817/744-4738 |
| Fossil Hill Middle Sch<br>3821 Staghorn Cir S, Fort Worth 76137<br>Jennifer Gonzales | 7-8 | T | 955<br>53 | 52% | 817/744-3050<br>Fax 817/744-3138 |
| Fossil Ridge High Sch<br>4101 Thompson Rd, Fort Worth 76244<br>Dave Hadley | 9-12 | T | 1,163<br>150 | 46% | 817/744-1700<br>Fax 817/744-1738 [f] |
| Freedom Elem Sch<br>5401 Wall Price Keller Rd, Keller 76244<br>Gary Mantz | K-4 | | 559<br>33 | 33% | 817/744-4800<br>Fax 817/744-4838 |
| Friendship Elem Sch<br>5400 Shiver Rd, Keller 76244<br>Casey Necessary | K-4 | T | 549 | 43% | 817/744-6200<br>Fax 817/744-6238 |
| Heritage Elem Sch<br>4001 Thompson Rd, Keller 76244<br>Edwina West-Dukes | K-4 | GT | 485<br>35 | 42% | 817/744-4900<br>Fax 817/744-4938 |
| Hidden Lakes Elem Sch<br>900 Preston Ln, Keller 76248<br>Melanie Graham | K-4 | | 400<br>36 | 3% | 817/744-5000<br>Fax 817/744-5038 |
| Hillwood Middle Sch<br>8250 Parkwood Hill Blvd, Fort Worth 76137<br>Kathleen Eckert | 7-8 | | 1,222<br>20 | 31% | 817/744-3350<br>Fax 817/744-3438 |
| Independence Elem Sch<br>11773 Bray Birch Ln, Fort Worth 76244<br>Mark Basham | K-4 | | 562 | 19% | 817/744-6100<br>Fax 817/744-6138 |
| Indian Springs Middle Sch<br>305 Bursey Rd, Keller 76248<br>Sandy Troudt | 5-8 | | 982<br>40 | 13% | 817/744-3200<br>Fax 817/744-3238 [f][t] |
| Keller Ctr Advanced Learning<br>201 Bursey Rd, Keller 76248<br>Leslee Shepherd | 9-12 | V | 4,000 | | 817/743-8000<br>Fax 817/743-8038 |
| Keller High Sch<br>601 Pate Orr Rd N, Keller 76248<br>Lisa Simmons | 9-12 | GV | 3,079 | 7% | 817/744-1400<br>Fax 817/744-1438 |
| Ⓐ Keller Learning Center<br>250 College Ave, Keller 76248<br>Dr Angel Lara | 9-12 | V | 49<br>7 | 27% | 817/744-4465<br>Fax 817/741-1269 |
| Keller Middle Sch<br>300 College Ave, Keller 76248<br>Amanda Burruel | 7-8 | V | 1,019<br>40 | 6% | 817/744-2900<br>Fax 817/744-2938 |
| Keller-Harvel Elem Sch<br>635 Norma Ln, Keller 76248<br>Leslie Tewell | K-4 | | 457<br>34 | 25% | 817/744-5100<br>Fax 817/744-5138 |
| Liberty Elem Sch<br>1101 W McDonwell School Rd, Colleyville 76034<br>Janet Travis | K-4 | | 435<br>25 | 4% | 817/744-6000<br>Fax 817/744-6038 |
| Lone Star Elem Sch<br>4647 Shiver Rd, Fort Worth 76244<br>Steve Hurst | K-4 | | 801<br>38 | 21% | 817/744-5200<br>Fax 817/744-5238 |
| North Riverside Elem Sch<br>7900 N Riverside Dr, Fort Worth 76137<br>Allison Boyd | K-4 | T | 394 | 61% | 817/744-5300<br>Fax 817/744-5338 |
| Park Glen Elem Sch<br>5100 Glen Canyon Rd, Fort Worth 76137<br>Marcia Formby | K-4 | | 597<br>32 | 22% | 817/744-5400<br>Fax 817/744-5438 |
| Parkview Elem Sch<br>6900 Bayberry Dr, Fort Worth 76137<br>Erin Appling | K-4 | GI | 556<br>38 | 61% | 817/744-5500<br>Fax 817/744-5538 |

---

| | | | |
|---|---|---|---|
| **79** Student Personnel | **91** Safety/Security | **275** Response To Intervention | **298** Grant Writer/Ptnrships |
| **80** Driver Ed/Safety | **92** Magnet School | **277** Remedial Math K-12 | **750** Chief Innovation Officer |
| **81** Gifted/Talented | **93** Parental Involvement | **280** Literacy Coach | **751** Chief of Staff |
| **82** Video Services | **95** Tech Prep Program | **285** STEM | **752** Social Emotional Learning |
| **83** Substance Abuse Prev | **97** Chief Infomation Officer | **286** Digital Learning | |
| **84** Erate | **98** Chief Technology Officer | **288** Common Core Standards | **Other School Types** |
| **85** AIDS Education | **270** Character Education | **294** Accountability | Ⓐ = Alternative School |
| **88** Alternative/At Risk | **271** Migrant Education | **295** Network System | Ⓒ = Charter School |
| **89** Multi-Cultural Curriculum | **273** Teacher Mentor | **296** Title II Programs | Ⓜ = Magnet School |
| **90** Social Work | **274** Before/After Sch | **297** Webmaster | Ⓨ = Year-Round School |

**School Programs**
A = Alternative Program
G = Adult Classes
M = Magnet Program
T = Title I Schoolwide
V = Career & Tech Ed Programs

**Social Media**
[f] = Facebook
[t] = Twitter

New Schools are shaded
New Superintendents and Principals are bold
Personnel with email addresses are underscored

# TX—357

| Parkwood Hill Intermediate Sch | 5-6 | | 1,190 | 29% | 817/744-4000 |
|---|---|---|---|---|---|
| 8201 Parkwood Hill Blvd, Fort Worth 76137 | | | | | Fax 817/744-4038 |
| Brad Taylor | | | | | 🅕🅣 |

| Ridgeview Elem Sch | K-4 | | 698 | 17% | 817/744-6600 |
|---|---|---|---|---|---|
| 1601 Marshall Ridge Pkwy, Keller 76248 | | | | | Fax 817/744-6638 |
| Becky Wilder | | | | | |

| Shady Grove Elem Sch | K-4 | | 457 | 7% | 817/744-5600 |
|---|---|---|---|---|---|
| 1400 Sarah Brooks Dr, Keller 76248 | | | 36 | | Fax 817/744-5638 |
| Anna Renfro | | | | | |

| Sunset Valley Elem Sch | K-4 | | 445 | 37% | 817/743-8200 |
|---|---|---|---|---|---|
| 2032 Canchim St, Fort Worth 76131 | | | | | |
| Kristen Eriksen | | | | | |

| Timber Creek High Sch | 9-12 | | 3,246 | 22% | 817/744-2300 |
|---|---|---|---|---|---|
| 12350 Timberland Blvd, Fort Worth 76244 | | | | | Fax 817/744-2338 |
| Michelle Somerhalder | | | | | |

| Timberview Middle Sch | 5-8 | | 1,240 | 15% | 817/744-2600 |
|---|---|---|---|---|---|
| 10300 N Riverside Dr, Fort Worth 76244 | | | | | Fax 817/744-2638 |
| Charles Erwin | | | | | |

| Trinity Meadows Interm Sch | 5-6 | | 983 | 34% | 817/744-4300 |
|---|---|---|---|---|---|
| 3500 Keller Hicks Rd, Keller 76244 | | | | | Fax 817/744-4338 |
| Susan Mackey | | | | | |

| Trinity Springs Middle Sch | 7-8 | | 992 | 29% | 817/744-3500 |
|---|---|---|---|---|---|
| 3550 Keller Hicks Rd, Fort Worth 76244 | | | | | Fax 817/744-3538 |
| Justin Barrett | | | | | |

| Vista Ridge Middle Sch | 5-7 | T | 500 | 44% | 817/743-8400 |
|---|---|---|---|---|---|
| 3201 Thompson Rd, Fort Worth 76177 | | | | | |
| Tracy Arsenault | | | | | |

| Whitley Road Elem Sch | K-4 | T | 449 | 60% | 817/744-5800 |
|---|---|---|---|---|---|
| 7600 Whitley Rd, Watauga 76148 | | | 38 | | Fax 817/744-5838 |
| Rodrigo Cano | | | | | 🅕🅣 |

| Willis Lane Elem Sch | K-4 | | 525 | 15% | 817/744-5700 |
|---|---|---|---|---|---|
| 1620 Willis Ln, Keller 76248 | | | 40 | | Fax 817/744-5738 |
| Cheryl Hudson | | | | | |

| Woodland Springs Elem Sch | K-4 | | 578 | 19% | 817/744-5900 |
|---|---|---|---|---|---|
| 12120 Woodland Springs Dr, Keller 76244 | | | | | Fax 817/744-5938 |
| Cindy Daniel | | | | | |

---

● **Kennedale Ind School Dist** PID: 01054030　　817/563-8000
120 W Kennedale Pkwy, Kennedale 76060　　Fax 817/483-3610

**Schools:** 6 \ **Teachers:** 202 \ **Students:** 3,000 \ **Special Ed Students:** 256 \ **LEP Students:** 240 \ **Ethnic:** Asian 4%, African American 26%, Hispanic 25%, Caucasian 44% \ **Exp:** $348 (High) \ **Poverty:** 12% \ **Title I:** $500,908 \ **Special Education:** $509,000 \ **Open-Close:** 08/12 - 05/27 \ **DTBP:** $176 (High) \ 🅕

| | | | |
|---|---|---|---|
| Chad Gee | 1 | Jimmy Adams | 2 |
| Eileen Mode | 3 | Laurie Humiston | 4* |
| Richard Barrett | 6,83 | Teresa Vasquez | 7* |
| Charity Woods | 8,58 | Jan Cleere | 8,69,73* |
| Dr Melissa Glenn | 8,11,57,68,88,294,296,298 | Dr Julie Vu | 15 |
| Alison Boubel | 16* | Stephanie Devlin | 36* |
| John Hunt | 67 | Brandy King | 68 |
| Tracy Williams | 71 | Logan Barrett | 91 |
| Brian Franklin | 295 | | |

| Public Schs..Principal | Grd | Prgm | Enr/#Cls | SN | |
|---|---|---|---|---|---|
| James A Arthur Interm Sch | 5-6 | T | 493 | 45% | 817/563-8300 |
| 100 E Mistletoe Dr, Kennedale 76060 | | | 20 | | Fax 817/483-3628 |
| Caroline Clark | | | | | |
| James F DeLaney Elem Sch | PK-4 | T | 593 | 46% | 817/563-8400 |
| 180 W Kennedale Pkwy, Kennedale 76060 | | | 25 | | Fax 817/483-3653 |
| Kari Pride | | | | | |
| Ⓐ Kennedale Alternative Ed Prog | 1-12 | | 100 | | 817/563-8060 |
| 100 W Kennedale Pkwy, Kennedale 76060 | | | 3 | | Fax 817/483-3674 |
| Carol Bryson | | | | | |

---

| Kennedale High Sch | 9-12 | T | 497 | 37% | 817/563-8100 |
|---|---|---|---|---|---|
| 901 Wildcat Way, Kennedale 76060 | | | | | Fax 817/563-3718 |
| Michael Cagle | | | | | |

| Kennedale Junior High Sch | 7-8 | T | 493 | 46% | 817/563-8200 |
|---|---|---|---|---|---|
| 930 Corry A Edwards Dr, Kennedale 76060 | | | | | Fax 817/483-3655 |
| Reggie Rhines | | | | | |

| R F Patterson Elem Sch | K-4 | T | 444 | 55% | 817/563-8600 |
|---|---|---|---|---|---|
| 6621 Kelly Elliott Rd, Arlington 76001 | | | 23 | | Fax 817/483-3638 |
| Khourie Jones | | | | | |

---

● **Lake Worth Ind School Dist** PID: 01054078　　817/306-4200
6805 Telephone Rd, Lake Worth 76135　　Fax 817/237-5284

**Schools:** 6 \ **Teachers:** 240 \ **Students:** 3,000 \ **Special Ed Students:** 331 \ **LEP Students:** 644 \ **Ethnic:** Asian 1%, African American 18%, Hispanic 60%, Native American: 1%, Caucasian 20% \ **Exp:** $551 (High) \ **Poverty:** 21% \ **Title I:** $894,499 \ **Special Education:** $503,000 \ **Open-Close:** 08/19 - 05/27 \ **DTBP:** $316 (High)

| | | | |
|---|---|---|---|
| Rosemary Neshyba | 1 | Jaclyn West | 2 |
| Tina Robinson | 4,7 | Carla Dodd | 5 |
| Tracy Welch | 6 | Eric Tingle | 8,294 |
| Lori Aguilar | 9,57 | Shawna Clouser | 10,280 |
| Sherry Dickens | 11,298 | Stephanie Harbin | 58,77 |
| Donna Hutson | 67 | Joel McClain | 68 |
| Mary Diaz | 69 | Gary Kirkendall | 73,76,295 |
| Art Urquidi | 79 | Jessica Gauthier | 297 |

| Public Schs..Principal | Grd | Prgm | Enr/#Cls | SN | |
|---|---|---|---|---|---|
| Effie Morris Elem Sch | PK-4 | AT | 357 | 85% | 817/306-4260 |
| 3801 Merrett Dr, Lake Worth 76135 | | | 37 | | Fax 817/237-3625 |
| Kristina Sosebee | | | | | |
| Lake Worth High Sch | 9-12 | ATV | 878 | 73% | 817/306-4230 |
| 4210 Boat Club Rd, Lake Worth 76135 | | | 50 | | Fax 817/237-4583 |
| Bobby Stults | | | | | |
| Lucyle Collins Middle Sch | 7-8 | AT | 517 | 81% | 817/306-4250 |
| 3651 Santos Dr, Fort Worth 76106 | | | 38 | | Fax 817/624-7058 |
| Kathy Harmon | | | | | |
| Marilyn J Miller Elem Sch | PK-4 | AT | 566 | 85% | 817/306-4280 |
| 5250 Estrella St, Fort Worth 76106 | | | 28 | | Fax 817/624-9007 |
| Brent McClain | | | | | |
| Marine Creek Leadership Acad | PK-4 | AT | 451 | 84% | 817/306-4270 |
| 4801 Huffines Blvd, Lake Worth 76135 | | | 16 | | Fax 817/238-6726 |
| Carrie Harrison | | | | | |
| N A Howry Intermediate Sch | 5-6 | ATV | 511 | 85% | 817/306-4240 |
| 4000 Dakota Trl, Lake Worth 76135 | | | 41 | | Fax 817/237-3687 |
| Dr Sylonda Burns | | | | | |

---

● **Mansfield Ind School Dist** PID: 01054119　　817/299-6300
605 E Broad St, Mansfield 76063　　Fax 817/473-5465

**Schools:** 46 \ **Teachers:** 2,263 \ **Students:** 35,626 \ **Special Ed Students:** 3,299 \ **LEP Students:** 3,253 \ **Ethnic:** Asian 8%, African American 32%, Hispanic 27%, Caucasian 33% \ **Exp:** $291 (Med) \ **Poverty:** 9% \ **Title I:** $4,428,981 \ **Special Education:** $4,304,000 \ **Open-Close:** 08/12 - 05/26 \ **DTBP:** $188 (High) \ 🅣

| | | | |
|---|---|---|---|
| Dr Kimberley Cantu | 1 | Ed Harper | 2 |
| Jeff Brogden | 3,5,15 | Dr Paul Cash | 3 |
| Scott Shafer | 3 | Rita Denton | 4 |
| Phillip O'Neal | 6 | Dr Sean Scott | 8,15,288,294 |
| Donald Williams | 15,71 | Janice North | 16,73 |
| Dr Russell Sanders | 20,23* | Christie Alfred | 27,31,74* |
| Holly McCanlies | 36,83 | Marie Medina | 39,81 |
| Amy Senato | 43* | Joshua Garcia | 57 |
| Lesa Shocklee | 58 | Karen Marcucci | 67 |
| Dr Jennifer Stoecker | 68 | David Wright | 79 |

| | | | | | | | |
|---|---|---|---|---|---|---|---|
| 1 Superintendent | 8 Curric/Instruct K-12 | 19 Chief Financial Officer | 29 Family/Consumer Science | 39 Social Studies K-12 | 49 English/Lang Arts Elem | 59 Special Education Elem | 69 Academic Assessment |
| 2 Bus/Finance/Purchasing | 9 Curric/Instruct Elem | 20 Art K-12 | 30 Adult Education | 40 Social Studies Elem | 50 English/Lang Arts Sec | 60 Special Education Sec | 70 Research/Development |
| 3 Buildings And Grounds | 10 Curric/Instruct Sec | 21 Art Elem | 31 Career/Sch-to-Work K-12 | 41 Social Studies Sec | 51 Reading K-12 | 61 Foreign/World Lang K-12 | 71 Public Information |
| 4 Food Service | 11 Federal Program | 22 Art Sec | 32 Career/Sch-to-Work Elem | 42 Science K-12 | 52 Reading Elem | 62 Foreign/World Lang Elem | 72 Summer School |
| 5 Transportation | 12 Title I | 23 Music K-12 | 33 Career/Sch-to-Work Sec | 43 Science Elem | 53 Reading Sec | 63 Foreign/World Lang Sec | 73 Instructional Tech |
| 6 Athletic | 13 Title V | 24 Music Elem | 34 Early Childhood Ed | 44 Science Sec | 54 Remedial Reading K-12 | 64 Religious Education K-12 | 74 Inservice Training |
| 7 Health Services | 15 Asst Superintendent | 25 Music Sec | 35 Health/Phys Education | 45 Math K-12 | 55 Remedial Reading Elem | 65 Religious Education Elem | 75 Marketing/Distributive |
| | 16 Instructional Media Svcs | 26 Business Education | 36 Guidance Services K-12 | 46 Math Elem | 56 Remedial Reading Sec | 66 Religious Education Sec | 76 Info Systems |
| | 17 Chief Operations Officer | 27 Career & Tech Ed | 37 Guidance Services Elem | 47 Math Sec | 57 Bilingual/ELL | 67 School Board President | 77 Psychological Assess |
| | 18 Chief Academic Officer | 28 Technology Education | 38 Guidance Services Sec | 48 English/Lang Arts K-12 | 58 Special Education K-12 | 68 Teacher Personnel | 78 Affirmative Action |

Dr Kelvin Stroy ............................ 79
Jimmy Womack ........................... 91
Lynn Phears .............................. 295
Terri Franks ............................... 81*
Staci Buck ................................. 275
Alicia Alford ............................... 297

| Public Schs..Principal | Grd | Prgm | Enr/#Cls | SN | |
|---|---|---|---|---|---|
| Alice Ponder Elem Sch<br>101 Pleasant Ridge Dr, Mansfield 76063<br>David Thayer | PK-4 | T | 645<br>35 | 70% | 817/299-7700<br>Fax 817/473-5658 |
| Anna May Daulton Elem Sch<br>2607 N Grand Peninsula Dr, Grand Prairie 75054<br>Alycen Phan | PK-4 | | 743<br>50 | 14% | 817/299-6640<br>Fax 817/453-6570 |
| Annette Perry Elem Sch<br>1261 S Main St, Mansfield 76063<br>Willie Wimbrey | PK-4 | T | 430 | 47% | 817/804-2800<br>Fax 817/453-6760 |
| Asa Low Jr Intermediate Sch<br>1526 N Walnut Creek Dr, Mansfield 76063<br>Jason Short | 5-6 | | 811 | 39% | 817/299-3640<br>Fax 817/453-6577 |
| Ben Barber Innovation Academy<br>1120 W Debbie Ln, Mansfield 76063<br>Catharine Hudgins | Voc | G | 1,200 | | 682/314-1600<br>Fax 817/453-6840 |
| Brooks Wester Middle Sch<br>1520 N Walnut Creek Dr, Mansfield 76063<br>Kourtney Gates | 7-8 | GV | 949 | 33% | 682/314-1800<br>Fax 817/453-7213 |
| Carol Holt Elem Sch<br>7321 Ledbetter Rd, Arlington 76001<br>Thelma Foster | PK-4 | T | 468<br>35 | 56% | 817/299-6460<br>Fax 817/561-3888 |
| Charlotte Anderson Elem Sch<br>2122 W Nathan Lowe Rd, Arlington 76017<br>Sheira Petty | PK-4 | T | 408<br>52 | 70% | 817/299-7760<br>Fax 817/472-3216 |
| Cora Spencer Elem Sch<br>3140 S Camino Lagos, Grand Prairie 75054<br>Jocelyn Hobdy | PK-4 | | 558 | 17% | 817/299-6680<br>Fax 817/453-6580 |
| Cross Timbers Intermediate Sch<br>2934 Russell Rd, Arlington 76001<br>Gina Rietfors | 5-6 | T | 742<br>60 | 66% | 817/299-3560<br>Fax 817/561-3814 |
| D P Morris Elem Sch<br>7900 Tin Cup Dr, Arlington 76001<br>Tara Sublette | PK-4 | T | 505<br>55 | 75% | 817/299-7860<br>Fax 817/473-5362 |
| Danny Jones Middle Sch<br>4500 E Broad St, Mansfield 76063<br>**Sharlonda Kennedy** | 7-8 | | 1,106<br>60 | 18% | 682/314-4600<br>Fax 817/453-7380 |
| Della Icenhower Interm Sch<br>8100 Webb Ferrell Rd, Arlington 76002<br>Mendy Gregory | 5-6 | T | 861 | 57% | 817/299-2700<br>Fax 817/453-6890 |
| Donna Shepard Intermediate Sch<br>1280 Highway 1187, Mansfield 76063<br>Matthew Brown | 5-6 | T | 891<br>60 | 53% | 817/299-5940<br>Fax 817/453-6812 |
| Dr Jandrucko Early Learners<br>7811 S Collins St, Arlington 76002<br>Kristi Cobb | PK-K | | 250 | | 817/299-7650 |
| Early College HS at Timberview<br>7700 S Watson Rd, Arlington 76002<br>Erica Bennett | 9-9 | | 72 | 53% | 682/314-1391<br>Fax 817/472-2978 |
| Elizabeth Smith Elem Sch<br>701 S Holland Rd, Mansfield 76063<br>Lea Boiles | PK-4 | | 620 | 21% | 817/299-6980<br>Fax 817/453-7340 |
| Erma Nash Elem Sch<br>1050 Magnolia St, Mansfield 76063<br>Kia McAdams | PK-4 | T | 540<br>36 | 67% | 817/299-6900<br>Fax 817/453-7300 |
| Frontier High Sch<br>1120 W Debbie Ln, Mansfield 76063<br>Catherine Hudgins | 11-12 | | 128 | 35% | 682/314-1600<br>Fax 817/453-6840 |
| Glenn Harmon Elem Sch<br>5700 Petra Dr, Arlington 76017<br>Robyn Rinearson | PK-4 | T | 560<br>51 | 88% | 817/299-7780<br>Fax 817/472-3228 |

| | | | | | |
|---|---|---|---|---|---|
| Imogene Gideon Elem Sch<br>1201 Mansfield Webb Rd, Arlington 76002<br>Shanee Charles | PK-4 | T | 332<br>36 | 63% | 817/299-7800<br>Fax 817/472-3292 |
| J L Boren Elem Sch<br>1401 Country Club Dr, Mansfield 76063<br>Tracy Johnson | PK-4 | | 538<br>30 | 17% | 817/299-7740<br>Fax 817/473-5727 |
| James L Coble Middle Sch<br>1200 Ballweg Rd, Arlington 76002<br>**Travis Moore** | 7-8 | T | 906 | 53% | 682/314-4900<br>Fax 817/548-2152 |
| Janet Brockett Elem Sch<br>810 Dove Meadows Dr, Arlington 76002<br>Tamara Liddell | PK-4 | T | 565<br>45 | 58% | 817/299-6620<br>Fax 817/453-6835 |
| Jerry Knight STEM Academy<br>1524 N Walnut Creek Dr, Mansfield 76063<br>**Victoria Webster** | 6-8 | | 285 | | 817/299-5090<br>Fax 817/473-5658 |
| Judy K Miller Elem Sch<br>403 N Holland Rd, Mansfield 76063<br>Jenny Roberson | PK-4 | | 522 | 30% | 817/299-7550<br>Fax 817/473-5706 |
| Kenneth Davis Elem Sch<br>900 Eden Rd, Arlington 76001<br>**Adam Bender** | PK-4 | T | 419<br>39 | 71% | 817/299-7840<br>Fax 817/472-3267 |
| Lake Ridge High Sch<br>101 N Day Miar Rd, Mansfield 76063<br>**Ashley Alloway** | 9-12 | | 2,632 | 25% | 682/314-0400<br>Fax 817/548-2110 |
| Legacy High Sch<br>1263 N Main St Unit A, Mansfield 76063<br>Dr Shelly Butler | 9-12 | | 2,173 | 38% | 682/314-0600<br>Fax 817/453-7653 |
| Linda Jobe Middle Sch<br>2491 Gertie Barrett Rd, Mansfield 76063<br>Joseph Harmonson | 7-8 | T | 896 | 47% | 682/314-4400<br>Fax 817/561-3899 |
| Louise Cabaniss Elem Sch<br>6080 Mirabella Blvd, Grand Prairie 75052<br>Sheryl Suchsland | PK-4 | T | 556 | 51% | 817/299-6480<br>Fax 817/472-3030 |
| Mansfield High Sch<br>3001 E Broad St, Mansfield 76063<br>Trent Dowd | 9-12 | GV | 2,417 | 24% | 682/314-0100<br>Fax 817/473-5424 |
| Martha Reid Elem Sch<br>500 Country Club Dr, Arlington 76002<br>Catherine McGuinness | PK-4 | | 531<br>37 | 40% | 817/299-6960<br>Fax 817/453-7360 |
| Mary Jo Sheppard Elem Sch<br>1701 FM 1187, Mansfield 76063<br>Darrell LeJeune | PK-4 | T | 433 | 54% | 817/299-6600<br>Fax 817/453-6870 |
| Mary Lillard Intermediate Sch<br>1301 N Day Miar Rd, Mansfield 76063<br>Matthew Herzberg | 5-6 | | 1,048 | 21% | 817/276-6260<br>Fax 817/548-2285 |
| Mary Orr Intermediate Sch<br>2900 E Broad St, Mansfield 76063<br>Duane Thurston | 5-6 | T | 920<br>50 | 43% | 817/299-2600<br>Fax 817/473-5747 |
| Nancy Neal Elem Sch<br>280 Nelson Wyatt Rd, Mansfield 76063<br>Tameka Patton | PK-4 | | 474 | 32% | 817/299-1270<br>Fax 817/561-3820 |
| Roberta Tipps Elem Sch<br>3001 N Walnut Creek Dr, Mansfield 76063<br>Cristina Hernandez | PK-4 | | 598 | 37% | 817/299-6920<br>Fax 817/453-7320 |
| Rogene Worley Middle Sch<br>500 Pleasant Ridge Dr, Mansfield 76063<br>Marcus Brannon | 7-8 | V | 903<br>59 | 42% | 682/314-5100<br>Fax 817/473-5623 |
| Summit High Sch<br>1071 Turner Warnell Rd, Arlington 76001<br>Todd Taylor | 9-12 | TV | 2,127<br>120 | 61% | 682/314-0800<br>Fax 817/473-5732 |
| T A Howard Middle Sch<br>7501 Calender Rd, Arlington 76001<br>Erica Gorruso | 7-8 | TV | 888<br>80 | 68% | 682/314-1050<br>Fax 817/561-3840 |
| Tarver-Rendon Elem Sch<br>6065 Retta Mansfield Rd, Burleson 76028<br>Jamie Norwood-Miller | PK-4 | T | 626<br>27 | 48% | 817/299-7880<br>Fax 817/453-6599 |

Ⓐ The Phoenix Academy    7-12   GT   150   64% 682/314-1700
902 E Broad St, Mansfield 76063     35     Fax 817/473-5477
Regenia Crane

Thelma Jones Elem Sch    PK-4   T   469   59% 817/299-6940
7650 S Watson Rd, Arlington 76002     Fax 817/472-3247
Mico Rhines

Timberview High Sch    9-12   T   1,879   51% 682/314-1300
7700 S Watson Rd, Arlington 76002     Fax 817/472-2978
Derrell Douglas    🅵 🆃

Willie E Brown Elem Sch    PK-4    535   19% 817/299-5860
1860 Cannon Dr, Mansfield 76063     29     Fax 817/473-5392
Kyna Eastlick

---

● **White Settlement Ind Sch Dist** PID: 01054183    817/367-1300
401 S Cherry Ln, Fort Worth 76108     Fax 817/367-1351

**Schools:** 9 \ **Teachers:** 423 \ **Students:** 6,909 \ **Special Ed Students:** 652 \
**LEP Students:** 763 \ **Ethnic:** Asian 1%, African American 10%, Hispanic 43%,
Caucasian 45% \ **Exp:** $458 (High) \ **Poverty:** 13% \ **Title I:** $1,089,671 \
**Special Education:** $1,220,000 \ **Open-Close:** 09/09 - 06/04 \ **DTBP:** $181
(High) \ 🅵 🆃

| Public Schs..Principal | Grd | Prgm | Enr/#Cls | SN | |
|---|---|---|---|---|---|
| Blue Haze Elem Sch<br>601 Blue Haze Dr, Fort Worth 76108<br>Emily Estes | PK-4 | T | 628<br>27 | 47% | 817/367-2583<br>Fax 817/367-1381 |
| Brewer High Sch<br>1025 W Loop 820 N, Fort Worth 76108<br>Jeff Seeton | 9-12 | T | 1,954<br>70 | 49% | 817/367-1200<br>Fax 817/367-1241 |
| Brewer Middle Sch<br>1000 S Cherry Ln, Fort Worth 76108<br>Sherri Kottwitz | 7-8 | T | 556<br>55 | 60% | 817/367-1267<br>Fax 817/367-1268 |
| Ⓐ Daep<br>7911 Gibbs Dr, WHT Settlemt 76108<br>Jennifer Heddins | 9-12 | | 53 | | 817/367-1364<br>Fax 817/367-1366 |
| Ⓜ Fine Arts Academy<br>8301 Downe Dr, Fort Worth 76108<br>Kerry Cooper | K-6 | T | 319<br>15 | 41% | 817/367-5396<br>Fax 817/367-1396 |
| Liberty Elem Sch<br>7976 Whitney Dr, Fort Worth 76108<br>Michael Dickinson | PK-4 | T | 596<br>38 | 74% | 817/367-1312<br>Fax 817/367-1313 |
| North Elem Sch<br>9850 Legacy Dr, Fort Worth 76108<br>Connie Bitters | PK-4 | T | 683<br>30 | 62% | 817/367-1323<br>Fax 817/367-1308 |
| Tannahill Intermediate Sch<br>701 American Flyer Blvd, Fort Worth 76108<br>Randy Summerhill | 5-6 | T | 984<br>46 | 58% | 817/367-1370<br>Fax 817/367-1371 |
| West Elem Sch<br>8901 White Settlement Rd, Fort Worth 76108<br>Courtney Harbuck | PK-4 | T | 452<br>22 | 80% | 817/367-1334<br>Fax 817/367-1333 |

---

# TARRANT CATHOLIC SCHOOLS

● **Diocese of Fort Worth Ed Off** PID: 01054339    817/560-3300
800 W Loop 820 S, Fort Worth 76108     Fax 817/945-9371

**Schools:** 19 \ **Students:** 4,700

Listing includes only schools located in this county. See District Index for
location of Diocesan Offices.

| Catholic Schs..Principal | Grd | Prgm | Enr/#Cls | SN |
|---|---|---|---|---|
| All Saints Catholic Sch<br>2006 N Houston St, Fort Worth 76164<br>Arica Prado | PK-8 | | 155<br>8 | 817/624-2670<br>Fax 817/624-1221 |
| Cassata High Sch<br>1400 Hemphill St, Fort Worth 76104<br>Brian Lott | 9-12 | GV | 100<br>7 | 817/926-1745<br>Fax 817/926-3132 |
| Holy Family Catholic Sch<br>6146 Pershing Ave, Fort Worth 76107<br>Ann Walters | PK-8 | | 232<br>16 | 817/737-4201<br>Fax 817/738-1542 |
| Holy Trinity Catholic Sch<br>3750 William D Tate Ave, Grapevine 76051<br>Jeffrey Heiple | PK-8 | | 300<br>30 | 817/421-8000<br>Fax 817/421-4468 |
| Nolan Catholic High Sch<br>4501 Bridge St, Fort Worth 76103<br>William Perales | 9-12 | | 797<br>55 | 817/457-2920<br>Fax 817/496-9775 |
| Our Lady of Victory Sch<br>3320 Hemphill St, Fort Worth 76110<br>Linda Kuntz | PK-8 | | 104<br>9 | 817/924-5123<br>Fax 817/923-9621 |
| St Andrew Catholic Sch<br>3304 Dryden Rd, Fort Worth 76109<br>Melissa Kasmeier | PK-8 | | 695<br>30 | 817/924-8917<br>Fax 817/921-1490 |
| St Elizabeth Ann Seton Sch<br>2016 Willis Ln, Keller 76248<br>Sam Vanderplas | PK-8 | | 482<br>28 | 817/431-4845<br>Fax 817/431-1865 |
| St George Sch<br>824 Hudgins Ave, Fort Worth 76111<br>Nikki Leafgreen | PK-8 | | 80<br>10 | 817/222-1221<br>Fax 817/838-0424 |
| St John the Apostle Cath Sch<br>7421 Glenview Dr, N Richlnd Hls 76180<br>Amy Felton | PK-8 | | 210<br>20 | 817/284-2228<br>Fax 817/284-1800 |
| St Joseph Catholic Sch<br>2015 SW Green Oaks Blvd, Arlington 76017<br>Diane Price | PK-8 | | 464<br>20 | 817/419-6800<br>Fax 817/419-7080<br>🅵 🆃 |
| St Maria Goretti Sch<br>1200 S Davis Dr, Arlington 76013<br>Laura Behee | PK-8 | | 455<br>20 | 817/275-5081<br>Fax 817/460-0048 |
| St Peter the Apostle Sch<br>1201 S Cherry Ln, WHT Settlemt 76108<br>Lisa Giardino | PK-8 | | 100<br>10 | 817/246-2032<br>Fax 817/246-4900 |
| St Rita Catholic Sch<br>712 Weiler Blvd, Fort Worth 76112<br>Mary Burns | PK-8 | | 175<br>11 | 817/451-9383<br>Fax 817/446-4465 |

---

| | | | | | | | | | |
|---|---|---|---|---|---|---|---|---|---|
| 1 | Superintendent | 8 | Curric/Instruct K-12 | 19 | Chief Financial Officer | 29 | Family/Consumer Science | 39 | Social Studies K-12 |
| 2 | Bus/Finance/Purchasing | 9 | Curric/Instruct Elem | 20 | Art K-12 | 30 | Adult Education | 40 | Social Studies Elem |
| 3 | Buildings And Grounds | 10 | Curric/Instruct Sec | 21 | Art Elem | 31 | Career/Sch-to-Work K-12 | 41 | Social Studies Sec |
| 4 | Food Service | 11 | Federal Program | 22 | Art Sec | 32 | Career/Sch-to-Work Elem | 42 | Science K-12 |
| 5 | Transportation | 12 | Title I | 23 | Music K-12 | 33 | Career/Sch-to-Work Sec | 43 | Science Elem |
| 6 | Athletic | 13 | Title V | 24 | Music Elem | 34 | Early Childhood Ed | 44 | Science Sec |
| 7 | Health Services | 15 | Asst Superintendent | 25 | Music Sec | 35 | Health/Phys Education | 45 | Math K-12 |
| | | 16 | Instructional Media Svcs | 26 | Business Education | 36 | Guidance Services K-12 | 46 | Math Elem |
| | | 17 | Chief Operations Officer | 27 | Career & Tech Ed | 37 | Guidance Services Elem | 47 | Math Sec |
| | | 18 | Chief Academic Officer | 28 | Technology Education | 38 | Guidance Services Sec | 48 | English/Lang Arts K-12 |

| | | | | | | | |
|---|---|---|---|---|---|---|---|
| 49 | English/Lang Arts Elem | 59 | Special Education Elem | 69 | Academic Assessment |
| 50 | English/Lang Arts Sec | 60 | Special Education Sec | 70 | Research/Development |
| 51 | Reading K-12 | 61 | Foreign/World Lang K-12 | 71 | Public Information |
| 52 | Reading Elem | 62 | Foreign/World Lang Elem | 72 | Summer School |
| 53 | Reading Sec | 63 | Foreign/World Lang Sec | 73 | Instructional Tech |
| 54 | Remedial Reading K-12 | 64 | Religious Education K-12 | 74 | Inservice Training |
| 55 | Remedial Reading Elem | 65 | Religious Education Elem | 75 | Marketing/Distributive |
| 56 | Remedial Reading Sec | 66 | Religious Education Sec | 76 | Info Systems |
| 57 | Bilingual/ELL | 67 | School Board President | 77 | Psychological Assess |
| 58 | Special Education K-12 | 68 | Teacher Personnel | 78 | Affirmative Action |

## TARRANT PRIVATE SCHOOLS

| Private Schs..Principal | Grd | Prgm | Enr/#Cls | SN |
|---|---|---|---|---|
| All Saints Episcopal Sch<br>9700 Saints Cir, Fort Worth 76108<br>Dr Thaddeus Bird | PK-12 | | 1,000<br>50 | 817/560-5700<br>Fax 817/560-5716 |
| Azle Christian Sch<br>1801 S Stewart St, Azle 76020<br>April Geeslin | PK-12 | | 110 | 817/444-9964<br>Fax 817/444-9914 |
| Barbara Gordon Montessori Sch<br>1513 Hall Johnson Rd, Colleyville 76034<br>Charlane Baccus | PK-6 | | 160<br>8 | 817/354-6670<br>Fax 817/354-6665<br>🅵 🆃 |
| Bethesda Christian Sch<br>4700 N Beach St, Fort Worth 76137<br>Freda Chadwick | K-12 | | 400<br>28 | 817/281-6446<br>Fax 817/281-1560 |
| Burton Adventist Academy<br>4611 Kelly Elliott Rd, Arlington 76017<br>Ellen Thomas | PK-12 | | 325<br>21 | 817/572-0081<br>Fax 817/561-4237 |
| Calvary Christian Academy<br>1401 Oakhurst Scenic Dr, Fort Worth 76111<br>Lance Miller | PK-12 | | 400<br>30 | 817/332-3351<br>Fax 817/332-4621 |
| Christian Life Preparatory Sch<br>5253 Altamesa Blvd, Fort Worth 76123<br>Zachary Henry | K-12 | | 200 | 817/293-1500 |
| Clariden Sch<br>100 Clariden Ranch Rd, Southlake 76092<br>Sallie Wells \ Robyn Folmar | PK-12 | | 87<br>10 | 682/237-0400<br>Fax 682/831-0300 |
| Country Day Sch of Arlington<br>1105 W Randol Mill Rd, Arlington 76012<br>Joyce Hunt-French | PK-1 | | 83<br>20 | 817/275-0851<br>Fax 817/275-0263 |
| Covenant Christian Academy<br>901 Cheek Sparger Rd, Colleyville 76034<br>Myrandi Ballesteros \ Susan Cook \ Justice Kerr | PK-12 | | 416 | 817/281-4333<br>Fax 682/334-0367<br>🅵 🆃 |
| Covenant Classical Sch<br>1701 Wind Star Way, Fort Worth 76108<br>Eric Cook \ Lori Beck | K-12 | | 161 | 817/820-0884<br>Fax 817/246-5027<br>🅵 🆃 |
| Crossroads Christian Academy<br>3512 Roberts Cut Off Rd, Fort Worth 76114<br>Chuck Mays | 8-12 | | 52<br>1 | 817/378-0100<br>Fax 817/378-8778 |
| Crown of Life Lutheran Sch<br>6605 Pleasant Run Rd, Colleyville 76034<br>Laura Cleland | PK-8 | | 160<br>15 | 817/251-1881<br>Fax 817/421-9263 |
| Ekklesia Christian Sch<br>1200 Bessie St, Fort Worth 76104<br>Michele Chambers | PK-6 | | 31<br>3 | 817/332-1202<br>🅵 |
| Faith Christian Sch<br>730 E Worth St, Grapevine 76051<br>Sharon Neely \ Kory Hicks \ Keith Hall | PK-12 | | 800<br>31 | 817/442-9144<br>Fax 817/442-9904<br>🅵 🆃 |
| Fellowship Academy<br>1021 N Bowman Springs Rd, Kennedale 76060<br>Shauna Moore | PK-12 | | 320<br>17 | 817/483-2400<br>Fax 817/483-2404 |
| Flint Academy<br>2111 Roosevelt Dr, Arlington 76013<br>Dr Paula Flint | PK-12 | | 90<br>17 | 817/277-0620<br>Fax 817/549-0004 |
| Fort Worth Academy<br>7301 Dutch Branch Rd, Fort Worth 76132<br>Shannon Elders | K-8 | | 240<br>24 | 817/370-1191<br>Fax 817/294-1323<br>🅵 🆃 |
| Fort Worth Christian Sch<br>6200 Holiday Ln, N Richlnd Hls 76180 | PK-12 | | 850<br>70 | 817/281-6504<br>Fax 817/281-7063 |
| Ft Worth Adventist Jr Academy<br>3040 Sycamore School Rd, Fort Worth 76133<br>Fred Esquivel | PK-8 | | 85<br>5 | 817/370-7177 |
| Ft Worth Country Day Sch<br>4200 Country Day Ln, Fort Worth 76109<br>Trey Blair \ John Stephens \ Stephen Stackhouse \ Alexis Stern | K-12 | | 1,100<br>75 | 817/732-7718<br>Fax 817/377-3425 |
| Fusion Academy-Southlake<br>301 State St Ste 200, Southlake 76092<br>Stephen Schwartz | 6-12 | | 50 | 817/416-0306 |
| Grace Prep Academy<br>PO Box 170958, Arlington 76003<br>Dr Marc Evans | K-12 | | 450<br>18 | 817/557-3399<br>Fax 817/557-4300 |
| Green Oaks Sch<br>5508 Chaperito Trl, Arlington 76016<br>Leigh Weedman | Spec | | 65 | 817/496-5100<br>Fax 817/496-5104 |
| Harvest Christian Academy<br>7200 Denton Hwy, Watauga 76148<br>Sheila Bothe | PK-12 | | 600<br>40 | 817/485-1660<br>Fax 817/514-6279 |
| High Point Prep Academy<br>2400 E Arbrook Blvd, Arlington 76014<br>Stephen Collins | K-12 | | 157<br>25 | 817/394-3100<br>Fax 817/394-3101 |
| Hill School of Fort Worth<br>4817 Odessa Ave, Fort Worth 76133<br>Roxanne Breyer | Spec | | 175<br>23 | 817/923-9482<br>Fax 817/923-4894<br>🅵 |
| Inspire Academy<br>55 Main St Ste 290, Colleyville 76034<br>Dana Judd | Spec | | 30 | 817/966-4821 |
| Key Sch<br>3947 E Loop 820 S, Fort Worth 76119<br>Leslie Vasquez \ Chad Meeks \ Leigh Bryant | Spec | G | 100<br>22 | 817/446-3738<br>Fax 817/496-3299 |
| Lake Country Christian Sch<br>7050 Lake Country Dr, Fort Worth 76179<br>Sarah Deckert \ Josh Williams | PK-12 | | 410<br>31 | 817/236-8703<br>Fax 817/236-1103 |
| Legacy Classical Chrn Academy<br>12501 Highway 287, Haslet 76052<br>Belinda Henson | PK-12 | | 85 | 817/382-2322 |
| Merryhill Sch<br>711 W Arbrook Blvd, Arlington 76015<br>Michelle Bechtel | PK-6 | | 300 | 817/472-9494<br>Fax 817/468-8348<br>🅵 |
| Messiah Luth Classical Academy<br>1308 Whitley Rd, Keller 76248<br>Alison Smith | PK-9 | | 155 | 817/431-5486<br>Fax 817/898-0365 |
| Metroplex Chapel Academy<br>601 E Airport Fwy, Euless 76039<br>Renee Delorge | PK-6 | | 100<br>7 | 817/267-1000<br>Fax 817/267-5000 |
| Montessori Academy-Arlington<br>3428 W Arkansas Ln, Arlington 76016<br>Pam Dunbar | PK-6 | | 260<br>12 | 817/274-1548<br>Fax 817/274-6951 |
| Montessori Children's House<br>3420 Clayton Rd E, Fort Worth 76116<br>Amy Henderson | PK-8 | | 200<br>5 | 817/732-0252<br>Fax 817/732-6601 |
| Nazarene Christian Academy<br>2001 E Main St, Crowley 76036<br>Nancy Shonamon | K-12 | | 385 | 817/297-7003<br>Fax 817/297-1509 |
| New Life Academy<br>601 E Airport Fwy, Euless 76039<br>Renee Delorge | PK-6 | | 60 | 817/267-1000 |
| North Park Christian Academy<br>7025 Mid Cities Blvd, N Richlnd Hls 76182<br>Jane Edwards | PK-3 | | 40<br>5 | 817/498-8456<br>Fax 817/428-2060 |
| North Texas Leadership Academy<br>10200 Alta Vista Rd, Keller 76244<br>Jennifer Pasteur | PK-4 | | 75 | 817/562-2931<br>Fax 817/562-2058 |
| Northstar Sch<br>4620 Park Springs Blvd, Arlington 76017<br>Lisa Odom | 7-12 | | 52 | 817/478-5852<br>Fax 817/478-7252 |
| Novus Academy<br>204 N Dooley St Ste 100, Grapevine 76051<br>Kathleen Edwards | K-12 | | 70 | 817/488-4555<br>Fax 817/488-4533 |
| Pantego Christian Academy<br>2351 Country Club Dr, Mansfield 76063<br>Elizabeth Birdwell | PK-5 | | 150<br>13 | 817/522-5900<br>Fax 682/518-0823 |

| | | | | |
|---|---|---|---|---|
| **79** Student Personnel | **91** Safety/Security | **275** Response To Intervention | **298** Grant Writer/Ptnrships | **School Programs** |
| **80** Driver Ed/Safety | **92** Magnet School | **277** Remedial Math K-12 | **750** Chief Innovation Officer | **A** = Alternative Program |
| **81** Gifted/Talented | **93** Parental Involvement | **280** Literacy Coach | **751** Chief of Staff | **G** = Adult Classes |
| **82** Video Services | **95** Tech Prep Program | **285** STEM | **752** Social Emotional Learning | **M** = Magnet Program |
| **83** Substance Abuse Prev | **97** Chief Infomation Officer | **286** Digital Learning | | **T** = Title I Schoolwide |
| **84** Erate | **98** Chief Technology Officer | **288** Common Core Standards | **Other School Types** | **V** = Career & Tech Ed Programs |
| **85** AIDS Education | **270** Character Education | **294** Accountability | Ⓐ = Alternative School | |
| **88** Alternative/At Risk | **271** Migrant Education | **295** Network System | Ⓒ = Charter School | **New Schools are shaded** |
| **89** Multi-Cultural Curriculum | **273** Teacher Mentor | **296** Title II Programs | Ⓜ = Magnet School | **New Superintendents and Principals are bold** |
| **90** Social Work | **274** Before/After Sch | **297** Webmaster | Ⓨ = Year-Round School | **Personnel with email addresses are underscored** |

**Social Media**

🅵 = Facebook

🆃 = Twitter

# TX—361

| | | | |
|---|---|---|---|
| Pantego Christian Academy<br>2201 W Park Row Dr, Arlington 76013<br>Elizabeth Birdwell \ Michael Beeson | PK-12 | 797<br>50 | 817/460-3315<br>Fax 817/548-9288 🅣 |
| Park Row Chrn Academy<br>915 W Park Row Dr, Arlington 76013<br>Paula Gibson | PK-6 | 200<br>15 | 817/277-1021<br>Fax 817/277-1385 |
| Premier Academy<br>4040 Heritage Trace Pkwy, Keller 76244<br>Chris Cross | PK-5 | 250<br>14 | 817/745-0034<br>Fax 817/741-4588 |
| Redeemer Lutheran Sch<br>4513 Williams Rd, Fort Worth 76116<br>Page Nickell | PK-5 | 50<br>8 | 817/560-0032 |
| Rivertree Academy<br>5439 Bonnell Ave, Fort Worth 76107<br>Emily Williams | PK-5 | 30 | 817/420-9310 |
| Saint Peters Classical Sch<br>7601 Bellaire Dr S, Fort Worth 76132<br>Jeanette Johnson | K-12 | 75<br>13 | 817/294-0124<br>Fax 817/288-0180 🅕 |
| Southwest Christian Sch-Prep<br>6901 Altamesa Blvd, Fort Worth 76123<br>Dr Joey Richards \ Coby Bird | 7-12 | 603 | 817/294-9596 |
| Southwest Christian Sch<br>6801 Dan Danciger Rd, Fort Worth 76133<br>Justin Kirk | PK-6 | 400<br>25 | 817/294-0350<br>Fax 817/294-0752 |
| Spurling Christian Academy<br>1200 High Point Rd, Arlington 76015<br>Linda Sands | PK-12 | 25 | 817/465-1122<br>Fax 817/391-1443 |
| St Ignatius College Prep Sch<br>8109 Shelton Dr, Fort Worth 76120<br>Victor Nguyen | 9-12 | 200 | 817/801-4801 |
| St Paul Lutheran Sch<br>1800 West Fwy, Fort Worth 76102<br>Scott Browning | PK-8 | 223<br>13 | 817/332-4563<br>Fax 817/332-2640 🅕 |
| St Paul's Preparatory Academy<br>6900 US 287 Hwy, Arlington 76001<br>Amy Maumus \ Gayla Rockwell | PK-12 | 290 | 817/561-3500<br>Fax 817/561-3408 |
| Starpoint Sch<br>2825 Stadium Dr, Fort Worth 76109<br>Marilyn Tolbert | Spec | 66<br>6 | 817/257-7141<br>Fax 817/257-7168 |
| Tate Springs Christian Sch<br>4001 Little Rd, Arlington 76016<br>Halley Steinhilber | K-6 | 325 | 817/478-7091<br>Fax 817/483-8283 |
| Temple Christian Sch<br>6824 Randol Mill Rd, Fort Worth 76120<br>Shelena Schweitzer | K-12 | 475<br>26 | 817/457-0770<br>Fax 817/457-0777 |
| The Jane Justin Sch<br>1300 W Lancaster Ave, Fort Worth 76102<br>Casey Mann | Spec | 70 | 817/390-2831<br>Fax 817/390-2851 |
| The Oakridge Sch<br>5900 W Pioneer Pkwy, Arlington 76013<br>Dr Sarah Schecter \ Britt Robinson \ Jim Andersen | PK-12 | 850 | 817/451-4994<br>Fax 817/457-6681 |
| Trinity Baptist Temple Academy<br>6045 Wj Boaz Rd, Fort Worth 76179<br>Kelley McDowell | PK-12 | 135<br>13 | 817/237-4255<br>Fax 817/237-5233 |
| Trinity Valley Sch<br>7500 Dutch Branch Rd, Fort Worth 76132<br>Sandy McNutt \ Jeffrey Snyder \ Kyle Kahuda | K-12  V | 971<br>78 | 817/321-0100<br>Fax 817/321-0105 🅕🅣 |
| Vanguard International Academy<br>1600 S Center St, Arlington 76010<br>Ibrahim Abu Abdulrahman | 8-11 | 23 | 817/274-6444 |
| Walnut Creek Private Sch<br>1751 N Walnut Creek Dr, Mansfield 76063<br>Ladonna Morgan | PK-5 | 150 | 817/473-4406<br>Fax 817/453-8755 |
| Wedgewood Academy<br>4833 Selkirk Dr, Fort Worth 76109<br>Rachel Wittich | Spec | 61 | 817/924-9095 |

## TARRANT REGIONAL CENTERS

- **Region 11 Ed Service Center** PID: 01054171
  1451 S Cherry Ln, WHT Settlemt 76108
  817/740-3600
  Fax 817/740-7600

| | | | |
|---|---|---|---|
| Dr Clyde Steelman | 1,11 | Brandilyn DePalma | 2 |
| Laura Weir | 2 | John Petree | 15,58,69,73,74 |
| Rory Peacock | 15,295 | Tiffany Green | 68 |
| Teela Watson | 70 | Lori Burton | 71 |
| David Sons | 76 | Shari King | 298 |

## TAYLOR COUNTY

## TAYLOR PUBLIC SCHOOLS

- **Abilene Ind School Dist** PID: 01054523
  241 Pine St, Abilene 79601
  325/677-1444
  Fax 325/794-1324

> **Schools:** 26 \ **Teachers:** 1,091 \ **Students:** 17,000 \
> **Special Ed Students:** 2,136 \ **LEP Students:** 926 \ **College-Bound:** 48%
> \ **Ethnic:** Asian 2%, African American 14%, Hispanic 46%, Caucasian
> 37% \ **Exp:** $250 (Med) \ **Poverty:** 26% \ **Title I:** $6,832,937 \
> **Special Education:** $3,437,000 \ **Open-Close:** 08/20 - 05/27 \ **DTBP:** $188
> (High)

| | | | |
|---|---|---|---|
| Dr David Young | 1 | Lisa Metcalf | 2 |
| Melissa Irby | 2 | Juan Rodriguez | 3 |
| Scott McLean | 3,4,5,15 | Phil Blue | 6,35 |
| Linda Langston | 7 | Kimberly Brumley | 8 |
| Alison Sims | 9 | Gustavo Villanueva | 10,15,27,31 |
| Cheryl Cunningham | 11,48,57 | Joseph Waldron | 15,68 |
| Jay Lester | 20,23 | Mignon Lawson | 30* |
| Jennifer Putnam | 34* | Ross Thomas | 39 |
| Teri Reece | 58 | Daryl Zeller | 67 |
| Jeannette Forehand | 69,294 | Gregory Fleming | 71 |
| Cary Owens | 76,295 | Dr Dan Dukes | 79 |
| Charles Caddell | 297 | | |

| Public Schs..Principal | Grd | Prgm | Enr/#Cls | SN |
|---|---|---|---|---|
| Abilene High Sch<br>2800 N 6th St, Abilene 79603<br>Michael Garcia | 9-12 | TV | 2,126 | 63%  325/677-1731<br>Fax 325/794-1387 |
| Adult Education<br>1929 S 11th St, Abilene 79602<br>Mignon Lawson | Adult | | 250<br>8 | 325/671-4419<br>Fax 325/794-1327 |
| ⊛ Atems High Sch<br>650 US Highway 80 E, Abilene 79601<br>Jeffrey Howle | 9-12 | V | 329 | 325/794-4140 |
| Austin Elem Sch<br>2341 Greenbriar Dr, Abilene 79605<br>Alison Camp | PK-5 | T | 510<br>25 | 42%  325/690-3920<br>Fax 325/794-1350 |
| Bassetti Elem Sch<br>5749 US Highway 277 S, Abilene 79606<br>**Cecelia Zertuche** | PK-5 | T | 454<br>30 | 71%  325/690-3720<br>Fax 325/794-1351 |
| Bonham Elem Sch<br>4250 Potomac Ave, Abilene 79605<br>Kyle Wiskow | PK-5 | T | 457<br>28 | 77%  325/690-3745<br>Fax 325/794-1352 |
| Bowie Elem Sch<br>2034 Jeanette St, Abilene 79602<br>Tina Jones | PK-5 | T | 476<br>32 | 81%  325/671-4770<br>Fax 325/794-1353 |

| School | Grd | Prgm | Enr | #Cls | % | Phone |
|---|---|---|---|---|---|---|
| Byron Craig Middle Sch<br>702 S Judge Ely Blvd, Abilene 79602<br>**Debra Stewart** | 6-8 | TV | 960 | | 71% | 325/794-4100<br>Fax 325/794-1385 |
| Clack Middle Sch<br>1610 Corsicana Ave, Abilene 79605<br>Todd Bramwell | 6-8 | TV | 888 | 55 | 72% | 325/692-1961<br>Fax 325/794-1371 |
| Cooper High Sch<br>3639 Sayles Blvd, Abilene 79605<br>Lyndsey Williamson | 9-12 | TV | 1,777 | | 60% | 325/691-1000<br>Fax 325/794-1375 |
| Dyess Elem Sch<br>402 Delaware Rd, Abilene 79605<br>**Chad Drake** | PK-5 | T | 456 | | 46% | 325/690-3795<br>Fax 325/794-1355 |
| Holland Medical High Sch<br>2200 Hickory St, Abilene 79601<br>Lyndsey Williamson | Voc | | 150 | | | 325/794-4120<br>Fax 325/794-1372 |
| Jackson Elem Sch<br>2650 S 32nd St, Abilene 79605<br>Debra Hollingsworth | PK-5 | T | 437 | | 69% | 325/690-3602<br>Fax 325/794-1357 |
| Jefferson Achievement Ctr<br>1741 S 14th St, Abilene 79602<br>Jane Allred | Spec | | 80 | 6 | 88% | 325/794-4150<br>Fax 325/794-1367 |
| Johnston Elem Sch<br>3602 N 12th St, Abilene 79603<br>Jeffrey Brokovich | PK-5 | T | 550 | 25 | 82% | 325/671-4845<br>Fax 325/794-1358 |
| Lee Elem Sch<br>1026 N Pioneer Dr, Abilene 79603<br>Andy Blessing | K-5 | T | 481 | 40 | 86% | 325/671-4895<br>Fax 325/794-1359 |
| Long Early Childhood Center<br>3600 Sherry Ln, Abilene 79603<br>Jennifer Putnam | PK-PK | T | 786 | 18 | 86% | 325/671-4594<br>Fax 325/794-1368 |
| Madison Middle Sch<br>3145 Barrow St, Abilene 79605<br>Joshua Newton | 6-8 | TV | 623 | 40 | 69% | 325/692-5661<br>Fax 325/794-1313 |
| Mann Middle Sch<br>2545 Mimosa Dr, Abilene 79603<br>Kathryn Walker | 6-8 | TV | 882 | 31 | 74% | 325/672-8493<br>Fax 325/794-1374 |
| Martinez Elem Sch<br>1250 Merchant St, Abilene 79603<br>Mildred Petty | PK-5 | T | 463 | 20 | 92% | 325/794-4160 |
| Ortiz Elem Sch<br>2550 Vogel St, Abilene 79603<br>Debra Stewart | K-5 | T | 588 | 36 | 92% | 325/671-4945<br>Fax 325/794-1361 |
| Reagan Elem Sch<br>5340 Hartford St, Abilene 79605<br>Leslye Roberts | PK-5 | T | 326 | 34 | 88% | 325/690-3627<br>Fax 325/794-1362 |
| Taylor Elem Sch<br>916 E North 13th St, Abilene 79601<br>Keri Thornburg | PK-5 | T | 529 | 25 | 62% | 325/671-4970<br>Fax 325/794-1364 |
| Thomas Elem Sch<br>1240 Lakeside Dr, Abilene 79602<br>Cindy Hay | K-5 | T | 367 | 26 | 71% | 325/671-4995<br>Fax 325/794-1365 |
| Ward Elem Sch<br>3750 Paint Brush Dr, Abilene 79606<br>Dawn Ripple | PK-5 | T | 480 | 29 | 43% | 325/690-3666<br>Fax 325/794-1366 |
| Ⓐ Woodson Center for Excellence<br>342 Cockerell Dr, Abilene 79601<br>Jaime Tindall | 9-12 | | 166 | 9 | 75% | 325/671-4736<br>Fax 325/676-1528 |

● **Jim Ned Cons Ind School Dist** PID: 01054896
441 Graham St, Tuscola 79562
325/554-7500
Fax 325/554-7740

> **Schools:** 4 \ **Teachers:** 94 \ **Students:** 1,360 \ **Special Ed Students:** 139 \ **LEP Students:** 3 \ **Ethnic:** African American 1%, Hispanic 11%, Caucasian 88% \ **Exp:** $441 (High) \ **Poverty:** 11% \ **Title I:** $129,647 \ **Open-Close:** 08/19 - 05/26 \ **DTBP:** $348 (High)

| | | | |
|---|---|---|---|
| Dr Glen Teal .................1 | | Hunter Cooley ............2,11,19,294 | |
| Douglas Taylor ...............4* | | Scott Carlilse ..........................5 | |
| Raenese Byrom .............7,85 | | Cristi Doty ...............8,288* | |
| Debbie Harris ................12 | | Marja Swart ...............16,82* | |
| Carla Cooley ........38,69,83,88* | | Mendi Jeter .................58 | |
| Matt Higgins ................67 | | Dana Kiner ..............73,286,295* | |

| Public Schs..Principal | Grd | Prgm | Enr/#Cls | SN | |
|---|---|---|---|---|---|
| Buffalo Gap Elem Sch<br>665 Vine St, Buffalo Gap 79508<br>**Alana McClure** | PK-5 | | 303<br>12 | 20% | 325/572-3533<br>Fax 325/572-4824 |
| Jim Ned High Sch<br>830 Garza Ave, Tuscola 79562<br>Treva Gambrell | 9-12 | V | 336<br>30 | 18% | 325/554-7755<br>Fax 325/554-7733 |
| Jim Ned Middle Sch<br>830 Garza Ave, Tuscola 79562<br>Jay Wise | 6-8 | | 327<br>24 | 25% | 325/554-7870<br>Fax 325/554-7750 |
| Lawn Elem Sch<br>525 4th Street, Lawn 79530<br>Debbie Harris | PK-5 | | 267<br>35 | | 325/583-2256<br>Fax 325/583-2679 |

● **Merkel Ind School Dist** PID: 01054925
1512 S 5th, Merkel 79536
325/928-5813
Fax 325/928-3910

> **Schools:** 3 \ **Teachers:** 98 \ **Students:** 1,073 \ **Special Ed Students:** 170 \ **LEP Students:** 23 \ **College-Bound:** 44% \ **Ethnic:** African American 1%, Hispanic 28%, Caucasian 71% \ **Exp:** $283 (Med) \ **Poverty:** 20% \ **Title I:** $323,196 \ **Open-Close:** 08/17 - 05/27 \ **DTBP:** $486 (High)

| | | | |
|---|---|---|---|
| Joseph O'Malley ..................1 | | Lane Petty ..........................2 | |
| Royce Fowler ........................3 | | Brin Reed ...........................4 | |
| Britt Hart ..............................6 | | Nan Wiley ...................57,271 | |
| Nan Wiley .................57,271* | | Kyle Doan .........................67 | |
| Rachael Byers .............69,83,88* | | Suzie Steckly .....................73 | |

| Public Schs..Principal | Grd | Prgm | Enr/#Cls | SN | |
|---|---|---|---|---|---|
| Merkel Elem Sch<br>1602 S 5th, Merkel 79536<br>Daniel Kotara | PK-5 | T | 494<br>17 | 66% | 325/928-4795<br>Fax 325/928-3174 |
| Merkel High Sch<br>2000 S 7th St, Merkel 79536<br>James Stevens | 9-12 | ATV | 307<br>40 | 55% | 325/928-4667<br>Fax 325/928-4684<br>🅕 |
| Merkel Middle Sch<br>302 Ash, Merkel 79536<br>Larry Bills | 6-8 | T | 272<br>27 | 57% | 325/928-5511<br>Fax 325/928-3138 |

● **Trent Isn School Dist** PID: 01054987
12821 E I 20, Trent 79561
325/862-6125
Fax 325/862-6448

> **Schools:** 1 \ **Teachers:** 17 \ **Students:** 150 \ **Special Ed Students:** 23 \ **College-Bound:** 50% \ **Ethnic:** Asian 1%, African American 1%, Hispanic 10%, Caucasian 89% \ **Exp:** $510 (High) \ **Poverty:** 25% \ **Title I:** $41,545 \ **Open-Close:** 08/20 - 05/26 \ **DTBP:** $352 (High)

| | | | |
|---|---|---|---|
| Charles Carter ........1,11,83,288 | | Kayla Swanzy ......................2 | |
| Greg Rains ...........................3* | | Patsy Williams ....................4* | |
| Derrick Newlun .....................5 | | Chris Ellison ......................6 | |
| Dora Bayne ..........................16 | | Marie Alambar ...............57,58* | |
| J Pickens .............................67 | | Tricia Spikes ..............73,295* | |

| Public Schs..Principal | Grd | Prgm | Enr/#Cls | SN | |
|---|---|---|---|---|---|
| Trent Sch<br>12821 East I 20, Trent 79561<br>Vanessa Oakley | PK-12 | TV | 150<br>23 | 64% | 325/862-6125 |

● **Wylie Ind School Dist** PID: 01055008    325/692-4353
6251 Buffalo Gap Rd, Abilene 79606    Fax 325/695-3438

---

**Schools:** 7 \ **Teachers:** 287 \ **Students:** 5,000 \ **Special Ed Students:** 332 \ **LEP Students:** 70 \ **Ethnic:** Asian 3%, African American 4%, Hispanic 20%, Caucasian 72% \ **Exp:** $209 (Med) \ **Poverty:** 8% \ **Title I:** $316,260 \ **Special Education:** $606,000 \ **Open-Close:** 08/19 - 05/26 \ **DTBP:** $153 (High)

---

| | | |
|---|---|---|
| Joey Light ...............................1 | Carol Smith .............................2,11,296,298 | |
| Craig Bessent ...................3,5,91 | Melanie Brewer ...................................4 | |
| Clay Martin ..........................6 | Corrissa Parris ...................................7* | |
| Terry Hagler .........................8 | Jennifer Greenough ...........................16 | |
| Lisa Salmon ...........34,57,69,83,273* | Greggory Ruffin ...............................35* | |
| Darla Swanner ..........36,85,88,271 | Shauni Vaughn ..........................58,271 | |
| Steve Keenum .....................67 | Robin McVay .....................................68 | |
| Tony Spradlin ......................73 | Jackie Powell ...................................76 | |
| Kimberly Cheek ...................81* | Brad McVay .....................................295 | |

| Public Schs..Principal | Grd | Prgm | Enr/#Cls | SN | |
|---|---|---|---|---|---|
| Wylie East Elem Sch<br>7401 Maple St, Abilene 79602<br>Kim McMillan | PK-4 | | 940 | 29% | 325/437-2330<br>Fax 325/437-2379 |
| Wylie East Junior High Sch<br>1682 Colony Hill Rd, Abilene 79602<br>Rob Goodenough | 5-8 | | 678 | | 325/437-2360<br>Fax 325/692-5786 |
| Wylie High Sch<br>4502 Antilley Rd, Abilene 79606<br>Tim Smith | 9-12 | | 1,235<br>65 | 14% | 325/690-1181<br>Fax 325/690-0320<br>🅵 🅴 |
| Wylie Intermediate Sch<br>3158 Beltway S, Abilene 79606<br>Phil Boone | 3-4 | | 692<br>28 | 25% | 325/692-7961<br>Fax 325/695-4647 |
| Wylie West Early Childhood Ctr<br>6249 Buffalo Gap Rd, Abilene 79606<br>Lisa Salmon | PK-K | | 187 | 32% | 325/437-2351<br>Fax 325/695-4645 |
| Wylie West Elem Sch<br>7650 Hardwick Rd, Abilene 79606<br>Lisa Bessent | 1-2 | | 698<br>19 | 19% | 325/692-6554<br>Fax 325/695-4645 |
| Wylie West Junior High Sch<br>4134 Beltway S, Abilene 79606<br>Aaron Amonett | 5-8 | | 686<br>30 | 20% | 325/695-1910<br>Fax 325/692-5786 |

## TAYLOR PRIVATE SCHOOLS

| Private Schs..Principal | Grd | Prgm | Enr/#Cls | SN | |
|---|---|---|---|---|---|
| A Habitat for Learning Daycare<br>3242 Beltway S, Abilene 79606<br>Michelle Van Horn | PK-PK | | 40 | | 325/692-2481<br>Fax 325/691-0655 |
| Abilene Christian Sch<br>2550 N Judge Ely Blvd, Abilene 79601<br>Cindy Johnson \ Van Gravitt | PK-12 | | 300<br>20 | | 325/672-6200<br>Fax 325/672-1202 |
| Cornerstone Christian Sch<br>718 Barrow St, Abilene 79605<br>Robbye Benningfield | PK-5 | | 45<br>6 | | 325/676-8232<br>Fax 325/437-2432 |
| Kenley Sch<br>1434 Matador St, Abilene 79605<br>Qi Hang | 1-8 | | 69<br>5 | | 325/698-3220<br>Fax 325/692-7387<br>🅵 |
| St John's Episcopal Sch<br>1600 Sherman Dr, Abilene 79605<br>Rebecca McMillion | PK-5 | | 260<br>14 | | 325/695-8870<br>Fax 325/698-1532 |

## TAYLOR REGIONAL CENTERS

● **Region 14 Ed Service Center** PID: 01054975    325/675-8600
1850 State Highway 351, Abilene 79601    Fax 325/675-8659

| | | |
|---|---|---|
| Ronnie Kincaid ...........................1 | Emily Jeffrey .............................2 | |
| Dr Rose Burks ............7,8,27,31,88 | Emilia Moreno .........................11,57 | |
| Lisa White ...........................36,58,77 | Dr Gene Shelhamer ...................67 | |
| Robb McClellan ........................73 | Misty Bloomingdale ...................74 | |
| Rod Pruitt ...........................83,85 | Donna Scherr .........................275 | |

## TERRELL COUNTY

## TERRELL PUBLIC SCHOOLS

● **Terrell Co Ind School Dist** PID: 01055046    432/345-2515
302 2nd St, Sanderson 79848    Fax 432/345-2404

---

**Schools:** 1 \ **Teachers:** 13 \ **Students:** 108 \ **Special Ed Students:** 14 \ **LEP Students:** 4 \ **College-Bound:** 50% \ **Ethnic:** Asian 3%, African American 2%, Hispanic 59%, Caucasian 36% \ **Exp:** $475 (High) \ **Poverty:** 21% \ **Title I:** $34,085 \ **Open-Close:** 08/13 - 05/14 \ **DTBP:** $428 (High) \ 🅵 🅴

---

| | | |
|---|---|---|
| Amanda Mangallan ...........................1 | Blain Chriesman .............................2 | |
| Sam Mangallan ...............................3 | Violita McDonald .........................13,83* | |
| Thad Cleveland ...............................67 | David Carrasco .............................73* | |

| Public Schs..Principal | Grd | Prgm | Enr/#Cls | SN | |
|---|---|---|---|---|---|
| Sanderson Public Sch<br>302 2nd Street, Sanderson 79848<br>Amanda Magallan | PK-12 | TV | 108<br>20 | 50% | 432/345-2515 |

## TERRY COUNTY

## TERRY PUBLIC SCHOOLS

● **Brownfield Ind Sch Dist** PID: 01055084    806/637-2591
601 E Tahoka Rd, Brownfield 79316    Fax 806/637-9208

---

**Schools:** 4 \ **Teachers:** 125 \ **Students:** 1,623 \ **Special Ed Students:** 153 \ **LEP Students:** 126 \ **College-Bound:** 40% \ **Ethnic:** African American 4%, Hispanic 75%, Caucasian 20% \ **Exp:** $624 (High) \ **Poverty:** 31% \ **Title I:** $915,451 \ **Special Education:** $466,000 \ **Open-Close:** 08/24 - 05/28 \ **DTBP:** $340 (High) \ 🅵 🅴

---

| | | |
|---|---|---|
| Chris Smith ...............................1 | David Martinez .............................2,19,68 | |
| Brian Paiva ...............................3 | Beverly Webb .................................4 | |
| Melissa Oliva .......................8,11,15 | Sarah Douglas .............................31* | |
| Geoff Cooper ...........................67 | Chris Martinez .........................73,286 | |
| Mary Valdonado .......................271 | Lauren Phelps .............................752 | |

---

| Public Schs..Principal | Grd | Prgm | Enr/#Cls | SN |
|---|---|---|---|---|
| Bright Beginnings Academic Ctr<br>1202 Seagraves Rd, Brownfield 79316<br>Paul Coronado | PK-PK | T | 169 | 94% 806/637-0757<br>Fax 806/637-0119 |
| Brownfield High Sch<br>701 Cub Dr, Brownfield 79316<br>Gionet Cooper | 9-12 | ATV | 104<br>54 | 73% 806/637-4523<br>Fax 806/637-3801 |
| Brownfield Middle Sch<br>1001 E Broadway St, Brownfield 79316<br>Artemio Ontiveros | 6-8 | TV | 361<br>30 | 78% 806/637-7521<br>Fax 806/637-2919 |
| Oak Grove Elem Sch<br>1000 E Cactus Ln, Brownfield 79316<br>Vicki Hathaway | K-5 | T | 730<br>29 | 83% 806/637-6455<br>Fax 806/637-3636 |

● **Meadow Ind School Dist** PID: 01055149
604 4th St, Meadow 79345
806/539-2246
Fax 806/539-2529

**Schools:** 1 \ **Teachers:** 28 \ **Students:** 285 \ **Special Ed Students:** 32 \
**LEP Students:** 18 \ **Ethnic:** Hispanic 72%, Caucasian 28% \ **Exp:** $724
(High) \ **Poverty:** 34% \ **Title I:** $126,176 \ **Open-Close:** 08/11 - 05/27 \
**DTBP:** $327 (High)

Darrian Dover ...........................................1   Joshua Connor ..........................................6
Stacey Dover ...................................11,60   Stacy Gamez ..........................................34*
Sherryll Barclay ...............................36,69*   Keith Harrison ..........................................67
Blane Britton ......................................73*

| Public Schs..Principal | Grd | Prgm | Enr/#Cls | SN |
|---|---|---|---|---|
| Meadow Sch<br>604 4th St, Meadow 79345<br>**Tabitha Coffman** \ Dennis Berger \ Bric Turner | PK-12 | T | 285<br>35 | 77% 806/539-2246 |

● **Wellman Union Ind School Dist** PID: 01055199
505 Terry St, Wellman 79378
806/637-4910
Fax 806/637-2585

**Schools:** 1 \ **Teachers:** 26 \ **Students:** 335 \ **Special Ed Students:** 16
\ **LEP Students:** 33 \ **Ethnic:** African American 1%, Hispanic 45%,
Caucasian 54% \ **Exp:** $573 (High) \ **Poverty:** 38% \ **Title I:** $73,392 \
**Open-Close:** 08/19 - 05/27 \ **DTBP:** $338 (High)

Ben Prowell .....................................1,11   Deborah Lambert ........................................2
Rudy Alvarado ...................................3*   Angie Cavazos ..........................................4*
Rudy Alvarado ...................................5   Brian Sepkowipz ..........................................6
Bridget Brown .....................12,271,275*   Megan Becker ...............36,69,83,85,88*
James Harlan .....................................67   Roger Chase ...............................73,286*

| Public Schs..Principal | Grd | Prgm | Enr/#Cls | SN |
|---|---|---|---|---|
| Wellman-Union Sch<br>505 Terry St, Wellman 79378<br>Bridget Brown \ **Kyle Conatser** | PK-12 | TV | 335<br>30 | 54% 806/637-4619 |

## THROCKMORTON PUBLIC SCHOOLS

● **Throckmorton Ind School Dist** PID: 01055228
210 College St, Throckmorton 76483
940/849-2411
Fax 940/849-3345

**Schools:** 1 \ **Teachers:** 14 \ **Students:** 158 \ **Special Ed Students:** 9 \
**College-Bound:** 100% \ **Ethnic:** African American 2%, Hispanic 17%,
Caucasian 81% \ **Exp:** $1,133 (High) \ **Poverty:** 19% \ **Title I:** $45,693 \
**Open-Close:** 08/13 - 05/18 \ **DTBP:** $350 (High) \ 📘

Dr Michelle Cline ..................................1   Brittney Woods ..........................................2
Ray Fowler .....................................3,5   Rhonda Riley ...........8,11,74,275,288,294,296
Amy Anthony .............................36,69,270   Kathy Thorp ..........................................67
Candi Key ...............................73,84,295

| Public Schs..Principal | Grd | Prgm | Enr/#Cls | SN |
|---|---|---|---|---|
| Throckmorton Sch<br>210 College St, Throckmorton 76483<br>Rhonda Riley | PK-12 | T | 158<br>10 | 69% 940/849-9981<br>📘 |

● **Woodson Ind School Dist** PID: 01055254
207 E Hill St, Woodson 76491
940/345-6521
Fax 940/345-6549

**Schools:** 1 \ **Teachers:** 18 \ **Students:** 144 \ **Special Ed Students:** 19 \
**College-Bound:** 67% \ **Ethnic:** Hispanic 20%, Caucasian 80% \ **Exp:** $940
(High) \ **Poverty:** 28% \ **Title I:** $23,916 \ **Open-Close:** 08/12 - 05/20 \
**DTBP:** $632 (High) \ 📘

Casey Adams .........................1,11,83,288   Melissa Vickers .....................................2,298
Caleb Hagle ..........................................3   Rhonda Brockman ..........................................4*
Brent Mills .....................................8,57,76   Margaret Mathiews ...........................58,79*
Gary Brockman ....................................67

| Public Schs..Principal | Grd | Prgm | Enr/#Cls | SN |
|---|---|---|---|---|
| Woodson Sch<br>207 E Hill St, Woodson 76491<br>Brent Mills | PK-12 | TV | 144<br>14 | 62% 940/345-6521 |

## TITUS PUBLIC SCHOOLS

● **Chapel Hill Ind School Dist** PID: 01055307
1069 County Road 4660, Mt Pleasant 75455
903/572-8096
Fax 903/572-1086

**Schools:** 3 \ **Teachers:** 80 \ **Students:** 1,050 \ **Special Ed Students:** 103 \
**LEP Students:** 150 \ **Ethnic:** Asian 1%, African American 3%, Hispanic 39%,
Caucasian 57% \ **Exp:** $712 (High) \ **Poverty:** 24% \ **Title I:** $219,342 \
**Special Education:** $5,000 \ **Open-Close:** 08/19 - 05/27 \ **DTBP:** $350 (High)
\ 📘

| | | | |
|---|---|---|---|
| 79 Student Personnel | 91 Safety/Security | 275 Response To Intervention | 298 Grant Writer/Ptnrships |
| 80 Driver Ed/Safety | 92 Magnet School | 277 Remedial Math K-12 | 750 Chief Innovation Officer |
| 81 Gifted/Talented | 93 Parental Involvement | 280 Literacy Coach | 751 Chief of Staff |
| 82 Video Services | 95 Tech Prep Program | 285 STEM | 752 Social Emotional Learning |
| 83 Substance Abuse Prev | 97 Chief Infomation Officer | 286 Digital Learning | |
| 84 Erate | 98 Chief Technology Officer | 288 Common Core Standards | **Other School Types** |
| 85 AIDS Education | 270 Character Education | 294 Accountability | Ⓐ = Alternative School |
| 88 Alternative/At Risk | 271 Migrant Education | 295 Network System | Ⓒ = Charter School |
| 89 Multi-Cultural Curriculum | 273 Teacher Mentor | 296 Title II Programs | Ⓜ = Magnet School |
| 90 Social Work | 274 Before/After Sch | 297 Webmaster | Ⓨ = Year-Round School |

**School Programs**
A = Alternative Program
G = Adult Classes
M = Magnet Program
T = Title I Schoolwide
V = Career & Tech Ed Programs

**Social Media**
📘 = Facebook
📱 = Twitter

New Schools are shaded
New Superintendents and Principals are bold
Personnel with email addresses are underscored

**TX—365**

| Marc Levesque | 1 |
| Justin Edwards | 3,5,17 |
| Dave Schmitt | 6 |
| Telly Hall | 16,73,98,286 |
| Christina Reid | 58* |
| Mike Edwards | 67 |
| Jessie Bratton | 274* |

| Mike Hall | 2 |
| Sherry Eargle | 4 |
| Lacy Robinson | 8,11,57,271,273,296,298 |
| Cassie Crane | 38 |
| Christina Reid | 58 |
| Stephine Craig | 270 |

| Public Schs..Principal | Grd | Prgm | Enr/#Cls | SN |
|---|---|---|---|---|
| Chapel Hill Elem Sch<br>1069 County Road 4660, Mt Pleasant 75455<br>Misty Lake | PK-5 | T | 407<br>25 | 50% 903/572-4586<br>Fax 903/577-9176<br>f |
| Chapel Hill High Sch<br>1069 County Road 4660, Mt Pleasant 75455<br>Marcus Ysasi | 9-12 | ATV | 360 | 43% 903/572-3925<br>Fax 903/572-3850 |
| Chapel Hill Junior High Sch<br>1069 County Road 4660, Mt Pleasant 75455<br>Matthew Dunn | 6-8 | TV | 237<br>21 | 50% 903/572-3925<br>Fax 903/572-9747 |

• **Harts Bluff Ind School Dist** PID: 01055345     903/577-1146
1402 Farm Rd, Mt Pleasant 75455     Fax 903/577-8710

---

**Schools:** 1 \ **Teachers:** 42 \ **Students:** 675 \ **Special Ed Students:** 39
\ **LEP Students:** 207 \ **Ethnic:** African American 2%, Hispanic 51%,
Caucasian 47% \ **Exp:** $424 (High) \ **Poverty:** 20% \ **Title I:** $151,485 \
**Open-Close:** 08/19 - 05/26 \ **DTBP:** $357 (High)

---

| Dr Bobby Rice | 1,11,83 |
| Ray Flinn | 3* |
| Michael Thomasson | 8* |
| Carole Dickerson | 12,16,57,69,88,270,273* |
| Penney Parker | 59* |
| Sabrina Stobnicki | 79,90* |
| Josh Viggerstaff | 275 |

| Craig Craven | 2 |
| Wayne Phillips | 5,73* |
| Tracie Rose | 9* |
| Carole Dickerson | 15,296 |
| Dr Bradshaw Colton | 67 |
| Melissa Rice | 271* |

| Public Schs..Principal | Grd | Prgm | Enr/#Cls | SN |
|---|---|---|---|---|
| Harts Bluff Elem Sch<br>1402 Farm Rd, Mt Pleasant 75455<br>Tracie Rose \ **Erika Ponce De Leon** | PK-8 | AT | 675<br>32 | 66% 903/577-1146 |

• **Mt Pleasant Ind School Dist** PID: 01055369     903/575-2000
2230 N Edwards Ave, Mt Pleasant 75455     Fax 903/575-2014

---

**Schools:** 8 \ **Teachers:** 404 \ **Students:** 5,100 \ **Special Ed Students:** 619
\ **LEP Students:** 2,140 \ **College-Bound:** 62% \ **Ethnic:** Asian 1%,
African American 12%, Hispanic 71%, Caucasian 17% \ **Exp:** $377 (High)
\ **Poverty:** 29% \ **Title I:** $2,131,778 \ **Open-Close:** 08/19 - 05/20 \
**DTBP:** $158 (High) \ t

---

| Judd Marshall | 1 |
| Russell Luck | 3 |
| Ritchie Pinkard | 6 |
| Shirley Peterson | 11* |
| Eva Beles | 57* |
| Yvonne Hampton | 67 |
| Kelly Cowan | 71* |
| Dustin Cook | 79 |
| Ronnie Humphrey | 91 |

| Stacie Thompson | 2,19 |
| Laura Stewart | 4* |
| Debra Malone | 7,15,68 |
| Mike Lide | 15 |
| Marilyn Logan | 58 |
| Shelley Derrick | 69* |
| Noe Arzate | 73,76,295* |
| Gina Landrum | 81 |

| Public Schs..Principal | Grd | Prgm | Enr/#Cls | SN |
|---|---|---|---|---|
| Annie Sims Elem Sch<br>1801 E 1st St, Mt Pleasant 75455<br>Tonya Murray | K-4 | T | 526<br>30 | 77% 903/575-2062<br>Fax 903/575-2067 |
| E C Brice Elem Sch<br>311 Cedar St, Mt Pleasant 75455<br>Steven Toney | K-4 | T | 481<br>26 | 76% 903/575-2057<br>Fax 903/575-2061 |

| Public Schs..Principal | Grd | Prgm | Enr/#Cls | SN |
|---|---|---|---|---|
| Frances Corprew Elem Sch<br>909 School St, Mt Pleasant 75455<br>Amanda Jones | K-4 | T | 424<br>24 | 91% 903/575-2050<br>Fax 903/575-2052 |
| Mount Pleasant High Sch<br>2110 N Edwards Ave, Mt Pleasant 75455<br>Craig Bailey | 9-12 | TV | 368<br>104 | 71% 903/575-2020<br>Fax 903/575-2036 |
| Mt Pleasant Child Dev Center<br>1602 W Ferguson Rd, Mt Pleasant 75455<br>Jamie Cook | PK-PK | T | 478<br>25 | 97% 903/575-2092<br>Fax 903/575-2077 |
| Mt Pleasant Junior High Sch<br>2801 Old Paris Rd, Mt Pleasant 75455<br>Jeff Turner | 7-8 | T | 714<br>45 | 72% 903/575-2110<br>Fax 903/575-2117 |
| P E Wallace Middle Sch<br>504 Dunn Ave, Mt Pleasant 75455<br>Nathan Rider | 5-6 | T | 390<br>49 | 83% 903/575-2040<br>Fax 903/575-2047 |
| Vivian Fowler Elem Sch<br>502 N Otyson St, Mt Pleasant 75455<br>Cindy Davis | K-4 | T | 428<br>24 | 83% 903/575-2070<br>Fax 903/575-2075 |

## TITUS PRIVATE SCHOOLS

| Private Schs..Principal | Grd | Prgm | Enr/#Cls | SN |
|---|---|---|---|---|
| Mt Pleasant Christian Sch<br>300 S Florey Ave, Mt Pleasant 75455<br>Tony McNatt | 1-12 | | 10<br>3 | 903/577-1550 |

# TOM GREEN COUNTY

## TOM GREEN PUBLIC SCHOOLS

• **Christoval Ind School Dist** PID: 01055486     325/896-2520
20065 3rd St, Christoval 76935     Fax 325/896-7405

---

**Schools:** 2 \ **Teachers:** 45 \ **Students:** 505 \ **Special Ed Students:** 54
\ **College-Bound:** 84% \ **Ethnic:** Hispanic 22%, Native American: 1%,
Caucasian 76% \ **Exp:** $677 (High) \ **Poverty:** 9% \ **Title I:** $49,656 \
**Open-Close:** 08/28 - 05/28 \ **DTBP:** $342 (High)

---

| Dr David Walker | 1 |
| Dave Goad | 3 |
| Tracy McDonald | 5 |
| Tracy Knighton | 9,11,88* |
| Staci Jenkins | 10,69* |
| Deidre Scherz | 60* |
| Cindy Jackson | 76 |

| Sherry Wheeler | 2 |
| Isabel Salinas | 4 |
| Scott Richardson | 6* |
| John Choate | 10,60,73,288,296* |
| Jill Novak | 59* |
| Duff Hallman | 67 |
| Josh Terrill | 295* |

| Public Schs..Principal | Grd | Prgm | Enr/#Cls | SN |
|---|---|---|---|---|
| Christoval Elem Sch<br>20000 Rudd Rd, Christoval 76935<br>Tracy Knighton | PK-5 | T | 237<br>15 | 39% 325/896-2446<br>Fax 325/896-1145 |
| Christoval Jr Sr High Sch<br>20454 Ranch Rd 2084, Christoval 76935<br>John Choate | 6-12 | AV | 194<br>21 | 27% 325/896-2355<br>Fax 325/896-2671 |

| | | | | | | | | | | | |
|---|---|---|---|---|---|---|---|---|---|---|---|
| 1 | Superintendent | 8 | Curric/Instruct K-12 | 19 | Chief Financial Officer | 29 | Family/Consumer Science | 39 | Social Studies K-12 | 49 | English/Lang Arts Elem |
| 2 | Bus/Finance/Purchasing | 9 | Curric/Instruct Elem | 20 | Art K-12 | 30 | Adult Education | 40 | Social Studies Elem | 50 | English/Lang Arts Sec |
| 3 | Buildings And Grounds | 10 | Curric/Instruct Sec | 21 | Art Elem | 31 | Career/Sch-to-Work K-12 | 41 | Social Studies Sec | 51 | Reading K-12 |
| 4 | Food Service | 11 | Federal Program | 22 | Art Sec | 32 | Career/Sch-to-Work Elem | 42 | Science K-12 | 52 | Reading Elem |
| 5 | Transportation | 12 | Title I | 23 | Music K-12 | 33 | Career/Sch-to-Work Sec | 43 | Science Elem | 53 | Reading Sec |
| 6 | Athletic | 13 | Title V | 24 | Music Elem | 34 | Early Childhood Ed | 44 | Science Sec | 54 | Remedial Reading K-12 |
| 7 | Health Services | 15 | Asst Superintendent | 25 | Music Sec | 35 | Health/Phys Education | 45 | Math K-12 | 55 | Remedial Reading Elem |
| | | 16 | Instructional Media Svcs | 26 | Business Education | 36 | Guidance Services K-12 | 46 | Math Elem | 56 | Remedial Reading Sec |
| | | 17 | Chief Operations Officer | 27 | Career & Tech Ed | 37 | Guidance Services Elem | 47 | Math Sec | 57 | Bilingual/ELL |
| | | 18 | Chief Academic Officer | 28 | Technology Education | 38 | Guidance Services Sec | 48 | English/Lang Arts K-12 | 58 | Special Education K-12 |

| | | | |
|---|---|---|---|
| 59 | Special Education Elem | 69 | Academic Assessment |
| 60 | Special Education Sec | 70 | Research/Development |
| 61 | Foreign/World Lang K-12 | 71 | Public Information |
| 62 | Foreign/World Lang Elem | 72 | Summer School |
| 63 | Foreign/World Lang Sec | 73 | Instructional Tech |
| 64 | Religious Education K-12 | 74 | Inservice Training |
| 65 | Religious Education Elem | 75 | Marketing/Distributive |
| 66 | Religious Education Sec | 76 | Info Systems |
| 67 | School Board President | 77 | Psychological Assess |
| 68 | Teacher Personnel | 78 | Affirmative Action |

## Grape Creek Ind School Dist PID: 01055515
8207 US Highway 87 N, San Angelo 76901

325/658-7823

Fax 325/658-8719

**Schools:** 3 \ **Teachers:** 93 \ **Students:** 1,160 \ **Special Ed Students:** 182 \ **LEP Students:** 60 \ **College-Bound:** 37% \ **Ethnic:** African American 1%, Hispanic 47%, Caucasian 51% \ **Exp:** $517 (High) \ **Poverty:** 27% \ **Title I:** $481,111 \ **Special Education:** $15,000 \ **Open-Close:** 08/26 - 05/21 \ **DTBP:** $219 (High)

Angie Smetana ....................................1
David Augustine ..................................5
Jordan Cox ...........11,57,58,285,286,288,296*
Dianne James ....................................67
Caleb Rodriguez .................................73
Teri Deweber ....................................298

Theresa Bird ......................................2
Jajean Johnston ..................................7*
Renita Dylan .....................................38*
Kimberly Hancock ..............................69,88*
Dan LaFave ......................................297*

| Public Schs..Principal | Grd | Prgm | Enr/#Cls | SN | |
|---|---|---|---|---|---|
| Grape Creek Elem Sch<br>9633 N Grape Creek Rd, San Angelo 76901<br>Dana Felts | PK-5 | T | 284<br>45 | 63%<br>Fax | 325/655-1735<br>325/658-2623 |
| Grape Creek High Sch<br>8834 N Grape Creek Rd, San Angelo 76901<br>Trey Gardner | 9-12 | T | 300<br>25 | 53%<br>Fax | 325/653-1852<br>325/653-3568 |
| Grape Creek Middle Sch<br>9633 N Grape Creek Rd, San Angelo 76901<br>Timothy Jetton | 6-8 | T | 184<br>35 | 60%<br>Fax | 325/655-1735<br>325/657-2997 |

## San Angelo Ind School Dist PID: 01055539
1621 University Ave, San Angelo 76904

325/947-3700

Fax 325/947-3822

**Schools:** 25 \ **Teachers:** 934 \ **Students:** 14,520 \ **Special Ed Students:** 1,559 \ **LEP Students:** 683 \ **College-Bound:** 61% \ **Ethnic:** Asian 1%, African American 4%, Hispanic 61%, Caucasian 34% \ **Exp:** $421 (High) \ **Poverty:** 23% \ **Title I:** $5,737,921 \ **Special Education:** $3,167,000 \ **Open-Close:** 08/19 - 05/28 \ **DTBP:** $167 (High) \ 🇹

Dr Carl Dethloff .................................1
David Creek .......................................3
Rodney Chant .................................6,35
Dr Jana Rueter ...............................8,15
Wesley Underwood ..........................8,18
Dr Farrah Gomez ...........................15,68
Tiffany Huebner ...........................20,23,81
Christy Diego ....................................57
Lanny Layman ....................................67
Whitney Watson Wood ..........................71
Laura Howard .....................................73
Monte Althaus ....................................91*

Dr George McFarland ..........................2,15
Michelle Helms ....................................4
Melissa Schumpert ................................7
Shelly Huddleston .............................8,18
Stephanie Free ...................................11
Shelly Hullihen ...................................15
Joy Gay .........................................27,31
Dian Underwood ..................................58
Rebecca Cline ...................................69*
Charlyn Doyle ...........................73,76,84,297
Sharon Wermuth ..................................76

| Public Schs..Principal | Grd | Prgm | Enr/#Cls | SN | |
|---|---|---|---|---|---|
| Alta Loma Elem Sch<br>1700 N Garfield St, San Angelo 76901<br>Lauri Herndon | PK-5 | T | 283<br>17 | 80%<br>Fax | 325/947-3914<br>325/947-3952 |
| Austin Elem Sch<br>700 N Van Buren St, San Angelo 76901<br>Brooke Kalnbach | PK-5 | T | 462<br>45 | 62%<br>Fax | 325/659-3636<br>325/657-4089 |
| Belaire Elem Sch<br>700 Stephen St, San Angelo 76905<br>Lindsay Carr | K-5 | T | 317<br>20 | 69%<br>Fax | 325/659-3639<br>325/657-4093 |
| Bonham Elem Sch<br>4630 Southland Blvd, San Angelo 76904<br>Heidi Wierzowiecki | K-5 | | 602<br>23 | 29%<br>Fax | 325/947-3917<br>325/947-3945 |
| Bowie Elem Sch<br>3700 Forest Trl, San Angelo 76904<br>Darius Flowers | K-5 | T | 453<br>24 | 56%<br>Fax | 325/947-3921<br>325/947-3947 |

| | Grd | Prgm | Enr/#Cls | SN | |
|---|---|---|---|---|---|
| Bradford Elem Sch<br>2302 Bradford St, San Angelo 76903<br>Berta Carrasco | PK-5 | T | 387<br>20 | 89%<br>Fax | 325/659-3645<br>325/659-3692 |
| Ⓐ Carver Learning Center<br>301 W 9th St, San Angelo 76903<br>Claudia Becerra | K-12 | | 47<br>9 | 72%<br>Fax | 325/659-3648<br>325/657-4087 |
| Central Freshman Campus<br>218 N Oakes St, San Angelo 76903<br>**Mr Waters** | 9-9 | V | 765 | Fax | 325/659-3576<br>325/659-3583 |
| Central High Sch<br>655 Caddo St, San Angelo 76901<br>Bill Waters | 10-12 | GTV | 2,042<br>120 | 43%<br>Fax | 325/659-3434<br>325/659-3413 |
| Crockett Elem Sch<br>2104 Johnson Ave, San Angelo 76904<br>Clayton Hubbard | K-5 | T | 346<br>30 | 59%<br>Fax | 325/947-3925<br>325/947-3951 |
| Fannin Elem Sch<br>1702 Wilson St, San Angelo 76901<br>Dave Danner | PK-5 | T | 306<br>22 | 88%<br>Fax | 325/947-3930<br>325/947-3944 |
| Ⓜ Ft Concho Elem Sch<br>310 E Washington Dr, San Angelo 76903<br>Lori Barton | K-5 | T | 467<br>23 | 39%<br>Fax<br>🇹 | 325/659-3654<br>325/657-4083 |
| Glenmore Elem Sch<br>323 Penrose St, San Angelo 76903<br>Teri Gould | PK-5 | T | 477<br>23 | 50%<br>Fax | 325/659-3657<br>325/657-4086 |
| Glenn Middle Sch<br>2201 University Ave, San Angelo 76904<br>Michael Kalnbach | 6-8 | TV | 1,328<br>55 | 46%<br>Fax | 325/947-3841<br>325/947-3847 |
| Goliad Elem Sch<br>120 E 39th St, San Angelo 76903<br>Zachary Ramirez | K-5 | T | 515<br>27 | 70%<br>Fax | 325/659-3660<br>325/657-4097 |
| Holiman Elem Sch<br>1900 Ricks Dr, San Angelo 76905<br>Ginger Luther | K-5 | T | 381<br>20 | 53%<br>Fax | 325/659-3663<br>325/659-3696 |
| Lake View High Sch<br>900 E 43rd St, San Angelo 76903<br>**Zachary Ramirez** | 9-12 | TV | 971<br>55 | 67%<br>Fax | 325/659-3500<br>325/653-8661 |
| Lamar Elem Sch<br>3444 School House Dr, San Angelo 76904<br>Sharon Lane | K-5 | T | 573<br>32 | 41%<br>Fax | 325/947-3900<br>325/947-3901 |
| Lee Middle Sch<br>2500 Sherwood Way, San Angelo 76901<br>Amy Lemaster | 6-8 | TV | 1,130<br>53 | 54%<br>Fax | 325/947-3871<br>325/947-3890 |
| Lincoln Middle Sch<br>255 Lake View Heroes Dr, San Angelo 76903<br>Joe Gandar | 6-8 | TV | 873<br>58 | 72%<br>Fax | 325/659-3550<br>325/659-3559 |
| McGill Elem Sch<br>201 Millspaugh St, San Angelo 76901<br>Dr John Rueter | PK-5 | T | 329<br>29 | 67%<br>Fax | 325/947-3934<br>325/947-3946 |
| Pays Sch<br>1820 Knickerbocker Rd, San Angelo 76904<br>Claudia Becerra | 11-12 | AV | 62 | Fax | 325/947-3912<br>325/949-4323 |
| Reagan Elem Sch<br>1600 Volney St, San Angelo 76903<br>Brandy Tyner | PK-5 | T | 369<br>20 | 78%<br>Fax | 325/659-3666<br>325/657-4096 |
| San Jacinto Elem Sch<br>800 Spaulding St, San Angelo 76903<br>Kimberly Spurgers | K-5 | T | 317<br>26 | 88%<br>Fax<br>🇹 | 325/659-3675<br>325/657-4092 |
| Ⓜ Santa Rita Elem Sch<br>615 S Madison St, San Angelo 76901<br>Kay Scott | K-5 | T | 375<br>25 | 38%<br>Fax<br>🇹 | 325/659-3672<br>325/657-4094 |

## Veribest Ind School Dist PID: 01055826
10062 Highway 380, Veribest 76886

325/655-2851
Fax 325/655-3355

**Schools:** 1 \ **Teachers:** 23 \ **Students:** 275 \ **Special Ed Students:** 28 \ **LEP Students:** 18 \ **College-Bound:** 75% \ **Ethnic:** Asian 1%, African American 1%, Hispanic 44%, Native American: 1%, Caucasian 54% \ **Exp:** $763 (High) \ **Poverty:** 23% \ **Title I:** $78,525 \ **Open-Close:** 08/21 - 05/21 \ **DTBP:** $345 (High)

| | | | |
|---|---|---|---|
| Ryder Appleton | 1,11,288 | Denise Dusek | 2 |
| Brenda Neill | 4* | Rick Lancaster | 5 |
| Laura Eubank | 9 | Glen Jones | 10 |
| Kelly Hannah | 12,69,83,270 | Chrys Martin | 16 |
| Lee Cauley | 51* | Mark Kellermeier | 67 |
| Lahne Burns | 73,286* | | |

| Public Schs..Principal | Grd | Prgm | Enr/#Cls | SN |
|---|---|---|---|---|
| Veribest Sch | PK-12 | ATV | 275 | 36% 325/655-2851 |
| 10062 FM Highway 380, Veribest 76886 | | | 30 | Fax 325/655-0551 |
| Amber Palmer \ Laura Eubank \ Glen Jones | | | | |

## Wall Ind School Dist PID: 01055840
8065 Loop 570, Wall 76957

325/651-7790

**Schools:** 4 \ **Teachers:** 113 \ **Students:** 1,100 \ **Special Ed Students:** 81 \ **LEP Students:** 19 \ **College-Bound:** 99% \ **Ethnic:** Hispanic 20%, Caucasian 79% \ **Exp:** $418 (High) \ **Poverty:** 12% \ **Title I:** $122,772 \ **Open-Close:** 08/20 - 05/28 \ **DTBP:** $357 (High)

| | | | |
|---|---|---|---|
| Russell Dacy | 1,11 | Charlotte Weishuhn | 2 |
| Lanier Duderstadt | 3,91 | Lisa Glasscock | 4 |
| Jeremy Williams | 5,6,8,85,92 | Kim Rollwitz | 7* |
| Kelly Granzin | 9 | Dr Mildred Seimonds | 57 |
| Brandy York | 58 | Chris Wilde | 67 |
| Cheryl Marsh | 68 | Suzette McIntyre | 73,295* |

| Public Schs..Principal | Grd | Prgm | Enr/#Cls | SN |
|---|---|---|---|---|
| Ⓐ Fairview Accelerated Sch | 6-12 | | 42 | 325/651-7656 |
| 2405 Fairview School Rd, San Angelo 76904 | | | 6 | Fax 325/651-8504 |
| Bert Johnson | | | | |
| Wall Elem Sch | PK-5 | T | 462 | 16% 325/651-7790 |
| 8065 Loop 570, Wall 76957 | | | 25 | |
| Kelly Granzin | | | | |
| Wall High Sch | 9-12 | | 269 | 12% 325/651-7521 |
| 8065 Loop 570, Wall 76957 | | | 30 | Fax 325/651-9419 |
| Ryan Snowden | | | | |
| Wall Middle Sch | 6-8 | | 270 | 19% 325/651-7648 |
| 8065 Loop 570, Wall 76957 | | | 29 | Fax 325/651-9664 |
| Matt Rivers | | | | |

## Water Valley Ind School Dist PID: 01055888
18000 Wildcat Dr, Water Valley 76958

325/484-2478
Fax 325/484-3359

**Schools:** 2 \ **Teachers:** 34 \ **Students:** 300 \ **Special Ed Students:** 45 \ **LEP Students:** 5 \ **College-Bound:** 85% \ **Ethnic:** African American 2%, Hispanic 24%, Caucasian 73% \ **Exp:** $601 (High) \ **Poverty:** 29% \ **Title I:** $137,049 \ **Open-Close:** 08/17 - 05/20 \ **DTBP:** $375 (High)

| | | | |
|---|---|---|---|
| Fabian Gomez | 1,83 | Tanis McCoy | 2,11 |
| Dant Hughes | 3,5 | Cheryl Schobajsa | 4* |
| Nathan Hayes | 6 | Tracy Randolf | 7 |
| Deenna Blanton | 8,16,31,58,69,83,88,288 | Pamela Ashley | 36* |
| Dane Hoover | 57,73,297 | Perri Brown | 57* |
| Charles Holler | 67 | | |

| Public Schs..Principal | Grd | Prgm | Enr/#Cls | SN |
|---|---|---|---|---|
| Water Valley Elem Sch | PK-6 | AT | 195 | 57% 325/484-2478 |
| 15575 Adams Ave, Water Valley 76958 | | | 11 | Fax 325/484-2473 |
| Deeanna Blanton | | | | |
| Water Valley Jr Sr High Sch | 7-12 | AT | 104 | 49% 325/484-2478 |
| 17886 Wildcat Dr, Water Valley 76958 | | | 20 | Fax 325/484-2462 |
| Deeanna Blanton | | | | |

# TOM GREEN CATHOLIC SCHOOLS

## Diocese of San Angelo Ed Off PID: 01055929
804 Ford St, San Angelo 76905

325/651-7500
Fax 325/651-6688

**Schools:** 3 \ **Students:** 1,000

Listing includes only schools located in this county. See District Index for location of Diocesan Offices.

Joan Wilmes ....1

| Catholic Schs..Principal | Grd | Prgm | Enr/#Cls | SN |
|---|---|---|---|---|
| Angelo Catholic Sch | PK-8 | | 127 | 325/949-1747 |
| 2315 A and M Ave, San Angelo 76904 | | | 8 | Fax 325/942-1547 |
| Gracie Gonzalez | | | | |

# TOM GREEN PRIVATE SCHOOLS

| Private Schs..Principal | Grd | Prgm | Enr/#Cls | SN |
|---|---|---|---|---|
| Cornerstone Christian Sch | PK-12 | | 200 | 325/655-3439 |
| 1502 N Jefferson St, San Angelo 76901 | | | 16 | Fax 325/658-8998 |
| Cynthia Robinson \ Todd Nichols | | | | |
| San Angelo Christian Academy | K-12 | | 87 | 325/651-8363 |
| 518 Country Club Rd, San Angelo 76904 | | | 8 | Fax 325/651-1682 |
| Betty Shook | | | | |
| Trinity Lutheran Sch | PK-8 | | 72 | 325/947-1275 |
| 3516 Lutheran Way, San Angelo 76904 | | | 9 | Fax 325/947-1377 |
| Ron Fritsche | | | | |

# TOM GREEN REGIONAL CENTERS

## Region 15 Ed Service Center PID: 01055814
612 S Irene St, San Angelo 76903

325/658-6571
Fax 325/655-4823

| | | | |
|---|---|---|---|
| Casey Callahan | 1,11 | Charity Vasquez | 2 |
| David Bedford | 8 | Laura Strube | 15 |
| Hector Pineda | 34 | Jam Page | 58 |
| Randon Lance | 295 | | |

| | | | | | | | |
|---|---|---|---|---|---|---|---|
| 1 Superintendent | 8 Curric/Instruct K-12 | 19 Chief Financial Officer | 29 Family/Consumer Science | 39 Social Studies K-12 | 49 English/Lang Arts Elem | 59 Special Education Elem | 69 Academic Assessment |
| 2 Bus/Finance/Purchasing | 9 Curric/Instruct Elem | 20 Art K-12 | 30 Adult Education | 40 Social Studies Elem | 50 English/Lang Arts Sec | 60 Special Education Sec | 70 Research/Development |
| 3 Buildings And Grounds | 10 Curric/Instruct Sec | 21 Art Elem | 31 Career/Sch-to-Work K-12 | 41 Social Studies Sec | 51 Reading K-12 | 61 Foreign/World Lang K-12 | 71 Public Information |
| 4 Food Service | 11 Federal Program | 22 Art Sec | 32 Career/Sch-to-Work Elem | 42 Science K-12 | 52 Reading Elem | 62 Foreign/World Lang Elem | 72 Summer School |
| 5 Transportation | 12 Title I | 23 Music K-12 | 33 Career/Sch-to-Work Sec | 43 Science Elem | 53 Reading Sec | 63 Foreign/World Lang Sec | 73 Instructional Tech |
| 6 Athletic | 13 Title V | 24 Music Elem | 34 Early Childhood Ed | 44 Science Sec | 54 Remedial Reading K-12 | 64 Religious Education K-12 | 74 Inservice Training |
| 7 Health Services | 15 Asst Superintendent | 25 Music Sec | 35 Health/Phys Education | 45 Math K-12 | 55 Remedial Reading Elem | 65 Religious Education Elem | 75 Marketing/Distributive |
| | 16 Instructional Media Svcs | 26 Business Education | 36 Guidance Services K-12 | 46 Math Elem | 56 Remedial Reading Sec | 66 Religious Education Sec | 76 Info Systems |
| | 17 Chief Operations Officer | 27 Career & Tech Ed | 37 Guidance Services Elem | 47 Math Sec | 57 Bilingual/ELL | 67 School Board President | 77 Psychological Assess |
| | 18 Chief Academic Officer | 28 Technology Education | 38 Guidance Services Sec | 48 English/Lang Arts K-12 | 58 Special Education K-12 | 68 Teacher Personnel | 78 Affirmative Action |

## TRAVIS COUNTY

## TRAVIS PUBLIC SCHOOLS

● **Austin Ind School Dist** PID: 01055993     512/414-1700
4000 S Ih 35 Frontage Rd, Austin 78704     Fax 512/414-1486

**Schools:** 117 \ **Teachers:** 5,540 \ **Students:** 80,950 \
**Special Ed Students:** 9,661 \ **LEP Students:** 19,112 \ **College-Bound:** 89%
\ **Ethnic:** Asian 5%, African American 7%, Hispanic 57%, Caucasian
31% \ **Exp:** $271 (Med) \ **Poverty:** 16% \ **Title I:** $27,485,731 \
**Special Education:** $14,290,000 \ **Bilingual Education:** $190,000 \
**Open-Close:** 08/18 - 05/26 \ **DTBP:** $192 (High) \ 🇫 🇹

<table>
<tr><td>Dr Stephanie Elizalde .......... 1</td><td>Nicole Conley-Johnson .......... 2</td></tr>
<tr><td>Louis Zachary .......... 3</td><td>Matias Segura .......... 3</td></tr>
<tr><td>Anneliese Tanner .......... 4</td><td>Kris Hafezizadeh .......... 5</td></tr>
<tr><td>Leal Anderson .......... 6</td><td>Tracy Spinner .......... 7</td></tr>
<tr><td>Dr Lisa Goodnow .......... 8,288</td><td>Dr Mary Thomas .......... 11,296,298,752</td></tr>
<tr><td>Jacob Reach .......... 15,751</td><td>Elizabeth Polk .......... 16</td></tr>
<tr><td>Alan Lambert .......... 20,23</td><td>Tammy Caesar .......... 31</td></tr>
<tr><td>Ami Cortez .......... 34</td><td>Michele Rusnak .......... 35</td></tr>
<tr><td>Tracilynn Wright .......... 36,88</td><td>Akweta Hickman .......... 58</td></tr>
<tr><td>Erin Barbier .......... 61</td><td>Geronimo Rodriguez .......... 67</td></tr>
<tr><td>Dr Fernando Medina .......... 68</td><td>Melissa Sabatino .......... 71</td></tr>
<tr><td>Reyne Telles .......... 71</td><td>Kevin Schwartz .......... 73,76,295</td></tr>
<tr><td>Dr Andri Lyons .......... 79</td><td>Rhonda Boyer .......... 81</td></tr>
<tr><td>Ashley Gonzalez .......... 91</td><td>Dennis McFall .......... 274</td></tr>
<tr><td>Debra Ready .......... 294</td><td>Tim Carrington .......... 295</td></tr>
<tr><td>Camille Lochet .......... 297</td><td></td></tr>
</table>

● **Austin ISD Elem School Area** PID: 04032304     512/414-0038
1111 W 6th St, Austin 78703     Fax 512/414-9977

Gilbert Hicks .......... 15

| Public Schs..Principal | Grd | Prgm | Enr/#Cls | SN |
|---|---|---|---|---|
| Allison Elem Sch<br>515 Vargas Rd, Austin 78741<br>**Lupe Molina** | PK-5 | T | 446<br>30 | 92% 512/414-2004<br>Fax 512/414-1070 |
| Andrews Elem Sch<br>6801 Northeast Dr, Austin 78723<br>Diana Vallejo | PK-5 | T | 310<br>40 | 89% 512/414-1770<br>Fax 512/926-6635<br>🇫🇹 |
| Barrington Elem Sch<br>400 Cooper Dr, Austin 78753<br>Gilma Sanchez | PK-5 | T | 500 | 96% 512/414-2008<br>Fax 512/836-4077 |
| Barton Hills Elem Sch<br>2108 Barton Hills Dr, Austin 78704<br>Kathryn Achtermann | PK-6 | | 394<br>40 | 8% 512/414-2013<br>Fax 512/841-3849<br>🇫🇹 |
| Bear Creek Elem Sch<br>12801 Escarpment Blvd, Austin 78739<br>**David Crissey** | PK-5 | | 522 | 512/414-0040<br>Fax 512/414-0050 |
| Becker Elem Sch<br>906 W Milton St, Austin 78704<br>**Travis Barrett** | PK-5 | T | 445<br>25 | 26% 512/414-2019<br>Fax 512/442-1759 |
| Blackshear Elem Sch<br>1712 E 11th St, Austin 78702<br>Rick Garner | PK-5 | T | 395<br>17 | 65% 512/414-2021<br>Fax 512/477-7640 |
| Blanton Elem Sch<br>5408 Westminster Dr, Austin 78723<br>Dora Molina | PK-6 | T | 516<br>40 | 61% 512/414-2026<br>Fax 512/926-8553 |
| Blazier Elem Sch<br>8601 Vertex Blvd, Austin 78744<br>Ana Pena-Wilk | PK-5 | T | 754<br>45 | 71% 512/841-8800<br>Fax 512/841-8801 |
| Boone Elem Sch<br>8101 Croftwood Dr, Austin 78749<br>Alan Stevens | PK-5 | T | 517<br>44 | 44% 512/414-2537<br>Fax 512/280-3307 |
| Brentwood Elem Sch<br>6700 Arroyo Seco, Austin 78757<br>Amber LaRoche | PK-5 | | 656<br>17 | 19% 512/414-2039<br>Fax 512/453-8928 |
| Brown Elem Sch<br>7801 Guadalupe St, Austin 78752<br>Veronica Sharp | PK-5 | | 408<br>30 | 512/414-2047<br>Fax 512/414-4293 |
| Bryker Woods Elem Sch<br>3309 Kerbey Ln, Austin 78703<br>Kristina Muehling | PK-6 | | 407<br>21 | 11% 512/414-2054<br>Fax 512/459-9047 |
| Campbell Elem Sch<br>2613 Rogers Ave, Austin 78722<br>Keith Moore | PK-5 | T | 167<br>35 | 87% 512/414-2056<br>Fax 512/841-1246 |
| Casey Elem Sch<br>9400 Texas Oaks Dr, Austin 78748<br>Lina Villarreal | PK-5 | T | 532<br>42 | 67% 512/841-6900<br>Fax 512/841-6925 |
| Casis Elem Sch<br>2710 Exposition Blvd, Austin 78703<br>Samuel Tinnon | PK-5 | | 709<br>40 | 5% 512/414-2062<br>Fax 512/414-7168 |
| Clayton Elem Sch<br>7525 La Crosse Ave, Austin 78739<br>Amy Gonzales | PK-5 | | 695<br>40 | 2% 512/841-9200<br>Fax 512/841-9201 |
| Cook Elem Sch<br>1511 Cripple Creek Dr, Austin 78758<br>Priscilla Emamian | PK-5 | T | 436<br>46 | 91% 512/414-2510<br>Fax 512/837-5983 |
| Cowan Elem Sch<br>2817 Kentish Dr, Austin 78748<br>Travis Brunner | PK-5 | | 748<br>29 | 31% 512/841-2700<br>Fax 512/841-2755 |
| Cunningham Elem Sch<br>2200 Berkeley Ave, Austin 78745<br>Heather Petruzzini | PK-5 | T | 352 | 66% 512/414-2067<br>Fax 512/441-6006<br>🇫🇹 |
| Davis Elem Sch<br>5214 Duval Rd, Austin 78727<br>Jennifer Daniels | PK-5 | | 745<br>35 | 24% 512/414-2580<br>Fax 512/346-7384 |
| Dawson Elem Sch<br>3001 S 1st St, Austin 78704<br>Tania Jedele | PK-5 | T | 317<br>23 | 75% 512/414-2070<br>Fax 512/442-5765 |
| Doss Elem Sch<br>7005 Northledge Dr, Austin 78731<br>Nathan Steenport | PK-5 | | 789<br>36 | 18% 512/414-2365<br>Fax 512/345-0013 |
| Frank & Sue McBee Elem Sch<br>1001 W Braker Ln, Austin 78758<br>Yvette Celorio-Reyes | PK-5 | T | 402<br>35 | 95% 512/841-2500<br>Fax 512/841-2333 |
| Galindo Elem Sch<br>3800 S 2nd St, Austin 78704<br>Natascha Barreto-Romero | PK-5 | T | 494<br>54 | 88% 512/414-1756<br>Fax 512/414-0448 |
| Govalle Elem Sch<br>3601 Govalle Ave, Austin 78702<br>Paula Reyes | PK-5 | T | 433<br>30 | 91% 512/414-2078<br>Fax 512/414-3760 |
| Graham Elem Sch<br>11211 Tom Adams Dr, Austin 78753<br>Ercilia Paredes | PK-5 | T | 436<br>55 | 81% 512/414-2395<br>Fax 512/835-4562<br>🇫🇹 |
| Guerrero Thompson Elem Sch<br>102 E Rundberg Ln, Austin 78753<br>Briana Garcia | PK-5 | T | 557 | 97% 512/414-8400<br>Fax 512/414-8401 |
| Gullett Elem Sch<br>6310 Treadwell Blvd, Austin 78757<br>Tisha Brown | PK-5 | | 606<br>25 | 8% 512/414-2082<br>Fax 512/451-2036 |
| Harris Elem Sch<br>1711 Wheless Ln, Austin 78723<br>Ana Maria Dwiggins | PK-5 | T | 461<br>44 | 96% 512/414-2085<br>Fax 512/929-4640 |

| School | Grades | | Enroll | % | Phone |
|--------|--------|---|--------|---|-------|
| Hart Elem Sch<br>8301 Furness Dr, Austin 78753<br>Sonia Tosh | PK-5 | T | 565<br>37 | 95% | 512/841-2100<br>Fax 512/841-2190 |
| Highland Park Elem Sch<br>4900 Fairview Dr, Austin 78731<br>Katie Pena | K-5 | | 651<br>26 | 7% | 512/414-2090<br>Fax 512/414-2626 |
| Hill Elem Sch<br>8601 Tallwood Dr, Austin 78759<br>Jack Drummond | PK-5 | | 1,003<br>35 | 10% | 512/414-2369<br>Fax 512/841-8105 |
| Houston Elem Sch<br>5409 Ponciana Dr, Austin 78744<br>Alberto Alonso | PK-5 | T | 519 | 94% | 512/414-2517<br>Fax 512/448-4869 |
| Jordan Elem Sch<br>6711 Johnny Morris Rd, Austin 78724<br>Adrienne Williams | PK-5 | T | 536<br>40 | 95% | 512/414-2578<br>Fax 512/926-8299 |
| Joslin Elem Sch<br>4500 Manchaca Rd, Austin 78745<br>Chaolin Chang | PK-5 | T | 236 | 63% | 512/414-2094<br>Fax 512/841-3483 |
| Kiker Elem Sch<br>5913 La Crosse Ave, Austin 78739<br>David Crissey | PK-5 | | 1,094 | 4% | 512/414-2584<br>Fax 512/288-5779 |
| Kocurek Elem Sch<br>9800 Curlew Dr, Austin 78748<br>Heather Parmelee | PK-5 | T | 491<br>33 | 66% | 512/414-2547<br>Fax 512/282-7824 |
| Langford Elem Sch<br>2206 Blue Meadow Dr, Austin 78744<br>Dounna Poth | PK-5 | T | 544<br>65 | 94% | 512/414-1765<br>Fax 512/414-5930 |
| Linder Elem Sch<br>2800 Metcalfe Rd, Austin 78741<br>Melissa Rodriguez | 1-5 | T | 383<br>41 | 89% | 512/414-2398<br>Fax 512/447-3222 |
| Lucy Read Pre-K Sch<br>2608 Richcreek Rd, Austin 78757<br>Ami Cortes | PK-PK | | 304 | | 512/419-9400<br>Fax 512/414-9401 |
| Maplewood Elem Sch<br>3808 Maplewood Ave, Austin 78722<br>Vickie Jacobson | PK-6 | G | 481<br>16 | 34% | 512/414-4402<br>Fax 512/472-8559 |
| Mathews Elem Sch<br>906 W Lynn St, Austin 78703<br>Grace Brewster | PK-6 | | 417<br>24 | 30% | 512/414-4406<br>Fax 512/414-7157 |
| Menchaca Elem Sch<br>1218 W FM 1626, Manchaca 78652<br>Eliza Loyola | PK-5 | | 655<br>38 | | 512/414-2333<br>Fax 512/414-5340 |
| Mills Elem Sch<br>6201 Davis Ln, Austin 78749<br>Lalla Beachum | PK-5 | | 789<br>50 | 7% | 512/841-2400<br>Fax 512/841-2490 |
| Norman-Sims Elem Sch<br>1203 Springdale Rd, Austin 78721<br>Wendy Mills | PK-5 | T | 300<br>28 | 95% | 512/414-2347<br>Fax 512/926-6321 |
| Oak Hill Elem Sch<br>6101 Patton Ranch Rd, Austin 78735<br>Lori Komassa | PK-5 | T | 820<br>40 | 43% | 512/414-2336<br>Fax 512/892-2279 |
| Oak Springs Elem Sch<br>3601 Webberville Rd, Austin 78702<br>**Cynthia Jackson** | PK-5 | T | 225<br>20 | 99% | 512/414-4413<br>Fax 512/472-5005 |
| Odom Elem Sch<br>1010 Turtle Creek Blvd, Austin 78745<br>Sondra McWilliams | PK-5 | T | 378<br>38 | 88% | 512/414-2388<br>Fax 512/443-6170 |
| Ortega Elem Sch<br>1135 Garland Ave, Austin 78721<br>Jen Stephens | PK-5 | T | 212<br>18 | 90% | 512/414-4417<br>Fax 512/929-7906 |
| Overton Elem Sch<br>7201 Colony Loop Dr, Austin 78724<br>Courtney Colvin | PK-5 | T | 477 | 97% | 512/841-9300<br>Fax 512/841-9316 |
| Padron Elem Sch<br>2011 W Rundberg Ln, Austin 78758<br>Rafael Soriano | PK-5 | T | 718 | 96% | 512/841-9600<br>Fax 512/719-3135 |
| Palm Elem Sch<br>7601 Dixie Dr, Austin 78744<br>Rhoda Coleman | PK-5 | T | 400<br>35 | 91% | 512/414-2545<br>Fax 512/280-2769 |
| Patton Elem Sch<br>6001 Westcreek Dr, Austin 78749<br>Amanda Brantley | PK-5 | | 882<br>40 | 24% | 512/414-1780<br>Fax 512/892-6541 |
| Pecan Springs Elem Sch<br>3100 Rogge Ln, Austin 78723<br>Andrea Williams | PK-5 | T | 342<br>47 | 95% | 512/414-4445<br>Fax 512/414-4029 |
| Perez Elem Sch<br>7500 S Pleasant Valley Rd, Austin 78744<br>Kara Santibanez | PK-5 | T | 525 | 89% | 512/841-9100<br>Fax 512/841-9101 |
| Pickle Elem Sch<br>1101 Wheatley Ave, Austin 78752<br>**Rosa Waters** | PK-5 | T | 459<br>34 | 97% | 512/841-8400<br>Fax 512/841-8444 |
| Pillow Elem Sch<br>3025 Crosscreek Dr, Austin 78757<br>Yvette Cardenas | PK-5 | T | 460<br>35 | 77% | 512/414-2350<br>Fax 512/467-2513 |
| Pleasant Hill Elem Sch<br>6405 Circle S Rd, Austin 78745<br>Kristi Cisneros | PK-5 | T | 438<br>46 | 91% | 512/414-4453<br>Fax 512/442-4741 |
| Reilly Elem Sch<br>405 Denson Dr, Austin 78752<br>Corrine Saenz | PK-5 | T | 193<br>22 | 63% | 512/414-4464<br>Fax 512/453-1193 |
| Ridgetop Elem Sch<br>5005 Caswell Ave, Austin 78751<br>Kara Schultz | PK-5 | | 338<br>14 | 25% | 512/414-4469<br>Fax 512/459-9187 |
| Rodriguez Elem Sch<br>4400 Franklin Park Dr, Austin 78744<br>Monica Mills | PK-5 | T | 444<br>53 | 98% | 512/841-7200<br>Fax 512/841-7205 |
| Rosedale Sch<br>2117 W 49th St, Austin 78756<br>Elizabeth Dickey | Spec | | 123<br>13 | 35% | 512/414-3617<br>Fax 512/458-6754 |
| Ross Baldwin Elem Sch<br>12200 Meridian Park Blvd, Austin 78739<br>Jennifer Murray | PK-5 | | 743 | 13% | 512/841-8900<br>Fax 512/841-8901 |
| Russell Lee Elem Sch<br>3308 Hampton Rd, Austin 78705<br>John Hewlett | PK-6 | | 398<br>20 | 18% | 512/414-2098<br>Fax 512/414-0940 |
| Sanchez Elem Sch<br>73 San Marcos St, Austin 78702<br>Azucena Garcia | PK-5 | T | 500<br>25 | 92% | 512/414-4423<br>Fax 512/472-9493 |
| St Elmo Elem Sch<br>600 W Saint Elmo Rd, Austin 78745<br>**Ben McCormack** | PK-5 | T | 299<br>30 | 86% | 512/414-4477<br>Fax 512/442-6871 |
| Summitt Elem Sch<br>12207 Brigadoon Ln, Austin 78727<br>Kelly Friede | PK-5 | | 763<br>33 | 32% | 512/414-4484<br>Fax 512/832-1458 |
| Sunset Valley Elem Sch<br>3000 Jones Rd, Austin 78745<br>Marizza Marquez | PK-5 | T | 502<br>32 | 47% | 512/414-2392<br>Fax 512/892-7206 |
| Timothy Baranoff Elem Sch<br>12009 Buckingham Gate Rd, Austin 78748<br>Beth Cantu | PK-5 | | 840<br>41 | 13% | 512/841-7100<br>Fax 512/841-7104 |
| Travis Heights Elem Sch<br>2010 Alameda Dr, Austin 78704<br>Michelle Navarro | PK-5 | T | 446<br>40 | 66% | 512/414-4495<br>Fax 512/442-9537 |
| Uphaus Early Childhood Center<br>5200 Freidrich Ln, Austin 78744<br>Claudia Santamaria | PK-K | | 347 | 92% | 512/414-5520<br>Fax 512/326-1031 |
| Walnut Creek Elem Sch<br>401 W Braker Ln, Austin 78753<br>Dinorah Bores | PK-5 | T | 568<br>51 | 95% | 512/414-4499<br>Fax 512/837-6789 |
| Widen Elem Sch<br>5605 Nuckols Crossing Rd, Austin 78744<br>Jennifer Pace | PK-5 | T | 447<br>40 | 96% | 512/414-2556<br>Fax 512/441-8971 |

---

| | | | | | | | | | | | | |
|---|---|---|---|---|---|---|---|---|---|---|---|---|
| 1 | Superintendent | 8 | Curric/Instruct K-12 | 19 | Chief Financial Officer | 29 | Family/Consumer Science | 39 | Social Studies K-12 | 49 | English/Lang Arts Elem | 59 | Special Education Elem | 69 | Academic Assessment |
| 2 | Bus/Finance/Purchasing | 9 | Curric/Instruct Elem | 20 | Art K-12 | 30 | Adult Education | 40 | Social Studies Elem | 50 | English/Lang Arts Sec | 60 | Special Education Sec | 70 | Research/Development |
| 3 | Buildings And Grounds | 10 | Curric/Instruct Sec | 21 | Art Elem | 31 | Career/Sch-to-Work K-12 | 41 | Social Studies Sec | 51 | Reading K-12 | 61 | Foreign/World Lang K-12 | 71 | Public Information |
| 4 | Food Service | 11 | Federal Program | 22 | Art Sec | 32 | Career/Sch-to-Work Elem | 42 | Science K-12 | 52 | Reading Elem | 62 | Foreign/World Lang Elem | 72 | Summer School |
| 5 | Transportation | 12 | Title I | 23 | Music K-12 | 33 | Career/Sch-to-Work Sec | 43 | Science Elem | 53 | Reading Sec | 63 | Foreign/World Lang Sec | 73 | Instructional Tech |
| 6 | Athletic | 13 | Title V | 24 | Music Elem | 34 | Early Childhood Ed | 44 | Science Sec | 54 | Remedial Reading K-12 | 64 | Religious Education K-12 | 74 | Inservice Training |
| 7 | Health Services | 14 | Asst Superintendent | 25 | Music Sec | 35 | Health/Phys Education | 45 | Math K-12 | 55 | Remedial Reading Elem | 65 | Religious Education Elem | 75 | Marketing/Distributive |
| | | 15 | Asst Superintendent | 26 | Business Education | 36 | Guidance Services K-12 | 46 | Math Elem | 56 | Remedial Reading Sec | 66 | Religious Education Sec | 76 | Info Systems |
| | | 16 | Instructional Media Svcs | 27 | Career & Tech Ed | 37 | Guidance Services Elem | 47 | Math Sec | 57 | Bilingual/ELL | 67 | School Board President | 77 | Psychological Assess |
| | | 17 | Chief Operations Officer | 28 | Technology Education | 38 | Guidance Services Sec | 48 | English/Lang Arts K-12 | 58 | Special Education K-12 | 68 | Teacher Personnel | 78 | Affirmative Action |
| | | 18 | Chief Academic Officer | | | | | | | | | | | | |

| Public Schs..Principal | Grd | Prgm | Enr/#Cls | SN | |
|---|---|---|---|---|---|
| Williams Elem Sch<br>500 Mairo St, Austin 78748<br>Natalie Villanueva | PK-5 | T | 411 | 74% | 512/414-2525<br>Fax 512/292-3041 |
| Winn Elem Sch<br>3500 Susquehanna Ln, Austin 78723<br>Anayansi Blessum | PK-5 | T | 220<br>40 | 84% | 512/414-2390<br>Fax 512/926-9211 |
| Wooldridge Elem Sch<br>1412 Norseman Ter, Austin 78758<br>Sheri Mull | PK-5 | T | 473<br>44 | 95% | 512/414-2353<br>Fax 512/339-6583<br>f t |
| Wooten Elem Sch<br>1406 Dale Dr, Austin 78757<br>Angelo San Segundo | PK-5 | T | 402<br>45 | 96% | 512/414-2315<br>Fax 512/459-9227 |
| Zavala Elem Sch<br>310 Robert T Martinez Jr St, Austin 78702<br>Jose Mejia | PK-5 | T | 266<br>30 | 97% | 512/414-2318<br>Fax 512/477-2361 |
| Zilker Elem Sch<br>1900 Bluebonnet Ln, Austin 78704<br>Alicia Hill | PK-5 | | 499<br>30 | 18% | 512/414-2327<br>Fax 512/442-3992 |

- **Austin ISD High School Area** PID: 04032328    512/414-1942
  1111 W 6th St, Austin 78703    Fax 512/414-1782

Sheila Henry .......................... 15

| Public Schs..Principal | Grd | Prgm | Enr/#Cls | SN | |
|---|---|---|---|---|---|
| A N McCallum High Sch<br>5600 Sunshine Dr, Austin 78756<br>Brandi Hosack | 9-12 | V | 1,769 | 21% | 512/414-2519<br>Fax 512/453-2599 |
| Akins Early College High Sch<br>10701 S 1st St, Austin 78748<br>Kristina Salazar | 9-12 | T | 2,802<br>120 | 62% | 512/841-9900<br>Fax 512/841-9903 |
| Ⓐ Alternative Learning Center<br>4900 Gonzales St, Austin 78702<br>Chris Jones | 6-12 | | 55<br>9 | 73% | 512/414-2554<br>Fax 512/476-2809 |
| Anderson High Sch<br>8403 Mesa Dr, Austin 78759<br>Sammi Harrison | 9-12 | AV | 2,226 | 25% | 512/414-2538<br>Fax 512/414-7961 |
| Austin High Sch<br>1715 W Cesar Chavez St, Austin 78703<br>Amy Taylor | 9-12 | AV | 2,328 | 25% | 512/414-2505<br>Fax 512/414-7373 |
| Clifton Career Dev Sch<br>1519 Coronado Hills Dr, Austin 78752<br>David Dishner | Voc | | 200 | | 512/414-3614<br>Fax 512/323-2646 |
| Crockett High Sch<br>5601 Manchaca Rd, Austin 78745<br>Kori Crawford | 9-12 | ATV | 1,464<br>100 | 67% | 512/414-2532<br>Fax 512/841-7740 |
| Eastside Memorial High Sch<br>1012 Arthur Stiles Rd, Austin 78721<br>Miguel Garcia | 9-12 | ATV | 396<br>80 | 90% | 512/414-5810<br>Fax 512/841-5935 |
| Garza Independence High Sch<br>1600 Chicon St, Austin 78702<br>Dr Linda Webb | 11-12 | GV | 162<br>10 | 31% | 512/414-8600<br>Fax 512/414-8610 |
| Ⓐ Graduation Prep Acad-Navarro<br>Ⓒ 1201 Payton Gin Rd, Austin 78758<br>Kevin Owens | 9-12 | | 84 | 69% | 512/414-2896<br>Fax 512/832-1203 |
| Ⓐ Graduation Prep Academy-Travis<br>Ⓒ 1211 E Oltorf St, Austin 78704<br>Eliseo Reyna | 9-12 | | 44 | 87% | 512/414-6635<br>Fax 512/707-0050 |
| International High Sch<br>1012 Arthur Stiles Rd, Austin 78721<br>Leticia Vega | 9-10 | | 203 | 96% | 512/414-6817<br>Fax 512/841-5621 |
| James Bowie High Sch<br>4103 W Slaughter Ln, Austin 78749<br>Mark Robinson | 9-12 | AV | 2,924 | 12% | 512/414-5247<br>Fax 512/292-0532 |
| Ⓜ Liberal Arts & Science Academy<br>7309 Lazy Creek Dr, Austin 78724<br>Stacia Crescenzi | 9-12 | | 1,239 | 10% | 512/414-5272<br>Fax 512/414-6050 |

| Public Schs..Principal | Grd | Prgm | Enr/#Cls | SN | |
|---|---|---|---|---|---|
| Lyndon B Johnson High Sch<br>7309 Lazy Creek Dr, Austin 78724<br>**Jon Bailey** | 9-12 | ATV | 842 | 80% | 512/414-2543<br>Fax 512/414-7022 |
| Navarro Early College High Sch<br>1201 Payton Gin Rd, Austin 78758<br>Steven Covin | 9-12 | TV | 1,549 | 85% | 512/414-2514<br>Fax 512/832-1203 |
| Northeast Early Clg High Sch<br>7104 Berkman Dr, Austin 78752<br>Alisia Longoria | 9-12 | ATV | 1,122 | 88% | 512/414-2523<br>Fax 512/452-7089 |
| Richards Young Women Leaders<br>2206 Prather Ln, Austin 78704<br>Kristina Waugh | 6-12 | | 856 | 51% | 512/414-3236<br>Fax 512/441-5208 |
| Travis Early College High Sch<br>1211 E Oltorf St, Austin 78704<br>Christina Hantgin | 9-12 | ATV | 1,249 | 79% | 512/414-2527<br>Fax 512/707-0050 |

- **Austin ISD Middle School Area** PID: 12033332    512/414-4481
  1111 W 6th St, Austin 78703    Fax 512/414-9977

Raul Moreno .......................... 15

| Public Schs..Principal | Grd | Prgm | Enr/#Cls | SN | |
|---|---|---|---|---|---|
| Bailey Middle Sch<br>4020 Lost Oasis Holw, Austin 78739<br>John Rocha | 6-8 | V | 1,003<br>75 | 33% | 512/414-4990<br>Fax 512/414-5434 |
| Bedichek Middle Sch<br>6800 Bill Hughes Rd, Austin 78745<br>Michael Herbin | 6-8 | GTV | 835<br>60 | 84% | 512/414-3265<br>Fax 512/414-3561 |
| Burnet Middle Sch<br>8401 Hathaway Dr, Austin 78757<br>Marvelia De La Rosa | 6-8 | TV | 924<br>76 | 92% | 512/414-3225<br>Fax 512/452-0695 |
| Covington Middle Sch<br>3700 Convict Hill Rd, Austin 78749<br>Tai Choice | 6-8 | TV | 696<br>60 | 60% | 512/414-3276<br>Fax 512/892-4547 |
| Dobie Middle Sch<br>1200 E Rundberg Ln, Austin 78753<br>Jesse De La Huerta | 6-8 | TV | 555 | 94% | 512/414-3270<br>Fax 512/836-8411<br>f t |
| Garcia Young Men's Leadership<br>7414 Johnny Morris Rd, Austin 78724<br>**Jose Mejia** | 6-8 | T | 411 | 95% | 512/841-9400<br>Fax 512/841-9401 |
| Gorzycki Middle Sch<br>7412 W Slaughter Ln, Austin 78749<br>Cathryn Mitchell | 6-8 | | 1,280 | 6% | 512/841-8600<br>Fax 512/841-8601<br>f t |
| Kealing Middle Sch<br>1607 Pennsylvania Ave, Austin 78702<br>Kenisha Coburn | 6-8 | TV | 1,230<br>30 | 34% | 512/414-3214<br>Fax 512/478-9133 |
| Lamar Middle Sch<br>6201 Wynona Ave, Austin 78757<br>Mayra Mondik | 6-8 | V | 1,193<br>60 | 22% | 512/414-3217<br>Fax 512/467-6862 |
| Ⓜ Lively Middle Sch<br>201 E Mary St, Austin 78704<br>Stacie Holiday | 6-8 | TV | 1,077<br>70 | 62% | 512/414-3207<br>Fax 512/441-3129 |
| Martin Middle Sch<br>1601 Haskell St, Austin 78702<br>Monica Conness | 6-8 | TV | 511<br>55 | 94% | 512/414-3243<br>Fax 512/320-0125 |
| Means Young Womens Ldrshp Acad<br>6401 N Hampton Dr, Austin 78723<br>Christina Almaraz | 6-8 | V | 370 | | 512/414-3234<br>Fax 512/926-6146 |
| Mendez Middle Sch<br>5106 Village Square Dr, Austin 78744<br>Joanna Rowley | 6-8 | GTV | 606 | 91% | 512/414-3284<br>Fax 512/442-5738 |
| Murchison Middle Sch<br>3700 N Hills Dr, Austin 78731<br>Beth Newton | 6-8 | | 1,408 | 23% | 512/414-3254<br>Fax 512/414-4570 |
| O Henry Middle Sch<br>2610 W 10th St, Austin 78703<br>Margaret Malott | 6-8 | V | 827<br>980 | 29% | 512/414-3229<br>Fax 512/477-7428 |

| | | | | | |
|---|---|---|---|---|---|
| Paredes Middle Sch<br>10100 S Mary Moore Searight Dr, Austin 78748<br>Vicente Salazar | 6-8 | T | 873 | 79% | 512/841-6800<br>Fax 512/841-7036 |
| Small Middle Sch<br>4801 Monterey Oaks Blvd, Austin 78749<br>Kenton Nelson | 6-8 | V | 1,277 | 27% | 512/841-6700<br>Fax 512/841-6703 |
| Webb Middle Sch<br>601 E Saint Johns Ave, Austin 78752<br>Raul Sanchez | 6-8 | TV | 681 | 96% | 512/414-3258<br>Fax 512/414-4194 |

● **Del Valle Ind School Dist** PID: 01056789  512/386-3010
5301 Ross Rd Ste 103, Del Valle 78617  Fax 512/386-3015

> **Schools:** 15 \ **Teachers:** 812 \ **Students:** 12,100 \
> **Special Ed Students:** 1,455 \ **LEP Students:** 4,153 \ **Ethnic:** Asian 1%,
> African American 9%, Hispanic 85%, Caucasian 5% \ **Exp:** $470 (High) \
> **Poverty:** 22% \ **Title I:** $4,013,162 \ **Special Education:** $2,617,000 \
> **Open-Close:** 08/24 - 06/03 \ **DTBP:** $143 (High) \ 🅣

| | | | |
|---|---|---|---|
| Annette Villerot | ...1 | David Edgas | 2,19 |
| David Edgar | 2,15 | Janice Patterson | 2 |
| Steven Alves | 3,91 | Karen Kovach | 4 |
| Humberto Araiza | 5 | Tawni Angel | 6 |
| Ray Prentice | 11 | Juan Orozco | 16 |
| Scott Wille | 34 | Leticia Hallmark | 39 |
| Rebecca Miller | 42 | Sonja Howard | 48 |
| Gaylen Clevenger | 58 | Jonathan Harris | 58,79 |
| Rebecca Birch | 67 | Todd Gratehouse | 73,76,84,98,295 |
| Gabril Munoz | 79 | Rocky Zepeda | 88 |
| Robert Garcia | 294 | Jena Gonzales | 298 |

| Public Schs..Principal | Grd | Prgm | Enr/#Cls | SN | |
|---|---|---|---|---|---|
| Baty Elem Sch<br>2101 Faro Dr, Austin 78741<br>Laura Gonzalez | PK-5 | T | 441 | 97% | 512/386-3450<br>Fax 512/386-3455 |
| Creedmoor Elem Sch<br>5604 FM 1327, Creedmoor 78610<br>Tj Moreno | PK-5 | T | 516 | 91% | 512/386-3950<br>Fax 512/386-3955 |
| Dailey Middle Sch<br>14000 Westall, Austin 78725<br>Mario Palacios | 6-8 | T | 829 | 87% | 512/386-3600<br>Fax 512/386-3605 |
| Ⓐ Del Valle Dist Alt Ed Program<br>4305 McKinney Falls Pkwy, Austin 78744<br>George Meave | PK-12 | | 150 | | 512/386-3180<br>Fax 512/386-3179 |
| Del Valle Elem Sch<br>5400 Ross Rd, Del Valle 78617<br>Jay Maines | PK-5 | T | 582 | 86% | 512/386-3350<br>Fax 512/386-3355 |
| Del Valle High Sch<br>5201 Ross Rd, Del Valle 78617<br>Joseph Welch | 9-12 | T | 3,135<br>70 | 74% | 512/386-3200<br>Fax 512/386-3205 |
| Del Valle Middle Sch<br>5500 Ross Rd, Del Valle 78617<br>Natasha Staten | 6-8 | T | 884 | 81% | 512/386-3400<br>Fax 512/247-3087 |
| Del Valle Opportunity Center<br>5301 Ross Rd Ste B, Del Valle 78617<br>Ray Macias | 9-12 | T | 119<br>13 | 88% | 512/386-3300<br>Fax 512/386-3316 |
| Hillcrest Elem Sch<br>6910 E William Cannon Dr, Austin 78744<br>Jennifer Eberly | PK-5 | T | 385<br>54 | 94% | 512/386-3550<br>Fax 512/386-3555 |
| Hornsby-Dunlap Elem Sch<br>13901 FM 969, Austin 78724<br>Helen Garcia | PK-5 | T | 466<br>32 | 87% | 512/386-3650<br>Fax 512/386-3655 |
| Joseph Gilbert Elem Sch<br>5412 Gilbert Rd, Austin 78724<br>Lindsay Gonzales | PK-5 | T | 641 | 91% | 512/386-3800<br>Fax 512/386-3805 |

| | | | | | |
|---|---|---|---|---|---|
| Newton Collins Elem Sch<br>7609 Apogee Blvd, Austin 78744<br>Suzi Wallace | PK-5 | T | 593 | 95% | 512/386-3900 |
| Ojeda Middle Sch<br>4900 McKinney Falls Pkwy, Austin 78744<br>Alex Torrez | 6-8 | T | 839 | 88% | 512/386-3500<br>Fax 512/386-3505 |
| Popham Elem Sch<br>7014 Elroy Rd, Del Valle 78617<br>Jennifer Spears | PK-5 | T | 591<br>42 | 85% | 512/386-3750<br>Fax 512/386-3755 |
| Smith Elem Sch<br>4209 Smith School Rd, Austin 78744<br>Francisca Maldonado | PK-5 | T | 424<br>47 | 87% | 512/386-3850<br>Fax 512/386-3855 |

● **Eanes Ind School Dist** PID: 01056844  512/732-9000
601 Camp Craft Rd, Austin 78746  Fax 512/732-9038

> **Schools:** 9 \ **Teachers:** 600 \ **Students:** 8,156 \ **Special Ed Students:** 702
> \ **LEP Students:** 181 \ **College-Bound:** 98% \ **Ethnic:** Asian 14%, African
> American 1%, Hispanic 14%, Caucasian 72% \ **Exp:** $183 (Low) \ **Poverty:** 3%
> \ **Title I:** $180,898 \ **Special Education:** $1,710,000 \ **Open-Close:** 08/19 -
> 05/26 \ **DTBP:** $171 (High) \ 🅕 🅣

| | | | |
|---|---|---|---|
| Dr Tom Leonard | 1 | Chris Scott | 2 |
| Maria Rockstead | 2 | Sylvie Pouget | 2 |
| Brian Bolek | 3 | Jeremy Trimble | 3,17 |
| Jerri Yznaga | 3 | Norman Hopkins | 3 |
| Steve Stracke | 4 | Todd Dodge | 6 |
| Todd Washburn | 8,15,36,275 | Carolyn Foote | 16* |
| Kerry Taylor | 20,23 | Lisa Groover | 30,274 |
| Molly May | 58 | Jennifer Champange | 67 |
| Laura Lee | 68 | Claudia McWhorter | 71 |
| Eric Wright | 76 | Kimberley Israel | 76 |
| Linda Rawlings | 79,752 | Jerri Lamirand | 81,285 |
| Matthew Zemo | 88 | Matt Greer | 91 |
| Beth Keith | 275 | Preston Jinnette | 295 |
| Pamela Van Dyke | 297 | | |

| Public Schs..Principal | Grd | Prgm | Enr/#Cls | SN | |
|---|---|---|---|---|---|
| Barton Creek Elem Sch<br>1314 Patterson Rd, Austin 78733<br>Tiffany Phelps | K-5 | | 488<br>23 | 2% | 512/732-9180<br>Fax 512/732-9189 |
| Bridge Point Elem Sch<br>6401 Cedar St, Austin 78746<br>Heather Meek | K-5 | | 636<br>37 | 2% | 512/732-9200<br>Fax 512/732-9209 |
| Cedar Creek Elem Sch<br>3301 Pinnacle Rd, Austin 78746<br>**Brad Wirht** | K-5 | | 523<br>18 | 5% | 512/732-9120<br>Fax 512/732-9129<br>🅕🅣 |
| Eanes Elem Sch<br>4101 Bee Caves Rd, Austin 78746<br>Lesley Ryan \ Charlotte Burke | PK-5 | | 658<br>27 | 1% | 512/732-9100<br>Fax 512/732-9109<br>🅕🅣 |
| Forest Trail Elem Sch<br>1203 S Capital of Texas Hwy, Austin 78746<br>Cody Spraberry | K-5 | | 569 | 2% | 512/732-9160<br>Fax 512/732-9169 |
| Hill Country Middle Sch<br>1300 Walsh Tarlton Ln, Austin 78746<br>Kathleen Sullivan | 6-8 | V | 1,053<br>55 | 3% | 512/732-9220<br>Fax 512/732-9229 |
| Valley View Elem Sch<br>1201 S Capital of Texas Hwy, Austin 78746<br>Jennifer Dusek | K-5 | | 483<br>35 | 8% | 512/732-9140<br>Fax 512/732-9149 |
| West Ridge Middle Sch<br>9201 Scenic Bluff Dr, Austin 78733<br>Dianne Carter | 6-8 | V | 931<br>60 | 4% | 512/732-9240<br>Fax 512/732-9249 |
| Westlake High Sch<br>4100 Westbank Dr, Austin 78746<br>Steven Ramsey | 9-12 | GV | 2,772<br>100 | 3% | 512/732-9280<br>Fax 512/732-9296 |

| | | | | | |
|---|---|---|---|---|---|
| 1 | Superintendent | 8 | Curric/Instruct K-12 | 19 | Chief Financial Officer |
| 2 | Bus/Finance/Purchasing | 9 | Curric/Instruct Elem | 20 | Art K-12 |
| 3 | Buildings And Grounds | 10 | Curric/Instruct Sec | 21 | Art Elem |
| 4 | Food Service | 11 | Federal Program | 22 | Art Sec |
| 5 | Transportation | 12 | Title I | 23 | Music K-12 |
| 6 | Athletic | 13 | Title V | 24 | Music Elem |
| 7 | Health Services | 15 | Asst Superintendent | 25 | Music Sec |
| | | 16 | Instructional Media Svcs | 26 | Business Education |
| | | 17 | Chief Operations Officer | 27 | Career & Tech Ed |
| | | 18 | Chief Academic Officer | 28 | Technology Education |

| | | | |
|---|---|---|---|
| 29 | Family/Consumer Science | 39 | Social Studies K-12 |
| 30 | Adult Education | 40 | Social Studies Elem |
| 31 | Career/Sch-to-Work K-12 | 41 | Social Studies Sec |
| 32 | Career/Sch-to-Work Elem | 42 | Science K-12 |
| 33 | Career/Sch-to-Work Sec | 43 | Science Elem |
| 34 | Early Childhood Ed | 44 | Science Sec |
| 35 | Health/Phys Education | 45 | Math K-12 |
| 36 | Guidance Services K-12 | 46 | Math Elem |
| 37 | Guidance Services Elem | 47 | Math Sec |
| 38 | Guidance Services Sec | 48 | English/Lang Arts K-12 |

| | | | |
|---|---|---|---|
| 49 | English/Lang Arts Elem | 59 | Special Education Elem |
| 50 | English/Lang Arts Sec | 60 | Special Education Sec |
| 51 | Reading K-12 | 61 | Foreign/World Lang K-12 |
| 52 | Reading Elem | 62 | Foreign/World Lang Elem |
| 53 | Reading Sec | 63 | Foreign/World Lang Sec |
| 54 | Remedial Reading K-12 | 64 | Religious Education K-12 |
| 55 | Remedial Reading Elem | 65 | Religious Education Elem |
| 56 | Remedial Reading Sec | 66 | Religious Education Sec |
| 57 | Bilingual/ELL | 67 | School Board President |
| 58 | Special Education K-12 | 68 | Teacher Personnel |

| | |
|---|---|
| 69 | Academic Assessment |
| 70 | Research/Development |
| 71 | Public Information |
| 72 | Summer School |
| 73 | Instructional Tech |
| 74 | Inservice Training |
| 75 | Marketing/Distributive |
| 76 | Info Systems |
| 77 | Psychological Assess |
| 78 | Affirmative Action |

• **Lago Vista Ind School Dist** PID: 01056870
8039 Bar K Ranch Rd, Lago Vista 78645

512/267-8300
Fax 512/267-8304

**Schools:** 4 \ **Teachers:** 93 \ **Students:** 1,500 \ **Special Ed Students:** 141 \
**LEP Students:** 64 \ **College-Bound:** 90% \ **Ethnic:** Asian 1%, Hispanic 24%,
Native American: 1%, Caucasian 74% \ **Exp:** $326 (High) \ **Poverty:** 11% \
**Title I:** $165,005 \ **Special Education:** $194,000 \ **Open-Close:** 08/13 -
05/26 \ **DTBP:** $363 (High)

| | | | |
|---|---|---|---|
| Darren Webb | 1 | Jason Stoner | 2,19 |
| Mark Beall | 3 | Stacey Widdecombe | 4 |
| Lisa Gordon | 5 | Craten Phillips | 6* |
| Regina Carmichael | 7,83,85* | Dr Suzy Lofton | 8,11,15,296 |
| Krystal Colhoff | 58,69 | David Scott | 67 |
| Russell Maynard | 73* | | |

| Public Schs..Principal | Grd | Prgm | Enr/#Cls | SN | |
|---|---|---|---|---|---|
| Lago Vista Elem Sch<br>20311 Dawn Dr, Lago Vista 78645<br>Michelle Jackson | PK-3 | | 361<br>32 | 30% | 512/267-8340<br>Fax 512/267-8362 |
| Lago Vista High Sch<br>5185 Lohmans Ford Rd, Lago Vista 78645<br>Heather Stoner | 9-12 | AV | 505<br>32 | 22% | 512/267-8300<br>Fax 512/267-8330 |
| Lago Vista Intermediate Sch<br>20801 FM 1431, Lago Vista 78645<br>Stacie Davis | 4-5 | | 245 | 27% | 512/267-8300<br>Fax 512/267-8363 |
| Lago Vista Middle Sch<br>20801 FM 1431, Lago Vista 78645<br>Eric Holt | 6-8 | | 392<br>35 | 24% | 512/267-8300<br>Fax 512/267-8329 |

• **Lake Travis Ind School Dist** PID: 02178653
3322 Ranch Road 620 S, Austin 78738

512/533-6000
Fax 512/533-6001

**Schools:** 10 \ **Teachers:** 603 \ **Students:** 10,410 \ **Special Ed Students:** 876
\ **LEP Students:** 615 \ **College-Bound:** 68% \ **Ethnic:** Asian 7%,
African American 2%, Hispanic 21%, Caucasian 70% \ **Exp:** $348 (High)
\ **Poverty:** 5% \ **Title I:** $413,495 \ **Special Education:** $1,408,000 \
**Open-Close:** 08/19 - 05/28 \ **DTBP:** $157 (High) \ 🅣

| | | | |
|---|---|---|---|
| Paul Norton | 1 | Angie Marsh | 2 |
| Brad Goerke | 2 | Johnny Hill | 2,15 |
| Rufus Myers | 2 | Tamara Odenthal | 2 |
| Richard Harrison | 3 | Robert Winovitch | 3 |
| Wesley Perkins | 3 | Marcie Kissko | 4 |
| Ryan Mikolaycik | 4 | Tanya Breazeale | 4 |
| Dan Lee | 5 | Rhonda Davis | 5 |
| Hank Carter | 6 | Michael Drinkwater | 6 |
| Jennifer Lyon | 7 | Elizabeth Deterra | 8 |
| Liz Sims | 9,57 | Mary Patin | 11,15,286 |
| Evalene Murphy | 15,68 | Holly Morris-Kuentz | 15 |
| Charles Aguillon | 20,23 | Rachel Behnke | 27 |
| Laura Abbott | 58,271 | Kim Flasch | 67 |
| Danielle Hinson | 68 | Kim Heinen | 68 |
| Kathy Burbank | 69,73,294 | Katie Kauffman | 70 |
| Dr Kevin Claypool | 70 | Marco Alvarado | 71 |
| Chris Woehl | 73,76,295 | Janis Jordan | 74 |
| Kathleen Hassenfratz | 83,85,270* | Kenneth Debord | 88 |
| Dionne Burnett | 93,274 | | |

| Public Schs..Principal | Grd | Prgm | Enr/#Cls | SN | |
|---|---|---|---|---|---|
| Bee Cave Elem Sch<br>14300 Hamilton Pool Rd, Austin 78738<br>Kim Kellner | PK-5 | | 678<br>32 | 5% | 512/533-6250<br>Fax 512/533-6251<br>🅕🅣 |
| Bee Cave Middle Sch<br>5400 Vail Dv, Austin 78738<br>Amanda Prehn | 6-8 | | 401 | | 737/931-2400<br>Fax 737/931-2401 |

| Public Schs..Principal | Grd | Prgm | Enr/#Cls | SN | |
|---|---|---|---|---|---|
| Hudson Bend Middle Sch<br>15600 Lariat Trl, Austin 78734<br>Thomas Payne | 6-8 | | 1,135 | 18% | 512/533-6400<br>Fax 512/533-6401 |
| Lake Pointe Elem Sch<br>11801 Sonoma Dr, Austin 78738<br>Kelly Freed | PK-5 | | 560<br>40 | 8% | 512/533-6500<br>Fax 512/533-6501<br>🅕🅣 |
| Lake Travis Elem Sch<br>15303 Kollmeyer Dr, Austin 78734<br>Mary Patterson \ **Angela Frankhouser** \ **Pam Schaeffer** | PK-5 | T | 793 | 47% | 512/533-6300<br>Fax 512/533-6301<br>🅣 |
| Lake Travis High Sch<br>3324 Ranch Road 620 S, Austin 78738<br>Gordon Butler | 9-12 | | 3,212 | 10% | 512/533-6100<br>Fax 512/533-6101 |
| Lake Travis Middle Sch<br>4932 Bee Creek Rd, Spicewood 78669<br>Lester Wolff | 6-8 | | 1,544 | 6% | 512/533-6200<br>Fax 512/264-2247 |
| Lakeway Elem Sch<br>1701 Lohmans Crossing Rd, Austin 78734<br>Sam Hicks | PK-5 | | 592<br>40 | 8% | 512/533-6350<br>Fax 512/533-6351<br>🅕🅣 |
| Serene Hills Elem Sch<br>3301 Serene Hills Ct, Austin 78738<br>Julie Nederveld | PK-5 | | 898 | 6% | 512/533-7400<br>Fax 512/533-7401 |
| West Cypress Hills Elem Sch<br>6112 Cypress Ranch Blvd, Spicewood 78669<br>Melanie Beninga | PK-5 | | 739 | 8% | 512/533-7500<br>Fax 512/533-7599<br>🅕 |

• **Manor Ind School Dist** PID: 01056894
10335 US Highway 290 E, Manor 78653

512/278-4000
Fax 512/278-4017

**Schools:** 16 \ **Teachers:** 626 \ **Students:** 9,200 \ **Special Ed Students:** 860
\ **LEP Students:** 3,453 \ **College-Bound:** 50% \ **Ethnic:** Asian 4%,
African American 21%, Hispanic 68%, Caucasian 7% \ **Exp:** $440 (High)
\ **Poverty:** 17% \ **Title I:** $1,856,879 \ **Special Education:** $1,263,000 \
**Bilingual Education:** $31,000 \ **Open-Close:** 08/14 - 05/21 \ **DTBP:** $126
(High) \ 🅕 🅣

| | | | |
|---|---|---|---|
| **Dr Andre Spencer** | 1 | Carla Stevens | 2 |
| Karen Chapoton | 2 | Melanie Boutwell | 2 |
| George Townsend | 4 | Jackie Fields | 5 |
| Jimmie Mitchell | 6 | Dr Brian Yearwood | 8,11,15,69,81,294,298 |
| Mikaela Perkins | 8,69,280,294,298* | Creslond Fannin | 11 |
| Alfredo Laredo | 16,73,98,286 | Renford Joseph | 20,23 |
| Jill Ranucci | 27 | Tamo King | 27 |
| Stacy Signaigo | 34 | Nanette Deaton | 36 |
| Courtney Webster | 39 | Claire Hodgin | 43 |
| Tammy Mayberry | 44 | Lakeyshia Brown | 46 |
| Dora Jackson | 47 | Lisa Kutsch | 47,69,285 |
| Lo DeWalt | 49 | Meredith Roddy | 57 |
| Michele McKinley | 58 | Elmer Fisher | 67 |
| Daniel Vera | 68 | Scott Thomas | 71 |
| Beth Chapoton | 76 | Chris Tawater | 76 |
| Rebecca Lott | 83 | Ryan Marcum | 91 |
| Dr Nathan Balasubcamania | 294 | David Gonzalez | 295 |

| Public Schs..Principal | Grd | Prgm | Enr/#Cls | SN | |
|---|---|---|---|---|---|
| Blake Manor Elem Sch<br>18010 Blake Manor Rd, Manor 78653<br>Maeloisa Morales | PK-5 | T | 487 | 80% | 512/278-4200<br>Fax 512/278-4209<br>🅕🅣 |
| Bluebonnet Trail Elem Sch<br>11316 Farmhaven Rd, Austin 78754<br>Angel DeLuna | PK-5 | T | 484<br>23 | 66% | 512/278-4125<br>Fax 512/278-4140 |
| Decker Elem Sch<br>8500 Decker Ln, Austin 78724<br>**Samuel Cauman** | K-5 | T | 431<br>44 | 91% | 512/278-4150<br>Fax 512/278-4174 |
| Decker Middle Sch<br>8104 Decker Ln, Austin 78724<br>Dayna Anthony-Swain | 6-8 | T | 715 | 77% | 512/278-4630<br>Fax 512/278-4654 |

| | | | | | |
|---|---|---|---|---|---|
| 79 Student Personnel | 91 Safety/Security | 275 Response To Intervention | 298 Grant Writer/Ptnrships | **School Programs** | **Social Media** |
| 80 Driver Ed/Safety | 92 Magnet School | 277 Remedial Math K-12 | 750 Chief Innovation Officer | A = Alternative Program | |
| 81 Gifted/Talented | 93 Parental Involvement | 280 Literacy Coach | 751 Chief of Staff | G = Adult Classes | 🅕 = Facebook |
| 82 Video Services | 95 Tech Prep Program | 285 STEM | 752 Social Emotional Learning | M = Magnet Program | |
| 83 Substance Abuse Prev | 97 Chief Infomation Officer | 286 Digital Learning | | T = Title I Schoolwide | 🅣 = Twitter |
| 84 Erate | 98 Chief Technology Officer | 288 Common Core Standards | **Other School Types** | V = Career & Tech Ed Programs | |
| 85 AIDS Education | 270 Character Education | 294 Accountability | Ⓐ = Alternative School | | |
| 88 Alternative/At Risk | 271 Migrant Education | 295 Network System | Ⓒ = Charter School | | |
| 89 Multi-Cultural Curriculum | 273 Teacher Mentor | 296 Title II Programs | Ⓜ = Magnet School | New Schools are shaded | |
| 90 Social Work | 274 Before/After Sch | 297 Webmaster | Ⓨ = Year-Round School | New Superintendents and Principals are bold<br>Personnel with email addresses are underscored | |

**TX—373**

| School | Grd | Prgm | Enr/#Cls | SN | Phone |
|---|---|---|---|---|---|
| Lagos Elem Sch<br>11817 Murchison St, Manor 78653<br>Malaki Hawkins | PK-5 | T | 350 | 71% | 512/278-4360<br>Fax 512/278-4361 |
| Manor Elem Early Learning Ctr<br>12904 Gregg Manor Rd, Manor 78653<br>Nicole Aguirre | PK-PK | T | 295<br>35 | 86% | 512/278-4100<br>Fax 512/278-4104 |
| Ⓐ Manor Excel Academy<br>600 E Parsons St, Manor 78653<br>Jerry Statos | 9-12 | T | 79 | 61% | 512/278-4851<br>Fax 512/278-4859 |
| Manor High Sch<br>12700 Gregg Manor Rd, Manor 78653<br>Jon Bailey | 9-10 | T | 900 | 69% | 512/278-4800<br>Fax 512/278-4803 |
| Manor Middle Sch<br>12900 Gregg Manor Rd, Manor 78653<br>Dr Marcus Jones | 6-8 | T | 771<br>80 | 77% | 512/278-4600<br>Fax 512/278-4285 🅣 |
| Manor New Tech High Sch<br>10323 US Highway 290 E, Manor 78653<br>Bobby Garcia | Voc | T | 177 | 57% | 512/278-4875<br>Fax 512/278-4880 |
| Manor New Tech Middle Sch<br>12116 Joyce Turner Dr, Manor 78653<br>**Francisco Ramirez** | 6-8 | T | 696 | 64% | 512/278-4300 |
| Manor Senior High Sch<br>14832 N FM 973 Rd, Manor 78653<br>**Brandon Powell** | 11-12 | GV | 900<br>53 | | 512/278-4665<br>Fax 512/278-4666 |
| Oak Meadows Elem Sch<br>5600 Decker Ln, Austin 78724<br>Salvador Vega | PK-5 | T | 603 | 92% | 512/278-4175<br>Fax 512/278-4199 |
| Pioneer Crossing Elem Sch<br>11300 Samsung Blvd, Austin 78754<br>Eddwina Flowers | PK-5 | T | 590 | 61% | 512/278-4250<br>Fax 512/278-4259 🅕🅣 |
| Presidential Meadows Elem Sch<br>13252 George Bush St, Manor 78653<br>Laura Krcmar | PK-5 | T | 541 | 78% | 512/278-4225<br>Fax 512/278-4231 |
| Shadowglen Elem Sch<br>12000 Shadowglen Trce, Manor 78653<br>Niccole Delestre | PK-5 | T | 656 | 61% | 512/278-4700<br>Fax 512/278-4701 |

● **Pflugerville Ind School Dist** PID: 01056935    512/594-0000
1401 W Pecan St, Pflugerville 78660    Fax 512/594-0011

> **Schools:** 33 \ **Teachers:** 1,819 \ **Students:** 26,269 \
> **Special Ed Students:** 2,857 \ **LEP Students:** 5,206 \ **College-Bound:** 57%
> \ **Ethnic:** Asian 8%, African American 16%, Hispanic 51%, Caucasian
> 24% \ **Exp:** $394 (High) \ **Poverty:** 13% \ **Title I:** $4,999,655 \
> **Special Education:** $3,646,000 \ **Bilingual Education:** $27,000 \
> **Open-Close:** 08/13 - 05/27 \ **DTBP:** $75 (Low) \ 🅕 🅣

| | | | |
|---|---|---|---|
| Dr Douglas Killian ...................1 | Craig Pruett .............................2 |
| Eduardo Ramos ................2,3,17 | David Vessling .........................3 |
| Geoff Holle ...............................4 | Todd Raymond .........................6 |
| Denise Kablaitis ...................7,91 | Brandi Baker .......................8,15 |
| Christine Fox ...........................11 | Dr Troy Galow ...................15,751 |
| Victor Valdez ...........16,73,76,295 | Manuel Gamez ...................20,23 |
| Traci Hendrix ..........................27 | Gema Henson ........................57 |
| Cara Schwartz ........................58 | Hutchison Hill .........................58 |
| Vernagene Mott .......................67 | Willie Watson .........................68 |
| Tamara Spencer .......................71 | David Greiner .........................76 |
| Shirley Bachus .......................81 | Karen Shah ..........................294 |

| Public Schs..Principal | Grd | Prgm | Enr/#Cls | SN | |
|---|---|---|---|---|---|
| Barron Elem Sch<br>14850 Harris Ridge Blvd, Pflugerville 78660<br>Natalia Gomez-Ramback | PK-5 | T | 562 | 83% | 512/594-4300<br>Fax 512/594-4305 🅕🅣 |
| Brookhollow Elem Sch<br>1200 N Railroad Ave, Pflugerville 78660<br>Lisa Harris | PK-5 | T | 436<br>40 | 44% | 512/594-5200<br>Fax 512/594-5205 |

| School | Grd | Prgm | Enr/#Cls | SN | Phone |
|---|---|---|---|---|---|
| Caldwell Elem Sch<br>1718 Picadilly Dr, Round Rock 78664<br>Colby Self | PK-5 | T | 568 | 61% | 512/594-6400<br>Fax 512/594-6405 |
| Cele Middle Sch<br>6000 Cele Rd, Pflugerville 78660<br>Ben O'Connor | 6-8 | TV | 1,123 | 40% | 512/594-3000 |
| Copperfield Elem Sch<br>12135 Thompkins Dr, Austin 78753<br>Georgie Arenaz | PK-5 | T | 411<br>55 | 75% | 512/594-5800<br>Fax 512/594-5805 |
| Dearing Elem Sch<br>4301 Gattis School Rd, Round Rock 78664<br>Christy Chandler | PK-5 | T | 585 | 48% | 512/594-4500<br>Fax 512/594-4505 |
| Delco Primary Sch<br>12900 Dessau Rd Ste A, Austin 78754<br>Miguel Castillo | PK-2 | T | 597 | 82% | 512/594-6200<br>Fax 512/594-6205 🅕🅣 |
| Dessau Elem Sch<br>1501 Dessau Ridge Ln, Austin 78754<br>Carolyn Parker | 3-5 | T | 542<br>33 | 85% | 512/594-4600<br>Fax 512/594-4605 |
| Dessau Middle Sch<br>12900 Dessau Rd, Austin 78754<br>Valerie Torres-Solis | 6-8 | T | 847 | 81% | 512/594-2600<br>Fax 512/594-2605 |
| Hendrickson High Sch<br>19201 Colorado Sand Dr, Pflugerville 78660<br>Daniel Garcia | 9-12 | V | 2,398<br>135 | 29% | 512/594-1100<br>Fax 512/594-1105 🅕🅣 |
| Highland Park Elem Sch<br>428 Kingston Lacy Blvd, Pflugerville 78660<br>Lizbeth Ruiz | PK-5 | T | 622 | 32% | 512/594-6800<br>Fax 512/594-6805 |
| John B Connally High Sch<br>13212 N Lamar Blvd, Austin 78753<br>Sheila Finley-Reed | 9-12 | TV | 827<br>50 | 69% | 512/594-0800<br>Fax 512/594-0805 |
| Kelly Lane Middle Sch<br>18900 Falcon Pointe Blvd, Pflugerville 78660<br>Dina Schaefer | 6-8 | V | 1,110<br>90 | 20% | 512/594-2800<br>Fax 512/594-2805 |
| Murchison Elem Sch<br>2215 Kelly Ln, Pflugerville 78660<br>Reese Weirich | PK-5 | | 833 | 12% | 512/594-6000<br>Fax 512/594-6005 |
| Northwest Elem Sch<br>14014 Thermal Dr, Austin 78728<br>Tana Ruckel | PK-5 | T | 478<br>32 | 79% | 512/594-4400<br>Fax 512/594-4405 🅕🅣 |
| Ⓐ Pace Sch<br>1401 W Pecan St B, Pflugerville 78660<br>Mike Harvey | 9-12 | | 112 | | 512/594-1900<br>Fax 512/594-1905 |
| Park Crest Middle Sch<br>1500 N Railroad Ave, Pflugerville 78660<br>Zachary Kleypas | 6-8 | TV | 909<br>50 | 46% | 512/594-2400<br>Fax 512/594-2405 |
| Parmer Lane Elem Sch<br>1806 W Parmer Ln, Austin 78727<br>Barry Miller | PK-5 | T | 480<br>37 | 69% | 512/594-4000<br>Fax 512/594-4005 |
| Pflugerville Elem Sch<br>701 Immanuel Rd, Pflugerville 78660<br>Genia Antoine | PK-5 | T | 466<br>29 | 55% | 512/594-3800<br>Fax 512/594-3805 🅕🅣 |
| Pflugerville High Sch<br>1301 W Pecan St, Pflugerville 78660<br>Ameka Durham-Hunt | 9-12 | TV | 2,058 | 47% | 512/594-0500<br>Fax 512/594-0505 |
| Pflugerville Middle Sch<br>1600 Settlers Valley Dr, Pflugerville 78660<br>Robert Stell | 6-8 | TV | 1,040<br>50 | 58% | 512/594-2000<br>Fax 512/594-2005 |
| Ⓐ Provan Opportunity Center<br>1401-A W Pecan St, Pflugerville 78660<br>Philip Clayton | K-12 | | 450<br>5 | | 512/594-3600<br>Fax 512/594-3605 |
| Riojas Elem Sch<br>3400 Crispin Hall Ln, Pflugerville 78660<br>Christi Siegel | PK-5 | | 636 | 20% | 512/594-4100<br>Fax 512/594-4105 |
| River Oaks Elem Sch<br>12401 Scofield Farms Dr, Austin 78758<br>Aracely Suarez | PK-5 | T | 441<br>25 | 87% | 512/594-5000<br>Fax 512/594-5005 🅕🅣 |

| | | | | |
|---|---|---|---|---|
| 1 Superintendent | 8 Curric/Instruct K-12 | 19 Chief Financial Officer | 29 Family/Consumer Science | 39 Social Studies K-12 | 49 English/Lang Arts Elem | 59 Special Education Elem | 69 Academic Assessment |
| 2 Bus/Finance/Purchasing | 9 Curric/Instruct Elem | 20 Art K-12 | 30 Adult Education | 40 Social Studies Elem | 50 English/Lang Arts Sec | 60 Special Education Sec | 70 Research/Development |
| 3 Buildings And Grounds | 10 Curric/Instruct Sec | 21 Art Elem | 31 Career/Sch-to-Work K-12 | 41 Social Studies Sec | 51 Reading K-12 | 61 Foreign/World Lang K-12 | 71 Public Information |
| 4 Food Service | 11 Federal Program | 22 Art Sec | 32 Career/Sch-to-Work Elem | 42 Science K-12 | 52 Reading Elem | 62 Foreign/World Lang Elem | 72 Summer School |
| 5 Transportation | 12 Title I | 23 Music K-12 | 33 Career/Sch-to-Work Sec | 43 Science Elem | 53 Reading Sec | 63 Foreign/World Lang Sec | 73 Instructional Tech |
| 6 Athletic | 13 Title V | 24 Music Elem | 34 Early Childhood Ed | 44 Science Sec | 54 Remedial Reading K-12 | 64 Religious Education K-12 | 74 Inservice Training |
| 7 Health Services | 14 Title V | 25 Music Sec | 35 Health/Phys Education | 45 Math K-12 | 55 Remedial Reading Elem | 65 Religious Education Elem | 75 Marketing/Distributive |
| | 15 Asst Superintendent | 26 Business Education | 36 Guidance Services K-12 | 46 Math Elem | 56 Remedial Reading Sec | 66 Religious Education Sec | 76 Info Systems |
| | 16 Instructional Media Svcs | 27 Career & Tech Ed | 37 Guidance Services Elem | 47 Math Sec | 57 Bilingual/ELL | 67 School Board President | 77 Psychological Assess |
| | 17 Chief Operations Officer | 28 Technology Education | 38 Guidance Services Sec | 48 English/Lang Arts K-12 | 58 Special Education K-12 | 68 Teacher Personnel | 78 Affirmative Action |

| | | | | | |
|---|---|---|---|---|---|
| Rowe Lane Elem Sch<br>3112 Speidel Dr, Pflugerville 78660<br>Rhonda Butcher | PK-5 | | 764<br>34 | 14% | 512/594-6600<br>Fax 512/594-6605 |
| Spring Hill Elem Sch<br>600 S Heatherwilde Blvd, Pflugerville 78660<br>Camille Ramirezlongori | PK-5 | T | 589<br>30 | 74% | 512/594-5400<br>Fax 512/594-5405 |
| Timmerman Elem Sch<br>412 Swenson Farms Blvd, Pflugerville 78660<br>Gregory Nestle | PK-5 | T | 544<br>25 | 60% | 512/594-4200<br>Fax 512/594-4205<br>f t |
| Vernagene Mott Elem Sch<br>20101 Hodde Ln, Pflugerville 78660<br>Tammy Rebecek | PK-5 | | 826 | | 512/594-4700 |
| Weiss High Sch<br>5201 Wolf Pack Dr, Pflugerville 78660<br>Paula Gamble | 9-10 | T | 807 | 49% | 512/594-1400 |
| Westview Middle Sch<br>1805 Scofield Ln, Austin 78727<br>**Alma Ramirez** | 6-8 | TV | 763<br>54 | 79% | 512/594-2200<br>Fax 512/594-2205<br>f t |
| Wieland Elem Sch<br>900 Tudor House Rd, Pflugerville 78660<br>Jared Stevenson | PK-5 | T | 388<br>27 | 67% | 512/594-3900<br>Fax 512/594-3905 |
| Windermere Elem Sch<br>1100 Picadilly Dr, Pflugerville 78660<br>Kate Shaum | 3-5 | T | 417<br>26 | 55% | 512/594-4800<br>Fax 512/594-4805<br>f t |
| Windermere Primary Sch<br>429 Grand Avenue Pkwy, Pflugerville 78660<br>Terri Floyd | PK-2 | T | 413 | 59% | 512/594-5600<br>Fax 512/594-5605 |

## TRAVIS CATHOLIC SCHOOLS

● **Diocese of Austin Ed Office** PID: 01420568        512/949-2497
6225 E Highway 290, Austin 78723                  Fax 512/949-2520

**Schools:** 21 \ **Students:** 5,141

Listing includes only schools located in this county. See District Index for location of Diocesan Offices.

Misty Poe ..............................1,11  Robert Whitworth ...............................8,15

| Catholic Schs..Principal | Grd | Prgm | Enr/#Cls | SN | |
|---|---|---|---|---|---|
| Cathedral School of St Mary<br>910 San Jacinto Blvd, Austin 78701<br>Robert Legros | PK-8 | | 140<br>11 | | 512/476-1480<br>Fax 512/476-9922 |
| San Juan Diego Cath High Sch<br>2512 S 1st St, Austin 78704<br>Daniel Tarin | 8-12 | | 160<br>17 | | 512/804-1935<br>Fax 512/804-1937<br>f t |
| St Austin Catholic Sch<br>1911 San Antonio St, Austin 78705<br>Tara Cevallos | PK-8 | | 215<br>16 | | 512/477-3751<br>Fax 512/477-3079 |
| St Gabriel's Catholic Sch<br>2500 Wimberly Ln, Austin 78735<br>Colleen Lynch \ Koy Severino | PK-8 | | 386<br>23 | | 512/327-7755<br>Fax 512/327-4334<br>f t |
| St Ignatius Martyr Cath Sch<br>120 W Oltorf St, Austin 78704<br>Fred Valle | PK-8 | | 268<br>13 | | 512/442-8547<br>Fax 512/442-8685<br>f t |
| St Louis Catholic Sch<br>2114 Saint Joseph Blvd, Austin 78757<br>Cindy Gee | PK-8 | | 245<br>18 | | 512/614-6622<br>Fax 512/454-7252<br>f t |
| St Michael's Catholic Academy<br>3000 Barton Creek Blvd, Austin 78735<br>Dr Dawn Nichols | 9-12 | | 388<br>29 | | 512/328-2323<br>Fax 512/328-2327<br>f |

| | | | | | |
|---|---|---|---|---|---|
| St Theresa's Catholic Sch<br>4311 Small Dr, Austin 78731<br>Brian Wheeler | PK-8 | | 350<br>20 | | 512/451-7105<br>Fax 512/451-8808 |

## TRAVIS PRIVATE SCHOOLS

| Private Schs..Principal | Grd | Prgm | Enr/#Cls | SN | |
|---|---|---|---|---|---|
| Academy of Thought & Industry<br>1701 Toomey Rd, Austin 78704<br>Michael Strong | 9-12 | | 401 | | 512/910-8980 |
| Acton Academy<br>1404 E Riverside Dr, Austin 78741<br>Laura Sandefer | 5-8 | | 100 | | 512/320-0596<br>f |
| Ahb Community Sch<br>4001 Speedway, Austin 78751<br>Shari Vars | K-8 | | 88 | | 512/299-5487 |
| Austin Eco Bilingual Sch-South<br>8707 Mountain Crest Dr, Austin 78735<br>Adriana Rodriguez | K-5 | | 125 | | 512/299-5731<br>Fax 512/432-5317 |
| Austin International Sch<br>4001 Adelphi Ln, Austin 78727<br>Audrey Talarico \ Emily Hopkins | PK-6 | | 90<br>7 | | 512/331-7806<br>Fax 512/219-5201<br>f t |
| Austin Jewish Academy<br>7300 Hart Ln, Austin 78731<br>Chris Aguero | K-8 | | 130<br>18 | | 512/735-8350<br>Fax 512/735-8351<br>f |
| Austin Montessori Sch<br>5006 Sunset Trl, Austin 78745<br>Grae Baker | PK-9 | | 330<br>13 | | 512/892-0253<br>Fax 512/891-9875 |
| Austin Peace Academy<br>5110 Manor Rd B, Austin 78723<br>Diana Abdi | PK-12 | | 220<br>14 | | 512/926-1737<br>Fax 512/926-9688 |
| Austin Sch Perform Visual Arts<br>1110 Guadalupe St, Austin 78701<br>Carol De Cardenas | 6-12 | | 25 | | 512/522-7782 |
| Brentwood Christian Sch<br>11908 N Lamar Blvd, Austin 78753<br>Mara Ashley \ Carol Johnson | PK-12 | | 700<br>45 | | 512/835-5983<br>Fax 512/835-2184 |
| Capitol School-Austin<br>2011 W Koenig Ln, Austin 78756<br>Jeannette Young | PK-4 | | 55<br>7 | | 512/467-7006<br>Fax 512/467-7025 |
| Fusion Academy-Austin<br>4701 Bee Caves Rd Ste 101, Austin 78746<br>Cody Pileski | 6-12 | | 80 | | 512/330-0188 |
| Girls' School of Austin<br>2007 McCall Rd, Austin 78703<br>Cathleen Eclarinal | K-8 | | 144 | | 512/478-7827<br>Fax 512/478-5456<br>f t |
| Griffin Sch<br>5001 Evans Ave, Austin 78751<br>Adam Wilson | 9-12 | | 80 | | 512/454-5797<br>Fax 512/454-5798 |
| Headwaters Sch<br>6305 Manchaca Rd, Austin 78745<br>Susie Demarest | PK-5 | | 545 | | 512/443-8843 |
| Headwaters Sch<br>807 Rio Grande St, Austin 78701<br>Ted Graf | 6-12 | | 500 | | 512/480-8142<br>Fax 512/480-0277 |
| Hebrew Prep School of Austin<br>2127 W Palmer Ln, Austin 78727<br>Rochel Levertov | PK-5 | | 50<br>6 | | 512/977-0770<br>Fax 512/499-8202 |
| Hill Country Christian Sch<br>12124 Ranch Road 620 N, Austin 78750<br>Jessica Tracy \ Matt Donnowitz | PK-12 | | 565 | | 512/331-7036<br>Fax 512/257-4190 |
| Huntington-Surrey Sch<br>4700 Grover Ave, Austin 78756<br>Catherine Cotman | 9-12 | | 70<br>6 | | 512/502-5400<br>Fax 512/457-0235 |

| | | | |
|---|---|---|---|
| Hyde Park Elem Middle Sch<br>3901 Speedway, Austin 78751<br>Kimmarie Suhr \ Dr Adam Creasy | PK-8 | 430 | 512/465-8338<br>Fax 512/371-1433 |
| Hyde Park High Sch<br>11400 N Mopac Expy, Austin 78759<br>Dr Chris Coy | 9-12 | 172 | 512/465-8333<br>Fax 512/827-2020 |
| Kirby Hall Sch<br>306 W 29th St, Austin 78705<br>Helen Roberts | PK-12 | 100<br>16 | 512/474-1770<br>Fax 512/474-1117<br>f |
| Magellan Int'l Sch-Anderson Ln<br>7938 Great Northern Blvd, Austin 78757<br>Sagrario Arguelles \ Nicolas Puga | K-8 | 145 | 512/782-2327 |
| Odyssey Sch<br>4407 Red River St, Austin 78751<br>John Brinson | Spec | 65<br>7 | 512/472-2262<br>Fax 512/236-9385<br>f |
| Paragon Prep Middle Sch<br>5206 Balcones Dr, Austin 78731<br>David McGrath | 5-8 | 160<br>8 | 512/459-5040<br>Fax 512/459-1875 |
| Rawson Saunders Sch<br>2614A Exposition Blvd, Austin 78703<br>Laura Steinbach | 1-8 | 100 | 512/476-8382<br>Fax 512/476-1132<br>f t |
| Redeemer Lutheran Sch<br>1500 W Anderson Ln, Austin 78757<br>Carol Mueller | PK-8 | 500<br>28 | 512/451-6478<br>Fax 512/610-8809<br>f |
| Regents School of Austin<br>3230 Travis Country Cir, Austin 78735<br>Ronnie Long \ Matt Jasinski \ Liz Benigno | K-12 | 1,000 | 512/899-8095<br>Fax 512/899-8623 |
| Regina Mater<br>1320B E 51st St, Austin 78723<br>Jarin Schiavolin | PK-12 | 25 | 512/524-1799 |
| Rise School of Austin<br>4800 Manor Rd Bldg J, Austin 78723<br>Emily Greer | Spec | 40 | 512/891-1682<br>Fax 512/494-4096<br>f t |
| St Andrew's Episcopal Sch<br>1112 W 31st St, Austin 78705<br>Kama Bruce \ Todd Stephenson | K-12 | 675<br>48 | 512/452-5779<br>Fax 512/299-9822<br>f t |
| St Francis Sch<br>300 E Huntland Dr, Austin 78752<br>Barbara Porter | PK-8 | 402 | 512/454-0848 |
| St Stephen's Episcopal Sch<br>6500 Saint Stephens Dr, Austin 78746<br>Magnus Maccow \ Kim Garey | 6-12 | 650 | 512/327-1213<br>Fax 512/327-1311<br>f t |
| Stonehill Christian Academy<br>4301 Kelly Ln, Pflugerville 78660<br>Chinyere Uyaniker | PK-8 | 13<br>4 | 512/763-2776 |
| Texas Neurorehab Center<br>1106 W Dittmar Rd, Austin 78745<br>Dottie Goodman | Spec GV | 53<br>7 | 512/444-4835<br>Fax 512/462-6636 |
| Trinity Episcopal Sch<br>3901 Bee Caves Rd, Austin 78746<br>Jennifer Morgan \ Shanna Hines \ Shanna Weiss | K-8 | 458 | 512/472-9525<br>Fax 512/472-2337<br>f t |
| Veritas Academy<br>13401 Escarpment Blvd, Austin 78739<br>Jef Fowler | PK-12 | 301<br>15 | 512/891-1673<br>Fax 512/891-1693 |
| Waterloo Sch<br>1511 S Congress Ave, Austin 78704<br>Craig Doerksen | 9-12 | 15 | 512/447-7781 |
| William's Community Sch<br>5209 Duval Rd, Austin 78727<br>Patsy Harris | Spec | 60 | 512/250-5700 |

## TRAVIS REGIONAL CENTERS

- **Region 13 Ed Service Center** PID: 02101545    512/919-5313
  5701 Springdale Rd, Austin 78723    Fax 512/919-5374

Dr Richard Elsasser ...........................1,11   Jesse Lopez .......................................8,15
Craig Spinn ............................................ 15   Millie Klein ............................................ 15

## TRINITY COUNTY

## TRINITY PUBLIC SCHOOLS

- **Apple Springs Ind School Dist** PID: 01057044    936/831-3344
  9120 FM 2501, Apple Springs 75926    Fax 936/831-2824

> **Schools:** 2 \ **Teachers:** 18 \ **Students:** 200 \ **Special Ed Students:** 36
> \ **College-Bound:** 67% \ **Ethnic:** African American 3%, Hispanic 8%,
> Caucasian 88% \ **Exp:** $448 (High) \ **Poverty:** 39% \ **Title I:** $121,342 \
> **Open-Close:** 08/20 - 05/28

Cody Moree ..............................................1   Cody Moree ..........................2,6,19,31,273*
Greg Cambell ............................................ 3*   Renee Turner ..........................................4*
Renee Turner ............................................4   Kevin Plott .................................................8
Loretta Eddins .........11,36,58,69,88,270,271*   Amanda Roden ...................................... 67
Lawanda Vazquez ...................... 73,76,98*

| Public Schs..Principal | Grd | Prgm | Enr/#Cls | SN | |
|---|---|---|---|---|---|
| Apple Springs Elem Sch<br>9120 Farm Road FM 2501, Apple Springs 75926<br>Kevin Plotts | PK-6 | T | 114<br>10 | 61% | 936/831-2241 |
| Apple Springs High Sch<br>9120 FM 2501, Apple Springs 75926<br>Kevin Plotts | 7-12 | TV | 75<br>14 | 60% | 936/831-2241 |

- **Centerville Ind School Dist** PID: 01057070    936/642-1597
  10327 N State Highway 94, Groveton 75845    Fax 936/642-2810

> **Schools:** 2 \ **Teachers:** 17 \ **Students:** 127 \ **Special Ed Students:** 14 \
> **College-Bound:** 70% \ **Ethnic:** Hispanic 7%, Caucasian 93% \ **Exp:** $601
> (High) \ **Poverty:** 26% \ **Title I:** $53,469 \ **Open-Close:** 08/17 - 05/28 \
> **DTBP:** $322 (High)

Mark Brown .........................................1,11   Terry Whittlesey ........................................2
Charles Ashworth ................................... 6*   Andja Sailer ................8,13,27,36,85,88,271*
Sheila Smith ........................................ 58   James Due ............................................. 67
Jennifer Westbrook .............................. 73*

| Public Schs..Principal | Grd | Prgm | Enr/#Cls | SN | |
|---|---|---|---|---|---|
| Centerville Elem Sch<br>10327 N State Highway 94, Groveton 75845<br>Andja Sailer | PK-6 | | 70<br>20 | | 936/642-1597<br>Fax 936/645-2810 |
| Centerville High Sch<br>10327 N State Highway 94, Groveton 75845<br>Andja Sailer | 7-12 | TV | 64<br>14 | 59% | 936/642-1597<br>Fax 936/645-2810 |

## Groveton Ind School Dist PID: 01057109
207 North Main St, Groveton 75845

936/642-1473
Fax 936/642-1628

**Schools:** 2 \ **Teachers:** 64 \ **Students:** 750 \ **Special Ed Students:** 105 \
**LEP Students:** 9 \ **Ethnic:** Asian 1%, African American 7%, Hispanic 15%,
Caucasian 78% \ **Exp:** $631 (High) \ **Poverty:** 24% \ **Title I:** $303,141 \
**Open-Close:** 08/13 - 05/28 \ **DTBP:** $345 (High)

| | | | |
|---|---|---|---|
| Don Hamilton | 1,11,57,83 | Luther Cockrell | 3 |
| Debbie Wilson | 4* | John Abshier | 5 |
| Richard Steubing | 6 | Virginia Redden | 7,35,85* |
| Amanda Stubblefield | 9,74,91 | Bryan Finch | 10,88,270 |
| Teresa Anderson | 16,82* | Dorothy Kennedy | 36,69* |
| Susan Kitchens | 54* | Mark Folds | 67 |
| Melody Benton | 68 | Jack Ledbetter | 73,83,295* |

| Public Schs..Principal | Grd | Prgm | Enr/#Cls | SN | |
|---|---|---|---|---|---|
| Groveton Elem Sch | PK-5 | T | 350 | 66% | 936/642-1182 |
| 421 N Magee St, Groveton 75845 | | | 24 | | Fax 936/642-3254 |
| Amanda Stubblefield | | | | | |
| Groveton Jr Sr High Sch | 6-12 | ATV | 389 | 61% | 936/642-1128 |
| 207 North Main Street, Groveton 75845 | | | 30 | | Fax 936/642-1616 |
| Bryan Finch | | | | | |

## Trinity Ind School Dist PID: 01057147
101 W Jefferson St, Trinity 75862

936/594-3569
Fax 936/594-8425

**Schools:** 3 \ **Teachers:** 93 \ **Students:** 1,188 \ **Special Ed Students:** 117
\ **LEP Students:** 93 \ **College-Bound:** 50% \ **Ethnic:** African American
17%, Hispanic 25%, Caucasian 57% \ **Exp:** $282 (Med) \ **Poverty:** 29% \
**Title I:** $478,440 \ **Special Education:** $151,000 \ **Open-Close:** 08/26 -
05/28 \ **DTBP:** $350 (High)

| | | | |
|---|---|---|---|
| John Kaufman | 1 | Luann Gallant | 2,11,74,84,296 |
| Gill Cambelle | 3,4,5,11,288 | Patrick Goodman | 6 |
| Rachel Kriner | 7* | Natalie Barrett | 8 |
| Emily Murray | 27 | David Keithley | 58 |
| Kevin Searcy | 67 | Ashley LaRue | 69,83* |
| Barry Coleman | 73,295 | | |

| Public Schs..Principal | Grd | Prgm | Enr/#Cls | SN | |
|---|---|---|---|---|---|
| Lansberry Elem Sch | PK-5 | T | 542 | 87% | 936/594-3567 |
| 400 S Maple St, Trinity 75862 | | | 50 | | Fax 936/594-2646 |
| Kelli Robinson | | | | | |
| Trinity High Sch | 9-12 | GTV | 349 | 65% | 936/594-3560 |
| 500 E Caroline St, Trinity 75862 | | | 20 | | Fax 936/594-2162 |
| Brittaney Cassidy | | | | | |
| Trinity Middle Sch | 6-8 | T | 297 | 76% | 936/594-2321 |
| 500 E Caroline St, Trinity 75862 | | | 20 | | Fax 936/594-3041 |
| Brittaney Cassidy | | | | | |

# TYLER COUNTY

## TYLER PUBLIC SCHOOLS

## Chester Ind School Dist PID: 01057197
273 Yellow Jacket Dr, Chester 75936

936/969-2211
Fax 936/969-2080

**Schools:** 2 \ **Teachers:** 18 \ **Students:** 184 \ **Special Ed Students:** 25
\ **College-Bound:** 66% \ **Ethnic:** African American 5%, Hispanic 3%,
Caucasian 91% \ **Exp:** $301 (High) \ **Poverty:** 17% \ **Title I:** $48,308 \
**Open-Close:** 08/14 - 05/28 \ **DTBP:** $331 (High) \ **f**

| | | | |
|---|---|---|---|
| Cory Hines | 1,83 | Stephanie Williams | 2 |
| Marty Thompson | 3 | Amanda Poundes | 4 |
| Betty Whitworth | 16* | Shelly Wilkinson | 58 |
| Shelly Wilkinson | 58* | Ray McKnight | 67 |
| Michelle Cowan | 73 | | |

| Public Schs..Principal | Grd | Prgm | Enr/#Cls | SN | |
|---|---|---|---|---|---|
| Chester Elem Sch | PK-5 | T | 86 | 61% | 936/969-2211 |
| 273 Yellow Jacket Dr, Chester 75936 | | | 8 | | Fax 936/969-3079 |
| Katie Loughner | | | | | |
| Chester High Sch | 6-12 | TV | 98 | 44% | 936/969-2211 |
| 273 Yellow Jacket Dr, Chester 75936 | | | 12 | | Fax 936/969-3079 |
| **Katy Loughner** | | | | | |

## Colmesneil Ind School Dist PID: 01057226
610 W Elder St, Colmesneil 75938

409/837-5757
Fax 409/837-9107

**Schools:** 2 \ **Teachers:** 38 \ **Students:** 450 \ **Special Ed Students:** 59
\ **College-Bound:** 49% \ **Ethnic:** African American 2%, Hispanic 7%,
Caucasian 91% \ **Exp:** $446 (High) \ **Poverty:** 20% \ **Title I:** $106,215 \
**Open-Close:** 08/13 - 05/27 \ **DTBP:** $335 (High)

| | | | |
|---|---|---|---|
| Eldon Franco | 1 | Wonda Ryan | 2 |
| Dana Setwalker | 4* | Ramon Follmar | 5 |
| Cody Day | 6 | Walter McAlpin | 10,69,271,275* |
| Kathy Gobert | 16,73,295* | Jennifer Dunson | 58 |
| Kris Lindsey | 67 | | |

| Public Schs..Principal | Grd | Prgm | Enr/#Cls | SN | |
|---|---|---|---|---|---|
| Colmesneil Elem Sch | PK-6 | T | 253 | 65% | 409/837-5757 |
| 610 W Elder St, Colmesneil 75938 | | | 14 | | Fax 409/837-9119 |
| Yvette Carlton | | | | | |
| Colmesneil High Sch | 7-12 | GTV | 200 | 52% | 409/837-2225 |
| 610 W Elder St, Colmesneil 75938 | | | 8 | | Fax 409/837-5759 |
| Walter McAlpin | | | | | |

## Spurger Ind School Dist PID: 01057252
12212 Highway 92 S, Spurger 77660

409/429-3464
Fax 409/429-3770

**Schools:** 2 \ **Teachers:** 34 \ **Students:** 400 \ **Special Ed Students:** 52 \
**LEP Students:** 7 \ **Ethnic:** Asian 1%, Hispanic 7%, Native American: 1%,
Caucasian 91% \ **Exp:** $297 (Med) \ **Poverty:** 22% \ **Title I:** $114,237 \
**Open-Close:** 08/13 - 05/28 \ **DTBP:** $430 (High)

| | | | |
|---|---|---|---|
| Morgan Wright | 1 | Connie Griffith | 2,19 |
| Doug Jenkins | 3,5 | Leona Callaway | 4* |
| Arlene Robinson | 9,69,83* | Joyce Tippett | 16* |
| Buck Hudson | 27* | Randall Rose | 57* |

Patti Tucker ............................................58*
Andrea Wilson .................. 73,84,97,98,295
Jason Drake ........................................ 298

Carroll Hatton ....................................... 67
Stefanie Miller ............................... 92,271

| Public Schs..Principal | Grd | Prgm | Enr/#Cls | SN | |
|---|---|---|---|---|---|
| Spurger Elem Sch<br>12212 Highway 92 N, Spurger 77660<br>Jason Drake | PK-5 | T | 181<br>16 | 69% | 409/429-3464 |
| Spurger High Sch<br>12212 Highway 92 S, Spurger 77660<br>**Amanda Hatton** | 6-12 | T | 191<br>20 | 60% | 409/429-3464 |

- **Warren Ind School Dist** PID: 01057288
  375 FM 3290, Warren 77664

  409/547-2241
  Fax 409/547-3405

> **Schools:** 4 \ **Teachers:** 94 \ **Students:** 1,200 \ **Special Ed Students:** 131
> \ **LEP Students:** 9 \ **Ethnic:** Asian 1%, African American 1%, Hispanic 6%,
> Native American: 1%, Caucasian 91% \ **Exp:** $258 (Med) \ **Poverty:** 23% \
> **Title I:** $320,769 \ **Open-Close:** 08/13 - 05/27 \ **DTBP:** $341 (High)

Dr Tammy Boyette ..................................1
Burke Dagle ......................................3,5
Jay Buckner ........................................ 6*
Mike Paddie ........................ 8,11,74,83
Rex Currie ..........................................27*
Bridgette Toelr ..............................58,69
Roy Moore ...................................73,295

Terry Ling ..............................................2
Tammy Heriard ......................................4
Janice Nott ...........................8,11,61,296
Carrie Standley ...................................16*
Paula Chesser .....................................29*
Rocky Burks ........................................ 67

| Public Schs..Principal | Grd | Prgm | Enr/#Cls | SN | |
|---|---|---|---|---|---|
| Fred Elem Sch<br>140-County Road 4650, Fred 77616<br>Katy Hicks | PK-5 | T | 210<br>15 | 69% | 409/429-3240<br>Fax 409/429-3488 |
| Warren Elem Sch<br>307 FM 3290 S, Warren 77664<br>Robyn Glosson | PK-5 | T | 382<br>28 | 64% | 409/547-2240<br>Fax 409/547-0146 |
| Warren High Sch<br>395 FM 3290 S, Warren 77664<br>James Swinney | 9-12 | TV | 229<br>25 | 45% | 409/547-2240<br>Fax 409/547-0214 |
| Warren Junior High Sch<br>395 FM 3290 S, Warren 77664<br>Kristina Wiedman | 6-8 | T | 300<br>25 | 51% | 409/547-2246<br>Fax 409/547-2740 |

- **Woodville Ind School Dist** PID: 01057331
  505 N Charlton St, Woodville 75979

  409/283-3752
  Fax 409/283-7962

> **Schools:** 4 \ **Teachers:** 107 \ **Students:** 1,300 \ **Special Ed Students:** 188
> \ **LEP Students:** 50 \ **College-Bound:** 75% \ **Ethnic:** Asian 1%, African
> American 24%, Hispanic 10%, Native American: 3%, Caucasian 62% \
> **Exp:** $521 (High) \ **Poverty:** 26% \ **Title I:** $505,052 \ **Open-Close:** 08/13 -
> 05/27 \ **DTBP:** $337 (High)

Lisa Meysembourg ............................1,57
Dwight Hollingsworth .......................3,91
Ronald Brown ........................................5
Jimmy Tucker ...................................... 67
Angela Hollingsworth ....................83,85*

Cody Jarrott ................................. 2,11,15
Linda Johnson ........................................4
Jennifer Dunsom ................................. 58
Jeremy Coker ...................... 73,76,84,295
Jason Hicks ........................................ 88*

| Public Schs..Principal | Grd | Prgm | Enr/#Cls | SN | |
|---|---|---|---|---|---|
| Wheat Elem Sch<br>306 Kirby Dr, Woodville 75979<br>Gina Greaff | PK-2 | T | 297<br>20 | 71% | 409/283-2452<br>Fax 409/331-3409 |
| Woodville High Sch<br>700 Eagle Dr, Woodville 75979<br>**Rusty Minyard** | 9-12 | ATV | 344<br>63 | 56% | 409/283-3714<br>Fax 409/331-3427 |

| Public Schs..Principal | Grd | Prgm | Enr/#Cls | SN | |
|---|---|---|---|---|---|
| Woodville Intermediate Sch<br>401 N Charlton St, Woodville 75979<br>**Bonnie Trammell** | 3-5 | T | 289<br>21 | 66% | 409/283-2549<br>Fax 409/331-3412 |
| Woodville Middle Sch<br>500 Eagle Dr, Woodville 75979<br>**Kevin Frauenberger** | 6-8 | TV | 305<br>25 | 67% | 409/283-7109<br>Fax 409/331-3418 |

## TYLER PRIVATE SCHOOLS

| Private Schs..Principal | Grd | Prgm | Enr/#Cls | SN | |
|---|---|---|---|---|---|
| St Paul's Episcopal Sch<br>1707 W Bluff St, Woodville 75979<br>Sharon Brown | PK-5 | | 28<br>3 | | 409/283-7555 |

# UPSHUR COUNTY

## UPSHUR PUBLIC SCHOOLS

- **Big Sandy Ind School Dist** PID: 01057379
  401 N Wildcat Dr, Big Sandy 75755

  903/636-5287
  Fax 903/636-5117

> **Schools:** 3 \ **Teachers:** 69 \ **Students:** 667 \ **Special Ed Students:** 81
> \ **LEP Students:** 20 \ **Ethnic:** African American 11%, Hispanic 12%,
> Caucasian 76% \ **Exp:** $615 (High) \ **Poverty:** 17% \ **Title I:** $213,799 \
> **Special Education:** $70,000 \ **Open-Close:** 08/26 - 05/28 \ **DTBP:** $358
> (High)

Mike Burns ............................................1
Joan Ford ...............................................4
Larry Minter ......................................... 6*
Jay Ratcliff .......................................... 11
Jamey Childress ................................. 67

Mary Troboy ..........................................2
Michael Crews ......................................5
Susan Williams ..................................... 7*
Peggy Oden ...................................58,93
Moriah Phillips .................. 73,76,286,295

| Public Schs..Principal | Grd | Prgm | Enr/#Cls | SN | |
|---|---|---|---|---|---|
| Big Sandy Elem Sch<br>401 N Wildcat Dr, Big Sandy 75755<br>**Andrea Blavier** | PK-5 | T | 314<br>35 | 70% | 903/636-5287<br>Fax 903/636-5311 |
| Big Sandy High Sch<br>401 N Wildcat Dr, Big Sandy 75755<br>Kim Stradley | 9-12 | TV | 206<br>17 | 59% | 903/636-5287<br>Fax 903/636-5111 |
| Big Sandy Junior High Sch<br>401 N Wildcat Dr, Big Sandy 75755<br>Kimberly Stradley | 6-8 | T | 147<br>10 | 65% | 903/636-5287<br>Fax 903/636-5111 |

- **Gilmer Ind School Dist** PID: 01057408
  500 S Trinity St, Gilmer 75644

  903/841-7400
  Fax 903/843-5279

> **Schools:** 4 \ **Teachers:** 171 \ **Students:** 2,437 \ **Special Ed Students:** 224
> \ **LEP Students:** 196 \ **College-Bound:** 49% \ **Ethnic:** African American
> 12%, Hispanic 22%, Native American: 1%, Caucasian 65% \ **Exp:** $350
> (High) \ **Poverty:** 20% \ **Title I:** $720,389 \ **Special Education:** $330,000 \
> **Open-Close:** 08/12 - 05/20 \ **DTBP:** $510 (High) \

Rick Albritton ........................................1
Hoby Holder ..........................................3
Roberta Jones .......................................4
Matt Turner ......................................... 6*
Dawn Harris ..........................11,15,273

Beverly Bobo .........................................2
Jerry Davis ............................................3
Greg Hanlin ...........................................5
Delinda Wall .........................8,57,83,271
Greg Watson ....................................... 15

| | | | | | | | | |
|---|---|---|---|---|---|---|---|---|
| **1** Superintendent | **8** Curric/Instruct K-12 | **19** Chief Financial Officer | **29** Family/Consumer Science | **39** Social Studies K-12 | **49** English/Lang Arts Elem | **59** Special Education Elem | **69** Academic Assessment | |
| **2** Bus/Finance/Purchasing | **9** Curric/Instruct Elem | **20** Art K-12 | **30** Adult Education | **40** Social Studies Elem | **50** English/Lang Arts Sec | **60** Special Education Sec | **70** Research/Development | |
| **3** Buildings And Grounds | **10** Curric/Instruct Sec | **21** Art Elem | **31** Career/Sch-to-Work K-12 | **41** Social Studies Sec | **51** Reading K-12 | **61** Foreign/World Lang K-12 | **71** Public Information | |
| **4** Food Service | **11** Federal Program | **22** Art Sec | **32** Career/Sch-to-Work Elem | **42** Science K-12 | **52** Reading Elem | **62** Foreign/World Lang Elem | **72** Summer School | |
| **5** Transportation | **12** Title I | **23** Music K-12 | **33** Career/Sch-to-Work Sec | **43** Science Elem | **53** Reading Sec | **63** Foreign/World Lang Sec | **73** Instructional Tech | |
| **6** Athletic | **13** Title V | **24** Music Elem | **34** Early Childhood Ed | **44** Science Sec | **54** Remedial Reading K-12 | **64** Religious Education K-12 | **74** Inservice Training | |
| **7** Health Services | **15** Asst Superintendent | **25** Music Sec | **35** Health/Phys Education | **45** Math K-12 | **55** Remedial Reading Elem | **65** Religious Education Elem | **75** Marketing/Distributive | |
| | **16** Instructional Media Svcs | **26** Business Education | **36** Guidance Services K-12 | **46** Math Elem | **56** Remedial Reading Sec | **66** Religious Education Sec | **76** Info Systems | |
| | **17** Chief Operations Officer | **27** Career & Tech Ed | **37** Guidance Services Elem | **47** Math Sec | **57** Bilingual/ELL | **67** School Board President | **77** Psychological Assess | |
| **TX—378** | **18** Chief Academic Officer | **28** Technology Education | **38** Guidance Services Sec | **48** English/Lang Arts K-12 | **58** Special Education K-12 | **68** Teacher Personnel | **78** Affirmative Action | |

Dr Peggy Oden .................................58　Mark Skinner .........................................67
Charlyn Harrel ...............................69　Jeff Hamilton ....................................71,79
Rusty Ivey ......................................73　Karen Holyfield ......................................76

| Public Schs..Principal | Grd | Prgm | Enr/#Cls | SN | |
|---|---|---|---|---|---|
| Bruce Junior High Sch<br>111 Bruce St, Gilmer 75645<br>**Bill Bradshaw** | 7-8 | T | 353<br>25 | 70% | 903/841-7600<br>Fax 903/843-6108 |
| Gilmer Elem Sch<br>1625 US Highway 271 N, Gilmer 75644<br>Kim Kemp | PK-4 | T | 933<br>30 | 78% | 903/841-7700<br>Fax 903/797-3773 |
| Gilmer High Sch<br>850 Buffalo St, Gilmer 75644<br>**Brian Bowman** | 9-12 | TV | 708<br>60 | 58% | 903/841-7500<br>Fax 903/843-2171 |
| Gilmer Intermediate Sch<br>1623 US Highway 271 N, Gilmer 75644<br>Gina Treadway | 5-6 | T | 389<br>16 | 72% | 903/841-7800<br>Fax 903/797-6346 |

- **Harmony Ind School Dist** PID: 01057458　　　903/725-5492
  9788 State Highway 154 W, Big Sandy 75755　　　Fax 903/725-6737

> **Schools:** 4 \ **Teachers:** 86 \ **Students:** 1,050 \ **Special Ed Students:** 70
> \ **LEP Students:** 43 \ **Ethnic:** African American 1%, Hispanic 15%,
> Caucasian 84% \ **Exp:** $461 (High) \ **Poverty:** 20% \ **Title I:** $245,481 \
> **Open-Close:** 08/17 - 05/26 \ **DTBP:** $352 (High)

Dennis Glenn ...............................1,83　Lena Williamson .....................................2
Mike Powell ......................................3　Terry Ward ..............................................4
Bo Bohannan ....................................5　Tim Russell ............................................6*
Dr Peggy Oden ...............................58　Jerry Key .................................................67
Tammy Swanner ............................68　Tory Cunningham .............................73,76
Amy Denman .................................294

| Public Schs..Principal | Grd | Prgm | Enr/#Cls | SN | |
|---|---|---|---|---|---|
| Harmony High Sch<br>9788 State Highway 154 W, Big Sandy 75755<br>Michael Alphin | 9-12 | | 324<br>24 | 39% | 903/725-5495<br>Fax 903/725-7079 |
| Harmony Irons-Smith Interm Sch<br>9788 State Highway 154 W, Big Sandy 75755<br>**Lynn Whitaker** | 4-5 | T | 158<br>8 | 51% | 903/725-7077<br>Fax 903/725-7370 |
| Harmony Junior High Sch<br>9788 State Highway 154 W, Big Sandy 75755<br>Lonnie Henry | 6-8 | T | 270<br>24 | 54% | 903/725-5485<br>Fax 903/725-7270 |
| James E Poole Elem Sch<br>9788 State Highway 154 W, Big Sandy 75755<br>**Diane Chevalier** | PK-3 | | 345<br>23 | | 903/725-5496<br>Fax 903/725-7078 |

- **New Diana Ind School Dist** PID: 01057484　　　903/663-8000
  1373 US Highway 259 S, Diana 75640　　　Fax 903/241-7393

> **Schools:** 3 \ **Teachers:** 81 \ **Students:** 1,073 \ **Special Ed Students:** 67
> \ **LEP Students:** 17 \ **College-Bound:** 68% \ **Ethnic:** African American
> 7%, Hispanic 14%, Caucasian 79% \ **Exp:** $360 (High) \ **Poverty:** 12% \
> **Title I:** $192,301 \ **Special Education:** $107,000 \ **Open-Close:** 08/17 -
> 05/27 \ **DTBP:** $333 (High) \ f

Carl Key ...............................................1　Melinda Benson .............................2,71,97
Bruce Jeffery ....................................3*　Toni Druschke .......................................4*
Scott Farler .........8,57,58,69,271,274,288　Melissa Ryan .................................11,298
Jeff Hamilton ....................................67　Sharon Wager .................................73,295*

| Public Schs..Principal | Grd | Prgm | Enr/#Cls | SN | |
|---|---|---|---|---|---|
| New Diana High Sch<br>11826 State Highway 154 E, Diana 75640<br>**John Gross** | 9-12 | ATV | 324<br>23 | 36% | 903/663-8001<br>Fax 903/663-2200 |

| Public Schs..Principal | Grd | Prgm | Enr/#Cls | SN | |
|---|---|---|---|---|---|
| New Diana Middle Sch<br>11854 State Highway 154 E, Diana 75640<br>John Gross | 6-8 | T | 262<br>12 | 44% | 903/663-8002<br>Fax 903/663-1812<br>f |
| Robert F Hunt Elem Sch<br>11150 State Highway 154 E, Diana 75640<br>**Ashley Zucosky** | PK-5 | T | 487<br>25 | 46% | 903/663-8004<br>Fax 903/663-7375 |

- **Ore City Ind School Dist** PID: 01057525　　　903/968-3300
  100 Rebel Rd N, Ore City 75683　　　Fax 903/708-6485

> **Schools:** 3 \ **Teachers:** 76 \ **Students:** 850 \ **Special Ed Students:** 105
> \ **LEP Students:** 42 \ **Ethnic:** African American 6%, Hispanic 17%, Native
> American: 1%, Caucasian 77% \ **Exp:** $530 (High) \ **Poverty:** 30% \
> **Title I:** $376,759 \ **Special Education:** $150,000 \ **Open-Close:** 08/10 -
> 05/21 \ **DTBP:** $343 (High) \ t

Lynn Heflin ..........................................1　Talina McElhany ......................................2
Jim West .........................................3,5　Donna Denton ..........................................4
Ron Bruhmer ......................................6　Mindy Hamilton .......................................7*
Matilda Anderson ..........8,11,57,69,288,294　Deb Tilley ...............................................33*
Elise Peterson ..................................37　Teddy Ott ........................................58,270
Ms Berryman ....................................67　Shelly Draper .........................................68
Zack Thomas ....................................73　Kim Freeman .........................................88*
Lesa Wright ....................................285*

| Public Schs..Principal | Grd | Prgm | Enr/#Cls | SN | |
|---|---|---|---|---|---|
| Ore City Elem Sch<br>1000 US Highway 259 S, Ore City 75683<br>Chad Miller | PK-5 | TV | 411<br>30 | 72% | 903/968-3300<br>Fax 903/968-6903 |
| Ore City High Sch<br>100 Rebel Rd N, Ore City 75683<br>Nathan Heflin | 9-12 | T | 263<br>20 | 56% | 903/968-3300<br>Fax 903/968-8726 |
| Ore City Middle Sch<br>100 Rebel Rd N, Ore City 75683<br>Beau Vincent | 6-8 | T | 230<br>12 | 67% | 903/968-3300<br>Fax 903/968-4446 |

- **Union Grove Ind School Dist** PID: 01057551　　　903/845-5509
  11220 Union Grove Rd, Gladewater 75647　　　Fax 903/845-6178

> **Schools:** 2 \ **Teachers:** 63 \ **Students:** 754 \ **Special Ed Students:** 40 \
> **LEP Students:** 14 \ **College-Bound:** 58% \ **Ethnic:** African American 1%,
> Hispanic 7%, Native American: 1%, Caucasian 91% \ **Exp:** $649 (High) \
> **Poverty:** 14% \ **Title I:** $120,537 \ **Open-Close:** 08/10 - 05/26 \ **DTBP:** $553
> (High) \ f t

Kelly Moore .........................................1　Laurice Marshall .................................2,11
Chris Wayt .......................................3,5　Cynthia Vance ........................................4*
Scotty Lament ....................................6　Jodie Mayhan ...........................................7
Sherrill Ballard .............................11,296　Inga Davis ..........................................16,82*
December Wimberley .................57,271*　Tracy Webb .............................................58*
Terri Woodfin ..................................68　Kyle Adams .......................................73,84
Kelly Klein ......................................298　Jaclyn Watson ......................................752

| Public Schs..Principal | Grd | Prgm | Enr/#Cls | SN | |
|---|---|---|---|---|---|
| Union Grove Elem Sch<br>11220 Union Grove Rd, Gladewater 75647<br>Lynn Whitaker | PK-6 | T | 411<br>25 | 51% | 903/845-3481<br>Fax 903/845-6270 |
| Union Grove Jr Sr High Sch<br>11220 Union Grove Rd, Gladewater 75647<br>**Rachel Evers** | 7-12 | | 343<br>34 | 43% | 903/845-5506<br>Fax 903/845-3003<br>f t |

- **Union Hill Ind School Dist** PID: 01057587
  2197 FM 2088, Gilmer 75644

  903/762-2140
  Fax 903/762-6845

**Schools:** 1 \ **Teachers:** 37 \ **Students:** 325 \ **Special Ed Students:** 21 \ **LEP Students:** 10 \ **College-Bound:** 85% \ **Ethnic:** African American 7%, Hispanic 14%, Native American: 1%, Caucasian 78% \ **Exp:** $535 (High) \ **Poverty:** 24% \ **Title I:** $103,717 \ **Open-Close:** 08/31 - 05/27 \ **DTBP:** $1,257 (High)

Dr Troy Batts .................................1,11
Don Sinquefield .............................. 3,5
Dr John Denson ................................ 8*
Sara Batts .........................10,88,271*
James Parker ................................... 67
Melissa Hoelscher ........................... 76
Kyle Youngblood ............................... 2
Hilda Nelms ......................................4*
Dr John Denson .................................. 8
Michel Lain .....................................16*
Mark Massingill ...............................73*

| Public Schs..Principal | Grd | Prgm | Enr/#Cls | SN |
|---|---|---|---|---|
| Union Hill Sch<br>2197 FM 2088, Gilmer 75644<br>Sara Batts \ Dr John Denson | PK-12 | TV | 325<br>28 | 51% 903/762-2138<br>Fax 903/762-6742 |

## UPTON COUNTY

## UPTON PUBLIC SCHOOLS

- **McCamey Ind School Dist** PID: 01057616
  112 E 11th St, Mc Camey 79752

  432/652-3666
  Fax 432/652-4219

**Schools:** 3 \ **Teachers:** 42 \ **Students:** 560 \ **Special Ed Students:** 52 \ **LEP Students:** 26 \ **College-Bound:** 50% \ **Ethnic:** African American 2%, Hispanic 73%, Native American: 1%, Caucasian 24% \ **Exp:** $536 (High) \ **Poverty:** 23% \ **Title I:** $154,565 \ **Open-Close:** 08/17 - 05/27 \ **DTBP:** $329 (High)

**Michael Valencia** ................................... 1
Michelle Falcon ...................................... 4
Leann McGraw ................................. 10,57
Luann Elliott ..................31,36,69,83,85,88*
Gail Molder ........................................ 2,11,26
Dana McWilliams ...........................5,295,297
Sara Hill ........................................... 23
Charollete Jones ................................ 67

| Public Schs..Principal | Grd | Prgm | Enr/#Cls | SN |
|---|---|---|---|---|
| McCamey High Sch<br>1201 S Burleson, Mc Camey 79752<br>Michael Valencia | 9-12 | TV | 145<br>25 | 62% 432/652-3666<br>Fax 432/652-4245 |
| McCamey Middle Sch<br>200 E 11th St, Mc Camey 79752<br>Blanca Smith | 5-8 | T | 151<br>16 | 78% 432/652-3666<br>Fax 432/652-4246 |
| McCamey Primary Sch<br>400 E 11th St, Mc Camey 79752<br>Michelle Schreiner | PK-4 | T | 228<br>20 | 75% 432/652-3666<br>Fax 432/652-4247 |

- **Rankin Ind School Dist** PID: 01057654
  1201 N Upton St, Rankin 79778

  432/693-2461
  Fax 432/693-2353

**Schools:** 2 \ **Teachers:** 37 \ **Students:** 294 \ **Special Ed Students:** 22 \ **LEP Students:** 23 \ **College-Bound:** 70% \ **Ethnic:** African American 1%, Hispanic 45%, Native American: 1%, Caucasian 53% \ **Exp:** $1,497 (High) \ **Poverty:** 10% \ **Title I:** $26,519 \ **Open-Close:** 08/10 - 05/20 \ **DTBP:** $337 (High)

Samuel Wyatt ...................................... 1
Tracy Clanton .................................... 3,5
Garret Avalos ...................................... 6
Elidia Gallardo .................................. 11
Jon Bright .........................................58*
Amanda Evridge ................................. 67
Adrian Gallardo .............................83,88*
Dawn Wyatt ......................................... 2
Reyna Rodriguez ................................. 4
Amy Cura ............................................ 7
Olga Martinez .................................... 57
Carrie Templeton ............................... 60
Michele Ricker .............................. 73,295

| Public Schs..Principal | Grd | Prgm | Enr/#Cls | SN |
|---|---|---|---|---|
| James D Gossett Elem Sch<br>511 W 12th St, Rankin 79778<br>Brad Riker | PK-5 | T | 149<br>14 | 54% 432/693-2455<br>Fax 432/693-2552 |
| Rankin High Sch<br>1201 Upton St, Rankin 79778<br>Adrian Gallardo | 7-12 | TV | 108<br>20 | 47% 432/693-2451<br>Fax 432/693-2453 |

## UVALDE COUNTY

## UVALDE PUBLIC SCHOOLS

- **Knippa Ind School Dist** PID: 01057692
  100 Kessler Ln, Knippa 78870

  830/934-2176
  Fax 830/934-2490

**Schools:** 1 \ **Teachers:** 36 \ **Students:** 460 \ **Special Ed Students:** 31 \ **LEP Students:** 14 \ **College-Bound:** 80% \ **Ethnic:** Asian 2%, Hispanic 58%, Caucasian 40% \ **Exp:** $414 (High) \ **Poverty:** 52% \ **Title I:** $172,738 \ **Open-Close:** 08/20 - 05/21 \ **DTBP:** $322 (High) \ 🔲 🔲

Elda Alejandro .................................... 1
Ted Sanderlin ..................................... 67
Melissa Garza ...........................8,12,298
Joe Cordova ......................................73*

| Public Schs..Principal | Grd | Prgm | Enr/#Cls | SN |
|---|---|---|---|---|
| Knippa Sch<br>100 Kessler Ln, Knippa 78870<br>Melissa Garza | PK-12 | T | 460<br>17 | 35% 830/934-2176<br>Fax 830/934-2390 |

- **Sabinal Ind School Dist** PID: 01057733
  409 W Cullins St, Sabinal 78881

  830/988-2472
  Fax 830/988-7151

**Schools:** 2 \ **Teachers:** 38 \ **Students:** 429 \ **Special Ed Students:** 53 \ **LEP Students:** 24 \ **College-Bound:** 72% \ **Ethnic:** Hispanic 81%, Native American: 1%, Caucasian 19% \ **Exp:** $541 (High) \ **Poverty:** 28% \ **Title I:** $190,881 \ **Open-Close:** 08/26 - 05/21 \ **DTBP:** $341 (High)

Richard Grill ....................................... 1
Andy Lopez ...................................... 3,5*
Jason Keller ...................................... 6*
Michael Neuman ................................ 15
Michael Casas ................................. 23*
Bob Nunley ........................................ 67
Steve Alvarado .................................. 88
Michael Neuman .............2,8,11,36,69,77,91*
Shea Gilleland .................................... 4
Cecilia Reyes ..................................... 7*
Monica DeLeon ................................ 16*
Beatriz Valenzuela ........................... 38*
Howard Karre ....................73,286,295*
Beth Brady ...................................... 275*

| Public Schs..Principal | Grd | Prgm | Enr/#Cls | SN |
|---|---|---|---|---|
| Sabinal Elem Sch<br>900 W Pickford St, Sabinal 78881<br>Beth Brady | PK-5 | T | 168<br>20 | 79% 830/988-2436<br>Fax 830/988-7142 |
| Sabinal High Sch<br>409 W Cullins St, Sabinal 78881<br>Steve Alvarado | 6-12 | TV | 261<br>40 | 81% 830/988-2475<br>Fax 830/988-7170 |

| | | | | | |
|---|---|---|---|---|---|
| 1 Superintendent | 8 Curric/Instruct K-12 | 19 Chief Financial Officer | 29 Family/Consumer Science | 39 Social Studies K-12 | 49 English/Lang Arts Elem | 59 Special Education Elem | 69 Academic Assessment |
| 2 Bus/Finance/Purchasing | 9 Curric/Instruct Elem | 20 Art K-12 | 30 Adult Education | 40 Social Studies Elem | 50 English/Lang Arts Sec | 60 Special Education Sec | 70 Research/Development |
| 3 Buildings And Grounds | 10 Curric/Instruct Sec | 21 Art Elem | 31 Career/Sch-to-Work K-12 | 41 Social Studies Sec | 51 Reading K-12 | 61 Foreign/World Lang K-12 | 71 Public Information |
| 4 Food Service | 11 Federal Program | 22 Art Sec | 32 Career/Sch-to-Work Elem | 42 Science K-12 | 52 Reading Elem | 62 Foreign/World Lang Elem | 72 Summer School |
| 5 Transportation | 12 Title I | 23 Music K-12 | 33 Career/Sch-to-Work Sec | 43 Science Elem | 53 Reading Sec | 63 Foreign/World Lang Sec | 73 Instructional Tech |
| 6 Athletic | 13 Title V | 24 Music Elem | 34 Early Childhood Ed | 44 Science Sec | 54 Remedial Reading K-12 | 64 Religious Education K-12 | 74 Inservice Training |
| 7 Health Services | 14 Asst Superintendent | 25 Music Sec | 35 Health/Phys Education | 45 Math K-12 | 55 Remedial Reading Elem | 65 Religious Education Elem | 75 Marketing/Distributive |
| | 16 Instructional Media Svcs | 26 Business Education | 36 Guidance Services K-12 | 46 Math Elem | 56 Remedial Reading Sec | 66 Religious Education Sec | 76 Info Systems |
| **TX—380** | 17 Chief Operations Officer | 27 Career & Tech Ed | 37 Guidance Services Elem | 47 Math Sec | 57 Bilingual/ELL | 67 School Board President | 77 Psychological Assess |
| | 18 Chief Academic Officer | 28 Technology Education | 38 Guidance Services Sec | 48 English/Lang Arts K-12 | 58 Special Education K-12 | 68 Teacher Personnel | 78 Affirmative Action |

● **Utopia Ind School Dist** PID: 01057769
258 School St, Utopia 78884

830/966-1928
Fax 830/966-6162

**Schools:** 1 \ **Teachers:** 20 \ **Students:** 210 \ **Special Ed Students:** 27 \ **LEP Students:** 9 \ **College-Bound:** 90% \ **Ethnic:** Asian 1%, Hispanic 24%, Caucasian 74% \ **Exp:** $549 (High) \ **Poverty:** 18% \ **Title I:** $45,540 \ **Open-Close:** 08/20 - 05/25 \ **DTBP:** $358 (High)

| | | |
|---|---|---|
| Michael Derry ............... 1,11,288 | Karen Heideman ........................... 2 | |
| Kim Reyes ...................... 4* | Alan Harris ................................ 6* | |
| Patti McCaleb ................ 7* | Julie Mazurek ...... 8,12,57,74,271,274,296 | |
| Theresa Loman .............. 16* | Carol Calk ................................. 58* | |
| Steve Darden ................ 67 | David Carter ........................ 73,76 | |

| Public Schs..Principal | Grd | Prgm | Enr/#Cls | SN | |
|---|---|---|---|---|---|
| Utopia Sch<br>258 School St, Utopia 78884<br>Bryan Hernandez | PK-12 | TV | 210<br>30 | 41% | 830/966-3339 |

● **Uvalde Cons Ind School Dist** PID: 01057795
1000 N Getty St, Uvalde 78801

830/278-6655
Fax 830/591-4909

**Schools:** 8 \ **Teachers:** 280 \ **Students:** 4,221 \ **Special Ed Students:** 435 \ **LEP Students:** 274 \ **Ethnic:** Hispanic 90%, Caucasian 10% \ **Exp:** $448 (High) \ **Poverty:** 32% \ **Title I:** $2,252,071 \ **Special Education:** $791,000 \ **Open-Close:** 08/17 - 05/27 \ **DTBP:** $158 (High)

| | | |
|---|---|---|
| Dr Hal Harrell ....................... 1 | Billie Collins ........................... 2,19 | |
| Leo Hicks ............................. 4 | Russell Lee ................................ 5 | |
| Traci Dillard ....................... 7* | Michael Rodriguez ............... 8,15,285 | |
| Dr Sandra Garza ................ 10 | Beth Reavis .................... 11,15,296 | |
| Mario Feron ....................... 57 | Victor Baron ............................. 58 | |
| Javier Flores ..................... 67 | Anne Marie Espinoza ................. 71 | |
| Cash Keith ......................... 73 | | |

| Public Schs..Principal | Grd | Prgm | Enr/#Cls | SN | |
|---|---|---|---|---|---|
| Anthon Elem Sch<br>224 N Benson Rd, Uvalde 78801<br>**Beatrice Martinez** | 1-2 | T | 678<br>32 | 82% | 830/591-2988<br>Fax 830/591-2993 |
| Batesville Elem Sch<br>496 Garden St, Batesville 78829<br>Felicitos Flores | PK-6 | T | 98<br>14 | 94% | 830/376-4221<br>Fax 830/376-4223 |
| Ⓐ Crossroads Academy High Sch<br>601 Dean St, Uvalde 78801<br>Dr Hector Lopez | 11-12 | | 80 | | 830/333-7002 |
| Dalton Early Childhood Center<br>600 N 4th St, Uvalde 78801<br>Abraham Contreras | PK-K | T | 300<br>36 | 82% | 830/591-4933<br>Fax 830/591-4936 |
| Flores Elem Sch<br>901 N Getty St, Uvalde 78801<br>Michelle Rodriguez | 5-6 | T | 605<br>18 | 86% | 830/591-2976<br>Fax 830/591-2987 |
| Morales Junior High Sch<br>615 Studer St, Uvalde 78801<br>Isidro Escamilla | 7-8 | TV | 668<br>52 | 81% | 830/591-2980<br>Fax 830/591-2975 |
| Robb Elem Sch<br>715 Old Carrizo Rd, Uvalde 78801<br>Abraham Gonzales \ **Abraham Contreras** | 3-4 | T | 597<br>27 | 87% | 830/591-4947<br>Fax 830/591-4937 |
| Uvalde High Sch<br>1 Coyote Trl, Uvalde 78801<br>Elizabeth Sandoval | 9-12 | TV | 1,207 | 75% | 830/591-2950<br>Fax 830/591-2961 |

## UVALDE CATHOLIC SCHOOLS

● **Archdiocese San Antonio Ed Off** PID: 00999724
Listing includes only schools located in this county. See District Index for location of Diocesan Offices.

| Catholic Schs..Principal | Grd | Prgm | Enr/#Cls | SN | |
|---|---|---|---|---|---|
| Sacred Heart Sch<br>401 W Leona St, Uvalde 78801<br>Janice Estrada | PK-6 | | 51<br>8 | | 830/278-2661<br>Fax 830/279-0634 |

## UVALDE PRIVATE SCHOOLS

| Private Schs..Principal | Grd | Prgm | Enr/#Cls | SN | |
|---|---|---|---|---|---|
| St Philip's Episcopal Sch<br>343 N Getty St, Uvalde 78801<br>Jean Chisum | PK-3 | | 65<br>7 | | 830/278-1350<br>Fax 830/278-2093 |

## VAL VERDE COUNTY

## VAL VERDE PUBLIC SCHOOLS

● **Comstock Ind School Dist** PID: 01057898
101 Sanderson St, Comstock 78837

432/292-4444
Fax 432/292-4436

**Schools:** 1 \ **Teachers:** 18 \ **Students:** 199 \ **Special Ed Students:** 14 \ **LEP Students:** 5 \ **College-Bound:** 100% \ **Ethnic:** Asian 1%, African American 2%, Hispanic 52%, Caucasian 46% \ **Exp:** $522 (High) \ **Poverty:** 19% \ **Title I:** $33,421 \ **Special Education:** $22,000 \ **Open-Close:** 08/14 - 05/20 \ **DTBP:** $304 (High) \ 🅵 🅣

| | | |
|---|---|---|
| Orlie Wolfenbarger ............. 1,11,83 | Amie Smith .............................. 2 | |
| Tina Meza ............................ 2 | Queta Vela ............................ 4* | |
| Rita Sanchez ............... 4,58,69,73* | Laura Parker .......... 6,8,69,74,273,274 | |
| Valarie Sanchez .................. 12 | Karin Greene ........................ 16* | |
| Bill Zuberbueler ................. 67 | | |

| Public Schs..Principal | Grd | Prgm | Enr/#Cls | SN | |
|---|---|---|---|---|---|
| Comstock Sch<br>101 Sanderson St, Comstock 78837<br>Laura Parker | K-12 | T | 199<br>18 | 31% | 432/292-4444 |

● **San Felipe-Del Rio Cons Ind SD** PID: 01057941
315 Griner St, Del Rio 78840

830/778-4000
Fax 830/774-9840

**Schools:** 12 \ **Teachers:** 631 \ **Students:** 10,472 \ **Special Ed Students:** 1,061 \ **LEP Students:** 1,695 \ **Ethnic:** African American 1%, Hispanic 94%, Caucasian 5% \ **Exp:** $411 (High) \ **Poverty:** 29% \ **Title I:** $3,874,405 \ **Special Education:** $1,977,000 \ **Open-Close:** 08/19 - 05/21 \ **DTBP:** $172 (High) \ 🅵 🅣

| | | |
|---|---|---|
| Carlos Rios ........................... 1 | Henry Arredondo .................. 2,19 | |
| Ric Smith ............................. 6 | Aida Gomez ............................. 8 | |
| Waymond Meza .................... 67 | Aidee Garcia .......................... 68 | |
| Leslie Hayenga ............... 73,286 | Michelle Gonzalez ................. 280 | |

| | | | |
|---|---|---|---|
| 79 Student Personnel | 91 Safety/Security | 275 Response To Intervention | 298 Grant Writer/Ptnrships |
| 80 Driver Ed/Safety | 92 Magnet School | 277 Remedial Math K-12 | 750 Chief Innovation Officer |
| 81 Gifted/Talented | 93 Parental Involvement | 280 Literacy Coach | 751 Chief of Staff |
| 82 Video Services | 95 Tech Prep Program | 285 STEM | 752 Social Emotional Learning |
| 83 Substance Abuse Prev | 97 Chief Infomation Officer | 286 Digital Learning | |
| 84 Erate | 98 Chief Technology Officer | 288 Common Core Standards | **Other School Types** |
| 85 AIDS Education | 270 Character Education | 294 Accountability | Ⓐ = Alternative School |
| 88 Alternative/At Risk | 271 Migrant Education | 295 Network System | Ⓒ = Charter School |
| 89 Multi-Cultural Curriculum | 273 Teacher Mentor | 296 Title II Programs | Ⓜ = Magnet School |
| 90 Social Work | 274 Before/After Sch | 297 Webmaster | Ⓨ = Year-Round School |

**School Programs**
A = Alternative Program
G = Adult Classes
M = Magnet Program
T = Title I Schoolwide
V = Career & Tech Ed Programs

**Social Media**
🅵 = Facebook
🅣 = Twitter

New Schools are shaded
New Superintendents and Principals are bold
Personnel with email addresses are underscored

Gilbert Vazquez .................................. 295

| Public Schs..Principal | Grd | Prgm | Enr/#Cls | SN |
|---|---|---|---|---|
| Buena Vista Elem Sch<br>100 Echo Valley Dr, Del Rio 78840<br>Jennifer Sutton | K-5 | T | 754<br>34 | 50% 830/778-4600<br>Fax 830/774-9875 |
| Del Rio Freshman Sch<br>90 Memorial Dr, Del Rio 78840<br>Patricia Rodriguez | 9-9 | TV | 819 | 67% 830/778-4400<br>Fax 830/774-9873 |
| Del Rio High Sch<br>100 Memorial Dr, Del Rio 78840<br>Jose Perez | 10-12 | ATV | 2,134<br>100 | 70% 830/778-4300<br>Fax 830/774-9320 |
| Del Rio Middle Sch<br>720 E De La Rosa St, Del Rio 78840<br>Sergio Jimenez | 7-8 | TV | 1,537 | 72% 830/778-4500<br>Fax 830/778-4912 |
| Dr Fermin Calderon Elem Sch<br>Highway 90 E, Del Rio 78840<br>Jane Villarreal | PK-5 | T | 536<br>38 | 85% 830/778-4620<br>Fax 830/774-9975 |
| Dr Lonnie Green Elem Sch<br>905 W Cantu Rd, Del Rio 78840<br>Cheryl Pond | K-5 | T | 794<br>60 | 70% 830/778-4750<br>Fax 830/774-9532 |
| Garfield Elem Sch<br>300 W Martin St, Del Rio 78840<br>Denise Rubio | PK-5 | T | 532<br>46 | 86% 830/778-4700<br>Fax 830/774-9928 |
| Irene C Cardwell Elem Sch<br>1009 Avenue J, Del Rio 78840<br>Rufina Adams | PK-PK | T | 496<br>32 | 91% 830/778-4650<br>Fax 830/774-9855 |
| Lamar Elem Sch<br>301 Waters Ave, Del Rio 78840<br>Iris Oca | K-5 | T | 541<br>52 | 85% 830/778-4730<br>Fax 830/774-9493 |
| North Heights Elem Sch<br>2003 N Main St, Del Rio 78840<br>Maytte Soliz | PK-5 | T | 545<br>22 | 80% 830/778-4777<br>Fax 830/778-4772 |
| Ruben Chavira Elem Sch<br>2253 S US Hwy 277, Del Rio 78840<br>Maria Correa | K-5 | T | 496<br>40 | 86% 830/778-4660<br>Fax 830/778-4921 |
| San Felipe Memorial Middle Sch<br>1207 W Garza St, Del Rio 78840<br>Celia Zuniga-Barrera | 6-6 | T | 695<br>35 | 74% 830/778-4560<br>Fax 830/778-4920 |

## VAL VERDE CATHOLIC SCHOOLS

• **Archdiocese San Antonio Ed Off** PID: 00999724
Listing includes only schools located in this county. See District Index for location of Diocesan Offices.

| Catholic Schs..Principal | Grd | Prgm | Enr/#Cls | SN |
|---|---|---|---|---|
| Sacred Heart Sch<br>209 E Greenwood St, Del Rio 78840<br>Araceli Faz | PK-8 | | 266<br>16 | 830/775-3274<br>Fax 830/774-2836 |

## VAL VERDE PRIVATE SCHOOLS

| Private Schs..Principal | Grd | Prgm | Enr/#Cls | SN |
|---|---|---|---|---|
| Bible Way Christian Academy<br>409 E Cortinas St, Del Rio 78840<br>Cynthia McCrea | PK-8 | | 200 | 830/775-9921<br>Fax 830/775-2475 |
| St James Episcopal Sch<br>206 W Greenwood St, Del Rio 78840<br>Kate Delosontas | PK-5 | | 147<br>18 | 830/775-9911<br>Fax 830/488-6228 |

## VAN ZANDT COUNTY

## VAN ZANDT PUBLIC SCHOOLS

• **Canton Ind School Dist** PID: 01058086
1045 S Buffalo St, Canton 75103
903/567-4179
Fax 903/567-2370

**Schools:** 4 \ **Teachers:** 150 \ **Students:** 2,300 \ **Special Ed Students:** 180 \ **LEP Students:** 74 \ **College-Bound:** 63% \ **Ethnic:** Asian 1%, African American 2%, Hispanic 13%, Native American 1%, Caucasian 83% \ **Exp:** $431 (High) \ **Poverty:** 11% \ **Title I:** $221,971 \ **Special Education:** $397,000 \ **Open-Close:** 08/17 - 05/21 \ **DTBP:** $344 (High)

| | | | |
|---|---|---|---|
| Dr Brain Nicoles ..................................... 1 | | Denise Stone .......................................... 2,84 | |
| Thomas Stewart ..................................... 3 | | Christy McClelen ....................................... 4 | |
| Dawn Loftin ............................................ 5 | | Robert Ivey ............................................. 6* | |
| Sunday Elerson ....................................... 7 | | Kristin Rose ....................................... 16,82* | |
| Christie Guy ........................................... 57* | | Daphne Thompson ................................... 58 | |
| Kenith Pruitt ........................................... 67 | | Stan Jontra ........................................ 73,295* | |
| Kari Webster .................................... 76,79 | | | |

| Public Schs..Principal | Grd | Prgm | Enr/#Cls | SN |
|---|---|---|---|---|
| Canton Elem Sch<br>1163 S Buffalo St, Canton 75103<br>Kelly Lamar | PK-2 | T | 497<br>30 | 50% 903/567-6521<br>Fax 903/567-5373<br>t |
| Canton High Sch<br>1110 W Highway 243, Canton 75103<br>Dusty Spencer | 9-12 | | 625<br>60 | 28% 903/567-6561<br>Fax 903/567-6562<br>t |
| Canton Intermediate Sch<br>1190 W Highway 243, Canton 75103<br>Angela McLeod | 3-5 | T | 495<br>35 | 44% 903/567-6418<br>Fax 903/567-2956 |
| Canton Junior High Sch<br>1115 S Buffalo St, Canton 75103<br>Dawn Boyd | 6-8 | T | 519<br>30 | 36% 903/567-4329<br>Fax 903/567-1298 |

• **Edgewood Ind School Dist** PID: 01058115
804 E Pine St, Edgewood 75117
903/896-4332
Fax 903/896-4306

**Schools:** 4 \ **Teachers:** 78 \ **Students:** 950 \ **Special Ed Students:** 124 \ **LEP Students:** 24 \ **College-Bound:** 42% \ **Ethnic:** African American 4%, Hispanic 12%, Caucasian 84% \ **Exp:** $535 (High) \ **Poverty:** 16% \ **Title I:** $194,995 \ **Special Education:** $191,000 \ **Open-Close:** 09/01 - 05/28 \ **DTBP:** $330 (High) \ f

| | | | |
|---|---|---|---|
| Kristin Prater ......................................... 1 | | Sharon Jones ........................................... 2 | |
| William Thornton ................................. 3,5 | | Jason Seal ............................................... 6 | |
| Kathy Harper ......................................... 7 | | Becky Goodwin ......... 8,11,69,83,88,288 | |
| Meggie Erwin ....................................... 36* | | Nikki Tyndell ........................................ 57* | |
| Kelli Sassell ........................................ 58 | | Roy Soto ............................................... 67 | |
| Faye McBride ....................................... 68 | | Lori Tollier ........................................... 73* | |

| Public Schs..Principal | Grd | Prgm | Enr/#Cls | SN |
|---|---|---|---|---|
| Edgewood Elem Sch<br>804 E Pine St, Edgewood 75117<br>Kristi Jones | PK-2 | T | 185<br>11 | 57% 903/896-4773<br>f |
| Edgewood High Sch<br>804 E Pine St, Edgewood 75117<br>Mark Kellogg | 9-12 | T | 297<br>35 | 45% 903/896-4856<br>Fax 903/896-1050 |

| | | | | | |
|---|---|---|---|---|---|
| 1 | Superintendent | 8 | Curric/Instruct K-12 | 19 | Chief Financial Officer |
| 2 | Bus/Finance/Purchasing | 9 | Curric/Instruct Elem | 20 | Art K-12 |
| 3 | Buildings And Grounds | 10 | Curric/Instruct Sec | 21 | Art Elem |
| 4 | Food Service | 11 | Federal Program | 22 | Art Sec |
| 5 | Transportation | 12 | Title I | 23 | Music K-12 |
| 6 | Athletic | 13 | Title V | 24 | Music Elem |
| 7 | Health Services | 14 | Asst Superintendent | 25 | Music Sec |
| | | 15 | Instructional Media Svcs | 26 | Business Education |
| | | 16 | Chief Operations Officer | 27 | Career & Tech Ed |
| | | 17 | Chief Academic Officer | 28 | Technology Education |

| | | | |
|---|---|---|---|
| 29 | Family/Consumer Science | 39 | Social Studies K-12 |
| 30 | Adult Education | 40 | Social Studies Elem |
| 31 | Career/Sch-to-Work K-12 | 41 | Social Studies Sec |
| 32 | Career/Sch-to-Work Elem | 42 | Science K-12 |
| 33 | Career/Sch-to-Work Sec | 43 | Science Elem |
| 34 | Early Childhood Ed | 44 | Science Sec |
| 35 | Health/Phys Education | 45 | Math K-12 |
| 36 | Guidance Services K-12 | 46 | Math Elem |
| 37 | Guidance Services Elem | 47 | Math Sec |
| 38 | Guidance Services Sec | 48 | English/Lang Arts K-12 |

| | | | |
|---|---|---|---|
| 49 | English/Lang Arts Elem | 59 | Special Education Elem |
| 50 | English/Lang Arts Sec | 60 | Special Education Sec |
| 51 | Reading K-12 | 61 | Foreign/World Lang K-12 |
| 52 | Reading Elem | 62 | Foreign/World Lang Elem |
| 53 | Reading Sec | 63 | Foreign/World Lang Sec |
| 54 | Remedial Reading K-12 | 64 | Religious Education K-12 |
| 55 | Remedial Reading Elem | 65 | Religious Education Elem |
| 56 | Remedial Reading Sec | 66 | Religious Education Sec |
| 57 | Bilingual/ELL | 67 | School Board President |
| 58 | Special Education K-12 | 68 | Teacher Personnel |

| | |
|---|---|
| 69 | Academic Assessment |
| 70 | Research/Development |
| 71 | Public Information |
| 72 | Summer School |
| 73 | Instructional Tech |
| 74 | Inservice Training |
| 75 | Marketing/Distributive |
| 76 | Info Systems |
| 77 | Psychological Assess |
| 78 | Affirmative Action |

| | | | | | | |
|---|---|---|---|---|---|---|
| Edgewood Intermediate Sch | 3-5 | T | 213 | 52% | 903/896-2143 | |
| 804 E Pine St, Edgewood 75117 | | | 21 | | Fax 903/896-7056 | |
| Shannon Orsborn | | | | | | �facebook |
| Edgewood Middle Sch | 6-8 | T | 255 | 44% | 903/896-1530 | |
| 804 E Pine St, Edgewood 75117 | | | 15 | | Fax 903/896-7349 | |
| Kassi Mays | | | | | | |

## ● Fruitvale Ind School Dist PID: 01058141

244 Vz County Road 1910, Fruitvale 75127

903/896-1191
Fax 903/896-1011

**Schools:** 3 \ **Teachers:** 36 \ **Students:** 425 \ **Special Ed Students:** 43 \ **LEP Students:** 12 \ **College-Bound:** 49% \ **Ethnic:** African American 1%, Hispanic 11%, Caucasian 87% \ **Exp:** $716 (High) \ **Poverty:** 28% \ **Title I:** $121,356 \ **Special Education:** $122,000 \ **Open-Close:** 08/13 - 05/28 \ **DTBP:** $350 (High)

| | | | |
|---|---|---|---|
| Rebecca Bain ............1 | Wendy Milam ............2 | | |
| Wallie Kroontje ............3* | Angela Clark ............8,11,89,296* | | |
| Susan McCann ............19,73,298 | Terry Furrh ............57* | | |
| Heath Yates ............67 | Amanda Masterson ............69,85,88,270* | | |
| Zach Masterson ............93* | Randy Mills ............98,295* | | |
| Charles Hartford ............285 | | | |

| Public Schs..Principal | Grd | Prgm | Enr/#Cls | SN | |
|---|---|---|---|---|---|
| Fruitvale Junior High Sch | 6-8 | T | 97 | 66% | 903/896-4363 |
| 141 Vz County Road 1901, Fruitvale 75127 | | | 19 | | Fax 903/896-4216 |
| Charles Harford | | | | | |
| Fruitvale Senior High Sch | 9-12 | GTV | 103 | 54% | 903/896-4363 |
| 141 Vz County Road 1901, Fruitvale 75127 | | | 15 | | Fax 903/896-4216 |
| Charles Harford | | | | | |
| Hallie Randall Elem Sch | PK-5 | T | 225 | 68% | 903/896-4466 |
| 131 Vz County Road 1901, Fruitvale 75127 | | | 15 | | Fax 903/896-4800 |
| Zach Masterson | | | | | |

## ● Grand Saline Ind School Dist PID: 01058165

400 Stadium Dr, Grand Saline 75140

903/962-7546
Fax 903/962-7464

**Schools:** 4 \ **Teachers:** 77 \ **Students:** 1,100 \ **Special Ed Students:** 117 \ **LEP Students:** 132 \ **College-Bound:** 5% \ **Ethnic:** Asian 1%, African American 1%, Hispanic 29%, Caucasian 69% \ **Exp:** $591 (High) \ **Poverty:** 22% \ **Title I:** $354,865 \ **Special Education:** $209,000 \ **Open-Close:** 08/24 - 05/28 \ **DTBP:** $354 (High)

| | | | |
|---|---|---|---|
| Micha Lewis ............1 | Laura Griffith ............2 | | |
| Patricia Vaughn ............4 | Joe Drennon ............6 | | |
| Debby Morse ......8,11,73,83,286,288,296,298 | Robin Goff ............31,274* | | |
| Kim Brewington ............58 | Matt Strictland ............67 | | |
| Lori Hooton ............82* | | | |

| Public Schs..Principal | Grd | Prgm | Enr/#Cls | SN | |
|---|---|---|---|---|---|
| Grand Saline Elem Sch | PK-2 | T | 257 | 69% | 903/962-7526 |
| 405 Stadium Dr, Grand Saline 75140 | | | 15 | | Fax 903/962-7438 |
| Lori Hooton | | | | | |
| Grand Saline High Sch | 9-12 | ATV | 67 | 50% | 903/962-7533 |
| 500 Stadium Dr, Grand Saline 75140 | | | 20 | | Fax 903/962-7482 |
| Ricky LaPrade | | | | | |
| Grand Saline Intermediate Sch | 3-5 | T | 252 | 64% | 903/962-5515 |
| 200 Stadium Dr, Grand Saline 75140 | | | 25 | | Fax 903/962-3783 |
| Tina Core | | | | | |
| Grand Saline Middle Sch | 6-8 | TV | 221 | 62% | 903/962-7537 |
| 400 Stadium Dr, Grand Saline 75140 | | | 20 | | Fax 903/962-7474 |
| Leland Hand | | | | | |

## ● Martin's Mill Ind Sch Dist PID: 01058191

301 FM 1861, Ben Wheeler 75754

903/479-3872
Fax 903/479-3711

**Schools:** 1 \ **Teachers:** 43 \ **Students:** 230 \ **Special Ed Students:** 53 \ **LEP Students:** 45 \ **College-Bound:** 75% \ **Ethnic:** African American 1%, Hispanic 20%, Caucasian 78% \ **Exp:** $798 (High) \ **Poverty:** 26% \ **Title I:** $184,186 \ **Special Education:** $86,000 \ **Open-Close:** 08/21 - 05/28 \ **DTBP:** $357 (High)

| | | | |
|---|---|---|---|
| James Oliver ............1 | Michelle Butcher ............2* | | |
| Gary Gordon ............3,5 | Tina Morse ............4* | | |
| Jake Bell ............6* | Rachel Martin ............8,16,73,82* | | |
| Suzette Stringer ............8,16,73,286* | Tina Stringer ............9,11,88,296,298* | | |
| Robin Gandy ............36,57,69,83,270* | Casey Swain ............58* | | |
| Dan Morrow ............67 | Casey Swain ............77 | | |
| Amber McLemore ............85* | | | |

| Public Schs..Principal | Grd | Prgm | Enr/#Cls | SN | |
|---|---|---|---|---|---|
| Martin's Mill Sch | PK-12 | ATV | 230 | 40% | 903/479-3234 |
| 301 FM 1861, Ben Wheeler 75754 | | | 35 | | Fax 903/479-3486 |
| Suzette Stringer \ Audra Latimer | | | | | |

## ● Van Ind School Dist PID: 01058232

549 E Texas St, Van 75790

903/963-8713
Fax 903/963-8797

**Schools:** 5 \ **Teachers:** 152 \ **Students:** 2,400 \ **Special Ed Students:** 270 \ **LEP Students:** 153 \ **College-Bound:** 92% \ **Ethnic:** Asian 1%, African American 3%, Hispanic 22%, Caucasian 74% \ **Exp:** $626 (High) \ **Poverty:** 16% \ **Title I:** $506,910 \ **Special Education:** $423,000 \ **Open-Close:** 09/03 - 05/28 \ **DTBP:** $363 (High) \ 🐦

| | | | |
|---|---|---|---|
| Don Dunn ............1 | Danny Morrow ............2,3,19,76 | | |
| Jared Moffatt ............6 | Dr Donna Wallace ............8,54,69,288,294,296 | | |
| Richard Pride ............11,58 | Karla Rainey ............27* | | |
| Scott Thomas ............67 | Jason Johnson ............73 | | |
| Glenn Hervieux ............84 | Thomas Robertson ............91 | | |
| Kalen Hanson ............295 | | | |

| Public Schs..Principal | Grd | Prgm | Enr/#Cls | SN | |
|---|---|---|---|---|---|
| J E Rhodes Elem Sch | PK-1 | T | 309 | 69% | 903/963-8386 |
| 250 N Pecan St, Van 75790 | | | 40 | | Fax 903/963-5586 |
| Jonnie Smith | | | | | |
| Van High Sch | 9-12 | TV | 768 | 44% | 903/963-8623 |
| 985 N Maple, Van 75790 | | | 50 | | Fax 903/963-5591 |
| Jeffery Hutchins | | | | | |
| Van Intermediate Sch | 2-3 | T | 357 | 60% | 903/963-8331 |
| 349 E Texas, Van 75790 | | | | | Fax 903/963-5582 |
| Marty Moore | | | | | |
| Van Junior High Sch | 7-8 | T | 356 | 54% | 903/963-8321 |
| 630 S Oak St, Van 75790 | | | 33 | | Fax 903/963-3277 |
| Jeremy Peterson | | | | | |
| Van Middle Sch | 4-6 | T | 561 | 57% | 903/963-1461 |
| 14300 State Hwy 110, Van 75790 | | | | | Fax 903/963-1472 |
| Shelby Davidson | | | | | |

## ● Wills Point Ind School Dist PID: 01058270

338 W North Commerce St, Wills Point 75169

903/873-3161
Fax 903/873-2462

**Schools:** 5 \ **Teachers:** 173 \ **Students:** 2,500 \ **Special Ed Students:** 299 \ **LEP Students:** 204 \ **College-Bound:** 43% \ **Ethnic:** African American 5%, Hispanic 26%, Native American: 1%, Caucasian 67% \ **Exp:** $324 (High) \ **Poverty:** 21% \ **Title I:** $710,012 \ **Special Education:** $468,000 \ **Open-Close:** 08/17 - 05/21 \ **DTBP:** $158 (High) \ 🐦

| | | | |
|---|---|---|---|
| Scott Caloss ............1 | Cheree Ivy ............2 | | |
| Mark Kellogg ............3 | Susan Pace ............4 | | |

Brian Stokes .............................................5
Tammi Lide ...............................................7*
Kendrea Entrop ..............................11,16,58
Melanie Mullin ..........................16,73,295
Nancy Morris ..........................................73

Tommy Poynter .........................................6
Barbi McMath ........8,15,285,286,288,294,298
Jeff Russell ............................................15
George Wilcoxson ...................................67
Donna Rowland .......................................98

| Public Schs..Principal | Grd | Prgm | Enr/#Cls | SN |
|---|---|---|---|---|
| Earnest O Woods Interm Sch<br>307 Wingo Way, Wills Point 75169<br>David Brown | 2-4 | T | 527<br>30 | 71% 903/873-5100<br>Fax 903/873-3134 |
| Wills Point High Sch<br>1800 W South Commerce St, Wills Point 75169<br>Brian Clements | 9-12 | TV | 713<br>50 | 56% 903/873-5100<br>Fax 903/873-6008 |
| Wills Point Junior High Sch<br>200 Tiger Dr, Wills Point 75169<br>Casey Cochran | 7-8 | T | 403<br>35 | 63% 903/873-5100<br>Fax 903/873-4873 |
| Wills Point Middle Sch<br>101 School St, Wills Point 75169<br>**Kelly Harle** | 5-6 | T | 405<br>26 | 70% 903/873-5100<br>Fax 903/873-2465 |
| Wills Point Primary Sch<br>447 Terrace Dr, Wills Point 75169<br>Kimberly Cole-White | PK-1 | T | 336<br>25 | 79% 903/873-5100<br>Fax 903/873-3051 |

## VAN ZANDT PRIVATE SCHOOLS

| Private Schs..Principal | Grd | Prgm | Enr/#Cls | SN |
|---|---|---|---|---|
| New Frontiers Christian Acad<br>24385 Interstate 20, Wills Point 75169<br>Dawn Perez | K-12 | | 37 | 903/873-2440 |

# VICTORIA COUNTY

## VICTORIA PUBLIC SCHOOLS

• **Bloomington Ind School Dist** PID: 01058311    361/333-8016
131 N Williams St, Placedo 77977    Fax 361/333-8026

**Schools:** 5 \ **Teachers:** 60 \ **Students:** 850 \ **Special Ed Students:** 121 \ **LEP Students:** 156 \ **Ethnic:** African American 4%, Hispanic 86%, Caucasian 10% \ **Exp:** $772 (High) \ **Poverty:** 26% \ **Title I:** $318,937 \ **Open-Close:** 08/12 - 05/27 \ **DTBP:** $345 (High)

Mark Anglin ..............................................1
Jeraldo Diaz ......................................3,91
Chris Horn ..............................................6*
Sally Horelka ..........................................16
Deloris White ..........................................67
Toi Tippin .........................................83,285

Randy Meyer ................................2,5,11,15
Gary Hatter .............................................4*
Sylvia Hernandez ....................................8*
Dora Hernandez .................................57,58*
Elliott Sung ...........................73,98,286,295

| Public Schs..Principal | Grd | Prgm | Enr/#Cls | SN |
|---|---|---|---|---|
| Bloomington Elem Sch<br>200 N Leonard St, Bloomington 77951<br>Carl Frisch | 2-5 | T | 264<br>32 | 87% 361/333-8003<br>Fax 361/333-8007 |
| Bloomington Middle Sch<br>2781 FM 616, Bloomington 77951<br>Lou Torres | 6-8 | TV | 207<br>12 | 78% 361/333-8008<br>Fax 361/333-8010 |
| Bloomington Senior High Sch<br>2781 FM 616, Bloomington 77951<br>Lina Moore | 9-12 | ATV | 248<br>25 | 63% 361/333-8011<br>Fax 361/333-8015 |

Ⓐ Crossroads Connect Academy    9-12    40    361/237-3061
2785 FM 616, Bloomington 77951
**Sylvia Hernandez**

| | Grd | Prgm | Enr/#Cls | SN |
|---|---|---|---|---|
| Placedo Elem Sch<br>167 N William St, Placedo 77977<br>Lou Torres | PK-1 | T | 131<br>12 | 85% 361/333-8000<br>Fax 361/333-8002 |

• **Nursery ISD School Dist** PID: 01058414    361/575-6882
13254 Nursery Dr, Victoria 77904    Fax 361/576-9212

**Schools:** 1 \ **Teachers:** 9 \ **Students:** 155 \ **Special Ed Students:** 10 \ **LEP Students:** 3 \ **Ethnic:** Asian 1%, African American 4%, Hispanic 36%, Caucasian 60% \ **Exp:** $386 (High) \ **Poverty:** 14% \ **Title I:** $45,098 \ **Open-Close:** 08/17 - 06/11 \ **DTBP:** $350 (High)

Larry Gieski ..........................1,11,73,288
Jennifer Thibodeaux ...............................6*
Neal Stevenson ......................................67

Lisa Sauceda ...........................................4*
Jennifer Southern ..................................12*

| Public Schs..Principal | Grd | Prgm | Enr/#Cls | SN |
|---|---|---|---|---|
| Nursery Elem Sch<br>13254 Nursery Dr, Victoria 77904<br>Chris Ulcak | PK-5 | T | 155<br>8 | 59% 361/575-6882 |

• **Victoria Ind School Dist** PID: 01058440    361/576-3131
102 Profit Dr, Victoria 77901    Fax 361/788-9643

**Schools:** 23 \ **Teachers:** 985 \ **Students:** 13,900 \ **Special Ed Students:** 1,620 \ **LEP Students:** 800 \ **College-Bound:** 60% \ **Ethnic:** Asian 1%, African American 7%, Hispanic 66%, Caucasian 26% \ **Exp:** $422 (High) \ **Poverty:** 19% \ **Title I:** $4,150,070 \ **Special Education:** $3,135,000 \ **Bilingual Education:** $84,000 \ **Open-Close:** 08/12 - 05/27 \ **DTBP:** $185 (High)

Dr Quintin Shepherd ................................1
John Urbano .......................................3,91
Angie Sherman .........................................5
Murphey Stuart ........................................7
Tammy Sestak .....................................9,93
Michelle Yates .......................................11
Dr Gregory Bonewald ..........................15,68
Linda Dueser .........................16,82,286
Carol Dippel ..........................................34
Teralee Barnett ......................................40
Susan Johnson .......................................47
Sarah Bradley .........................................50
Kelli Cotton .......................................58,77*
Carla Schaefer ..................................69,294
Samantha Schulte ................73,76,295
Roberto Gonzalez ...................................83*

Frances Koch ......................................2,15
Dana Bigham ...........................................4
Bobby Jackwright ....................................6
Dr Susanne Carroll ........................8,15,74
Sherri Hathaway .....................................10
Tammy Nobles ...................................13,79
Lisa Blundell ..........................................15
Jason Levin ......................................20,23
Kim Motley ............................................36
Mica Hernandez ....................................41
Ashlee Dornak ........................................49
Alejandro Mojica ........................57,89,271
Kevin Vanhook .......................................67
Shawna Currie ........................................71
Alyese Tate ............................................81
Melanie Rodriguez ................................297

| Public Schs..Principal | Grd | Prgm | Enr/#Cls | SN |
|---|---|---|---|---|
| Aloe Elem Sch<br>62 Chaparral Rd, Victoria 77905<br>Kristina Hurley | PK-5 | T | 408<br>27 | 55% 361/788-9509<br>Fax 361/788-9662 |
| Career & Technology Institute<br>104 Profit Dr, Victoria 77901<br>Melissa Correll | Voc | | 200<br>9 | 361/788-9288<br>Fax 361/788-9656 |
| Chandler Elem Sch<br>5105 Guy Grant Rd, Victoria 77904<br>Melanie Steed | PK-5 | T | 553<br>27 | 69% 361/788-9587<br>Fax 361/788-9590 |
| Ⓥ Crain Elem Sch<br>2706 N Azalea St, Victoria 77901<br>Renee Harper | PK-5 | MT | 390<br>50 | 85% 361/573-7453<br>Fax 361/574-3411 |
| DeLeon Elem Sch<br>1002 Santa Barbara St, Victoria 77904<br>Selina Reyna | PK-5 | T | 525<br>25 | 44% 361/788-9553<br>Fax 361/788-9634 |

| | | | | | | | | |
|---|---|---|---|---|---|---|---|---|
| 1 Superintendent | 8 Curric/Instruct K-12 | 19 Chief Financial Officer | 29 Family/Consumer Science | 39 Social Studies K-12 | 49 English/Lang Arts Elem | 59 Special Education Elem | 69 Academic Assessment |
| 2 Bus/Finance/Purchasing | 9 Curric/Instruct Elem | 20 Art K-12 | 30 Adult Education | 40 Social Studies Sec | 50 English/Lang Arts Sec | 60 Special Education Sec | 70 Research/Development |
| 3 Buildings And Grounds | 10 Curric/Instruct Sec | 21 Art Elem | 31 Career/Sch-to-Work K-12 | 41 Social Studies Sec | 51 Reading K-12 | 61 Foreign/World Lang K-12 | 71 Public Information |
| 4 Food Service | 11 Federal Program | 22 Art Sec | 32 Career/Sch-to-Work Elem | 42 Science K-12 | 52 Reading Elem | 62 Foreign/World Lang Elem | 72 Summer School |
| 5 Transportation | 12 Title I | 23 Music K-12 | 33 Career/Sch-to-Work Sec | 43 Science Sec | 53 Reading Sec | 63 Foreign/World Lang Sec | 73 Instructional Tech |
| 6 Athletic | 13 Title V | 24 Music Elem | 34 Early Childhood Ed | 44 Science Sec | 54 Remedial Reading K-12 | 64 Religious Education K-12 | 74 Inservice Training |
| 7 Health Services | 14 Instructional Media Svcs | 25 Music Sec | 35 Health/Phys Education | 45 Math K-12 | 55 Remedial Reading Elem | 65 Religious Education Elem | 75 Marketing/Distributive |
| | 15 Asst Superintendent | 26 Business Education | 36 Guidance Services K-12 | 46 Math Elem | 56 Remedial Reading Sec | 66 Religious Education Sec | 76 Info Systems |
| | 16 Instructional Media Svcs | 27 Career & Tech Ed | 37 Guidance Services Elem | 47 Math Sec | 57 Bilingual/ELL | 67 School Board President | 77 Psychological Assess |
| | 17 Chief Operations Officer | 28 Technology Education | 38 Guidance Services Sec | 48 English/Lang Arts K-12 | 58 Special Education K-12 | 68 Teacher Personnel | 78 Affirmative Action |
| | 18 Chief Academic Officer | | | | | | |

Ⓜ Dudley Magnet Sch — PK-5 T 369 81% 361/788-9517
3307 Callis St, Victoria 77901 — 27 — Fax 361/788-9523
Steven Carroll

Ella Schorlemmer Elem Sch — PK-5 T 544 53% 361/788-2860
2564 Mallette St, Victoria 77904 — Fax 361/788-9283
Elizabeth Chandler

Harold Cade Middle Sch — 6-8 T 875 54% 361/788-2840
611 Tropical Dr, Victoria 77904 — Fax 361/788-2886
Jill Lau

Ⓨ Hopkins Elem Sch — PK-5 MT 418 93% 361/788-9527
110 Hopkins St, Victoria 77901 — 30 — Fax 361/788-9635
Leandra Hill

Howell Middle Sch — 6-8 T 885 58% 361/578-1561
2502 Fannin Dr, Victoria 77901 — 64 — Fax 361/788-9547
Jo Jones

Ⓐ Liberty Campus — 9-12 T 187 71% 361/788-9650
1110 Sam Houston Dr, Victoria 77901 — 10 — Fax 361/788-9013
Sheila Garcia

Mission Valley Elem Sch — PK-5 T 251 41% 361/788-9514
12063 FM 236, Victoria 77905 — 12 — Fax 361/788-9689
Eric Amsler

Ⓨ O'Connor Elem Sch — PK-5 MT 334 80% 361/788-9572
3402 Bobolink St, Victoria 77901 — 33 — Fax 361/788-9575
Vickie Dunseth

Patti Welder Middle Sch — 6-8 T 210 79% 361/575-4553
1604 E North St, Victoria 77901 — 80 — Fax 361/788-9629
Denise Canchola

Rowland Elem Sch — PK-5 T 448 77% 361/788-9549
2706 Leary Ln, Victoria 77901 — 27 — Fax 361/788-9902
Tammy Garza

Shields Elem Sch — PK-5 T 373 89% 361/788-9593
3400 Bluebonnet St, Victoria 77901 — 42 — Fax 361/788-9691
Kelly Gabrysch

Smith Elem Sch — PK-5 T 491 77% 361/788-9605
2901 Erwin Ave, Victoria 77901 — 35 — Fax 361/788-9688
Michelle Graves

Stroman Middle Sch — 6-8 T 758 78% 361/578-2711
3002 E North St, Victoria 77901 — Fax 361/788-9800
Dawn Maroney

Torres Elem Sch — PK-5 T 457 83% 361/788-2850
4208 Lone Tree Rd, Victoria 77901 — Fax 361/788-9278
Crystal Rice

Vickers Elem Sch — PK-5 T 514 42% 361/788-9579
708 Glascow St, Victoria 77904 — 20 — Fax 361/788-9663
Troy White

Victoria East High Sch — 9-12 TV 1,886 56% 361/788-2820
4103 E Mockingbird Ln, Victoria 77904 — 100 — Fax 361/788-2826
Justin Gabrysch

Ⓐ Victoria Juv Justice Center — 6-12 M 35 361/575-0399
Ⓨ 97 Foster Field Dr, Victoria 77904
Christine Martin

Victoria West High Sch — 9-12 TV 1,761 53% 361/788-2830
307 Tropical Dr, Victoria 77904 — Fax 361/788-2836
Debbie Crick

## VICTORIA CATHOLIC SCHOOLS

● **Diocese of Victoria Ed Office** PID: 02181727 — 361/573-0828
1505 E Mesquite Ln, Victoria 77901 — Fax 361/573-5725

| Schools: 13 \ Students: 2,827 |

Listing includes only schools located in this county. See District Index for location of Diocesan Offices.

Dr John Quary ........................................1  Tony Martinez ...........................................2

| Catholic Schs..Principal | Grd | Prgm | Enr/#Cls | SN |
|---|---|---|---|---|
| Nazareth Academy<br>206 W Convent St, Victoria 77901<br>Sr Evelyn Korenek | PK-8 | | 356<br>20 | 361/573-6651<br>Fax 361/573-1829 |
| Our Lady of Victory Sch<br>1311 E Mesquite Ln, Victoria 77901<br>Justin Matias | PK-8 | | 501<br>20 | 361/575-5391<br>Fax 361/575-3473 |
| St Joseph High Sch<br>110 E Red River St, Victoria 77901<br>John Gilley | 9-12 | | 337<br>30 | 361/573-2446<br>Fax 361/573-4221<br>f |

## VICTORIA PRIVATE SCHOOLS

| Private Schs..Principal | Grd | Prgm | Enr/#Cls | SN |
|---|---|---|---|---|
| Faith Academy<br>2002 E Mockingbird Ln, Victoria 77904<br>Larry Long \ Terry Neinast | PK-12 | | 329<br>17 | 361/573-2484<br>Fax 361/572-4602<br>f t |
| Northside Baptist Sch<br>4100 N Laurent St, Victoria 77901<br>Jan Chilcoat | PK-5 | | 128<br>9 | 361/578-1568 |
| Trinity Episcopal Sch<br>1504 N Moody St, Victoria 77901<br>Kristy Nelson | PK-8 | | 220<br>20 | 361/573-3220<br>Fax 361/573-2964 |
| Victoria Christian Sch<br>3310 N Ben Jordan St, Victoria 77901<br>Catherine Key | PK-8 | | 98 | 361/573-5345<br>Fax 361/578-3367 |
| Vine Sch<br>2911 N Azalea St, Victoria 77901<br>Erin Hatley | Spec | | 18 | 361/212-8463 |

## VICTORIA REGIONAL CENTERS

● **Region 3 Ed Service Center** PID: 01058438 — 361/573-0731
1905 Leary Ln, Victoria 77901 — Fax 361/576-4804

Charlotte Baker ...............................1  Jennifer Sappington ........................2,19
Laura Ratliff ...............................2,3,15  Carly Shock .......................................4
Linda Ledwig ..............................15,34  Marybeth Matula ..........................15,76
Mitzi McAfee .....................................15  Laura Sprinkle ...............................286
Lisa Hernandez ..............................298

## WALKER COUNTY

### WALKER PUBLIC SCHOOLS

• **Huntsville Ind School Dist** PID: 01058672
441 FM 2821 Rd E, Huntsville 77320
936/435-6300
Fax 936/435-6648

**Schools:** 9 \ **Teachers:** 400 \ **Students:** 6,500 \ **Special Ed Students:** 688 \ **LEP Students:** 965 \ **Ethnic:** Asian 1%, African American 28%, Hispanic 36%, Native American: 1%, Caucasian 35% \ **Exp:** $474 (High) \ **Poverty:** 26% \ **Title I:** $2,380,206 \ **Special Education:** $1,378,000 \ **Open-Close:** 08/19 - 05/27 \ **DTBP:** $159 (High)

| | | | |
|---|---|---|---|
| Dr Scott Sheppard | 1 | Paul Brown | 2,19 |
| William Roberts | 2,15,17,76 | Larry Brown | 3 |
| Rodney Merek | 3 | Henery Tapia | 4 |
| Charles McGowen | 5 | Rodney Southern | 6 |
| Ana Thomas | 7,8,16,57,68,81,273 | Rebecca Presley | 7 |
| Dr Jamey Johnson | 10 | Leigh Kovalchik | 11,296 |
| Marcus Forney | 15,36,83,88,270 | Matthew Lahey | 16,286* |
| John Green | 23* | Gary Evans | 27 |
| Mary Stanford | 27,285 | Kelley Tieterse | 58 |
| Greg Nelson | 67 | Angee Andrus | 69,294 |
| Shannon Duncan | 71 | Nadine Pharries | 73 |
| Teresa Bridge | 76 | Leroy Morales | 79 |
| Sally Dallas | 90 | Morllo Faulkner | 295 |

| Public Schs..Principal | Grd | Prgm | Enr/#Cls | SN |
|---|---|---|---|---|
| Estella Stewart Elem Sch<br>3400 Boettcher Dr, Huntsville 77340<br>**Kimberly Fox** | K-4 | T | 513<br>40 | 71% 936/435-6700<br>Fax 936/293-2809 |
| Huntsville Elem Sch<br>87 M L King Blvd, Huntsville 77320<br>**Christy Cross** | K-4 | T | 605<br>44 | 74% 936/435-6850<br>Fax 936/293-2896 |
| Huntsville High Sch<br>515 FM 2821 Rd E, Huntsville 77320<br>**Paul Trevino** | 9-12 | T | 1,708<br>80 | 53% 936/435-6100<br>Fax 936/293-2609 |
| Huntsville Intermediate Sch<br>431 Highway 190 E, Huntsville 77340<br>**Racheal Branch** | 5-6 | T | 955<br>60 | 64% 936/435-6500<br>Fax 936/293-2712 |
| Mance Park Middle Sch<br>1010 8th St, Huntsville 77320<br>Joshua Campbell | 7-8 | T | 882<br>67 | 60% 936/435-6400<br>Fax 936/435-6617 |
| Mary McAshan Gibbs PK Center<br>441 FM 2821 Rd E, Huntsville 77320<br>Jessie Anderson | PK-PK | T | 385<br>17 | 99% 936/435-6550<br>Fax 936/293-2826 |
| Samuel Houston Elem Sch<br>1641 7th St, Huntsville 77320<br>**Natasha Simmons** | K-4 | T | 445<br>30 | 70% 936/435-6750<br>Fax 936/439-1223 |
| Scott Johnson Elem Sch<br>603 Highway 190 E, Huntsville 77340<br>Shannon Williams | K-4 | T | 645<br>28 | 69% 936/435-6250<br>Fax 936/293-2876 |
| Texas Online Preparatory Sch<br>1955 Lakeway Dr Ste 250B, Lewisville 75057<br>Blanda Watt \ Elizabeth Nelson \ Rebecca Finka | 3-12 | | 2,000 | 888/263-6497 |

• **New Waverly Ind School Dist** PID: 01058737
355 Front St, New Waverly 77358
936/344-6751
Fax 936/344-2438

**Schools:** 4 \ **Teachers:** 84 \ **Students:** 1,000 \ **Special Ed Students:** 84 \ **LEP Students:** 40 \ **College-Bound:** 10% \ **Ethnic:** African American 16%, Hispanic 14%, Native American: 1%, Caucasian 69% \ **Exp:** $210 (Med) \ **Poverty:** 26% \ **Title I:** $343,665 \ **Special Education:** $199,000 \ **Open-Close:** 08/13 - 05/20 \ **DTBP:** $350 (High)

| | | | |
|---|---|---|---|
| Dr Darol Hail | 1 | Michele Chitwood | 2 |
| James Sanders | 3 | Jewel Gregory | 4 |
| Roland Oliphant | 5 | Dean Schaub | 6* |
| Celeste Roberts | 7* | Stephanie Brock | 8,11,288,298* |
| Dusky Hall | 16,73,295 | Debbie Choate | 36,85,286 |
| Candice Reynolds | 37* | Kim Shoulders | 58* |
| Anthony Barge | 67 | Cade Reece | 83,88* |
| Gloria Murphy | 280 | | |

| Public Schs..Principal | Grd | Prgm | Enr/#Cls | SN |
|---|---|---|---|---|
| New Waverly Elem Sch<br>335 FM 1375 West, New Waverly 77358<br>**Tiffany Wedgeworth** | PK-3 | T | 287<br>37 | 62% 936/344-2900<br>Fax 936/344-2905 |
| New Waverly High Sch<br>9464 Highway 75 S, New Waverly 77358<br>Kristopher Drane | 9-12 | T | 307<br>25 | 41% 936/344-6451<br>Fax 936/344-6113 |
| New Waverly Intermediate Sch<br>215 Clara Rudd Ln, New Waverly 77358<br>Kathy Lepley | 4-5 | T | 159<br>8 | 48% 936/344-6601<br>Fax 936/344-2331 |
| New Waverly Junior High Sch<br>1111 Front St, New Waverly 77358<br>Dudley Hawkes | 6-8 | T | 222<br>19 | 53% 936/344-2246<br>Fax 936/344-8313 |

### WALKER PRIVATE SCHOOLS

| Private Schs..Principal | Grd | Prgm | Enr/#Cls | SN |
|---|---|---|---|---|
| Alpha Omega Academy<br>3891 Highway 30 W, Huntsville 77340<br>Paul Davidheizar | PK-12 | | 400<br>40 | 936/438-8833<br>Fax 936/438-8844 |
| Summit Christian Academy<br>3122 Montgomery Rd, Huntsville 77340<br>Krystal Nunez | 1-12 | | 120<br>8 | 936/295-9601<br>Fax 936/295-9236 |

### WALKER REGIONAL CENTERS

• **Region 6 Ed Service Center** PID: 01058763
3332 Montgomery Rd, Huntsville 77340
936/435-8400
Fax 936/435-8484

| | | | |
|---|---|---|---|
| Michael Holland | 1 | Robert Lindeman | 2,19 |
| Dr Brian Zemlicka | 15,71 | Tally Jo Stout | 27,31 |
| Kristine Haymae | 30 | Dr Catherine George | 58 |
| Bonney Monjaras | 68 | Jayne Tavenner | 69 |
| Dr John Conley | 73 | | |

| | | | | | |
|---|---|---|---|---|---|
| 1 | Superintendent | 8 | Curric/Instruct K-12 | 19 | Chief Financial Officer |
| 2 | Bus/Finance/Purchasing | 9 | Curric/Instruct Elem | 20 | Art K-12 |
| 3 | Buildings And Grounds | 10 | Curric/Instruct Sec | 21 | Art Elem |
| 4 | Food Service | 11 | Federal Program | 22 | Art Sec |
| 5 | Transportation | 12 | Title I | 23 | Music K-12 |
| 6 | Athletic | 13 | Title V | 24 | Music Elem |
| 7 | Health Services | 15 | Asst Superintendent | 25 | Music Sec |
| | | 16 | Instructional Media Svcs | 26 | Business Education |
| | | 17 | Chief Operations Officer | 27 | Career & Tech Ed |
| | | 18 | Chief Academic Officer | 28 | Technology Education |

| | | | | | |
|---|---|---|---|---|---|
| 29 | Family/Consumer Science | 39 | Social Studies K-12 | 49 | English/Lang Arts Elem |
| 30 | Adult Education | 40 | Social Studies Elem | 50 | English/Lang Arts Sec |
| 31 | Career/Sch-to-Work K-12 | 41 | Social Studies Sec | 51 | Reading K-12 |
| 32 | Career/Sch-to-Work Elem | 42 | Science K-12 | 52 | Reading Elem |
| 33 | Career/Sch-to-Work Sec | 43 | Science Elem | 53 | Reading Sec |
| 34 | Early Childhood Ed | 44 | Science Sec | 54 | Remedial Reading K-12 |
| 35 | Health/Phys Education | 45 | Math K-12 | 55 | Remedial Reading Elem |
| 36 | Guidance Services K-12 | 46 | Math Elem | 56 | Remedial Reading Sec |
| 37 | Guidance Services Elem | 47 | Math Sec | 57 | Bilingual/ELL |
| 38 | Guidance Services Sec | 48 | English/Lang Arts K-12 | 58 | Special Education K-12 |

| | | | |
|---|---|---|---|
| 59 | Special Education Elem | 69 | Academic Assessment |
| 60 | Special Education Sec | 70 | Research/Development |
| 61 | Foreign/World Lang K-12 | 71 | Public Information |
| 62 | Foreign/World Lang Elem | 72 | Summer School |
| 63 | Foreign/World Lang Sec | 73 | Instructional Tech |
| 64 | Religious Education K-12 | 74 | Inservice Training |
| 65 | Religious Education Elem | 75 | Marketing/Distributive |
| 66 | Religious Education Sec | 76 | Info Systems |
| 67 | School Board President | 77 | Psychological Assess |
| 68 | Teacher Personnel | 78 | Affirmative Action |

# WALLER COUNTY

## WALLER PUBLIC SCHOOLS

• **Hempstead Ind School Dist** PID: 01058775     979/826-3304
1440 13th St, Hempstead 77445     Fax 979/826-5510

Schools: 3 \ **Teachers:** 130 \ **Students:** 1,600 \ **Special Ed Students:** 117 \ **LEP Students:** 421 \ **Ethnic:** Asian 1%, African American 26%, Hispanic 61%, Caucasian 12% \ **Exp:** $342 (High) \ **Poverty:** 22% \ **Title I:** $694,356 \ **Special Education:** $364,000 \ **Open-Close:** 08/24 - 05/27 \ **DTBP:** $558 (High)

| | | | |
|---|---|---|---|
| Dr Angela Gutsch | 1,11 | Kevin Mathis | 2 |
| Eddie Brown | 5 | Bobby Spain | 6* |
| Erin Meadows | 8 | Eric Mullens | 11,69,88,271,274,296,298 |
| Mandy Dempsey | 16,82* | J Kevin Mathis | 19 |
| Consuelo Yamaguchi | 57 | Courtney Williams | 58 |
| Ricky Pearce | 67 | Mabisha Crawford | 68 |
| Laurie Bettis | 71 | Alex Miller | 73,98,295,297 |
| Mabisha Stubblefield | 74 | Aaron Meadow | 88 |

| Public Schs..Principal | Grd | Prgm | Enr/#Cls | SN | |
|---|---|---|---|---|---|
| Hempstead Elem Sch<br>1340 13th St, Hempstead 77445<br>Samantha Ray-Mullens | PK-5 | T | 827<br>50 | 91% | 979/826-2452<br>Fax 979/826-5524 |
| Hempstead High Sch<br>801 Donoho Street, Hempstead 77445<br>Eric Mullens | 9-12 | AGTV | 415<br>50 | 73% | 979/826-3331<br>Fax 979/826-4779 |
| Hempstead Middle Sch<br>2532 9th St, Hempstead 77445<br>Erika Douglas | 6-8 | TV | 347<br>48 | 82% | 979/826-2530<br>Fax 979/826-5583 |

• **Royal Ind School Dist** PID: 01058816     281/934-2248
3714 FM 359, Pattison 77466     Fax 281/934-2846

Schools: 4 \ **Teachers:** 166 \ **Students:** 2,400 \ **Special Ed Students:** 200 \ **LEP Students:** 959 \ **College-Bound:** 57% \ **Ethnic:** African American 15%, Hispanic 75%, Caucasian 10% \ **Exp:** $478 (High) \ **Poverty:** 23% \ **Title I:** $781,034 \ **Special Education:** $402,000 \ **Open-Close:** 08/12 - 05/20 \ **DTBP:** $331 (High)

| | | | |
|---|---|---|---|
| Stacy Ackley | 1 | Gladys Hein | 2 |
| Sandy Mayberry | 2 | Derrick Dabney | 3,5 |
| Greg Anderson | 6 | Kendra Strange | 8 |
| Susan Cardiff | 11,69,294,296,298 | Ronnie Melton | 27,31* |
| Tonya Woods Gage | 58 | Elton Foster | 67 |
| Debbie Ulrich | 68 | Mike Nicholas | 73,295 |
| Stephanie Hein | 79 | | |

| Public Schs..Principal | Grd | Prgm | Enr/#Cls | SN | |
|---|---|---|---|---|---|
| Royal Early Childhood Center<br>2300 Durkin Rd, Brookshire 77423<br>Aronda Green | PK-K | T | 341<br>17 | 79% | 281/934-3181<br>Fax 281/934-3186 |
| Royal Elem Sch<br>2222 Durkin Rd, Brookshire 77423<br>Aronda Green | 1-5 | T | 932<br>16 | 84% | 281/934-3166<br>Fax 281/934-3358 |
| Royal High Sch<br>34499 Royal Rd, Brookshire 77423<br>Tony Runnels | 9-12 | ATV | 630<br>45 | 75% | 281/934-2215<br>Fax 281/934-2866 |

| Royal Junior High Sch<br>2520 Durkin Road, Brookshire 77423<br>Orlando Vargas | 6-8 | ATV | 523<br>30 | 88% | 281/934-2241<br>Fax 281/934-2329 |
|---|---|---|---|---|---|

• **Waller Ind School Dist** PID: 01058866     936/931-3685
2214 Waller St, Waller 77484     Fax 936/372-5576

Schools: 8 \ **Teachers:** 465 \ **Students:** 7,700 \ **Special Ed Students:** 568 \ **LEP Students:** 2,012 \ **College-Bound:** 53% \ **Ethnic:** Asian 1%, African American 9%, Hispanic 55%, Caucasian 35% \ **Exp:** $402 (High) \ **Poverty:** 17% \ **Title I:** $1,489,579 \ **Special Education:** $1,036,000 \ **Open-Close:** 08/24 - 05/27 \ **DTBP:** $153 (High)

| | | | |
|---|---|---|---|
| Kevin Moran | 1 | Kim Peinly | 2 |
| Mike Marcus | 2,19 | Guy Thomas | 3 |
| Molly Warzon | 4 | Joe Mooneyham | 5,91 |
| Jim Phillips | 6* | Kelly Baehren | 8,11,18,288,298,752 |
| Sharon Bey | 36 | Diane Dewease | 47 |
| Carrie Lentz | 49 | Jorge Alvarado | 57 |
| Jan Oatess | 58 | David Kaminski | 67 |
| Mike Brooks | 68 | Donna Suggitt | 69 |
| Sarah Marcus | 71 | Rosa Ojeda | 76,97,286 |

| Public Schs..Principal | Grd | Prgm | Enr/#Cls | SN | |
|---|---|---|---|---|---|
| Evelyn Turlington Elem Sch<br>23400 Hegar Rd, Hockley 77447<br>Kristen Eckerman | PK-5 | T | 830 | 65% | 936/372-0100<br>Fax 936/372-3868 |
| Fields Store Elem Sch<br>31670 Giboney Rd, Waller 77484<br>Melissa Crosby | PK-5 | T | 652<br>41 | 58% | 936/931-4050<br>Fax 936/372-4100 |
| Herman Jones Elem Sch<br>35723 Owens Rd, Prairie View 77446<br>Ashley Kinney | PK-5 | | 640<br>12 | | 936/372-4200<br>Fax 936/857-5050 |
| It Holleman Elem Sch<br>2200 Brazeal St, Waller 77484<br>Ashley Abke | PK-5 | T | 679<br>36 | 65% | 936/372-9196<br>Fax 936/372-2468 |
| Roberts Road Elem Sch<br>24920 Zube Rd, Hockley 77447<br>Amy Carranza | PK-5 | T | 648<br>50 | 70% | 936/931-0300<br>Fax 281/373-3164 |
| Schultz Junior High Sch<br>19455 Stokes Rd, Waller 77484<br>Hannah Gates | 6-8 | T | 942<br>52 | 59% | 936/931-9103<br>Fax 936/372-9302 |
| Waller High Sch<br>20950 Fields Store Rd, Waller 77484<br>Stephanie Fletcher | 9-12 | T | 1,861 | 59% | 936/372-3654<br>Fax 936/372-4114 |
| Waller Junior High Sch<br>2402 Waller St, Waller 77484<br>Tanya Carrejo | 6-8 | T | 820<br>50 | 69% | 936/931-1353<br>Fax 936/931-4044 |

## WARD COUNTY

## WASHINGTON COUNTY

### WARD PUBLIC SCHOOLS

### WASHINGTON PUBLIC SCHOOLS

● **Grandfalls-Royalty Ind SD** PID: 01058919　　432/547-2266
115 Ave C, Grandfalls 79742　　　　　　　　　　Fax 432/547-2960

**Schools:** 1 \ **Teachers:** 16 \ **Students:** 184 \ **Special Ed Students:** 15
\ **College-Bound:** 40% \ **Ethnic:** African American 5%, Hispanic 65%,
Caucasian 30% \ **Exp:** $429 (High) \ **Poverty:** 15% \ **Title I:** $27,289 \
**Open-Close:** 08/13 - 05/21 \ **DTBP:** $359 (High)

| | | | |
|---|---|---|---|
| Brett Starkweather | 1,11,73 | Lorraine Natividad | 2 |
| Rosa Vasquez | 4 | Jeff Corean | 6,8 |
| Amanda Herrera | 28,286 | Linda Kuhn | 58* |
| Mark Kuhn | 67 | Brett Starkweather | 73* |
| Toyse Eaton | 83,752 | | |

| Public Schs..Principal | Grd | Prgm | Enr/#Cls | SN | |
|---|---|---|---|---|---|
| Grandfalls Royalty Sch | PK-12 | T | 184 | 58% | 432/547-2266 |
| 115 Ave C, Grandfalls 79742 | | | 35 | | |
| **Charles Chesser** | | | | | |

● **Monahans-Wickett-Pyote ISD** PID: 01058957　　432/943-6711
606 S Betty Ave, Monahans 79756　　　　　　　　Fax 432/943-2307

**Schools:** 6 \ **Teachers:** 135 \ **Students:** 2,300 \ **Special Ed Students:** 219
\ **LEP Students:** 214 \ **College-Bound:** 50% \ **Ethnic:** Asian 1%,
African American 5%, Hispanic 62%, Caucasian 32% \ **Exp:** $643 (High)
\ **Poverty:** 16% \ **Title I:** $430,369 \ **Special Education:** $467,000 \
**Open-Close:** 08/19 - 05/27 \ **DTBP:** $347 (High)

| | | | |
|---|---|---|---|
| Kellye Riley | 1 | Sarah Harris | 2 |
| Jeff Jones | 3 | Tammy Sanchez | 4* |
| Leif Tefertiller | 5 | Frederek Staugh | 6 |
| Ann McCallester | 7* | Doug Doege | 8,11,57,69,298 |
| Kimberley Thomas | 30,38* | Anthony Ayundis | 58 |
| Donna Garcia | 67 | Allen Fox | 73,295,297* |
| Allen Fox | 84 | | |

| Public Schs..Principal | Grd | Prgm | Enr/#Cls | SN | |
|---|---|---|---|---|---|
| Cullender Kindergarten | PK-K | T | 258 | 53% | 432/943-5252 |
| 1100 S Leon Ave, Monahans 79756 | | | 14 | | Fax 432/943-4768 |
| Jeannie Jackson | | | | | |
| Ⓐ Monahans Education Center HS | 9-12 | T | 23 | 50% | 432/943-2019 |
| 813 S Alice Ave, Monahans 79756 | | | 4 | | Fax 432/943-2593 |
| Chad Smith | | | | | |
| Monahans High Sch | 9-12 | TV | 212 | 40% | 432/943-2519 |
| 809 S Betty Ave, Monahans 79756 | | | 40 | | Fax 432/943-3327 |
| Patty Acosta | | | | | |
| Sudderth Elem Sch | 4-6 | T | 578 | 61% | 432/943-5101 |
| 701 N Carol Ave, Monahans 79756 | | | 13 | | Fax 432/943-2685 |
| **Kim Thomas** | | | | | |
| Tatom Elem Sch | 1-3 | T | 567 | 56% | 432/943-2769 |
| 1600 S Calvin Ave, Monahans 79756 | | | 14 | | Fax 432/943-3952 |
| Jill Steen | | | | | |
| Walker Junior High Sch | 7-8 | T | 349 | 48% | 432/943-4622 |
| 800 S Faye Ave, Monahans 79756 | | | 24 | | Fax 432/943-3723 |
| Mayna Benavides | | | | | |

● **Brenham Ind School Dist** PID: 01059042　　979/277-3700
711 E Mansfield St, Brenham 77833　　　　　　Fax 979/277-3701

**Schools:** 7 \ **Teachers:** 366 \ **Students:** 5,000 \ **Special Ed Students:** 645
\ **LEP Students:** 536 \ **College-Bound:** 57% \ **Ethnic:** Asian 2%, African
American 22%, Hispanic 35%, Caucasian 41% \ **Exp:** $264 (Med) \
**Poverty:** 18% \ **Title I:** $1,135,588 \ **Special Education:** $1,013,000 \
**Open-Close:** 08/19 - 05/27 \ **DTBP:** $156 (High)

| | | | |
|---|---|---|---|
| **Dr Tylor Chaplin** | 1 | Kim Weatherby | 2 |
| Phillip Derkowski | 3 | Omian Toran | 5 |
| Elliot Allen | 6 | Dr Jamey Johnson | 8,15 |
| Paul Aschenbeck | 15 | Kim Strauss | 16,73,76,295 |
| Eric Rettig | 23* | Cody Stelter | 27,28* |
| Sarah Broesche | 34,58 | Steve Skrla | 36 |
| Lori Wamble | 57,81 | Natalie Lange | 67 |
| Christie Olivarez | 68 | Jessica Johnston | 71 |
| Sarah Cook | 294 | Shawn Mays | 752* |

| Public Schs..Principal | Grd | Prgm | Enr/#Cls | SN | |
|---|---|---|---|---|---|
| Alton Elem Sch | PK-4 | T | 409 | 61% | 979/277-3870 |
| 1210 S Market St, Brenham 77833 | | | 40 | | Fax 979/277-3871 |
| Michael Ogg | | | | | |
| Brenham Elem Sch | PK-4 | T | 610 | 67% | 979/277-3880 |
| 1000 W Blue Bell Rd, Brenham 77833 | | | 41 | | Fax 979/277-3881 |
| Kim Rocka | | | | | |
| Brenham High Sch | 9-12 | V | 1,495 | 48% | 979/277-3800 |
| 525 A H Ehrig Dr, Brenham 77833 | | | 200 | | Fax 979/277-3801 |
| Joseph Chandler | | | | | |
| Brenham Junior High Sch | 7-8 | T | 785 | 54% | 979/277-3830 |
| 1200 Carlee Dr, Brenham 77833 | | | 60 | | Fax 979/277-3831 |
| Bryan Bryant | | | | | |
| Brenham Middle Sch | 5-6 | T | 753 | 61% | 979/277-3845 |
| 1600 S Blue Bell Rd, Brenham 77833 | | | 30 | | Fax 979/277-3846 |
| Peggy Still | | | | | |
| Krause Elem Sch | PK-4 | T | 528 | 67% | 979/277-3860 |
| 2201 E Stone St, Brenham 77833 | | | 50 | | Fax 979/277-3861 |
| Courtney Mason | | | | | |
| Ⓐ Pride Academy | 11-12 | | 30 | | 979/277-3890 |
| 1301 S Market St, Brenham 77833 | | | 5 | | Fax 979/277-3891 |
| Allan Colvin | | | | | |

● **Burton Ind School Dist** PID: 01059107　　979/289-3131
701 N Railroad St, Burton 77835　　　　　　　Fax 979/289-3076

**Schools:** 2 \ **Teachers:** 39 \ **Students:** 440 \ **Special Ed Students:** 47
\ **LEP Students:** 25 \ **College-Bound:** 70% \ **Ethnic:** African American
14%, Hispanic 21%, Caucasian 64% \ **Exp:** $524 (High) \ **Poverty:** 13% \
**Title I:** $74,192 \ **Open-Close:** 08/20 - 05/28 \ **DTBP:** $344 (High) \ 🆕

| | | | |
|---|---|---|---|
| Dr Edna Kennedy | 1,73,83 | Caitlyn Blakey | 2 |
| Ronnie Hohlt | 3 | Amy Jozwiak | 4 |
| Jason Hodde | 6* | Melinda Fuchs | 8,12,69,88,270,288,296* |
| Angela Rhodes | 31,79,88,270 | Kristie Hess | 58 |
| Demetrius Colvin | 67 | Tracie Kramer | 68 |

| | | | | | | | |
|---|---|---|---|---|---|---|---|
| 1 | Superintendent | 8 | Curric/Instruct K-12 | 19 | Chief Financial Officer | 29 | Family/Consumer Science |
| 2 | Bus/Finance/Purchasing | 9 | Curric/Instruct Elem | 20 | Art K-12 | 30 | Adult Education |
| 3 | Buildings And Grounds | 10 | Curric/Instruct Sec | 21 | Art Elem | 31 | Career/Sch-to-Work K-12 |
| 4 | Food Service | 11 | Federal Program | 22 | Art Sec | 32 | Career/Sch-to-Work Elem |
| 5 | Transportation | 12 | Title I | 23 | Music K-12 | 33 | Career/Sch-to-Work Sec |
| 6 | Athletic | 13 | Title V | 24 | Music Elem | 34 | Early Childhood Ed |
| 7 | Health Services | 15 | Asst Superintendent | 25 | Music Sec | 35 | Health/Phys Education |
| | | 16 | Instructional Media Svcs | 26 | Business Education | 36 | Guidance Services K-12 |
| | | 17 | Chief Operations Officer | 27 | Career & Tech Ed | 37 | Guidance Services Elem |
| | | 18 | Chief Academic Officer | 28 | Technology Education | 38 | Guidance Services Sec |

| | | | | | | | |
|---|---|---|---|---|---|---|---|
| 39 | Social Studies K-12 | 49 | English/Lang Arts Elem | 59 | Special Education Elem | 69 | Academic Assessment |
| 40 | Social Studies Elem | 50 | English/Lang Arts Sec | 60 | Special Education Sec | 70 | Research/Development |
| 41 | Social Studies Sec | 51 | Reading K-12 | 61 | Foreign/World Lang K-12 | 71 | Public Information |
| 42 | Science K-12 | 52 | Reading Elem | 62 | Foreign/World Lang Elem | 72 | Summer School |
| 43 | Science Elem | 53 | Reading Sec | 63 | Foreign/World Lang Sec | 73 | Instructional Tech |
| 44 | Science Sec | 54 | Remedial Reading K-12 | 64 | Religious Education K-12 | 74 | Inservice Training |
| 45 | Math K-12 | 55 | Remedial Reading Elem | 65 | Religious Education Elem | 75 | Marketing/Distributive |
| 46 | Math Elem | 56 | Remedial Reading Sec | 66 | Religious Education Sec | 76 | Info Systems |
| 47 | Math Sec | 57 | Bilingual/ELL | 67 | School Board President | 77 | Psychological Assess |
| 48 | English/Lang Arts K-12 | 58 | Special Education K-12 | 68 | Teacher Personnel | 78 | Affirmative Action |

| Public Schs..Principal | Grd | Prgm | Enr/#Cls | SN | |
|---|---|---|---|---|---|
| Burton Elem Sch<br>12504 W Cedar St, Burton 77835<br>Melinda Fuchs | PK-6 | T | 218<br>12 | 56% | 979/289-2175<br>Fax 979/289-0170 |
| Burton High Sch<br>917 N Main St, Burton 77835<br>Matthew Wamble | 7-12 | TV | 193<br>14 | 54% | 979/289-3830<br>Fax 979/289-4609 |

## WASHINGTON PRIVATE SCHOOLS

| Private Schs..Principal | Grd | Prgm | Enr/#Cls | SN | |
|---|---|---|---|---|---|
| Citadel Christian Sch<br>2111 S Blue Bell Rd, Brenham 77833<br>Shelia Suders | PK-8 | | 28<br>16 | | 979/830-8480<br>Fax 979/830-1687 |
| First Baptist Church Sch<br>302 Pahl St, Brenham 77833<br>Nancy Jahns | PK-6 | | 275<br>15 | | 979/836-6411<br>Fax 979/836-3269 |
| Grace Lutheran Sch<br>1212 W Jefferson St, Brenham 77833<br>Thomas Obersat | PK-8 | | 78<br>10 | | 979/836-2030<br>Fax 979/836-0510 |
| Johnson Ferguson Academy<br>1102 E Main St, Brenham 77833<br>Dr Patricia Larke | K-4 | | 3<br>1 | | 979/836-4156<br>Fax 979/836-1361 |

## WEBB COUNTY

## WEBB PUBLIC SCHOOLS

- **Laredo Ind School Dist** PID: 01059183    956/273-1000
  1702 Houston St, Laredo 78040    Fax 956/273-1403

**Schools:** 33 \ **Teachers:** 1,445 \ **Students:** 23,737 \
**Special Ed Students:** 2,100 \ **LEP Students:** 11,205 \ **College-Bound:** 69%
\ **Ethnic:** Hispanic 99%, Caucasian 1% \ **Exp:** $404 (High) \ **Poverty:** 43% \
**Title I:** $16,673,008 \ **Special Education:** $4,654,000 \ **Open-Close:** 08/12 -
05/27 \ **DTBP:** $195 (High)

| | | | |
|---|---|---|---|
| Dr Silvia Rios ..................................1 | Flor Ayala ..............................2,19 |
| Hector Mejia .................................2 | Roberto Cuellar .........................4 |
| Esteban Rangel ............................5 | Silvia Barrera .........................6,35 |
| Dr Gerardo Cruz ...........................8 | Myrtala Ramirez ........................9 |
| Oralia Cortez ............................11* | Oralia Cortez ..........................11 |
| Roberta Ramirez .......................15,68 | Mely Paez ..............................16 |
| Rogelio Garcia .......................27,31* | Rogelio Garcia .......................27,31 |
| Brenda Sepulveda ................34,73,76 | Itzamara Rendon ......................34 |
| Rosina Silva ...........................36,88 | Cynthia Cruz ..........................57 |
| Raul Gomez ...............................58 | Hector Noyola .........................67 |
| Delma Alaniz-Ramos .................69,294 | Veronica Castillon ....................71 |
| Maggie Martinez .......................79,83 | Scott Roberts .........................298 |

| Public Schs..Principal | Grd | Prgm | Enr/#Cls | SN | |
|---|---|---|---|---|---|
| Alma A Pierce Elem Sch<br>800 E Eistetter St, Laredo 78041<br>Noralva Johnson | PK-5 | T | 734<br>45 | 99% | 956/273-4300<br>Fax 956/273-4395 |
| Anita T Dovalina Elem Sch<br>1700 Anna Ave, Laredo 78040<br>Karla Pena | PK-5 | T | 348<br>40 | 98% | 956/273-3320<br>Fax 956/273-3395 |

| Public Schs..Principal | Grd | Prgm | Enr/#Cls | SN | |
|---|---|---|---|---|---|
| Antonio Bruni Elem Sch<br>1508 San Eduardo Ave, Laredo 78040<br>Michelle Martinez | PK-5 | T | 604<br>35 | 99% | 956/273-3000<br>Fax 956/273-3095 |
| C L Milton Elem Sch<br>2500 E Ash St, Laredo 78043<br>Cecilia McGee | PK-5 | T | 925<br>47 | 94% | 956/273-4200<br>Fax 956/795-4295 |
| C M MacDonell Elem Sch<br>1606 Benavides St, Laredo 78040<br>Erika Rodriguez | PK-5 | T | 449<br>30 | 99% | 956/273-4000<br>Fax 956/273-4095 |
| D D Hachar Elem Sch<br>3000 Guadalupe St, Laredo 78043<br>Cynthia Villarreal | PK-5 | T | 535<br>28 | 96% | 956/273-3500<br>Fax 956/273-3595 |
| Don Jose Gallego Elem Sch<br>520 Clark Blvd, Laredo 78040<br>Jorge Silva | PK-5 | T | 747<br>33 | 97% | 956/273-3100<br>Fax 956/273-3195 |
| Ⓜ Dr Dennis Cantu Health Sci Sch<br>2002 San Bernardo Ave, Laredo 78040<br>Geraldine Arredondo | 9-12 | V | 305 | | 956/795-3874<br>Fax 956/795-3875 |
| Dr Joaquin Cigarroa Middle Sch<br>2600 Palo Blanco St, Laredo 78046<br>Jose Cerda | 6-8 | ATV | 1,329<br>88 | 98% | 956/273-6100<br>Fax 956/273-6195 |
| Dr Leo Cigarroa High Sch<br>2600 Zacatecas St, Laredo 78046<br>Jose Inzaola | 9-12 | ATV | 1,555<br>100 | 97% | 956/273-6800<br>Fax 956/273-9075 |
| Francisco Farias Elem Sch<br>1510 Chicago St, Laredo 78041<br>San Juana Garza | PK-5 | T | 568<br>42 | 99% | 956/273-3400<br>Fax 956/273-3495 |
| Ⓐ Francisco S Lara Academy<br>Ⓜ 2901 E Travis St, Laredo 78043<br>Armando Molina | 6-12 | G | 70<br>20 | 98% | 956/273-7900<br>Fax 956/726-0350 |
| H B Zachry Elem Sch<br>3200 Chacota St, Laredo 78046<br>Diana Martinez | PK-5 | T | 629<br>35 | 96% | 956/273-4900<br>Fax 956/273-4995 |
| Ⓜ Hector Garcia Early Clg HS<br>5241 University Blvd Cowart Hl, Laredo 78041<br>Jose Iznaola | 9-12 | T | 213 | 87% | 956/273-7700<br>Fax 956/273-7795 |
| Heights Elem Sch<br>1208 Market St, Laredo 78040<br>Adriana Padilla | PK-5 | T | 471<br>25 | 96% | 956/273-3600<br>Fax 956/273-3695 |
| Honore Ligarde Elem Sch<br>2800 S Canada Ave, Laredo 78046<br>Elba Contreras | PK-5 | T | 740<br>45 | 97% | 956/273-3900<br>Fax 956/273-3995 |
| J A Kawas Elem Sch<br>2100 S Milmo Ave, Laredo 78046<br>Alberto Resendez | PK-5 | T | 445<br>32 | 99% | 956/273-3700<br>Fax 956/273-3795 |
| J W Nixon High Sch<br>2000 E Plum St, Laredo 78043<br>Cassandra Mendoza | 9-12 | ATV | 2,236<br>80 | 92% | 956/273-7400<br>Fax 956/273-7495 |
| J Z Leyendecker Elem Sch<br>1311 Garden St, Laredo 78040<br>Maria Oviedo | PK-5 | T | 506<br>40 | 98% | 956/273-3800<br>Fax 956/273-3895 |
| Ⓐ Jose A Valdez High Sch<br>1619 Victoria St, Laredo 78040<br>Lizzy Newsome | 9-12 | | 100 | | 956/273-8000<br>Fax 956/273-8095 |
| Joseph C Martin Elem Sch<br>1600 Monterrey Ave, Laredo 78040<br>Amy Cruz | PK-5 | T | 608<br>28 | 99% | 956/273-4100<br>Fax 956/273-4195 |
| Katherine Tarver Elem Sch<br>3200 Tilden Ave, Laredo 78040<br>Sara Montemayor | PK-5 | T | 431<br>33 | 94% | 956/273-4800<br>Fax 956/273-4895 |
| L J Christen Middle Sch<br>2001 Santa Maria Ave, Laredo 78040<br>Sandra Garcia | 6-8 | ATV | 1,187<br>100 | 100% | 956/273-6400<br>Fax 956/273-6495 |
| Leon Daiches Elem Sch<br>1401 Green St, Laredo 78040<br>Lisa Soto | PK-5 | T | 493<br>34 | 98% | 956/273-3200<br>Fax 956/273-3295 |

| | | | | | |
|---|---|---|---|---|---|
| 79 Student Personnel | 91 Safety/Security | 275 Response To Intervention | 298 Grant Writer/Ptnrships | **School Programs** | **Social Media** |
| 80 Driver Ed/Safety | 92 Magnet School | 277 Remedial Math K-12 | 750 Chief Innovation Officer | A = Alternative Program | |
| 81 Gifted/Talented | 93 Parental Involvement | 280 Literacy Coach | 751 Chief of Staff | G = Adult Classes | 🅵 = Facebook |
| 82 Video Services | 95 Tech Prep Program | 285 STEM | 752 Social Emotional Learning | M = Magnet Program | |
| 83 Substance Abuse Prev | 97 Chief Infomation Officer | 286 Digital Learning | | T = Title I Schoolwide | 🆃 = Twitter |
| 84 Erate | 98 Chief Technology Officer | 288 Common Core Standards | **Other School Types** | V = Career & Tech Ed Programs | |
| 85 AIDS Education | 270 Character Education | 294 Accountability | Ⓐ = Alternative School | | |
| 88 Alternative/At Risk | 271 Migrant Education | 295 Network System | Ⓒ = Charter School | New Schools are shaded | |
| 89 Multi-Cultural Curriculum | 273 Teacher Mentor | 296 Title II Programs | Ⓜ = Magnet School | New Superintendents and Principals are bold | |
| 90 Social Work | 274 Before/After Sch | 297 Webmaster | Ⓨ = Year-Round School | Personnel with email addresses are underscored | |

## TX—389

| School | Grd | Prgm | Enr/#Cls | SN | Phone |
|--------|-----|------|----------|-----|-------|
| M B Lamar Middle Sch<br>1818 N Arkansas Ave, Laredo 78043<br>Eduardo Lopez | 6-8 | ATV | 1,369<br>60 | 96% | 956/273-6200<br>Fax 956/273-6395 |
| M S Ryan Elem Sch<br>2401 Clark Blvd, Laredo 78043<br>Elsa Flores | PK-5 | | 837<br>45 | | 956/273-4400<br>Fax 956/273-4495 |
| Memorial Middle Sch<br>2002 Marcella Ave, Laredo 78040<br>Melissa Valdez | 6-8 | ATV | 490<br>45 | 98% | 956/273-6600<br>Fax 956/273-6795 |
| Raymond & Tirza Martin HS<br>2002 San Bernardo Ave, Laredo 78040<br>Guillermo Pro | 9-12 | ATV | 2,004<br>100 | 97% | 956/273-7100<br>Fax 956/273-7394 |
| Ⓜ Sabas Perez Eng & Tech Sch<br>2600 Zacatecas St, Laredo 78046<br>Alfredo Perez | 9-12 | V | 305 | | 956/795-3800<br>Fax 956/273-9075 |
| Sanchez-Ochoa Elem Sch<br>211 E Ash St, Laredo 78040<br>Rosalba Martinez | PK-5 | T | 671<br>40 | 98% | 956/273-4500<br>Fax 956/273-4595 |
| Santa Maria Elem Sch<br>3817 Santa Maria Ave, Laredo 78041<br>Jose De Leon | PK-5 | T | 573<br>35 | 100% | 956/273-4600<br>Fax 956/273-4695 |
| Santo Nino Elem Sch<br>2701 Bismark St, Laredo 78043<br>Jose Perez | PK-5 | T | 706<br>45 | 93% | 956/273-4700<br>Fax 956/273-4795 |
| Ⓜ Trevino Comm & Fine Art Sch<br>2102 E Lyon St, Laredo 78043<br>Dr Martha Villarreal | 9-12 | | 687<br>28 | | 956/273-7800<br>Fax 956/273-7895 |

● **United Ind School Dist**  PID: 01059470                     956/473-6201
201 Lindenwood Dr, Laredo 78045                              Fax 956/473-6476

**Schools:** 48 \ **Teachers:** 2,585 \ **Students:** 48,174 \
**Special Ed Students:** 3,989 \ **LEP Students:** 13,682 \ **College-Bound:** 51%
\ **Ethnic:** Hispanic 99%, Caucasian 1% \ **Exp:** $367 (High) \ **Poverty:** 27% \
**Title I:** $18,259,285 \ **Special Education:** $6,533,000 \ **Open-Close:** 08/24 -
05/28 \ **DTBP:** $191 (High)

| | | | |
|---|---|---|---|
| Roberto Santos | 1 | Cordelia Flores-Jackson | 2 |
| Eduardo Zuniga | 2,3,5,15,73,79 | Laida Benavides | 2,15 |
| Enrique Rangel | 3,15 | Mike Garza | 3,7,15 |
| Rogelio Gutierrez | 3 | Raul Ramirez | 4 |
| Joe Aranda | 5 | Bobby Cruz | 6* |
| Irene Rosales | 7* | David Gonzalez | 8,15 |
| Cynthia Rodriguez | 9 | David Canales | 10 |
| Dolores Barrera | 10 | Rebecca Morales | 11,93,271 |
| David Garcia | 15,68 | Gloria Rendon | 15 |
| Celia Taboada | 16,74 | Gerardo Rodriguez | 20,23* |
| Angelica Sanchez | 27,31 | Cordelia Cuellar | 34 |
| Melissa Chapa Ramirez | 36,83,274 | Maria Arambula-Ruiz | 57,61 |
| Cynthia Ramirez | 58 | Ramiro Veliz | 67 |
| Christina Casanova | 69 | Melissa Cruz | 70 |
| Rocio Moore | 71 | Hector Perez | 73,76,286,295 |
| Judith Garcia | 73 | Laura Garcia | 76 |
| Lisa Marie Dunn-Flores | 81 | Rene Cruz | 84 |
| Annette Perez | 88 | Ray Garner | 91 |
| Ricardo Rangel | 91 | Dr Cordelia Martinez-Nava | 275 |
| Emma Leza | 294 | Dr Edith Landeck | 298 |

| Public Schs..Principal | Grd | Prgm | Enr/#Cls | SN | Phone |
|-----------------------|-----|------|----------|-----|-------|
| Alicia Ruiz Elem Sch<br>1717 Los Presidentes Ave, Laredo 78046<br>Michelle Cantu | PK-5 | T | 774<br>65 | 82% | 956/473-3300<br>Fax 956/473-3399 |
| Amparo Gutierrez Elem Sch<br>505 Calle Del Norte, Laredo 78041<br>Laura Vasquez | PK-5 | T | 412<br>51 | 78% | 956/473-4400<br>Fax 956/473-4499 |
| Antonio Gonzalez Middle Sch<br>5208 Santa Claudia, Laredo 78043<br>Clotilde Gamez | 6-8 | T | 685 | 86% | 956/473-7000<br>Fax 956/473-7099 |

| School | Grd | Prgm | Enr/#Cls | SN | Phone |
|--------|-----|------|----------|-----|-------|
| Barbara Fasken Elem Sch<br>11111 Atlanta Dr, Laredo 78045<br>Melba Gutierrez | PK-5 | T | 748 | 65% | 956/473-4700<br>Fax 956/473-4799 |
| Bonnie Garcia Elem Sch<br>1453 Concord Hills Blvd, Laredo 78046<br>Patricia Lanas | PK-5 | T | 684 | 84% | 956/473-8900<br>Fax 956/473-8999 |
| Charles Borchers Elem Sch<br>9551 Backwoods Trl, Laredo 78045<br>Mucia Flores | PK-5 | T | 667<br>35 | 43% | 956/473-7200<br>Fax 956/473-7299 |
| Clark Elem Sch<br>500 W Hillside Rd, Laredo 78041<br>Gabriela Perez | PK-5 | T | 381<br>32 | 90% | 956/473-4600<br>Fax 956/473-4699 |
| Clark Middle Sch<br>500 W Hillside Rd, Laredo 78041<br>Pamela Arredondo | 6-8 | | 698<br>52 | 86% | 956/473-7500<br>Fax 956/473-7599 |
| Col Santos Benavides Elem Sch<br>10702 Kirby Dr, Laredo 78045<br>Adriana Vela | PK-5 | T | 913<br>60 | 36% | 956/473-4900<br>Fax 956/473-4999 |
| Dr Henry Cuellar Elem Sch<br>6431 Casa Del Sol Blvd, Laredo 78043<br>Andrea Sanchez | PK-5 | T | 561<br>34 | 90% | 956/473-2700<br>Fax 956/473-2799 |
| Dr Malakoff Elem Sch<br>2810 Havana, Laredo 78045<br>Anna Martinez | PK-5 | T | 643 | 55% | 956/473-4800<br>Fax 956/473-4899 |
| Dr S Perez Elem Sch<br>500 Sierra Vista Blvd, Laredo 78046<br>Salud Hernandez | PK-5 | T | 583<br>48 | 92% | 956/473-3600<br>Fax 956/473-3699 |
| Elias Herrera Middle Sch<br>8800 McPherson Rd, Laredo 78045<br>Carlos Martinez | 6-8 | | 401 | | 956/473-6900<br>Fax 956/473-6999 |
| Finley Elem Sch<br>2001 Lowry Rd, Laredo 78045<br>Kristina Chapa | PK-5 | T | 399<br>35 | 88% | 956/473-4500<br>Fax 956/473-4599 |
| Freedom Elem Sch<br>415 Eg Ranch Rd, Laredo 78046<br>Laura De Los Santos | PK-5 | | 531 | | 956/473-1600<br>Fax 956/473-1699 |
| George Washington Middle Sch<br>10306 Riverbank Dr, Laredo 78045<br>Dorothy Porter | 6-8 | AT | 1,256<br>74 | 77% | 956/473-7600<br>Fax 956/473-7699 |
| J B Alexander 9th Grade HS<br>4601 Victory Dr, Laredo 78045<br>Eva Alicia Calcaneo | 9-9 | | 900 | | 956/473-1300<br>Fax 956/473-1399 |
| J B Alexander High Sch<br>3600 E Del Mar Blvd, Laredo 78041<br>Ernesto Sandoval | 10-12 | TV | 1,892<br>125 | 56% | 956/473-5800<br>Fax 956/473-5999 |
| J B Jones Muller Elem Sch<br>4430 Muller Blvd, Laredo 78045<br>Mayra Ramirez | PK-5 | T | 812<br>40 | 77% | 956/473-3900<br>Fax 956/473-3999 |
| J W Arndt Elem Sch<br>610 Santa Martha Blvd, Laredo 78046<br>Juanita Zepeda | PK-5 | T | 698<br>40 | 96% | 956/473-2800<br>Fax 956/473-2899 |
| Juarez-Lincoln Elem Sch<br>1003 Espejo Molina Rd, Laredo 78046<br>Roberto Ortiz | PK-5 | T | 598<br>40 | 94% | 956/473-3000<br>Fax 956/473-3099 |
| Kazen Elem Sch<br>9620 Albany Dr, Laredo 78045<br>Monica Arriaga | PK-5 | T | 474<br>50 | 83% | 956/473-4200<br>Fax 956/473-4299 |
| Kennedy-Zapata Elem Sch<br>3809 Espejo Molina Rd, El Cenizo 78046<br>Thelma Martinez | PK-5 | T | 158 | 94% | 956/473-4100<br>Fax 956/473-4199 |
| Killam Elem Sch<br>5315 Fairfield Dr, Laredo 78043<br>Agapito Palizo | PK-5 | T | 647 | 87% | 956/473-2600<br>Fax 956/473-2699 |
| Lamar Bruni Vergara Middle Sch<br>5910 Saint Luke, Laredo 78046<br>Clarissa Flores | 6-8 | T | 1,013 | 94% | 956/473-6600<br>Fax 956/473-6699 |

| # | | # | | # | | # | | # | | # | | # | |
|---|---|---|---|---|---|---|---|---|---|---|---|---|---|
| 1 | Superintendent | 8 | Curric/Instruct K-12 | 19 | Chief Financial Officer | 29 | Family/Consumer Science | 39 | Social Studies K-12 | 49 | English/Lang Arts Elem | 59 | Special Education Elem | 69 | Academic Assessment |
| 2 | Bus/Finance/Purchasing | 9 | Curric/Instruct Elem | 20 | Art K-12 | 30 | Adult Education | 40 | Social Studies Elem | 50 | English/Lang Arts Sec | 60 | Special Education Sec | 70 | Research/Development |
| 3 | Buildings And Grounds | 10 | Curric/Instruct Sec | 21 | Art Elem | 31 | Career/Sch-to-Work K-12 | 41 | Social Studies Sec | 51 | Reading K-12 | 61 | Foreign/World Lang K-12 | 71 | Public Information |
| 4 | Food Service | 11 | Federal Program | 22 | Art Sec | 32 | Career/Sch-to-Work Elem | 42 | Science K-12 | 52 | Reading Elem | 62 | Foreign/World Lang Elem | 72 | Summer School |
| 5 | Transportation | 12 | Title I | 23 | Music K-12 | 33 | Career/Sch-to-Work Sec | 43 | Science Elem | 53 | Reading Sec | 63 | Foreign/World Lang Sec | 73 | Instructional Tech |
| 6 | Athletic | 13 | Title V | 24 | Music Elem | 34 | Early Childhood Ed | 44 | Science Sec | 54 | Remedial Reading K-12 | 64 | Religious Education K-12 | 74 | Inservice Training |
| 7 | Health Services | 15 | Asst Superintendent | 25 | Music Sec | 35 | Health/Phys Education | 45 | Math K-12 | 55 | Remedial Reading Elem | 65 | Religious Education Elem | 75 | Marketing/Distributive |
| | | 16 | Instructional Media Svcs | 26 | Business Education | 36 | Guidance Services K-12 | 46 | Math Elem | 56 | Remedial Reading Sec | 66 | Religious Education Sec | 76 | Info Systems |
| | | 17 | Chief Operations Officer | 27 | Career & Tech Ed | 37 | Guidance Services Elem | 47 | Math Sec | 57 | Bilingual/ELL | 67 | School Board President | 77 | Psychological Assess |
| | | 18 | Chief Academic Officer | 28 | Technology Education | 38 | Guidance Services Sec | 48 | English/Lang Arts K-12 | 58 | Special Education K-12 | 68 | Teacher Personnel | 78 | Affirmative Action |

| | | | | | |
|---|---|---|---|---|---|
| Los Obispos Middle Sch<br>4801 S Ejido Ave, Laredo 78046<br>Jessica Salazar | 6-8 | TV | 1,001 | 96% | 956/473-7800<br>Fax 956/473-7899 |
| Lyndon B Johnson High Sch<br>5626 Cielito Lindo, Laredo 78046<br>Armando Salazar | 9-12 | AGTV | 2,981 | 92% | 956/473-5100<br>Fax 956/473-5281 |
| Matias De Llano Jr Elem Sch<br>1415 Shiloh Dr, Laredo 78045<br>Diana Korrodi | PK-5 | T | 492<br>32 | 65% | 956/473-4000<br>Fax 956/473-4099 |
| Newman Elem Sch<br>1300 Alta Vista Dr, Laredo 78041<br>Leticia Garcia | PK-5 | T | 543<br>33 | 88% | 956/473-3800<br>Fax 956/473-3899 |
| Nye Elem Sch<br>101 E Del Mar Blvd, Laredo 78041<br>Cynthia Caballero | PK-5 | T | 792<br>53 | 73% | 956/473-3700<br>Fax 956/473-3799 |
| Paciano Prada Elem Sch<br>510 Soria Dr, Laredo 78046<br>Vanessa Saldana | PK-5 | T | 653<br>45 | 93% | 956/473-3500<br>Fax 956/473-3599 |
| Raul Perales Middle Sch<br>410 Eg Ranch Rd, Laredo 78043<br>Martha Alvarez | 6-8 | T | 451 | 89% | 956/473-6800<br>Fax 956/473-6899 |
| Rodolfo Centeno Elem Sch<br>2710 La Pita Mangana Rd, Laredo 78046<br>Amabilia Gonzalez | PK-5 | T | 855 | 91% | 956/473-8800<br>Fax 956/473-8899 |
| Roosevelt Elem Sch<br>3301 Sierra Vista Blvd, Laredo 78046<br>Sylvia Ruiz | PK-5 | T | 619<br>47 | 97% | 956/473-3400<br>Fax 956/473-3499 |
| Salinas Elem Sch<br>3611 Alfredo Cantu Dr, Laredo 78046<br>Abraham Rodriguez | PK-5 | T | 732<br>35 | 81% | 956/473-3200<br>Fax 956/473-3299 |
| Salvador Garcia Middle Sch<br>499 Pena Dr, Laredo 78046<br>Quetzalcoatl Palapa | 6-8 | AT | 297<br>40 | 96% | 956/473-5000<br>Fax 956/473-5099 |
| San Isidro Elem Sch<br>11021 Bucky Houdman Blvd, Laredo 78045<br>Dr Myrtha Villareal | PK-5 | | 645 | 30% | 956/473-6700<br>Fax 956/473-6799 |
| Senator Judith Zaffirini ES<br>5210 Santa Claudia, Laredo 78043<br>Claudia Benavides | PK-5 | T | 483 | 81% | 956/473-2900<br>Fax 956/473-2999 |
| Trautman Elem Sch<br>810 Lindenwood Dr, Laredo 78045<br>Melissa Shinn | PK-5 | T | 719<br>40 | 47% | 956/473-3100<br>Fax 956/473-3199 |
| Trautmann Middle Sch<br>8501 Curly Ln, Laredo 78045<br>Leticia Menchaca | 6-8 | TV | 1,718<br>50 | 46% | 956/473-7400<br>Fax 956/473-7499 |
| United High 9th Grade HS<br>2811 Hillcroft Dr, Laredo 78045<br>Arlene Trevino | 9-9 | | 1,000 | | 956/473-2400<br>Fax 956/473-2499 |
| United High Sch<br>2811 United Ave, Laredo 78045<br>Alberto Aleman | 10-12 | TV | 2,200<br>100 | 60% | 956/473-5600<br>Fax 956/473-1980 |
| United Middle Sch<br>700 E Del Mar Blvd, Laredo 78041<br>Rosana Arizola | 6-8 | T | 1,149 | 51% | 956/473-7300<br>Fax 956/473-7399 |
| United South High 9th Grade HS<br>3819 Aguanieve Dr, Laredo 78046<br>Olga Cantu | 9-9 | | 795 | | 956/473-1400<br>Fax 956/473-1499 |
| United South High Sch<br>4001 Los Presidentes Ave, Laredo 78046<br>Adriana Ramirez | 10-12 | TV | 2,300 | 85% | 956/473-5400<br>Fax 956/473-5599 |
| United South Middle Sch<br>3707 Los Presidentes Ave, Laredo 78046<br>Carlos Valdez | 6-8 | GT | 1,367<br>40 | 83% | 956/473-7700<br>Fax 956/473-7799 |
| Ⓐ United Step Academy<br>1600 Espejo Molina Rd, Laredo 78046<br>Gerardo Rodriguez | 6-12 | T | 71<br>16 | 95% | 956/473-6500<br>Fax 956/473-6599 |

| | | | | | |
|---|---|---|---|---|---|
| Veterans Memorial Elem Sch<br>5909 Saint Luke, Laredo 78046<br>Luz Serna Ramirez | PK-5 | T | 754 | 91% | 956/473-1200<br>Fax 956/473-1299 |

- **Webb Cons Ind School Dist** PID: 01059145     361/747-5415
  619 Avenue F, Bruni 78344        Fax 361/747-5202

> **Schools:** 3 \ **Teachers:** 27 \ **Students:** 238 \ **Special Ed Students:** 35
> \ **LEP Students:** 18 \ **College-Bound:** 56% \ **Ethnic:** African American
> 2%, Hispanic 94%, Caucasian 4% \ **Exp:** $1,276 (High) \ **Poverty:** 42% \
> **Title I:** $215,354 \ **Special Education:** $83,000 \ **Open-Close:** 07/24 - 05/25
> \ **DTBP:** $350 (High)

| | |
|---|---|
| Beto Gonzalez ...........................................1 | Martha Gonzalez ................................. 2,4 |
| Ruben Davila .............................................3 | Alvaro Carreon ........................................5* |
| Sylvia Garcia .............................................7 | Sandra Castillo ............8,11,16,57,58,69,275* |
| Jenette Black ..............................19,84,296 | Melissa Pena ........................................ 67 |
| Alexis Salinas ................................. 73,286 | Jesus Dominguez .................................. 91 |

| Public Schs..Principal | Grd | Prgm | Enr/#Cls | | SN |
|---|---|---|---|---|---|
| Bruni High Sch<br>619 Avenue F, Bruni 78344<br>H Garza | 9-12 | ATV | 57 | 70% | 361/747-5415<br>Fax 361/747-5301 |
| Bruni Middle Sch<br>619 Avenue F, Bruni 78344<br>Josie Castillo | 6-8 | T | 58<br>10 | 90% | 361/747-5415 |
| Oilton Elem Sch<br>619 Avenue F, Bruni 78344<br>Josie Castillo | PK-5 | T | 123<br>16 | 83% | 361/586-5415<br>Fax 361/586-4979 |

## WEBB CATHOLIC SCHOOLS

- **Diocese of Laredo Ed Office** PID: 04938095    956/753-5208
  1201 Corpus Christi St, Laredo 78040     Fax 956/753-5203

> **Schools:** 4 \ **Students:** 1,627 \ **Open-Close:** 08/17 - 05/27

Listing includes only schools located in this county. See District Index for location of Diocesan Offices.

| | |
|---|---|
| Dr Guadalupe Perez ..................................1 | Lizzy Flores ............................................2 |
| Melinda Sepulveda .................................68 | Luis Martinez ................................. 76,295 |

| Catholic Schs..Principal | Grd | Prgm | Enr/#Cls | SN |
|---|---|---|---|---|
| Blessed Sacrament Sch<br>1501 N Bartlett Ave, Laredo 78043<br>Selma Santos | PK-8 | | 250<br>13 | 956/722-1222<br>Fax 956/712-2002 |
| St Augustine Elem Middle Sch<br>1300 Galveston St, Laredo 78040<br>Barbra Zurita | PK-8 | | 300<br>10 | 956/724-1176<br>Fax 956/724-9891 |
| St Augustine High Sch<br>1300 Galveston St, Laredo 78040<br>Olga Gentry | 9-12 | | 627<br>38 | 956/724-8131<br>Fax 956/724-2770<br>⒡ⓣ |

## WEBB PRIVATE SCHOOLS

| Private Schs..Principal | Grd | Prgm | Enr/#Cls | SN |
|---|---|---|---|---|
| Mary Help of Christians Sch<br>10 E Del Mar Blvd, Laredo 78041<br>Sr Vuong DO | K-8 | | 614<br>33 | 956/722-3966<br>Fax 956/722-1413 |

United Day Sch  PK-8  390  956/723-7261
1701 San Isidro Pkwy, Laredo 78045  25  Fax 956/718-4048
Jessica Rivera

## WHARTON COUNTY

## WHARTON PUBLIC SCHOOLS

● **Boling Ind School Dist** PID: 01059535  979/657-2770
301 Texas Ave, Boling 77420  Fax 979/657-3265

Schools: 3 \ **Teachers:** 72 \ **Students:** 1,137 \ **Special Ed Students:** 87
\ **LEP Students:** 67 \ **College-Bound:** 67% \ **Ethnic:** African American
10%, Hispanic 54%, Caucasian 36% \ **Exp:** $463 (High) \ **Poverty:** 15% \
**Title I:** $142,174 \ **Open-Close:** 08/13 - 05/20 \ **DTBP:** $301 (High)

| | | |
|---|---|---|
| Wade Stidevent ...................................1,83 | Cherry Page ................................................2 |
| Larry Fisher ..........................................3,5 | Mark Salais .................................................4 |
| Kevin Urbanek ........................................6 | Nicole Folmar .............................................7* |
| Bryan Blanar ...................8,11,15,58,285,298 | Inez Kucera .................................................9 |
| Sarah Wilkins ........................................36* | Linda Taylor ..............................................57 |
| Donald Sciba ..........................................67 | Terrell Jessen ...........................................73* |

| Public Schs..Principal | Grd | Prgm | Enr/#Cls | SN |
|---|---|---|---|---|
| Boling High Sch<br>407 Atlantic St, Boling 77420<br>Keith Jedlicka | 9-12 | T | 371<br>25 | 47% 979/657-2816<br>Fax 979/657-2026 |
| Iago Junior High Sch<br>200 Gift St, Boling 77420<br>Gerald Floyd | 6-8 | TV | 270<br>20 | 59% 979/657-2826<br>Fax 979/657-2828 |
| Newgulf Elem Sch<br>1867 Burning Stone Dr, Boling 77420<br>Inez Kucera | PK-5 | AT | 496<br>30 | 58% 979/657-2837<br>Fax 979/657-3604 |

● **East Bernard Ind Sch Dist** PID: 01059573  979/335-7519
723 College St, East Bernard 77435  Fax 979/335-6561

Schools: 3 \ **Teachers:** 82 \ **Students:** 950 \ **Special Ed Students:** 72
\ **LEP Students:** 34 \ **Ethnic:** African American 6%, Hispanic 29%,
Caucasian 65% \ **Exp:** $595 (High) \ **Poverty:** 16% \ **Title I:** $158,846 \
**Open-Close:** 08/20 - 05/28 \ **DTBP:** $350 (High) \ 🇫 🇪

| | |
|---|---|
| Courtney Hudgins ......................................1 | Becky Kovar ..........................2,11,294,296 |
| Wade Bosse .............................................6* | Sandra Dusek ............................................7* |
| Kimberly Sulak ..............8,31,83,88,270,271* | Philip Gaudette .....................................9,273* |
| Lacey Christ ...........................................58 | Robert Gouduea .......................................67 |
| Jennifer Rieger ........................................69 | Abram Kubena ...........................73,84,295 |

| Public Schs..Principal | Grd | Prgm | Enr/#Cls | SN |
|---|---|---|---|---|
| East Bernard Elem Sch<br>723 College St, East Bernard 77435<br>Philip Gaudette | PK-4 | T | 341<br>17 | 43% 979/335-7519<br>Fax 979/335-6341 |
| East Bernard High Sch<br>723 College St, East Bernard 77435<br>Jeremy Janczak | 9-12 | AV | 318<br>35 | 27% 979/335-7519<br>Fax 979/335-6085 |
| East Bernard Jr High Sch<br>723 College St, East Bernard 77435<br>**David Janecek** | 5-8 | | 268<br>17 | 38% 979/335-7519<br>Fax 979/335-6415 |

● **El Campo Ind School Dist** PID: 01059602  979/543-6771
700 W Norris St, El Campo 77437  Fax 979/543-1670

Schools: 5 \ **Teachers:** 237 \ **Students:** 4,500 \ **Special Ed Students:** 340
\ **LEP Students:** 419 \ **Ethnic:** African American 10%, Hispanic 65%,
Caucasian 24% \ **Exp:** $567 (High) \ **Poverty:** 26% \ **Title I:** $1,257,249 \
**Open-Close:** 08/19 - 05/21 \ **DTBP:** $159 (High)

| | |
|---|---|
| Bob Calligan ............................................1 | David Bright ...............................2,3,15,17 |
| Jeff Balcar .........................................3,91 | Chelsea Akadie .........................................4 |
| Mark Freeman ..........................................5 | Wayne Condra ..........................................6* |
| Monica Ott .............................................7* | Doloris Trevino ...............8,15,18,57,271,274 |
| Alicia Stary ..............................11,294,296 | Christopher Skinner ........................16,73,82 |
| Amy Bosse ..............................................58 | James Russell ...........................................67 |
| Terese Faas ........................................68,79 | Tana Martin .............................................69 |
| Thomas Krenek .........................76,84,286 | Donald Oldag ...........................................295 |

| Public Schs..Principal | Grd | Prgm | Enr/#Cls | SN |
|---|---|---|---|---|
| El Campo High Sch<br>600 W Norris St, El Campo 77437<br>Demetric Wells | 9-12 | ATV | 1,127<br>82 | 58% 979/543-6341<br>Fax 979/543-2528 |
| El Campo Middle Sch<br>4010 FM 2765 Rd, El Campo 77437<br>**Alicia Stary** | 6-8 | AT | 863<br>50 | 71% 979/543-6362<br>Fax 979/541-5210 |
| Hutchins Elem Sch<br>1006 Roberts St, El Campo 77437<br>Elizabeth Tupa | 2-3 | T | 563<br>41 | 77% 979/543-5481<br>Fax 979/543-2418<br>🇪 |
| Myatt Elem Sch<br>501 W Webb St, El Campo 77437<br>Mauri Couey | PK-1 | T | 653<br>35 | 85% 979/543-7514<br>Fax 979/543-5188 |
| Northside Elem Sch<br>2610 Meadow Ln, El Campo 77437<br>Rebecca Crowell | 4-5 | T | 535<br>24 | 72% 979/543-5812<br>Fax 979/578-0682 |

● **Louise Ind School Dist** PID: 01059664  979/648-2982
408 2nd St, Louise 77455  Fax 979/648-2520

Schools: 3 \ **Teachers:** 42 \ **Students:** 510 \ **Special Ed Students:** 28
\ **LEP Students:** 67 \ **College-Bound:** 53% \ **Ethnic:** Asian 1%, African
American 4%, Hispanic 61%, Caucasian 34% \ **Exp:** $472 (High) \
**Poverty:** 18% \ **Title I:** $100,898 \ **Open-Close:** 08/27 - 06/01 \ **DTBP:** $345
(High)

| | |
|---|---|
| Dr Garth Oliver ..........................................1 | Pam Wagner ..............................................2 |
| Mike Briden .......................................3,5,91 | Shae Barker ...............................................4 |
| Heath Clawson ........................................6* | Kathryn Peterson ......................................8 |
| Traci Harvey .............................................38 | Donna Kutac ...........................................57* |
| Linda Alderson .........................................67 | Sandra Holik ...........................73,286,295* |

| Public Schs..Principal | Grd | Prgm | Enr/#Cls | SN |
|---|---|---|---|---|
| Louise Elem Sch<br>408 2nd St, Louise 77455<br>Brady Peterson | PK-5 | T | 230<br>21 | 70% 979/648-2262 |
| Louise High Sch<br>505 Hackberry St, Louise 77455<br>Donna Kutac | 9-12 | T | 159<br>16 | 55% 979/648-2202<br>Fax 979/648-2142 |
| Louise Junior High Sch<br>408 2nd St, Louise 77455<br>Brady Peterson | 6-8 | T | 121 | 69% 979/648-2262 |

| | | | | | | | |
|---|---|---|---|---|---|---|---|
| 1 | Superintendent | 8 | Curric/Instruct K-12 | 19 | Chief Financial Officer | 29 | Family/Consumer Science |
| 2 | Bus/Finance/Purchasing | 9 | Curric/Instruct Elem | 20 | Art K-12 | 30 | Adult Education |
| 3 | Buildings And Grounds | 10 | Curric/Instruct Sec | 21 | Art Elem | 31 | Career/Sch-to-Work K-12 |
| 4 | Food Service | 11 | Federal Program | 22 | Art Sec | 32 | Career/Sch-to-Work Elem |
| 5 | Transportation | 12 | Title I | 23 | Music K-12 | 33 | Career/Sch-to-Work Sec |
| 6 | Athletic | 13 | Title V | 24 | Music Elem | 34 | Early Childhood Ed |
| 7 | Health Services | 15 | Asst Superintendent | 25 | Music Sec | 35 | Health/Phys Education |
| | | 16 | Instructional Media Svcs | 26 | Business Education | 36 | Guidance Services K-12 |
| | | 17 | Chief Operations Officer | 27 | Career & Tech Ed | 37 | Guidance Services Elem |
| | | 18 | Chief Academic Officer | 28 | Technology Education | 38 | Guidance Services Sec |

| | | | | | | | |
|---|---|---|---|---|---|---|---|
| 39 | Social Studies K-12 | 49 | English/Lang Arts Elem | 59 | Special Education Elem | 69 | Academic Assessment |
| 40 | Social Studies Elem | 50 | English/Lang Arts Sec | 60 | Special Education Sec | 70 | Research/Development |
| 41 | Social Studies Sec | 51 | Reading K-12 | 61 | Foreign/World Lang K-12 | 71 | Public Information |
| 42 | Science K-12 | 52 | Reading Elem | 62 | Foreign/World Lang Elem | 72 | Summer School |
| 43 | Science Elem | 53 | Reading Sec | 63 | Foreign/World Lang Sec | 73 | Instructional Tech |
| 44 | Science Sec | 54 | Remedial Reading K-12 | 64 | Religious Education K-12 | 74 | Inservice Training |
| 45 | Math K-12 | 55 | Remedial Reading Elem | 65 | Religious Education Elem | 75 | Marketing/Distributive |
| 46 | Math Elem | 56 | Remedial Reading Sec | 66 | Religious Education Sec | 76 | Info Systems |
| 47 | Math Sec | 57 | Bilingual/ELL | 67 | School Board President | 77 | Psychological Assess |
| 48 | English/Lang Arts K-12 | 58 | Special Education K-12 | 68 | Teacher Personnel | 78 | Affirmative Action |

## Wharton Ind School Dist PID: 01059690
2100 N Fulton St, Wharton 77488

979/532-3612
Fax 979/532-6228

**Schools:** 5 \ **Teachers:** 146 \ **Students:** 2,015 \ **Special Ed Students:** 223 \ **LEP Students:** 247 \ **Ethnic:** Asian 1%, African American 25%, Hispanic 62%, Caucasian 12% \ **Exp:** $422 (High) \ **Poverty:** 21% \ **Title I:** $600,454 \ **Special Education:** $501,000 \ **Open-Close:** 08/14 - 05/28 \ **DTBP:** $360 (High) \ 🅵 🆃

| | | | | |
|---|---|---|---|---|
| Dr Michael O'Guin | .....1 | Kim Moses | ....2,84 | |
| Randall Meyer | .....3,15,19,68 | Alison Robeledo | ....4 | |
| Chad Butler | .....6 | Diana Garcia | ....7* | |
| Gayle Parenica | .....8 | David Calbert | ....58 | |
| Kimberly Somer | .....58,90* | Curtis Evans | ....67 | |
| Heath Roddy | .....73,297 | Anna Sanders | ....82* | |

| Public Schs..Principal | Grd | Prgm | Enr/#Cls | SN | |
|---|---|---|---|---|---|
| C G Sivells Elem Sch<br>1605 N Alabama Rd, Wharton 77488<br>**Dana Foyt** | PK-2 | T | 494<br>70 | 81% | 979/532-6866<br>Fax 979/532-6873 |
| Ⓐ Wharton Alternative Sch<br>1010 N Rusk St, Wharton 77488<br>Kim Harris | 7-12 | V | 60<br>4 | | 979/532-6262<br>Fax 979/532-6266 |
| Wharton Elem Sch<br>2030 E Boling Hwy, Wharton 77488<br>Pamela Lechler | 3-6 | T | 630<br>45 | 77% | 979/532-6882<br>Fax 979/532-6884<br>🅵 🆃 |
| Wharton High Sch<br>1 Tiger Ave, Wharton 77488<br>Jerrell Barron | 9-12 | TV | 591<br>60 | 65% | 979/532-6800<br>Fax 979/532-6807<br>🅵 🆃 |
| Wharton Junior High Sch<br>1120 N Rusk St, Wharton 77488<br>Olatunji Oduwole | 7-8 | GT | 300<br>44 | 73% | 979/532-6840<br>Fax 979/532-6849 |

## WHARTON CATHOLIC SCHOOLS

## Diocese of Victoria Ed Office PID: 02181727
Listing includes only schools located in this county. See District Index for location of Diocesan Offices.

| Catholic Schs..Principal | Grd | Prgm | Enr/#Cls | SN | |
|---|---|---|---|---|---|
| St Philip Catholic Sch<br>302 W Church St, El Campo 77437<br>Gwen Edwards | PK-8 | | 330<br>12 | | 979/543-2901<br>Fax 979/578-8835<br>🆃 |

## WHARTON PRIVATE SCHOOLS

| Private Schs..Principal | Grd | Prgm | Enr/#Cls | SN | |
|---|---|---|---|---|---|
| Faith Christian Academy<br>5227 FM 1301 Rd, Wharton 77488<br>Sandra Allen | PK-12 | | 100 | | 979/531-1000 |

## WHEELER PUBLIC SCHOOLS

## Ft Elliott Cons Ind Sch Dist PID: 01059779
501 E Wilson Ave, Briscoe 79011

806/375-2454
Fax 806/375-2327

**Schools:** 1 \ **Teachers:** 18 \ **Students:** 146 \ **Special Ed Students:** 12 \ **LEP Students:** 3 \ **College-Bound:** 30% \ **Ethnic:** Hispanic 13%, Caucasian 87% \ **Exp:** $507 (High) \ **Poverty:** 8% \ **Title I:** $12,768 \ **Open-Close:** 08/21 - 05/21 \ **DTBP:** $350 (High)

| | | | | |
|---|---|---|---|---|
| Frank Belcher | .....1,11,73,83 | Gwen Gibson | ....2 | |
| Brandon Mahler | .....8,88,273,286,752 | Kevin Meek | ....27* | |
| Susan Hughes | .....58 | Bret Begert | ....67 | |

| Public Schs..Principal | Grd | Prgm | Enr/#Cls | SN | |
|---|---|---|---|---|---|
| Ft Elliott Sch<br>501 E Wilson Road, Briscoe 79011<br>Brandon Mahler | PK-12 | V | 146<br>18 | 32% | 806/375-2454 |

## Kelton Ind School Dist PID: 01059808
16703 FM 2697, Wheeler 79096

806/826-5795
Fax 806/826-5737

**Schools:** 1 \ **Teachers:** 15 \ **Students:** 84 \ **Special Ed Students:** 11 \ **LEP Students:** 9 \ **College-Bound:** 100% \ **Ethnic:** Asian 3%, African American 1%, Hispanic 39%, Caucasian 57% \ **Exp:** $1,400 (High) \ **Poverty:** 12% \ **Open-Close:** 08/17 - 05/21

| | | | | |
|---|---|---|---|---|
| Leslie Berry | .....1,57,288 | Melanie Alls | ....2,16 | |
| Sherylene Willam | .....2 | Barbara Harris | ....7* | |
| Karen Byrum | .....58* | Bret Buckingham | ....67 | |

| Public Schs..Principal | Grd | Prgm | Enr/#Cls | SN | |
|---|---|---|---|---|---|
| Kelton Sch<br>16703 FM 2697, Wheeler 79096<br>Leslie Berry | PK-12 | T | 84<br>29 | 49% | 806/826-5795 |

## Shamrock Ind School Dist PID: 01059858
100 S Illinois St, Shamrock 79079

806/256-3492
Fax 806/256-3628

**Schools:** 3 \ **Teachers:** 40 \ **Students:** 342 \ **Special Ed Students:** 50 \ **LEP Students:** 16 \ **College-Bound:** 80% \ **Ethnic:** Asian 1%, African American 4%, Hispanic 34%, Native American: 1%, Caucasian 60% \ **Exp:** $713 (High) \ **Poverty:** 25% \ **Title I:** $131,343 \ **Open-Close:** 08/28 - 05/25 \ **DTBP:** $340 (High)

| | | | | |
|---|---|---|---|---|
| Kenneth Shields | .....1 | Connie Jones | ....2 | |
| Christi Evans | .....4* | Monte Cornett | ....5 | |
| Jody Guy | .....6* | Amanda Bell | ....7* | |
| Kenneth Shields | .....12,57* | Laramie Jernigan | ....16,73* | |
| Lanna Reeves | .....34,58 | Richard Hall | ....67 | |
| Jennifer Peevey | .....69 | | | |

| Public Schs..Principal | Grd | Prgm | Enr/#Cls | SN | |
|---|---|---|---|---|---|
| Shamrock Elem Sch<br>100 S Illinois St, Shamrock 79079<br>Andy Glass | PK-5 | T | 159<br>14 | 68% | 806/256-3227 |

| Shamrock High Sch | 9-12 | TV | 104 | 55% | 806/256-2241 |
| 100 S Illinois St, Shamrock 79079 | | | 25 | | |
| Blaze Herring | | | | | |

| Shamrock Junior High Sch | 6-8 | T | 79 | 67% | 806/256-3227 |
| 100 S Illinois St, Shamrock 79079 | | | 20 | | |
| Frank Berngen | | | | | |

● **Wheeler Ind School Dist** PID: 01059896   806/826-5241
1 Mustang Dr, Wheeler 79096   Fax 806/826-3118

**Schools:** 1 \ **Teachers:** 41 \ **Students:** 441 \ **Special Ed Students:** 49
\ **LEP Students:** 84 \ **College-Bound:** 72% \ **Ethnic:** Hispanic 59%,
Native American: 1%, Caucasian 40% \ **Exp:** $483 (High) \ **Poverty:** 18% \
**Title I:** $100,088 \ **Open-Close:** 08/21 - 05/21 \ **DTBP:** $424 (High)

| Bryan Markham | 1,11,83 | Stacie Horton | 2,19,298 |
| Randi Barr | 4* | Chris Evans | 6* |
| David Dale | 8,81,270,273* | Heather Hardcastle | 12,296* |
| Cecil Thomas | 16,73* | Angie Ware | 27* |
| Stacey Finsterwald | 57* | Jennifer Houska | 58 |
| Dr Leanne Hillhouse | 67 | Erin Shaw | 69* |

| Public Schs..Principal | Grd | Prgm | Enr/#Cls | SN | |
|---|---|---|---|---|---|
| Wheeler Sch | PK-12 | T | 441 | 52% | 806/826-5241 |
| 1 Mustang Dr, Wheeler 79096 | | | 40 | | |
| Mike Bailey \ **Heather Hardcastle** | | | | | |

# WICHITA COUNTY

# WICHITA PUBLIC SCHOOLS

● **Burkburnett Ind Sch Dist** PID: 01059925   940/569-3326
100 N Avenue D, Burkburnett 76354   Fax 940/569-4776

**Schools:** 6 \ **Teachers:** 245 \ **Students:** 3,350 \ **Special Ed Students:** 411
\ **LEP Students:** 42 \ **Ethnic:** Asian 1%, African American 7%, Hispanic 20%,
Native American: 1%, Caucasian 71% \ **Exp:** $461 (High) \ **Poverty:** 14% \
**Title I:** $566,152 \ **Special Education:** $937,000 \ **Open-Close:** 08/12 -
05/26 \ **DTBP:** $184 (High) \ 

| Tylor Chaplin | 1 | Laura Richards | 2 |
| Scott Simmons | 3,91 | Debbie Welch | 4 |
| Anthony West | 5 | Danny Nix | 6* |
| Missy Mayfield | 8,27,57,69,74,88,286,288 | Dr Jim Russell | 11,15 |
| Brad Owen | 16,73,82,295 | Casey Hunter | 27,298 |
| Audrey Ash | 58,271 | Frank Andrajack | 67 |
| Elizabeth Nolan | 81* | Anna Black | 83,88* |

| Public Schs..Principal | Grd | Prgm | Enr/#Cls | SN | |
|---|---|---|---|---|---|
| Burkburnett High Sch | 9-12 | TV | 670 | 39% | 940/569-1411 |
| 109 W Kramer Rd, Burkburnett 76354 | | | 80 | | Fax 940/569-9700 |
| Vance Morris | | | | | |
| Burkburnett Middle Sch | 6-8 | T | 685 | 50% | 940/569-3381 |
| 108 S Avenue D, Burkburnett 76354 | | | 80 | | Fax 940/569-7116 |
| Michael Baughman | | | | | |
| Ⓐ Gateway Alternative Ed Center | 1-12 | | 25 | | 940/569-0850 |
| 200 E 3rd St, Burkburnett 76354 | | | 4 | | Fax 940/569-3030 |
| Anna Black | | | | | |
| I C Evans Elem Sch | PK-5 | T | 734 | 62% | 940/569-3311 |
| 1015 S Berry St, Burkburnett 76354 | | | 26 | | Fax 940/569-2719 |
| Michelle Wiese | | | | | |

| John Tower Elem Sch | PK-5 | T | 331 | 42% | 940/855-3221 |
| 5200 Hooper Dr, Wichita Falls 76306 | | | 38 | | Fax 940/855-9812 |
| Jason Nolan | | | | | |

| Overton Ray Elem Sch | 3-5 | T | 330 | 55% | 940/569-5253 |
| 345 D W Taylor Pathway, Burkburnett 76354 | | | 53 | | |
| Kendy Johnston | | | | | |

● **City View Ind School Dist** PID: 01059999   940/855-4042
1025 City View Dr, Wichita Falls 76306   Fax 940/851-8889

**Schools:** 2 \ **Teachers:** 84 \ **Students:** 921 \ **Special Ed Students:** 132
\ **LEP Students:** 26 \ **College-Bound:** 51% \ **Ethnic:** Asian 1%, African
American 11%, Hispanic 33%, Native American: 1%, Caucasian 54% \
**Exp:** $863 (High) \ **Poverty:** 21% \ **Title I:** $214,306 \ **Open-Close:** 08/20 -
05/21 \ **DTBP:** $216 (High)

| Tony Bushong | 1 | Debbie McDaris | 2 |
| Dub Ewing | 3 | Daphne Ramsey | 4 |
| William Ewing | 5 | Rudy Hawkins | 6* |
| Carrie Hughes | 8,11,16,57,69,88,273 | Meridith Utley | 10,31,83 |
| Chuck Thompson | 16* | Michael Long | 67 |
| Jeff St Andre | 73,84,295 | Lana Wampler | 76 |

| Public Schs..Principal | Grd | Prgm | Enr/#Cls | SN | |
|---|---|---|---|---|---|
| City View Elem Sch | PK-6 | T | 461 | 83% | 940/855-2351 |
| 1023 City View Dr, Wichita Falls 76306 | | | 31 | | Fax 940/855-7943 |
| **Ronda Moffett** | | | | | |
| City View Jr Sr High Sch | 7-12 | ATV | 460 | 62% | 940/855-7511 |
| 1600 City View Dr, Wichita Falls 76306 | | | 32 | | Fax 940/851-5027 |
| Scott Boswell \ **Christina McDaniel** | | | | | |

● **Electra Ind School Dist** PID: 01060015   940/495-3683
400 E Roosevelt Ave, Electra 76360   Fax 940/495-3945

**Schools:** 3 \ **Teachers:** 42 \ **Students:** 391 \ **Special Ed Students:** 50
\ **LEP Students:** 5 \ **College-Bound:** 47% \ **Ethnic:** Asian 1%, African
American 6%, Hispanic 17%, Native American: 1%, Caucasian 76% \
**Exp:** $460 (High) \ **Poverty:** 21% \ **Title I:** $147,069 \ **Open-Close:** 08/26 -
05/21 \ **DTBP:** $606 (High)

| Ted West | 1 | Laura Lee Brock | 2,8,11,27,31,88,273 |
| Debra Malone | 4 | Brian Ramsey | 6* |
| Steven Wallace | 9,54* | Janet Goodwin | 11,57,271* |
| Angela Schlegel | 58 | Wayne Cranford | 67 |
| Renneth Reed | 73,295* | Scott Hogue | 83 |
| Rayann Stevens | 275* | | |

| Public Schs..Principal | Grd | Prgm | Enr/#Cls | SN | |
|---|---|---|---|---|---|
| Electra Elem Sch | PK-6 | T | 255 | 71% | 940/432-3815 |
| 621 S Bailey St, Electra 76360 | | | 24 | | Fax 940/495-3627 |
| **Dr Jim Russell** | | | | | |
| Electra Jr Senior High Sch | 7-12 | TV | 136 | 59% | 940/432-3812 |
| 200 Anderson Ave, Electra 76360 | | | 23 | | Fax 940/257-2815 |
| **Don Hasley** | | | | | |
| Ⓐ Texoma Alternative Center | 4-12 | | 40 | | 940/592-1410 |
| 205 N Colorado St, Iowa Park 76367 | | | 4 | | Fax 940/592-1486 |
| Rosie Flanigan | | | | | |

| 1 | Superintendent | 8 | Curric/Instruct K-12 | 19 | Chief Financial Officer | 29 | Family/Consumer Science | 39 | Social Studies K-12 | 49 | English/Lang Arts Elem | 59 | Special Education Elem | 69 | Academic Assessment |
|---|---|---|---|---|---|---|---|---|---|---|---|---|---|---|---|
| 2 | Bus/Finance/Purchasing | 9 | Curric/Instruct Elem | 20 | Art K-12 | 30 | Adult Education | 40 | Social Studies Elem | 50 | English/Lang Arts Sec | 60 | Special Education Sec | 70 | Research/Development |
| 3 | Buildings And Grounds | 10 | Curric/Instruct Sec | 21 | Art Elem | 31 | Career/Sch-to-Work K-12 | 41 | Social Studies Sec | 51 | Reading K-12 | 61 | Foreign/World Lang K-12 | 71 | Public Information |
| 4 | Food Service | 11 | Federal Program | 22 | Art Sec | 32 | Career/Sch-to-Work Elem | 42 | Science K-12 | 52 | Reading Elem | 62 | Foreign/World Lang Elem | 72 | Summer School |
| 5 | Transportation | 12 | Title I | 23 | Music K-12 | 33 | Career/Sch-to-Work Sec | 43 | Science Elem | 53 | Reading Sec | 63 | Foreign/World Lang Sec | 73 | Instructional Tech |
| 6 | Athletic | 13 | Title V | 24 | Music Elem | 34 | Early Childhood Ed | 44 | Science Sec | 54 | Remedial Reading K-12 | 64 | Religious Education K-12 | 74 | Inservice Training |
| 7 | Health Services | 14 | Asst Superintendent | 25 | Music Sec | 35 | Health/Phys Education | 45 | Math K-12 | 55 | Remedial Reading Elem | 65 | Religious Education Elem | 75 | Marketing/Distributive |
| | | 16 | Instructional Media Svcs | 26 | Business Education | 36 | Guidance Services K-12 | 46 | Math Elem | 56 | Remedial Reading Sec | 66 | Religious Education Sec | 76 | Info Systems |
| | | 17 | Chief Operations Officer | 27 | Career & Tech Ed | 37 | Guidance Services Elem | 47 | Math Sec | 57 | Bilingual/ELL | 67 | School Board President | 77 | Psychological Assess |
| | | 18 | Chief Academic Officer | 28 | Technology Education | 38 | Guidance Services Sec | 48 | English/Lang Arts K-12 | 58 | Special Education K-12 | 68 | Teacher Personnel | 78 | Affirmative Action |

- **Iowa Park Consolidated Ind SD** PID: 01060065    940/592-4193
  328 E Highway St, Iowa Park 76367    Fax 940/592-2136

**Schools:** 4 \ **Teachers:** 132 \ **Students:** 1,421 \ **Special Ed Students:** 217 \ **LEP Students:** 10 \ **Ethnic:** Asian 1%, Hispanic 13%, Native American: 1%, Caucasian 86% \ **Exp:** $471 (High) \ **Poverty:** 11% \ **Title I:** $214,022 \ **Open-Close:** 08/14 - 05/20 \ **DTBP:** $550 (High) \ [f] [t]

| | | |
|---|---|---|
| Steve Moody ........................1 | Sharon Godwin ...........2,11,19,298 | |
| Tim Kingcade ........................3 | Serena Criswell ..........................4 | |
| Ned Miller ........................5 | Aubrey Sims ..........................6* | |
| Jodie Schlaud .........8,73,285,286,288 | Brandy Rhoades .......................36* | |
| Anjela Schlegel ........................58 | Jeff Rhoades ..........................67 | |
| Cindy Bartow ........................68 | Mike Parchman ........................76 | |
| Cindy Teichman ........................79 | | |

| Public Schs..Principal | Grd | Prgm | Enr/#Cls | SN |
|---|---|---|---|---|
| **Bradford Elem Sch** <br> 809 Texowa Rd, Iowa Park 76367 <br> Brandi Swenson | 3-5 | T | 442 <br> 26 | 41%   940/592-5841 <br> Fax 940/592-2059 |
| **Iowa Park High Sch** <br> 1 Bob Dawson Dr, Iowa Park 76367 <br> Leah Russell | 9-12 | V | 286 <br> 50 | 36%   940/592-2144 <br> Fax 940/592-2583 |
| **Kidwell Elem Sch** <br> 1200 N 3rd St, Iowa Park 76367 <br> James Kennedy | PK-2 | T | 412 <br> 28 | 55%   940/592-4322 <br> Fax 940/592-2487 |
| **W F George Middle Sch** <br> 412 E Cash St, Iowa Park 76367 <br> Darla Biddy | 6-8 | T | 281 <br> 40 | 38%   940/592-2196 <br> Fax 940/592-2801 |

- **Wichita Falls Ind School Dist** PID: 01060132    940/235-1000
  1104 Broad St, Wichita Falls 76301

**Schools:** 28 \ **Teachers:** 1,006 \ **Students:** 14,500 \ **Special Ed Students:** 1,669 \ **LEP Students:** 1,081 \ **College-Bound:** 46% \ **Ethnic:** Asian 3%, African American 15%, Hispanic 38%, Native American: 1%, Caucasian 44% \ **Exp:** $187 (Low) \ **Poverty:** 22% \ **Title I:** $4,635,204 \ **Special Education:** $2,612,000 \ **Open-Close:** 08/14 - 05/21 \ **DTBP:** $187 (High) \ [f]

| | | |
|---|---|---|
| Michael Kuhrt ........................1 | Alicia Woodard ..........................2 | |
| Denise Brown ........................2 | Tim Sherrod ..........................2,19 | |
| Christopher Fain ........................3 | Scot Hafley ..........................6 | |
| Debi Mills ........................7 | Misti Spear ..........................9 | |
| Debbie Dippery ........................10,36 | Jackie Wheat ..........................11 | |
| Peter Griffiths ........................15,286 | Shad McGaha ...............16,73,76,98,295 | |
| Kelly Strenski ........................20,23 | Michelle Wood ..........................27,31 | |
| Synthia Kirby ........................27,31,73,95* | Dr Travis Armstrong ......................34 | |
| Julie Henderson ........................35,83,85 | Sherry Parker ..........................39 | |
| Greta Benavides ........................57 | Alefia Paris-Toulon ......................58 | |
| Elizabeth Yeager ........................67 | Cyndy Kohl ..........................68 | |
| Shannon Kuhrt ........................69 | Ashley Thomas ..........................71 | |
| Frank Murray ........................73 | Dr Linda Muehlberger ....................79,93 | |
| Ward Roberts ........................81 | Betsi Morton ..........................88 | |
| Bill Horton ........................91 | Jessica Wilkins ..........................297 | |

| Public Schs..Principal | Grd | Prgm | Enr/#Cls | SN |
|---|---|---|---|---|
| Ⓜ **Barwise Middle Sch** <br> 3807 Kemp Blvd, Wichita Falls 76308 <br> Peter Braveboy | 6-8 | TV | 1,179 <br> 39 | 73%   940/235-1108 <br> Fax 940/235-1109 |
| **Booker T Washington ES** <br> 1300 Harding St, Wichita Falls 76301 <br> Angela Rooney | PK-5 | T | 264 <br> 15 | 91%   940/235-1196 <br> Fax 940/235-1197 |
| **Brook Village Eec** <br> 2222 Brook Ave, Wichita Falls 76301 <br> Letitia Willis | PK-K | | 251 <br> 14 | 940/235-1132 <br> Fax 940/235-1133 |
| Ⓜ **Burgess Elem Sch** <br> 3106 Maurine St, Wichita Falls 76306 <br> Jeff Hill | PK-5 | T | 271 <br> 36 | 87%   940/235-1136 <br> Fax 940/235-1137 |
| **Career Education Center** <br> 500 E Hatton Rd, Wichita Falls 76302 <br> Synthia Kirby | Voc | | 150 | 940/235-4316 |
| **Crockett Elem Sch** <br> 3015 Avenue I, Wichita Falls 76309 <br> Jesse Thomas | K-5 | T | 481 <br> 35 | 67%   940/235-1140 <br> Fax 940/235-1141 |
| **Cunningham Elem Sch** <br> 4100 Pool St, Wichita Falls 76308 <br> Donna Martin | PK-5 | T | 444 <br> 28 | 66%   940/235-1144 <br> Fax 940/235-1145 |
| Ⓐ **Denver Alternative Center** <br> 3115 5th St, Wichita Falls 76301 <br> Linda Nichols | K-12 | | 150 <br> 9 | 940/235-1101 <br> Fax 940/235-1102 |
| **Fain Elem Sch** <br> 1562 Norman St, Wichita Falls 76302 <br> Clarisa Richie | PK-5 | T | 438 <br> 27 | 62%   940/235-1148 <br> Fax 940/235-1149 |
| **Farris Early Childhood Center** <br> 710 Burkburnett Rd, Wichita Falls 76306 <br> Letitia Willis | PK-PK | T | 213 <br> 16 | 99%   940/235-4302 <br> Fax 940/235-4303 |
| **Fowler Elem Sch** <br> 5100 Ridgecrest Dr, Wichita Falls 76310 <br> Alexandra Martin | PK-5 | T | 547 <br> 28 | 43%   940/235-1152 <br> Fax 940/235-1153 |
| **Franklin Elem Sch** <br> 2112 Speedway Ave, Wichita Falls 76308 <br> Angie Betts | PK-5 | T | 414 <br> 36 | 52%   940/235-1156 <br> Fax 940/235-1157 |
| **Haynes Northwest Academy** <br> 1705 Katherine Dr, Wichita Falls 76306 <br> Lori Apple | PK-5 | T | 182 <br> 25 | 82%   940/235-1160 <br> Fax 940/235-1161 |
| Ⓜ **Hirschi High Sch** <br> 3106 Borton St, Wichita Falls 76306 <br> Doug Albus | 9-12 | TV | 206 <br> 80 | 75%   940/235-1070 <br> Fax 940/235-1300 |
| **Jefferson Elem Sch** <br> 4628 Mistletoe Dr, Wichita Falls 76310 <br> Erica Adkins | PK-5 | T | 447 <br> 23 | 59%   940/235-1168 <br> Fax 940/235-1169 |
| Ⓜ **Kirby Middle Sch** <br> 1715 Loop 11, Wichita Falls 76306 <br> Shannon Cunningham | 6-8 | TV | 414 <br> 39 | 87%   940/235-1113 <br> Fax 940/235-1114 |
| **Lamar Elem Sch** <br> 2206 Lucas Ave, Wichita Falls 76301 <br> Amanda Garcia | PK-5 | T | 326 <br> 25 | 91%   940/235-1172 <br> Fax 940/235-1173 |
| Ⓜ **McNiel Middle Sch** <br> 4712 Barnett Rd, Wichita Falls 76310 <br> Summer Bynum | 6-8 | TV | 1,223 <br> 50 | 49%   940/235-1118 <br> Fax 940/235-1119 |
| **Milam Elem Sch** <br> 2901 Boren Ave, Wichita Falls 76308 <br> Gena Ayers | PK-5 | T | 450 <br> 34 | 70%   940/235-1176 <br> Fax 940/235-1305 <br> [f] |
| **North West Head Start Center** <br> 2310 Seymour Hwy, Wichita Falls 76301 <br> Letitia Willis | PK-PK | T | 51 | 94%   940/235-4307 |
| Ⓜ **Rider High Sch** <br> 4611 Cypress Ave, Wichita Falls 76310 <br> Dr Cody Blair | 9-12 | TV | 1,520 <br> 90 | 42%   940/235-1077 <br> Fax 940/235-1301 |
| **Rosewood Head Start Center** <br> 503 N Rosewood Ave, Wichita Falls 76301 <br> Letitia Willis | PK-PK | T | 81 <br> 7 | 96%   940/235-4309 <br> Fax 940/766-4126 |
| Ⓜ **Scotland Park Elem Sch** <br> 1415 N 5th St, Wichita Falls 76306 <br> Laura Scott | PK-5 | T | 422 <br> 26 | 91%   940/235-1180 <br> Fax 940/235-1303 |
| **Sheppard AFB Elem Sch** <br> 301 Anderson Dr, Sheppard Afb 76311 <br> Cindy Waddell | PK-6 | | 294 <br> 18 | 29%   940/235-1184 <br> Fax 940/235-1185 |
| **Southern Hills Elem Sch** <br> 3920 Armory Rd, Wichita Falls 76302 <br> Kacy Hunter | PK-5 | T | 462 <br> 29 | 80%   940/235-1188 <br> Fax 940/235-1304 |

| West Foundation Elem Sch | K-5 | | 425 | 33% 940/235-1192 |
| 5220 Lake Wellington Pkwy, Wichita Falls 76310 | | | 28 | Fax 940/235-1193 |
| Kim Smith | | | | |
| Ⓜ Wichita Falls High Sch | 9-12 | TV | 1,248 | 68% 940/235-1084 |
| 2149 Avenue H, Wichita Falls 76309 | | | | Fax 940/235-1310 |
| Christy Nash | | | | |
| Zundy Elem Sch | K-5 | T | 566 | 90% 940/235-1123 |
| 1706 Polk St, Wichita Falls 76309 | | | 25 | Fax 940/235-1124 |
| Becky Hernandez | | | | |

## WICHITA CATHOLIC SCHOOLS

- **Diocese of Fort Worth Ed Off** PID: 01054339
  Listing includes only schools located in this county. See District Index for location of Diocesan Offices.

| Catholic Schs..Principal | Grd | Prgm | Enr/#Cls | SN |
|---|---|---|---|---|
| Notre Dame Catholic Sch | PK-12 | | 260 | 940/692-6041 |
| 2821 Lansing Blvd, Wichita Falls 76309 | | | 25 | Fax 940/692-2811 |
| Rachel Gutgsell | | | | |

## WICHITA PRIVATE SCHOOLS

| Private Schs..Principal | Grd | Prgm | Enr/#Cls | SN |
|---|---|---|---|---|
| Bible Baptist Christian Sch | PK-12 | | 22 | 940/723-2446 |
| 1606 30th St, Wichita Falls 76302 | | | 3 | Fax 940/763-0712 |
| Dj James | | | | |
| Christ Academy | PK-12 | | 240 | 940/692-2853 |
| 5105 Stone Lake Dr, Wichita Falls 76310 | | | 20 | Fax 940/692-2657 |
| Tim Callaway | | | | ￼ |
| Wichita Christian Sch | K-12 | | 200 | 940/763-1347 |
| 1615 Midwestern Pkwy, Wichita Falls 76302 | | | | Fax 940/687-0744 |
| Courtney Cummings \ Julie Foster | | | | |

## WICHITA REGIONAL CENTERS

- **Region 9 Ed Service Center** PID: 01060120    940/322-6928
  301 Loop 11, Wichita Falls 76306    Fax 940/767-3836

| Wes Pierce | 1 | Janay Litz | 2 |
| Cindy Moses | 8,58,77,275 | Darren Francis | 15,16,73 |
| Michael Chapman | 27,31,36 | | |

## WILBARGER COUNTY

## WILBARGER PUBLIC SCHOOLS

- **Harrold Ind School Dist** PID: 01060508    940/886-2213
  18106 Stewart St, Harrold 76364    Fax 940/886-2215

> **Schools:** 1 \ **Teachers:** 14 \ **Students:** 106 \ **Special Ed Students:** 13 \ **College-Bound:** 90% \ **Ethnic:** Asian 2%, Hispanic 35%, Native American: 1%, Caucasian 62% \ **Exp:** $927 (High) \ **Poverty:** 23% \ **Open-Close:** 08/20 - 05/28 \ ￼

| David Thweatt | 1,11,73 | Lynn Dhane | 2,16,271* |
| Craig Templeton | 8,57,69,83,88,273* | Carla Clayton | 58* |
| Tim Clouse | 67 | | |

| Public Schs..Principal | Grd | Prgm | Enr/#Cls | SN |
|---|---|---|---|---|
| Harrold Sch | K-12 | V | 106 | 63% 940/886-2213 |
| 18106 Stewart St, Harrold 76364 | | | 17 | |
| Craig Templeton | | | | |

- **Northside Ind School Dist** PID: 01060534    940/552-2551
  18040 US Highway 283, Vernon 76384    Fax 940/553-4919

> **Schools:** 1 \ **Teachers:** 17 \ **Students:** 222 \ **Special Ed Students:** 20 \ **LEP Students:** 3 \ **College-Bound:** 75% \ **Ethnic:** Asian 1%, African American 3%, Hispanic 32%, Native American: 1%, Caucasian 62% \ **Exp:** $966 (High) \ **Poverty:** 19% \ **Title I:** $1,409 \ **Open-Close:** 08/14 - 05/21 \ **DTBP:** $341 (High) \ ￼ ￼

| Mark Haught | 1 | Karen Skinner | 2,84 |
| Debra Vincent | 4 | Jeremy Reeder | 6* |
| Kim Bria | 7* | Molly Lemon | 8,11,73* |
| Lori Woods | 57* | Dawn Wilkinson | 58,88* |
| Phoebe Reeves | 67 | Shari Coody | 286* |

| Public Schs..Principal | Grd | Prgm | Enr/#Cls | SN |
|---|---|---|---|---|
| Northside Sch | K-12 | TV | 222 | 41% 940/552-2551 |
| 18040 US Highway 283, Vernon 76384 | | | 20 | |
| Molly Lemon | | | | ￼￼ |

- **Vernon Ind School Dist** PID: 01060560    940/553-1900
  1713 Wilbarger St Ste 203, Vernon 76384    Fax 940/553-3802

> **Schools:** 6 \ **Teachers:** 141 \ **Students:** 1,700 \ **Special Ed Students:** 271 \ **LEP Students:** 212 \ **Ethnic:** Asian 6%, African American 10%, Hispanic 44%, Native American: 1%, Caucasian 40% \ **Exp:** $556 (High) \ **Poverty:** 21% \ **Title I:** $522,379 \ **Open-Close:** 08/17 - 05/21 \ **DTBP:** $333 (High) \ ￼ ￼

| Jeff Byrd | 1 | Tammi Wrinkle | 2 |
| Jimmy Anderson | 3,5 | Tammie Newcomer | 4 |
| Matthew Hoover | 6* | Hope Appel | 8,11,57,69,288,294,298 |
| Blaise Boswell | 16,73,295 | Toni Waldo | 58,275,286 |
| Emory Byars | 67 | Trisha Dillingham | 83,90 |

| Public Schs..Principal | Grd | Prgm | Enr/#Cls | SN |
|---|---|---|---|---|
| Central Elem Sch | 2-3 | | 278 | 940/553-1859 |
| 1300 Paradise St, Vernon 76384 | | | 20 | Fax 940/553-1138 |
| **Stefanie Merrell** | | | | |

| | | | | | | | | | | | | |
|---|---|---|---|---|---|---|---|---|---|---|---|---|
| 1 | Superintendent | 8 | Curric/Instruct K-12 | 19 | Chief Financial Officer | 29 | Family/Consumer Science | 39 | Social Studies K-12 | 49 | English/Lang Arts Elem | 59 | Special Education Elem | 69 | Academic Assessment |
| 2 | Bus/Finance/Purchasing | 9 | Curric/Instruct Elem | 20 | Art K-12 | 30 | Adult Education | 40 | Social Studies Elem | 50 | English/Lang Arts Sec | 60 | Special Education Sec | 70 | Research/Development |
| 3 | Buildings And Grounds | 10 | Curric/Instruct Sec | 21 | Art Elem | 31 | Career/Sch-to-Work K-12 | 41 | Social Studies Sec | 51 | Reading K-12 | 61 | Foreign/World Lang K-12 | 71 | Public Information |
| 4 | Food Service | 11 | Federal Program | 22 | Art Sec | 32 | Career/Sch-to-Work Elem | 42 | Science K-12 | 52 | Reading Elem | 62 | Foreign/World Lang Elem | 72 | Summer School |
| 5 | Transportation | 12 | Title I | 23 | Music K-12 | 33 | Career/Sch-to-Work Sec | 43 | Science Elem | 53 | Reading Sec | 63 | Foreign/World Lang Sec | 73 | Instructional Tech |
| 6 | Athletic | 13 | Title V | 24 | Music Elem | 34 | Early Childhood Ed | 44 | Science Sec | 54 | Remedial Reading K-12 | 64 | Religious Education K-12 | 74 | Inservice Training |
| 7 | Health Services | 15 | Asst Superintendent | 25 | Music Sec | 35 | Health/Phys Education | 45 | Math K-12 | 55 | Remedial Reading Elem | 65 | Religious Education Elem | 75 | Marketing/Distributive |
| | | 16 | Instructional Media Svcs | 26 | Business Education | 36 | Guidance Services K-12 | 46 | Math Elem | 56 | Remedial Reading Sec | 66 | Religious Education Sec | 76 | Info Systems |
| | | 17 | Chief Operations Officer | 27 | Career & Tech Ed | 37 | Guidance Services Elem | 47 | Math Sec | 57 | Bilingual/ELL | 67 | School Board President | 77 | Psychological Assess |
| | | 18 | Chief Academic Officer | 28 | Technology Education | 38 | Guidance Services Sec | 48 | English/Lang Arts K-12 | 58 | Special Education K-12 | 68 | Teacher Personnel | 78 | Affirmative Action |

| | Grd | Prgm | Enr/#Cls | SN | |
|---|---|---|---|---|---|
| McCord Elem Sch<br>2915 Sand Rd, Vernon 76384<br>Scott Mills | PK-1 | T | 341<br>25 | 78% | 940/553-4381<br>Fax 940/552-0056 |
| Shive Elem Sch<br>3130 Bacon St, Vernon 76384<br>Stefanie Merrell | 4-5 | T | 310<br>17 | 73% | 940/553-4309<br>Fax 940/552-5597 |
| Vernon High Sch<br>2102 Yucca Ln, Vernon 76384<br>Tommy Cummings | 9-12 | ATV | 149<br>45 | 58% | 940/553-3377<br>Fax 940/553-4531 |
| Vernon Middle Sch<br>2200 Yamparika St, Vernon 76384<br>Debbie Pearce | 6-8 | ATV | 299<br>40 | 68% | 940/552-6231<br>Fax 940/552-0504 |
| Ⓐ Visd Alternative Ed Sch<br>2211 London St, Vernon 76384<br>Joe Hennessee | K-12 | | 20<br>2 | | 940/552-2252<br>Fax 940/552-6999 |

## WILLACY COUNTY

## WILLACY PUBLIC SCHOOLS

### • Lasara Ind School Dist PID: 01060637
11932 Jones St, Lasara 78561

956/642-3271
Fax 956/642-3751

Schools: 2 \ Teachers: 32 \ Students: 368 \ Special Ed Students: 32 \ LEP Students: 56 \ College-Bound: 42% \ Ethnic: Hispanic 99%, Native American: 1%, \ Exp: $807 (High) \ Poverty: 37% \ Title I: $195,927 \ Open-Close: 08/26 - 05/28 \ DTBP: $350 (High) \ 🇫 🇹

| | | | |
|---|---|---|---|
| Sara Alvarado .................................1 | | Rogelio Cantu ...............................2,68,91 | |
| Mary Cazares ..................................4* | | Ted Gutierrez ................................5* | |
| Roy Vega .......................................6* | | Cynthia Ramos .......8,11,69,74,271,273,285* | |
| Ray Garza ..............................16,73,295 | | Karen McInnis ..............36,83,88,270,275* | |
| Christina Vargas .............................58* | | Rolando Velazquez ...............................67 | |

| Public Schs..Principal | Grd | Prgm | Enr/#Cls | SN | |
|---|---|---|---|---|---|
| Lasara Elem Sch<br>11932 Jones St, Lasara 78561<br>Israel Quintanilla | PK-8 | GTV | 258<br>25 | 81% | 956/642-3271<br><br>🇫🇹 |
| Lasara High Sch<br>11932 Jones St, Lasara 78561<br>Israel Quintanilla | 9-12 | T | 110 | 77% | 956/642-3271 |

### • Lyford Cons Ind School Dist PID: 01060651
8204 Simon Gomez Rd, Lyford 78569

956/347-3900
Fax 956/347-5588

Schools: 3 \ Teachers: 109 \ Students: 1,422 \ Special Ed Students: 119 \ LEP Students: 120 \ College-Bound: 55% \ Ethnic: Hispanic 97%, Caucasian 2% \ Exp: $674 (High) \ Poverty: 43% \ Title I: $924,651 \ Open-Close: 08/31 - 06/04 \ DTBP: $359 (High)

| | | |
|---|---|---|
| Dr Kristen Brown ...................................1 | Elisa Rosas .........................................2 |
| Jesse Orozco .........................3,5,17,91 | Ariel Abregon ......................................4 |
| Israel Gonzalez ...................................6 | Bibiana Bernal ....................................7 |
| Veronica Ramon ..................................8 | Dolly Rocha ...........................16,82,93 |
| Laura Juarez .......................................58 | Marina Rivera ...................................67 |
| Melissa Pimertel ...............................69* | Clarisa De La Fuente ........................71 |
| Gilbert Gonzalez ................................73 | Mayra Aguirre .................................271 |

| Public Schs..Principal | Grd | Prgm | Enr/#Cls | SN | |
|---|---|---|---|---|---|
| Lyford Elem Sch<br>13094 High School Circle, Lyford 78569<br>Alma Alvarez | PK-5 | T | 576<br>36 | 86% | 956/347-3911<br>Fax 956/347-3577 |
| Lyford High Sch<br>8201 High School Circle, Lyford 78569<br>Michelle DeWitt | 9-12 | ATV | 499<br>40 | 79% | 956/347-3909<br>Fax 956/347-5034 |
| Lyford Middle Sch<br>12820 Glen Lofton Ave, Lyford 78569<br>Raul Gonzalez | 6-8 | AT | 347<br>30 | 83% | 956/347-3910<br>Fax 956/347-2351 |

### • Raymondville Ind Sch Dist PID: 01060716
419 FM 3168, Raymondville 78580

956/689-2471
Fax 956/689-8180

Schools: 5 \ Teachers: 151 \ Students: 2,000 \ Special Ed Students: 211 \ LEP Students: 151 \ College-Bound: 42% \ Ethnic: Hispanic 99%, Caucasian 1% \ Exp: $427 (High) \ Poverty: 46% \ Title I: $1,556,364 \ Open-Close: 08/26 - 05/28 \ DTBP: $350 (High)

| | | |
|---|---|---|
| Stetson Roane ......................................1 | David Longoria ..............................2,19 |
| Kayla Arce ...........................................2 | Oscar Gutierrez ...............................3,5 |
| Norma Cavazos ..................................4 | Santos Zuniga ...................................5 |
| Frank Cantu .........................................6 | Andrea Mungia ...............................8,69 |
| Ben Clinton ...................................11,15 | Denise Butler ...................................58 |
| John Solis ..........................................67 | David Flores .....................................73 |

| Public Schs..Principal | Grd | Prgm | Enr/#Cls | SN | |
|---|---|---|---|---|---|
| L C Smith Elem Sch<br>700 N 1st St, Raymondville 78580<br>**Sylvia Ramos** | PK-5 | T | 389<br>32 | 94% | 956/689-8172<br>Fax 956/689-5871 |
| Myra Green Middle Sch<br>419 FM 3168, Raymondville 78580<br>Raul Valdez | 6-8 | AT | 155<br>50 | 88% | 956/689-8171<br>Fax 956/689-2302 |
| Pittman Elem Sch<br>258 E Harris St, Raymondville 78580<br>Sulema Davila | PK-5 | T | 501<br>47 | 89% | 956/689-8173<br>Fax 956/689-1141 |
| Raymondville High Sch<br>601 FM 3168, Raymondville 78580<br>Sandra Nieto | 9-12 | ATV | 511<br>60 | 86% | 956/689-8170<br>Fax 956/689-3640 |
| Ⓐ Raymondville Options Academy<br>512 E Rodriguez Ave, Raymondville 78580<br>Frank Garcia | 9-12 | T | 61 | 100% | 956/689-8185 |

### • San Perlita Ind School Dist PID: 01060780
22987 Trojan Dr, San Perlita 78590

956/248-5563
Fax 956/248-5561

Schools: 1 \ Teachers: 24 \ Students: 269 \ Special Ed Students: 25 \ LEP Students: 27 \ College-Bound: 100% \ Ethnic: Hispanic 86%, Caucasian 14% \ Exp: $755 (High) \ Poverty: 41% \ Title I: $124,854 \ Open-Close: 08/12 - 05/21 \ DTBP: $361 (High) \ 🇫 🇹

| | | |
|---|---|---|
| Albert Pena .........................................1 | Debra Rodriguez .................................2 |
| Nathaniel Garza ..................................6* | Adrian Montemayor ......................8,58* |
| Janie Livas ..................................11,298* | Kisch Russell .....................11,84,298 |
| Melissa Guadiana ..............................67 | Crystal Hernandez ............................69* |
| Armando Torres .............................73,295* | Judith Johnson ................................294 |

| Public Schs..Principal | Grd | Prgm | Enr/#Cls | SN | |
|---|---|---|---|---|---|
| San Perlita Sch<br>22987 Trojan Dr, San Perlita 78590<br>Adrian Montemayor \ Laurie Kilborn | PK-12 | T | 269<br>30 | 80% | 956/248-5250<br>Fax 956/248-5103 |

---

## WILLIAMSON COUNTY

## WILLIAMSON PUBLIC SCHOOLS

- **Coupland Ind School Dist** PID: 01060819　　512/856-2422
  620 S Commerce St, Coupland 78615　　　　　Fax 512/856-2222

**Schools:** 1 \ **Teachers:** 13 \ **Students:** 165 \ **Special Ed Students:** 16 \
**LEP Students:** 15 \ **Ethnic:** Asian 1%, African American 1%, Hispanic 29%,
Native American: 1%, Caucasian 68% \ **Exp:** $494 (High) \ **Poverty:** 21% \
**Title I:** $59,925 \ **Open-Close:** 08/19 - 05/27 \ **DTBP:** $365 (High)

| | | |
|---|---|---|
| Tammy Brinkman .................. 1,11,57,83 | Cindy Olson .............. 2,71,274,294,298 | |
| Cecilia Stuckly ...................... 16,82* | Kandice Samuelson ................ 67 | |

| Public Schs..Principal | Grd | Prgm | Enr/#Cls | SN |
|---|---|---|---|---|
| Coupland Elem Sch<br>620 S Commerce St, Coupland 78615<br>Tammy Brinkman | K-8 | | 165<br>13 | 40% 512/856-2422 |

- **Florence Ind School Dist** PID: 01060833　　254/793-2850
  306 College Ave, Florence 76527　　　　　Fax 254/793-3055

**Schools:** 3 \ **Teachers:** 82 \ **Students:** 957 \ **Special Ed Students:** 113
\ **LEP Students:** 241 \ **Ethnic:** African American 2%, Hispanic 50%,
Caucasian 48% \ **Exp:** $556 (High) \ **Poverty:** 10% \ **Title I:** $132,593 \
**Special Education:** $205,000 \ **Open-Close:** 08/13 - 05/27 \ **DTBP:** $353
(High) \ 🇫 🇹

| | | |
|---|---|---|
| Paul Michaelewicz ..................... 1 | Eric Banfield ........................ 2,19 | |
| Dalton West ............................ 3 | Lillian Barnet ........................ 4 | |
| Lisa Ragsdale .......................... 5 | Drew Bridges ........................ 6 | |
| Lila West ............................. 8* | Sharon Gibson ............. 11,58,296 | |
| Jenny Strack ..................... 16,82* | Vanessa Freed ...................... 57 | |
| Ed Navarette ......................... 67 | Amy Branton ........................ 68 | |
| Chad Blackman .............. 73,98,295* | Judy Stapper ........................ 76 | |

| Public Schs..Principal | Grd | Prgm | Enr/#Cls | SN |
|---|---|---|---|---|
| Florence Elem Sch<br>304 College Ave, Florence 76527<br>Dr Kay Bradford | PK-5 | T | 455<br>25 | 69% 254/793-2497<br>Fax 254/793-3158<br>🇫🇹 |
| Florence High Sch<br>401 FM 970, Florence 76527<br>Steve Elder | 9-12 | ATV | 242<br>30 | 50% 254/793-2495<br>Fax 254/793-3784<br>🇫🇹 |
| Florence Middle Sch<br>12551 S Hwy 195, Florence 76527<br>Catherine Beckerley | 6-8 | T | 260<br>19 | 57% 254/793-2504<br>Fax 254/793-3054 |

- **Georgetown Ind School Dist** PID: 01060869　　512/943-5000
  507 E University Ave, Georgetown 78626　　　Fax 512/943-5004

**Schools:** 18 \ **Teachers:** 858 \ **Students:** 12,403 \
**Special Ed Students:** 1,265 \ **LEP Students:** 1,526 \ **College-Bound:** 59%
\ **Ethnic:** Asian 2%, African American 4%, Hispanic 45%, Caucasian
48% \ **Exp:** $270 (Med) \ **Poverty:** 8% \ **Title I:** $1,247,021 \
**Special Education:** $1,537,000 \ **Open-Close:** 08/20 - 05/28 \ **DTBP:** $188
(High) \ 🇹

| | | |
|---|---|---|
| Dr Fred Brent .......................... 1 | Carol Malcik ........................ 2 | |
| Tonya Blesing ......................... 2 | Courtney Acosta ............... 3,7,36,91 | |

| | | |
|---|---|---|
| David Biesheuvel .................... 3 | Heather Stoner ................... 3,78 |
| Kirby Campbell ...................... 3 | Jean Caldwell ....................... 4 |
| Tray Mitchell ........................ 4 | David Gray .......................... 5 |
| Jason Dean .......................... 6 | David Raniey ...................... 7,36 |
| Terri Conrad ................. 8,74,273 | Tiffany Walker ............. 8,11,57,58 |
| Janna Jackson ..................... 11 | Lisa Napper ...................... 15,68 |
| Pam Sanchez ....................... 19 | Carol Watson ..................... 20,23 |
| Bretton Schulz ...................... 27 | Tiffany Pullen ................... 40,52 |
| Jennifer Kearney .............. 41,50,53 | Paige Hoellen ...................... 42 |
| Tony Bonazzi ....................... 45 | Dana Johnson ...................... 58 |
| Scott Stribling ...................... 67 | Sue Harrison ....................... 68 |
| Deb Jacobson ...................... 69 | Lannon Heflin ....... 70,73,98,286,750 |
| Melinda Brasher .................... 71 | Donnie Bruton ...................... 73 |
| Jordan Folks ........................ 74 | Mary Mitchem .................... 76,79 |
| Carey Thornell ................... 274* | Kim Garcia ....................... 286 |
| Wes Vanicer ...................... 294 | Michael McKenzie ................ 295 |

| Public Schs..Principal | Grd | Prgm | Enr/#Cls | SN |
|---|---|---|---|---|
| Annie Purl Elem Sch<br>1953 Maple St, Georgetown 78626<br>Denisse Baldwin | PK-5 | T | 732<br>37 | 76% 512/943-5080<br>Fax 512/943-5089<br>🇹 |
| Carver Elem Sch<br>4901 Scenic Lake Dr, Georgetown 78626<br>Nancy Bottlinger | PK-5 | T | 851<br>33 | 41% 512/943-5070<br>Fax 512/943-5079 |
| Charles Forbes Middle Sch<br>1911 NE Inner Loop, Georgetown 78626<br>Justin Del Bosque | 6-8 | T | 603<br>80 | 39% 512/943-5150<br>Fax 512/943-5159 |
| Ⓐ Chip Richarte High Sch<br>2295 N Austin Ave, Georgetown 78626<br>Roby Dyer | 9-12 | GTV | 62<br>8 | 67% 512/943-5120<br>Fax 512/943-5121 |
| Douglas Benold Middle Sch<br>3407 Northwest Blvd, Georgetown 78628<br>Brandon Jayroe | 6-8 | | 826<br>40 | 28% 512/943-5090<br>Fax 512/943-5099 |
| Eastview High Sch<br>4490 E University Ave, Georgetown 78626<br>Latoya Easter | 9-12 | TV | 1,675<br>60 | 47% 512/943-1800<br>Fax 512/943-1819 |
| George Wagner Middle Sch<br>1621 Rockride Ln, Georgetown 78626<br>Danielle Holloway | 6-8 | T | 734 | 49% 512/943-1830<br>Fax 512/943-1839 |
| Ⓐ Georgetown Alt Program<br>502 County Road 104, Georgetown 78626<br>Spiller Kelly | 6-12 | | 23<br>4 | 56% 512/943-5196<br>Fax 512/943-5197 |
| Georgetown High Sch<br>2211 N Austin Ave, Georgetown 78626<br>Brian Johnson | 9-12 | V | 1,977 | 25% 512/943-5100<br>Fax 512/943-5109 |
| Jack Frost Elem Sch<br>711 Lakeway Dr, Georgetown 78628<br>**Tamara Marbibi** | PK-5 | T | 260<br>28 | 64% 512/943-5020<br>Fax 512/943-5028 |
| James Mitchell Elem Sch<br>1601 Rockride Ln, Georgetown 78626<br>Meredith Gandy | PK-5 | T | 675 | 60% 512/943-1820<br>Fax 512/943-1829 |
| James Tippit Middle Sch<br>1601 Leander Rd, Georgetown 78628<br>Alfonso Longoria | 6-8 | T | 358 | 63% 512/943-5040<br>Fax 512/943-5049 |
| Jo Ann Ford Elem Sch<br>210 Woodlake Dr, Georgetown 78633<br>Jessica McMullen | PK-5 | | 470 | 10% 512/943-5180<br>Fax 512/943-5189 |
| Pat Cooper Elem Sch<br>1921 NE Inner Loop, Georgetown 78626<br>Tish Ptomey | PK-5 | T | 531<br>30 | 61% 512/943-5060<br>Fax 512/943-5069 |
| Raye McCoy Elem Sch<br>401 Bellaire Dr, Georgetown 78628<br>Jennifer Guidry | PK-5 | | 518<br>22 | 16% 512/943-5030<br>Fax 512/943-5039 |
| Village Elem Sch<br>400 Village Commons Blvd, Georgetown 78633<br>Laura Sloan | PK-5 | T | 504<br>18 | 42% 512/943-5140<br>Fax 512/943-5149<br>🇹 |

| | | | | | | | |
|---|---|---|---|---|---|---|---|
| **1** Superintendent | **8** Curric/Instruct K-12 | **19** Chief Financial Officer | **29** Family/Consumer Science | **39** Social Studies K-12 | **49** English/Lang Arts Elem | **59** Special Education Elem | **69** Academic Assessment |
| **2** Bus/Finance/Purchasing | **9** Curric/Instruct Elem | **20** Art K-12 | **30** Adult Education | **40** Social Studies Elem | **50** English/Lang Arts Sec | **60** Special Education Sec | **70** Research/Development |
| **3** Buildings And Grounds | **10** Curric/Instruct Sec | **21** Art Elem | **31** Career/Sch-to-Work K-12 | **41** Social Studies Sec | **51** Reading K-12 | **61** Foreign/World Lang K-12 | **71** Public Information |
| **4** Food Service | **11** Federal Program | **22** Art Sec | **32** Career/Sch-to-Work Elem | **42** Science K-12 | **52** Reading Elem | **62** Foreign/World Lang Elem | **72** Summer School |
| **5** Transportation | **12** Title I | **23** Music K-12 | **33** Career/Sch-to-Work Sec | **43** Science Elem | **53** Reading Sec | **63** Foreign/World Lang Sec | **73** Instructional Tech |
| **6** Athletic | **13** Title V | **24** Music Elem | **34** Early Childhood Ed | **44** Science Sec | **54** Remedial Reading K-12 | **64** Religious Education K-12 | **74** Inservice Training |
| **7** Health Services | **15** Asst Superintendent | **25** Music Sec | **35** Health/Phys Education | **45** Math K-12 | **55** Remedial Reading Elem | **65** Religious Education Elem | **75** Marketing/Distributive |
| | **16** Instructional Media Svcs | **26** Business Education | **36** Guidance Services K-12 | **46** Math Elem | **56** Remedial Reading Sec | **66** Religious Education Sec | **76** Info Systems |
| | **17** Chief Operations Officer | **27** Career & Tech Ed | **37** Guidance Services Elem | **47** Math Sec | **57** Bilingual/ELL | **67** School Board President | **77** Psychological Assess |
| | **18** Chief Academic Officer | **28** Technology Education | **38** Guidance Services Sec | **48** English/Lang Arts K-12 | **58** Special Education K-12 | **68** Teacher Personnel | **78** Affirmative Action |

| | | | | | |
|---|---|---|---|---|---|
| **Williams Elem Sch** | PK-5 | | 850 | | 512/943-5160 |
| 4101 Southwestern Blvd, Georgetown 78626 | | | | | |
| **Jeanna Sniffin** | | | | | |

| | | | | | |
|---|---|---|---|---|---|
| Wolf Ranch Elem Sch | PK-5 | T | 850 | 47% | 512/943-5050 |
| 1210 Jay Wolf Dr, Georgetown 78628 | | | 22 | | Fax 512/943-5059 |
| Jacob Donnell | | | | | ▣ |

● **Granger Ind School Dist** PID: 01060912    512/859-2613
300 N Colorado St, Granger 76530    Fax 512/859-2446

**Schools:** 1 \ **Teachers:** 37 \ **Students:** 426 \ **Special Ed Students:** 42 \ **LEP Students:** 56 \ **College-Bound:** 62% \ **Ethnic:** African American 3%, Hispanic 46%, Caucasian 51% \ **Exp:** $706 (High) \ **Poverty:** 8% \ **Title I:** $52,134 \ **Open-Close:** 08/26 - 05/28 \ **DTBP:** $341 (High) \ ▣ ▣

| | | | |
|---|---|---|---|
| Randy Willis | 1 | Louise Thornton | 2,19 |
| Marlena Sustaita | 4 | Stephen Brosch | 6 |
| Erica Moczygemba | 7* | Sara Cooper | 8* |
| Amber Thorsen | 11,36,69,752* | Tommy Filla | 67 |
| Andrea Dolan | 73* | Jimmie Baker | 286* |

| Public Schs..Principal | Grd | Prgm | Enr/#Cls | SN | |
|---|---|---|---|---|---|
| Granger Sch | PK-12 | TV | 426 | 64% | 512/859-2173 |
| 300 N Colorado St, Granger 76530 | | | 45 | | |
| Mike Abbott \ **Tawnya Shirocky** | | | | | |

● **Hutto Ind School Dist** PID: 01060948    512/759-3771
200 College St, Hutto 78634    Fax 512/759-4797

**Schools:** 10 \ **Teachers:** 491 \ **Students:** 8,129 \ **Special Ed Students:** 950 \ **LEP Students:** 769 \ **Ethnic:** Asian 1%, African American 14%, Hispanic 47%, Caucasian 38% \ **Exp:** $507 (High) \ **Poverty:** 6% \ **Title I:** $428,228 \ **Special Education:** $874,000 \ **Open-Close:** 08/18 - 05/27 \ **DTBP:** $135 (High) \ ▣ ▣

| | | | |
|---|---|---|---|
| Dr Celina Thomas | 1 | Caleb Sted | 2 |
| Glen Graham | 2,15 | Anna Martin | 4 |
| David Uecker | 5 | Kenfra Estes | 7 |
| Robert Sormani | 8,15,68,79,88,288 | Elva Torres | 11,57,294,296 |
| Dr Stacy Koerth | 58 | Billie Logiudice | 67 |
| Melissa Haney | 69 | Todd Robison | 71 |
| David Oestreicher | 73,76,295 | | |

| Public Schs..Principal | Grd | Prgm | Enr/#Cls | SN | |
|---|---|---|---|---|---|
| Benjamin Doc Kerley Elem Sch | PK-5 | | 540 | | 512/759-5410 |
| 800 Hay Barn Ln, Hutto 78634 | | | | | Fax 512/759-5411 |
| Kyle Ruggirello | | | | | |
| Cottonwood Creek Elem Sch | PK-5 | T | 651 | 46% | 512/759-5430 |
| 3160 Limmer Loop, Hutto 78634 | | | | | Fax 512/759-5431 |
| Linda Pachicano | | | | | |
| Farley Middle Sch | 6-8 | T | 916 | 37% | 512/759-2050 |
| 303 County Road 137, Hutto 78634 | | | 60 | | Fax 512/759-2033 |
| Mark Willoughby | | | | | ▣▣ |
| Howard Norman Elem Sch | PK-5 | | 751 | 33% | 512/759-5480 |
| 101 Llano River Trl, Hutto 78634 | | | | | Fax 512/759-5481 |
| Carrie Abrams | | | | | |
| Hutto Elem Sch | PK-5 | T | 407 | 35% | 512/759-2094 |
| 100 Mager Ln, Hutto 78634 | | | 42 | | Fax 512/759-4778 |
| Gaye Rosser | | | | | |
| Hutto High Sch | 9-12 | V | 1,576 | 37% | 512/759-4700 |
| 101 Chris Kelley Blvd, Hutto 78634 | | | 50 | | Fax 512/759-4757 |
| Roy Christian | | | | | ▣▣ |
| Hutto Middle Sch | 6-8 | T | 853 | 43% | 512/759-4541 |
| 1005 Exchange Blvd, Hutto 78634 | | | 30 | | Fax 512/759-4753 |
| Jason McAuliffe | | | | | ▣▣ |

| | | | | | |
|---|---|---|---|---|---|
| Nadine Johnson Elem Sch | PK-5 | T | 423 | 34% | 512/759-5400 |
| 480 Carl Stern Dr, Hutto 78634 | | | 40 | | Fax 512/759-5401 |
| **Bridgit Reichel** | | | | | ▣▣ |
| Ray Elem Sch | PK-5 | T | 676 | 43% | 512/759-5450 |
| 225 Swindoll Ln, Hutto 78634 | | | | | Fax 512/759-5451 |
| Alexis Campbell | | | | | ▣▣ |
| Veterans Hill Elem Sch | PK-5 | TV | 693 | 47% | 512/759-3030 |
| 555 Limmer Loop, Round Rock 78665 | | | | | Fax 512/759-5485 |
| Misty Patureau | | | | | |

● **Jarrell Ind School Dist** PID: 01060974    512/746-2124
312 N 5th St, Jarrell 76537    Fax 512/746-2518

**Schools:** 5 \ **Teachers:** 121 \ **Students:** 1,800 \ **Special Ed Students:** 226 \ **LEP Students:** 260 \ **Ethnic:** Asian 1%, African American 5%, Hispanic 52%, Caucasian 41% \ **Exp:** $583 (High) \ **Poverty:** 9% \ **Title I:** $133,944 \ **Special Education:** $261,000 \ **Open-Close:** 08/19 - 05/27 \ **DTBP:** $350 (High) \ ▣

| | | | |
|---|---|---|---|
| Keith Boles | 1 | James Garrett | 2 |
| Gretchen Mathys | 3 | Tim Copeland | 3 |
| Maria Manzo | 4 | Jackie Ivicic | 5 |
| Drew Sumner | 6 | Brandi O'Neill | 7 |
| Kathleen Crowe | 8,285,286,288,298 | Shanda Bizel | 27 |
| Laura Buckley | 37,273* | Monica Gonzalez | 57 |
| Jeff Conaway | 58,275 | Michael Cosimeno | 67 |
| Vanessa Ashcraft | 73 | Krissy Gryseeles | 76 |
| Joseph Hubbard | 295 | | |

| Public Schs..Principal | Grd | Prgm | Enr/#Cls | SN | |
|---|---|---|---|---|---|
| Igo Elem Sch | PK-5 | | 401 | | 512/746-4805 |
| 1601 County Rd 314, Jarrell 76537 | | | | | |
| Jack Wilson | | | | | |
| Jarrell Elem Sch | PK-3 | T | 479 | 63% | 512/746-2170 |
| 1615 County Road 313, Jarrell 76537 | | | | | Fax 512/746-2575 |
| Andrea David | | | | | |
| Jarrell High Sch | 9-12 | TV | 379 | 52% | 512/746-2188 |
| 1100 W FM 487, Jarrell 76537 | | | | | |
| James Larremore | | | | | |
| Jarrell Intermediate Sch | 4-5 | T | 250 | 55% | 512/746-4805 |
| 502 N 5th St, Jarrell 76537 | | | | | |
| Jack Wilson | | | | | |
| Jarrell Middle Sch | 6-8 | TV | 412 | 60% | 512/746-4180 |
| 101 E Avenue F, Jarrell 76537 | | | | | Fax 512/746-4280 |
| Jeremy Hill | | | | | |

● **Leander Ind School Dist** PID: 01061007    512/570-0000
204 W South St, Leander 78641    Fax 512/570-0054

**Schools:** 44 \ **Teachers:** 2,690 \ **Students:** 43,000 \ **Special Ed Students:** 4,810 \ **LEP Students:** 2,336 \ **College-Bound:** 70% \ **Ethnic:** Asian 9%, African American 4%, Hispanic 26%, Caucasian 60% \ **Exp:** $301 (High) \ **Poverty:** 5% \ **Title I:** $2,306,253 \ **Special Education:** $5,087,000 \ **Open-Close:** 08/13 - 05/27 \ **DTBP:** $174 (High) \ ▣ ▣

| | | | |
|---|---|---|---|
| Dr Bruce Gearing | 1 | Dana Paulson | 2 |
| Stephen Bentley | 3,4,5 | Steve Smith | 4 |
| Myron Wilson | 5 | Jody Hormann | 6 |
| Bryan Miller | 7,79,91 | Dr Matt Bentz | 8,18 |
| Kendra Winans | 11 | Devin Padavil | 15 |
| John Graham | 15 | Dr Laurelyn Arterbury | 15 |
| Sarah Grissom | 15 | Becky Calzada | 16 |
| Jimmy Disler | 17 | Elaine Cogburn | 19 |
| Peter Warshaw | 20,23 | Camille Clay | 27,31 |
| Steve Clark | 36 | Tina Dozier | 57 |
| Kimberly Waltmon | 58 | Trish Bode | 67 |

---

| | |
|---|---|
| Eddie Curran ........................68 | Karie McSpadden ....................68 |
| Brenda Cruz .....................69,294 | Corey Ryan ..........................71 |
| Terrece Harris .....................73 | Susan Cole .....................74,273 |
| Jason Johnston .....................76 | Russell Bundy ......................91 |
| Jason Miller ........................98 | Jennifer Freeman ..................275 |

| Public Schs..Principal | Grd | Prgm | Enr/#Cls | SN | |
|---|---|---|---|---|---|
| Bagdad Elem Sch<br>800 Deercreek Ln, Leander 78641<br>Christine Hilbun | PK-5 | T | 607 | 64% | 512/570-5900<br>Fax 512/570-5905 |
| Block House Creek Elem Sch<br>401 Creek Run Dr, Leander 78641<br>Dr Deana Cady | PK-5 | | 625<br>41 | 25% | 512/570-7600<br>Fax 512/570-7605 |
| Camacho Elem Sch<br>501 Municipal Dr, Leander 78641<br>Gena Fleming | PK-5 | T | 776 | 40% | 512/570-7800<br>Fax 512/570-7805 |
| Canyon Ridge Middle Sch<br>12601 Country Trl, Austin 78732<br>**Wendy Sturdevant** | 6-8 | | 1,265<br>80 | 5% | 512/570-3500<br>Fax 512/570-3505 |
| Cedar Park High Sch<br>2150 Cypress Creek Rd, Cedar Park 78613<br>John Sloan | 9-12 | V | 2,081 | 12% | 512/570-1200<br>Fax 512/570-1205 |
| Cedar Park Middle Sch<br>2100 Sunchase Blvd, Cedar Park 78613<br>Keith Morgan | 6-8 | | 1,314 | 12% | 512/570-3100<br>Fax 512/570-3105 |
| Cox Elem Sch<br>1001 Brushy Creek Rd, Cedar Park 78613<br>Charlie Rodriguez | PK-5 | | 530 | 14% | 512/570-6000<br>Fax 512/570-6005 |
| Cypress Elem Sch<br>2900 El Salido Pkwy, Cedar Park 78613<br>Kristen Alex | PK-5 | | 553<br>40 | 15% | 512/570-5400<br>Fax 512/570-5405 |
| Danielson Middle Sch<br>1061 Collarborative Way, Leander 78641<br>**Mark Koller** | 6-8 | | 970 | | 512/570-3900 |
| Deer Creek Elem Sch<br>2420 Zeppelin Dr, Cedar Park 78613<br>Matthew Calkins | PK-5 | | 680 | 5% | 512/570-6300<br>Fax 512/570-6305 |
| Faubion Elem Sch<br>1209 Cypress Creek Rd, Cedar Park 78613<br>Donna LeJeune | PK-5 | T | 381<br>32 | 34% | 512/570-7500<br>Fax 512/570-7505 |
| Four Points Middle Sch<br>9700 McNeil Dr, Austin 78750<br>Steve Crawford | 6-8 | | 292 | 20% | 512/570-3700<br>Fax 512/570-3705 |
| Giddens Elem Sch<br>1500 Timberwood Dr, Cedar Park 78613<br>Sally Hill | PK-5 | T | 582 | 43% | 512/570-5600<br>Fax 512/570-5605 |
| Glenn High Sch<br>1320 Collaborative Way, Leander 78641<br>Arturo Lomeli | 9-12 | | 1,587 | 33% | 512/570-1400<br>Fax 512/570-1405 |
| Grandview Hills Elem Sch<br>12024 Vista Parke Dr, Austin 78726<br>Kathy Sparksgoecke | PK-5 | T | 426 | 35% | 512/570-6800<br>Fax 512/570-6805 |
| Henry Middle Sch<br>100 N Vista Ridge Pkwy, Cedar Park 78613<br>Dr David Ellis | 6-8 | | 1,364 | 23% | 512/570-3400<br>Fax 512/570-3405 |
| Knowles Elem Sch<br>2101 Cougar Country, Cedar Park 78613<br>Lara Labbe-Maginel | PK-5 | T | 596<br>55 | 59% | 512/570-6200<br>Fax 512/570-6205 |
| Larkspur Elem Sch<br>424 Rusk Bluff Ave, Leander 78641<br>Tracie Montanio | K-5 | | 440 | | 512/570-8100<br>Fax 512/570-8105 |
| Laura Welch Bush Elem Sch<br>12600 Country Trails Ln, Austin 78732<br>**Jon Bailon-Valdez** | PK-5 | | 596<br>38 | 2% | 512/570-6100<br>Fax 512/570-6105 |
| Leander High Sch<br>3301 S Bagdad Rd, Leander 78641<br>Chris Simpson | 9-12 | AV | 2,153 | 24% | 512/570-1000<br>Fax 512/570-1005 |
| Leander Middle Sch<br>410 S West Dr, Leander 78641<br>Josh Haug | 6-8 | T | 1,111 | 39% | 512/570-3200<br>Fax 512/570-3205 |
| ⓐ Leo Center<br>300 S West Dr, Leander 78641<br>Cathy White | K-12 | V | 30<br>9 | | 512/570-2230<br>Fax 512/570-2234 |
| Mason Elem Sch<br>1501 N Lakeline Blvd, Cedar Park 78613<br>Abby Kennell | PK-5 | | 656<br>47 | 27% | 512/570-5500<br>Fax 512/570-5505 |
| Monta Jane Akin Elem Sch<br>3261 Barley Rd, Leander 78641<br>Beckie Webster | PK-5 | | 849 | 7% | 512/570-8000<br>Fax 512/570-8005 |
| Naumann Elem Sch<br>1201 Brighton Bend Ln, Cedar Park 78613<br>Shanita Kozlowski | PK-5 | | 480<br>56 | 23% | 512/570-5800<br>Fax 512/570-5805 |
| ⓐ New Hope High Sch<br>401 S West Dr, Leander 78641<br>Barbara Spelman | 9-12 | V | 43<br>4 | | 512/570-2200<br>Fax 512/570-2204 |
| Parkside Elem Sch<br>301 Garner Park Dr, Georgetown 78628<br>Lauren Meeks | PK-5 | | 957 | 3% | 512/570-7100<br>Fax 512/570-7105 |
| Plain Elem Sch<br>501 S Brook Dr, Leander 78641<br>Evelyn Crisp | PK-5 | | 938 | 24% | 512/570-6600<br>Fax 512/570-6605 |
| Pleasant Hill Elem Sch<br>1800 Horizon Park Blvd, Leander 78641<br>Heather Robbins | PK-5 | | 629 | 28% | 512/570-6400<br>Fax 512/570-6405 |
| Reed Elem Sch<br>1515 Little Elm Trl, Cedar Park 78613<br>Paige Collier | PK-5 | | 767 | | 512/570-7700<br>Fax 512/570-7705 |
| River Place Elem Sch<br>6500 Sitio Del Rio Blvd, Austin 78730<br>Christina Pasak | PK-5 | | 664 | 22% | 512/570-6900<br>Fax 512/570-6905 |
| River Ridge Elem Sch<br>12900 Tierra Grande Trl, Austin 78732<br>Shelley Roberts | PK-5 | | 601 | 2% | 512/570-7300<br>Fax 512/570-7305 |
| Ronald Reagan Elem Sch<br>1700 E Park St, Cedar Park 78613<br>Marianne Norman | PK-5 | | 753 | 11% | 512/570-7200<br>Fax 512/570-7205 |
| Rouse High Sch<br>1222 Raider Way, Leander 78641<br>Christine Simpson | 9-12 | A | 1,688 | 16% | 512/570-2000<br>Fax 512/570-2005 |
| Running Brushy Middle Sch<br>2303 N Lakeline Blvd, Cedar Park 78613<br>Jim Rose | 6-8 | T | 1,227<br>50 | 35% | 512/570-3300<br>Fax 512/570-3305 |
| Rutledge Elem Sch<br>11501 Staked Plains Dr, Austin 78717<br>Elizabeth Mohler | PK-5 | | 763 | 10% | 512/570-6500<br>Fax 512/570-6505 |
| Steiner Ranch Elem Sch<br>4001 N Quinlan Park Rd, Austin 78732<br>Angela Hodges | PK-5 | | 465<br>37 | 12% | 512/570-5700<br>Fax 512/570-5705 |
| Stiles Middle Sch<br>3250 Barley Rd, Leander 78641<br>Melody Maples | 6-8 | | 1,404 | 9% | 512/570-3800<br>Fax 512/570-3805 |
| Vandegrift High Sch<br>9500 McNeil Dr, Austin 78750<br>Charles Little | 9-12 | | 2,709 | 7% | 512/570-2300<br>Fax 512/570-2305 |
| Vista Ridge High Sch<br>200 S Vista Ridge Pkwy, Cedar Park 78613<br>Paul Johnson | 9-12 | | 2,384 | 17% | 512/570-1800<br>Fax 512/570-1805 |
| Westside Elem Sch<br>300 Ryan Jordan Ln, Cedar Park 78613<br>Amanda Lillard | PK-5 | | 567 | 8% | 512/570-7000<br>Fax 512/570-7005 |
| Whitestone Elem Sch<br>2000 Crystal Falls Pkwy, Leander 78641<br>Niki Prindle | PK-5 | | 791<br>60 | 29% | 512/570-7400<br>Fax 512/570-7405 |

| | | | |
|---|---|---|---|
| 1 Superintendent | 8 Curric/Instruct K-12 | 19 Chief Financial Officer | 29 Family/Consumer Science |
| 2 Bus/Finance/Purchasing | 9 Curric/Instruct Elem | 20 Art K-12 | 30 Adult Education |
| 3 Buildings And Grounds | 10 Curric/Instruct Sec | 21 Art Elem | 31 Career/Sch-to-Work K-12 |
| 4 Food Service | 11 Federal Program | 22 Art Sec | 32 Career/Sch-to-Work Elem |
| 5 Transportation | 12 Title I | 23 Music K-12 | 33 Career/Sch-to-Work Sec |
| 6 Athletic | 13 Title V | 24 Music Elem | 34 Early Childhood Ed |
| 7 Health Services | 15 Asst Superintendent | 25 Music Sec | 35 Health/Phys Education |
| | 16 Instructional Media Svcs | 26 Business Education | 36 Guidance Services K-12 |
| | 17 Chief Operations Officer | 27 Career & Tech Ed | 37 Guidance Services Elem |
| | 18 Chief Academic Officer | 28 Technology Education | 38 Guidance Services Sec |

| | | | |
|---|---|---|---|
| 39 Social Studies K-12 | 49 English/Lang Arts Elem | 59 Special Education Elem | 69 Academic Assessment |
| 40 Social Studies Elem | 50 English/Lang Arts Sec | 60 Special Education Sec | 70 Research/Development |
| 41 Social Studies Sec | 51 Reading K-12 | 61 Foreign/World Lang K-12 | 71 Public Information |
| 42 Science K-12 | 52 Reading Elem | 62 Foreign/World Lang Elem | 72 Summer School |
| 43 Science Elem | 53 Reading Sec | 63 Foreign/World Lang Sec | 73 Instructional Tech |
| 44 Science Sec | 54 Remedial Reading K-12 | 64 Religious Education K-12 | 74 Inservice Training |
| 45 Math K-12 | 55 Remedial Reading Elem | 65 Religious Education Elem | 75 Marketing/Distributive |
| 46 Math Elem | 56 Remedial Reading Sec | 66 Religious Education Sec | 76 Info Systems |
| 47 Math Sec | 57 Bilingual/ELL | 67 School Board President | 77 Psychological Assess |
| 48 English/Lang Arts K-12 | 58 Special Education K-12 | 68 Teacher Personnel | 78 Affirmative Action |

| | | | | | |
|---|---|---|---|---|---|
| **Wiley Middle Sch** | 6-8 | T | 1,072 | 28% | 512/570-3600 |
| 1526 Raider Way, Leander 78641 | | | | | Fax 512/570-3605 |
| **Angela Hodges** | | | | | |
| **Winkley Elem Sch** | PK-5 | | 685 | 10% | 512/570-6700 |
| 2100 Pow Wow, Leander 78641 | | | | | Fax 512/570-6705 |
| Davina Stringer | | | | | |

● **Liberty Hill Ind School Dist** PID: 01061069    512/260-5580
301 Forrest St, Liberty Hill 78642    Fax 512/260-5581

**Schools:** 6 \ **Teachers:** 295 \ **Students:** 4,000 \ **Special Ed Students:** 396 \ **LEP Students:** 170 \ **Ethnic:** Asian 1%, African American 1%, Hispanic 22%, Caucasian 75% \ **Exp:** $375 (High) \ **Poverty:** 5% \ **Title I:** $194,470 \ **Special Education:** $591,000 \ **Open-Close:** 08/20 - 05/27 \ **DTBP:** $148 (High)

| | | | |
|---|---|---|---|
| Steven Snell | 1 | Erin Jarrett | 2 |
| Jennifer Hanna | 2,19 | Mary Sheffield | 4 |
| Meleia Cox | 5 | Jeff Walker | 6,35,85* |
| Kelly Keene | 7 | Dr Toni Hicks | 8,15,88,294 |
| Summer Neary | 11,296 | Brad Mansfield | 15 |
| Jay Olivier | 16 | Lauaren Claymon | 16,82* |
| Kristy Kercheville | 31,57* | Laura Elder | 37 |
| Lara Chapman | 38* | Candy Tijerina | 57,271 |
| Elyse Tarlton | 58,69 | Clay Cole | 67 |
| Paul Urban | 76 | | |

| Public Schs..Principal | Grd | Prgm | Enr/#Cls | SN | |
|---|---|---|---|---|---|
| **Bill Burden Elem Sch** | PK-4 | | 667 | 30% | 512/260-4400 |
| 315 Stonewall Pkwy, Liberty Hill 78642 | | | | | Fax 512/260-4410 |
| Tanya Lambert | | | | | |
| **Liberty Hill Elem Sch** | PK-4 | | 352 | 29% | 512/379-3260 |
| 1400 Loop 332, Liberty Hill 78642 | | | 21 | | Fax 512/379-3256 |
| Heather Collison | | | | | |
| **Liberty Hill High Sch** | 9-12 | | 1,228 | 17% | 512/260-5500 |
| 16500 W State Highway 29, Liberty Hill 78642 | | | 45 | | Fax 512/260-5510 |
| Jonathan Bever | | | | | |
| **Liberty Hill Intermediate Sch** | 5-6 | | 376 | 24% | 512/379-3200 |
| 101 Loop 332, Liberty Hill 78642 | | | 20 | | Fax 512/379-3210 |
| Josh Curtis | | | | | |
| **Liberty Hill Middle Sch** | 7-8 | | 324 | 23% | 512/379-3300 |
| 13125 W State Highway 29, Liberty Hill 78642 | | | 35 | | Fax 512/379-3310 |
| Travis Motal | | | | | |
| **Rancho Sienna Elem Sch** | PK-4 | | 695 | 20% | 512/260-4450 |
| 751 Bonnet Blvd, Georgetown 78628 | | | | | Fax 512/260-4460 |
| Melanie Bowman | | | | | |

● **Round Rock Ind School Dist** PID: 01061083    512/464-5000
1311 Round Rock Ave, Round Rock 78681    Fax 512/464-5090

**Schools:** 54 \ **Teachers:** 3,382 \ **Students:** 51,008 \ **Special Ed Students:** 4,897 \ **LEP Students:** 4,729 \ **College-Bound:** 64% \ **Ethnic:** Asian 18%, African American 9%, Hispanic 32%, Caucasian 40% \ **Exp:** $227 (Med) \ **Poverty:** 6% \ **Title I:** $4,651,708 \ **Special Education:** $8,545,000 \ **Bilingual Education:** $69,000 \ **Open-Close:** 08/20 - 05/27 \ **DTBP:** $203 (High) \ 🅣

| | | | |
|---|---|---|---|
| Dr Steve Flores | 1 | Danny Poolman | 2 |
| Sara Kohn | 2 | David Hoedebeck | 3 |
| Terry Worcester | 3,17 | Yana Koleva | 4 |
| Tina Fausett | 5 | Dr Daniel Presley | 6,7,91 |
| Dwayne Weirich | 6 | Brandy Hafner | 7 |
| Darrell Emanuel | 8 | Mandy Estes | 8,18 |
| Ryan Smith | 8 | Laura Segars | 11,57,271 |
| Margo Vogelpohl | 12,34 | Carla Amacher | 15 |
| John Yonker | 15 | Dr Nancy Guerrero | 15 |
| Natalie Nichols | 15 | Rebecca Donald | 15 |

| | | |
|---|---|---|
| Amy Uselman | 16 | |
| Dr Kenneth Adix | 19 | |
| Dr Christina Wiswell | 36 | |
| Marie Gonzalez | 58 | |
| Annette Vierra | 68 | |
| Debbie Lewis | 69,294 | |
| Jeffrey Uselman | 73,286 | |
| Mark Gabehart | 76 | |
| Michelle Swain | 81,92 | |
| Kimberly Berry-Corie | 88,275 | |
| Regina Payne | 277 | |
| Rachelle Finck | 752 | |
| Dr Lora Darden | 16,27 | |
| Sheri Bonds | 27,31 | |
| Maria Green | 57 | |
| Amy Weir | 67 | |
| Dr Cathy Malerba | 69 | |
| Jenny Lacoste-Caputo | 71 | |
| Edie Binns | 74 | |
| Roger Adair | 76 | |
| Scott Stansbury | 84,295 | |
| Jeff Yarbrough | 91 | |
| Melissa McCarroll | 280 | |

| Public Schs..Principal | Grd | Prgm | Enr/#Cls | SN | |
|---|---|---|---|---|---|
| **Anderson Mill Elem Sch** | PK-5 | T | 520 | 62% | 512/428-3700 |
| 10610 Salt Mill Holw, Austin 78750 | | | 20 | | Fax 512/428-3790 |
| Amanda Molina | | | | | |
| **Blackland Prairie Elem Sch** | PK-5 | | 833 | 11% | 512/424-8600 |
| 2005 Via Sonoma Dr, Round Rock 78665 | | | 38 | | Fax 512/424-8690 |
| **Sue Hildebrand** | | | | | |
| **Bluebonnet Elem Sch** | PK-5 | T | 357 | 81% | 512/428-7700 |
| 1010 Chisholm Valley Dr, Round Rock 78681 | | | 32 | | Fax 512/428-7790 |
| Samuel Soto | | | | | |
| **Brushy Creek Elem Sch** | PK-5 | | 713 | 21% | 512/428-3000 |
| 3800 Stonebridge Dr, Round Rock 78681 | | | 40 | | Fax 512/428-3080 |
| Jennifer Strong | | | | | |
| **C D Fulkes Middle Sch** | 6-8 | TV | 770 | 68% | 512/428-3100 |
| 300 W Anderson Ave, Round Rock 78664 | | | | | Fax 512/428-3240 |
| Rebekah Van Ryn | | | | | |
| **Cactus Ranch Elem Sch** | PK-5 | | 963 | 3% | 512/424-8000 |
| 2901 Goldenoak Cir, Round Rock 78681 | | | 32 | | Fax 512/424-8090 |
| Vicki Crain | | | | | |
| **Caldwell Heights Elem Sch** | PK-5 | T | 805 | 57% | 512/428-7300 |
| 4010 Eagles Nest St, Round Rock 78665 | | | 25 | | Fax 512/428-7390 |
| Michelle Montalvo | | | | | |
| **Canyon Creek Elem Sch** | K-5 | | 438 | 5% | 512/428-2800 |
| 10210 Ember Glen Dr, Austin 78726 | | | 31 | | Fax 512/428-2890 |
| April Crawford | | | | | |
| **Canyon Vista Middle Sch** | 6-8 | V | 1,406 | 12% | 512/464-8100 |
| 8455 Spicewood Springs Rd, Austin 78759 | | | | | Fax 512/464-8210 |
| Nicole Hagerty | | | | | |
| **Cedar Ridge High Sch** | 9-12 | | 2,753 | 29% | 512/704-0100 |
| 2801 Gattis School Rd, Round Rock 78664 | | | | | Fax 512/704-0280 |
| Jiae Kim-Batra | | | | | |
| **Cedar Valley Middle Sch** | 6-8 | V | 1,296 | 10% | 512/428-2300 |
| 8139 Racine Trl, Austin 78717 | | | 45 | | Fax 512/428-2420 |
| Zac Oldham | | | | | |
| **Chandler Oaks Elem Sch** | K-5 | | 567 | 14% | 512/704-0400 |
| 3800 Stone Oak Dr, Round Rock 78681 | | | | | Fax 512/704-0490 |
| Kelley Hirt | | | | | |
| **Chisholm Trail Middle Sch** | 6-8 | V | 943 | 38% | 512/428-2500 |
| 500 Oakridge Dr, Round Rock 78681 | | | 69 | | Fax 512/428-2629 |
| Steven Swain | | | | | |
| **Claude Berkman Elem Sch** | PK-5 | T | 432 | 81% | 512/464-8250 |
| 400 W Anderson Ave, Round Rock 78664 | | | 39 | | Fax 512/464-8315 |
| Kathy Cawthron | | | | | |
| **Deep Wood Elem Sch** | PK-5 | | 351 | 29% | 512/464-4400 |
| 705 Saint Williams Ave, Round Rock 78681 | | | 22 | | Fax 512/464-4494 |
| Reba Mussey | | | | | |
| **Deerpark Middle Sch** | 6-8 | TV | 924 | 42% | 512/464-6600 |
| 8849 Anderson Mill Rd, Austin 78729 | | | | | Fax 512/464-6740 |
| Jonathan Smith | | | | | 🅣 |
| **Double File Trail Elem Sch** | PK-5 | T | 648 | 43% | 512/428-7400 |
| 2400 Chandler Creek Blvd, Round Rock 78665 | | | 34 | | Fax 512/428-7490 |
| Alifia Britton | | | | | |
| **Early Clg High Sch** | 9-10 | | 250 | 35% | 512/704-1650 |
| 4400 College Park, Round Rock 78665 | | | | | |
| **Dr Elizabeth Wilson** | | | | | |

England Elem Sch   PK-5   1,225   5% 512/704-1200
8801 Pearson Ranch Rd, Austin 78717     Fax 512/704-1290
Jana Stowe

Fern Bluff Elem Sch   K-5   609   9% 512/428-2100
17815 Park Valley Dr, Round Rock 78681   52   Fax 512/428-2160
**Tyler Hultman**

Forest Creek Elem Sch   K-5   842   10% 512/464-5350
3505 Forest Creek Dr, Round Rock 78664   45   Fax 512/464-5430
Denise Sharp

Forest North Elem Sch   PK-5   T   402   49% 512/464-6750
13414 Broadmeade Ave, Austin 78729     Fax 512/464-6794
Amy Jacobs

Gattis Elem Sch   PK-5   T   673   43% 512/428-2000
2920 Round Rock Ranch Blvd, Round Rock 78665   45   Fax 512/428-2065
Jennifer Lucas

Goals Learning Center   Spec   50   512/464-5153
1311 Round Rock Ave Bldg 800, Round Rock 78681     Fax 512/428-7940
Dennis Hardesty

Great Oaks Elem Sch   PK-5   762   11% 512/464-6850
16455 S Great Oaks Dr, Round Rock 78681   50   Fax 512/464-6930
Heath Frazer

Hopewell Middle Sch   6-8   V   1,217   35% 512/464-5200
1535 Gulf Way, Round Rock 78665     Fax 512/464-5349
Lynda Garinger

James Garland Walsh Middle Sch   6-8   1,345   12% 512/704-0800
3850 Walsh Ranch Blvd, Round Rock 78681     Fax 512/704-0940
Brenda Heath-Agnew

Joe Lee Johnson Elem Sch   PK-5   T   750   48% 512/704-1400
2800 Sauls Dr, Austin 78728     Fax 512/704-1490
Marc Scott

Jollyville Elem Sch   PK-5   T   453   38% 512/428-2200
6720 Corpus Christi Dr, Austin 78729   30   Fax 512/428-2299
Scott Morgan

Kathy Caraway Elem Sch   PK-5   876   8% 512/464-5500
11104 Oak View Dr, Austin 78759   25   Fax 512/464-5590
Katrina Bailey

Laurel Mountain Elem Sch   K-5   730   4% 512/464-4300
10111 D K Ranch Rd, Austin 78759   38   Fax 512/464-4390
Doriane Marvel

Linda Herrington Elem Sch   PK-5   1,116   19% 512/704-1900
2850 Paloma Lake Blvd, Round Rock 78665     Fax 512/704-1990
Julie Nelson

Live Oak Elem Sch   PK-5   T   598   41% 512/428-3800
8607 Anderson Mill Rd, Austin 78729   40   Fax 512/428-3890
**Brian Braudrick**

McNeil High Sch   9-12   V   2,673   24% 512/464-6300
5720 McNeil Dr, Austin 78729   100   Fax 512/464-6550
Amanda Johnson

Neysa Callison Elem Sch   PK-5   T   788   65% 512/704-0700
1750 Thompson Trl, Round Rock 78664     Fax 512/704-0790
Penny Oates

Noel Grisham Middle Sch   6-8   V   442   31% 512/428-2650
10805 School House Ln, Austin 78750   45   Fax 512/428-2790
**Amanda Serna**

Old Town Elem Sch   PK-5   715   30% 512/428-7600
2200 Chaparral Dr, Round Rock 78681   36   Fax 512/428-7690
Jessica Schock

Patsy Sommer Elem Sch   PK-5   1,257   3% 512/704-0600
16200 Avery Ranch Blvd, Austin 78717     Fax 512/704-0690
Nancy Varljen

Pearson Ranch Middle Sch   6-8   883   19% 512/704-1500
8901 Pearson Ranch Rd, Austin 78717
Kim Winters

Pfc Robert Hernandez Mid Sch   6-8   T   534   59% 512/424-8800
1901 Sunrise Rd, Round Rock 78664     Fax 512/424-8940
Dr Patricia Ephlin

Pond Springs Elem Sch   PK-5   596   25% 512/464-4200
7825 Elkhorn Mountain Trl, Austin 78729   43   Fax 512/464-4290
Brooke Elarms

Purple Sage Elem Sch   PK-5   487   34% 512/428-3500
11801 Tanglebriar Trl, Austin 78750   11   Fax 512/428-3590
Sara Nelson

Ridgeview Middle Sch   6-8   1,370   21% 512/424-8400
2000 Via Sonoma Dr, Round Rock 78665   60   Fax 512/424-8540
Travis Mutscher

Round Rock High Sch   9-12   GV   3,501   13% 512/464-6000
201 Deep Wood Dr, Round Rock 78681     Fax 512/464-6190
Matthew Groff

Ⓐ Round Rock Opportunity Center   6-12   250   66% 512/428-2900
931 Luther Peterson, Round Rock 78665   22   Fax 512/428-2943
**Donald Bosier**

Spicewood Elem Sch   K-5   846   7% 512/428-3600
11601 Olson Dr, Austin 78750   32   Fax 512/428-3690
Teyan Allen

Stony Point High Sch   9-12   TV   2,598   38% 512/428-7000
1801 Tiger Trl, Round Rock 78664     Fax 512/428-7280
Anthony Watson

Ⓐ Success High Sch   9-12   335   47% 512/704-1300
500 Gattis School Rd, Round Rock 78664     Fax 512/704-1390
Thomasine Stewart

Teravista Elem Sch   PK-5   876   19% 512/704-0500
4419 Teravista Club Dr, Round Rock 78665     Fax 512/704-0590
Michael Wakefield

Union Hill Elem Sch   PK-5   T   774   69% 512/424-8700
1511 Gulf Way, Round Rock 78665   39   Fax 512/424-8790
Kimberly Connelly

Vic Robertson Elem Sch   PK-5   T   438   71% 512/428-3300
1415 Bayland St, Round Rock 78664   30   Fax 512/428-3370
Kyle Borel

Wells Branch Elem Sch   PK-5   T   483   60% 512/428-3400
14650 Merriltown Rd, Austin 78728   39   Fax 512/428-3490
Eliza Gordon

Westwood High Sch   9-12   GV   2,756   15% 512/464-4000
12400 Mellow Meadow Dr, Austin 78750   130   Fax 512/464-4020
Mario Acosta

Xenia Voigt Elem Sch   PK-5   T   586   73% 512/428-7500
1201 Cushing Dr, Round Rock 78664     Fax 512/428-7590
Cheryl Hester

• **Taylor Ind School Dist**   PID: 01061162     512/365-1391
3101 N Main St Ste 104, Taylor 76574     Fax 512/365-3800

> **Schools:** 7 \ **Teachers:** 239 \ **Students:** 3,200 \ **Special Ed Students:** 330 \ **LEP Students:** 402 \ **College-Bound:** 51% \ **Ethnic:** Asian 1%, African American 9%, Hispanic 64%, Caucasian 27% \ **Exp:** $443 (High) \ **Poverty:** 14% \ **Title I:** $666,159 \ **Open-Close:** 08/20 - 05/27 \ **DTBP:** $178 (High)

| | | | |
|---|---|---|---|
| Keith Brown | 1 | Lorine David | 2 |
| Johnnie Horn | 3 | Lori Wilbanks | 3 |
| Lindsay Gage | 4 | Carl Caldwell | 5 |
| Robert Little | 6 | Dr George Willey | 8,18,275 |
| Jennifer Patschke | 11,296,298 | Rodney Fausett | 15 |
| Sandra Martinez | 57* | Sandra Martinez | 57,271 |
| Robert Stevens | 58 | Marco Ortiz | 67 |
| Debbie Matthys | 69 | Tim Crow | 71,76 |
| Andrew Maddox | 88* | Jamie Sellers | 295 |

| Public Schs..Principal | Grd | Prgm | Enr/#Cls | SN |
|---|---|---|---|---|
| Legacy Early College High Sch<br>516 N Main St, Taylor 76574<br>Ron Roth | 9-12 | T | 190 | 45% 512/352-9596<br>Fax 512/309-4477 |

| | | | | | | | |
|---|---|---|---|---|---|---|---|
| 1 | Superintendent | 8 | Curric/Instruct K-12 | 19 | Chief Financial Officer | 29 | Family/Consumer Science |
| 2 | Bus/Finance/Purchasing | 9 | Curric/Instruct Elem | 20 | Art K-12 | 30 | Adult Education |
| 3 | Buildings And Grounds | 10 | Curric/Instruct Sec | 21 | Art Elem | 31 | Career/Sch-to-Work K-12 |
| 4 | Food Service | 11 | Federal Program | 22 | Art Sec | 32 | Career/Sch-to-Work Elem |
| 5 | Transportation | 12 | Title I | 23 | Music K-12 | 33 | Career/Sch-to-Work Sec |
| 6 | Athletic | 13 | Title V | 24 | Music Elem | 34 | Early Childhood Ed |
| 7 | Health Services | 15 | Asst Superintendent | 25 | Music Sec | 35 | Health/Phys Education |
| | | 16 | Instructional Media Svcs | 26 | Business Education | 36 | Guidance Services K-12 |
| | | 17 | Chief Operations Officer | 27 | Career & Tech Ed | 37 | Guidance Services Elem |
| | | 18 | Chief Academic Officer | 28 | Technology Education | 38 | Guidance Services Sec |

| | | | | | | | |
|---|---|---|---|---|---|---|---|
| 39 | Social Studies K-12 | 49 | English/Lang Arts Elem | 59 | Special Education Elem | 69 | Academic Assessment |
| 40 | Social Studies Elem | 50 | English/Lang Arts Sec | 60 | Special Education Sec | 70 | Research/Development |
| 41 | Social Studies Sec | 51 | Reading K-12 | 61 | Foreign/World Lang K-12 | 71 | Public Information |
| 42 | Science K-12 | 52 | Reading Elem | 62 | Foreign/World Lang Elem | 72 | Summer School |
| 43 | Science Elem | 53 | Reading Sec | 63 | Foreign/World Lang Sec | 73 | Instructional Tech |
| 44 | Science Sec | 54 | Remedial Reading K-12 | 64 | Religious Education K-12 | 74 | Inservice Training |
| 45 | Math K-12 | 55 | Remedial Reading Elem | 65 | Religious Education Elem | 75 | Marketing/Distributive |
| 46 | Math Elem | 56 | Remedial Reading Sec | 66 | Religious Education Sec | 76 | Info Systems |
| 47 | Math Sec | 57 | Bilingual/ELL | 67 | School Board President | 77 | Psychological Assess |
| 48 | English/Lang Arts K-12 | 58 | Special Education K-12 | 68 | Teacher Personnel | 78 | Affirmative Action |

| | Grd | Prgm | Enr/#Cls | SN |
|---|---|---|---|---|
| Main Street Imtermediate Sch<br>3101 N Main St Ste 105, Taylor 76574<br>Marcelina Cobb | 4-5 | T | 437<br>32 | 71% 512/365-1999<br>Fax 512/309-4471 |
| Naomi Pasemann Elem Sch<br>2809 North Dr, Taylor 76574<br>Renee Duckworth | 1-3 | T | 636<br>33 | 68% 512/352-1016<br>Fax 512/309-4461 |
| T H Johnson Elem Sch<br>3100 Duck Ln, Taylor 76574<br>Jenni Cork | PK-K | T | 216 | 73% 512/352-2275<br>Fax 512/365-7112 |
| Taylor High Sch<br>355 FM 973, Taylor 76574<br>Andrew Maddox | 9-12 | AGTV | 844<br>80 | 55% 512/365-6326<br>Fax 512/365-1351 |
| Taylor Middle Sch<br>304 Carlos G Parker Blvd NW, Taylor 76574<br>Chelsey Ellison | 6-8 | AT | 691<br>45 | 65% 512/352-2815<br>Fax 512/365-8589 |
| Ⓐ Taylor Opportunity Center<br>1004 Dellinger St, Taylor 76574<br>Andrew Maddox | 6-12 | | 50 | 512/365-8089<br>Fax 512/309-4481 |

- **Thrall Ind School Dist** PID: 01061227      512/898-0062
201 S Bounds St, Thrall 76578      Fax 512/898-5349

**Schools:** 3 \ **Teachers:** 56 \ **Students:** 750 \ **Special Ed Students:** 73
\ **LEP Students:** 17 \ **Ethnic:** African American 2%, Hispanic 31%,
Caucasian 67% \ **Exp:** $470 (High) \ **Poverty:** 9% \ **Title I:** $74,645 \
**Open-Close:** 08/10 - 05/27 \ **DTBP:** $376 (High)

| | | | |
|---|---|---|---|
| Tommy Hooker | 1 | Blake Schneider | 2 |
| Joan Sladek | 3,5 | Jeni Anders | 4 |
| Rick Porter | 6 | Jolena Pokorny | 11,285 |
| Bryan Holubec | 67 | Susan Burkhart | 73,84 |

| Public Schs..Principal | Grd | Prgm | Enr/#Cls | SN |
|---|---|---|---|---|
| Thrall Elem Sch<br>201 S Bounds St, Thrall 76578<br>Sherri Maruska | PK-5 | T | 305<br>17 | 39% 512/898-5293<br>Fax 512/898-2879 |
| Thrall High Sch<br>201 S Bounds St, Thrall 76578<br>Travis Dube | 9-12 | AV | 157<br>12 | 26% 512/898-5193<br>Fax 512/898-2132 |
| Thrall Middle Sch<br>201 S Bounds St, Thrall 76578<br>Kim Luton | 6-8 | | 152<br>10 | 33% 512/898-5328<br>Fax 512/898-2132 |

## WILLIAMSON CATHOLIC SCHOOLS

- **Diocese of Austin Ed Office** PID: 01420568
Listing includes only schools located in this county. See District Index for
location of Diocesan Offices.

| Catholic Schs..Principal | Grd | Prgm | Enr/#Cls | SN |
|---|---|---|---|---|
| Holy Family Catholic Sch<br>9400 Neenah Ave, Austin 78717<br>Kelly Laster | PK-8 | | 514 | 512/246-4455<br>Fax 512/246-4454 |
| St Dominic Savio Catholic HS<br>9300 Neenah Ave, Austin 78717<br>Enrique Garcia | 9-12 | | 365 | 512/388-8846<br>Fax 512/388-1335 |
| St Helen Catholic Sch<br>2700 E University Ave, Georgetown 78626<br>Mary Sims | PK-8 | | 189<br>8 | 512/868-0744<br>Fax 512/869-3244 |
| St Mary's Sch<br>520 Washburn St, Taylor 76574<br>Heidi Altman | PK-8 | | 161<br>10 | 512/352-2313<br>Fax 512/365-5313 |

## WILLIAMSON PRIVATE SCHOOLS

| Private Schs..Principal | Grd | Prgm | Enr/#Cls | SN |
|---|---|---|---|---|
| Applegate Adventist Jr Academy<br>4 Applegate Cir, Round Rock 78665<br>Ingrid Stanley | PK-8 | | 24 | 512/388-7870 |
| Challenger School-Avery Rnch<br>15101 Avery Ranch Blvd, Austin 78717<br>Molly Bauer | PK-7 | | 116 | 512/341-8000<br>Fax 512/331-2951 |
| Community Montessori Sch<br>500 Pleasant Valley Dr, Georgetown 78626<br>Becki Hardie | PK-6 | | 148<br>9 | 512/863-7920<br>Fax 512/819-9617<br>f |
| Concordia High Sch<br>1500 Royston Ln Ste A, Round Rock 78664<br>Mike Doering | 9-12 | | 101<br>10 | 512/248-2547<br>Fax 512/252-3839 |
| Grace Academy<br>225 Grace Blvd, Georgetown 78633<br>Dr David Diener | K-12 | | 188<br>11 | 512/864-9500<br>Fax 512/868-5429 |
| Guidepost Montessori-Brush Crk<br>3017 Polar Ln, Cedar Park 78613 | PK-6 | | 401 | 512/259-3333<br>Fax 512/259-3331<br>f t |
| McCasland Christian Academy<br>915 Rockmoor Dr, Georgetown 78628<br>Jennifer Stoops | 1-5 | | 50 | 512/863-9903 |
| Round Rock Christian Academy<br>301 N Lake Creek Dr, Round Rock 78681<br>Tiffany Jaksch \ Kelly Counts | PK-12 | | 530 | 512/255-4491 |
| Summit Christian Academy<br>2121 Cypress Creek Rd, Cedar Park 78613<br>Shelley Jordan | PK-12 | | 300<br>20 | 512/250-1369<br>Fax 512/257-1851<br>f t |
| Zion Lutheran Sch<br>6101 FM 1105, Georgetown 78626<br>Thomas Wrege | PK-8 | | 200<br>12 | 512/863-5345<br>Fax 512/869-5659 |

## WILSON COUNTY

## WILSON PUBLIC SCHOOLS

- **Floresville Ind School Dist** PID: 01061265      830/393-5300
1200 5th St, Floresville 78114      Fax 830/393-5399

**Schools:** 5 \ **Teachers:** 247 \ **Students:** 3,000 \ **Special Ed Students:** 368
\ **LEP Students:** 201 \ **College-Bound:** 45% \ **Ethnic:** African American
1%, Hispanic 66%, Caucasian 32% \ **Exp:** $419 (High) \ **Poverty:** 16% \
**Title I:** $840,166 \ **Special Education:** $702,000 \ **Open-Close:** 08/24 -
05/28 \ **DTBP:** $184 (High) \ f

| | | | |
|---|---|---|---|
| Dr Sherri Bays | 1 | Michael Schroller | 2,15,17,91 |
| Darrell Towley | 3 | Scott Andlesey | 4 |
| Mary Aaron | 5 | Andrew Rohrf | 6 |
| Donna Lynn | 7,85 | Chris Galloway | 8 |
| Dr Rhonda Wade | 9,36,83 | Greta Warren | 11 |
| Jessica Stanush | 15,68,78,79,273 | Denise Knight | 27 |
| Debbie Akers | 58 | Penny Smith | 67 |
| James Urbanczyk | 73,295,297 | Angela Garcia | 88,274* |
| Jessica Grant | 90 | Melvin Albert | 295 |

| 79 | Student Personnel | 91 | Safety/Security | 275 | Response To Intervention | 298 | Grant Writer/Ptnrships |
|---|---|---|---|---|---|---|---|
| 80 | Driver Ed/Safety | 92 | Magnet School | 277 | Remedial Math K-12 | 750 | Chief Innovation Officer |
| 81 | Gifted/Talented | 93 | Parental Involvement | 280 | Literacy Coach | 751 | Chief of Staff |
| 82 | Video Services | 95 | Tech Prep Program | 285 | STEM | 752 | Social Emotional Learning |
| 83 | Substance Abuse Prev | 97 | Chief Infomation Officer | 286 | Digital Learning | | |
| 84 | Erate | 98 | Chief Technology Officer | 288 | Common Core Standards | | |
| 85 | AIDS Education | 270 | Character Education | 294 | Accountability | | |
| 88 | Alternative/At Risk | 271 | Migrant Education | 295 | Network System | | |
| 89 | Multi-Cultural Curriculum | 273 | Teacher Mentor | 296 | Title II Programs | | |
| 90 | Social Work | 274 | Before/After Sch | 297 | Webmaster | | |

**School Programs**
A = Alternative Program
G = Adult Classes
M = Magnet Program
T = Title I Schoolwide
V = Career & Tech Ed Programs

**Other School Types**
Ⓐ = Alternative School
Ⓒ = Charter School
Ⓜ = Magnet School
Ⓨ = Year-Round School

**Social Media**
f = Facebook
t = Twitter

New Schools are shaded
New Superintendents and Principals are bold
Personnel with email addresses are underscored

**TX—403**

| Public Schs..Principal | Grd | Prgm | Enr/#Cls | SN | |
|---|---|---|---|---|---|
| Ⓐ Floresville Alternative Ctr<br>335 Alternative Ln, Floresville 78114<br>Angela Garcia | 6-12 | | 85<br>5 | 76% | 830/393-5368<br>Fax 830/393-5706 |
| Floresville High Sch<br>1813 Tiger Ln, Floresville 78114<br>Marcia Gonzales | 9-12 | TV | 961<br>60 | 44% | 830/393-5370<br>Fax 830/393-5719 |
| Floresville Middle Sch<br>2601 B St, Floresville 78114<br>David Lehman | 6-8 | T | 632<br>80 | 52% | 830/393-5350<br>Fax 830/393-5359 🅵🆃 |
| Floresville North Elem Sch<br>14905 FM 775, Floresville 78114<br>Heather Brooks | PK-5 | T | 615<br>29 | 55% | 830/393-5310<br>Fax 830/393-5315 |
| Floresville South Elem Sch<br>2000 Tiger Ln, Floresville 78114<br>Leanne Marshall | PK-5 | T | 888<br>39 | 64% | 830/393-5325<br>Fax 830/393-5746 🅵🆃 |

● **La Vernia Ind School Dist** PID: 01061318
13600 US Highway 87 W, La Vernia 78121

830/779-6600
Fax 830/779-2304

**Schools:** 4 \ **Teachers:** 219 \ **Students:** 2,400 \ **Special Ed Students:** 354 \ **LEP Students:** 104 \ **College-Bound:** 55% \ **Ethnic:** African American 1%, Hispanic 31%, Caucasian 67% \ **Exp:** $295 (Med) \ **Poverty:** 9% \ **Title I:** $316,260 \ **Special Education:** $407,000 \ **Open-Close:** 08/19 - 05/27 \ **DTBP:** $141 (High) \ 🅵 🆃

| | | | |
|---|---|---|---|
| Hensley Cone | 1 | Amy Cowley | 2,5,15,19 |
| Jeremy Deck | 3,17 | Adellea Freeman-Wright | 4 |
| Chris Taber | 6* | Kasey Dickson | 7,83,85* |
| Dana Grubb | 8 | Roseann Armendarvi | 11,57,58 |
| Jeff Towns | 67 | Max Flores | 68 |
| Toni Riester-Wood | 69 | Angela Turner | 73,98,295,297 |
| Michael Duffik | 91 | | |

| Public Schs..Principal | Grd | Prgm | Enr/#Cls | SN | |
|---|---|---|---|---|---|
| La Vernia High Sch<br>225 Bluebonnet Rd, La Vernia 78121<br>Anthony Kosub | 9-12 | V | 579 | 23% | 830/779-6630<br>Fax 830/779-3218 |
| La Vernia Intermediate Sch<br>369 S FM 1346, La Vernia 78121<br>Helen Hubert | 3-5 | | 497<br>38 | 29% | 830/779-6640<br>Fax 830/779-2519 |
| La Vernia Junior High Sch<br>195 Bluebonnet Rd, La Vernia 78121<br>Andrea Carter | 6-8 | | 532<br>25 | 26% | 830/779-6650<br>Fax 830/779-6651 |
| La Vernia Primary Sch<br>249 S FM 1346, La Vernia 78121<br>Shelley Keck | PK-2 | | 826<br>29 | 30% | 830/779-6660<br>Fax 830/779-7031 |

● **Poth Ind School Dist** PID: 01061344
510 Titcomb St, Poth 78147

830/484-3330
Fax 830/484-2961

**Schools:** 3 \ **Teachers:** 68 \ **Students:** 858 \ **Special Ed Students:** 104 \ **LEP Students:** 51 \ **College-Bound:** 58% \ **Ethnic:** Hispanic 47%, Caucasian 52% \ **Exp:** $421 (High) \ **Poverty:** 8% \ **Title I:** $66,788 \ **Special Education:** $111,000 \ **Open-Close:** 08/13 - 05/21 \ **DTBP:** $345 (High) \ 🅵

| | | | |
|---|---|---|---|
| Paula Renken | 1,11 | Jennifer Johnson | 2 |
| James Molina | 3 | Scott Brysch | 3 |
| Betty Moy | 4 | Philip Zwicke | 5,79,91 |
| Jeffrey Luna | 6 | Casse Landrum | 7,35* |
| Susie Martinez | 8,69* | Karla Brysch | 12* |
| Bradon Lyssy | 19 | Ronnie Wieding | 27* |
| Nicole Dziuk | 31,36,83* | Martizes Suzi | 57 |
| Lori Spencer | 58,752* | Les Miller | 67 |
| Max Calhoun | 73 | Danette Lyssy | 280 |
| Josh Wadsworth | 294 | | |

| Public Schs..Principal | Grd | Prgm | Enr/#Cls | SN | |
|---|---|---|---|---|---|
| Poth Elem Sch<br>210 Brinkoeter St, Poth 78147<br>Karla Brysch | PK-5 | T | 377<br>19 | 40% | 830/484-3321<br>Fax 830/484-0197 🅵 |
| Poth High Sch<br>506 N Dickson St, Poth 78147<br>Todd Deaver | 9-12 | | 120<br>22 | 31% | 830/484-3322<br>Fax 830/484-3304 |
| Poth Junior High Sch<br>505 N Dickson St, Poth 78147<br>Laura Kroll | 6-8 | | 188<br>22 | 37% | 830/484-3323<br>Fax 830/484-3682 |

● **Stockdale Ind School Dist** PID: 01061382
503 S 4th St, Stockdale 78160

830/996-3551
Fax 830/996-1071

**Schools:** 3 \ **Teachers:** 74 \ **Students:** 820 \ **Special Ed Students:** 129 \ **LEP Students:** 33 \ **Ethnic:** African American 1%, Hispanic 49%, Caucasian 50% \ **Exp:** $573 (High) \ **Poverty:** 22% \ **Title I:** $258,497 \ **Open-Close:** 08/21 - 05/28 \ **DTBP:** $346 (High)

| | | | |
|---|---|---|---|
| Daniel Fuller | 1 | Becky Stewart | 2 |
| Samaris Velazquez | 4 | Roxanne Moczgemba | 8,11,57,69,296 |
| Sharon Dunn | 9,35,88,288* | Susan Loep | 9 |
| Sandra Lynn | 10* | Salvadore Urrabazo | 67 |
| Billy Polasek | 73 | Pam Burrier | 76 |

| Public Schs..Principal | Grd | Prgm | Enr/#Cls | SN | |
|---|---|---|---|---|---|
| Stockdale Elem Sch<br>503 S 4th St, Stockdale 78160<br>Brigit Lucas | PK-5 | T | 349<br>21 | 60% | 830/996-1612<br>Fax 830/996-3236 |
| Stockdale High Sch<br>503 S 4th St, Stockdale 78160<br>Sandra Lynn | 9-12 | TV | 163<br>15 | 51% | 830/996-3103<br>Fax 830/996-9071 |
| Stockdale Junior High Sch<br>503 S 4th St, Stockdale 78160<br>Sharon Dunn | 6-8 | T | 136<br>10 | 60% | 830/996-3153<br>Fax 830/996-3055 |

## WILSON CATHOLIC SCHOOLS

● **Archdiocese San Antonio Ed Off** PID: 00999724
Listing includes only schools located in this county. See District Index for location of Diocesan Offices.

| Catholic Schs..Principal | Grd | Prgm | Enr/#Cls | SN | |
|---|---|---|---|---|---|
| Sacred Heart Catholic Sch<br>1007 Trail St, Floresville 78114<br>Hilary Reile | PK-6 | | 125<br>6 | | 830/393-2117<br>Fax 830/393-6968 🅵🆃 |

## WILSON PRIVATE SCHOOLS

| Private Schs..Principal | Grd | Prgm | Enr/#Cls | SN | |
|---|---|---|---|---|---|
| La Vernia Christian Agape Acad<br>10688 US Highway 87 W, La Vernia 78121<br>Bob Middleton | K-12 | | 15 | | 830/779-6361<br>Fax 830/779-2402 |

| | | | | | | | |
|---|---|---|---|---|---|---|---|
| 1 Superintendent | 8 Curric/Instruct K-12 | 19 Chief Financial Officer | 29 Family/Consumer Science | 39 Social Studies K-12 | 49 English/Lang Arts Elem | 59 Special Education Elem | 69 Academic Assessment |
| 2 Bus/Finance/Purchasing | 9 Curric/Instruct Elem | 20 Art K-12 | 30 Adult Education | 40 Social Studies Elem | 50 English/Lang Arts Sec | 60 Special Education Sec | 70 Research/Development |
| 3 Buildings And Grounds | 10 Curric/Instruct Sec | 21 Art Elem | 31 Career/Sch-to-Work K-12 | 41 Social Studies Sec | 51 Reading K-12 | 61 Foreign/World Lang K-12 | 71 Public Information |
| 4 Food Service | 11 Federal Program | 22 Art Sec | 32 Career/Sch-to-Work Elem | 42 Science K-12 | 52 Reading Elem | 62 Foreign/World Lang Elem | 72 Summer School |
| 5 Transportation | 12 Title I | 23 Music K-12 | 33 Career/Sch-to-Work Sec | 43 Science Elem | 53 Reading Sec | 63 Foreign/World Lang Sec | 73 Instructional Tech |
| 6 Athletic | 13 Title V | 24 Music Elem | 34 Early Childhood Ed | 44 Science Sec | 54 Remedial Reading K-12 | 64 Religious Education K-12 | 74 Inservice Training |
| 7 Health Services | 15 Asst Superintendent | 25 Music Sec | 35 Health/Phys Education | 45 Math K-12 | 55 Remedial Reading Elem | 65 Religious Education Elem | 75 Marketing/Distributive |
| | 16 Instructional Media Svcs | 26 Business Education | 36 Guidance Services K-12 | 46 Math Elem | 56 Remedial Reading Sec | 66 Religious Education Sec | 76 Info Systems |
| | 17 Chief Operations Officer | 27 Career & Tech Ed | 37 Guidance Services Elem | 47 Math Sec | 57 Bilingual/ELL | 67 School Board President | 77 Psychological Assess |
| | 18 Chief Academic Officer | 28 Technology Education | 38 Guidance Services Sec | 48 English/Lang Arts K-12 | 58 Special Education K-12 | 68 Teacher Personnel | 78 Affirmative Action |

| | |
|---|---|
| **WINKLER COUNTY** | **WISE COUNTY** |

## WINKLER PUBLIC SCHOOLS

## WISE PUBLIC SCHOOLS

● **Kermit Ind School Dist** PID: 01061423
601 S Poplar St, Kermit 79745
432/586-1000
Fax 432/586-1016

Schools: 3 \ **Teachers:** 83 \ **Students:** 1,397 \ **Special Ed Students:** 121 \
**LEP Students:** 287 \ **Ethnic:** Asian 1%, African American 1%, Hispanic 81%,
Caucasian 17% \ **Exp:** $756 (High) \ **Poverty:** 19% \ **Title I:** $350,458 \
**Open-Close:** 08/24 - 05/27 \ **DTBP:** $352 (High)

| | | |
|---|---|---|
| Dr Denise Shetter ....................................1 | Gayle Fuqua ............................................2 |
| Gabe Espino .................................3,5,91 | Iyana Matthews ......................................4 |
| Charles Ross ...........................................6 | Remona Sherry ......................................7 |
| William Armstrong ........ 8,83,88,288,294,298 | Mark Patrick ............................. 16,73,295* |
| Amanda Urias .........................31,36,270* | Roxanne Greer ......................................58 |
| Lee Lentz-Edwards ...............................67 | Angela Florez ........................................79 |

| Public Schs..Principal | Grd | Prgm | Enr/#Cls | SN | |
|---|---|---|---|---|---|
| Kermit Elem Sch | PK-4 | T | 571 | 78% | 432/586-1020 |
| 201 N East Ave, Kermit 79745 | | | 18 | | Fax 432/586-1023 |
| Sonia Gonzales | | | | | |
| Kermit High Sch | 9-12 | TV | 373 | 64% | 432/586-1050 |
| 912 E Tommy Thompson St, Kermit 79745 | | | 35 | | Fax 432/586-1055 |
| Daniel Sharp | | | | | |
| Kermit Junior High Sch | 5-8 | TV | 453 | 72% | 432/586-1040 |
| 1000 Tommy Thompson St, Kermit 79745 | | | 30 | | Fax 432/586-1045 |
| Laura Miller | | | | | |

● **Wink Loving Ind School Dist** PID: 01061485
200 N Rosey Dodd Ave, Wink 79789
432/527-3880
Fax 432/527-3505

Schools: 2 \ **Teachers:** 40 \ **Students:** 420 \ **Special Ed Students:** 35
\ **LEP Students:** 18 \ **Ethnic:** African American 2%, Hispanic 47%,
Caucasian 51% \ **Exp:** $1,064 (High) \ **Poverty:** 12% \ **Title I:** $55,978 \
**Open-Close:** 08/17 - 05/21 \ **DTBP:** $340 (High)

| | | |
|---|---|---|
| Scotty Carman ......................................1 | Geanna Coker ........................................2 |
| Mickey Underwood ...............................4 | Brian Gibson ........................................6* |
| Courtney Woody ...........................7,85* | Kittie Gibson ........................................8* |
| Priscilla Salgado ........... 8,11,36,69,83,88,93* | Lance Wineinger ..................................9* |
| Darryl Schwierjohn ..............................23* | Kimberly Licon ...........................51,271* |
| Luis Salcido ..........................................58 | Peter Lara ............................................61* |
| Brad White ............................................67 | Micheal Dawkins ........73,76,98,286,295,298* |

| Public Schs..Principal | Grd | Prgm | Enr/#Cls | SN | |
|---|---|---|---|---|---|
| Wink Elem Sch | PK-6 | AT | 249 | 43% | 432/527-3880 |
| 200 Rosey Dodd St, Wink 79789 | | | 18 | | |
| Lance Wineinger | | | | | |
| Wink High Sch | 7-12 | AGTV | 194 | 38% | 432/527-3880 |
| 200 Rosey Dodd St, Wink 79789 | | | 28 | | |
| Kittie Gibson | | | | | [t] |

● **Alvord Ind School Dist** PID: 01061526
100 Mosley Ln, Alvord 76225
940/427-5975
Fax 940/427-2313

Schools: 3 \ **Teachers:** 57 \ **Students:** 700 \ **Special Ed Students:** 83 \
**LEP Students:** 25 \ **Ethnic:** Hispanic 12%, Caucasian 87% \ **Exp:** $536 (High)
\ **Poverty:** 9% \ **Title I:** $73,663 \ **Open-Close:** 08/20 - 05/27

| | | |
|---|---|---|
| Dr Randy Brown ....................................1 | Cindy Tackett ........................................2 |
| Jeremy Russell ......................................5 | Peter Hart ............................................6* |
| Asisela Palmer ...............................7,85* | Bonnie Foreman ...............8,69,83,270* |
| Charles Mann .........................11,73,295* | Daniel Ruddick .....................................67 |

| Public Schs..Principal | Grd | Prgm | Enr/#Cls | SN | |
|---|---|---|---|---|---|
| Alvord Elem Sch | PK-5 | T | 318 | 45% | 940/427-2881 |
| 711 W Stadium Dr, Alvord 76225 | | | 31 | | Fax 940/427-2377 |
| Bridget Williams | | | | | |
| Alvord High Sch | 9-12 | V | 211 | 33% | 940/427-9643 |
| 1049 W Bypass 287, Alvord 76225 | | | | | Fax 940/427-9648 |
| Aaron Tefertiller | | | | | |
| Alvord Middle Sch | 6-8 | | 171 | 35% | 940/427-5511 |
| 328 S FM 1655, Alvord 76225 | | | 11 | | Fax 940/427-2461 |
| Jessica Bull | | | | | |

● **Boyd Ind School Dist** PID: 01061552
600 Knox Ave, Boyd 76023
940/433-2327
Fax 940/433-9569

Schools: 4 \ **Teachers:** 95 \ **Students:** 1,281 \ **Special Ed Students:** 91 \
**LEP Students:** 54 \ **College-Bound:** 53% \ **Ethnic:** African American 1%,
Hispanic 17%, Native American 1%, Caucasian 81% \ **Exp:** $217 (Med) \
**Poverty:** 10% \ **Title I:** $129,320 \ **Open-Close:** 08/19 - 05/27 \ **DTBP:** $349
(High)

| | | |
|---|---|---|
| Dr Tamara Bardy ....................................1 | Julie Maddix ..........................................2 |
| James McDonald ....................................3 | Sharon Nelson ......................................5 |
| Brandon Hopkins ...................................6* | Chris Chapaton ...............................8,15 |
| Krystle Duncan ......................................58 | Bill Childress ........................................67 |
| Christine Magrita ..................................73 | |

| Public Schs..Principal | Grd | Prgm | Enr/#Cls | SN | |
|---|---|---|---|---|---|
| Boyd Elem Sch | PK-3 | T | 380 | 58% | 940/433-9520 |
| 500 E Morton Ave, Boyd 76023 | | | 20 | | Fax 940/433-9536 |
| Anke Bracey | | | | | |
| Boyd High Sch | 9-12 | AV | 410 | 38% | 940/433-9580 |
| 700 Knox Ave, Boyd 76023 | | | 22 | | Fax 940/433-2713 |
| **Chelsea Reeves \ Christine Magryta** | | | | | |
| Boyd Intermediate Sch | 4-6 | T | 278 | 45% | 940/433-9540 |
| 550 Knox Ave, Boyd 76023 | | | 14 | | Fax 940/433-8568 |
| **Morgan Harrison** | | | | | |
| Boyd Middle Sch | 7-8 | | 213 | 43% | 940/433-9560 |
| 550 Knox Ave, Boyd 76023 | | | 20 | | Fax 940/433-9548 |
| Daniel Bourgeois | | | | | |

| | | | | |
|---|---|---|---|---|
| 79 Student Personnel | 91 Safety/Security | 275 Response To Intervention | 298 Grant Writer/Ptnrships | **School Programs** |
| 80 Driver Ed/Safety | 92 Magnet School | 277 Remedial Math K-12 | 750 Chief Innovation Officer | **A = Alternative Program** |
| 81 Gifted/Talented | 93 Parental Involvement | 280 Literacy Coach | 751 Chief of Staff | **G = Adult Classes** |
| 82 Video Services | 95 Tech Prep Program | 285 STEM | 752 Social Emotional Learning | **M = Magnet Program** |
| 83 Substance Abuse Prev | 97 Chief Infomation Officer | 286 Digital Learning | | **T = Title I Schoolwide** |
| 84 Erate | 98 Chief Technology Officer | 288 Common Core Standards | **Other School Types** | **V = Career & Tech Ed Programs** |
| 85 AIDS Education | 270 Character Education | 294 Accountability | Ⓐ = Alternative School | |
| 88 Alternative/At Risk | 271 Migrant Education | 295 Network System | Ⓒ = Charter School | **New Schools are shaded** |
| 89 Multi-Cultural Curriculum | 273 Teacher Mentor | 296 Title II Programs | Ⓜ = Magnet School | **New Superintendents and Principals are bold** |
| 90 Social Work | 274 Before/After Sch | 297 Webmaster | Ⓨ = Year-Round School | **Personnel with email addresses are underscored** |

**Social Media**

[f] = Facebook

[t] = Twitter

## • Bridgeport Ind School Dist PID: 01061588    940/683-5124
2107 15th St, Bridgeport 76426          Fax 940/683-4268

**Schools:** 5 \ **Teachers:** 161 \ **Students:** 1,994 \ **Special Ed Students:** 209 \ **LEP Students:** 501 \ **College-Bound:** 43% \ **Ethnic:** African American 1%, Hispanic 53%, Native American: 1%, Caucasian 46% \ **Exp:** $391 (High) \ **Poverty:** 15% \ **Title I:** $498,932 \ **Open-Close:** 08/14 - 05/20 \ **DTBP:** $343 (High)

| | |
|---|---|
| Brandon Peavey ..................................1 | Debi Meng ..........................................2 |
| Kurt Kronenberger ...................3,5,15,68 | Shelley Laaser ...................................4 |
| Terry Rye ..........................................5* | Shannon Wilson .................................6 |
| Dr Adam Hile .........................8,15,72 | Patricia Hernandez 11,57,69,271,288,296,298 |
| Travis Hood .....................................58 | Tom Talley ........................................67 |
| Leslie Henson .................................73 | Roger Egle ..................73,76,286,295* |

| Public Schs..Principal | Grd | Prgm | Enr/#Cls | SN | |
|---|---|---|---|---|---|
| Ⓐ Alternative Learning Center 1101 17th St, Bridgeport 76426 Laura Williams | 1-12 | | 25 4 | | 940/683-1830 Fax 940/683-3582 |
| Bridgeport Elem Sch 1408 Elementary Dr, Bridgeport 76426 Martha Bock | PK-2 | T | 414 50 | 71% | 940/683-5955 Fax 940/683-5079 |
| Bridgeport High Sch 1 Maroon Dr, Bridgeport 76426 Jaime Sturdivant | 9-12 | ATV | 625 45 | 57% | 940/683-4064 Fax 940/683-4014 |
| Bridgeport Intermediate Sch 1400 US Highway 380, Bridgeport 76426 Mallory Marr | 3-5 | T | 470 32 | 73% | 940/683-5784 Fax 940/683-4086 |
| Bridgeport Middle Sch 702 17th St, Bridgeport 76426 Steven Valkenaar | 6-8 | ATV | 485 36 | 70% | 940/683-2273 Fax 940/683-5812 |

## • Chico Ind School Dist PID: 01061629    940/644-2228
503 W Sherman St, Chico 76431        Fax 940/644-0055

**Schools:** 3 \ **Teachers:** 52 \ **Students:** 600 \ **Special Ed Students:** 56 \ **LEP Students:** 51 \ **College-Bound:** 52% \ **Ethnic:** African American 1%, Hispanic 28%, Native American: 1%, Caucasian 69% \ **Exp:** $435 (High) \ **Poverty:** 17% \ **Title I:** $139,399 \ **Open-Close:** 08/20 - 05/28 \ **DTBP:** $365 (High)

| | |
|---|---|
| William Higgins ..................................1 | Melody Parr .......................................2 |
| Shelli Lieser .....................................4 | Maury Martin ........................5,58,273 |
| Randi Miller ......................................6 | Brent Hand ......................................8* |
| Linda Duck .........................12,280* | Tim Raley ..........................................67 |
| Breann Cox ...................................73 | Karen Decker ...............................275* |
| Debbie Peyton ........................295,297 | |

| Public Schs..Principal | Grd | Prgm | Enr/#Cls | SN | |
|---|---|---|---|---|---|
| Chico Elem Sch 1120 Park Rd, Chico 76431 Karen Decker | PK-5 | AT | 274 23 | 72% | 940/644-2220 Fax 940/644-2193 |
| Chico High Sch 263 FM 2952, Chico 76431 Randy Brawner | 9-12 | ATV | 162 22 | 65% | 940/644-5783 Fax 940/644-1932 |
| Chico Middle Sch 1205 W Sherman St, Chico 76431 Monte Sewell | 6-8 | AT | 134 12 | 64% | 940/644-5550 Fax 940/644-5876 |

## • Decatur Ind School Dist PID: 01061655    940/393-7100
307 S Cates St, Decatur 76234        Fax 940/627-3141

**Schools:** 5 \ **Teachers:** 224 \ **Students:** 3,390 \ **Special Ed Students:** 392 \ **LEP Students:** 469 \ **College-Bound:** 59% \ **Ethnic:** Asian 1%, African American 1%, Hispanic 34%, Native American: 1%, Caucasian 63% \ **Exp:** $329 (High) \ **Poverty:** 11% \ **Title I:** $369,297 \ **Special Education:** $592,000 \ **Open-Close:** 08/14 - 05/20 \ **DTBP:** $181 (High) \ 🅵

| | |
|---|---|
| **Dr Coburn** .......................................1 | Cindy Tatum ...............................2,15 |
| Rusty Berg ........................................3 | Shelly Lasser ....................................4 |
| Steve White ......................................5 | Mike Fuller ........................................6 |
| Dr Shane Conklin ........8,31,57,69,70,271,274 | Meredith Culpepper ...........11,68,83,88,298 |
| April Whisenant ..............................58 | Charlie Tibbels ...............................67 |
| Jennifer Terrell ................................69 | Troy Bagwell ..................................73* |
| David Jackson ...............................295 | |

| Public Schs..Principal | Grd | Prgm | Enr/#Cls | SN | |
|---|---|---|---|---|---|
| Carson Elem Sch 2100 S Business 287, Decatur 76234 Craig Weston | PK-5 | T | 464 30 | 39% | 940/393-7500 Fax 940/627-4792 |
| Decatur High Sch 750 E Eagle Smt, Decatur 76234 **Dr Jadie Matthew** | 9-12 | TV | 1,053 55 | 43% | 940/393-7200 Fax 940/626-4520 🅵 |
| McCarroll Middle Sch 1201 W Thompson St, Decatur 76234 **Roby Nunn** | 6-8 | TV | 495 25 | 49% | 940/393-7300 Fax 940/627-2497 🅵 |
| Rann Elem Sch 1300 Deer Park Rd, Decatur 76234 **Galindo Vargas** | PK-5 | T | 563 35 | 53% | 940/393-7600 Fax 940/627-6198 |
| Young Elem Sch 379 Buchanan Rd, Decatur 76234 Lana Coffman | PK-5 | T | 520 | 60% | 940/393-7400 Fax 940/627-0082 |

## • North Lamar Ind School Dist PID: 01036636    903/737-2000
3130 N Main St, Paradise 76073        Fax 903/669-0129

**Schools:** 7 \ **Teachers:** 220 \ **Students:** 2,417 \ **Special Ed Students:** 342 \ **LEP Students:** 72 \ **College-Bound:** 67% \ **Ethnic:** Asian 1%, African American 5%, Hispanic 11%, Native American: 2%, Caucasian 81% \ **Exp:** $387 (High) \ **Poverty:** 15% \ **Title I:** $512,756 \ **Open-Close:** 08/13 - 05/21 \ **DTBP:** $160 (High)

| | |
|---|---|
| Kelli Stewart ......................................1 | Melissa Darrow .................................2 |
| Tami Miles .................................2,296 | Rick Landis .......................................3 |
| Diana McGregor ..............................4* | Clint Hildreath ..................................5 |
| Kendall Kirk ....................................6* | Justine Wideman ..................7,35,85* |
| Angela Chadwick .........................8,285 | Leslie Watson ..... 11,15,58,83,88,275,294,296 |
| Debbie Basden ..............................16* | Wes Brown ..................27,31,271* |
| Jeff Martin .......................................67 | Carla Coleman .............................71 |
| Glenda Parsons .....................73,95,295* | Jodie Ingram ...................................73 |
| Launa Doyal ..............................297* | Launa Doyal ...................................297 |

| Public Schs..Principal | Grd | Prgm | Enr/#Cls | SN | |
|---|---|---|---|---|---|
| Aaron Parker Elem Sch 98 Cr 4412, Powderly 75473 Kristin Hughes | PK-5 | T | 203 16 | 65% | 903/732-3066 Fax 903/669-0139 |
| Cecil Everett Elem Sch 3201 Lewis Ln, Paris 75460 Lora Sanders | 2-3 | T | 274 | 49% | 903/737-2061 Fax 903/669-0169 |
| Frank Stone Middle Sch 3201 Lewis Ln, Paris 75460 Lindsey Miller | 6-8 | T | 585 55 | 50% | 903/737-2041 Fax 903/669-0149 |
| Geneva Bailey Intermediate Sch 3201 Lewis Ln, Paris 75460 Angela Compton | 4-5 | T | 311 18 | 52% | 903/737-7971 Fax 903/669-0179 |

---

| | | | | | | | | |
|---|---|---|---|---|---|---|---|---|
| **1** Superintendent | **8** Curric/Instruct K-12 | **19** Chief Financial Officer | **29** Family/Consumer Science | **39** Social Studies K-12 | **49** English/Lang Arts Elem | **59** Special Education Elem | **69** Academic Assessment |
| **2** Bus/Finance/Purchasing | **9** Curric/Instruct Elem | **20** Art K-12 | **30** Adult Education | **40** Social Studies Elem | **50** English/Lang Arts Sec | **60** Special Education Sec | **70** Research/Development |
| **3** Buildings And Grounds | **10** Curric/Instruct Sec | **21** Art Elem | **31** Career/Sch-to-Work K-12 | **41** Social Studies Sec | **51** Reading K-12 | **61** Foreign/World Lang K-12 | **71** Public Information |
| **4** Food Service | **11** Federal Program | **22** Art Sec | **32** Career/Sch-to-Work Elem | **42** Science K-12 | **52** Reading Elem | **62** Foreign/World Lang Elem | **72** Summer School |
| **5** Transportation | **12** Title I | **23** Music K-12 | **33** Career/Sch-to-Work Sec | **43** Science Elem | **53** Reading Sec | **63** Foreign/World Lang Sec | **73** Instructional Tech |
| **6** Athletic | **13** Title V | **24** Music Elem | **34** Early Childhood Ed | **44** Science Sec | **54** Remedial Reading K-12 | **64** Religious Education K-12 | **74** Inservice Training |
| **7** Health Services | **14** Instructional Media Svcs | **25** Music Sec | **35** Health/Phys Education | **45** Math K-12 | **55** Remedial Reading Elem | **65** Religious Education Elem | **75** Marketing/Distributive |
| | **15** Asst Superintendent | **26** Business Education | **36** Guidance Services K-12 | **46** Math Elem | **56** Remedial Reading Sec | **66** Religious Education Sec | **76** Info Systems |
| | **16** Chief Operations Officer | **27** Career & Tech Ed | **37** Guidance Services Elem | **47** Math Sec | **57** Bilingual/ELL | **67** School Board President | **77** Psychological Assess |
| | **17** Chief Academic Officer | **28** Technology Education | **38** Guidance Services Sec | **48** English/Lang Arts K-12 | **58** Special Education K-12 | **68** Teacher Personnel | **78** Affirmative Action |

| ⒶLamar-Delta Alternative Ctr | 6-12 | | 30 | | 903/737-7963 |
| 3201 Lewis Ln, Paris 75460 | | | 2 | | Fax 903/669-0193 |
| Tracie Harris | | | | | |
| North Lamar High Sch | 9-12 | TV | 762 | 43% | 903/737-2011 |
| 3201 Lewis Ln, Paris 75460 | | | 65 | | Fax 903/669-0119 |
| **Mark Keith** | | | | | |
| W L Higgins Elem Sch | PK-1 | T | 272 | 64% | 903/737-2081 |
| 3201 Lewis Ln, Paris 75460 | | | 22 | | Fax 903/669-0189 |
| Lori Malone | | | | | |

- **Paradise Ind School Dist** PID: 01061722    940/969-2501
  338 School House Rd, Paradise 76073    Fax 940/969-5008

> **Schools:** 4 \ **Teachers:** 97 \ **Students:** 1,209 \ **Special Ed Students:** 135
> \ **LEP Students:** 35 \ **Ethnic:** African American 1%, Hispanic 13%,
> Caucasian 86% \ **Exp:** $218 (Med) \ **Poverty:** 14% \ **Title I:** $175,069 \
> **Open-Close:** 08/17 - 05/27 \ **DTBP:** $340 (High) \ ⓕ

| | | | |
|---|---|---|---|
| Dr Paul Uttley ...............................1 | | Summer Mathis .....................................2,19 | |
| Greg Fletcher ................................3 | | Joe Koch ..................................................6 | |
| Robin Gibson ...........8,11,15,74,271,296 | | Dr Joyce Hardy .....................................15,69 | |
| Lana McGehee ..............................16* | | Robin Garrett .........................................37* | |
| Cherie Gopffarth .........................38,83,88 | | Jennifer Crawford ..................................59* | |
| Homer Mundy ................................67 | | Doug Bryant .........................................73,76,286 | |

| Public Schs..Principal | Grd | Prgm | Enr/#Cls | SN | |
|---|---|---|---|---|---|
| Paradise Elem Sch | PK-3 | T | 373 | 39% | 940/969-5046 |
| 340 Schoolhouse Rd, Paradise 76073 | | | 18 | | Fax 940/969-5043 |
| **Melissa Cota** | | | | | |
| Paradise High Sch | 9-12 | V | 351 | 28% | 940/969-5010 |
| 338 School House Rd, Paradise 76073 | | | 20 | | Fax 940/969-5009 |
| Mark Mathis | | | | | |
| Paradise Intermediate Sch | 4-5 | | 176 | 28% | 940/969-5032 |
| 338 School House Rd, Paradise 76073 | | | 12 | | Fax 940/969-5031 |
| Kristin Gage | | | | | |
| Paradise Junior High Sch | 6-8 | V | 309 | 33% | 940/969-5034 |
| 338 School House Rd, Paradise 76073 | | | | | Fax 940/969-5025 |
| **Nicki Carter** | | | | | |

- **Slidell Ind School Dist** PID: 01061758    940/535-5260
  1 Greyhound Ln, Slidell 76267    Fax 832/426-3424

> **Schools:** 2 \ **Teachers:** 21 \ **Students:** 350 \ **Special Ed Students:** 18 \
> **LEP Students:** 34 \ **Ethnic:** Hispanic 30%, Caucasian 69% \ **Exp:** $465 (High)
> \ **Poverty:** 11% \ **Title I:** $42,233 \ **Open-Close:** 08/19 - 05/26 \ **DTBP:** $532
> (High)

| | | | |
|---|---|---|---|
| Taylor Williams ...............................1 | | Irene Wilson ...........................................2,12 | |
| Robert Oney ...............3,5,73,76,295* | | Casey Pierce ..........................................6* | |
| Marty Bratcher-Hair ....8,11,15,16,57,58,286* | | Marty Bratcher-Hair ...............................15,58 | |
| Tim Fletcher ................................67 | | | |

| Public Schs..Principal | Grd | Prgm | Enr/#Cls | SN | |
|---|---|---|---|---|---|
| Slidell Elem Sch | PK-3 | | 129 | | 940/466-3118 |
| 17347 FM 455, Decatur 76234 | | | 10 | | Fax 940/466-3016 |
| Theresa Stevens | | | | | |
| Slidell Secondary Sch | 5-12 | T | 153 | 52% | 940/535-5260 |
| 1 Greyhound Ln, Slidell 76267 | | | 12 | | |
| Theresa Stevens | | | | | |

## WISE PRIVATE SCHOOLS

| Private Schs..Principal | Grd | Prgm | Enr/#Cls | SN | |
|---|---|---|---|---|---|
| Victory Christian Academy | PK-12 | | 401 | | 940/626-4730 |
| 600 W Mulberry St, Decatur 76234 | | | | | Fax 972/954-3492 |
| Allen Bates | | | | | |

## WOOD COUNTY

## WOOD PUBLIC SCHOOLS

- **Alba-Golden Ind School Dist** PID: 01061784    903/768-2472
  1373 County Road 2377, Alba 75410    Fax 903/768-2130

> **Schools:** 2 \ **Teachers:** 79 \ **Students:** 588 \ **Special Ed Students:** 120
> \ **LEP Students:** 16 \ **College-Bound:** 37% \ **Ethnic:** Hispanic 9%,
> Caucasian 90% \ **Exp:** $638 (High) \ **Poverty:** 25% \ **Title I:** $304,916 \
> **Open-Close:** 08/26 - 05/28 \ **DTBP:** $340 (High)

| | | | |
|---|---|---|---|
| Cole McClendon ..................................1 | | Brenda Kelley .........................................2 | |
| Derek Smith ........................................6* | | Deitra Bizzell .........................................8* | |
| Michele Glidewell ...............................9* | | Jennifer Wigington .................................11 | |
| Michelle Randell ..................................58* | | Jason Stovall .........................................67 | |
| Dina Allred .........................................69* | | Michael Scott .........................................73,98 | |
| Starla Bryant ........................................88* | | | |

| Public Schs..Principal | Grd | Prgm | Enr/#Cls | SN | |
|---|---|---|---|---|---|
| Alba-Golden Elem Sch | PK-5 | T | 419 | 56% | 903/768-2472 |
| 1373 County Road 2377, Alba 75410 | | | 22 | | Fax 903/768-2593 |
| Kevin Wright | | | | | |
| Alba-Golden Jr Sr High Sch | 6-12 | T | 169 | 56% | 903/768-2472 |
| 1373 County Road 2377, Alba 75410 | | | 56 | | Fax 903/768-2303 |
| Brandon Bohannan \ Michael Mize | | | | | |

- **Hawkins Ind School Dist** PID: 01061813    903/769-2181
  179 Hawk Dr, Hawkins 75765    Fax 903/769-0505

> **Schools:** 3 \ **Teachers:** 60 \ **Students:** 750 \ **Special Ed Students:** 95
> \ **LEP Students:** 10 \ **College-Bound:** 75% \ **Ethnic:** African American
> 10%, Hispanic 7%, Caucasian 83% \ **Exp:** $474 (High) \ **Poverty:** 25% \
> **Title I:** $262,003 \ **Open-Close:** 08/13 - 05/21 \ **DTBP:** $378 (High)

| | | | |
|---|---|---|---|
| Stephanie McConnell ...........................1 | | Robby Fair ..............................................2 | |
| Troy Love ............................................3,5 | | Lesa Gibson ...........................................4 | |
| Scott Evans .........................................6,91 | | Natalie Hlavenka ...................................7* | |
| Dionne Williams ...........8,11,83,88,296,298 | | Carol Davis .............................................58 | |
| Robbie White .......................................67 | | Sharon Love ...........................................68 | |
| Mike Henderson .................................73,295* | | Morris Lyon .............................................84 | |
| Cristi Parson ......................................288 | | | |

| Public Schs..Principal | Grd | Prgm | Enr/#Cls | SN | |
|---|---|---|---|---|---|
| Hawkins Elem Sch | PK-5 | T | 320 | 70% | 903/769-0536 |
| 231 Hawk Dr, Hawkins 75765 | | | 25 | | Fax 903/769-0513 |
| Stephanie McConnell | | | | | |
| Hawkins High Sch | 9-12 | ATV | 222 | 60% | 903/769-0571 |
| 231 Hawk Dr, Hawkins 75765 | | | 35 | | Fax 903/769-0573 |
| Elisa Henninger | | | | | |

| Hawkins Middle Sch | 6-8 | 145 | 903/769-0552 |
|---|---|---|---|
| 231 Hawk Dr, Hawkins 75765 | | 15 | Fax 903/769-0573 |
| Elisa Henninger | | | |

## ● Mineola Ind School Dist PID: 01061851    903/569-2448
1695 W Loop 564, Mineola 75773    Fax 903/569-5155

**Schools:** 4 \ **Teachers:** 132 \ **Students:** 1,556 \ **Special Ed Students:** 156 \ **LEP Students:** 181 \ **College-Bound:** 55% \ **Ethnic:** Asian 1%, African American 6%, Hispanic 35%, Native American: 1%, Caucasian 57% \ **Exp:** $422 (High) \ **Poverty:** 24% \ **Title I:** $514,286 \ **Open-Close:** 08/13 - 05/21 \ **DTBP:** $353 (High)

| | | |
|---|---|---|
| Cody Mize ............1 | William Bjork ............2,15 | |
| Rick Browning ............3 | Kim Myers ............4 | |
| Sherri Harding ............5 | Luke Blackwell ............6* | |
| Jennifer Knipp ........8,57,58,69,74,88,271,286 | Carolyn Standford ............16 | |
| David Sauer ............27 | Dr John Abott ............67 | |
| Joseph Armstrong ............73,77,84,295 | Dr Kim Tunnell ............83 | |
| Melisia Foster ............85* | | |

| Public Schs..Principal | Grd | Prgm | Enr/#Cls | SN | |
|---|---|---|---|---|---|
| Mineola Elem Sch | 3-5 | T | 386 | 69% | 903/569-2466 |
| 900 W Patten St, Mineola 75773 | | | 20 | | Fax 903/569-3061 |
| Stacy Morris | | | | | |
| Mineola High Sch | 9-12 | TV | 471 | 53% | 903/569-3000 |
| 900 W Patten St, Mineola 75773 | | | 34 | | Fax 903/569-1930 |
| David Sauer | | | | | |
| Mineola Middle Sch | 6-8 | GT | 363 | 60% | 903/569-5338 |
| 1050 W Loop 564, Mineola 75773 | | | 30 | | Fax 903/569-5339 |
| Kendall Gould | | | | | 📘📧 |
| Mineola Primary Sch | PK-2 | GT | 336 | 70% | 903/569-5488 |
| 1695 W Loop 564, Mineola 75773 | | | 25 | | Fax 903/569-5489 |
| Jole Ray | | | | | |

## ● Quitman Ind School Dist PID: 01061904    903/763-5000
600 N Winnsboro St, Quitman 75783    Fax 903/763-2710

**Schools:** 3 \ **Teachers:** 85 \ **Students:** 1,083 \ **Special Ed Students:** 139 \ **LEP Students:** 45 \ **College-Bound:** 48% \ **Ethnic:** African American 3%, Hispanic 16%, Caucasian 81% \ **Exp:** $519 (High) \ **Poverty:** 19% \ **Title I:** $293,492 \ **Open-Close:** 08/17 - 05/21 \ **DTBP:** $350 (High)

| | |
|---|---|
| Rhonda Turner ............1 | Kayla Mars ............2,68 |
| Steve Schoon ............3,5,91 | Vinny Bass ............4 |
| Teresa Bradshaw ............5 | Bryan Oakes ............6 |
| Stacy Vandersthaas ............7* | Chris Mason ............8,11,57,69,88,285,296,298 |
| June Sims ............37* | Dr Jeremy Smith ............67 |
| Scott Turner ............73,295 | |

| Public Schs..Principal | Grd | Prgm | Enr/#Cls | SN | |
|---|---|---|---|---|---|
| Quitman Elem Sch | PK-5 | T | 475 | 64% | 903/763-5000 |
| 902 E Goode St, Quitman 75783 | | | 41 | | Fax 903/763-4151 |
| **Brittany Eldred** | | | | | |
| Quitman High Sch | 9-12 | TV | 326 | 57% | 903/763-5000 |
| 1101 E Goode St, Quitman 75783 | | | 30 | | Fax 903/763-2589 |
| Dana Hamrick | | | | | |
| Quitman Junior High Sch | 6-8 | ATV | 282 | 60% | 903/763-5000 |
| 1101 E Goode St, Quitman 75783 | | | 20 | | Fax 903/763-2589 |
| Chrystal Ballard | | | | | |

## ● Winnsboro Ind School Dist PID: 01061942    903/342-3737
207 E Pine St, Winnsboro 75494    Fax 903/342-3380

**Schools:** 3 \ **Teachers:** 112 \ **Students:** 1,422 \ **Special Ed Students:** 167 \ **LEP Students:** 108 \ **College-Bound:** 80% \ **Ethnic:** Asian 1%, African American 3%, Hispanic 18%, Caucasian 78% \ **Exp:** $651 (High) \ **Poverty:** 20% \ **Title I:** $363,426 \ **Special Education:** $256,000 \ **Open-Close:** 08/13 - 05/27 \ **DTBP:** $341 (High)

| | |
|---|---|
| Susan Morton ............1 | Mary Ann Lanier ............2 |
| Roger Spakes ............3,5 | Kisha Smith ............4* |
| William Cummings ............5 | Steve Pinnell ............6* |
| Erika Martin ............7 | Torri Miller ............8,11,58,76,286,288,298* |
| Debbie May ............38,85,88* | Rena Wagner ............57* |
| Mary Ellen Knight ............58 | Chris McElyea ............67 |
| Craig Anderson ............73,84,295 | Adriana Weems ............76 |
| Jody Hettich ............91* | David Pinell ............285* |

| Public Schs..Principal | Grd | Prgm | Enr/#Cls | SN | |
|---|---|---|---|---|---|
| Memorial Middle Sch | 5-8 | T | 436 | 57% | 903/342-5711 |
| 505 S Chestnut St, Winnsboro 75494 | | | 40 | | Fax 903/342-6689 |
| Jeff Akin | | | | | |
| Winnsboro Elem Sch | PK-4 | T | 523 | 60% | 903/342-3548 |
| 310 W Coke Rd, Winnsboro 75494 | | | 36 | | Fax 903/342-6858 |
| Pam Gambrel | | | | | |
| Winnsboro High Sch | 9-12 | T | 463 | 45% | 903/342-3641 |
| 409 Newsome St, Winnsboro 75494 | | | 32 | | Fax 903/342-3645 |
| David Pinell | | | | | |

## ● Yantis Ind School Dist PID: 01061980    903/383-2463
105 W Oak St, Yantis 75497    Fax 903/383-7620

**Schools:** 2 \ **Teachers:** 30 \ **Students:** 350 \ **Special Ed Students:** 35 \ **LEP Students:** 43 \ **College-Bound:** 50% \ **Ethnic:** Hispanic 31%, Native American: 1%, Caucasian 68% \ **Exp:** $319 (High) \ **Poverty:** 33% \ **Title I:** $190,285 \ **Open-Close:** 08/13 - 05/21 \ **DTBP:** $350 (High)

| | |
|---|---|
| Tracey Helfferich ............1 | Belinda Brown ............2,19 |
| Mitzi McLane ............4 | Staci Gammill ............7* |
| Tracey Helfferich ............8,11,298* | Johnathan Pollard ............16,73,82,84,286 |
| Janan Stravnacky ............31,69,83,88,270,271,288 | Marla Gilbreath ............57 |
| Deanna Alexander ............58* | Melissa Stephens ............67 |

| Public Schs..Principal | Grd | Prgm | Enr/#Cls | SN | |
|---|---|---|---|---|---|
| Imagene Glenn Elem Sch | PK-5 | | 199 | | 903/383-2462 |
| 105 W Oak St, Yantis 75497 | | | 13 | | Fax 903/383-2463 |
| Tracey Helfferich | | | | | |
| Yantis Sch | PK-12 | ATV | 155 | 66% | 903/383-2462 |
| 105 W Oak St, Yantis 75497 | | | 27 | | Fax 903/383-2463 |
| Tracey Helfferich \ Buddy Winstead | | | | | |

| | | | | | | | |
|---|---|---|---|---|---|---|---|
| 1 | Superintendent | 8 | Curric/Instruct K-12 | 19 | Chief Financial Officer | 29 | Family/Consumer Science |
| 2 | Bus/Finance/Purchasing | 9 | Curric/Instruct Elem | 20 | Art K-12 | 30 | Adult Education |
| 3 | Buildings And Grounds | 10 | Curric/Instruct Sec | 21 | Art Elem | 31 | Career/Sch-to-Work K-12 |
| 4 | Food Service | 11 | Federal Program | 22 | Art Sec | 32 | Career/Sch-to-Work Elem |
| 5 | Transportation | 12 | Title I | 23 | Music K-12 | 33 | Career/Sch-to-Work Sec |
| 6 | Athletic | 13 | Title V | 24 | Music Elem | 34 | Early Childhood Ed |
| 7 | Health Services | 14 | Asst Superintendent | 25 | Music Sec | 35 | Health/Phys Education |
| | | 15 | Asst Superintendent | 26 | Business Education | 36 | Guidance Services K-12 |
| | | 16 | Instructional Media Svcs | 27 | Career & Tech Ed | 37 | Guidance Services Elem |
| | | 17 | Chief Operations Officer | 28 | Technology Education | 38 | Guidance Services Sec |
| | | 18 | Chief Academic Officer | | | | |

| | | | | | | | |
|---|---|---|---|---|---|---|---|
| 39 | Social Studies K-12 | 49 | English/Lang Arts Elem | 59 | Special Education Elem | 69 | Academic Assessment |
| 40 | Social Studies Elem | 50 | English/Lang Arts Sec | 60 | Special Education Sec | 70 | Research/Development |
| 41 | Social Studies Sec | 51 | Reading K-12 | 61 | Foreign/World Lang K-12 | 71 | Public Information |
| 42 | Science K-12 | 52 | Reading Elem | 62 | Foreign/World Lang Elem | 72 | Summer School |
| 43 | Science Elem | 53 | Reading Sec | 63 | Foreign/World Lang Sec | 73 | Instructional Tech |
| 44 | Science Sec | 54 | Remedial Reading K-12 | 64 | Religious Education K-12 | 74 | Inservice Training |
| 45 | Math K-12 | 55 | Remedial Reading Elem | 65 | Religious Education Elem | 75 | Marketing/Distributive |
| 46 | Math Elem | 56 | Remedial Reading Sec | 66 | Religious Education Sec | 76 | Info Systems |
| 47 | Math Sec | 57 | Bilingual/ELL | 67 | School Board President | 77 | Psychological Assess |
| 48 | English/Lang Arts K-12 | 58 | Special Education K-12 | 68 | Teacher Personnel | 78 | Affirmative Action |

## YOAKUM COUNTY

## YOAKUM PUBLIC SCHOOLS

- **Denver City Ind School Dist** PID: 01062013    806/592-5900
  501 Mustang Dr, Denver City 79323    Fax 806/592-5909

**Schools:** 5 \ **Teachers:** 120 \ **Students:** 1,741 \ **Special Ed Students:** 121 \ **LEP Students:** 297 \ **College-Bound:** 52% \ **Ethnic:** Asian 1%, African American 1%, Hispanic 82%, Caucasian 16% \ **Exp:** $343 (High) \ **Poverty:** 14% \ **Title I:** $232,732 \ **Open-Close:** 08/20 - 05/21 \ **DTBP:** $133 (High)

| | | | |
|---|---|---|---|
| Mr Azam | 1 | Lachrisa Rains | 2,19 |
| Shannon Bressler | 2 | Butch Johnson | 3 |
| Jennifer Jordon | 4 | Kelly Adams | 4,8,11,58,83,88,271* |
| Alonzo Diaz | 5 | Steve Taylor | 6* |
| Vee Ann Carter | 7,85* | Priscilla Summers | 16,82* |
| Jerry Fortenberry | 27,73 | Kristy Kostelich | 27* |
| Kelli Hilburn | 37* | Brad Woosley | 67 |
| Angie Benningield | 68 | Kathy Guetersloh | 77* |
| Cindy Bessire | 79 | | |

| Public Schs..Principal | Grd | Prgm | Enr/#Cls | SN | |
|---|---|---|---|---|---|
| Denver City High Sch<br>601 Mustang Dr, Denver City 79323<br>Ricky Martinez | 9-12 | TV | 484<br>45 | 39% | 806/592-5950<br>Fax 806/592-5959 |
| Dodson Primary Sch<br>600 N Soland Ave, Denver City 79323<br>Elizabeth Calk | PK-2 | T | 428 | 66% | 806/592-5931 |
| Excalibur Sch<br>601 Mustang Dr, Denver City 79323<br>Rick Martinez | 9-12 | | 6<br>1 | | 806/592-5950<br>Fax 806/592-5959 |
| Kelley Elem Sch<br>500 N Soland Ave, Denver City 79323<br>Lori Alexander | 3-5 | T | 400<br>48 | 58% | 806/592-5920<br>Fax 806/592-5929 |
| William G Gravitt Jr High Sch<br>419 Mustang Dr, Denver City 79323<br>Billy Moore | 6-8 | TV | 391<br>40 | 52% | 806/592-5940<br>Fax 806/592-5949 |

- **Plains Ind School Dist** PID: 01062063    806/456-7401
  811 Cowboy Way, Plains 79355    Fax 806/456-4325

**Schools:** 3 \ **Teachers:** 39 \ **Students:** 475 \ **Special Ed Students:** 36 \ **LEP Students:** 66 \ **College-Bound:** 93% \ **Ethnic:** Hispanic 66%, Caucasian 34% \ **Exp:** $584 (High) \ **Poverty:** 19% \ **Title I:** $129,609 \ **Open-Close:** 08/19 - 05/21 \ **DTBP:** $331 (High) \ 🇫 🇹

| | | | |
|---|---|---|---|
| Robert McClean | 1,11,83 | Jesenia Suarez | 2 |
| Mary Parra | 4 | Mike Taylor | 5 |
| Ron Welch | 6 | Cindy Hopkins | 7 |
| George Mendez | 8 | Kim Gass | 16* |
| Sharon Mendez | 36 | Gloria Covarrubias | 57,271* |
| Kyle Martin | 67 | John Harris | 73,295 |

| Public Schs..Principal | Grd | Prgm | Enr/#Cls | SN | |
|---|---|---|---|---|---|
| Plains Elem Sch<br>811 Cowboy Way, Plains 79355<br>Traci Heflin | PK-5 | T | 201<br>17 | 69% | 806/456-7401 |

| Public Schs..Principal | Grd | Prgm | Enr/#Cls | SN | |
|---|---|---|---|---|---|
| Plains High Sch<br>811 Cowboy Way, Plains 79355<br>Jorge Mendez | 9-12 | ATV | 124<br>12 | 57% | 806/456-7401 |
| Plains Middle Sch<br>811 Cowboy Way, Plains 79355<br>Benjamin Taylor | 5-8 | TV | 137<br>14 | 70% | 806/456-7401 |

## YOUNG COUNTY

## YOUNG PUBLIC SCHOOLS

- **Graham Ind School Dist** PID: 01062104    940/549-0595
  400 3rd St, Graham 76450    Fax 940/549-8656

**Schools:** 5 \ **Teachers:** 168 \ **Students:** 2,354 \ **Special Ed Students:** 271 \ **LEP Students:** 253 \ **College-Bound:** 32% \ **Ethnic:** African American 1%, Hispanic 30%, Native American: 1%, Caucasian 68% \ **Exp:** $357 (High) \ **Poverty:** 18% \ **Title I:** $560,160 \ **Special Education:** $481,000 \ **Open-Close:** 08/31 - 05/28 \ **DTBP:** $317 (High) \ 🇫

| | | | |
|---|---|---|---|
| Sonny Cruse | 1 | Don Davis | 2,15 |
| Jerry Davidson | 3,5,91 | Jodi Arispe | 4* |
| Kenneth Davidson | 6* | Stacy Key | 7* |
| Gary Browning | 8,288 | Natalie Husen | 11,58 |
| Robert Loomis | 15,38,68,69,88,296 | Meredith Lucas | 67 |
| Chris Rasile | 73,286,295 | Blake Davis | 83,91 |

| Public Schs..Principal | Grd | Prgm | Enr/#Cls | SN | |
|---|---|---|---|---|---|
| Crestview Elem Sch<br>1317 Old Jacksboro Rd, Graham 76450<br>Amanda Townley | 1-3 | T | 534<br>27 | | 940/549-6023<br>Fax 940/549-6025 |
| Graham High Sch<br>1000 Brazos St, Graham 76450<br>Joe Gordy | 9-12 | T | 347<br>65 | 48% | 940/549-1504<br>Fax 940/549-4031 |
| Graham Junior High Sch<br>1000 2nd St, Graham 76450<br>Ginger Robbins | 6-8 | T | 552<br>38 | 58% | 940/549-2002<br>Fax 940/549-6991 |
| Pioneer Elem Sch<br>1425 1st St, Graham 76450<br>Donna Gatlin | PK-K | T | 246<br>13 | 75% | 940/549-2442<br>Fax 940/549-2460<br>🇫 🇹 |
| Woodland Elem Sch<br>1219 Cliff Dr, Graham 76450<br>Audra Barrett | 4-5 | T | 368<br>18 | 60% | 940/549-4090<br>Fax 940/549-4093 |

- **Newcastle Ind School Dist** PID: 01062166    940/846-3531
  505 Washington Ave, Newcastle 76372    Fax 940/846-3452

**Schools:** 1 \ **Teachers:** 19 \ **Students:** 205 \ **Special Ed Students:** 20 \ **LEP Students:** 4 \ **College-Bound:** 55% \ **Ethnic:** Hispanic 21%, Caucasian 79% \ **Exp:** $674 (High) \ **Poverty:** 28% \ **Title I:** $105,443 \ **Open-Close:** 08/07 - 05/21 \ **DTBP:** $370 (High)

| | | | |
|---|---|---|---|
| Evan Cardwell | 1,11,83 | Shirley Rhodes | 2,84 |
| Elaine Manuel | 3,5 | Cindy Hager | 4 |
| Julian Menchaca | 6 | Gena Phillips | 7 |
| Debbie Wilkinson | 8,88,285,288* | Melanie Lowe | 54,57* |
| Shae Humphrey | 58 | Tradd Strawbridge | 67 |
| Christy Eli | 73,286,295* | Sherri McMillan | 270* |

---

| | | | | | |
|---|---|---|---|---|---|
| 79 | Student Personnel | 91 | Safety/Security | 275 | Response To Intervention |
| 80 | Driver Ed/Safety | 92 | Magnet School | 277 | Remedial Math K-12 |
| 81 | Gifted/Talented | 93 | Parental Involvement | 280 | Literacy Coach |
| 82 | Video Services | 95 | Tech Prep Program | 285 | STEM |
| 83 | Substance Abuse Prev | 97 | Chief Infomation Officer | 286 | Digital Learning |
| 84 | Erate | 98 | Chief Technology Officer | 288 | Common Core Standards |
| 85 | AIDS Education | 270 | Character Education | 294 | Accountability |
| 88 | Alternative/At Risk | 271 | Migrant Education | 295 | Network System |
| 89 | Multi-Cultural Curriculum | 273 | Teacher Mentor | 296 | Title II Programs |
| 90 | Social Work | 274 | Before/After Sch | 297 | Webmaster |

| | |
|---|---|
| 298 | Grant Writer/Ptnrships |
| 750 | Chief Innovation Officer |
| 751 | Chief of Staff |
| 752 | Social Emotional Learning |

**Other School Types**
Ⓐ = Alternative School
© = Charter School
Ⓜ = Magnet School
Ⓨ = Year-Round School

**School Programs**
A = Alternative Program
G = Adult Classes
M = Magnet Program
T = Title I Schoolwide
V = Career & Tech Ed Programs

New Schools are shaded
New Superintendents and Principals are bold
Personnel with email addresses are underscored

**Social Media**
🇫 = Facebook
🇹 = Twitter

| Public Schs..Principal | Grd | Prgm | Enr/#Cls | SN |
|---|---|---|---|---|
| Newcastle Sch<br>505 Washington Ave, Newcastle 76372<br>Debbie Wilkinson | PK-12 | TV | 205<br>23 | 62% 940/846-3531 |

---

• **Olney Ind School Dist** PID: 01062192      940/564-3519
809 W Hamilton St, Olney 76374      Fax 940/564-5205

**Schools:** 3 \ **Teachers:** 72 \ **Students:** 639 \ **Special Ed Students:** 86 \ **LEP Students:** 27 \ **College-Bound:** 64% \ **Ethnic:** Asian 1%, African American 2%, Hispanic 40%, Caucasian 56% \ **Exp:** $582 (High) \ **Poverty:** 17% \ **Title I:** $171,989 \ **Open-Close:** 08/14 - 05/14 \ **DTBP:** $350 (High) \ 🇫 🇹

| | | | |
|---|---|---|---|
| Dr Greg Roach | 1 | Debbie Pace | 2 |
| Tim Orsak | 2,84 | Elaine Reno | 8,12,288,298 |
| Tony Nichol | 16,73 | Charlotte Mahler | 57* |
| Cristi Little | 58 | Jake Bailey | 67 |
| Jenny Walker | 68 | | |

| Public Schs..Principal | Grd | Prgm | Enr/#Cls | SN |
|---|---|---|---|---|
| Olney Elem Sch<br>801 W Hamilton St, Olney 76374<br>Gunter Rodriguez | PK-5 | T | 310<br>30 | 71% 940/564-5608<br>Fax 940/564-3518 |
| Olney High Sch<br>704 W Grove St, Olney 76374<br>Matt Caffey | 9-12 | AT | 178<br>20 | 63% 940/564-5637<br>Fax 940/564-5733 |
| Olney Junior High Sch<br>300 S Avenue H, Olney 76374<br>Amanda Barrientes | 6-8 | T | 151<br>14 | 68% 940/564-3517<br>Fax 940/564-8824<br>🇫🇹 |

## YOUNG PRIVATE SCHOOLS

| Private Schs..Principal | Grd | Prgm | Enr/#Cls | SN |
|---|---|---|---|---|
| Open Door Christian Sch<br>735 Oak St, Graham 76450<br>Brandi Menard | PK-6 | | 120 | 940/549-2339 |

## ZAPATA COUNTY

## ZAPATA PUBLIC SCHOOLS

• **Zapata Co Ind School Dist** PID: 01062245      956/765-6546
1302 Glenn St, Zapata 78076      Fax 956/765-8350

**Schools:** 6 \ **Teachers:** 227 \ **Students:** 3,500 \ **Special Ed Students:** 379 \ **LEP Students:** 985 \ **Ethnic:** Hispanic 99%, Caucasian 1% \ **Exp:** $370 (High) \ **Poverty:** 46% \ **Title I:** $2,643,165 \ **Special Education:** $605,000 \ **Open-Close:** 08/03 - 06/11 \ **DTBP:** $158 (High)

| | | | |
|---|---|---|---|
| Carlos Gonzalez | 1 | Patricia Gonzalez | 2 |
| Theresa Hein | 2 | Pedro Morales | 3,5,17 |
| Lesvia Cuellar | 4 | Joel Lopez | 6 |
| Connie Gray | 8,42,93,288* | Crisella Gutierrez | 8 |
| Hildeliza Garza | 8 | Suzette Barrera | 11,294,298 |
| Janie Rodriguez | 31,36,81,85,88 | Rebecca Flores | 57 |
| Carmen Zavala | 58 | Ricardo Ramirez | 67 |
| Rogelia Gonzales | 68 | Anna Martinez | 69 |

| | | | | |
|---|---|---|---|---|
| Gilbert Flores | 73,76,98,286,295 | Raymond Moya | | 91 |

| Public Schs..Principal | Grd | Prgm | Enr/#Cls | SN |
|---|---|---|---|---|
| A L Benavides Elem Sch<br>307 Lincoln Ave, San Ygnacio 78067<br>Diana Brandon | PK-5 | T | 53<br>6 | 85% 956/765-5611<br>Fax 956/765-3942 |
| Villarreal Elem Sch<br>805 Mira Flores Ave, Zapata 78076<br>Marlen Guerra | PK-5 | T | 394<br>35 | 95% 956/765-4321<br>Fax 956/765-5124 |
| Zapata High Sch<br>2009 State Highway 16, Zapata 78076<br>Gerardo Garcia \ **Jerry Garcia** | 9-12 | TV | 947<br>66 | 84% 956/765-0280<br>Fax 956/765-0274 |
| Zapata Middle Sch<br>702 E 17th Ave, Zapata 78076<br>Marlen Guerra | 6-8 | T | 771<br>60 | 87% 956/765-6542<br>Fax 956/765-9204 |
| Zapata North Elem Sch<br>1302 Glenn St, Zapata 78076<br>Elma Almaraz | PK-5 | T | 524<br>28 | 80% 956/765-6917<br>Fax 956/765-8512 |
| Zapata South Elem Sch<br>500 Delmar St, Zapata 78076<br>Dahlia Garcia | PK-5 | T | 511<br>25 | 79% 956/765-4332<br>Fax 956/765-3320 |

## ZAVALA COUNTY

## ZAVALA PUBLIC SCHOOLS

• **Crystal City Ind School Dist** PID: 01062295      830/374-2367
613 W Zavala St, Crystal City 78839      Fax 830/374-8022

**Schools:** 5 \ **Teachers:** 121 \ **Students:** 1,950 \ **Special Ed Students:** 222 \ **LEP Students:** 45 \ **Ethnic:** African American 1%, Hispanic 98%, \ **Exp:** $233 (Med) \ **Poverty:** 43% \ **Title I:** $1,309,823 \ **Special Education:** $364,000 \ **Open-Close:** 08/24 - 05/28 \ **DTBP:** $350 (High)

| | | | |
|---|---|---|---|
| Edward Churchill | 1 | Magdalena Flores | 2,4,19 |
| Irene Melendrez | 3,5 | Esmerelda Gonzales | 4 |
| David Lopez | 6* | Marina Pruvino | 7,85 |
| Sandra Alvarado | 16* | Casandra Mata | 37 |
| Erma Martinez | 57 | Alma Semdejo | 58 |
| Victor Bonilla | 67 | Jesse Guajardo | 73 |
| Sarah Garcia | 79 | Norma Geraza | 288* |
| Rene Juajardo | 288* | Dina Briones | 752 |

| Public Schs..Principal | Grd | Prgm | Enr/#Cls | SN |
|---|---|---|---|---|
| Benito Juarez Middle Sch<br>1000 Javalina Dr, Crystal City 78839<br>Carmel Diaz | 5-6 | T | 299<br>20 | 82% 830/374-8105<br>Fax 830/374-0043 |
| Crystal City High Sch<br>1101 N 11th St, Crystal City 78839<br>Jorge Cerna | 9-12 | TV | 526<br>30 | 78% 830/374-2341<br>Fax 830/374-8012 |
| Dr Tomas Rivera Elem Sch<br>909 Javalina Dr, Crystal City 78839<br>Andi Guerrero | PK-1 | T | 409 | 91% 830/374-8078<br>Fax 830/374-8024 |
| Lorenzo De Zavala Elem Sch<br>901 Javalina Dr, Crystal City 78839<br>Veronica Hoffman | 2-4 | T | 402<br>25 | 88% 830/374-8080<br>Fax 830/374-8092 |
| Sterling H Fly Jr High Sch<br>715 E Crockett Street, Crystal City 78839<br>Robert Alvarado | 7-8 | T | 301<br>25 | 83% 830/374-2371<br>Fax 830/374-8103 |

---

| | | | | | | | |
|---|---|---|---|---|---|---|---|
| 1 | Superintendent | 8 | Curric/Instruct K-12 | 19 | Chief Financial Officer | 29 | Family/Consumer Science |
| 2 | Bus/Finance/Purchasing | 9 | Curric/Instruct Elem | 20 | Art K-12 | 30 | Adult Education |
| 3 | Buildings And Grounds | 10 | Curric/Instruct Sec | 21 | Art Elem | 31 | Career/Sch-to-Work K-12 |
| 4 | Food Service | 11 | Federal Program | 22 | Art Sec | 32 | Career/Sch-to-Work Elem |
| 5 | Transportation | 12 | Title I | 23 | Music K-12 | 33 | Career/Sch-to-Work Sec |
| 6 | Athletic | 13 | Title V | 24 | Music Elem | 34 | Early Childhood Ed |
| 7 | Health Services | 15 | Asst Superintendent | 25 | Music Sec | 35 | Health/Phys Education |
| | | 16 | Instructional Media Svcs | 26 | Business Education | 36 | Guidance Services K-12 |
| | | 17 | Chief Operations Officer | 27 | Career & Tech Ed | 37 | Guidance Services Elem |
| | | 18 | Chief Academic Officer | 28 | Technology Education | 38 | Guidance Services Sec |

| | | | | | | | |
|---|---|---|---|---|---|---|---|
| 39 | Social Studies K-12 | 49 | English/Lang Arts Elem | 59 | Special Education Elem | 69 | Academic Assessment |
| 40 | Social Studies Elem | 50 | English/Lang Arts Sec | 60 | Special Education Sec | 70 | Research/Development |
| 41 | Social Studies Sec | 51 | Reading K-12 | 61 | Foreign/World Lang K-12 | 71 | Public Information |
| 42 | Science K-12 | 52 | Reading Elem | 62 | Foreign/World Lang Elem | 72 | Summer School |
| 43 | Science Elem | 53 | Reading Sec | 63 | Foreign/World Lang Sec | 73 | Instructional Tech |
| 44 | Science Sec | 54 | Remedial Reading K-12 | 64 | Religious Education K-12 | 74 | Inservice Training |
| 45 | Math K-12 | 55 | Remedial Reading Elem | 65 | Religious Education Elem | 75 | Marketing/Distributive |
| 46 | Math Elem | 56 | Remedial Reading Sec | 66 | Religious Education Sec | 76 | Info Systems |
| 47 | Math Sec | 57 | Bilingual/ELL | 67 | School Board President | 77 | Psychological Assess |
| 48 | English/Lang Arts K-12 | 58 | Special Education K-12 | 68 | Teacher Personnel | 78 | Affirmative Action |

- **La Pryor Ind School Dist** PID: 01062374          830/365-4000
  311 E Highway 57, La Pryor 78872          Fax 830/365-4006

---

**Schools:** 2 \ **Teachers:** 42 \ **Students:** 500 \ **Special Ed Students:** 58
\ **LEP Students:** 26 \ **Ethnic:** Hispanic 97%, Caucasian 3% \ **Exp:** $566
(High) \ **Poverty:** 38% \ **Title I:** $271,993 \ **Special Education:** $98,000 \
**Open-Close:** 08/14 - 05/21 \ **DTBP:** $343 (High) \ 🅵 🅴

---

| | | | |
|---|---|---|---|
| Matthew McHazlett | 1 | Becky Garcia | 2 |
| John Gaitan | 3,5,91 | Elispo Aguero | 6 |
| Reina Gallegos | 11,296 | Maryann Perez | 57 |
| Rick Rodriguez | 58 | Marcel Valdez | 67 |
| Roque Olaslaugua | 73 | Aimee Mann | 88 |

| Public Schs..Principal | Grd | Prgm | Enr/#Cls | SN | |
|---|---|---|---|---|---|
| La Pryor Elem Sch | PK-6 | T | 288 | 87% | 830/365-4009 |
| 511 Estes St, La Pryor 78872 | | | 15 | | Fax 830/365-4021 |
| Esequiel De La Fuente | | | | | |
| La Pryor High Sch | 7-12 | ATV | 215 | 79% | 830/365-4007 |
| 315 E Edith St, La Pryor 78872 | | | | | Fax 830/365-4026 |
| Rachel Lambert | | | | | |

## PUBLIC SCHOOL DISTRICTS

| SCHOOL DISTRICT | NO. OF SCHOOLS | ENROLL-MENT | COUNTY | PAGE |
|---|---|---|---|---|
| Abbott Ind School Dist | 1 | 280 | Hill | 229 |
| Abernathy Ind School Dist | 3 | 850 | Hale | 179 |
| Abilene Ind School Dist | 26 | 17,000 | Taylor | 362 |
| Academy Ind School Dist | 5 | 1,602 | Bell | 29 |
| Adrian Ind School Dist | 1 | 120 | Oldham | 310 |
| Advantage Academy Admin Office | 4 | 1,650 | Dallas | 100 |
| Agua Dulce Ind School Dist | 2 | 374 | Nueces | 305 |
| Alamo Heights Ind School Dist | 5 | 4,800 | Bexar | 33 |
| Alba-Golden Ind School Dist | 2 | 588 | Wood | 407 |
| Albany Ind School Dist | 2 | 512 | Shackelford | 336 |
| Aldine Ind School Dist | 82 | 67,331 | Harris | 184 |
| Aldine ISD-Elem Sch Team 1 | | | Harris | 184 |
| Aldine ISD-Elem Sch Team 2 | | | Harris | 184 |
| Aldine ISD-Elem Sch Team 3 | | | Harris | 185 |
| Aldine ISD-High Sch Team | | | Harris | 185 |
| Aldine ISD-Middle Sch Team | | | Harris | 186 |
| Aldine ISD-Primary Team | | | Harris | 186 |
| Aledo Ind School Dist | 10 | 6,000 | Parker | 315 |
| Alice Ind School Dist | 9 | 4,784 | Jim Wells | 248 |
| Alief Ind School Dist | 46 | 46,000 | Harris | 186 |
| Allen Ind School Dist | 24 | 21,404 | Collin | 80 |
| Alpine Ind School Dist | 3 | 965 | Brewster | 60 |
| Alto Ind School Dist | 3 | 664 | Cherokee | 76 |
| Alvarado Ind School Dist | 6 | 3,500 | Johnson | 249 |
| Alvin Ind School Dist | 31 | 25,926 | Brazoria | 54 |
| Alvord Ind School Dist | 3 | 700 | Wise | 405 |
| Amarillo Ind School Dist | 55 | 33,311 | Potter | 320 |
| Amherst Ind School Dist | 1 | 130 | Lamb | 263 |
| Anahuac Ind School Dist | 3 | 950 | Chambers | 75 |
| Anderson-Shiro Cons Ind SD | 2 | 879 | Grimes | 176 |
| Andrews Ind School Dist | 6 | 4,200 | Andrews | 19 |
| Angleton Ind School Dist | 9 | 6,787 | Brazoria | 55 |
| Anna Ind School Dist | 6 | 3,800 | Collin | 81 |
| Anson Ind School Dist | 3 | 700 | Jones | 252 |
| Anthony Ind School Dist | 3 | 795 | El Paso | 136 |
| Anton Ind School Dist | 1 | 185 | Hockley | 232 |
| Apple Springs Ind School Dist | 2 | 200 | Trinity | 376 |
| Aquilla Ind School Dist | 1 | 330 | Hill | 230 |
| Aransas Co Ind School Dist | 4 | 2,975 | Aransas | 22 |
| Aransas Pass Ind School Dist | 5 | 1,484 | San Patricio | 333 |
| Archer City Ind School Dist | 2 | 505 | Archer | 22 |
| Argyle Ind School Dist | 5 | 3,100 | Denton | 124 |
| Arlington Ind School Dist | 78 | 59,500 | Tarrant | 346 |
| Arp Ind School Dist | 3 | 870 | Smith | 339 |
| Aspermont Ind School Dist | 2 | 214 | Stonewall | 344 |
| Athens Ind School Dist | 5 | 3,000 | Henderson | 218 |
| Atlanta Ind School Dist | 5 | 1,760 | Cass | 73 |
| Aubrey Ind School Dist | 5 | 2,500 | Denton | 124 |
| Austin Ind School Dist | 117 | 80,950 | Travis | 369 |
| Austin ISD Elem School Area | | | Travis | 369 |
| Austin ISD High School Area | | | Travis | 371 |
| Austin ISD Middle School Area | | | Travis | 371 |
| Austwell Tivoli Ind SD | 2 | 140 | Refugio | 326 |
| Avalon Ind School Dist | 1 | 350 | Ellis | 144 |
| Avery Ind School Dist | 2 | 323 | Red River | 325 |
| Avinger Ind School Dist | 1 | 140 | Cass | 73 |
| Axtell Ind School Dist | 2 | 580 | McLennan | 281 |
| Azle Ind School Dist | 12 | 5,900 | Tarrant | 348 |
| Baird Ind School Dist | 3 | 289 | Callahan | 65 |
| Ballinger Ind School Dist | 3 | 798 | Runnels | 329 |
| Balmorhea Ind School Dist | 1 | 165 | Reeves | 325 |
| Bandera Ind School Dist | 4 | 2,120 | Bandera | 26 |
| Bangs Ind School Dist | 3 | 868 | Brown | 61 |
| Banquete Ind School Dist | 3 | 900 | Nueces | 305 |
| Barbers Hill Ind School Dist | 8 | 5,214 | Chambers | 75 |
| Bartlett Ind School Dist | 3 | 380 | Bell | 29 |
| Bastrop Ind School Dist | 15 | 11,000 | Bastrop | 26 |
| Bay City Ind School Dist | 5 | 3,670 | Matagorda | 278 |
| Beaumont Ind School Dist | 27 | 18,000 | Jefferson | 244 |
| Beckville Ind School Dist | 2 | 700 | Panola | 314 |
| Beeville Ind School Dist | 6 | 3,400 | Bee | 28 |
| Bellevue Ind School Dist | 1 | 140 | Clay | 77 |
| Bells Ind School Dist | 3 | 850 | Grayson | 170 |
| Bellville Ind School Dist | 6 | 2,200 | Austin | 24 |
| Belton Ind School Dist | 17 | 11,950 | Bell | 29 |
| Ben Bolt-Palito Blanco ISD | 2 | 520 | Jim Wells | 248 |
| Benavides Ind School Dist | 2 | 320 | Duval | 132 |
| Benjamin Ind School Dist | 1 | 108 | Knox | 261 |
| Big Sandy Ind School Dist | 1 | 484 | Polk | 319 |
| Big Sandy Ind School Dist | 3 | 667 | Upshur | 378 |
| Big Spring Ind School Dist | 9 | 4,000 | Howard | 236 |
| Birdville Ind School Dist | 33 | 23,513 | Tarrant | 348 |
| Bishop Cons Ind School Dist | 5 | 1,380 | Nueces | 305 |
| Blackwell Cons Ind Sch Dist | 1 | 150 | Nolan | 304 |
| Blanco Ind School Dist | 3 | 1,020 | Blanco | 49 |
| Bland Ind School Dist | 3 | 700 | Hunt | 238 |
| Blanket Ind School Dist | 1 | 145 | Brown | 61 |
| Bloomburg Ind School Dist | 1 | 272 | Cass | 73 |
| Blooming Grove Ind School Dist | 3 | 950 | Navarro | 302 |
| Bloomington Ind School Dist | 5 | 850 | Victoria | 384 |
| Blue Ridge Ind School Dist | 3 | 975 | Collin | 81 |
| Bluff Dale Ind Sch Dist | 1 | 222 | Erath | 147 |
| Blum Ind School Dist | 1 | 344 | Hill | 230 |
| Boerne Ind School Dist | 12 | 9,000 | Kendall | 257 |
| Boles Ind School Dist | 3 | 545 | Hunt | 238 |
| Boling Ind School Dist | 3 | 1,137 | Wharton | 392 |
| Bonham Ind School Dist | 5 | 1,850 | Fannin | 149 |
| Booker Ind School Dist | 2 | 371 | Lipscomb | 270 |
| Borden Co Ind School Dist | 1 | 214 | Borden | 49 |
| Borger Ind School Dist | 6 | 2,700 | Hutchinson | 240 |
| Bosqueville Ind School Dist | 3 | 699 | McLennan | 281 |
| Bovina Ind School Dist | 3 | 460 | Parmer | 317 |
| Bowie Ind School Dist | 4 | 1,720 | Montague | 292 |
| Boyd Ind School Dist | 4 | 1,281 | Wise | 405 |
| Boys Ranch Ind School Dist | 3 | 240 | Oldham | 310 |
| Brackett Ind School Dist | 3 | 570 | Kinney | 260 |
| Brady Ind School Dist | 4 | 1,050 | McCulloch | 280 |
| Braination Schools | 8 | 818 | Bexar | 33 |
| Brazos Ind School Dist | 4 | 700 | Austin | 25 |
| Brazosport Ind School Dist | 19 | 12,000 | Brazoria | 55 |
| Breckenridge Ind School Dist | 5 | 1,413 | Stephens | 344 |
| Bremond Ind School Dist | 3 | 500 | Robertson | 327 |
| Brenham Ind School Dist | 7 | 5,000 | Washington | 388 |
| Bridge City Ind School Dist | 4 | 3,057 | Orange | 311 |
| Bridgeport Ind School Dist | 5 | 1,994 | Wise | 406 |
| Broaddus Ind School Dist | 2 | 400 | San Augustine | 332 |
| Brock Ind School Dist | 4 | 1,476 | Parker | 315 |
| Bronte Ind School Dist | 2 | 225 | Coke | 79 |
| Brookeland Ind School Dist | 1 | 380 | Jasper | 243 |
| Brookesmith Ind School Dist | 3 | 200 | Brown | 61 |
| Brooks Co Ind School Dist | 4 | 1,470 | Brooks | 61 |
| Brownfield Ind Sch Dist | 4 | 1,623 | Terry | 364 |
| Brownsboro Ind School Dist | 7 | 2,800 | Henderson | 218 |
| Brownsville Ind School Dist | 54 | 44,356 | Cameron | 66 |
| Brownwood Ind School Dist | 7 | 3,500 | Brown | 62 |
| Bruceville-Eddy Ind Sch Dist | 4 | 630 | McLennan | 281 |
| Bryan Ind School Dist | 24 | 16,134 | Brazos | 58 |
| Bryson Ind School Dist | 1 | 241 | Jack | 241 |
| Buckholts Ind School Dist | 1 | 132 | Milam | 290 |
| Buena Vista Ind School Dist | 1 | 250 | Pecos | 318 |
| Buffalo Ind School Dist | 4 | 900 | Leon | 266 |
| Bullard Ind School Dist | 6 | 2,700 | Smith | 339 |
| Buna Ind School Dist | 3 | 1,497 | Jasper | 243 |
| Burkburnett Ind Sch Dist | 6 | 3,350 | Wichita | 394 |
| Burkeville Ind School Dist | 2 | 250 | Newton | 303 |
| Burleson Ind School Dist | 18 | 13,268 | Johnson | 249 |
| Burnet Cons Ind Sch Dist | 6 | 3,000 | Burnet | 63 |
| Burton Ind School Dist | 2 | 440 | Washington | 388 |
| Bushland Ind School Dist | 3 | 1,400 | Potter | 321 |
| Bynum Ind School Dist | 1 | 195 | Hill | 230 |
| Caddo Mills Ind Sch Dist | 5 | 2,000 | Hunt | 238 |
| Calallen Ind School Dist | 5 | 3,914 | Nueces | 305 |

| SCHOOL DISTRICT | NO. OF SCHOOLS | ENROLL-MENT | COUNTY | PAGE | SCHOOL DISTRICT | NO. OF SCHOOLS | ENROLL-MENT | COUNTY | PAGE |
|---|---|---|---|---|---|---|---|---|---|
| Caldwell Ind School Dist | 5 | 1,750 | Burleson | 63 | Coppell Ind School Dist | 18 | 13,500 | Dallas | 102 |
| Calhoun Co Ind School Dist | 7 | 3,738 | Calhoun | 65 | Copperas Cove Ind School Dist | 11 | 8,200 | Coryell | 96 |
| Callisburg Ind School Dist | 2 | 1,100 | Cooke | 94 | Corpus Christi Ind Sch Dist | 58 | 37,000 | Nueces | 306 |
| Calvert Ind School Dist | 1 | 166 | Robertson | 327 | Corrigan-Camden Ind Sch Dist | 3 | 830 | Polk | 319 |
| Cameron Ind School Dist | 4 | 1,684 | Milam | 290 | Corsicana Ind School Dist | 9 | 6,000 | Navarro | 302 |
| Campbell Ind School Dist | 1 | 300 | Hunt | 238 | Cotton Center Ind School Dist | 1 | 125 | Hale | 179 |
| Canadian Ind School Dist | 4 | 860 | Hemphill | 218 | Cotulla Ind School Dist | 4 | 1,180 | La Salle | 262 |
| Canton Ind School Dist | 4 | 2,300 | Van Zandt | 382 | Coupland Ind School Dist | 1 | 165 | Williamson | 398 |
| Canutillo Ind School Dist | 10 | 6,200 | El Paso | 136 | Covington ISD School Dist | 1 | 390 | Hill | 230 |
| Canyon Ind School Dist | 16 | 11,000 | Randall | 323 | Crandall Ind School Dist | 8 | 4,700 | Kaufman | 254 |
| Carlisle Ind School Dist | 1 | 587 | Rusk | 330 | Crane Ind School Dist | 3 | 1,172 | Crane | 97 |
| Carrizo Spgs Cons Ind SD | 4 | 2,200 | Dimmit | 131 | Cranfills Gap ISD School Dist | 1 | 120 | Bosque | 50 |
| Carroll Independent Sch Dist | 11 | 8,000 | Tarrant | 349 | Crawford Ind School Dist | 2 | 560 | McLennan | 282 |
| Carrollton-Farmers Branch ISD | 37 | 24,500 | Dallas | 100 | Crockett Co Cons Common SD | 3 | 720 | Crockett | 98 |
| Carthage Ind School Dist | 6 | 2,600 | Panola | 314 | Crockett Ind School Dist | 5 | 1,331 | Houston | 235 |
| Castleberry Ind School Dist | 7 | 3,574 | Tarrant | 349 | Crosby Ind School Dist | 7 | 6,350 | Harris | 188 |
| Cayuga Ind School Dist | 1 | 564 | Anderson | 18 | Crosbyton Cons Ind Sch Dist | 2 | 330 | Crosby | 98 |
| Cedar Hill Ind School Dist | 14 | 7,866 | Dallas | 101 | Cross Plains Ind Sch Dist | 2 | 340 | Callahan | 66 |
| Celeste Ind School Dist | 3 | 480 | Hunt | 238 | Cross Roads Ind School Dist | 3 | 545 | Henderson | 218 |
| Celina Ind School Dist | 6 | 2,600 | Collin | 81 | Crowell Ind School Dist | 2 | 230 | Foard | 153 |
| Center Ind School Dist | 6 | 2,600 | Shelby | 337 | Crowley Ind School Dist | 25 | 15,215 | Tarrant | 350 |
| Center Point Ind School Dist | 3 | 569 | Kerr | 258 | Crystal City Ind School Dist | 5 | 1,950 | Zavala | 410 |
| Centerville Ind School Dist | 2 | 700 | Leon | 267 | Cuero Ind School Dist | 4 | 1,990 | De Witt | 121 |
| Centerville Ind School Dist | 2 | 127 | Trinity | 376 | Culberson Co Allamoore Ind SD | 1 | 378 | Culberson | 99 |
| Central Heights Ind Sch Dist | 3 | 1,100 | Nacogdoches | 300 | Cumby Ind School Dist | 2 | 400 | Hopkins | 234 |
| Central Ind School Dist | 3 | 1,400 | Angelina | 20 | Cushing Ind School Dist | 2 | 524 | Nacogdoches | 300 |
| Channelview Ind School Dist | 13 | 9,700 | Harris | 188 | Cypress-Fairbanks Ind Sch Dist | 92 | 113,256 | Harris | 188 |
| Channing Ind School Dist | 1 | 173 | Hartley | 214 | D'Hanis Ind School Dist | 1 | 368 | Medina | 286 |
| Chapel Hill Ind School Dist | 5 | 3,513 | Smith | 339 | Daingerfield-Lone Star Ind SD | 4 | 970 | Morris | 299 |
| Chapel Hill Ind School Dist | 3 | 1,050 | Titus | 365 | Dalhart Ind School Dist | 4 | 1,700 | Dallam | 99 |
| Charlotte Ind School Dist | 3 | 450 | Atascosa | 23 | Dallas Ind School Dist | 233 | 153,861 | Dallas | 102 |
| Cherokee Ind School Dist | 1 | 112 | San Saba | 335 | Damon Ind School Dist | 1 | 144 | Brazoria | 56 |
| Chester Ind School Dist | 2 | 184 | Tyler | 377 | Danbury Ind School Dist | 3 | 840 | Brazoria | 56 |
| Chico Ind School Dist | 3 | 600 | Wise | 406 | Darrouzett Ind School Dist | 1 | 105 | Lipscomb | 270 |
| Childress Ind School Dist | 4 | 1,052 | Childress | 77 | Dawson Ind School Dist | 1 | 140 | Dawson | 121 |
| Chillicothe ISD School Dist | 2 | 200 | Hardeman | 182 | Dawson Ind School Dist | 1 | 512 | Navarro | 302 |
| Chilton Ind School Dist | 1 | 540 | Falls | 148 | Dayton Ind School Dist | 7 | 5,400 | Liberty | 268 |
| China Spring Ind School Dist | 5 | 2,748 | McLennan | 281 | De Kalb Ind School Dist | 3 | 650 | Bowie | 51 |
| Chireno ISD School Dist | 1 | 400 | Nacogdoches | 300 | De Leon Ind School Dist | 3 | 720 | Comanche | 93 |
| Chisum Ind School Dist | 3 | 1,020 | Lamar | 262 | Decatur Ind School Dist | 5 | 3,390 | Wise | 406 |
| Christoval Ind School Dist | 2 | 505 | Tom Green | 366 | Deer Park Ind School Dist | 16 | 13,000 | Harris | 191 |
| Cisco Independent Sch Dist | 4 | 830 | Eastland | 133 | Del Valle Ind School Dist | 15 | 12,100 | Travis | 372 |
| City View Ind School Dist | 2 | 921 | Wichita | 394 | Dell City Ind School Dist | 1 | 61 | Hudspeth | 237 |
| Clarendon Cons Ind Sch Dist | 3 | 450 | Donley | 131 | Denison Ind School Dist | 9 | 3,885 | Grayson | 171 |
| Clarksville Ind School Dist | 2 | 534 | Red River | 325 | Denton Ind School Dist | 42 | 33,485 | Denton | 124 |
| Claude Ind School Dist | 1 | 308 | Armstrong | 23 | Denver City Ind School Dist | 5 | 1,741 | Yoakum | 409 |
| Clear Creek Ind School Dist | 46 | 42,042 | Galveston | 162 | DeSoto Ind School Dist | 14 | 9,872 | Dallas | 108 |
| Cleburne Ind School Dist | 12 | 6,749 | Johnson | 250 | Detroit Ind School Dist | 3 | 530 | Red River | 325 |
| Cleveland Ind School Dist | 7 | 6,338 | Liberty | 267 | Devers Ind School Dist | 1 | 176 | Liberty | 268 |
| Clifton Ind School Dist | 3 | 1,000 | Bosque | 49 | Devine Ind School Dist | 4 | 1,900 | Medina | 286 |
| Clint Ind School Dist | 14 | 11,522 | El Paso | 136 | Dew Ind School Dist | 1 | 155 | Freestone | 160 |
| Clyde Consolidated Ind SD | 4 | 1,440 | Callahan | 66 | Deweyville Ind School Dist | 2 | 575 | Orange | 311 |
| Coahoma Ind School Dist | 3 | 1,061 | Howard | 237 | Diboll Ind School Dist | 5 | 1,800 | Angelina | 20 |
| Coldspring-Oakhurst Cons ISD | 4 | 1,465 | San Jacinto | 332 | Dickinson Ind School Dist | 14 | 10,400 | Galveston | 164 |
| Coleman Ind School Dist | 3 | 869 | Coleman | 79 | Dilley Ind School Dist | 4 | 950 | Frio | 161 |
| College Station Ind Sch Dist | 19 | 14,000 | Brazos | 59 | Dime Box Ind School Dist | 1 | 160 | Lee | 266 |
| Collinsville Ind School Dist | 2 | 540 | Grayson | 171 | Dimmitt Ind School Dist | 4 | 1,230 | Castro | 74 |
| Colmesneil Ind School Dist | 2 | 450 | Tyler | 377 | Divide ISD School Dist | 1 | 23 | Kerr | 258 |
| Colorado Ind School Dist | 4 | 900 | Mitchell | 292 | Dodd City Ind School Dist | 1 | 364 | Fannin | 150 |
| Columbia Brazoria ISD | 5 | 2,681 | Brazoria | 56 | Donna Ind School Dist | 22 | 14,459 | Hidalgo | 220 |
| Columbus Ind School Dist | 4 | 1,494 | Colorado | 90 | Doss Consolidated Common SD | 1 | 25 | Gillespie | 167 |
| Comal Ind School Dist | 33 | 23,800 | Comal | 91 | Douglass Ind School Dist | 1 | 440 | Nacogdoches | 300 |
| Comanche Ind School Dist | 4 | 1,325 | Comanche | 93 | Dripping Springs Ind Sch Dist | 7 | 6,400 | Hays | 215 |
| Comfort Ind School Dist | 3 | 1,052 | Kendall | 257 | Driscoll Ind School Dist | 1 | 281 | Nueces | 307 |
| Commerce Independent Sch Dist | 4 | 1,442 | Hunt | 239 | Dublin Ind School Dist | 3 | 1,121 | Erath | 147 |
| Community Ind School Dist | 4 | 2,600 | Collin | 81 | Dumas Ind School Dist | 9 | 4,300 | Moore | 298 |
| Como Pickton Cons Ind SD | 1 | 700 | Hopkins | 234 | Duncanville Ind School Dist | 19 | 12,250 | Dallas | 108 |
| Comstock Ind School Dist | 1 | 199 | Val Verde | 381 | Eagle Mtn-Saginaw Ind Sch Dist | 27 | 21,000 | Tarrant | 351 |
| Connally Ind School Dist | 6 | 2,300 | McLennan | 282 | Eagle Pass Ind School Dist | 23 | 15,000 | Maverick | 279 |
| Conroe Ind School Dist | 65 | 64,500 | Montgomery | 294 | Eanes Ind School Dist | 9 | 8,156 | Travis | 372 |
| Coolidge Ind School Dist | 2 | 295 | Limestone | 269 | Early Ind School Dist | 4 | 1,200 | Brown | 62 |
| Cooper Ind School Dist | 2 | 800 | Delta | 123 | East Bernard Ind Sch Dist | 3 | 950 | Wharton | 392 |

| SCHOOL DISTRICT | NO. OF SCHOOLS | ENROLL-MENT | COUNTY | PAGE | SCHOOL DISTRICT | NO. OF SCHOOLS | ENROLL-MENT | COUNTY | PAGE |
|---|---|---|---|---|---|---|---|---|---|
| East Central Ind School Dist | 12 | 10,146 | Bexar | 34 | Gatesville Ind School Dist | 5 | 2,744 | Coryell | 96 |
| East Chambers Ind School Dist | 4 | 1,534 | Chambers | 76 | Gause Ind School Dist | 1 | 170 | Milam | 290 |
| Eastland Ind School Dist | 3 | 1,000 | Eastland | 133 | George West Ind School Dist | 4 | 1,100 | Live Oak | 271 |
| Ector Co Ind School Dist | 42 | 32,391 | Ector | 134 | Georgetown Ind School Dist | 18 | 12,403 | Williamson | 398 |
| Ector Ind School Dist | 1 | 260 | Fannin | 150 | Gholson Ind School Dist | 1 | 246 | McLennan | 282 |
| Edcouch Elsa Ind School Dist | 8 | 5,450 | Hidalgo | 220 | Giddings Ind School Dist | 4 | 1,900 | Lee | 266 |
| Eden Cons Ind School Dist | 2 | 230 | Concho | 94 | Gilmer Ind School Dist | 4 | 2,437 | Upshur | 378 |
| Edgewood Ind School Dist | 21 | 10,881 | Bexar | 34 | Gladewater Ind School Dist | 4 | 1,700 | Gregg | 174 |
| Edgewood Ind School Dist | 4 | 950 | Van Zandt | 382 | Glasscock Co Ind School Dist | 1 | 292 | Glasscock | 168 |
| Edinburg Cons Ind School Dist | 43 | 34,500 | Hidalgo | 221 | Glen Rose Ind School Dist | 4 | 1,970 | Somervell | 342 |
| Edna Ind School Dist | 4 | 1,328 | Jackson | 242 | Godley Ind School Dist | 5 | 2,027 | Johnson | 250 |
| El Campo Ind School Dist | 5 | 4,500 | Wharton | 392 | Gold-Burg Ind School Dist | 1 | 127 | Montague | 293 |
| El Paso Ind School Dist | 86 | 57,315 | El Paso | 137 | Goldthwaite Consolidated ISD | 3 | 555 | Mills | 291 |
| El Paso ISD-Elementary | | | El Paso | 137 | Goliad Ind School Dist | 3 | 1,325 | Goliad | 168 |
| El Paso ISD-High Schools | | | El Paso | 138 | Gonzales Ind School Dist | 6 | 2,875 | Gonzales | 169 |
| El Paso ISD-Middle Schools | | | El Paso | 139 | Goodrich Ind School Dist | 2 | 218 | Polk | 319 |
| Electra Ind School Dist | 3 | 391 | Wichita | 394 | Goose Creek Cons Ind Sch Dist | 28 | 24,000 | Harris | 192 |
| Elgin Ind School Dist | 7 | 4,500 | Bastrop | 27 | Gordon Ind School Dist | 1 | 210 | Palo Pinto | 313 |
| Elkhart Ind School Dist | 4 | 1,250 | Anderson | 18 | Gorman Ind School Dist | 3 | 287 | Eastland | 133 |
| Elysian Fields Ind School Dist | 3 | 889 | Harrison | 213 | Grady Ind School Dist | 1 | 233 | Martin | 277 |
| Ennis Ind School Dist | 11 | 5,800 | Ellis | 144 | Graford Ind School Dist | 2 | 340 | Palo Pinto | 313 |
| Era Ind School Dist | 1 | 454 | Cooke | 94 | Graham Ind School Dist | 5 | 2,354 | Young | 409 |
| Etoile Ind School Dist | 1 | 100 | Nacogdoches | 300 | Granbury Ind School Dist | 11 | 6,971 | Hood | 233 |
| Eula Ind School Dist | 3 | 441 | Callahan | 66 | Grand Prairie Ind School Dist | 42 | 29,334 | Dallas | 111 |
| Eustace Ind School Dist | 4 | 1,566 | Henderson | 219 | Grand Saline Ind School Dist | 4 | 1,100 | Van Zandt | 383 |
| Evadale Ind School Dist | 2 | 394 | Jasper | 243 | Grandfalls-Royalty Ind SD | 1 | 184 | Ward | 388 |
| Evant Ind School Dist | 1 | 249 | Coryell | 96 | Grandview Ind School Dist | 3 | 1,365 | Johnson | 251 |
| Everman Ind School Dist | 11 | 6,345 | Tarrant | 351 | Grandview-Hopkins Ind Sch Dist | 1 | 50 | Gray | 169 |
| Excelsior Ind School Dist | 1 | 80 | Shelby | 337 | Granger Ind School Dist | 1 | 426 | Williamson | 399 |
| Ezzell Ind School Dist | 1 | 85 | Lavaca | 264 | Grape Creek Ind School Dist | 3 | 1,160 | Tom Green | 367 |
| Fabens Ind School Dist | 5 | 2,000 | El Paso | 139 | Grapeland Ind School Dist | 3 | 600 | Houston | 235 |
| Fairfield Ind School Dist | 4 | 1,800 | Freestone | 160 | Grapevine-Colleyville Ind SD | 21 | 14,000 | Tarrant | 355 |
| Falls City Ind School Dist | 2 | 340 | Karnes | 253 | Greenville Ind School Dist | 12 | 5,400 | Hunt | 239 |
| Fannindel Ind School Dist | 2 | 200 | Delta | 124 | Greenwood Ind School Dist | 4 | 2,831 | Midland | 288 |
| Farmersville Ind School Dist | 4 | 1,594 | Collin | 82 | Gregory-Portland Ind Sch Dist | 7 | 4,600 | San Patricio | 333 |
| Farwell Ind School Dist | 3 | 539 | Parmer | 317 | Groesbeck Ind School Dist | 4 | 1,500 | Limestone | 269 |
| Fayetteville Ind School Dist | 1 | 260 | Fayette | 151 | Groom Ind School Dist | 1 | 145 | Carson | 72 |
| Ferris Ind School Dist | 5 | 2,400 | Ellis | 144 | Groveton Ind School Dist | 2 | 750 | Trinity | 377 |
| Flatonia Ind School Dist | 3 | 580 | Fayette | 151 | Gruver Ind School Dist | 3 | 450 | Hansford | 181 |
| Florence Ind School Dist | 3 | 957 | Williamson | 398 | Gunter Ind School Dist | 3 | 1,000 | Grayson | 171 |
| Floresville Ind School Dist | 5 | 3,000 | Wilson | 403 | Gustine Ind School Dist | 1 | 134 | Comanche | 93 |
| Flour Bluff Ind School Dist | 7 | 5,750 | Nueces | 307 | Guthrie Common School Dist | 1 | 95 | King | 260 |
| Floydada Ind School Dist | 2 | 700 | Floyd | 153 | Hale Center Ind School Dist | 3 | 628 | Hale | 180 |
| Follett Ind School Dist | 1 | 165 | Lipscomb | 270 | Hallettsville Ind Sch Dist | 3 | 1,100 | Lavaca | 265 |
| Forestburg Ind School Dist | 1 | 173 | Montague | 293 | Hallsburg Ind School Dist | 1 | 170 | McLennan | 282 |
| Forney Ind School Dist | 14 | 9,681 | Kaufman | 254 | Hallsville Ind School Dist | 5 | 5,000 | Harrison | 213 |
| Forsan Ind School Dist | 2 | 771 | Howard | 237 | Hamilton Ind School Dist | 3 | 789 | Hamilton | 181 |
| Fort Davis Ind School Dist | 2 | 225 | Jeff Davis | 244 | Hamlin Collegiate Ind Sch Dist | 2 | 430 | Jones | 252 |
| Franklin Ind School Dist | 3 | 1,100 | Robertson | 327 | Hamshire Fannett Ind Sch Dist | 4 | 1,934 | Jefferson | 245 |
| Frankston Ind School Dist | 3 | 766 | Anderson | 18 | Happy Ind School Dist | 2 | 248 | Swisher | 345 |
| Fredericksburg Ind School Dist | 6 | 3,200 | Gillespie | 167 | Hardin Ind School Dist | 3 | 1,700 | Liberty | 268 |
| Freer Ind School Dist | 3 | 701 | Duval | 132 | Hardin Jefferson Ind Sch Dist | 4 | 2,300 | Hardin | 182 |
| Frenship Ind School Dist | 13 | 9,900 | Lubbock | 272 | Harlandale Ind School Dist | 24 | 14,500 | Bexar | 35 |
| Friendswood Ind Sch Dist | 6 | 6,000 | Galveston | 164 | Harleton Ind School Dist | 3 | 716 | Harrison | 213 |
| Friona Ind School Dist | 4 | 1,045 | Parmer | 318 | Harlingen Cons Ind School Dist | 31 | 18,600 | Cameron | 68 |
| Frisco Ind School Dist | 72 | 63,015 | Collin | 82 | Harmony Ind School Dist | 4 | 1,050 | Upshur | 379 |
| Frost Ind School Dist | 2 | 368 | Navarro | 302 | Harper Ind School Dist | 3 | 557 | Gillespie | 168 |
| Fruitvale Ind School Dist | 3 | 425 | Van Zandt | 383 | Harrold Ind School Dist | 1 | 106 | Wilbarger | 396 |
| Ft Bend Ind School Dist | 82 | 79,076 | Fort Bend | 153 | Hart Ind School Dist | 2 | 206 | Castro | 75 |
| Ft Elliott Cons Ind Sch Dist | 1 | 146 | Wheeler | 393 | Hartley Ind School Dist | 1 | 205 | Hartley | 215 |
| Ft Hancock Ind School Dist | 3 | 377 | Hudspeth | 237 | Harts Bluff Ind School Dist | 1 | 675 | Titus | 366 |
| Ft Sam Houston Ind School Dist | 2 | 1,560 | Bexar | 35 | Haskell Cons Ind School Dist | 3 | 550 | Haskell | 215 |
| Ft Stockton Ind School Dist | 5 | 2,469 | Pecos | 318 | Hawkins Ind School Dist | 3 | 750 | Wood | 407 |
| Ft Worth Ind School Dist | 134 | 89,000 | Tarrant | 352 | Hawley Ind School Dist | 3 | 784 | Jones | 253 |
| Gainesville Ind School Dist | 6 | 3,100 | Cooke | 95 | Hays Cons Ind School Dist | 25 | 20,063 | Hays | 216 |
| Galena Park Ind School Dist | 27 | 21,045 | Harris | 191 | Hearne Ind School Dist | 3 | 766 | Robertson | 327 |
| Galveston Ind School Dist | 11 | 7,000 | Galveston | 164 | Hedley Ind School Dist | 1 | 112 | Donley | 132 |
| Ganado Ind School Dist | 3 | 700 | Jackson | 242 | Hemphill Ind School Dist | 3 | 906 | Sabine | 331 |
| Garland Ind School Dist | 72 | 55,848 | Dallas | 109 | Hempstead Ind School Dist | 3 | 1,600 | Waller | 387 |
| Garner Ind School Dist | 1 | 212 | Parker | 315 | Henderson Ind School Dist | 6 | 3,400 | Rusk | 330 |
| Garrison Ind School Dist | 3 | 682 | Nacogdoches | 301 | Henrietta Ind School Dist | 3 | 937 | Clay | 78 |
| Gary Ind School Dist | 1 | 443 | Panola | 314 | Hereford Ind School Dist | 9 | 4,100 | Deaf Smith | 123 |

| SCHOOL DISTRICT | NO. OF SCHOOLS | ENROLL-MENT | COUNTY | PAGE | SCHOOL DISTRICT | NO. OF SCHOOLS | ENROLL-MENT | COUNTY | PAGE |
|---|---|---|---|---|---|---|---|---|---|
| Hermleigh Ind School Dist | 1 | 275 | Scurry | 336 | Kemp Ind School Dist | 4 | 1,236 | Kaufman | 255 |
| Hico Ind School Dist | 2 | 563 | Hamilton | 181 | Kenedy Co Wide Common Sch Dist | 1 | 80 | Kenedy | 258 |
| Hidalgo Ind School Dist | 7 | 2,600 | Hidalgo | 222 | Kenedy Ind School Dist | 3 | 500 | Karnes | 254 |
| Higgins Ind School Dist | 1 | 96 | Lipscomb | 270 | Kennard Ind Sch Dist | 1 | 256 | Houston | 236 |
| High Island Ind Sch Dist | 1 | 135 | Galveston | 165 | Kennedale Ind School Dist | 6 | 3,000 | Tarrant | 358 |
| Highland Ind School Dist | 1 | 239 | Nolan | 304 | Kerens Ind School Dist | 3 | 600 | Navarro | 303 |
| Highland Park Ind Sch Dist | 8 | 7,000 | Dallas | 112 | Kermit Ind School Dist | 3 | 1,397 | Winkler | 405 |
| Highland Park Ind School Dist | 3 | 864 | Potter | 322 | Kerrville Ind School Dist | 10 | 4,800 | Kerr | 259 |
| Hillsboro Ind School Dist | 5 | 2,000 | Hill | 230 | Kilgore Ind School Dist | 5 | 4,086 | Gregg | 174 |
| Hitchcock Ind School Dist | 4 | 1,600 | Galveston | 165 | Killeen Ind School Dist | 53 | 45,500 | Bell | 30 |
| Holland Ind School Dist | 3 | 636 | Bell | 30 | Kingsville Ind School Dist | 8 | 3,050 | Kleberg | 260 |
| Holliday Ind School Dist | 3 | 1,051 | Archer | 22 | Kirbyville Cons Ind Sch Dist | 3 | 1,500 | Jasper | 244 |
| Hondo Ind School Dist | 4 | 1,838 | Medina | 287 | Klein Ind School Dist | 49 | 53,292 | Harris | 201 |
| Honey Grove Ind School Dist | 3 | 614 | Fannin | 150 | Klondike Ind School Dist | 1 | 249 | Dawson | 121 |
| Hooks Ind School Dist | 3 | 884 | Bowie | 51 | Knippa Ind School Dist | 1 | 460 | Uvalde | 380 |
| Houston Ind School Dist | 276 | 207,809 | Harris | 193 | Knox City-O'Brien Cons Ind SD | 3 | 280 | Knox | 261 |
| Houston ISD-Achieve 180 | | | Harris | 193 | Kopperl Ind School Dist | 1 | 200 | Bosque | 50 |
| Houston ISD-East Area | | | Harris | 194 | Kountze Ind School Dist | 4 | 767 | Hardin | 183 |
| Houston ISD-North Area | | | Harris | 195 | Kress Ind School Dist | 2 | 242 | Swisher | 345 |
| Houston ISD-Northwest Area | | | Harris | 196 | Krum Ind School Dist | 5 | 2,100 | Denton | 126 |
| Houston ISD-South Area | | | Harris | 197 | La Feria Ind School Dist | 7 | 2,880 | Cameron | 69 |
| Houston ISD-West Area | | | Harris | 198 | La Gloria Ind School Dist | 1 | 108 | Jim Wells | 248 |
| Howe Ind School Dist | 4 | 1,100 | Grayson | 171 | La Grange Ind School Dist | 3 | 2,350 | Fayette | 151 |
| Hubbard Ind School Dist | 1 | 107 | Bowie | 51 | La Joya Ind School Dist | 41 | 27,000 | Hidalgo | 222 |
| Hubbard Ind School Dist | 2 | 422 | Hill | 230 | La Porte Ind School Dist | 13 | 7,679 | Harris | 203 |
| Huckabay Ind School Dist | 1 | 250 | Erath | 147 | La Poynor Ind School Dist | 1 | 470 | Henderson | 219 |
| Hudson Ind School Dist | 5 | 2,950 | Angelina | 20 | La Pryor Ind School Dist | 2 | 500 | Zavala | 411 |
| Huffman Ind School Dist | 4 | 3,600 | Harris | 200 | La Vega Ind School Dist | 5 | 3,140 | McLennan | 282 |
| Hughes Springs Ind Sch Dist | 3 | 1,145 | Cass | 73 | La Vernia Ind School Dist | 4 | 2,400 | Wilson | 404 |
| Hull Daisetta Ind School Dist | 3 | 453 | Liberty | 268 | La Villa Ind School Dist | 3 | 555 | Hidalgo | 223 |
| Humble Ind School Dist | 47 | 43,189 | Harris | 200 | Lackland Ind School Dist | 2 | 1,000 | Bexar | 37 |
| Hunt Ind School Dist | 1 | 204 | Kerr | 258 | Lago Vista Ind School Dist | 4 | 1,500 | Travis | 373 |
| Huntington Ind School Dist | 5 | 1,750 | Angelina | 20 | Lake Dallas Ind School Dist | 5 | 4,000 | Denton | 126 |
| Huntsville Ind School Dist | 9 | 6,500 | Walker | 386 | Lake Travis Ind School Dist | 10 | 10,410 | Travis | 373 |
| Hurst-Euless-Bedford ISD | 31 | 23,000 | Tarrant | 356 | Lake Worth Ind School Dist | 6 | 3,000 | Tarrant | 358 |
| Hutto Ind School Dist | 10 | 8,129 | Williamson | 399 | Lamar Cons Ind School Dist | 46 | 34,806 | Fort Bend | 157 |
| Idalou Ind School Dist | 3 | 984 | Lubbock | 272 | Lamesa Ind School Dist | 5 | 1,800 | Dawson | 121 |
| Industrial Ind School Dist | 4 | 1,100 | Jackson | 243 | Lampasas Ind School Dist | 5 | 3,400 | Lampasas | 264 |
| Ingleside Ind School Dist | 5 | 2,046 | San Patricio | 333 | Lancaster Ind School Dist | 11 | 7,600 | Dallas | 114 |
| Ingram Ind School Dist | 3 | 1,100 | Kerr | 259 | Laneville Ind School Dist | 1 | 157 | Rusk | 330 |
| Int'l Leadership of Texas Dist | 19 | 19,100 | Dallas | 112 | Laredo Ind School Dist | 33 | 23,737 | Webb | 389 |
| Iola Ind School Dist | 2 | 527 | Grimes | 177 | Lasara Ind School Dist | 2 | 368 | Willacy | 397 |
| Iowa Park Consolidated Ind SD | 4 | 1,421 | Wichita | 395 | Latexo Ind School Dist | 2 | 475 | Houston | 236 |
| Ira Ind School Dist | 1 | 275 | Scurry | 336 | Lazbuddie Ind School Dist | 1 | 168 | Parmer | 318 |
| Iraan-Sheffield Ind Sch Dist | 3 | 375 | Pecos | 318 | Leakey Ind School Dist | 1 | 279 | Real | 324 |
| Iredell Ind School Dist | 1 | 138 | Bosque | 50 | Leander Ind School Dist | 44 | 43,000 | Williamson | 399 |
| Irion Co Ind School Dist | 2 | 300 | Irion | 241 | Leary Ind School Dist | 1 | 119 | Bowie | 51 |
| Irving Ind School Dist | 38 | 33,901 | Dallas | 113 | Lefors Ind School Dist | 1 | 168 | Gray | 170 |
| Italy Ind School Dist | 2 | 600 | Ellis | 145 | Leggett Ind School Dist | 1 | 167 | Polk | 319 |
| Itasca Ind School Dist | 3 | 670 | Hill | 231 | Leon Ind School Dist | 2 | 700 | Leon | 267 |
| Jacksboro Ind Sch Dist | 3 | 1,023 | Jack | 242 | Leonard Ind School Dist | 4 | 878 | Fannin | 150 |
| Jacksonville Ind School Dist | 8 | 5,091 | Cherokee | 76 | Levelland Ind School Dist | 6 | 2,936 | Hockley | 232 |
| Jarrell Ind School Dist | 5 | 1,800 | Williamson | 399 | Leveretts Chapel Ind Sch Dist | 1 | 240 | Rusk | 330 |
| Jasper Ind School Dist | 4 | 2,400 | Jasper | 243 | Lewisville Ind School Dist | 71 | 52,300 | Denton | 126 |
| Jayton-Girard Ind School Dist | 1 | 143 | Kent | 258 | Lexington Ind School Dist | 3 | 1,066 | Lee | 266 |
| Jefferson Ind School Dist | 4 | 1,324 | Marion | 277 | Liberty Hill Ind School Dist | 6 | 4,000 | Williamson | 401 |
| Jim Hogg Co Ind School Dist | 3 | 1,100 | Jim Hogg | 247 | Liberty Ind School Dist | 4 | 2,227 | Liberty | 269 |
| Jim Ned Cons Ind School Dist | 4 | 1,360 | Taylor | 363 | Liberty-Eylau Ind School Dist | 4 | 2,465 | Bowie | 51 |
| Joaquin Ind School Dist | 3 | 680 | Shelby | 337 | Lindale Ind School Dist | 6 | 4,200 | Smith | 339 |
| Johnson City Ind School Dist | 3 | 650 | Blanco | 49 | Linden Kildare Cons Ind SD | 3 | 647 | Cass | 74 |
| Jonesboro Ind School Dist | 1 | 330 | Coryell | 97 | Lindsay Ind School Dist | 2 | 500 | Cooke | 95 |
| Joshua Ind School Dist | 10 | 5,626 | Johnson | 251 | Lingleville Ind School Dist | 1 | 282 | Erath | 148 |
| Jourdanton Ind School Dist | 4 | 1,200 | Atascosa | 23 | Lipan Ind School Dist | 1 | 413 | Hood | 233 |
| Judson Ind School Dist | 33 | 23,000 | Bexar | 36 | Little Cypress Mauriceville SD | 6 | 3,100 | Orange | 311 |
| Junction Ind School Dist | 3 | 605 | Kimble | 259 | Little Elm Ind School Dist | 9 | 8,100 | Denton | 128 |
| Karnack Ind School Dist | 1 | 145 | Harrison | 214 | Littlefield Ind School Dist | 4 | 1,300 | Lamb | 263 |
| Karnes City Ind School Dist | 5 | 1,062 | Karnes | 253 | Livingston Ind School Dist | 7 | 3,963 | Polk | 319 |
| Katy Ind School Dist | 72 | 84,299 | Fort Bend | 155 | Llano Ind School Dist | 4 | 1,701 | Llano | 271 |
| Kaufman Ind School Dist | 7 | 3,500 | Kaufman | 255 | Lockhart Ind School Dist | 9 | 6,350 | Caldwell | 64 |
| Keene Ind School Dist | 4 | 1,011 | Johnson | 251 | Lockney Independent Sch Dist | 3 | 450 | Floyd | 153 |
| Keller Ind School Dist | 42 | 35,352 | Tarrant | 357 | Lohn Ind School Dist | 1 | 100 | McCulloch | 280 |
| Kelton Ind School Dist | 1 | 84 | Wheeler | 393 | Lometa Ind School Dist | 1 | 300 | Lampasas | 264 |

| SCHOOL DISTRICT | NO. OF SCHOOLS | ENROLL-MENT | COUNTY | PAGE | SCHOOL DISTRICT | NO. OF SCHOOLS | ENROLL-MENT | COUNTY | PAGE |
|---|---|---|---|---|---|---|---|---|---|
| London Ind School Dist | 1 | 900 | Nueces | 308 | Millsap Ind School Dist | 3 | 989 | Parker | 315 |
| Lone Oak Ind School Dist | 4 | 1,000 | Hunt | 239 | Mineola Ind School Dist | 4 | 1,556 | Wood | 408 |
| Longview Ind School Dist | 13 | 8,700 | Gregg | 174 | Mineral Wells Ind School Dist | 6 | 3,200 | Palo Pinto | 313 |
| Loop Ind School Dist | 1 | 124 | Gaines | 162 | Mission Cons Ind School Dist | 23 | 16,000 | Hidalgo | 225 |
| Loraine Ind School Dist | 1 | 142 | Mitchell | 292 | Monahans-Wickett-Pyote ISD | 6 | 2,300 | Ward | 388 |
| Lorena Ind School Dist | 4 | 1,673 | McLennan | 283 | Montague Ind School Dist | 1 | 166 | Montague | 293 |
| Lorenzo Ind School Dist | 2 | 250 | Crosby | 98 | Monte Alto Ind School Dist | 3 | 900 | Hidalgo | 226 |
| Los Fresnos Cons Ind Sch Dist | 16 | 10,379 | Cameron | 69 | Montgomery Ind School Dist | 10 | 9,048 | Montgomery | 296 |
| Louise Ind School Dist | 3 | 510 | Wharton | 392 | Moody Ind School Dist | 3 | 660 | McLennan | 284 |
| Lovejoy Ind School Dist | 6 | 4,424 | Collin | 84 | Moran Ind School Dist | 1 | 105 | Shackelford | 336 |
| Lovelady Ind School Dist | 2 | 510 | Houston | 236 | Morgan Ind School Dist | 1 | 130 | Bosque | 50 |
| Lubbock Ind School Dist | 48 | 26,000 | Lubbock | 272 | Morgan Mill Ind School Dist | 1 | 125 | Erath | 148 |
| Lubbock-Cooper Ind Sch Dist | 9 | 6,000 | Lubbock | 274 | Morton Ind School Dist | 3 | 400 | Cochran | 78 |
| Lueders-Avoca Ind School Dist | 2 | 100 | Jones | 253 | Motley Co Ind School Dist | 1 | 162 | Motley | 299 |
| Lufkin Ind School Dist | 15 | 8,000 | Angelina | 21 | Moulton Ind School Dist | 2 | 300 | Lavaca | 265 |
| Luling Ind School Dist | 4 | 1,400 | Caldwell | 64 | Mount Vernon Ind School Dist | 3 | 1,570 | Franklin | 160 |
| Lumberton Ind School Dist | 5 | 3,437 | Hardin | 183 | Mt Calm Ind School Dist | 2 | 200 | Hill | 231 |
| Lyford Cons Ind School Dist | 3 | 1,422 | Willacy | 397 | Mt Enterprise Ind School Dist | 1 | 398 | Rusk | 330 |
| Lytle Ind School Dist | 4 | 1,309 | Atascosa | 24 | Mt Pleasant Ind School Dist | 8 | 5,100 | Titus | 366 |
| Mabank Ind School Dist | 8 | 3,664 | Kaufman | 255 | Muenster Ind School Dist | 2 | 481 | Cooke | 95 |
| Madisonville Cons ISD | 4 | 2,233 | Madison | 276 | Muleshoe Ind School Dist | 4 | 1,450 | Bailey | 25 |
| Magnolia Ind School Dist | 16 | 13,100 | Montgomery | 295 | Mullin Ind School Dist | 6 | 294 | Mills | 291 |
| Malakoff Ind School Dist | 5 | 1,300 | Henderson | 219 | Mumford Ind School Dist | 1 | 612 | Brazos | 59 |
| Malone Independent School Dist | 1 | 178 | Hill | 231 | Munday Consolidated Ind SD | 2 | 392 | Knox | 262 |
| Malta Ind School Dist | 1 | 225 | Bowie | 52 | Murchison Ind Sch Dist | 1 | 200 | Henderson | 219 |
| Manor Ind School Dist | 16 | 9,200 | Travis | 373 | Nacogdoches Ind School Dist | 10 | 6,400 | Nacogdoches | 301 |
| Mansfield Ind School Dist | 46 | 35,626 | Tarrant | 358 | Natalia Ind School Dist | 4 | 1,000 | Medina | 287 |
| Marathon Ind School Dist | 1 | 55 | Brewster | 60 | Navarro Ind School Dist | 4 | 1,909 | Guadalupe | 178 |
| Marble Falls Ind School Dist | 7 | 4,000 | Burnet | 64 | Navasota Ind School Dist | 6 | 3,000 | Grimes | 177 |
| Marfa Ind School Dist | 2 | 342 | Presidio | 322 | Nazareth Ind School Dist | 1 | 253 | Castro | 75 |
| Marion Ind School Dist | 4 | 1,500 | Guadalupe | 177 | Neches Ind School Dist | 2 | 330 | Anderson | 18 |
| Marlin Ind School Dist | 3 | 821 | Falls | 149 | Nederland Ind School Dist | 8 | 5,214 | Jefferson | 245 |
| Marshall Ind School Dist | 7 | 5,345 | Harrison | 214 | Needville Ind School Dist | 4 | 3,228 | Fort Bend | 159 |
| Mart Ind School Dist | 2 | 426 | McLennan | 283 | New Boston Ind School Dist | 4 | 1,198 | Bowie | 52 |
| Martin's Mill Ind Sch Dist | 1 | 230 | Van Zandt | 383 | New Braunfels Ind School Dist | 15 | 9,220 | Comal | 92 |
| Martinsville Ind School Dist | 1 | 400 | Nacogdoches | 301 | New Caney Ind School Dist | 19 | 15,000 | Montgomery | 296 |
| Mason Ind School Dist | 3 | 674 | Mason | 278 | New Deal Ind School Dist | 3 | 750 | Lubbock | 274 |
| Matagorda Ind School Dist | 1 | 120 | Matagorda | 278 | New Diana Ind School Dist | 3 | 1,073 | Upshur | 379 |
| Mathis Ind School Dist | 4 | 1,600 | San Patricio | 334 | New Home Ind School Dist | 1 | 580 | Lynn | 275 |
| Maud Ind School Dist | 1 | 475 | Bowie | 52 | New Summerfield Ind Sch Dist | 1 | 544 | Cherokee | 76 |
| May Ind School Dist | 2 | 230 | Brown | 62 | New Waverly Ind School Dist | 4 | 1,000 | Walker | 386 |
| Maypearl Ind School Dist | 4 | 1,040 | Ellis | 145 | Newcastle Ind School Dist | 1 | 205 | Young | 409 |
| McAllen Ind School Dist | 31 | 24,000 | Hidalgo | 224 | Newton Ind School Dist | 3 | 1,041 | Newton | 304 |
| McCamey Ind School Dist | 3 | 560 | Upton | 380 | Nixon-Smiley Cons Ind Sch Dist | 3 | 1,076 | Gonzales | 169 |
| McDade Ind School Dist | 1 | 370 | Bastrop | 27 | Nocona Ind School Dist | 3 | 725 | Montague | 293 |
| McGregor Ind School Dist | 4 | 1,342 | McLennan | 283 | Nordheim Ind School Dist | 1 | 149 | De Witt | 122 |
| McKinney Ind School Dist | 31 | 24,335 | Collin | 84 | Normangee Ind School Dist | 3 | 605 | Leon | 267 |
| McLean Ind School Dist | 1 | 236 | Gray | 170 | North East Ind School Dist | 74 | 66,759 | Bexar | 37 |
| McLeod Ind School Dist | 1 | 388 | Cass | 74 | North Hopkins Ind School Dist | 1 | 550 | Hopkins | 234 |
| McMullen Co Ind Sch Dist | 1 | 289 | McMullen | 286 | North Lamar Ind School Dist | 7 | 2,417 | Wise | 406 |
| Meadow Ind School Dist | 1 | 285 | Terry | 365 | North Zulch Ind School Dist | 1 | 310 | Madison | 276 |
| Medina Ind School Dist | 2 | 300 | Bandera | 26 | Northside Ind School Dist | 124 | 106,863 | Bexar | 39 |
| Medina Valley Ind School Dist | 7 | 5,087 | Medina | 287 | Northside Ind School Dist | 1 | 222 | Wilbarger | 396 |
| Melissa Ind School Dist | 4 | 3,102 | Collin | 85 | Northwest Ind School Dist | 31 | 25,000 | Denton | 128 |
| Memphis Ind School Dist | 4 | 400 | Hall | 180 | Nueces Canyon Cons Ind SD | 2 | 264 | Edwards | 135 |
| Menard Ind School Dist | 2 | 305 | Menard | 288 | Nursery ISD School Dist | 1 | 155 | Victoria | 384 |
| Mercedes Ind School Dist | 9 | 4,781 | Hidalgo | 225 | O'Donnell Ind School Dist | 2 | 300 | Lynn | 276 |
| Meridian Ind School Dist | 4 | 475 | Bosque | 50 | Oakwood Ind School Dist | 2 | 199 | Leon | 267 |
| Merkel Ind School Dist | 3 | 1,073 | Taylor | 363 | Odem-Edroy Ind School Dist | 4 | 900 | San Patricio | 334 |
| Mesquite Ind School Dist | 48 | 38,266 | Dallas | 115 | Oglesby Ind School Dist | 1 | 180 | Coryell | 97 |
| Mexia Ind School Dist | 5 | 1,800 | Limestone | 270 | Olfen Ind School Dist | 1 | 205 | Runnels | 329 |
| Meyersville Ind School Dist | 1 | 137 | De Witt | 122 | Olney Ind School Dist | 3 | 639 | Young | 410 |
| Miami Ind School Dist | 1 | 190 | Roberts | 327 | Olton Ind School Dist | 3 | 600 | Lamb | 263 |
| Midland Ind School Dist | 40 | 26,000 | Midland | 288 | Onalaska Ind School Dist | 2 | 1,056 | Polk | 320 |
| Midlothian Ind School Dist | 11 | 9,500 | Ellis | 145 | Orange Grove Ind School Dist | 4 | 1,850 | Jim Wells | 248 |
| Midway Ind School Dist | 1 | 134 | Clay | 78 | Orangefield Ind School Dist | 3 | 1,785 | Orange | 312 |
| Midway Ind School Dist | 10 | 8,100 | McLennan | 283 | Ore City Ind School Dist | 3 | 850 | Upshur | 379 |
| Milano Ind School Dist | 3 | 419 | Milam | 290 | Overton Ind School Dist | 2 | 500 | Rusk | 331 |
| Mildred Ind School Dist | 1 | 730 | Navarro | 303 | Paducah Ind School Dist | 1 | 200 | Cottle | 97 |
| Miles Ind School Dist | 1 | 480 | Runnels | 329 | Paint Creek Ind School Dist | 1 | 108 | Haskell | 215 |
| Milford Ind School Dist | 1 | 240 | Ellis | 146 | Paint Rock Ind School Dist | 1 | 225 | Concho | 94 |
| Miller Grove Ind School Dist | 1 | 345 | Hopkins | 234 | Palacios Ind School Dist | 4 | 1,506 | Matagorda | 278 |

| SCHOOL DISTRICT | NO. OF SCHOOLS | ENROLL- MENT | COUNTY | PAGE | SCHOOL DISTRICT | NO. OF SCHOOLS | ENROLL- MENT | COUNTY | PAGE |
|---|---|---|---|---|---|---|---|---|---|
| Palestine Ind School Dist | 6 | 3,300 | Anderson | 18 | Richards Ind School Dist | 1 | 180 | Grimes | 177 |
| Palmer Ind School Dist | 3 | 1,300 | Ellis | 146 | Richardson Ind School Dist | 56 | 38,700 | Dallas | 116 |
| Palo Pinto Ind Sch Dist 906 | 1 | 100 | Palo Pinto | 313 | Richland Springs Ind Sch Dist | 1 | 123 | San Saba | 335 |
| Pampa Ind School Dist | 7 | 3,500 | Gray | 170 | Riesel Ind School Dist | 2 | 660 | McLennan | 284 |
| Panhandle Ind School Dist | 3 | 670 | Carson | 72 | Rio Grande City Ind Sch Dist | 18 | 10,175 | Starr | 342 |
| Panther Creek Cons Ind SD | 1 | 150 | Coleman | 79 | Rio Hondo Ind School Dist | 3 | 1,650 | Cameron | 70 |
| Paradise Ind School Dist | 4 | 1,209 | Wise | 407 | Rio Vista Ind School Dist | 3 | 755 | Johnson | 251 |
| Paris Ind School Dist | 8 | 3,900 | Lamar | 262 | Rising Star Ind Sch Dist | 2 | 150 | Eastland | 133 |
| Pasadena Ind School Dist | 68 | 53,157 | Harris | 203 | River Road Ind School Dist | 4 | 1,278 | Potter | 322 |
| Patton Springs Ind School Dist | 1 | 97 | Dickens | 131 | Rivercrest Ind School Dist | 3 | 700 | Red River | 325 |
| Pawnee Ind School Dist | 1 | 550 | Bee | 28 | Riviera Ind School Dist | 2 | 440 | Kleberg | 261 |
| Pearland Ind School Dist | 23 | 21,917 | Brazoria | 56 | Robert Lee Ind School Dist | 1 | 260 | Coke | 79 |
| Pearsall Ind School Dist | 4 | 2,100 | Frio | 161 | Robinson Ind School Dist | 5 | 2,200 | McLennan | 284 |
| Peaster Ind School Dist | 3 | 1,210 | Parker | 316 | Robstown Ind School Dist | 7 | 2,000 | Nueces | 308 |
| Pecos-Barstow-Toyah Ind SD | 5 | 2,700 | Reeves | 326 | Roby Cons Ind School Dist | 2 | 277 | Fisher | 152 |
| Penelope ISD School Dist | 1 | 215 | Hill | 231 | Rochelle Ind School Dist | 1 | 179 | McCulloch | 281 |
| Perrin-Whitt Cons Ind Sch Dist | 2 | 340 | Jack | 242 | Rockdale Ind School Dist | 4 | 1,432 | Milam | 290 |
| Perryton Ind School Dist | 6 | 2,217 | Ochiltree | 310 | Rocksprings Ind School Dist | 1 | 289 | Edwards | 135 |
| Petersburg Ind School Dist | 1 | 280 | Hale | 180 | Rockwall Ind School Dist | 22 | 17,078 | Rockwall | 328 |
| Petrolia Cons Ind School Dist | 2 | 450 | Clay | 78 | Rogers Ind School Dist | 3 | 869 | Bell | 32 |
| Pettus Ind School Dist | 2 | 400 | Bee | 28 | Roma Ind School Dist | 10 | 6,000 | Starr | 343 |
| Pewitt Cons Ind School Dist | 3 | 870 | Morris | 299 | Roosevelt Ind School Dist | 3 | 1,012 | Lubbock | 274 |
| Pflugerville Ind School Dist | 33 | 26,269 | Travis | 374 | Ropes Ind School Dist | 1 | 479 | Hockley | 232 |
| Pharr-San Juan-Alamo Ind SD | 42 | 32,000 | Hidalgo | 226 | Roscoe Collegiate Ind Sch Dist | 3 | 593 | Nolan | 304 |
| Pilot Point Ind School Dist | 4 | 1,400 | Denton | 129 | Rosebud-Lott Ind School Dist | 3 | 637 | Falls | 149 |
| Pine Tree Ind School Dist | 8 | 4,700 | Gregg | 175 | Rotan Ind School Dist | 2 | 240 | Fisher | 152 |
| Pittsburg Ind School Dist | 5 | 2,356 | Camp | 72 | Round Rock Ind School Dist | 54 | 51,008 | Williamson | 401 |
| Plains Ind School Dist | 3 | 475 | Yoakum | 409 | Round Top-Carmine Ind Sch Dist | 2 | 267 | Fayette | 151 |
| Plainview Ind School Dist | 10 | 4,717 | Hale | 180 | Royal Ind School Dist | 4 | 2,400 | Waller | 387 |
| Plano Ind School Dist | 73 | 52,692 | Collin | 85 | Royse City Ind School Dist | 9 | 6,300 | Rockwall | 328 |
| Pleasant Grove Ind School Dist | 4 | 2,200 | Bowie | 52 | Rule Ind School Dist | 1 | 114 | Haskell | 215 |
| Pleasanton Ind School Dist | 4 | 3,540 | Atascosa | 24 | Runge Ind School Dist | 1 | 238 | Karnes | 254 |
| Plemons-Stinnett-Phillips CISD | 3 | 731 | Hutchinson | 240 | Rusk Ind School Dist | 5 | 1,979 | Cherokee | 77 |
| Point Isabel Ind Sch Dist | 4 | 2,017 | Cameron | 70 | S & S Cons Ind School Dist | 3 | 896 | Grayson | 172 |
| Ponder Ind School Dist | 3 | 1,600 | Denton | 130 | Sabinal Ind School Dist | 2 | 429 | Uvalde | 380 |
| Poolville Ind School Dist | 3 | 550 | Parker | 316 | Sabine Ind School Dist | 3 | 1,495 | Gregg | 175 |
| Port Aransas Ind School Dist | 3 | 480 | Nueces | 308 | Sabine Pass Ind School Dist | 1 | 354 | Jefferson | 247 |
| Port Arthur Ind School Dist | 16 | 9,000 | Jefferson | 246 | Salado Ind School Dist | 3 | 2,056 | Bell | 32 |
| Port Neches-Groves Ind SD | 10 | 5,000 | Jefferson | 246 | Saltillo Ind School Dist | 1 | 276 | Hopkins | 234 |
| Post Ind School Dist | 3 | 566 | Garza | 167 | Sam Rayburn Ind School Dist | 1 | 525 | Fannin | 150 |
| Poteet Ind School Dist | 4 | 1,339 | Atascosa | 24 | San Angelo Ind School Dist | 25 | 14,520 | Tom Green | 367 |
| Poth Ind School Dist | 3 | 858 | Wilson | 404 | San Antonio Ind School Dist | 94 | 48,178 | Bexar | 42 |
| Pottsboro Ind School Dist | 3 | 1,384 | Grayson | 172 | San Augustine Ind School Dist | 2 | 720 | San Augustine | 332 |
| Prairie Lea Ind School Dist | 1 | 216 | Caldwell | 65 | San Benito Cons Ind Sch Dist | 18 | 10,600 | Cameron | 70 |
| Prairie Valley Ind School Dist | 1 | 167 | Montague | 293 | San Diego Ind School Dist | 3 | 1,385 | Duval | 132 |
| Prairiland Ind School Dist | 4 | 1,088 | Lamar | 263 | San Elizario Ind School Dist | 6 | 3,560 | El Paso | 139 |
| Premont Ind School Dist | 2 | 705 | Jim Wells | 248 | San Felipe-Del Rio Cons Ind SD | 12 | 10,472 | Val Verde | 381 |
| Presidio Ind School Dist | 3 | 1,162 | Presidio | 323 | San Isidro Ind School Dist | 1 | 200 | Starr | 343 |
| Priddy Ind School Dist | 1 | 115 | Mills | 292 | San Marcos Cons Ind Sch Dist | 12 | 8,200 | Hays | 216 |
| Princeton Ind School Dist | 9 | 5,567 | Collin | 87 | San Perlita Ind School Dist | 1 | 269 | Willacy | 397 |
| Pringle-Morse Cons ISD | 1 | 125 | Hansford | 182 | San Saba Ind School Dist | 3 | 717 | San Saba | 335 |
| Progreso Ind School Dist | 5 | 1,900 | Hidalgo | 227 | San Vicente Ind School Dist | 1 | 13 | Brewster | 60 |
| Prosper Ind School Dist | 18 | 19,000 | Collin | 88 | Sands Consolidated ISD | 1 | 247 | Dawson | 121 |
| Quanah Ind School Dist | 3 | 525 | Hardeman | 182 | Sanford-Fritch Ind School Dist | 3 | 687 | Hutchinson | 241 |
| Queen City Ind School Dist | 4 | 1,005 | Cass | 74 | Sanger Ind School Dist | 7 | 2,660 | Denton | 130 |
| Quinlan Ind School Dist | 5 | 2,516 | Hunt | 240 | Santa Anna Ind School Dist | 2 | 250 | Coleman | 79 |
| Quitman Ind School Dist | 3 | 1,083 | Wood | 408 | Santa Fe Ind School Dist | 5 | 4,794 | Galveston | 165 |
| Rains Ind School Dist | 4 | 1,500 | Rains | 323 | Santa Gertrudis Ind Sch Dist | 2 | 800 | Kleberg | 261 |
| Ralls Ind School Dist | 4 | 485 | Crosby | 98 | Santa Maria Ind School Dist | 4 | 691 | Cameron | 71 |
| Ramirez Common School Dist | 1 | 37 | Duval | 132 | Santa Rosa Ind School Dist | 3 | 960 | Cameron | 71 |
| Randolph Field Ind School Dist | 3 | 1,442 | Bexar | 42 | Santo Ind School Dist | 2 | 451 | Palo Pinto | 313 |
| Ranger Ind School Dist | 1 | 350 | Eastland | 133 | Savoy Ind School Dist | 2 | 320 | Fannin | 150 |
| Rankin Ind School Dist | 2 | 294 | Upton | 380 | Schertz-Cibolo-Univ City ISD | 17 | 15,925 | Guadalupe | 178 |
| Raymondville Ind Sch Dist | 5 | 2,000 | Willacy | 397 | Schleicher Co Ind Sch Dist | 3 | 540 | Schleicher | 335 |
| Reagan Co Ind School Dist | 3 | 850 | Reagan | 324 | School of Excellence In Ed | 4 | 649 | Bexar | 45 |
| Red Lick Ind School Dist | 1 | 520 | Bowie | 52 | Schulenburg Ind School Dist | 2 | 700 | Fayette | 152 |
| Red Oak Ind School Dist | 8 | 6,000 | Ellis | 146 | Scurry Rosser Ind School Dist | 3 | 1,037 | Kaufman | 256 |
| Redwater Ind School Dist | 4 | 1,076 | Bowie | 53 | Seagraves Ind School Dist | 3 | 547 | Gaines | 162 |
| Refugio Ind School Dist | 3 | 654 | Refugio | 326 | Sealy Ind School Dist | 4 | 2,669 | Austin | 25 |
| Ricardo Ind School Dist | 1 | 670 | Kleberg | 261 | Seguin Ind School Dist | 13 | 7,048 | Guadalupe | 178 |
| Rice Cons Ind School Dist | 7 | 1,325 | Colorado | 90 | Seminole Ind School Dist | 6 | 2,619 | Gaines | 162 |
| Rice Ind School Dist | 4 | 975 | Navarro | 303 | Seymour Ind School Dist | 3 | 582 | Baylor | 28 |

| SCHOOL DISTRICT | NO. OF SCHOOLS | ENROLL-MENT | COUNTY | PAGE | SCHOOL DISTRICT | NO. OF SCHOOLS | ENROLL-MENT | COUNTY | PAGE |
|---|---|---|---|---|---|---|---|---|---|
| Shallowater Ind School Dist | 4 | 1,351 | Lubbock | 274 | Texas City Ind School Dist | 14 | 9,000 | Galveston | 166 |
| Shamrock Ind School Dist | 3 | 342 | Wheeler | 393 | Texhoma Ind School Dist | 1 | 130 | Sherman | 338 |
| Sharyland Ind School Dist | 14 | 10,295 | Hidalgo | 227 | Texline Ind School Dist | 1 | 180 | Dallam | 99 |
| Shelbyville Ind School Dist | 3 | 790 | Shelby | 337 | Thorndale Ind School Dist | 3 | 650 | Milam | 291 |
| Sheldon Ind School Dist | 12 | 8,500 | Harris | 205 | Thrall Ind School Dist | 3 | 750 | Williamson | 403 |
| Shepherd Ind School Dist | 4 | 2,041 | San Jacinto | 333 | Three Rivers Ind School Dist | 2 | 628 | Live Oak | 271 |
| Sherman Ind School Dist | 12 | 7,500 | Grayson | 172 | Three Way Ind School Dist | 2 | 190 | Erath | 148 |
| Shiner Ind School Dist | 2 | 650 | Lavaca | 265 | Throckmorton Ind School Dist | 1 | 158 | Throckmorton | 365 |
| Sidney Ind School Dist | 1 | 139 | Comanche | 94 | Tidehaven Ind School Dist | 4 | 980 | Matagorda | 279 |
| Sierra Blanca Ind School Dist | 1 | 103 | Hudspeth | 237 | Timpson Ind School Dist | 3 | 628 | Shelby | 338 |
| Silsbee Ind School Dist | 4 | 2,800 | Hardin | 183 | Tioga Ind School Dist | 1 | 639 | Grayson | 172 |
| Silverton Ind School Dist | 1 | 174 | Briscoe | 61 | Tolar Ind School Dist | 3 | 800 | Hood | 233 |
| Simms Ind School Dist | 3 | 500 | Bowie | 53 | Tom Bean Ind School Dist | 3 | 620 | Grayson | 173 |
| Sinton Ind School Dist | 4 | 1,339 | San Patricio | 334 | Tomball Ind School Dist | 20 | 16,289 | Harris | 208 |
| Sivells Bend Ind School Dist | 1 | 57 | Cooke | 95 | Tornillo Ind School Dist | 4 | 950 | El Paso | 141 |
| Skidmore Tynan Ind SD | 3 | 850 | Bee | 29 | Trent Isn School Dist | 1 | 150 | Taylor | 363 |
| Slaton Ind School Dist | 4 | 950 | Lubbock | 275 | Trenton Ind School Dist | 3 | 573 | Fannin | 151 |
| Slidell Ind School Dist | 2 | 350 | Wise | 407 | Trinidad Ind School Dist | 1 | 145 | Henderson | 219 |
| Slocum ISD School Dist | 1 | 400 | Anderson | 19 | Trinity Ind School Dist | 3 | 1,188 | Trinity | 377 |
| Smithville Ind School Dist | 5 | 1,800 | Bastrop | 27 | Troup Ind School Dist | 3 | 1,100 | Smith | 340 |
| Smyer Ind School Dist | 2 | 415 | Hockley | 232 | Troy Ind School Dist | 4 | 1,600 | Bell | 33 |
| Snook Ind School Dist | 1 | 500 | Burleson | 63 | Tulia Ind School Dist | 3 | 1,040 | Swisher | 345 |
| Snyder Ind School Dist | 4 | 2,700 | Scurry | 336 | Tuloso-Midway Ind School Dist | 5 | 3,043 | Nueces | 308 |
| Socorro Ind School Dist | 50 | 44,992 | El Paso | 140 | Turkey-Quitaque Cons Ind SD | 1 | 185 | Hall | 181 |
| Somerset Ind School Dist | 7 | 3,990 | Bexar | 45 | Tyler Ind School Dist | 29 | 18,000 | Smith | 340 |
| Somerville Ind School Dist | 3 | 550 | Burleson | 63 | Union Grove Ind School Dist | 2 | 754 | Upshur | 379 |
| Sonora Ind School Dist | 3 | 767 | Sutton | 345 | Union Hill Ind School Dist | 1 | 325 | Upshur | 380 |
| South San Antonio Ind Sch Dist | 16 | 8,800 | Bexar | 45 | United Ind School Dist | 48 | 48,174 | Webb | 390 |
| South Texas Ind School Dist | 6 | 4,245 | Cameron | 71 | UT Tyler University Acad Dist | 3 | 400 | Smith | 341 |
| Southland Ind School Dist | 1 | 123 | Garza | 167 | Utopia Ind School Dist | 1 | 210 | Uvalde | 381 |
| Southside Ind School Dist | 9 | 5,800 | Bexar | 46 | Uvalde Cons Ind School Dist | 8 | 4,221 | Uvalde | 381 |
| Southwest Ind School Dist | 19 | 13,928 | Bexar | 46 | Valentine Ind School Dist | 1 | 34 | Jeff Davis | 244 |
| Spearman Ind School Dist | 3 | 834 | Hansford | 182 | Valley Mills Ind School Dist | 2 | 600 | Bosque | 50 |
| Splendora Ind School Dist | 6 | 4,200 | Montgomery | 297 | Valley View Ind School Dist | 8 | 4,300 | Hidalgo | 228 |
| Spring Branch Ind School Dist | 47 | 35,300 | Harris | 205 | Valley View ISD-Cooke Co | 1 | 875 | Cooke | 95 |
| Spring Creek Ind School Dist | 1 | 110 | Hutchinson | 241 | Van Alstyne Ind School Dist | 4 | 1,576 | Grayson | 173 |
| Spring Hill Ind School Dist | 4 | 2,100 | Gregg | 175 | Van Ind School Dist | 5 | 2,400 | Van Zandt | 383 |
| Spring Ind School Dist | 41 | 35,600 | Harris | 207 | Van Vleck Ind School Dist | 4 | 1,027 | Matagorda | 279 |
| Springlake-Earth Ind Sch Dist | 2 | 370 | Lamb | 264 | Vega Ind School Dist | 2 | 370 | Oldham | 310 |
| Springtown Ind School Dist | 6 | 3,470 | Parker | 316 | Venus Ind School Dist | 4 | 2,095 | Johnson | 252 |
| Spur Ind School Dist | 1 | 235 | Dickens | 131 | Veribest Ind School Dist | 1 | 275 | Tom Green | 368 |
| Spurger Ind School Dist | 2 | 400 | Tyler | 377 | Vernon Ind School Dist | 6 | 1,700 | Wilbarger | 396 |
| St Jo Ind School Dist | 2 | 330 | Montague | 293 | Victoria Ind School Dist | 23 | 13,900 | Victoria | 384 |
| Stafford Municipal Sch Dist | 7 | 3,600 | Fort Bend | 159 | Vidor Ind School Dist | 7 | 4,400 | Orange | 312 |
| Stamford Ind School Dist | 3 | 630 | Jones | 253 | Vysehrad Ind School Dist | 1 | 115 | Lavaca | 265 |
| Stanton Ind School Dist | 3 | 1,053 | Martin | 277 | Waco Ind School Dist | 24 | 15,050 | McLennan | 284 |
| Stephenville Ind School Dist | 6 | 3,650 | Erath | 148 | Waelder Ind School Dist | 1 | 317 | Gonzales | 169 |
| Sterling City Ind School Dist | 2 | 320 | Sterling | 344 | Walcott Ind School Dist | 1 | 146 | Deaf Smith | 123 |
| Stockdale Ind School Dist | 3 | 820 | Wilson | 404 | Wall Ind School Dist | 4 | 1,100 | Tom Green | 368 |
| Stratford Ind School Dist | 3 | 560 | Sherman | 338 | Waller Ind School Dist | 8 | 7,700 | Waller | 387 |
| Strawn Ind School Dist | 1 | 160 | Palo Pinto | 314 | Walnut Bend Ind School Dist | 1 | 72 | Cooke | 96 |
| Sudan Ind School Dist | 2 | 424 | Lamb | 264 | Walnut Springs Ind Sch Dist | 1 | 187 | Bosque | 51 |
| Sulphur Bluff Ind School Dist | 1 | 230 | Hopkins | 235 | Warren Ind School Dist | 4 | 1,200 | Tyler | 378 |
| Sulphur Springs Ind Sch Dist | 9 | 4,400 | Hopkins | 235 | Waskom Ind School Dist | 3 | 850 | Harrison | 214 |
| Sundown Ind School Dist | 3 | 595 | Hockley | 232 | Water Valley Ind School Dist | 2 | 300 | Tom Green | 368 |
| Sunnyvale Ind School Dist | 3 | 2,200 | Dallas | 117 | Waxahachie Ind School Dist | 16 | 9,481 | Ellis | 146 |
| Sunray Ind School Dist | 3 | 556 | Moore | 299 | Weatherford Ind School Dist | 12 | 8,000 | Parker | 316 |
| Sweeny Ind School Dist | 3 | 1,926 | Brazoria | 57 | Webb Cons Ind School Dist | 3 | 238 | Webb | 391 |
| Sweet Home Ind School Dist | 1 | 140 | Lavaca | 265 | Weimar Ind School Dist | 3 | 629 | Colorado | 91 |
| Sweetwater ISD School Dist | 7 | 1,888 | Nolan | 304 | Wellington Ind School Dist | 3 | 530 | Collingsworth | 90 |
| Taft Ind School Dist | 3 | 1,154 | San Patricio | 334 | Wellman Union Ind School Dist | 1 | 335 | Terry | 365 |
| Tahoka Ind School Dist | 3 | 600 | Lynn | 276 | Wells Ind School Dist | 2 | 280 | Cherokee | 77 |
| Tarkington Ind School Dist | 4 | 1,810 | Liberty | 269 | Weslaco Ind School Dist | 19 | 18,000 | Hidalgo | 228 |
| Tatum Ind School Dist | 4 | 1,461 | Rusk | 331 | West Hardin Co Cons Sch Dist | 2 | 525 | Hardin | 183 |
| Taylor Ind School Dist | 7 | 3,200 | Williamson | 402 | West Ind School Dist | 4 | 826 | McLennan | 285 |
| Teague Ind School Dist | 3 | 1,160 | Freestone | 161 | West Orange-Cove Cons ISD | 4 | 2,485 | Orange | 312 |
| Temple Ind School Dist | 15 | 8,700 | Bell | 32 | West Oso Ind School Dist | 4 | 1,946 | Nueces | 309 |
| Tenaha Ind School Dist | 1 | 542 | Shelby | 337 | West Rusk Co Cons Ind Sch Dist | 4 | 980 | Rusk | 331 |
| Terlingua Common School Dist | 2 | 105 | Brewster | 60 | West Sabine Ind Sch Dist | 2 | 578 | Sabine | 332 |
| Terrell Co Ind School Dist | 1 | 108 | Terrell | 364 | Westbrook Ind School Dist | 1 | 272 | Mitchell | 292 |
| Terrell Ind School Dist | 10 | 4,711 | Kaufman | 256 | Westhoff Ind School Dist | 1 | 80 | De Witt | 122 |
| Texarkana Ind School Dist | 13 | 7,174 | Bowie | 53 | Westphalia Ind School Dist | 1 | 155 | Falls | 149 |

| SCHOOL DISTRICT | NO. OF SCHOOLS | ENROLL- MENT | COUNTY | PAGE |
|---|---|---|---|---|
| Westwood Ind School Dist | 4 | 1,500 | Anderson | 19 |
| Wharton Ind School Dist | 5 | 2,015 | Wharton | 393 |
| Wheeler Ind School Dist | 1 | 441 | Wheeler | 394 |
| White Deer Ind School Dist | 2 | 360 | Carson | 73 |
| White Oak Ind School Dist | 4 | 1,496 | Gregg | 176 |
| White Settlement Ind Sch Dist | 9 | 6,909 | Tarrant | 360 |
| Whiteface Con Ind School Dist | 2 | 345 | Cochran | 78 |
| Whitehouse Ind School Dist | 8 | 4,800 | Smith | 341 |
| Whitesboro Ind School Dist | 4 | 1,540 | Grayson | 173 |
| Whitewright Ind School Dist | 3 | 823 | Grayson | 173 |
| Whitharral Ind School Dist | 1 | 175 | Hockley | 233 |
| Whitney Ind School Dist | 4 | 1,311 | Hill | 231 |
| Wichita Falls Ind School Dist | 28 | 14,500 | Wichita | 395 |
| Wildorado Ind Sch Dist | 1 | 210 | Oldham | 311 |
| Willis Ind School Dist | 9 | 6,709 | Montgomery | 297 |
| Wills Point Ind School Dist | 5 | 2,500 | Van Zandt | 383 |
| Wilson Ind School Dist | 1 | 94 | Lynn | 276 |
| Wimberley Ind School Dist | 4 | 2,500 | Hays | 217 |
| Windthorst Ind School Dist | 3 | 390 | Archer | 23 |
| Wink Loving Ind School Dist | 2 | 420 | Winkler | 405 |
| Winnsboro Ind School Dist | 3 | 1,422 | Wood | 408 |
| Winona Ind School Dist | 4 | 1,050 | Smith | 341 |
| Winters Ind School Dist | 3 | 525 | Runnels | 329 |
| Woden Ind School Dist | 3 | 780 | Nacogdoches | 301 |
| Wolfe City Ind School Dist | 3 | 646 | Hunt | 240 |
| Woodsboro Ind School Dist | 2 | 441 | Refugio | 326 |
| Woodson Ind School Dist | 1 | 144 | Throckmorton | 365 |
| Woodville Ind School Dist | 4 | 1,300 | Tyler | 378 |
| Wortham Ind School Dist | 3 | 500 | Freestone | 161 |
| Wylie Ind School Dist | 20 | 17,500 | Collin | 88 |
| Wylie Ind School Dist | 7 | 5,000 | Taylor | 364 |
| Yantis Ind School Dist | 2 | 350 | Wood | 408 |
| Yoakum Ind School Dist | 5 | 1,500 | De Witt | 122 |
| Yorktown Ind School Dist | 3 | 513 | De Witt | 122 |
| Ysleta Ind School Dist | 57 | 40,304 | El Paso | 141 |
| Zapata Co Ind School Dist | 6 | 3,500 | Zapata | 410 |
| Zavalla Ind School Dist | 2 | 300 | Angelina | 21 |
| Zephyr Ind School Dist | 1 | 208 | Brown | 62 |

## CATHOLIC DIOCESE

| SCHOOL DISTRICT | NO. OF SCHOOLS | ENROLL- MENT | COUNTY | PAGE |
|---|---|---|---|---|
| Archdiocese Galveston-Houston | 55 | 18,631 | Harris | 209 |
| Archdiocese San Antonio Ed Off | 39 | 13,050 | Bexar | 47 |
| Diocese Corpus Christi Ed Off | 16 | 3,300 | Nueces | 309 |
| Diocese of Amarillo Ed Office | 5 | 850 | Potter | 322 |
| Diocese of Austin Ed Office | 21 | 5,141 | Travis | 375 |
| Diocese of Beaumont Sch Office | 5 | 1,500 | Jefferson | 247 |
| Diocese of Brownsville Ed Off | 12 | 2,831 | Hidalgo | 229 |
| Diocese of Dallas Ed Office | 35 | 14,823 | Dallas | 118 |
| Diocese of El Paso Ed Office | 11 | 2,700 | El Paso | 143 |
| Diocese of Fort Worth Ed Off | 19 | 4,700 | Tarrant | 360 |
| Diocese of Laredo Ed Office | 4 | 1,627 | Webb | 391 |
| Diocese of Lubbock Ed Office | 1 | 360 | Lubbock | 275 |
| Diocese of San Angelo Ed Off | 3 | 1,000 | Tom Green | 368 |
| Diocese of Tyler Ed Office | 4 | 1,300 | Smith | 342 |
| Diocese of Victoria Ed Office | 13 | 2,827 | Victoria | 385 |

## COUNTY CENTERS

| SCHOOL DISTRICT | NO. OF SCHOOLS | ENROLL- MENT | COUNTY | PAGE |
|---|---|---|---|---|
| Dallas Co Schools | | | Dallas | 99 |
| Harris Co Dept of Ed | | | Harris | 184 |
| Kenedy Co Schools | | | Kenedy | 257 |

## REGIONAL CENTERS

| SCHOOL DISTRICT | NO. OF SCHOOLS | ENROLL- MENT | COUNTY | PAGE |
|---|---|---|---|---|
| Burleson Milam Spec Serv Co-op | | | Milam | 291 |
| Region 1 Ed Service Center | | | Hidalgo | 229 |
| Region 2 Ed Service Center | | | Nueces | 309 |
| Region 3 Ed Service Center | | | Victoria | 385 |
| Region 4 Ed Service Center | | | Harris | 213 |
| Region 5 Ed Service Center | | | Jefferson | 247 |
| Region 6 Ed Service Center | | | Walker | 386 |
| Region 7 Ed Service Center | | | Gregg | 176 |
| Region 8 Ed Service Center | | | Camp | 72 |
| Region 9 Ed Service Center | | | Wichita | 396 |
| Region 10 Ed Service Center | | | Dallas | 120 |
| Region 11 Ed Service Center | | | Tarrant | 362 |
| Region 12 Ed Service Center | | | McLennan | 286 |
| Region 13 Ed Service Center | | | Travis | 376 |
| Region 14 Ed Service Center | | | Taylor | 364 |
| Region 15 Ed Service Center | | | Tom Green | 368 |
| Region 16 Ed Service Center | | | Randall | 324 |
| Region 17 Ed Service Center | | | Lubbock | 275 |
| Region 18 Ed Service Center | | | Midland | 290 |
| Region 19 Ed Service Center | | | El Paso | 144 |
| Region 20 Ed Service Center | | | Bexar | 48 |

| COUNTY<br>District/City | NO. OF<br>SCHOOLS | ENROLL-<br>MENT | PAGE |
|---|---|---|---|
| **ANDERSON** | | | |
| Cayuga Ind School Dist/Tenn Colony | 1 | 564 | 18 |
| Elkhart Ind School Dist/Elkhart | 4 | 1,250 | 18 |
| Frankston Ind School Dist/Frankston | 3 | 766 | 18 |
| Neches Ind School Dist/Neches | 2 | 330 | 18 |
| Palestine Ind School Dist/Palestine | 6 | 3,300 | 18 |
| Slocum ISD School Dist/Elkhart | 1 | 400 | 19 |
| Westwood Ind School Dist/Palestine | 4 | 1,500 | 19 |
| **ANDREWS** | | | |
| Andrews Ind School Dist/Andrews | 6 | 4,200 | 19 |
| **ANGELINA** | | | |
| Central Ind School Dist/Pollok | 3 | 1,400 | 20 |
| Diboll Ind School Dist/Diboll | 5 | 1,800 | 20 |
| Hudson Ind School Dist/Lufkin | 5 | 2,950 | 20 |
| Huntington Ind School Dist/Huntington | 5 | 1,750 | 20 |
| Lufkin Ind School Dist/Lufkin | 15 | 8,000 | 21 |
| Zavalla Ind School Dist/Zavalla | 2 | 300 | 21 |
| **ARANSAS** | | | |
| Aransas Co Ind School Dist/Rockport | 4 | 2,975 | 22 |
| **ARCHER** | | | |
| Archer City Ind School Dist/Archer City | 2 | 505 | 22 |
| Holliday Ind School Dist/Holliday | 3 | 1,051 | 22 |
| Windthorst Ind School Dist/Windthorst | 3 | 390 | 23 |
| **ARMSTRONG** | | | |
| Claude Ind School Dist/Claude | 1 | 308 | 23 |
| **ATASCOSA** | | | |
| Charlotte Ind School Dist/Charlotte | 3 | 450 | 23 |
| Jourdanton Ind School Dist/Jourdanton | 4 | 1,200 | 23 |
| Lytle Ind School Dist/Lytle | 4 | 1,309 | 24 |
| Pleasanton Ind School Dist/Pleasanton | 4 | 3,540 | 24 |
| Poteet Ind School Dist/Poteet | 4 | 1,339 | 24 |
| **AUSTIN** | | | |
| Bellville Ind School Dist/Bellville | 6 | 2,200 | 24 |
| Brazos Ind School Dist/Wallis | 4 | 700 | 25 |
| Sealy Ind School Dist/Sealy | 4 | 2,669 | 25 |
| **BAILEY** | | | |
| Muleshoe Ind School Dist/Muleshoe | 4 | 1,450 | 25 |
| **BANDERA** | | | |
| Bandera Ind School Dist/Bandera | 4 | 2,120 | 26 |
| Medina Ind School Dist/Medina | 2 | 300 | 26 |
| **BASTROP** | | | |
| Bastrop Ind School Dist/Bastrop | 15 | 11,000 | 26 |
| Elgin Ind School Dist/Elgin | 7 | 4,500 | 27 |
| McDade Ind School Dist/Mc Dade | 1 | 370 | 27 |
| Smithville Ind School Dist/Smithville | 5 | 1,800 | 27 |
| **BAYLOR** | | | |
| Seymour Ind School Dist/Seymour | 3 | 582 | 28 |
| **BEE** | | | |
| Beeville Ind School Dist/Beeville | 6 | 3,400 | 28 |
| Pawnee Ind School Dist/Pawnee | 1 | 550 | 28 |
| Pettus Ind School Dist/Pettus | 2 | 400 | 28 |
| Skidmore Tynan Ind SD/Skidmore | 3 | 850 | 29 |
| **BELL** | | | |
| Academy Ind School Dist/LTL RVR Acad | 5 | 1,602 | 29 |
| Bartlett Ind School Dist/Bartlett | 3 | 380 | 29 |
| Belton Ind School Dist/Belton | 17 | 11,950 | 29 |
| Holland Ind School Dist/Holland | 3 | 636 | 30 |
| Killeen Ind School Dist/Killeen | 53 | 45,500 | 30 |
| Rogers Ind School Dist/Rogers | 3 | 869 | 32 |
| Salado Ind School Dist/Salado | 3 | 2,056 | 32 |
| Temple Ind School Dist/Temple | 15 | 8,700 | 32 |
| Troy Ind School Dist/Troy | 4 | 1,600 | 33 |
| **BEXAR** | | | |
| Alamo Heights Ind School Dist/San Antonio | 5 | 4,800 | 33 |
| Archdiocese San Antonio Ed Off/San Antonio | 39 | 13,050 | 47 |
| Braination Schools/San Antonio | 8 | 818 | 33 |
| East Central Ind School Dist/San Antonio | 12 | 10,146 | 34 |
| Edgewood Ind School Dist/San Antonio | 21 | 10,881 | 34 |
| Ft Sam Houston Ind School Dist/San Antonio | 2 | 1,560 | 35 |
| Harlandale Ind School Dist/San Antonio | 24 | 14,500 | 35 |
| Judson Ind School Dist/Live Oak | 33 | 23,000 | 36 |
| Lackland Ind School Dist/San Antonio | 2 | 1,000 | 37 |
| North East Ind School Dist/San Antonio | 74 | 66,759 | 37 |
| Northside Ind School Dist/San Antonio | 124 | 106,863 | 39 |

| COUNTY<br>District/City | NO. OF<br>SCHOOLS | ENROLL-<br>MENT | PAGE |
|---|---|---|---|
| Randolph Field Ind School Dist/Universal Cty | 3 | 1,442 | 42 |
| Region 20 Ed Service Center/San Antonio | | | 48 |
| San Antonio Ind School Dist/San Antonio | 94 | 48,178 | 42 |
| School of Excellence In Ed/San Antonio | 4 | 649 | 45 |
| Somerset Ind School Dist/Somerset | 7 | 3,990 | 45 |
| South San Antonio Ind Sch Dist/San Antonio | 16 | 8,800 | 45 |
| Southside Ind School Dist/San Antonio | 9 | 5,800 | 46 |
| Southwest Ind School Dist/San Antonio | 19 | 13,928 | 46 |
| **BLANCO** | | | |
| Blanco Ind School Dist/Blanco | 3 | 1,020 | 49 |
| Johnson City Ind School Dist/Johnson City | 3 | 650 | 49 |
| **BORDEN** | | | |
| Borden Co Ind School Dist/Gail | 1 | 214 | 49 |
| **BOSQUE** | | | |
| Clifton Ind School Dist/Clifton | 3 | 1,000 | 49 |
| Cranfills Gap ISD School Dist/Cranfills Gap | 1 | 120 | 50 |
| Iredell Ind School Dist/Iredell | 1 | 138 | 50 |
| Kopperl Ind School Dist/Kopperl | 1 | 200 | 50 |
| Meridian Ind School Dist/Meridian | 4 | 475 | 50 |
| Morgan Ind School Dist/Morgan | 1 | 130 | 50 |
| Valley Mills Ind School Dist/Valley Mills | 2 | 600 | 50 |
| Walnut Springs Ind Sch Dist/Walnut Spgs | 1 | 187 | 51 |
| **BOWIE** | | | |
| De Kalb Ind School Dist/De Kalb | 3 | 650 | 51 |
| Hooks Ind School Dist/Hooks | 3 | 884 | 51 |
| Hubbard Ind School Dist/De Kalb | 1 | 107 | 51 |
| Leary Ind School Dist/Texarkana | 1 | 119 | 51 |
| Liberty-Eylau Ind School Dist/Texarkana | 4 | 2,465 | 51 |
| Malta Ind School Dist/New Boston | 1 | 225 | 52 |
| Maud Ind School Dist/Maud | 1 | 475 | 52 |
| New Boston Ind School Dist/New Boston | 4 | 1,198 | 52 |
| Pleasant Grove Ind School Dist/Texarkana | 4 | 2,200 | 52 |
| Red Lick Ind School Dist/Texarkana | 1 | 520 | 52 |
| Redwater Ind School Dist/Redwater | 4 | 1,076 | 53 |
| Simms Ind School Dist/Simms | 3 | 500 | 53 |
| Texarkana Ind School Dist/Texarkana | 13 | 7,174 | 53 |
| **BRAZORIA** | | | |
| Alvin Ind School Dist/Alvin | 31 | 25,926 | 54 |
| Angleton Ind School Dist/Angleton | 9 | 6,787 | 55 |
| Brazosport Ind School Dist/Clute | 19 | 12,000 | 55 |
| Columbia Brazoria ISD/West Columbia | 5 | 2,681 | 56 |
| Damon Ind School Dist/Damon | 1 | 144 | 56 |
| Danbury Ind School Dist/Danbury | 3 | 840 | 56 |
| Pearland Ind School Dist/Pearland | 23 | 21,917 | 56 |
| Sweeny Ind School Dist/Sweeny | 3 | 1,926 | 57 |
| **BRAZOS** | | | |
| Bryan Ind School Dist/Bryan | 24 | 16,134 | 58 |
| College Station Ind Sch Dist/College Sta | 19 | 14,000 | 59 |
| Mumford Ind School Dist/Mumford | 1 | 612 | 59 |
| **BREWSTER** | | | |
| Alpine Ind School Dist/Alpine | 3 | 965 | 60 |
| Marathon Ind School Dist/Marathon | 1 | 55 | 60 |
| San Vicente Ind School Dist/Bg BND NTL Pk | 1 | 13 | 60 |
| Terlingua Common School Dist/Terlingua | 2 | 105 | 60 |
| **BRISCOE** | | | |
| Silverton Ind School Dist/Silverton | 1 | 174 | 61 |
| **BROOKS** | | | |
| Brooks Co Ind School Dist/Falfurrias | 4 | 1,470 | 61 |
| **BROWN** | | | |
| Bangs Ind School Dist/Bangs | 3 | 868 | 61 |
| Blanket Ind School Dist/Blanket | 1 | 145 | 61 |
| Brookesmith Ind School Dist/Brookesmith | 3 | 200 | 61 |
| Brownwood Ind School Dist/Brownwood | 7 | 3,500 | 62 |
| Early Ind School Dist/Early | 4 | 1,200 | 62 |
| May Ind School Dist/May | 2 | 230 | 62 |
| Zephyr Ind School Dist/Zephyr | 1 | 208 | 62 |
| **BURLESON** | | | |
| Caldwell Ind School Dist/Caldwell | 5 | 1,750 | 63 |
| Snook Ind School Dist/Snook | 1 | 500 | 63 |
| Somerville Ind School Dist/Somerville | 3 | 550 | 63 |
| **BURNET** | | | |
| Burnet Cons Ind Sch Dist/Burnet | 6 | 3,000 | 63 |
| Marble Falls Ind School Dist/Marble Falls | 7 | 4,000 | 64 |
| **CALDWELL** | | | |
| Lockhart Ind School Dist/Lockhart | 9 | 6,350 | 64 |
| Luling Ind School Dist/Luling | 4 | 1,400 | 64 |

| COUNTY<br>District/City | NO. OF<br>SCHOOLS | ENROLL-<br>MENT | PAGE |
|---|---|---|---|
| Prairie Lea Ind School Dist/Prairie Lea | 1 | 216 | 65 |
| **CALHOUN** | | | |
| Calhoun Co Ind School Dist/Port Lavaca | 7 | 3,738 | 65 |
| **CALLAHAN** | | | |
| Baird Ind School Dist/Baird | 3 | 289 | 65 |
| Clyde Consolidated Ind SD/Clyde | 4 | 1,440 | 66 |
| Cross Plains Ind Sch Dist/Cross Plains | 2 | 340 | 66 |
| Eula Ind School Dist/Clyde | 3 | 441 | 66 |
| **CAMERON** | | | |
| Brownsville Ind School Dist/Brownsville | 54 | 44,356 | 66 |
| Harlingen Cons Ind School Dist/Harlingen | 31 | 18,600 | 68 |
| La Feria Ind School Dist/La Feria | 7 | 2,880 | 69 |
| Los Fresnos Cons Ind Sch Dist/Los Fresnos | 16 | 10,379 | 69 |
| Point Isabel Ind Sch Dist/Port Isabel | 4 | 2,017 | 70 |
| Rio Hondo Ind School Dist/Rio Hondo | 3 | 1,650 | 70 |
| San Benito Cons Ind Sch Dist/San Benito | 18 | 10,600 | 70 |
| Santa Maria Ind School Dist/Santa Maria | 4 | 691 | 71 |
| Santa Rosa Ind School Dist/Santa Rosa | 3 | 960 | 71 |
| South Texas Ind School Dist/Mercedes | 6 | 4,245 | 71 |
| **CAMP** | | | |
| Pittsburg Ind School Dist/Pittsburg | 5 | 2,356 | 72 |
| Region 8 Ed Service Center/Pittsburg | | | 72 |
| **CARSON** | | | |
| Groom Ind School Dist/Groom | 1 | 145 | 72 |
| Panhandle Ind School Dist/Panhandle | 3 | 670 | 72 |
| White Deer Ind School Dist/White Deer | 2 | 360 | 73 |
| **CASS** | | | |
| Atlanta Ind School Dist/Atlanta | 5 | 1,760 | 73 |
| Avinger Ind School Dist/Avinger | 1 | 140 | 73 |
| Bloomburg Ind School Dist/Bloomburg | 1 | 272 | 73 |
| Hughes Springs Ind Sch Dist/Hughes Spgs | 3 | 1,145 | 73 |
| Linden Kildare Cons Ind SD/Linden | 3 | 647 | 74 |
| McLeod Ind School Dist/Mc Leod | 1 | 388 | 74 |
| Queen City Ind School Dist/Queen City | 4 | 1,005 | 74 |
| **CASTRO** | | | |
| Dimmitt Ind School Dist/Dimmitt | 4 | 1,230 | 74 |
| Hart Ind School Dist/Hart | 2 | 206 | 75 |
| Nazareth Ind School Dist/Nazareth | 1 | 253 | 75 |
| **CHAMBERS** | | | |
| Anahuac Ind School Dist/Anahuac | 3 | 950 | 75 |
| Barbers Hill Ind School Dist/Mont Belvieu | 8 | 5,214 | 75 |
| East Chambers Ind School Dist/Winnie | 4 | 1,534 | 76 |
| **CHEROKEE** | | | |
| Alto Ind School Dist/Alto | 3 | 664 | 76 |
| Jacksonville Ind School Dist/Jacksonville | 8 | 5,091 | 76 |
| New Summerfield Ind Sch Dist/New Summerfld | 1 | 544 | 76 |
| Rusk Ind School Dist/Rusk | 5 | 1,979 | 77 |
| Wells Ind School Dist/Wells | 2 | 280 | 77 |
| **CHILDRESS** | | | |
| Childress Ind School Dist/Childress | 4 | 1,052 | 77 |
| **CLAY** | | | |
| Bellevue Ind School Dist/Bellevue | 1 | 140 | 77 |
| Henrietta Ind School Dist/Henrietta | 3 | 937 | 78 |
| Midway Ind School Dist/Henrietta | 1 | 134 | 78 |
| Petrolia Cons Ind School Dist/Petrolia | 2 | 450 | 78 |
| **COCHRAN** | | | |
| Morton Ind School Dist/Morton | 3 | 400 | 78 |
| Whiteface Con Ind School Dist/Whiteface | 2 | 345 | 78 |
| **COKE** | | | |
| Bronte Ind School Dist/Bronte | 2 | 225 | 79 |
| Robert Lee Ind School Dist/Robert Lee | 1 | 260 | 79 |
| **COLEMAN** | | | |
| Coleman Ind School Dist/Coleman | 3 | 869 | 79 |
| Panther Creek Cons Ind SD/Voss | 1 | 150 | 79 |
| Santa Anna Ind School Dist/Santa Anna | 2 | 250 | 79 |
| **COLLIN** | | | |
| Allen Ind School Dist/Allen | 24 | 21,404 | 80 |
| Anna Ind School Dist/Anna | 6 | 3,800 | 81 |
| Blue Ridge Ind School Dist/Blue Ridge | 3 | 975 | 81 |
| Celina Ind School Dist/Celina | 6 | 2,600 | 81 |
| Community Ind School Dist/Nevada | 4 | 2,600 | 81 |
| Farmersville Ind School Dist/Farmersville | 4 | 1,594 | 82 |
| Frisco Ind School Dist/Frisco | 72 | 63,015 | 82 |
| Lovejoy Ind School Dist/Allen | 6 | 4,424 | 84 |

| COUNTY<br>District/City | NO. OF<br>SCHOOLS | ENROLL-<br>MENT | PAGE |
|---|---|---|---|
| McKinney Ind School Dist/McKinney | 31 | 24,335 | 84 |
| Melissa Ind School Dist/Melissa | 4 | 3,102 | 85 |
| Plano Ind School Dist/Plano | 73 | 52,692 | 85 |
| Princeton Ind School Dist/Princeton | 9 | 5,567 | 87 |
| Prosper Ind School Dist/Prosper | 18 | 19,000 | 88 |
| Wylie Ind School Dist/Wylie | 20 | 17,500 | 88 |
| **COLLINGSWORTH** | | | |
| Wellington Ind School Dist/Wellington | 3 | 530 | 90 |
| **COLORADO** | | | |
| Columbus Ind School Dist/Columbus | 4 | 1,494 | 90 |
| Rice Cons Ind School Dist/Altair | 7 | 1,325 | 90 |
| Weimar Ind School Dist/Weimar | 3 | 629 | 91 |
| **COMAL** | | | |
| Comal Ind School Dist/New Braunfels | 33 | 23,800 | 91 |
| New Braunfels Ind School Dist/New Braunfels | 15 | 9,220 | 92 |
| **COMANCHE** | | | |
| Comanche Ind School Dist/Comanche | 4 | 1,325 | 93 |
| De Leon Ind School Dist/De Leon | 3 | 720 | 93 |
| Gustine Ind School Dist/Gustine | 1 | 134 | 93 |
| Sidney Ind School Dist/Sidney | 1 | 139 | 94 |
| **CONCHO** | | | |
| Eden Cons Ind School Dist/Eden | 2 | 230 | 94 |
| Paint Rock Ind School Dist/Paint Rock | 1 | 225 | 94 |
| **COOKE** | | | |
| Callisburg Ind School Dist/Gainesville | 2 | 1,100 | 94 |
| Era Ind School Dist/Era | 1 | 454 | 94 |
| Gainesville Ind School Dist/Gainesville | 6 | 3,100 | 95 |
| Lindsay Ind School Dist/Lindsay | 2 | 500 | 95 |
| Muenster Ind School Dist/Muenster | 2 | 481 | 95 |
| Sivells Bend Ind School Dist/Gainesville | 1 | 57 | 95 |
| Valley View ISD-Cooke Co/Valley View | 1 | 875 | 95 |
| Walnut Bend Ind School Dist/Gainesville | 1 | 72 | 96 |
| **CORYELL** | | | |
| Copperas Cove Ind School Dist/Copperas Cove | 11 | 8,200 | 96 |
| Evant Ind School Dist/Evant | 1 | 249 | 96 |
| Gatesville Ind School Dist/Gatesville | 5 | 2,744 | 96 |
| Jonesboro Ind School Dist/Jonesboro | 1 | 330 | 97 |
| Oglesby Ind School Dist/Oglesby | 1 | 180 | 97 |
| **COTTLE** | | | |
| Paducah Ind School Dist/Paducah | 1 | 200 | 97 |
| **CRANE** | | | |
| Crane Ind School Dist/Crane | 3 | 1,172 | 97 |
| **CROCKETT** | | | |
| Crockett Co Cons Common SD/Ozona | 3 | 720 | 98 |
| **CROSBY** | | | |
| Crosbyton Cons Ind Sch Dist/Crosbyton | 2 | 330 | 98 |
| Lorenzo Ind School Dist/Lorenzo | 2 | 250 | 98 |
| Ralls Ind School Dist/Ralls | 4 | 485 | 98 |
| **CULBERSON** | | | |
| Culberson Co Allamoore Ind SD/Van Horn | 1 | 378 | 99 |
| **DALLAM** | | | |
| Dalhart Ind School Dist/Dalhart | 4 | 1,700 | 99 |
| Texline Ind School Dist/Texline | 1 | 180 | 99 |
| **DALLAS** | | | |
| Advantage Academy Admin Office/Duncanville | 4 | 1,650 | 100 |
| Carrollton-Farmers Branch ISD/Carrollton | 37 | 24,500 | 100 |
| Cedar Hill Ind School Dist/Cedar Hill | 14 | 7,866 | 101 |
| Coppell Ind School Dist/Coppell | 18 | 13,500 | 102 |
| Dallas Co Schools/Dallas | | | 99 |
| Dallas Ind School Dist/Dallas | 233 | 153,861 | 102 |
| DeSoto Ind School Dist/Desoto | 14 | 9,872 | 108 |
| Diocese of Dallas Ed Office/Dallas | 35 | 14,823 | 118 |
| Duncanville Ind School Dist/Duncanville | 19 | 12,250 | 108 |
| Garland Ind School Dist/Garland | 72 | 55,848 | 109 |
| Grand Prairie Ind School Dist/Grand Prairie | 42 | 29,334 | 111 |
| Highland Park Ind Sch Dist/Dallas | 8 | 7,000 | 112 |
| Int'l Leadership of Texas Dist/Richardson | 19 | 19,100 | 112 |
| Irving Ind School Dist/Irving | 38 | 33,901 | 113 |
| Lancaster Ind School Dist/Lancaster | 11 | 7,600 | 114 |
| Mesquite Ind School Dist/Mesquite | 48 | 38,266 | 115 |
| Region 10 Ed Service Center/Richardson | | | 120 |
| Richardson Ind School Dist/Richardson | 56 | 38,700 | 116 |
| Sunnyvale Ind School Dist/Sunnyvale | 3 | 2,200 | 117 |
| **DAWSON** | | | |

| COUNTY<br>District/City | NO. OF<br>SCHOOLS | ENROLL-<br>MENT | PAGE |
|---|---|---|---|
| Dawson Ind School Dist/Welch | 1 | 140 | 121 |
| Klondike Ind School Dist/Lamesa | 1 | 249 | 121 |
| Lamesa Ind School Dist/Lamesa | 5 | 1,800 | 121 |
| Sands Consolidated ISD/Ackerly | 1 | 247 | 121 |
| **DE WITT** | | | |
| Cuero Ind School Dist/Cuero | 4 | 1,990 | 121 |
| Meyersville Ind School Dist/Meyersville | 1 | 137 | 122 |
| Nordheim Ind School Dist/Nordheim | 1 | 149 | 122 |
| Westhoff Ind School Dist/Westhoff | 1 | 80 | 122 |
| Yoakum Ind School Dist/Yoakum | 5 | 1,500 | 122 |
| Yorktown Ind School Dist/Yorktown | 3 | 513 | 122 |
| **DEAF SMITH** | | | |
| Hereford Ind School Dist/Hereford | 9 | 4,100 | 123 |
| Walcott Ind School Dist/Hereford | 1 | 146 | 123 |
| **DELTA** | | | |
| Cooper Ind School Dist/Cooper | 2 | 800 | 123 |
| Fannindel Ind School Dist/Ladonia | 2 | 200 | 124 |
| **DENTON** | | | |
| Argyle Ind School Dist/Argyle | 5 | 3,100 | 124 |
| Aubrey Ind School Dist/Aubrey | 5 | 2,500 | 124 |
| Denton Ind School Dist/Denton | 42 | 33,485 | 124 |
| Krum Ind School Dist/Krum | 5 | 2,100 | 126 |
| Lake Dallas Ind School Dist/Lake Dallas | 5 | 4,000 | 126 |
| Lewisville Ind School Dist/Lewisville | 71 | 52,300 | 126 |
| Little Elm Ind School Dist/Little Elm | 9 | 8,100 | 128 |
| Northwest Ind School Dist/Justin | 31 | 25,000 | 128 |
| Pilot Point Ind School Dist/Pilot Point | 4 | 1,400 | 129 |
| Ponder Ind School Dist/Ponder | 3 | 1,600 | 130 |
| Sanger Ind School Dist/Sanger | 7 | 2,660 | 130 |
| **DICKENS** | | | |
| Patton Springs Ind School Dist/Afton | 1 | 97 | 131 |
| Spur Ind School Dist/Spur | 1 | 235 | 131 |
| **DIMMIT** | | | |
| Carrizo Spgs Cons Ind SD/Carrizo Spgs | 4 | 2,200 | 131 |
| **DONLEY** | | | |
| Clarendon Cons Ind Sch Dist/Clarendon | 3 | 450 | 131 |
| Hedley Ind School Dist/Hedley | 1 | 112 | 132 |
| **DUVAL** | | | |
| Benavides Ind School Dist/Benavides | 2 | 320 | 132 |
| Freer Ind School Dist/Freer | 3 | 701 | 132 |
| Ramirez Common School Dist/Realitos | 1 | 37 | 132 |
| San Diego Ind School Dist/San Diego | 3 | 1,385 | 132 |
| **EASTLAND** | | | |
| Cisco Independent Sch Dist/Cisco | 4 | 830 | 133 |
| Eastland Ind School Dist/Eastland | 3 | 1,000 | 133 |
| Gorman Ind School Dist/Gorman | 3 | 287 | 133 |
| Ranger Ind School Dist/Ranger | 1 | 350 | 133 |
| Rising Star Ind Sch Dist/Rising Star | 2 | 150 | 133 |
| **ECTOR** | | | |
| Ector Co Ind School Dist/Odessa | 42 | 32,391 | 134 |
| **EDWARDS** | | | |
| Nueces Canyon Cons Ind SD/Barksdale | 2 | 264 | 135 |
| Rocksprings Ind School Dist/Rocksprings | 1 | 289 | 135 |
| **EL PASO** | | | |
| Anthony Ind School Dist/Anthony | 3 | 795 | 136 |
| Canutillo Ind School Dist/El Paso | 10 | 6,200 | 136 |
| Clint Ind School Dist/El Paso | 14 | 11,522 | 136 |
| Diocese of El Paso Ed Office/El Paso | 11 | 2,700 | 143 |
| El Paso Ind School Dist/El Paso | 86 | 57,315 | 137 |
| El Paso ISD-Elementary/El Paso | | | 137 |
| El Paso ISD-High Schools/El Paso | | | 138 |
| El Paso ISD-Middle Schools/El Paso | | | 139 |
| Fabens Ind School Dist/Fabens | 5 | 2,000 | 139 |
| Region 19 Ed Service Center/El Paso | | | 144 |
| San Elizario Ind School Dist/San Elizario | 6 | 3,560 | 139 |
| Socorro Ind School Dist/El Paso | 50 | 44,992 | 140 |
| Tornillo Ind School Dist/Tornillo | 4 | 950 | 141 |
| Ysleta Ind School Dist/El Paso | 57 | 40,304 | 141 |
| **ELLIS** | | | |
| Avalon Ind School Dist/Avalon | 1 | 350 | 144 |
| Ennis Ind School Dist/Ennis | 11 | 5,800 | 144 |
| Ferris Ind School Dist/Ferris | 5 | 2,400 | 144 |
| Italy Ind School Dist/Italy | 2 | 600 | 145 |
| Maypearl Ind School Dist/Maypearl | 4 | 1,040 | 145 |
| Midlothian Ind School Dist/Midlothian | 11 | 9,500 | 145 |
| Milford Ind School Dist/Milford | 1 | 240 | 146 |

| COUNTY<br>District/City | NO. OF<br>SCHOOLS | ENROLL-<br>MENT | PAGE |
|---|---|---|---|
| Palmer Ind School Dist/Palmer | 3 | 1,300 | 146 |
| Red Oak Ind School Dist/Red Oak | 8 | 6,000 | 146 |
| Waxahachie Ind School Dist/Waxahachie | 16 | 9,481 | 146 |
| **ERATH** | | | |
| Bluff Dale Ind Sch Dist/Bluff Dale | 1 | 222 | 147 |
| Dublin Ind School Dist/Dublin | 3 | 1,121 | 147 |
| Huckabay Ind School Dist/Stephenville | 1 | 250 | 147 |
| Lingleville Ind School Dist/Lingleville | 1 | 282 | 148 |
| Morgan Mill Ind School Dist/Morgan Mill | 1 | 125 | 148 |
| Stephenville Ind School Dist/Stephenville | 6 | 3,650 | 148 |
| Three Way Ind School Dist/Stephenville | 2 | 190 | 148 |
| **FALLS** | | | |
| Chilton Ind School Dist/Chilton | 1 | 540 | 148 |
| Marlin Ind School Dist/Marlin | 3 | 821 | 149 |
| Rosebud-Lott Ind School Dist/Lott | 3 | 637 | 149 |
| Westphalia Ind School Dist/Lott | 1 | 155 | 149 |
| **FANNIN** | | | |
| Bonham Ind School Dist/Bonham | 5 | 1,850 | 149 |
| Dodd City Ind School Dist/Dodd City | 1 | 364 | 150 |
| Ector Ind School Dist/Ector | 1 | 260 | 150 |
| Honey Grove Ind School Dist/Honey Grove | 3 | 614 | 150 |
| Leonard Ind School Dist/Leonard | 4 | 878 | 150 |
| Sam Rayburn Ind School Dist/Ivanhoe | 1 | 525 | 150 |
| Savoy Ind School Dist/Savoy | 2 | 320 | 150 |
| Trenton Ind School Dist/Trenton | 3 | 573 | 151 |
| **FAYETTE** | | | |
| Fayetteville Ind School Dist/Fayetteville | 1 | 260 | 151 |
| Flatonia Ind School Dist/Flatonia | 3 | 580 | 151 |
| La Grange Ind School Dist/La Grange | 3 | 2,350 | 151 |
| Round Top-Carmine Ind Sch Dist/Carmine | 2 | 267 | 151 |
| Schulenburg Ind School Dist/Schulenburg | 2 | 700 | 152 |
| **FISHER** | | | |
| Roby Cons Ind School Dist/Roby | 2 | 277 | 152 |
| Rotan Ind School Dist/Rotan | 2 | 240 | 152 |
| **FLOYD** | | | |
| Floydada Ind School Dist/Floydada | 2 | 700 | 153 |
| Lockney Independent Sch Dist/Lockney | 3 | 450 | 153 |
| **FOARD** | | | |
| Crowell Ind School Dist/Crowell | 2 | 230 | 153 |
| **FORT BEND** | | | |
| Ft Bend Ind School Dist/Sugar Land | 82 | 79,076 | 153 |
| Katy Ind School Dist/Katy | 72 | 84,299 | 155 |
| Lamar Cons Ind School Dist/Rosenberg | 46 | 34,806 | 157 |
| Needville Ind School Dist/Needville | 4 | 3,228 | 159 |
| Stafford Municipal Sch Dist/Stafford | 7 | 3,600 | 159 |
| **FRANKLIN** | | | |
| Mount Vernon Ind School Dist/Mount Vernon | 3 | 1,570 | 160 |
| **FREESTONE** | | | |
| Dew Ind School Dist/Teague | 1 | 155 | 160 |
| Fairfield Ind School Dist/Fairfield | 4 | 1,800 | 160 |
| Teague Ind School Dist/Teague | 5 | 1,160 | 161 |
| Wortham Ind School Dist/Wortham | 3 | 500 | 161 |
| **FRIO** | | | |
| Dilley Ind School Dist/Dilley | 4 | 950 | 161 |
| Pearsall Ind School Dist/Pearsall | 4 | 2,100 | 161 |
| **GAINES** | | | |
| Loop Ind School Dist/Loop | 1 | 124 | 162 |
| Seagraves Ind School Dist/Seagraves | 3 | 547 | 162 |
| Seminole Ind School Dist/Seminole | 6 | 2,619 | 162 |
| **GALVESTON** | | | |
| Clear Creek Ind School Dist/League City | 46 | 42,042 | 162 |
| Dickinson Ind School Dist/Dickinson | 14 | 10,400 | 164 |
| Friendswood Ind Sch Dist/Friendswood | 6 | 6,000 | 164 |
| Galveston Ind School Dist/Galveston | 11 | 7,000 | 164 |
| High Island Ind Sch Dist/High Island | 1 | 135 | 165 |
| Hitchcock Ind School Dist/Hitchcock | 4 | 1,600 | 165 |
| Santa Fe Ind School Dist/Santa Fe | 5 | 4,794 | 165 |
| Texas City Ind School Dist/Texas City | 14 | 9,000 | 166 |
| **GARZA** | | | |
| Post Ind School Dist/Post | 3 | 566 | 167 |
| Southland Ind School Dist/Southland | 1 | 123 | 167 |
| **GILLESPIE** | | | |
| Doss Consolidated Common SD/Doss | 1 | 25 | 167 |
| Fredericksburg Ind School Dist/Fredericksbrg | 6 | 3,200 | 167 |

| COUNTY<br>District/City | NO. OF<br>SCHOOLS | ENROLL-<br>MENT | PAGE |
|---|---|---|---|
| **HILL** | | | |
| Abbott Ind School Dist/Abbott | 1 | 280 | 229 |
| Aquilla Ind School Dist/Aquilla | 1 | 330 | 230 |
| Blum Ind School Dist/Blum | 1 | 344 | 230 |
| Bynum Ind School Dist/Bynum | 1 | 195 | 230 |
| Covington ISD School Dist/Covington | 1 | 390 | 230 |
| Hillsboro Ind School Dist/Hillsboro | 5 | 2,000 | 230 |
| Hubbard Ind School Dist/Hubbard | 2 | 422 | 230 |
| Itasca Ind School Dist/Itasca | 3 | 670 | 231 |
| Malone Independent School Dist/Malone | 1 | 178 | 231 |
| Mt Calm Ind School Dist/Mount Calm | 2 | 200 | 231 |
| Penelope ISD School Dist/Penelope | 1 | 215 | 231 |
| Whitney Ind School Dist/Whitney | 4 | 1,311 | 231 |
| **HOCKLEY** | | | |
| Anton Ind School Dist/Anton | 1 | 185 | 232 |
| Levelland Ind School Dist/Levelland | 6 | 2,936 | 232 |
| Ropes Ind School Dist/Ropesville | 1 | 479 | 232 |
| Smyer Ind School Dist/Smyer | 2 | 415 | 232 |
| Sundown Ind School Dist/Sundown | 3 | 595 | 232 |
| Whitharral Ind School Dist/Whitharral | 1 | 175 | 233 |
| **HOOD** | | | |
| Granbury Ind School Dist/Granbury | 11 | 6,971 | 233 |
| Lipan Ind School Dist/Lipan | 1 | 413 | 233 |
| Tolar Ind School Dist/Tolar | 3 | 800 | 233 |
| **HOPKINS** | | | |
| Como Pickton Cons Ind SD/Como | 1 | 700 | 234 |
| Cumby Ind School Dist/Cumby | 2 | 400 | 234 |
| Miller Grove Ind School Dist/Cumby | 1 | 345 | 234 |
| North Hopkins Ind School Dist/Sulphur Spgs | 1 | 550 | 234 |
| Saltillo Ind School Dist/Saltillo | 1 | 276 | 234 |
| Sulphur Bluff Ind School Dist/Sulphur Bluff | 1 | 230 | 235 |
| Sulphur Springs Ind Sch Dist/Sulphur Spgs | 9 | 4,400 | 235 |
| **HOUSTON** | | | |
| Crockett Ind School Dist/Crockett | 5 | 1,331 | 235 |
| Grapeland Ind School Dist/Grapeland | 3 | 600 | 235 |
| Kennard Ind Sch Dist/Kennard | 1 | 256 | 236 |
| Latexo Ind School Dist/Latexo | 2 | 475 | 236 |
| Lovelady Ind School Dist/Lovelady | 2 | 510 | 236 |
| **HOWARD** | | | |
| Big Spring Ind School Dist/Big Spring | 9 | 4,000 | 236 |
| Coahoma Ind School Dist/Coahoma | 3 | 1,061 | 237 |
| Forsan Ind School Dist/Forsan | 2 | 771 | 237 |
| **HUDSPETH** | | | |
| Dell City Ind School Dist/Dell City | 1 | 61 | 237 |
| Ft Hancock Ind School Dist/Fort Hancock | 3 | 377 | 237 |
| Sierra Blanca Ind School Dist/Sierra Blanca | 1 | 103 | 237 |
| **HUNT** | | | |
| Bland Ind School Dist/Merit | 3 | 700 | 238 |
| Boles Ind School Dist/Quinlan | 3 | 545 | 238 |
| Caddo Mills Ind Sch Dist/Caddo Mills | 5 | 2,000 | 238 |
| Campbell Ind School Dist/Campbell | 1 | 300 | 238 |
| Celeste Ind School Dist/Celeste | 3 | 480 | 238 |
| Commerce Independent Sch Dist/Commerce | 4 | 1,442 | 239 |
| Greenville Ind School Dist/Greenville | 12 | 5,400 | 239 |
| Lone Oak Ind School Dist/Lone Oak | 4 | 1,000 | 239 |
| Quinlan Ind School Dist/Quinlan | 5 | 2,516 | 240 |
| Wolfe City Ind School Dist/Wolfe City | 3 | 646 | 240 |
| **HUTCHINSON** | | | |
| Borger Ind School Dist/Borger | 6 | 2,700 | 240 |
| Plemons-Stinnett-Phillips CISD/Stinnett | 3 | 731 | 240 |
| Sanford-Fritch Ind School Dist/Fritch | 3 | 687 | 241 |
| Spring Creek Ind School Dist/Skellytown | 1 | 110 | 241 |
| **IRION** | | | |
| Irion Co Ind School Dist/Mertzon | 2 | 300 | 241 |
| **JACK** | | | |
| Bryson Ind School Dist/Bryson | 1 | 241 | 241 |
| Jacksboro Ind Sch Dist/Jacksboro | 3 | 1,023 | 242 |
| Perrin-Whitt Cons Ind Sch Dist/Perrin | 2 | 340 | 242 |
| **JACKSON** | | | |
| Edna Ind School Dist/Edna | 4 | 1,328 | 242 |
| Ganado Ind School Dist/Ganado | 3 | 700 | 242 |
| Industrial Ind School Dist/Vanderbilt | 4 | 1,100 | 243 |
| **JASPER** | | | |
| Brookeland Ind School Dist/Brookeland | 1 | 380 | 243 |
| Buna Ind School Dist/Buna | 3 | 1,497 | 243 |
| Evadale Ind School Dist/Evadale | 2 | 394 | 243 |

| COUNTY<br>District/City | NO. OF<br>SCHOOLS | ENROLL-<br>MENT | PAGE |
|---|---|---|---|
| Jasper Ind School Dist/Jasper | 4 | 2,400 | 243 |
| Kirbyville Cons Ind Sch Dist/Kirbyville | 3 | 1,500 | 244 |
| **JEFF DAVIS** | | | |
| Fort Davis Ind School Dist/Fort Davis | 2 | 225 | 244 |
| Valentine Ind School Dist/Valentine | 1 | 34 | 244 |
| **JEFFERSON** | | | |
| Beaumont Ind School Dist/Beaumont | 27 | 18,000 | 244 |
| Diocese of Beaumont Sch Office/Beaumont | 5 | 1,500 | 247 |
| Hamshire Fannett Ind Sch Dist/Hamshire | 4 | 1,934 | 245 |
| Nederland Ind School Dist/Nederland | 8 | 5,214 | 245 |
| Port Arthur Ind School Dist/Port Arthur | 16 | 9,000 | 246 |
| Port Neches-Groves Ind SD/Port Neches | 10 | 5,000 | 246 |
| Region 5 Ed Service Center/Beaumont | | | 247 |
| Sabine Pass Ind School Dist/Sabine Pass | 1 | 354 | 247 |
| **JIM HOGG** | | | |
| Jim Hogg Co Ind School Dist/Hebbronville | 3 | 1,100 | 247 |
| **JIM WELLS** | | | |
| Alice Ind School Dist/Alice | 9 | 4,784 | 248 |
| Ben Bolt-Palito Blanco ISD/Ben Bolt | 2 | 520 | 248 |
| La Gloria Ind School Dist/Falfurrias | 1 | 108 | 248 |
| Orange Grove Ind School Dist/Orange Grove | 4 | 1,850 | 248 |
| Premont Ind School Dist/Premont | 2 | 705 | 248 |
| **JOHNSON** | | | |
| Alvarado Ind School Dist/Alvarado | 6 | 3,500 | 249 |
| Burleson Ind School Dist/Burleson | 18 | 13,268 | 249 |
| Cleburne Ind School Dist/Cleburne | 12 | 6,749 | 250 |
| Godley Ind School Dist/Godley | 5 | 2,027 | 250 |
| Grandview Ind School Dist/Grandview | 3 | 1,365 | 251 |
| Joshua Ind School Dist/Joshua | 10 | 5,626 | 251 |
| Keene Ind School Dist/Keene | 4 | 1,011 | 251 |
| Rio Vista Ind School Dist/Rio Vista | 3 | 755 | 251 |
| Venus Ind School Dist/Venus | 4 | 2,095 | 252 |
| **JONES** | | | |
| Anson Ind School Dist/Anson | 3 | 700 | 252 |
| Hamlin Collegiate Ind Sch Dist/Hamlin | 2 | 430 | 252 |
| Hawley Ind School Dist/Hawley | 3 | 784 | 253 |
| Lueders-Avoca Ind School Dist/Lueders | 2 | 100 | 253 |
| Stamford Ind School Dist/Stamford | 3 | 630 | 253 |
| **KARNES** | | | |
| Falls City Ind School Dist/Falls City | 2 | 340 | 253 |
| Karnes City Ind School Dist/Karnes City | 5 | 1,062 | 253 |
| Kenedy Ind School Dist/Kenedy | 3 | 500 | 254 |
| Runge Ind School Dist/Runge | 1 | 238 | 254 |
| **KAUFMAN** | | | |
| Crandall Ind School Dist/Crandall | 8 | 4,700 | 254 |
| Forney Ind School Dist/Forney | 14 | 9,681 | 254 |
| Kaufman Ind School Dist/Kaufman | 7 | 3,500 | 255 |
| Kemp Ind School Dist/Kemp | 4 | 1,236 | 255 |
| Mabank Ind School Dist/Mabank | 8 | 3,664 | 255 |
| Scurry Rosser Ind School Dist/Scurry | 3 | 1,037 | 256 |
| Terrell Ind School Dist/Terrell | 10 | 4,711 | 256 |
| **KENDALL** | | | |
| Boerne Ind School Dist/Boerne | 12 | 9,000 | 257 |
| Comfort Ind School Dist/Comfort | 3 | 1,052 | 257 |
| **KENEDY** | | | |
| Kenedy Co Schools/Sarita | | | 257 |
| Kenedy Co Wide Common Sch Dist/Sarita | 1 | 80 | 258 |
| **KENT** | | | |
| Jayton-Girard Ind School Dist/Jayton | 1 | 143 | 258 |
| **KERR** | | | |
| Center Point Ind School Dist/Center Point | 3 | 569 | 258 |
| Divide ISD School Dist/Mountain Home | 1 | 23 | 258 |
| Hunt Ind School Dist/Hunt | 1 | 204 | 258 |
| Ingram Ind School Dist/Ingram | 3 | 1,100 | 259 |
| Kerrville Ind School Dist/Kerrville | 10 | 4,800 | 259 |
| **KIMBLE** | | | |
| Junction Ind School Dist/Junction | 3 | 605 | 259 |
| **KING** | | | |
| Guthrie Common School Dist/Guthrie | 1 | 95 | 260 |
| **KINNEY** | | | |
| Brackett Ind School Dist/Brackettville | 3 | 570 | 260 |
| **KLEBERG** | | | |
| Kingsville Ind School Dist/Kingsville | 8 | 3,050 | 260 |

| COUNTY<br>District/City | NO. OF<br>SCHOOLS | ENROLL-<br>MENT | PAGE |
|---|---|---|---|
| Ricardo Ind School Dist/Kingsville | 1 | 670 | 261 |
| Riviera Ind School Dist/Riviera | 2 | 440 | 261 |
| Santa Gertrudis Ind Sch Dist/Kingsville | 2 | 800 | 261 |
| **KNOX** | | | |
| Benjamin Ind School Dist/Benjamin | 1 | 108 | 261 |
| Knox City-O'Brien Cons Ind SD/Knox City | 3 | 280 | 261 |
| Munday Consolidated Ind SD/Munday | 2 | 392 | 262 |
| **LA SALLE** | | | |
| Cotulla Ind School Dist/Cotulla | 4 | 1,180 | 262 |
| **LAMAR** | | | |
| Chisum Ind School Dist/Paris | 3 | 1,020 | 262 |
| Paris Ind School Dist/Paris | 8 | 3,900 | 262 |
| Prairiland Ind School Dist/Pattonville | 4 | 1,088 | 263 |
| **LAMB** | | | |
| Amherst Ind School Dist/Amherst | 1 | 130 | 263 |
| Littlefield Ind School Dist/Littlefield | 4 | 1,300 | 263 |
| Olton Ind School Dist/Olton | 3 | 600 | 263 |
| Springlake-Earth Ind Sch Dist/Earth | 2 | 370 | 264 |
| Sudan Ind School Dist/Sudan | 2 | 424 | 264 |
| **LAMPASAS** | | | |
| Lampasas Ind School Dist/Lampasas | 5 | 3,400 | 264 |
| Lometa Ind School Dist/Lometa | 1 | 300 | 264 |
| **LAVACA** | | | |
| Ezzell Ind School Dist/Hallettsville | 1 | 85 | 264 |
| Hallettsville Ind Sch Dist/Hallettsville | 3 | 1,100 | 265 |
| Moulton Ind School Dist/Moulton | 2 | 300 | 265 |
| Shiner Ind School Dist/Shiner | 2 | 650 | 265 |
| Sweet Home Ind School Dist/Sweet Home | 1 | 140 | 265 |
| Vysehrad Ind School Dist/Hallettsville | 1 | 115 | 265 |
| **LEE** | | | |
| Dime Box Ind School Dist/Dime Box | 1 | 160 | 266 |
| Giddings Ind School Dist/Giddings | 4 | 1,900 | 266 |
| Lexington Ind School Dist/Lexington | 3 | 1,066 | 266 |
| **LEON** | | | |
| Buffalo Ind School Dist/Buffalo | 4 | 900 | 266 |
| Centerville Ind School Dist/Centerville | 2 | 700 | 267 |
| Leon Ind School Dist/Jewett | 2 | 700 | 267 |
| Normangee Ind School Dist/Normangee | 3 | 605 | 267 |
| Oakwood Ind School Dist/Oakwood | 2 | 199 | 267 |
| **LIBERTY** | | | |
| Cleveland Ind School Dist/Cleveland | 7 | 6,338 | 267 |
| Dayton Ind School Dist/Dayton | 7 | 5,400 | 268 |
| Devers Ind School Dist/Devers | 1 | 176 | 268 |
| Hardin Ind School Dist/Hardin | 3 | 1,700 | 268 |
| Hull Daisetta Ind School Dist/Daisetta | 3 | 453 | 268 |
| Liberty Ind School Dist/Liberty | 4 | 2,227 | 269 |
| Tarkington Ind School Dist/Cleveland | 4 | 1,810 | 269 |
| **LIMESTONE** | | | |
| Coolidge Ind School Dist/Coolidge | 2 | 295 | 269 |
| Groesbeck Ind School Dist/Groesbeck | 4 | 1,500 | 269 |
| Mexia Ind School Dist/Mexia | 5 | 1,800 | 270 |
| **LIPSCOMB** | | | |
| Booker Ind School Dist/Booker | 2 | 371 | 270 |
| Darrouzett Ind School Dist/Darrouzett | 1 | 105 | 270 |
| Follett Ind School Dist/Follett | 1 | 165 | 270 |
| Higgins Ind School Dist/Higgins | 1 | 96 | 270 |
| **LIVE OAK** | | | |
| George West Ind School Dist/George West | 4 | 1,100 | 271 |
| Three Rivers Ind School Dist/Three Rivers | 2 | 628 | 271 |
| **LLANO** | | | |
| Llano Ind School Dist/Llano | 4 | 1,701 | 271 |
| **LUBBOCK** | | | |
| Diocese of Lubbock Ed Office/Lubbock | 1 | 360 | 275 |
| Frenship Ind School Dist/Wolfforth | 13 | 9,900 | 272 |
| Idalou Ind School Dist/Idalou | 3 | 984 | 272 |
| Lubbock Ind School Dist/Lubbock | 48 | 26,000 | 272 |
| Lubbock-Cooper Ind Sch Dist/Lubbock | 9 | 6,000 | 274 |
| New Deal Ind School Dist/New Deal | 3 | 750 | 274 |
| Region 17 Ed Service Center/Lubbock | | | 275 |
| Roosevelt Ind School Dist/Lubbock | 3 | 1,012 | 274 |
| Shallowater Ind School Dist/Shallowater | 4 | 1,351 | 274 |
| Slaton Ind School Dist/Slaton | 4 | 950 | 275 |
| **LYNN** | | | |
| New Home Ind School Dist/New Home | 1 | 580 | 275 |

| COUNTY<br>District/City | NO. OF<br>SCHOOLS | ENROLL-<br>MENT | PAGE |
|---|---|---|---|
| O'Donnell Ind School Dist/Odonnell | 2 | 300 | 276 |
| Tahoka Ind School Dist/Tahoka | 3 | 600 | 276 |
| Wilson Ind School Dist/Wilson | 1 | 94 | 276 |
| **MADISON** | | | |
| Madisonville Cons ISD/Madisonville | 4 | 2,233 | 276 |
| North Zulch Ind School Dist/North Zulch | 1 | 310 | 276 |
| **MARION** | | | |
| Jefferson Ind School Dist/Jefferson | 4 | 1,324 | 277 |
| **MARTIN** | | | |
| Grady Ind School Dist/Lenorah | 1 | 233 | 277 |
| Stanton Ind School Dist/Stanton | 3 | 1,053 | 277 |
| **MASON** | | | |
| Mason Ind School Dist/Mason | 3 | 674 | 278 |
| **MATAGORDA** | | | |
| Bay City Ind School Dist/Bay City | 5 | 3,670 | 278 |
| Matagorda Ind School Dist/Matagorda | 1 | 120 | 278 |
| Palacios Ind School Dist/Palacios | 4 | 1,506 | 278 |
| Tidehaven Ind School Dist/Elmaton | 4 | 980 | 279 |
| Van Vleck Ind School Dist/Van Vleck | 4 | 1,027 | 279 |
| **MAVERICK** | | | |
| Eagle Pass Ind School Dist/Eagle Pass | 23 | 15,000 | 279 |
| **MCCULLOCH** | | | |
| Brady Ind School Dist/Brady | 4 | 1,050 | 280 |
| Lohn Ind School Dist/Lohn | 1 | 100 | 280 |
| Rochelle Ind School Dist/Rochelle | 1 | 179 | 281 |
| **MCLENNAN** | | | |
| Axtell Ind School Dist/Axtell | 2 | 580 | 281 |
| Bosqueville Ind School Dist/Waco | 3 | 699 | 281 |
| Bruceville-Eddy Ind Sch Dist/Eddy | 4 | 630 | 281 |
| China Spring Ind School Dist/China Spring | 5 | 2,748 | 281 |
| Connally Ind School Dist/Waco | 6 | 2,300 | 282 |
| Crawford Ind School Dist/Crawford | 2 | 560 | 282 |
| Gholson Ind School Dist/Waco | 1 | 246 | 282 |
| Hallsburg Ind School Dist/Waco | 1 | 170 | 282 |
| La Vega Ind School Dist/Waco | 5 | 3,140 | 282 |
| Lorena Ind School Dist/Lorena | 4 | 1,673 | 283 |
| Mart Ind School Dist/Mart | 2 | 426 | 283 |
| McGregor Ind School Dist/Mc Gregor | 4 | 1,342 | 283 |
| Midway Ind School Dist/Woodway | 10 | 8,100 | 283 |
| Moody Ind School Dist/Moody | 3 | 660 | 284 |
| Region 12 Ed Service Center/Waco | | | 286 |
| Riesel Ind School Dist/Riesel | 2 | 660 | 284 |
| Robinson Ind School Dist/Robinson | 5 | 2,200 | 284 |
| Waco Ind School Dist/Waco | 24 | 15,050 | 284 |
| West Ind School Dist/West | 4 | 826 | 285 |
| **MCMULLEN** | | | |
| McMullen Co Ind Sch Dist/Tilden | 1 | 289 | 286 |
| **MEDINA** | | | |
| D'Hanis Ind School Dist/D Hanis | 1 | 368 | 286 |
| Devine Ind School Dist/Devine | 4 | 1,900 | 286 |
| Hondo Ind School Dist/Hondo | 4 | 1,838 | 287 |
| Medina Valley Ind School Dist/Castroville | 7 | 5,087 | 287 |
| Natalia Ind School Dist/Natalia | 4 | 1,000 | 287 |
| **MENARD** | | | |
| Menard Ind School Dist/Menard | 2 | 305 | 288 |
| **MIDLAND** | | | |
| Greenwood Ind School Dist/Midland | 4 | 2,831 | 288 |
| Midland Ind School Dist/Midland | 40 | 26,000 | 288 |
| Region 18 Ed Service Center/Midland | | | 290 |
| **MILAM** | | | |
| Buckholts Ind School Dist/Buckholts | 1 | 132 | 290 |
| Burleson Milam Spec Serv Co-op/Milano | | | 291 |
| Cameron Ind School Dist/Cameron | 4 | 1,684 | 290 |
| Gause Ind School Dist/Gause | 1 | 170 | 290 |
| Milano Ind School Dist/Milano | 3 | 419 | 290 |
| Rockdale Ind School Dist/Rockdale | 4 | 1,432 | 290 |
| Thorndale Ind School Dist/Thorndale | 3 | 650 | 291 |
| **MILLS** | | | |
| Goldthwaite Consolidated ISD/Goldthwaite | 3 | 555 | 291 |
| Mullin Ind School Dist/Mullin | 6 | 294 | 291 |
| Priddy Ind School Dist/Priddy | 1 | 115 | 292 |
| **MITCHELL** | | | |
| Colorado Ind School Dist/Colorado City | 4 | 900 | 292 |
| Loraine Ind School Dist/Loraine | 1 | 142 | 292 |

| COUNTY District/City | NO. OF SCHOOLS | ENROLL-MENT | PAGE |
|---|---|---|---|
| Westbrook Ind School Dist/Westbrook | 1 | 272 | 292 |
| **MONTAGUE** | | | |
| Bowie Ind School Dist/Bowie | 4 | 1,720 | 292 |
| Forestburg Ind School Dist/Forestburg | 1 | 173 | 293 |
| Gold-Burg Ind School Dist/Bowie | 1 | 127 | 293 |
| Montague Ind School Dist/Montague | 1 | 166 | 293 |
| Nocona Ind School Dist/Nocona | 3 | 725 | 293 |
| Prairie Valley Ind School Dist/Nocona | 1 | 167 | 293 |
| St Jo Ind School Dist/Saint Jo | 2 | 330 | 293 |
| **MONTGOMERY** | | | |
| Conroe Ind School Dist/Conroe | 65 | 64,500 | 294 |
| Magnolia Ind School Dist/Magnolia | 16 | 13,100 | 295 |
| Montgomery Ind School Dist/Montgomery | 10 | 9,048 | 296 |
| New Caney Ind School Dist/New Caney | 19 | 15,000 | 296 |
| Splendora Ind School Dist/Splendora | 6 | 4,200 | 297 |
| Willis Ind School Dist/Willis | 9 | 6,709 | 297 |
| **MOORE** | | | |
| Dumas Ind School Dist/Dumas | 9 | 4,300 | 298 |
| Sunray Ind School Dist/Sunray | 3 | 556 | 299 |
| **MORRIS** | | | |
| Daingerfield-Lone Star Ind SD/Daingerfield | 4 | 970 | 299 |
| Pewitt Cons Ind School Dist/Omaha | 3 | 870 | 299 |
| **MOTLEY** | | | |
| Motley Co Ind School Dist/Matador | 1 | 162 | 299 |
| **NACOGDOCHES** | | | |
| Central Heights Ind Sch Dist/Nacogdoches | 3 | 1,100 | 300 |
| Chireno ISD School Dist/Chireno | 1 | 400 | 300 |
| Cushing Ind School Dist/Cushing | 2 | 524 | 300 |
| Douglass Ind School Dist/Douglass | 1 | 440 | 300 |
| Etoile Ind School Dist/Etoile | 1 | 100 | 300 |
| Garrison Ind School Dist/Garrison | 3 | 682 | 301 |
| Martinsville Ind School Dist/Nacogdoches | 1 | 400 | 301 |
| Nacogdoches Ind School Dist/Nacogdoches | 10 | 6,400 | 301 |
| Woden Ind School Dist/Nacogdoches | 3 | 780 | 301 |
| **NAVARRO** | | | |
| Blooming Grove Ind School Dist/Blooming GRV | 3 | 950 | 302 |
| Corsicana Ind School Dist/Corsicana | 9 | 6,000 | 302 |
| Dawson Ind School Dist/Dawson | 1 | 512 | 302 |
| Frost Ind School Dist/Frost | 2 | 368 | 302 |
| Kerens Ind School Dist/Kerens | 3 | 600 | 303 |
| Mildred Ind School Dist/Corsicana | 1 | 730 | 303 |
| Rice Ind School Dist/Rice | 4 | 975 | 303 |
| **NEWTON** | | | |
| Burkeville Ind School Dist/Burkeville | 2 | 250 | 303 |
| Newton Ind School Dist/Newton | 3 | 1,041 | 304 |
| **NOLAN** | | | |
| Blackwell Cons Ind Sch Dist/Blackwell | 1 | 150 | 304 |
| Highland Ind School Dist/Roscoe | 1 | 239 | 304 |
| Roscoe Collegiate Ind Sch Dist/Roscoe | 3 | 593 | 304 |
| Sweetwater ISD School Dist/Sweetwater | 7 | 1,888 | 304 |
| **NUECES** | | | |
| Agua Dulce Ind School Dist/Agua Dulce | 2 | 374 | 305 |
| Banquete Ind School Dist/Banquete | 3 | 900 | 305 |
| Bishop Cons Ind School Dist/Bishop | 5 | 1,380 | 305 |
| Calallen Ind School Dist/Corp Christi | 5 | 3,914 | 305 |
| Corpus Christi Ind Sch Dist/Corp Christi | 58 | 37,000 | 306 |
| Diocese Corpus Christi Ed Off/Corp Christi | 16 | 3,300 | 309 |
| Driscoll Ind School Dist/Driscoll | 1 | 281 | 307 |
| Flour Bluff Ind School Dist/Corp Christi | 7 | 5,750 | 307 |
| London Ind School Dist/Corp Christi | 1 | 900 | 308 |
| Port Aransas Ind School Dist/Port Aransas | 3 | 480 | 308 |
| Region 2 Ed Service Center/Corp Christi | | | 309 |
| Robstown Ind School Dist/Robstown | 7 | 2,000 | 308 |
| Tuloso-Midway Ind School Dist/Corp Christi | 5 | 3,043 | 308 |
| West Oso Ind School Dist/Corp Christi | 4 | 1,946 | 309 |
| **OCHILTREE** | | | |
| Perryton Ind School Dist/Perryton | 6 | 2,217 | 310 |
| **OLDHAM** | | | |
| Adrian Ind School Dist/Adrian | 1 | 120 | 310 |
| Boys Ranch Ind School Dist/Boys Ranch | 3 | 240 | 310 |
| Vega Ind School Dist/Vega | 2 | 370 | 310 |
| Wildorado Ind Sch Dist/Wildorado | 1 | 210 | 311 |
| **ORANGE** | | | |
| Bridge City Ind School Dist/Bridge City | 4 | 3,057 | 311 |
| Deweyville Ind School Dist/Orange | 2 | 575 | 311 |
| Little Cypress Mauriceville SD/Orange | 6 | 3,100 | 311 |

| COUNTY District/City | NO. OF SCHOOLS | ENROLL-MENT | PAGE |
|---|---|---|---|
| Orangefield Ind School Dist/Orange | 3 | 1,785 | 312 |
| Vidor Ind School Dist/Vidor | 7 | 4,400 | 312 |
| West Orange-Cove Cons ISD/Orange | 4 | 2,485 | 312 |
| **PALO PINTO** | | | |
| Gordon Ind School Dist/Gordon | 1 | 210 | 313 |
| Graford Ind School Dist/Graford | 2 | 340 | 313 |
| Mineral Wells Ind School Dist/Mineral Wells | 6 | 3,200 | 313 |
| Palo Pinto Ind Sch Dist 906/Palo Pinto | 1 | 100 | 313 |
| Santo Ind School Dist/Santo | 2 | 451 | 313 |
| Strawn Ind School Dist/Strawn | 1 | 160 | 314 |
| **PANOLA** | | | |
| Beckville Ind School Dist/Beckville | 2 | 700 | 314 |
| Carthage Ind School Dist/Carthage | 6 | 2,600 | 314 |
| Gary Ind School Dist/Gary | 1 | 443 | 314 |
| **PARKER** | | | |
| Aledo Ind School Dist/Aledo | 10 | 6,000 | 315 |
| Brock Ind School Dist/Brock | 4 | 1,476 | 315 |
| Garner Ind School Dist/Weatherford | 1 | 212 | 315 |
| Millsap Ind School Dist/Millsap | 3 | 989 | 315 |
| Peaster Ind School Dist/Weatherford | 3 | 1,210 | 316 |
| Poolville Ind School Dist/Poolville | 3 | 550 | 316 |
| Springtown Ind School Dist/Springtown | 6 | 3,470 | 316 |
| Weatherford Ind School Dist/Weatherford | 12 | 8,000 | 316 |
| **PARMER** | | | |
| Bovina Ind School Dist/Bovina | 3 | 460 | 317 |
| Farwell Ind School Dist/Farwell | 3 | 539 | 317 |
| Friona Ind School Dist/Friona | 4 | 1,045 | 318 |
| Lazbuddie Ind School Dist/Lazbuddie | 1 | 168 | 318 |
| **PECOS** | | | |
| Buena Vista Ind School Dist/Imperial | 1 | 250 | 318 |
| Ft Stockton Ind School Dist/Fort Stockton | 5 | 2,469 | 318 |
| Iraan-Sheffield Ind Sch Dist/Iraan | 3 | 375 | 318 |
| **POLK** | | | |
| Big Sandy Ind School Dist/Livingston | 1 | 484 | 319 |
| Corrigan-Camden Ind Sch Dist/Corrigan | 3 | 830 | 319 |
| Goodrich Ind School Dist/Goodrich | 2 | 218 | 319 |
| Leggett Ind School Dist/Leggett | 1 | 167 | 319 |
| Livingston Ind School Dist/Livingston | 7 | 3,963 | 319 |
| Onalaska Ind School Dist/Onalaska | 2 | 1,056 | 320 |
| **POTTER** | | | |
| Amarillo Ind School Dist/Amarillo | 55 | 33,311 | 320 |
| Bushland Ind School Dist/Amarillo | 3 | 1,400 | 321 |
| Diocese of Amarillo Ed Office/Amarillo | 5 | 850 | 322 |
| Highland Park Ind School Dist/Amarillo | 3 | 864 | 322 |
| River Road Ind School Dist/Amarillo | 4 | 1,278 | 322 |
| **PRESIDIO** | | | |
| Marfa Ind School Dist/Marfa | 2 | 342 | 322 |
| Presidio Ind School Dist/Presidio | 3 | 1,162 | 323 |
| **RAINS** | | | |
| Rains Ind School Dist/Emory | 4 | 1,500 | 323 |
| **RANDALL** | | | |
| Canyon Ind School Dist/Canyon | 16 | 11,000 | 323 |
| Region 16 Ed Service Center/Amarillo | | | 324 |
| **REAGAN** | | | |
| Reagan Co Ind School Dist/Big Lake | 3 | 850 | 324 |
| **REAL** | | | |
| Leakey Ind School Dist/Leakey | 1 | 279 | 324 |
| **RED RIVER** | | | |
| Avery Ind School Dist/Avery | 2 | 323 | 325 |
| Clarksville Ind School Dist/Clarksville | 2 | 534 | 325 |
| Detroit Ind School Dist/Detroit | 3 | 530 | 325 |
| Rivercrest Ind School Dist/Bogata | 3 | 700 | 325 |
| **REEVES** | | | |
| Balmorhea Ind School Dist/Balmorhea | 1 | 165 | 325 |
| Pecos-Barstow-Toyah Ind SD/Pecos | 5 | 2,700 | 326 |
| **REFUGIO** | | | |
| Austwell Tivoli Ind SD/Tivoli | 2 | 140 | 326 |
| Refugio Ind School Dist/Refugio | 3 | 654 | 326 |
| Woodsboro Ind School Dist/Woodsboro | 2 | 441 | 326 |
| **ROBERTS** | | | |
| Miami Ind School Dist/Miami | 1 | 190 | 327 |
| **ROBERTSON** | | | |
| Bremond Ind School Dist/Bremond | 3 | 500 | 327 |

| COUNTY<br>District/City | NO. OF<br>SCHOOLS | ENROLL-<br>MENT | PAGE |
|---|---|---|---|
| Calvert Ind School Dist/Calvert | 1 | 166 | 327 |
| Franklin Ind School Dist/Franklin | 3 | 1,100 | 327 |
| Hearne Ind School Dist/Hearne | 3 | 766 | 327 |
| **ROCKWALL** | | | |
| Rockwall Ind School Dist/Rockwall | 22 | 17,078 | 328 |
| Royse City Ind School Dist/Royse City | 9 | 6,300 | 328 |
| **RUNNELS** | | | |
| Ballinger Ind School Dist/Ballinger | 3 | 798 | 329 |
| Miles Ind School Dist/Miles | 1 | 480 | 329 |
| Olfen Ind School Dist/Rowena | 1 | 205 | 329 |
| Winters Ind School Dist/Winters | 3 | 525 | 329 |
| **RUSK** | | | |
| Carlisle Ind School Dist/Henderson | 1 | 587 | 330 |
| Henderson Ind School Dist/Henderson | 6 | 3,400 | 330 |
| Laneville Ind School Dist/Laneville | 1 | 157 | 330 |
| Leveretts Chapel Ind Sch Dist/Overton | 1 | 240 | 330 |
| Mt Enterprise Ind School Dist/Mt Enterprise | 1 | 398 | 330 |
| Overton Ind School Dist/Overton | 2 | 500 | 331 |
| Tatum Ind School Dist/Tatum | 4 | 1,461 | 331 |
| West Rusk Co Cons Ind Sch Dist/New London | 4 | 980 | 331 |
| **SABINE** | | | |
| Hemphill Ind School Dist/Hemphill | 3 | 906 | 331 |
| West Sabine Ind Sch Dist/Pineland | 2 | 578 | 332 |
| **SAN AUGUSTINE** | | | |
| Broaddus Ind School Dist/Broaddus | 2 | 400 | 332 |
| San Augustine Ind School Dist/San Augustine | 2 | 720 | 332 |
| **SAN JACINTO** | | | |
| Coldspring-Oakhurst Cons ISD/Coldspring | 4 | 1,465 | 332 |
| Shepherd Ind School Dist/Shepherd | 4 | 2,041 | 333 |
| **SAN PATRICIO** | | | |
| Aransas Pass Ind School Dist/Aransas Pass | 5 | 1,484 | 333 |
| Gregory-Portland Ind Sch Dist/Portland | 7 | 4,600 | 333 |
| Ingleside Ind School Dist/Ingleside | 5 | 2,046 | 333 |
| Mathis Ind School Dist/Mathis | 4 | 1,600 | 334 |
| Odem-Edroy Ind School Dist/Odem | 4 | 900 | 334 |
| Sinton Ind School Dist/Sinton | 4 | 1,339 | 334 |
| Taft Ind School Dist/Taft | 3 | 1,154 | 334 |
| **SAN SABA** | | | |
| Cherokee Ind School Dist/Cherokee | 1 | 112 | 335 |
| Richland Springs Ind Sch Dist/Richland Spgs | 1 | 123 | 335 |
| San Saba Ind School Dist/San Saba | 3 | 717 | 335 |
| **SCHLEICHER** | | | |
| Schleicher Co Ind Sch Dist/Eldorado | 3 | 540 | 335 |
| **SCURRY** | | | |
| Hermleigh Ind School Dist/Hermleigh | 1 | 275 | 336 |
| Ira Ind School Dist/Ira | 1 | 275 | 336 |
| Snyder Ind School Dist/Snyder | 4 | 2,700 | 336 |
| **SHACKELFORD** | | | |
| Albany Ind School Dist/Albany | 2 | 512 | 336 |
| Moran Ind School Dist/Moran | 1 | 105 | 336 |
| **SHELBY** | | | |
| Center Ind School Dist/Center | 6 | 2,600 | 337 |
| Excelsior Ind School Dist/Center | 1 | 80 | 337 |
| Joaquin Ind School Dist/Joaquin | 3 | 680 | 337 |
| Shelbyville Ind School Dist/Shelbyville | 3 | 790 | 337 |
| Tenaha Ind School Dist/Tenaha | 1 | 542 | 337 |
| Timpson Ind School Dist/Timpson | 3 | 628 | 338 |
| **SHERMAN** | | | |
| Stratford Ind School Dist/Stratford | 3 | 560 | 338 |
| Texhoma Ind School Dist/Texhoma | 1 | 130 | 338 |
| **SMITH** | | | |
| Arp Ind School Dist/Arp | 3 | 870 | 339 |
| Bullard Ind School Dist/Bullard | 6 | 2,700 | 339 |
| Chapel Hill Ind School Dist/Tyler | 5 | 3,513 | 339 |
| Diocese of Tyler Ed Office/Tyler | 4 | 1,300 | 342 |
| Lindale Ind School Dist/Lindale | 6 | 4,200 | 339 |
| Troup Ind School Dist/Troup | 3 | 1,100 | 340 |
| Tyler Ind School Dist/Tyler | 29 | 18,000 | 340 |
| UT Tyler University Acad Dist/Tyler | 3 | 400 | 341 |
| Whitehouse Ind School Dist/Whitehouse | 8 | 4,800 | 341 |
| Winona Ind School Dist/Winona | 4 | 1,050 | 341 |
| **SOMERVELL** | | | |
| Glen Rose Ind School Dist/Glen Rose | 4 | 1,970 | 342 |

| COUNTY<br>District/City | NO. OF<br>SCHOOLS | ENROLL-<br>MENT | PAGE |
|---|---|---|---|
| **STARR** | | | |
| Rio Grande City Ind Sch Dist/Rio Grande Cy | 18 | 10,175 | 342 |
| Roma Ind School Dist/Roma | 10 | 6,000 | 343 |
| San Isidro Ind School Dist/San Isidro | 1 | 200 | 343 |
| **STEPHENS** | | | |
| Breckenridge Ind School Dist/Breckenridge | 5 | 1,413 | 344 |
| **STERLING** | | | |
| Sterling City Ind School Dist/Sterling City | 2 | 320 | 344 |
| **STONEWALL** | | | |
| Aspermont Ind School Dist/Aspermont | 2 | 214 | 344 |
| **SUTTON** | | | |
| Sonora Ind School Dist/Sonora | 3 | 767 | 345 |
| **SWISHER** | | | |
| Happy Ind School Dist/Happy | 2 | 248 | 345 |
| Kress Ind School Dist/Kress | 2 | 242 | 345 |
| Tulia Ind School Dist/Tulia | 3 | 1,040 | 345 |
| **TARRANT** | | | |
| Arlington Ind School Dist/Arlington | 78 | 59,500 | 346 |
| Azle Ind School Dist/Azle | 12 | 5,900 | 348 |
| Birdville Ind School Dist/Haltom City | 33 | 23,513 | 348 |
| Carroll Independent Sch Dist/Southlake | 11 | 8,000 | 349 |
| Castleberry Ind School Dist/Fort Worth | 7 | 3,574 | 349 |
| Crowley Ind School Dist/Crowley | 25 | 15,215 | 350 |
| Diocese of Fort Worth Ed Off/Fort Worth | 19 | 4,700 | 360 |
| Eagle Mtn-Saginaw Ind Sch Dist/Saginaw | 27 | 21,000 | 351 |
| Everman Ind School Dist/Fort Worth | 11 | 6,345 | 351 |
| Ft Worth Ind School Dist/Fort Worth | 134 | 89,000 | 352 |
| Grapevine-Colleyville Ind SD/Grapevine | 21 | 14,000 | 355 |
| Hurst-Euless-Bedford ISD/Bedford | 31 | 23,000 | 356 |
| Keller Ind School Dist/Keller | 42 | 35,352 | 357 |
| Kennedale Ind School Dist/Kennedale | 6 | 3,000 | 358 |
| Lake Worth Ind School Dist/Lake Worth | 6 | 3,000 | 358 |
| Mansfield Ind School Dist/Mansfield | 46 | 35,626 | 358 |
| Region 11 Ed Service Center/WHT Settlemt | | | 362 |
| White Settlement Ind Sch Dist/Fort Worth | 9 | 6,909 | 360 |
| **TAYLOR** | | | |
| Abilene Ind School Dist/Abilene | 26 | 17,000 | 362 |
| Jim Ned Cons Ind School Dist/Tuscola | 4 | 1,360 | 363 |
| Merkel Ind School Dist/Merkel | 3 | 1,073 | 363 |
| Region 14 Ed Service Center/Abilene | | | 364 |
| Trent Isn School Dist/Trent | 1 | 150 | 363 |
| Wylie Ind School Dist/Abilene | 7 | 5,000 | 364 |
| **TERRELL** | | | |
| Terrell Co Ind School Dist/Sanderson | 1 | 108 | 364 |
| **TERRY** | | | |
| Brownfield Ind Sch Dist/Brownfield | 4 | 1,623 | 364 |
| Meadow Ind School Dist/Meadow | 1 | 285 | 365 |
| Wellman Union Ind School Dist/Wellman | 1 | 335 | 365 |
| **THROCKMORTON** | | | |
| Throckmorton Ind School Dist/Throckmorton | 1 | 158 | 365 |
| Woodson Ind School Dist/Woodson | 1 | 144 | 365 |
| **TITUS** | | | |
| Chapel Hill Ind School Dist/Mt Pleasant | 3 | 1,050 | 365 |
| Harts Bluff Ind School Dist/Mt Pleasant | 1 | 675 | 366 |
| Mt Pleasant Ind School Dist/Mt Pleasant | 8 | 5,100 | 366 |
| **TOM GREEN** | | | |
| Christoval Ind School Dist/Christoval | 2 | 505 | 366 |
| Diocese of San Angelo Ed Off/San Angelo | 3 | 1,000 | 368 |
| Grape Creek Ind School Dist/San Angelo | 3 | 1,160 | 367 |
| Region 15 Ed Service Center/San Angelo | | | 368 |
| San Angelo Ind School Dist/San Angelo | 25 | 14,520 | 367 |
| Veribest Ind School Dist/Veribest | 1 | 275 | 368 |
| Wall Ind School Dist/Wall | 4 | 1,100 | 368 |
| Water Valley Ind School Dist/Water Valley | 2 | 300 | 368 |
| **TRAVIS** | | | |
| Austin Ind School Dist/Austin | 117 | 80,950 | 369 |
| Austin ISD Elem School Area/Austin | | | 369 |
| Austin ISD High School Area/Austin | | | 371 |
| Austin ISD Middle School Area/Austin | | | 371 |
| Del Valle Ind School Dist/Del Valle | 15 | 12,100 | 372 |
| Diocese of Austin Ed Office/Austin | 21 | 5,141 | 375 |
| Eanes Ind School Dist/Austin | 9 | 8,156 | 372 |
| Lago Vista Ind School Dist/Lago Vista | 4 | 1,500 | 373 |
| Lake Travis Ind School Dist/Austin | 10 | 10,410 | 373 |
| Manor Ind School Dist/Manor | 16 | 9,200 | 373 |
| Pflugerville Ind School Dist/Pflugerville | 33 | 26,269 | 374 |

| COUNTY District/City | NO. OF SCHOOLS | ENROLL-MENT | PAGE |
|---|---|---|---|
| Region 13 Ed Service Center/Austin | | | 376 |
| **TRINITY** | | | |
| Apple Springs Ind School Dist/Apple Springs | 2 | 200 | 376 |
| Centerville Ind School Dist/Groveton | 2 | 127 | 376 |
| Groveton Ind School Dist/Groveton | 2 | 750 | 377 |
| Trinity Ind School Dist/Trinity | 3 | 1,188 | 377 |
| **TYLER** | | | |
| Chester Ind School Dist/Chester | 2 | 184 | 377 |
| Colmesneil Ind School Dist/Colmesneil | 2 | 450 | 377 |
| Spurger Ind School Dist/Spurger | 2 | 400 | 377 |
| Warren Ind School Dist/Warren | 4 | 1,200 | 378 |
| Woodville Ind School Dist/Woodville | 4 | 1,300 | 378 |
| **UPSHUR** | | | |
| Big Sandy Ind School Dist/Big Sandy | 3 | 667 | 378 |
| Gilmer Ind School Dist/Gilmer | 4 | 2,437 | 378 |
| Harmony Ind School Dist/Big Sandy | 4 | 1,050 | 379 |
| New Diana Ind School Dist/Diana | 3 | 1,073 | 379 |
| Ore City Ind School Dist/Ore City | 3 | 850 | 379 |
| Union Grove Ind School Dist/Gladewater | 2 | 754 | 379 |
| Union Hill Ind School Dist/Gilmer | 1 | 325 | 380 |
| **UPTON** | | | |
| McCamey Ind School Dist/Mc Camey | 3 | 560 | 380 |
| Rankin Ind School Dist/Rankin | 2 | 294 | 380 |
| **UVALDE** | | | |
| Knippa Ind School Dist/Knippa | 1 | 460 | 380 |
| Sabinal Ind School Dist/Sabinal | 2 | 429 | 380 |
| Utopia Ind School Dist/Utopia | 1 | 210 | 381 |
| Uvalde Cons Ind School Dist/Uvalde | 8 | 4,221 | 381 |
| **VAL VERDE** | | | |
| Comstock Ind School Dist/Comstock | 1 | 199 | 381 |
| San Felipe-Del Rio Cons Ind SD/Del Rio | 12 | 10,472 | 381 |
| **VAN ZANDT** | | | |
| Canton Ind School Dist/Canton | 4 | 2,300 | 382 |
| Edgewood Ind School Dist/Edgewood | 4 | 950 | 382 |
| Fruitvale Ind School Dist/Fruitvale | 3 | 425 | 383 |
| Grand Saline Ind School Dist/Grand Saline | 4 | 1,100 | 383 |
| Martin's Mill Ind Sch Dist/Ben Wheeler | 1 | 230 | 383 |
| Van Ind School Dist/Van | 5 | 2,400 | 383 |
| Wills Point Ind School Dist/Wills Point | 5 | 2,500 | 383 |
| **VICTORIA** | | | |
| Bloomington Ind School Dist/Placedo | 5 | 850 | 384 |
| Diocese of Victoria Ed Office/Victoria | 13 | 2,827 | 385 |
| Nursery ISD/Victoria | 1 | 155 | 384 |
| Region 3 Ed Service Center/Victoria | | | 385 |
| Victoria Ind School Dist/Victoria | 23 | 13,900 | 384 |
| **WALKER** | | | |
| Huntsville Ind School Dist/Huntsville | 9 | 6,500 | 386 |
| New Waverly Ind School Dist/New Waverly | 4 | 1,000 | 386 |
| Region 6 Ed Service Center/Huntsville | | | 386 |
| **WALLER** | | | |
| Hempstead Ind School Dist/Hempstead | 3 | 1,600 | 387 |
| Royal Ind School Dist/Pattison | 4 | 2,400 | 387 |
| Waller Ind School Dist/Waller | 8 | 7,700 | 387 |
| **WARD** | | | |
| Grandfalls-Royalty Ind SD/Grandfalls | 1 | 184 | 388 |
| Monahans-Wickett-Pyote ISD/Monahans | 6 | 2,300 | 388 |
| **WASHINGTON** | | | |
| Brenham Ind School Dist/Brenham | 7 | 5,000 | 388 |
| Burton Ind School Dist/Burton | 2 | 440 | 388 |
| **WEBB** | | | |
| Diocese of Laredo Ed Office/Laredo | 4 | 1,627 | 391 |
| Laredo Ind School Dist/Laredo | 33 | 23,737 | 389 |
| United Ind School Dist/Laredo | 48 | 48,174 | 390 |
| Webb Cons Ind School Dist/Bruni | 3 | 238 | 391 |
| **WHARTON** | | | |
| Boling Ind School Dist/Boling | 3 | 1,137 | 392 |
| East Bernard Ind Sch Dist/East Bernard | 3 | 950 | 392 |
| El Campo Ind School Dist/El Campo | 5 | 4,500 | 392 |
| Louise Ind School Dist/Louise | 3 | 510 | 392 |
| Wharton Ind School Dist/Wharton | 5 | 2,015 | 393 |
| **WHEELER** | | | |
| Ft Elliott Cons Ind Sch Dist/Briscoe | 1 | 146 | 393 |
| Kelton Ind School Dist/Wheeler | 1 | 84 | 393 |
| Shamrock Ind School Dist/Shamrock | 3 | 342 | 393 |

| COUNTY District/City | NO. OF SCHOOLS | ENROLL-MENT | PAGE |
|---|---|---|---|
| Wheeler Ind School Dist/Wheeler | 1 | 441 | 394 |
| **WICHITA** | | | |
| Burkburnett Ind Sch Dist/Burkburnett | 6 | 3,350 | 394 |
| City View Ind School Dist/Wichita Falls | 2 | 921 | 394 |
| Electra Ind School Dist/Electra | 3 | 391 | 394 |
| Iowa Park Consolidated Ind SD/Iowa Park | 4 | 1,421 | 395 |
| Region 9 Ed Service Center/Wichita Falls | | | 396 |
| Wichita Falls Ind School Dist/Wichita Falls | 28 | 14,500 | 395 |
| **WILBARGER** | | | |
| Harrold Ind School Dist/Harrold | 1 | 106 | 396 |
| Northside Ind School Dist/Vernon | 1 | 222 | 396 |
| Vernon Ind School Dist/Vernon | 6 | 1,700 | 396 |
| **WILLACY** | | | |
| Lasara Ind School Dist/Lasara | 2 | 368 | 397 |
| Lyford Cons Ind School Dist/Lyford | 3 | 1,422 | 397 |
| Raymondville Ind Sch Dist/Raymondville | 5 | 2,000 | 397 |
| San Perlita Ind School Dist/San Perlita | 1 | 269 | 397 |
| **WILLIAMSON** | | | |
| Coupland Ind School Dist/Coupland | 1 | 165 | 398 |
| Florence Ind School Dist/Florence | 3 | 957 | 398 |
| Georgetown Ind School Dist/Georgetown | 18 | 12,403 | 398 |
| Granger Ind School Dist/Granger | 1 | 426 | 399 |
| Hutto Ind School Dist/Hutto | 10 | 8,129 | 399 |
| Jarrell Ind School Dist/Jarrell | 5 | 1,800 | 399 |
| Leander Ind School Dist/Leander | 44 | 43,000 | 399 |
| Liberty Hill Ind School Dist/Liberty Hill | 6 | 4,000 | 401 |
| Round Rock Ind School Dist/Round Rock | 54 | 51,008 | 401 |
| Taylor Ind School Dist/Taylor | 7 | 3,200 | 402 |
| Thrall Ind School Dist/Thrall | 3 | 750 | 403 |
| **WILSON** | | | |
| Floresville Ind School Dist/Floresville | 5 | 3,000 | 403 |
| La Vernia Ind School Dist/La Vernia | 4 | 2,400 | 404 |
| Poth Ind School Dist/Poth | 3 | 858 | 404 |
| Stockdale Ind School Dist/Stockdale | 3 | 820 | 404 |
| **WINKLER** | | | |
| Kermit Ind School Dist/Kermit | 3 | 1,397 | 405 |
| Wink Loving Ind School Dist/Wink | 2 | 420 | 405 |
| **WISE** | | | |
| Alvord Ind School Dist/Alvord | 3 | 700 | 405 |
| Boyd Ind School Dist/Boyd | 4 | 1,281 | 405 |
| Bridgeport Ind School Dist/Bridgeport | 5 | 1,994 | 406 |
| Chico Ind School Dist/Chico | 3 | 600 | 406 |
| Decatur Ind School Dist/Decatur | 5 | 3,390 | 406 |
| North Lamar Ind School Dist/Paradise | 7 | 2,417 | 406 |
| Paradise Ind School Dist/Paradise | 4 | 1,209 | 407 |
| Slidell Ind School Dist/Slidell | 2 | 350 | 407 |
| **WOOD** | | | |
| Alba-Golden Ind School Dist/Alba | 2 | 588 | 407 |
| Hawkins Ind School Dist/Hawkins | 3 | 750 | 407 |
| Mineola Ind School Dist/Mineola | 4 | 1,556 | 408 |
| Quitman Ind School Dist/Quitman | 3 | 1,083 | 408 |
| Winnsboro Ind School Dist/Winnsboro | 3 | 1,422 | 408 |
| Yantis Ind School Dist/Yantis | 2 | 350 | 408 |
| **YOAKUM** | | | |
| Denver City Ind School Dist/Denver City | 5 | 1,741 | 409 |
| Plains Ind School Dist/Plains | 3 | 475 | 409 |
| **YOUNG** | | | |
| Graham Ind School Dist/Graham | 5 | 2,354 | 409 |
| Newcastle Ind School Dist/Newcastle | 1 | 205 | 409 |
| Olney Ind School Dist/Olney | 3 | 639 | 410 |
| **ZAPATA** | | | |
| Zapata Co Ind School Dist/Zapata | 6 | 3,500 | 410 |
| **ZAVALA** | | | |
| Crystal City Ind School Dist/Crystal City | 5 | 1,950 | 410 |
| La Pryor Ind School Dist/La Pryor | 2 | 500 | 411 |

| NAME/District | JOB FUNCTIONS | PAGE |
|---|---|---|
| **A** | | |
| Aaron, Hunter/Azle Ind School Dist | 4 | 348 |
| Aaron, Mary/Floresville Ind School Dist | 5 | 403 |
| Abadie, Melissa/Waxahachie Ind School Dist | 43,285 | 146 |
| Abalos, Delma/Ector Co Ind School Dist | 67 | 134 |
| Abaraham, Ollie/Post Ind School Dist | 5 | 167 |
| Abbott, Clarissa/McAllen Ind School Dist | 39 | 224 |
| Abbott, Laura/Lake Travis Ind School Dist | 58,271 | 373 |
| Abbott, Paula/Mart Ind School Dist | 4 | 283 |
| Abbott, Tonya/Poteet Ind School Dist | 16,82 | 24 |
| Abernethy, Elizabeth/Region 7 Ed Service Center | 1 | 176 |
| Abila, Samantha/Dublin Ind School Dist | 58 | 147 |
| Abitua, Jesse/Benavides Ind School Dist | 67 | 132 |
| Abla, Kurtis/Dalhart Ind School Dist | 88 | 99 |
| Ables, Mitch/Hawley Ind School Dist | 6 | 253 |
| Abott, John, Dr/Mineola Ind School Dist | 67 | 408 |
| Abrams, Dalton/UT Tyler University Acad Dist | 73 | 341 |
| Abregon, Ariel/Lyford Cons Ind School Dist | 4 | 397 |
| Abrigo, Janie/Roscoe Collegiate Ind Sch Dist | 58 | 304 |
| Abrigo, Yolanda/Alice Ind School Dist | 16,73,76,82,286,295 | 248 |
| Abshier, Cody/Liberty Ind School Dist | 1 | 269 |
| Abshier, John/Groveton Ind School Dist | 5 | 377 |
| Abundez, Paul/La Villa Ind School Dist | 274 | 224 |
| Abundis, David/South San Antonio Ind Sch Dist | 11,296 | 45 |
| Acevedo, Evaristo/Klondike Ind School Dist | 3 | 121 |
| Aceves, Debra, Dr/Donna Ind School Dist | 13,57,61,81 | 220 |
| Ach, Rachel/Borger Ind School Dist | 16 | 240 |
| Acker, Marvin/Jacksonville Ind School Dist | 91 | 76 |
| **Acklery, Stacy/**Goliad Ind School Dist | 1 | 168 |
| Ackley, Karol/Paris Ind School Dist | 11 | 262 |
| Ackley, Stacy/Royal Ind School Dist | 1 | 387 |
| Acklin, Teresa/Prairie Lea Ind School Dist | 6 | 65 |
| Ackmann, Leslie/Weatherford Ind School Dist | 58,275 | 316 |
| Acock, Dana/Grand Prairie Ind School Dist | 5 | 111 |
| Acosta, Adrian/Houston Ind School Dist | 73 | 193 |
| Acosta, Courtney/Georgetown Ind School Dist | 3,7,36,91 | 398 |
| Acosta, Henry/Northside Ind School Dist | 15 | 39 |
| Acosta, Jorge/Irving Ind School Dist | 68 | 113 |
| Acosta, Simona/Pecos-Barstow-Toyah Ind SD | 7 | 326 |
| Adair, Roger/Round Rock Ind School Dist | 76 | 401 |
| Adam, Jerry, Dr/Comfort Ind School Dist | 8,12,57,74,83,288 | 257 |
| Adame, Jimmy/Taft Ind School Dist | 67 | 334 |
| Adame, Roger/Mercedes Ind School Dist | 6 | 225 |
| Adami, Francis/Freer Ind School Dist | 6 | 132 |
| Adami, Randolph/Spring Branch Ind School Dist | 91 | 206 |
| Adams-Molina, Georgeanna/Buffalo Ind School Dist | 11,73,271,286 | 266 |
| Adams, Amanda/West Ind School Dist | 8 | 285 |
| Adams, Angela/Winona Ind School Dist | 13,58 | 341 |
| Adams, Carolyn/Gruver Ind School Dist | 60 | 181 |
| Adams, Casey/Woodson Ind School Dist | 1,11,83,288 | 365 |
| Adams, Cynthia/Industrial Ind School Dist | 58 | 243 |
| Adams, Donna/Jasper Ind School Dist | 5 | 243 |
| Adams, Felicia/Houston Ind School Dist | 73 | 193 |
| Adams, Greta/Anna Ind School Dist | 16 | 81 |
| Adams, Jason/Fairfield Ind School Dist | 1 | 160 |
| Adams, Jennifer/Frisco Ind School Dist | 81 | 82 |
| Adams, Jennifer/Tomball Ind School Dist | 42 | 208 |
| Adams, Jimmy/Kennedale Ind School Dist | 2 | 358 |
| Adams, John/El Paso Ind School Dist | 35 | 137 |
| Adams, Kamara/Kingsville Ind School Dist | 8,15 | 260 |
| Adams, Katie/UT Tyler University Acad Dist | 27 | 341 |
| Adams, Keith/Sunnyvale Ind School Dist | 3 | 117 |
| Adams, Kelly/Denver City Ind School Dist | 4,8,11,58,83,88,271 | 409 |
| Adams, Kyle/Union Grove Ind School Dist | 73,84 | 379 |
| Adams, Lisa/Temple Ind School Dist | 10,15 | 32 |
| Adams, Matt/Azle Ind School Dist | 2,11 | 348 |
| Adams, Matt/Peaster Ind School Dist | 1 | 316 |
| Adams, Molly/Aransas Co Ind School Dist | 12 | 22 |
| Adams, Shannon/Evadale Ind School Dist | 3,5,91 | 243 |
| Adams, Shay/Lovejoy Ind School Dist | 2,19 | 84 |
| Adams, Sheila/Lufkin Ind School Dist | 71 | 21 |
| Adams, Tammy/West Hardin Co Cons Sch Dist | 7 | 183 |
| Adams, Travis/Guthrie Common School Dist | 67 | 260 |
| Adams, Vicky/Hillsboro Ind School Dist | 1 | 230 |

| NAME/District | JOB FUNCTIONS | PAGE |
|---|---|---|
| Adcock, Katrina/Kopperl Ind School Dist | 1,73 | 50 |
| Adcock, Steve/Evant Ind School Dist | 3,17 | 96 |
| Adcox, Garri/Hurst-Euless-Bedford ISD | 46 | 356 |
| Adermann, Carin/Northside Ind School Dist | 69 | 39 |
| Adix, Kenneth, Dr/Round Rock Ind School Dist | 19 | 401 |
| Adkin, William/Judson Ind School Dist | 2,19,73 | 36 |
| Adkins, Craig/Jacksboro Ind Sch Dist | 3,4,91 | 242 |
| Adkins, Cyril/Smithville Ind School Dist | 6 | 27 |
| Adkins, Mike/Ector Co Ind School Dist | 71 | 134 |
| Adkins, Norman/Millsap Ind School Dist | 3 | 315 |
| Adkinson, Christi/Roby Cons Ind School Dist | 4 | 152 |
| Adkinson, Rebecca/Excelsior Ind School Dist | 34 | 337 |
| Adkison, Amie/Garrison Ind School Dist | 7 | 301 |
| Adrian, Stacy/Crowley Ind School Dist | 2,19 | 350 |
| Agee, Danny/Salado Ind School Dist | 3,5 | 32 |
| Aghazadian, Megan/Texas Dept of Education | 3,11,15,68,70 | 1 |
| Aguero, Elispo/La Pryor Ind School Dist | 6 | 411 |
| Aguero, Oscar/Marfa Ind School Dist | 1 | 322 |
| Aguilar, Abel/Weslaco Ind School Dist | 15 | 228 |
| Aguilar, Anna/Sulphur Springs Ind Sch Dist | 57,271 | 235 |
| Aguilar, Antonio/La Feria Ind School Dist | 2,19 | 69 |
| Aguilar, Hortencia/Fort Davis Ind School Dist | 13 | 244 |
| Aguilar, Lori/Lake Worth Ind School Dist | 9,57 | 358 |
| Aguilar, Magdalena, Dr/Socorro Ind School Dist | 88 | 140 |
| Aguilar, Racheal/Tornillo Ind School Dist | 31 | 141 |
| Aguilera, Becky/Palacios Ind School Dist | 91 | 278 |
| Aguillon, Charles/Lake Travis Ind School Dist | 20,23 | 373 |
| Aguirre-Baeza, Louisa/Ysleta Ind School Dist | 8,15 | 141 |
| Aguirre, Andreas/San Saba Ind School Dist | 6 | 335 |
| Aguirre, Angelica/Tahoka Ind School Dist | 16,73,98,286,295 | 276 |
| Aguirre, Angelica/Tahoka Ind School Dist | 73,98,286 | 276 |
| Aguirre, Armando, Dr/Region 19 Ed Service Center | 1 | 144 |
| Aguirre, Margarita/Pharr-San Juan-Alamo Ind SD | 58 | 226 |
| Aguirre, Mayra/Lyford Cons Ind School Dist | 271 | 397 |
| Aguirre, Norma/Tornillo Ind School Dist | 4 | 141 |
| Agular, Matthew/Dilley Ind School Dist | 73 | 161 |
| Ahumada, Irene/Ysleta Ind School Dist | 15 | 141 |
| Ailara, Michelle/Red Oak Ind School Dist | 15,68,79 | 146 |
| Airheart, Eric/Trinidad Ind School Dist | 67 | 219 |
| Akadie, Chelsea/El Campo Ind School Dist | 4 | 392 |
| Akers, Debbie/Floresville Ind School Dist | 58 | 403 |
| Akers, Ellen/Pearland Ind School Dist | 69 | 56 |
| Akin, Gina/Kilgore Ind School Dist | 58 | 174 |
| Akin, Lynn/Lubbock Ind School Dist | 79,88 | 272 |
| Akin, Shelby/Pleasant Grove Ind School Dist | 75,298 | 52 |
| Akins, Jennifer/McKinney Ind School Dist | 36 | 84 |
| Akins, Sue/Anna Ind School Dist | 8,15 | 81 |
| Akridge, Tonja/Lufkin Ind School Dist | 90,93 | 21 |
| Akuna, James/Lockhart Ind School Dist | 4 | 64 |
| Alaman, Kandy/Coahoma Ind School Dist | 67 | 237 |
| Alambar, Marie/Trent Isn School Dist | 57,58 | 363 |
| Alana, Nancy/Granbury Ind School Dist | 67 | 233 |
| Alandzes, Mandy/Braination Schools | 4 | 33 |
| Alanis, Claudia/Midland Ind School Dist | 294 | 288 |
| Alanis, Frank/Progreso Ind School Dist | 67 | 227 |
| Alaniz-Ramos, Delma/Laredo Ind School Dist | 69,294 | 389 |
| Alaniz, Adelina/Mission Cons Ind School Dist | 45 | 225 |
| Alaniz, Eduardo/Mission Cons Ind School Dist | 88 | 225 |
| Alaniz, Noe/Rio Hondo Ind School Dist | 2 | 70 |
| Alaniz, Samuel/Medina Valley Ind School Dist | 71 | 287 |
| Alarcon, Theresa/Point Isabel Ind Sch Dist | 1 | 70 |
| Alavardo, Sara/San Benito Cons Ind Sch Dist | 15,68 | 70 |
| Alawneh, John, Dr/Katy Ind School Dist | 71,76,97,286 | 156 |
| Albert, Melvin/Floresville Ind School Dist | 295 | 403 |
| Albracht, Ralph/Nazareth Ind School Dist | 3,5 | 75 |
| Albright, James/Aspermont Ind School Dist | 3,91 | 344 |
| Albright, Janet/Spring Hill Ind School Dist | 4 | 175 |
| Albritton, Jodie/Bullard Ind School Dist | 69 | 339 |
| Albritton, Rick/Gilmer Ind School Dist | 1 | 378 |
| Albro, Josh/Burnet Cons Ind Sch Dist | 5 | 63 |
| Albus, Anthony/Whitharral Ind School Dist | 67 | 233 |
| Albus, Joe/Knox City-O'Brien Cons Ind SD | 67 | 261 |
| Alcorn, Bill/Haskell Cons Ind School Dist | 1 | 215 |
| Alcorta, Andrew/Anton Ind School Dist | 4 | 232 |
| Alcorta, Joe, Dr/Dalhart Ind School Dist | 1,11 | 99 |
| Aldarado, Mary/Greenwood Ind School Dist | 57,271 | 288 |

| NAME/District | JOB FUNCTIONS | PAGE |
|---|---|---|
| Anaya, Marlen/Los Fresnos Cons Ind Sch Dist | 68 | 69 |
| Ancelet, Jackie/Groesbeck Ind School Dist | 3 | 269 |
| Anchondo, Oscar/El Paso Ind School Dist | 5 | 137 |
| Anders, Dustin/Loraine Ind School Dist | 1 | 292 |
| Anders, Jeni/Thrall Ind School Dist | 4 | 403 |
| Andersen, Cynthia/La Porte Ind School Dist | 58 | 203 |
| Anderson, Amy/Angleton Ind School Dist | 4 | 55 |
| Anderson, Aniece/Holliday Ind School Dist | 36,83,88,93,271 | 22 |
| Anderson, Anne/Texas City Ind School Dist | 8 | 166 |
| Anderson, Chris/Red Oak Ind School Dist | 6,35 | 146 |
| Anderson, Christopher, Dr/Arlington Ind School Dist | 20 | 346 |
| Anderson, Craig/Winnsboro Ind School Dist | 73,84,295 | 408 |
| Anderson, Darren/Wolfe City Ind School Dist | 6 | 240 |
| Anderson, David/Comal Ind School Dist | 2,19 | 91 |
| Anderson, Denise/Bovina Ind School Dist | 1 | 317 |
| Anderson, Emily/Donna Ind School Dist | 43 | 220 |
| Anderson, Grant/Little Elm Ind School Dist | 2,15,19 | 128 |
| Anderson, Greg/Greenville Ind School Dist | 3 | 239 |
| Anderson, Greg/Royal Ind School Dist | 6 | 387 |
| Anderson, Jackie/Allen Ind School Dist | 4 | 80 |
| Anderson, Jens/Elgin Ind School Dist | 6 | 27 |
| Anderson, Jimmy/Dickinson Ind School Dist | 3 | 164 |
| Anderson, Jimmy/Vernon Ind School Dist | 3,5 | 396 |
| Anderson, John/Red Oak Ind School Dist | 67 | 146 |
| Anderson, John/Sealy Ind School Dist | 4 | 25 |
| Anderson, John/Seymour Ind School Dist | 1 | 28 |
| Anderson, Julia Faye/Laneville Ind School Dist | 92,93,270 | 330 |
| Anderson, Justin/Hull Daisetta Ind School Dist | 10,13 | 268 |
| Anderson, Kelli/Spring Ind School Dist | 9 | 207 |
| Anderson, Kimberly/Harlingen Cons Ind School Dist | 2 | 68 |
| Anderson, Kimberly/Trenton Ind School Dist | 2 | 151 |
| Anderson, Leal/Austin Ind School Dist | 6 | 369 |
| Anderson, Lindsay/Keller Ind School Dist | 8,15 | 357 |
| Anderson, Lori/Lindale Ind School Dist | 11 | 339 |
| Anderson, Matilda/Ore City Ind School Dist | 8,11,57,69,288,294 | 379 |
| Anderson, Randy/Lindale Ind School Dist | 73,84,295 | 339 |
| Anderson, Robert/Midway Ind School Dist | 5 | 283 |
| Anderson, Robna/Stanton Ind School Dist | 58 | 277 |
| Anderson, Russell/Hubbard Ind School Dist | 6 | 230 |
| Anderson, Shane/Connally Ind School Dist | 6 | 282 |
| Anderson, Stacy/White Oak Ind School Dist | 5 | 176 |
| Anderson, Tameka/Alief Ind School Dist | 274 | 186 |
| Anderson, Tanya/Azle Ind School Dist | 1 | 348 |
| Anderson, Teresa/Groveton Ind School Dist | 16,82 | 377 |
| Anderson, Terry/Paris Ind School Dist | 3 | 262 |
| Anderson, Tracy/Harlandale Ind School Dist | 27,31 | 35 |
| Anderson, Valerie/Lamar Cons Ind School Dist | 81 | 157 |
| Anderson, Vonnie/Big Spring Ind School Dist | 27,294 | 236 |
| Anderton, Amy/Dallas Ind School Dist | 61 | 102 |
| Andlesey, Scott/Floresville Ind School Dist | 4 | 403 |
| Andrajack, Frank/Burkburnett Ind Sch Dist | 67 | 394 |
| Andre, Steve/Mesquite Ind School Dist | 20,23 | 115 |
| Andress, Paul/Denton Ind School Dist | 3 | 124 |
| Andrews, Brenda/North Zulch Ind School Dist | 4 | 276 |
| Andrews, Jenna/Como Pickton Cons Ind SD | 11,58,298 | 234 |
| Andrews, Judy/Excelsior Ind School Dist | 11,57,76,88,286,288,296,298 | 337 |
| Andrews, Kathryn/Deer Park Ind School Dist | 39,81 | 191 |
| Andrews, Sally/Vidor Ind School Dist | 71 | 312 |
| Andrews, Tracy/Canutillo Ind School Dist | 27 | 136 |
| Andrus, Alan/North Zulch Ind School Dist | 1,11 | 276 |
| Andrus, Angee/Huntsville Ind School Dist | 69,294 | 386 |
| Andrus, Darrel/Jourdanton Ind School Dist | 6 | 23 |
| Andrus, James/Slaton Ind School Dist | 8,11,15,74,88,275,294 | 275 |
| Andrus, Jennifer/North Zulch Ind School Dist | 285 | 276 |
| Andrus, Lea-Ann/North Zulch Ind School Dist | 8,288 | 276 |
| Angel-Cundieff, Rita/Brazosport Ind School Dist | 57,89,93 | 55 |
| Angel, Lance/Bryan Ind School Dist | 6 | 58 |
| Angel, Lance/Palestine Ind School Dist | 6 | 18 |
| Angel, Tawni/Del Valle Ind School Dist | 6 | 372 |
| Angerer, Martha/Southland Ind School Dist | 58 | 167 |
| Angerstein, Josephine/Clint Ind School Dist | 58 | 136 |
| Anglesee, Scott/Kerrville Ind School Dist | 4 | 259 |
| Anglin, Mark/Bloomington Ind School Dist | 1 | 384 |
| Anguiano, Maria/Crowley Ind School Dist | 57 | 350 |
| Antes, Kathy/Leakey Ind School Dist | 2,297 | 324 |
| Anthony, Amy/Throckmorton Ind School Dist | 36,69,270 | 365 |
| Anthony, Philip/Princeton Ind School Dist | 3 | 87 |
| Antley, Tina, Dr/Pleasant Grove Ind School Dist | 57,63,271 | 52 |
| Antoine, Roland/Dallas Ind School Dist | 73,76,295 | 102 |
| Antoline, Carlos, Dr/Ft Worth Ind School Dist | 77 | 352 |
| Antonio Lara, Marco/South Texas Ind School Dist | 1 | 71 |
| Anzualda, Maria/Brooks Co Ind School Dist | 271 | 61 |
| Apeldace, Bea/San Elizario Ind School Dist | 12,271 | 139 |
| Apodaca, Beatriz/San Elizario Ind School Dist | 12 | 139 |
| Apodaca, Jorge/Ft Hancock Ind School Dist | 5 | 237 |
| Appel, Hope/Vernon Ind School Dist | 8,11,57,69,288,294,298 | 396 |
| Appelt, Jason/Vysehrad Ind School Dist | 1,11,83,84 | 265 |
| Applegate, Angie, Dr/Coppell Ind School Dist | 8,15,69 | 102 |
| Appleton, Ryder/Veribest Ind School Dist | 1,11,288 | 368 |
| Aquero-Ramirez, Melissa/Pharr-San Juan-Alamo Ind SD | 68 | 226 |
| Ara, Rosie/Brownsville Ind School Dist | 16 | 66 |
| Aragon, Jake/Dumas Ind School Dist | 73,76,95,295 | 298 |
| Araiza, Humberto/Del Valle Ind School Dist | 5 | 372 |
| Araiza, Humberto/Eagle Pass Ind School Dist | 5 | 279 |
| Arambula-Ruiz, Maria/United Ind School Dist | 57,61 | 390 |
| Aranda, Joe/United Ind School Dist | 5 | 390 |
| Araujo, Daniel/Los Fresnos Cons Ind Sch Dist | 76 | 69 |
| Arbogast, Ted/Terlingua Common School Dist | 73,285,295 | 60 |
| Arce, Kayla/Raymondville Ind Sch Dist | 2 | 397 |
| Arce, Paul/Rio Hondo Ind School Dist | 297 | 70 |
| Archie, Patricia/Sheldon Ind School Dist | 67 | 205 |
| Archuleta, Rita/Dell City Ind School Dist | 2,12 | 237 |
| Ard, James/Onalaska Ind School Dist | 3,4 | 320 |
| Ard, Susan/Cleveland Ind School Dist | 71 | 267 |
| Areal, Maria/Carrizo Spgs Cons Ind SD | 8,288 | 131 |
| Arevalo, Faviola/Joshua Ind School Dist | 57 | 251 |
| Arfsten, Leslynn/Walcott Ind School Dist | 2 | 123 |
| Arias, Carrie/Friona Ind School Dist | 34,58 | 318 |
| Arias, Jimmy/Friona Ind School Dist | 6 | 318 |
| Arismendi, Jennifer/Corpus Christi Ind Sch Dist | 13,58,77 | 306 |
| Arispe, Jodi/Graham Ind School Dist | 4 | 409 |
| Arispe, Sara/Ft Worth Ind School Dist | 15,294 | 352 |
| Arledge, Jenny/Sulphur Springs Ind Sch Dist | 26,27,31,75,95 | 235 |
| Armacost, Christopher/Hitchcock Ind School Dist | 3,73,84,97,98 | 165 |
| Armand, Richard/Region 4 Ed Service Center | 286 | 213 |
| Armendarez, Ann/Windthorst Ind School Dist | 12,57,275 | 23 |
| Armendariz, Ruben/Presidio Ind School Dist | 3,5 | 323 |
| Armendarvi, Roseann/La Vernia Ind School Dist | 11,57,58 | 404 |
| Armstrong, Caroline/Richardson Ind School Dist | 57 | 116 |
| Armstrong, Dan/Plano Ind School Dist | 15,16,73,76,295 | 85 |
| Armstrong, Jewell/Hallsburg Ind School Dist | 2 | 282 |
| Armstrong, Jim, Dr/West Hardin Co Cons Sch Dist | 1 | 183 |
| Armstrong, Joseph/Mineola Ind School Dist | 73,77,84,295 | 408 |
| Armstrong, Randy/White Settlement Ind Sch Dist | 67 | 360 |
| Armstrong, Tracy/Beaumont Ind School Dist | 3,12,34,88,295,750 | 244 |
| Armstrong, Travis, Dr/Wichita Falls Ind School Dist | 34 | 395 |
| Armstrong, Viana/Ferris Ind School Dist | 57 | 145 |
| Armstrong, Wanda/Chisum Ind School Dist | 4 | 262 |
| Armstrong, William/Kermit Ind School Dist | 8,83,88,288,294,298 | 405 |
| Armwood, Jackie, Dr/Alief Ind School Dist | 79 | 186 |
| Arnett, Karen/Redwater Ind School Dist | 79 | 53 |
| Arnold, Daniel/Calvert Ind School Dist | 73 | 327 |
| Arnold, Justin/Overton Ind School Dist | 6 | 331 |
| Arnold, Michelle/Ranger Ind School Dist | 11 | 133 |
| Arnold, Veronica/Sulphur Springs Ind Sch Dist | 4 | 235 |
| Arnst, Karl/Three Rivers Ind School Dist | 67 | 271 |
| Arocha-Gill, Teresa, Dr/Judson Ind School Dist | 58,275 | 36 |
| Arredondo, Azel/Edinburg Cons Ind School Dist | 39 | 221 |
| Arredondo, Henry/San Felipe-Del Rio Cons Ind SD | 2,19 | 381 |
| Arredondo, Jenny/San Antonio Ind School Dist | 4 | 42 |
| **Arrendondo, Jorge/**Pharr-San Juan-Alamo Ind SD | 1 | 226 |
| Arrington, Dara/Gunter Ind School Dist | 8,11,296 | 171 |
| Arrington, John/Arp Ind School Dist | 1 | 339 |
| Arriola, Suzette/East Central Ind School Dist | 6 | 34 |
| Arrona, Vanessa/Edinburg Cons Ind School Dist | 44 | 221 |
| Arrott, Brian/Ballinger Ind School Dist | 58 | 329 |
| Arsuaga, Tony/Taft Ind School Dist | 83,91 | 334 |
| Arteaga, Fabian/Winona Ind School Dist | 91 | 341 |
| Arterbury, Laurelyn, Dr/Leander Ind School Dist | 15 | 399 |
| Artho, Rhonda/Dumas Ind School Dist | 286 | 298 |
| Arthur, Leighanne/Burleson Ind School Dist | 10 | 249 |
| **Arthur, Steve/**Sam Rayburn Ind School Dist | 1 | 150 |

| 1 | Superintendent | 16 | Instructional Media Svcs | 30 | Adult Education | 44 | Science Sec | 58 | Special Education K-12 | 72 | Summer School | 88 | Alternative/At Risk | 277 | Remedial Math K-12 |
|---|---|---|---|---|---|---|---|---|---|---|---|---|---|---|---|
| 2 | Bus/Finance/Purchasing | 17 | Chief Operations Officer | 31 | Career/Sch-to-Work K-12 | 45 | Math K-12 | 59 | Special Education Elem | 73 | Instructional Tech | 89 | Multi-Cultural Curriculum | 280 | Literacy Coach |
| 3 | Buildings And Grounds | 18 | Chief Academic Officer | 32 | Career/Sch-to-Work Elem | 46 | Math Elem | 60 | Special Education Sec | 74 | Inservice Training | 90 | Social Work | 285 | STEM |
| 4 | Food Service | 19 | Chief Financial Officer | 33 | Career/Sch-to-Work Sec | 47 | Math Sec | 61 | Foreign/World Lang K-12 | 75 | Marketing/Distributive | 91 | Safety/Security | 286 | Digital Learning |
| 5 | Transportation | 20 | Art K-12 | 34 | Early Childhood Ed | 48 | English/Lang Arts K-12 | 62 | Foreign/World Lang Elem | 76 | Info Systems | 92 | Magnet School | 288 | Common Core Standards |
| 6 | Athletic | 21 | Art Elem | 35 | Health/Phys Education | 49 | English/Lang Arts Elem | 63 | Foreign/World Lang Sec | 77 | Psychological Assess | 93 | Parental Involvement | 294 | Accountability |
| 7 | Health Services | 22 | Art Sec | 36 | Guidance Services K-12 | 50 | English/Lang Arts Sec | 64 | Religious Education K-12 | 78 | Affirmative Action | 95 | Tech Prep Program | 295 | Network System |
| 8 | Curric/Instruct K-12 | 23 | Music K-12 | 37 | Guidance Services Elem | 51 | Reading K-12 | 65 | Religious Education Elem | 79 | Student Personnel | 97 | Chief Information Officer | 296 | Title II Programs |
| 9 | Curric/Instruct Elem | 24 | Music Elem | 38 | Guidance Services Sec | 52 | Reading Elem | 66 | Religious Education Sec | 80 | Driver Ed/Safety | 98 | Chief Technology Officer | 297 | Webmaster |
| 10 | Curric/Instruct Sec | 25 | Music Sec | 39 | Social Studies K-12 | 53 | Reading Sec | 67 | School Board President | 81 | Gifted/Talented | 270 | Character Education | 298 | Grant Writer/Ptnrships |
| 11 | Federal Program | 26 | Business Education | 40 | Social Studies Elem | 54 | Remedial Reading K-12 | 68 | Teacher Personnel | 82 | Video Services | 271 | Migrant Education | 750 | Chief Innovation Officer |
| 12 | Title I | 27 | Career & Tech Ed | 41 | Social Studies Sec | 55 | Remedial Reading Elem | 69 | Academic Assessment | 83 | Substance Abuse Prev | 273 | Teacher Mentor | 751 | Chief of Staff |
| 13 | Title V | 28 | Technology Education | 42 | Science K-12 | 56 | Remedial Reading Sec | 70 | Research/Development | 84 | Erate | 274 | Before/After Sch | 752 | Social Emotional Learning |
| 15 | Asst Superintendent | 29 | Family/Consumer Science | 43 | Science Elem | 57 | Bilingual/ELL | 71 | Public Information | 85 | AIDS Education | 275 | Response To Intervention | | |

| NAME/District | JOB FUNCTIONS | PAGE | NAME/District | JOB FUNCTIONS | PAGE |
|---|---|---|---|---|---|
| Baker, Brent/Region 8 Ed Service Center | 16,73 | 72 | Barber, Rachel/Tyler Ind School Dist | 7 | 340 |
| Baker, Brian/North Zulch Ind School Dist | 67 | 276 | Barber, Stacey/Shallowater Ind School Dist | 73,84,297 | 274 |
| Baker, Brooke/Midway Ind School Dist | 83 | 283 | Barbier, Erin/Austin Ind School Dist | 61 | 369 |
| Baker, Bruce/Crockett Ind School Dist | 5 | 235 | Barbosa, Alonzo/Edinburg Cons Ind School Dist | 5 | 221 |
| Baker, Carolyn/Woodsboro Ind School Dist | 7 | 326 | Barcenez, Frances/Southwest Ind School Dist | 11 | 46 |
| Baker, Charlotte/Region 3 Ed Service Center | 1 | 385 | Barck, Cathy/Garland Ind School Dist | 73 | 109 |
| Baker, Claudia/Vysehrad Ind School Dist | 73,286 | 265 | Barclay, Sherryll/Meadow Ind School Dist | 36,69 | 365 |
| Baker, Danny/Coolidge Ind School Dist | 6 | 269 | Barclay, TJ/Vega Ind School Dist | 67 | 310 |
| Baker, Darla/Splendora Ind School Dist | 2 | 297 | **Bardy, Tamara, Dr/**Boyd Ind School Dist | 1 | 405 |
| Baker, David/Rochelle Ind School Dist | 3,5 | 281 | Bares, Hubert/Campbell Ind School Dist | 2 | 238 |
| Baker, Henry/Trenton Ind School Dist | 67 | 151 | Bares, Noelle/Greenville Ind School Dist | 7,83,88 | 239 |
| Baker, Jay/Stanton Ind School Dist | 73,295 | 277 | Barganski, Linda, Dr/Flour Bluff Ind School Dist | 11,83,298 | 307 |
| Baker, Jennifer/Alief Ind School Dist | 27 | 186 | Barge, Anthony/New Waverly Ind School Dist | 67 | 386 |
| Baker, Jimmie/Granger Ind School Dist | 286 | 399 | Barge, James/Zavalla Ind School Dist | 67 | 21 |
| Baker, Judy/Harlingen Cons Ind School Dist | 4,7 | 68 | Barger, Dustin/Petrolia Cons Ind School Dist | 67 | 78 |
| Baker, Julie/Aledo Ind School Dist | 16,82 | 315 | Barger, Skyla/Petrolia Cons Ind School Dist | 4 | 78 |
| Baker, Katie/Lumberton Ind School Dist | 4 | 183 | Barham, Justin/Mildred Ind School Dist | 73 | 303 |
| Baker, Kyle/Sam Rayburn Ind School Dist | 3 | 150 | Barker, Brent/Eagle Mtn-Saginaw Ind Sch Dist | 6 | 351 |
| Baker, Melody/Pampa Ind School Dist | 76 | 170 | Barker, Denise/Region 10 Ed Service Center | 297 | 121 |
| Baker, Michael/Hays Cons Ind School Dist | 3 | 216 | Barker, Shae/Louise Ind School Dist | 4 | 392 |
| Baker, Rick/Center Ind School Dist | 3,5 | 337 | Barker, Wendell/Palo Pinto Ind Sch Dist 906 | 11,36,73,83 | 313 |
| Baker, Rocky/Carlisle Ind School Dist | 6 | 330 | Barker, Wendell/Palo Pinto Ind Sch Dist 906 | 1,84 | 313 |
| Baker, Shannon/Mildred Ind School Dist | 1,11 | 303 | Barley, Pepperjo/Jourdanton Ind School Dist | 11 | 23 |
| Baker, Stella/Tenaha Ind School Dist | 7 | 338 | Barlow, Billy/Fairfield Ind School Dist | 91 | 160 |
| Baker, Susan/Liberty Ind School Dist | 16 | 269 | Barlow, Cindy/Kirbyville Cons Ind Sch Dist | 4 | 244 |
| Baker, Tammy/Malakoff Ind School Dist | 5 | 219 | Barlow, Kevin, Dr/Arlington Ind School Dist | 70,294 | 346 |
| Baker, Tess/Redwater Ind School Dist | 2 | 53 | Barnard, Chris/Celeste Ind School Dist | 67 | 239 |
| Baker, Wanda, Dr/Bryan Ind School Dist | 57,271 | 58 | Barnes, Arlen/Follett Ind School Dist | 73,76 | 270 |
| Baker, Will/Southwest Ind School Dist | 68 | 46 | Barnes, Dana, Dr/Eagle Mtn-Saginaw Ind Sch Dist | 27,30,31 | 351 |
| Balasubcamania, Nathan, Dr/Manor Ind School Dist | 294 | 373 | Barnes, Ed/Bandera Ind School Dist | 3 | 26 |
| Balaszi, Angie/Jourdanton Ind School Dist | 2 | 23 | Barnes, Lannie/Van Alstyne Ind School Dist | 3,5 | 173 |
| Balcar, Jeff/El Campo Ind School Dist | 3,91 | 392 | Barnes, Lauri/Cypress-Fairbanks Ind Sch Dist | 58 | 189 |
| Balderas, Ramiro/Valley View Ind School Dist | 27 | 228 | Barnes, Marion/Channelview Ind School Dist | 295 | 188 |
| Baldwin, Bryan/Seymour Ind School Dist | 67 | 28 | Barnet, Lillian/Florence Ind School Dist | 4 | 398 |
| Baldwin, Elvia, Dr/Alief Ind School Dist | 36 | 186 | Barnett, Bryce/Blackwell Cons Ind Sch Dist | 27 | 304 |
| Baldwin, Heather/Wimberley Ind School Dist | 4 | 217 | Barnett, Christy/Levelland Ind School Dist | 9 | 232 |
| Baldwin, Owen/Wimberley Ind School Dist | 5 | 217 | Barnett, Joe/Frenship Ind School Dist | 73,98,297 | 272 |
| Baldwin, Tricia/Tomball Ind School Dist | 69 | 208 | Barnett, Martha/Franklin Ind School Dist | 69 | 327 |
| Ball, Amanda/Little Elm Ind School Dist | 74 | 128 | Barnett, Melissa/Oakwood Ind School Dist | 4 | 267 |
| Ball, Andy/Clifton Ind School Dist | 1 | 49 | Barnett, Teralee/Victoria Ind School Dist | 40 | 384 |
| Ball, Brin/Panther Creek Cons Ind SD | 58 | 79 | Barnett, Tonya/Coolidge Ind School Dist | 4 | 269 |
| Ball, Janette, Dr/Judson Ind School Dist | 1 | 36 | Barnette, Barbara/Cross Plains Ind Sch Dist | 4 | 66 |
| Ball, Josh/Aquilla Ind School Dist | 6 | 230 | Barnhart, Carol/Calallen Ind School Dist | 5 | 305 |
| Ball, Travis/Chisum Ind School Dist | 67 | 262 | Barnwell, Jackie/New Boston Ind School Dist | 2,12 | 52 |
| Ball, Veronica/Archdiocese San Antonio Ed Off | 36,79 | 47 | Barnwell, Rob/Jefferson Ind School Dist | 1 | 277 |
| Ballard, Brad/Rosebud-Lott Ind School Dist | 6 | 149 | Baron, Victor/Uvalde Cons Ind School Dist | 58 | 381 |
| Ballard, Jeff/Prairiland Ind School Dist | 1 | 263 | Baronet, Shana/Brady Ind School Dist | 37 | 280 |
| Ballard, Kathy/Carthage Ind School Dist | 2 | 314 | Barr, Billy/Industrial Ind School Dist | 3 | 243 |
| Ballard, Robin/Lake Dallas Ind School Dist | 73 | 126 | Barr, Glendell/Baird Ind School Dist | 73,295 | 65 |
| Ballard, Sherrill/Union Grove Ind School Dist | 11,296 | 379 | Barr, Mary Beth/Tomball Ind School Dist | 280 | 208 |
| Ballenger, Richard, Dr/Gary Ind School Dist | 8,15,58,69 | 314 | Barr, Norman/Elysian Fields Ind School Dist | 3 | 213 |
| Ballew, Ray/Schleicher Co Ind Sch Dist | 2 | 335 | Barr, Randi/Wheeler Ind School Dist | 4 | 394 |
| Ballinger, Josh/Tioga Ind School Dist | 15 | 172 | Barraza, Debi/Sands Consolidated ISD | 271 | 121 |
| Ballinger, Tony/Morgan Mill Ind School Dist | 67 | 148 | Barraza, Phillip/El Paso Ind School Dist | 20,23 | 137 |
| Bancroft, George/Big Spring Ind School Dist | 15 | 236 | Barrera, Diana/Somerset Ind School Dist | 9,88 | 45 |
| Banda, Ivonne/Taft Ind School Dist | 2 | 334 | Barrera, Dolores/United Ind School Dist | 10 | 390 |
| Bandy, Todd/Floydada Ind School Dist | 6 | 153 | Barrera, George/Barbers Hill Ind School Dist | 67 | 75 |
| Bane, Justin/Richards Ind School Dist | 6 | 177 | Barrera, Hartadelia/Roma Ind School Dist | 58 | 343 |
| Bane, Justin/Richards Ind School Dist | 6 | 177 | Barrera, Jorge/Eagle Pass Ind School Dist | 67 | 279 |
| Banfield, Eric/Florence Ind School Dist | 2,19 | 398 | Barrera, Leslie/Archdiocese Galveston-Houston | 73 | 209 |
| Banfield, Sue/Belton Ind School Dist | 34 | 29 | Barrera, Mike, Dr/Ben Bolt-Palito Blanco ISD | 1 | 248 |
| Bang, Shari/Smithville Ind School Dist | 58 | 27 | Barrera, Rolando/Rio Grande City Ind Sch Dist | 7 | 342 |
| Banks, David/Lamar Cons Ind School Dist | 295 | 157 | Barrera, Silvia/Laredo Ind School Dist | 6,35 | 389 |
| Banks, James/Texas City Ind School Dist | 73 | 166 | Barrera, Suzette/Zapata Co Ind School Dist | 11,294,298 | 410 |
| Banks, Yolanda/Int'l Leadership of Texas Dist | 4 | 112 | Barrett, Debbie/Pasadena Ind School Dist | 58 | 203 |
| Bannowsky, Amy/Menard Ind School Dist | 1 | 288 | Barrett, Jay Be/Farwell Ind School Dist | 67 | 317 |
| Bany, Rebecca/Shepherd Ind School Dist | 16 | 333 | Barrett, Logan/Kennedale Ind School Dist | 91 | 358 |
| Barajas, Melinda/Mathis Ind School Dist | 67 | 334 | Barrett, Natalie/Trinity Ind School Dist | 8 | 377 |
| Barajas, Rafael/Southwest Ind School Dist | 3 | 46 | Barrett, Richard/Kennedale Ind School Dist | 6,83 | 358 |
| Barajas, Rene/Northside Ind School Dist | 2,15 | 39 | Barrick, Brett/Mineral Wells Ind School Dist | 5 | 313 |
| Barbarick, Lisa/Nacogdoches Ind School Dist | 2,19 | 301 | Barrick, Brett/Mineral Wells Ind School Dist | 5 | 313 |
| Barbaroux, Paula/Grapevine-Colleyville Ind SD | 3,17 | 355 | Barrientes, Estela/Brownsville Ind School Dist | 271 | 66 |
| Barbay, Darrell/Jasper Ind School Dist | 6 | 243 | Barrientez, Michael/Loraine Ind School Dist | 31 | 292 |
| Barbee, Jay/Higgins Ind School Dist | 67 | 270 | Barrier, Nathan/Hardin Ind School Dist | 6 | 268 |
| Barber, Duane/Whitehouse Ind School Dist | 4,5,15 | 341 | Barriga, Ethel/Presidio Ind School Dist | 67 | 323 |
| Barber, Lareta/Lazbuddie Ind School Dist | 7 | 318 | Barrington, Shirley/Bishop Cons Ind School Dist | 42,45 | 305 |

| | | | | | | | | | |
|---|---|---|---|---|---|---|---|---|---|
| 1 | Superintendent | 16 | Instructional Media Svcs | 30 | Adult Education | 44 | Science Sec | 58 | Special Education K-12 | 72 | Summer School | 88 | Alternative/At Risk | 277 | Remedial Math K-12 |
| 2 | Bus/Finance/Purchasing | 17 | Chief Operations Officer | 31 | Career/Sch-to-Work K-12 | 45 | Math K-12 | 59 | Special Education Elem | 73 | Instructional Tech | 89 | Multi-Cultural Curriculum | 280 | Literacy Coach |
| 3 | Buildings And Grounds | 18 | Chief Academic Officer | 32 | Career/Sch-to-Work Elem | 46 | Math Elem | 60 | Special Education Sec | 74 | Inservice Training | 90 | Social Work | 285 | STEM |
| 4 | Food Service | 19 | Chief Financial Officer | 33 | Career/Sch-to-Work Sec | 47 | Math Sec | 61 | Foreign/World Lang K-12 | 75 | Marketing/Distributive | 91 | Safety/Security | 286 | Digital Learning |
| 5 | Transportation | 20 | Art K-12 | 34 | Early Childhood Ed | 48 | English/Lang Arts K-12 | 62 | Foreign/World Lang Elem | 76 | Info Systems | 92 | Magnet School | 288 | Common Core Standards |
| 6 | Athletic | 21 | Art Elem | 35 | Health/Phys Education | 49 | English/Lang Arts Elem | 63 | Foreign/World Lang Sec | 77 | Psychological Assess | 93 | Parental Involvement | 294 | Accountability |
| 7 | Health Services | 22 | Art Sec | 36 | Guidance Services K-12 | 50 | English/Lang Arts Sec | 64 | Religious Education K-12 | 78 | Affirmative Action | 95 | Tech Prep Program | 295 | Network System |
| 8 | Curric/Instruct K-12 | 23 | Music K-12 | 37 | Guidance Services Elem | 51 | Reading K-12 | 65 | Religious Education Elem | 79 | Student Personnel | 97 | Chief Information Officer | 296 | Title II Programs |
| 9 | Curric/Instruct Sec | 24 | Music Elem | 38 | Guidance Services Sec | 52 | Reading Elem | 66 | Religious Education Sec | 80 | Driver Ed/Safety | 98 | Chief Technology Officer | 297 | Webmaster |
| 10 | Curric/Instruct Sec | 25 | Music Sec | 39 | Social Studies K-12 | 53 | Reading Sec | 67 | School Board President | 81 | Gifted/Talented | 270 | Character Education | 298 | Grant Writer/Ptnrships |
| 11 | Federal Program | 26 | Business Education | 40 | Social Studies Elem | 54 | Remedial Reading K-12 | 68 | Teacher Personnel | 82 | Video Services | 271 | Migrant Education | 750 | Chief Innovation Officer |
| 12 | Title I | 27 | Career & Tech Ed | 41 | Social Studies Sec | 55 | Remedial Reading Elem | 69 | Academic Assessment | 83 | Substance Abuse Prev | 273 | Teacher Mentor | 751 | Chief of Staff |
| 13 | Title V | 28 | Technology Education | 42 | Science K-12 | 56 | Remedial Reading Sec | 70 | Research/Development | 84 | Erate | 274 | Before/After Sch | 752 | Social Emotional Learning |
| 15 | Asst Superintendent | 29 | Family/Consumer Science | 43 | Science Elem | 57 | Bilingual/ELL | 71 | Public Information | 85 | AIDS Education | 275 | Response To Intervention | | |

| | | | | | | | | | | |
|---|---|---|---|---|---|---|---|---|---|---|
| 1 | Superintendent | 16 | Instructional Media Svcs | 30 | Adult Education | 44 | Science Sec | 58 | Special Education K-12 | 72 | Summer School |
| 2 | Bus/Finance/Purchasing | 17 | Chief Operations Officer | 31 | Career/Sch-to-Work K-12 | 45 | Math K-12 | 59 | Special Education Elem | 73 | Instructional Tech |
| 3 | Buildings And Grounds | 18 | Chief Academic Officer | 32 | Career/Sch-to-Work Elem | 46 | Math Elem | 60 | Special Education Sec | 74 | Inservice Training |
| 4 | Food Service | 19 | Chief Financial Officer | 33 | Career/Sch-to-Work Sec | 47 | Math Sec | 61 | Foreign/World Lang K-12 | 75 | Marketing/Distributive |
| 5 | Transportation | 20 | Art K-12 | 34 | Early Childhood Ed | 48 | English/Lang Arts K-12 | 62 | Foreign/World Lang Elem | 76 | Info Systems |
| 6 | Athletic | 21 | Art Elem | 35 | Health/Phys Education | 49 | English/Lang Arts Elem | 63 | Foreign/World Lang Sec | 77 | Psychological Assess |
| 7 | Health Services | 22 | Art Sec | 36 | Guidance Services K-12 | 50 | English/Lang Arts Sec | 64 | Religious Education K-12 | 78 | Affirmative Action |
| 8 | Curric/Instruct K-12 | 23 | Music K-12 | 37 | Guidance Services Elem | 51 | Reading K-12 | 65 | Religious Education Elem | 79 | Student Personnel |
| 9 | Curric/Instruct Elem | 24 | Music Elem | 38 | Guidance Services Sec | 52 | Reading Elem | 66 | Religious Education Sec | 80 | Driver Ed/Safety |
| 10 | Curric/Instruct Sec | 25 | Music Sec | 39 | Social Studies K-12 | 53 | Reading Sec | 67 | School Board President | 81 | Gifted/Talented |
| 11 | Federal Program | 26 | Business Education | 40 | Social Studies Elem | 54 | Remedial Reading K-12 | 68 | Teacher Personnel | 82 | Video Services |
| 12 | Title I | 27 | Career & Tech Ed | 41 | Social Studies Sec | 55 | Remedial Reading Elem | 69 | Academic Assessment | 83 | Substance Abuse Prev |
| 13 | Title V | 28 | Technology Education | 42 | Science K-12 | 56 | Remedial Reading Sec | 70 | Research/Development | 84 | Erate |
| 15 | Asst Superintendent | 29 | Family/Consumer Science | 43 | Science Elem | 57 | Bilingual/ELL | 71 | Public Information | 85 | AIDS Education |

| | | | | |
|---|---|---|---|---|
| 88 | Alternative/At Risk | 277 | Remedial Math K-12 |
| 89 | Multi-Cultural Curriculum | 280 | Literacy Coach |
| 90 | Social Work | 285 | STEM |
| 91 | Safety/Security | 286 | Digital Learning |
| 92 | Magnet School | 288 | Common Core Standards |
| 93 | Parental Involvement | 294 | Accountability |
| 95 | Tech Prep Program | 295 | Network System |
| 97 | Chief Infomation Officer | 296 | Title II Programs |
| 98 | Chief Technology Officer | 297 | Webmaster |
| 270 | Character Education | 298 | Grant Writer/Ptnrships |
| 271 | Migrant Education | 750 | Chief Innovation Officer |
| 273 | Teacher Mentor | 751 | Chief of Staff |
| 274 | Before/After Sch | 752 | Social Emotional Learning |
| 275 | Response to Intervention | | |

| NAME/District | JOB FUNCTIONS | PAGE |
|---|---|---|
| Bloomingdale, Misty/Region 14 Ed Service Center | 74 | 364 |
| Blount, Brad/Paducah Ind School Dist | 67 | 97 |
| Blount, Irene/Paducah Ind School Dist | 2 | 97 |
| Blount, Wayne/Region 17 Ed Service Center | 2,3,4,15,76 | 275 |
| Bludau, Joann/Hallettsville Ind Sch Dist | 1 | 265 |
| Blue, Frankie/Dumas Ind School Dist | 58,275 | 298 |
| Blue, Misty/Kerens Ind School Dist | 37,57 | 303 |
| Blue, Patti/Gustine Ind School Dist | 1,11,73 | 93 |
| Blue, Phil/Abilene Ind School Dist | 6,35 | 362 |
| Bluhm, Bernadette/Karnes City Ind School Dist | 7 | 253 |
| Blum, Karen/Tarkington Ind School Dist | 4 | 269 |
| Blundell, Lisa/Victoria Ind School Dist | 15 | 384 |
| Board, Gregg/Channelview Ind School Dist | 91 | 188 |
| Boatner, Olivia/Aldine Ind School Dist | 92 | 184 |
| Bobbitt, Brian/New Boston Ind School Dist | 1 | 52 |
| Bobbitt, Charlie/Crockett Ind School Dist | 73,297 | 235 |
| Bobbitt, Leah/West Rusk Co Cons Ind Sch Dist | 8,15,288 | 331 |
| Bobino, Sabrina/High Island Ind Sch Dist | 5 | 165 |
| Bobo, Beverly/Gilmer Ind School Dist | 2 | 378 |
| Bobo, Ryan/Cotton Center Ind School Dist | 1 | 179 |
| Bocanegra, Edward/Pearsall Ind School Dist | 6 | 161 |
| Bodden, Renee/Nederland Ind School Dist | 4 | 245 |
| Bode, Trish/Leander Ind School Dist | 67 | 399 |
| Bodwell, Carol/Princeton Ind School Dist | 67 | 87 |
| Boedeker, Kim/Melissa Ind School Dist | 69 | 85 |
| Boehme, Braden/Jourdanton Ind School Dist | 5 | 23 |
| Boehs, Kenneth/Canyon Ind School Dist | 295 | 323 |
| Boeker, Lewis/Forsan Ind School Dist | 67 | 237 |
| Boettger, Cavin, Dr/Denison Ind School Dist | 31 | 171 |
| Boge, Victoria/London Ind School Dist | 2 | 308 |
| Boggas, Kristi/Trinidad Ind School Dist | 4 | 219 |
| Boggs, Holly/Morton Ind School Dist | 9,11,57,88 | 78 |
| Bogle, Katrina/Hamlin Collegiate Ind Sch Dist | 73,76,84,295 | 252 |
| Bogt, Holly/Kerrville Ind School Dist | 71 | 259 |
| Bohannan, Bo/Harmony Ind School Dist | 5 | 379 |
| Bohannon, David/North East Ind School Dist | 2 | 37 |
| Bohannon, Dawn/Ector Ind School Dist | 16,73 | 150 |
| Bohling, Kathryn/Mesquite Ind School Dist | 2,3,15 | 115 |
| Bohlken, Shannon/Roosevelt Ind School Dist | 37 | 274 |
| Bohn, Susan, Dr/Aledo Ind School Dist | 1 | 315 |
| Boiles, Donna/Whitesboro Ind School Dist | 36,69,77 | 173 |
| Boitmann, Jona/Princeton Ind School Dist | 2,11,15,298 | 87 |
| Boldrin, Stacey/Yorktown Ind School Dist | 5 | 122 |
| Bolek, Brian/Eanes Ind School Dist | 3 | 372 |
| Bolen, Judy, Dr/Wylie Ind School Dist | 69,294 | 88 |
| Boles, Charles/Cumby Ind School Dist | 6 | 234 |
| **Boles, Keith/**Jarrell Ind School Dist | 1 | 399 |
| Boles, Zachery/Tomball Ind School Dist | 2 | 208 |
| Bolin, Kim/Center Point Ind School Dist | 58 | 258 |
| Bolt, Heather/Queen City Ind School Dist | 77 | 74 |
| Boltie, Lisa/Southwest Ind School Dist | 69,294 | 46 |
| Bolton, David/Alvin Ind School Dist | 3 | 54 |
| Bolton, Neil/Cedar Hill Ind School Dist | 76,295 | 101 |
| Bolton, Tina/Neches Ind School Dist | 2 | 18 |
| Bomar, Jerry/Groesbeck Ind School Dist | 6 | 269 |
| Bomberger, Chris/Denton Ind School Dist | 4 | 124 |
| Bonazzi, Tony/Georgetown Ind School Dist | 45 | 398 |
| Bond, Shalon/Dallas Ind School Dist | 39 | 102 |
| Bonds, Sheri/Round Rock Ind School Dist | 27,31 | 401 |
| Bonewald, Gregory, Dr/Victoria Ind School Dist | 15,68 | 384 |
| Bonilla, Filiberto/Hays Cons Ind School Dist | 5 | 216 |
| Bonilla, Victor/Crystal City Ind School Dist | 67 | 410 |
| Bonner, Jason/Jefferson Ind School Dist | 67 | 277 |
| Bonner, Joe/Panhandle Ind School Dist | 3 | 72 |
| Bonner, Kayce/Kerens Ind School Dist | 58 | 303 |
| Bonner, Mark/Joaquin Ind School Dist | 3 | 337 |
| Bonser, Sara/Plano Ind School Dist | 1 | 85 |
| Booher, Kim/Holliday Ind School Dist | 69,79 | 22 |
| Boonau, Stephanie/Henderson Ind School Dist | 8,11,57,88,286,288,296,298 | 330 |
| Boone, Mike/San Marcos Cons Ind Sch Dist | 4 | 216 |
| Boone, Reggie/Humble Ind School Dist | 76 | 200 |
| Boone, Ryan/Dickinson Ind School Dist | 2,3,15 | 164 |
| Booth, Ashton/Giddings Ind School Dist | 58 | 266 |
| Booth, Brenda/El Paso Ind School Dist | 69 | 137 |
| Booth, John/De Kalb Ind School Dist | 1 | 51 |
| Booth, Veronica/Clint Ind School Dist | 27 | 136 |

| NAME/District | JOB FUNCTIONS | PAGE |
|---|---|---|
| Boothe, Deanna/White Oak Ind School Dist | 84 | 176 |
| Boothe, Sharon/Greenville Ind School Dist | 8,15,74 | 239 |
| Boothe, Stacey/Sanford-Fritch Ind School Dist | 67 | 241 |
| Boozer, Stacy/Dimmitt Ind School Dist | 11,296 | 74 |
| Borchardt, Cheri/Lorena Ind School Dist | 8,11,57,76,286,288,296,751 | 283 |
| Borchardt, Eric/Krum Ind School Dist | 67 | 126 |
| Bordelon, Cindi/Nederland Ind School Dist | 38 | 245 |
| Borden, Cory/Cleburne Ind School Dist | 58 | 250 |
| Borden, Cynthia/Seguin Ind School Dist | 8,11,57,69,77,83,294 | 178 |
| Borden, Nathan/Riviera Ind School Dist | 6 | 261 |
| **Bordner, Jennifer/**Cherokee Ind School Dist | 1 | 335 |
| Bordousky, Karen/Ingram Ind School Dist | 83,275,294 | 259 |
| Boren, Catherine/Bosqueville Ind School Dist | 2 | 281 |
| Boren, Justin/Whitesboro Ind School Dist | 67 | 173 |
| Boren, Martha/Tenaha Ind School Dist | 8,11,69 | 338 |
| Borkert, Penelope/School of Excellence In Ed | 58 | 45 |
| Bornemeier, Misty/Dalhart Ind School Dist | 16,82 | 99 |
| Borrego, Lucia/Socorro Ind School Dist | 8,18 | 140 |
| Borrego, Marie/Culberson Co Allamoore Ind SD | 4 | 99 |
| Borreson, Diane/Hays Cons Ind School Dist | 73,98 | 216 |
| Bos, Michael/Borger Ind School Dist | 73,84,295 | 240 |
| Boseman, Lenise/Como Pickton Cons Ind SD | 2 | 234 |
| **Bosley, Melissa/**Wortham Ind School Dist | 1,11 | 161 |
| Bosse, Amy/El Campo Ind School Dist | 58 | 392 |
| Bosse, Amy/Rice Cons Ind School Dist | 58 | 90 |
| Bosse, Wade/East Bernard Ind Sch Dist | 6 | 392 |
| Bostic, Robert, Dr/Stafford Municipal Sch Dist | 1 | 159 |
| Bostick, Charity/Aldine Ind School Dist | 50 | 184 |
| Bostick, Larry/Santa Anna Ind School Dist | 73 | 80 |
| Boswell, Blaise/Vernon Ind School Dist | 16,73,295 | 396 |
| Boswell, Cecelia/Waco Ind School Dist | 81 | 284 |
| Botard, Mack/Oakwood Ind School Dist | 67 | 267 |
| Botello, Elaine/Waco Ind School Dist | 15 | 284 |
| Botello, Jorge/Edinburg Cons Ind School Dist | 69 | 221 |
| Bott, Kevin/Lampasas Ind School Dist | 8,11,57,83,286,288,296,298 | 264 |
| Boubel, Alison/Kennedale Ind School Dist | 16 | 358 |
| Boudreaux, Victor/Bremond Ind School Dist | 3 | 327 |
| Boughton, Nathan, Dr/Cleveland Ind School Dist | 15 | 267 |
| Bouliane, Nancy/Navasota Ind School Dist | 16 | 177 |
| Boullion, Brad/Hardin Jefferson Ind Sch Dist | 2,3 | 182 |
| Boulware, Alice/Zavalla Ind School Dist | 2 | 21 |
| Bourland, Linda/Weatherford Ind School Dist | 42 | 316 |
| Bourn, Loretta/Cypress-Fairbanks Ind Sch Dist | 23 | 189 |
| Bousquet, Melissa/Waxahachie Ind School Dist | 7 | 146 |
| Boutte, Andre/Port Arthur Ind School Dist | 6 | 246 |
| Boutwell, Melanie/Manor Ind School Dist | 2 | 373 |
| Bowben, Melinda/Waskom Ind School Dist | 38 | 214 |
| Bowdoin, Geoffery/Leon Ind School Dist | 8,11,274,296 | 267 |
| Bowen, Bob/Munday Consolidated Ind SD | 5 | 262 |
| Bowen, Bridgette/Bangs Ind School Dist | 73,76 | 61 |
| Bowen, Bridgette/Bangs Ind School Dist | 295 | 61 |
| Bowen, Kathleen, Dr/Lamar Cons Ind School Dist | 68 | 157 |
| Bower, Greg/Como Pickton Cons Ind SD | 1 | 234 |
| Bowers, Cherie/Santa Fe Ind School Dist | 4 | 165 |
| Bowie, Kalean/Angleton Ind School Dist | 79 | 55 |
| Bowie, Sheila/Winona Ind School Dist | 2,298 | 341 |
| Bowlin, Emily/Tenaha Ind School Dist | 68 | 338 |
| Bowlin, Terry/Tenaha Ind School Dist | 5,17,298 | 338 |
| Bowling, Mike/Peaster Ind School Dist | 67 | 316 |
| Bowling, Ritchie/Maypearl Ind School Dist | 1 | 145 |
| Bowman, Blake/Joshua Ind School Dist | 3 | 251 |
| Bowman, Katie/Birdville Ind School Dist | 2 | 348 |
| Bowman, Kimberly/Munday Consolidated Ind SD | 73,273,286,295 | 262 |
| Bowser, Jacob/Castleberry Ind School Dist | 76 | 350 |
| Bowyer, Beth/Blanket Ind School Dist | 67 | 61 |
| Boxell, Nardeen/Plano Ind School Dist | 11 | 85 |
| Boxwell, Cindy/Perryton Ind School Dist | 16 | 310 |
| Boyce, Charles/Onalaska Ind School Dist | 73,84,286 | 320 |
| Boyce, Joy/Richards Ind School Dist | 2 | 177 |
| Boyce, William/Richards Ind School Dist | 8,57,73,74,271,295 | 177 |
| Boyce, William/Richards Ind School Dist | 1,11 | 177 |
| Boyd, Angela/Hillsboro Ind School Dist | 8 | 230 |
| Boyd, Cella/West Oso Ind School Dist | 67 | 309 |
| Boyd, Dennis/Pampa Ind School Dist | 295 | 170 |
| Boyd, Felicia/Slaton Ind School Dist | 34 | 275 |
| Boyd, Kent/Temple Ind School Dist | 2,15 | 32 |

| NAME/District | JOB FUNCTIONS | PAGE | NAME/District | JOB FUNCTIONS | PAGE |
|---|---|---|---|---|---|
| Bridges, Ronda/Lometa Ind School Dist | 2 | 264 | Brooks, Tina/Stratford Ind School Dist | 4 | 338 |
| Bridgman, Mark/Winters Ind School Dist | 5 | 329 | Brooks, Tony/Athens Ind School Dist | 73,76,286 | 218 |
| Briese, John/Millsap Ind School Dist | 73 | 315 | Brooks, Wesley/Midway Ind School Dist | 2,15 | 283 |
| Briggs, Julie/Richardson Ind School Dist | 16 | 116 | Broome, Richard/Medina Valley Ind School Dist | 5 | 287 |
| Briggs, Reese/Hemphill Ind School Dist | 1 | 331 | Brosch, Stephen/Granger Ind School Dist | 6 | 399 |
| Briggs, Tonya/New Boston Ind School Dist | 27 | 52 | Broscoss, Julee/Slaton Ind School Dist | 1 | 275 |
| Bright, David/El Campo Ind School Dist | 2,3,15,17 | 392 | Brosnahan, Carla/Cypress-Fairbanks Ind Sch Dist | 15 | 189 |
| Bright, Jon/Rankin Ind School Dist | 58 | 380 | Brothers, Ray/Fayetteville Ind School Dist | 16,31,73,295 | 151 |
| Bright, Michelle/Seagraves Ind School Dist | 58 | 162 | Brou, Jason/Aransas Pass Ind School Dist | 73 | 333 |
| Bright, Roxanne/London Ind School Dist | 4 | 308 | Broumbley, Joni/Hico Ind School Dist | 4 | 181 |
| Bright, Tammy/Cleburne Ind School Dist | 12,15,296 | 250 | Broumley, Dana/Hico Ind School Dist | 37 | 181 |
| Briles, Art/Mount Vernon Ind School Dist | 6 | 160 | Broumley, Keith/Hico Ind School Dist | 67 | 181 |
| Brim, Amanda/Lewisville Ind School Dist | 71 | 126 | Broussard, Colby/Bellevue Ind School Dist | 6 | 77 |
| Brink, Heather/Central Ind School Dist | 4 | 20 | Brower, Aaron/Maud Ind School Dist | 67 | 52 |
| Brink, Justin/Robinson Ind School Dist | 295 | 284 | Brown, A Tracie/Arlington Ind School Dist | 15 | 346 |
| Brinker, Joseph/Marshall Ind School Dist | 5 | 214 | Brown, Allen/Pasadena Ind School Dist | 76 | 203 |
| Brinkley, Boone/Oglesby Ind School Dist | 3,5 | 97 | Brown, Amanda/River Road Ind School Dist | 67 | 322 |
| Brinkley, Molly/Pampa Ind School Dist | 73 | 170 | Brown, Angela/Coppell Ind School Dist | 75 | 102 |
| Brinkman, Tammy/Coupland Ind School Dist | 1,11,57,83 | 398 | Brown, Anthony/Galveston Ind School Dist | 67 | 165 |
| Brinkman, Tammy/Iola Ind School Dist | 11,271,273 | 177 | Brown, Anthony/Paint Rock Ind School Dist | 67 | 94 |
| Brinlee, Ricky/Howe Ind School Dist | 3,5 | 171 | Brown, Barbara/Marlin Ind School Dist | 4 | 149 |
| Brinson, Lisa/Deweyville Ind School Dist | 7,85 | 311 | Brown, Becky/Miller Grove Ind School Dist | 4 | 234 |
| Brinson, Steve/Bridge City Ind School Dist | 83,91 | 311 | Brown, Belinda/Yantis Ind School Dist | 2,19 | 408 |
| Brinson, Terri/Early Ind School Dist | 79 | 62 | Brown, Blair/Panhandle Ind School Dist | 1,11 | 72 |
| Briones, Dina/Crystal City Ind School Dist | 752 | 410 | Brown, Blake/Harleton Ind School Dist | 295 | 213 |
| Briones, Judy/Marathon Ind School Dist | 67 | 60 | Brown, Brenda/Hull Daisetta Ind School Dist | 4 | 268 |
| Brisbin, Lauren/Belton Ind School Dist | 57,280 | 29 | Brown, Bridget/Wellman Union Ind School Dist | 12,271,275 | 365 |
| Brisco, Kristine/Snook Ind School Dist | 67 | 63 | Brown, Brittanie/Henrietta Ind School Dist | 4 | 78 |
| Briscoe, Beth/Needville Ind School Dist | 8,11,15,69,271 | 159 | Brown, Cayla/Hubbard Ind School Dist | 752 | 51 |
| Brisero, Cynthia/Edcouch Elsa Ind School Dist | 36,85 | 220 | Brown, Chad/Comanche Ind School Dist | 5 | 93 |
| Brison, Alan/Pittsburg Ind School Dist | 67 | 72 | Brown, Chesney/Hondo Ind School Dist | 7 | 287 |
| Britt, Jim/Bowie Ind School Dist | 73,84,295 | 292 | Brown, Connie/Van Vleck Ind School Dist | 4 | 279 |
| Brittain, Jason/Angleton Ind School Dist | 6 | 55 | Brown, Danny/Tyler Ind School Dist | 83,91 | 340 |
| Brittain, Tim/Huffman Ind School Dist | 2,11,19 | 200 | Brown, Darrell, Dr/Birdville Ind School Dist | 1 | 348 |
| Britting, Susan/Breckenridge Ind School Dist | 58 | 344 | Brown, David/Bandera Ind School Dist | 16,82,84,295,297 | 26 |
| Britton, Blane/Meadow Ind School Dist | 73 | 365 | Brown, David, Dr/Van Alstyne Ind School Dist | 1 | 173 |
| Britton, Delwin/Sundown Ind School Dist | 67 | 232 | Brown, Debbie/Hays Cons Ind School Dist | 275 | 216 |
| Britton, Nancy/East Central Ind School Dist | 4 | 34 | Brown, Denise/Wichita Falls Ind School Dist | 2 | 395 |
| Britton, Patrick/School of Excellence In Ed | 67 | 45 | Brown, Eddie/Hempstead Ind School Dist | 5 | 387 |
| Broadhurst, Lance/Littlefield Ind School Dist | 67 | 263 | Brown, Fred/Sands Consolidated ISD | 5 | 121 |
| Broadus, Amy/Kilgore Ind School Dist | 68 | 174 | Brown, Glenn/Everman Ind School Dist | 3 | 351 |
| Broadwater, Sheri/Longview Ind School Dist | 11,54,298 | 174 | Brown, Gradyne, Dr/Garland Ind School Dist | 15,68 | 109 |
| Brock, Brooke/Athens Ind School Dist | 58 | 218 | Brown, Greg/Plainview Ind School Dist | 15 | 180 |
| Brock, Jennifer, Dr/Region 4 Ed Service Center | 34,39,48,51,57 | 213 | Brown, Jamie/Cedar Hill Ind School Dist | 71 | 101 |
| Brock, Katie/Collinsville Ind School Dist | 37 | 171 | Brown, Jamie/San Antonio Ind School Dist | 69 | 42 |
| Brock, Kenneth/Baird Ind School Dist | 67 | 65 | Brown, Jana/Simms Ind School Dist | 2,296 | 53 |
| Brock, Laura Lee/Electra Ind School Dist | 2,8,11,27,31,88,273 | 394 | Brown, Jason/Liberty-Eylau Ind School Dist | 16,73 | 51 |
| Brock, Matt/Pampa Ind School Dist | 67 | 170 | Brown, Jason/Pottsboro Ind School Dist | 73,286,295 | 172 |
| Brock, Megan/Snook Ind School Dist | 36 | 63 | Brown, Julie/White Deer Ind School Dist | 69,88 | 73 |
| Brock, Stephanie/New Waverly Ind School Dist | 8,11,288,298 | 386 | Brown, Kalith/Dawson Ind School Dist | 67 | 121 |
| Brockett, Marie/Bruceville-Eddy Ind Sch Dist | 11,69,294,296,298 | 281 | Brown, Kareen, Dr/Galena Park Ind School Dist | 81 | 191 |
| Brockett, Rhonda/Ponder Ind School Dist | 16,82 | 130 | Brown, Kathleen/Duncanville Ind School Dist | 15,68 | 108 |
| Brockman, Beth, Dr/Plano Ind School Dist | 15,68 | 85 | Brown, Keith/Taylor Ind School Dist | 1 | 402 |
| Brockman, Gary/Woodson Ind School Dist | 67 | 365 | Brown, Kenneth/Boys Ranch Ind School Dist | 1 | 310 |
| Brockman, Rhonda/Woodson Ind School Dist | 4 | 365 | Brown, Khristie/Grapevine-Colleyville Ind SD | 34 | 355 |
| Broesche, Sarah/Brenham Ind School Dist | 34,58 | 388 | Brown, Kristen/Barbers Hill Ind School Dist | 59 | 75 |
| Brogden, Jeff/Mansfield Ind School Dist | 3,5,15 | 358 | Brown, Kristen/Clarendon Cons Ind Sch Dist | 2 | 131 |
| Broner Westerl, Debra/Klein Ind School Dist | 27 | 202 | Brown, Kristen, Dr/Lyford Cons Ind School Dist | 1 | 397 |
| Bronis, Juan/La Feria Ind School Dist | 67 | 69 | Brown, Kristine/Little Cypress Mauriceville SD | 35,75 | 311 |
| Bronson, Cindy/Lovejoy Ind School Dist | 43 | 84 | Brown, Kyle/Reagan Co Ind School Dist | 83,88 | 324 |
| Brooks, Aaron/Harper Ind School Dist | 11 | 168 | Brown, Lakeyshia/Manor Ind School Dist | 46 | 373 |
| Brooks, Amy/Comanche Ind School Dist | 4 | 93 | Brown, Larry/Huntsville Ind School Dist | 3 | 386 |
| Brooks, Angela/Houston Ind School Dist | 298 | 193 | Brown, Mark/Centerville Ind School Dist | 1,11 | 376 |
| Brooks, Anthony/Mexia Ind School Dist | 295 | 270 | Brown, Mark/Gary Ind School Dist | 6 | 314 |
| Brooks, Dawn/Adrian Ind School Dist | 8,288 | 310 | Brown, Mary/Hallsville Ind School Dist | 2,19 | 213 |
| Brooks, Jamie/Whitesboro Ind School Dist | 2 | 173 | Brown, Melanie/Clyde Consolidated Ind SD | 4 | 66 |
| Brooks, Justin/Greenwood Ind School Dist | 67 | 288 | Brown, Michael/Kilgore Ind School Dist | 3,5 | 174 |
| Brooks, Keith, Dr/Sheldon Ind School Dist | 10 | 205 | Brown, Michelle/Dallas Ind School Dist | 58 | 102 |
| Brooks, Kim/Highland Park Ind Sch Dist | 81 | 112 | Brown, Monet/Whitehouse Ind School Dist | 68 | 341 |
| Brooks, Marie/Marion Ind School Dist | 4 | 177 | Brown, Pam/Lubbock-Cooper Ind Sch Dist | 36,69 | 274 |
| Brooks, Melvin/Shiner Ind School Dist | 3 | 265 | Brown, Pamela/Lancaster Ind School Dist | 15,57,68,79,81 | 114 |
| Brooks, Michael/Frenship Ind School Dist | 5 | 272 | Brown, Patrick/Los Fresnos Cons Ind Sch Dist | 6 | 69 |
| Brooks, Mike/Waller Ind School Dist | 68 | 387 | Brown, Patti/Borger Ind School Dist | 58,275 | 240 |
| Brooks, Scott/Canutillo Ind School Dist | 6 | 136 | Brown, Patti/Panhandle Ind School Dist | 58 | 73 |
| Brooks, Shelly/Miami Ind School Dist | 57 | 327 | Brown, Paul/Huntsville Ind School Dist | 2,19 | 386 |
| Brooks, Stephanie/Redwater Ind School Dist | 67 | 53 | Brown, Perri/Water Valley Ind School Dist | 57 | 368 |

| NAME/District | JOB FUNCTIONS | PAGE |
|---|---|---|
| Burfiend, Michael/Stamford Ind School Dist | 73 | 253 |
| Burg, Meredith/Montgomery Ind School Dist | 58,79 | 296 |
| Burger, Camille/Ingleside Ind School Dist | 58 | 334 |
| Burger, Jerry/Wilson Ind School Dist | 1,83 | 276 |
| Burger, Monty/Brazosport Ind School Dist | 3,17,73,98 | 55 |
| Burgess, Rickey/Everman Ind School Dist | 67 | 351 |
| Burgess, Tonya/McGregor Ind School Dist | 9,31 | 283 |
| Burghardt, Becky/College Station Ind Sch Dist | 69 | 59 |
| Burguss, April/Lorenzo Ind School Dist | 16,82 | 98 |
| Burk, Randy, Dr/Hamlin Collegiate Ind Sch Dist | 1 | 252 |
| Burke, Candice/Crandall Ind School Dist | 58 | 254 |
| Burke, Jeff, Dr/Splendora Ind School Dist | 1 | 297 |
| Burke, Matthew/La Porte Ind School Dist | 20,23 | 203 |
| Burke, Michelle/Spring Branch Ind School Dist | 57 | 205 |
| Burkett, Stephanie/Bruceville-Eddy Ind Sch Dist | 31,36,83,88,271 | 281 |
| Burkhart, Jerry/Richland Springs Ind Sch Dist | 6 | 335 |
| Burkhart, Susan/Thrall Ind School Dist | 73,84 | 403 |
| Burkholder, Karla, Dr/Schertz-Cibolo-Univ City ISD | 73 | 178 |
| Burks, Rocky/Warren Ind School Dist | 67 | 378 |
| Burks, Rose, Dr/Region 14 Ed Service Center | 7,8,27,31,88 | 364 |
| Burks, Sean/Corrigan-Camden Ind Sch Dist | 67 | 319 |
| Burleson, Jeramy/Kaufman Ind School Dist | 6 | 255 |
| Burleson, Lois/Clyde Consolidated Ind SD | 7 | 66 |
| Burleson, Todd/Westbrook Ind School Dist | 1 | 292 |
| Burley, Ecomet/Harris Co Dept of Ed | 91 | 184 |
| Burnell, Rhonda/Copperas Cove Ind School Dist | 58 | 96 |
| Burnett, B J/Lometa Ind School Dist | 4 | 264 |
| Burnett, Brandy/Liberty-Eylau Ind School Dist | 12,68 | 51 |
| Burnett, Dionne/Lake Travis Ind School Dist | 93,274 | 373 |
| Burnett, John/Bremond Ind School Dist | 57,271 | 327 |
| Burnett, Samuel/Brownwood Ind School Dist | 6 | 62 |
| Burnett, Tammy/Neches Ind School Dist | 288 | 18 |
| Burnette, Sanya/Arp Ind School Dist | 58 | 339 |
| Burney, Mitchell/Anna Ind School Dist | 4 | 81 |
| Burns, Barbara/Denton Ind School Dist | 67 | 125 |
| Burns, Charla/Pettus Ind School Dist | 38,69,83 | 28 |
| Burns, Cheryl/Smithville Ind School Dist | 1 | 27 |
| Burns, Deborah/Iredell Ind School Dist | 2 | 50 |
| Burns, Jana/Region 10 Ed Service Center | 15 | 120 |
| **Burns, Jimmy/**Friona Ind School Dist | 1 | 318 |
| Burns, Joseph, Dr/Copperas Cove Ind School Dist | 1 | 96 |
| Burns, Judy/East Central Ind School Dist | 2,19 | 34 |
| Burns, Kade/Mason Ind School Dist | 285 | 278 |
| Burns, Kelly/Redwater Ind School Dist | 1 | 53 |
| Burns, Ken/Aledo Ind School Dist | 5 | 315 |
| Burns, Lahne/Veribest Ind School Dist | 73,286 | 368 |
| **Burns, Mike/**Big Sandy Ind School Dist | 1 | 378 |
| Burrell, Connie/Harleton Ind School Dist | 4 | 213 |
| Burrier, Pam/Stockdale Ind School Dist | 76 | 404 |
| Burris, Brad/Marshall Ind School Dist | 67 | 214 |
| Burris, Cody/Tornillo Ind School Dist | 6 | 141 |
| Burris, Jon/Hamshire Fannett Ind Sch Dist | 8,11,88,271,273,294 | 245 |
| Burroughs, Renee/Denison Ind School Dist | 10 | 171 |
| Burroughs, Willie/San Antonio Ind School Dist | 3,17 | 42 |
| Burrow, Macy/Texhoma Ind School Dist | 4 | 338 |
| Burrow, Scott/Pringle-Morse Cons ISD | 1,11,73 | 182 |
| Burrus, Jennifer/Muleshoe Ind School Dist | 9 | 25 |
| Burt, Jamie/Pasadena Ind School Dist | 79 | 203 |
| Burton, Chris/Coleman Ind School Dist | 5 | 79 |
| Burton, Christy/Cleburne Ind School Dist | 57 | 250 |
| Burton, Jayne/Boerne Ind School Dist | 48,51 | 257 |
| Burton, Jodi/Judson Ind School Dist | 11,296,298 | 36 |
| Burton, Lori/Region 11 Ed Service Center | 71 | 362 |
| Burton, Maggie/Morgan Mill Ind School Dist | 270,271 | 148 |
| Burwell, Paddy/Westhoff Ind School Dist | 67 | 122 |
| Busa, Kathleen/Navasota Ind School Dist | 7 | 177 |
| Busalacchi, Sherri/Advantage Academy Admin Office | 71 | 100 |
| Busby, Adam/Nederland Ind School Dist | 295 | 245 |
| Busby, Amy, Dr/Montgomery Ind School Dist | 73,76,79,286,295 | 296 |
| Buser, Shawn/West Hardin Co Cons Sch Dist | 73,273,295 | 183 |
| Bush, Kenneth/Galena Park Ind School Dist | 5 | 191 |
| Bush, Leanne/Melissa Ind School Dist | 57 | 85 |
| Bush, Travis/Seguin Ind School Dist | 6 | 178 |
| Bushfield, Victor/Pearland Ind School Dist | 297 | 56 |
| Bushong, Tony/City View Ind School Dist | 1 | 394 |
| Bustamante, Patty/Arlington Ind School Dist | 79 | 346 |

| NAME/District | JOB FUNCTIONS | PAGE |
|---|---|---|
| Bustillos, Monica/Archdiocese San Antonio Ed Off | 2 | 47 |
| Bustos, Victoria/San Antonio Ind School Dist | 36 | 42 |
| Butcher, Michelle/Martin's Mill Ind Sch Dist | 2 | 383 |
| Butler, Ann/Whitehouse Ind School Dist | 42,81 | 341 |
| Butler, Bill/Andrews Ind School Dist | 2 | 19 |
| Butler, Chad/Wharton Ind School Dist | 6 | 393 |
| Butler, Dan/Cotton Center Ind School Dist | 73,83,88,270 | 179 |
| Butler, Denise/Raymondville Ind Sch Dist | 58 | 397 |
| Butler, Drew/Henderson Ind School Dist | 67 | 330 |
| Butler, Dwight/Granbury Ind School Dist | 6 | 233 |
| Butler, Jill/Gruver Ind School Dist | 57 | 181 |
| Butler, Lois, Dr/School of Excellence In Ed | 84 | 45 |
| Butler, Michael/Center Point Ind School Dist | 67 | 258 |
| Butler, Michelle/Kingsville Ind School Dist | 4 | 260 |
| Butler, Michelle/Region 12 Ed Service Center | 77 | 286 |
| Butler, Monica/Hemphill Ind School Dist | 9,273 | 331 |
| Butler, Sally/Hemphill Ind School Dist | 2,11 | 331 |
| Butler, Sonya/Lancaster Ind School Dist | 98,295 | 114 |
| Butler, Terry/Knox City-O'Brien Cons Ind SD | 3 | 261 |
| Butler, Tom/Sabine Pass Ind School Dist | 3,5 | 247 |
| Buttrum, Becky/Hubbard Ind School Dist | 16 | 51 |
| Butts, Jeff/Ballinger Ind School Dist | 1 | 329 |
| Byars, Emory/Vernon Ind School Dist | 67 | 396 |
| Bye, Mickey/Kress Ind School Dist | 5 | 345 |
| Byers, Janet/Deer Park Ind School Dist | 15,79,91 | 191 |
| Byers, Paul/Galveston Ind School Dist | 3 | 164 |
| Byers, Rachael/Merkel Ind School Dist | 69,83,88 | 363 |
| Bymaster, Bryan/Bland Ind School Dist | 2,15,88 | 238 |
| Bynard, Brandon/Red Lick Ind School Dist | 1 | 52 |
| Byno, Kristin, Dr/Richardson Ind School Dist | 8,15 | 116 |
| Bynum, Charlotte/Lufkin Ind School Dist | 2 | 21 |
| Bynum, Debbie/Ector Co Ind School Dist | 74 | 134 |
| Bynum, Tina/Irving Ind School Dist | 48,51 | 113 |
| Byrd, Allison/Hamshire Fannett Ind Sch Dist | 2,11,15 | 245 |
| Byrd, Anita/Central Ind School Dist | 8,88 | 20 |
| Byrd, Chad/Petersburg Ind School Dist | 67 | 180 |
| Byrd, Christen/Henderson Ind School Dist | 2 | 330 |
| Byrd, Jeff/Vernon Ind School Dist | 1 | 396 |
| Byrd, Mark/Whitney Ind School Dist | 6 | 231 |
| Byrne, Bev/Whiteface Con Ind School Dist | 31 | 78 |
| Byrne, Beverly/Whiteface Con Ind School Dist | 36,69,83,85,88,270 | 78 |
| Byrne, Carla/Ector Co Ind School Dist | 27,31 | 134 |
| Byrne, Treva/Midway Ind School Dist | 58 | 78 |
| Byrnes, Tina/Center Ind School Dist | 4 | 337 |
| Byrom, Brenda/Valley Mills Ind School Dist | 2,68 | 50 |
| Byrom, Raenese/Jim Ned Cons Ind School Dist | 7,85 | 363 |
| Byrum, Joey/Rockwall Ind School Dist | 68 | 328 |
| Byrum, Karen/Kelton Ind School Dist | 58 | 393 |

### C

| NAME/District | JOB FUNCTIONS | PAGE |
|---|---|---|
| Cabaniss, Keith/Holland Ind School Dist | 295 | 30 |
| Cabavule, Serapio/Friona Ind School Dist | 5 | 318 |
| Cabazos, Jorge/Mission Cons Ind School Dist | 16,68,73,76,95,295,297 | 225 |
| Cabrera, Charles/Robstown Ind School Dist | 23 | 308 |
| Cabrera, Juan/El Paso Ind School Dist | 1,288 | 137 |
| **Cabrera, Juan/**El Paso ISD-Elementary | 1 | 137 |
| **Cabrera, Juan/**El Paso ISD-High Schools | 1 | 138 |
| **Cabrera, Juan/**El Paso ISD-Middle Schools | 1 | 139 |
| Cabrera, Juan/UT Tyler University Acad Dist | 3 | 341 |
| Cabrera, Tricia/Thorndale Ind School Dist | 36,88 | 291 |
| Caddell, Charles/Abilene Ind School Dist | 297 | 362 |
| Caddell, Jennifer/Knox City-O'Brien Cons Ind SD | 58 | 261 |
| Caddell, Jennifer/Munday Consolidated Ind SD | 58 | 262 |
| Caddell, Jennifer/Stamford Ind School Dist | 67 | 253 |
| Caddell, Kimberly, Dr/Garland Ind School Dist | 69,70,294 | 109 |
| Caddell, Linda/Rule Ind School Dist | 57 | 215 |
| Caddell, Rodney/Levelland Ind School Dist | 91,751 | 232 |
| Cade, Clay/Snyder Ind School Dist | 3 | 336 |
| Cade, Laura/Clint Ind School Dist | 71 | 136 |
| Cadena, Leticia/Roma Ind School Dist | 16,73,84,89,297 | 343 |
| Cadena, Roland/Devine Ind School Dist | 38 | 286 |
| Caesar, Tammy/Austin Ind School Dist | 31 | 369 |
| Caesar-White, Felecia/Houston Ind School Dist | 35 | 193 |
| Caffey, Deanne/S & S Cons Ind School Dist | 4 | 172 |
| Caffey, Doug/Sidney Ind School Dist | 67 | 94 |
| Caffey, John/Yorktown Ind School Dist | 6 | 122 |

| | | | | | | |
|---|---|---|---|---|---|---|
| 1 Superintendent | 16 Instructional Media Svcs | 30 Adult Education | 44 Science Sec | 58 Special Education K-12 | 72 Summer School | 88 Alternative/At Risk | 277 Remedial Math K-12 |
| 2 Bus/Finance/Purchasing | 17 Chief Operations Officer | 31 Career/Sch-to-Work K-12 | 45 Math K-12 | 59 Special Education Elem | 73 Instructional Tech | 89 Multi-Cultural Curriculum | 280 Literacy Coach |
| 3 Buildings And Grounds | 18 Chief Academic Officer | 32 Career/Sch-to-Work Elem | 46 Math Elem | 60 Special Education Sec | 74 Inservice Training | 90 Social Work | 285 STEM |
| 4 Food Service | 19 Chief Financial Officer | 33 Career/Sch-to-Work Sec | 47 Math Sec | 61 Foreign/World Lang K-12 | 75 Marketing/Distributive | 91 Safety/Security | 286 Digital Learning |
| 5 Transportation | 20 Art K-12 | 34 Early Childhood Ed | 48 English/Lang Arts K-12 | 62 Foreign/World Lang Elem | 76 Info Systems | 92 Magnet School | 288 Common Core Standards |
| 6 Athletic | 21 Art Elem | 35 Health/Phys Education | 49 English/Lang Arts Elem | 63 Foreign/World Lang Sec | 77 Psychological Assess | 93 Parental Involvement | 294 Accountability |
| 7 Health Services | 22 Art Sec | 36 Guidance Services K-12 | 50 English/Lang Arts Sec | 64 Religious Education K-12 | 78 Affirmative Action | 95 Tech Prep Program | 295 Network System |
| 8 Curric/Instruct K-12 | 23 Music K-12 | 37 Guidance Services Elem | 51 Reading K-12 | 65 Religious Education Elem | 79 Student Personnel | 97 Chief Information Officer | 296 Title II Programs |
| 9 Curric/Instruct Elem | 24 Music Elem | 38 Guidance Services Sec | 52 Reading Elem | 66 Religious Education Sec | 80 Driver Ed/Safety | 98 Chief Technology Officer | 297 Webmaster |
| 10 Curric/Instruct Sec | 25 Music Sec | 39 Social Studies K-12 | 53 Reading Sec | 67 Teacher Personnel | 81 Gifted/Talented | 270 Character Education | 298 Grant Writer/Ptnrships |
| 11 Federal Program | 26 Business Education | 40 Social Studies Elem | 54 Remedial Reading K-12 | 68 Teacher Personnel | 82 Video Services | 271 Migrant Education | 750 Chief Innovation Officer |
| 12 Title I | 27 Career & Tech Ed | 41 Social Studies Sec | 55 Remedial Reading Elem | 69 Academic Assessment | 83 Substance Abuse Prev | 273 Teacher Mentor | 751 Chief of Staff |
| 13 Title V | 28 Technology Education | 42 Science K-12 | 56 Remedial Reading Sec | 70 Research/Development | 84 Erate | 274 Before/After Sch | 752 Social Emotional Learning |
| 15 Asst Superintendent | 29 Family/Consumer Science | 43 Science Elem | 57 Bilingual/ELL | 71 Public Information | 85 AIDS Education | 275 Response To Intervention | |

| NAME/District | JOB FUNCTIONS | PAGE | NAME/District | JOB FUNCTIONS | PAGE |
|---|---|---|---|---|---|
| Cantu, Ronnie/Harlandale Ind School Dist | 9 | 35 | Carrillo, Carlos/Canutillo Ind School Dist | 91 | 136 |
| Cantu, Sheila/La Porte Ind School Dist | 2 | 203 | Carrillo, Sandra/Canutillo Ind School Dist | 34 | 136 |
| Cantwell, Nancy/Harper Ind School Dist | 57,271 | 168 | Carrington, Kathy/Joaquin Ind School Dist | 11,58 | 337 |
| Canuteson, Ashley, Dr/Midway Ind School Dist | 27,31 | 283 | Carrington, Tim/Austin Ind School Dist | 295 | 369 |
| Caperton, Brian/Whitney Ind School Dist | 3,5,91 | 231 | Carrington, Wade/Hurst-Euless-Bedford ISD | 42 | 356 |
| Capps, Ted/Bland Ind School Dist | 73,286 | 238 | Carrington, Wendy/Arlington Ind School Dist | 88 | 346 |
| Capra, Jennifer/Pasadena Ind School Dist | 30 | 203 | Carrizales, Lupita/Odem-Edroy Ind School Dist | 274 | 334 |
| Carabajal, Bob/Carroll Independent Sch Dist | 3 | 349 | Carrol, Blake/New Caney Ind School Dist | 15 | 296 |
| Caralez, Michael/Somerset Ind School Dist | 2,19 | 45 | Carroll, Adam/Cranfills Gap ISD School Dist | 6 | 50 |
| Caraway, Christy/Honey Grove Ind School Dist | 68 | 150 | Carroll, Charles/Ft Worth Ind School Dist | 8,18 | 352 |
| Caraway, J/Honey Grove Ind School Dist | 3 | 150 | **Carroll, Cody/**Holliday Ind School Dist | 1 | 22 |
| Carden, Corey/Kennard Ind Sch Dist | 6 | 236 | Carroll, Karen/Idalou Ind School Dist | 10,31 | 272 |
| Carden, Cory/Kennard Ind Sch Dist | 6 | 236 | Carroll, Leann/Birdville Ind School Dist | 36,77,83,85,88 | 348 |
| Carden, Ken/Whitesboro Ind School Dist | 3 | 173 | Carroll, Pamela/Lancaster Ind School Dist | 78 | 114 |
| Cardenas-Rubio, Alma/Brownsville Ind School Dist | 8,15 | 66 | Carroll, Philip/Tuloso-Midway Ind School Dist | 2,19,75 | 308 |
| Cardenas, David/Devine Ind School Dist | 3 | 286 | Carroll, Raymond/Anthony Ind School Dist | 296 | 136 |
| Cardenas, Louis/Alamo Heights Ind School Dist | 3 | 33 | Carroll, Samantha/Paint Creek Ind School Dist | 54,58,271 | 215 |
| Cardiff, Susan/Royal Ind School Dist | 11,69,294,296,298 | 387 | Carroll, Sharon/Melissa Ind School Dist | 8,11,36,69,294 | 85 |
| Cardona, Michael/San Marcos Cons Ind Sch Dist | 1 | 216 | Carroll, Susanne, Dr/Victoria Ind School Dist | 8,15,74 | 384 |
| Cardoza, Patrick/Kaufman Ind School Dist | 5 | 255 | Carroll, Tim/Allen Ind School Dist | 71,97 | 80 |
| Cardwell, Evan/Newcastle Ind School Dist | 1,11,83 | 409 | Carruthers, Heidi/Gunter Ind School Dist | 68 | 171 |
| Carey, Bobby/Krum Ind School Dist | 3,5 | 126 | Cartagena, Lorena/Socorro Ind School Dist | 12 | 140 |
| Carey, John/Rice Cons Ind School Dist | 67 | 90 | Cartas, Tracy/Frisco Ind School Dist | 58 | 82 |
| Carey, Kristin/Tolar Ind School Dist | 73,295 | 233 | Carter, Alissa/Plainview Ind School Dist | 73 | 180 |
| Carley, Lawanda/Texas Dept of Education | 74 | 1 | Carter, Amy/Sweeny Ind School Dist | 2,19 | 57 |
| Carlilse, Scott/Jim Ned Cons Ind School Dist | 5 | 363 | Carter, Ashley/Plano Ind School Dist | 44 | 85 |
| Carlin, Howard/Forney Ind School Dist | 295 | 255 | Carter, Becky/Austwell Tivoli Ind SD | 4 | 326 |
| Carlisle, Dayren/Conroe Ind School Dist | 57 | 294 | Carter, Brian/Northwest Ind School Dist | 2,15,19 | 128 |
| Carlisle, Scott/Comanche Ind School Dist | 91 | 93 | Carter, Cara/Northwest Ind School Dist | 2,16,19,73,76,95,286 | 128 |
| Carlson, Michael/Diocese of Fort Worth Ed Off | 6 | 360 | Carter, Carey/Mineral Wells Ind School Dist | 8,16,54,69,74,273,294 | 313 |
| Carlton, B/Garner Ind School Dist | 3,5 | 315 | Carter, Carra/Seymour Ind School Dist | 34 | 28 |
| Carlton, Cyndi/Killeen Ind School Dist | 76 | 30 | **Carter, Charles/**Trent Isn School Dist | 1,11,83,288 | 363 |
| Carlton, Denise/Gorman Ind School Dist | 73 | 133 | Carter, Clay/Jacksonville Ind School Dist | 4 | 76 |
| Carman, Nate, Dr/San Benito Cons Ind Sch Dist | 1 | 70 | Carter, David/Rockwall Ind School Dist | 2,19 | 328 |
| Carman, Scotty/Wink Loving Ind School Dist | 1 | 405 | Carter, David/Utopia Ind School Dist | 73,76 | 381 |
| Carmichael, Regina/Lago Vista Ind School Dist | 7,83,85 | 373 | Carter, Debbie/Texline Ind School Dist | 2,84 | 99 |
| Carnagey, Trish/Farmersville Ind School Dist | 11,57,280 | 82 | Carter, Denise/Houston Ind School Dist | 40 | 193 |
| Carnathan, Jennifer/Channelview Ind School Dist | 19 | 188 | Carter, Gary/Plano Ind School Dist | 83 | 85 |
| Carnes, Charlie/Northside Ind School Dist | 91 | 39 | Carter, Hank/Lake Travis Ind School Dist | 6 | 373 |
| Carnes, Heather/Winona Ind School Dist | 11,271 | 341 | Carter, Hanna/Forsan Ind School Dist | 8,68,79,273 | 237 |
| Carney, Brady/Muenster Ind School Dist | 6 | 95 | Carter, Jason/Roby Cons Ind School Dist | 8,69,73,285,296,298 | 152 |
| Carney, Jodi/Lovelady Ind School Dist | 54 | 236 | Carter, Jimmie/Seymour Ind School Dist | 27 | 28 |
| Carnigney, Donna/Petersburg Ind School Dist | 8,57,58,271,274 | 180 | Carter, Jordan/Knox City-O'Brien Cons Ind SD | 298 | 261 |
| Caroll, Lizatte/Tornillo Ind School Dist | 57,68 | 141 | Carter, Jorgannie/Pearland Ind School Dist | 2,19,76 | 56 |
| Carpenter, David/Huffman Ind School Dist | 73,84,295 | 200 | Carter, Kenny/Hubbard Ind School Dist | 73,295 | 230 |
| Carpenter, Eric/Big Sandy Ind School Dist | 1,11 | 319 | Carter, Lacy/Hallsville Ind School Dist | 69,83,294 | 213 |
| Carpenter, Gary/Woodsboro Ind School Dist | 6 | 326 | Carter, Laquita/Spring Ind School Dist | 15,81 | 207 |
| Carpenter, John/McGregor Ind School Dist | 4 | 283 | Carter, Leonard/Seguin Ind School Dist | 295 | 179 |
| Carpenter, Keith/Hardin Ind School Dist | 3 | 268 | Carter, Mike/Bloomburg Ind School Dist | 3 | 73 |
| Carpenter, Larry/Waco Ind School Dist | 20,23 | 284 | Carter, Mike/Junction Ind School Dist | 1 | 259 |
| Carpenter, Scott/Prairie Valley Ind School Dist | 67 | 293 | Carter, Rachel/Bosqueville Ind School Dist | 73,286,295 | 281 |
| Carpenter, Sonya/Rockwall Ind School Dist | 11,34,88,298 | 328 | **Carter, Ralph/**Lipan Ind School Dist | 1 | 233 |
| Carpenter, Steve/Dell City Ind School Dist | 67 | 237 | Carter, Randy/Boys Ranch Ind School Dist | 73,295 | 310 |
| Carpio, Mario/Whitewright Ind School Dist | 3 | 173 | Carter, Tim/Ropes Ind School Dist | 8,12,273 | 232 |
| Carr, D/Como Pickton Cons Ind SD | 67 | 234 | Carter, Vee Ann/Denver City Ind School Dist | 7,85 | 409 |
| Carr, Dustin/Sulphur Bluff Ind School Dist | 1,11 | 235 | Carthel, Clint/Cotton Center Ind School Dist | 67 | 179 |
| Carr, Jason/Lufkin Ind School Dist | 295 | 21 | Cartwright, Brock/Claude Ind School Dist | 1,11 | 23 |
| Carr, Ron/Miami Ind School Dist | 3,5 | 327 | Cartwright, Cody/Texhoma Ind School Dist | 67 | 338 |
| Carr, Vicki/Tolar Ind School Dist | 2 | 233 | Cartwright, Debra/Port Arthur Ind School Dist | 58,83,88 | 246 |
| Carr, Yolanda/Odem-Edroy Ind School Dist | 1 | 334 | Cartwright, Greg/Allen Ind School Dist | 2,19 | 80 |
| Carrabine, Ginger/Bryan Ind School Dist | 15,751 | 58 | Cartwright, Missy/Texhoma Ind School Dist | 11,73,83,275,286,288 | 338 |
| Carrales, Norma/Santa Gertrudis Ind Sch Dist | 4 | 261 | Caruthers, Brian/Granbury Ind School Dist | 5 | 233 |
| Carranza, Alejandro/La Joya Ind School Dist | 43 | 222 | Carver, Donna/Seymour Ind School Dist | 57,271 | 28 |
| Carrasco, Angela/Woodsboro Ind School Dist | 2 | 326 | Carver, Shelley/New Deal Ind School Dist | 8,69 | 274 |
| Carrasco, David/Socorro Ind School Dist | 3 | 140 | Carwell, Tiffany/Westwood Ind School Dist | 11,57,69,83,285,294,298 | 19 |
| Carrasco, David/Terrell Co Ind School Dist | 73 | 364 | Cary, Gabriel/Medina Valley Ind School Dist | 11 | 287 |
| Carrasco, Jesus/Anthony Ind School Dist | 4 | 136 | Casall, MacKenzie/Duncanville Ind School Dist | 36,58,77 | 108 |
| Carrasco, Laura/Int'l Leadership of Texas Dist | 8,18 | 112 | Casanova, Christina/United Ind School Dist | 69 | 390 |
| Carrasco, Martha/Canutillo Ind School Dist | 68 | 136 | Casarez, Carrie/Whiteface Con Ind School Dist | 16 | 78 |
| Carrasco, Maryann/Hart Ind School Dist | 67 | 75 | Casarez, Christopher/Tuloso-Midway Ind School Dist | 15,91 | 308 |
| Carrasco, Samuel/Presidio Ind School Dist | 30,69 | 323 | Casarez, Kenneth/Castleberry Ind School Dist | 10 | 349 |
| Carrell, Jean/Pittsburg Ind School Dist | 57,271 | 72 | Casas, Cynthia/La Feria Ind School Dist | 4 | 69 |
| Carreon, Alvaro/Webb Cons Ind School Dist | 5 | 391 | Casas, Maria, Dr/Brooks Co Ind School Dist | 1 | 61 |
| Carreon, Rita/Eagle Pass Ind School Dist | 46,277 | 279 | Casas, Michael/Sabinal Ind School Dist | 23 | 380 |
| Carrera, Israel/Waco Ind School Dist | 3,15 | 284 | Case, Becky/Gold-Burg Ind School Dist | 67 | 293 |
| Carriger, Will/Skidmore Tynan Ind SD | 67 | 29 | Case, Diane/Red Oak Ind School Dist | 297 | 146 |

| NAME/District | JOB FUNCTIONS | PAGE | NAME/District | JOB FUNCTIONS | PAGE |
|---|---|---|---|---|---|
| Chapman, Ester/Port Arthur Ind School Dist | 5 | 246 | Choiniere, Sharon/Iola Ind School Dist | 2 | 177 |
| Chapman, John, Dr/Carrollton-Farmers Branch ISD | 1 | 100 | Choundhury, Mohammed/San Antonio Ind School Dist | 70,750 | 42 |
| Chapman, Judy/West Rusk Co Cons Ind Sch Dist | 57 | 331 | Chriesman, Blain/Terrell Co Ind School Dist | 2 | 364 |
| Chapman, Karry/Grand Prairie Ind School Dist | 68 | 111 | Christ, Lacey/East Bernard Ind Sch Dist | 58 | 392 |
| Chapman, Kodi/New Home Ind School Dist | 58 | 275 | Christian, Andrew/Aquilla Ind School Dist | 8,88 | 230 |
| Chapman, Lara/Liberty Hill Ind School Dist | 38 | 401 | Christian, Andrew/Aquilla Ind School Dist | 2,8,15,88 | 230 |
| Chapman, Mandi/Ennis Ind School Dist | 58 | 144 | Christian, Barbara/Malone Independent School Dist | 58,270,273 | 231 |
| Chapman, Marcy/Tom Bean Ind School Dist | 27 | 173 | Christian, Hayley/Farwell Ind School Dist | 36,88,270 | 317 |
| Chapman, Maynard/Elysian Fields Ind School Dist | 1 | 213 | Christian, Jenny/Dallas Ind School Dist | 42,285 | 102 |
| Chapman, Michael/Region 9 Ed Service Center | 27,31,36 | 396 | Christian, Keisha/Evadale Ind School Dist | 7,85 | 243 |
| Chapman, Monte/Weatherford Ind School Dist | 5,15,68,78 | 316 | Christian, Sherry/Dallas Ind School Dist | 15,88 | 102 |
| Chapman, Steve/Hurst-Euless-Bedford ISD | 1 | 356 | Christianson, Emily/Crandall Ind School Dist | 294 | 254 |
| Chapoton, Beth/Manor Ind School Dist | 76 | 373 | Christie, Heather/Bastrop Ind School Dist | 294 | 26 |
| Chapoton, Karen/Manor Ind School Dist | 2 | 373 | Christopher, Rebekah/Denton Ind School Dist | 752 | 125 |
| Chappa, Joe/George West Ind School Dist | 3 | 271 | Christopherson, Judith/Spring Branch Ind School Dist | 7 | 205 |
| Chappell, Charmaine/Beckville Ind School Dist | 2 | 314 | Chrzanowski, Maria/Amarillo Ind School Dist | 81 | 320 |
| Charanza, Ashley/Caldwell Ind School Dist | 4 | 63 | Chuca, Miguel/Region 1 Ed Service Center | 73,76,286 | 229 |
| Chares, Timito/Eagle Pass Ind School Dist | 271 | 279 | Church, Katelyn/Wilson Ind School Dist | 73 | 276 |
| Charles, Courtney/Port Arthur Ind School Dist | 41 | 246 | Church, Keith/Wilson Ind School Dist | 16 | 276 |
| Charlton, Shelly/Leon Ind School Dist | 54 | 267 | Churchill, Edward/Crystal City Ind School Dist | 1 | 410 |
| Chase, John/Forney Ind School Dist | 2,19 | 254 | Cielencki, Cayla/Amarillo Ind School Dist | 42 | 320 |
| Chase, Roger/Wellman Union Ind School Dist | 73,286 | 365 | Cieri, Ashley/Waxahachie Ind School Dist | 286 | 146 |
| Chatelain, Stefanie/Edgewood Ind School Dist | 7 | 34 | Cieszlak, Lucia/Eagle Mtn-Saginaw Ind Sch Dist | 2 | 351 |
| Chatfield, Chuck/Crowell Ind School Dist | 5 | 153 | Cikanek, Kathy/Ennis Ind School Dist | 8,15,69 | 144 |
| Chatman, Kim/Gladewater Ind School Dist | 3,17,83 | 174 | Cimmings, April/Central Ind School Dist | 76 | 20 |
| Chauveaux, Mark/Godley Ind School Dist | 6 | 250 | Cipolla, Denise/Conroe Ind School Dist | 36 | 294 |
| Chavarria, Amanda/West Oso Ind School Dist | 76 | 309 | Cipriano, Juan/Santa Rosa Ind School Dist | 6 | 71 |
| Chavarria, Martin/Charlotte Ind School Dist | 3,5 | 23 | Cisneros, Eve/Beeville Ind School Dist | 2 | 28 |
| Chavarria, Raul/Crockett Co Cons Common SD | 1 | 98 | Cisneros, Jesse/Sweeny Ind School Dist | 91 | 57 |
| Chavera, George/Ramirez Common School Dist | 67 | 132 | Civis, Leah/Banquete Ind School Dist | 4 | 305 |
| Chavers, Eric/Fairfield Ind School Dist | 67 | 160 | Clancy, Brian/San Antonio Ind School Dist | 6 | 42 |
| Chaves, Rodrigo/Conroe Ind School Dist | 7,30,88,93,271 | 294 | Clandenen, Sue Ann/Llano Ind School Dist | 2 | 271 |
| Chavez, Anna/Little Elm Ind School Dist | 2 | 128 | Clanton, Tracy/Rankin Ind School Dist | 3,5 | 380 |
| Chavez, David/Donna Ind School Dist | 16,73,76,295 | 220 | Clardy, Dick/Ft Worth Ind School Dist | 23 | 352 |
| Chavez, Gloria/Ysleta Ind School Dist | 73,76 | 141 | Clardy, Karen/Richardson Ind School Dist | 67 | 116 |
| Chavez, Juan, Dr/Brownsville Ind School Dist | 27,31 | 66 | Clark, Amy/Sweetwater ISD School Dist | 31,38,88 | 304 |
| Chavez, Micheal/Springtown Ind School Dist | 5,79 | 316 | Clark, Angela/Fruitvale Ind School Dist | 8,11,89,296 | 383 |
| Chavez, Phillip/Edgewood Ind School Dist | 8,15,18 | 34 | Clark, Bridget/Gregory-Portland Ind Sch Dist | 2,19 | 333 |
| Chavez, Rene/Clint Ind School Dist | 68 | 136 | Clark, Cindy/Baird Ind School Dist | 2 | 65 |
| Chavez, Tomas/Ft Hancock Ind School Dist | 73 | 237 | Clark, Darin/Perryton Ind School Dist | 71 | 310 |
| Chavez, Veronica/La Joya Ind School Dist | 50 | 222 | Clark, Darla/Hurst-Euless-Bedford ISD | 9,15 | 356 |
| Chavira, Hector/Rio Hondo Ind School Dist | 15 | 70 | Clark, Elizabeth, Dr/Birdville Ind School Dist | 8,15 | 348 |
| Chavira, Manny/El Paso Ind School Dist | 91 | 137 | Clark, Ellen/Lancaster Ind School Dist | 67 | 114 |
| Cheatham, Patricia/Coppell Ind School Dist | 57 | 102 | Clark, Gay/Ferris Ind School Dist | 4 | 144 |
| Cheek, Dale/Maypearl Ind School Dist | 3,5 | 145 | Clark, Jennifer/Melissa Ind School Dist | 58 | 85 |
| Cheek, Faith Ann, Dr/Pecos-Barstow-Toyah Ind SD | 271 | 326 | Clark, Jennifer/Prairiland Ind School Dist | 11,38,69,83,88,270,752 | 263 |
| Cheek, Kimberly/Wylie Ind School Dist | 81 | 364 | Clark, Joe/Spring Ind School Dist | 20,23 | 207 |
| Cheek, Steve/Chillicothe ISD School Dist | 3 | 182 | Clark, Karrie/Vidor Ind School Dist | 34,57,58,77 | 312 |
| Cheetum, Carla/Alpine Ind School Dist | 752 | 60 | Clark, Lisa/Rains Ind School Dist | 73,295 | 323 |
| Chenausky, Shelly/Socorro Ind School Dist | 4 | 140 | Clark, Mary Ann/El Paso ISD-High Schools | 92 | 138 |
| Cheney, Darrell/Channelview Ind School Dist | 73,84 | 188 | Clark, Melissa/O'Donnell Ind School Dist | 2 | 276 |
| Chenoweth, Katie/Region 7 Ed Service Center | 2,68,71 | 176 | Clark, Michelle/Elkhart Ind School Dist | 16,82 | 18 |
| Cheslock, Jason/Poolville Ind School Dist | 9,59 | 316 | Clark, Randy/Walnut Bend Ind School Dist | 67 | 96 |
| Chesnut, Christian/UT Tyler University Acad Dist | 2 | 341 | Clark, Rebecca/Benjamin Ind School Dist | 7 | 261 |
| Chesser, Brandon/Eastland Ind School Dist | 12 | 133 | Clark, Robby/Krum Ind School Dist | 6 | 126 |
| Chesser, Paula/Warren Ind School Dist | 29 | 378 | Clark, Ryan/Schertz-Cibolo-Univ City ISD | 91 | 178 |
| Chester, Mark/Blue Ridge Ind School Dist | 6 | 81 | Clark, Sandy/Orange Grove Ind School Dist | 36 | 248 |
| Chevalier, Jessica/Houston Ind School Dist | 57,280 | 193 | Clark, Sedric/Gladewater Ind School Dist | 1 | 174 |
| Chiarelli, April/Burleson Ind School Dist | 9,18,34 | 249 | Clark, Sherry/Wildorado Ind Sch Dist | 12 | 311 |
| Chiboroski, Susan/Goose Creek Cons Ind Sch Dist | 20,23 | 192 | Clark, Steve/Leander Ind School Dist | 36 | 399 |
| Chide, Wendy/Dickinson Ind School Dist | 88 | 164 | Clark, Tim/Richardson Ind School Dist | 71 | 116 |
| Childers, Willis/Chilton Ind School Dist | 3 | 148 | Clark, Viann/Pringle-Morse Cons ISD | 271 | 182 |
| Childress, Bill/Boyd Ind School Dist | 67 | 405 | Clark, Yvonne/Klein Ind School Dist | 7 | 201 |
| Childress, Don/Fannindel Ind School Dist | 16 | 124 | Clarkson, Lesa/Prairiland Ind School Dist | 4 | 263 |
| Childress, Dwight/Crockett Co Cons Common SD | 67 | 98 | Claunch, Suann/Ft Worth Ind School Dist | 57 | 352 |
| Childress, Jamey/Big Sandy Ind School Dist | 67 | 378 | Clausen, Mike/La Porte Ind School Dist | 3,15,17,91 | 203 |
| Chism, Heather/Kilgore Ind School Dist | 295 | 174 | Clavell, Deanna/Shepherd Ind School Dist | 2 | 333 |
| Chisum, Kevin/Guthrie Common School Dist | 1,83 | 260 | Clawson, Heath/Louise Ind School Dist | 6 | 392 |
| Chisum, McKenzie/Guthrie Common School Dist | 57,271 | 260 | Claxon, Mary/Crawford Ind School Dist | 38 | 282 |
| Chitwood, Michele/New Waverly Ind School Dist | 2 | 386 | Clay, Anita/Texarkana Ind School Dist | 2 | 53 |
| Chlapecka, Ross/Bells Ind School Dist | 73,76,84,97,98,286 | 170 | Clay, Camille/Leander Ind School Dist | 27,31 | 399 |
| Choate, Barry/Athens Ind School Dist | 3,4,5 | 218 | Clay, Steve/El Paso Ind School Dist | 69,70,294 | 137 |
| Choate, Debbie/New Waverly Ind School Dist | 36,85,286 | 386 | Clay, Toni/Athens Ind School Dist | 71 | 218 |
| Choate, John/Christoval Ind School Dist | 10,60,73,288,296 | 366 | Clayburn, Ashley, Dr/Cypress-Fairbanks Ind Sch Dist | 15,294 | 189 |
| Choate, Merideth/Frisco Ind School Dist | 57 | 82 | Claycomb, Becky/Texline Ind School Dist | 31,90 | 99 |
| Chohlis, Ashley/East Central Ind School Dist | 71,79 | 34 | Claymon, Lauaren/Liberty Hill Ind School Dist | 16,82 | 401 |

| NAME/District | JOB FUNCTIONS | PAGE |
|---|---|---|
| Claypool, Kevin, Dr/Lake Travis Ind School Dist | 70 | 373 |
| Clayton, Carla/Harrold Ind School Dist | 58 | 396 |
| Clayton, John/Grandview Ind School Dist | 73,95,295 | 251 |
| Clayton, Raachelle/George West Ind School Dist | 7 | 271 |
| **Clayton, Scot**/Henrietta Ind School Dist | 1 | 78 |
| Cleary, Brian/Bandera Ind School Dist | 4 | 26 |
| Cleaver, Max/Hays Cons Ind School Dist | 17 | 216 |
| Cleere, Jan/Kennedale Ind School Dist | 8,69,73 | 358 |
| Cleere, Roger/Ector Co Ind School Dist | 5 | 134 |
| Clem, Dale/New Home Ind School Dist | 3 | 275 |
| Clement, Sherri/Aubrey Ind School Dist | 4 | 124 |
| Clements, Bryan/Galena Park Ind School Dist | 91 | 191 |
| Clements, Jody, Dr/Longview Ind School Dist | 68,74,93,296 | 174 |
| Clements, John/Buffalo Ind School Dist | 83 | 266 |
| Cleveland, Jess/Scurry Rosser Ind School Dist | 6 | 256 |
| Cleveland, Royce/Region 19 Ed Service Center | 2 | 144 |
| Cleveland, Sunny/Lovejoy Ind School Dist | 4 | 84 |
| Cleveland, Thad/Terrell Co Ind School Dist | 67 | 364 |
| Clevenger, Denise/Advantage Academy Admin Office | 280 | 100 |
| Clevenger, Gaylen/Del Valle Ind School Dist | 58 | 372 |
| Clevenger, Theodore/Bartlett Ind School Dist | 1 | 29 |
| Click, Shan/Eden Cons Ind School Dist | 67 | 94 |
| Clifton, Denise/Blooming Grove Ind School Dist | 37 | 302 |
| Clifton, Karen/Ranger Ind School Dist | 67 | 133 |
| Clifton, Megan/Crowell Ind School Dist | 16 | 153 |
| Clifton, Mona/Comanche Ind School Dist | 7 | 93 |
| Clifton, Sharon/George West Ind School Dist | 4 | 271 |
| Cline, Donna/Clint Ind School Dist | 2,19 | 136 |
| Cline, Kelly/Spring Ind School Dist | 11,15 | 207 |
| Cline, Michelle, Dr/Throckmorton Ind School Dist | 1 | 365 |
| Cline, Nancy/Carrollton-Farmers Branch ISD | 67 | 100 |
| Cline, Rebecca/San Angelo Ind School Dist | 69 | 367 |
| Cline, Ron/Paint Rock Ind School Dist | 1,11 | 94 |
| Clinton, Ben/Raymondville Ind Sch Dist | 11,15 | 397 |
| Clopton, Kell/Kaufman Ind School Dist | 15,68,88 | 255 |
| Cloud, David/South San Antonio Ind Sch Dist | 16,73 | 45 |
| Cloud, Kenneth/Tomball Ind School Dist | 76 | 208 |
| Cloud, Rhonda/Hearne Ind School Dist | 4 | 327 |
| Clouse, Christy/Lindale Ind School Dist | 58 | 339 |
| Clouse, Tim/Harrold Ind School Dist | 67 | 396 |
| Clouser, Shawna/Lake Worth Ind School Dist | 10,280 | 358 |
| Clover, Cortney/Little Elm Ind School Dist | 58 | 128 |
| Clower, Scott/Gladewater Ind School Dist | 6 | 174 |
| Cloy, Michael/Brownwood Ind School Dist | 67 | 62 |
| Clugston, Steve/Pine Tree Ind School Dist | 1 | 175 |
| Clymer, Amanda/Dallas Ind School Dist | 57 | 102 |
| Clynch, Kim/Harleton Ind School Dist | 16 | 213 |
| Cmaidalka, Brian/Dickinson Ind School Dist | 5 | 164 |
| Coachman, Andrea/McKinney Ind School Dist | 50 | 84 |
| Coats, Lorrie/Plainview Ind School Dist | 5 | 180 |
| Coats, Shannon/Queen City Ind School Dist | 4 | 74 |
| Cob, Darryl, Dr/DeSoto Ind School Dist | 68,78 | 108 |
| Cobarrubias, Rosie, Dr/Monte Alto Ind School Dist | 1 | 226 |
| Cobb, Bruce/Canyon Ind School Dist | 67 | 323 |
| Cobb, Chris/Pewitt Cons Ind School Dist | 2,19 | 299 |
| Cobb, Cindy/Frenship Ind School Dist | 8,15,74,273 | 272 |
| Cobb, Courtney/Alpine Ind School Dist | 4 | 60 |
| Cobb, Derek/Frenship Ind School Dist | 3 | 272 |
| Cobb, Jennifer, Dr/Spring Ind School Dist | 15,69,70,294 | 207 |
| Cobb, Marilyn/Atlanta Ind School Dist | 2,15 | 73 |
| Cobb, Martin/Spring Hill Ind School Dist | 2,19 | 175 |
| Cobb, Melissa/Waxahachie Ind School Dist | 30 | 146 |
| Cobb, Robert/Dickinson Ind School Dist | 15 | 164 |
| Cobb, Ryan/Tidehaven Ind School Dist | 3 | 279 |
| Cobb, Samantha/Martinsville Ind School Dist | 2 | 301 |
| Cobb, Tracy/Corrigan-Camden Ind Sch Dist | 58 | 319 |
| Cobos, Dolores/Klondike Ind School Dist | 4 | 121 |

| NAME/District | JOB FUNCTIONS | PAGE |
|---|---|---|
| Cobos, Dolores/Klondike Ind School Dist | 4 | 121 |
| Coburn, Billy/Little Elm Ind School Dist | 91 | 128 |
| **Coburn, Dr**/Decatur Ind School Dist | 1 | 406 |
| Coburn, Harold/Elysian Fields Ind School Dist | 67 | 213 |
| Coburn, Joseph, Dr/Lewisville Ind School Dist | 7,72,91 | 126 |
| Cochran, Jarrett/Comal Ind School Dist | 73,76,295,297 | 91 |
| Cochran, Jason/Eastland Ind School Dist | 1,83 | 133 |
| Cochran, Lisa/Midway Ind School Dist | 58 | 283 |
| Cochran, William/Motley Co Ind School Dist | 1 | 299 |
| Cochrane, Judy/Hooks Ind School Dist | 2 | 51 |
| Cochrane, Karla/Palmer Ind School Dist | 2 | 146 |
| Cockrell, Luther/Groveton Ind School Dist | 3 | 377 |
| Cockrum, Kenneth/North Hopkins Ind School Dist | 5 | 234 |
| Cockrum, Lisa/Wells Ind School Dist | 57 | 77 |
| Cockrum, Lisa/Wells Ind School Dist | 8,11,69,294 | 77 |
| Cody, Robert/Sulphur Springs Ind Sch Dist | 67 | 235 |
| Coffee, Lawanda/Spring Branch Ind School Dist | 12 | 205 |
| Coffelt, Bradley/Whitney Ind School Dist | 27 | 231 |
| Coffey, Keith/Aquilla Ind School Dist | 12 | 230 |
| Cofper, Melinda/Peaster Ind School Dist | 16 | 316 |
| Cogburn, Elaine/Dripping Springs Ind Sch Dist | 2 | 215 |
| Cogburn, Elaine/Leander Ind School Dist | 19 | 399 |
| Cogburn, Ray/Region 16 Ed Service Center | 1 | 324 |
| Cogdell, Danny/Little Elm Ind School Dist | 3 | 128 |
| Cohen, Alan/Dallas Ind School Dist | 34 | 102 |
| Coker, Geanna/Wink Loving Ind School Dist | 2 | 405 |
| Coker, Jeremy/Woodville Ind School Dist | 73,76,84,295 | 378 |
| Coker, Jon/Abbott Ind School Dist | 57,58,79,280,296 | 229 |
| Coker, Kent/Reagan Co Ind School Dist | 60,752 | 324 |
| Coker, Marie/Keller Ind School Dist | 57 | 357 |
| Colbert, Cecilia/Diocese of Dallas Ed Office | 19 | 118 |
| Colbert, Dean/Aldine Ind School Dist | 6 | 184 |
| Colbert, James/Harris Co Dept of Ed | 1 | 184 |
| Cole, Amy/Galena Park Ind School Dist | 11 | 191 |
| Cole, Brian/Brazosport Ind School Dist | 11,16,34,69,73,271,285,286 | 55 |
| Cole, Christina/Cypress-Fairbanks Ind Sch Dist | 15 | 189 |
| Cole, Clay/Liberty Hill Ind School Dist | 67 | 401 |
| Cole, Judy/Bridge City Ind School Dist | 67 | 311 |
| Cole, Julie/Hurst-Euless-Bedford ISD | 67 | 356 |
| Cole, Shannon, Dr/Irving Ind School Dist | 58,74 | 113 |
| Cole, Susan/Leander Ind School Dist | 74,273 | 400 |
| Coleman, Alton/Gregory-Portland Ind Sch Dist | 5 | 333 |
| Coleman, Barry/Trinity Ind School Dist | 73,295 | 377 |
| Coleman, Carla/North Lamar Ind School Dist | 71 | 406 |
| Coleman, Debbie/Nixon-Smiley Cons Ind Sch Dist | 16 | 169 |
| Coleman, Derrell, Dr/Carrollton-Farmers Branch ISD | 15,751 | 100 |
| Coleman, Jennifer/Gainesville Ind School Dist | 73,98 | 95 |
| Coleman, Lawrence/West Rusk Co Cons Ind Sch Dist | 1 | 331 |
| Coleman, Roy/Lumberton Ind School Dist | 5 | 183 |
| Coleman, Susan/Aransas Pass Ind School Dist | 16 | 333 |
| Coleman, Tim/Pewitt Cons Ind School Dist | 5 | 299 |
| Coleman, Todd/Beaumont Ind School Dist | 5 | 244 |
| Coleman, Tonja/Gary Ind School Dist | 81 | 314 |
| Coleman, Wayne/Jacksonville Ind School Dist | 6 | 76 |
| Colhoff, Krystal/Lago Vista Ind School Dist | 58,69 | 373 |
| **Collavo, Lana**/Natalia Ind School Dist | 1 | 287 |
| Collazo, Sheila/Somerset Ind School Dist | 8,15,57,271 | 45 |
| Collida, Joanna/Dodd City Ind School Dist | 274 | 150 |
| Collier, Melody/Hawley Ind School Dist | 2,8,11,57,288 | 253 |
| Collier, Twiana/Aldine Ind School Dist | 2 | 184 |
| Collingsworth, Roselle/Grandview-Hopkins Ind Sch Dist | 4 | 169 |
| Collins, Amy/Hallsville Ind School Dist | 34,58,90 | 213 |
| Collins, Betty/Rusk Ind School Dist | 8,27,57,74,88,271,296,298 | 77 |
| Collins, Billie/Uvalde Cons Ind School Dist | 2,19 | 381 |
| Collins, Cathy/Ft Bend Ind School Dist | 274 | 154 |
| Collins, Chad/Lovejoy Ind School Dist | 67 | 84 |
| Collins, Chad/Scurry Rosser Ind School Dist | 15 | 256 |

| NAME/District | JOB FUNCTIONS | PAGE | NAME/District | JOB FUNCTIONS | PAGE |
|---|---|---|---|---|---|
| Collins, Christi/Nueces Canyon Cons Ind SD | 58,83 | 135 | Cook, Solomon/Humble Ind School Dist | 91 | 200 |
| Collins, Jeanann/Princeton Ind School Dist | 71 | 87 | Cook, Stephanie, Dr/Frisco Ind School Dist | 36 | 82 |
| Collins, Karen/Community Ind School Dist | 7,85 | 81 | Cook, Tammie/Vega Ind School Dist | 8,31,36,69,83,270 | 310 |
| Collins, Kelli/Zavalla Ind School Dist | 36 | 21 | Cook, Tracy/Hooks Ind School Dist | 8,11,30,34,36,57,288,296 | 51 |
| Collins, Kortni/Eula Ind School Dist | 270 | 66 | Cooke, Mrs/Aransas Pass Ind School Dist | 1 | 333 |
| Collins, Lisa/Rio Vista Ind School Dist | 81 | 251 | Cooksy, Rodney/Int'l Leadership of Texas Dist | 15 | 112 |
| Collins, Tim/Arlington Ind School Dist | 5 | 346 | Cooley, Carla/Jim Ned Cons Ind School Dist | 38,69,83,88 | 363 |
| Collmorgen, Joe/Central Ind School Dist | 2,3 | 20 | Cooley, Hunter/Jim Ned Cons Ind School Dist | 2,11,19,294 | 363 |
| Collum, Jeff/Hallsville Ind School Dist | 1 | 213 | Coonkin, Clinit/Clarendon Cons Ind Sch Dist | 6 | 131 |
| Colson, Harold/Pilot Point Ind School Dist | 15 | 129 | Cooper, Aimee/Advantage Academy Admin Office | 8 | 100 |
| Colton, Bradshaw, Dr/Harts Bluff Ind School Dist | 67 | 366 | Cooper, Brian/Greenwood Ind School Dist | 3,15 | 288 |
| Colvert, Jeremy/Leon Ind School Dist | 6 | 267 | Cooper, Chris/Sherman Ind School Dist | 76 | 172 |
| Colvin, Demetrius/Burton Ind School Dist | 67 | 388 | Cooper, Debbie/Red Lick Ind School Dist | 9,11,57,69,74,88 | 52 |
| Colvin, Lou/Como Pickton Cons Ind SD | 38 | 234 | Cooper, Donna/Brookeland Ind School Dist | 3,5 | 243 |
| Combs, Daniel, Dr/Alvin Ind School Dist | 2,15,19,71 | 54 | Cooper, Geoff/Brownfield Ind Sch Dist | 67 | 364 |
| Combs, Mike/Lindale Ind School Dist | 67 | 339 | Cooper, Jason/Lewisville Ind School Dist | 31 | 126 |
| Comeaux, Erin/Pasadena Ind School Dist | 11 | 203 | Cooper, John/Lipan Ind School Dist | 67 | 233 |
| Comeaux, Michael/Anna Ind School Dist | 1 | 81 | Cooper, John/Snook Ind School Dist | 3 | 63 |
| Comer, Norma/Richardson Ind School Dist | 76,295 | 116 | Cooper, Kary, Dr/Plano Ind School Dist | 4,5,15,35,68,91 | 85 |
| Comneck, Mark/Angleton Ind School Dist | 8,15 | 55 | Cooper, Keri/Pleasanton Ind School Dist | 57,288,296 | 24 |
| Compton, Alice/Avalon Ind School Dist | 2 | 144 | Cooper, Kyle/Gatesville Ind School Dist | 6 | 96 |
| Compton, Nate/Lone Oak Ind School Dist | 6 | 239 | Cooper, Lynette/Bay City Ind School Dist | 7 | 278 |
| Compton, Tommy/Clifton Ind School Dist | 3,5 | 49 | Cooper, Madeline/Liberty-Eylau Ind School Dist | 26 | 51 |
| Conaway, Jeff/Jarrell Ind School Dist | 58,275 | 399 | Cooper, Rebbeca/New Deal Ind School Dist | 12,57 | 274 |
| Concha, Alfredo/Lackland Ind School Dist | 3,4,5,73,76,91,295 | 37 | Cooper, Richard/Corrigan-Camden Ind Sch Dist | 1 | 319 |
| Concha, Beveylon/Judson Ind School Dist | 4 | 36 | Cooper, Sara/Granger Ind School Dist | 8 | 399 |
| Concres, Marena/La Joya Ind School Dist | 9 | 222 | Cooper, Sherry/Leonard Ind School Dist | 4 | 150 |
| Condarco, Mary/Junction Ind School Dist | 4 | 259 | Cooper, Tim/San Saba Ind School Dist | 73,286,295 | 335 |
| Condra, Randy/Crosby Ind School Dist | 67 | 188 | Cope, Brandon/Riesel Ind School Dist | 1 | 284 |
| Condra, Wayne/El Campo Ind School Dist | 6 | 392 | Cope, John/Ft Worth Ind School Dist | 297 | 352 |
| Condron, Mark/Hudson Ind School Dist | 297 | 20 | Cope, Kristi/Industrial Ind School Dist | 16 | 243 |
| Cone, Hensley/La Vernia Ind School Dist | 1 | 404 | Copelan, Casey/Cushing Ind School Dist | 3,73 | 300 |
| Conger, Eddie/Int'l Leadership of Texas Dist | 1 | 112 | Copeland, Derek/New Deal Ind School Dist | 5 | 274 |
| Conklin, Mike/Northwest Ind School Dist | 91 | 129 | Copeland, Jim/Pottsboro Ind School Dist | 67 | 172 |
| Conklin, Shane, Dr/Decatur Ind School Dist | 8,31,57,69,70,271,274 | 406 | Copeland, Kendra/Salado Ind School Dist | 57 | 32 |
| Conley-Johnson, Nicole/Austin Ind School Dist | 2 | 369 | Copeland, Shelly/Spring Ind School Dist | 4 | 207 |
| Conley, John, Dr/Region 6 Ed Service Center | 73 | 386 | Copeland, Sunshine/Orangefield Ind School Dist | 16 | 312 |
| Connally, Melanie/Priddy Ind School Dist | 2 | 292 | Copeland, Tim/Jarrell Ind School Dist | 3 | 399 |
| Connally, Paula/Bronte Ind School Dist | 58,280 | 79 | Copley, Jamie/Follett Ind School Dist | 1,11 | 270 |
| Connell, Jeremy/San Marcos Cons Ind Sch Dist | 295 | 217 | Copp, Judy/Northwest Ind School Dist | 67 | 129 |
| Connelly, Brad/Celeste Ind School Dist | 1 | 239 | Coppock, Joyce/Darrouzett Ind School Dist | 36,275,288 | 270 |
| Conner, Arron/Bridge City Ind School Dist | 27 | 311 | Corbett, Patrick/Bryan Ind School Dist | 20,23 | 58 |
| Conner, Jacob/Irion Co Ind School Dist | 6 | 241 | Corbin, Leeann/Redwater Ind School Dist | 8,11,57,69,83,273,288,296 | 53 |
| Conner, Maryellen/Dayton Ind School Dist | 68,273 | 268 | Corbin, Sarah/Buffalo Ind School Dist | 4 | 266 |
| Connor, Jim/Columbus Ind School Dist | 8 | 90 | Corcan, Tommy/Glen Rose Ind School Dist | 3,5,15,17,68,83,91 | 342 |
| Connor, Joshua/Meadow Ind School Dist | 6 | 365 | Corcoran, Patrick/Munday Consolidated Ind SD | 6,35 | 262 |
| Connors, Deborah/Humble Ind School Dist | 2 | 200 | Cordell, Cole/Region 16 Ed Service Center | 2 | 324 |
| Connot, Lance/Rivercrest Ind School Dist | 6 | 325 | Corder, Angela/Kaufman Ind School Dist | 73,76 | 255 |
| Conrad, Dana/Spur Ind School Dist | 58 | 131 | Cordova, Courtney/Glen Rose Ind School Dist | 69,288 | 342 |
| Conrad, Scott/Sherman Ind School Dist | 3 | 172 | Cordova, Joe/Knippa Ind School Dist | 73 | 380 |
| Conrad, Terri/Georgetown Ind School Dist | 8,74,273 | 398 | Cordova, Toni/Dallas Ind School Dist | 71 | 102 |
| Conring, Kathy/Cisco Independent Sch Dist | 69,83 | 133 | Corean, Jeff/Grandfalls-Royalty Ind SD | 6,8 | 388 |
| Contreras, Austin/Corsicana Ind School Dist | 73,295 | 302 | Corean, Jeff/Rochelle Ind School Dist | 6,9,74,288 | 281 |
| Contreras, Carlos/Dell City Ind School Dist | 8,11,88,285,288,294 | 237 | Coreo, Beatrice/Stratford Ind School Dist | 271 | 338 |
| Contreras, Chris/Hardin Ind School Dist | 2,19 | 268 | Corley, Jolynn, Dr/Nacogdoches Ind School Dist | 11,294 | 301 |
| Contreras, Sam/Pecos-Barstow-Toyah Ind SD | 67 | 326 | Cormier, Mandy/Hamshire Fannett Ind Sch Dist | 34 | 245 |
| Contrucci, John/Junction Ind School Dist | 6 | 259 | Cornejo, Maggie/Schertz-Cibolo-Univ City ISD | 4 | 178 |
| Contu, Nora, Dr/Pharr-San Juan-Alamo Ind SD | 10 | 226 | Cornelison, Steffani/Lindsay Ind School Dist | 752 | 95 |
| Conway, Nina/Robstown Ind School Dist | 2,19 | 308 | Cornelius, John/Sudan Ind School Dist | 6 | 264 |
| Conway, Shelly/Anna Ind School Dist | 67 | 81 | Cornett, Dilia/San Benito Cons Ind Sch Dist | 9 | 70 |
| Coody, Shari/Northside Ind School Dist | 286 | 396 | Cornett, Monte/Shamrock Ind School Dist | 5 | 393 |
| Cook, Amy/Friona Ind School Dist | 16 | 318 | Cornish, Kaaron/Mt Calm Ind School Dist | 58 | 231 |
| Cook, Carter/Ft Worth Ind School Dist | 16 | 352 | Corona, Melissa/Lockhart Ind School Dist | 58,81 | 64 |
| Cook, Donna/Central Ind School Dist | 16,82 | 20 | Corona, Nicholas/El Paso Ind School Dist | 3,4,5 | 137 |
| Cook, Dustin/Mt Pleasant Ind School Dist | 79 | 366 | Coronado, Sergio/Canutillo Ind School Dist | 67 | 136 |
| Cook, Grant/Tarkington Ind School Dist | 67 | 269 | Coronado, Sergio/Progreso Ind School Dist | 1 | 227 |
| Cook, Justus/Hull Daisetta Ind School Dist | 73,295 | 268 | Corral, Jesus/El Paso Ind School Dist | 73 | 137 |
| Cook, Keith/Roby Cons Ind School Dist | 1,11 | 152 | Corrales, Cynthia/Ysleta Ind School Dist | 93 | 141 |
| Cook, Kimberly/Milford Ind School Dist | 67 | 146 | Correa, Bea/Glasscock Co Ind School Dist | 57 | 168 |
| Cook, Laura/Lubbock Ind School Dist | 61 | 272 | Correa, Nolan/Humble Ind School Dist | 15,79 | 200 |
| Cook, Leigh/Keller Ind School Dist | 11,298 | 357 | Correll, Andrew/Levelland Ind School Dist | 6,35 | 232 |
| Cook, Lynwood/Neches Ind School Dist | 3,85,91 | 18 | Cortez, Ami/Austin Ind School Dist | 34 | 369 |
| Cook, Nicci/Frankston Ind School Dist | 1,11,57 | 18 | Cortez, Debbie/San Elizario Ind School Dist | 42,45,277 | 139 |
| Cook, Rebecca/Cypress-Fairbanks Ind Sch Dist | 73 | 189 | Cortez, Eddie/Carrizo Spgs Cons Ind SD | 91 | 131 |
| Cook, Sarah/Brenham Ind School Dist | 294 | 388 | Cortez, Eric/Austwell Tivoli Ind SD | 11,57,88 | 326 |
| Cook, Sarah/Memphis Ind School Dist | 67 | 181 | Cortez, Fiosncio/Muleshoe Ind School Dist | 5 | 25 |

| NAME/District | JOB FUNCTIONS | PAGE |
|---|---|---|
| Daniel, Traci/Bonham Ind School Dist | 8,11,57,83,285,288,294 | 149 |
| Daniels, Micki/Rockdale Ind School Dist | 57 | 290 |
| Daniels, Raily/Timpson Ind School Dist | 2 | 338 |
| Daniels, Toni/Itasca Ind School Dist | 4 | 231 |
| Danilowicz, Raymond/Lewisville Ind School Dist | 4 | 126 |
| Danke, Lisa/Valley Mills Ind School Dist | 4 | 50 |
| Dankel, Amy/McKinney Ind School Dist | 67 | 84 |
| Dannheim, Marisa/Olfen Ind School Dist | 58 | 329 |
| Darden, Lora, Dr/Round Rock Ind School Dist | 16,27 | 401 |
| Darden, Steve/Utopia Ind School Dist | 67 | 381 |
| Darden, Thomas/Cooper Ind School Dist | 67 | 124 |
| Darnell, Ann/Socorro Ind School Dist | 298 | 140 |
| Darragh, Sheron, Dr/Region 7 Ed Service Center | 8,74 | 176 |
| Darrow, Brandon/Miller Grove Ind School Dist | 67 | 234 |
| Darrow, Melissa/Clarksville Ind School Dist | 2 | 325 |
| Darrow, Melissa/North Lamar Ind School Dist | 2 | 406 |
| Daugherty, Olivia/Pasadena Ind School Dist | 298 | 203 |
| Daugherty, Teresa/Killeen Ind School Dist | 69,294 | 30 |
| Daugherty, Zachary/Tidehaven Ind School Dist | 73,295 | 279 |
| Davant, Tamara/Tidehaven Ind School Dist | 31,36,85 | 279 |
| Davenport, Allison/Garland Ind School Dist | 2 | 109 |
| Davenport, Kenny/Silsbee Ind School Dist | 91 | 183 |
| Davenport, Mattew/Whitesboro Ind School Dist | 8,15 | 173 |
| Davenport, Michelle/Huffman Ind School Dist | 34,57,58,77,88,271 | 200 |
| David, Danny/Pilot Point Ind School Dist | 6 | 129 |
| David, Lorine/Taylor Ind School Dist | 2 | 402 |
| Davidson, Ben/Livingston Ind School Dist | 2,19 | 319 |
| Davidson, Cassie/Pilot Point Ind School Dist | 4 | 129 |
| Davidson, Jeff/Commerce Independent Sch Dist | 6 | 239 |
| Davidson, Jerry/Graham Ind School Dist | 3,5,91 | 409 |
| Davidson, Kenneth/Graham Ind School Dist | 6 | 409 |
| Davidson, Mary/Marble Falls Ind School Dist | 4 | 64 |
| Davie, Cindy/Hull Daisetta Ind School Dist | 5 | 268 |
| Davies, Robert/Harlingen Cons Ind School Dist | 6 | 68 |
| Davila, Angel/Seagraves Ind School Dist | 37 | 162 |
| Davila, Diana/Edinburg Cons Ind School Dist | 7 | 221 |
| Davila, Michael/Kingsville Ind School Dist | 6 | 260 |
| Davila, Michelle/Seagraves Ind School Dist | 11,296,298 | 162 |
| Davila, Ruben/Webb Cons Ind School Dist | 3 | 391 |
| Davila, Sam/Conroe Ind School Dist | 5 | 294 |
| Davilla, Perla/Aldine Ind School Dist | 11 | 184 |
| Davis, Amanda/Sundown Ind School Dist | 37,270 | 232 |
| Davis, Amy/Crosby Ind School Dist | 73,98,295,297 | 188 |
| Davis, April/Texarkana Ind School Dist | 58 | 53 |
| Davis, Audra/Whiteface Con Ind School Dist | 57,271 | 78 |
| Davis, Blake/Graham Ind School Dist | 83,91 | 409 |
| Davis, Blayne/Mumford Ind School Dist | 11 | 59 |
| Davis, Brad/Grandview Ind School Dist | 6 | 251 |
| Davis, Carla/Winona Ind School Dist | 5 | 341 |
| Davis, Carol/Hawkins Ind School Dist | 58 | 407 |
| Davis, Carolyn/Eustace Ind School Dist | 4 | 219 |
| Davis, Cecilia/Judson Ind School Dist | 15 | 36 |
| Davis, Charlotte, Dr/Aldine Ind School Dist | 15,79,275 | 184 |
| Davis, Christie/Crosby Ind School Dist | 34 | 188 |
| Davis, Christine/Frisco Ind School Dist | 58 | 82 |
| Davis, Cindy/Seymour Ind School Dist | 2,8,11,83,88,296,298 | 28 |
| Davis, Cliff/Kerens Ind School Dist | 3 | 303 |
| Davis, Danny/Lubbock-Cooper Ind Sch Dist | 15 | 274 |
| Davis, Dewaski/Liberty-Eylau Ind School Dist | 6 | 51 |
| Davis, Diana/Los Fresnos Cons Ind Sch Dist | 7 | 69 |
| Davis, Don/Graham Ind School Dist | 2,15 | 409 |
| Davis, Donna/Pecos-Barstow-Toyah Ind SD | 58 | 326 |
| Davis, Elna/Grand Prairie Ind School Dist | 15 | 111 |
| Davis, Gay/Meyersville Ind School Dist | 16,57,73,295 | 122 |
| Davis, Gloria/San Antonio Ind School Dist | 7 | 42 |
| Davis, Greg/Connally Ind School Dist | 67 | 282 |
| Davis, Inga/Union Grove Ind School Dist | 16,82 | 379 |

| NAME/District | JOB FUNCTIONS | PAGE |
|---|---|---|
| Davis, Jay/Hearne Ind School Dist | 79 | 327 |
| Davis, Jenifer/Booker Ind School Dist | 58 | 270 |
| Davis, Jerry/Gilmer Ind School Dist | 3 | 378 |
| Davis, John/Leonard Ind School Dist | 27 | 150 |
| Davis, Kenneth, Dr/Houston ISD-South Area | 15 | 197 |
| Davis, Kennith, Dr/Houston Ind School Dist | 15,78 | 193 |
| Davis, Kevin/Baird Ind School Dist | 3,5 | 65 |
| Davis, Kim/Ft Bend Ind School Dist | 70 | 153 |
| Davis, King/Sheldon Ind School Dist | 1 | 205 |
| Davis, Kristen/Barbers Hill Ind School Dist | 16,73,76,82,295 | 75 |
| Davis, Kristi/Bangs Ind School Dist | 83 | 61 |
| Davis, Larry/DeSoto Ind School Dist | 6,35 | 108 |
| Davis, Laurie/Frenship Ind School Dist | 73 | 272 |
| Davis, Lisa/Angleton Ind School Dist | 10 | 55 |
| Davis, Lisa/Grandview Ind School Dist | 7,85 | 251 |
| Davis, Melissa/Lewisville Ind School Dist | 275 | 126 |
| Davis, Michael/Cushing Ind School Dist | 1 | 300 |
| Davis, Michael/Judson Ind School Dist | 295 | 36 |
| Davis, Michael/New Summerfield Ind Sch Dist | 67 | 76 |
| Davis, Michelle/Graford Ind School Dist | 2 | 313 |
| **Davis, Mike**/Krum Ind School Dist | 1 | 126 |
| Davis, Nathan/Dayton Ind School Dist | 76,295 | 268 |
| Davis, Pam/Millsap Ind School Dist | 34 | 315 |
| Davis, Phyllis/Anson Ind School Dist | 58 | 252 |
| Davis, Randy, Dr/Carrollton-Farmers Branch ISD | 68 | 100 |
| Davis, Renee/Crosby Ind School Dist | 5 | 188 |
| Davis, Rhonda/Lake Travis Ind School Dist | 5 | 373 |
| Davis, Rhonda/Plano Ind School Dist | 81 | 85 |
| Davis, Rick/Leakey Ind School Dist | 16,73,295 | 324 |
| Davis, Rick/Midland Ind School Dist | 67 | 288 |
| Davis, Robin/Grapevine-Colleyville Ind SD | 83 | 355 |
| Davis, Rosie/Springlake-Earth Ind Sch Dist | 2 | 264 |
| Davis, Ryan/Grandview-Hopkins Ind Sch Dist | 67 | 169 |
| Davis, Scott, Dr/Crosby Ind School Dist | 1 | 188 |
| Davis, Shannon/Amarillo Ind School Dist | 57,93 | 320 |
| Davis, Shawn/Texarkana Ind School Dist | 11,58,85,274,275 | 53 |
| Davis, Sherry/Childress Ind School Dist | 36 | 77 |
| Davis, Sheryl/Waco Ind School Dist | 2,19 | 284 |
| Davis, Stephanie/Grandview Ind School Dist | 38,69,83,270 | 251 |
| Davis, Stephen, Dr/Wylie Ind School Dist | 10 | 88 |
| Davis, Steven/Runge Ind School Dist | 6 | 254 |
| Davis, Susie/Laneville Ind School Dist | 7,85 | 330 |
| Davis, Todd, Dr/Aldine Ind School Dist | 18 | 184 |
| Davis, Tonya/Henderson Ind School Dist | 4 | 330 |
| Davis, Traci/Grand Prairie Ind School Dist | 15 | 111 |
| Davis, Trevor/Lovejoy Ind School Dist | 295 | 84 |
| Davis, Twyla/McLeod Ind School Dist | 52,55 | 74 |
| Dawkins, Micheal/Wink Loving Ind School Dist | 73,76,98,286,295,298 | 405 |
| Dawson, Brandi/Lewisville Ind School Dist | 16 | 126 |
| Dawson, Jimmy/Granbury Ind School Dist | 27 | 233 |
| Dawson, Kristin/Lovejoy Ind School Dist | 16 | 84 |
| Dawson, Renee/Westbrook Ind School Dist | 67 | 292 |
| Dawson, Tim/Boles Ind School Dist | 4 | 238 |
| Dawson, Yvonne/Lamar Cons Ind School Dist | 2 | 157 |
| Day, Betty/Ector Ind School Dist | 58 | 150 |
| Day, Cody/Colmesneil Ind School Dist | 6 | 377 |
| Day, Kay Lynn/Midlothian Ind School Dist | 15,79 | 145 |
| Day, Louise/Flour Bluff Ind School Dist | 15 | 307 |
| Day, Sam/Caddo Mills Ind Sch Dist | 5 | 238 |
| De La Fuente, Clarisa/Lyford Cons Ind School Dist | 71 | 397 |
| De La Fuente, Senaida/Hart Ind School Dist | 58 | 75 |
| De La Garza, Jeff/Plainview Ind School Dist | 79 | 180 |
| De La Rosa, Mario/Carrollton-Farmers Branch ISD | 91 | 100 |
| De La Rosa, Michael/Weslaco Ind School Dist | 88 | 228 |
| De La Santos, Linda/Roby Cons Ind School Dist | 57,271 | 152 |
| De La Sierra, Blanca/Irving Ind School Dist | 57 | 113 |
| De La Torre, Xavier, Dr/Ysleta Ind School Dist | 1 | 141 |

| | | | | | | | |
|---|---|---|---|---|---|---|---|
| 1 | Superintendent | 16 | Instructional Media Svcs | 30 | Adult Education | 44 | Science Sec |
| 2 | Bus/Finance/Purchasing | 17 | Chief Operations Officer | 31 | Career/Sch-to-Work K-12 | 45 | Math K-12 |
| 3 | Buildings And Grounds | 18 | Chief Academic Officer | 32 | Career/Sch-to-Work Elem | 46 | Math Elem |
| 4 | Food Service | 19 | Chief Financial Officer | 33 | Career/Sch-to-Work Sec | 47 | Math Sec |
| 5 | Transportation | 20 | Art K-12 | 34 | Early Childhood Ed | 48 | English/Lang Arts K-12 |
| 6 | Athletic | 21 | Art Elem | 35 | Health/Phys Education | 49 | English/Lang Arts Elem |
| 7 | Health Services | 22 | Art Sec | 36 | Guidance Services K-12 | 50 | English/Lang Arts Sec |
| 8 | Curric/Instruct K-12 | 23 | Music K-12 | 37 | Guidance Services Elem | 51 | Reading K-12 |
| 9 | Curric/Instruct Elem | 24 | Music Elem | 38 | Guidance Services Sec | 52 | Reading Elem |
| 10 | Curric/Instruct Sec | 25 | Music Sec | 39 | Social Studies K-12 | 53 | Reading Sec |
| 11 | Federal Program | 26 | Business Education | 40 | Social Studies Elem | 54 | Remedial Reading K-12 |
| 12 | Title I | 27 | Career & Tech Ed | 41 | Social Studies Sec | 55 | Remedial Reading Elem |
| 13 | Title V | 28 | Technology Education | 42 | Science K-12 | 56 | Remedial Reading Sec |
| 15 | Asst Superintendent | 29 | Family/Consumer Science | 43 | Science Elem | 57 | Bilingual/ELL |

| | | | | | | | |
|---|---|---|---|---|---|---|---|
| 58 | Special Education K-12 | 72 | Summer School | 88 | Alternative/At Risk | 277 | Remedial Math K-12 |
| 59 | Special Education Elem | 73 | Instructional Tech | 89 | Multi-Cultural Curriculum | 280 | Literacy Coach |
| 60 | Special Education Sec | 74 | Inservice Training | 90 | Social Work | 285 | STEM |
| 61 | Foreign/World Lang K-12 | 75 | Marketing/Distributive | 91 | Safety/Security | 286 | Digital Learning |
| 62 | Foreign/World Lang Elem | 76 | Info Systems | 92 | Magnet School | 288 | Common Core Standards |
| 63 | Foreign/World Lang Sec | 77 | Psychological Assess | 93 | Parental Involvement | 294 | Accountability |
| 64 | Religious Education K-12 | 78 | Affirmative Action | 95 | Tech Prep Program | 295 | Network System |
| 65 | Religious Education Elem | 79 | Student Personnel | 96 | Chief Infomation Officer | 296 | Title II Programs |
| 66 | Religious Education Sec | 80 | Driver Ed/Safety | 97 | Webmaster | 297 | Webmaster |
| 67 | School Board President | 81 | Gifted/Talented | 98 | Chief Technology Officer | 298 | Grant Writer/Ptnrships |
| 68 | Teacher Personnel | 82 | Video Services | 270 | Character Education | 750 | Chief Innovation Officer |
| 69 | Academic Assessment | 83 | Substance Abuse Prev | 271 | Migrant Education | 751 | Chief of Staff |
| 70 | Research/Development | 84 | Erate | 273 | Teacher Mentor | 752 | Social Emotional Learning |
| 71 | Public Information | 85 | AIDS Education | 274 | Before/After Sch | | |
| | | | | | 275 | Response To Intervention | |

| NAME/District | JOB FUNCTIONS | PAGE |
|---|---|---|
| Dickerson, Carole/Harts Bluff Ind School Dist | 12,16,57,69,88,270,273 | 366 |
| Dickerson, Carole/Harts Bluff Ind School Dist | 15,296 | 366 |
| Dickerson, Donnie/Burkeville Ind School Dist | 3,5 | 303 |
| Dickerson, Julia/Little Cypress Mauriceville SD | 9,57,81,271,288 | 311 |
| Dickerson, Pam/Burkeville Ind School Dist | 2,286 | 303 |
| Dickerson, Stewart/Early Ind School Dist | 3,5 | 62 |
| Dickey, Carole/Centerville Ind School Dist | 2,4,15,298 | 267 |
| Dickison, Elizabeth/Lometa Ind School Dist | 69,83,88 | 264 |
| Dickson, Amy/Karnack Ind School Dist | 1,11 | 214 |
| Dickson, Andy/De Leon Ind School Dist | 6 | 93 |
| Dickson, Heath/Post Ind School Dist | 1 | 167 |
| Dickson, Kasey/La Vernia Ind School Dist | 7,83,85 | 404 |
| Diego, Christy/San Angelo Ind School Dist | 57 | 367 |
| Diehl, Jared/Channelview Ind School Dist | 5 | 188 |
| Dieringer, Laura/Glasscock Co Ind School Dist | 51,54 | 168 |
| Dierlam, Shari/Calhoun Co Ind School Dist | 7 | 65 |
| Dieterich, Brandon/Axtell Ind School Dist | 76,751 | 281 |
| Dieterich, Bryan/Breckenridge Ind School Dist | 3 | 344 |
| Dietiker, Diane/La Vega Ind School Dist | 16 | 282 |
| Dietrich, Adam/Splendora Ind School Dist | 67 | 297 |
| Dietrich, Mickie/Alvin Ind School Dist | 2 | 54 |
| Diets, Jeremy/Era Ind School Dist | 5 | 94 |
| Dietz, Dee/Palestine Ind School Dist | 58 | 18 |
| Dietz, Diana/Luling Ind School Dist | 5 | 65 |
| Dietz, Joel/Whiteface Con Ind School Dist | 73,98 | 78 |
| Dildine, Sarah/Hughes Springs Ind Sch Dist | 1,57 | 74 |
| Diles, Jennifer/Celeste Ind School Dist | 7,85 | 239 |
| Diles, Tom/Woodsboro Ind School Dist | 10,273 | 326 |
| Dill, Jane/North Zulch Ind School Dist | 83 | 276 |
| Dillard, Jill/Llano Ind School Dist | 16,82 | 271 |
| Dillard, Kelli/Eden Cons Ind School Dist | 286 | 94 |
| Dillard, Kerry/Hull Daisetta Ind School Dist | 31 | 268 |
| Dillard, Nancy/Waskom Ind School Dist | 2 | 214 |
| Dillard, Rhonda/Frenship Ind School Dist | 68,78 | 272 |
| Dillard, Robert/Littlefield Ind School Dist | 1 | 263 |
| Dillard, Stacey/Princeton Ind School Dist | 6 | 87 |
| Dillard, Traci/Uvalde Cons Ind School Dist | 7 | 381 |
| Dillingham, Trisha/Vernon Ind School Dist | 83,90 | 396 |
| Dillon, David/Lovejoy Ind School Dist | 3,5 | 84 |
| Dillon, Matt/Canadian Ind School Dist | 3 | 218 |
| Dillon, Renae/Goose Creek Cons Ind Sch Dist | 27,92 | 192 |
| Dillon, Shana/Boerne Ind School Dist | 81 | 257 |
| Dillon, Stacey/Lovejoy Ind School Dist | 71 | 84 |
| Dills, Alice/Celeste Ind School Dist | 12,36,69,83,88,273 | 239 |
| Dimas, Velinda/Lamesa Ind School Dist | 68 | 121 |
| Dimmitt, Julia/Houston Ind School Dist | 68 | 193 |
| Dingle, Debbie, Dr/North East Ind School Dist | 61 | 37 |
| Dinkelmann, Johan/Somerset Ind School Dist | 6 | 45 |
| Dippel, Carol/Victoria Ind School Dist | 34 | 384 |
| Dippery, Debbie/Wichita Falls Ind School Dist | 10,36 | 395 |
| Dirkse, Amy/Meridian Ind School Dist | 7 | 50 |
| Disler, Jimmy/Leander Ind School Dist | 17 | 399 |
| Ditto, Jim/China Spring Ind School Dist | 3,5 | 281 |
| Dixon, Althea/Paris Ind School Dist | 8,15,294 | 262 |
| Dixon, Andrea/Kerrville Ind School Dist | 286 | 259 |
| Dixon, James/Industrial Ind School Dist | 6 | 243 |
| Dixon, Jeb/Oglesby Ind School Dist | 6 | 97 |
| Dixon, Jeff/Alvarado Ind School Dist | 6 | 249 |
| Dixon, Kevin/Ferris Ind School Dist | 58 | 145 |
| Dixon, Nkrumah/College Station Ind Sch Dist | 68 | 59 |
| Dixon, Shantina, Dr/Bryan Ind School Dist | 77 | 58 |
| Dluhos, Sarah/College Station Ind Sch Dist | 4 | 59 |
| Doan, Jamie/Trenton Ind School Dist | 270 | 151 |
| Doan, Kyle/Merkel Ind School Dist | 67 | 363 |
| Dobbs, Renea/Goose Creek Cons Ind Sch Dist | 2 | 192 |
| Dobecka, Tory/West Ind School Dist | 8 | 285 |
| Dobson, Pete/Pawnee Ind School Dist | 67 | 28 |

| NAME/District | JOB FUNCTIONS | PAGE |
|---|---|---|
| Dobson, Randal/Mexia Ind School Dist | 83,91 | 270 |
| Docken, Carla/Hurst-Euless-Bedford ISD | 36,88,270 | 356 |
| Dockens, Deborah, Dr/Eagle Mtn-Saginaw Ind Sch Dist | 68,79 | 351 |
| Dockery, Kristin/Patton Springs Ind School Dist | 4 | 131 |
| Dodd, Carla/Lake Worth Ind School Dist | 5 | 358 |
| Dodds, Darrell/Greenwood Ind School Dist | 2,15 | 288 |
| Dodds, Debbie/Greenwood Ind School Dist | 73,295 | 288 |
| Dodge, Todd/Eanes Ind School Dist | 6 | 372 |
| Dodson, James/Kirbyville Cons Ind Sch Dist | 3 | 244 |
| Dodson, Tony/Groom Ind School Dist | 16,295 | 72 |
| Doege, Doug/Monahans-Wickett-Pyote ISD | 8,11,57,69,298 | 388 |
| Doepken, Marny/Clear Creek Ind School Dist | 39 | 162 |
| Doering, Lori/Lewisville Ind School Dist | 47 | 126 |
| Dohnalik, Jason/Cameron Ind School Dist | 67 | 290 |
| Dolan, Andrea/Granger Ind School Dist | 73 | 399 |
| Dollarhide, Tony/Texarkana Ind School Dist | 83,91 | 53 |
| Domain, Melinda, Dr/Ferris Ind School Dist | 12,15,27,79,88,296,298 | 145 |
| Dominguez, David/Elkhart Ind School Dist | 57 | 18 |
| Dominguez, Faustina/Alice Ind School Dist | 79 | 248 |
| Dominguez, Jesus/Webb Cons Ind School Dist | 91 | 391 |
| Dominguez, Laura/Braination Schools | 58 | 33 |
| Dominguez, Mario/Fabens Ind School Dist | 73,84,91 | 139 |
| Dominguez, Mark/Buena Vista Ind School Dist | 1,11,83 | 318 |
| Dominguez, Tommy/Balmorhea Ind School Dist | 67 | 325 |
| Dominquez, Mike/Stratford Ind School Dist | 1,73,83 | 338 |
| Dominqueze, Shelly/Aransas Pass Ind School Dist | 8,16,57,88,271,273,286,288 | 333 |
| Donaghey, Andy/Weatherford Ind School Dist | 23,27 | 316 |
| Donaghey, Kady/Weatherford Ind School Dist | 27,31,75 | 316 |
| Donald, Ben, Dr/Carthage Ind School Dist | 67 | 314 |
| Donald, Rebecca/Round Rock Ind School Dist | 15 | 401 |
| Donaldson, Felicia/Everman Ind School Dist | 5,7,15,36,68,78,80,298 | 351 |
| Donato, Jennifer/Pleasanton Ind School Dist | 2,19 | 24 |
| Donaubauer, Gloria/Runge Ind School Dist | 58 | 254 |
| Donham, Shawn/Benjamin Ind School Dist | 3 | 261 |
| Donnell, Stephanie/Bushland Ind School Dist | 37,83,85 | 321 |
| Donovan, Jennifer/Hitchcock Ind School Dist | 2,19,296 | 165 |
| Dorcz, Monica/Huffman Ind School Dist | 45 | 200 |
| Doris, Jim/Texas Dept of Education | 20,23 | 1 |
| Dornak, Ashlee/Victoria Ind School Dist | 49 | 384 |
| Doron, Amy/Spring Hill Ind School Dist | 270 | 175 |
| Doskocil, Cheyenne/Rogers Ind School Dist | 68,297 | 32 |
| Dossey, Jim/Montgomery Ind School Dist | 67 | 296 |
| Dossey, Julie/Klondike Ind School Dist | 36,69,88,270,271 | 121 |
| Dossey, Macey/Mesquite Ind School Dist | 7 | 115 |
| Dossey, Matt/Jonesboro Ind School Dist | 1,11,73,83 | 97 |
| Doty, Cristi/Jim Ned Cons Ind School Dist | 8,288 | 363 |
| Doucet, Chad/South San Antonio Ind Sch Dist | 2 | 45 |
| Doug, Crosby/New Caney Ind School Dist | 295 | 296 |
| Dougherty, Mark/Sharyland Ind School Dist | 3,91 | 227 |
| Dougherty, Ruth/Channelview Ind School Dist | 76 | 188 |
| Doughty, Katie/Grapeland Ind School Dist | 10 | 235 |
| Doughty, Marilyn/Corpus Christi Ind Sch Dist | 76,295 | 306 |
| Douglas, Christopher/Southside Ind School Dist | 58 | 46 |
| Douglas, Imo/Midland Ind School Dist | 7 | 288 |
| Douglas, Jennifer/Galveston Ind School Dist | 4 | 164 |
| Douglas, Robert/Aransas Co Ind School Dist | 5 | 22 |
| Douglas, Sarah/Brownfield Ind Sch Dist | 31 | 364 |
| Douglas, Susan/Bland Ind School Dist | 16 | 238 |
| Douglas, Thomas/Pasadena Ind School Dist | 3 | 203 |
| Dove, Dwayne/Breckenridge Ind School Dist | 28,73,297 | 344 |
| Dove, Jason/Deer Park Ind School Dist | 20,23 | 191 |
| Dovel, Christy/Dalhart Ind School Dist | 38 | 99 |
| Dover, Darrian/Meadow Ind School Dist | 1 | 365 |
| Dover, Greg/Rusk Ind School Dist | 3 | 77 |
| Dover, Stacey/Meadow Ind School Dist | 11,60 | 365 |
| Dow, Bill/Huckabay Ind School Dist | 11,67 | 147 |
| Dowdy, Sandra/Hays Cons Ind School Dist | 8,18 | 216 |

| NAME/District | JOB FUNCTIONS | PAGE | NAME/District | JOB FUNCTIONS | PAGE |
|---|---|---|---|---|---|
| Dowdy, Tammy/Dickinson Ind School Dist | 71 | 164 | Duhon, Brenda, Dr/Port Neches-Groves Ind SD | 8,15,69,73,74,288,294,298 | 246 |
| Dowell, Cheryl/Stephenville Ind School Dist | 4 | 148 | Duke, Georgette/Texarkana Ind School Dist | 274 | 53 |
| Downey, Cheryl/Sivells Bend Ind School Dist | 11 | 95 | Duke, Kim/Darrouzett Ind School Dist | 2 | 270 |
| Downing, Shane/Holland Ind School Dist | 1,57 | 30 | Duke, Krystal/Wortham Ind School Dist | 38 | 161 |
| Downs, Deanna/De Leon Ind School Dist | 57 | 93 | Duke, Sandra/Brownsboro Ind School Dist | 34,58,77 | 218 |
| Downs, Karen/Avery Ind School Dist | 11,296 | 325 | Duke, Sharon/Central Heights Ind Sch Dist | 27,31 | 300 |
| Doyal, Ashley/Krum Ind School Dist | 4 | 126 | Dukes, Dan, Dr/Abilene Ind School Dist | 79 | 362 |
| Doyal, Launa/North Lamar Ind School Dist | 297 | 406 | Dulude, David/Waskom Ind School Dist | 83 | 214 |
| Doyal, Launa/North Lamar Ind School Dist | 297 | 406 | Dulworth, Rhonda/Corsicana Ind School Dist | 31 | 302 |
| Doyle, Charlyn/San Angelo Ind School Dist | 73,76,84,297 | 367 | Dumont, Tab/Pleasanton Ind School Dist | 6 | 24 |
| Doyle, Jd/Schleicher Co Ind Sch Dist | 73,76,286,295 | 335 | Dunavant, Beth Anne/Pittsburg Ind School Dist | 8,11,88,285,288,294,296,298 | 72 |
| Doyle, Kendra/San Antonio Ind School Dist | 8 | 42 | Dunbar, Melissa/Medina Ind School Dist | 11,58 | 26 |
| Doyle, Sara/Cranfills Gap ISD School Dist | 2 | 50 | Duncan, Brad/Anna Ind School Dist | 15 | 81 |
| Doyno, Paul, Dr/Rio Grande City Ind Sch Dist | 298 | 343 | Duncan, Dayne/Groesbeck Ind School Dist | 2,4,5,91 | 269 |
| Dozier, Phyllis/Longview Ind School Dist | 4 | 174 | Duncan, Kayla/Kerens Ind School Dist | 4 | 303 |
| Dozier, Tina/Leander Ind School Dist | 57 | 399 | Duncan, Krystle/Boyd Ind School Dist | 58 | 405 |
| Drab, Gary/La Grange Ind School Dist | 67 | 151 | Duncan, Lee/White Settlement Ind Sch Dist | 8 | 360 |
| Drabek, Carlett/Navarro Ind School Dist | 4 | 178 | Duncan, Lisa/Ector Co Ind School Dist | 45 | 134 |
| Dragoescu, Justin/New Boston Ind School Dist | 16,73,295 | 52 | Duncan, Marcie/Wolfe City Ind School Dist | 4 | 240 |
| Dragon, Les/Three Rivers Ind School Dist | 1 | 271 | Duncan, Melanie/Tenaha Ind School Dist | 4 | 338 |
| Drake, Jason/Spurger Ind School Dist | 298 | 378 | Duncan, Pam/Cisco Independent Sch Dist | 7 | 133 |
| Drake, Traci/Hubbard Ind School Dist | 12 | 51 | Duncan, Rebecca/Sweetwater ISD School Dist | 27 | 304 |
| Drake, Traci/Hubbard Ind School Dist | 1,11,83 | 51 | Duncan, Scot/Hooks Ind School Dist | 67 | 51 |
| Dranowsky, George/East Central Ind School Dist | 91 | 34 | Duncan, Shannon/Huntsville Ind School Dist | 71 | 386 |
| Draper, Brad/Frenship Ind School Dist | 67 | 272 | Duncan, Tiffany/Dripping Springs Ind Sch Dist | 68 | 215 |
| Draper, Shelly/Ore City Ind School Dist | 68 | 379 | Duncan, Tim/White Settlement Ind Sch Dist | 68 | 360 |
| Drastata, David/Comal Ind School Dist | 67 | 91 | Duncan, Tom/Mt Calm Ind School Dist | 6 | 231 |
| Drawhorn, Sheri/Port Neches-Groves Ind SD | 2 | 246 | Duncum, Jared, Dr/Sweetwater ISD School Dist | 11,15,18,57,61,288 | 304 |
| Dray, Nicole/San Marcos Cons Ind Sch Dist | 8,12,36,83,277,294 | 217 | Dungen, Jeff/Alvin Ind School Dist | 5 | 54 |
| Drennan, Greg/Plemons-Stinnett-Phillips CISD | 3,5,91 | 241 | Duniven, Lynn/Highland Ind School Dist | 2 | 304 |
| Drennon, Joe/Grand Saline Ind School Dist | 6 | 383 | Dunlap, Becca/Plainview Ind School Dist | 2 | 180 |
| Drew, Debbie/Avery Ind School Dist | 1 | 325 | Dunlap, Brian/Mt Calm Ind School Dist | 67 | 231 |
| Drew, James/Ft Bend Ind School Dist | 20 | 153 | Dunlap, Terry/Bellevue Ind School Dist | 58,296 | 77 |
| Drews, Celia, Dr/Mexia Ind School Dist | 8,11,15 | 270 | Dunn-Flores, Lisa Marie/United Ind School Dist | 81 | 390 |
| Drews, Celia, Dr/Mexia Ind School Dist | 13,296 | 270 | Dunn, Dirk/Ira Ind School Dist | 67 | 336 |
| Drews, Lynn/Bremond Ind School Dist | 69,270 | 327 | Dunn, Don/Van Ind School Dist | 1 | 383 |
| Driesbach, Amy/Schertz-Cibolo-Univ City ISD | 67 | 178 | Dunn, Kelly/Meyersville Ind School Dist | 1,11 | 122 |
| Driggers, Rachael/Greenville Ind School Dist | 69,70,294 | 239 | Dunn, Sharon/Stockdale Ind School Dist | 9,35,88,288 | 404 |
| Drilling, Christi/Grapevine-Colleyville Ind SD | 2 | 355 | Dunn, Tonya/Post Ind School Dist | 38 | 167 |
| Drinkwater, Amanda/Lewisville Ind School Dist | 20,23 | 126 | Dunn, Wendy/Mexia Ind School Dist | 38 | 270 |
| Drinkwater, Michael/Lake Travis Ind School Dist | 6 | 373 | Dunnam, Nancy/Region 18 Ed Service Center | 76 | 290 |
| Driscoll, Terry/Abernathy Ind School Dist | 73,76,286 | 179 | Dunne-Oldfield, Tiffany/Spring Ind School Dist | 71,93 | 207 |
| Driskall, Dahria/Friendswood Ind Sch Dist | 13,58 | 164 | Dunniven, Britney/Lockney Independent Sch Dist | 7 | 153 |
| Driskell, Jamie/Malakoff Ind School Dist | 6 | 219 | Dunsom, Jennifer/Woodville Ind School Dist | 58 | 378 |
| Driskill, Elita/Arlington Ind School Dist | 73 | 346 | Dunson, Jennifer/Colmesneil Ind School Dist | 58 | 377 |
| Driskill, Jamie/Frisco Ind School Dist | 71 | 82 | Duplechain, Erica/Hearne Ind School Dist | 2 | 327 |
| Driver, Darryl/Roosevelt Ind School Dist | 5 | 274 | Duplichain, Jeff/Alto Ind School Dist | 67 | 76 |
| Driver, Jamie/Whitharral Ind School Dist | 58 | 233 | DuPont, Laura, Dr/Clear Creek Ind School Dist | 67 | 163 |
| Driver, Tom/Port Aransas Ind School Dist | 73 | 308 | DuPont, Michelle/Kenedy Co Wide Common Sch Dist | 81 | 258 |
| Droddy, Eric/Queen City Ind School Dist | 6 | 74 | Dupre, Charles, Dr/Ft Bend Ind School Dist | 1 | 153 |
| Drollinger, Tony/Arlington Ind School Dist | 2 | 346 | Duque, Sebastian/La Joya Ind School Dist | 8,69 | 222 |
| Dromgoole, Emma, Dr/Edgewood Ind School Dist | 20,23 | 34 | Duran, Angela/Sweetwater ISD School Dist | 5 | 304 |
| Drum, Lewis/Motley Co Ind School Dist | 67 | 299 | Duran, Christy/Diocese of Lubbock Ed Office | 2 | 275 |
| Drummond, Deanna/Sidney Ind School Dist | 73,98,298 | 94 | Duran, Kathy/Lytle Ind School Dist | 2 | 24 |
| Druschke, Toni/New Diana Ind School Dist | 4 | 379 | Duran, Laura/El Paso Ind School Dist | 4 | 137 |
| **Duarte, Melissa, Dr/**Texas City Ind School Dist | 1 | 166 | Duran, Nancy/Killeen Ind School Dist | 31 | 30 |
| Dube, Kathy/Lexington Ind School Dist | 2 | 266 | Duran, Shirley/Boles Ind School Dist | 93 | 238 |
| Dube, Mark/McDade Ind School Dist | 67 | 27 | Duran, Umberto/Eagle Pass Ind School Dist | 297 | 279 |
| Dubose, Bill/Abernathy Ind School Dist | 67 | 179 | Durand, Jocelyn/Boerne Ind School Dist | 71 | 257 |
| Dubose, Heather/Runge Ind School Dist | 36,69,83,88 | 254 | Durand, Mark/Jasper Ind School Dist | 67 | 243 |
| Dubose, Steven/Overton Ind School Dist | 1,11 | 331 | Duree, Sandra/Barbers Hill Ind School Dist | 8,15,275,280,286 | 75 |
| Duck, Linda/Chico Ind School Dist | 12,280 | 406 | Duren, Ella/Maud Ind School Dist | 69 | 52 |
| Duck, Troy/Wildorado Ind Sch Dist | 1,11,73 | 311 | Durham, Kelly/St Jo Ind School Dist | 36,69 | 293 |
| Dudenhoeffer, Dana/Gainesville Ind School Dist | 8 | 95 | Durham, Tucker/Alpine Ind School Dist | 2,19 | 60 |
| Duderstadt, Lanier/Wall Ind School Dist | 3,91 | 368 | Durham, Ulla/San Marcos Cons Ind Sch Dist | 2 | 216 |
| Dudley, Cara/Centerville Ind School Dist | 8,11,285,286 | 267 | Durick, Kimberly/Prairie Lea Ind School Dist | 58 | 65 |
| Dudley, Rachel/Priddy Ind School Dist | 71 | 292 | Duron, Jodi, Dr/Elgin Ind School Dist | 1 | 27 |
| Due, James/Centerville Ind School Dist | 67 | 376 | Durrant, Dayan/Marshall Ind School Dist | 285 | 214 |
| Duenas, Juan/Sheldon Ind School Dist | 9,288 | 205 | Durrwachter, Sonya/Calallen Ind School Dist | 34,57,58,72,88,271 | 305 |
| Duenez, Linda/Austwell Tivoli Ind SD | 60 | 326 | Dusebout, Paul/Willis Ind School Dist | 3,4 | 297 |
| Duenez, Luis/Weatherford Ind School Dist | 91 | 316 | Dusek, Denise/Veribest Ind School Dist | 2 | 368 |
| Duerr, Alan/Hays Cons Ind School Dist | 295 | 216 | Dusek, Sandra/East Bernard Ind Sch Dist | 7 | 392 |
| Dueser, Linda/Victoria Ind School Dist | 16,82,286 | 384 | Dutcher, Larry/Rosebud-Lott Ind School Dist | 73 | 149 |
| Duffer, Stefanie/Caddo Mills Ind Sch Dist | 73 | 238 | Dutton, Donnie/Leakey Ind School Dist | 6 | 324 |
| Duffik, Michael/La Vernia Ind School Dist | 91 | 404 | Dutton, Matt/Huffman Ind School Dist | 67 | 200 |
| Duffney, Janice/Coppell Ind School Dist | 76 | 102 | Duty, David/Bruceville-Eddy Ind Sch Dist | 67 | 281 |

| NAME/District | JOB FUNCTIONS | PAGE |
|---|---|---|
| DuVall, Lynn/Poolville Ind School Dist | 67 | 316 |
| Duvon, Catherine/Shelbyville Ind School Dist | 13,57,58 | 337 |
| Dvorak, Jane/Ferris Ind School Dist | 10,85 | 144 |
| Dvorak, Jane/Kemp Ind School Dist | 8,11,286 | 255 |
| Dworaczyk, Dana/Calhoun Co Ind School Dist | 27 | 65 |
| Dworkin, James/Int'l Leadership of Texas Dist | 2,19 | 112 |
| Dwyer, Jane/Nixon-Smiley Cons Ind Sch Dist | 8,57,69,88,273,286,288,298 | 169 |
| Dyar, Tom/Burleson Ind School Dist | 68 | 249 |
| Dyer, Amy/Sealy Ind School Dist | 73,76,295 | 25 |
| Dyer, Jeff/Navasota Ind School Dist | 68 | 177 |
| Dyer, Lisa/Fayetteville Ind School Dist | 57 | 151 |
| Dyer, Micah, Dr/Cuero Ind School Dist | 1 | 121 |
| Dyer, Michael/Dayton Ind School Dist | 11,80,296 | 268 |
| Dyer, Susan/Plano Ind School Dist | 49 | 85 |
| Dykes, Dana/Athens Ind School Dist | 91 | 218 |
| Dykes, Mark/Collinsville Ind School Dist | 1 | 171 |
| Dykman, Jeannia/Tyler Ind School Dist | 34,58 | 340 |
| Dykstra, Dirk/East Central Ind School Dist | 73 | 34 |
| Dykstra, Valerie/Devine Ind School Dist | 58 | 286 |
| Dylan, Renita/Grape Creek Ind School Dist | 38 | 367 |
| Dynis, Deana/Coppell Ind School Dist | 81 | 102 |
| Dziuk, Nicole/Poth Ind School Dist | 31,36,83 | 404 |

## E

| NAME/District | JOB FUNCTIONS | PAGE |
|---|---|---|
| Eads, Kassi/Dublin Ind School Dist | 68,78 | 147 |
| Eager, Cheryl/Krum Ind School Dist | 16 | 126 |
| Eakin, David/Lamar Cons Ind School Dist | 76,95 | 157 |
| **Ealy, Clark, Dr**/Schertz-Cibolo-Univ City ISD | 1 | 178 |
| Eargle, Sherry/Chapel Hill Ind School Dist | 4 | 366 |
| Earhart, Mark/Kress Ind School Dist | 6 | 345 |
| Earl, Debbie/Tulia Ind School Dist | 4 | 345 |
| Earley, Dandy/Alvarado Ind School Dist | 69 | 249 |
| Earlie, Xandra/Aldine Ind School Dist | 44 | 184 |
| Earnshaw, Kayla/Llano Ind School Dist | 4 | 271 |
| Earrientes, Joey/Tahoka Ind School Dist | 3 | 276 |
| Earthman, Kim/Conroe Ind School Dist | 79 | 294 |
| Easterly, Brandon/Comfort Ind School Dist | 6 | 257 |
| Easterwood, Shay/Brady Ind School Dist | 6 | 280 |
| Eastman, John/Troup Ind School Dist | 6 | 340 |
| Eastman, William/Clear Creek Ind School Dist | 61 | 163 |
| Eastwood, Dyanna/San Marcos Cons Ind Sch Dist | 7 | 216 |
| Eaton, Jimmy/Comanche Ind School Dist | 5 | 93 |
| Eaton, Toyse/Grandfalls-Royalty Ind SD | 83,752 | 388 |
| Eaves, Brian/Denison Ind School Dist | 71 | 171 |
| Ebell, Steven, Dr/Clear Creek Ind School Dist | 8,15 | 162 |
| Eberlan, Allen/San Augustine Ind School Dist | 3,91 | 332 |
| Eberlan, Skipper/Etoile Ind School Dist | 3,5 | 300 |
| Echavaria, Teresa/Friona Ind School Dist | 7 | 318 |
| Eckel, Joseph/Rusk Ind School Dist | 5 | 77 |
| Eckenrod, Tiffany/Beaumont Ind School Dist | 4 | 244 |
| Eckert, Dean/Harper Ind School Dist | 3,5 | 168 |
| Eckert, Dean/Harper Ind School Dist | 3,5 | 168 |
| Eddins, Loretta/Apple Springs Ind School Dist | 11,36,58,69,88,270,271 | 376 |
| Eddy, Carri/Northwest Ind School Dist | 12,36,57,83,271,274 | 128 |
| Eder, Nancy/Diocese of Fort Worth Ed Off | 7 | 360 |
| Edgar, David/Deer Park Ind School Dist | 2,15 | 191 |
| Edgar, David/Del Valle Ind School Dist | 2,15 | 372 |
| Edgar, David/Lampasas Ind School Dist | 3 | 264 |
| Edgar, Dina/Galena Park Ind School Dist | 2,15 | 191 |
| Edgar, Lisa/Copperas Cove Ind School Dist | 8,12,74,275 | 96 |
| Edgas, David/Del Valle Ind School Dist | 2,19 | 372 |
| Edgemon, Trevor/Lubbock-Cooper Ind Sch Dist | 5 | 274 |
| Edison, David, Dr/Aquilla Ind School Dist | 1,11 | 230 |
| Edmonds, Jana/Loraine Ind School Dist | 58 | 292 |
| Edmondson, Joshua/Honey Grove Ind School Dist | 16,73 | 150 |
| Edmonson, Scott/Brookesmith Ind School Dist | 6,35 | 61 |
| Edwards-Scott, Michelle, Dr/Irving Ind School Dist | 58 | 113 |

| NAME/District | JOB FUNCTIONS | PAGE |
|---|---|---|
| Edwards, Barry/Bastrop Ind School Dist | 1 | 26 |
| Edwards, Chris/Hughes Springs Ind Sch Dist | 6 | 74 |
| Edwards, Courtney/Llano Ind School Dist | 38 | 271 |
| Edwards, Damon, Dr/Schertz-Cibolo-Univ City ISD | 8,15,68,73 | 178 |
| Edwards, David/Smithville Ind School Dist | 11 | 27 |
| Edwards, Erik/Goldthwaite Consolidated ISD | 3 | 291 |
| Edwards, Jami/Meridian Ind School Dist | 2 | 50 |
| Edwards, Jessica/Galveston Ind School Dist | 58 | 165 |
| Edwards, Justin/Chapel Hill Ind School Dist | 3,5,17 | 366 |
| Edwards, Kim/Meridian Ind School Dist | 1,11,84 | 50 |
| Edwards, Kim/Mesquite Ind School Dist | 36 | 115 |
| Edwards, Lisa/Aldine Ind School Dist | 49 | 184 |
| Edwards, Lori/Quinlan Ind School Dist | 57 | 240 |
| Edwards, Mac/Llano Ind School Dist | 1 | 271 |
| Edwards, Matt/Turkey-Quitaque Cons Ind SD | 5 | 181 |
| Edwards, Mike/Chapel Hill Ind School Dist | 67 | 366 |
| Edwards, Nanette/Ranger Ind School Dist | 27,31 | 133 |
| Edwards, Natalie/Goose Creek Cons Ind Sch Dist | 4 | 192 |
| Edwards, Phil/Angleton Ind School Dist | 1 | 55 |
| Edwards, Rick/Joshua Ind School Dist | 15 | 251 |
| Edwards, Robbie/Holland Ind School Dist | 10,11,57,83,275,285 | 30 |
| Edwards, Stephen/Hamshire Fannett Ind Sch Dist | 15,73 | 245 |
| Edwards, Thelissa/Humble Ind School Dist | 58 | 200 |
| Edwards, Travis/Hitchcock Ind School Dist | 1 | 165 |
| Edwardsen, Jennifer, Dr/Hays Cons Ind School Dist | 31,34,36,81,274 | 216 |
| Egger, Jim/McAllen Ind School Dist | 20,23 | 224 |
| Eggerton, Jonathan/Hallsburg Ind School Dist | 15,280,285,294,296,298 | 282 |
| Egle, Roger/Bridgeport Ind School Dist | 73,76,286,295 | 406 |
| Ehlers, Paul/Lubbock-Cooper Ind Sch Dist | 67 | 274 |
| Ehrlich, Frances/Karnes City Ind School Dist | 274 | 253 |
| Eiben, Suzanne/Palestine Ind School Dist | 15,68 | 18 |
| Eichman, Jeff/Coldspring-Oakhurst Cons ISD | 11 | 332 |
| Eichman, Jon/Devine Ind School Dist | 5 | 286 |
| Eichman, Missy/Coldspring-Oakhurst Cons ISD | 73,286 | 332 |
| Eilers, Anthony/Mount Vernon Ind School Dist | 73,295 | 160 |
| Eilers, Stacy/La Grange Ind School Dist | 15 | 151 |
| Elandary, Juliana/Lovejoy Ind School Dist | 4 | 84 |
| Elbert, Michael/Sinton Ind School Dist | 58 | 334 |
| Elder, John/Coleman Ind School Dist | 6 | 79 |
| Elder, Laura/Liberty Hill Ind School Dist | 37 | 401 |
| Eldredge, Dana/Eagle Mtn-Saginaw Ind Sch Dist | 27 | 351 |
| Eldredge, Wendy, Dr/Crandall Ind School Dist | 1 | 254 |
| Eldredge, Billy/Wolfe City Ind School Dist | 31,69,77 | 240 |
| Eldridge, Patricia/Mullin Ind School Dist | 4 | 291 |
| Eldridge, Vickie/Muenster Ind School Dist | 16 | 95 |
| Elerson, Sunday/Canton Ind School Dist | 7 | 382 |
| Elester, Sally/Big Sandy Ind School Dist | 8,31,69,83,88 | 319 |
| Elhabr, Kamal/San Antonio Ind School Dist | 3,15 | 42 |
| Eli, Christy/Newcastle Ind School Dist | 73,286,295 | 409 |
| Elias, Sheila/Ysleta Ind School Dist | 11,298 | 141 |
| **Elizalde, Stephanie, Dr**/Austin Ind School Dist | 1 | 369 |
| Elizalde, Travis/Broaddus Ind School Dist | 67 | 332 |
| Elizando, Anna/Tuloso-Midway Ind School Dist | 68,78 | 308 |
| Elizondo, Daniel/Silsbee Ind School Dist | 71 | 183 |
| Elizondo, Maribelle/McAllen Ind School Dist | 58 | 224 |
| **Elizondo, Paz**/La Villa Ind School Dist | 1 | 223 |
| Elledge, Kiera/Hurst-Euless-Bedford ISD | 16,285 | 356 |
| Eller, Jackie/Bells Ind School Dist | 3 | 170 |
| Elley, Alissa/Navarro Ind School Dist | 73,286,295,298 | 178 |
| Ellington, Russell/Thorndale Ind School Dist | 3 | 291 |
| Elliot, Bill/Celina Ind School Dist | 6 | 81 |
| Elliott, Alicia/Athens Ind School Dist | 67 | 218 |
| Elliott, Ariel/Greenwood Ind School Dist | 1 | 288 |
| Elliott, Gary/Amarillo Ind School Dist | 2 | 320 |
| Elliott, Gary/Copperas Cove Ind School Dist | 3,5,91 | 96 |
| Elliott, Gina/North East Ind School Dist | 68 | 37 |
| Elliott, Lindsey/Joshua Ind School Dist | 274 | 251 |

| NAME/District | JOB FUNCTIONS | PAGE |
|---|---|---|
| Elliott, Luann/McCamey Ind School Dist | 31,36,69,83,85,88 | 380 |
| Elliott, Nicole/Peaster Ind School Dist | 73,76,286,295 | 316 |
| Ellis, Amy, Dr/Rockwall Ind School Dist | 8 | 328 |
| Ellis, Andrea, Dr/Commerce Independent Sch Dist | 27,31 | 239 |
| Ellis, Kevin/Texas Dept of Education | 67 | 1 |
| Ellis, Kim/Waco Ind School Dist | 8,15 | 284 |
| Ellis, Linda/Grand Prairie Ind School Dist | 1 | 111 |
| Ellis, Roger/Gold-Burg Ind School Dist | 1 | 293 |
| **Ellis, Roger/**Rio Hondo Ind School Dist | 1 | 70 |
| Ellis, Scott/Kemp Ind School Dist | 3,5 | 255 |
| Ellis, Stacey/Terrell Ind School Dist | 68,79,273 | 256 |
| Ellison, Chris/Trent Isn School Dist | 6 | 363 |
| Ellison, Jennifer/Southwest Ind School Dist | 10 | 46 |
| Ellison, Krista/Happy Ind School Dist | 9,45,48,51,85,274,288 | 345 |
| Ellison, Phillip/Spring Ind School Dist | 2 | 207 |
| Ellison, Tommy/Medina Valley Ind School Dist | 3 | 287 |
| Ellisor, Stephenie/Etoile Ind School Dist | 7 | 300 |
| Ellsworth, Betty/Henrietta Ind School Dist | 67 | 78 |
| Elms, Mark/Pampa Ind School Dist | 47 | 170 |
| Elridge, Curtis/St Jo Ind School Dist | 1 | 293 |
| Elrod, Katie/Gordon Ind School Dist | 8,16,36,74 | 313 |
| Elrod, Keith/Hico Ind School Dist | 2,298 | 181 |
| Elsasser, Richard, Dr/Region 13 Ed Service Center | 1,11 | 376 |
| Elsbecker, Leon/Sanger Ind School Dist | 73,295 | 130 |
| Ely, Chad/Sunray Ind School Dist | 3,5 | 299 |
| Ely, Diana/Northside Ind School Dist | 74 | 39 |
| Ely, Stacy/Franklin Ind School Dist | 8,11,74,294,296 | 327 |
| Emanuel, Darrell/Round Rock Ind School Dist | 8 | 401 |
| Emerson, Dolores/Brownsville Ind School Dist | 9 | 66 |
| Emerson, Sarah/Clarendon Cons Ind Sch Dist | 2 | 131 |
| Emerson, Troy/Sulphur Bluff Ind School Dist | 5 | 235 |
| Emfinger, Keith/Lamesa Ind School Dist | 16,73,286,295 | 121 |
| **Emrich, John/**Crockett Ind School Dist | 1 | 235 |
| Encinia, Jennifer/Mathis Ind School Dist | 68 | 334 |
| Engle, Debbie/Valentine Ind School Dist | 1,11,57,83 | 244 |
| Engle, Karen/Clear Creek Ind School Dist | 10,15 | 162 |
| Engle, Kathryn/Central Heights Ind Sch Dist | 8,16,57,271,274 | 300 |
| Englehart, Kenneth/Medina Valley Ind School Dist | 84,98 | 287 |
| English, Amy/Beckville Ind School Dist | 57 | 314 |
| English, Lacy/Aspermont Ind School Dist | 67 | 344 |
| English, Latrishia/Rivercrest Ind School Dist | 57 | 325 |
| English, Todd/Hardin Ind School Dist | 73,286 | 268 |
| Engstrom, Heather/Kerrville Ind School Dist | 8,15,288 | 259 |
| Enlow, Blake/Bowie Ind School Dist | 1 | 292 |
| Enlue, Laurie/El Paso Ind School Dist | 15,58 | 137 |
| Enoch, Maria/Tidehaven Ind School Dist | 57,271 | 279 |
| Enos, Brandon/Goliad Ind School Dist | 8,15 | 168 |
| Enriquez, Micheal/Pettus Ind School Dist | 6 | 28 |
| Entrop, Kendrea/Wills Point Ind School Dist | 11,16,58 | 384 |
| Epley, Mandy/Comal Ind School Dist | 68 | 91 |
| Epperson, Barbara/Belton Ind School Dist | 81 | 29 |
| Eppes, Steve/Kountze Ind School Dist | 67 | 183 |
| Epps, Cleota/Little Elm Ind School Dist | 68 | 128 |
| Epps, Mechelle, Dr/Galena Park Ind School Dist | 15 | 191 |
| Erickson, Jimmy/Motley Co Ind School Dist | 2 | 299 |
| Ernhart, Paige/Miles Ind School Dist | 31 | 329 |
| Ernst, Barbi/Clifton Ind School Dist | 73 | 49 |
| Erwin, Donald/Coolidge Ind School Dist | 3,5 | 269 |
| Erwin, John/Era Ind School Dist | 31,36,69,83,85 | 94 |
| Erwin, Meggie/Edgewood Ind School Dist | 36 | 382 |
| Escalante, Heather/Caldwell Ind School Dist | 2,19 | 63 |
| Escalon, Melissa/Weslaco Ind School Dist | 91 | 228 |
| Escamilla, Beverly/Diocese of Beaumont Sch Office | 68 | 247 |
| Escamita, Judith/McAllen Ind School Dist | 73,76,295 | 224 |
| Escarcega, Vanessa/Dimmitt Ind School Dist | 4 | 74 |
| Eschenburg, Emily/Sealy Ind School Dist | 10,57,271 | 25 |
| Escobar, Daniel/Socorro Ind School Dist | 71 | 140 |
| Escobar, Helen/Roma Ind School Dist | 71 | 343 |
| Escobar, Jaime/Roma Ind School Dist | 6,35 | 343 |
| Escobar, Joaquin/Carrizo Spgs Cons Ind SD | 6 | 131 |
| Eshbaugh, Calvin/Academy Ind School Dist | 67 | 29 |
| Eslick, Brianne/Spearman Ind School Dist | 95 | 182 |
| Esparza, April/Diocese Corpus Christi Ed Off | 7 | 309 |
| Esparza, Ricardo/Roma Ind School Dist | 5 | 343 |
| Esparza, Susan/Brackett Ind School Dist | 68 | 260 |
| Espino, Billy/Ft Stockton Ind School Dist | 67 | 318 |

| NAME/District | JOB FUNCTIONS | PAGE |
|---|---|---|
| Espino, Gabe/Kermit Ind School Dist | 3,5,91 | 405 |
| Espinosa, Stephanie, Dr/Northwest Ind School Dist | 74,273,296 | 129 |
| Espinoza, Anne Marie/Uvalde Cons Ind School Dist | 71 | 381 |
| Espinoza, Christina/Hermleigh Ind School Dist | 60 | 336 |
| Espinoza, Jose, Dr/Socorro Ind School Dist | 1 | 140 |
| Espinoza, Kari/Harlandale Ind School Dist | 48,51,54,61,280 | 35 |
| Esqueda, Ana/Ysleta Ind School Dist | 57 | 141 |
| Esquibel, Armando/Lytle Ind School Dist | 5 | 24 |
| Esquivel, Cris/McAllen Ind School Dist | 91 | 224 |
| Esquivel, Sergio/Sharyland Ind School Dist | 297 | 227 |
| Essberg, Brenda/Ft Bend Ind School Dist | 2 | 153 |
| Essig, Jason/Boerne Ind School Dist | 73,286 | 257 |
| Estes, Caroly/Goliad Ind School Dist | 2 | 168 |
| Estes, Kenfra/Hutto Ind School Dist | 7 | 399 |
| Estes, Kenneth, Dr/Alvarado Ind School Dist | 1 | 249 |
| Estes, Mandy/Round Rock Ind School Dist | 8,18 | 401 |
| Estes, Nocona/Dublin Ind School Dist | 4 | 147 |
| Estrada, Amy/Idalou Ind School Dist | 58 | 272 |
| Estrada, Ben/Los Fresnos Cons Ind Sch Dist | 69 | 69 |
| Estrada, Dora/Edinburg Cons Ind School Dist | 16,82 | 221 |
| Estrada, Iris/Corpus Christi Ind Sch Dist | 34 | 306 |
| Estrada, Noel/Agua Dulce Ind School Dist | 67 | 305 |
| Estrada, Ram/Lamar Cons Ind School Dist | 20,23 | 157 |
| Estrada, Rebecca/Lackland Ind School Dist | 2,13,19 | 37 |
| Estrada, Tiffany/Eden Cons Ind School Dist | 31 | 94 |
| Estrades, Mark/Lockhart Ind School Dist | 1 | 64 |
| Etter, Sarah/Magnolia Ind School Dist | 286 | 295 |
| Ettredge, Barbara/Pilot Point Ind School Dist | 2,19 | 129 |
| Etzler, Michele/Hallettsville Ind Sch Dist | 35,83,85 | 265 |
| Etzler, Tim/Ricardo Ind School Dist | 73,84 | 261 |
| Eubank, Laura/Veribest Ind School Dist | 9 | 368 |
| Eubank, Sonia/Region 19 Ed Service Center | 2,15 | 144 |
| **Eubanks, Ben/**Iredell Ind School Dist | 1 | 50 |
| Eubanks, Lynne/Columbia Brazoria ISD | 76 | 56 |
| Eubanks, Reta/Saltillo Ind School Dist | 58 | 234 |
| Eubanks, Sylvia/Lufkin Ind School Dist | 57,271 | 21 |
| Euler, Kendall/Little Elm Ind School Dist | 76 | 128 |
| Evans, Amber/Chireno ISD School Dist | 4 | 300 |
| Evans, Ashley/Duncanville Ind School Dist | 41 | 108 |
| Evans, Chris/Wheeler Ind School Dist | 6 | 394 |
| Evans, Christi/Shamrock Ind School Dist | 4 | 393 |
| Evans, Curtis/Wharton Ind School Dist | 67 | 393 |
| Evans, Dana/Timpson Ind School Dist | 58 | 338 |
| Evans, Darrell/Dew Ind School Dist | 1,11 | 160 |
| Evans, Darrell/Nederland Ind School Dist | 69 | 245 |
| Evans, Emily/Teague Ind School Dist | 2 | 161 |
| Evans, Gary/Huntsville Ind School Dist | 27 | 386 |
| Evans, Jason/Sulphur Springs Ind Sch Dist | 69,294 | 235 |
| Evans, Karen/Sonora Ind School Dist | 73,98,286 | 345 |
| Evans, Kim/Midland Ind School Dist | 27,31 | 288 |
| Evans, Lauri/Rains Ind School Dist | 76 | 323 |
| Evans, Linda/Iola Ind School Dist | 4 | 177 |
| Evans, Louis/Harris Co Dept of Ed | 67 | 184 |
| Evans, Megan/Clear Creek Ind School Dist | 69 | 163 |
| Evans, Pamela/Houston Ind School Dist | 11,296 | 193 |
| Evans, Phil/Frisco Ind School Dist | 8 | 82 |
| Evans, Scott/Hawkins Ind School Dist | 6,91 | 407 |
| Evans, Teresa/Crosby Ind School Dist | 4 | 188 |
| Evenson, Ruth/Hereford Ind School Dist | 5 | 123 |
| Everest, Kathryn/Ft Worth Ind School Dist | 36 | 352 |
| Everett, Aiden/Runge Ind School Dist | 84 | 254 |
| Everett, Aiden/Runge Ind School Dist | 28,73,286 | 254 |
| Everett, Chris/Columbus Ind School Dist | 5 | 90 |
| Everett, David/McGregor Ind School Dist | 8,11,15,83 | 283 |
| Everett, Terry/Henderson Ind School Dist | 8,39,42,48,51,54,61 | 330 |
| Everette, Christie/Snook Ind School Dist | 9,11,88 | 63 |
| Eversole, Wes/Lake Dallas Ind School Dist | 2,15,19 | 126 |
| Everson, Melissa/Benjamin Ind School Dist | 57,58,271,286 | 261 |
| Evertt, Joel/Hereford Ind School Dist | 3 | 123 |
| Evins, Staci/Moody Ind School Dist | 67 | 284 |
| Evridge, Amanda/Rankin Ind School Dist | 67 | 380 |
| Ewing, Dub/City View Ind School Dist | 3 | 394 |
| Ewing, Michael/Ft Bend Ind School Dist | 88 | 154 |
| Ewing, William/City View Ind School Dist | 5 | 394 |
| Ewton, Galen/Collinsville Ind School Dist | 2 | 171 |
| Eyeington, Tom/Socorro Ind School Dist | 3,15,17 | 140 |

| | | | | | | | | |
|---|---|---|---|---|---|---|---|---|
| 1 | Superintendent | 16 | Instructional Media Svcs | 30 | Adult Education | 44 | Science Sec | |
| 2 | Bus/Finance/Purchasing | 17 | Chief Operations Officer | 31 | Career/Sch-to-Work K-12 | 45 | Math K-12 | |
| 3 | Buildings And Grounds | 18 | Chief Academic Officer | 32 | Career/Sch-to-Work Elem | 46 | Math Elem | |
| 4 | Food Service | 19 | Chief Financial Officer | 33 | Career/Sch-to-Work Sec | 47 | Math Sec | |
| 5 | Transportation | 20 | Art K-12 | 34 | Early Childhood Ed | 48 | English/Lang Arts K-12 | |
| 6 | Athletic | 21 | Art Elem | 35 | Health/Phys Education | 49 | English/Lang Arts Elem | |
| 7 | Health Services | 22 | Art Sec | 36 | Guidance Services K-12 | 50 | English/Lang Arts Sec | |
| 8 | Curric/Instruct K-12 | 23 | Music K-12 | 37 | Guidance Services Elem | 51 | Reading K-12 | |
| 9 | Curric/Instruct Elem | 24 | Music Elem | 38 | Guidance Services Sec | 52 | Reading Elem | |
| 10 | Curric/Instruct Sec | 25 | Music Sec | 39 | Social Studies K-12 | 53 | Reading Sec | |
| 11 | Federal Program | 26 | Business Education | 40 | Social Studies Elem | 54 | Remedial Reading K-12 | |
| 12 | Title I | 27 | Career & Tech Ed | 41 | Social Studies Sec | 55 | Remedial Reading Elem | |
| 13 | Title V | 28 | Technology Education | 42 | Science K-12 | 56 | Remedial Reading Sec | |
| 15 | Asst Superintendent | 29 | Family/Consumer Science | 43 | Science Elem | 57 | Bilingual/ELL | |

| | | | | | |
|---|---|---|---|---|---|
| 58 | Special Education K-12 | 72 | Summer School | 88 | Alternative/At Risk |
| 59 | Special Education Elem | 73 | Instructional Tech | 89 | Multi-Cultural Curriculum |
| 60 | Special Education Sec | 74 | Inservice Training | 90 | Social Work |
| 61 | Foreign/World Lang K-12 | 75 | Marketing/Distributive | 91 | Safety/Security |
| 62 | Foreign/World Lang Elem | 76 | Info Systems | 92 | Magnet School |
| 63 | Foreign/World Lang Sec | 77 | Psychological Assess | 93 | Parental Involvement |
| 64 | Religious Education K-12 | 78 | Affirmative Action | 95 | Tech Prep Program |
| 65 | Religious Education Elem | 79 | Student Personnel | 96 | Title II Programs |
| 66 | Religious Education Sec | 80 | Driver Ed/Safety | 97 | Chief Information Officer |
| 67 | School Board President | 81 | Gifted/Talented | 98 | Chief Technology Officer |
| 68 | Teacher Personnel | 82 | Video Services | 270 | Character Education |
| 69 | Academic Assessment | 83 | Substance Abuse Prev | 271 | Migrant Education |
| 70 | Research/Development | 84 | Erate | 273 | Teacher Mentor |
| 71 | Public Information | 85 | AIDS Education | 274 | Before/After Sch |
| | | | | 275 | Response To Intervention |

| | |
|---|---|
| 277 | Remedial Math K-12 |
| 280 | Literacy Coach |
| 285 | STEM |
| 286 | Digital Learning |
| 288 | Common Core Standards |
| 294 | Accountability |
| 295 | Network System |
| 296 | Title III Programs |
| 297 | Webmaster |
| 298 | Grant Writer/Ptnrshps |
| 750 | Chief Innovation Officer |
| 751 | Chief of Staff |
| 752 | Social Emotional Learning |

| NAME/District | JOB FUNCTIONS | PAGE | NAME/District | JOB FUNCTIONS | PAGE |
|---|---|---|---|---|---|
| Fields, Melissa/Marble Falls Ind School Dist | 69,294 | 64 | Fletcher, Linda/Pasadena Ind School Dist | 20,23 | 203 |
| Fields, Milton/Judson Ind School Dist | 3,15,91 | 36 | Fletcher, Shane/Leonard Ind School Dist | 6 | 150 |
| Fields, Sara/Campbell Ind School Dist | 58 | 238 | Fletcher, Sue/Zavalla Ind School Dist | 4 | 21 |
| Fieszel, Jacob/Gunter Ind School Dist | 6 | 171 | Fletcher, Tim/Slidell Ind School Dist | 67 | 407 |
| Figarelli, Joseph/Garland Ind School Dist | 20,23 | 109 | Fletcher, Toby/Llano Ind School Dist | 31,83,88 | 271 |
| Figueroa, Anthony/Wolfe City Ind School Dist | 1,83 | 240 | Flinchum, Thomas/Gold-Burg Ind School Dist | 8,11,36,69,83,88 | 293 |
| Fikes, Chris/Evadale Ind School Dist | 16,73,76,84,286,295 | 243 | Fling, Jason/Yoakum Ind School Dist | 16,73,76,84,295,298 | 122 |
| Filda, David/Cotulla Ind School Dist | 6 | 262 | Flinn, Ray/Harts Bluff Ind School Dist | 3 | 366 |
| Filipow, Jamie/Houston Ind School Dist | 41 | 193 | Flint, Ryan/Irving Ind School Dist | 42 | 113 |
| Filipp, Ace/Danbury Ind School Dist | 16,82 | 56 | Flippin, Amy/Coleman Ind School Dist | 83,85,270,273 | 79 |
| Filla, Tommy/Granger Ind School Dist | 67 | 399 | Flippin, Susan/Plainview Ind School Dist | 16 | 180 |
| Fillmore, Cheryl/West Oso Ind School Dist | 6 | 309 | Flippo, Chris/Sam Rayburn Ind School Dist | 67 | 150 |
| Finch, Bryan/Groveton Ind School Dist | 10,88,270 | 377 | Flood, Matt/Goose Creek Cons Ind Sch Dist | 73,76,98 | 192 |
| Finch, Danny/Perryton Ind School Dist | 83 | 310 | Flores-Jackson, Cordelia/United Ind School Dist | 2 | 390 |
| Finch, Danny/Spring Creek Ind School Dist | 8 | 241 | Flores, Anita/Plainview Ind School Dist | 271 | 180 |
| Fincher, Judy/Brady Ind School Dist | 73,84 | 280 | Flores, Barbara/Comfort Ind School Dist | 2,11 | 257 |
| Fincher, Lisa/Ennis Ind School Dist | 2,19,296,298 | 144 | Flores, Bernice/Spearman Ind School Dist | 4 | 182 |
| Finck, Rachelle/Round Rock Ind School Dist | 752 | 401 | Flores, Daniel/Stafford Municipal Sch Dist | 2 | 159 |
| Finger, Kami/Lubbock Ind School Dist | 58 | 272 | Flores, David/Alice Ind School Dist | 2,19 | 248 |
| Fink, Nathan/Marble Falls Ind School Dist | 73,295 | 64 | Flores, David/Raymondville Ind Sch Dist | 73 | 397 |
| Finley, Danny/Coolidge Ind School Dist | 67 | 269 | Flores, Diane/Ysleta Ind School Dist | 9 | 141 |
| Finley, Debbie/Loraine Ind School Dist | 2 | 292 | Flores, Edgwyna/Haskell Cons Ind School Dist | 4 | 215 |
| Finley, Jennifer/Dallas Ind School Dist | 7 | 102 | Flores, Gilbert/Zapata Co Ind School Dist | 73,76,98,286,295 | 410 |
| Finley, Lindy/Jacksonville Ind School Dist | 2 | 76 | Flores, Itza/Edcouch Elsa Ind School Dist | 58 | 220 |
| Finley, Stacy/Santo Ind School Dist | 4 | 313 | Flores, Javier/Uvalde Cons Ind School Dist | 67 | 381 |
| Finn, Donnie/Fredericksburg Ind School Dist | 3,11,15,79,91 | 167 | Flores, Jenny/Lubbock Ind School Dist | 16 | 272 |
| Finnell, John/Cleburne Ind School Dist | 67 | 250 | Flores, Jorge/La Joya Ind School Dist | 27 | 222 |
| Finney, Lawanda, Dr/Port Arthur Ind School Dist | 93,273 | 246 | Flores, Jose/La Joya Ind School Dist | 11 | 222 |
| Finster, Dwana/Calhoun Co Ind School Dist | 88 | 65 | Flores, Kimberly/Lamar Cons Ind School Dist | 275 | 157 |
| Finsterwald, Stacey/Wheeler Ind School Dist | 57 | 394 | Flores, Krystle/Alice Ind School Dist | 4 | 248 |
| Fiolek, Brian/Crockett Ind School Dist | 3 | 235 | Flores, Lizzy/Diocese of Laredo Ed Office | 2 | 391 |
| Fiorini, Robert/Palacios Ind School Dist | 73,295 | 278 | Flores, Magdalena/Crystal City Ind School Dist | 2,4,19 | 410 |
| Fischer, Jessica/Comal Ind School Dist | 5 | 91 | Flores, Marina/Grapevine-Colleyville Ind SD | 79 | 355 |
| Fischer, Karen/Gruver Ind School Dist | 2,11 | 181 | Flores, Marissa/Santa Gertrudis Ind Sch Dist | 7 | 261 |
| Fishbeck, Christie/Dew Ind School Dist | 16,73,295,297 | 160 | Flores, Max/La Vernia Ind School Dist | 68 | 404 |
| Fishbeck, Kevin/Moulton Ind School Dist | 6 | 265 | Flores, Melinda/La Joya Ind School Dist | 10 | 222 |
| Fisher, Corgie/S & S Cons Ind School Dist | 3,5 | 172 | Flores, Monica/Pawnee Ind School Dist | 4 | 28 |
| Fisher, David/Lometa Ind School Dist | 1,11 | 264 | Flores, Orlando/Fabens Ind School Dist | 67 | 139 |
| Fisher, Debbie/Olfen Ind School Dist | 4 | 329 | Flores, Patty/Rocksprings Ind School Dist | 2 | 135 |
| Fisher, Denise/Castleberry Ind School Dist | 42 | 350 | Flores, Raymond/Irion Co Ind School Dist | 73,295 | 241 |
| Fisher, Elmer/Manor Ind School Dist | 67 | 373 | Flores, Rebecca/Zapata Co Ind School Dist | 57 | 410 |
| Fisher, George/Paris Ind School Dist | 67 | 262 | Flores, Rene/Houston Ind School Dist | 285 | 193 |
| Fisher, Jeff/Rains Ind School Dist | 2,15 | 323 | Flores, Richard/Southwest Ind School Dist | 20,23 | 46 |
| Fisher, Jimmy/Brownwood Ind School Dist | 295 | 62 | Flores, Rick/Weslaco Ind School Dist | 77,294 | 228 |
| Fisher, Julie/Terrell Ind School Dist | 11,36,69,275,288,296 | 256 | Flores, Robin/Kopperl Ind School Dist | 76 | 50 |
| Fisher, Larry/Boling Ind School Dist | 3,5 | 392 | Flores, Rosalinda/San Diego Ind School Dist | 16 | 132 |
| Fisher, Leanne/Frenship Ind School Dist | 288 | 272 | Flores, Rose/Seagraves Ind School Dist | 57 | 162 |
| Fisher, Robert/Brownsville Ind School Dist | 76,95,286 | 66 | Flores, Sandy/Rule Ind School Dist | 2 | 215 |
| Fisher, Ron/Flour Bluff Ind School Dist | 91 | 307 | Flores, Stephanie/Coppell Ind School Dist | 58 | 102 |
| Fisher, Tiffany/Shallowater Ind School Dist | 57 | 274 | Flores, Steve, Dr/Round Rock Ind School Dist | 1 | 401 |
| Fisk, Dara/Mount Vernon Ind School Dist | 77 | 160 | Flores, Tony/El Paso Ind School Dist | 73 | 137 |
| Fisk, Sherri/Valley Mills Ind School Dist | 7 | 50 | Flores, Vincinte/Irion Co Ind School Dist | 67 | 241 |
| Fisk, Tiffany/Bushland Ind School Dist | 38,83 | 321 | Flores, Yolanda/Irving Ind School Dist | 81 | 113 |
| Fitch, Pam/Nacogdoches Ind School Dist | 67 | 301 | Florez, Angela/Kermit Ind School Dist | 79 | 405 |
| Fite, Drenon/Tatum Ind School Dist | 15,68 | 331 | Flower, Jenny/Groesbeck Ind School Dist | 7 | 269 |
| Fitts, David, Dr/Region 8 Ed Service Center | 1 | 72 | Flowers, David/Huntington Ind School Dist | 1 | 20 |
| Fitzgerald, Karen/Midlothian Ind School Dist | 15,71,76,750 | 145 | Flowers, Kelly, Dr/Sherman Ind School Dist | 9 | 172 |
| Fitzhenry, Derek/Sheldon Ind School Dist | 6,35 | 205 | Floyd, Brittany/Gunter Ind School Dist | 2 | 171 |
| Fitzhugh, Sarah, Dr/Lewisville Ind School Dist | 69,294 | 126 | Floyd, Cheryl/Paint Creek Ind School Dist | 1 | 215 |
| Fitzpatrick, Dianna/La Grange Ind School Dist | 19 | 151 | Floyd, Jason/Calallen Ind School Dist | 67 | 305 |
| Fitzpatrick, Steffany/Santa Anna Ind School Dist | 36,57,69,83,271,285 | 80 | Floyd, Jennifer/Seagraves Ind School Dist | 7,85 | 162 |
| Flaim, Diane/Dripping Springs Ind Sch Dist | 8,15 | 215 | Floyd, Scott/White Oak Ind School Dist | 73,295 | 176 |
| Flanary, Patty/Glen Rose Ind School Dist | 286 | 342 | Flusche, Darryl/Canyon Ind School Dist | 1 | 323 |
| Flannery, Sylvia/Kerrville Ind School Dist | 27,31,57,81,271 | 259 | Flynn, Jane/Cleburne Ind School Dist | 286 | 250 |
| Flasch, Kim/Lake Travis Ind School Dist | 67 | 373 | Flynt, Sherri/Huntington Ind School Dist | 38,69 | 20 |
| Flater, Janes/Connally Ind School Dist | 2,15 | 282 | Fogerson, Tracy/Lubbock-Cooper Ind Sch Dist | 58 | 274 |
| Flecter, Todd/Slocum ISD School Dist | 3 | 19 | Fojtik, Katie/Edna Ind School Dist | 7 | 242 |
| Fleet, Penny/Spring Hill Ind School Dist | 8,15,74 | 175 | Folds, Mark/Groveton Ind School Dist | 67 | 377 |
| Fleitman, Susie/Muenster Ind School Dist | 5 | 95 | Foley, Kelly/Lufkin Ind School Dist | 76 | 21 |
| Fleming, David/Spring Hill Ind School Dist | 5 | 175 | Folkerts, James/Bushland Ind School Dist | 3,5 | 321 |
| Fleming, Gregory/Abilene Ind School Dist | 71 | 362 | Folks, Jordan/Georgetown Ind School Dist | 74 | 398 |
| Fleming, Jennifer/Keller Ind School Dist | 36 | 357 | Follmar, Ramon/Colmesneil Ind School Dist | 5 | 377 |
| Flencher, Amanda/Somerville Ind School Dist | 2 | 63 | Followwell, Kimberly/Murchison Ind Sch Dist | 1,11,83 | 219 |
| Fletcher, Beverly/Ft Worth Ind School Dist | 20 | 352 | Folmar, Annette/Prosper Ind School District | 2,19 | 88 |
| Fletcher, Greg/Paradise Ind School Dist | 3 | 407 | Folmar, Nicole/Boling Ind School Dist | 7 | 392 |
| Fletcher, Greg/Zavalla Ind School Dist | 5 | 21 | Fontenot, Nicole/Jacksonville Ind School Dist | 7 | 76 |

| | | | | | | | |
|---|---|---|---|---|---|---|---|
| 1 Superintendent | 16 Instructional Media Svcs | 30 Adult Education | 44 Science Sec | 58 Special Education K-12 | 72 Summer School | 88 Alternative/At Risk | 277 Remedial Math K-12 |
| 2 Bus/Finance/Purchasing | 17 Chief Operations Officer | 31 Career/Sch-to-Work K-12 | 45 Math K-12 | 59 Special Education Elem | 73 Instructional Tech | 89 Multi-Cultural Curriculum | 280 Literacy Coach |
| 3 Buildings And Grounds | 18 Chief Academic Officer | 32 Career/Sch-to-Work Elem | 46 Math Elem | 60 Special Education Sec | 74 Inservice Training | 90 Social Work | 285 STEM |
| 4 Food Service | 19 Chief Financial Officer | 33 Career/Sch-to-Work Sec | 47 Math Sec | 61 Foreign/World Lang K-12 | 75 Marketing/Distributive | 91 Safety/Security | 286 Digital Learning |
| 5 Transportation | 20 Art K-12 | 34 Early Childhood Ed | 48 English/Lang Arts K-12 | 62 Foreign/World Lang Elem | 76 Info Systems | 92 Magnet School | 288 Common Core Standards |
| 6 Athletic | 21 Art Elem | 35 Health/Phys Education | 49 English/Lang Arts Elem | 63 Foreign/World Lang Sec | 77 Psychological Assess | 93 Parental Involvement | 294 Accountability |
| 7 Health Services | 22 Art Sec | 36 Guidance Services K-12 | 50 English/Lang Arts Sec | 64 Religious Education K-12 | 78 Affirmative Action | 95 Tech Prep Program | 295 Network System |
| 8 Curric/Instruct K-12 | 23 Music K-12 | 37 Guidance Services Elem | 51 Reading K-12 | 65 Religious Education Elem | 79 Student Personnel | 97 Chief Infomation Officer | 296 Title II Programs |
| 9 Curric/Instruct Elem | 24 Music Elem | 38 Guidance Services Sec | 52 Reading Elem | 66 Religious Education Sec | 80 Driver Ed/Safety | 98 Chief Technology Officer | 297 Webmaster |
| 10 Curric/Instruct Sec | 25 Music Sec | 39 Social Studies K-12 | 53 Reading Sec | 67 School Board President | 81 Gifted/Talented | 270 Character Education | 298 Grant Writer/Ptnrships |
| 11 Federal Program | 26 Business Education | 40 Social Studies Elem | 54 Remedial Reading K-12 | 68 Teacher Personnel | 82 Video Services | 271 Migrant Education | 750 Chief Innovation Officer |
| 12 Title I | 27 Career & Tech Ed | 41 Social Studies Sec | 55 Remedial Reading Elem | 69 Academic Assessment | 83 Substance Abuse Prev | 273 Teacher Mentor | 751 Chief of Staff |
| 13 Title V | 28 Technology Education | 42 Science K-12 | 56 Remedial Reading Sec | 70 Research/Development | 84 Erate | 274 Before/After Sch | 752 Social Emotional Learning |
| 15 Asst Superintendent | 29 Family/Consumer Science | 43 Science Elem | 57 Bilingual/ELL | 71 Public Information | 85 AIDS Education | 275 Response To Intervention | |

| NAME/District | JOB FUNCTIONS | PAGE |
|---|---|---|
| Freeman, Michael/Richardson Ind School Dist | 92 | 116 |
| Freeman, Noreen/Alto Ind School Dist | 58 | 76 |
| Freeman, Shelley/Birdville Ind School Dist | 2 | 348 |
| Freeman, Steve/New Caney Ind School Dist | 68 | 296 |
| Freeman, Tonya/Liberty Ind School Dist | 37 | 269 |
| Freese, Carol/Coppell Ind School Dist | 76 | 102 |
| Fregia, Hollie/Little Cypress Mauriceville SD | 19 | 311 |
| Frei, Dwayne/Troy Ind School Dist | 83,88 | 33 |
| French, Corinne/Valley View ISD-Cooke Co | 67 | 95 |
| French, John/Kountze Ind School Dist | 5 | 183 |
| **French, Micheal/**Farmersville Ind School Dist | 1 | 82 |
| French, Rebecca/Lexington Ind School Dist | 8,11,74,271 | 266 |
| French, Rebecca/Lexington Ind School Dist | 273,288,296 | 266 |
| Frey, Matt/Plano Ind School Dist | 73 | 85 |
| Freytag, Chris/Flatonia Ind School Dist | 6 | 151 |
| Friar, Carlin/Boerne Ind School Dist | 67 | 257 |
| Frias, Holly/Garland Ind School Dist | 4 | 109 |
| Friday, Jamie/Texarkana Ind School Dist | 8 | 53 |
| Friddle, Amy/Como Pickton Cons Ind SD | 57,73,76,271,286,288 | 234 |
| Friddle, Mindy/Como Pickton Cons Ind SD | 4 | 234 |
| Fried, Rita/Roscoe Collegiate Ind Sch Dist | 2 | 304 |
| Friel, Kris/Tulia Ind School Dist | 84,295 | 345 |
| Frierson, Amy/Texarkana Ind School Dist | 43,46 | 53 |
| Friese, Galadriel/San Antonio Ind School Dist | 57 | 42 |
| Friess, Kay/Sonora Ind School Dist | 38 | 345 |
| Fritsche, Charles/Dime Box Ind School Dist | 67 | 266 |
| Froneberger, Dan/Sulphur Springs Ind Sch Dist | 3 | 235 |
| Frost, Diane, Dr/Corsicana Ind School Dist | 1 | 302 |
| Frunza-Tanca, Gabi/Houston Ind School Dist | 61 | 193 |
| Fry, Brian/Palmer Ind School Dist | 8,74,285,286,288 | 146 |
| Fry, Matthew/Liberty-Eylau Ind School Dist | 71 | 51 |
| Fryar, Bobby/Reagan Co Ind School Dist | 1 | 324 |
| Frye, Della/Midland Ind School Dist | 34 | 288 |
| Fryman, Kimberly/Mt Enterprise Ind School Dist | 57 | 330 |
| Fryrear, Sundy/Bryan Ind School Dist | 4 | 58 |
| Fuchs, Candace/Joshua Ind School Dist | 2 | 251 |
| Fuchs, Debbie/Clear Creek Ind School Dist | 6,35 | 162 |
| Fuchs, Kristy/Glasscock Co Ind School Dist | 2,11,296 | 168 |
| Fuchs, Melinda/Burton Ind School Dist | 8,12,69,88,270,288,296 | 388 |
| Fudge, Barney/Texas Dept of Education | 35 | 1 |
| Fuenmayor, Susana, Dr/Pearland Ind School Dist | 57 | 56 |
| Fuentes, Lindsey/College Station Ind Sch Dist | 58,77 | 59 |
| Fuenties, Justin/Houston Ind School Dist | 92 | 193 |
| Fuerte-Luna, Jenise/Edinburg Cons Ind School Dist | 275 | 221 |
| Fulgham, Carri/Lubbock Ind School Dist | 73,286 | 272 |
| Fuller, Christina/Teague Ind School Dist | 57 | 161 |
| Fuller, Daniel/Stockdale Ind School Dist | 1 | 404 |
| Fuller, Joye/Eula Ind School Dist | 7 | 66 |
| Fuller, Kim, Dr/Richardson Ind School Dist | 11,298 | 116 |
| Fuller, Margie/Grandview Ind School Dist | 2,19 | 251 |
| Fuller, Mike/Decatur Ind School Dist | 6 | 406 |
| Fuller, Ryan/Joaquin Ind School Dist | 1 | 337 |
| Fuller, Sancy/Lovejoy Ind School Dist | 7,57,58 | 84 |
| Fuller, Shannon/East Central Ind School Dist | 8 | 34 |
| Fullerton, Diane/Granbury Ind School Dist | 58 | 233 |
| Fulmer, Jeff/Brock Ind School Dist | 5 | 315 |
| Fulp, Shannon/Greenville Ind School Dist | 73,76,295 | 239 |
| Fulton, Elise/Diocese of Beaumont Sch Office | 67 | 247 |
| Fulton, Randy/Frost Ind School Dist | 6 | 302 |
| Funk, Terry/El Paso Ind School Dist | 76 | 137 |
| Fuqua, Bryan/Robinson Ind School Dist | 73,84 | 284 |
| Fuqua, Gayle/Kermit Ind School Dist | 2 | 405 |
| Furbee, Brian/Normangee Ind School Dist | 73,82,286 | 267 |
| Furbush, Jane/Hunt Ind School Dist | 7,83,85 | 258 |
| Furgeson, Susan/Pampa Ind School Dist | 58,81,88 | 170 |
| Furlow, Lorin/Brazosport Ind School Dist | 58,77,90,296 | 55 |
| Furlow, Mike/Shelbyville Ind School Dist | 69,273 | 337 |
| Furr, Cindy/Springlake-Earth Ind Sch Dist | 10,69,270 | 264 |
| Furrh, Terry/Fruitvale Ind School Dist | 57 | 383 |
| Fussell, Cindy, Dr/Region 5 Ed Service Center | 58 | 247 |

## G

| NAME/District | JOB FUNCTIONS | PAGE |
|---|---|---|
| Gabehart, Mark/Round Rock Ind School Dist | 76 | 401 |
| Gabriel, Nicole/Region 18 Ed Service Center | 7,8,73,74,85 | 290 |
| Gabrisch, Kelly/Humble Ind School Dist | 68 | 200 |
| Gaeta, Victoria/Southwest Ind School Dist | 30,274 | 46 |

| NAME/District | JOB FUNCTIONS | PAGE |
|---|---|---|
| Gage, Dana/Milano Ind School Dist | 4 | 290 |
| Gage, Joey/Milano Ind School Dist | 5 | 290 |
| Gage, Lindsay/Taylor Ind School Dist | 4 | 402 |
| Gage, Stephanie/Milano Ind School Dist | 2,11 | 290 |
| Gage, Theresa/Lamar Cons Ind School Dist | 49,52 | 157 |
| Gagne, Laurie, Dr/Highland Park Ind Sch Dist | 58 | 112 |
| Gaillard, Sahala/Gruver Ind School Dist | 7 | 181 |
| Gain, Kerry/Comal Ind School Dist | 8,15 | 91 |
| Gainer, Joee/Everman Ind School Dist | 2,19 | 351 |
| Gaines, Lashun/Elgin Ind School Dist | 275 | 27 |
| Gainey, Dan/Colorado Ind School Dist | 6 | 292 |
| Gaitan, John/La Pryor Ind School Dist | 3,5,91 | 411 |
| Gaitan, Nora/Charlotte Ind School Dist | 2,11 | 23 |
| Gajdica, Kendra/Ferris Ind School Dist | 9 | 144 |
| Gajewski, Mary/Sealy Ind School Dist | 11,88,296 | 25 |
| Galamore, Sherry/Magnolia Ind School Dist | 42 | 295 |
| Galan, Valerie/Edgewood Ind School Dist | 88 | 34 |
| Galaviz, April/Canutillo Ind School Dist | 69,70,294 | 136 |
| Galaviz, Pedro, Dr/Canutillo Ind School Dist | 1 | 136 |
| Galbreath, Charles/Sanger Ind School Dist | 6 | 130 |
| Galbreath, Ronnie/Joshua Ind School Dist | 67 | 251 |
| Galetti, Tracey/Ganado Ind School Dist | 4 | 242 |
| Galetti, Tracey/Ganado Ind School Dist | 4 | 242 |
| Galindo, Betty/Edgewood Ind School Dist | 2 | 34 |
| Galindo, Brandi/Milford Ind School Dist | 4 | 146 |
| Galindo, Dorian, Dr/North East Ind School Dist | 69,70,294 | 37 |
| Galindo, Lamar/Taft Ind School Dist | 58 | 334 |
| Galindo, Magda/Houston Ind School Dist | 271 | 193 |
| Galindo, Ray/Northside Ind School Dist | 15 | 39 |
| Galindo, Richard/Balmorhea Ind School Dist | 73 | 325 |
| Gall, Adrienne/Lewisville Ind School Dist | 9 | 126 |
| Gallagher, Arlene/Alvarado Ind School Dist | 58 | 249 |
| Gallagher, Daniel/Little Elm Ind School Dist | 1 | 128 |
| Gallagos, Susan/Freer Ind School Dist | 58 | 132 |
| Gallant, Luann/Trinity Ind School Dist | 2,11,74,84,296 | 377 |
| Gallardo, Adrian/Rankin Ind School Dist | 83,88 | 380 |
| Gallardo, Elidia/Rankin Ind School Dist | 11 | 380 |
| Gallegos, Denise/Brownsville Ind School Dist | 73,285 | 66 |
| Gallegos, Gloria/Pasadena Ind School Dist | 11,15,57,271,274,296 | 203 |
| Gallegos, Reina/La Pryor Ind School Dist | 11,296 | 411 |
| Gallegos, Robert/San Elizario Ind School Dist | 7,35,83,91 | 139 |
| Gallegos, Stephanie/Tuloso-Midway Ind School Dist | 4 | 308 |
| Galley, Sandra/Detroit Ind School Dist | 4,79 | 325 |
| Galligan, John/Childress Ind School Dist | 73,295 | 77 |
| Galloway, Chris/Floresville Ind School Dist | 8 | 403 |
| Galloway, Steven/Columbia Brazoria ISD | 1 | 56 |
| Galm, Patricia/Bandera Ind School Dist | 58 | 26 |
| Galow, Troy, Dr/Pflugerville Ind School Dist | 15,751 | 374 |
| Galvan, Adam/Lockhart Ind School Dist | 15,73,76,271 | 64 |
| Galvan, Bobby/Ben Bolt-Palito Blanco ISD | 8,11,76,296,298 | 248 |
| Galvan, Daniel/Alice Ind School Dist | 5 | 248 |
| Galvan, Haylie/Vega Ind School Dist | 2 | 310 |
| Galvan, Manuel/Ballinger Ind School Dist | 67 | 329 |
| Galvan, Mike/Tidehaven Ind School Dist | 5 | 279 |
| Galvan, Nora/Pharr-San Juan-Alamo Ind SD | 16 | 226 |
| Galvan, Rosie/Hidalgo Ind School Dist | 4 | 222 |
| Galvan, Sofia/Irving Ind School Dist | 88,275 | 113 |
| Galvan, Victor/Aransas Pass Ind School Dist | 67 | 333 |
| Galvez, Thomas/Medina Valley Ind School Dist | 20 | 287 |
| Galvin, Jacob/Seguin Ind School Dist | 4 | 178 |
| Gamel, Merlina/Mason Ind School Dist | 73 | 278 |
| Gamell, Maria, Dr/Eagle Mtn-Saginaw Ind Sch Dist | 68 | 351 |
| Gamez, Laura/San Antonio Ind School Dist | 48 | 42 |
| Gamez, Manuel/Pflugerville Ind School Dist | 20,23 | 374 |
| Gamez, Stacy/Meadow Ind School Dist | 34 | 365 |
| Gammill, Staci/Yantis Ind School Dist | 7 | 408 |
| Gandillon, Joe/Howe Ind School Dist | 73,76,298 | 171 |
| Gandy, Brian/Douglass Ind School Dist | 8,57,271,273 | 300 |
| Gandy, Elizabeth/Evant Ind School Dist | 42 | 96 |
| Gandy, Misty/Eden Cons Ind School Dist | 1,11,73 | 94 |
| Gandy, Robin/Martin's Mill Ind Sch Dist | 36,57,69,83,270 | 383 |
| Gann, Angie/Stamford Ind School Dist | 58 | 253 |
| Gann, Cynthia/Hondo Ind School Dist | 58,77 | 287 |
| Gann, Linda/Boerne Ind School Dist | 45 | 257 |
| Gant, Chequita/Maud Ind School Dist | 76 | 52 |
| Garakani, Leslie/Midlothian Ind School Dist | 73,98 | 145 |

| NAME/District | JOB FUNCTIONS | PAGE | NAME/District | JOB FUNCTIONS | PAGE |
|---|---|---|---|---|---|
| Garay, Javier/Fabens Ind School Dist | 3,5 | 139 | Garcia, Monica/Judson Ind School Dist | 36 | 36 |
| Garcia, Able/Balmorhea Ind School Dist | 57 | 325 | Garcia, Norma/Harlingen Cons Ind School Dist | 57 | 68 |
| Garcia, Adriana/Pharr-San Juan-Alamo Ind SD | 27,31 | 226 | Garcia, Olga/Harlingen Cons Ind School Dist | 76 | 68 |
| Garcia, Aidee/San Felipe-Del Rio Cons Ind SD | 68 | 381 | Garcia, Orlando/Pharr-San Juan-Alamo Ind SD | 6 | 226 |
| Garcia, Alma, Dr/Alice Ind School Dist | 11,57,270,296 | 248 | Garcia, Oscar/Brownsville Ind School Dist | 91 | 66 |
| Garcia, Amanda/Poteet Ind School Dist | 2,3 | 24 | Garcia, Paula/Slaton Ind School Dist | 4 | 275 |
| Garcia, Angela/Floresville Ind School Dist | 88,274 | 403 | Garcia, Robert/Del Valle Ind School Dist | 294 | 372 |
| Garcia, Anna/Refugio Ind School Dist | 16,82 | 326 | Garcia, Robert/Maypearl Ind School Dist | 3,5,91 | 145 |
| Garcia, Arturo/Robstown Ind School Dist | 6 | 308 | Garcia, Rogelio/Laredo Ind School Dist | 27,31 | 389 |
| Garcia, Becky/La Pryor Ind School Dist | 2 | 411 | Garcia, Rogelio/Laredo Ind School Dist | 27,31 | 389 |
| Garcia, Blanca, Dr/El Paso ISD-Elementary | 15 | 137 | Garcia, Roy/Cypress-Fairbanks Ind Sch Dist | 15 | 189 |
| Garcia, Carlos/Tornillo Ind School Dist | 73,76 | 141 | Garcia, Samuel/Socorro Ind School Dist | 2 | 140 |
| Garcia, Carmen/Edcouch Elsa Ind School Dist | 8,11,15,296 | 220 | Garcia, Sarah/Crystal City Ind School Dist | 79 | 410 |
| Garcia, Charlie/Mission Cons Ind School Dist | 67 | 225 | Garcia, Sergio/Weslaco Ind School Dist | 15 | 228 |
| Garcia, Charmaine/Stafford Municipal Sch Dist | 11,58,275 | 159 | Garcia, Sharla/Waco Ind School Dist | 298 | 284 |
| Garcia, Cindy, Dr/Driscoll Ind School Dist | 1 | 307 | Garcia, Shelley/Crane Ind School Dist | 58 | 97 |
| Garcia, Conrado/West Oso Ind School Dist | 1 | 309 | Garcia, Sue/Barbers Hill Ind School Dist | 34,58,77 | 75 |
| Garcia, Cynthia/Los Fresnos Cons Ind Sch Dist | 16 | 69 | Garcia, Sylvia/Webb Cons Ind School Dist | 7 | 391 |
| Garcia, Dalia/Harlingen Cons Ind School Dist | 294 | 68 | Garcia, Tasha/Seminole Ind School Dist | 69 | 162 |
| Garcia, Dalia/Southwest Ind School Dist | 8,15,58,73,74 | 46 | Garcia, Veronica/Rio Grande City Ind Sch Dist | 271 | 343 |
| Garcia, Dan/Devine Ind School Dist | 84 | 286 | Garcie, Kelye/Port Aransas Ind School Dist | 9 | 308 |
| Garcia, Daniel/Harlingen Cons Ind School Dist | 58 | 68 | Gardea, Margarita/Houston Ind School Dist | 9 | 193 |
| Garcia, Danny/Ft Worth Ind School Dist | 91 | 352 | Gardenhire, Jay/Hondo Ind School Dist | 67 | 287 |
| Garcia, David/Hurst-Euless-Bedford ISD | 2,15 | 356 | Gardner, Chad/College Station Ind Sch Dist | 30,274 | 59 |
| Garcia, David/United Ind School Dist | 15,68 | 390 | Gardner, Heidi/Brownwood Ind School Dist | 11,31,57,88,285,296 | 62 |
| Garcia, Denise/San Marcos Cons Ind Sch Dist | 2 | 216 | Gardner, Rick/Humble Ind School Dist | 15,68,78,273 | 200 |
| Garcia, Devanira/Brownsville Ind School Dist | 74 | 66 | Gardner, Robin/Junction Ind School Dist | 38,83,85,270 | 260 |
| Garcia, Diana/Wharton Ind School Dist | 7 | 393 | Gardner, Roy/Angleton Ind School Dist | 16,27,31,88 | 55 |
| Garcia, Donna/Monahans-Wickett-Pyote ISD | 67 | 388 | Gardner, Sheila/Wolfe City Ind School Dist | 8,73,286,288 | 240 |
| Garcia, Edna/Plainview Ind School Dist | 11,57,93,271 | 180 | Gardzina, Margaret/Liberty Ind School Dist | 8,11 | 269 |
| Garcia, Elda, Dr/Corpus Christi Ind Sch Dist | 69,294 | 306 | Gargg, Kasey/Central Ind School Dist | 2 | 20 |
| Garcia, Eloy/Hidalgo Ind School Dist | 73,84,295 | 222 | Garibay, Cornelio/Culberson Co Allamoore Ind SD | 5 | 99 |
| Garcia, Erica/Hale Center Ind School Dist | 4 | 180 | Garica, Dimitrio/Kenedy Ind School Dist | 67 | 254 |
| Garcia, Erica/Weslaco Ind School Dist | 93 | 228 | Garis, Chris/Aransas Co Ind School Dist | 295 | 22 |
| Garcia, Francis/Boerne Ind School Dist | 54 | 257 | Garison, Ross/Denton Ind School Dist | 73,286 | 125 |
| Garcia, Grace/Alice Ind School Dist | 58 | 248 | Garland, Diane/Cypress-Fairbanks Ind Sch Dist | 8,16 | 189 |
| Garcia, Gregorio, Dr/Brownsville Ind School Dist | 298 | 66 | Garland, Shay/Magnolia Ind School Dist | 48 | 295 |
| Garcia, Jacob/Harlandale Ind School Dist | 5 | 35 | Garlic, John/Weslaco Ind School Dist | 11 | 228 |
| Garcia, Jacob/Waelder Ind School Dist | 6 | 169 | Garlock, Steve/Iraan-Sheffield Ind Sch Dist | 67 | 318 |
| Garcia, Javier/Rio Grande City Ind Sch Dist | 91 | 343 | Garn, Jesse/Midway Ind School Dist | 98 | 283 |
| Garcia, Jerry/Kenedy Ind School Dist | 3,91 | 254 | Garner, Brian/Whitewright Ind School Dist | 1 | 173 |
| Garcia, Joe/Dalhart Ind School Dist | 3 | 99 | Garner, Ray/United Ind School Dist | 91 | 390 |
| Garcia, Joe/Stamford Ind School Dist | 3,91 | 253 | Garnett, Mark, Dr/Spearman Ind School Dist | 67 | 182 |
| Garcia, Joshua/Mansfield Ind School Dist | 57 | 358 | Garrett, Daphany/Mildred Ind School Dist | 36,69,83,85,270 | 303 |
| Garcia, Josie/South Texas Ind School Dist | 58 | 71 | Garrett, James/Jarrell Ind School Dist | 2 | 399 |
| Garcia, Juana/Bryan Ind School Dist | 271 | 58 | Garrett, Joel/Lamar Cons Ind School Dist | 27,31 | 157 |
| Garcia, Juana/Hartley Ind School Dist | 271,273 | 215 | Garrett, Matthew/Lewisville Ind School Dist | 91 | 126 |
| Garcia, Judith/United Ind School Dist | 73 | 390 | Garrett, Pat/Walnut Springs Ind Sch Dist | 1,11,84 | 51 |
| Garcia, Karl/Freer Ind School Dist | 73,84,295 | 132 | Garrett, Robin/Paradise Ind School Dist | 37 | 407 |
| Garcia, Kim/Georgetown Ind School Dist | 286 | 398 | Garrett, Shelley/Garland Ind School Dist | 15,91 | 109 |
| Garcia, Krista/Northside Ind School Dist | 58 | 39 | Garrison, Karen/Spring Ind School Dist | 71 | 207 |
| Garcia, Larry/McMullen Co Ind Sch Dist | 3,5 | 286 | Garrison, Todd/Kaufman Ind School Dist | 2,19 | 255 |
| Garcia, Laura/United Ind School Dist | 76 | 390 | Gartrell, Louise/Garland Ind School Dist | 35 | 109 |
| Garcia, Lawrence/Beeville Ind School Dist | 84 | 28 | Garvey, Nancy/Coppell Ind School Dist | 73,286 | 102 |
| Garcia, Lee, Dr/Brownsville Ind School Dist | 76 | 66 | Garvey, Tonya/Carrollton-Farmers Branch ISD | 47 | 100 |
| Garcia, Liodolee/Killeen Ind School Dist | 57,271 | 30 | Gary, Staci/Port Neches-Groves Ind SD | 9,57 | 246 |
| Garcia, Lupe/Weslaco Ind School Dist | 5 | 228 | Garza-Viator, Angela/La Porte Ind School Dist | 68,78 | 203 |
| Garcia, Magdalena/Channelview Ind School Dist | 57 | 188 | Garza-Viator, Angela/La Porte Ind School Dist | 68 | 203 |
| Garcia, Manuel/Roma Ind School Dist | 76 | 343 | Garza, Andrea/La Joya Ind School Dist | 58,77 | 222 |
| Garcia, Maria/East Chambers Ind School Dist | 57 | 76 | Garza, Angelica/Edgewood Ind School Dist | 76 | 34 |
| Garcia, Maria/Edcouch Elsa Ind School Dist | 8,15 | 220 | Garza, Anjanett/McAllen Ind School Dist | 11 | 224 |
| Garcia, Maria, Dr/Amarillo Ind School Dist | 58 | 320 | Garza, Anthony, Dr/Edinburg Cons Ind School Dist | 10 | 221 |
| Garcia, Maricela/Rio Grande City Ind Sch Dist | 58 | 343 | Garza, Arnold/Alice Ind School Dist | 23 | 248 |
| Garcia, Mario/Eagle Pass Ind School Dist | 4 | 279 | Garza, Brandon/Magnolia Ind School Dist | 11,36,275,294 | 295 |
| Garcia, Marty/Moody Ind School Dist | 6 | 284 | Garza, Clem/La Joya Ind School Dist | 73,84 | 222 |
| Garcia, Melissa/Channing Ind School Dist | 58 | 214 | Garza, Daniel/Devine Ind School Dist | 73 | 286 |
| Garcia, Miguel/Ft Worth Ind School Dist | 274 | 352 | Garza, Deborah/Sharyland Ind School Dist | 68 | 227 |

| NAME/District | JOB FUNCTIONS | PAGE |
|---|---|---|
| Garza, Elena/Edcouch Elsa Ind School Dist | 4 | 220 |
| Garza, Emily/Pharr-San Juan-Alamo Ind SD | 2 | 226 |
| Garza, Erica/Hays Cons Ind School Dist | 74 | 216 |
| Garza, Estella/San Antonio Ind School Dist | 90 | 42 |
| Garza, Geneva/Eden Cons Ind School Dist | 36,57,69,83,270 | 94 |
| Garza, Gilbert/Edinburg Cons Ind School Dist | 1 | 221 |
| Garza, Gina/Jim Hogg Co Ind School Dist | 8 | 247 |
| Garza, Guadalupe/Rio Grande City Ind Sch Dist | 39 | 343 |
| Garza, Hildeliza/Zapata Co Ind School Dist | 8 | 410 |
| Garza, Jennifer/Hidalgo Ind School Dist | 71 | 222 |
| Garza, Jesse, Dr/Los Fresnos Cons Ind Sch Dist | 73,286 | 69 |
| Garza, Juan/Tomball Ind School Dist | 68 | 208 |
| Garza, Judy/Skidmore Tynan Ind SD | 270 | 29 |
| Garza, Larry/San Antonio Ind School Dist | 2,19 | 42 |
| Garza, Leonel/Los Fresnos Cons Ind Sch Dist | 67 | 69 |
| Garza, Leslie/Woodsboro Ind School Dist | 9,11 | 326 |
| Garza, Letty/Driscoll Ind School Dist | 59 | 307 |
| Garza, Liz/Ballinger Ind School Dist | 2 | 329 |
| Garza, Luis/Roma Ind School Dist | 15,68,83,273 | 343 |
| Garza, Marie/La Villa Ind School Dist | 4 | 223 |
| Garza, Marisa/San Isidro Ind School Dist | 36,88 | 343 |
| Garza, Martha/Hidalgo Ind School Dist | 8 | 222 |
| Garza, Mary/Brownsville Ind School Dist | 2 | 66 |
| Garza, Matthew/Ben Bolt-Palito Blanco ISD | 2 | 248 |
| Garza, Melissa/Knippa Ind School Dist | 8,12,298 | 380 |
| Garza, Mike/United Ind School Dist | 3,7,15 | 390 |
| Garza, Mirella/Edinburg Cons Ind School Dist | 43 | 221 |
| Garza, Monika/Ricardo Ind School Dist | 69,88,270 | 261 |
| Garza, Nancy/Mercedes Ind School Dist | 4 | 225 |
| Garza, Nathaniel/San Perlita Ind School Dist | 6 | 397 |
| Garza, Neil/Weslaco Ind School Dist | 58 | 228 |
| Garza, Noemie/Ricardo Ind School Dist | 4 | 261 |
| Garza, Ramon/Galena Park Ind School Dist | 67 | 191 |
| Garza, Ray/Aransas Co Ind School Dist | 67 | 22 |
| Garza, Ray/D'Hanis Ind School Dist | 3 | 286 |
| Garza, Ray/Lasara Ind School Dist | 16,73,295 | 397 |
| Garza, Rebecca/Pharr-San Juan-Alamo Ind SD | 15,68 | 226 |
| Garza, Roel/Banquete Ind School Dist | 27 | 305 |
| Garza, Rogelio/Edinburg Cons Ind School Dist | 6,35 | 221 |
| Garza, Romeo/Pharr-San Juan-Alamo Ind SD | 91 | 226 |
| Garza, Sandra, Dr/Uvalde Cons Ind School Dist | 10 | 381 |
| Garza, Sara/Brownsville Ind School Dist | 36,752 | 66 |
| Garza, Susana, Dr/Jim Hogg Co Ind School Dist | 1 | 247 |
| Garza, Sylvia/Edcouch Elsa Ind School Dist | 2 | 220 |
| Garza, Traci/Seagraves Ind School Dist | 2 | 162 |
| Garza, Veronica/Mathis Ind School Dist | 58 | 334 |
| Garza, Victor/La Joya Ind School Dist | 6 | 222 |
| Garza, Vilma/Rio Grande City Ind Sch Dist | 1 | 342 |
| Gasaway, Jeff/Marble Falls Ind School Dist | 2,15 | 64 |
| Gasiorowski, Mike/Friendswood Ind Sch Dist | 76 | 164 |
| Gaskamp, Collin/Blanco Ind School Dist | 73 | 49 |
| Gaskin, Stacy/Buffalo Ind School Dist | 7 | 266 |
| Gaskins, Gretchen/Alief Ind School Dist | 39 | 186 |
| Gaspard, James/Kirbyville Cons Ind Sch Dist | 16,73,295 | 244 |
| Gasper, Christina/Lueders-Avoca Ind School Dist | 8 | 253 |
| Gasper, Christopher/Lueders-Avoca Ind School Dist | 6 | 253 |
| Gass, Kim/Plains Ind School Dist | 16 | 409 |
| Gassman, Melissa/Prosper Ind School Dist | 57 | 88 |
| Gast, Stephanie/Millsap Ind School Dist | 7 | 315 |
| Gaston, Jeremy/Hearne Ind School Dist | 16,73,82,295 | 327 |
| **Gaston, Jill**/Wells Ind School Dist | 1 | 77 |
| Gates, B J/Burnet Cons Ind Sch Dist | 9 | 63 |
| Gates, Cristy/Sheldon Ind School Dist | 3,17 | 205 |
| Gates, Ginger, Dr/Region 4 Ed Service Center | 58 | 213 |
| Gates, Simeon/Bryan Ind School Dist | 5 | 58 |
| Gates, Theresa/Rusk Ind School Dist | 38,91 | 77 |
| Gatewood, Kellie/Cayuga Ind School Dist | 2 | 18 |
| Gatlin, Jeff/Miller Grove Ind School Dist | 27 | 234 |
| Gatlin, Kyle/Henderson Ind School Dist | 5 | 330 |
| Gatlin, Ron/El Paso Ind School Dist | 2 | 137 |
| Gatlin, Winston/Southwest Ind School Dist | 4 | 46 |
| Gau, Tim/Littlefield Ind School Dist | 73,84,295 | 263 |
| Gaudette, Philip/East Bernard Ind Sch Dist | 9,273 | 392 |
| Gauntt, Debbie/Coppell Ind School Dist | 275 | 102 |
| Gausemeier, Valerie/Rosebud-Lott Ind School Dist | 2 | 149 |
| Gauthier, Jennifer/Orangefield Ind School Dist | 73,76,84,295 | 312 |
| Gauthier, Jessica/Lake Worth Ind School Dist | 297 | 358 |
| Gauthier, Julie/Port Neches-Groves Ind SD | 15,91,296 | 246 |
| Gavina, Yolanda/Hereford Ind School Dist | 11,83,271,274 | 123 |
| Gaw, Kathy/Hallsville Ind School Dist | 26,27,29,75,95 | 213 |
| Gawryszewski, Bryan/Fairfield Ind School Dist | 5,79,294 | 160 |
| Gay, Joy/San Angelo Ind School Dist | 27,31 | 367 |
| Gay, Richard/Spring Branch Ind School Dist | 2 | 205 |
| Gayle, James/Angleton Ind School Dist | 91 | 55 |
| Gaylord, Angie/Dallas Ind School Dist | 74 | 102 |
| Gaynor, Arlena/Dallas Ind School Dist | 48,51,280 | 102 |
| Gazlick, Donna/Wolfe City Ind School Dist | 88 | 240 |
| Geans, Phyllis/Port Arthur Ind School Dist | 2,15 | 246 |
| Gearing, Bruce/Dripping Springs Ind Sch Dist | 1 | 215 |
| Gearing, Bruce, Dr/Leander Ind School Dist | 1 | 399 |
| Gee, Chad/Kennedale Ind School Dist | 1 | 358 |
| Geer, Richard/Forney Ind School Dist | 7,88,270 | 254 |
| Genella, Laura/Sweeny Ind School Dist | 52 | 57 |
| Genovese, Diane/Aransas Pass Ind School Dist | 76 | 333 |
| George, Abraham/Sheldon Ind School Dist | 2,19 | 205 |
| George, Bobby/Detroit Ind School Dist | 5 | 325 |
| George, Catherine, Dr/Bryan Ind School Dist | 58 | 58 |
| George, Catherine, Dr/Region 6 Ed Service Center | 58 | 386 |
| George, Chad/Kirbyville Cons Ind Sch Dist | 67 | 244 |
| George, Debra/Elgin Ind School Dist | 2,19 | 27 |
| George, Dusty/Tulia Ind School Dist | 3 | 345 |
| George, Elaine/Lorena Ind School Dist | 5 | 283 |
| George, Lee/Buffalo Ind School Dist | 5 | 266 |
| George, Ranjan/Carroll Independent Sch Dist | 5 | 349 |
| George, Sonya/Galena Park Ind School Dist | 2,3,15,19,68 | 191 |
| George, Vickie/London Ind School Dist | 4,19 | 308 |
| Georges-Penny, Serena/Schertz-Cibolo-Univ City ISD | 8,74 | 178 |
| Geraza, Norma/Crystal City Ind School Dist | 288 | 410 |
| Gerber, K'Lynn/Nazareth Ind School Dist | 2 | 75 |
| Gerber, Marty/Nazareth Ind School Dist | 67 | 75 |
| Gerber, Sherry/Hico Ind School Dist | 73 | 181 |
| Gerhart, Linda/Barbers Hill Ind School Dist | 11,57,271,298 | 75 |
| Gerlach, Christine/Ysleta Ind School Dist | 2 | 141 |
| Gerlich, Bryan/Grapevine-Colleyville Ind SD | 6 | 355 |
| Gertson, Connie/Rice Cons Ind School Dist | 16 | 90 |
| Gertson, Ralph/Rice Cons Ind School Dist | 73,295 | 90 |
| Geske, Bob/El Paso Ind School Dist | 67 | 137 |
| Geske, Bob/El Paso ISD-Elementary | 67 | 137 |
| Geske, Lindsey/Sonora Ind School Dist | 16 | 345 |
| Getwood, Melvin, Dr/Port Arthur Ind School Dist | 10,11,15,36,288,298 | 246 |
| Geye, Susan/Everman Ind School Dist | 16,73,286,295 | 351 |
| Gholson, James/Karnack Ind School Dist | 2 | 214 |
| Gholson, Theresa/Hamlin Collegiate Ind Sch Dist | 3,5 | 252 |
| Giacona, Wanna, Dr/Galena Park Ind School Dist | 15 | 191 |
| Gibbin, Matthew, Dr/Richardson Ind School Dist | 79,83 | 116 |
| Gibbons, Tim/Tulia Ind School Dist | 5 | 345 |
| Gibbs, Christopher/Forney Ind School Dist | 3 | 254 |
| Gibbs, Terry/Winona Ind School Dist | 3 | 341 |
| Gibbs, Tony/Chapel Hill Ind School Dist | 295 | 339 |
| Gibson, Amanda/College Station Ind Sch Dist | 42 | 59 |
| Gibson, Brian/New Braunfels Ind School Dist | 5,91 | 92 |
| Gibson, Brian/Wink Loving Ind School Dist | 6 | 405 |
| Gibson, Cody/Crawford Ind School Dist | 3 | 282 |
| Gibson, Gwen/Ft Elliott Cons Ind Sch Dist | 2 | 393 |
| Gibson, Heath/Hermleigh Ind School Dist | 73 | 336 |
| Gibson, Jerry, Dr/Marshall Ind School Dist | 1 | 214 |
| Gibson, Josh/Pleasant Grove Ind School Dist | 6 | 52 |
| Gibson, Justin/Jayton-Girard Ind School Dist | 58 | 258 |
| Gibson, Kittie/Wink Loving Ind School Dist | 8 | 405 |
| Gibson, Lesa/Hawkins Ind School Dist | 4 | 407 |
| **Gibson, Robert**/Idalou Ind School Dist | 1 | 272 |
| Gibson, Robert/Schleicher Co Ind Sch Dist | 1,11 | 335 |
| Gibson, Robin/Paradise Ind School Dist | 8,11,15,74,271,296 | 407 |
| Gibson, Ron/Loraine Ind School Dist | 67 | 292 |
| Gibson, Sharon/Fairfield Ind School Dist | 2 | 160 |
| Gibson, Sharon/Florence Ind School Dist | 11,58,296 | 398 |
| Giddens, Leigh/Dallas Co Schools | 5 | 99 |
| Giddens, Martha/Avinger Ind School Dist | 88 | 73 |
| Gidst-Barrow, Michelle/Venus Ind School Dist | 58 | 252 |
| Giesenschlag, Missi/Cameron Ind School Dist | 2 | 290 |
| **Gieski, Larry/**Nursery ISD School Dist | 1,11,73,288 | 384 |
| Gifford, Candy/Palacios Ind School Dist | 4 | 278 |

| | | | | | | | | | | |
|---|---|---|---|---|---|---|---|---|---|---|
| 1 | Superintendent | 16 | Instructional Media Svcs | 30 | Adult Education | 44 | Science Sec | 58 | Special Education K-12 | 72 | Summer School |
| 2 | Bus/Finance/Purchasing | 17 | Chief Operations Officer | 31 | Career/Sch-to-Work K-12 | 45 | Math K-12 | 59 | Special Education Elem | 73 | Instructional Tech |
| 3 | Buildings And Grounds | 18 | Chief Academic Officer | 32 | Career/Sch-to-Work Elem | 46 | Math Elem | 60 | Special Education Sec | 74 | Inservice Training |
| 4 | Food Service | 19 | Chief Financial Officer | 33 | Career/Sch-to-Work Sec | 47 | Math Sec | 61 | Foreign/World Lang K-12 | 75 | Marketing/Distributive |
| 5 | Transportation | 20 | Art K-12 | 34 | Early Childhood Ed | 48 | English/Lang Arts K-12 | 62 | Foreign/World Lang Elem | 76 | Info Systems |
| 6 | Athletic | 21 | Art Elem | 35 | Health/Phys Education | 49 | English/Lang Arts Elem | 63 | Foreign/World Lang Sec | 77 | Psychological Assess |
| 7 | Health Services | 22 | Art Sec | 36 | Guidance Services K-12 | 50 | English/Lang Arts Sec | 64 | Religious Education K-12 | 78 | Affirmative Action |
| 8 | Curric/Instruct K-12 | 23 | Music K-12 | 37 | Guidance Services Elem | 51 | Reading K-12 | 65 | Religious Education Elem | 79 | Student Personnel |
| 9 | Curric/Instruct Elem | 24 | Music Elem | 38 | Guidance Services Sec | 52 | Reading Elem | 66 | Religious Education Sec | 80 | Driver Ed/Safety |
| 10 | Curric/Instruct Sec | 25 | Music Sec | 39 | Social Studies K-12 | 53 | Reading Sec | 67 | School Board President | 81 | Gifted/Talented |
| 11 | Federal Program | 26 | Business Education | 40 | Social Studies Elem | 54 | Remedial Reading K-12 | 68 | Teacher Personnel | 82 | Video Services |
| 12 | Title I | 27 | Career & Tech Ed | 41 | Social Studies Sec | 55 | Remedial Reading Elem | 69 | Academic Assessment | 83 | Substance Abuse Prev |
| 13 | Title V | 28 | Technology Education | 42 | Science K-12 | 56 | Remedial Reading Sec | 70 | Research/Development | 84 | Erate |
| 15 | Asst Superintendent | 29 | Family/Consumer Science | 43 | Science Elem | 57 | Bilingual/ELL | 71 | Public Information | 85 | AIDS Education |

| | | | |
|---|---|---|---|
| 88 | Alternative/At Risk | 277 | Remedial Math K-12 |
| 89 | Multi-Cultural Curriculum | 280 | Literacy Coach |
| 90 | Social Work | 285 | STEM |
| 91 | Safety/Security | 286 | Digital Learning |
| 92 | Magnet School | 288 | Common Core Standards |
| 93 | Parental Involvement | 294 | Accountability |
| 95 | Tech Prep Program | 295 | Network System |
| 97 | Chief Information Officer | 296 | Title II Programs |
| 98 | Chief Technology Officer | 297 | Webmaster |
| 270 | Character Education | 298 | Grant Writer/Ptnrships |
| 271 | Migrant Education | 750 | Chief Innovation Officer |
| 273 | Teacher Mentor | 751 | Chief of Staff |
| 274 | Before/After Sch | 752 | Social Emotional Learning |
| 275 | Response To Intervention | | |

| NAME/District | JOB FUNCTIONS | PAGE | NAME/District | JOB FUNCTIONS | PAGE |
|---|---|---|---|---|---|
| Gomez, Yolanda/Pharr-San Juan-Alamo Ind SD | 271 | 226 | Gonzalez, Roberto/Victoria Ind School Dist | 83 | 384 |
| Gonazales, Alicia/Sundown Ind School Dist | 4 | 232 | Gonzalez, Ronnie/Navasota Ind School Dist | 15,17 | 177 |
| Gongora, Elizabeth/Sharyland Ind School Dist | 57 | 227 | Gonzalez, Sharlene/Crandall Ind School Dist | 57 | 254 |
| Gonzales, Adam/Poteet Ind School Dist | 295 | 24 | Gonzalez, Teresa/Sharyland Ind School Dist | 11,271 | 227 |
| Gonzales, Angela/Rio Vista Ind School Dist | 58 | 251 | Gonzalez, Victoria/Ft Hancock Ind School Dist | 2 | 237 |
| Gonzales, Carla, Dr/El Paso ISD-High Schools | 15 | 138 | Gonzalez, Virginio/Edcouch Elsa Ind School Dist | 68 | 220 |
| Gonzales, Chayo/Alpine Ind School Dist | 3,5 | 60 | Gonzalez, Yliana/Ramirez Common School Dist | 1 | 132 |
| Gonzales, Corrin/Bridge City Ind School Dist | 58 | 311 | Gonzalez, Zabi/McKinney Ind School Dist | 57 | 84 |
| Gonzales, Dann/Miami Ind School Dist | 16 | 327 | Gooch, Jason/Iola Ind School Dist | 67 | 177 |
| Gonzales, Esmerelda/Crystal City Ind School Dist | 4 | 410 | Goodall, Steven/Luling Ind School Dist | 73,76 | 65 |
| Gonzales, Jeff/Teague Ind School Dist | 67 | 161 | Goode, Luke/Elkhart Ind School Dist | 6 | 18 |
| Gonzales, Jena/Del Valle Ind School Dist | 298 | 372 | Gooden, Charles/Pearland Ind School Dist | 67 | 56 |
| Gonzales, Jennifer/Malakoff Ind School Dist | 4 | 219 | Gooden, Todd/La Vega Ind School Dist | 15,68,74,78,273 | 282 |
| Gonzales, Julie/Amherst Ind School Dist | 4 | 263 | Goodgion, Phillip/New Deal Ind School Dist | 73 | 274 |
| Gonzales, Karen, Dr/White Settlement Ind Sch Dist | 34 | 360 | Goodlett, Bridget/College Station Ind Sch Dist | 4 | 59 |
| Gonzales, Leandro/Grady Ind School Dist | 1,83 | 277 | Goodman, Crystal/Bryan Ind School Dist | 68 | 58 |
| Gonzales, Linda/Abernathy Ind School Dist | 271 | 179 | Goodman, Greg/Clear Creek Ind School Dist | 20,23 | 162 |
| Gonzales, Lisa, Dr/Kemp Ind School Dist | 1 | 255 | Goodman, Patrick/Trinity Ind School Dist | 6 | 377 |
| Gonzales, Luis/San Benito Cons Ind Sch Dist | 93 | 70 | Goodman, Riley/Sundown Ind School Dist | 3,5 | 232 |
| Gonzales, Maria/Brownsville Ind School Dist | 34 | 66 | Goodnow, Lisa, Dr/Austin Ind School Dist | 8,288 | 369 |
| Gonzales, Maria/Edcouch Elsa Ind School Dist | 81 | 220 | Goodson, Christopher, Dr/Richardson Ind School Dist | 15,68 | 116 |
| Gonzales, Mario/Rocksprings Ind School Dist | 73 | 135 | Goodson, Pam/Spring Branch Ind School Dist | 67 | 206 |
| Gonzales, Mike, Dr/Port Neches-Groves Ind SD | 1 | 246 | Goodwin, Becky/Edgewood Ind School Dist | 11 | 34 |
| Gonzales, Patricia/Hondo Ind School Dist | 2 | 287 | Goodwin, Becky/Edgewood Ind School Dist | 8,11,69,83,88,288 | 382 |
| Gonzales, Robert/Seguin Ind School Dist | 3 | 178 | Goodwin, Dwight/Arlington Ind School Dist | 95 | 346 |
| Gonzales, Rogelia/Zapata Co Ind School Dist | 68 | 410 | Goodwin, Gerald/Aransas Co Ind School Dist | 2 | 22 |
| Gonzales, Tammy/Knox City-O'Brien Cons Ind SD | 2,4,11,19 | 261 | Goodwin, Glen/Big Sandy Ind School Dist | 67 | 319 |
| Gonzalez, Adam/Poteet Ind School Dist | 73,295 | 24 | Goodwin, Janet/Electra Ind School Dist | 11,57,271 | 394 |
| Gonzalez, Angela/Godley Ind School Dist | 58 | 250 | Goodwin, Kathy/Tatum Ind School Dist | 4 | 331 |
| Gonzalez, Angela, Dr/Santa Rosa Ind School Dist | 1 | 71 | Goodwin, Renee/Stephenville Ind School Dist | 13,69,294 | 148 |
| Gonzalez, Anna/Galena Park Ind School Dist | 298 | 191 | Goodwin, Sasha/Glasscock Co Ind School Dist | 35,85 | 168 |
| Gonzalez, Armand/Austwell Tivoli Ind SD | 73,285 | 326 | Goodwin, Traci/Pasadena Ind School Dist | 74 | 203 |
| Gonzalez, Ashley/Austin Ind School Dist | 91 | 369 | Goolsby, Sara/Willis Ind School Dist | 57,81,275 | 297 |
| Gonzalez, Benita/Archdiocese Galveston-Houston | 58 | 209 | Gopffarth, Cherie/Paradise Ind School Dist | 38,83,88 | 407 |
| Gonzalez, Beto/Webb Cons Ind School Dist | 1 | 391 | Goranson, Jackie/Ezzell Ind School Dist | 2 | 264 |
| Gonzalez, Carlos/Zapata Co Ind School Dist | 1 | 410 | Gorden, Tim/Mildred Ind School Dist | 3,5 | 303 |
| Gonzalez, Cornelio, Dr/Region 1 Ed Service Center | 1 | 229 | Gordon, Donald/Hillsboro Ind School Dist | 16,73,76,97,295 | 230 |
| Gonzalez, Dario/Brackett Ind School Dist | 57 | 260 | Gordon, Dorothea, Dr/Grand Prairie Ind School Dist | 58 | 111 |
| Gonzalez, David/Manor Ind School Dist | 295 | 373 | Gordon, Gary/Martin's Mill Ind Sch Dist | 3,5 | 383 |
| Gonzalez, David/United Ind School Dist | 8,15 | 390 | Gordon, Gwen/Azle Ind School Dist | 58 | 348 |
| Gonzalez, Dera/Rotan Ind School Dist | 57 | 152 | Gordon, Jim/Vidor Ind School Dist | 73 | 312 |
| Gonzalez, Eric/Robstown Ind School Dist | 88,275 | 308 | Gordon, Laurie/Little Cypress Mauriceville SD | 11 | 311 |
| Gonzalez, Gerardo/Mission Cons Ind School Dist | 69,77 | 225 | Gordon, Lisa/Lago Vista Ind School Dist | 5 | 373 |
| Gonzalez, Gilbert/Lyford Cons Ind School Dist | 73 | 397 | Gordy, Cheryl/Klein Ind School Dist | 11 | 201 |
| Gonzalez, Gilberto/Eagle Pass Ind School Dist | 1 | 279 | Gore, Jerry/Buna Ind School Dist | 58 | 243 |
| Gonzalez, Gina/Rio Grande City Ind Sch Dist | 11,296 | 342 | Gore, Leah/Sulphur Bluff Ind School Dist | 31,36,294 | 235 |
| Gonzalez, Isabelle/San Benito Cons Ind Sch Dist | 71 | 70 | Gorena, Jackie, Dr/Irving Ind School Dist | 8,57,58,69,70,74 | 113 |
| Gonzalez, Ismael/Sharyland Ind School Dist | 2,15 | 227 | Gorene, Belinda/Sharyland Ind School Dist | 15,68,71,79 | 227 |
| Gonzalez, Israel/Lyford Cons Ind School Dist | 6 | 397 | Gosch, Lacey/Navarro Ind School Dist | 8,11,57,271,273,288,294 | 178 |
| Gonzalez, Israel/Southwest Ind School Dist | 57 | 46 | Gosett, Eric/New Deal Ind School Dist | 2,19 | 274 |
| Gonzalez, J, Dr/McAllen Ind School Dist | 1 | 224 | **Goss, Micheal/**Boles Ind School Dist | 1,83 | 238 |
| Gonzalez, James/Cleveland Ind School Dist | 73,295 | 267 | Goss, Mikayle/Wolfe City Ind School Dist | 11,271,296 | 240 |
| Gonzalez, Jennifer/Floydada Ind School Dist | 37,83,88,752 | 153 | Gossett, Chris/Region 17 Ed Service Center | 16,73 | 275 |
| Gonzalez, Jodi/Spur Ind School Dist | 2,11 | 131 | Gossett, Claylene/Rochelle Ind School Dist | 2 | 281 |
| Gonzalez, Kimberly/Edgewood Ind School Dist | 73 | 34 | Gossett, Jason/Klein Ind School Dist | 2 | 201 |
| Gonzalez, Kristina, Dr/Premont Ind School Dist | 12,15 | 249 | Gossett, Reginald/Troup Ind School Dist | 16,73 | 340 |
| Gonzalez, Laura/Fort Davis Ind School Dist | 73 | 244 | Gott, Abe/Blackwell Cons Ind Sch Dist | 1 | 304 |
| Gonzalez, Lee/Robstown Ind School Dist | 3 | 308 | Gouduea, Robert/East Bernard Ind Sch Dist | 67 | 392 |
| Gonzalez, Luis/Southwest Ind School Dist | 36 | 46 | Gough, Jennifer/Leveretts Chapel Ind Sch Dist | 4,73 | 330 |
| Gonzalez, Marcial/Culberson Co Allamoore Ind SD | 3 | 99 | Gould, Paul/Frankston Ind School Dist | 6 | 18 |
| Gonzalez, Marie/Round Rock Ind School Dist | 58 | 401 | Gouldy, Loretta/Wildorado Ind Sch Dist | 7 | 311 |
| Gonzalez, Mark/Driscoll Ind School Dist | 3 | 307 | Goundrey, Colleen/Barbers Hill Ind School Dist | 7 | 75 |
| Gonzalez, Martha/Webb Cons Ind School Dist | 2,4 | 391 | Govan, Charissa/Dallas Ind School Dist | 275 | 102 |
| Gonzalez, Melanie/Weatherford Ind School Dist | 46 | 316 | Gowens, Sandra/New Deal Ind School Dist | 67 | 274 |
| Gonzalez, Melissa/Refugio Ind School Dist | 1 | 326 | Gowin, Flossie/Milford Ind School Dist | 57 | 146 |
| Gonzalez, Michelle/Fabens Ind School Dist | 15,288 | 139 | Goytia, Corina/Socorro Ind School Dist | 271 | 140 |
| Gonzalez, Michelle/San Felipe-Del Rio Cons Ind SD | 280 | 381 | Gracia, Cassandra/Schertz-Cibolo-Univ City ISD | 27,31,36,69 | 178 |
| Gonzalez, Monica/Jarrell Ind School Dist | 57 | 399 | Gracia, Leticia/Calallen Ind School Dist | 4 | 305 |
| Gonzalez, Monica/Region 19 Ed Service Center | 16,73 | 144 | Graeber, Pennie/Waco Ind School Dist | 275 | 284 |
| Gonzalez, Nephalit/Santa Rosa Ind School Dist | 76 | 71 | Graf, Edward/Eagle Pass Ind School Dist | 6,35 | 279 |
| Gonzalez, Patricia/Zapata Co Ind School Dist | 2 | 410 | Graf, Nathan/San Antonio Ind School Dist | 5 | 42 |
| Gonzalez, Paula/McAllen Ind School Dist | 6 | 224 | Graf, Thomas/Redwater Ind School Dist | 6 | 53 |
| Gonzalez, Pedro/Fabens Ind School Dist | 83 | 139 | Graham, Becky/Texarkana Ind School Dist | 58 | 53 |
| Gonzalez, Raul/La Joya Ind School Dist | 5 | 222 | Graham, Bradley/Colorado Ind School Dist | 73,295 | 292 |
| Gonzalez, Richard/Robstown Ind School Dist | 5,27,73,76,84,286 | 308 | Graham, Brant, Dr/Burkeville Ind School Dist | 1,11 | 303 |
| Gonzalez, Rick/Riviera Ind School Dist | 73,84 | 261 | Graham, Donna/Burkeville Ind School Dist | 58 | 303 |

| NAME/District | JOB FUNCTIONS | PAGE |
|---|---|---|
| Graham, Gary/Grapeland Ind School Dist | 27,298 | 235 |
| Graham, Glen/Hutto Ind School Dist | 2,15 | 399 |
| Graham, Jack/Diocese of Brownsville Ed Off | 2 | 229 |
| Graham, John/Leander Ind School Dist | 15 | 399 |
| Graham, Kelsee/Colorado Ind School Dist | 7,85 | 292 |
| Graham, Kim/Timpson Ind School Dist | 91 | 338 |
| Graham, Korey/Karnes City Ind School Dist | 5 | 253 |
| Graham, Leslie/Archer City Ind School Dist | 69,83,88 | 22 |
| Graham, Patti/West Hardin Co Cons Sch Dist | 3,5 | 183 |
| Graham, Ronald/Burkeville Ind School Dist | 67 | 303 |
| Graham, Tellunce/Cedar Hill Ind School Dist | 15,79 | 101 |
| Graham, Tonya/O'Donnell Ind School Dist | 8,42,57,58,69,81 | 276 |
| Grahmann, Ashley/Flatonia Ind School Dist | 8 | 151 |
| Grahmann, Stepahnie/Hallettsville Ind Sch Dist | 34 | 265 |
| **Grandjean, Todd**/Devine Ind School Dist | 1 | 286 |
| Grange, Shane/White Deer Ind School Dist | 67 | 73 |
| Granger, Elijah/Lancaster Ind School Dist | 1 | 114 |
| Grant, Jessica/Floresville Ind School Dist | 90 | 403 |
| Grant, Tiffany/San Antonio Ind School Dist | 15,751 | 42 |
| Grantham, Karen/Bushland Ind School Dist | 2 | 321 |
| Granzin, Kelly/Wall Ind School Dist | 9 | 368 |
| Grape, Magda/Grand Prairie Ind School Dist | 57 | 111 |
| Gratehouse, Todd/Del Valle Ind School Dist | 73,76,84,98,295 | 372 |
| Graves, Gary/Post Ind School Dist | 3 | 167 |
| Graves, Jack/Santa Anna Ind School Dist | 6 | 80 |
| Graves, Leah/Medina Valley Ind School Dist | 45 | 287 |
| Graves, Mehgan/Vega Ind School Dist | 58 | 310 |
| Graves, Rena/Mart Ind School Dist | 2 | 283 |
| Graves, Wendy/Montgomery Ind School Dist | 9,11,15,16,34,57,270,274 | 296 |
| Gravey, Thomas/Mullin Ind School Dist | 273 | 291 |
| Grawunder, Suzanne/Bellville Ind School Dist | 7 | 25 |
| Gray, Billy/Goose Creek Cons Ind Sch Dist | 3 | 192 |
| **Gray, Brian/**White Oak Ind School Dist | 1 | 176 |
| Gray, Carrie/Detroit Ind School Dist | 58 | 325 |
| Gray, Connie/Zapata Co Ind School Dist | 8,42,93,288 | 410 |
| Gray, Craig/Region 10 Ed Service Center | 286 | 121 |
| Gray, David/Georgetown Ind School Dist | 5 | 398 |
| Gray, David/Waco Ind School Dist | 5 | 284 |
| Gray, Joyce/Strawn Ind School Dist | 57 | 314 |
| Gray, Julie/Eustace Ind School Dist | 34 | 219 |
| Gray, Rita/Brownsboro Ind School Dist | 11,57,69,88,271,274,275,752 | 218 |
| Gray, Robert/Rice Ind School Dist | 91 | 303 |
| Gray, Roxann/Comanche Ind School Dist | 76 | 93 |
| Gray, Tony/Farmersville Ind School Dist | 67 | 82 |
| Greaves, Lori/Lubbock Ind School Dist | 48,51 | 272 |
| Greeling, Chrissy/Keller Ind School Dist | 46 | 357 |
| Green, Amanda/Penelope ISD School Dist | 57 | 231 |
| Green, Angela/Italy Ind School Dist | 37 | 145 |
| Green, Brent/Littlefield Ind School Dist | 6 | 263 |
| Green, Burt/Brock Ind School Dist | 3 | 315 |
| Green, Clay/Ganado Ind School Dist | 67 | 242 |
| Green, Don/Somerset Ind School Dist | 67 | 45 |
| Green, Georgina/Savoy Ind School Dist | 4 | 150 |
| Green, Jennifer/Clifton Ind School Dist | 4 | 49 |
| Green, Jennifer/La Porte Ind School Dist | 11,69,288,294,296,298 | 203 |
| Green, John/Huntsville Ind School Dist | 23 | 386 |
| Green, Leesa/Region 7 Ed Service Center | 69,294 | 176 |
| Green, Maria/Round Rock Ind School Dist | 57 | 401 |
| Green, Matthew/Llano Ind School Dist | 6 | 271 |
| Green, Paula/Conroe Ind School Dist | 68 | 294 |
| Green, Staci/Waskom Ind School Dist | 58 | 214 |
| Green, Stephanie/Adrian Ind School Dist | 2 | 310 |
| Green, Stryker/Texline Ind School Dist | 5 | 99 |
| Green, Tara/Normangee Ind School Dist | 4 | 267 |
| Green, Tiffany/Region 11 Ed Service Center | 68 | 362 |
| Greene, Jeff/Deer Park Ind School Dist | 5 | 191 |
| Greene, Jonas, Dr/Lewisville Ind School Dist | 285 | 126 |
| Greene, Karin/Comstock Ind School Dist | 16 | 381 |
| Greene, Patty/New Boston Ind School Dist | 8,11,57,69,273,298 | 52 |
| Greeney, Brian, Dr/Willis Ind School Dist | 8,15 | 297 |
| Greening, Candy/Panhandle Ind School Dist | 4 | 72 |
| Greenough, Jennifer/Wylie Ind School Dist | 16 | 364 |
| Greenwood, Julie/Santa Gertrudis Ind Sch Dist | 83,85 | 261 |
| Greer, Alyce/Gainesville Ind School Dist | 2,19 | 95 |
| Greer, Matt/Eanes Ind School Dist | 91 | 372 |
| Greer, Reagan/Rice Ind School Dist | 69,270 | 303 |
| Greer, Roxanne/Kermit Ind School Dist | 58 | 405 |
| Greer, Tatiana/Pampa Ind School Dist | 57,271 | 170 |
| Greer, Todd/Gary Ind School Dist | 1 | 314 |
| Greer, Zach/Millsap Ind School Dist | 73 | 315 |
| Gregg, Byron/Kaufman Ind School Dist | 67 | 255 |
| Gregg, Mary Ann/Kemp Ind School Dist | 57 | 255 |
| Greggerson, Tami/Splendora Ind School Dist | 8,69,72,81,88,271,285 | 297 |
| Gregorski, Ken, Dr/Katy Ind School Dist | 1 | 155 |
| Gregory, Jewel/New Waverly Ind School Dist | 4 | 386 |
| Gregson, Lane/Oakwood Ind School Dist | 73 | 267 |
| Gregson, Layne/Centerville Ind School Dist | 76,295 | 267 |
| Greig, Melody/Richardson Ind School Dist | 2 | 116 |
| Greiner, David/Pflugerville Ind School Dist | 76 | 374 |
| Grell-Boethel, Lynn/Columbia Brazoria ISD | 11,36,57,77,79,83,88,296 | 56 |
| Grenier, Brian/Randolph Field Ind School Dist | 73,98,295 | 42 |
| Gresham, Tina/Ganado Ind School Dist | 280 | 242 |
| Grey, Christina/Woodsboro Ind School Dist | 73,79,295 | 326 |
| Grey, Karen/Crosby Ind School Dist | 15,68 | 188 |
| Gribble, Sherri/Chisum Ind School Dist | 294 | 262 |
| Grieb, Dana/Royse City Ind School Dist | 39,50 | 328 |
| Griedl, Jake/Marshall Ind School Dist | 6 | 214 |
| Griffey, Nancy/Cayuga Ind School Dist | 83,85 | 18 |
| Griffien, Michael/Northwest Ind School Dist | 15 | 128 |
| Griffin, Chris/Region 12 Ed Service Center | 58 | 286 |
| Griffin, Darvis/Waco Ind School Dist | 73,98 | 284 |
| Griffin, Dawn/Robinson Ind School Dist | 27,31 | 284 |
| Griffin, Debra/Maypearl Ind School Dist | 36,83,85,270 | 145 |
| Griffin, Gary/Brackett Ind School Dist | 6 | 260 |
| Griffin, Jesse/Mullin Ind School Dist | 2 | 291 |
| Griffin, Joe/Keller Ind School Dist | 73,76,98,295 | 357 |
| Griffin, Joe/Waskom Ind School Dist | 4 | 214 |
| Griffin, Julie/Stephenville Ind School Dist | 76 | 148 |
| Griffin, Kriss/Schleicher Co Ind Sch Dist | 67 | 335 |
| Griffin, Larry/Lingleville Ind School Dist | 67 | 148 |
| Griffin, Marc/Hemphill Ind School Dist | 88 | 331 |
| Griffin, Melanie/Northwest Ind School Dist | 47 | 129 |
| Griffin, Natalie/Mineral Wells Ind School Dist | 11,57,81,271,298 | 313 |
| Griffin, Tamira/McKinney Ind School Dist | 15,68,270,273 | 84 |
| Griffis, Weston/Spring Hill Ind School Dist | 6 | 175 |
| Griffith, Barbara/Ft Worth Ind School Dist | 71 | 352 |
| Griffith, Cathy/Pottsboro Ind School Dist | 4 | 172 |
| Griffith, Connie/Spurger Ind School Dist | 2,19 | 377 |
| Griffith, Jeremy/Sundown Ind School Dist | 8,34,57 | 232 |
| Griffith, Kaci/Colorado Ind School Dist | 38 | 292 |
| Griffith, Karen/San Marcos Cons Ind Sch Dist | 15 | 217 |
| Griffith, Laura/Grand Saline Ind School Dist | 2 | 383 |
| Griffith, Lori/La Poynor Ind School Dist | 57 | 219 |
| Griffiths, Peter/Wichita Falls Ind School Dist | 15,286 | 395 |
| Griffon, Mark/Friendswood Ind Sch Dist | 72 | 164 |
| Griffth, Karen/Corpus Christi Ind Sch Dist | 2,15 | 306 |
| Grigar, Melody/Rice Cons Ind School Dist | 8,11,15,83,88,288,296,298 | 90 |
| Grijalva, Timothy/Cleburne Ind School Dist | 73 | 250 |
| Grill, Richard/Sabinal Ind School Dist | 1 | 380 |
| Grill, Tish/Boerne Ind School Dist | 2,15 | 257 |
| Grimes, Dallas/Roosevelt Ind School Dist | 1 | 274 |
| Grimes, Greg/McKinney Ind School Dist | 76 | 84 |
| Grimes, Justin/College Station Ind Sch Dist | 83,88 | 59 |
| Grimes, Margie/Goose Creek Cons Ind Sch Dist | 2,19 | 192 |

| NAME/District | JOB FUNCTIONS | PAGE | NAME/District | JOB FUNCTIONS | PAGE |
|---|---|---|---|---|---|
| Grimes, Perry/Woden Ind School Dist | 67 | 301 | Gumes, Samantha/Era Ind School Dist | 7 | 94 |
| Grimes, Tracy/Olfen Ind School Dist | 67 | 329 | Gunnels, Susan/Reagan Co Ind School Dist | 2,79 | 324 |
| Grimes, Tracy/Paint Rock Ind School Dist | 2 | 94 | Gunter, Coleen/Sivells Bend Ind School Dist | 57 | 95 |
| Grimet, Howard/Katy Ind School Dist | 35 | 156 | Gunter, Jenny/Dayton Ind School Dist | 69,294 | 268 |
| Grimm, Jennifer/Lorena Ind School Dist | 73,295 | 283 | Gunter, Steve/Idalou Ind School Dist | 8,11,274 | 272 |
| Grimm, Rusty/Lorena Ind School Dist | 5,79,83,91,294 | 283 | Gustifsan, Kendra/Jonesboro Ind School Dist | 8,12,286 | 97 |
| Grimsley, Bobby/Abernathy Ind School Dist | 3,91 | 179 | Guterrez, Daniel/Sudan Ind School Dist | 58 | 264 |
| Grimsley, Keri/Godley Ind School Dist | 9 | 250 | Guthals, Deirdre/Farwell Ind School Dist | 57 | 317 |
| Grimsley, Richard/Dallas Ind School Dist | 27,31 | 102 | Gutierrez, Christina/Bishop Cons Ind School Dist | 1 | 305 |
| Grisham, Nikki/Hawley Ind School Dist | 31,285 | 253 | Gutierrez, Crisella/Zapata Co Ind School Dist | 8 | 410 |
| Grissom, Sarah/Leander Ind School Dist | 15 | 399 | Gutierrez, David/Ennis Ind School Dist | 4 | 144 |
| Grissom, Wayne/Lufkin Ind School Dist | 5 | 21 | Gutierrez, Grant/Smithville Ind School Dist | 67 | 27 |
| Grmela, Jimmy/Kerrville Ind School Dist | 69 | 259 | Gutierrez, Jennifer/North East Ind School Dist | 9 | 37 |
| Groce, Susan/Caldwell Ind School Dist | 8 | 63 | Gutierrez, Jessica/London Ind School Dist | 12,271 | 308 |
| Groff, Suzy/Bandera Ind School Dist | 71 | 26 | Gutierrez, Jiovana/Ysleta Ind School Dist | 68 | 141 |
| Grogan, April/Avinger Ind School Dist | 73 | 73 | Gutierrez, Manuela/Fabens Ind School Dist | 16 | 139 |
| Grogan, Eric/Rice Cons Ind School Dist | 271 | 90 | Gutierrez, Matthew, Dr/Seguin Ind School Dist | 1 | 178 |
| Grogan, Jason/Wimberley Ind School Dist | 16,73,76,98,295 | 217 | Gutierrez, Oscar/Raymondville Ind Sch Dist | 3,5 | 397 |
| Grohler, Wendy/McAllen Ind School Dist | 42 | 224 | Gutierrez, Rene, Dr/Brownsville Ind School Dist | 1 | 66 |
| Grona, Juanice/Harper Ind School Dist | 67 | 168 | Gutierrez, Robert/San Marcos Cons Ind Sch Dist | 3,91 | 216 |
| Grona, Shannon/North East Ind School Dist | 67 | 37 | Gutierrez, Rogelio/United Ind School Dist | 3 | 390 |
| Grooban, Shelby/Rotan Ind School Dist | 2 | 152 | Gutierrez, Samantha/Penelope ISD School Dist | 2,11 | 231 |
| Groomes, Kenneth/San Saba Ind School Dist | 3 | 335 | Gutierrez, Steven, Dr/Tomball Ind School Dist | 17 | 208 |
| Grooms, Andrea, Dr/Katy Ind School Dist | 15,71,93 | 156 | Gutierrez, Tamara/Pampa Ind School Dist | 7 | 170 |
| Groover, Lisa/Eanes Ind School Dist | 30,274 | 372 | Gutierrez, Ted/Lasara Ind School Dist | 5 | 397 |
| Groves, Josh/Winona Ind School Dist | 12,296 | 341 | Gutierrez, Veronica, Dr/Mathis Ind School Dist | 45 | 334 |
| Groves, Kody/Mesquite Ind School Dist | 6 | 115 | Gutsch, Angela, Dr/Hempstead Ind School Dist | 1,11 | 387 |
| Growlaski, Kenney/Bremond Ind School Dist | 5,10,83,88 | 327 | Guy, Christie/Canton Ind School Dist | 57 | 382 |
| Grubb, Dana/La Vernia Ind School Dist | 8 | 404 | Guy, Jody/Shamrock Ind School Dist | 6 | 393 |
| Grubb, Kay/Paris Ind School Dist | 85 | 262 | Guzman, Carlos/Roma Ind School Dist | 1 | 343 |
| Grubbs, Travis/High Island Ind Sch Dist | 1 | 165 | Guzman, Dalia/Edinburg Cons Ind School Dist | 8,15 | 221 |
| Gruhlkey, Tonya/Walcott Ind School Dist | 271 | 123 | Guzman, Gustavo/Valley View Ind School Dist | 285 | 228 |
| Gruhn, Todd/Trenton Ind School Dist | 70,73 | 151 | Guzman, Susan/Luling Ind School Dist | 68 | 65 |
| Grumbles, Amy/Sands Consolidated ISD | 2 | 121 | Gwaltney, Dayna/Comfort Ind School Dist | 7,85 | 257 |
| Grunseich, John/Bellevue Ind School Dist | 67 | 77 | Gwinn, Bryan/Ft Bend Ind School Dist | 2,19 | 153 |
| Gruwell, Lori/New Braunfels Ind School Dist | 74 | 92 | | | |
| Gryseeles, Krissy/Jarrell Ind School Dist | 76 | 399 | **H** | | |
| Guadiana, Melissa/San Perlita Ind School Dist | 67 | 397 | Habekutt, Nancy/Higgins Ind School Dist | 270 | 270 |
| Guajardo, Elizabeth/Elgin Ind School Dist | 4 | 27 | Hachmeister, Paige/Sanger Ind School Dist | 4 | 130 |
| Guajardo, Gina/Sinton Ind School Dist | 11,83,296 | 334 | Hackett, Chris/Pittsburg Ind School Dist | 4 | 72 |
| Guajardo, Jesse/Crystal City Ind School Dist | 73 | 410 | Hackley, Brent/Jacksboro Ind Sch Dist | 67 | 242 |
| Guajardo, Leslie, Dr/Denton Ind School Dist | 274 | 125 | Hadaway, Lee/Wylie Ind School Dist | 73,74 | 88 |
| Guanzon, Angelica/Hidalgo Ind School Dist | 8 | 222 | Haden, Amy/Evadale Ind School Dist | 69 | 243 |
| Guenther, Codi/Weimar Ind School Dist | 11 | 91 | Haden, Tammi/Brookeland Ind School Dist | 2 | 243 |
| Guereca, Luis/Iredell Ind School Dist | 6 | 50 | Haehn, Anne/Lake Dallas Ind School Dist | 2,11 | 126 |
| Guerra, Albert/Hidalgo Ind School Dist | 3,68 | 222 | Hafezizadeh, Kris/Austin Ind School Dist | 5 | 369 |
| Guerra, Alejandro/Elgin Ind School Dist | 5 | 27 | Haffey, Keith, Dr/Spring Branch Ind School Dist | 69,294 | 206 |
| Guerra, Andrew/Gregory-Portland Ind Sch Dist | 16,73,84,295 | 333 | Hafford, Joshua/Burleson Ind School Dist | 39 | 249 |
| Guerra, Darrell/La Feria Ind School Dist | 3,5 | 69 | Hafley, Scot/Wichita Falls Ind School Dist | 6 | 395 |
| Guerra, Evangelina/Hitchcock Ind School Dist | 58 | 165 | Hafner, Brandy/Round Rock Ind School Dist | 7 | 401 |
| Guerra, Maria Luisa/Corpus Christi Ind Sch Dist | 8,15 | 306 | Hagan, Mike/Brady Ind School Dist | 5 | 280 |
| Guerra, Miriam, Dr/La Feria Ind School Dist | 11,27,285 | 69 | Hagar, Mike/Alamo Heights Ind School Dist | 2,15 | 33 |
| Guerra, Noemi/Bastrop Ind School Dist | 271 | 26 | Hagar, Tanya/Pasadena Ind School Dist | 27 | 203 |
| Guerra, Servando/Brooks Co Ind School Dist | 67 | 61 | Hagdorn, Lindie/West Oso Ind School Dist | 73,297 | 309 |
| Guerreo, Christina/Ft Sam Houston Ind School Dist | 6 | 35 | Hagedorn, Scott/Sabine Pass Ind School Dist | 73 | 247 |
| Guerrero, Angie/Corpus Christi Ind Sch Dist | 7 | 306 | Hageman, Becky/Kenedy Co Wide Common Sch Dist | 73,97,98 | 258 |
| Guerrero, Audelia/Irving Ind School Dist | 295 | 113 | Hagemen, Becky/Kenedy Co Schools | 73 | 257 |
| Guerrero, Cynthia/Pasadena Ind School Dist | 68,273 | 203 | Hager, Cindy/Newcastle Ind School Dist | 4 | 409 |
| Guerrero, Megan/Harlandale Ind School Dist | 285 | 35 | Haggan, Paul/Argyle Ind School Dist | 77,83,88,275 | 124 |
| Guerrero, Nancy, Dr/Round Rock Ind School Dist | 15 | 401 | Haggard, Eric/Irving Ind School Dist | 39 | 113 |
| Guerrero, Roberto/Hidalgo Ind School Dist | 5 | 222 | Haggard, Eric/Plano Ind School Dist | 41 | 85 |
| Guerrero, Susan/Crosbyton Cons Ind Sch Dist | 4 | 98 | Haggen, Paul/Argyle Ind School Dist | 77,88,275 | 124 |
| Guerry, Larry/Crandall Ind School Dist | 2,19 | 254 | Haggerton, Kathy/Blum Ind School Dist | 4 | 230 |
| Guess, June/Ranger Ind School Dist | 16 | 133 | Hagle, Caleb/Woodson Ind School Dist | 3 | 365 |
| Guest, Mike/Weatherford Ind School Dist | 67 | 316 | Hagle, Heather/Chireno ISD School Dist | 8,11,79,275,286,294,296 | 300 |
| Guetersloh, Kathy/Denver City Ind School Dist | 77 | 409 | Hagler, Jaime/Vidor Ind School Dist | 93 | 312 |
| Guetersloh, Michelle/Sterling City Ind School Dist | 11,298 | 344 | Hagler, Terry/Wylie Ind School Dist | 8 | 364 |
| Guidry, Rachel/Beaumont Ind School Dist | 36,83 | 244 | Hail, Darol, Dr/New Waverly Ind School Dist | 1 | 386 |
| Guidry, Wayne, Dr/Spring Hill Ind School Dist | 1 | 175 | Haisler, Betsy/Aldine Ind School Dist | 57 | 184 |
| Guillen, Candace/South Texas Ind School Dist | 93 | 71 | Halbert, Christy/Walnut Springs Ind Sch Dist | 8,12,57,88,288 | 51 |
| Guillen, Noe/Los Fresnos Cons Ind Sch Dist | 11,271 | 69 | Hale, Alisha/Dodd City Ind School Dist | 7 | 150 |
| Guillory, Jennifer/Center Ind School Dist | 11,37,57,271 | 337 | Hale, Bobbie/Ira Ind School Dist | 8,11,57,69,270,273,752 | 336 |
| Guillory, Maisha/Aldine Ind School Dist | 7 | 184 | Hale, Bonnie/Bandera Ind School Dist | 36,83,88 | 26 |
| Guinn, Kimberly/Carrollton-Farmers Branch ISD | 12,69,294 | 100 | Hale, Donna/Miami Ind School Dist | 1,11 | 327 |
| Guiturrez, Sarah/Jourdanton Ind School Dist | 7 | 23 | Hale, Jennifer/Carlisle Ind School Dist | 8,31,69,270 | 330 |
| Gully, Madelaine/Greenwood Ind School Dist | 7,83,85 | 288 | Hale, Kami/Goose Creek Cons Ind Sch Dist | 48,61 | 192 |

| | | | | | |
|---|---|---|---|---|---|
| 1 Superintendent | 16 Instructional Media Svcs | 30 Adult Education | 44 Science Sec | 58 Special Education K-12 | 72 Summer School |
| 2 Bus/Finance/Purchasing | 17 Chief Operations Officer | 31 Career/Sch-to-Work K-12 | 45 Math K-12 | 59 Special Education Elem | 73 Instructional Tech |
| 3 Buildings And Grounds | 18 Chief Academic Officer | 32 Career/Sch-to-Work Elem | 46 Math Elem | 60 Special Education Sec | 74 Inservice Training |
| 4 Food Service | 19 Chief Financial Officer | 33 Career/Sch-to-Work Sec | 47 Math Sec | 61 Foreign/World Lang K-12 | 75 Marketing/Distributive |
| 5 Transportation | 20 Art K-12 | 34 Early Childhood Ed | 48 English/Lang Arts K-12 | 62 Foreign/World Lang Elem | 76 Info Systems |
| 6 Athletic | 21 Art Elem | 35 Health/Phys Education | 49 English/Lang Arts Elem | 63 Foreign/World Lang Sec | 77 Psychological Assess |
| 7 Health Services | 22 Art Sec | 36 Guidance Services K-12 | 50 English/Lang Arts Sec | 64 Religious Education K-12 | 78 Affirmative Action |
| 8 Curric/Instruct K-12 | 23 Music K-12 | 37 Guidance Services Elem | 51 Reading K-12 | 65 Religious Education Elem | 79 Student Personnel |
| 9 Curric/Instruct Elem | 24 Music Elem | 38 Guidance Services Sec | 52 Reading Elem | 66 Religious Education Sec | 80 Driver Ed/Safety |
| 10 Curric/Instruct Sec | 25 Music Sec | 39 Social Studies K-12 | 53 Reading Sec | 67 School Board President | 81 Gifted/Talented |
| 11 Federal Program | 26 Business Education | 40 Social Studies Elem | 54 Remedial Reading K-12 | 68 Teacher Personnel | 82 Video Services |
| 12 Title I | 27 Career & Tech Ed | 41 Social Studies Sec | 55 Remedial Reading Elem | 69 Academic Assessment | 83 Substance Abuse Prev |
| 13 Title V | 28 Technology Education | 42 Science K-12 | 56 Remedial Reading Sec | 70 Research/Development | 84 Erate |
| 15 Asst Superintendent | 29 Family/Consumer Science | 43 Science Elem | 57 Bilingual/ELL | 71 Public Information | 85 AIDS Education |

| | |
|---|---|
| 88 Alternative/At Risk | 277 Remedial Math K-12 |
| 89 Multi-Cultural Curriculum | 280 Literacy Coach |
| 90 Social Work | 285 STEM |
| 91 Safety/Security | 286 Digital Learning |
| 92 Magnet School | 288 Common Core Standards |
| 93 Parental Involvement | 294 Accountability |
| 95 Tech Prep Program | 295 Network System |
| 96 Chief Information Officer | 296 Title II Programs |
| 97 Chief Information Officer | 297 Webmaster |
| 98 Chief Technology Officer | 298 Grant Writer/Ptnrships |
| 270 Character Education | 750 Chief Innovation Officer |
| 271 Migrant Education | 751 Chief of Staff |
| 273 Teacher Mentor | 752 Social Emotional Learning |
| 274 Before/After Sch | |
| 275 Response To Intervention | |

| NAME/District | JOB FUNCTIONS | PAGE | NAME/District | JOB FUNCTIONS | PAGE |
|---|---|---|---|---|---|
| Hanson, Zana, Dr/Ft Stockton Ind School Dist | 58 | 318 | Harrington, Kevin/McGregor Ind School Dist | 58,275 | 283 |
| Hanssard, Patti/Santa Fe Ind School Dist | 68,71,79 | 165 | Harrington, Kevin/Moody Ind School Dist | 58 | 284 |
| Harbin, Stepahnie/Lake Worth Ind School Dist | 58,77 | 358 | Harrington, Kevin/Oglesby Ind School Dist | 58 | 97 |
| Harbour, Jonathan/Walnut Springs Ind Sch Dist | 58 | 51 | Harrington, Kurt/Palestine Ind School Dist | 67 | 19 |
| Hardaway, Debbie/Prairie Lea Ind School Dist | 4 | 65 | Harrington, Paul/Clint Ind School Dist | 4 | 136 |
| Hardaway, Shelley/Prairie Lea Ind School Dist | 27 | 65 | Harris, Alan/Utopia Ind School Dist | 6 | 381 |
| Hardcastle, Heather/Wheeler Ind School Dist | 12,296 | 394 | Harris, Barbara/Kelton Ind School Dist | 7 | 393 |
| Hardee, Kyle/Centerville Ind School Dist | 6 | 267 | Harris, Carol/Neches Ind School Dist | 57 | 18 |
| Harden, Kyle/Crandall Ind School Dist | 6 | 254 | Harris, Cathy/Prairie Valley Ind School Dist | 79 | 293 |
| Harden, Rusty/Sulphur Springs Ind Sch Dist | 15,68 | 235 | Harris, Cohnie/Royse City Ind School Dist | 4 | 328 |
| Hardin, Ashley/Axtell Ind School Dist | 69 | 281 | Harris, Dagmar/Killeen Ind School Dist | 10 | 30 |
| Hardin, Barry/Holliday Ind School Dist | 67 | 22 | Harris, David, Dr/Galena Park Ind School Dist | 15 | 191 |
| Hardin, Corey/Gainesville Ind School Dist | 67 | 95 | Harris, Dawn/Gilmer Ind School Dist | 11,15,273 | 378 |
| Hardin, Dustin/Humble Ind School Dist | 73,76 | 200 | Harris, Debbie/Jim Ned Cons Ind School Dist | 12 | 363 |
| Hardin, Gary/Crosbyton Cons Ind Sch Dist | 2 | 98 | Harris, Elizabeth/Devers Ind School Dist | 1,11,57,288 | 268 |
| Hardin, Wayne/Clarendon Cons Ind Sch Dist | 67 | 131 | Harris, Elizabeth/Devers Ind School Dist | 12,57,83 | 268 |
| Harding, Diane/Palestine Ind School Dist | 16 | 18 | Harris, Gay/Beckville Ind School Dist | 3,5 | 314 |
| Harding, Sherri/Mineola Ind School Dist | 5 | 408 | Harris, Grif/Bynum Ind School Dist | 67 | 230 |
| Hardy, Joyce, Dr/Paradise Ind School Dist | 15,69 | 407 | Harris, Hoyt/Aledo Ind School Dist | 67 | 315 |
| Hardy, Kimberley/Luling Ind School Dist | 16,82 | 65 | Harris, Jeff/College Station Ind Sch Dist | 67 | 59 |
| Hardy, Michelle/Silsbee Ind School Dist | 7 | 183 | Harris, John/Ector Ind School Dist | 67 | 150 |
| Hardy, Steve/Spring Hill Ind School Dist | 73 | 175 | Harris, John/Plains Ind School Dist | 73,295 | 409 |
| Hardy, Velvet/Fort Davis Ind School Dist | 2 | 244 | Harris, Jonathan/Del Valle Ind School Dist | 58,79 | 372 |
| Hare, Amanda/Lorenzo Ind School Dist | 9,274 | 98 | Harris, Leslie/Chilton Ind School Dist | 8,12,69,88 | 148 |
| Hare, Kalliier/De Leon Ind School Dist | 8 | 93 | Harris, Linda/Dayton Ind School Dist | 67 | 268 |
| Hargis, Kent/Grandview-Hopkins Ind Sch Dist | 1,11,288 | 169 | Harris, Lindsay/Iola Ind School Dist | 31,270 | 177 |
| Hargis, Linda/Bruceville-Eddy Ind Sch Dist | 16,82 | 281 | Harris, Nichole/Bridge City Ind School Dist | 36 | 311 |
| Hargrave, Deidra/Devers Ind School Dist | 4 | 268 | Harris, Rickie/West Orange-Cove Cons ISD | 1 | 312 |
| Hargrove, Amber/Pine Tree Ind School Dist | 76 | 175 | Harris, Ron/Fairfield Ind School Dist | 3 | 160 |
| Hargrove, Julie/Duncanville Ind School Dist | 79 | 108 | Harris, Ronnie/Blackwell Cons Ind Sch Dist | 3,5 | 304 |
| Hargrove, Marie/Anson Ind School Dist | 2 | 252 | Harris, Sam/Galena Park Ind School Dist | 20,23 | 191 |
| Hargrove, Pauline, Dr/Little Cypress Mauriceville SD | 1 | 311 | Harris, Sarah/Monahans-Wickett-Pyote ISD | 2 | 388 |
| Harkrider, Tim/Willis Ind School Dist | 1 | 297 | Harris, Sheree/Boles Ind School Dist | 36,83 | 238 |
| Harlan, Billy/Academy Ind School Dist | 1 | 29 | Harris, Terrece/Leander Ind School Dist | 73 | 400 |
| Harlan, James/Wellman Union Ind School Dist | 67 | 365 | Harris, Terrell/Kerens Ind School Dist | 6 | 303 |
| Harlan, Melanie/Forney Ind School Dist | 81 | 255 | Harris, Terry/Richardson Ind School Dist | 68 | 116 |
| Harland, Danielle/Texhoma Ind School Dist | 2,71 | 338 | Harris, Tim/Navasota Ind School Dist | 67 | 177 |
| Harle, Carol, Dr/Northside Ind School Dist | 67 | 39 | Harris, Zachary/Smithville Ind School Dist | 3,5 | 27 |
| Harman, Lucy/Hunt Ind School Dist | 1,11,73 | 258 | Harrison, Darla/Jayton-Girard Ind School Dist | 31,69,83,88 | 258 |
| Harmon, Brent/Sterling City Ind School Dist | 3 | 344 | Harrison, Dierdre/Lufkin Ind School Dist | 77 | 21 |
| Harmon, Vicki/Angleton Ind School Dist | 9 | 55 | Harrison, Keith/Meadow Ind School Dist | 67 | 365 |
| Harmon, Wayne/Liberty-Eylau Ind School Dist | 3 | 51 | Harrison, Mark/Celeste Ind School Dist | 3,5 | 239 |
| Harmsen, Keith/Crockett Co Cons Common SD | 73,295 | 98 | Harrison, Marshall/Sunray Ind School Dist | 1,11,57 | 299 |
| Harmsen, Lisa/Crockett Co Cons Common SD | 2 | 98 | Harrison, Monica/Red Lick Ind School Dist | 67 | 52 |
| Harness, Bill/Conroe Ind School Dist | 91 | 294 | Harrison, Monica/Texarkana Ind School Dist | 81 | 53 |
| Haro, Angie/Region 19 Ed Service Center | 27,73 | 144 | Harrison, Nick/West Rusk Co Cons Ind Sch Dist | 6 | 331 |
| Harp, Bill/Pleasant Grove Ind School Dist | 4,68,83 | 52 | Harrison, Richard/Lake Travis Ind School Dist | 3 | 373 |
| Harp, Bret/Avery Ind School Dist | 6 | 325 | Harrison, Sharanda/Hitchcock Ind School Dist | 68 | 165 |
| Harper, Daniel/Edna Ind School Dist | 2,19 | 242 | Harrison, Sherry/New Braunfels Ind School Dist | 67 | 92 |
| Harper, Ed/Mansfield Ind School Dist | 2 | 358 | Harrison, Sue/Georgetown Ind School Dist | 68 | 398 |
| Harper, Gay/Laneville Ind School Dist | 4 | 330 | Harrison, Susan/Woden Ind School Dist | 16 | 301 |
| Harper, Jay/Harper Ind School Dist | 9,58 | 168 | Harrison, Theresa/Petrolia Cons Ind School Dist | 2,84 | 78 |
| Harper, Kathy/Edgewood Ind School Dist | 7 | 382 | Harrist, Sidney/Atlanta Ind School Dist | 1 | 73 |
| Harper, Lana/Eagle Pass Ind School Dist | 30,74,83,90,93,273,274 | 279 | Harryman, Mary/Pasadena Ind School Dist | 4 | 203 |
| Harper, Lisa/Palacios Ind School Dist | 7 | 278 | Hart, Amy, Dr/Denton Ind School Dist | 81 | 125 |
| Harper, Mike/Harleton Ind School Dist | 5 | 213 | Hart, Britt/Merkel Ind School Dist | 6 | 363 |
| Harper, Nathan/Medina Valley Ind School Dist | 295 | 287 | Hart, Cindy/Deer Park Ind School Dist | 45 | 191 |
| Harper, Ryan/Whitesboro Ind School Dist | 1 | 173 | Hart, Courtney/Lewisville Ind School Dist | 11 | 126 |
| Harper, Shelly/Gatesville Ind School Dist | 73 | 96 | Hart, Jaelynn/East Central Ind School Dist | 7 | 34 |
| Harpole, Jeremy/Collinsville Ind School Dist | 298 | 171 | Hart, Kelly/Gruver Ind School Dist | 16 | 181 |
| Harral, Tony/Ballinger Ind School Dist | 3,5 | 329 | Hart, Lori/Denton Ind School Dist | 69 | 125 |
| Harrel, Charlyn/Gilmer Ind School Dist | 69 | 379 | Hart, Peter/Alvord Ind School Dist | 6 | 405 |
| Harrell, Alyta/Pasadena Ind School Dist | 15,70 | 203 | Hartenett, Laticha/Fort Davis Ind School Dist | 58 | 244 |
| Harrell, Hal, Dr/Uvalde Cons Ind School Dist | 1 | 381 | Hartford, Charles/Fruitvale Ind School Dist | 285 | 383 |
| Harrell, Kayela/Sudan Ind School Dist | 69,288 | 264 | Hartford, David/Boles Ind School Dist | 73,76,295 | 238 |
| Harrell, Kayla/Maud Ind School Dist | 83,85,88,270,752 | 52 | Hartgraves, Jon/Hico Ind School Dist | 1,11,84 | 181 |
| Harrell, Rick/Crandall Ind School Dist | 67 | 254 | Hartioz, Jerrod/Leon Ind School Dist | 73 | 267 |
| Harrell, Sam Edd/Silsbee Ind School Dist | 67 | 183 | **Hartley, Rick/**Blooming Grove Ind School Dist | 1 | 302 |
| Harrell, Scott/Pasadena Ind School Dist | 74 | 203 | Hartling, Marisa/Houston Ind School Dist | 53 | 193 |
| Harrell, Scott/Sudan Ind School Dist | 1,11 | 264 | Hartman, James/Ferris Ind School Dist | 1 | 144 |
| Harrell, Sherra/Grady Ind School Dist | 58 | 277 | Hartmann, Michelle/Pawnee Ind School Dist | 1,11,84 | 28 |
| Harrell, Zac/Athens Ind School Dist | 6 | 218 | Hartnett, Desiree/Galveston Ind School Dist | 57 | 165 |
| Harrington, Deanna/Frost Ind School Dist | 2 | 302 | **Harvell, Amy/**Rice Ind School Dist | 1 | 303 |
| Harrington, Joe, Dr/Hurst-Euless-Bedford ISD | 8,15 | 356 | Harvey, Bill, Dr/Calhoun Co Ind School Dist | 67 | 65 |
| Harrington, Julie/Crosbyton Cons Ind Sch Dist | 73,295 | 98 | Harvey, Brad/Kerrville Ind School Dist | 5 | 259 |
| Harrington, Kevin/Crawford Ind School Dist | 58 | 282 | Harvey, Isabel/Sabine Pass Ind School Dist | 36,270 | 247 |

| NAME/District | JOB FUNCTIONS | PAGE | NAME/District | JOB FUNCTIONS | PAGE |
|---|---|---|---|---|---|
| Harvey, Jeff/Fayetteville Ind School Dist | 1,11,83 | 151 | Haynes, Deanna/Eustace Ind School Dist | 8,12,57 | 219 |
| Harvey, Michael/Lamar Cons Ind School Dist | 42 | 157 | Haynes, Denise/Deer Park Ind School Dist | 42 | 191 |
| Harvey, Traci/Louise Ind School Dist | 38 | 392 | Haynes, Jacob/La Poynor Ind School Dist | 67 | 219 |
| Harwell, Eddie/Nacogdoches Ind School Dist | 90 | 301 | Haynes, Jimmy/Brownsville Ind School Dist | 3,15 | 66 |
| Haskins, Chad/Lubbock Ind School Dist | 81,92,286 | 272 | Haynes, Larry/West Orange-Cove Cons ISD | 11 | 312 |
| Hasley, Donald/Nacogdoches Ind School Dist | 27 | 301 | Haynes, Sherri/McLean Ind School Dist | 67 | 170 |
| Hasley, Katrina, Dr/Plano Ind School Dist | 8,15,27,34,57 | 85 | Haynie, Dennis/Andrews Ind School Dist | 16,73,95 | 19 |
| Hassenfratz, Kathleen/Lake Travis Ind School Dist | 83,85,270 | 373 | Haynie, Joe/Crowell Ind School Dist | 67 | 153 |
| Hassler, Javon/Higgins Ind School Dist | 16,73,286 | 270 | Haynie, Mary/Ysleta Ind School Dist | 2 | 141 |
| Hastey, Lizette/Post Ind School Dist | 37 | 167 | Hays, Amber/Littlefield Ind School Dist | 12,34,57 | 263 |
| Hastings, Cindy/Hamlin Collegiate Ind Sch Dist | 31,36,57,83,88,751 | 252 | Hays, Blake/Sherman Ind School Dist | 10 | 172 |
| Hastings, John/Seguin Ind School Dist | 76 | 179 | Hays, Wanda/Cuero Ind School Dist | 7 | 121 |
| Hastings, Julie/Waxahachie Ind School Dist | 11,298 | 146 | Hayward, David/Damon Ind School Dist | 1,73 | 56 |
| Hatch, John/Garland Ind School Dist | 39 | 109 | Hazzard, Preston/Frisco Ind School Dist | 20 | 82 |
| Hatch, Nannette/Diocese Corpus Christi Ed Off | 15 | 309 | Head, Scott/Lake Dallas Ind School Dist | 6 | 126 |
| Hatcher, Zevely/Kilgore Ind School Dist | 8 | 174 | Head, Tom/Alvarado Ind School Dist | 67 | 249 |
| Hathaway, Bill/Luling Ind School Dist | 4 | 65 | Head, Tracy/La Grange Ind School Dist | 8 | 151 |
| Hathaway, Robin/West Orange-Cove Cons ISD | 2 | 312 | Headlee, Glenn/Ft Worth Ind School Dist | 4 | 352 |
| Hathaway, Sherri/Victoria Ind School Dist | 10 | 384 | Headnot, Denitro/Jasper Ind School Dist | 73,76,295 | 243 |
| Hatley, Lisa/Dumas Ind School Dist | 9,34 | 298 | Heafley, Tracy/Yorktown Ind School Dist | 38 | 122 |
| Hatter, Gary/Bloomington Ind School Dist | 4 | 384 | Heard, Clint/Montgomery Ind School Dist | 6,35 | 296 |
| Hatton, Carroll/Spurger Ind School Dist | 67 | 378 | Hearn, Irene/Boles Ind School Dist | 7 | 238 |
| Hauberd, Carl/Alvin Ind School Dist | 67 | 54 | Hearn, Paul/Mineral Wells Ind School Dist | 2,19 | 313 |
| Haugeberg, Eric/Temple Ind School Dist | 13,15,79 | 32 | Hearne, Debbie/Bryson Ind School Dist | 8,12,69 | 241 |
| Hauger, Bob/Bryson Ind School Dist | 67 | 241 | Hearron, Shannon/Harleton Ind School Dist | 7 | 213 |
| Haught, Mark/Northside Ind School Dist | 1 | 396 | Heath, Cliff/Bosqueville Ind School Dist | 10 | 281 |
| Hauk, Kyle/Buckholts Ind School Dist | 6 | 290 | Heath, Jason/Anna Ind School Dist | 6 | 81 |
| Hauk, Monica/Bartlett Ind School Dist | 16,73,295 | 29 | Heath, Kyle, Dr/Cleburne Ind School Dist | 1 | 250 |
| Haussie, Gentry/Lackland Ind School Dist | 58,77 | 37 | Heath, Phyllis/Chillicothe ISD School Dist | 73 | 182 |
| Havard, Daniel/West Sabine Ind Sch Dist | 16,73,295 | 332 | Heath, Susan/College Station Ind Sch Dist | 34 | 59 |
| Havey, Holly/Medina Valley Ind School Dist | 88 | 287 | Heathington, Dani/Muleshoe Ind School Dist | 15 | 25 |
| Hawkins, Ben/Lindsay Ind School Dist | 67 | 95 | Heathington, Misty/Hawley Ind School Dist | 270,271,273 | 253 |
| Hawkins, Brent, Dr/Livingston Ind School Dist | 1 | 319 | Heathman, Jerid/Murchison Ind Sch Dist | 6 | 219 |
| Hawkins, Kristi/Mt Calm Ind School Dist | 2,11 | 231 | **Hebert, Anita/**Shallowater Ind School Dist | 1 | 274 |
| Hawkins, Mike/Bruceville-Eddy Ind Sch Dist | 5 | 281 | Hebert, Forrest/Channing Ind School Dist | 8,74,83 | 214 |
| Hawkins, Mildred/Bay City Ind School Dist | 4 | 278 | Heck, Austin/Nazareth Ind School Dist | 27 | 75 |
| Hawkins, Randy/Winona Ind School Dist | 67 | 341 | Heck, Patricia/Panhandle Ind School Dist | 58 | 73 |
| Hawkins, Rudy/City View Ind School Dist | 6 | 394 | Heckman, Coleman, Dr/Northside Ind School Dist | 77 | 39 |
| Hawkins, Scott/Thorndale Ind School Dist | 6 | 291 | Hecks, Cesioy/Aspermont Ind School Dist | 73 | 344 |
| Hawkins, Yolanda/Queen City Ind School Dist | 2 | 74 | Heddins, Jennifer/White Settlement Ind Sch Dist | 30,80 | 360 |
| Hawley, Aaron, Dr/Ector Co Ind School Dist | 20,23 | 134 | Hedges, David/Petrolia Cons Ind School Dist | 1 | 78 |
| Hawley, David/Denison Ind School Dist | 67 | 171 | Heers, Lou/Muenster Ind School Dist | 9,11,271 | 95 |
| Haws, Amy/Bynum Ind School Dist | 36 | 230 | Heeth, Karen/Spring Branch Ind School Dist | 15,68 | 205 |
| Haws, Josh/Bynum Ind School Dist | 3,5 | 230 | Heflin, Lannon/Georgetown Ind School Dist | 70,73,98,286,750 | 398 |
| Hawthorne, Leighann/Memphis Ind School Dist | 8 | 181 | Heflin, Lynn/Ore City Ind School Dist | 1 | 379 |
| Hawvermale, Lindsey/Ranger Ind School Dist | 8 | 133 | Hefner, Bill/Rice Cons Ind School Dist | 1,11 | 90 |
| Hayenga, Leslie/San Felipe-Del Rio Cons Ind SD | 73,286 | 381 | Heid, Kristi/Sabine Pass Ind School Dist | 1 | 247 |
| Hayes-Ramirez, Heather/Alief Ind School Dist | 4 | 186 | Heidel, Patti/Columbia Brazoria ISD | 8,54,275,280 | 56 |
| Hayes, Amy/Temple Ind School Dist | 68 | 32 | Heideman, Karen/Utopia Ind School Dist | 2 | 381 |
| Hayes, Andy/Karnack Ind School Dist | 5 | 214 | Heier, Linda/Randolph Field Ind School Dist | 11 | 42 |
| Hayes, Britt/Region 18 Ed Service Center | 2 | 290 | Hein, Gladys/Royal Ind School Dist | 2 | 387 |
| Hayes, Cori/Forestburg Ind School Dist | 6 | 293 | Hein, Richard/Sanford-Fritch Ind School Dist | 2,11 | 241 |
| Hayes, David/Wortham Ind School Dist | 8,271,273 | 161 | Hein, Stephanie/Royal Ind School Dist | 79 | 387 |
| Hayes, Houston/Humble Ind School Dist | 20 | 200 | Hein, Theresa/Zapata Co Ind School Dist | 2 | 410 |
| Hayes, Melanie/Dawson Ind School Dist | 36,69,88 | 121 | Heinen, Kim/Lake Travis Ind School Dist | 68 | 373 |
| Hayes, Michael/Silverton Ind School Dist | 2 | 61 | Heinrich, Darla/Lubbock-Cooper Ind Sch Dist | 11 | 274 |
| Hayes, Nathan/Water Valley Ind School Dist | 6 | 368 | Heinroth, Michael/Sweeny Ind School Dist | 37 | 57 |
| Hayes, Robert/Bryan Ind School Dist | 76 | 58 | Heironimus, Brian/Angleton Ind School Dist | 295 | 55 |
| Hayes, Sandra/Richardson Ind School Dist | 3,15 | 116 | Heisel, Stan/Terrell Ind School Dist | 5,73,76,295 | 256 |
| Hayes, Shannon/Royse City Ind School Dist | 58,79 | 328 | Helfferich, Tracey/Yantis Ind School Dist | 8,11,298 | 408 |
| Hayes, Sheri/Bishop Cons Ind School Dist | 16,82,84 | 305 | Helfferich, Tracey/Yantis Ind School Dist | 1 | 408 |
| Hayes, Stephanie/Bullard Ind School Dist | 4 | 339 | Helge, Nicholas/Whitewright Ind School Dist | 73 | 173 |
| Hayes, Sue/Region 10 Ed Service Center | 2,19 | 120 | Heller, Don/Anson Ind School Dist | 67 | 252 |
| Hayes, Tami/Ropes Ind School Dist | 58 | 232 | Hellor, Melissa/Richardson Ind School Dist | 74,750 | 116 |
| Haygood, Blake/New Braunfels Ind School Dist | 81 | 92 | Helmcamp, Jack/Buffalo Ind School Dist | 67 | 266 |
| Haymae, Kristine/Region 6 Ed Service Center | 30 | 386 | Helmcamp, Janet/Cleburne Ind School Dist | 69,81 | 250 |
| Haymark, Wade/Conroe Ind School Dist | 7,35 | 294 | Helmer, Kevin/Chireno ISD School Dist | 16,73,295 | 300 |

| | | | | | | | | | |
|---|---|---|---|---|---|---|---|---|---|
| 1 | Superintendent | 16 | Instructional Media Svcs | 30 | Adult Education | 44 | Science Sec | 58 | Special Education K-12 |
| 2 | Bus/Finance/Purchasing | 17 | Chief Operations Officer | 31 | Career/Sch-to-Work K-12 | 45 | Math K-12 | 59 | Special Education Elem |
| 3 | Buildings And Grounds | 18 | Chief Academic Officer | 32 | Career/Sch-to-Work Elem | 46 | Math Elem | 60 | Special Education Sec |
| 4 | Food Service | 19 | Chief Financial Officer | 33 | Career/Sch-to-Work Sec | 47 | Math Sec | 61 | Foreign/World Lang K-12 |
| 5 | Transportation | 20 | Art K-12 | 34 | Early Childhood Ed | 48 | English/Lang Arts K-12 | 62 | Foreign/World Lang Elem |
| 6 | Athletic | 21 | Art Elem | 35 | Health/Phys Education | 49 | English/Lang Arts Elem | 63 | Foreign/World Lang Sec |
| 7 | Health Services | 22 | Art Sec | 36 | Guidance Services K-12 | 50 | English/Lang Arts Sec | 64 | Religious Education K-12 |
| 8 | Curric/Instruct K-12 | 23 | Music K-12 | 37 | Guidance Services Elem | 51 | Reading K-12 | 65 | Religious Education Elem |
| 9 | Curric/Instruct Elem | 24 | Music Elem | 38 | Guidance Services Sec | 52 | Reading Elem | 66 | Religious Education Sec |
| 10 | Curric/Instruct Sec | 25 | Music Sec | 39 | Social Studies K-12 | 53 | Reading Sec | 67 | School Board President |
| 11 | Federal Program | 26 | Business Education | 40 | Social Studies Elem | 54 | Remedial Reading K-12 | 68 | Teacher Personnel |
| 12 | Title I | 27 | Career & Tech Ed | 41 | Social Studies Sec | 55 | Remedial Reading Elem | 69 | Academic Assessment |
| 13 | Title V | 28 | Technology Education | 42 | Science K-12 | 56 | Remedial Reading Sec | 70 | Research/Development |
| 14 | Asst Superintendent | 29 | Family/Consumer Science | 43 | Science Elem | 57 | Bilingual/ELL | 71 | Public Information |

| | | | | | | | | | |
|---|---|---|---|---|---|---|---|---|---|
| 72 | Summer School | 88 | Alternative/At Risk | 277 | Remedial Math K-12 |
| 73 | Instructional Tech | 89 | Multi-Cultural Curriculum | 280 | Literacy Coach |
| 74 | Inservice Training | 90 | Social Work | 285 | STEM |
| 75 | Marketing/Distributive | 91 | Safety/Security | 286 | Digital Learning |
| 76 | Info Systems | 92 | Magnet School | 288 | Common Core Standards |
| 77 | Psychological Assess | 93 | Parental Involvement | 294 | Accountability |
| 78 | Affirmative Action | 95 | Tech Prep Program | 295 | Network System |
| 79 | Student Personnel | 97 | Chief Infomation Officer | 296 | Title II Programs |
| 80 | Driver Ed/Safety | 98 | Chief Technology Officer | 297 | Webmaster |
| 81 | Gifted/Talented | 270 | Character Education | 298 | Grant Writer/Ptnrships |
| 82 | Video Services | 271 | Migrant Education | 750 | Chief Innovation Officer |
| 83 | Substance Abuse Prev | 273 | Teacher Mentor | 751 | Chief of Staff |
| 84 | Erate | 274 | Before/After Sch | 752 | Social Emotional Learning |
| 85 | AIDS Education | 275 | Response To Intervention | | |

| NAME/District | JOB FUNCTIONS | PAGE | NAME/District | JOB FUNCTIONS | PAGE |
|---|---|---|---|---|---|
| Helms, Ashley/Plano Ind School Dist | 10 | 85 | Hernandez, Cheryl/Beaumont Ind School Dist | 2,19 | 244 |
| Helms, Jody/Rotan Ind School Dist | 9 | 152 | Hernandez, Cindy/Buckholts Ind School Dist | 4 | 290 |
| Helms, Michelle/San Angelo Ind School Dist | 4 | 367 | Hernandez, Cindy/Walcott Ind School Dist | 4 | 123 |
| Helms, Robert/Irion Co Ind School Dist | 2 | 241 | Hernandez, Crystal/San Perlita Ind School Dist | 69 | 397 |
| Hemann, Ronnie/Region 7 Ed Service Center | 3,15,68 | 176 | Hernandez, Cynthia/Corpus Christi Ind Sch Dist | 280 | 306 |
| Hembree, Jeff/South Texas Ind School Dist | 11,57,73,76,285,286,295,296 | 71 | Hernandez, Daisy/Hart Ind School Dist | 36 | 75 |
| Hemby, William/Celina Ind School Dist | 3,15 | 81 | Hernandez, Dayna/Klein Ind School Dist | 15,71,79 | 201 |
| Hemmila, Jaclyn/Carroll Independent Sch Dist | 22,44,47 | 349 | Hernandez, Debbie/Point Isabel Ind Sch Dist | 69 | 70 |
| Hempel, Craig/Mexia Ind School Dist | 4 | 270 | Hernandez, Deborah/Harlandale Ind School Dist | 7 | 35 |
| Hemphill, Allison/Angleton Ind School Dist | 298 | 55 | Hernandez, Denise/West Oso Ind School Dist | 3,5 | 309 |
| Hemphill, Bebetta/Garland Ind School Dist | 79 | 109 | Hernandez, Dora/Bloomington Ind School Dist | 57,58 | 384 |
| Hemphill, Danny/Evant Ind School Dist | 84 | 96 | Hernandez, Eden, Dr/Bishop Cons Ind School Dist | 8,11,34,58,69,73,81,83 | 305 |
| Hemphill, Kim/Smithville Ind School Dist | 16 | 27 | Hernandez, Eduardo, Dr/Edgewood Ind School Dist | 1 | 34 |
| Henderson, Angela/El Paso ISD-Middle Schools | 15 | 139 | Hernandez, Elizabeth/Teague Ind School Dist | 69 | 161 |
| Henderson, Ernest/Orange Grove Ind School Dist | 8,11,57,69,74,275,294 | 248 | Hernandez, Hector/Boerne Ind School Dist | 91 | 257 |
| Henderson, Julie/Wichita Falls Ind School Dist | 35,83,85 | 395 | Hernandez, Horacio/San Elizario Ind School Dist | 295 | 139 |
| Henderson, Kathy/Aransas Co Ind School Dist | 2,19 | 22 | Hernandez, Janice/Southwest Ind School Dist | 71 | 46 |
| Henderson, Mike/Hawkins Ind School Dist | 73,295 | 407 | Hernandez, Joe/Calhoun Co Ind School Dist | 3,5,91 | 65 |
| Henderson, Shannon/Queen City Ind School Dist | 8,11,36,69,72,73,285 | 74 | Hernandez, John/East Central Ind School Dist | 79 | 34 |
| Henderson, Shelly/McLean Ind School Dist | 54,280 | 170 | Hernandez, Kelbi/Hart Ind School Dist | 76 | 75 |
| Henderson, Stacy/Dawson Ind School Dist | 1 | 302 | Hernandez, Kristi/Region 4 Ed Service Center | 71 | 213 |
| Henderson, Suzette/Era Ind School Dist | 2,11 | 94 | Hernandez, Letty/Culberson Co Allamoore Ind SD | 67 | 99 |
| Henderson, Tracy/Kennard Ind Sch Dist | 5 | 236 | Hernandez, Linda/Roosevelt Ind School Dist | 8,11,69,83,273,274,286,296 | 274 |
| Henderson, Wayne/Sands Consolidated ISD | 1 | 121 | Hernandez, Lisa/Region 3 Ed Service Center | 298 | 385 |
| Hendrick, Irana/Overton Ind School Dist | 16 | 331 | Hernandez, Lucero/Canutillo Ind School Dist | 88 | 136 |
| Hendrick, Sue/Kerrville Ind School Dist | 5 | 259 | Hernandez, Lupe/Evant Ind School Dist | 4 | 96 |
| Hendricks, Jackie, Dr/Princeton Ind School Dist | 8,15,36,57,271,288 | 87 | Hernandez, Magda/Irving Ind School Dist | 1 | 113 |
| Hendricks, Mary/Commerce Independent Sch Dist | 11,296 | 239 | Hernandez, Maria/Crane Ind School Dist | 7 | 97 |
| Hendricks, Mike/Dawson Ind School Dist | 3,4,5 | 121 | Hernandez, Maria/Crane Ind School Dist | 7 | 97 |
| Hendricks, Terry/Munday Consolidated Ind SD | 3 | 262 | Hernandez, Marie/Weatherford Ind School Dist | 10,280 | 316 |
| Hendrickson, Curtis/Pottsboro Ind School Dist | 5 | 172 | Hernandez, Marie/Weatherford Ind School Dist | 57 | 316 |
| Hendrickson, Jessica/Gordon Ind School Dist | 2,19 | 313 | Hernandez, Melissa/Lubbock Ind School Dist | 57 | 272 |
| Hendrickson, Kathryn/Eustace Ind School Dist | 58 | 219 | Hernandez, Mica/Victoria Ind School Dist | 41 | 384 |
| Hendrix, Laura/Aquilla Ind School Dist | 58 | 230 | Hernandez, Mike/Slaton Ind School Dist | 3,5 | 275 |
| Hendrix, Traci/Pflugerville Ind School Dist | 27 | 374 | Hernandez, Olivia/San Antonio Ind School Dist | 15,57,271 | 42 |
| Hendry, Mary/Diboll Ind School Dist | 69 | 20 | Hernandez, Patricia/Bridgeport Ind School Dist | 11,57,69,271,288,296,298 | 406 |
| Henke, Charles/Schulenburg Ind School Dist | 69 | 152 | Hernandez, Patrick/Tuloso-Midway Ind School Dist | 3,5 | 308 |
| Henke, Kendra/McKinney Ind School Dist | 44 | 84 | Hernandez, Renee/Allen Ind School Dist | 16 | 80 |
| Hennessey, Carla/Montague Ind School Dist | 1,11,83 | 293 | Hernandez, Richard/Harlandale Ind School Dist | 2,15 | 35 |
| Hennig, Grace/Itasca Ind School Dist | 36,83 | 231 | Hernandez, Roland, Dr/Corpus Christi Ind Sch Dist | 1 | 306 |
| Henry, Justin/Dallas Ind School Dist | 67 | 102 | Hernandez, Rolando/La Joya Ind School Dist | 4 | 222 |
| Henry, Kenneth/Cypress-Fairbanks Ind Sch Dist | 79 | 189 | Hernandez, Rosemary/Edgewood Ind School Dist | 34 | 34 |
| Henry, Kristi/Anahuac Ind School Dist | 38,79 | 75 | Hernandez, Sandra/Cuero Ind School Dist | 4 | 121 |
| Henry, Mark, Dr/Cypress-Fairbanks Ind Sch Dist | 1 | 188 | Hernandez, Shannon/Ft Worth Ind School Dist | 45 | 352 |
| Henry, Rosemary, Dr/Diocese Corpus Christi Ed Off | 1,11 | 309 | Hernandez, Sylvia/Bloomington Ind School Dist | 8 | 384 |
| Henry, Roy/Kopperl Ind School Dist | 31,36,83 | 50 | Hernandez, Victor/Clint Ind School Dist | 57 | 136 |
| Henry, Sharon, Dr/Conroe Ind School Dist | 49 | 294 | Hernandez, Victor/Corpus Christi Ind Sch Dist | 10,16 | 306 |
| Henry, Sheila/Austin ISD High School Area | 15 | 371 | Hernandez, Victor/Gregory-Portland Ind Sch Dist | 67 | 333 |
| Hensley, Andrea/Cleburne Ind School Dist | 68 | 250 | Hernandez, Victor/Plainview Ind School Dist | 2 | 180 |
| Hensley, Nielan/De Kalb Ind School Dist | 91 | 51 | Hernandez, Yvonne/Kress Ind School Dist | 285 | 345 |
| Hensley, Patti/New Deal Ind School Dist | 7,85 | 274 | Hernando, Noah/Sanford-Fritch Ind School Dist | 73,84 | 241 |
| Hensley, Wanda/Winona Ind School Dist | 271 | 341 | Herndon, Sommer/Center Ind School Dist | 38,69 | 337 |
| Henson, Barry/White Oak Ind School Dist | 3 | 176 | Hernendez, Adrian/Galena Park Ind School Dist | 295 | 191 |
| Henson, Darryl, Dr/Cedar Hill Ind School Dist | 15 | 101 | Herrera, Amanda/Grandfalls-Royalty Ind SD | 28,286 | 388 |
| Henson, Gema/Pflugerville Ind School Dist | 57 | 374 | Herrera, Hector/Dayton Ind School Dist | 91 | 268 |
| Henson, Kathleen/Hemphill Ind School Dist | 4 | 331 | Herrera, Karen, Dr/Killeen Ind School Dist | 20,23 | 30 |
| Henson, Kim/Rusk Ind School Dist | 68 | 77 | Herrera, Marcie/Sheldon Ind School Dist | 76 | 205 |
| Henson, Leslie/Bridgeport Ind School Dist | 73 | 406 | Herrera, Maria/Whitney Ind School Dist | 57 | 231 |
| Henson, Reggie/Kilgore Ind School Dist | 67 | 174 | Herrera, Marianna/Flatonia Ind School Dist | 271 | 151 |
| Herbel, Dene, Dr/Millsap Ind School Dist | 67 | 315 | Herrera, Rolando/Mercedes Ind School Dist | 3 | 225 |
| Herbst, Myra/Humble Ind School Dist | 49,51 | 200 | Herrin, Emily/Hays Cons Ind School Dist | 286 | 216 |
| Herbstritt, Tracee/Childress Ind School Dist | 4 | 77 | Herrin, Rick/Aledo Ind School Dist | 71 | 315 |
| Herenadez, Guan/Progreso Ind School Dist | 2 | 227 | Herrin, Rick/Argyle Ind School Dist | 98 | 124 |
| Herew, Carey/Center Ind School Dist | 34,58 | 337 | Herring, Cheryl/Junction Ind School Dist | 2,84 | 259 |
| Hergert, Adrienne/Rockwall Ind School Dist | 7,35 | 328 | Herring, Cliff/Southside Ind School Dist | 73 | 46 |
| Heriard, Tammy/Warren Ind School Dist | 4 | 378 | Herring, Gloria/Atlanta Ind School Dist | 16 | 73 |
| Hermes, Adam/Burnet Cons Ind Sch Dist | 73 | 63 | Herring, Jason/Refugio Ind School Dist | 6 | 326 |
| Hermes, Kevin/Banquete Ind School Dist | 6 | 305 | Herring, Kathy/Comanche Ind School Dist | 2 | 93 |
| Hermesmeyer, Angie/Goldthwaite Consolidated ISD | 6,285 | 291 | Herring, Lisa/Refugio Ind School Dist | 2,11,57,69,74,270,294,298 | 326 |
| Hermesmeyer, Stephen/Comanche Ind School Dist | 6 | 93 | Herring, Tana/Elkhart Ind School Dist | 12,298 | 18 |
| Hernadez, Maggie/Calhoun Co Ind School Dist | 8,15,57,69,74,271 | 65 | Herron, Kevin/Central Heights Ind Sch Dist | 6 | 300 |
| Hernanadez, Christian/Temple Ind School Dist | 71 | 32 | Hershey, Paige/Spring Branch Ind School Dist | 6 | 205 |
| Hernandez, Alicia/Weatherford Ind School Dist | 4 | 316 | Hertz, Taffi/East Central Ind School Dist | 8,15 | 34 |
| Hernandez, Arianna/Pharr-San Juan-Alamo Ind SD | 71 | 226 | Hervieux, Glenn/Van Ind School Dist | 84 | 383 |
| Hernandez, Benny/Mathis Ind School Dist | 1,57,83 | 334 | Heryford, Mary/Seagraves Ind School Dist | 38 | 162 |
| Hernandez, Cathy/La Feria Ind School Dist | 1 | 69 | Heskett, Christopher, Dr/Covington ISD School Dist | 1 | 230 |

Job Function Legend:

1 Superintendent
2 Bus/Finance/Purchasing
3 Buildings And Grounds
4 Food Service
5 Transportation
6 Athletic
7 Health Services
8 Curric/Instruct K-12
9 Curric/Instruct Elem
10 Curric/Instruct Sec
11 Federal Program
12 Title I
13 Title V
15 Asst Superintendent
16 Instructional Media Svcs
17 Chief Operations Officer
18 Chief Academic Officer
19 Chief Financial Officer
20 Art K-12
21 Art Elem
22 Art Sec
23 Music K-12
24 Music Elem
25 Music Sec
26 Business Education
27 Career & Tech Ed
28 Technology Education
29 Family/Consumer Science
30 Adult Education
31 Career/Sch-to-Work K-12
32 Career/Sch-to-Work Elem
33 Career/Sch-to-Work Sec
34 Early Childhood Ed
35 Health/Phys Education
36 Guidance Services K-12
37 Guidance Services Elem
38 Guidance Services Sec
39 Social Studies K-12
40 Social Studies Elem
41 Social Studies Sec
42 Science K-12
43 Science Elem
44 Science Sec
45 Math K-12
46 Math Elem
47 Math Sec
48 English/Lang Arts K-12
49 English/Lang Arts Elem
50 English/Lang Arts Sec
51 Reading K-12
52 Reading Elem
53 Reading Sec
54 Remedial Reading K-12
55 Remedial Reading Elem
56 Remedial Reading Sec
57 Bilingual/ELL
58 Special Education K-12
59 Special Education Elem
60 Special Education Sec
61 Foreign/World Lang K-12
62 Foreign/World Lang Elem
63 Foreign/World Lang Sec
64 Religious Education K-12
65 Religious Education Elem
66 Religious Education Sec
67 School Board President
68 Teacher Personnel
69 Academic Assessment
70 Research/Development
71 Public Information
72 Summer School
73 Instructional Tech
74 Inservice Training
75 Marketing/Distributive
76 Info Systems
77 Psychological Assess
78 Affirmative Action
79 Student Personnel
80 Driver Ed/Safety
81 Gifted/Talented
82 Video Services
83 Substance Abuse Prev
84 Erate
85 AIDS Education
88 Alternative/At Risk
89 Multi-Cultural Curriculum
90 Social Work
91 Safety/Security
92 Magnet School
93 Parental Involvement
95 Tech Prep Program
97 Chief Information Officer
98 Chief Technology Officer
270 Character Education
271 Migrant Education
273 Teacher Mentor
274 Before/After Sch
275 Response to Intervention
277 Remedial Math K-12
280 Literacy Coach
285 STEM
286 Digital Learning
288 Common Core Standards
294 Accountability
295 Network System
296 Title II Programs
297 Webmaster
298 Grant Writer/Ptnrships
750 Chief Innovation Officer
751 Chief of Staff
752 Social Emotional Learning

| NAME/District | JOB FUNCTIONS | PAGE | NAME/District | JOB FUNCTIONS | PAGE |
|---|---|---|---|---|---|
| Hobden, Bonita/Kaufman Ind School Dist | 68 | 255 | Holland, Brad/Stanton Ind School Dist | 2,19 | 277 |
| Hobson, Bobby/Douglass Ind School Dist | 67 | 300 | Holland, Brandy/Tyler Ind School Dist | 11 | 340 |
| Hobson, Brad/Milano Ind School Dist | 3 | 290 | Holland, Carrie/Region 7 Ed Service Center | 2,15 | 176 |
| Hocott, Kim/Pearland Ind School Dist | 16,71 | 56 | Holland, David/Birdville Ind School Dist | 69,294 | 348 |
| Hodde, Jason/Burton Ind School Dist | 6 | 388 | Holland, Julie/Alvarado Ind School Dist | 16,73,295 | 249 |
| Hodge, Donna/Keller Ind School Dist | 81 | 357 | Holland, Kim/Moran Ind School Dist | 8,69,288 | 336 |
| Hodge, Paul/Lockhart Ind School Dist | 295 | 64 | Holland, Michael/Region 6 Ed Service Center | 1 | 386 |
| Hodge, Remy/Marlin Ind School Dist | 8 | 149 | Holland, Tony/Claude Ind School Dist | 58 | 23 |
| Hodge, Trevelyan/Liberty-Eylau Ind School Dist | 67 | 51 | Holle, Geoff/Pflugerville Ind School Dist | 4 | 374 |
| Hodges, Becky/Patton Springs Ind School Dist | 2 | 131 | Holleman, Tish/Paris Ind School Dist | 2 | 262 |
| Hodges, Blake/De Kalb Ind School Dist | 67 | 51 | Holler, Charles/Water Valley Ind School Dist | 67 | 368 |
| Hodges, Brad/Anderson-Shiro Cons Ind SD | 6 | 176 | Hollie, Gil/Temple Ind School Dist | 274 | 32 |
| Hodges, Brenda/Salado Ind School Dist | 4 | 32 | Holligan, Alicia/Region 17 Ed Service Center | 36,77 | 275 |
| Hodges, Cynthia/Killeen Ind School Dist | 285 | 30 | Hollingsworth, Angela/Woodville Ind School Dist | 83,85 | 378 |
| Hodges, Lisa/Allen Ind School Dist | 68 | 80 | Hollingsworth, Charla/Alief Ind School Dist | 16,280 | 186 |
| Hodges, Randy/Rotan Ind School Dist | 73 | 152 | Hollingsworth, Chyrl/Blooming Grove Ind School Dist | 7 | 302 |
| Hodges, Stan/Hull Daisetta Ind School Dist | 6 | 268 | Hollingsworth, Dwight/Woodville Ind School Dist | 3,91 | 378 |
| Hodges, Terri/Stephenville Ind School Dist | 2 | 148 | Hollingsworth, Jerry/Bandera Ind School Dist | 1 | 26 |
| Hodgin, Claire/Manor Ind School Dist | 43 | 373 | Hollingsworth, Lacey/Axtell Ind School Dist | 58 | 281 |
| Hodkinson, Andy/Carlisle Ind School Dist | 3,5 | 330 | Hollingsworth, Rusty/Crosby Ind School Dist | 3 | 188 |
| Hodnett, Brian/Haskell Cons Ind School Dist | 6 | 215 | Hollingsworth, Tara/Haskell Cons Ind School Dist | 58 | 215 |
| Hodson, Joyce/Killeen Ind School Dist | 298 | 30 | Hollins, Jonnelle/Houston Ind School Dist | 274 | 193 |
| Hodson, Julie/Spring Branch Ind School Dist | 11,298 | 205 | Hollins, Tony/Pine Tree Ind School Dist | 3,15 | 175 |
| Hoedebeck, David/Round Rock Ind School Dist | 3 | 401 | Holloman, Casey/Bellville Ind School Dist | 8,11,36,57,69,83,88 | 25 |
| Hoehn, Sheila/Oglesby Ind School Dist | 76 | 97 | Holloway, Brett/Brookeland Ind School Dist | 67 | 243 |
| Hoellen, Paige/Georgetown Ind School Dist | 42 | 398 | Holloway, Charles, Dr/Tioga Ind School Dist | 1 | 172 |
| Hoelscher, Melissa/Union Hill Ind School Dist | 76 | 380 | Holloway, Cindy/Troy Ind School Dist | 2 | 33 |
| Hoelscher, Russell/Olfen Ind School Dist | 73,286,295 | 329 | Holloway, Deanne/Flatonia Ind School Dist | 16,73 | 151 |
| Hoelscher, Russell/Paint Rock Ind School Dist | 73 | 94 | Holloway, Deborah/Killeen Ind School Dist | 34 | 30 |
| Hoelscher, Shahala/Highland Ind School Dist | 36,69 | 304 | Holloway, Deirdre/Ft Bend Ind School Dist | 11 | 153 |
| Hoelting, Cory/Nazareth Ind School Dist | 73,295 | 75 | Holloway, Harold/Elkhart Ind School Dist | 67 | 18 |
| Hoff, Elizabeth/Blanco Ind School Dist | 16,82 | 49 | Holloway, Jeanne/Chireno ISD School Dist | 2,11 | 300 |
| Hoffman, Kevin/Mart Ind School Dist | 6 | 283 | Holloway, Melody/Elkhart Ind School Dist | 38 | 18 |
| Hoffmann, Sean/Seguin Ind School Dist | 71 | 179 | Hollway, Leah/Broaddus Ind School Dist | 2,11 | 332 |
| Hoffpauir, Gary/East Chambers Ind School Dist | 67 | 76 | Hollway, Lucas/Broaddus Ind School Dist | 1,83 | 332 |
| Hoffpauir, Lynda/Region 5 Ed Service Center | 76 | 247 | Holly, Mike/Post Ind School Dist | 67 | 167 |
| Hofmann, Shannon/Mason Ind School Dist | 58,752 | 278 | Holly, Tom/Midland Ind School Dist | 73,76,295,297 | 288 |
| Hogan, Aaron/College Station Ind Sch Dist | 48 | 59 | Holman, Jason/Tatum Ind School Dist | 6 | 331 |
| Hogan, Albrey/Southwest Ind School Dist | 752 | 46 | Holman, Shane/Giddings Ind School Dist | 8,11,57,58,83,88,288,296 | 266 |
| Hogan, Cody/Stanton Ind School Dist | 6 | 277 | Holmes, Adrianne/Humble Ind School Dist | 298 | 200 |
| Hogan, Jenifer/Quinlan Ind School Dist | 36 | 240 | Holmes, Brent/Teague Ind School Dist | 73,295 | 161 |
| Hogan, Nadine/Hays Cons Ind School Dist | 58 | 216 | Holmes, Carrie/Iraan-Sheffield Ind Sch Dist | 16 | 318 |
| Hogg, Jeff/Overton Ind School Dist | 27 | 331 | Holmgreen, Ron/Granbury Ind School Dist | 15 | 233 |
| Hogg, Jimmy/Cedar Hill Ind School Dist | 91 | 101 | Holt, Brian, Dr/Booker Ind School Dist | 1 | 270 |
| Hogue, Aaron/Dawson Ind School Dist | 3,5 | 302 | **Holt, Brian, Dr/**Randolph Field Ind School Dist | 1 | 42 |
| Hogue, Brenda/Shelbyville Ind School Dist | 4 | 337 | Holt, Dennis/Graford Ind School Dist | 1 | 313 |
| Hogue, Scott/Electra Ind School Dist | 83 | 394 | Holt, Laura, Dr/Birdville Ind School Dist | 12,58 | 348 |
| Hohenberger, Denicia/Cooper Ind School Dist | 1,11,57 | 123 | Holt, Leann/Rocksprings Ind School Dist | 58 | 135 |
| Hohenberger, Steven/Paris Ind School Dist | 6 | 262 | Holt, Wesley/Connally Ind School Dist | 1 | 282 |
| Hohlt, Ronnie/Burton Ind School Dist | 3 | 388 | Holtkamp, Leslie, Dr/Bryan Ind School Dist | 8 | 58 |
| Hohmann, Alissa/Coleman Ind School Dist | 36 | 79 | Holub, Phil/Seymour Ind School Dist | 3,5 | 28 |
| Hoke, Janine/Alief Ind School Dist | 74 | 186 | Holubec, Bryan/Thrall Ind School Dist | 67 | 403 |
| Holacka, Karin, Dr/Duncanville Ind School Dist | 15,79 | 108 | Holyfield, Karen/Gilmer Ind School Dist | 76 | 379 |
| Holbert, Cheryl/Henrietta Ind School Dist | 31,69,83,85 | 78 | Holzapfel, Malinda/Woden Ind School Dist | 73,76 | 301 |
| Holbrook, Dianne, Dr/Huntington Ind School Dist | 8,11,57,69,88,280,285,298 | 20 | Holzhaus, Paul/Medina Valley Ind School Dist | 2,5,15 | 287 |
| Holbrooks, Todd/Borden Co Ind School Dist | 67 | 49 | Homann, Michael/Medina Valley Ind School Dist | 2,15 | 287 |
| Holcomb, Jennifer/Weatherford Ind School Dist | 274 | 316 | Homann, Mike/Pettus Ind School Dist | 1,11 | 28 |
| Holcomb, Kim/Corsicana Ind School Dist | 8,15,34,39 | 302 | Homann, Tanya/Lockhart Ind School Dist | 2 | 64 |
| Holcomb, Pam/Garland Ind School Dist | 73 | 109 | Homer, Bonita/Elgin Ind School Dist | 58 | 27 |
| Holcomb, Pamela/Burnet Cons Ind Sch Dist | 4 | 63 | Homeyer, Lori/Refugio Ind School Dist | 58 | 326 |
| Holcombe, Coy, Dr/Eustace Ind School Dist | 1,73 | 219 | Homeyer, Lori/Woodsboro Ind School Dist | 58 | 326 |
| Holcombe, Laurie/Malakoff Ind School Dist | 58 | 219 | Hommel, Chad/Clarendon Cons Ind Sch Dist | 5 | 131 |
| Holcombe, Rex/Floydada Ind School Dist | 11,57,73,81,84,271,295,296 | 153 | Homstead, Gracie/Benjamin Ind School Dist | 4 | 261 |
| Holden, Russell/Oakwood Ind School Dist | 1 | 267 | Honeycutt, Judy/Silsbee Ind School Dist | 27,95 | 183 |
| Holder, Brett/Shallowater Ind School Dist | 5 | 274 | Honold, Eduardo/Harris Co Dept of Ed | 30 | 184 |
| Holder, David/Castleberry Ind School Dist | 67 | 350 | Honts, Sandy/Anthony Ind School Dist | 8,11,58 | 136 |
| Holder, Glenda/Clear Creek Ind School Dist | 81 | 163 | Honza, Bill/Ennis Ind School Dist | 71 | 144 |
| Holder, Hoby/Gilmer Ind School Dist | 3 | 378 | Honzell, Marcy/Carlisle Ind School Dist | 2 | 330 |
| Holder, Jamie/Lindale Ind School Dist | 3,15,76 | 339 | Hood, Aaron/Robert Lee Ind School Dist | 1,11 | 79 |
| Holding, Jeanette/Henrietta Ind School Dist | 7 | 78 | Hood, Greg/Whitehouse Ind School Dist | 67 | 341 |
| Holfpauir, Kenny/West Hardin Co Cons Sch Dist | 6 | 183 | Hood, John/Rusk Ind School Dist | 4,11,288 | 77 |
| Holiday, Kevin/Spring Ind School Dist | 73 | 207 | Hood, Sean/Lewisville Ind School Dist | 50 | 126 |
| Holik, Sandra/Louise Ind School Dist | 73,286,295 | 392 | Hood, Travis/Bridgeport Ind School Dist | 58 | 406 |
| Holland, Adam/La Porte Ind School Dist | 71 | 203 | Hook, Mike/Claude Ind School Dist | 3,5 | 23 |
| Holland, Amber/Gruver Ind School Dist | 9 | 181 | Hooker, Tommy/Thrall Ind School Dist | 1 | 403 |
| Holland, Ana/Point Isabel Ind Sch Dist | 8,16,57,69,72,85,273,274 | 70 | Hooper, Fay/Borger Ind School Dist | 2 | 240 |

| NAME/District | JOB FUNCTIONS | PAGE |
|---|---|---|
| Hooper, Marbella/Angleton Ind School Dist | 57,81 | 55 |
| Hooper, Richard/Ponder Ind School Dist | 31,73,297 | 130 |
| Hooten, Kathleen/Commerce Independent Sch Dist | 67 | 239 |
| Hooten, Kenneth/Linden Kildare Cons Ind SD | 2 | 74 |
| Hooten, Kenton/Lockney Independent Sch Dist | 3,5 | 153 |
| Hooton, Lori/Grand Saline Ind School Dist | 82 | 383 |
| Hoover, Creed/Booker Ind School Dist | 67 | 270 |
| Hoover, Dane/Water Valley Ind School Dist | 57,73,297 | 368 |
| Hoover, Matt/Crowley Ind School Dist | 297 | 350 |
| Hoover, Matthew/Vernon Ind School Dist | 6 | 396 |
| Hope, Michael/Robinson Ind School Dist | 1 | 284 |
| Hopkins, Brandon/Boyd Ind School Dist | 6 | 405 |
| Hopkins, Cindy/Plains Ind School Dist | 7 | 409 |
| Hopkins, Justin/Mullin Ind School Dist | 42 | 291 |
| Hopkins, Kim/Sam Rayburn Ind School Dist | 16 | 150 |
| Hopkins, Norman/Eanes Ind School Dist | 3 | 372 |
| Hopkins, Patty/Gordon Ind School Dist | 4 | 313 |
| Hopkins, Tony/Friendswood Ind Sch Dist | 67 | 164 |
| Hopper, Carlton/Austwell Tivoli Ind SD | 67 | 326 |
| Hopper, Craig/De Leon Ind School Dist | 58 | 93 |
| Hopper, Creig/Rising Star Ind Sch Dist | 58 | 133 |
| Hopper, James/Venus Ind School Dist | 1 | 252 |
| Hopson, Donna/Quinlan Ind School Dist | 85 | 240 |
| Hopson, Lily/Livingston Ind School Dist | 294 | 319 |
| Horelica, Missy/Devers Ind School Dist | 16,69 | 268 |
| Horelka, Sally/Bloomington Ind School Dist | 16 | 384 |
| Hormann, Jody/Leander Ind School Dist | 6 | 399 |
| Horn, Chris/Bloomington Ind School Dist | 6 | 384 |
| Horn, Johnnie/Taylor Ind School Dist | 3 | 402 |
| Horn, Julie/Navasota Ind School Dist | 42,45 | 177 |
| Horn, Kelly/Arlington Ind School Dist | 3 | 346 |
| Hornacky, Libby/Shiner Ind School Dist | 7 | 265 |
| Hornback, Jackie/Sweeny Ind School Dist | 2 | 57 |
| Hornberger, David/Alamo Heights Ind School Dist | 67 | 33 |
| Horner, Jeff/Midland Ind School Dist | 10 | 288 |
| Hornsby, Ann/Cross Roads Ind School Dist | 2 | 218 |
| Hornsby, Janice/Axtell Ind School Dist | 31,73,83,286,298 | 281 |
| Horrice, Shirley/Bynum Ind School Dist | 4 | 230 |
| Horton, Bill/Wichita Falls Ind School Dist | 91 | 395 |
| Horton, Pam/Aquilla Ind School Dist | 70 | 230 |
| Horton, Paula/Jasper Ind School Dist | 2,294 | 243 |
| Horton, Robert, Dr/Conroe Ind School Dist | 20,23 | 294 |
| Horton, Stacie/Wheeler Ind School Dist | 2,19,298 | 394 |
| Horton, Tamela, Dr/Arlington Ind School Dist | 8 | 346 |
| Hosek, Tracy/Keller Ind School Dist | 42 | 357 |
| Hosford, Debbie/Denison Ind School Dist | 4 | 171 |
| Hoskin, Anne/Alief Ind School Dist | 47 | 186 |
| Hoskins, Ken/Lazbuddie Ind School Dist | 285 | 318 |
| Hottman, Sarah/Etoile Ind School Dist | 1,11 | 300 |
| Houck, Lettie/Spring Ind School Dist | 57 | 207 |
| Hough, Eric/Aubrey Ind School Dist | 2,19 | 124 |
| Houlbec, Cody/Rochelle Ind School Dist | 27 | 281 |
| House, Kelli/Avery Ind School Dist | 2 | 325 |
| Houska, Jennifer/Wheeler Ind School Dist | 58 | 394 |
| Houston, Brandon/Buffalo Ind School Dist | 6,35 | 266 |
| Houston, Cheryl/Seminole Ind School Dist | 7,85 | 162 |
| Houy, Dawn/Valentine Ind School Dist | 8,36,288 | 244 |
| Howard-Schwind, Michelle, Dr/DeSoto Ind School Dist | 8,15 | 108 |
| Howard, Aimee/Farmersville Ind School Dist | 7 | 82 |
| Howard, Amy/Grapeland Ind School Dist | 57,271 | 235 |
| Howard, Chris/Connally Ind School Dist | 57,69,294 | 282 |
| Howard, Dee/Wimberley Ind School Dist | 8,11,15,286,288,296,298 | 217 |
| **Howard, Drew, Dr**/Sweetwater ISD School Dist | 1 | 304 |
| Howard, Elaine/Boerne Ind School Dist | 68,79 | 257 |
| Howard, Jean/Cooper Ind School Dist | 271 | 124 |
| Howard, Jeff/Brownsboro Ind School Dist | 3,5,91 | 218 |
| Howard, Joy/Borger Ind School Dist | 4 | 240 |

| NAME/District | JOB FUNCTIONS | PAGE |
|---|---|---|
| Howard, Laura/San Angelo Ind School Dist | 73 | 367 |
| Howard, Lisa/China Spring Ind School Dist | 11,58 | 281 |
| Howard, Mason/Brazosport Ind School Dist | 67 | 55 |
| Howard, Matthew/Winters Ind School Dist | 73,295 | 329 |
| Howard, Mindy/Troy Ind School Dist | 27,33,273 | 33 |
| Howard, Misty/Wimberley Ind School Dist | 57 | 217 |
| Howard, Sandy/Lipan Ind School Dist | 271 | 233 |
| Howard, Sonja/Del Valle Ind School Dist | 48 | 372 |
| Howard, Stephanie, Dr/Ector Co Ind School Dist | 3,6,68 | 134 |
| Howard, Steve/May Ind School Dist | 1 | 62 |
| Howard, Suzie/Ricardo Ind School Dist | 7,85 | 261 |
| Howard, Tana/Sands Consolidated ISD | 69,83,270 | 121 |
| Howard, Teresa/Clyde Consolidated Ind SD | 16 | 66 |
| Howard, Tonia/Lancaster Ind School Dist | 18,74 | 114 |
| Howe, Stephanie/Crawford Ind School Dist | 4 | 282 |
| Howell, Alyssa/Houston Ind School Dist | 47 | 193 |
| Howell, Brandi/Darrouzett Ind School Dist | 4 | 270 |
| Howell, Sandra/Little Elm Ind School Dist | 6 | 128 |
| Howell, Tracy/Leonard Ind School Dist | 271 | 150 |
| Howes, Rusty/Panhandle Ind School Dist | 73,295 | 73 |
| Howeth, Christie/Knox City-O'Brien Cons Ind SD | 34,69,270 | 261 |
| Howeth, Colin/Knox City-O'Brien Cons Ind SD | 1,84 | 261 |
| Howey, Todd/San Antonio Ind School Dist | 6,42 | 42 |
| Hoya, Henry/Broaddus Ind School Dist | 5 | 332 |
| Hoyer, Randy, Dr/Orange Grove Ind School Dist | 1 | 248 |
| Hruska, Jed/Reagan Co Ind School Dist | 67 | 324 |
| Hruska, Jessica/Harlingen Cons Ind School Dist | 73 | 68 |
| Hruska, Mike/Dripping Springs Ind Sch Dist | 3 | 215 |
| Hryhorchuk, Sharlene/Deweyville Ind School Dist | 4 | 311 |
| Hubanek, Greg/San Marcos Cons Ind Sch Dist | 73,76,295 | 217 |
| Hubbard, Brandon/Chilton Ind School Dist | 1,11 | 148 |
| Hubbard, Joseph/Jarrell Ind School Dist | 295 | 399 |
| Hubbard, Kim/Peaster Ind School Dist | 12,271 | 316 |
| Hubble, Casey/Breckenridge Ind School Dist | 6 | 344 |
| Huber, Brandon/Goliad Ind School Dist | 67 | 168 |
| Huber, Mollie/Troy Ind School Dist | 38 | 33 |
| Huber, Patricia/Goliad Ind School Dist | 9,34 | 168 |
| Huckabee, Justin/McLeod Ind School Dist | 16,73,286,295 | 74 |
| Huckaby, Chad/Martinsville Ind School Dist | 73,76 | 301 |
| Huddleston, Gena/East Chambers Ind School Dist | 2 | 76 |
| Huddleston, Norman/Hallsburg Ind School Dist | 67 | 282 |
| Huddleston, Shelly/San Angelo Ind School Dist | 8,18 | 367 |
| Huddleston, Sigrid/Sidney Ind School Dist | 8,58,88 | 94 |
| Hudgens, Robin/Borger Ind School Dist | 5 | 240 |
| Hudgeons, Jennifer/Cuero Ind School Dist | 16 | 121 |
| Hudgins, Courtney/East Bernard Ind Sch Dist | 1 | 392 |
| Hudson, Buck/Spurger Ind School Dist | 27 | 377 |
| Hudson, Cheryl/Lingleville Ind School Dist | 36,83 | 148 |
| Hudson, Emma/Miller Grove Ind School Dist | 58,88 | 234 |
| Hudson, Gerald, Dr/Cedar Hill Ind School Dist | 1 | 101 |
| Hudson, Jason/Cumby Ind School Dist | 67 | 234 |
| Hudson, Jason/Wylie Ind School Dist | 27 | 88 |
| Hudson, Kenny/Royse City Ind School Dist | 11,15,296 | 328 |
| Hudson, Larry/Richardson Ind School Dist | 5 | 116 |
| Hudson, Les/Bastrop Ind School Dist | 79 | 26 |
| Hudson, Logan/Miami Ind School Dist | 67 | 327 |
| Hudson, Natalie/Goose Creek Cons Ind Sch Dist | 58 | 192 |
| Hudson, Robert/Westphalia Ind School Dist | 1,11 | 149 |
| Hudson, Robert/Westphalia Ind School Dist | 6,69,83,270 | 149 |
| Hudson, Sha-Ree/Neches Ind School Dist | 8,12,69,83,88,285,752 | 18 |
| Hudson, Tijuana/Duncanville Ind School Dist | 88 | 108 |
| Hudson, Warren/Venus Ind School Dist | 73 | 252 |
| Hudson, Zach/Mabank Ind School Dist | 6 | 256 |
| Huebner, Tiffany/San Angelo Ind School Dist | 20,23,81 | 367 |
| Huerta, Armando/Odem-Edroy Ind School Dist | 6 | 334 |
| Huerta, Brittany/Sundown Ind School Dist | 7 | 232 |
| Huerta, Rosie/Mathis Ind School Dist | 5 | 334 |

| NAME/District | JOB FUNCTIONS | PAGE | NAME/District | JOB FUNCTIONS | PAGE |
|---|---|---|---|---|---|
| Hues, Tommy/Shepherd Ind School Dist | 73,84 | 333 | Husen, Natalie/Graham Ind School Dist | 11,58 | 409 |
| Hueske, Debbie/Corrigan-Camden Ind Sch Dist | 4 | 319 | Husfeld, Earl/Aledo Ind School Dist | 2,19 | 315 |
| Huey, Flint/Hondo Ind School Dist | 88 | 287 | Hussaker, Michelle/Hawley Ind School Dist | 7 | 253 |
| Huey, Kathy/White Settlement Ind Sch Dist | 4 | 360 | Hutchins, Climet/Goodrich Ind School Dist | 3,5 | 319 |
| Huff, Audra/Three Rivers Ind School Dist | 11,52,58,286,296 | 271 | Hutchins, Darla/Midway Ind School Dist | 11,73,84,286 | 78 |
| Huff, Brian/Castleberry Ind School Dist | 84,295 | 350 | Hutchinson, Kathy/Levelland Ind School Dist | 12,58 | 232 |
| Huff, Cidney/Grapeland Ind School Dist | 69,79 | 235 | Hutchinson, Leslie/Paducah Ind School Dist | 8 | 97 |
| Huff, Eric/Aubrey Ind School Dist | 3,17 | 124 | Hutchison, Christine/Brackett Ind School Dist | 77,88 | 260 |
| Huff, Hudson/Keller Ind School Dist | 3 | 357 | Hutchison, David/College Station Ind Sch Dist | 73 | 59 |
| Huff, Karen/Coleman Ind School Dist | 2 | 79 | Hutchison, Kenneth/Blooming Grove Ind School Dist | 3,5 | 302 |
| Hugg, Randall/Killeen Ind School Dist | 6 | 30 | Hutsell, Richard/Elysian Fields Ind School Dist | 2 | 213 |
| Hughes, Carissa/Coahoma Ind School Dist | 35,83,85 | 237 | Hutson, Donna/Lake Worth Ind School Dist | 67 | 358 |
| Hughes, Carrie/City View Ind School Dist | 8,11,16,57,69,88,273 | 394 | Hutto, Karen/Hudson Ind School Dist | 4 | 20 |
| Hughes, Danielle/Robinson Ind School Dist | 57 | 284 | Hyde, Brady/Rocksprings Ind School Dist | 67 | 135 |
| Hughes, Dant/Water Valley Ind School Dist | 3,5 | 368 | Hyde, David/Navarro Ind School Dist | 295 | 178 |
| Hughes, Heather, Dr/Eagle Mtn-Saginaw Ind Sch Dist | 58,77 | 351 | Hyde, Duane/Highland Ind School Dist | 1,11 | 304 |
| Hughes, Holly/Clear Creek Ind School Dist | 9,15 | 162 | Hyde, Jk/Mabank Ind School Dist | 73,295,297 | 256 |
| Hughes, Jason/Lewisville Ind School Dist | 3 | 126 | Hyde, Kelly/Navarro Ind School Dist | 5 | 178 |
| Hughes, Jessica Lily/Spring Branch Ind School Dist | 16 | 205 | Hyde, Shalana/Hudson Ind School Dist | 7 | 20 |
| Hughes, John/Birdville Ind School Dist | 3 | 348 | Hyde, Tonya, Dr/Lackland Ind School Dist | 8,11,57,83,88,288 | 37 |
| Hughes, John/Kaufman Ind School Dist | 3 | 255 | Hyles, Lisa/Maypearl Ind School Dist | 8 | 145 |
| Hughes, Luann/Rockwall Ind School Dist | 16,73,76,82,295 | 328 | Hymer, Josh/Bremond Ind School Dist | 73,76 | 327 |
| Hughes, Mary/Shallowater Ind School Dist | 7,12,15,69,275,295 | 274 | Hyndran, Justin/Southland Ind School Dist | 3,5 | 167 |
| Hughes, Robyn/Conroe Ind School Dist | 4 | 294 | Hysinger, Monty/Dumas Ind School Dist | 1 | 298 |
| Hughes, Scotty/West Hardin Co Cons Sch Dist | 67 | 183 | | | |
| Hughes, Susan/Ft Elliott Cons Ind Sch Dist | 58 | 393 | | | |
| Hughes, Sylvia/Amarillo Ind School Dist | 57,271 | 320 | Iacoponelli, Mark/Cuero Ind School Dist | 2,15 | 121 |
| Hughes, Vada/Lufkin Ind School Dist | 42 | 21 | Ibanez, Matt/Buna Ind School Dist | 295 | 243 |
| Huime, Mindy/Midway Ind School Dist | 274 | 283 | Ibarra, Edgar/Mission Cons Ind School Dist | 57 | 225 |
| Hulbert, Jonathan/East Central Ind School Dist | 69 | 34 | Ibarra, Hugo/Bryan Ind School Dist | 71 | 58 |
| Hulett, Brian/Springtown Ind School Dist | 6 | 316 | Ibarra, Laticia/Mission Cons Ind School Dist | 6 | 225 |
| Hull, Teresa/Cypress-Fairbanks Ind Sch Dist | 751 | 189 | Ibarra, Martin/Chapel Hill Ind School Dist | 67 | 339 |
| Hullender, Deanne/Dallas Co Schools | 16,70 | 99 | Ibarra, Norma, Dr/Brownsville Ind School Dist | 10 | 66 |
| Hullender, Deanne/Hurst-Euless-Bedford ISD | 71 | 356 | Ibarra, Sylvia/McAllen Ind School Dist | 8,15 | 224 |
| Hullihen, Shelly/San Angelo Ind School Dist | 15 | 367 | Icenhower, Kim/Texarkana Ind School Dist | 73 | 53 |
| Hullman, David/Eastland Ind School Dist | 67 | 133 | Ideus, John/Sweeny Ind School Dist | 91 | 57 |
| Hulme, Thom/Coppell Ind School Dist | 67 | 102 | Igo, Tony/Smyer Ind School Dist | 9,11,57,271 | 232 |
| Humiston, Laurie/Kennedale Ind School Dist | 4 | 358 | Ikard, Tricia/Maypearl Ind School Dist | 58 | 145 |
| Humphrey, Beverly/Lancaster Ind School Dist | 6,71 | 114 | Imnan, Natalie/Bloomburg Ind School Dist | 17,69,273 | 73 |
| Humphrey, Concan/Bonham Ind School Dist | 5 | 149 | Inboden, Cheryl/Deweyville Ind School Dist | 16 | 311 |
| Humphrey, Deanna/Anahuac Ind School Dist | 11,36,57,58,69,83,88 | 75 | Indelicato, Anthony, Dr/Ft Bend Ind School Dist | 15,70,751 | 153 |
| Humphrey, Megan/Rockwall Ind School Dist | 46 | 328 | Ingle, Regina/Morton Ind School Dist | 271 | 78 |
| Humphrey, Ronnie/Mt Pleasant Ind School Dist | 91 | 366 | Ingram, Jennell/Texarkana Ind School Dist | 273 | 53 |
| Humphrey, Shae/Newcastle Ind School Dist | 58 | 409 | Ingram, Jennifer/Evant Ind School Dist | 2 | 96 |
| Humphrey, Troy/Walnut Bend Ind School Dist | 1,11,73,83 | 96 | Ingram, Jodie/North Lamar Ind School Dist | 73 | 406 |
| Humphreys, Connie/Rochelle Ind School Dist | 58 | 281 | Ingram, Kelly/Region 4 Ed Service Center | 8,15 | 213 |
| Humphries, Jamie/Honey Grove Ind School Dist | 76 | 150 | Inman, Robert/Hudson Ind School Dist | 295 | 20 |
| Hunger, Tena/Nueces Canyon Cons Ind SD | 297 | 135 | Inman, Suzie/Texarkana Ind School Dist | 7 | 53 |
| Hungteres, Debbie/Wellington Ind School Dist | 4 | 90 | Inman, Suzie/Texarkana Ind School Dist | 7 | 53 |
| Hunkapillar, Cortney/Denison Ind School Dist | 2 | 171 | Irby, Melissa/Abilene Ind School Dist | 2 | 362 |
| Hunt, Becky/Allen Ind School Dist | 27,31 | 80 | Irvin, Jack/Pine Tree Ind School Dist | 5,91 | 175 |
| Hunt, Beth/Tomball Ind School Dist | 4 | 208 | Irvin, Jeff/Quinlan Ind School Dist | 1 | 240 |
| Hunt, Brad/Coppell Ind School Dist | 1 | 102 | Irwin, Dale/Arp Ind School Dist | 6 | 339 |
| Hunt, Brian/Hico Ind School Dist | 57 | 181 | Irwin, Danny/Nueces Canyon Cons Ind SD | 67 | 135 |
| Hunt, Bud/Miles Ind School Dist | 3,5 | 329 | Irwin, Lori/Idalou Ind School Dist | 57,69,270,271 | 272 |
| Hunt, Jan/Crane Ind School Dist | 1 | 97 | Isaacs, Caloby/Goodrich Ind School Dist | 8,288 | 319 |
| Hunt, John/Kennedale Ind School Dist | 67 | 358 | Isabel, Connie/Lancaster Ind School Dist | 69 | 114 |
| Hunt, Laura/Whitney Ind School Dist | 288,298 | 231 | Ishmael, Clint/Grandview Ind School Dist | 67 | 251 |
| Hunter, Casey/Burkburnett Ind Sch Dist | 27,298 | 394 | Iske, Kris/White Oak Ind School Dist | 6 | 176 |
| Hunter, Kandi/Arlington Ind School Dist | 45 | 346 | Isnhower, Lynn/Quanah Ind School Dist | 4 | 182 |
| Hunter, Mark/Highland Park Ind Sch Dist | 295 | 112 | Israel, Kimberley/Eanes Ind School Dist | 76 | 372 |
| Hunter, Robert/Rockdale Ind School Dist | 5 | 290 | Ivey, Jami/Athens Ind School Dist | 10,15 | 218 |
| Hunter, Sam/Munday Consolidated Ind SD | 67 | 262 | Ivey, Karen/Hardin Ind School Dist | 8 | 268 |
| Hunter, Tommy, Dr/Sanger Ind School Dist | 1 | 130 | Ivey, Keitha/Amarillo Ind School Dist | 76 | 320 |
| Hurd, Clifford/Palmer Ind School Dist | 5 | 146 | Ivey, Kyle/Central Ind School Dist | 73,286 | 20 |
| Hurst, Curtis/Priddy Ind School Dist | 6 | 292 | Ivey, Martin, Dr/Brock Ind School Dist | 67 | 315 |
| Hurst, Kashonda/Humble Ind School Dist | 68 | 200 | Ivey, Robert/Canton Ind School Dist | 6 | 382 |
| Hurst, Luke/McKinney Ind School Dist | 81 | 84 | Ivey, Rusty/Gilmer Ind School Dist | 73 | 379 |
| Hurst, Monica/Iola Ind School Dist | 73,295 | 177 | Ivey, Tracie/Sam Rayburn Ind School Dist | 2,12 | 150 |
| Hurst, Terry/Bland Ind School Dist | 67 | 238 | Ivicic, Jackie/Jarrell Ind School Dist | 5 | 399 |
| Hurst, Thyrun, Dr/Calvert Ind School Dist | 1 | 327 | Ivy, Adam/Thorndale Ind School Dist | 1,11 | 291 |
| Hurt, Chantele/Blum Ind School Dist | 57 | 230 | Ivy, Anne/Ponder Ind School Dist | 38,88 | 130 |
| Hurtado, Carolina/Kerrville Ind School Dist | 3,91 | 259 | Ivy, Cheree/Wills Point Ind School Dist | 2 | 383 |
| Huschke, Krystal/McMullen Co Ind Sch Dist | 2 | 286 | Ivy, Cindy/Nacogdoches Ind School Dist | 36,69 | 301 |
| Huseman, Colby/Crosbyton Cons Ind Sch Dist | 6 | 98 | Ivy, Keith/Aubrey Ind School Dist | 6 | 124 |
| Huseman, Mike/Tulia Ind School Dist | 2 | 345 | Ivy, Wade/Kerrville Ind School Dist | 15,68,78,79 | 259 |

| NAME/District | JOB FUNCTIONS | PAGE | NAME/District | JOB FUNCTIONS | PAGE |
|---|---|---|---|---|---|
| Jennings, Wayne/Plainview Ind School Dist | 295 | 180 | Johnson, Julea/Bryan Ind School Dist | 73 | 58 |
| Jennings, William/Channelview Ind School Dist | 6,7,35,85 | 188 | Johnson, Julie/Kaufman Ind School Dist | 58 | 255 |
| Jensen, Jennifer/North East Ind School Dist | 285 | 37 | Johnson, Keith/Caldwell Ind School Dist | 73,76 | 63 |
| Jensen, Pam/Leon Ind School Dist | 58 | 267 | Johnson, Kenneth/Judson Ind School Dist | 5 | 36 |
| Jentsch, Clint/Grandview Ind School Dist | 37 | 251 | Johnson, Kim/Kemp Ind School Dist | 2 | 255 |
| Jerkins, Greg/Stafford Municipal Sch Dist | 5 | 159 | Johnson, Kim/Mesquite Ind School Dist | 58 | 115 |
| Jernegen, Farrah/Hallettsville Ind Sch Dist | 73,295 | 265 | Johnson, Kimberly/Midway Ind School Dist | 46 | 283 |
| Jernigan, Laramie/Shamrock Ind School Dist | 16,73 | 393 | Johnson, Kimberly/Wolfe City Ind School Dist | 7 | 240 |
| Jessee, Stanley/Rivercrest Ind School Dist | 1 | 325 | Johnson, Kyle/Westwood Ind School Dist | 2 | 19 |
| Jessen, Terrell/Boling Ind School Dist | 73 | 392 | Johnson, Kyndra/Richardson Ind School Dist | 285 | 116 |
| Jessie, Shirrell/Corsicana Ind School Dist | 4 | 302 | Johnson, Lance/S & S Cons Ind School Dist | 11,83 | 172 |
| Jester, Linda/Whitewright Ind School Dist | 67 | 173 | Johnson, Lauren/Lubbock Ind School Dist | 4 | 272 |
| Jestis, Heather/Scurry Rosser Ind School Dist | 58 | 256 | Johnson, Laurie/Hale Center Ind School Dist | 38,83 | 180 |
| Jeter, Mendi/Jim Ned Cons Ind School Dist | 58 | 363 | Johnson, Linda/Woodville Ind School Dist | 4 | 378 |
| Jeter, Neil/Troy Ind School Dist | 1 | 33 | Johnson, Mandy/Bangs Ind School Dist | 5 | 61 |
| Jett, Jeri/Borger Ind School Dist | 2 | 240 | Johnson, Margaret/Joshua Ind School Dist | 98 | 251 |
| Jette, Jeanna/Marble Falls Ind School Dist | 298 | 64 | Johnson, Maria/Ft Bend Ind School Dist | 7 | 153 |
| Jimenez, Israel/Nixon-Smiley Cons Ind Sch Dist | 68 | 169 | Johnson, Mark/Giddings Ind School Dist | 67 | 266 |
| Jimenez, Manuel/Olton Ind School Dist | 5 | 263 | Johnson, Marsha/Kaufman Ind School Dist | 294 | 255 |
| Jimenez, Margarito/Progreso Ind School Dist | 6 | 227 | Johnson, Mary/Lumberton Ind School Dist | 73,286,297 | 183 |
| Jimenez, Rudy/North East Ind School Dist | 15 | 37 | Johnson, Michael/Hallsburg Ind School Dist | 73,286 | 282 |
| Jimenez, Sandra/Lubbock-Cooper Ind Sch Dist | 57,271 | 274 | Johnson, Michael/Henrietta Ind School Dist | 6 | 78 |
| Jimerson, Bret, Dr/Burleson Ind School Dist | 1 | 249 | Johnson, Michael/Malone Independent School Dist | 76 | 231 |
| Jimerson, Terence/Jefferson Ind School Dist | 88 | 277 | Johnson, Michael/Westphalia Ind School Dist | 73,76,295 | 149 |
| Jimmerson, Antwain/Jefferson Ind School Dist | 6 | 277 | Johnson, Michelle/Silsbee Ind School Dist | 4 | 183 |
| Jinkins, Mike/Huntington Ind School Dist | 91 | 20 | Johnson, Mid, Dr/Timpson Ind School Dist | 1 | 338 |
| Jinks, Robert/Katy Ind School Dist | 91 | 156 | Johnson, Molly/Breckenridge Ind School Dist | 8,11,69,88,273,296 | 344 |
| Jinnette, Preston/Eanes Ind School Dist | 295 | 372 | Johnson, Monica/Arp Ind School Dist | 37 | 339 |
| Jobe, Laura/Mesquite Ind School Dist | 71,297 | 115 | Johnson, Nancy/Dublin Ind School Dist | 7 | 147 |
| Joffre, Cassie/Italy Ind School Dist | 16 | 145 | Johnson, Nicholas/DeSoto Ind School Dist | 27,285 | 108 |
| Joffre, Lee/Italy Ind School Dist | 8 | 145 | Johnson, Paige/Dublin Ind School Dist | 69 | 147 |
| Johns, Nicole/Galena Park Ind School Dist | 275 | 191 | Johnson, Pam/Hale Center Ind School Dist | 67 | 180 |
| Johns, Wendell/Clear Creek Ind School Dist | 5 | 162 | Johnson, Peggy, Dr/La Vega Ind School Dist | 9,11,294,296,298 | 282 |
| Johnson, Adrian, Dr/Hearne Ind School Dist | 1 | 327 | Johnson, Randy/Forsan Ind School Dist | 1 | 237 |
| Johnson, Andy/Simms Ind School Dist | 8,11,298 | 53 | Johnson, Richard/Bay City Ind School Dist | 2,19 | 278 |
| Johnson, Angela/Archdiocese Galveston-Houston | 15 | 209 | Johnson, Robin/Blanco Ind School Dist | 7 | 49 |
| Johnson, Ann, Dr/Humble Ind School Dist | 8,18 | 200 | Johnson, Sarah/Palestine Ind School Dist | 36 | 18 |
| Johnson, Annette/Timpson Ind School Dist | 73,76 | 338 | Johnson, Shane/Cushing Ind School Dist | 83,91 | 300 |
| Johnson, Barbara/Dallas Ind School Dist | 35 | 102 | Johnson, Shane/Cushing Ind School Dist | 5,83,91 | 300 |
| Johnson, Billy/Crowley Ind School Dist | 15,79,83,85 | 350 | Johnson, Sharon/Bruceville-Eddy Ind Sch Dist | 9 | 281 |
| Johnson, Billy/Marlin Ind School Dist | 67 | 149 | Johnson, Shellie/Keller Ind School Dist | 71 | 357 |
| Johnson, Bridget/Aransas Co Ind School Dist | 68 | 22 | Johnson, Slade/Wells Ind School Dist | 73,295,296 | 77 |
| Johnson, Bridget/Canyon Ind School Dist | 58 | 323 | Johnson, Stace/Waxahachie Ind School Dist | 46 | 146 |
| Johnson, Butch/Denver City Ind School Dist | 3 | 409 | Johnson, Stacy/Springtown Ind School Dist | 34,58 | 316 |
| Johnson, Carleen/Alief Ind School Dist | 7 | 186 | Johnson, Steve/Lockhart Ind School Dist | 67 | 64 |
| Johnson, Carol/Quanah Ind School Dist | 83 | 182 | Johnson, Steve/Miller Grove Ind School Dist | 1,11,83 | 234 |
| Johnson, Casey/Center Point Ind School Dist | 8,12,16,73,79,286 | 258 | Johnson, Sunni, Dr/Northwest Ind School Dist | 49,52,55 | 129 |
| Johnson, Cherrhunda/Galena Park Ind School Dist | 71 | 191 | Johnson, Susan/Corsicana Ind School Dist | 71,76,93,297 | 302 |
| Johnson, Christine/Aransas Pass Ind School Dist | 58 | 333 | Johnson, Susan/Magnolia Ind School Dist | 45 | 295 |
| Johnson, Connie/Spring Hill Ind School Dist | 69 | 175 | Johnson, Susan/Victoria Ind School Dist | 47 | 384 |
| Johnson, Dana/Georgetown Ind School Dist | 58 | 398 | Johnson, Teresa/School of Excellence In Ed | 11,298 | 45 |
| Johnson, Debbie/Lexington Ind School Dist | 16,82 | 266 | Johnson, Terry/Karnes City Ind School Dist | 67 | 253 |
| Johnson, Debbie/Maud Ind School Dist | 4 | 52 | Johnson, Terry/McDade Ind School Dist | 2,3,5,91 | 27 |
| Johnson, Deitra/Splendora Ind School Dist | 71 | 297 | Johnson, Tom/North East Ind School Dist | 16,73 | 37 |
| Johnson, Dina/Blanco Ind School Dist | 8,11,57,88,271,288,294 | 49 | **Johnson, Tom/**Quanah Ind School Dist | 1 | 182 |
| Johnson, Dixie/Tulia Ind School Dist | 34,58,275 | 345 | Johnson, Tracy/Keller Ind School Dist | 15,68 | 357 |
| Johnson, Eileen/Henderson Ind School Dist | 58,77 | 330 | Johnson, Victrina/Trinidad Ind School Dist | 58 | 219 |
| Johnson, Eileen/Prosper Ind School Dist | 4 | 88 | Johnson, Wanda/Tom Bean Ind School Dist | 58 | 173 |
| Johnson, Frank/Holliday Ind School Dist | 6 | 22 | Johnson, Whitney/Tomball Ind School Dist | 4 | 208 |
| Johnson, Jamey, Dr/Brenham Ind School Dist | 8,15 | 388 | Johnson, Yvonne/Shepherd Ind School Dist | 67 | 333 |
| Johnson, Jamey, Dr/Huntsville Ind School Dist | 10 | 386 | Johnston, Bill, Dr/Red Oak Ind School Dist | 2,19 | 146 |
| Johnson, Jason/Daingerfield-Lone Star Ind SD | 16,73,295 | 299 | Johnston, Chris/Celeste Ind School Dist | 73 | 239 |
| Johnson, Jason/Van Ind School Dist | 73 | 383 | Johnston, Debbie/Newton Ind School Dist | 8,69 | 304 |
| Johnson, Jay/Cypress-Fairbanks Ind Sch Dist | 28 | 189 | Johnston, Drew/Newton Ind School Dist | 6 | 304 |
| Johnson, Jeanie, Dr/Midway Ind School Dist | 15,79,91 | 283 | Johnston, Jajean/Grape Creek Ind School Dist | 7 | 367 |
| Johnson, Jeff/Leonard Ind School Dist | 11,15,296 | 150 | Johnston, Jason/Leander Ind School Dist | 76 | 400 |
| Johnson, Jennifer/Comal Ind School Dist | 79,275 | 91 | Johnston, Jessica/Brenham Ind School Dist | 71 | 388 |
| Johnson, Jennifer/Poth Ind School Dist | 2 | 404 | Johnston, Lana/Brazos Ind School Dist | 58 | 25 |
| Johnson, Jennifer/Rains Ind School Dist | 1,11 | 323 | Johnston, Mary, Dr/Rockwall Ind School Dist | 9,18 | 328 |
| Johnson, Jennifer/Rockwall Ind School Dist | 47 | 328 | Johnston, Ryan/Region 2 Ed Service Center | 2,76 | 309 |
| Johnson, Jessica, Dr/Dayton Ind School Dist | 1 | 268 | Johnston, Sonya/Whitehouse Ind School Dist | 36,69,83 | 341 |
| Johnson, Jody/Vega Ind School Dist | 1,11 | 310 | Johnston, Susan/Sulphur Springs Ind Sch Dist | 58 | 235 |
| Johnson, Joel/Northwest Ind School Dist | 6,35 | 128 | Johnstone, Whitcomb, Dr/Irving Ind School Dist | 70 | 113 |
| Johnson, John/Tyler Ind School Dist | 79 | 340 | Jolivette, Alishia/Houston Ind School Dist | 3 | 193 |
| **Johnson, Josh/**Leveretts Chapel Ind Sch Dist | 1 | 330 | Jolly, Cynthia/Tahoka Ind School Dist | 16 | 276 |
| Johnson, Judith/San Perlita Ind School Dist | 294 | 397 | Jolly, Darin, Dr/North Hopkins Ind School Dist | 1 | 234 |

| NAME/District | JOB FUNCTIONS | PAGE |
|---|---|---|
| Jolly, Linda/Region 18 Ed Service Center | 58 | 290 |
| Jondron, Dacia/Princeton Ind School Dist | 7 | 87 |
| Jones, Akiko/Mt Enterprise Ind School Dist | 58 | 330 |
| Jones, Akiko/Overton Ind School Dist | 58 | 331 |
| Jones, Becky/Comanche Ind School Dist | 58 | 93 |
| Jones, Beth/San Antonio Ind School Dist | 58,77 | 42 |
| Jones, Bill/Gause Ind School Dist | 67 | 290 |
| Jones, Blanca/Beaumont Ind School Dist | 57 | 244 |
| Jones, Bob/Sherman Ind School Dist | 6 | 172 |
| Jones, Bobbie/Terlingua Common School Dist | 11,83 | 60 |
| Jones, Brad/Gause Ind School Dist | 1,11 | 290 |
| Jones, Brad/Rule Ind School Dist | 1 | 215 |
| Jones, Cami/Hardin Ind School Dist | 11,57,296 | 268 |
| Jones, Carolyn/Garner Ind School Dist | 2,13 | 315 |
| Jones, Carolyn/Leakey Ind School Dist | 5 | 324 |
| Jones, Casey/Hamilton Ind School Dist | 6 | 181 |
| Jones, Cecelia/Little Elm Ind School Dist | 71 | 128 |
| Jones, Chad/Sinton Ind School Dist | 1 | 334 |
| Jones, Chad, Dr/Lamar Cons Ind School Dist | 16,286 | 157 |
| Jones, Charlotte/Milano Ind School Dist | 76 | 290 |
| Jones, Charollete/McCamey Ind School Dist | 67 | 380 |
| Jones, Cheryl/Tom Bean Ind School Dist | 16,73,82 | 173 |
| Jones, Connie/Shamrock Ind School Dist | 2 | 393 |
| Jones, Craig/Kirbyville Cons Ind Sch Dist | 6 | 244 |
| Jones, Dale/Ira Ind School Dist | 13 | 336 |
| Jones, David/Kerrville Ind School Dist | 6 | 259 |
| Jones, Deb/Blanket Ind School Dist | 69,83,85,88 | 61 |
| Jones, Debbie/Columbia Brazoria ISD | 5 | 56 |
| Jones, Deborah/Central Heights Ind Sch Dist | 58 | 300 |
| Jones, Debra/Adrian Ind School Dist | 7 | 310 |
| Jones, Dwayne/Crowley Ind School Dist | 2 | 350 |
| Jones, Emily/Burleson Ind School Dist | 4 | 249 |
| Jones, Etola/Shelbyville Ind School Dist | 67 | 337 |
| Jones, Glen/Veribest Ind School Dist | 10 | 368 |
| Jones, Greg/Detroit Ind School Dist | 2,11 | 325 |
| Jones, Jason/Blackwell Cons Ind Sch Dist | 67 | 304 |
| Jones, Jason/McMullen Co Ind Sch Dist | 1 | 286 |
| Jones, Jeff/Anna Ind School Dist | 91 | 81 |
| Jones, Jeff/Glasscock Co Ind School Dist | 6 | 168 |
| Jones, Jeff/Monahans-Wickett-Pyote ISD | 3 | 388 |
| Jones, Jeff/Wortham Ind School Dist | 67 | 161 |
| Jones, Jennifer/Tyler Ind School Dist | 9,36 | 340 |
| Jones, Jill/Blackwell Cons Ind Sch Dist | 2 | 304 |
| Jones, Jim/Quanah Ind School Dist | 2 | 182 |
| Jones, Joey/Longview Ind School Dist | 2,19 | 174 |
| Jones, Joey/Schleicher Co Ind Sch Dist | 5 | 335 |
| Jones, Joffery, Dr/Klein Ind School Dist | 91 | 202 |
| Jones, Kayce/College Station Ind Sch Dist | 59 | 59 |
| Jones, Keith/McLeod Ind School Dist | 91 | 74 |
| Jones, Keith, Dr/Deweyville Ind School Dist | 1,11 | 311 |
| Jones, Kellie/Greenville Ind School Dist | 5 | 239 |
| Jones, Kevin/Harleton Ind School Dist | 73,76 | 213 |
| Jones, Kristie/Pewitt Cons Ind School Dist | 11,288 | 299 |
| Jones, Kurt/Burnet Cons Ind Sch Dist | 6 | 63 |
| Jones, Lanell/Aransas Pass Ind School Dist | 4 | 333 |
| Jones, Laurl/George West Ind School Dist | 76 | 271 |
| Jones, Leann/Palmer Ind School Dist | 31 | 146 |
| Jones, Lisa/Crosby Ind School Dist | 2,11,19 | 188 |
| Jones, Lisa/Era Ind School Dist | 12,57 | 94 |
| Jones, Lisa/Houston Ind School Dist | 7 | 193 |
| Jones, Lisa/Tahoka Ind School Dist | 2,4,12,19 | 276 |
| Jones, Lois/Santa Fe Ind School Dist | 90 | 165 |
| Jones, Lori/Northside Ind School Dist | 15,73 | 39 |
| Jones, Maria/Burleson Ind School Dist | 57 | 249 |
| Jones, Maria/Mineral Wells Ind School Dist | 67 | 313 |
| Jones, Mary/Eastland Ind School Dist | 2 | 133 |
| Jones, Mary/Sunray Ind School Dist | 275 | 299 |
| Jones, Mary, Dr/Eagle Mtn-Saginaw Ind Sch Dist | 11,69,88,271,296 | 351 |
| Jones, Marybeth/Sunray Ind School Dist | 35,36,69,83 | 299 |
| Jones, Matthew/New Braunfels Ind School Dist | 16,73,295 | 92 |
| Jones, Michelle/Hamlin Collegiate Ind Sch Dist | 58 | 252 |
| Jones, Mike/Lamar Cons Ind School Dist | 5 | 157 |
| Jones, Mike/Trenton Ind School Dist | 6 | 151 |
| Jones, Mike/Valley Mills Ind School Dist | 67 | 50 |
| Jones, Naiomo/Lockney Independent Sch Dist | 11 | 153 |
| Jones, Niki/Region 8 Ed Service Center | 7,271 | 72 |
| Jones, Patrick/Midland Ind School Dist | 8,18 | 288 |
| Jones, Paul/Boys Ranch Ind School Dist | 6,15,275 | 310 |
| Jones, Paul/Paris Ind School Dist | 1 | 262 |
| Jones, Racheal/Burnet Cons Ind Sch Dist | 11,16,27,57,83,296,298 | 63 |
| Jones, Randy/Athens Ind School Dist | 2,19 | 218 |
| Jones, Robert/Balmorhea Ind School Dist | 6 | 325 |
| Jones, Roberta/Gilmer Ind School Dist | 4 | 378 |
| Jones, Ron/Tyler Ind School Dist | 15,68,751 | 340 |
| Jones, Samantha/De Leon Ind School Dist | 4,11,271,286,298 | 93 |
| Jones, Shane/Lampasas Ind School Dist | 2,19 | 264 |
| Jones, Shannon/Huffman Ind School Dist | 91 | 200 |
| Jones, Sharon/Edgewood Ind School Dist | 2 | 382 |
| Jones, Shawn/Huntington Ind School Dist | 6 | 20 |
| Jones, Sheila/Quinlan Ind School Dist | 58 | 240 |
| Jones, Stacy/Cross Plains Ind Sch Dist | 8,69,83,88,275,294 | 66 |
| Jones, Tamera/Leary Ind School Dist | 59 | 51 |
| Jones, Tammy/Troup Ind School Dist | 1 | 340 |
| Jones, Taygon/Montague Ind School Dist | 67 | 293 |
| Jones, Terisa/Sonora Ind School Dist | 90,752 | 345 |
| Jones, Terrell/Texline Ind School Dist | 1 | 99 |
| Jones, Thresha/Bloomburg Ind School Dist | 67 | 73 |
| Jones, Tiffanie/Mt Enterprise Ind School Dist | 36,69,83,88 | 330 |
| Jones, Tiffany/Clifton Ind School Dist | 8,11 | 49 |
| Jones, Timothy/Dallas Co Schools | 3 | 99 |
| Jones, Todd/Era Ind School Dist | 8 | 94 |
| Jones, Traci/Harleton Ind School Dist | 270 | 213 |
| Jones, Vernora/Tyler Ind School Dist | 12 | 340 |
| Jones, Wes/Granbury Ind School Dist | 68 | 233 |
| Jontra, Stan/Canton Ind School Dist | 73,295 | 382 |
| Jopling, Sandra/Lytle Ind School Dist | 83 | 24 |
| Jordan, Bethany/Pasadena Ind School Dist | 2 | 203 |
| Jordan, Byron/Mt Enterprise Ind School Dist | 1,11 | 330 |
| Jordan, Darelle/Wimberley Ind School Dist | 7,83,85 | 217 |
| Jordan, Dave/Iola Ind School Dist | 3 | 177 |
| Jordan, Elizabeth/Kountze Ind School Dist | 4 | 183 |
| Jordan, Fabiola/Socorro Ind School Dist | 45 | 140 |
| Jordan, Janis/Lake Travis Ind School Dist | 74 | 373 |
| Jordan, Janis, Dr/Northside Ind School Dist | 8,15 | 39 |
| Jordan, Jaretha/Crowley Ind School Dist | 74 | 350 |
| Jordan, Jaretha, Dr/Irving Ind School Dist | 9 | 113 |
| Jordan, Melissa/Devers Ind School Dist | 2,295 | 268 |
| Jordan, Michael/San Antonio Ind School Dist | 88 | 42 |
| Jordan, Sue/Belton Ind School Dist | 67 | 29 |
| Jordan, Vondell/Mason Ind School Dist | 280 | 278 |
| Jordon, Jennifer/Denver City Ind School Dist | 4 | 409 |
| Joseph, Renferd/Alief Ind School Dist | 20,23 | 186 |
| Joseph, Renferd/Manor Ind School Dist | 20,23 | 373 |
| Joseph, Roosevelt/Coldspring-Oakhurst Cons ISD | 91 | 332 |
| Joseph, Stacy/Forney Ind School Dist | 16,73 | 255 |
| Joslin, Chris/Coahoma Ind School Dist | 6 | 237 |
| **Joslin, Cristal/West Sabine Ind Sch Dist** | 1 | 332 |
| Josselet, Kent/Ponder Ind School Dist | 2,15,286 | 130 |
| Jost, Doug/Glasscock Co Ind School Dist | 67 | 168 |
| Joubert, Maggie/Bridge City Ind School Dist | 4 | 311 |
| Joyner, Veronica/Garland Ind School Dist | 61 | 109 |
| Jozwiak, Amy/Burton Ind School Dist | 4 | 388 |
| Juajardo, Rene/Crystal City Ind School Dist | 288 | 410 |
| Juarez, Laura/Lyford Cons Ind School Dist | 58 | 397 |

| | | | | |
|---|---|---|---|---|
| 1 Superintendent | 16 Instructional Media Svcs | 30 Adult Education | 44 Science Sec | 58 Special Education K-12 | 72 Summer School | 88 Alternative/At Risk | 277 Remedial Math K-12 |
| 2 Bus/Finance/Purchasing | 17 Chief Operations Officer | 31 Career/Sch-to-Work K-12 | 45 Math K-12 | 59 Special Education Elem | 73 Instructional Tech | 89 Multi-Cultural Curriculum | 280 Literacy Coach |
| 3 Buildings And Grounds | 18 Chief Academic Officer | 32 Career/Sch-to-Work Elem | 46 Math Elem | 60 Special Education Sec | 74 Inservice Training | 90 Social Work | 285 STEM |
| 4 Food Service | 19 Chief Financial Officer | 33 Career/Sch-to-Work Sec | 47 Math Sec | 61 Foreign/World Lang K-12 | 75 Marketing/Distributive | 91 Safety/Security | 286 Digital Learning |
| 5 Transportation | 20 Art K-12 | 34 Early Childhood Ed | 48 English/Lang Arts K-12 | 62 Foreign/World Lang Elem | 76 Info Systems | 92 Magnet School | 288 Common Core Standards |
| 6 Athletic | 21 Art Elem | 35 Health/Phys Education | 49 English/Lang Arts Elem | 63 Foreign/World Lang Sec | 77 Psychological Assess | 93 Parental Involvement | 294 Accountability |
| 7 Health Services | 22 Art Sec | 36 Guidance Services K-12 | 50 English/Lang Arts Sec | 64 Religious Education K-12 | 78 Affirmative Action | 95 Tech Prep Program | 295 Network System |
| 8 Curric/Instruct K-12 | 23 Music K-12 | 37 Guidance Services Elem | 51 Reading K-12 | 65 Religious Education Elem | 79 Student Personnel | 97 Chief Information Officer | 296 Title II Programs |
| 9 Curric/Instruct Elem | 24 Music Elem | 38 Guidance Services Sec | 52 Reading Elem | 66 Religious Education Sec | 80 Driver Ed/Safety | 98 Chief Technology Officer | 297 Webmaster |
| 10 Curric/Instruct Sec | 25 Music Sec | 39 Social Studies K-12 | 53 Reading Sec | 67 School Board President | 81 Gifted/Talented | 270 Character Education | 298 Grant Writer/Ptnrships |
| 11 Federal Program | 26 Business Education | 40 Social Studies Elem | 54 Remedial Reading K-12 | 68 Teacher Personnel | 82 Video Services | 271 Migrant Education | 750 Chief Innovation Officer |
| 12 Title I | 27 Career & Tech Ed | 41 Social Studies Sec | 55 Remedial Reading Elem | 69 Academic Assessment | 83 Substance Abuse Prev | 273 Teacher Mentor | 751 Chief of Staff |
| 13 Title V | 28 Technology Education | 42 Science K-12 | 56 Remedial Reading Sec | 70 Research/Development | 84 Erate | 274 Before/After Sch | 752 Social Emotional Learning |
| 15 Asst Superintendent | 29 Family/Consumer Science | 43 Science Elem | 57 Bilingual/ELL | 71 Public Information | 85 AIDS Education | 275 Response To Intervention | |

| NAME/District | JOB FUNCTIONS | PAGE | NAME/District | JOB FUNCTIONS | PAGE |
|---|---|---|---|---|---|
| Juarez, Mike/Silverton Ind School Dist | 3,5 | 61 | Keene, Kelly/Liberty Hill Ind School Dist | 7 | 401 |
| Juban, Anda/Hallsville Ind School Dist | 81 | 213 | Keener, Michelle/Deer Park Ind School Dist | 4 | 191 |
| Judie, Robert/Chilton Ind School Dist | 5 | 148 | Keeney, Chris/Perrin-Whitt Cons Ind Sch Dist | 67 | 242 |
| Juergens, Kelly/Celina Ind School Dist | 67 | 81 | Keeney, Mike/Aldine Ind School Dist | 71 | 184 |
| Juggs, Ashley/Jonesboro Ind School Dist | 2 | 97 | Keenum, Steve/Wylie Ind School Dist | 67 | 364 |
| Julian, Joy/Wells Ind School Dist | 58 | 77 | Keese, Gabe/Lufkin Ind School Dist | 45 | 21 |
| Junco, Marianne/Santa Fe Ind School Dist | 2 | 165 | Keeton, Wendy/Sam Rayburn Ind School Dist | 8,11,69,73,271,275,286,295 | 150 |
| Jungman, Suzi/Lufkin Ind School Dist | 285 | 21 | Kehoe, Mark/Azle Ind School Dist | 68 | 348 |
| Junkin, Courtney/Marion Ind School Dist | 16,297 | 177 | Keith, Beth/Eanes Ind School Dist | 275 | 372 |
| Juntti, Christopher/Lamar Cons Ind School Dist | 3,4,5,15,73 | 157 | Keith, Cash/Uvalde Cons Ind School Dist | 73 | 381 |
| Jurado, Alicia/Childress Ind School Dist | 57 | 77 | Keith, Daniel/Tulia Ind School Dist | 8,11,57,285,286,288,298 | 345 |
| Jurado, David/Memphis Ind School Dist | 6 | 181 | Keith, Karen/Lingleville Ind School Dist | 58 | 148 |
| Jurecek, Lisa/Orange Grove Ind School Dist | 16,82 | 248 | Keith, Marc, Dr/Tarkington Ind School Dist | 1 | 269 |
| Jurek, Dennis/Bellville Ind School Dist | 2,19 | 24 | Keith, Ray/Happy Ind School Dist | 1 | 345 |
| Jurek, Donald/East Central Ind School Dist | 5 | 34 | Keithley, David/Trinity Ind School Dist | 58 | 377 |
| Jurek, Stephen/Weimar Ind School Dist | 3 | 91 | Kelanic, Jack/Dallas Ind School Dist | 73,98 | 102 |
| Justiss, Joseph/Paris Ind School Dist | 5 | 262 | Kelchner, Laura/Spring Ind School Dist | 76 | 207 |
| | | | Kellas, Deb/Lindale Ind School Dist | 57 | 339 |
| **K** | | | Keller Perkins, Stephine/Medina Valley Ind School Dist | 58 | 287 |
| Kablaitis, Denise/Pflugerville Ind School Dist | 7,91 | 374 | Keller, Gloria/Karnes City Ind School Dist | 5 | 253 |
| Kaffka, Daniel/Santa Maria Ind School Dist | 91 | 71 | Keller, Jason/Sabinal Ind School Dist | 6 | 380 |
| Kahl, Scott/Arlington Ind School Dist | 15,68,79 | 346 | Keller, Jon/Gladewater Ind School Dist | 67 | 174 |
| Kahlden, Ryan/Waxahachie Ind School Dist | 2,15 | 146 | Keller, Taylor/Comal Ind School Dist | 42 | 91 |
| Kaiser, Bettinae/South San Antonio Ind Sch Dist | 2,19 | 45 | Kellermeier, Mark/Veribest Ind School Dist | 67 | 368 |
| Kajs, Jeffrey/Lewisville Ind School Dist | 79 | 126 | Kelley, Brenda/Alba-Golden Ind School Dist | 2 | 407 |
| Kalbas, Edie/Farwell Ind School Dist | 2,11 | 317 | Kelley, Charles/Killeen Ind School Dist | 91 | 30 |
| Kale, Eric/Hico Ind School Dist | 27 | 181 | Kelley, Christina/Atlanta Ind School Dist | 34,58 | 73 |
| Kalina, Cindy/Schulenburg Ind School Dist | 7,85 | 152 | Kelley, Michaelann, Dr/Aldine Ind School Dist | 20 | 184 |
| Kalina, Kim/Marshall Ind School Dist | 60 | 214 | Kelley, Mike/Springtown Ind School Dist | 1 | 316 |
| Kallus, Sherry/Holland Ind School Dist | 274 | 30 | Kelley, Rebecca/Brazosport Ind School Dist | 2,19 | 55 |
| Kaluzas, Elizabeth/Hubbard Ind School Dist | 2 | 230 | Kelley, Richard/River Road Ind School Dist | 1 | 322 |
| Kaminski, David/Waller Ind School Dist | 67 | 387 | Kelley, Tim/Eula Ind School Dist | 1 | 66 |
| Kammerer, William/Iredell Ind School Dist | 273 | 50 | Kelley, Tom/Yoakum Ind School Dist | 1 | 122 |
| Kamradt, Christopher/Spring Branch Ind School Dist | 4 | 205 | Kellogg, Mark/Wills Point Ind School Dist | 3 | 383 |
| Kane, Diedra/Wellington Ind School Dist | 8 | 90 | Kelly, Chad, Dr/Jacksonville Ind School Dist | 1 | 76 |
| Kane, Marnie/Wellington Ind School Dist | 20 | 90 | Kelly, Corey/Needville Ind School Dist | 73 | 159 |
| Kanierin, Jenny/Crosby Ind School Dist | 298 | 188 | Kelly, Frank/Madisonville Cons ISD | 3,91 | 276 |
| Kanipes, Mark/Santa Fe Ind School Dist | 6 | 165 | Kelly, Jean/Laneville Ind School Dist | 50 | 330 |
| Karl, Carla/Gold-Burg Ind School Dist | 3 | 293 | Kelly, Jennifer/Anna Ind School Dist | 33 | 81 |
| Karnes, Jason/Godley Ind School Dist | 15 | 250 | Kelly, Jennifer/Columbia Brazoria ISD | 58,69 | 56 |
| Karr, Lisa/Hurst-Euless-Bedford ISD | 27,28 | 356 | Kelly, John, Dr/Pearland Ind School Dist | 1 | 56 |
| Karre, Howard/Sabinal Ind School Dist | 73,286,295 | 380 | Kelly, Melissa/Gunter Ind School Dist | 73 | 171 |
| Kasch, Bob/Spring Creek Ind School Dist | 67 | 241 | Kelly, Mike/Valley Mills Ind School Dist | 1,11 | 50 |
| Kasel, Tim/Farwell Ind School Dist | 3,5,91 | 317 | Kelly, Susan/Carrollton-Farmers Branch ISD | 34,54 | 100 |
| Kaser, Brie/Community Ind School Dist | 16,73,76,286,295 | 81 | Kelly, Trudy/Carrollton-Farmers Branch ISD | 71 | 100 |
| Kasper, Brian/Longview Ind School Dist | 31 | 174 | Kelly, Wayne/San Saba Ind School Dist | 1,83 | 335 |
| Kasper, Jennifer/East Central Ind School Dist | 8 | 34 | Kelmm, Karin/McKinney Ind School Dist | 35 | 84 |
| Kasper, Melanie/Salado Ind School Dist | 58 | 32 | Kelsey, Lena/Latexo Ind School Dist | 28,73,286 | 236 |
| Kassaw, Kim/Lufkin Ind School Dist | 58 | 21 | Kelso, John/Greenville Ind School Dist | 67 | 239 |
| Kassen, Jennifer/Valley View ISD-Cooke Co | 4 | 95 | Kelsoe, Kelli/Castleberry Ind School Dist | 16 | 350 |
| Kassman, Lisa/Katy Ind School Dist | 3,70 | 156 | Kemp, Allen/Perryton Ind School Dist | 3 | 310 |
| Kates, Matt/La Grange Ind School Dist | 6 | 151 | Kemp, Allison/Palmer Ind School Dist | 29 | 146 |
| Kates, Melissa/Duncanville Ind School Dist | 15,751 | 108 | Kemp, Christian/Hardin Jefferson Ind Sch Dist | 28 | 182 |
| Kates, Stephanie/La Grange Ind School Dist | 81 | 151 | Kemp, Ken/Collinsville Ind School Dist | 16,73,295 | 171 |
| Katrina, Garrett/Plainview Ind School Dist | 9 | 180 | Kemp, Mark/Aransas Pass Ind School Dist | 11 | 333 |
| Kattner, Vicki/Godley Ind School Dist | 16 | 250 | Kemper, James/Corrigan-Camden Ind Sch Dist | 3,5 | 319 |
| Kauffman, Katie/Lake Travis Ind School Dist | 70 | 373 | Kemper, Mary/Coppell Ind School Dist | 45 | 102 |
| Kaufman, John/Trinity Ind School Dist | 1 | 377 | Kendall, Jim/Kerens Ind School Dist | 2 | 303 |
| Kaufmann, Pam/Rockdale Ind School Dist | 8,11,15,58,288,296,298 | 290 | Kendrick, Kenny/Humble Ind School Dist | 3 | 200 |
| Kaup, Keith/Spring Ind School Dist | 5 | 207 | Kendrick, Marshall/Pasadena Ind School Dist | 67 | 203 |
| Kautz, Jeff/Stratford Ind School Dist | 5 | 338 | Kendrick, Rhonda/Crockett Ind School Dist | 68 | 235 |
| Kautz, Lynette/Stratford Ind School Dist | 2,11,84,296 | 338 | Kennedy, Catherine, Dr/Ysleta Ind School Dist | 15 | 141 |
| Kay, Patricia, Dr/Crosby Ind School Dist | 15,31,68 | 188 | Kennedy, David/Westhoff Ind School Dist | 1,11,73,83,84 | 122 |
| Kazanas, George, Dr/Midway Ind School Dist | 1 | 283 | Kennedy, Dorothy/Groveton Ind School Dist | 36,69 | 377 |
| Keach, Kristy/George West Ind School Dist | 11,69 | 271 | Kennedy, Edna, Dr/Burton Ind School Dist | 1,73,83 | 388 |
| Keahey, Mark/Region 10 Ed Service Center | 4 | 120 | Kennedy, John/Somerset Ind School Dist | 295 | 45 |
| Keal, Hugo/Edinburg Cons Ind School Dist | 47 | 221 | Kennedy, Maria/El Paso Ind School Dist | 6 | 137 |
| Kearley, Donna/Denton Ind School Dist | 16 | 125 | Kennedy, Rhonda/Covington ISD School Dist | 4 | 230 |
| Kearney, Jennifer/Georgetown Ind School Dist | 41,50,53 | 398 | Kennedy, Suzanne/Bonham Ind School Dist | 34 | 149 |
| Keasler, Steve/Carroll Independent Sch Dist | 6 | 349 | Kenney, Kathy/New Braunfels Ind School Dist | 68 | 92 |
| Keating, Shannon/Bells Ind School Dist | 4 | 170 | Kent, Cay/Kirbyville Cons Ind Sch Dist | 19 | 244 |
| Kechnie, J P/Weatherford Ind School Dist | 3 | 316 | Kent, Katrina/Iraan-Sheffield Ind Sch Dist | 4 | 318 |
| Keeler, Stephen/Benjamin Ind School Dist | 67 | 261 | Keough, Michael/Canyon Ind School Dist | 76,98 | 323 |
| Keeling, Justin/Douglass Ind School Dist | 1 | 300 | Kerbow, Gary/Carrollton-Farmers Branch ISD | 2,19 | 100 |
| Keeling, Whitney/Waskom Ind School Dist | 6 | 214 | Kercheville, Kristy/Liberty Hill Ind School Dist | 31,57 | 401 |
| Keen, Susan/Lancaster Ind School Dist | 58 | 114 | Kerin, Pat/Shallowater Ind School Dist | 4 | 274 |

| | | | | | | | | |
|---|---|---|---|---|---|---|---|---|
| 1 | Superintendent | 16 | Instructional Media Svcs | 30 | Adult Education | 44 | Science Sec | |
| 2 | Bus/Finance/Purchasing | 17 | Chief Operations Officer | 31 | Career/Sch-to-Work K-12 | 45 | Math K-12 | |
| 3 | Buildings And Grounds | 18 | Chief Academic Officer | 32 | Career/Sch-to-Work Elem | 46 | Math Elem | |
| 4 | Food Service | 19 | Chief Financial Officer | 33 | Career/Sch-to-Work Sec | 47 | Math Sec | |
| 5 | Transportation | 20 | Art K-12 | 34 | Early Childhood Ed | 48 | English/Lang Arts K-12 | |
| 6 | Athletic | 21 | Art Elem | 35 | Health/Phys Education | 49 | English/Lang Arts Elem | |
| 7 | Health Services | 22 | Art Sec | 36 | Guidance Services K-12 | 50 | English/Lang Arts Sec | |
| 8 | Curric/Instruct K-12 | 23 | Music K-12 | 37 | Guidance Services Elem | 51 | Reading K-12 | |
| 9 | Curric/Instruct Elem | 24 | Music Elem | 38 | Guidance Services Sec | 52 | Reading Elem | |
| 10 | Curric/Instruct Sec | 25 | Music Sec | 39 | Social Studies K-12 | 53 | Reading Sec | |
| 11 | Federal Program | 26 | Business Education | 40 | Social Studies Elem | 54 | Remedial Reading K-12 | |
| 12 | Title I | 27 | Career & Tech Ed | 41 | Social Studies Sec | 55 | Remedial Reading Elem | |
| 13 | Title V | 28 | Technology Education | 42 | Science K-12 | 56 | Remedial Reading Sec | |
| 15 | Asst Superintendent | 29 | Family/Consumer Science | 43 | Science Elem | 57 | Bilingual/ELL | |

| | | | | | |
|---|---|---|---|---|---|
| 58 | Special Education K-12 | 72 | Summer School | 88 | Alternative/At Risk |
| 59 | Special Education Elem | 73 | Instructional Tech | 89 | Multi-Cultural Curriculum |
| 60 | Special Education Sec | 74 | Inservice Training | 90 | Social Work |
| 61 | Foreign/World Lang K-12 | 75 | Marketing/Distributive | 91 | Safety/Security |
| 62 | Foreign/World Lang Elem | 76 | Info Systems | 92 | Magnet School |
| 63 | Foreign/World Lang Sec | 77 | Psychological Assess | 93 | Parental Involvement |
| 64 | Religious Education K-12 | 78 | Affirmative Action | 95 | Tech Prep Program |
| 65 | Religious Education Elem | 79 | Student Personnel | 97 | Chief Information Officer |
| 66 | Religious Education Sec | 80 | Driver Ed/Safety | 98 | Chief Technology Officer |
| 67 | Teacher Personnel | 81 | Gifted/Talented | 270 | Character Education |
| 68 | Academic Assessment | 83 | Substance Abuse Prev | 271 | Migrant Education |
| 69 | Research/Development | 84 | Erate | 273 | Teacher Mentor |
| 70 | Public Information | 85 | AIDS Education | 274 | Before/After Sch |
| 71 | | | | 275 | Response To Intervention |

| | |
|---|---|
| 277 | Remedial Math K-12 |
| 280 | Literacy Coach |
| 285 | STEM |
| 286 | Digital Learning |
| 288 | Common Core Standards |
| 294 | Accountability |
| 295 | Network System |
| 296 | Title II Program |
| 297 | Webmaster |
| 298 | Grant Writer/Ptnrships |
| 750 | Chief Innovation Officer |
| 751 | Chief of Staff |
| 752 | Social Emotional Learning |

| NAME/District | JOB FUNCTIONS | PAGE | NAME/District | JOB FUNCTIONS | PAGE |
|---|---|---|---|---|---|
| Klein, Millie/Region 13 Ed Service Center | 15 | 376 | Koskelin, Shela/Mabank Ind School Dist | 31 | 256 |
| Klein, Stephanie/Sam Rayburn Ind School Dist | 37 | 150 | Kostelich, Kristy/Denver City Ind School Dist | 27 | 409 |
| Klein, Suzanne/Irving Ind School Dist | 45 | 113 | Koster, Gena, Dr/Keller Ind School Dist | 58 | 357 |
| Kleinhans, Angela/Montague Ind School Dist | 16,73 | 293 | Kotsopoulos, Renee/Garland Ind School Dist | 7,85 | 109 |
| Klement, Carol/Muenster Ind School Dist | 2 | 95 | Kotula, Colette/Everman Ind School Dist | 11 | 351 |
| Klemstein, Jodi/Comfort Ind School Dist | 16 | 257 | Kouba, Ronda/Deer Park Ind School Dist | 8,15,296 | 191 |
| Klepac, Robert/Bay City Ind School Dist | 67 | 278 | Kovach, Karen/Del Valle Ind School Dist | 4 | 372 |
| **Klimitchek, Missy, Dr**/Industrial Ind School Dist | 1,11 | 243 | Kovacs, Kelly/Schertz-Cibolo-Univ City ISD | 8,11,18,27,58,74 | 178 |
| Kline, Andrea/Waxahachie Ind School Dist | 41 | 146 | Kovalchik, Leigh/Huntsville Ind School Dist | 11,296 | 386 |
| Kline, Julie/St Jo Ind School Dist | 73,76,82 | 293 | Kovar, Becky/East Bernard Ind Sch Dist | 2,11,294,296 | 392 |
| Klink, Renessa/Wellington Ind School Dist | 69,83,88 | 90 | Kovar, Jacqueline/Rice Cons Ind School Dist | 31 | 90 |
| Kloepper, Eliabeth/Llano Ind School Dist | 85 | 271 | Kovar, John/Thorndale Ind School Dist | 11,83 | 291 |
| Klopper, Cathy/Texarkana Ind School Dist | 285 | 53 | Kovar, Shannon/Grapevine-Colleyville Ind SD | 69,294 | 355 |
| Klopzman, Jeffrey/Lubbock Ind School Dist | 71 | 272 | Kozma, Brian/Bartlett Ind School Dist | 6 | 29 |
| Kluttz, Les/Sweeny Ind School Dist | 79 | 57 | Kraft, Jeanne/Paris Ind School Dist | 71 | 262 |
| Knaub, Marla/South Texas Ind School Dist | 2,15 | 71 | Krajca, Kristi/Mesquite Ind School Dist | 27,31 | 115 |
| Knaus, Connie/Holland Ind School Dist | 4 | 30 | Kram, Ken/Weimar Ind School Dist | 67 | 91 |
| Knickerbocker, Tessa/Ballinger Ind School Dist | 38 | 329 | Kramer, Joan/Fredericksburg Ind School Dist | 30 | 167 |
| Knight, Adam/Alto Ind School Dist | 73 | 76 | Kramer, Richard/Nueces Canyon Cons Ind SD | 27 | 135 |
| Knight, Adrian/Spring Hill Ind School Dist | 294 | 175 | Kramer, Toby/Nueces Canyon Cons Ind SD | 59 | 135 |
| Knight, Beverly/Little Cypress Mauriceville SD | 58,72,270 | 311 | Kramer, Tracie/Burton Ind School Dist | 68 | 388 |
| Knight, Denise/Floresville Ind School Dist | 27 | 403 | Kramme, Debbie/Ft Sam Houston Ind School Dist | 68 | 35 |
| Knight, Jill/Plemons-Stinnett-Phillips CISD | 73,76 | 241 | Kranz, Stephanie/Lovejoy Ind School Dist | 273 | 84 |
| Knight, Jim/Lamesa Ind School Dist | 1 | 121 | Krause, Calvin/Round Top-Carmine Ind Sch Dist | 67 | 151 |
| Knight, Lisa/Midlothian Ind School Dist | 11,57,271,296,298 | 145 | Krause, Curtis/Giddings Ind School Dist | 5 | 266 |
| Knight, Mary Ellen/Winnsboro Ind School Dist | 58 | 408 | Krchnak, Brenda/Snook Ind School Dist | 1 | 63 |
| Knight, Robert/Ft Stockton Ind School Dist | 83 | 318 | Kreiter, Erich/Friendswood Ind Sch Dist | 91 | 164 |
| Knight, Robert/Hondo Ind School Dist | 10,31 | 287 | Krenek, Thomas/El Campo Ind School Dist | 76,84,286 | 392 |
| Knight, Thomas/Ferris Ind School Dist | 11,54,57,68,69,74,83,294 | 144 | Kretchmar, Ted/Crowley Ind School Dist | 11,294,296 | 350 |
| Knighton, Tracy/Christoval Ind School Dist | 9,11,88 | 366 | Krichnak, Randall/Sealy Ind School Dist | 5 | 25 |
| Knipp, Jennifer/Mineola Ind School Dist | 8,57,58,69,74,88,271,286 | 408 | Kridler, Gene/Gonzales Ind School Dist | 3,5,17 | 169 |
| Knisely, Keith/Skidmore Tynan Ind SD | 73,84 | 29 | Kriegel, Angela/Liberty Ind School Dist | 76 | 269 |
| Knobloch, Cd/Archer City Ind School Dist | 1,11 | 22 | Kriner, Rachel/Trinity Ind School Dist | 7 | 377 |
| Knopp, Tyson/Linden Kildare Cons Ind SD | 73 | 74 | Krippel, John/Humble Ind School Dist | 68 | 200 |
| Knostman, Ryan/Aransas Pass Ind School Dist | 6 | 333 | Kroeger, Brian/Splendora Ind School Dist | 68 | 297 |
| Knowlton, John/Deer Park Ind School Dist | 2 | 191 | Kroeker, Duane/Ingram Ind School Dist | 6 | 259 |
| Knowlton, Tonya/Lexington Ind School Dist | 1 | 266 | Kroll, Carrie/Dripping Springs Ind Sch Dist | 67 | 215 |
| Knox, Ashton/West Orange-Cove Cons ISD | 8,296 | 312 | Kroll, Micheal/Karnes City Ind School Dist | 27,28 | 253 |
| Knox, Heather/West Orange-Cove Cons ISD | 58,90,91 | 312 | Krone, Mickey/Forney Ind School Dist | 5 | 254 |
| Knox, Karl/School of Excellence In Ed | 2,11 | 45 | Kronenberger, Kurt/Bridgeport Ind School Dist | 3,5,15,68 | 406 |
| Knox, Retta/Hart Ind School Dist | 13,35,83,85,88 | 75 | Kroontje, Wallie/Fruitvale Ind School Dist | 3 | 383 |
| Knudsen, Tina/Lockhart Ind School Dist | 2,19 | 64 | Krsnak, Becki/Midlothian Ind School Dist | 9 | 145 |
| Knudson, Stacey/San Antonio Ind School Dist | 46 | 42 | Krueger, Jennifer/Northside Ind School Dist | 7 | 39 |
| Kobosky, David/Gunter Ind School Dist | 295 | 171 | Krueger, Thomas/Southwest Ind School Dist | 3 | 46 |
| Koch, Allen/Carthage Ind School Dist | 8,69,294 | 314 | Krumm, Lisa/Chapel Hill Ind School Dist | 9,69 | 339 |
| Koch, Frances/Victoria Ind School Dist | 2,15 | 384 | Krunnow, Elicia/Bosqueville Ind School Dist | 57 | 281 |
| Koch, Joe/Paradise Ind School Dist | 6 | 407 | Krusemark, Stony/Knox City-O'Brien Cons Ind SD | 73,88,98,286 | 261 |
| Kocian, Penny/Axtell Ind School Dist | 2,10,11,35,57,88 | 281 | Krusleski, Jerry/Magnolia Ind School Dist | 27,31,39,73 | 295 |
| Koehl, Kenny/Columbus Ind School Dist | 3 | 90 | Kubecka, Denise/Cypress-Fairbanks Ind Sch Dist | 8,15,27 | 188 |
| Koelzer, James/Muenster Ind School Dist | 3 | 95 | Kubena, Abram/East Bernard Ind Sch Dist | 73,84,295 | 392 |
| Koerth, Stacy, Dr/Hutto Ind School Dist | 58 | 399 | Kucera, David/Penelope ISD School Dist | 67 | 231 |
| Koester, Steve/Goose Creek Cons Ind Sch Dist | 73,286 | 192 | Kucera, Inez/Boling Ind School Dist | 9 | 392 |
| Kohl, Cyndy/Wichita Falls Ind School Dist | 68 | 395 | Kucera, Joe, Dr/Lorena Ind School Dist | 1 | 283 |
| Kohler, Theresa, Dr/Crowley Ind School Dist | 68 | 350 | Kucera, Tony/Van Vleck Ind School Dist | 67 | 279 |
| Kohn, Sara/Round Rock Ind School Dist | 2 | 401 | Kuchler, Kathy/Industrial Ind School Dist | 7 | 243 |
| Kohrman, Jeff/Spring Ind School Dist | 295 | 207 | Kuddes, Kathy/Plano Ind School Dist | 20,23 | 85 |
| Kolbeck, Bryon/Lewisville Ind School Dist | 73,98 | 126 | Kuecker, Rachelle/Round Top-Carmine Ind Sch Dist | 6,10,88 | 151 |
| Kolby, Amberly/Navasota Ind School Dist | 8,69 | 177 | Kuehler, Kyle/Borden Co Ind School Dist | 73,84 | 49 |
| Kole, Jason/Quanah Ind School Dist | 6 | 182 | Kuehler, Ron/Groom Ind School Dist | 67 | 72 |
| Kolek, Richard/Johnson City Ind School Dist | 1 | 49 | Kuenstler, Katherine/Yorktown Ind School Dist | 1 | 122 |
| Kolenda, Joe/Spring Branch Ind School Dist | 31 | 205 | Kuhn, John, Dr/Mineral Wells Ind School Dist | 1 | 313 |
| Koleva, Yana/Round Rock Ind School Dist | 4 | 401 | Kuhn, Linda/Grandfalls-Royalty Ind SD | 58 | 388 |
| Kolodziej, Kellie/Kenedy Ind School Dist | 7 | 254 | Kuhn, Mark/Grandfalls-Royalty Ind SD | 67 | 388 |
| Konderla, Joya/Garrison Ind School Dist | 37 | 301 | Kuhrt, Michael/Wichita Falls Ind School Dist | 1 | 395 |
| Konz, Wendy/Lake Dallas Ind School Dist | 5 | 126 | Kuhrt, Shannon/Wichita Falls Ind School Dist | 69 | 395 |
| Koonce, David/Lewisville Ind School Dist | 76 | 126 | Kujawa, Rose/Bremond Ind School Dist | 16 | 327 |
| Koons, Jim/Keller Ind School Dist | 5 | 357 | Kukla, Lisa/Harlandale Ind School Dist | 16 | 35 |
| Koop, Diane/Ganado Ind School Dist | 7 | 242 | Kulpa, Dawn/San Antonio Ind School Dist | 275 | 42 |
| Koopman, Robert/Friendswood Ind Sch Dist | 6 | 164 | Kunde, Kevin, Dr/Marion Ind School Dist | 67 | 177 |
| Kopowski, Sara/Keller Ind School Dist | 8,275,296 | 357 | Kunschik, Veronica/Crowley Ind School Dist | 750 | 350 |
| Koran, Candace/Lumberton Ind School Dist | 16,82 | 183 | Kuntz, Lindsay/Medina Ind School Dist | 8,16,57,83,288 | 26 |
| Korenek, Genelle/Rockdale Ind School Dist | 2 | 290 | Kupatt, Leslie/Rule Ind School Dist | 31,69,270 | 215 |
| Kornegay, Brent/George West Ind School Dist | 6,35 | 271 | Kurmes, Michele/Keene Ind School Dist | 58 | 251 |
| Kortan, Maria/Harlingen Cons Ind School Dist | 74 | 68 | Kusack, Laura/Moulton Ind School Dist | 36,69 | 265 |
| Kosar, Tim/Keene Ind School Dist | 91 | 251 | Kusak, Glen/Yoakum Ind School Dist | 67 | 122 |
| **Koskelin, Brad**/Mabank Ind School Dist | 1 | 256 | Kutac, Donna/Louise Ind School Dist | 57 | 392 |

| NAME/District | JOB FUNCTIONS | PAGE | NAME/District | JOB FUNCTIONS | PAGE |
|---|---|---|---|---|---|
| Larson, Crystal/High Island Ind Sch Dist | 2 | 165 | Leaf, Buster/Terrell Ind School Dist | 6 | 256 |
| Larson, Todd/Region 1 Ed Service Center | 58 | 229 | Leafloor, Garry/Highland Park Ind School Dist | 3 | 322 |
| LaRue, Ashley/Lovelady Ind School Dist | 8,11,57,58,270,298 | 236 | Leal, Armando/Quanah Ind School Dist | 3 | 182 |
| LaRue, Ashley/Trinity Ind School Dist | 69,83 | 377 | Leal, Gilbert/Brownsville Ind School Dist | 6 | 66 |
| LaRue, Eddie/Paris Ind School Dist | 295 | 262 | Leal, Jennifer/Rockwall Ind School Dist | 81 | 328 |
| LaRue, Ralph/Nacogdoches Ind School Dist | 3 | 301 | Leal, Jose/Los Fresnos Cons Ind Sch Dist | 3 | 69 |
| Lasater, Thad/College Station Ind Sch Dist | 2 | 59 | Leal, Maria/La Joya Ind School Dist | 298 | 222 |
| Lascsak, Justin/Mineral Wells Ind School Dist | 286 | 313 | Leal, Robin/Maypearl Ind School Dist | 4 | 145 |
| Lashaway, Jay/Seminole Ind School Dist | 2 | 162 | Leal, Romero/Edinburg Cons Ind School Dist | 46 | 221 |
| Lashbrook, Brianna/Sudan Ind School Dist | 4 | 264 | **Leamon, Sean/**Winters Ind School Dist | 1 | 329 |
| Lasher, Lenny/Castleberry Ind School Dist | 6,7,35 | 349 | Lear, Pamela/Dallas Ind School Dist | 751 | 102 |
| Lasiter, Cliff/Slocum ISD School Dist | 1 | 19 | Leath, Christi/Goose Creek Cons Ind Sch Dist | 74,81,273 | 192 |
| Lass, Mike/Lockney Independent Sch Dist | 67 | 153 | Lebherz, Beverly/North East Ind School Dist | 69 | 37 |
| Lasser, Shelly/Decatur Ind School Dist | 4 | 406 | LeBlanc, Lakeisha/Channelview Ind School Dist | 71 | 188 |
| Lasseygne, Amber/Allen Ind School Dist | 2 | 80 | LeBlanc, Matthew/Bryan Ind School Dist | 71 | 58 |
| Lassiter, Ross/Olton Ind School Dist | 6 | 263 | LeBlanc, Nina, Dr/West Orange-Cove Cons ISD | 8,11,17,57,58,91,273,288 | 312 |
| Laster, Nancy/Marlin Ind School Dist | 16 | 149 | LeBlanc, Susan/Barbers Hill Ind School Dist | 4 | 75 |
| Lathan, Grenita, Dr/Houston Ind School Dist | 1 | 193 | LeBlanc, Tim/Barbers Hill Ind School Dist | 295 | 75 |
| Latiolais, Pam/Channelview Ind School Dist | 10 | 188 | Lebleu, Michelle/Angleton Ind School Dist | 58,77 | 55 |
| Latterell, Pennie/Sonora Ind School Dist | 7,83,85 | 345 | Leblew, Michele/Little Cypress Mauriceville SD | 5 | 311 |
| Laubhan, Kenton/Follett Ind School Dist | 67 | 270 | Lebuhn, Erin/Gonzales Ind School Dist | 752 | 169 |
| Laude, Julie/Midway Ind School Dist | 2 | 78 | Ledbetter, Jack/Groveton Ind School Dist | 73,83,295 | 377 |
| Lauer, Cathy/Nixon-Smiley Cons Ind Sch Dist | 1,11,83 | 169 | Ledbetter, Lane, Dr/Midlothian Ind School Dist | 1 | 145 |
| Laughinghouse, Stephanie/Hondo Ind School Dist | 11,54,57,83,271,273,275,296 | 287 | Ledbetter, Robert/Dalhart Ind School Dist | 67 | 99 |
| Laughlin, Erin/Hamshire Fannett Ind Sch Dist | 16 | 245 | Ledesna, Sylvia/Edinburg Cons Ind School Dist | 81 | 221 |
| Launius, Keri, Dr/Galveston Ind School Dist | 74 | 165 | Ledford, Thomas/Argyle Ind School Dist | 3 | 124 |
| Lautzenheifer, Andy/Medina Ind School Dist | 67 | 26 | Ledwig, Linda/Region 3 Ed Service Center | 15,34 | 385 |
| Laux, Lily/Texas Dept of Education | 15,34,69,286 | 1 | Lee-Winslow, Debbie/Mercedes Ind School Dist | 286 | 225 |
| Lavake, Ashley/Stratford Ind School Dist | 12 | 338 | Lee, Andy/Mt Enterprise Ind School Dist | 2,68,73,76 | 330 |
| Lavan, Raysield/Beaumont Ind School Dist | 20,23 | 244 | Lee, Andy/Mt Enterprise Ind School Dist | 84 | 331 |
| Lavender, Joseph/Liberty-Eylau Ind School Dist | 295 | 52 | Lee, Ardianne, Dr/Beaumont Ind School Dist | 16 | 244 |
| Lavender, Kristin/Bushland Ind School Dist | 752 | 321 | Lee, Beverley/Somerset Ind School Dist | 69,294 | 45 |
| Laverett, Julie/Blum Ind School Dist | 58 | 230 | Lee, Brant/Central Ind School Dist | 67 | 20 |
| Lawing, Kimberly/Aransas Co Ind School Dist | 73 | 22 | Lee, Christopher/Garrison Ind School Dist | 5 | 301 |
| Lawler, Corbett/Killeen Ind School Dist | 67 | 30 | Lee, Cody/Weatherford Ind School Dist | 76,286 | 316 |
| Lawless, Erica/Sunnyvale Ind School Dist | 11,58 | 117 | Lee, Dan/Lake Travis Ind School Dist | 5 | 373 |
| Lawrence, Amy/Denton Ind School Dist | 36 | 125 | Lee, Danzel/Corsicana Ind School Dist | 36,79,294 | 302 |
| Lawrence, Christy/Clear Creek Ind School Dist | 34 | 162 | Lee, David/Malta Ind School Dist | 6,9,57,69,74,270 | 52 |
| Lawrence, Cindy, Dr/Richardson Ind School Dist | 58 | 116 | Lee, Deann/Millsap Ind School Dist | 1,11 | 315 |
| Lawrence, Colton/Midway Ind School Dist | 4 | 283 | Lee, Debbie/Garland Ind School Dist | 36 | 109 |
| Lawrence, Cynthia/Lumberton Ind School Dist | 8 | 183 | Lee, Dewaine/Strawn Ind School Dist | 6 | 314 |
| Lawrence, Gayla/Irving Ind School Dist | 20 | 113 | Lee, Donny, Dr/Buna Ind School Dist | 1 | 243 |
| Lawrence, Howard/Rising Star Ind Sch Dist | 67 | 133 | Lee, Donny, Dr/Oakwood Ind School Dist | 288 | 267 |
| Lawrence, Leslie/Cross Plains Ind Sch Dist | 4,11 | 66 | Lee, Emily/De Kalb Ind School Dist | 11,69 | 51 |
| Lawrence, Teresa/Rising Star Ind Sch Dist | 2 | 133 | Lee, Gerald/Cleveland Ind School Dist | 3 | 267 |
| Lawrence, Yvonne/Liberty Ind School Dist | 69 | 269 | Lee, Ginger/Timpson Ind School Dist | 4 | 338 |
| Lawson, Amanda/Leggett Ind School Dist | 36,69,88 | 319 | Lee, Heather/George West Ind School Dist | 31 | 271 |
| Lawson, Denise/Holliday Ind School Dist | 76 | 22 | Lee, Honey/White Settlement Ind Sch Dist | 88 | 360 |
| Lawson, Heather/Bonham Ind School Dist | 7 | 149 | Lee, Ingrid/Region 4 Ed Service Center | 294 | 213 |
| Lawson, Ike/Happy Ind School Dist | 3,5 | 345 | **Lee, Jack, Dr/**Bullard Ind School Dist | 1 | 339 |
| Lawson, Jill/Glen Rose Ind School Dist | 4 | 342 | Lee, Jeffrey/Seguin Ind School Dist | 295 | 179 |
| Lawson, Jim/Royse City Ind School Dist | 3 | 328 | Lee, Judy/Dickinson Ind School Dist | 4 | 164 |
| Lawson, Kim, Dr/Katy Ind School Dist | 9 | 156 | Lee, Kim/Texarkana Ind School Dist | 40,49 | 53 |
| Lawson, Lisa/Gainesville Ind School Dist | 7,85 | 95 | Lee, Kristi/Newton Ind School Dist | 2 | 304 |
| Lawson, Lisa/Whitewright Ind School Dist | 16,286 | 173 | Lee, Kristi, Dr/Bastrop Ind School Dist | 71,298 | 26 |
| Lawson, Megan/White Oak Ind School Dist | 19 | 176 | Lee, Laura/Eanes Ind School Dist | 68 | 372 |
| Lawson, Mignon/Abilene Ind School Dist | 30 | 362 | Lee, Marcus/Buckholts Ind School Dist | 73 | 290 |
| Lawson, Ronnie/Chilton Ind School Dist | 73,286 | 148 | Lee, Margaret/Texas City Ind School Dist | 2,15 | 166 |
| Lawson, Sherri/Spring Branch Ind School Dist | 5 | 205 | Lee, Martha/Cushing Ind School Dist | 2 | 300 |
| Lawver, Ron/London Ind School Dist | 91 | 308 | Lee, Michelle/Mt Enterprise Ind School Dist | 16,270 | 330 |
| Laxson, Felicia/Menard Ind School Dist | 36,83,88,275 | 288 | Lee, Robin/Leggett Ind School Dist | 16 | 319 |
| Layman, Janna/Leonard Ind School Dist | 2,298 | 150 | Lee, Russell/Uvalde Cons Ind School Dist | 5 | 381 |
| Layman, Lanny/San Angelo Ind School Dist | 67 | 367 | Leech, Stan/Boerne Ind School Dist | 6,35 | 257 |
| Layne, Brandon/Ferris Ind School Dist | 6,35 | 144 | Leeper, Lynly/Ysleta Ind School Dist | 17,19 | 141 |
| Layne, Garrett/Rogers Ind School Dist | 12,34,277 | 32 | Lefevers, Toby/Ector Co Ind School Dist | 73 | 134 |
| Layne, Scott/Dallas Ind School Dist | 3,17 | 102 | Leffew, Mike/Sanford-Fritch Ind School Dist | 73 | 241 |
| Layton, Done/Malakoff Ind School Dist | 1 | 219 | Leflet, Yarda/Marble Falls Ind School Dist | 11,88 | 64 |
| Lazar, Scott/Klein Ind School Dist | 3 | 201 | Leftwich, Pam/Lubbock Ind School Dist | 69,70,294 | 272 |
| Lazarine, Barbara/Lufkin Ind School Dist | 9,15,74 | 21 | Leger, Rita/Port Arthur Ind School Dist | 43,285 | 246 |
| Lazcano, Elsa/Ector Co Ind School Dist | 69 | 134 | Legg, Carroll/Sudan Ind School Dist | 5 | 264 |
| Lazrine, Diane/Gause Ind School Dist | 2 | 290 | Legg, Kelly/Dumas Ind School Dist | 8,11,15,88,296 | 298 |
| Leach, Derek/Henrietta Ind School Dist | 73,76 | 78 | Leggett, Vanakan/Navasota Ind School Dist | 12 | 177 |
| Leach, Derek/Midway Ind School Dist | 67 | 78 | Legore, Kristen/Seguin Ind School Dist | 79,90 | 179 |
| Leach, Evan/Killeen Ind School Dist | 2 | 30 | LeGrande, Kim/Mabank Ind School Dist | 4 | 256 |
| Leach, Michele/Region 8 Ed Service Center | 2,3,19 | 72 | Lehnhoff, Scott/Schertz-Cibolo-Univ City ISD | 6,35 | 178 |
| Leach, Randy/Granbury Ind School Dist | 3,91 | 233 | Lehr, Ron/Marshall Ind School Dist | 73,84,295 | 214 |

| NAME/District | JOB FUNCTIONS | PAGE |
|---|---|---|
| Leib, Mary/Gatesville Ind School Dist | 67 | 96 |
| Leigh, Kimberly/Early Ind School Dist | 4 | 62 |
| Leirer, Lisa/Lovejoy Ind School Dist | 274 | 84 |
| Leivas, Larry/Dimmitt Ind School Dist | 2,3 | 74 |
| LeJeune, Adam/Marlin Ind School Dist | 16,288 | 149 |
| Lejune, Bethany/Jonesboro Ind School Dist | 36 | 97 |
| Leloux, Cathy/Leggett Ind School Dist | 2,4,11 | 319 |
| Lemere, Jody/Pleasanton Ind School Dist | 73,95,297 | 24 |
| Lemieux, Vick/Wolfe City Ind School Dist | 295 | 240 |
| Lemley, Brett/Ft Bend Ind School Dist | 10,15 | 153 |
| Lemley, Jeff/Graford Ind School Dist | 67 | 313 |
| LeMoine, Emily/Tenaha Ind School Dist | 2,294 | 338 |
| Lemon, Lisa/Chapel Hill Ind School Dist | 2 | 339 |
| Lemon, Molly/Northside Ind School Dist | 8,11,73 | 396 |
| Lemond, Stormy/Forney Ind School Dist | 28 | 255 |
| Lemonier, Gabrielle, Dr/DeSoto Ind School Dist | 15 | 108 |
| Lemons, Jennifer/Bryan Ind School Dist | 76,79 | 58 |
| Lenamon, James/McGregor Ind School Dist | 1 | 283 |
| Lenamon, Michelle/McGregor Ind School Dist | 16 | 283 |
| Lenart, Brenda/Abbott Ind School Dist | 2 | 229 |
| Lennon, Jullia/Avery Ind School Dist | 7 | 325 |
| Lenoard, Paul/Haskell Cons Ind School Dist | 67 | 215 |
| Lentz-Edwards, Lee/Kermit Ind School Dist | 67 | 405 |
| Lentz, Carrie/Waller Ind School Dist | 49 | 387 |
| Lenz, Steven/Chapel Hill Ind School Dist | 3,4,5,91 | 339 |
| Lenz, Wade/Hartley Ind School Dist | 67 | 215 |
| **Leo, Maria, Dr**/Dilley Ind School Dist | 1 | 161 |
| Leon, Arcelia/Medina Valley Ind School Dist | 8,69 | 287 |
| Leonard, Charla/Aspermont Ind School Dist | 2 | 344 |
| Leonard, Karen/Childress Ind School Dist | 2 | 77 |
| Leonard, Randy/Klondike Ind School Dist | 73,295 | 121 |
| Leonard, Tom, Dr/Eanes Ind School Dist | 1 | 372 |
| Leopold, Kathy/Dripping Springs Ind Sch Dist | 16,73,76,297 | 215 |
| Leopold, Rob/Windthorst Ind School Dist | 73,84,295 | 23 |
| Leopold, Scott/Columbus Ind School Dist | 2,19 | 90 |
| Leos, Jennifer/Cleveland Ind School Dist | 4 | 267 |
| Leos, Melissa/Anthony Ind School Dist | 271 | 136 |
| Lererio, Marclella/Fabens Ind School Dist | 4 | 139 |
| Lerma, Carlos/Mission Cons Ind School Dist | 5 | 225 |
| Lerma, Laurie/Alice Ind School Dist | 81 | 248 |
| Lerma, Parisa/Mineral Wells Ind School Dist | 58,275 | 313 |
| Leschber, Deby/Thorndale Ind School Dist | 73,286,295 | 291 |
| Lester, Don/DeSoto Ind School Dist | 3 | 108 |
| Lester, Jay/Abilene Ind School Dist | 20,23 | 362 |
| Lester, Karla, Dr/Ft Worth Ind School Dist | 73 | 352 |
| Lesueur, Larkin/Humble Ind School Dist | 27,31 | 200 |
| Leuba, Ginny/Linden Kildare Cons Ind SD | 58 | 74 |
| Levandoski, Barbara/Cypress-Fairbanks Ind Sch Dist | 8,15,34,58 | 188 |
| Levario, Gloria/Dallas Co Schools | 67 | 99 |
| Levels, Levatta/DeSoto Ind School Dist | 15,79 | 108 |
| Levesque, Marc/Chapel Hill Ind School Dist | 1 | 366 |
| Levien, Luke/Junction Ind School Dist | 67 | 260 |
| Levin, Jason/Victoria Ind School Dist | 20,23 | 384 |
| Levingston, Ceretha, Dr/Liberty-Eylau Ind School Dist | 11,15,80,298 | 51 |
| Levrier, Henry/Point Isabel Ind Sch Dist | 2,3,11,27,30,83,296 | 70 |
| Levy-David, Carmela/Ft Bend Ind School Dist | 15,34 | 153 |
| Lewis, Bill/Seguin Ind School Dist | 16,73,76 | 178 |
| Lewis, Carol/Hallsburg Ind School Dist | 4 | 282 |
| Lewis, Cindy/Community Ind School Dist | 4 | 81 |
| Lewis, Claude/Bonham Ind School Dist | 3 | 149 |
| Lewis, Dave/Rochelle Ind School Dist | 1,11 | 281 |
| Lewis, David/Arlington Ind School Dist | 4 | 346 |
| Lewis, Dean/Friendswood Ind Sch Dist | 5 | 164 |
| Lewis, Debbie/Fredericksburg Ind School Dist | 29 | 167 |
| Lewis, Debbie/Round Rock Ind School Dist | 69,294 | 401 |
| Lewis, Janie/Callisburg Ind School Dist | 2,12 | 94 |
| Lewis, Jason/Richland Springs Ind Sch Dist | 67 | 335 |
| Lewis, Kelley/Lubbock Ind School Dist | 2 | 272 |
| Lewis, Lee/Moran Ind School Dist | 6 | 336 |
| Lewis, Lezley, Dr/Ft Worth Ind School Dist | 74 | 352 |
| Lewis, Mandi/Sherman Ind School Dist | 2 | 172 |
| Lewis, Maureen, Dr/Longview Ind School Dist | 58 | 174 |
| Lewis, Micha/Grand Saline Ind School Dist | 1 | 383 |
| Lewis, Nyda/Ft Worth Ind School Dist | 30 | 352 |
| Lewis, Pat/Marlin Ind School Dist | 2,19 | 149 |
| Lewis, Patricia/Grand Prairie Ind School Dist | 11,15 | 111 |
| Lewis, Randy/Gorman Ind School Dist | 3,5 | 133 |
| Lewis, Rich/Forestburg Ind School Dist | 73,286 | 293 |
| Lewis, Sharen/Blooming Grove Ind School Dist | 4 | 302 |
| Lewis, Terry/Savoy Ind School Dist | 67 | 150 |
| Leza, Emma/United Ind School Dist | 294 | 390 |
| Libby, Leanne/Corpus Christi Ind Sch Dist | 71 | 306 |
| Licon, Kimberly/Wink Loving Ind School Dist | 51,271 | 405 |
| Licon, Sandra/San Elizario Ind School Dist | 67 | 139 |
| Lide, Mike/Mt Pleasant Ind School Dist | 15 | 366 |
| Lide, Tammi/Wills Point Ind School Dist | 7 | 384 |
| Lieb, James/Pringle-Morse Cons ISD | 67 | 182 |
| Liebman, Amanda/Academy Ind School Dist | 69 | 29 |
| Lieck, Sandra/Carrollton-Farmers Branch ISD | 7 | 100 |
| Lied, Cindy/Pringle-Morse Cons ISD | 280 | 182 |
| Liefer, Pene/Bastrop Ind School Dist | 68 | 26 |
| Liepman, Virginia/San Augustine Ind School Dist | 1 | 332 |
| Lieser, Shelli/Chico Ind School Dist | 4 | 406 |
| Liewehr, Jason/Carrollton-Farmers Branch ISD | 68 | 100 |
| Liggins, Demetrus, Dr/Greenville Ind School Dist | 1 | 239 |
| Light, Joey/Wylie Ind School Dist | 1 | 364 |
| Lightfoot, Delana/Ingleside Ind School Dist | 73,286 | 334 |
| Lightfoot, Jimmy/Gladewater Ind School Dist | 8,12,15,79,296 | 174 |
| Lile, Brent/Booker Ind School Dist | 6 | 270 |
| Lilley, Vickie/Daingerfield-Lone Star Ind SD | 34,58,275 | 299 |
| Lilley, Vickie/Pewitt Cons Ind School Dist | 58 | 299 |
| Limbaugh, Duane/Schulenburg Ind School Dist | 1 | 152 |
| Limmer, Josh/Comfort Ind School Dist | 3,5,91 | 257 |
| Limon, Jeanette/Socorro Ind School Dist | 40 | 140 |
| Limvorratre, Ashley/Carrollton-Farmers Branch ISD | 297 | 100 |
| Lin, Dawn/Wylie Ind School Dist | 4 | 88 |
| Lincoln, Charles/Crowley Ind School Dist | 6 | 350 |
| Lincomm, Mary/Grand Prairie Ind School Dist | 7,85 | 111 |
| Lindeman, Robert/Region 6 Ed Service Center | 2,19 | 386 |
| Lindeman, Todd/Aldine ISD-High Sch Team | 15 | 185 |
| Lindholm, Jon/Marion Ind School Dist | 68 | 177 |
| Lindholm, Kelly/Marion Ind School Dist | 1,83 | 177 |
| Lindley, Alene/Katy Ind School Dist | 81 | 156 |
| Lindsey, Gary/Dallas Co Schools | 1 | 99 |
| Lindsey, Jennifer/Memphis Ind School Dist | 295,298 | 181 |
| Lindsey, Kenneth/Anna Ind School Dist | 3 | 81 |
| Lindsey, Kris/Colmesneil Ind School Dist | 67 | 377 |
| Lindsey, Lara/McKinney Ind School Dist | 16,73 | 84 |
| Lindsey, Melinda/Kennard Ind Sch Dist | 1,11,73 | 236 |
| Lindsey, Preston/Troup Ind School Dist | 5 | 340 |
| Line, Debbie/Post Ind School Dist | 4 | 167 |
| Linebarger, Les/Nacogdoches Ind School Dist | 71 | 301 |
| Linex, Amy/Red Oak Ind School Dist | 76 | 146 |
| Ling, Terry/Warren Ind School Dist | 2 | 378 |
| Link, Stephanie/Elkhart Ind School Dist | 7 | 18 |
| Linley, Tim/Dallas Ind School Dist | 20,23 | 102 |
| Linman, Clint/McLean Ind School Dist | 6 | 170 |
| Linnstaedter, Jeff/Lorena Ind School Dist | 2,19 | 283 |
| Linthicum, Kyle/Spring Hill Ind School Dist | 295 | 175 |
| Linton, Pamela, Dr/Frisco Ind School Dist | 68,78 | 82 |
| Lintzen, Todd/Bridge City Ind School Dist | 1 | 311 |
| Linwood, Ann/Avinger Ind School Dist | 67 | 73 |
| Lionberger, Jay/Peaster Ind School Dist | 3 | 316 |
| Lipe, Mike/Schertz-Cibolo-Univ City ISD | 20,23 | 178 |

| NAME/District | JOB FUNCTIONS | PAGE |
|---|---|---|
| Lippa, Adriana/Brownsville Ind School Dist | 58 | 66 |
| Lippard, Stephanie/Sherman Ind School Dist | 54,57,74,77,271,273,277 | 172 |
| Lipscomb, Claudell/Bryan Ind School Dist | 5 | 58 |
| Liptack, Charlotte/Alvin Ind School Dist | 39,48 | 54 |
| Lira, Adam/Splendora Ind School Dist | 27,31 | 297 |
| Lisby, Ronnie/Venus Ind School Dist | 3 | 252 |
| Lischka, Grant/Bellville Ind School Dist | 67 | 25 |
| Liska, Karen/Spring Branch Ind School Dist | 15 | 205 |
| Lister, Charles/Rio Vista Ind School Dist | 73,295 | 251 |
| Little, Amy/Westwood Ind School Dist | 54 | 19 |
| Little, Cristi/Olney Ind School Dist | 58 | 410 |
| Little, Deborah/Abbott Ind School Dist | 298 | 229 |
| Little, Imelda/Irving Ind School Dist | 9 | 113 |
| Little, Laura/Castleberry Ind School Dist | 294 | 350 |
| Little, Robert/Taylor Ind School Dist | 6 | 402 |
| Little, Shellie/Gorman Ind School Dist | 7 | 133 |
| **Little, Tim/**Baird Ind School Dist | 1 | 65 |
| Little, Valerie/Prosper Ind School Dist | 6 | 88 |
| Littlefield, Michael/Harlandale Ind School Dist | 10 | 35 |
| Littlefields, Brad/Millsap Ind School Dist | 5 | 315 |
| Littlejohn, Jim/Clint Ind School Dist | 10,15 | 136 |
| Litton, Steve/Pewitt Cons Ind School Dist | 3,17 | 299 |
| Littrell, Kacie/Leonard Ind School Dist | 31,36,58,69,83,88 | 150 |
| Litvik, Kenny/Nederland Ind School Dist | 3,5 | 245 |
| Litz, Janay/Region 9 Ed Service Center | 2 | 396 |
| Livas, Janie/San Perlita Ind School Dist | 11,298 | 397 |
| Lively, Debra/Teague Ind School Dist | 4 | 161 |
| Lively, Kenneth/Westwood Ind School Dist | 27 | 19 |
| Lively, Virginia/Alvin Ind School Dist | 39 | 54 |
| Livingston, Mandi/La Vega Ind School Dist | 5 | 282 |
| Llamas, Anna/Jourdanton Ind School Dist | 271 | 23 |
| Llanez, Mesinda/Alpine Ind School Dist | 58 | 60 |
| Llanez, Mesinda/Marfa Ind School Dist | 58 | 322 |
| Lloyd, Donnie/Andrews Ind School Dist | 5 | 19 |
| Lloyd, Michael/Midland Ind School Dist | 73 | 288 |
| Loan, Tim/Amarillo Ind School Dist | 3 | 320 |
| Lochet, Camille/Austin Ind School Dist | 297 | 369 |
| Lock, Richard/Southside Ind School Dist | 6 | 46 |
| Lock, Tonya/Lefors Ind School Dist | 271 | 170 |
| Locker, Amy/Magnolia Ind School Dist | 8,69 | 295 |
| Lockesimmons, Tia/Houston Ind School Dist | 81 | 193 |
| Lockett, Dale/Southwest Ind School Dist | 73,286 | 46 |
| Lockett, Gwendolyn/Aldine Ind School Dist | 40 | 184 |
| Lockett, Marcella/London Ind School Dist | 57 | 308 |
| Lockhart, Luanne/Mumford Ind School Dist | 2 | 59 |
| Locklin, Jamie/Alamo Heights Ind School Dist | 73,295 | 33 |
| Loeffler, Evelyn/Sierra Blanca Ind School Dist | 1,11,73,83 | 237 |
| Loep, Susan/Stockdale Ind School Dist | 9 | 404 |
| Loer, Sarah/Nixon-Smiley Cons Ind Sch Dist | 73 | 169 |
| Loera, Armando/El Paso Ind School Dist | 16 | 137 |
| Loera, Omega/Ector Co Ind School Dist | 81 | 134 |
| Loffey, Rich/Grand Prairie Ind School Dist | 79 | 111 |
| Loftin, Dawn/Canton Ind School Dist | 5 | 382 |
| Loftis, Robert/Laneville Ind School Dist | 67 | 330 |
| Lofton, Jeff/Idalou Ind School Dist | 6 | 272 |
| Lofton, Kathy/West Hardin Co Cons Sch Dist | 4 | 183 |
| Lofton, Suzy, Dr/Lago Vista Ind School Dist | 8,11,15,296 | 373 |
| Logan, Marilyn/Mt Pleasant Ind School Dist | 58 | 366 |
| Logan, Stephen/Burleson Ind School Dist | 76,98,295 | 249 |
| Logiudice, Billie/Hutto Ind School Dist | 67 | 399 |
| Lokie, Charlie/Lake Dallas Ind School Dist | 9,57,274 | 126 |
| Loman, Theresa/Utopia Ind School Dist | 16 | 381 |
| Lomax, Brittney/Ira Ind School Dist | 4 | 336 |
| London, Greg/Bryson Ind School Dist | 1,11 | 241 |
| Londow, Kathy/Port Arthur Ind School Dist | 68,79 | 246 |
| Londrie, Valarie/Los Fresnos Cons Ind Sch Dist | 9 | 69 |
| Long Botham, Pamela, Dr/Cuero Ind School Dist | 8,11,15,57,88,285,288,298 | 121 |
| Long, Asheley/Wellington Ind School Dist | 7 | 90 |
| Long, Bill/Harper Ind School Dist | 73,295 | 168 |
| Long, Clayton/Lipan Ind School Dist | 3 | 233 |
| Long, Cynthia/Campbell Ind School Dist | 4 | 238 |
| Long, Danny/Conroe Ind School Dist | 6 | 294 |
| Long, Gail/Hurst-Euless-Bedford ISD | 69 | 356 |
| Long, Jon/Schleicher Co Ind Sch Dist | 6 | 335 |
| Long, Michael/City View Ind School Dist | 67 | 394 |
| Long, Mitchell/East Chambers Ind School Dist | 16,73,288 | 76 |
| Long, Patricia/Pleasant Grove Ind School Dist | 26 | 52 |
| Long, Shannon/College Station Ind Sch Dist | 73 | 59 |
| Long, Shelli/Sterling City Ind School Dist | 68 | 344 |
| Long, Sherry/Crosby Ind School Dist | 9,37 | 188 |
| Longley, Cathy/Santo Ind School Dist | 12,57 | 313 |
| Longoria, David/Raymondville Ind Sch Dist | 2,19 | 397 |
| Longoria, Margie/Taft Ind School Dist | 4 | 334 |
| Longoria, Rose/Brownsville Ind School Dist | 8,15 | 66 |
| Longorio, Faith/Goose Creek Cons Ind Sch Dist | 39 | 192 |
| Lonsford, Jennifer/Cedar Hill Ind School Dist | 58 | 101 |
| Lookabaugh, Greg/Harris Co Dept of Ed | 3 | 184 |
| Loomis, Chrystal/Roby Cons Ind School Dist | 83,85,88,270,273 | 152 |
| Loomis, Doug/Amarillo Ind School Dist | 1 | 320 |
| Loomis, Robert/Graham Ind School Dist | 15,38,68,69,88,296 | 409 |
| Looney, Susan/Highland Park Ind School Dist | 73 | 322 |
| Loper, Tim/Tyler Ind School Dist | 3 | 340 |
| Lopez, Andy/Covington ISD School Dist | 67 | 230 |
| Lopez, Andy/Sabinal Ind School Dist | 3,5 | 380 |
| Lopez, Angel/Taft Ind School Dist | 8,11,57 | 334 |
| Lopez, Brynn/Fayetteville Ind School Dist | 8,36,270,273 | 151 |
| Lopez, Cesar/Brownsville Ind School Dist | 3 | 66 |
| Lopez, Chris/S & S Cons Ind School Dist | 67 | 172 |
| Lopez, Connie/Region 1 Ed Service Center | 2,15,19 | 229 |
| Lopez, David/Crystal City Ind School Dist | 6 | 410 |
| Lopez, David/Plainview Ind School Dist | 3 | 180 |
| Lopez, Debbie/Skidmore Tynan Ind SD | 16 | 29 |
| Lopez, Diana/Ferris Ind School Dist | 76 | 145 |
| Lopez, Diane/Midland Ind School Dist | 9 | 288 |
| Lopez, Erin/Athens Ind School Dist | 4 | 218 |
| Lopez, Fernando/Pharr-San Juan-Alamo Ind SD | 3 | 226 |
| Lopez, Frank/Andrews Ind School Dist | 297 | 19 |
| Lopez, Frank/Ricardo Ind School Dist | 6 | 261 |
| Lopez, Genaro/Coppell Ind School Dist | 3,5,91 | 102 |
| Lopez, George/Weslaco Ind School Dist | 271 | 228 |
| Lopez, Gerry/Santa Gertrudis Ind Sch Dist | 73 | 261 |
| Lopez, Ivan/Bushland Ind School Dist | 73,286,295,297 | 321 |
| Lopez, Jesse/Region 13 Ed Service Center | 8,15 | 376 |
| Lopez, Joel/Zapata Co Ind School Dist | 6 | 410 |
| Lopez, Johnnie/Kenedy Ind School Dist | 5 | 254 |
| Lopez, Jose/El Paso Ind School Dist | 751 | 137 |
| Lopez, Juan/Point Isabel Ind Sch Dist | 58 | 70 |
| Lopez, Leo/Texas Dept of Education | 2,15,19 | 1 |
| Lopez, Linda/La Joya Ind School Dist | 9 | 222 |
| Lopez, Marin/Rio Grande City Ind Sch Dist | 3 | 342 |
| Lopez, Melissa/Region 1 Ed Service Center | 27 | 229 |
| Lopez, Monica/Iraan-Sheffield Ind Sch Dist | 7,83,85 | 318 |
| Lopez, Nick/Westbrook Ind School Dist | 3,5 | 292 |
| Lopez, Orlando/San Benito Cons Ind Sch Dist | 67 | 70 |
| Lopez, Oscar/Robstown Ind School Dist | 67 | 308 |
| Lopez, Paula/Poteet Ind School Dist | 5 | 24 |
| Lopez, Pedro/Houston Ind School Dist | 91 | 193 |
| Lopez, Pete/Lueders-Avoca Ind School Dist | 67 | 253 |
| Lopez, Ricardo, Dr/Garland Ind School Dist | 1 | 109 |
| Lopez, Rosie/Snyder Ind School Dist | 57 | 336 |
| Lopez, Sandra/Brownsville Ind School Dist | 8,15 | 66 |
| Lopez, Sebastian/Barbers Hill Ind School Dist | 295 | 75 |
| Lopez, Shanna/Rice Ind School Dist | 67 | 303 |
| Lopez, Sherry/Buckholts Ind School Dist | 2,68 | 290 |
| Lopez, Sonja, Dr/Montgomery Ind School Dist | 7,15,68,71,273 | 296 |
| Lopez, Vangie/Taft Ind School Dist | 271 | 334 |
| Lopez, Vicki/Archer City Ind School Dist | 285 | 22 |
| Loredo, Augustine/Goose Creek Cons Ind Sch Dist | 67 | 192 |
| Lorenz, Emily/Calallen Ind School Dist | 15,68,83 | 305 |
| Losoya, Adam/Buckholts Ind School Dist | 67 | 290 |
| Lotspeich, Catrina/Temple Ind School Dist | 20,23 | 32 |
| Lott, Rebecca/Manor Ind School Dist | 83 | 373 |
| Lott, Richard/Nixon-Smiley Cons Ind Sch Dist | 67 | 169 |
| Loud, Wonderful/Lubbock Ind School Dist | 68 | 272 |
| Louder, Jermey/Stanton Ind School Dist | 67 | 277 |
| Lough, Betty/Whitehouse Ind School Dist | 8,11,57,74,85,273,274,296 | 341 |
| Loughmiller, Dale/Paris Ind School Dist | 73 | 262 |
| Loupe, Todd/Little Cypress Mauriceville SD | 10,30,36,69,85,88 | 311 |
| Lovaasen, Martha/Elysian Fields Ind School Dist | 9 | 213 |
| Lovato, Krystal/Int'l Leadership of Texas Dist | 12,298 | 112 |
| Love, Catina/Longview Ind School Dist | 69 | 174 |
| Love, Elisa/Paducah Ind School Dist | 4 | 97 |

| NAME/District | JOB FUNCTIONS | PAGE | NAME/District | JOB FUNCTIONS | PAGE |
|---|---|---|---|---|---|
| MacLeod, Carol/Brookeland Ind School Dist | 58 | 243 | Mangallan, Amanda/Terrell Co Ind School Dist | 1 | 364 |
| Madden, Amanda/Sabine Ind School Dist | 7 | 175 | Mangallan, Sam/Terrell Co Ind School Dist | 3 | 364 |
| Maddix, Julie/Boyd Ind School Dist | 2 | 405 | Maniatis, Joni/Alief Ind School Dist | 275 | 186 |
| Maddox, Andrew/Taylor Ind School Dist | 88 | 402 | Manley, David/Killeen Ind School Dist | 9,15 | 30 |
| Maddox, Dodie/Southwest Ind School Dist | 73 | 46 | Manley, Mark/Sweeny Ind School Dist | 27 | 57 |
| Maddox, Elizabeth/Bartlett Ind School Dist | 4 | 29 | Mann, Aimee/La Pryor Ind School Dist | 88 | 411 |
| Maddox, Kellie/Memphis Ind School Dist | 7 | 181 | Mann, Charles/Alvord Ind School Dist | 11,73,295 | 405 |
| Maddox, Mike/Lindale Ind School Dist | 6,35,83 | 339 | Mann, Jeff/College Station Ind Sch Dist | 9,74 | 59 |
| Maddux, Mary/Clifton Ind School Dist | 68 | 49 | Mann, Matthew, Dr/Pleasanton Ind School Dist | 1 | 24 |
| Madison, Caitlin/Int'l Leadership of Texas Dist | 71 | 112 | Manning, Emily/Ponder Ind School Dist | 11,34,57,59,274 | 130 |
| Madison, Michelle/Peaster Ind School Dist | 9,57,88 | 316 | Manning, Joan/Copperas Cove Ind School Dist | 67 | 96 |
| Madkins, Sheilda/School of Excellence In Ed | 1 | 45 | Manning, Kristen/Hurst-Euless-Bedford ISD | 47 | 356 |
| Madrid, Gil/Ft Stockton Ind School Dist | 15 | 318 | Mannino, Gina/Bridge City Ind School Dist | 11,15,271,274,294 | 311 |
| Madrid, Marla/Brackett Ind School Dist | 2,11,84 | 260 | Manor, Teresa/Miami Ind School Dist | 2 | 327 |
| Madrid, Rebecca/Socorro Ind School Dist | 7 | 140 | Manriquez, Ernesto/San Benito Cons Ind Sch Dist | 58 | 70 |
| Madrigal, Fidencio/La Gloria Ind School Dist | 6 | 248 | Mansell, Nicole, Dr/Irving Ind School Dist | 71 | 113 |
| **Madrigal, Hector/**Karnes City Ind School Dist | 1 | 253 | Mansfield, Brad/Liberty Hill Ind School Dist | 15 | 401 |
| Madrigal, Racao/Rio Hondo Ind School Dist | 4 | 70 | Mansfield, Tracy/Aldine Ind School Dist | 43 | 184 |
| Maeker, Christy/Katy Ind School Dist | 36,77 | 156 | Mansfield, William/Overton Ind School Dist | 73 | 331 |
| Maeker, Monica/New Home Ind School Dist | 2 | 275 | Mansker, Clark/Pettus Ind School Dist | 2 | 28 |
| Magallon, Perla/San Elizario Ind School Dist | 95 | 139 | Manson, Bobby/Celina Ind School Dist | 91 | 81 |
| MaGee, Patsy/Beaumont Ind School Dist | 42 | 244 | Manuel, Dianna/Frisco Ind School Dist | 27,31 | 82 |
| MaGee, Sarah/Sealy Ind School Dist | 34 | 25 | Manuel, Elaine/Newcastle Ind School Dist | 3,5 | 409 |
| MaGee, Suzanne/Little Cypress Mauriceville SD | 4 | 311 | Manuel, Lacey/Godley Ind School Dist | 4 | 250 |
| Magers, Lisa/Cleburne Ind School Dist | 71,93 | 250 | Manzo, Maria/Jarrell Ind School Dist | 4 | 399 |
| Maglievaz, Carmen/Natalia Ind School Dist | 9 | 287 | Manzo, Roberto/Texas Dept of Education | 57 | 1 |
| **Maglisceau, Thopmas, Dr/**Celina Ind School Dist | 1 | 81 | Maples, Billy/Bushland Ind School Dist | 4 | 321 |
| Maglothin, James/Zavalla Ind School Dist | 73 | 21 | Maples, Reene/Van Alstyne Ind School Dist | 2,11 | 173 |
| Magnum, Laura/Redwater Ind School Dist | 7 | 53 | Marable, Dana/De Leon Ind School Dist | 1 | 93 |
| Magrita, Christine/Boyd Ind School Dist | 73 | 405 | Marable, Michelle/New Caney Ind School Dist | 3 | 296 |
| Magura, Lorianne/Lytle Ind School Dist | 71 | 24 | Marak, Kristin/Hallettsville Ind Sch Dist | 2 | 265 |
| Mahalitc, Janet/Rice Cons Ind School Dist | 76 | 90 | Marak, Lisa/Weimar Ind School Dist | 57 | 91 |
| Maham, Jill/Avery Ind School Dist | 11 | 325 | Marak, Terry/Region 12 Ed Service Center | 2,19 | 286 |
| Mahan, Dana/Dawson Ind School Dist | 58 | 121 | Marburger, James/Lexington Ind School Dist | 5 | 266 |
| Mahan, Josh/De Leon Ind School Dist | 67 | 93 | Marbut, Melissa/Whitney Ind School Dist | 8,12,273 | 231 |
| Maher, Stephanie/S & S Cons Ind School Dist | 2 | 172 | Marcellus, Angela/Int'l Leadership of Texas Dist | 79 | 112 |
| Mahfouz, Monica/Region 5 Ed Service Center | 8,27,31 | 247 | March, Leslie/Hudson Ind School Dist | 58 | 20 |
| Mahler, Brandon/Ft Elliott Cons Ind Sch Dist | 8,88,273,286,752 | 393 | Marchbanks, Barbara/McDade Ind School Dist | 1,11,288 | 27 |
| Mahler, Charlotte/Olney Ind School Dist | 57 | 410 | Marchena, Katie/Lamar Cons Ind School Dist | 8 | 157 |
| Mahone, Debra/Elgin Ind School Dist | 298 | 27 | Marcucci, Karen/Mansfield Ind School Dist | 67 | 358 |
| Maige, Stan/Garland Ind School Dist | 28,295 | 109 | Marcum, Ryan/Manor Ind School Dist | 91 | 373 |
| Maika, Sean, Dr/North East Ind School Dist | 1 | 37 | Marcus, Mere/Brock Ind School Dist | 4 | 315 |
| Maines, Travis/Vidor Ind School Dist | 15,68 | 312 | Marcus, Mike/Waller Ind School Dist | 2,19 | 387 |
| Mainord, Peggy/Irving Ind School Dist | 42 | 113 | Marcus, Sarah/Waller Ind School Dist | 71 | 387 |
| Maiorano, Tammy/San Marcos Cons Ind Sch Dist | 58,77 | 217 | Marek, Courtney/Brazos Ind School Dist | 2 | 25 |
| Majors, Ann/Sundown Ind School Dist | 69,83,85,88,273 | 232 | Marek, Fran/Joshua Ind School Dist | 1 | 251 |
| Malandruccolo, Kevin/Hays Cons Ind School Dist | 69,294 | 216 | Marek, Kimberly/Rogers Ind School Dist | 57 | 32 |
| Malcik, Carol/Georgetown Ind School Dist | 2 | 398 | Marek, Lindsey/Goose Creek Cons Ind Sch Dist | 285 | 192 |
| Malcom, Marci, Dr/Lake Dallas Ind School Dist | 15 | 126 | Mares, Rosemary/Hondo Ind School Dist | 15,69,74,91 | 287 |
| Maldonado, Arnold/Odem-Edroy Ind School Dist | 3 | 334 | Maresh, Madalyn/Edna Ind School Dist | 11,298 | 242 |
| Maldonado, Jennifer/Harlingen Cons Ind School Dist | 286 | 68 | Margoitta, Vince/Marlin Ind School Dist | 3,5 | 149 |
| Maldonado, Marlene/Cotulla Ind School Dist | 38 | 262 | Mariappa, Lucy/Int'l Leadership of Texas Dist | 97 | 112 |
| Maldonado, Monica/Diocese Corpus Christi Ed Off | 73 | 309 | Marin, Manuel/Plainview Ind School Dist | 3 | 180 |
| Maldonado, Phillip/Southland Ind School Dist | 271 | 167 | Marion, Chelaine/Texas Dept of Education | 48,51 | 1 |
| Maldonado, Valarie/Southwest Ind School Dist | 7 | 46 | Mariscal, Juanita/Mercedes Ind School Dist | 42 | 225 |
| Malechuk, Brian, Dr/Katy Ind School Dist | 58 | 156 | Markert, Kay/Prairie Lea Ind School Dist | 57 | 65 |
| Malenack, Rachelle/Fredericksburg Ind School Dist | 30 | 167 | Markert, Larry/Prairie Lea Ind School Dist | 1,11 | 65 |
| Maler, Kevin/West Ind School Dist | 5 | 285 | Markgraf, Dondi/Ferris Ind School Dist | 3 | 144 |
| Malerba, Cathy, Dr/Round Rock Ind School Dist | 69 | 401 | Markham, Bryan/Wheeler Ind School Dist | 1,11,83 | 394 |
| Mallick, George/Dallas Ind School Dist | 76 | 102 | Marks, Ginna/Everman Ind School Dist | 58 | 351 |
| Mallory-Sneed, Wilma/Advantage Academy Admin Office | 2,11,19,298 | 100 | Marks, Sequetta/Dallas Ind School Dist | 11 | 102 |
| Mallory, Jessica/Strawn Ind School Dist | 288 | 314 | Marks, Vance/Johnson City Ind School Dist | 3,91 | 49 |
| Malloy, Holli/Galena Park Ind School Dist | 15 | 191 | Marlar, Corey/La Porte Ind School Dist | 3,5,73 | 203 |
| Malmberg, Kathy/Denton Ind School Dist | 7 | 124 | Marlar, Lynley/La Porte Ind School Dist | 2 | 203 |
| Malone, Chris/Grand Prairie Ind School Dist | 73,98 | 111 | Marlin, Traci/Midway Ind School Dist | 71 | 283 |
| Malone, Debra/Electra Ind School Dist | 4 | 394 | Marquez, Angelica/Ralls Ind School Dist | 271 | 98 |
| Malone, Debra/Mt Pleasant Ind School Dist | 7,15,68 | 366 | Marquez, Cheryl/Detroit Ind School Dist | 57 | 325 |
| Malone, Jennifer/Tatum Ind School Dist | 69 | 331 | Marquez, Chris/Pearsall Ind School Dist | 91 | 161 |
| Malone, Joe/Wimberley Ind School Dist | 67 | 217 | Marquez, Fernando/Ysleta Ind School Dist | 27,31 | 141 |
| Malone, Lisa/Paris Ind School Dist | 58 | 262 | Marquez, Liza/Socorro Ind School Dist | 34 | 140 |
| Malone, Robin/Amarillo Ind School Dist | 67 | 320 | Marr, Brian/Klein Ind School Dist | 88 | 202 |
| Malovets, Tracie/Rogers Ind School Dist | 2 | 32 | Mars, Kayla/Quitman Ind School Dist | 2,68 | 408 |
| Manca, Amanda/Texarkana Ind School Dist | 76 | 53 | Marschall, Toni/Harper Ind School Dist | 16 | 168 |
| Mancha, Guillermo/Brackett Ind School Dist | 1 | 260 | Marsh, Amanda/Winona Ind School Dist | 8 | 341 |
| Mancias, Renee/Braination Schools | 76 | 33 | Marsh, Angie/Lake Travis Ind School Dist | 2 | 373 |
| Mancillas, Yvette/Pharr-San Juan-Alamo Ind SD | 34 | 226 | Marsh, Cheryl/Wall Ind School Dist | 68 | 368 |

| NAME/District | JOB FUNCTIONS | PAGE | NAME/District | JOB FUNCTIONS | PAGE |
|---|---|---|---|---|---|
| Martinez, Pete/Iola Ind School Dist | 6,83,88 | 177 | Matthews, David/Grady Ind School Dist | 67 | 277 |
| Martinez, Ricardo/Borden Co Ind School Dist | 295 | 49 | Matthews, Iyana/Kermit Ind School Dist | 4 | 405 |
| Martinez, Rick/Belton Ind School Dist | 3 | 29 | Matthews, James/Wylie Ind School Dist | 76 | 88 |
| Martinez, Robin/Calhoun Co Ind School Dist | 2 | 65 | Matthews, Jeff/Vidor Ind School Dist | 6,35 | 312 |
| Martinez, Rosalinda/Goldthwaite Consolidated ISD | 57 | 291 | Matthews, John, Dr/Celina Ind School Dist | 15,68 | 81 |
| Martinez, Ruth/Poteet Ind School Dist | 7,83,85 | 24 | Matthews, Kevin, Dr/Pottsboro Ind School Dist | 1 | 172 |
| Martinez, Sandra/Clint Ind School Dist | 48 | 136 | Matthews, Patti/Anna Ind School Dist | 76 | 81 |
| Martinez, Sandra/La Villa Ind School Dist | 19 | 223 | Matthews, Phillip/Little Cypress Mauriceville SD | 3,91 | 311 |
| Martinez, Sandra/Taylor Ind School Dist | 57 | 402 | Matthews, Ray/Teague Ind School Dist | 15 | 161 |
| Martinez, Sandra/Taylor Ind School Dist | 57,271 | 402 | Matthews, Spencer/Kountze Ind School Dist | 73,295 | 183 |
| Martinez, Sara/Seguin Ind School Dist | 88 | 179 | Matthews, Teresa/Hudson Ind School Dist | 90 | 20 |
| Martinez, Simon/Santa Maria Ind School Dist | 73 | 71 | Matthews, Teresa/Kountze Ind School Dist | 16 | 183 |
| Martinez, Sonya/Pearsall Ind School Dist | 8,68,69,79 | 161 | Matthews, Vickie/Walcott Ind School Dist | 57 | 123 |
| Martinez, Suanne/Mathis Ind School Dist | 4 | 334 | Matthys, Debbie/Taylor Ind School Dist | 69 | 402 |
| Martinez, Susie/Poth Ind School Dist | 8,69 | 404 | Mattingly, Kim/Cross Roads Ind School Dist | 31,69,85 | 219 |
| Martinez, Tony/Diocese of Victoria Ed Office | 2 | 385 | Mattingly, Mike, Dr/Denton Ind School Dist | 8,15 | 124 |
| Martinez, Tresa/Haskell Cons Ind School Dist | 271 | 215 | Matula, Marybeth/Region 3 Ed Service Center | 15,76 | 385 |
| Martinez, Veronica/Fabens Ind School Dist | 16 | 139 | Mault, Brenda/Big Spring Ind School Dist | 297 | 236 |
| Martinez, Veronica/Galena Park Ind School Dist | 34,57 | 191 | Mauricio, Curtis/Irving Ind School Dist | 8 | 113 |
| Martischnig, Whitney/Seymour Ind School Dist | 60 | 28 | Maxfield, Kyle/Bangs Ind School Dist | 6 | 61 |
| Marts, Renee/Lewisville Ind School Dist | 43 | 126 | Maxwell, Brad/Leonard Ind School Dist | 1 | 150 |
| Marwitz, Jill/Holland Ind School Dist | 67 | 30 | Maxwell, Connie/Olton Ind School Dist | 67 | 263 |
| Marwitz, Stanton/Zephyr Ind School Dist | 1,83,84 | 62 | Maxwell, Jon, Dr/Lamar Cons Ind School Dist | 11,27,69,70,79,81,294 | 157 |
| Marx, David/Texas Dept of Education | 2 | 1 | Maxwell, Mike/Pleasanton Ind School Dist | 295 | 24 |
| Mascheck, Brent/Columbia Brazoria ISD | 6 | 56 | Maxwell, Nathan/Pampa Ind School Dist | 68,74,78,273 | 170 |
| Masek, Andy/Giddings Ind School Dist | 3,5 | 266 | **Maxwell, Nathan, Dr/**Ralls Ind School Dist | 1 | 98 |
| Masick, Christina/Spring Branch Ind School Dist | 15,71,73,76,97,295 | 205 | May, Aubrey/Frost Ind School Dist | 4 | 302 |
| Masinger, James/West Rusk Co Cons Ind Sch Dist | 3 | 331 | May, Cathy/McLeod Ind School Dist | 1 | 74 |
| Mask, Leanne/Lytle Ind School Dist | 67 | 24 | May, Deanna/Franklin Ind School Dist | 57 | 327 |
| Mason, Bruce/West Rusk Co Cons Ind Sch Dist | 5 | 331 | May, Debbie/Winnsboro Ind School Dist | 38,85,88 | 408 |
| Mason, Chris/Quitman Ind School Dist | 8,11,57,69,88,285,296,298 | 408 | May, Eddy/De Kalb Ind School Dist | 6 | 51 |
| Mason, Lane/Wildorado Ind Sch Dist | 67 | 311 | May, Gene/Callisburg Ind School Dist | 3,5 | 94 |
| Mason, Ralph/Andrews Ind School Dist | 6 | 19 | May, Kaci/Tahoka Ind School Dist | 57 | 276 |
| Mason, Shawn/Crosbyton Cons Ind Sch Dist | 1 | 98 | May, Lori/Denison Ind School Dist | 58,77 | 171 |
| Mason, Stacy/Crosbyton Cons Ind Sch Dist | 11,69,77 | 98 | May, Molly/Eanes Ind School Dist | 58 | 372 |
| Mason, Wayne/Excelsior Ind School Dist | 1 | 337 | May, Wendy/Redwater Ind School Dist | 31,36,93,270,271,274 | 53 |
| Massengale, John/East Central Ind School Dist | 67 | 34 | May, Wendy/Redwater Ind School Dist | 31,36,93,270,271,274 | 53 |
| Massey, Amy/Schertz-Cibolo-Univ City ISD | 27 | 178 | May, Wendy/Simms Ind School Dist | 57,69,83,85,88,270 | 53 |
| Massey, Brandi/Balmorhea Ind School Dist | 58,286 | 325 | Maya, Taina/Killeen Ind School Dist | 71 | 30 |
| Massey, Chad/Brock Ind School Dist | 6 | 315 | Mayberry, Sandy/Royal Ind School Dist | 2 | 387 |
| Massey, Danny/Brazosport Ind School Dist | 1 | 55 | Mayberry, Tammy/Manor Ind School Dist | 44 | 373 |
| Massey, Doug/Klein Ind School Dist | 4 | 201 | Mayeaux, Dolly/Galena Park Ind School Dist | 69,294 | 191 |
| **Massey, John/**Balmorhea Ind School Dist | 1,11 | 325 | Mayer, Courtney/Northside Ind School Dist | 81 | 39 |
| Massey, Obid/Itasca Ind School Dist | 5 | 231 | Mayer, Lisa/Deer Park Ind School Dist | 48 | 191 |
| Massingill, Mark/Union Hill Ind School Dist | 73 | 380 | Mayfield, Carol/Brownsboro Ind School Dist | 68 | 218 |
| Masterson, Amanda/Fruitvale Ind School Dist | 69,85,88,270 | 383 | Mayfield, Cindy/Holliday Ind School Dist | 3 | 22 |
| Masterson, Zach/Fruitvale Ind School Dist | 93 | 383 | Mayfield, Heather/Castleberry Ind School Dist | 76 | 350 |
| Mata, Casandra/Crystal City Ind School Dist | 37 | 410 | Mayfield, Missy/Burkburnett Ind Sch Dist | 8,27,57,69,74,88,286,288 | 394 |
| Mata, Enrique/Sharyland Ind School Dist | 5 | 227 | Mayhan, Jodie/Union Grove Ind School Dist | 7 | 379 |
| Mata, Ernie/Point Isabel Ind Sch Dist | 5 | 70 | Maynard, Kristi/Turkey-Quitaque Cons Ind SD | 4 | 181 |
| Mata, Monica/La Villa Ind School Dist | 2 | 223 | Maynard, Russell/Lago Vista Ind School Dist | 73 | 373 |
| Matchett, Amy/Van Vleck Ind School Dist | 37 | 279 | Mayo, Carol/Diocese of Dallas Ed Office | 73 | 118 |
| Matheny, Kevin/Central Heights Ind Sch Dist | 5 | 300 | Mayo, Judy/Fredericksburg Ind School Dist | 7 | 167 |
| Mathes, Cliff/Ennis Ind School Dist | 58 | 144 | Mays, Chance, Dr/Mt Enterprise Ind School Dist | 10 | 330 |
| Mathesen, Jennie/Temple Ind School Dist | 58 | 32 | Mays, Kecia/Arlington Ind School Dist | 67 | 346 |
| Matheson, Stacey/Danbury Ind School Dist | 11,73,76,295 | 56 | Mays, Lisa/Troy Ind School Dist | 4 | 33 |
| Mathews, David/Dawson Ind School Dist | 67 | 302 | Mays, Shawn/Brenham Ind School Dist | 752 | 388 |
| Mathews, Dusty/Lexington Ind School Dist | 7 | 266 | Maze, Jerry/Region 12 Ed Service Center | 1 | 286 |
| Mathews, Malisa/Liberty-Eylau Ind School Dist | 4 | 51 | Mazurek, Julie/Utopia Ind School Dist | 8,12,57,74,271,274,296 | 381 |
| Mathews, Michelle/Franklin Ind School Dist | 2 | 327 | Mazzagate, Roy/Little Cypress Mauriceville SD | 16,297 | 311 |
| Mathieu, Troy/Grand Prairie Ind School Dist | 17 | 111 | McAda, Donna/Mesquite Ind School Dist | 69 | 115 |
| Mathiews, Margaret/Woodson Ind School Dist | 58,79 | 365 | McAdams, Sunday/Seymour Ind School Dist | 16,82 | 28 |
| Mathis, Earl/Sweeny Ind School Dist | 67 | 57 | McAfee, Mitzi/Region 3 Ed Service Center | 15 | 385 |
| Mathis, J Kevin/Hempstead Ind School Dist | 19 | 387 | McAlister, Leighanne/Maypearl Ind School Dist | 2 | 145 |
| Mathis, John/Galveston Ind School Dist | 76,84,295 | 165 | McAlpin, Shaun/Orangefield Ind School Dist | 2,15,298 | 312 |
| Mathis, Kevin/Hempstead Ind School Dist | 2 | 387 | McAlpin, Walter/Colmesneil Ind School Dist | 10,69,271,275 | 377 |
| Mathis, Summer/Paradise Ind School Dist | 2,19 | 407 | McAnally, Rosalea/White Deer Ind School Dist | 73 | 73 |
| Mathis, Tiffany/Lamar Cons Ind School Dist | 58 | 157 | McAndrew, Wende/Hawley Ind School Dist | 4 | 253 |
| Mathys, Gretchen/Jarrell Ind School Dist | 3 | 399 | McAnear, Melissa/Cypress-Fairbanks Ind Sch Dist | 2 | 188 |
| Matlock, Dale/Everman Ind School Dist | 6 | 351 | McBain, Kelly/Socorro Ind School Dist | 70 | 140 |
| Matney, Allison, Dr/Houston Ind School Dist | 294 | 193 | McBee, Morgan/Lefors Ind School Dist | 2 | 170 |
| Matney, Allison, Dr/Katy Ind School Dist | 69,70,294 | 156 | McBrayer, Cassidy, Dr/Hawley Ind School Dist | 1 | 253 |
| Matranga, Mike/Texas City Ind School Dist | 91 | 166 | McBride, Faye/Edgewood Ind School Dist | 68 | 382 |
| Matson, Craig/Douglass Ind School Dist | 58 | 300 | McBride, Kristi/Schulenburg Ind School Dist | 8,11,16,286 | 152 |
| Mattern, Shawn/Elkhart Ind School Dist | 5 | 18 | McBride, Ticia/Lumberton Ind School Dist | 57 | 183 |
| Matthews, Brenda/Columbia Brazoria ISD | 68 | 56 | McBride, Vicki/Garner Ind School Dist | 4 | 315 |

| | | | | | | | | | |
|---|---|---|---|---|---|---|---|---|---|
| 1 | Superintendent | 16 | Instructional Media Svcs | 30 | Adult Education | 44 | Science Sec | 58 | Special Education K-12 |
| 2 | Bus/Finance/Purchasing | 17 | Chief Operations Officer | 31 | Career/Sch-to-Work K-12 | 45 | Math K-12 | 59 | Special Education Elem |
| 3 | Buildings And Grounds | 18 | Chief Academic Officer | 32 | Career/Sch-to-Work Elem | 46 | Math Elem | 60 | Special Education Sec |
| 4 | Food Service | 19 | Chief Financial Officer | 33 | Career/Sch-to-Work Sec | 47 | Math Sec | 61 | Foreign/World Lang K-12 |
| 5 | Transportation | 20 | Art K-12 | 34 | Early Childhood Ed | 48 | English/Lang Arts K-12 | 62 | Foreign/World Lang Elem |
| 6 | Athletic | 21 | Art Elem | 35 | Health/Phys Education | 49 | English/Lang Arts Elem | 63 | Foreign/World Lang Sec |
| 7 | Health Services | 22 | Art Sec | 36 | Guidance Services K-12 | 50 | English/Lang Arts Sec | 64 | Religious Education K-12 |
| 8 | Curric/Instruct K-12 | 23 | Music K-12 | 37 | Guidance Services Elem | 51 | Reading K-12 | 65 | Religious Education Elem |
| 9 | Curric/Instruct Elem | 24 | Music Elem | 38 | Guidance Services Sec | 52 | Reading Elem | 66 | Religious Education Sec |
| 10 | Curric/Instruct Sec | 25 | Music Sec | 39 | Social Studies K-12 | 53 | Reading Sec | 67 | School Board President |
| 11 | Federal Program | 26 | Business Education | 40 | Social Studies Elem | 54 | Remedial Reading K-12 | 68 | Teacher Personnel |
| 12 | Title I | 27 | Career & Tech Ed | 41 | Social Studies Sec | 55 | Remedial Reading Elem | 69 | Academic Assessment |
| 13 | Title V | 28 | Technology Education | 42 | Science K-12 | 56 | Remedial Reading Sec | 70 | Research/Development |
| 15 | Asst Superintendent | 29 | Family/Consumer Science | 43 | Science Elem | 57 | Bilingual/ELL | 71 | Public Information |

| | | | | |
|---|---|---|---|---|
| 72 | Summer School | 88 | Alternative/At Risk | 277 Remedial Math K-12 |
| 73 | Instructional Tech | 89 | Multi-Cultural Curriculum | 280 Literacy Coach |
| 74 | Inservice Training | 90 | Social Work | 285 STEM |
| 75 | Marketing/Distributive | 91 | Safety/Security | 286 Digital Learning |
| 76 | Info Systems | 92 | Magnet School | 288 Common Core Standards |
| 77 | Psychological Assess | 93 | Parental Involvement | 294 Accountability |
| 78 | Affirmative Action | 95 | Tech Prep Program | 295 Network System |
| 79 | Student Personnel | 97 | Chief Infomation Officer | 296 Title II Programs |
| 80 | Driver Ed/Safety | 98 | Chief Technology Officer | 297 Webmaster |
| 81 | Gifted/Talented | 270 Character Education | 298 Grant Writer/Ptnrships |
| 82 | Video Services | 271 Migrant Education | 750 Chief Innovation Officer |
| 83 | Substance Abuse Prev | 273 Teacher Mentor | 751 Chief of Staff |
| 84 | Erate | 274 Before/After Sch | 752 Social Emotional Learning |
| 85 | AIDS Education | 275 Response To Intervention | |

| NAME/District | JOB FUNCTIONS | PAGE | NAME/District | JOB FUNCTIONS | PAGE |
|---|---|---|---|---|---|
| McDurham, Robin, Dr/Waco Ind School Dist | 10 | 284 | McKinnon, Jeff/Nederland Ind School Dist | 69 | 245 |
| McEachern, Brad/Hardin Jefferson Ind Sch Dist | 1 | 182 | McKinnon, Reeann/Glasscock Co Ind School Dist | 4 | 168 |
| McEachern, Mike/Huffman Ind School Dist | 6 | 200 | McKinny, Suzy/Magnolia Ind School Dist | 9 | 295 |
| McElhany, Talina/Ore City Ind School Dist | 2 | 379 | McKittrick, Matt/Godley Ind School Dist | 67 | 250 |
| McElroy, Samantha/Huntington Ind School Dist | 4 | 20 | McKnight, Ray/Chester Ind School Dist | 67 | 377 |
| McElyea, Chris/Winnsboro Ind School Dist | 67 | 408 | McKnight, Schronda/Bryan Ind School Dist | 34 | 58 |
| McEntyre, Lori/Paris Ind School Dist | 4 | 262 | McKnight, Winnie/Lovelady Ind School Dist | 7 | 236 |
| McEwen, Kathy/Port Arthur Ind School Dist | 69 | 246 | McKown, Joan/Iola Ind School Dist | 54 | 177 |
| McFadden, Duane/Montgomery Ind School Dist | 10,15 | 296 | McLain, Tammy/Dimmitt Ind School Dist | 286 | 74 |
| McFadden, Leslie/Garrison Ind School Dist | 58 | 301 | McLamore, Mitch/Petrolia Cons Ind School Dist | 6 | 78 |
| McFall, Dennis/Austin Ind School Dist | 274 | 369 | McLane, Mitzi/Yantis Ind School Dist | 4 | 408 |
| McFarland, George, Dr/San Angelo Ind School Dist | 2,15 | 367 | McLaren, Steve/Klondike Ind School Dist | 1,11 | 121 |
| McFarland, Michael, Dr/Crowley Ind School Dist | 1 | 350 | McLarty, Patrick/Ponder Ind School Dist | 3,5 | 130 |
| McFarland, Steve/Gladewater Ind School Dist | 5 | 174 | McLarty, Paul/Clear Creek Ind School Dist | 2,3,15 | 162 |
| McFarlin, Vonda/Gainesville Ind School Dist | 8 | 95 | McLarty, Sam/Center Point Ind School Dist | 4,5 | 258 |
| McFarlind, John/Keene Ind School Dist | 6 | 251 | McLaughlin, Bill, Dr/Walcott Ind School Dist | 1,11,288 | 123 |
| McGaha, Shad/Wichita Falls Ind School Dist | 16,73,76,98,295 | 395 | McLean, Denise/Beaumont Ind School Dist | 71 | 244 |
| McGahey, Suzanne/Keller Ind School Dist | 39 | 357 | McLean, Denise/Klein Ind School Dist | 297 | 202 |
| McGan, Bryan/Hale Center Ind School Dist | 73 | 180 | McLean, Holly/Gruver Ind School Dist | 73 | 181 |
| McGane, Sherra/Cedar Hill Ind School Dist | 2 | 101 | McLean, Scott/Abilene Ind School Dist | 3,4,5,15 | 362 |
| McGavock, Deborah/Hico Ind School Dist | 31,36,69 | 181 | McLear, Blare/Calallen Ind School Dist | 10,69 | 305 |
| McGee, Blanca/Grand Prairie Ind School Dist | 752 | 111 | McLemore, Amber/Martin's Mill Ind Sch Dist | 85 | 383 |
| McGee, Dustin/Liberty Ind School Dist | 15 | 269 | McLendon, Deeanna/Blanco Ind School Dist | 8,31,36,69,83 | 49 |
| McGee, Karla/Crosby Ind School Dist | 58 | 188 | McLendon, Gerry/Morton Ind School Dist | 5 | 78 |
| McGee, Rayanne/Texline Ind School Dist | 31,58 | 99 | McLeod, Kimberly/Harris Co Dept of Ed | 8,15 | 184 |
| McGeehee, Ben/Sweetwater ISD School Dist | 6,35 | 304 | McLeod, Michael/Mason Ind School Dist | 6 | 278 |
| McGehee, Lana/Paradise Ind School Dist | 16 | 407 | McLerran, Patti/San Augustine Ind School Dist | 2 | 332 |
| McGhee, Cori/North East Ind School Dist | 31 | 37 | McLver, Ryan/Weimar Ind School Dist | 6 | 91 |
| McGill, Pat/Harleton Ind School Dist | 67 | 213 | McMahan, Glenda/Sunnyvale Ind School Dist | 69,88,270 | 117 |
| McGilvary, Steven/Coppell Ind School Dist | 73,98 | 102 | McMains, Julia, Dr/Palacios Ind School Dist | 8,11,16,57,58,271,273,274 | 278 |
| McGinley, James/Higgins Ind School Dist | 3 | 270 | McManners, Mike/Iola Ind School Dist | 27 | 177 |
| McGinn, Kelly/Stephenville Ind School Dist | 8,288 | 148 | McManus, Becky/Barbers Hill Ind School Dist | 2,15 | 75 |
| McGinnis, Jeff/Snyder Ind School Dist | 73 | 336 | McManus, Kim/Caldwell Ind School Dist | 69 | 63 |
| McGinnis, Linda/Comanche Ind School Dist | 73 | 93 | McMath, Barbi/Wills Point Ind School Dist | 8,15,285,286,288,294,298 | 384 |
| McGowan, Jenny, Dr/Klein Ind School Dist | 1,288 | 201 | McMeans, Bart/Borden Co Ind School Dist | 8,11,57,69,88,294,296 | 49 |
| McGowan, Lucy/Walcott Ind School Dist | 67 | 123 | McMichael, Mechelle/Hubbard Ind School Dist | 73,76,270 | 51 |
| McGowen, Charles/Huntsville Ind School Dist | 5 | 386 | McMillan, Sherri/Newcastle Ind School Dist | 270 | 409 |
| McGowen, Donnie/Weatherford Ind School Dist | 30 | 316 | McMillian, Bonnie/Carthage Ind School Dist | 7 | 314 |
| McGowen, Robby, Dr/Region 4 Ed Service Center | 15,79 | 213 | McMillian, David/Santa Fe Ind School Dist | 5 | 165 |
| McGraw, Leann/McCamey Ind School Dist | 10,57 | 380 | McMillion, Paula/Anna Ind School Dist | 11,57 | 81 |
| McGraw, Sherry/Sulphur Springs Ind Sch Dist | 2 | 235 | McMillon, Lacey/Red Lick Ind School Dist | 2 | 52 |
| McGregor, Diana/North Lamar Ind School Dist | 4 | 406 | McMullan, Mary/Bronte Ind School Dist | 16,73,82,286,295,297 | 79 |
| McGregor, Heather/Region 8 Ed Service Center | 74,294 | 72 | McMurtry, Brad/Troy Ind School Dist | 3,68,79,288 | 33 |
| McGuane, Julie/Lamar Cons Ind School Dist | 50,53 | 157 | McMurtry, Gary/Troy Ind School Dist | 67 | 33 |
| McGuire, Julie/Arlington Ind School Dist | 11 | 346 | McMurtry, Linda/Malakoff Ind School Dist | 16,82 | 219 |
| McGuire, Paul/Clyde Consolidated Ind SD | 295 | 66 | McNab, Maggie/Lubbock-Cooper Ind Sch Dist | 88 | 274 |
| McHam, Terry/Connally Ind School Dist | 5 | 282 | McNabb, Jean/Ropes Ind School Dist | 59 | 232 |
| McHazlett, Matthew/La Pryor Ind School Dist | 1 | 411 | McNabb, Terry/Aubrey Ind School Dist | 15 | 124 |
| McHenry, Robert/Springtown Ind School Dist | 73,98,286,295 | 316 | McNaird, Vickie/Tioga Ind School Dist | 4 | 172 |
| McHenry, Rodney/Garland Ind School Dist | 68 | 109 | McNeely, Clay/Hereford Ind School Dist | 67 | 123 |
| McIlcain, Michielle/De Leon Ind School Dist | 285 | 93 | McNeely, Deborah/Aldine Ind School Dist | 275 | 184 |
| McIlveene, Cindy/Wolfe City Ind School Dist | 2 | 240 | McNeely, Debra/Conroe Ind School Dist | 50,63 | 294 |
| McInnis, Karen/Lasara Ind School Dist | 36,83,88,270,275 | 397 | McNeely, Janet/Weatherford Ind School Dist | 11 | 316 |
| McIntosh, Matt/Gladewater Ind School Dist | 3 | 174 | McNeill, Diane/Sweeny Ind School Dist | 5 | 57 |
| McIntrye, Amber/Princeton Ind School Dist | 69 | 87 | McNelly, Curt/Miles Ind School Dist | 9 | 329 |
| **McIntyre, Donald/**Princeton Ind School Dist | 1 | 87 | McNutt, Jamie/Winona Ind School Dist | 16,82 | 341 |
| McIntyre, Suzette/Wall Ind School Dist | 73,295 | 368 | McNutt, Michelle/Stephenville Ind School Dist | 57 | 148 |
| McIver, Dasha/Terrell Ind School Dist | 2 | 256 | McNutt, Shelli/Bremond Ind School Dist | 9 | 327 |
| McKamie, David/Region 12 Ed Service Center | 79 | 286 | McPhaul, Tracey/Reagan Co Ind School Dist | 73,295 | 324 |
| McKay, Ginger/Goose Creek Cons Ind Sch Dist | 11,298 | 192 | McPherson, Cindy/North Hopkins Ind School Dist | 4 | 234 |
| McKay, Michael/Galena Park Ind School Dist | 15,68 | 191 | McPherson, Diane/Happy Ind School Dist | 4 | 345 |
| McKee, Ashley/Eustace Ind School Dist | 67 | 219 | McPherson, Liuren/Blum Ind School Dist | 31,69,83,88 | 230 |
| McKee, Jamie/Karnes City Ind School Dist | 84 | 253 | McPherson, Richard/Blum Ind School Dist | 67 | 230 |
| McKee, Jennifer/Irving Ind School Dist | 34 | 113 | McPherson, Toni/Beaumont Ind School Dist | 73 | 244 |
| McKee, Norma/Rio Grande City Ind Sch Dist | 93 | 343 | McQuagge, Dina/Freer Ind School Dist | 33,38 | 132 |
| McKeever, Kevin/Lamar Cons Ind School Dist | 3 | 157 | McQuagge, Steve/Freer Ind School Dist | 67 | 132 |
| McKelvain, Travis/Edgewood Ind School Dist | 68 | 34 | McQuarters, Alvin/Irving Ind School Dist | 97,98 | 113 |
| McKenzie, Michael/Georgetown Ind School Dist | 295 | 398 | McQuary, Beverly/Mildred Ind School Dist | 2 | 303 |
| McKenzie, Tonya/Breckenridge Ind School Dist | 7 | 344 | McReery, Lisa/Henderson Ind School Dist | 27,31 | 330 |
| McKethan, Donna/Waco Ind School Dist | 27,31 | 284 | McSpadden, Karie/Leander Ind School Dist | 68 | 400 |
| McKinley, Michele/Manor Ind School Dist | 58 | 373 | McSwain, James/Houston ISD-West Area | 15 | 198 |
| McKinney, Bridget/Alief Ind School Dist | 46 | 186 | McSwain, Mike/Brock Ind School Dist | 2,19 | 315 |
| McKinney, Carlton/Nixon-Smiley Cons Ind Sch Dist | 6 | 169 | McTee, Sonya/Trenton Ind School Dist | 4 | 151 |
| McKinney, Lynn/Aledo Ind School Dist | 11,15,296 | 315 | McThatter, Brett/Port Neches-Groves Ind SD | 285 | 246 |
| McKinney, Mark/Santa Fe Ind School Dist | 5 | 165 | McVay, Brad/Wylie Ind School Dist | 295 | 364 |
| McKinney, Sharon/Port Aransas Ind School Dist | 1 | 308 | McVay, Robin/Wylie Ind School Dist | 68 | 364 |

| # | | # | | # | | # | | # | |
|---|---|---|---|---|---|---|---|---|---|
| 1 | Superintendent | 16 | Instructional Media Svcs | 30 | Adult Education | 44 | Science Sec | 58 | Special Education K-12 |
| 2 | Bus/Finance/Purchasing | 17 | Chief Operations Officer | 31 | Career/Sch-to-Work K-12 | 45 | Math K-12 | 59 | Special Education Elem |
| 3 | Buildings And Grounds | 18 | Chief Academic Officer | 32 | Career/Sch-to-Work Elem | 46 | Math Elem | 60 | Special Education Sec |
| 4 | Food Service | 19 | Chief Financial Officer | 33 | Career/Sch-to-Work Sec | 47 | Math Sec | 61 | Foreign/World Lang K-12 |
| 5 | Transportation | 20 | Art K-12 | 34 | Early Childhood Ed | 48 | English/Lang Arts K-12 | 62 | Foreign/World Lang Elem |
| 6 | Athletic | 21 | Art Elem | 35 | Health/Phys Education | 49 | English/Lang Arts Elem | 63 | Foreign/World Lang Sec |
| 7 | Health Services | 22 | Art Sec | 36 | Guidance Services K-12 | 50 | English/Lang Arts Sec | 64 | Religious Education K-12 |
| 8 | Curric/Instruct K-12 | 23 | Music K-12 | 37 | Guidance Services Elem | 51 | Reading K-12 | 65 | Religious Education Elem |
| 9 | Curric/Instruct Elem | 24 | Music Elem | 38 | Guidance Services Sec | 52 | Reading Elem | 66 | Religious Education Sec |
| 10 | Curric/Instruct Sec | 25 | Music Sec | 39 | Social Studies K-12 | 53 | Reading Sec | 67 | School Board President |
| 11 | Federal Program | 26 | Business Education | 40 | Social Studies Elem | 54 | Remedial Reading K-12 | 68 | Teacher Personnel |
| 12 | Title I | 27 | Career & Tech Ed | 41 | Social Studies Sec | 55 | Remedial Reading Elem | 69 | Academic Assessment |
| 13 | Title V | 28 | Technology Education | 42 | Science K-12 | 56 | Remedial Reading Sec | 70 | Research/Development |
| 15 | Asst Superintendent | 29 | Family/Consumer Science | 43 | Science Elem | 57 | Bilingual/ELL | 71 | Public Information |

| # | | # | | # | | # | |
|---|---|---|---|---|---|---|---|
| 72 | Summer School | 88 | Alternative/At Risk | 277 | Remedial Math K-12 | | |
| 73 | Instructional Tech | 89 | Multi-Cultural Curriculum | 280 | Literacy Coach | | |
| 74 | Inservice Training | 90 | Social Work | 285 | STEM | | |
| 75 | Marketing/Distributive | 91 | Safety/Security | 286 | Digital Learning | | |
| 76 | Info Systems | 92 | Magnet School | 288 | Common Core Standards | | |
| 77 | Psychological Assess | 93 | Parental Involvement | 294 | Accountability | | |
| 78 | Affirmative Action | 95 | Tech Prep Program | 295 | Network System | | |
| 79 | Student Personnel | 97 | Chief Information Officer | 296 | Title II Programs | | |
| 80 | Driver Ed/Safety | 98 | Chief Technology Officer | 297 | Webmaster | | |
| 81 | Gifted/Talented | 270 | Character Education | 298 | Grant Writer/Ptnrships | | |
| 82 | Video Services | 271 | Migrant Education | 750 | Chief Innovation Officer | | |
| 83 | Substance Abuse Prev | 273 | Teacher Mentor | 751 | Chief of Staff | | |
| 84 | Erate | 274 | Before/After Sch | 752 | Social Emotional Learning | | |
| 85 | AIDS Education | 275 | Response To Intervention | | | | |

| NAME/District | JOB FUNCTIONS | PAGE |
|---|---|---|
| Meza-Chavez, Jeannie, Dr/San Elizario Ind School Dist | 1 | 139 |
| Meza, Tina/Comstock Ind School Dist | 2 | 381 |
| Meza, Waymond/San Felipe-Del Rio Cons Ind SD | 67 | 381 |
| Michael, Amanda/Skidmore Tynan Ind SD | 7 | 29 |
| Michael, Stephen/Palmer Ind School Dist | 73 | 146 |
| Michaelewicz, Paul/Florence Ind School Dist | 1 | 398 |
| Michalec, Rose/Archdiocese Galveston-Houston | 2 | 209 |
| Micinski, Gary/Irving Ind School Dist | 19 | 113 |
| Mickelson, Kristi/Mullin Ind School Dist | 8,11,83,271,294 | 291 |
| Mickelson, Kristi/Mullin Ind School Dist | 1,73 | 291 |
| Mickelson, Steve/Brookesmith Ind School Dist | 1 | 61 |
| Miculka, James/Northside Ind School Dist | 20,23 | 39 |
| Middleton, Allison/Itasca Ind School Dist | 58,76,285,296 | 231 |
| Middleton, Mace/Happy Ind School Dist | 67 | 345 |
| Middleton, Maryann/Crowley Ind School Dist | 8 | 350 |
| Mierles, Leonel/Rio Grande City Ind Sch Dist | 6 | 342 |
| Migel, Galvan/Tidehaven Ind School Dist | 5 | 279 |
| Migl, Leann/Vysehrad Ind School Dist | 59,275 | 265 |
| Migura, Jason/Medina Valley Ind School Dist | 68 | 287 |
| Mijares, Ismael/Eagle Pass Ind School Dist | 2,15 | 279 |
| Mijares, Samuel/Eagle Pass Ind School Dist | 8,15,81,288 | 279 |
| Mika, Cyndy, Dr/Little Elm Ind School Dist | 11,15,70,294 | 128 |
| Mikeal, Laura/Hudson Ind School Dist | 34 | 20 |
| Mikesh, Holly/Center Ind School Dist | 68 | 337 |
| Mikeska, Charles/West Ind School Dist | 2,3,91 | 285 |
| Mikolaycik, Ryan/Lake Travis Ind School Dist | 4 | 373 |
| Miksch, Brett/Sweeny Ind School Dist | 6 | 57 |
| Milam, Brandon/Tatum Ind School Dist | 2 | 331 |
| Milam, Dwain/Jacksboro Ind Sch Dist | 1 | 242 |
| **Milam, Jessica/**San Vicente Ind School Dist | 1 | 60 |
| Milam, Wendy/Fruitvale Ind School Dist | 2 | 383 |
| Milan, Cynthia/Ft Stockton Ind School Dist | 7 | 318 |
| Miles, Tami/North Lamar Ind School Dist | 2,296 | 406 |
| Miles, Tina/Westbrook Ind School Dist | 59 | 292 |
| Milla, Jennifer/Edgewood Ind School Dist | 7 | 34 |
| Miller-Baker, Mary, Dr/Edgewood Ind School Dist | 34 | 34 |
| Miller, Alex/Hempstead Ind School Dist | 73,98,295,297 | 387 |
| Miller, Amy/Wortham Ind School Dist | 83,85 | 161 |
| Miller, Andrew/Moody Ind School Dist | 285 | 284 |
| Miller, Anna/Lumberton Ind School Dist | 71 | 183 |
| Miller, Bethany/Southland Ind School Dist | 11,296 | 167 |
| Miller, Billie/Quinlan Ind School Dist | 2 | 240 |
| Miller, Brian/Lackland Ind School Dist | 67 | 37 |
| Miller, Bryan/Leander Ind School Dist | 7,79,91 | 399 |
| Miller, Chris/Columbia Brazoria ISD | 15 | 56 |
| Miller, Christopher/Hallsville Ind School Dist | 91 | 213 |
| Miller, Christy/Palacios Ind School Dist | 2 | 278 |
| Miller, Chuck/De Leon Ind School Dist | 91 | 93 |
| Miller, Clint/Rising Star Ind Sch Dist | 6 | 133 |
| **Miller, Damenion/**Winona Ind School Dist | 1 | 341 |
| Miller, Darlene/Bovina Ind School Dist | 2 | 317 |
| Miller, Dawn/Midland Ind School Dist | 58,77 | 288 |
| Miller, Doug/Detroit Ind School Dist | 67 | 325 |
| Miller, Erica/Italy Ind School Dist | 69,88,271 | 145 |
| Miller, Jaime/Ector Co Ind School Dist | 8,280 | 134 |
| Miller, Jason/Leander Ind School Dist | 98 | 400 |
| Miller, Jeff/Rockdale Ind School Dist | 6 | 290 |
| Miller, Jennifer/Birdville Ind School Dist | 39,59 | 348 |
| Miller, Jennifer/Cypress-Fairbanks Ind Sch Dist | 73 | 189 |
| Miller, Jimmy/Roosevelt Ind School Dist | 6 | 274 |
| Miller, Julie/Irving Ind School Dist | 8 | 113 |
| Miller, Karen/Eagle Mtn-Saginaw Ind Sch Dist | 74,273 | 351 |
| Miller, Karie/Holliday Ind School Dist | 73,84,286 | 22 |
| Miller, Kay/Bandera Ind School Dist | 5 | 26 |
| Miller, Kelly/Dawson Ind School Dist | 2 | 302 |
| Miller, Kristi/Irion Co Ind School Dist | 4,10,11,296 | 241 |
| Miller, Leah/Copperas Cove Ind School Dist | 31,38 | 96 |
| Miller, Les/Poth Ind School Dist | 67 | 404 |
| Miller, Lyle/Floydada Ind School Dist | 67 | 153 |
| Miller, M-Lynn/Claude Ind School Dist | 73,76,286 | 23 |
| Miller, Matt/Carroll Independent Sch Dist | 15,68 | 349 |
| Miller, Melonie/La Gloria Ind School Dist | 16,57,59,273 | 248 |
| Miller, Mike/Judson Ind School Dist | 6 | 36 |
| Miller, Mikeal/Van Alstyne Ind School Dist | 6 | 173 |
| Miller, Ned/Iowa Park Consolidated Ind SD | 5 | 395 |
| Miller, Pam/Avinger Ind School Dist | 2 | 73 |

| NAME/District | JOB FUNCTIONS | PAGE |
|---|---|---|
| Miller, Patty/Itasca Ind School Dist | 3,5 | 231 |
| Miller, Paul/Clear Creek Ind School Dist | 3 | 162 |
| Miller, Paul/McGregor Ind School Dist | 7,15,91 | 283 |
| Miller, Randi/Chico Ind School Dist | 6 | 406 |
| Miller, Randy/Darrouzett Ind School Dist | 67 | 270 |
| Miller, Rebecca/Del Valle Ind School Dist | 42 | 372 |
| Miller, Richard/Center Ind School Dist | 73,76 | 337 |
| Miller, Robert/Edgewood Ind School Dist | 69,70 | 34 |
| Miller, Ryne/Marion Ind School Dist | 6 | 177 |
| Miller, Sarah/Sterling City Ind School Dist | 57,58 | 344 |
| Miller, Shawna, Dr/Lewisville Ind School Dist | 74 | 126 |
| Miller, Stan/Bovina Ind School Dist | 73,84,295 | 317 |
| Miller, Stefanie/Spurger Ind School Dist | 92,271 | 378 |
| Miller, Stephen/Olton Ind School Dist | 295 | 263 |
| Miller, Toby/Southland Ind School Dist | 1 | 167 |
| Miller, Toni/Kemp Ind School Dist | 27 | 255 |
| Miller, Torri/Winnsboro Ind School Dist | 8,11,58,76,286,288,298 | 408 |
| Miller, Wade/Tuloso-Midway Ind School Dist | 6 | 308 |
| Miller, William/Valentine Ind School Dist | 67 | 244 |
| Millerick, Tim/Sherman Ind School Dist | 67 | 172 |
| Millican, Chris/Aubrey Ind School Dist | 73,295 | 124 |
| **Millican, Jill/**Dimmitt Ind School Dist | 1 | 74 |
| Milligan, Mida, Dr/Garland Ind School Dist | 71 | 109 |
| Millner, Jeff/Canyon Ind School Dist | 3 | 323 |
| Mills-Oller, Kim/Post Ind School Dist | 8,11,15,69,270,273 | 167 |
| Mills, Andy/Rice Ind School Dist | 6 | 303 |
| Mills, Brent/Woodson Ind School Dist | 8,57,76 | 365 |
| Mills, Brooke/Pawnee Ind School Dist | 7 | 28 |
| Mills, Charla/Ralls Ind School Dist | 59 | 98 |
| Mills, Cheryl/Poteet Ind School Dist | 1,57 | 24 |
| Mills, Debi/Wichita Falls Ind School Dist | 7 | 395 |
| Mills, Dee Ann/Brock Ind School Dist | 12,298 | 315 |
| Mills, Linda/Randolph Field Ind School Dist | 68 | 42 |
| Mills, Randy/Fruitvale Ind School Dist | 98,295 | 383 |
| Mills, Sarah/Childress Ind School Dist | 8,11,58 | 77 |
| Milton, Kathy/Royse City Ind School Dist | 69,294 | 328 |
| Milton, Randy/Shepherd Ind School Dist | 4 | 333 |
| Mims, Jason/Forsan Ind School Dist | 2 | 237 |
| Mims, Mysti/Forsan Ind School Dist | 8,57,69,88,271 | 237 |
| Mincher, Diane/Tioga Ind School Dist | 11,88 | 172 |
| Ming, Keith/Liberty Ind School Dist | 33 | 269 |
| Minix, Winston/Grand Prairie Ind School Dist | 27,31 | 111 |
| Minjarez, Armando/Seagraves Ind School Dist | 6 | 162 |
| Minor, Josh/Hurst-Euless-Bedford ISD | 3 | 356 |
| Minor, Rodney/Int'l Leadership of Texas Dist | 5 | 112 |
| Minor, Todd/Montague Ind School Dist | 3,5 | 293 |
| Minschu, Jill/Fredericksburg Ind School Dist | 2,15 | 167 |
| Minter, Alvis/Mexia Ind School Dist | 3,5 | 270 |
| **Minter, Keith/**Hooks Ind School Dist | 1,73 | 51 |
| Minter, Larry/Big Sandy Ind School Dist | 6 | 378 |
| Minyard, Rusty/Evadale Ind School Dist | 83,288 | 243 |
| Miramontes, Gerogina/Tornillo Ind School Dist | 58 | 141 |
| Miranda, Mark/Spring Ind School Dist | 17 | 207 |
| Miranda, Patricia/Amarillo Ind School Dist | 7,85 | 320 |
| Miranda, Roxanne/Carrizo Spgs Cons Ind SD | 38 | 131 |
| Mircovich, Karen/Ingleside Ind School Dist | 11,57,69,83 | 334 |
| Mircovich, Troy/Ingleside Ind School Dist | 1 | 333 |
| **Mireles, James/**Perryton Ind School Dist | 1 | 310 |
| Mires, Kelly/Coppell Ind School Dist | 68 | 102 |
| Mitchell, Allison/Panhandle Ind School Dist | 9,74 | 73 |
| Mitchell, Amy/Crandall Ind School Dist | 4 | 254 |
| Mitchell, Byron/Elgin Ind School Dist | 67 | 27 |
| Mitchell, Cindy/Boles Ind School Dist | 3,5,17 | 238 |
| Mitchell, Gary/Broaddus Ind School Dist | 16,73,295 | 332 |
| Mitchell, Jimmie/Manor Ind School Dist | 6 | 373 |
| Mitchell, Lakeisha/Richardson Ind School Dist | 42 | 116 |
| Mitchell, Laurie/Katy Ind School Dist | 75 | 156 |
| Mitchell, Michelle/Pine Tree Ind School Dist | 4 | 175 |
| Mitchell, Pam/Pampa Ind School Dist | 8,11,15,30,72 | 170 |
| Mitchell, Pamela/Livingston Ind School Dist | 58 | 319 |
| Mitchell, Renee/Sweeny Ind School Dist | 36 | 57 |
| Mitchell, Richard/Strawn Ind School Dist | 1,11 | 314 |
| Mitchell, Shaelee/Weatherford Ind School Dist | 7,83 | 316 |
| Mitchell, Sunny/Bellevue Ind School District | 73,295 | 77 |
| Mitchell, Suzi/Hays Cons Ind School Dist | 27,31 | 216 |
| Mitchell, Tray/Georgetown Ind School Dist | 4 | 398 |

| NAME/District | JOB FUNCTIONS | PAGE |
|---|---|---|
| Mitchem, Mary/Georgetown Ind School Dist | 76,79 | 398 |
| Mixon, Cheryl/Ft Worth Ind School Dist | 34 | 352 |
| Mixon, Jason/San Augustine Ind School Dist | 8,11,15,69 | 332 |
| Miytchell, Jimmy/Edna Ind School Dist | 6 | 242 |
| Mize, Brenda/Burleson Ind School Dist | 2,19 | 249 |
| **Mize, Cody/**Mineola Ind School Dist | 1 | 408 |
| Mizell, Matthew/Trinidad Ind School Dist | 8,11,83,88,274,288 | 219 |
| Moats, James/Lindsay Ind School Dist | 73,84 | 95 |
| Moats, Mara/Edinburg Cons Ind School Dist | 74,285 | 221 |
| Mobley, Billy/Ballinger Ind School Dist | 73 | 329 |
| Mobley, Jennifer/Mesquite Ind School Dist | 11 | 115 |
| Mobley, Shane/Sealy Ind School Dist | 6 | 25 |
| Mocygemba, Angie/Schertz-Cibolo-Univ City ISD | 2 | 178 |
| Moczgemba, Roxanne/Stockdale Ind School Dist | 8,11,57,69,296 | 404 |
| Moczygemba, Cynthia/Randolph Field Ind School Dist | 4 | 42 |
| Moczygemba, Erica/Granger Ind School Dist | 7 | 399 |
| Moczygemba, Joey/Pleasanton Ind School Dist | 4 | 24 |
| Moczygemba, Kalyn/Falls City Ind School Dist | 2 | 253 |
| Moczygemba, Lisa/Karnes City Ind School Dist | 11,57,88,271,296 | 253 |
| Moczygemba, Randy/New Braunfels Ind School Dist | 1 | 92 |
| Mode, Eileen/Kennedale Ind School Dist | 3 | 358 |
| Modest, Anetta/Houston Ind School Dist | 74 | 193 |
| Modgling, Jack/Dripping Springs Ind Sch Dist | 58,275 | 215 |
| Moebes, Todd/Lockhart Ind School Dist | 6 | 64 |
| Moehlig, Scott/Alief Ind School Dist | 6 | 186 |
| Moeller, Delia/Flatonia Ind School Dist | 16,73 | 151 |
| Moffatt, Jared/Van Ind School Dist | 6 | 383 |
| Moffett, John/Claude Ind School Dist | 6,83,88,273,275,294 | 23 |
| Moffett, Lance/Fredericksburg Ind School Dist | 6 | 167 |
| Mohan, Cody/Cayuga Ind School Dist | 6 | 18 |
| Moharam, Hossiny/Randolph Field Ind School Dist | 3 | 42 |
| Moiser, Ginny/Dublin Ind School Dist | 2 | 147 |
| Mojica, Alejandro/Victoria Ind School Dist | 57,89,271 | 384 |
| Moke, Martha/New Braunfels Ind School Dist | 58 | 92 |
| Molano, Velma/Hidalgo Ind School Dist | 7 | 222 |
| Molder, Gail/McCamey Ind School Dist | 2,11,26 | 380 |
| Molina, Alexandra/McAllen Ind School Dist | 4 | 224 |
| Molina, James/Poth Ind School Dist | 3 | 404 |
| Molina, Nancy/Moody Ind School Dist | 16,69,73,286 | 284 |
| **Molinar, Frank/**White Settlement Ind Sch Dist | 1 | 360 |
| Molinar, Karen/Ft Worth Ind School Dist | 751 | 352 |
| Molinar, Monica/Aubrey Ind School Dist | 57,271 | 124 |
| Molinar, Savannah/Brackett Ind School Dist | 7 | 260 |
| Molsey, Micah/Nederland Ind School Dist | 67 | 245 |
| Molter, Matt/Lometa Ind School Dist | 67 | 264 |
| Momanyi, Timothy/Houston Ind School Dist | 2 | 193 |
| Money, Tracy/Forney Ind School Dist | 4 | 254 |
| Moneyhon, Jennifer/Mason Ind School Dist | 7,35 | 278 |
| Monjaras, Bonney/Region 6 Ed Service Center | 68 | 386 |
| Monjaras, Mario/Pettus Ind School Dist | 4 | 28 |
| Monk-Allen, Christina/San Antonio Ind School Dist | 27 | 42 |
| Monk, Bruce/Lovelady Ind School Dist | 67 | 236 |
| Monk, Kristin/Sulphur Springs Ind Sch Dist | 9,15 | 235 |
| Monreal, Julian/Southside Ind School Dist | 3 | 46 |
| Monroe, Judy/Tenaha Ind School Dist | 58 | 338 |
| Monroe, Scott/Carrollton-Farmers Branch ISD | 16,73,76,295 | 100 |
| Monroe, Tanya, Dr/Comfort Ind School Dist | 1 | 257 |
| Monsizias, Sam/Tahoka Ind School Dist | 5,91 | 276 |
| Monson, Ronda/Stephenville Ind School Dist | 298 | 148 |
| Montalbo, Nancy/Splendora Ind School Dist | 4 | 297 |
| Montalvo, Pamela/Sharyland Ind School Dist | 8,15 | 227 |
| Montalvo, Roldan/Jim Hogg Co Ind School Dist | 6 | 247 |
| Montanez, Esther/Lewisville Ind School Dist | 57 | 126 |
| Montano, Matthew/Texas Dept of Education | 15,57,58 | 1 |
| Montelongo, Anthony/Dimmitt Ind School Dist | 73,295 | 74 |
| Montemayor, Adrian/San Perlita Ind School Dist | 8,58 | 397 |
| Montemayor, David/Little Elm Ind School Dist | 67 | 128 |

| NAME/District | JOB FUNCTIONS | PAGE |
|---|---|---|
| Montemayor, Teresa/Levelland Ind School Dist | 2,19 | 232 |
| Montenegro, Jorge/Diocese of Fort Worth Ed Off | 2 | 360 |
| Montes, Alex/Clifton Ind School Dist | 67 | 49 |
| Montes, Missey/Itasca Ind School Dist | 4 | 231 |
| Montes, Wayne/Wells Ind School Dist | 67 | 77 |
| Montez, Garla/Aquilla Ind School Dist | 36,69,83 | 230 |
| Montez, Garla/Aquilla Ind School Dist | 36,57,69 | 230 |
| Montgomery, Amy/Garland Ind School Dist | 76 | 109 |
| Montgomery, Ava/Alief Ind School Dist | 8,15 | 186 |
| Montgomery, Christopher/Tomball Ind School Dist | 295 | 208 |
| Montgomery, Clay/Spearman Ind School Dist | 1 | 182 |
| Montgomery, Gina/River Road Ind School Dist | 73,295 | 322 |
| Montgomery, Gina/River Road Ind School Dist | 84 | 322 |
| Montgomery, John/Allen Ind School Dist | 67 | 80 |
| Montgomery, Kelli/Birdville Ind School Dist | 16,286 | 348 |
| Montgomery, Nancy/Strawn Ind School Dist | 4 | 314 |
| Montgomery, Rhiannon/Weatherford Ind School Dist | 73 | 316 |
| Montgomery, Rhiannon/Weatherford Ind School Dist | 73 | 316 |
| Montgomery, Robert/Albany Ind School Dist | 67 | 336 |
| Montgomery, Robert/McKinney Ind School Dist | 5,91 | 84 |
| Montgomery, Tracy/Weatherford Ind School Dist | 295 | 316 |
| Monto, Roseo/Bovina Ind School Dist | 88 | 317 |
| Montoya, Georgia/Pharr-San Juan-Alamo Ind SD | 298 | 226 |
| Monzingo, Denise, Dr/Rockdale Ind School Dist | 1 | 290 |
| Moody, Darcas/Splendora Ind School Dist | 5 | 297 |
| Moody, David/Pearland Ind School Dist | 15,68,79 | 56 |
| Moody, Jason/Brownsville Ind School Dist | 71 | 66 |
| Moody, Leslie/Westbrook Ind School Dist | 2 | 292 |
| Moody, Sam/Valley Mills Ind School Dist | 6 | 50 |
| Moody, Steve/Iowa Park Consolidated Ind SD | 1 | 395 |
| Moody, Tania/Levelland Ind School Dist | 67 | 232 |
| Moon, Dawn/Brookeland Ind School Dist | 7 | 243 |
| Moon, Lisa/Bruceville-Eddy Ind Sch Dist | 7,85 | 281 |
| Mooney, Charles/Plainview Ind School Dist | 3 | 180 |
| Mooney, Daiann/Grapevine-Colleyville Ind SD | 2,19 | 355 |
| Mooneyham, Cindy/Magnolia Ind School Dist | 5 | 295 |
| Mooneyham, Joe/Waller Ind School Dist | 5,91 | 387 |
| Moore Morrison, Nicole/Houston ISD-Achieve 180 | 15 | 193 |
| Moore-Ellis, Pam/Clear Creek Ind School Dist | 77 | 163 |
| Moore, Brian/Lamar Cons Ind School Dist | 36,69,70,294 | 157 |
| Moore, Brooks/Aledo Ind School Dist | 73,98,295 | 315 |
| Moore, Carmen/Gholson Ind School Dist | 2,13,296 | 282 |
| Moore, Carson/Gholson Ind School Dist | 3 | 282 |
| Moore, Chalet/Early Ind School Dist | 58 | 62 |
| Moore, Chenda/Pearland Ind School Dist | 36,83,88,275 | 56 |
| Moore, Cheri/George West Ind School Dist | 67 | 271 |
| Moore, Chris/Crandall Ind School Dist | 71 | 254 |
| Moore, Cindy/Canadian Ind School Dist | 2 | 218 |
| Moore, Courtney/Cuero Ind School Dist | 67 | 122 |
| Moore, David/Ft Bend Ind School Dist | 3 | 153 |
| Moore, Deanna/Schulenburg Ind School Dist | 58 | 152 |
| Moore, Derik/Sheldon Ind School Dist | 71 | 205 |
| Moore, George/Texarkana Ind School Dist | 15,88 | 53 |
| Moore, Hollis/Venus Ind School Dist | 11,15,83 | 252 |
| Moore, Jamie/Panhandle Ind School Dist | 2 | 72 |
| Moore, Jamye/Cotton Center Ind School Dist | 27 | 179 |
| Moore, Janan/Livingston Ind School Dist | 8,18,69,74 | 319 |
| Moore, Janette/Alto Ind School Dist | 57 | 76 |
| **Moore, John, Dr/**Galena Park Ind School Dist | 1 | 191 |
| Moore, Kala/Jacksonville Ind School Dist | 68 | 76 |
| Moore, Karen/Campbell Ind School Dist | 16,286 | 238 |
| Moore, Kelly/Union Grove Ind School Dist | 1 | 379 |
| Moore, Kimberley/Big Sandy Ind School Dist | 4 | 319 |
| Moore, Kimberly/West Oso Ind School Dist | 27,285 | 309 |
| Moore, Leland, Dr/Coldspring-Oakhurst Cons ISD | 1 | 332 |
| Moore, Mary-Jane/Tarkington Ind School Dist | 8,11,57,76,85,88,296,298 | 269 |
| Moore, Megan/Texline Ind School Dist | 31,90 | 99 |

| NAME/District | JOB FUNCTIONS | PAGE |
|---|---|---|
| Mosley, Dana/Lancaster Ind School Dist | 2 | 114 |
| Mosley, J D/Schertz-Cibolo-Univ City ISD | 3 | 178 |
| Mosley, Jean/Coppell Ind School Dist | 4 | 102 |
| Moss, Darla/Midland Ind School Dist | 2,19 | 288 |
| Moss, Jennifer/Connally Ind School Dist | 2 | 282 |
| Moss, Ron/Midland Ind School Dist | 36 | 288 |
| Moss, Terri/Bushland Ind School Dist | 58 | 321 |
| Mossige, Teresa, Dr/Lamar Cons Ind School Dist | 18 | 157 |
| Mostella, Paul/Tuloso-Midway Ind School Dist | 67 | 308 |
| Motes, Melissa/De Kalb Ind School Dist | 73 | 51 |
| Motley, Kim/Victoria Ind School Dist | 36 | 384 |
| Mott, Lisa/Waxahachie Ind School Dist | 8 | 146 |
| Mott, Vernagene/Pflugerville Ind School Dist | 67 | 374 |
| Moucoulis, Olga/Edgewood Ind School Dist | 15,751 | 34 |
| Moulton, Jeannie/Brackett Ind School Dist | 37,69 | 260 |
| Moulton, Kelli, Dr/Galveston Ind School Dist | 1 | 164 |
| Mount, Jamie/Humble Ind School Dist | 71 | 200 |
| Moutray, Rebecca/Centerville Ind School Dist | 83 | 267 |
| Moy, Betty/Poth Ind School Dist | 4 | 404 |
| Moy, Brian/North East Ind School Dist | 2 | 37 |
| Moya, Elizabeth/Ysleta Ind School Dist | 30 | 141 |
| Moya, Lisa/Bay City Ind School Dist | 8,18,57,69,88,285,288,294 | 278 |
| Moya, Raymond/Zapata Co Ind School Dist | 91 | 410 |
| Moyers, Dustan/Idalou Ind School Dist | 67 | 272 |
| Moynihan, David/Friendswood Ind Sch Dist | 4 | 164 |
| Muckensturm, Scott/Royse City Ind School Dist | 67 | 328 |
| Mueck, Martin/Navarro Ind School Dist | 3 | 178 |
| Muehlberger, Linda, Dr/Wichita Falls Ind School Dist | 79,93 | 395 |
| Mueller, Leann/Stamford Ind School Dist | 31,38 | 253 |
| Mueller, Mariana/Galveston Ind School Dist | 16,73 | 164 |
| Muery, Jana/McDade Ind School Dist | 2 | 27 |
| Muhl, Kirk/Lexington Ind School Dist | 6 | 266 |
| Muizers, Dennis/Lovejoy Ind School Dist | 8,15,69 | 84 |
| Mulanax, Eddie/Marshall Ind School Dist | 76 | 214 |
| Mulkey, Jennifer/Sanger Ind School Dist | 11,57,296 | 130 |
| Mullen, Mary/Lovejoy Ind School Dist | 8 | 84 |
| Mullens, Eric/Hempstead Ind School Dist | 11,69,88,271,274,296,298 | 387 |
| Muller, Robert, Dr/Belton Ind School Dist | 15 | 29 |
| Mullin, Melanie/Wills Point Ind School Dist | 16,73,295 | 384 |
| Mullins, Dathan/Lubbock Ind School Dist | 76,295 | 272 |
| Mullins, Jeremy/Tolar Ind School Dist | 6 | 233 |
| Mullins, Keith/Buna Ind School Dist | 67 | 243 |
| Mullins, Leatha/Dallas Co Schools | 15,71 | 99 |
| Mullins, Lisa, Dr/Pine Tree Ind School Dist | 8,39,48 | 175 |
| Mullins, Rene/Princeton Ind School Dist | 9 | 87 |
| Mulroney, Malcolm/Carrollton-Farmers Branch ISD | 3,17 | 100 |
| Mulvaney, Bernard/Goose Creek Cons Ind Sch Dist | 6 | 192 |
| Mundowski, Jason/Pilot Point Ind School Dist | 3 | 129 |
| Mundy, Homer/Paradise Ind School Dist | 67 | 407 |
| Mundy, Nefertari/Tomball Ind School Dist | 15,70,74 | 208 |
| Mungia, Andrea/Raymondville Ind Sch Dist | 8,69 | 397 |
| Munguia, Yesica/Paris Ind School Dist | 57 | 262 |
| Muniz, Jesse/Carrizo Spgs Cons Ind SD | 2 | 131 |
| Muniz, Noe/Roma Ind School Dist | 27,31,83,88 | 343 |
| Muniz, Norma/Ft Hancock Ind School Dist | 4 | 237 |
| Muniz, Oscar/McLean Ind School Dist | 1 | 170 |
| Munoz, April/Chapel Hill Ind School Dist | 57 | 339 |
| Munoz, Arminda/Weslaco Ind School Dist | 71 | 228 |
| Munoz, Chuck/Chapel Hill Ind School Dist | 84 | 339 |
| Munoz, Claudia/La Joya Ind School Dist | 49 | 222 |
| Munoz, Esmerelda, Dr/North East Ind School Dist | 11,27,34,36,69 | 37 |
| Munoz, Gabril/Del Valle Ind School Dist | 79 | 372 |
| Munoz, Jose/Eagle Pass Ind School Dist | 73,82,98,295 | 279 |
| Munoz, Leticia/Beeville Ind School Dist | 67 | 28 |
| Munoz, Lucy/La Joya Ind School Dist | 46 | 222 |
| Munoz, Martine/La Joya Ind School Dist | 15,68 | 222 |
| Munoz, Michael/Brackett Ind School Dist | 73 | 260 |

| NAME/District | JOB FUNCTIONS | PAGE |
|---|---|---|
| Munoz, Stephanie/San Marcos Cons Ind Sch Dist | 68 | 217 |
| Munoz, Yvonne/San Diego Ind School Dist | 8 | 132 |
| Munro, Loree/New Caney Ind School Dist | 81 | 296 |
| Murdock, Kirk/Eagle Mtn-Saginaw Ind Sch Dist | 73,295 | 351 |
| Murguia, Leo/Gold-Burg Ind School Dist | 6 | 293 |
| Muri, Scott, Dr/Ector Co Ind School Dist | 1 | 134 |
| Murillo, Danica/Seguin Ind School Dist | 74 | 179 |
| Murphey, Debra/Danbury Ind School Dist | 37 | 56 |
| Murphree, Amanda/Yoakum Ind School Dist | 7,85 | 122 |
| Murphy, Aaron/Columbia Brazoria ISD | 295 | 56 |
| Murphy, Alysha/Cotton Center Ind School Dist | 2 | 179 |
| Murphy, Brenda/Braination Schools | 8,18 | 33 |
| Murphy, Ethel/George West Ind School Dist | 58 | 271 |
| Murphy, Evalene/Lake Travis Ind School Dist | 15,68 | 373 |
| Murphy, Gloria/New Waverly Ind School Dist | 280 | 386 |
| Murphy, Kari/Deer Park Ind School Dist | 73,286,295 | 191 |
| Murphy, Keith/Melissa Ind School Dist | 1 | 85 |
| Murphy, Patrick/Iredell Ind School Dist | 11,73,83,288 | 50 |
| Murphy, Renae/Rockwall Ind School Dist | 71 | 328 |
| Murphy, Valerie/Cleveland Ind School Dist | 7 | 267 |
| Murphy, Vanessa/Hughes Springs Ind Sch Dist | 37 | 74 |
| Murr, Marty/Anahuac Ind School Dist | 6 | 75 |
| Murr, Marty/San Augustine Ind School Dist | 6 | 332 |
| Murr, Suzanne/Azle Ind School Dist | 27 | 348 |
| Murray, Amy/Burnet Cons Ind Sch Dist | 7 | 63 |
| Murray, Ana/Smithville Ind School Dist | 71,97 | 27 |
| Murray, Chuck/Crosby Ind School Dist | 3,91 | 188 |
| Murray, Emily/Trinity Ind School Dist | 27 | 377 |
| Murray, Frank/Wichita Falls Ind School Dist | 73 | 395 |
| Murray, Jeffery/Rule Ind School Dist | 67 | 215 |
| Murray, Lisa/Dawson Ind School Dist | 58 | 302 |
| Murray, Lou Ann/Cooper Ind School Dist | 7,85 | 124 |
| Murray, Mark/Arlington Ind School Dist | 76 | 346 |
| Murray, Mark/Pampa Ind School Dist | 27,31 | 170 |
| Murray, Robin/Tuloso-Midway Ind School Dist | 298 | 308 |
| Murray, Tina/Farmersville Ind School Dist | 76 | 82 |
| Murrell, Terry/Tulia Ind School Dist | 67 | 345 |
| Murry, Anjanette, Dr/Crandall Ind School Dist | 8,11,15,288 | 254 |
| Murry, Morgan/Ralls Ind School Dist | 77 | 98 |
| Murtell, John/Brazosport Ind School Dist | 9,15 | 55 |
| Musich, Sharon/Woodsboro Ind School Dist | 275 | 326 |
| Musick, Patricia/Willis Ind School Dist | 9 | 297 |
| Musick, Stu, Dr/Navasota Ind School Dist | 1 | 177 |
| Musquiz, Rodolfo/Eagle Pass Ind School Dist | 48,51,54,61,280,298 | 279 |
| Muzny, Sharon/La Grange Ind School Dist | 3,5 | 151 |
| Myatt, Darla/Muleshoe Ind School Dist | 34,58 | 25 |
| Myers, Diane/Friendswood Ind Sch Dist | 15 | 164 |
| Myers, Kathy/Commerce Independent Sch Dist | 85 | 239 |
| Myers, Kim/Mineola Ind School Dist | 4 | 408 |
| Myers, Patricia/Driscoll Ind School Dist | 73 | 307 |
| Myers, Rachel/Commerce Independent Sch Dist | 58 | 239 |
| Myers, Rufus/Lake Travis Ind School Dist | 2 | 373 |
| Myers, Susan/Texas City Ind School Dist | 8,15,16,36,274 | 166 |
| Myers, Teddye/Aspermont Ind School Dist | 8,36,69,83,88,270,271,275 | 344 |
| Mynar, Mary/Bosqueville Ind School Dist | 4 | 281 |
| Mynarcik, Larry/Bynum Ind School Dist | 1,11,83 | 230 |
| Mynarcik, Lori/La Vega Ind School Dist | 71 | 282 |
| Myres, Bryan/Godley Ind School Dist | 2,11,296 | 250 |

**N**

| NAME/District | JOB FUNCTIONS | PAGE |
|---|---|---|
| Nace, Michael/Amherst Ind School Dist | 84,295 | 263 |
| Nachlinger, Larry/Hermleigh Ind School Dist | 67 | 336 |
| Nacianceno, Arlando/La Joya Ind School Dist | 3,91 | 222 |
| Nail, Rusty/Madisonville Cons ISD | 6 | 276 |
| Najera, Cynthia/Socorro Ind School Dist | 67 | 140 |
| Nance, Darin/Alpine Ind School Dist | 73,98,295 | 60 |
| Nanez, Christopher/Brazos Ind School Dist | 67 | 25 |

| NAME/District | JOB FUNCTIONS | PAGE |
|---|---|---|
| Nanez, Lilian, Dr/Ector Co Ind School Dist | 8,15 | 134 |
| Nanny, Dwin/Panther Creek Cons Ind SD | 1,11 | 79 |
| Nanus, Jessie/Brazos Ind School Dist | 73,295 | 25 |
| Napper, Lisa/Georgetown Ind School Dist | 15,68 | 398 |
| Nardozza, Chelsea/UT Tyler University Acad Dist | 58 | 341 |
| Naseman, Becca/Brazos Ind School Dist | 31,69,83,85 | 25 |
| Nash, Charles/Centerville Ind School Dist | 67 | 267 |
| Nash, Kim/Springtown Ind School Dist | 4 | 316 |
| Nash, Richard/Kilgore Ind School Dist | 11,15 | 174 |
| Nasky, Holley/Irving Ind School Dist | 81 | 113 |
| Natividad, Fernando/Irving Ind School Dist | 2,4,11 | 113 |
| Natividad, Lorraine/Grandfalls-Royalty Ind SD | 2 | 388 |
| Naugher, Mariella/Hurst-Euless-Bedford ISD | 4 | 356 |
| Nauling, Autumn/North Zulch Ind School Dist | 16 | 276 |
| Nauman, Patti/Anahuac Ind School Dist | 8 | 75 |
| Naumann, Kevin/Marble Falls Ind School Dist | 67 | 64 |
| Nava, Ramiro, Dr/Somerset Ind School Dist | 58 | 45 |
| Nava, Yoelia/Sharyland Ind School Dist | 27 | 227 |
| Navarette, Ed/Florence Ind School Dist | 67 | 398 |
| Navariz, Danielle/Socorro Ind School Dist | 43 | 140 |
| Navarre, Becky, Dr/Ft Worth Ind School Dist | 15,95 | 352 |
| Navarro, Christian/Edcouch Elsa Ind School Dist | 6,35 | 220 |
| Navarro, Eva/Duncanville Ind School Dist | 7,85 | 108 |
| Navarro, Tommy/Pearsall Ind School Dist | 67 | 161 |
| Nazworth, Steven/Venus Ind School Dist | 8,271 | 252 |
| Ncelhaney, Roxanne/Palmer Ind School Dist | 79 | 146 |
| Neal, Angela/Region 10 Ed Service Center | 34 | 120 |
| Neal, Brian/Savoy Ind School Dist | 1 | 150 |
| Neal, Carolyn/North Hopkins Ind School Dist | 7 | 234 |
| Neal, Mike/Clyde Consolidated Ind SD | 73,286 | 66 |
| Neal, Rhonda/Winters Ind School Dist | 2,11 | 329 |
| Neal, Tracy/Huntington Ind School Dist | 67 | 20 |
| Neal, Tyler/Castleberry Ind School Dist | 48 | 350 |
| Neary, Summer/Liberty Hill Ind School Dist | 11,296 | 401 |
| Neblett, Jeff/Navasota Ind School Dist | 3 | 177 |
| Necessary, Keith/Jonesboro Ind School Dist | 3 | 97 |
| Ned, Charles, Dr/Humble Ind School Dist | 81 | 200 |
| Nedbalek, Phil/Westwood Ind School Dist | 5 | 19 |
| Needham, Debbie/New Caney Ind School Dist | 4 | 296 |
| Needham, Debbie/Waxahachie Ind School Dist | 73 | 146 |
| Neel, Diana/Oakwood Ind School Dist | 2,11,296 | 267 |
| Neel, Julie/Slocum ISD School Dist | 58 | 19 |
| Neely, Mitzi/White Oak Ind School Dist | 8,11,57,83,88,273,294,296 | 176 |
| Neff, Sally/Colorado Ind School Dist | 67 | 292 |
| Neglert, Jennifer/Bronte Ind School Dist | 8 | 79 |
| Neidert, Amy/Denison Ind School Dist | 9 | 171 |
| Neighbors, Lisa/Midland Ind School Dist | 9 | 288 |
| Neill, Brenda/Veribest Ind School Dist | 4 | 368 |
| Neira, Claudia/Int'l Leadership of Texas Dist | 68 | 112 |
| Nejtek, Kimberly/Westphalia Ind School Dist | 57,59 | 149 |
| Nelda Flores, Rosa/Roma Ind School Dist | 7 | 343 |
| Nelms, Hilda/Union Hill Ind School Dist | 4 | 380 |
| Nelson-Fluker, Shermika/Garland Ind School Dist | 298 | 109 |
| Nelson, Becky/Andrews Ind School Dist | 7 | 19 |
| Nelson, Becky/Mullin Ind School Dist | 57 | 291 |
| Nelson, Carol/Alvin Ind School Dist | 1 | 54 |
| Nelson, Davin/Daingerfield-Lone Star Ind SD | 6 | 299 |
| Nelson, Dawn/East Chambers Ind School Dist | 4 | 76 |
| Nelson, Ernest/Huffman Ind School Dist | 5 | 200 |
| Nelson, Garrett/Shallowater Ind School Dist | 67 | 274 |
| Nelson, Greg/Huntsville Ind School Dist | 67 | 386 |
| Nelson, Jay/Hallsville Ind School Dist | 67 | 213 |
| Nelson, Jennifer/Ennis Ind School Dist | 11,34,58 | 144 |
| Nelson, Jenny/Ganado Ind School Dist | 16,73,76,286,295,296 | 242 |
| Nelson, Keith/Llano Ind School Dist | 3 | 271 |
| Nelson, Kelisa/Region 16 Ed Service Center | 58,77 | 324 |
| Nelson, Mark/Breckenridge Ind School Dist | 4 | 344 |
| Nelson, Matthew/Snyder Ind School Dist | 58 | 336 |
| Nelson, Nicole/Lamar Cons Ind School Dist | 6 | 157 |
| Nelson, Rebecca/Weatherford Ind School Dist | 74 | 316 |
| Nelson, Sharon/Boyd Ind School Dist | 5 | 405 |
| Nelson, Susan/Franklin Ind School Dist | 16,28,73,297 | 327 |
| Nelson, Toni/Little Elm Ind School Dist | 7 | 128 |
| Nelson, Tyisha/Carroll Independent Sch Dist | 11,27,57,58,88 | 349 |
| Nelson, Vicki/Rice Cons Ind School Dist | 57 | 90 |
| Nericua, John/Ferris Ind School Dist | 295 | 145 |
| Nesbit, Michael/Medina Valley Ind School Dist | 8,15,69 | 287 |
| Neshyba, Rosemary/Lake Worth Ind School Dist | 1 | 358 |
| Netera, Eddie/Alpine Ind School Dist | 67 | 60 |
| Netherland, Jenni/Salado Ind School Dist | 3,4,5,17 | 32 |
| Netro, Tahnee/Mission Cons Ind School Dist | 58 | 225 |
| Netterville, Colleen/Greenville Ind School Dist | 58,68 | 239 |
| Neudorf, Ramona/Hart Ind School Dist | 73 | 75 |
| Neugebauer, Lena/Montgomery Ind School Dist | 4 | 296 |
| Neuhoff, Paul/Region 20 Ed Service Center | 2 | 48 |
| Neuman, Kami/Hondo Ind School Dist | 16,82 | 287 |
| Neuman, Michael/Sabinal Ind School Dist | 2,8,11,36,69,77,91 | 380 |
| Neuman, Michael/Sabinal Ind School Dist | 15 | 380 |
| New, Donald/Era Ind School Dist | 6 | 94 |
| Newby, Randy/Evant Ind School Dist | 16,73,76,97,98,285,295 | 96 |
| Newcom, Steven/Eagle Mtn-Saginaw Ind Sch Dist | 67 | 351 |
| Newcomb, Beverly/Center Point Ind School Dist | 31 | 258 |
| Newcomb, Cody/Center Point Ind School Dist | 1,83 | 258 |
| Newcomer, Tammie/Vernon Ind School Dist | 4 | 396 |
| Newhouse, Rhonda/Spring Ind School Dist | 67 | 207 |
| Newkirk, Tiffany/Comal Ind School Dist | 83,90 | 91 |
| Newlun, Derrick/Trent Isn School Dist | 5 | 363 |
| Newman, Belinda/Eagle Mtn-Saginaw Ind Sch Dist | 76 | 351 |
| Newman, Bobby/Nixon-Smiley Cons Ind Sch Dist | 3 | 169 |
| Newman, Casey/Woodsboro Ind School Dist | 73,91 | 326 |
| Newman, Donna, Dr/North East Ind School Dist | 8,15,58,68,79 | 37 |
| Newman, Ed/Region 12 Ed Service Center | 76 | 286 |
| Newman, Jarrod/Academy Ind School Dist | 73,295 | 29 |
| Newman, Joshua/Ferris Ind School Dist | 91 | 145 |
| Newman, Kasey/Karnes City Ind School Dist | 73 | 253 |
| Newman, Natasha/Morton Ind School Dist | 298 | 78 |
| Newman, Teara/Rusk Ind School Dist | 7 | 77 |
| Newsom, Kevin/Medina Ind School Dist | 1,73 | 26 |
| Newton, Becky/Navarro Ind School Dist | 58 | 178 |
| Newton, Garon/Highland Park Ind School Dist | 4 | 322 |
| Newton, Sandra/Tyler Ind School Dist | 20,23 | 340 |
| Neyman, Jessica/Killeen Ind School Dist | 68 | 30 |
| Nguyen, Nicole/Calhoun Co Ind School Dist | 4 | 65 |
| Nichol, Tony/Olney Ind School Dist | 16,73 | 410 |
| Nicholas, Beth/Mesquite Ind School Dist | 15,57,58,69,72,73,275 | 115 |
| Nicholas, Mike/Royal Ind School Dist | 73,295 | 387 |
| Nicholason, Amy/Blooming Grove Ind School Dist | 2 | 302 |
| Nichols, Blake/O'Donnell Ind School Dist | 6 | 276 |
| Nichols, Heather/Tomball Ind School Dist | 270 | 208 |
| Nichols, Larry/Calhoun Co Ind School Dist | 1 | 65 |
| Nichols, Michele/Garland Ind School Dist | 49 | 109 |
| Nichols, Mike/Academy Ind School Dist | 6 | 29 |
| Nichols, Natalie/Round Rock Ind School Dist | 15 | 401 |
| Nichols, Sarah/Hunt Ind School Dist | 16,297 | 258 |
| Nicholson, Justin/Campbell Ind School Dist | 3 | 238 |
| Nick, Angela/Winona Ind School Dist | 4 | 341 |
| Nick, Kara/Abernathy Ind School Dist | 36 | 179 |
| Nickerson, Erik/Dallas Ind School Dist | 79 | 102 |
| Nickle, Jeanie/Navasota Ind School Dist | 8,16 | 177 |
| Nicks, Joe/Kaufman Ind School Dist | 8,15,286,288 | 255 |
| Nicol, Kelly/Latexo Ind School Dist | 67 | 236 |
| **Nicoles, Brain, Dr**/Canton Ind School Dist | 1 | 382 |
| Niedziela, Joseph/Ft Worth Ind School Dist | 39 | 352 |
| Nielsen, David/Hurst-Euless-Bedford ISD | 297 | 356 |
| Nieman, Stina/New Home Ind School Dist | 76 | 275 |
| Niemeyer, Mike/Channelview Ind School Dist | 15 | 188 |
| Niemyer, Diane/Liberty-Eylau Ind School Dist | 88 | 51 |
| Nienstedt, Christy/Anderson-Shiro Cons Ind SD | 38 | 176 |
| Nies, Andy/River Road Ind School Dist | 2,8,11,74,88,270,294,296 | 322 |
| Nieto, Isidoro/Weslaco Ind School Dist | 67 | 228 |
| Nieto, Melissa/Harlingen Cons Ind School Dist | 68 | 68 |
| Nine, Mary/Perryton Ind School Dist | 58 | 310 |
| Nine, Mary/Spearman Ind School Dist | 58 | 182 |
| Nipps, Lamanda/Lamar Cons Ind School Dist | 2 | 157 |
| Nitsch, Karen/McAllen Ind School Dist | 81 | 224 |
| Niven, Scott/Allen Ind School Dist | 1 | 80 |
| Niven, Scott, Dr/Denton Ind School Dist | 48 | 125 |
| Nivins, Roosevelt/Community Ind School Dist | 1 | 81 |
| Nix, Amy/Texarkana Ind School Dist | 68 | 53 |
| Nix, Becky/Borden Co Ind School Dist | 58,275 | 49 |
| Nix, Dalton/Tolar Ind School Dist | 67 | 233 |
| Nix, Danny/Burkburnett Ind Sch Dist | 6 | 394 |

| NAME/District | JOB FUNCTIONS | PAGE | NAME/District | JOB FUNCTIONS | PAGE |
|---|---|---|---|---|---|
| Oglesby, Lori/Eula Ind School Dist | 31 | 66 | Orozco, Menivra/Petersburg Ind School Dist | 98 | 180 |
| Ogletree, Ben/Livingston Ind School Dist | 67 | 319 | Orozco, Victoria/El Paso Ind School Dist | 70 | 137 |
| Ogletree, John, Dr/Cypress-Fairbanks Ind Sch Dist | 67 | 189 | Orozlo, Jon/Waelder Ind School Dist | 1,11,73,83 | 169 |
| Ogwumike, Ify/Cypress-Fairbanks Ind Sch Dist | 15,79 | 189 | Orr, Bill/Ingram Ind School Dist | 2,19 | 259 |
| Ohlendorf, Kimberly/Magnolia Ind School Dist | 4 | 295 | Orr, Bill/Marion Ind School Dist | 2 | 177 |
| Ojeda, Linda/Marfa Ind School Dist | 6 | 322 | Orr, John/Plano Ind School Dist | 2 | 85 |
| Ojeda, Rosa/Waller Ind School Dist | 76,97,286 | 387 | Orr, Terry/Roby Cons Ind School Dist | 58 | 152 |
| Olaslaugua, Roque/La Pryor Ind School Dist | 73 | 411 | Orren, Christin/Terlingua Common School Dist | 57 | 60 |
| Oldag, Donald/El Campo Ind School Dist | 295 | 392 | Orsak, Tim/Olney Ind School Dist | 2,84 | 410 |
| Oles, Reagan/Canadian Ind School Dist | 9 | 218 | Orta, Nelson/Garland Ind School Dist | 74 | 109 |
| Olin Lawton, John/Dallas Ind School Dist | 91 | 102 | Ortega Ruiz, Elizabeth/Corpus Christi Ind Sch Dist | 20 | 306 |
| Oliphant, Holly/Shepherd Ind School Dist | 7 | 333 | Ortega, Alejo/Texhoma Ind School Dist | 3 | 338 |
| Oliphant, Holly/Shepherd Ind School Dist | 7 | 333 | Ortega, Jamie/Sharyland Ind School Dist | 2 | 227 |
| Oliphant, Roland/New Waverly Ind School Dist | 5 | 386 | Ortega, Mary Alice/Woodsboro Ind School Dist | 4 | 326 |
| Oliva, Adam/Idalou Ind School Dist | 3 | 272 | Ortega, Richard/Socorro Ind School Dist | 58,275 | 140 |
| Oliva, Efrain, Dr/Spring Ind School Dist | 15 | 207 | Ortega, Samando/Greenville Ind School Dist | 57 | 239 |
| Oliva, Melissa/Brownfield Ind Sch Dist | 8,11,15 | 364 | Ortega, Yvonne/Farwell Ind School Dist | 93 | 317 |
| Olivares, Ismael/Taft Ind School Dist | 3 | 334 | Ortegan, Audre/Fabens Ind School Dist | 79 | 139 |
| Olivares, Victor/Tyler Ind School Dist | 4 | 340 | Ortiz, Bertha, Dr/Edgewood Ind School Dist | 81 | 34 |
| Olivarez, Alfredo/Ricardo Ind School Dist | 3,16,83 | 261 | Ortiz, Carlos/Three Way Ind School Dist | 73 | 148 |
| Olivarez, Christie/Brenham Ind School Dist | 68 | 388 | Ortiz, Ernesto/El Paso Ind School Dist | 3 | 137 |
| Olivarez, Isabel/West Oso Ind School Dist | 69,294 | 309 | Ortiz, Gina/Karnes City Ind School Dist | 8,18,69,79,275,280,288,294 | 253 |
| Olivarez, Leonel/San Isidro Ind School Dist | 2,4 | 343 | Ortiz, Marco/Taylor Ind School Dist | 67 | 402 |
| Olivarez, Rogerio/Rio Grande City Ind Sch Dist | 23 | 342 | Ortiz, Mary/Poteet Ind School Dist | 90,93 | 24 |
| Olivas, Cassie/Blackwell Cons Ind Sch Dist | 16 | 304 | Ortiz, Milo/Aldine Ind School Dist | 3 | 184 |
| Olive, Lori/Oakwood Ind School Dist | 8,69 | 267 | Osagie, Andree, Dr/Lamar Cons Ind School Dist | 10,15 | 157 |
| Oliveira, Ana, Dr/La Joya Ind School Dist | 10 | 222 | Osborn, Donnie/Teague Ind School Dist | 6 | 161 |
| Oliver, Debbie/Midland Ind School Dist | 61 | 288 | Osborne, Charles/Burleson Ind School Dist | 11,69 | 249 |
| Oliver, Garth, Dr/Louise Ind School Dist | 1 | 392 | Osburn, Clay/Troy Ind School Dist | 73,295 | 33 |
| Oliver, Heather/Lometa Ind School Dist | 57,271 | 264 | Osei, James/Campbell Ind School Dist | 73,295 | 238 |
| Oliver, James/Martin's Mill Ind Sch Dist | 1 | 383 | Oshman, Melissa/Northside Ind School Dist | 76 | 39 |
| **Oliver, Joe/**Buckholts Ind School Dist | 1,11 | 290 | Osinski, David/Terrell Ind School Dist | 295 | 256 |
| Oliver, Karla/Plano Ind School Dist | 15,71,298 | 85 | Osten, Sharee/Greenville Ind School Dist | 4 | 239 |
| Oliver, Kathy/Santa Fe Ind School Dist | 58 | 165 | Oswald, Beth Anne/Archer City Ind School Dist | 84 | 22 |
| Oliver, Kaye/Texarkana Ind School Dist | 5 | 53 | Oswald, Bethann/Archer City Ind School Dist | 73,286,298 | 22 |
| Oliver, Marty/Godley Ind School Dist | 28,73,295 | 250 | Otero, Diana, Dr/Ysleta Ind School Dist | 58 | 141 |
| Oliver, Ricky/Zavalla Ind School Dist | 1 | 21 | Ott, Bobby, Dr/Temple Ind School Dist | 1 | 32 |
| Oliver, Robert/Colorado Ind School Dist | 5 | 292 | Ott, Monica/El Campo Ind School Dist | 7 | 392 |
| Oliver, Sharla/Zavalla Ind School Dist | 11,58,69 | 21 | Ott, Teddy/Ore City Ind School Dist | 58,270 | 379 |
| Oliver, Shirley/Lorena Ind School Dist | 4 | 283 | Ottis, Michelle/Matagorda Ind School Dist | 35 | 278 |
| Oliveras-Ortiz, Yanira, Dr/UT Tyler University Acad Dist | 67 | 341 | Ottmers, Deborah/Ector Co Ind School Dist | 19 | 134 |
| Olivier, Jay/Liberty Hill Ind School Dist | 16 | 401 | Ouellette, Michael/Katy Ind School Dist | 20,23 | 156 |
| Olivo, Diane/South San Antonio Ind Sch Dist | 7 | 45 | Ouren, Lora/Bryan Ind School Dist | 58 | 58 |
| Ollis, Greg/Channelview Ind School Dist | 1 | 188 | Ousley, Brian/Orangefield Ind School Dist | 4 | 312 |
| Olmos, Leticia/Farwell Ind School Dist | 4 | 317 | Ovalle Lopez, Maria/Klein Ind School Dist | 93 | 202 |
| Olmos, Lorena/Ysleta Ind School Dist | 297 | 141 | Ovalle, Rey/Los Fresnos Cons Ind Sch Dist | 4 | 69 |
| Olson, Andria/Lamar Cons Ind School Dist | 47 | 157 | Overbo, Trig/Jayton-Girard Ind School Dist | 1 | 258 |
| Olson, Chad/Pecos-Barstow-Toyah Ind SD | 6,35 | 326 | Overman, Megan/Eagle Mtn-Saginaw Ind Sch Dist | 71 | 351 |
| Olson, Cindy/Coupland Ind School Dist | 2,71,274,294,298 | 398 | Overstreet, Gary/Quinlan Ind School Dist | 5 | 240 |
| Olsovsky, Brandi/Yorktown Ind School Dist | 37 | 122 | Overstreet, Stephen/Tahoka Ind School Dist | 6 | 276 |
| Olvera, Carlos/Brownsville Ind School Dist | 57 | 66 | Owen, Brad/Burkburnett Ind Sch Dist | 16,73,82,295 | 394 |
| Oneal, Marva, Dr/Lamar Cons Ind School Dist | 11 | 157 | Owen, Dana/Friendswood Ind Sch Dist | 71,76 | 164 |
| Oneal, Thomas, Dr/Anna Ind School Dist | 2,15,19 | 81 | Owen, John/Aransas Co Ind School Dist | 31 | 22 |
| Oneil, Carl/Fredericksburg Ind School Dist | 73 | 167 | Owen, Kathy/Jayton-Girard Ind School Dist | 67 | 258 |
| Oneil, Lyndi/Schleicher Co Ind Sch Dist | 69,83,85,88,270,288 | 335 | Owen, Keith/Linden Kildare Cons Ind SD | 11,88,288,298 | 74 |
| Oneil, Patrick/Prosper Ind School Dist | 73 | 88 | Owen, Lonnie/Anderson-Shiro Cons Ind SD | 67 | 176 |
| Oneill, David/Hico Ind School Dist | 286 | 181 | Owen, Tandi/Forney Ind School Dist | 11,294 | 255 |
| Oney, Robert/Slidell Ind School Dist | 3,5,73,76,295 | 407 | Owen, Tina/Frankston Ind School Dist | 4 | 18 |
| Oniel, Ted/Keene Ind School Dist | 11,88,271 | 251 | Owens, Auttum/Leary Ind School Dist | 2,288 | 51 |
| Ontiveros, Jesse/Pearsall Ind School Dist | 3 | 161 | Owens, Auttumn/Hubbard Ind School Dist | 2 | 51 |
| Oppelt, Julie/Medina Valley Ind School Dist | 81 | 287 | Owens, Cary/Abilene Ind School Dist | 76,295 | 362 |
| Oquinn, Jana/Wells Ind School Dist | 2 | 77 | Owens, Cindy/Corrigan-Camden Ind Sch Dist | 2 | 319 |
| Ormiston, Chris/Boerne Ind School Dist | 42 | 257 | Owens, Frank/Campbell Ind School Dist | 67 | 238 |
| Orndorff, Vernon/Milford Ind School Dist | 1 | 146 | Owens, Greg/Sulphur Springs Ind Sch Dist | 6 | 235 |
| Ornelas, Eliud/Brownsville Ind School Dist | 5 | 66 | Owens, Jackie/Tarkington Ind School Dist | 37 | 269 |
| Ornelas, Hamie/Crosby Ind School Dist | 57 | 188 | Owens, Janette/White Settlement Ind Sch Dist | 2 | 360 |
| Ornelas, Herman/Columbia Brazoria ISD | 5 | 56 | Owens, Jennie/Hedley Ind School Dist | 73,295 | 132 |
| Orosco, Alejandro/Carrizo Spgs Cons Ind SD | 3,5 | 131 | Owens, Les/Venus Ind School Dist | 67 | 252 |
| Orosco, Denise/South San Antonio Ind Sch Dist | 70,76 | 45 | Owens, Melanie/Tarkington Ind School Dist | 5 | 269 |
| Orosco, Esperanza/Hays Cons Ind School Dist | 67 | 216 | Owens, Ola/Wolfe City Ind School Dist | 67 | 240 |
| Orozco, Christine/Medina Valley Ind School Dist | 93 | 287 | Owens, Scott/Mesquite Ind School Dist | 3 | 115 |
| Orozco, James/San Antonio Ind School Dist | 20 | 42 | Owens, Susie/Laneville Ind School Dist | 294 | 330 |
| Orozco, Jesse/Lyford Cons Ind School Dist | 3,5,17,91 | 397 | Owens, Tatiana, Dr/Port Arthur Ind School Dist | 57,271 | 246 |
| Orozco, Juan/Del Valle Ind School Dist | 16 | 372 | Owings, Kathy/Deer Park Ind School Dist | 69,294 | 191 |
| Orozco, Juan/Seguin Ind School Dist | 286 | 179 | Owings, Larry/May Ind School Dist | 73,76,286 | 62 |
| Orozco, Matilda, Dr/Int'l Leadership of Texas Dist | 15 | 112 | Owings, Michele/May Ind School Dist | 2 | 62 |

| NAME/District | JOB FUNCTIONS | PAGE | NAME/District | JOB FUNCTIONS | PAGE |
|---|---|---|---|---|---|
| Paschall, Theresa/Crowley Ind School Dist | 36 | 350 | Peavey, Brandon/Bridgeport Ind School Dist | 1 | 406 |
| Pasichnyk, Rob/Belton Ind School Dist | 4 | 29 | Pecina, Gesus/Progreso Ind School Dist | 73 | 227 |
| Paskell, Angela/San Antonio Ind School Dist | 42 | 42 | Pecina, Jesus/Progreso Ind School Dist | 76 | 227 |
| Passmore, Susan/Goose Creek Cons Ind Sch Dist | 71 | 192 | Pecina, Ruben/Dilley Ind School Dist | 58 | 161 |
| Patchke, Carla/Roosevelt Ind School Dist | 7 | 274 | Peck, Kelley/Buna Ind School Dist | 8,11,15,76,271 | 243 |
| Pate, David/Richardson Ind School Dist | 2,19 | 116 | Peck, Nita/George West Ind School Dist | 2 | 271 |
| Pate, James/Mabank Ind School Dist | 16 | 256 | Peckover, Bruce/Elgin Ind School Dist | 31 | 27 |
| Pate, Jason/Comanche Ind School Dist | 67 | 93 | Peddy, Gina/Carroll Independent Sch Dist | 8,61,81 | 349 |
| Pate, Johnny/Hubbard Ind School Dist | 57 | 51 | Pedersen, Jaclyn/UT Tyler University Acad Dist | 8,298 | 341 |
| Pate, Lynette/Yoakum Ind School Dist | 68,79 | 122 | Pederson, Lyndsey/Bynum Ind School Dist | 8,11,58,76,286,288 | 230 |
| Pate, Marnie/Port Aransas Ind School Dist | 67 | 308 | Pedroza, Blanca/Olton Ind School Dist | 271 | 263 |
| Pate, Mary/McMullen Co Ind Sch Dist | 73,76 | 286 | Peebles, Justin/La Vega Ind School Dist | 73,84,295 | 282 |
| Pate, Rose/Etoile Ind School Dist | 2,28 | 300 | Peeks, Judy/Avery Ind School Dist | 4 | 325 |
| Patek, Joseph/Aransas Co Ind School Dist | 1 | 22 | Peel, Rebecca/Thorndale Ind School Dist | 2 | 291 |
| Patek, Trina/Hallettsville Ind Sch Dist | 79 | 265 | Peeler, Barbra/Jourdanton Ind School Dist | 67 | 23 |
| Paterson, Karen/Anthony Ind School Dist | 16 | 136 | Peeples, Cesily/Marion Ind School Dist | 8 | 177 |
| Patillo, Paul/Region 20 Ed Service Center | 73,76,98 | 48 | Peeples, Scott/Sunray Ind School Dist | 67 | 299 |
| Patin, Mary/Lake Travis Ind School Dist | 11,15,286 | 373 | Peery, Susan/Alamo Heights Ind School Dist | 34 | 33 |
| Patin, Mitzi/Ft Bend Ind School Dist | 73,76 | 153 | Peese, Evelyn/Fredericksburg Ind School Dist | 5 | 167 |
| Patino, Maria/Lubbock Ind School Dist | 271 | 272 | Peet, Jennifer/Groom Ind School Dist | 2 | 72 |
| Patrick, Gay/Dallas Ind School Dist | 16 | 102 | Peets, Courtney/Burleson Ind School Dist | 7 | 249 |
| Patrick, Jay/Jefferson Ind School Dist | 73,295 | 277 | Peevey, Jennifer/Shamrock Ind School Dist | 69 | 393 |
| Patrick, Kati/Ira Ind School Dist | 7 | 336 | Pehl, Kit/Coppell Ind School Dist | 6 | 102 |
| Patrick, Mark/Kermit Ind School Dist | 16,73,295 | 405 | Peinly, Kim/Waller Ind School Dist | 2 | 387 |
| Patrick, Mary/Galveston Ind School Dist | 34,58 | 165 | Pelichet, Kyle/Corpus Christi Ind Sch Dist | 5 | 306 |
| Patrick, Scott/Llano Ind School Dist | 31,83,88 | 271 | Pelletier, Jennifer/Diocese of Fort Worth Ed Off | 1 | 360 |
| Patschke, Curtis/Lexington Ind School Dist | 17,18,19,73,286,295,298,750 | 266 | Peltier, Cynthia, Dr/Clear Creek Ind School Dist | 58,83,90,275 | 163 |
| Patschke, Jennifer/Taylor Ind School Dist | 11,296,298 | 402 | Peltier, Daryl/Danbury Ind School Dist | 67 | 56 |
| Patterson, Brian/Ira Ind School Dist | 6 | 336 | Peltier, Diane/Alvin Ind School Dist | 45 | 54 |
| Patterson, Brian/Ira Ind School Dist | 1 | 336 | Pelton, Robin/Brazosport Ind School Dist | 79,83,270,275 | 55 |
| Patterson, Britt/Rusk Ind School Dist | 67 | 77 | Pena-Rodriguez, Audrey/Point Isabel Ind Sch Dist | 4 | 70 |
| Patterson, Candi/Orangefield Ind School Dist | 31,36,69,83,93 | 312 | Pena, Aaron, Dr/Midway Ind School Dist | 8,15,288 | 283 |
| Patterson, Garrett/Collinsville Ind School Dist | 6 | 171 | Pena, Adolfo/Rio Grande City Ind Sch Dist | 15 | 342 |
| Patterson, Janice/Del Valle Ind School Dist | 2 | 372 | Pena, Adrian/Banquete Ind School Dist | 2 | 305 |
| Patterson, Julie/Cisco Independent Sch Dist | 58,74,92 | 133 | Pena, Albert/San Perlita Ind School Dist | 1 | 397 |
| Patterson, Kate/Blanco Ind School Dist | 58 | 49 | Pena, Annette/La Feria Ind School Dist | 57 | 69 |
| Patterson, Kate/Bryan Ind School Dist | 58 | 58 | Pena, Dora/Weslaco Ind School Dist | 4 | 228 |
| Patterson, Krystal/Latexo Ind School Dist | 7 | 236 | Pena, Janie/Weslaco Ind School Dist | 8 | 228 |
| Patterson, Michelle/Alief Ind School Dist | 49 | 186 | Pena, Jennifer/San Vicente Ind School Dist | 83,85,270 | 60 |
| Patterson, Paula/Sheldon Ind School Dist | 8,15,18 | 205 | Pena, Jennifer/Terlingua Common School Dist | 36 | 60 |
| Patterson, Stephen, Dr/Orangefield Ind School Dist | 1 | 312 | Pena, Leonila/San Benito Cons Ind Sch Dist | 16,76,286 | 70 |
| Patterson, Susan/Arlington Ind School Dist | 27 | 346 | Pena, Maricela/Robstown Ind School Dist | 30 | 308 |
| Patton, Cody/Tioga Ind School Dist | 6 | 172 | Pena, Melissa/Webb Cons Ind School Dist | 67 | 391 |
| **Patty, Rae Ann**/Waskom Ind School Dist | 1 | 214 | Pena, Minerva/Brownsville Ind School Dist | 67 | 66 |
| Paul, Eric/Galveston Ind School Dist | 27 | 164 | Pena, Noe/Edinburg Cons Ind School Dist | 73,286 | 221 |
| Paul, Sue/Douglass Ind School Dist | 36,69,83,88,270 | 300 | Pena, Pam/Carrollton-Farmers Branch ISD | 71,75 | 100 |
| Paulson, Dana/Leander Ind School Dist | 2 | 399 | Pena, Rob/Midland Ind School Dist | 42 | 288 |
| Pautsky, Susan/Chillicothe ISD School Dist | 4 | 182 | Pena, Rodrigo, Dr/San Diego Ind School Dist | 1 | 132 |
| Pavlovsky, Charles/Archdiocese Galveston-Houston | 68 | 209 | Pena, Sergio/Mission Cons Ind School Dist | 27,31 | 225 |
| Pawelek, Cynthia/Elgin Ind School Dist | 294 | 27 | Pena, Virginia/Riviera Ind School Dist | 2 | 261 |
| Pawelek, Todd/Falls City Ind School Dist | 1,11,83 | 253 | Pendarvis, Liz/Harleton Ind School Dist | 8,11,57,58,69,81,93 | 213 |
| Pawelek, Vanessa/Karnes City Ind School Dist | 2,17,68 | 253 | Pendegraft, Dana/Paint Creek Ind School Dist | 67 | 215 |
| Pawelk, Lindsy/Pleasanton Ind School Dist | 11,58 | 24 | Pendergrass, Susan/Whitharral Ind School Dist | 57 | 233 |
| Pawlik-Perales, Patti/Alamo Heights Ind School Dist | 297 | 33 | Pendlay, Nikki/Carrollton-Farmers Branch ISD | 2 | 100 |
| Paxon, Michael/Brackett Ind School Dist | 67 | 260 | Penn, Amber/Jacksonville Ind School Dist | 57,89,271 | 76 |
| Payne, Brenda/Richardson Ind School Dist | 9,15 | 116 | Penn, Kyle/Sunnyvale Ind School Dist | 2,17,752 | 117 |
| Payne, David/Lorena Ind School Dist | 295 | 283 | Penn, Terry/Rockwall Ind School Dist | 5 | 328 |
| Payne, Larry/Dumas Ind School Dist | 71,83 | 298 | Pennell, Amber/Farmersville Ind School Dist | 2,19,271 | 82 |
| Payne, Liesl/Irving Ind School Dist | 93 | 113 | Pennell, Elsa/San Antonio Ind School Dist | 93 | 42 |
| Payne, Michael/Carlisle Ind School Dist | 1,11,83 | 330 | Penney, Jennifer/Whitney Ind School Dist | 10,31,36,69,83,85,88 | 231 |
| Payne, Regina/Round Rock Ind School Dist | 277 | 401 | Penney, Pam/La Poynor Ind School Dist | 7,85 | 219 |
| Payne, Shalontae/Duncanville Ind School Dist | 27,31 | 108 | Pennington, Cathy/Poolville Ind School Dist | 8,11,57,58,69,271,296,298 | 316 |
| Payne, Stephanie/Lake Dallas Ind School Dist | 69 | 126 | Pennington, Stacy/Barbers Hill Ind School Dist | 73 | 75 |
| Payton, Kenneth/Groom Ind School Dist | 3 | 72 | Penny, Eary/Bosqueville Ind School Dist | 7 | 281 |
| Paz, Temoc/Sharyland Ind School Dist | 9 | 227 | Peno, Maris/Region 5 Ed Service Center | 7,298 | 247 |
| Peace, Angie/Bartlett Ind School Dist | 8,36,69,88 | 29 | Penrod, Eric, Dr/Killeen Ind School Dist | 15 | 30 |
| Peach, Ken/Boerne Ind School Dist | 20 | 257 | Penrod, Florence/Tom Bean Ind School Dist | 4 | 173 |
| Peacock, Rory/Region 11 Ed Service Center | 15,295 | 362 | Penton, Jennifer/Rockwall Ind School Dist | 40,280 | 328 |
| Peacock, Ryder/Albany Ind School Dist | 6 | 336 | Pepper, Kitsy/Memphis Ind School Dist | 298 | 181 |
| Peacock, Shannon/Bloomburg Ind School Dist | 83 | 73 | Pepper, Nancy/Devine Ind School Dist | 67 | 286 |
| Pear, Kellye/North East Ind School Dist | 11 | 37 | Perales, Aaron/Arlington Ind School Dist | 93 | 346 |
| Pearce, Ricky/Hempstead Ind School Dist | 67 | 387 | Perales, Carlos/Teague Ind School Dist | 3 | 161 |
| Pearson, Carrie/Keller Ind School Dist | 34 | 357 | Perales, Laura/Corpus Christi Ind Sch Dist | 73 | 306 |
| Pearson, Greg/Brownsboro Ind School Dist | 6,35 | 218 | Peredia, Lori/Ralls Ind School Dist | 7,35,85 | 98 |
| Pearson, Lisa/Livingston Ind School Dist | 2 | 319 | Perez, Aleida/San Antonio Ind School Dist | 34 | 42 |
| Pease, Ben/Lackland Ind School Dist | 76 | 37 | Perez, Alfonso/Roma Ind School Dist | 2 | 343 |

| NAME/District | JOB FUNCTIONS | PAGE |
|---|---|---|
| Phillips, Cassandra/Duncanville Ind School Dist | 67 | 108 |
| Phillips, Connie/Cuero Ind School Dist | 76,294 | 122 |
| Phillips, Craten/Lago Vista Ind School Dist | 6 | 373 |
| Phillips, Dedra/Sweeny Ind School Dist | 76 | 57 |
| Phillips, Gena/Newcastle Ind School Dist | 7 | 409 |
| Phillips, Jason/Forsan Ind School Dist | 6 | 237 |
| Phillips, Jeff/May Ind School Dist | 67 | 62 |
| Phillips, Jim/Waller Ind School Dist | 6 | 387 |
| Phillips, John/Bronte Ind School Dist | 9,11,52,55 | 79 |
| Phillips, Kentrell/Everman Ind School Dist | 8,73 | 351 |
| Phillips, Kim/Sanger Ind School Dist | 58 | 130 |
| Phillips, Leeton/St Jo Ind School Dist | 67 | 293 |
| Phillips, Mike/Marble Falls Ind School Dist | 3 | 64 |
| Phillips, Moriah/Big Sandy Ind School Dist | 73,76,286,295 | 378 |
| Phillips, Renae/Hallettsville Ind Sch Dist | 16 | 265 |
| Phillips, Scott/Franklin Ind School Dist | 67 | 327 |
| Phillips, Sherry/Danbury Ind School Dist | 273 | 56 |
| Phillips, Sherry/Danbury Ind School Dist | 15 | 56 |
| Phillips, Stacy/Sherman Ind School Dist | 7,36,69,83,275 | 172 |
| Phillips, Susan/Matagorda Ind School Dist | 1,11,57,83,288 | 278 |
| Phillips, Tera/Normangee Ind School Dist | 9,57,83,270,271,296 | 267 |
| Phillips, Terry/Clyde Consolidated Ind SD | 2 | 66 |
| Phillips, Tony/Lipan Ind School Dist | 6,8 | 233 |
| Phillips, Wayne/Harts Bluff Ind School Dist | 5,73 | 366 |
| Phipps, Robbie/Dawson Ind School Dist | 7 | 121 |
| Phipps, Scott/Crandall Ind School Dist | 73,76,98,286 | 254 |
| Piazza, Jason/Clear Creek Ind School Dist | 295 | 163 |
| Pichardo, Brandi/Leakey Ind School Dist | 67 | 324 |
| Pick, Paul/Grapeland Ind School Dist | 5 | 235 |
| Pickens, Dwan/Region 12 Ed Service Center | 57 | 286 |
| Pickens, J/Trent Isn School Dist | 67 | 363 |
| Pickett, Hubert/Everman Ind School Dist | 79 | 351 |
| Pickett, Tammy/Red Oak Ind School Dist | 5 | 146 |
| Picon, Raul/Port Arthur Ind School Dist | 297 | 246 |
| Picou, Kelsey/Robstown Ind School Dist | 71 | 308 |
| Piekarski, Martha/Canutillo Ind School Dist | 2,19 | 136 |
| Pieratt, Annaliza/D'Hanis Ind School Dist | 57 | 286 |
| Pierce, Casey/Slidell Ind School Dist | 6 | 407 |
| Pierce, Daniel/Cross Roads Ind School Dist | 6 | 219 |
| Pierce, Glen/Longview Ind School Dist | 76 | 174 |
| Pierce, Jim/Texhoma Ind School Dist | 295 | 338 |
| Pierce, Karyn/Amarillo Ind School Dist | 27,31 | 320 |
| Pierce, Robbie/Lytle Ind School Dist | 58 | 24 |
| Pierce, Tami/Dayton Ind School Dist | 2,15,19 | 268 |
| Pierce, Wayland/Glasscock Co Ind School Dist | 8,12,88,274 | 168 |
| Pierce, Wes/Region 9 Ed Service Center | 1 | 396 |
| Pietsch, Shelly/Bastrop Ind School Dist | 59 | 26 |
| Pigg, Donna/Turkey-Quitaque Cons Ind SD | 2 | 181 |
| Pike, Melissa/Llano Ind School Dist | 5 | 271 |
| Pike, Penny/Pine Tree Ind School Dist | 5 | 175 |
| Pike, Sue/Deer Park Ind School Dist | 76 | 191 |
| Piles, Harry/Lytle Ind School Dist | 8,15,275,286,288 | 24 |
| Pilgrim, Jerome/Irving Ind School Dist | 2 | 113 |
| Pilip, Christal/Prairiland Ind School Dist | 7 | 263 |
| Pilkey, Jacqueline, Dr/Killeen Ind School Dist | 58 | 30 |
| Pilkington, Debbie/Kennard Ind Sch Dist | 16,82 | 236 |
| Pimertel, Melissa/Lyford Cons Ind School Dist | 69 | 397 |
| Pina, Patricia/Goose Creek Cons Ind Sch Dist | 7 | 192 |
| Pineda, Hector/Region 15 Ed Service Center | 34 | 368 |
| Pineda, Maria/El Paso Ind School Dist | 2 | 137 |
| Pinedo, Monica/Marathon Ind School Dist | 57,83,271 | 60 |
| Pinegar, Lorrine/Clear Creek Ind School Dist | 71 | 163 |
| Pinell, David/Winnsboro Ind School Dist | 285 | 408 |
| Pinkard, Ritchie/Mt Pleasant Ind School Dist | 6 | 366 |
| Pinkston, Cassie/Lone Oak Ind School Dist | 73,76,297 | 239 |
| Pinnell, Steve/Winnsboro Ind School Dist | 6 | 408 |
| Pinner, Sandy/Chireno ISD School Dist | 36,57,69,83,88,93,271 | 300 |
| Pinson, Barbara/Maypearl Ind School Dist | 16 | 145 |
| Pinyan, Chris/Rio Vista Ind School Dist | 67 | 251 |
| Pipak, Molly/Plano Ind School Dist | 35 | 85 |
| Piper, Kristen/Brazosport Ind School Dist | 48,51,54 | 55 |
| Piper, Pam/Tom Bean Ind School Dist | 3 | 173 |
| Pipes, Lynne/Maypearl Ind School Dist | 59 | 145 |
| Pipkin, Linda/Hunt Ind School Dist | 67 | 258 |
| Pippin, Mable/Riviera Ind School Dist | 16 | 261 |
| Pirtele, Chad/Pleasant Grove Ind School Dist | 1 | 52 |

| NAME/District | JOB FUNCTIONS | PAGE |
|---|---|---|
| Pitcock, Daniel/Allen Ind School Dist | 3,5,15,91,295 | 80 |
| Pittenger, Donna/Katy Ind School Dist | 4 | 156 |
| Pittman, Brandi/Hughes Springs Ind Sch Dist | 7 | 74 |
| Pittman, Calvin/Lampasas Ind School Dist | 4 | 264 |
| Pittman, Michael/Post Ind School Dist | 6 | 167 |
| Pitts, Brian/Longview Ind School Dist | 73,295 | 174 |
| Pitts, Kevin/Richardson Ind School Dist | 6 | 116 |
| Pitts, Kevin, Dr/China Spring Ind School Dist | 15 | 281 |
| Pitts, Linda/Boles Ind School Dist | 67 | 238 |
| Pitts, Peter/Kingsville Ind School Dist | 2,68 | 260 |
| Piwetz, Tisha/Port Aransas Ind School Dist | 11,298 | 308 |
| Pizana, James/Seguin Ind School Dist | 3,5,79,91 | 178 |
| Pizzini, Gracie/San Diego Ind School Dist | 11,15,79 | 132 |
| Planey, Doug/Richardson Ind School Dist | 47 | 116 |
| Plant, Curtis/Kenedy Ind School Dist | 73,84 | 254 |
| Platt-Bryant, Linda/West Orange-Cove Cons ISD | 67 | 312 |
| Plauche, Lane/Sabine Pass Ind School Dist | 67 | 247 |
| Pleasant, Carl/Temple Ind School Dist | 88 | 32 |
| Pleasant, Toby/Spring Hill Ind School Dist | 3 | 175 |
| Pledger, Colette/Robinson Ind School Dist | 8,18 | 284 |
| Plott, Kathleen/Klein Ind School Dist | 81 | 202 |
| Plott, Kevin/Apple Springs Ind School Dist | 8 | 376 |
| Plowman, Monica/Everman Ind School Dist | 57 | 351 |
| Pluao, Lynn/Kerrville Ind School Dist | 11,58,83,88,275,298 | 259 |
| Plyler, Mignon/Sherman Ind School Dist | 73,295 | 172 |
| Poage, Liz/Lamesa Ind School Dist | 2,294 | 121 |
| Poage, Ron/Lampasas Ind School Dist | 73,295 | 264 |
| Pocius, Clayton/Flour Bluff Ind School Dist | 3,5 | 307 |
| Poe, Matt/Pottsboro Ind School Dist | 6 | 172 |
| Poe, Misty/Diocese of Austin Ed Office | 1,11 | 375 |
| Poenitzsch, Nicole/Dripping Springs Ind Sch Dist | 15 | 215 |
| **Poenitzsch, Nicole, Dr/Bellville Ind School Dist** | 1 | 24 |
| Poer, Mandy/Spring Creek Ind School Dist | 1,11,73,83 | 241 |
| Pogue, Michael/White Settlement Ind Sch Dist | 58 | 360 |
| Pohler, Jenny/Sweet Home Ind School Dist | 59,752 | 265 |
| Pokorny, Jolena/Thrall Ind School Dist | 11,285 | 403 |
| Poland, Denise/Aransas Co Ind School Dist | 9 | 22 |
| Polasek, Billy/Pawnee Ind School Dist | 73 | 28 |
| Polasek, Billy/Stockdale Ind School Dist | 73 | 404 |
| Polasek, Holly/Karnes City Ind School Dist | 16 | 253 |
| Polk, Brittanie/Gainesville Ind School Dist | 58 | 95 |
| Polk, Charles/Nederland Ind School Dist | 5 | 245 |
| Polk, Crystel/Crowley Ind School Dist | 298 | 350 |
| Polk, Elizabeth/Austin Ind School Dist | 16 | 369 |
| Polk, James/Gainesville Ind School Dist | 6 | 95 |
| Polk, Larry, Dr/Terrell Ind School Dist | 15,298 | 256 |
| Polk, Ray/Karnack Ind School Dist | 67 | 214 |
| Polk, Renee/Pilot Point Ind School Dist | 67 | 129 |
| Pollard, Barrett, Dr/Gatesville Ind School Dist | 1 | 96 |
| Pollard, Johnathan/Yantis Ind School Dist | 16,73,82,84,286 | 408 |
| Polomo, Ernesto/Gregory-Portland Ind Sch Dist | 3 | 333 |
| Polsen, Elaina/Clear Creek Ind School Dist | 71 | 163 |
| Polster, Misti/Hamilton Ind School Dist | 57 | 181 |
| Polzin, Dyann/Galveston Ind School Dist | 68,71 | 165 |
| Ponce, Geovanny/Houston ISD-East Area | 15 | 194 |
| Poncik, Callie/Academy Ind School Dist | 10,74,273 | 29 |
| Pond, Laurie/Hamlin Collegiate Ind Sch Dist | 8 | 252 |
| Pondant, Melanie/Longview Ind School Dist | 10 | 174 |
| Ponder, Barbara/Barbers Hill Ind School Dist | 15,68 | 75 |
| Ponder, Scott/Center Ind School Dist | 6 | 337 |
| Pones, Rosa/Brownsville Ind School Dist | 7 | 66 |
| Pool, Cathy/Tomball Ind School Dist | 7,35,85 | 208 |
| Pool, Lynn/Weatherford Ind School Dist | 78,79 | 316 |
| Poole, Becky/Buffalo Ind School Dist | 68,71 | 266 |
| Poole, Greg, Dr/Barbers Hill Ind School Dist | 1 | 75 |
| Poole, Lee/Hunt Ind School Dist | 6 | 258 |
| Poolman, Danny/Round Rock Ind School Dist | 2 | 401 |
| Poore, Mike/Nocona Ind School Dist | 5 | 293 |
| Pope, Amy/Sweeny Ind School Dist | 11,15,69,83,88,275,294,296 | 57 |
| Pope, Bonnie/Carthage Ind School Dist | 16 | 314 |
| Pope, Faith/Lockhart Ind School Dist | 9 | 64 |
| Pope, Gary/Lamesa Ind School Dist | 4 | 121 |
| Popham, Jacob/Loraine Ind School Dist | 6 | 292 |
| Poppy, Meggan, Dr/Bellville Ind School Dist | 34,37,58 | 25 |
| Porras, Amy/Ft Stockton Ind School Dist | 274 | 318 |
| Porter, Amy/Frankston Ind School Dist | 7 | 18 |

1 Superintendent 2 Bus/Finance/Purchasing 3 Buildings And Grounds 4 Food Service 5 Transportation 6 Athletic 7 Health Services 8 Curric/Instruct K-12 9 Curric/Instruct Elem 10 Curric/Instruct Sec 11 Federal Program 12 Title I 13 Title V 15 Asst Superintendent 16 Instructional Media Svcs 17 Chief Operations Officer 18 Chief Academic Officer 19 Chief Financial Officer 20 Art K-12 21 Art Elem 22 Art Sec 23 Music K-12 24 Music Elem 25 Music Sec 26 Business Education 27 Career & Tech Ed 28 Technology Education 29 Family/Consumer Science 30 Adult Education 31 Career/Sch-to-Work K-12 32 Career/Sch-to-Work Elem 33 Career/Sch-to-Work Sec 34 Early Childhood Ed 35 Health/Phys Education 36 Guidance Services K-12 37 Guidance Services Elem 38 Guidance Services Sec 39 Social Studies K-12 40 Social Studies Elem 41 Social Studies Sec 42 Science K-12 43 Science Elem 44 Science Sec 45 Math K-12 46 Math Elem 47 Math Sec 48 English/Lang Arts K-12 49 English/Lang Arts Elem 50 English/Lang Arts Sec 51 Reading K-12 52 Reading Elem 53 Reading Sec 54 Remedial Reading K-12 55 Remedial Reading Elem 56 Remedial Reading Sec 57 Bilingual/ELL 58 Special Education K-12 59 Special Education Elem 60 Special Education Sec 61 Foreign/World Lang K-12 62 Foreign/World Lang Elem 63 Foreign/World Lang Sec 64 Religious Education K-12 65 Religious Education Elem 66 Religious Education Sec 67 School Board President 68 Teacher Personnel 69 Academic Assessment 70 Research/Development 71 Public Information 72 Summer School 73 Instructional Tech 74 Inservice Training 75 Marketing/Distributive 76 Info Systems 77 Psychological Assess 78 Affirmative Action 79 Student Personnel 80 Driver Ed/Safety 81 Gifted/Talented 82 Video Services 83 Substance Abuse Prev 84 Erate 85 AIDS Education 88 Alternative/At Risk 89 Multi-Cultural Curriculum 90 Social Work 91 Safety/Security 92 Magnet School 93 Parental Involvement 95 Tech Prep Program 97 Chief Infomation Officer 98 Chief Technology Officer 270 Character Education 271 Migrant Education 273 Teacher Mentor 274 Before/After Sch 275 Response To Intervention 277 Remedial Math K-12 280 Literacy Coach 285 STEM 286 Digital Learning 288 Common Core Standards 294 Accountability 295 Network System 296 Title II Programs 297 Webmaster 298 Grant Writer/Ptnrships 750 Chief Innovation Officer 751 Chief of Staff 752 Social Emotional Learning

| NAME/District | JOB FUNCTIONS | PAGE | NAME/District | JOB FUNCTIONS | PAGE |
|---|---|---|---|---|---|
| Pruitt, John/Galveston Ind School Dist | 5 | 164 | Raga, Victor/Northside Ind School Dist | 57 | 39 |
| Pruitt, Kenith/Canton Ind School Dist | 67 | 382 | Ragland, Joan/Hudson Ind School Dist | 73 | 20 |
| Pruitt, Rod/Region 14 Ed Service Center | 83,85 | 364 | Ragle, Scott/Sands Consolidated ISD | 73 | 121 |
| Pruneda, Noe/Valley View Ind School Dist | 67 | 228 | Ragsdale, Lisa/Florence Ind School Dist | 5 | 398 |
| Pruski, Wayne/Schertz-Cibolo-Univ City ISD | 3,4,5,19 | 178 | Rahn, Terry/Krum Ind School Dist | 58,88 | 126 |
| Pruvino, Marina/Crystal City Ind School Dist | 7,85 | 410 | Raines, David/Leon Ind School Dist | 1 | 267 |
| Pryor, Ed/Coleman Ind School Dist | 11,69 | 79 | Rainey, Jason/Denton Ind School Dist | 68 | 125 |
| Psencik, Thomas/Hallettsville Ind Sch Dist | 6 | 265 | Rainey, Karla/Van Ind School Dist | 27 | 383 |
| Ptasnik, Misty/Hondo Ind School Dist | 9 | 287 | Rainey, Lacey, Dr/Denton Ind School Dist | 15 | 124 |
| Puckett, Jim Bob/Lovejoy Ind School Dist | 6 | 84 | Rainey, Lance/Melissa Ind School Dist | 2 | 85 |
| Puente, Alex/Flour Bluff Ind School Dist | 73,76,84,295 | 307 | Rainey, Lisa/McGregor Ind School Dist | 294 | 283 |
| Puente, Veronica/Rio Hondo Ind School Dist | 11,57,58,69 | 70 | Rains, Amber/Gainesville Ind School Dist | 57,275 | 95 |
| Puga, Soor-El/Marble Falls Ind School Dist | 57 | 64 | Rains, Greg/Trent Isn School Dist | 3 | 363 |
| Pugh, Denise/Savoy Ind School Dist | 2,76 | 150 | Rains, Lachrisa/Denver City Ind School Dist | 2,19 | 409 |
| Pugh, Donna/Levelland Ind School Dist | 11,31,57,88,271,274,296,298 | 232 | Rains, Renae/Iola Ind School Dist | 59 | 177 |
| Pugh, Kyle/Winona Ind School Dist | 73,84 | 341 | Rakestraw, Wally/Alief Ind School Dist | 73,295 | 186 |
| Pugsley, Kim/Rockwall Ind School Dist | 4 | 328 | Rakin, Sharron/Kemp Ind School Dist | 67 | 255 |
| **Puig, Marc, Dr/**South San Antonio Ind Sch Dist | 1 | 45 | Raley, Craig/Richardson Ind School Dist | 79 | 116 |
| Pulate, Penny/Johnson City Ind School Dist | 11,58,69 | 49 | Raley, Tim/Chico Ind School Dist | 67 | 406 |
| Pullen, Cindy/Angleton Ind School Dist | 68 | 55 | Rally, Joe/Lefors Ind School Dist | 6 | 170 |
| Pullen, Cyndy/Columbia Brazoria ISD | 273 | 56 | Ralston, Becky/Rogers Ind School Dist | 8,69,294 | 32 |
| Pullen, Tiffany/Georgetown Ind School Dist | 40,52 | 398 | Ralston, Terry/Clarendon Cons Ind Sch Dist | 3 | 131 |
| Pulliam, Lawana/Canadian Ind School Dist | 8,73 | 218 | Ramaker, Tonia/Aransas Co Ind School Dist | 7 | 22 |
| **Pulliam, Lynn/**Canadian Ind School Dist | 1 | 218 | Ramas, Kina/Morton Ind School Dist | 8 | 78 |
| Pullin, Clint/Walnut Springs Ind Sch Dist | 67 | 51 | Rambin, Ashley/Joaquin Ind School Dist | 36,57,271 | 337 |
| Pumphrey, Shonna/Lancaster Ind School Dist | 2,19 | 114 | Ramer, Ginger/Liberty Ind School Dist | 2,19 | 269 |
| Purdy, Randy/Region 2 Ed Service Center | 8,16,73 | 309 | **Ramerez, Juan/**Morgan Ind School Dist | 1,11,73,83 | 50 |
| Purgahn, Carmen/Deweyville Ind School Dist | 58 | 311 | Ramerez, Randel/Sundown Ind School Dist | 16,82,295 | 232 |
| Pursch, Victoria/New Braunfels Ind School Dist | 8,15,34,69,294 | 92 | Rameriz, Ben/Daingerfield-Lone Star Ind SD | 270 | 299 |
| Purser, Rusty/Greenwood Ind School Dist | 6 | 288 | Rameriz, Maryjane/Hearne Ind School Dist | 67 | 327 |
| Pursifull, Kyle/Allen Ind School Dist | 5 | 80 | Rameriz, Stephanie/Coahoma Ind School Dist | 4 | 237 |
| Purvis, Daniel/Cross Plains Ind Sch Dist | 6 | 66 | Ramey, Jamie/Ganado Ind School Dist | 58 | 242 |
| Pustejovsky, Annie/Waelder Ind School Dist | 4 | 169 | Ramirez, Alejandra/Floydada Ind School Dist | 27,75 | 153 |
| Pustejovsky, Ben/Abbott Ind School Dist | 5 | 229 | Ramirez, Alex/Anthony Ind School Dist | 295 | 136 |
| Pustejovsky, Bob/Abbott Ind School Dist | 67 | 229 | Ramirez, Amanda/Santa Gertrudis Ind Sch Dist | 2 | 261 |
| Pustejovsky, Channa/Abbott Ind School Dist | 8,11,58,88,285,288,294 | 229 | Ramirez, Angie/Corpus Christi Ind Sch Dist | 273 | 306 |
| Pustejovsky, Dale/Buena Vista Ind School Dist | 6 | 318 | Ramirez, Arminda/Mission Cons Ind School Dist | 271 | 225 |
| Pustejovsky, Ed/Abbott Ind School Dist | 3 | 229 | Ramirez, Arsenio/Seminole Ind School Dist | 5 | 162 |
| Pustejovsky, Eric/Abbott Ind School Dist | 1,57 | 229 | Ramirez, Becky/Ector Co Ind School Dist | 39 | 134 |
| Pustejovsky, Linda/Brazos Ind School Dist | 4 | 25 | Ramirez, Christopher/Harlandale Ind School Dist | 3 | 35 |
| Pustejovsky, Traci/Penelope ISD School Dist | 73 | 231 | Ramirez, Cynthia/United Ind School Dist | 58 | 390 |
| Puth, Nina/East Central Ind School Dist | 58 | 34 | Ramirez, Delia/Yorktown Ind School Dist | 76 | 122 |
| Putnal, Mike/Alvin Ind School Dist | 91 | 54 | Ramirez, Deonicio/Cotulla Ind School Dist | 67 | 262 |
| Putnam, Jennifer/Abilene Ind School Dist | 34 | 362 | Ramirez, Diane/Lake Dallas Ind School Dist | 7 | 126 |
| Putter, Renee/Carrollton-Farmers Branch ISD | 6,35 | 100 | Ramirez, Etna/Jim Hogg Co Ind School Dist | 67 | 247 |
| Puz, Melony/Port Arthur Ind School Dist | 44,53 | 246 | Ramirez, George/Stanton Ind School Dist | 5 | 277 |
| Pyburn, Steven/Hale Center Ind School Dist | 1 | 180 | Ramirez, Guillermo/Hidalgo Ind School Dist | 2,3,91 | 222 |
| Pyle, Patrick/San Antonio Ind School Dist | 39 | 42 | Ramirez, Heather/Cotulla Ind School Dist | 8,11,288,296,298,752 | 262 |
| Pyle, Tammy/Farmersville Ind School Dist | 4 | 82 | Ramirez, Ismael/Sierra Blanca Ind School Dist | 6 | 237 |
|  |  |  | Ramirez, Jennifer/Belton Ind School Dist | 58 | 29 |
| **Q** |  |  | Ramirez, Jose/Clint Ind School Dist | 39 | 136 |
| Quade, Marsha/Knox City-O'Brien Cons Ind SD | 9,57,271 | 261 | Ramirez, Juana/Southside Ind School Dist | 4 | 46 |
| Quarles, Breck/Palestine Ind School Dist | 5 | 18 | Ramirez, Kirstie/Point Isabel Ind Sch Dist | 11,270,271 | 70 |
| Quarles, Sandra/Daingerfield-Lone Star Ind SD | 1 | 299 | Ramirez, Liz/Fabens Ind School Dist | 7 | 139 |
| Quary, John, Dr/Diocese of Victoria Ed Office | 1 | 385 | Ramirez, Marla/College Station Ind Sch Dist | 57 | 59 |
| Queen, Danielle/Bronte Ind School Dist | 4 | 79 | Ramirez, Michael/Carrollton-Farmers Branch ISD | 35 | 100 |
| Quesada, Patricia, Dr/San Benito Cons Ind Sch Dist | 57 | 70 | Ramirez, Mike/Harlandale Ind School Dist | 91 | 35 |
| **Quesada, Roland, Dr/**George West Ind School Dist | 1 | 271 | Ramirez, Myrtala/Laredo Ind School Dist | 9 | 389 |
| Quick, Todd/Lufkin Ind School Dist | 6 | 21 | Ramirez, Nicole/La Grange Ind School Dist | 11 | 151 |
| Quinn, Elizabeth/Archdiocese Galveston-Houston | 64 | 209 | Ramirez, Patsy/Rio Grande City Ind Sch Dist | 4 | 342 |
| Quinn, Janice/Kerens Ind School Dist | 16 | 303 | Ramirez, Randy/Runge Ind School Dist | 2 | 254 |
| Quinn, Kaye/De Leon Ind School Dist | 12,31,36,69,85,88,270,296 | 93 | Ramirez, Raul/Dilley Ind School Dist | 5 | 161 |
| Quinn, Kim/Carrollton-Farmers Branch ISD | 11 | 100 | Ramirez, Raul/United Ind School Dist | 4 | 390 |
| Quintero, Frank/Progreso Ind School Dist | 5,91 | 227 | Ramirez, Rene/Anthony Ind School Dist | 3,5 | 136 |
| Quintna, Larry/Presidio Ind School Dist | 73 | 323 | Ramirez, Ricardo/Zapata Co Ind School Dist | 67 | 410 |
| Quiraz, Fernando/Brackett Ind School Dist | 3 | 260 | Ramirez, Roberta/Laredo Ind School Dist | 15,68 | 389 |
| Quiroga, Jesse/Edgewood Ind School Dist | 91 | 34 | **Ramirez, Rolando/**Southside Ind School Dist | 1 | 46 |
| Quisenberry, Chad/Devine Ind School Dist | 6 | 286 | Ramirez, Ruben/Devine Ind School Dist | 3 | 286 |
| Quisenberry, Melissa/Aledo Ind School Dist | 73 | 315 | Ramirez, Shannon/Devine Ind School Dist | 2 | 286 |
| Quisenberry, Stephen/Region 10 Ed Service Center | 68 | 120 | Ramirez, Stephanie/San Benito Cons Ind Sch Dist | 74 | 70 |
| **R** |  |  | Ramirez, Susanna/Grand Prairie Ind School Dist | 15,34,93 | 111 |
|  |  |  | Ramirez, Suzanne/Los Fresnos Cons Ind Sch Dist | 5 | 69 |
| Rabalais, Carla/Barbers Hill Ind School Dist | 71 | 75 | Ramirz, Alma/Robinson Ind School Dist | 4 | 284 |
| Rabalais, Don/Alvin Ind School Dist | 16,73,76,98 | 54 | Ramm, Justin/Lone Oak Ind School Dist | 67 | 239 |
| Radle, Patti/San Antonio Ind School Dist | 67 | 42 | Ramm, Michelle/Mesquite Ind School Dist | 5 | 115 |
| Raftery, Liz/Denton Ind School Dist | 4 | 124 | Ramon, Ralph/Snyder Ind School Dist | 67 | 336 |

| | | | | | |
|---|---|---|---|---|---|
| 1 Superintendent | 16 Instructional Media Svcs | 30 Adult Education | 44 Science Sec | 58 Special Education K-12 | 72 Summer School | 88 Alternative/At Risk | 277 Remedial Math K-12 |
| 2 Bus/Finance/Purchasing | 17 Chief Operations Officer | 31 Career/Sch-to-Work K-12 | 45 Math K-12 | 59 Special Education Elem | 73 Instructional Tech | 89 Multi-Cultural Curriculum | 280 Literacy Coach |
| 3 Buildings And Grounds | 18 Chief Academic Officer | 32 Career/Sch-to-Work Elem | 46 Math Elem | 60 Special Education Sec | 74 Inservice Training | 90 Social Work | 285 STEM |
| 4 Food Service | 19 Chief Financial Officer | 33 Career/Sch-to-Work Sec | 47 Math Sec | 61 Foreign/World Lang K-12 | 75 Marketing/Distributive | 91 Safety/Security | 286 Digital Learning |
| 5 Transportation | 20 Art K-12 | 34 Early Childhood Ed | 48 English/Lang Arts K-12 | 62 Foreign/World Lang Elem | 76 Info Systems | 92 Magnet School | 288 Common Core Standards |
| 6 Athletic | 21 Art Elem | 35 Health/Phys Education | 49 English/Lang Arts Elem | 63 Foreign/World Lang Sec | 77 Psychological Assess | 93 Parental Involvement | 294 Accountability |
| 7 Health Services | 22 Art Sec | 36 Guidance Services K-12 | 50 English/Lang Arts Sec | 64 Religious Education K-12 | 78 Affirmative Action | 95 Tech Prep Program | 295 Network System |
| 8 Curric/Instruct K-12 | 23 Music K-12 | 37 Guidance Services Elem | 51 Reading K-12 | 65 Religious Education Elem | 79 Student Personnel | 96 Title II Programs | 296 Title II Programs |
| 9 Curric/Instruct Elem | 24 Music Elem | 38 Guidance Services Sec | 52 Reading Elem | 66 Religious Education Sec | 80 Driver Ed/Safety | 97 Chief Information Officer | 297 Webmaster |
| 10 Curric/Instruct Sec | 25 Music Sec | 39 Social Studies K-12 | 53 Reading Sec | 67 School Board President | 81 Gifted/Talented | 98 Chief Technology Officer | 298 Grant Writer/Ptnrships |
| 11 Federal Program | 26 Business Education | 40 Social Studies Elem | 54 Remedial Reading K-12 | 68 Teacher Personnel | 82 Video Services | 270 Character Education | 750 Chief Innovation Officer |
| 12 Title I | 27 Career & Tech Ed | 41 Social Studies Sec | 55 Remedial Reading Elem | 69 Academic Assessment | 83 Substance Abuse Prev | 271 Migrant Education | 751 Chief of Staff |
| 13 Title V | 28 Technology Education | 42 Science K-12 | 56 Remedial Reading Sec | 70 Research/Development | 84 Erate | 273 Teacher Mentor | 752 Social Emotional Learning |
| 15 Asst Superintendent | 29 Family/Consumer Science | 43 Science Elem | 57 Bilingual/ELL | 71 Public Information | 85 AIDS Education | 274 Before/After Sch | |
| | | | | | | 275 Response To Intervention | |

| NAME/District | JOB FUNCTIONS | PAGE | NAME/District | JOB FUNCTIONS | PAGE |
|---|---|---|---|---|---|
| Reed, Brin/Merkel Ind School Dist | 4 | 363 | Ressler, Teresa/Brazos Ind School Dist | 8,11,57,74,271,294 | 25 |
| Reed, Colleen/Silverton Ind School Dist | 27,73,286,295 | 61 | Restivo, Rick/Columbus Ind School Dist | 67 | 90 |
| **Reed, Craig/**Dodd City Ind School Dist | 1,83 | 150 | Restivo, Rick/Melissa Ind School Dist | 67 | 85 |
| Reed, Gary/Wilson Ind School Dist | 3 | 276 | Retona, Cynthia/Socorro Ind School Dist | 15 | 140 |
| Reed, Glenn/Houston Ind School Dist | 19 | 193 | Rettig, Eric/Brenham Ind School Dist | 23 | 388 |
| Reed, Greg/Waxahachie Ind School Dist | 6 | 146 | Retzlaff, Allen/Lexington Ind School Dist | 3 | 266 |
| Reed, Jeanie/New Caney Ind School Dist | 286 | 296 | Revell, Elaine/Region 7 Ed Service Center | 4 | 176 |
| Reed, Jennifer/Mesquite Ind School Dist | 88 | 115 | Revels, Jeanette/Flour Bluff Ind School Dist | 68 | 307 |
| Reed, Julie/Pasadena Ind School Dist | 58,294 | 203 | Reville, Sherry/Quinlan Ind School Dist | 68 | 240 |
| Reed, Laura/Gholson Ind School Dist | 59 | 282 | Rex, Carlinda/Academy Ind School Dist | 9 | 29 |
| Reed, Matt/New Deal Ind School Dist | 1,11 | 274 | Rex, Twilla/Ennis Ind School Dist | 8,57,69,288 | 144 |
| Reed, Mike/Gordon Ind School Dist | 6 | 313 | Reyas, Erika/Duncanville Ind School Dist | 34,296 | 108 |
| Reed, Reagan/Terlingua Common School Dist | 6 | 60 | Reyenga, Shane/Kountze Ind School Dist | 8,11,15,69 | 183 |
| Reed, Reagan/Terlingua Common School Dist | 1 | 60 | **Reyenga, Shane/**Kountze Ind School Dist | 1 | 183 |
| Reed, Renneth/Electra Ind School Dist | 73,295 | 394 | Reyes, Brandon/Ector Co Ind School Dist | 4 | 134 |
| Reed, Roger/S & S Cons Ind School Dist | 1 | 172 | Reyes, Cecilia/Sabinal Ind School Dist | 7 | 380 |
| Reed, Sharon/Palestine Ind School Dist | 8,69 | 18 | Reyes, Corina/Petersburg Ind School Dist | 36 | 180 |
| Reed, Sheleah/Aldine Ind School Dist | 71 | 184 | Reyes, Galina/La Joya Ind School Dist | 4 | 222 |
| Reed, Tiffany/Kress Ind School Dist | 67 | 345 | Reyes, Jaime/Anthony Ind School Dist | 5 | 136 |
| Reeder, Jeremy/Northside Ind School Dist | 6 | 396 | Reyes, Jissel/Anthony Ind School Dist | 2 | 136 |
| Reel, Jodie/Guthrie Common School Dist | 8,31 | 260 | Reyes, Kim/Utopia Ind School Dist | 4 | 381 |
| Rees, Laurie/Kerrville Ind School Dist | 273 | 259 | Reyes, Laura/Kress Ind School Dist | 4 | 345 |
| Reese-Taylor, Pamela/Cedar Hill Ind School Dist | 7 | 101 | Reyes, Monica, Dr/Canutillo Ind School Dist | 7,30,34,36,85,88,93 | 136 |
| **Reese, Allen/**Mumford Ind School Dist | 1 | 59 | Reyes, Raquel/Hidalgo Ind School Dist | 8 | 222 |
| Reese, Chris/Birdville Ind School Dist | 91 | 348 | Reyes, Sam/School of Excellence In Ed | 4 | 45 |
| Reese, Stephanie/Lake Dallas Ind School Dist | 4 | 126 | Reyes, Velinda/San Isidro Ind School Dist | 67 | 343 |
| Reese, Stephen/Rivercrest Ind School Dist | 73,295 | 325 | Reyes, Veronica/Socorro Ind School Dist | 57 | 140 |
| Reeves, Catrina/Red Oak Ind School Dist | 68 | 146 | Reyna, Amy/Itasca Ind School Dist | 8,11 | 231 |
| Reeves, Deidra/Greenville Ind School Dist | 2,15,19 | 239 | Reyna, Dolores/Mission Cons Ind School Dist | 298 | 225 |
| Reeves, Eli/De Leon Ind School Dist | 2 | 93 | Reyna, Hector/Socorro Ind School Dist | 73,76,98,295,297 | 140 |
| Reeves, Farley/Frenship Ind School Dist | 2,15 | 272 | Reyna, Isidor/Skidmore Tynan Ind SD | 3 | 29 |
| Reeves, Lanna/Shamrock Ind School Dist | 34,58 | 393 | Reyna, Jacob/Jourdanton Ind School Dist | 3 | 23 |
| Reeves, Leshell/Elgin Ind School Dist | 8 | 27 | Reyna, Jessica/Deer Park Ind School Dist | 48 | 191 |
| Reeves, Marilin/Krum Ind School Dist | 274 | 126 | Reyna, Maricella/Lackland Ind School Dist | 4 | 37 |
| Reeves, Phoebe/Northside Ind School Dist | 67 | 396 | Reyna, Mario/McAllen Ind School Dist | 35 | 224 |
| Reeves, Rick/Conroe Ind School Dist | 2 | 294 | Reyna, Yolanda/Robstown Ind School Dist | 11,57,83 | 308 |
| Reeves, Russ/Rockwall Ind School Dist | 6 | 328 | **Reynolds-Perez, Cecilia, Dr/**Kingsville Ind School Dist | 1 | 260 |
| Register, Tina/Bryson Ind School Dist | 2 | 241 | Reynolds-Perez, Cissy, Dr/West Oso Ind School Dist | 8,15,68 | 309 |
| Rehkopf, Kristie/Floydada Ind School Dist | 38,69,288 | 153 | Reynolds, Bobby/Godley Ind School Dist | 3 | 250 |
| Reichardt, Ryan/Sealy Ind School Dist | 67 | 25 | Reynolds, Candice/New Waverly Ind School Dist | 37 | 386 |
| Reichelt, Christine/Conroe Ind School Dist | 81 | 294 | Reynolds, David/Bryan Ind School Dist | 27,31 | 58 |
| Reid, Brian/Bellville Ind School Dist | 73,286,295 | 25 | Reynolds, Ernie/Schertz-Cibolo-Univ City ISD | 7,10,91 | 178 |
| Reid, Christina/Chapel Hill Ind School Dist | 58 | 366 | Reynolds, Freda/Port Arthur Ind School Dist | 34 | 246 |
| Reid, Christina/Chapel Hill Ind School Dist | 58 | 366 | Reynolds, Josh/Bushland Ind School Dist | 6 | 321 |
| Reid, Dana/Frisco Ind School Dist | 81 | 82 | Reynolds, Kent, Dr/Hallsburg Ind School Dist | 1,11,83 | 282 |
| Reid, Linda/Rockwall Ind School Dist | 69,77,294 | 328 | Reynolds, Michelle/Lamar Cons Ind School Dist | 2 | 157 |
| **Reid, Melissa/**Pewitt Cons Ind School Dist | 1 | 299 | Reynolds, Monica/Beaumont Ind School Dist | 39,81 | 244 |
| Reid, Nikki/Aldine Ind School Dist | 91 | 184 | Reynolds, Penny/Godley Ind School Dist | 4 | 250 |
| Reid, Randy/Denison Ind School Dist | 2,15,91 | 171 | Reynolds, Royce/Ponder Ind School Dist | 6 | 130 |
| Reidlinger, Christopher, Dr/Amarillo Ind School Dist | 23 | 320 | Reynolds, Sandy/Little Cypress Mauriceville SD | 16 | 311 |
| Reimer, Eric/Splendora Ind School Dist | 3 | 297 | Reynolds, Steve/Adrian Ind School Dist | 1,11 | 310 |
| Reimonenq, Precious, Dr/Goose Creek Cons Ind Sch Dist | 31,36 | 192 | Reynolds, Thelma/Harlingen Cons Ind School Dist | 11 | 68 |
| Reina-Garza, Jessica/Mission Cons Ind School Dist | 49 | 225 | Reysinger, Renee/Carthage Ind School Dist | 3,4,5,15 | 314 |
| Reinart, Sara/Happy Ind School Dist | 27,30,31 | 345 | Reza, Tony/Socorro Ind School Dist | 2,19 | 140 |
| Reisner, Keely/Rockdale Ind School Dist | 69,77 | 290 | Rhinehart, Ed/Lindale Ind School Dist | 3 | 339 |
| Remchel, Alex/Academy Ind School Dist | 3,11,15,83,88,271,274 | 29 | Rhoades, Brandy/Iowa Park Consolidated Ind SD | 36 | 395 |
| Remick, Lorrie/Randolph Field Ind School Dist | 2,19,71 | 42 | Rhoades, Cindy/Dumas Ind School Dist | 79,294 | 298 |
| Remissong, Patricia, Dr/Copperas Cove Ind School Dist | 8,15,288 | 96 | Rhoades, Jeff/Iowa Park Consolidated Ind SD | 67 | 395 |
| Remmers, Pamela/Nordheim Ind School Dist | 67 | 122 | Rhoades, Ryan/Plainview Ind School Dist | 6 | 180 |
| Remschel, Alex/Shiner Ind School Dist | 1 | 265 | Rhoades, Stephen/Lufkin Ind School Dist | 27,31,75 | 21 |
| Rena, Shelley/Crosby Ind School Dist | 69 | 188 | Rhoades, Wendee/Ropes Ind School Dist | 7 | 232 |
| Rendon, Gloria/United Ind School Dist | 15 | 390 | Rhodes, Angela/Burton Ind School Dist | 31,79,88,270 | 388 |
| Rendon, Hilda/San Benito Cons Ind Sch Dist | 2,15 | 70 | Rhodes, Curtis/Needville Ind School Dist | 1 | 159 |
| Rendon, Itzamara/Laredo Ind School Dist | 34 | 389 | **Rhodes, Donald, Dr/**Crowell Ind School Dist | 1 | 153 |
| Reneau, Bart/Garrison Ind School Dist | 67 | 301 | Rhodes, Melissa/Needville Ind School Dist | 16 | 159 |
| Reneau, Kacie/Bloomburg Ind School Dist | 58 | 73 | Rhodes, Rick/Gregory-Portland Ind Sch Dist | 6 | 333 |
| Renegar, Lisa/San Elizario Ind School Dist | 39,48,69,81,88,275,294 | 139 | Rhodes, Shirley/Newcastle Ind School Dist | 2,84 | 409 |
| Renken, Paula/Poth Ind School Dist | 1,11 | 404 | Rhone, Kristi/Grandview Ind School Dist | 8,11,76,88,285,288,296,298 | 251 |
| Reno-Rollo, Kathryn/Lubbock Ind School Dist | 1 | 272 | Rhone, Kristi, Dr/Cleburne Ind School Dist | 9 | 250 |
| Reno, Elaine/Olney Ind School Dist | 8,12,288,298 | 410 | Riberou, Richard, Dr/Edcouch Elsa Ind School Dist | 1 | 220 |
| Rentz, Crystal/Dallas Ind School Dist | 72 | 102 | Rice-Imumwen, Christina/Spring Branch Ind School Dist | 27 | 205 |
| Renyolds, Troy/Splendora Ind School Dist | 11 | 297 | Rice-Wiltz, Christina/Alvin Ind School Dist | 27,31,95 | 54 |
| Rergel, Ren/Santa Rosa Ind School Dist | 3,5 | 71 | Rice, Ben/New Caney Ind School Dist | 73 | 296 |
| Rerich, Theresa/Weimar Ind School Dist | 4 | 91 | Rice, Bobby, Dr/Harts Bluff Ind School Dist | 1,11,83 | 366 |
| Resendez, Marco/Los Fresnos Cons Ind Sch Dist | 297 | 69 | Rice, Darrin/Conroe Ind School Dist | 2,19 | 294 |
| Ressler, Richard/New Caney Ind School Dist | 5 | 296 | Rice, Dawn/Lancaster Ind School Dist | 5 | 114 |

| NAME/District | JOB FUNCTIONS | PAGE | NAME/District | JOB FUNCTIONS | PAGE |
|---|---|---|---|---|---|
| Roan, James/Cooper Ind School Dist | 3 | 123 | Robles, Reynaldo/Monte Alto Ind School Dist | 2,4,17 | 226 |
| Roan, Richard/Cooper Ind School Dist | 12 | 124 | Robles, Ronald/Ingleside Ind School Dist | 3,5,92 | 333 |
| Roane, Stetson/Raymondville Ind Sch Dist | 1 | 397 | Roby, Deborah/Lewisville Ind School Dist | 81 | 126 |
| Roane, Warren, Dr/Humble Ind School Dist | 294 | 200 | Rocha, Andy/Refugio Ind School Dist | 67 | 326 |
| Robbins, Jessica/Aransas Co Ind School Dist | 57,69 | 22 | Rocha, Antonio/Friona Ind School Dist | 67 | 318 |
| Robbins, Patricia/Little Elm Ind School Dist | 71 | 128 | Rocha, Audrey/Progreso Ind School Dist | 4 | 227 |
| Robbins, Sheryl/Bruceville-Eddy Ind Sch Dist | 2,68 | 281 | Rocha, Dolly/Lyford Cons Ind School Dist | 16,82,93 | 397 |
| Robeledo, Alison/Wharton Ind School Dist | 4 | 393 | Rocha, Frances/Edcouch Elsa Ind School Dist | 15 | 220 |
| Roberson, Michelle/Meridian Ind School Dist | 58 | 50 | Rocha, Marnie/Canutillo Ind School Dist | 15 | 136 |
| Roberts, Allen/Alvin Ind School Dist | 15 | 54 | Rocha, Ruben/Corpus Christi Ind Sch Dist | 41 | 306 |
| Roberts, Anthony/Onalaska Ind School Dist | 1 | 320 | Rocha, Zelda/Progreso Ind School Dist | 57,88,93 | 227 |
| Roberts, Celeste/New Waverly Ind School Dist | 7 | 386 | Rockefeller, John/Zephyr Ind School Dist | 67 | 62 |
| Roberts, Chance/Bonham Ind School Dist | 67 | 149 | Rockstead, Maria/Eanes Ind School Dist | 2 | 372 |
| Roberts, Cherise/Stafford Municipal Sch Dist | 298 | 159 | Rockwood, Mike/Lamar Cons Ind School Dist | 71,751 | 157 |
| Roberts, Danny/Prosper Ind School Dist | 3 | 88 | Rodarmer, Paul/Tioga Ind School Dist | 67 | 172 |
| Roberts, Eric/College Station Ind Sch Dist | 60 | 59 | Roddy, Clint/Irving Ind School Dist | 6 | 113 |
| Roberts, Georgiann/Ft Worth Ind School Dist | 35 | 352 | Roddy, Heath/Wharton Ind School Dist | 73,297 | 393 |
| Roberts, Jennett/Natalia Ind School Dist | 73,286,295,297 | 287 | Roddy, Meredith/Manor Ind School Dist | 57 | 373 |
| Roberts, Jennifer, Dr/Lamar Cons Ind School Dist | 7,79 | 157 | Rodela, Joni/Lubbock Ind School Dist | 39 | 272 |
| Roberts, Joi/Paris Ind School Dist | 58 | 262 | Rodell, Angela/Centerville Ind School Dist | 16,73 | 267 |
| Roberts, Katherine/Venus Ind School Dist | 16 | 252 | Rodell, Courtney/Buffalo Ind School Dist | 2,11 | 266 |
| Roberts, Keri/Goldthwaite Consolidated ISD | 67 | 291 | Roden, Amanda/Apple Springs Ind School Dist | 67 | 376 |
| Roberts, Michael/Quinlan Ind School Dist | 16,73,295 | 240 | Roden, Gay/Venus Ind School Dist | 57 | 252 |
| Roberts, Nicole/Alief Ind School Dist | 58 | 186 | Roden, Kasie/Grand Prairie Ind School Dist | 285 | 111 |
| Roberts, Ross/Little Elm Ind School Dist | 15,79 | 128 | Roderick, Scott/Wylie Ind School Dist | 2,15 | 88 |
| Roberts, Scott/Laredo Ind School Dist | 298 | 389 | Roderiguez, Isaac, Dr/La Feria Ind School Dist | 8 | 69 |
| Roberts, Sharon/Mission Cons Ind School Dist | 15,81 | 225 | Rodgers, Brannon/Jacksboro Ind Sch Dist | 6,35 | 242 |
| Roberts, Teresa/Bangs Ind School Dist | 2 | 61 | Rodgers, Jackie/Bastrop Ind School Dist | 58 | 26 |
| Roberts, Troy/Huckabay Ind School Dist | 1,83 | 147 | Rodgers, Joel/Amherst Ind School Dist | 1,11,83 | 263 |
| Roberts, Ward/Wichita Falls Ind School Dist | 81 | 395 | Rodgers, Scott/Red Oak Ind School Dist | 10 | 146 |
| Roberts, William/Huntsville Ind School Dist | 2,15,17,76 | 386 | Rodgers, Wesley/Seagraves Ind School Dist | 67 | 162 |
| Robertson, Barbara/Conroe Ind School Dist | 7 | 294 | Rodguiez, Jorge/Stafford Municipal Sch Dist | 73,295 | 159 |
| Robertson, Bradley/Brownsboro Ind School Dist | 79,270 | 218 | Rodregez, Martin/Edcouch Elsa Ind School Dist | 5 | 220 |
| Robertson, Collin/Leon Ind School Dist | 67 | 267 | Rodriguez, Al/Elgin Ind School Dist | 15,68,71,78 | 27 |
| Robertson, Darlenea/Petersburg Ind School Dist | 2 | 180 | Rodriguez, Alex/Valley View Ind School Dist | 3,5 | 228 |
| Robertson, Donna/Smyer Ind School Dist | 2 | 232 | Rodriguez, Alfonso/La Joya Ind School Dist | 47 | 222 |
| Robertson, Jonathan/Sudan Ind School Dist | 73,286,298 | 264 | Rodriguez, Alva/Crosbyton Cons Ind Sch Dist | 57,271 | 98 |
| Robertson, Kelly/Alto Ind School Dist | 2 | 76 | Rodriguez, Ann/Hurst-Euless-Bedford ISD | 74 | 356 |
| Robertson, Robert/Klein Ind School Dist | 3,15 | 201 | Rodriguez, Barbara/San Antonio Ind School Dist | 11 | 42 |
| Robertson, Staci/Stamford Ind School Dist | 2,15 | 253 | Rodriguez, Brenda/Ft Sam Houston Ind School Dist | 4 | 35 |
| Robertson, Steve, Dr/Katy Ind School Dist | 15 | 156 | Rodriguez, Brenda/Mabank Ind School Dist | 2 | 256 |
| Robertson, Thomas/Van Ind School Dist | 91 | 383 | Rodriguez, Caleb/Grape Creek Ind School Dist | 73 | 367 |
| Robins, Becky/Goose Creek Cons Ind Sch Dist | 8 | 192 | Rodriguez, Carmelita/Brownsville Ind School Dist | 15,68,78 | 66 |
| Robins, Rodney/Ingram Ind School Dist | 91 | 259 | Rodriguez, Christine/Southside Ind School Dist | 297 | 46 |
| Robinson, Arlene/Spurger Ind School Dist | 9,69,83 | 377 | Rodriguez, Clemente/Kress Ind School Dist | 76 | 345 |
| Robinson, Becky/Judson Ind School Dist | 15 | 36 | Rodriguez, Connie, Dr/Dallas Ind School Dist | 77,90 | 102 |
| Robinson, Bo/Yoakum Ind School Dist | 6 | 122 | Rodriguez, Cynthia/United Ind School Dist | 9 | 390 |
| Robinson, Cody/Lovelady Ind School Dist | 3,5,91 | 236 | Rodriguez, Dawn/Aldine Ind School Dist | 69,70,294 | 184 |
| Robinson, Danielle/West Orange-Cove Cons ISD | 4 | 312 | Rodriguez, Debra/San Perlita Ind School Dist | 2 | 397 |
| Robinson, Dawn/Troy Ind School Dist | 34,37 | 33 | Rodriguez, Doug/Lubbock Ind School Dist | 15,68,78,751 | 272 |
| Robinson, Gary/Joshua Ind School Dist | 6 | 251 | Rodriguez, Edgar/Frankston Ind School Dist | 69,88,285 | 18 |
| Robinson, Geneva/La Poynor Ind School Dist | 31 | 219 | Rodriguez, Edward/Lackland Ind School Dist | 4 | 37 |
| Robinson, Ginger/Waxahachie Ind School Dist | 36,69,294 | 146 | Rodriguez, Erasmo/Beeville Ind School Dist | 15,91 | 28 |
| Robinson, Jeff/Waxahachie Ind School Dist | 76 | 146 | Rodriguez, Ernie/Allen Ind School Dist | 91 | 80 |
| Robinson, Julia/Royse City Ind School Dist | 8 | 328 | Rodriguez, Francisco/Roma Ind School Dist | 286 | 343 |
| Robinson, Karen/Meridian Ind School Dist | 69,83,85,88,273,274 | 50 | Rodriguez, Gerardo/United Ind School Dist | 20,23 | 390 |
| Robinson, Lacy/Chapel Hill Ind School Dist | 8,11,57,271,273,296,298 | 366 | Rodriguez, Geronimo/Austin Ind School Dist | 67 | 369 |
| Robinson, Lafreceia/Cooper Ind School Dist | 4 | 123 | Rodriguez, Gustavo/Ft Bend Ind School Dist | 5 | 153 |
| Robinson, Larry/Region 12 Ed Service Center | 68 | 286 | Rodriguez, Haydee/La Feria Ind School Dist | 36 | 69 |
| Robinson, Lisa/Sulphur Springs Ind Sch Dist | 8 | 235 | Rodriguez, Homero/Southwest Ind School Dist | 15,91 | 46 |
| Robinson, Lori/Natalia Ind School Dist | 8,271,285 | 287 | Rodriguez, Jaime/La Feria Ind School Dist | 93,271 | 69 |
| Robinson, Robert/Southwest Ind School Dist | 58,275 | 46 | Rodriguez, Jaime/Pettus Ind School Dist | 67 | 28 |
| Robinson, Sherrie/Houston Ind School Dist | 2 | 193 | Rodriguez, Janette/San Benito Cons Ind Sch Dist | 7 | 70 |
| Robinson, Tina/Lake Worth Ind School Dist | 4,7 | 358 | Rodriguez, Janie/Zapata Co Ind School Dist | 31,36,81,85,88 | 410 |
| Robison, Miles/Shepherd Ind School Dist | 6 | 333 | Rodriguez, Joe/Ft Bend Ind School Dist | 15 | 153 |
| Robison, Teresa/Follett Ind School Dist | 8,88,752 | 270 | Rodriguez, Joe/Ft Hancock Ind School Dist | 67 | 237 |
| Robison, Teresa/Follett Ind School Dist | 752 | 270 | Rodriguez, Juan/Abilene Ind School Dist | 3 | 362 |
| Robison, Todd/Hutto Ind School Dist | 71 | 399 | Rodriguez, Juanita/Donna Ind School Dist | 15,68,79,273 | 220 |
| Roble, Gelyn/Alief Ind School Dist | 43 | 186 | Rodriguez, Judi/Big Spring Ind School Dist | 4 | 236 |
| Robledo, David/Brownsville Ind School Dist | 19 | 66 | Rodriguez, Karla/Valley View Ind School Dist | 4 | 228 |
| Robledo, David/Santa Rosa Ind School Dist | 2,4,19 | 71 | Rodriguez, Laurie/Dickinson Ind School Dist | 58,77 | 164 |
| Robledo, Sandra/Schleicher Co Ind Sch Dist | 68 | 335 | Rodriguez, Lilly/Premont Ind School Dist | 83,752 | 249 |
| Robles Mendez, Deanna/Rio Grande City Ind Sch Dist | 2,19 | 342 | Rodriguez, Liza/Canutillo Ind School Dist | 71 | 136 |
| Robles, Janet/Pharr-San Juan-Alamo Ind SD | 19 | 226 | Rodriguez, Manuel/Valley View Ind School Dist | 20,23 | 228 |
| Robles, Maryhelen/Westhoff Ind School Dist | 2 | 122 | Rodriguez, Marcos/Harlandale Ind School Dist | 4 | 35 |
| Robles, Pete/Brazos Ind School Dist | 3,5 | 25 | Rodriguez, Maribel/Progreso Ind School Dist | 69,296 | 227 |

| | | | | | | |
|---|---|---|---|---|---|---|
| 1 Superintendent | 16 Instructional Media Svcs | 30 Adult Education | 44 Science Sec | 58 Special Education K-12 | 72 Summer School | 88 Alternative/At Risk | 277 Remedial Math K-12 |
| 2 Bus/Finance/Purchasing | 17 Chief Operations Officer | 31 Career/Sch-to-Work K-12 | 45 Math K-12 | 59 Special Education Elem | 73 Instructional Tech | 89 Multi-Cultural Curriculum | 280 Literacy Coach |
| 3 Buildings And Grounds | 18 Chief Academic Officer | 32 Career/Sch-to-Work Elem | 46 Math Elem | 60 Special Education Sec | 74 Inservice Training | 90 Social Work | 285 STEM |
| 4 Food Service | 19 Chief Financial Officer | 33 Career/Sch-to-Work Sec | 47 Math Sec | 61 Foreign/World Lang K-12 | 75 Marketing/Distributive | 91 Safety/Security | 286 Digital Learning |
| 5 Transportation | 20 Art K-12 | 34 Early Childhood Ed | 48 English/Lang Arts K-12 | 62 Foreign/World Lang Elem | 76 Info Systems | 92 Magnet School | 288 Common Core Standards |
| 6 Athletic | 21 Art Elem | 35 Health/Phys Education | 49 English/Lang Arts Elem | 63 Foreign/World Lang Sec | 77 Psychological Assess | 93 Parental Involvement | 294 Accountability |
| 7 Health Services | 22 Art Sec | 36 Guidance Services K-12 | 50 English/Lang Arts Sec | 64 Religious Education K-12 | 78 Affirmative Action | 95 Tech Prep Program | 295 Network System |
| 8 Curric/Instruct K-12 | 23 Music K-12 | 37 Guidance Services Elem | 51 Reading K-12 | 65 Religious Education Elem | 79 Student Personnel | 97 Chief Information Officer | 296 Title II Programs |
| 9 Curric/Instruct Elem | 24 Music Elem | 38 Guidance Services Sec | 52 Reading Elem | 66 Religious Education Sec | 80 Driver Ed/Safety | 98 Chief Technology Officer | 297 Webmaster |
| 10 Curric/Instruct Sec | 25 Music Sec | 39 Social Studies K-12 | 53 Reading Sec | 67 School Board President | 81 Gifted/Talented | 270 Character Education | 298 Grant Writer/Ptnrships |
| 11 Federal Program | 26 Business Education | 40 Social Studies Elem | 54 Remedial Reading K-12 | 68 Teacher Personnel | 82 Video Services | 271 Migrant Education | 750 Chief Innovation Officer |
| 12 Title I | 27 Career & Tech Ed | 41 Social Studies Sec | 55 Remedial Reading Elem | 69 Academic Assessment | 83 Substance Abuse Prev | 273 Teacher Mentor | 751 Chief of Staff |
| 13 Title V | 28 Technology Education | 42 Science K-12 | 56 Remedial Reading Sec | 70 Research/Development | 84 Erate | 274 Before/After Sch | 752 Social Emotional Learning |
| 15 Asst Superintendent | 29 Family/Consumer Science | 43 Science Elem | 57 Bilingual/ELL | 71 Public Information | 85 AIDS Education | 275 Response To Intervention | |

| NAME/District | JOB FUNCTIONS | PAGE | NAME/District | JOB FUNCTIONS | PAGE |
|---|---|---|---|---|---|
| Rowe, Christi/Central Ind School Dist | 37 | 20 | Russell, Jeff, Dr/Denton Ind School Dist | 15 | 124 |
| Rowe, Elizabeth/Chapel Hill Ind School Dist | 68 | 339 | Russell, Jeremy/Alvord Ind School Dist | 5 | 405 |
| Rowe, Ginger/Midway Ind School Dist | 81 | 283 | Russell, Jim, Dr/Burkburnett Ind Sch Dist | 11,15 | 394 |
| Rowe, Grady/Bellville Ind School Dist | 6 | 25 | Russell, Josh/Honey Grove Ind School Dist | 67 | 150 |
| Rowe, Pete/Caddo Mills Ind Sch Dist | 73 | 238 | Russell, Kayla/Bastrop Ind School Dist | 274 | 26 |
| Rowe, Pete/Mart Ind School Dist | 67 | 283 | Russell, Kisch/San Perlita Ind School Dist | 11,84,298 | 397 |
| Rowe, Rebecca/Scurry Rosser Ind School Dist | 7,85 | 256 | Russell, Kristen/Goliad Ind School Dist | 7 | 168 |
| Rowell, Tim/Flatonia Ind School Dist | 67 | 151 | Russell, Nikita, Dr/Everman Ind School Dist | 71 | 351 |
| Rower, Jennifer/Braination Schools | 3,5,17,68 | 33 | Russell, Rick/San Augustine Ind School Dist | 5 | 332 |
| Rowland, Donna/Wills Point Ind School Dist | 98 | 384 | Russell, Samantha/Gause Ind School Dist | 59,275 | 290 |
| Rowland, Jeff/Marble Falls Ind School Dist | 3 | 64 | Russell, Shawn/Early Ind School Dist | 67 | 62 |
| Royal, Tara/Miami Ind School Dist | 16,73,295 | 327 | Russell, Stewart/Livingston Ind School Dist | 3,91 | 319 |
| Royar, Greg/Argyle Ind School Dist | 16,73,76,295 | 124 | Russell, Stewart/Pasadena Ind School Dist | 91 | 203 |
| Roybal, Debbie/Denton Ind School Dist | 58 | 125 | Russell, Susanna/Garland Ind School Dist | 751 | 109 |
| Roybal, Joanette/Palmer Ind School Dist | 7 | 146 | Russell, Theresa/Gause Ind School Dist | 57 | 290 |
| Royce, Shannon/Carthage Ind School Dist | 38,270 | 314 | Russell, Tim/Harmony Ind School Dist | 6 | 379 |
| Rozelle, Carolyn/Northside Ind School Dist | 12 | 39 | **Russell, Wendi/**Navarro Ind School Dist | 1 | 178 |
| Rozneck, Paulett/Lubbock Ind School Dist | 7,83,85 | 272 | Russo, Joe/Huffman Ind School Dist | 4 | 200 |
| Rubio, Luciano/Harlingen Cons Ind School Dist | 5 | 68 | Rust, Amanda/Comfort Ind School Dist | 68 | 257 |
| Rubio, Manny/Grapevine-Colleyville Ind SD | 5 | 355 | Ruthart, Brad/Paris Ind School Dist | 91 | 262 |
| Rubio, Nancy/Dallas Ind School Dist | 92 | 102 | Rutherford, Jerrell/Springtown Ind School Dist | 3 | 316 |
| Rubio, Sandra/Honey Grove Ind School Dist | 57 | 150 | Rutherford, Leann/Irion Co Ind School Dist | 83,88,270 | 241 |
| Rucker, James/Sidney Ind School Dist | 1,11,73,83 | 94 | Rutherford, Nick/Sweetwater ISD School Dist | 76,84,95,286 | 304 |
| Rucker, Margo/Eden Cons Ind School Dist | 2 | 94 | Rutherford, Russ/Gainesville Ind School Dist | 20,23 | 95 |
| Rucker, Mindy/Henderson Ind School Dist | 45,72,277 | 330 | Rutherford, Susan/Santa Gertrudis Ind Sch Dist | 16,69,82,294 | 261 |
| Rudd, Charla, Dr/La Vega Ind School Dist | 8,15 | 282 | Rutkowski, John/Haskell Cons Ind School Dist | 73,84,286,295 | 215 |
| Ruddick, Daniel/Alvord Ind School Dist | 67 | 405 | Rutland, Marcy/Dayton Ind School Dist | 4 | 268 |
| Rudock, Michael/Peaster Ind School Dist | 5,8,11,68,69,78,83,298 | 316 | Rutledge, Albert/Argyle Ind School Dist | 5 | 124 |
| Rudolph, Nick/Peaster Ind School Dist | 288 | 316 | Rutledge, Charles/Cooper Ind School Dist | 73,76,295 | 124 |
| Rudy, Chad/Frisco Ind School Dist | 67 | 82 | Rutledge, Charles/Cooper Ind School Dist | 76 | 124 |
| Rueda, David/Anthony Ind School Dist | 6 | 136 | Rutledge, Seth/Prosper Ind School Dist | 81 | 88 |
| Ruedas, Brandy/Gustine Ind School Dist | 57 | 93 | Rutledge, Tracey/Rising Star Ind Sch Dist | 4 | 133 |
| Ruel Schafer, Deborah/Northside Ind School Dist | 31,34 | 39 | Ryan, Cheryl/Alvin Ind School Dist | 2 | 54 |
| Rueter, Jana, Dr/San Angelo Ind School Dist | 8,15 | 367 | Ryan, Corey/Leander Ind School Dist | 71 | 400 |
| Ruffin, Greggory/Wylie Ind School Dist | 35 | 364 | Ryan, Melissa/New Diana Ind School Dist | 11,298 | 379 |
| Ruffin, Mark/Normangee Ind School Dist | 1 | 267 | Ryan, Paul/Three Way Ind School Dist | 1,11,84 | 148 |
| Ruge, Carla/Denton Ind School Dist | 27,31 | 125 | Ryan, Robin, Dr/Grapevine-Colleyville Ind SD | 1 | 355 |
| Ruggeri, Mary/Lovejoy Ind School Dist | 37 | 84 | Ryan, Sara/Santa Fe Ind School Dist | 294 | 165 |
| Ruggerio, Christopher/Klein Ind School Dist | 11 | 201 | Ryan, Wonda/Colmesneil Ind School Dist | 2 | 377 |
| Ruggles, Mark, Dr/Lake Dallas Ind School Dist | 58 | 126 | Rychel, Ron/New Braunfels Ind School Dist | 11 | 92 |
| Ruiz Mills, Monica/San Marcos Cons Ind Sch Dist | 15,68,69 | 217 | Rye, Terry/Bridgeport Ind School Dist | 5 | 406 |
| Ruiz, Arnulfo/Hidalgo Ind School Dist | 271 | 222 | Ryman, Louis/Van Vleck Ind School Dist | 3 | 279 |
| Ruiz, Enrique/Brooks Co Ind School Dist | 8 | 61 | Ryon, Stephanie/College Station Ind Sch Dist | 286 | 59 |
| Ruiz, Esmarelda/Leakey Ind School Dist | 57 | 324 | | | |
| Ruiz, Manuel/Advantage Academy Admin Office | 3 | 100 | **S** | | |
| Ruiz, Oscar/San Diego Ind School Dist | 73 | 132 | Saavedra, Norma/Elgin Ind School Dist | 57 | 27 |
| Ruiz, Peter/North East Ind School Dist | 295 | 37 | Sabatino, Melissa/Austin Ind School Dist | 71 | 369 |
| Ruiz, Rene, Dr/Region 4 Ed Service Center | 74 | 213 | Sablatura, David/Spring Branch Ind School Dist | 27 | 205 |
| Ruiz, Rita/Irving Ind School Dist | 48 | 113 | Sack, Frank/Arlington Ind School Dist | 297 | 346 |
| Ruiz, Roxanne/Edgewood Ind School Dist | 4 | 34 | Sadler, Lisa/Prairie Valley Ind School Dist | 58 | 293 |
| Ruiz, Rumalda/Mission Cons Ind School Dist | 2,15 | 225 | Sadler, Melody/Groesbeck Ind School Dist | 11,58 | 269 |
| Ruiz, Sandra/Los Fresnos Cons Ind Sch Dist | 36,81,83 | 69 | Saenz, Cynthia/Edinburg Cons Ind School Dist | 57,271 | 221 |
| Ruiz, Steve/Lamesa Ind School Dist | 7 | 121 | Saenz, Eddie/Rio Grande City Ind Sch Dist | 8,16,73,76,82 | 342 |
| Ruiz, Willie/Alice Ind School Dist | 3,5,17,91 | 248 | Saenz, Eli/Waxahachie Ind School Dist | 295 | 146 |
| Rumfield, Alecia/Cotulla Ind School Dist | 58 | 262 | Saenz, Gisela, Dr/La Joya Ind School Dist | 1 | 222 |
| Rumsey, Jennifer/Bridge City Ind School Dist | 38 | 311 | Saenz, Jorge/Fabens Ind School Dist | 11,58 | 139 |
| Runnels, Daniel/Mercedes Ind School Dist | 69 | 225 | Saenz, Lory/Bovina Ind School Dist | 271 | 317 |
| Running, Mary/Cypress-Fairbanks Ind Sch Dist | 20,23 | 189 | Saenz, Zelda/Ben Bolt-Palito Blanco ISD | 67 | 248 |
| Rurup, Amanda/Eden Cons Ind School Dist | 58 | 94 | Saffel, Lisa/Rule Ind School Dist | 4 | 215 |
| Rusek, Pete/Midway Ind School Dist | 67 | 283 | Sailer, Andja/Centerville Ind School Dist | 8,13,27,36,85,88,271 | 376 |
| Rush, Stacy/Fredericksburg Ind School Dist | 68 | 167 | Saint Clair, Darrell/Snook Ind School Dist | 2,13,296,298 | 63 |
| Rushing, Elvis/West Orange-Cove Cons ISD | 16,73,82 | 312 | Salais, Mark/Boling Ind School Dist | 4 | 392 |
| Rushing, Lonnie/Clarksville Ind School Dist | 5 | 325 | Salazar-Zamora, Martha, Dr/Tomball Ind School Dist | 1 | 208 |
| Rusnak, Michele/Austin Ind School Dist | 35 | 369 | Salazar, Alex, Dr/Caldwell Ind School Dist | 15,18,57,88 | 63 |
| Russek, Charles/Moran Ind School Dist | 3,5 | 336 | Salazar, Amanda/Ft Bend Ind School Dist | 298 | 154 |
| Russell-Garcia, Bobbi/Ysleta Ind School Dist | 68 | 141 | Salazar, Gonzalo, Dr/Los Fresnos Cons Ind Sch Dist | 1 | 69 |
| Russell, Angela/Oglesby Ind School Dist | 57 | 97 | Salazar, Holly/London Ind School Dist | 58 | 308 |
| Russell, Anita/Pampa Ind School Dist | 2 | 170 | Salazar, Kevin/Goliad Ind School Dist | 6 | 168 |
| Russell, Benny/Excelsior Ind School Dist | 67 | 337 | Salazar, Marco/Advantage Academy Admin Office | 73,76,286,295 | 100 |
| Russell, Betsy/Marble Falls Ind School Dist | 68 | 64 | Salazar, Martha/La Gloria Ind School Dist | 67 | 248 |
| Russell, Billy/Hudson Ind School Dist | 3 | 20 | Salazar, Michelle/Venus Ind School Dist | 2,19,84,288 | 252 |
| Russell, Bonnie/Irving Ind School Dist | 76 | 113 | Salazar, Orlando/Corpus Christi Ind Sch Dist | 27,36,79,90,285 | 306 |
| Russell, David/Central Heights Ind Sch Dist | 1 | 300 | Salazar, Rafael/Northside Ind School Dist | 5 | 39 |
| Russell, Doug/Malta Ind School Dist | 67 | 52 | Salazar, Raul/San Antonio Ind School District | 35 | 42 |
| Russell, James/El Campo Ind School Dist | 67 | 392 | Salazar, Xochitl/Tomball Ind School Dist | 11 | 208 |
| Russell, Jeff/Wills Point Ind School Dist | 15 | 384 | Salcido, Betsabe/Ector Co Ind School Dist | 57 | 134 |

| NAME/District | JOB FUNCTIONS | PAGE | NAME/District | JOB FUNCTIONS | PAGE |
|---|---|---|---|---|---|
| Santoyo, Patricia/Hays Cons Ind School Dist | 34,274 | 216 | Schlaud, Jodie/Iowa Park Consolidated Ind SD | 8,73,285,286,288 | 395 |
| Sapia, Mike/Levelland Ind School Dist | 73,76,95,98,286,295,297 | 232 | Schlegel, Angela/Electra Ind School Dist | 58 | 394 |
| Sapp, Lorri/Midway Ind School Dist | 69 | 283 | Schlegel, Anjela/Iowa Park Consolidated Ind SD | 58 | 395 |
| Sappington, Jennifer/Region 3 Ed Service Center | 2,19 | 385 | Schluter, Traci/Cypress-Fairbanks Ind Sch Dist | 77 | 189 |
| Sappington, Nathan/Industrial Ind School Dist | 73,84,295 | 243 | Schmelzer, Tina/Medina Valley Ind School Dist | 7 | 287 |
| Sargent, Judy/Birdville Ind School Dist | 4 | 348 | Schmidt, Andrew/Garrison Ind School Dist | 3 | 301 |
| Sargent, Kristi/Itasca Ind School Dist | 69 | 231 | Schmidt, Cathy/Teague Ind School Dist | 288,296 | 161 |
| Sargent, Ricky/Hearne Ind School Dist | 6 | 327 | Schmidt, Don/Northside Ind School Dist | 15,79 | 39 |
| Sartain, J'Ann/UT Tyler University Acad Dist | 4 | 341 | Schmidt, Monica/Pringle-Morse Cons ISD | 16 | 182 |
| Sassell, Kelli/Edgewood Ind School Dist | 58 | 382 | Schmitt, Dave/Chapel Hill Ind School Dist | 6 | 366 |
| Satcher, Sharee/Palmer Ind School Dist | 4 | 146 | Schnautz, Brad, Dr/Grapevine-Colleyville Ind SD | 15 | 355 |
| Satterwhite, Cassie/Grapeland Ind School Dist | 9,34,36,69 | 235 | Schneider, Blake/Thrall Ind School Dist | 2 | 403 |
| Satterwhite, Macy/Lubbock-Cooper Ind Sch Dist | 15 | 274 | Schneider, Bubba/Damon Ind School Dist | 67 | 56 |
| Sattewhite, Cindy/Kerens Ind School Dist | 9 | 303 | Schneider, Dawn/Devine Ind School Dist | 79 | 286 |
| Sattler, Shawn/Doss Consolidated Common SD | 67 | 167 | Schneider, Kristi/Muenster Ind School Dist | 36,69,83,88,270 | 95 |
| Sauceda-Upshaw, Hedith, Dr/Conroe Ind School Dist | 8,74,273 | 294 | Schneider, Shelly/Damon Ind School Dist | 286 | 56 |
| Sauceda, Dora, Dr/Brownsville Ind School Dist | 8,15 | 66 | Schneider, Shelly/Damon Ind School Dist | 83 | 56 |
| Sauceda, Emily/Edgewood Ind School Dist | 58 | 34 | Schnider, Rodney/Dublin Ind School Dist | 1 | 147 |
| Sauceda, Evelyn/Nacogdoches Ind School Dist | 57,271 | 301 | Schnitger, Mike/Canyon Ind School Dist | 4 | 323 |
| Sauceda, Lisa/Nursery ISD School Dist | 4 | 384 | Schnucker, Kim/Dumas Ind School Dist | 274 | 298 |
| Saucedo, Arnold/Menard Ind School Dist | 67 | 288 | Schobajsa, Cheryl/Water Valley Ind School Dist | 4 | 368 |
| Saucedo, Diana/Eagle Pass Ind School Dist | 16 | 279 | Schobel, Matt/Columbus Ind School Dist | 6 | 90 |
| Saucedo, Flavio/Mumford Ind School Dist | 73 | 59 | Schoen, Kathryn/Round Top-Carmine Ind Sch Dist | 9 | 151 |
| Saucke, Mike/Hubbard Ind School Dist | 3 | 230 | Schoen, Sheila/Vidor Ind School Dist | 2 | 312 |
| Sauder, Reggie/Wellington Ind School Dist | 5 | 90 | Schoenhals, Nieda/Darrouzett Ind School Dist | 73,286,295 | 270 |
| Sauer, David/Mineola Ind School Dist | 27 | 408 | Schofield, Brenda/Region 5 Ed Service Center | 11,30 | 247 |
| Saul, Michael/Sweeny Ind School Dist | 79 | 57 | Scholz, Tracy, Dr/Alief Ind School Dist | 81 | 186 |
| Saunas, Oscar/Edinburg Cons Ind School Dist | 67 | 221 | Schonhoeft, Ross/Aransas Co Ind School Dist | 4 | 22 |
| Saunders, Eric/Tomball Ind School Dist | 3 | 208 | Schonhoeft, Ross/Ingleside Ind School Dist | 4 | 333 |
| Saunders, Karen/Morton Ind School Dist | 1 | 78 | Schoon, Steve/Quitman Ind School Dist | 3,5,91 | 408 |
| Saunders, Kimberly/Nordheim Ind School Dist | 2 | 122 | Schoppe, Theresa/Snook Ind School Dist | 68 | 63 |
| Savage, Lisa/Alvin Ind School Dist | 20,23 | 54 | Schorch, Holly/McMullen Co Ind Sch Dist | 58,83,88,270 | 286 |
| Savala, Janina/Crockett Co Cons Common SD | 11,57,288,296,298 | 98 | Schovajsa, Brandon/Round Top-Carmine Ind Sch Dist | 1,11,83 | 151 |
| Savanah, Ken/Stafford Municipal Sch Dist | 6 | 159 | Schovajsa, Chanda/Sudan Ind School Dist | 16,82 | 264 |
| Saveat, Cindy/Beaumont Ind School Dist | 79 | 244 | Schrader, Mark/Palestine Ind School Dist | 73,76,286 | 19 |
| Saveat, Rodney/Beaumont Ind School Dist | 35 | 244 | Schram, Sheila/Springtown Ind School Dist | 76 | 316 |
| Saverline, Charles/Ricardo Ind School Dist | 67 | 261 | Schramm, Hannah/Comal Ind School Dist | 74 | 91 |
| Savoy, Tim/Hays Cons Ind School Dist | 71 | 216 | Schreiber, Shirley/Northside Ind School Dist | 7 | 39 |
| Sawyer, Sandy/Robert Lee Ind School Dist | 16,73,76,286 | 79 | Schreitmueller, Joyce/Diocese of Dallas Ed Office | 11,30 | 118 |
| Saxon, Joey, Dr/Aubrey Ind School Dist | 67 | 124 | Schroader, Barbie/Borger Ind School Dist | 69,271,285 | 240 |
| Saxton, Ingia/Brock Ind School Dist | 79 | 315 | Schroeder, Dena/New Braunfels Ind School Dist | 69 | 92 |
| Saxton, Nikki/Leveretts Chapel Ind Sch Dist | 12 | 330 | Schroeder, Marshall/Conroe Ind School Dist | 3 | 294 |
| Sayavedra, Diana/Ft Bend Ind School Dist | 8,31,69,79 | 153 | Schroeder, Ronnie/Amherst Ind School Dist | 67 | 263 |
| Sayers, Georgia/Kirbyville Cons Ind Sch Dist | 1,11 | 244 | Schroedter, Jodi/Orange Grove Ind School Dist | 2 | 248 |
| Sayers, Nan/Diocese of Dallas Ed Office | 2 | 118 | Schroller, Michael/Floresville Ind School Dist | 2,15,17,91 | 403 |
| Saylack, Diana/Lovejoy Ind School Dist | 46 | 84 | Schronk, Odell/Grandview Ind School Dist | 5 | 251 |
| Saylor, Shannon, Dr/Aubrey Ind School Dist | 15,68,79 | 124 | Schuble, Henry/Columbia Brazoria ISD | 3 | 56 |
| Sazedj, Teresa, Dr/Stafford Municipal Sch Dist | 13,78,296 | 159 | Schuessler, Edwin/Westwood Ind School Dist | 73,98,286,295 | 19 |
| Scales, Kim/Hemphill Ind School Dist | 67 | 331 | Schuessler, Shelly/Llano Ind School Dist | 58 | 271 |
| Scamardo, Anthony/Mumford Ind School Dist | 67 | 59 | Schuler, Megan/Plano Ind School Dist | 7 | 85 |
| Scarborough, Michael/Mumford Ind School Dist | 6 | 59 | Schuler, Yvonne/Judson Ind School Dist | 30,274 | 36 |
| Scarbourgh, Megan/Grapevine-Colleyville Ind SD | 274 | 355 | Schulte, Glenn/Honey Grove Ind School Dist | 6 | 150 |
| Scarbrough, Carl, Dr/Alice Ind School Dist | 1 | 248 | Schulte, Ken/Brazosport Ind School Dist | 3 | 55 |
| Scates, Barbara/Excelsior Ind School Dist | 16,73,295,297 | 337 | Schulte, Samantha/Victoria Ind School Dist | 73,76,295 | 384 |
| Schaap, Mike/Smyer Ind School Dist | 6 | 232 | Schultz, Craig/Schulenburg Ind School Dist | 67 | 152 |
| Schacherl, Andrew/Shiner Ind School Dist | 67 | 265 | Schultz, Ida/Humble Ind School Dist | 2 | 200 |
| Schaefer, Carla/Victoria Ind School Dist | 69,294 | 384 | Schulz, Billy/Abbott Ind School Dist | 16,73,76,286,295 | 229 |
| Schaefer, Dan/Klein Ind School Dist | 2,19 | 201 | Schulz, Bretton/Georgetown Ind School Dist | 27 | 398 |
| Schaeffer, Kathryn/Carrollton-Farmers Branch ISD | 69,81 | 100 | Schulz, Chantel/Woodsboro Ind School Dist | 8,27,31,36,69,83,88,288 | 326 |
| Schafer, Brian/Eastland Ind School Dist | 5 | 133 | Schulz, Marcus/Splendora Ind School Dist | 6 | 297 |
| Schasteen, Karen/Clifton Ind School Dist | 58 | 49 | Schulze, Disa/Danbury Ind School Dist | 3,4,5,91 | 56 |
| Schaub, Dean/New Waverly Ind School Dist | 6 | 386 | Schulze, Lori/Odem-Edroy Ind School Dist | 10,11,285 | 334 |
| Schaum, Allison/Flour Bluff Ind School Dist | 8,12,13,15 | 307 | Schulze, Renee/Junction Ind School Dist | 11 | 259 |
| Scheffler, Dena/Sanger Ind School Dist | 3 | 130 | Schumacher, Kelly/Klein Ind School Dist | 15,68 | 201 |
| Scherr, Donna/Region 14 Ed Service Center | 275 | 364 | Schumacker, John/Gonzales Ind School Dist | 1 | 169 |
| Scherrer, Jennifer/Pleasanton Ind School Dist | 27,35,36,83 | 24 | Schumann, Carla/Comal Ind School Dist | 20,23 | 91 |
| Scherz, Deidre/Christoval Ind School Dist | 60 | 366 | Schumer, Nicole/Tyler Ind School Dist | 81 | 340 |
| Schesshir, Chrisntina/Floydada Ind School Dist | 79 | 153 | Schumpert, Melissa/San Angelo Ind School Dist | 7 | 367 |
| Schhade, Leaann/Garland Ind School Dist | 275 | 109 | Schuppert, Phillip/Forsan Ind School Dist | 3 | 237 |
| Schiele, Jim/Eagle Mtn-Saginaw Ind Sch Dist | 2,19 | 351 | Schuss, Brian/Katy Ind School Dist | 68 | 156 |
| Schiller, Dawn/Belton Ind School Dist | 69,70 | 29 | Schwake, Richard/McGregor Ind School Dist | 3,5 | 283 |
| Schilling, Karen/Farwell Ind School Dist | 69 | 317 | Schwartz, Cara/Pflugerville Ind School Dist | 58 | 374 |
| Schindewolf, Amy, Dr/Tomball Ind School Dist | 18 | 208 | Schwartz, Kevin/Austin Ind School Dist | 73,76,295 | 369 |
| Schintta, Mina, Dr/Ft Sam Houston Ind School Dist | 8,11,16,57,83,88,285,296 | 35 | Schwarz, Kim/Bosqueville Ind School Dist | 16 | 281 |
| | | | Schweitzer, Dawna/Birdville Ind School Dist | 42 | 348 |
| Schiro, Elsie/Ft Worth Ind School Dist | 19 | 352 | Schwertner, Paula/Bushland Ind School Dist | 16 | 321 |

| NAME/District | JOB FUNCTIONS | PAGE |
|---|---|---|
| Seymure, Crystal/Texhoma Ind School Dist | 271 | 338 |
| Sgulin, Anna/Tyler Ind School Dist | 57 | 340 |
| Shade, Chris/Denton Ind School Dist | 11,296,298 | 124 |
| Shafer, Brooklyn/Joshua Ind School Dist | 30 | 251 |
| Shafer, Scott/Mansfield Ind School Dist | 3 | 358 |
| Shafer, Tammy/Texas City Ind School Dist | 3 | 166 |
| Shaffer, Pam/Stanton Ind School Dist | 2 | 277 |
| Shah, Karen/Pflugerville Ind School Dist | 294 | 374 |
| Shahan, Christel/Munday Consolidated Ind SD | 27,36,69,77,88,294 | 262 |
| Shahan, Kevin/San Saba Ind School Dist | 67 | 335 |
| Shannon, Beverly/Hooks Ind School Dist | 88 | 51 |
| Shannon, Bobbie/South San Antonio Ind Sch Dist | 27 | 45 |
| Shannon, Tammy/Belton Ind School Dist | 2 | 29 |
| Sharp, Anna/San Augustine Ind School Dist | 58 | 332 |
| Sharp, Ed/Whitharral Ind School Dist | 1,11,73 | 233 |
| Sharp, Henry/Clarksville Ind School Dist | 11 | 325 |
| Sharp, Leslie/Borger Ind School Dist | 67 | 240 |
| Sharp, Randy/Bangs Ind School Dist | 3 | 61 |
| Sharp, Randy/Bastrop Ind School Dist | 73,84 | 26 |
| Sharp, Rex/Sabine Ind School Dist | 6 | 175 |
| Sharp, Vince/Anna Ind School Dist | 77,83 | 81 |
| Sharp, Vivian/West Rusk Co Cons Ind Sch Dist | 73 | 331 |
| Shatto, Steve/Pleasant Grove Ind School Dist | 3 | 52 |
| Shaver, Melissa/Region 16 Ed Service Center | 34 | 324 |
| Shaw, Amy/Trenton Ind School Dist | 31,83,85,88,273 | 151 |
| Shaw, Brent/Alvin Ind School Dist | 69,294 | 54 |
| Shaw, Cameron/Dawson Ind School Dist | 73,76,295 | 302 |
| Shaw, Connie/Seymour Ind School Dist | 4 | 28 |
| Shaw, Debbie/Midland Ind School Dist | 20,23 | 288 |
| Shaw, Diane/Garner Ind School Dist | 7,11,16,34,69 | 315 |
| Shaw, Erin/Wheeler Ind School Dist | 69 | 394 |
| Shaw, Gary/Springtown Ind School Dist | 2,19 | 316 |
| Shaw, Kayla/Klein Ind School Dist | 36,85 | 202 |
| Shaw, Pamela/Ft Bend Ind School Dist | 93 | 154 |
| Shaw, Pamela/Plemons-Stinnett-Phillips CISD | 4 | 241 |
| Shaw, Teresa/Calallen Ind School Dist | 7,85 | 305 |
| Shea, Tracy/Cleburne Ind School Dist | 286 | 250 |
| Shear, Pat/Region 4 Ed Service Center | 73,76 | 213 |
| Shedd, Tammy/Aransas Pass Ind School Dist | 295 | 333 |
| Sheeran, Diana/Brooks Co Ind School Dist | 11,88 | 61 |
| Sheets, Gene/Smyer Ind School Dist | 4 | 232 |
| Sheets, Sean/Alamo Heights Ind School Dist | 4 | 33 |
| Sheffield, Chad/Bloomburg Ind School Dist | 6 | 73 |
| Sheffield, Dani/Aldine Ind School Dist | 4 | 184 |
| Sheffield, Maria, Dr/Ft Worth Ind School Dist | 15,58 | 352 |
| Sheffield, Mary/Liberty Hill Ind School Dist | 4 | 401 |
| Sheffield, Scott/Whitney Ind School Dist | 5 | 231 |
| Sheffield, Vincent/El Paso Ind School Dist | 8,15,68,78 | 137 |
| Sheilds, Mike/McGregor Ind School Dist | 6 | 283 |
| Shelby, Debra/Texarkana Ind School Dist | 74 | 53 |
| Sheldon, Gwen/Azle Ind School Dist | 752 | 348 |
| Shelhamer, Gene, Dr/Region 14 Ed Service Center | 67 | 364 |
| Shelton, Brad/Midway Ind School Dist | 6 | 283 |
| Shelton, Gail/Gatesville Ind School Dist | 4 | 96 |
| Shelton, Heath/Leary Ind School Dist | 73,286 | 51 |
| Shelton, Holly/Amarillo Ind School Dist | 71 | 320 |
| Shelton, Kenneth/Pittsburg Ind School Dist | 5 | 72 |
| Shelton, Mary/Garland Ind School Dist | 50 | 109 |
| Shelton, Theresa/Laneville Ind School Dist | 1,11 | 330 |
| Shelton, Wendy/Waskom Ind School Dist | 57 | 214 |
| Shenault, David/Henderson Ind School Dist | 71,97 | 330 |
| Sheneman, Laura/Region 1 Ed Service Center | 16 | 229 |
| Shepard, Linda/Katy Ind School Dist | 57 | 156 |
| Shepard, Michael/Community Ind School Dist | 67 | 81 |
| Shepard, Nicole/Klein Ind School Dist | 16,71 | 201 |
| Shepherd, Cherly/Harleton Ind School Dist | 68 | 213 |
| Shepherd, Leslee/Keller Ind School Dist | 27 | 357 |
| Shepherd, Quintin, Dr/Victoria Ind School Dist | 1 | 384 |
| Shepherd, Tyler/Big Spring Ind School Dist | 11,34,57,58,88,271,296,298 | 236 |
| Shepherd, Wayne/Lone Oak Ind School Dist | 3 | 239 |
| Shepler, Gail/Mathis Ind School Dist | 2 | 334 |
| Sheppard, Scott, Dr/Huntsville Ind School Dist | 1 | 386 |
| Sheppard, Shelli/Madisonville Cons ISD | 27,38,69,75 | 276 |
| Sheppard, Sondra/Gause Ind School Dist | 4 | 290 |
| Sherman, Angie/Victoria Ind School Dist | 5 | 384 |
| Sherman, Julie, Dr/Port Arthur Ind School Dist | 77 | 246 |
| Sherman, Robin/Lockney Independent Sch Dist | 280 | 153 |
| Shermer, Joei/Wylie Ind School Dist | 9,54 | 88 |
| Sherrill, Kevin/Sonora Ind School Dist | 6 | 345 |
| Sherrin, Rachelle/Carrollton-Farmers Branch ISD | 4 | 100 |
| Sherrod, Tim/Wichita Falls Ind School Dist | 2,19 | 395 |
| Sherry, Remona/Kermit Ind School Dist | 7 | 405 |
| Sherwood, Peg/Spring Ind School Dist | 58 | 207 |
| Shetter, Denise, Dr/Kermit Ind School Dist | 1 | 405 |
| Shew, Dennis/Tarkington Ind School Dist | 2,15 | 269 |
| Shieldknight, Kristen/Spearman Ind School Dist | 73 | 182 |
| Shields, Kenneth/Shamrock Ind School Dist | 12,57 | 393 |
| Shields, Kenneth/Shamrock Ind School Dist | 1 | 393 |
| Shields, Sharon, Dr/La Vega Ind School Dist | 1 | 282 |
| Shields, Tammy/Celeste Ind School Dist | 2 | 239 |
| Shiels, Steven/Ft Bend Ind School Dist | 36,79,90,270,271 | 153 |
| Shiller, Todd/Belton Ind School Dist | 15,68,78,273 | 29 |
| Shimer, Ellen/Humble Ind School Dist | 34 | 200 |
| Shimomura, Leslie/Duncanville Ind School Dist | 16 | 108 |
| Shipley, Nancy/Krum Ind School Dist | 11,15 | 126 |
| Shipman, Bryan/Blackwell Cons Ind Sch Dist | 8,11,31,36,58,69,83 | 304 |
| Shipman, Lu Ann/Schleicher Co Ind Sch Dist | 16 | 335 |
| Shipman, Tammy/Huckabay Ind School Dist | 2 | 147 |
| Shipp, Greg/Conroe Ind School Dist | 27,31 | 294 |
| Shipp, Susan/Carrollton-Farmers Branch ISD | 42,280,285 | 100 |
| Shirey, Kandy/Scurry Rosser Ind School Dist | 9,34 | 256 |
| Shirley, Crystal/Terrell Ind School Dist | 2 | 256 |
| Shirley, Todd/Prosper Ind School Dist | 18 | 88 |
| Shivers, Sherry/Wortham Ind School Dist | 2 | 161 |
| Shock, Carly/Region 3 Ed Service Center | 4 | 385 |
| Shocklee, Lesa/Mansfield Ind School Dist | 58 | 358 |
| Shockner, Kim/Troup Ind School Dist | 274 | 340 |
| Shoemake, James/McKinney Ind School Dist | 4 | 84 |
| Shoemaker, Don/Central Heights Ind Sch Dist | 67 | 300 |
| Shoesmith, Tyler/North East Ind School Dist | 83,275,752 | 37 |
| Shofner, Cindy/Bloomburg Ind School Dist | 79 | 73 |
| Shofner, Kristi/New Caney Ind School Dist | 8 | 296 |
| Sholmire, Fred/Spring Ind School Dist | 3 | 207 |
| Shoppach, Kyle/Bruceville-Eddy Ind Sch Dist | 6 | 281 |
| Shore, Julie/North East Ind School Dist | 20,23 | 37 |
| Short, Scott/Ennis Ind School Dist | 16,28,73,76,82,84,286 | 144 |
| Shoulders, Kim/New Waverly Ind School Dist | 58 | 386 |
| Showell, Joseph/Birdville Ind School Dist | 79,93 | 348 |
| Shubert, Clyde/Dublin Ind School Dist | 3,5 | 147 |
| Shudde, Doug/Northside Ind School Dist | 16,73 | 39 |
| Shulman, Jackie, Dr/Santa Fe Ind School Dist | 8,12,34,288 | 165 |
| Shults, Jamie/Mission Cons Ind School Dist | 42 | 225 |
| Shultz, Angela/Sudan Ind School Dist | 57 | 264 |
| Shultz, Josh/Westwood Ind School Dist | 3,91 | 19 |
| Shuman, Jacqueline, Dr/Santa Fe Ind School Dist | 15 | 165 |
| Shurbet, Barbara/Mount Vernon Ind School Dist | 2 | 160 |
| Shute, Christian/Slaton Ind School Dist | 81 | 275 |
| Sibberson, Michael/Lometa Ind School Dist | 5,51 | 264 |
| Sibley, Derick/Pleasant Grove Ind School Dist | 2,11 | 52 |
| Sibley, Upenda/Lancaster Ind School Dist | 4 | 114 |
| Siem, Jordan/Azle Ind School Dist | 11 | 348 |
| Sifford, Nicole/Dew Ind School Dist | 7 | 160 |
| Sigee, Alicia/West Orange-Cove Cons ISD | 79 | 312 |
| Sigge, Thomas/Beaumont Ind School Dist | 67 | 244 |
| Sigler, Melissa/Everman Ind School Dist | 47 | 351 |
| Signaigo, Stacy/Manor Ind School Dist | 34 | 373 |
| Siler, Jill, Dr/Gunter Ind School Dist | 1 | 171 |
| Siler, Rebecca/Bronte Ind School Dist | 11,73,286,295,296,297 | 79 |
| Siler, Tim/Bronte Ind School Dist | 1,11 | 79 |
| Silguero, Alberto/Gregory-Portland Ind Sch Dist | 2 | 333 |
| Siller, Regina/Hawley Ind School Dist | 27 | 253 |
| Sills, Dawn/Temple Ind School Dist | 69,294 | 32 |
| Silva, Allison/Bay City Ind School Dist | 71 | 278 |
| Silva, Hector/College Station Ind Sch Dist | 5 | 59 |
| Silva, Julie/South San Antonio Ind Sch Dist | 58 | 45 |
| Silva, Lili/McAllen Ind School Dist | 27,31 | 224 |
| Silva, Maria/Canutillo Ind School Dist | 57,271 | 136 |
| Silva, Maria/Cleveland Ind School Dist | 8,11,16,57,69,285,294,296 | 267 |
| Silva, Melana/Calallen Ind School Dist | 10 | 305 |
| Silva, Ralph, Dr/Corpus Christi Ind Sch Dist | 273 | 306 |
| Silva, Rosina/Laredo Ind School Dist | 36,88 | 389 |
| Silva, Stephan/Skidmore Tynan Ind SD | 6 | 29 |

| | | | | |
|---|---|---|---|---|
| 1 Superintendent | 16 Instructional Media Svcs | 30 Adult Education | 44 Science Sec | 58 Special Education K-12 | 72 Summer School | 88 Alternative/At Risk | 277 Remedial Math K-12 |
| 2 Bus/Finance/Purchasing | 17 Chief Operations Officer | 31 Career/Sch-to-Work K-12 | 45 Math K-12 | 59 Special Education Elem | 73 Instructional Tech | 89 Multi-Cultural Curriculum | 280 Literacy Coach |
| 3 Buildings And Grounds | 18 Chief Academic Officer | 32 Career/Sch-to-Work Elem | 46 Math Elem | 60 Special Education Sec | 74 Inservice Training | 90 Social Work | 285 STEM |
| 4 Food Service | 19 Chief Financial Officer | 33 Career/Sch-to-Work Sec | 47 Math Sec | 61 Foreign/World Lang K-12 | 75 Marketing/Distributive | 91 Safety/Security | 286 Digital Learning |
| 5 Transportation | 20 Art K-12 | 34 Early Childhood Ed | 48 English/Lang Arts K-12 | 62 Foreign/World Lang Elem | 76 Info Systems | 92 Magnet School | 288 Common Core Standards |
| 6 Athletic | 21 Art Elem | 35 Health/Phys Education | 49 English/Lang Arts Elem | 63 Foreign/World Lang Sec | 77 Psychological Assess | 93 Parental Involvement | 294 Accountability |
| 7 Health Services | 22 Art Sec | 36 Guidance Services K-12 | 50 English/Lang Arts Sec | 64 Religious Education K-12 | 78 Affirmative Action | 95 Tech Prep Program | 295 Network System |
| 8 Curric/Instruct K-12 | 23 Music K-12 | 37 Guidance Services Elem | 51 Reading K-12 | 65 Religious Education Elem | 79 Student Personnel | 97 Chief Information Officer | 296 Title II Programs |
| 9 Curric/Instruct Elem | 24 Music Elem | 38 Guidance Services Sec | 52 Reading Elem | 66 Religious Education Sec | 80 Driver Ed/Safety | 98 Chief Technology Officer | 297 Webmaster |
| 10 Curric/Instruct Sec | 25 Music Sec | 39 Social Studies K-12 | 53 Reading Sec | 67 School Board President | 81 Gifted/Talented | 270 Character Education | 298 Grant Writer/Ptnrships |
| 11 Federal Program | 26 Business Education | 40 Social Studies Elem | 54 Remedial Reading K-12 | 68 Teacher Personnel | 82 Video Services | 271 Migrant Education | 750 Chief Innovation Officer |
| 12 Title I | 27 Career & Tech Ed | 41 Social Studies Sec | 55 Remedial Reading Elem | 69 Academic Assessment | 83 Substance Abuse Prev | 273 Teacher Mentor | 751 Chief of Staff |
| 13 Title V | 28 Technology Education | 42 Science K-12 | 56 Remedial Reading Sec | 70 Research/Development | 84 Erate | 274 Before/After Sch | 752 Social Emotional Learning |
| 15 Asst Superintendent | 29 Family/Consumer Science | 43 Science Elem | 57 Bilingual/ELL | 71 Public Information | 85 AIDS Education | 275 Response To Intervention | |

| NAME/District | JOB FUNCTIONS | PAGE |
|---|---|---|
| Smith, Cade, Dr/Brock Ind School Dist | 1 | 315 |
| Smith, Calvin/Timpson Ind School Dist | 285 | 338 |
| Smith, Carol/Wylie Ind School Dist | 2,11,296,298 | 364 |
| Smith, Chantay/Aldine Ind School Dist | 46 | 184 |
| Smith, Charlotte/Belton Ind School Dist | 7 | 29 |
| Smith, Chris/Brownfield Ind Sch Dist | 1 | 364 |
| Smith, Chris/Katy Ind School Dist | 2,19 | 155 |
| Smith, Christy/May Ind School Dist | 58 | 62 |
| Smith, Cliff/Refugio Ind School Dist | 73,295 | 326 |
| Smith, Craig/Hitchcock Ind School Dist | 6 | 165 |
| Smith, Craig/Poteet Ind School Dist | 297 | 24 |
| Smith, Dalton/Bullard Ind School Dist | 3,5,73 | 339 |
| Smith, Dalton/Bullard Ind School Dist | 5 | 339 |
| Smith, Darren/East Chambers Ind School Dist | 3,5,91 | 76 |
| Smith, David/Keller Ind School Dist | 4 | 357 |
| Smith, David/Luling Ind School Dist | 285 | 65 |
| Smith, David/Troup Ind School Dist | 8,11,57,69,83,88,273 | 340 |
| Smith, Dawn/Coldspring-Oakhurst Cons ISD | 4 | 332 |
| Smith, Dayna, Dr/Orangefield Ind School Dist | 11,34,57,58,88,271,275,296 | 312 |
| Smith, Deborah/Lubbock-Cooper Ind Sch Dist | 27 | 274 |
| Smith, Derek/Alba-Golden Ind School Dist | 6 | 407 |
| Smith, DeWitt/Region 18 Ed Service Center | 1 | 290 |
| Smith, Doug/Frenship Ind School Dist | 58 | 272 |
| Smith, Ella/Keene Ind School Dist | 4 | 251 |
| Smith, Eric/Natalia Ind School Dist | 67 | 287 |
| Smith, Gail, Dr/Lubbock Ind School Dist | 81 | 272 |
| Smith, Glen/Eula Ind School Dist | 3,91 | 66 |
| Smith, Greg, Dr/Clear Creek Ind School Dist | 1 | 162 |
| Smith, Gwinn/Comanche Ind School Dist | 37 | 93 |
| Smith, Heidi/Caddo Mills Ind Sch Dist | 2 | 238 |
| Smith, Jack/Jefferson Ind School Dist | 5 | 277 |
| Smith, Jacquelyn/Avinger Ind School Dist | 1,11 | 73 |
| Smith, James/Birdville Ind School Dist | 9,34 | 348 |
| Smith, Jana/Tioga Ind School Dist | 57,271 | 172 |
| Smith, Jason/Joshua Ind School Dist | 295 | 251 |
| Smith, Jay/Dime Box Ind School Dist | 8,73 | 266 |
| Smith, Jeff/Hale Center Ind School Dist | 6 | 180 |
| Smith, Jeff/Plano Ind School Dist | 6 | 85 |
| Smith, Jennifer/College Station Ind Sch Dist | 45 | 59 |
| Smith, Jennifer/Longview Ind School Dist | 16,73 | 174 |
| Smith, Jeremy, Dr/Quitman Ind School Dist | 67 | 408 |
| Smith, Jim/Mason Ind School Dist | 67 | 278 |
| Smith, Joe/Roscoe Collegiate Ind Sch Dist | 3,5 | 304 |
| Smith, John/Priddy Ind School Dist | 286 | 292 |
| Smith, Johnna/Bridge City Ind School Dist | 37 | 311 |
| Smith, Josh/Hudson Ind School Dist | 76,295 | 20 |
| Smith, Julie/Diboll Ind School Dist | 16 | 20 |
| Smith, Kamber/Shallowater Ind School Dist | 38 | 274 |
| Smith, Karen/Cypress-Fairbanks Ind Sch Dist | 15,19 | 189 |
| Smith, Kayne/Cypress-Fairbanks Ind Sch Dist | 5 | 188 |
| Smith, Keith/Madisonville Cons ISD | 1 | 276 |
| Smith, Kelli/Olton Ind School Dist | 16,82 | 263 |
| Smith, Kelly/Olton Ind School Dist | 8,31,58 | 263 |
| Smith, Kimberly/Alief Ind School Dist | 71 | 186 |
| Smith, Kimberly/Frisco Ind School Dist | 2,19 | 82 |
| Smith, Kisha/Winnsboro Ind School Dist | 4 | 408 |
| Smith, Kristy/Whitney Ind School Dist | 16,73,297 | 231 |
| Smith, Lamont, Dr/Elkhart Ind School Dist | 1 | 18 |
| Smith, Lamont, Dr/Lancaster Ind School Dist | 294 | 114 |
| Smith, Lana/Livingston Ind School Dist | 9,11,57,68,79,83,88,751 | 319 |
| Smith, Laney/Madisonville Cons ISD | 73 | 276 |
| Smith, Larry/Blanket Ind School Dist | 16,73 | 61 |
| Smith, Larry/Canadian Ind School Dist | 67 | 218 |
| Smith, Larry/Cleveland Ind School Dist | 5 | 267 |
| Smith, Larry/Mason Ind School Dist | 5,88 | 278 |
| Smith, Laura/Pittsburg Ind School Dist | 7 | 72 |
| Smith, Lepaula/Keller Ind School Dist | 17 | 357 |
| Smith, Lesley/China Spring Ind School Dist | 8 | 281 |
| Smith, Libby/Devers Ind School Dist | 6 | 268 |
| Smith, Lisha/Carlisle Ind School Dist | 31,36 | 330 |
| Smith, Lloyd/Murchison Ind Sch Dist | 67 | 219 |
| Smith, Louanne/Pleasant Grove Ind School Dist | 38 | 52 |
| Smith, Luke/Deweyville Ind School Dist | 67 | 311 |
| Smith, Marc, Dr/Duncanville Ind School Dist | 1 | 108 |
| Smith, Margaret/Bremond Ind School Dist | 4 | 327 |

| NAME/District | JOB FUNCTIONS | PAGE |
|---|---|---|
| Smith, Marie/West Sabine Ind Sch Dist | 57 | 332 |
| Smith, Marty/Paducah Ind School Dist | 3 | 97 |
| Smith, Mary/Aledo Ind School Dist | 27 | 315 |
| Smith, Matt/Humble Ind School Dist | 37 | 200 |
| **Smith, Matt, Dr**/Belton Ind School Dist | 1 | 29 |
| Smith, Melissa/Buffalo Ind School Dist | 88 | 266 |
| Smith, Melissa, Dr/Lamar Cons Ind School Dist | 88 | 157 |
| Smith, Michael/Comal Ind School Dist | 7,35 | 91 |
| Smith, Michael/Savoy Ind School Dist | 10 | 150 |
| Smith, Michelle/Lytle Ind School Dist | 1 | 24 |
| Smith, Monica/Floydada Ind School Dist | 8 | 153 |
| Smith, Monica/Irving Ind School Dist | 76 | 113 |
| Smith, Nicole/Waskom Ind School Dist | 8,69,288,298 | 214 |
| Smith, Penny/Floresville Ind School Dist | 67 | 403 |
| Smith, Rachel/Humble Ind School Dist | 46 | 200 |
| Smith, Randy/Silsbee Ind School Dist | 6 | 183 |
| Smith, Ric/San Felipe-Del Rio Cons Ind SD | 6 | 381 |
| Smith, Robert/Miller Grove Ind School Dist | 3 | 234 |
| Smith, Robin/Fairfield Ind School Dist | 76 | 160 |
| Smith, Ron/Lefors Ind School Dist | 3 | 170 |
| Smith, Roy/Brady Ind School Dist | 3 | 280 |
| Smith, Ryan/Round Rock Ind School Dist | 8 | 401 |
| Smith, Sandra/Greenwood Ind School Dist | 4 | 288 |
| Smith, Sandra/West Rusk Co Cons Ind Sch Dist | 67 | 331 |
| Smith, Shane/Irving Ind School Dist | 73 | 113 |
| Smith, Sheila/Centerville Ind School Dist | 58 | 376 |
| Smith, Sheila/Lewisville Ind School Dist | 68 | 126 |
| Smith, Shelia/Allen Ind School Dist | 15,68 | 80 |
| Smith, Sherri/Duncanville Ind School Dist | 74 | 108 |
| Smith, Stephanie/Liberty Ind School Dist | 68 | 269 |
| Smith, Stephanie/Priddy Ind School Dist | 58 | 292 |
| Smith, Steve/Leander Ind School Dist | 4 | 399 |
| Smith, Steven/Eustace Ind School Dist | 6 | 219 |
| Smith, Steven/Killeen Ind School Dist | 4 | 30 |
| Smith, Steven/Nueces Canyon Cons Ind SD | 3,5 | 135 |
| Smith, Stuart/Pampa Ind School Dist | 5 | 170 |
| Smith, Susan/Saltillo Ind School Dist | 4 | 234 |
| Smith, Tammy/Cushing Ind School Dist | 79 | 300 |
| Smith, Tammy/Midway Ind School Dist | 79 | 283 |
| Smith, Terri/Hurst-Euless-Bedford ISD | 50 | 356 |
| Smith, Todd/Azle Ind School Dist | 15 | 348 |
| Smith, Tony/Garner Ind School Dist | 6 | 315 |
| Smith, Tracy/Bishop Cons Ind School Dist | 39,48 | 305 |
| Smith, Tracy/Carrollton-Farmers Branch ISD | 9,15,275 | 100 |
| Smith, Tracy/Groesbeck Ind School Dist | 37 | 269 |
| Smith, Travis/New Home Ind School Dist | 67 | 275 |
| Smithers, Ludonna/Commerce Independent Sch Dist | 68,71,297 | 239 |
| Smithey, Theresa/Waxahachie Ind School Dist | 44 | 146 |
| Snapp, Julie/Howe Ind School Dist | 2 | 171 |
| Sneed, Kimberly/Flour Bluff Ind School Dist | 71 | 307 |
| Snell, Michelle/Joshua Ind School Dist | 10 | 251 |
| Snell, Steven/Liberty Hill Ind School Dist | 1 | 401 |
| Snelson, John/Dickinson Ind School Dist | 6 | 164 |
| Snider, Dianne/Gorman Ind School Dist | 68 | 133 |
| Snider, Kimberlyn/Neches Ind School Dist | 11 | 18 |
| Snider, Randy/Neches Ind School Dist | 1 | 18 |
| Snipes, David/Aquilla Ind School Dist | 67 | 230 |
| Snodgrass, Christie/Lohn Ind School Dist | 11,73 | 280 |
| Snodgrass, Kelley/Glen Rose Ind School Dist | 67 | 342 |
| Snook, Joshua/Winona Ind School Dist | 91 | 341 |
| Snow, Billy/Dallas Ind School Dist | 70,750 | 102 |
| Snow, Zach/Royse City Ind School Dist | 27,73,285,286 | 328 |
| Snyder, Dale/Hillsboro Ind School Dist | 2 | 230 |
| Snyder, Steven/Ingleside Ind School Dist | 71 | 334 |
| Snyder, Wayne/Region 8 Ed Service Center | 76 | 72 |
| Sodolak, Amy/Brazos Ind School Dist | 7 | 25 |
| Soileau, Benny, Dr/Huffman Ind School Dist | 1 | 200 |
| Soles, Nancy/Sweetwater ISD School Dist | 7,85 | 304 |
| Solice, Davette/Tornillo Ind School Dist | 2 | 141 |
| Solis, Cynthia/La Joya Ind School Dist | 74 | 222 |
| Solis, Emily/Frenship Ind School Dist | 71 | 272 |
| Solis, John/Raymondville Ind Sch Dist | 67 | 397 |
| Solis, Joshua/Bay City Ind School Dist | 73,76,98,295 | 278 |
| Solis, Juan/Terrell Ind School Dist | 79 | 256 |
| Solis, Judith, Dr/San Antonio Ind School Dist | 15 | 42 |
| Solis, Margarita/Community Ind School Dist | 57 | 81 |

| NAME/District | JOB FUNCTIONS | PAGE |
|---|---|---|
| Solis, Ricardo/Rio Grande City Ind Sch Dist | 5 | 342 |
| Solis, Rosie/San Diego Ind School Dist | 58,76 | 132 |
| Solis, Sulema/Pharr-San Juan-Alamo Ind SD | 7,35,85 | 226 |
| Solis, Yolanda/Karnes City Ind School Dist | 36 | 253 |
| Soliz-Garcia, Velma/Gregory-Portland Ind Sch Dist | 8,15,68 | 333 |
| Soliz, Lori/Sinton Ind School Dist | 7 | 334 |
| Soliz, Rosie/Benavides Ind School Dist | 58 | 132 |
| Solley, Donna/Birdville Ind School Dist | 8 | 348 |
| Solorio, Luis/Harlingen Cons Ind School Dist | 35 | 68 |
| Solorzano, Gina/Marble Falls Ind School Dist | 5 | 64 |
| Somer, Kimberly/Wharton Ind School Dist | 58,90 | 393 |
| Sommerfeld, Tiffany/Waco Ind School Dist | 36 | 284 |
| Sonia, Sonya/Bay City Ind School Dist | 34,58 | 278 |
| Sonnenburg, Jay/Katy Ind School Dist | 16 | 156 |
| Sonnier, Beth/Little Cypress Mauriceville SD | 68 | 311 |
| Sonntag, Shelley/Valley Mills Ind School Dist | 5 | 50 |
| Sons, Dana/Lewisville Ind School Dist | 73 | 126 |
| Sons, David/Region 11 Ed Service Center | 76 | 362 |
| Sooby, Donna/Ferris Ind School Dist | 295 | 145 |
| Soote, Nikole/Dumas Ind School Dist | 10,280 | 298 |
| Sootoo, Tiffany/Bellville Ind School Dist | 5 | 25 |
| Sopher, Veronica/Ft Bend Ind School Dist | 71 | 153 |
| Sophie, Weinheimer/Smithville Ind School Dist | 7 | 27 |
| Sormani, Robert/Hutto Ind School Dist | 8,15,68,79,88,288 | 399 |
| Sorola, Anthony, Dr/Lufkin Ind School Dist | 13,15,78 | 21 |
| Sorrell, Tom/Agua Dulce Ind School Dist | 73,76,84,286 | 305 |
| Sorrells, Gary/Lone Oak Ind School Dist | 2,5 | 239 |
| Sorters, Erica/Normangee Ind School Dist | 7 | 267 |
| Sosa, Juan/San Benito Cons Ind Sch Dist | 91 | 70 |
| Sosa, Luci/Corpus Christi Ind Sch Dist | 43 | 306 |
| Sotelo, Mario/Charlotte Ind School Dist | 1,83 | 23 |
| Soto, Arceli/San Benito Cons Ind Sch Dist | 4 | 70 |
| Soto, Donna/Livingston Ind School Dist | 5 | 319 |
| **Soto, Gerardo/**Harlandale Ind School Dist | 1 | 35 |
| Soto, Mark/San Marcos Cons Ind Sch Dist | 6 | 216 |
| Soto, Roy/Edgewood Ind School Dist | 67 | 382 |
| Souder, Diane/Wellington Ind School Dist | 2 | 90 |
| Southard, Brett/Littlefield Ind School Dist | 58 | 263 |
| Southard, Jon/Blooming Grove Ind School Dist | 67 | 302 |
| Southard, Krystal/Holliday Ind School Dist | 59 | 22 |
| Southard, Krystal/Holliday Ind School Dist | 59 | 22 |
| Southern, Jennifer/Nursery ISD School Dist | 12 | 384 |
| Southern, Rodney/Huntsville Ind School Dist | 6 | 386 |
| Sowell, Amanda/Broaddus Ind School Dist | 7,85 | 332 |
| Sowers, Stan/Eustace Ind School Dist | 5,15 | 219 |
| Soza, Chris/Beeville Ind School Dist | 6 | 28 |
| Spain, Bobby/Hempstead Ind School Dist | 6 | 387 |
| Spakes, Roger/Winnsboro Ind School Dist | 3,5 | 408 |
| Spakes, Tina/Strawn Ind School Dist | 67 | 314 |
| Spalloni, Natalie/Canutillo Ind School Dist | 48 | 136 |
| Spann, David/McKinney Ind School Dist | 71,73,97 | 84 |
| Sparkman, Keith/Winona Ind School Dist | 88 | 341 |
| Sparks, John/Big Spring Ind School Dist | 3,5 | 236 |
| Sparks, Karla/Somerville Ind School Dist | 1,11,83 | 63 |
| Sparks, Katie/East Chambers Ind School Dist | 7 | 76 |
| Sparks, Larry/West Ind School Dist | 67 | 285 |
| Sparks, Marcy/Socorro Ind School Dist | 16 | 140 |
| Sparks, Trey/College Station Ind Sch Dist | 295 | 59 |
| Sparks, Troy/Three Way Ind School Dist | 5 | 148 |
| Sparks, Viki/Region 7 Ed Service Center | 11 | 176 |
| Sparling, Rhonda/McLean Ind School Dist | 4 | 170 |
| Spaulding, Karen/Carrollton-Farmers Branch ISD | 46,277 | 100 |
| Spear, Misti/Wichita Falls Ind School Dist | 9 | 395 |
| Spear, Rick/Gordon Ind School Dist | 73,295 | 313 |
| Spearman, Jill/Leveretts Chapel Ind Sch Dist | 2 | 330 |
| Spears, Britt/Lubbock-Cooper Ind Sch Dist | 68 | 274 |
| Spears, Kermit/Ft Bend Ind School Dist | 68 | 153 |

| NAME/District | JOB FUNCTIONS | PAGE |
|---|---|---|
| Spears, Leann/Era Ind School Dist | 81 | 94 |
| Spears, Norman/Aransas Co Ind School Dist | 3,16,73 | 22 |
| Speck, Mark/Rockwall Ind School Dist | 68,74,79 | 328 |
| Speck, Paige/Pringle-Morse Cons ISD | 2,12,84,97,298 | 182 |
| Speed, Jo Ann/Navarro Ind School Dist | 2 | 178 |
| Speight, Jacob/Waskom Ind School Dist | 67 | 214 |
| Spence, Keari/Rockdale Ind School Dist | 7 | 290 |
| **Spencer, Andre, Dr/**Manor Ind School Dist | 1 | 373 |
| Spencer, Beverley/Lampasas Ind School Dist | 5 | 264 |
| Spencer, Bill/Elysian Fields Ind School Dist | 73,84 | 213 |
| Spencer, Helen/Harris Co Dept of Ed | 295 | 184 |
| Spencer, Kellie/Cedar Hill Ind School Dist | 15 | 101 |
| Spencer, Kim/Malakoff Ind School Dist | 2 | 219 |
| Spencer, Lori/Poth Ind School Dist | 58,752 | 404 |
| Spencer, Paul/Boerne Ind School Dist | 5 | 257 |
| Spencer, Reggy/Colorado Ind School Dist | 1 | 292 |
| Spencer, Tamara/Pflugerville Ind School Dist | 71 | 374 |
| Spenrath, Brad/Comfort Ind School Dist | 67 | 257 |
| Spicer, Kim, Dr/Wylie Ind School Dist | 15 | 88 |
| Spieckerman, Sutton/Zephyr Ind School Dist | 58 | 62 |
| Spikes, Bob/Lueders-Avoca Ind School Dist | 1,84 | 253 |
| Spikes, Tricia/Trent Isn School Dist | 73,295 | 363 |
| Spikeston, J/Gainesville Ind School Dist | 8 | 95 |
| Spindler, Carol/Sterling City Ind School Dist | 4 | 344 |
| Spinhirne, David/Channing Ind School Dist | 67 | 214 |
| Spinks, Sharon/Schleicher Co Ind Sch Dist | 285,298 | 335 |
| Spinn, Craig/Region 13 Ed Service Center | 15 | 376 |
| Spinner, Tracy/Austin Ind School Dist | 7 | 369 |
| Spivey, Chris/Sands Consolidated ISD | 3 | 121 |
| Spivey, Jana/Sands Consolidated ISD | 4 | 121 |
| Spivey, Reid/Garrison Ind School Dist | 1 | 301 |
| Spivey, Terry/Pleasant Grove Ind School Dist | 5,91 | 52 |
| Spoor, Jodi/Boerne Ind School Dist | 8,15,36,74,81,88,273 | 257 |
| Spradlin, Tony/Wylie Ind School Dist | 73 | 364 |
| Sprague, Mark/Krum Ind School Dist | 73 | 126 |
| Sprague, Roy/Cypress-Fairbanks Ind Sch Dist | 3,15,17 | 188 |
| Spreen, Mimi/Palestine Ind School Dist | 4 | 18 |
| Sprinkle, Laura/Region 3 Ed Service Center | 286 | 385 |
| Sprinkles, Kevin/Cameron Ind School Dist | 1 | 290 |
| Sprouse, David, Dr/Kerrville Ind School Dist | 67 | 259 |
| Spurlin, Cliff/McDade Ind School Dist | 16,73,295,297 | 27 |
| Spurlock, Becky/Azle Ind School Dist | 6 | 348 |
| Squires, Ron/Nordheim Ind School Dist | 73 | 122 |
| Squirrell, Vanessa/Galena Park Ind School Dist | 752 | 191 |
| Sriddle, Norma/Natalia Ind School Dist | 2 | 287 |
| Sriritarat, Rapee/Savoy Ind School Dist | 295 | 150 |
| Sritairat, Rapee/Savoy Ind School Dist | 73,84 | 150 |
| St Andre, Jeff/City View Ind School Dist | 73,84,295 | 394 |
| Stacey, Theresa/Morgan Ind School Dist | 67 | 50 |
| Stack, Becky/Deer Park Ind School Dist | 45 | 191 |
| Stacy, Lance/Lake Dallas Ind School Dist | 67 | 126 |
| Stafford, Stephanie/Sterling City Ind School Dist | 36,69,83,85 | 344 |
| Stafford, Tammi/Sweetwater ISD School Dist | 69 | 304 |
| Staggs, Ben/Perrin-Whitt Cons Ind Sch Dist | 6 | 242 |
| Stags, Tommy/Sands Consolidated ISD | 67 | 121 |
| Stahl, Mark/Boerne Ind School Dist | 3 | 257 |
| Stahnke, Curtis/Comanche Ind School Dist | 54 | 93 |
| Staley, Jim/Princeton Ind School Dist | 3 | 87 |
| Staley, Michele, Dr/Clear Creek Ind School Dist | 79 | 163 |
| Stallard, Robert/Ft Stockton Ind School Dist | 3 | 318 |
| Stallworth, Lance/Spring Branch Ind School Dist | 79 | 206 |
| Stambaugh, Holly/Joshua Ind School Dist | 68 | 251 |
| Stanaland, John/Turkey-Quitaque Cons Ind SD | 6 | 181 |
| Stancil, Jana/Fannindel Ind School Dist | 58 | 124 |
| Standford, Carolyn/Mineola Ind School Dist | 16 | 408 |
| Standifer, Brenda/Lone Oak Ind School Dist | 4 | 239 |
| Standlee, Becky/Dimmitt Ind School Dist | 2 | 74 |

| | | | | | | | | |
|---|---|---|---|---|---|---|---|---|
| 1 | Superintendent | 16 | Instructional Media Svcs | 30 | Adult Education | 44 | Science Sec | 58 | Special Education K-12 | 72 | Summer School | 88 | Alternative/At Risk | 277 | Remedial Math K-12 |
| 2 | Bus/Finance/Purchasing | 17 | Chief Operations Officer | 31 | Career/Sch-to-Work K-12 | 45 | Math K-12 | 59 | Special Education Elem | 73 | Instructional Tech | 89 | Multi-Cultural Curriculum | 280 | Literacy Coach |
| 3 | Buildings And Grounds | 18 | Chief Academic Officer | 32 | Career/Sch-to-Work Elem | 46 | Math Elem | 60 | Special Education Sec | 74 | Inservice Training | 90 | Social Work | 285 | STEM |
| 4 | Food Service | 19 | Chief Financial Officer | 33 | Career/Sch-to-Work Sec | 47 | Math Sec | 61 | Foreign/World Lang K-12 | 75 | Marketing/Distributive | 91 | Safety/Security | 286 | Digital Learning |
| 5 | Transportation | 20 | Art K-12 | 34 | Early Childhood Ed | 48 | English/Lang Arts K-12 | 62 | Foreign/World Lang Elem | 76 | Info Systems | 92 | Magnet School | 288 | Common Core Standards |
| 6 | Athletic | 21 | Art Elem | 35 | Health/Phys Education | 49 | English/Lang Arts Elem | 63 | Foreign/World Lang Sec | 77 | Psychological Assess | 93 | Parental Involvement | 294 | Accountability |
| 7 | Health Services | 22 | Art Sec | 36 | Guidance Services K-12 | 50 | English/Lang Arts Sec | 64 | Religious Education K-12 | 78 | Affirmative Action | 95 | Tech Prep Program | 295 | Network System |
| 8 | Curric/Instruct K-12 | 23 | Music K-12 | 37 | Guidance Services Elem | 51 | Reading K-12 | 65 | Religious Education Elem | 79 | Student Personnel | 97 | Chief Information Officer | 296 | Title II Programs |
| 9 | Curric/Instruct Elem | 24 | Music Elem | 38 | Guidance Services Sec | 52 | Reading Elem | 66 | Religious Education Sec | 80 | Driver Ed/Safety | 98 | Chief Technology Officer | 297 | Webmaster |
| 10 | Curric/Instruct Sec | 25 | Music Sec | 39 | Social Studies K-12 | 53 | Reading Sec | 67 | School Board President | 81 | Gifted/Talented | 270 | Character Education | 298 | Grant Writer/Ptnrships |
| 11 | Federal Program | 26 | Business Education | 40 | Social Studies Elem | 54 | Remedial Reading K-12 | 68 | Teacher Personnel | 82 | Video Services | 271 | Migrant Education | 750 | Chief Innovation Officer |
| 12 | Title I | 27 | Career & Tech Ed | 41 | Social Studies Sec | 55 | Remedial Reading Elem | 69 | Academic Assessment | 83 | Substance Abuse Prev | 273 | Teacher Mentor | 751 | Chief of Staff |
| 13 | Title V | 28 | Technology Education | 42 | Science K-12 | 56 | Remedial Reading Sec | 70 | Research/Development | 84 | Erate | 274 | Before/After Sch | 752 | Social Emotional Learning |
| 14 | Asst Superintendent | 29 | Family/Consumer Science | 43 | Science Elem | 57 | Bilingual/ELL | 71 | Public Information | 85 | AIDS Education | 275 | Response To Intervention | | |

| NAME/District | JOB FUNCTIONS | PAGE | NAME/District | JOB FUNCTIONS | PAGE |
|---|---|---|---|---|---|
| Standley, Carrie/Warren Ind School Dist | 16 | 378 | Stephens, Mandy/Sherman Ind School Dist | 4 | 172 |
| Stanfield, Carolyn/Freer Ind School Dist | 4 | 132 | Stephens, Melissa/Yantis Ind School Dist | 67 | 408 |
| Stanfield, Dana/Nazareth Ind School Dist | 26 | 75 | Stephens, Mike/Whitewright Ind School Dist | 91 | 173 |
| Stanford, Brandy/Salado Ind School Dist | 2,11 | 32 | Stephens, Pauli/Howe Ind School Dist | 38 | 171 |
| Stanford, Brent/Red Oak Ind School Dist | 3,5 | 146 | Stephens, Phylis/Burkeville Ind School Dist | 8,31,57,83,88,275,294 | 303 |
| Stanford, Carla/Corsicana Ind School Dist | 288 | 302 | Stephens, Rebecca/Mabank Ind School Dist | 8,11,57,69,83,88,294 | 256 |
| Stanford, Mary/Huntsville Ind School Dist | 27,285 | 386 | Stephens, Ricky, Dr/Keene Ind School Dist | 1 | 251 |
| Stanford, Steve/Comal Ind School Dist | 71 | 91 | Stephens, Scott/South San Antonio Ind Sch Dist | 4 | 45 |
| Stanford, Travis/Spring Branch Ind School Dist | 3,15 | 205 | Stephens, Tamika, Dr/Aldine Ind School Dist | 2,19 | 184 |
| Stanford, Wade/Westwood Ind School Dist | 1 | 19 | Stephens, Todd, Dr/Magnolia Ind School Dist | 1 | 295 |
| Stange, Frank/Alamo Heights Ind School Dist | 68,71 | 33 | Stephenson, Angelita/Coleman Ind School Dist | 58 | 79 |
| Stanghellini, Annett/Claude Ind School Dist | 4 | 23 | Stephenson, Ann/Avery Ind School Dist | 59 | 325 |
| Stanley, Betty/Sidney Ind School Dist | 4 | 94 | Stephenson, Janon/Glen Rose Ind School Dist | 7 | 342 |
| Stanley, Danny/Kilgore Ind School Dist | 57,69,81 | 174 | Steubing, Richard/Groveton Ind School Dist | 6 | 377 |
| Stanley, Ken/Coldspring-Oakhurst Cons ISD | 6,35 | 332 | Stevens, Bettye/Plemons-Stinnett-Phillips CISD | 2 | 240 |
| Stanley, Mark/Brownwood Ind School Dist | 73,286,295 | 62 | Stevens, Carla/Manor Ind School Dist | 2 | 373 |
| Stanley, Robert/North Hopkins Ind School Dist | 11 | 234 | Stevens, David/Arlington Ind School Dist | 91 | 346 |
| Stanley, Wendy, Dr/Anna Ind School Dist | 58 | 81 | Stevens, Jeffrey/Era Ind School Dist | 67 | 94 |
| Stanmore, Jonathan/Queen City Ind School Dist | 67 | 74 | Stevens, Marcia/Diocese of Beaumont Sch Office | 1 | 247 |
| Stanner, Charlotte/Atlanta Ind School Dist | 67 | 73 | Stevens, Rayann/Electra Ind School Dist | 275 | 394 |
| Stansberry, Amber/Edna Ind School Dist | 34,58,77 | 242 | Stevens, Robert/Taylor Ind School Dist | 58 | 402 |
| Stansberry, Cheryle/Aransas Pass Ind School Dist | 2 | 333 | Stevens, Tina/Millsap Ind School Dist | 4 | 315 |
| Stansbury, Scott/Round Rock Ind School Dist | 84,295 | 401 | Stevens, Trae/Mathis Ind School Dist | 6 | 334 |
| Stanush, Jessica/Floresville Ind School Dist | 15,68,78,79,273 | 403 | Stevens, Ty/Sterling City Ind School Dist | 285 | 344 |
| Stapper, Judy/Florence Ind School Dist | 76 | 398 | Stevenson, Alex/Dodd City Ind School Dist | 6 | 150 |
| Stark, Brittany/Pampa Ind School Dist | 38,83,90 | 170 | Stevenson, Neal/Nursery ISD School Dist | 67 | 384 |
| Starke, Adam, Dr/Socorro Ind School Dist | 11 | 140 | Stewart-Kooper, Gloria/Lamar Cons Ind School Dist | 57 | 157 |
| Starkey, Scott/Whitehouse Ind School Dist | 73 | 341 | Stewart, Ashley/Boerne Ind School Dist | 15 | 257 |
| Starkweather, Brett/Grandfalls-Royalty Ind SD | 73 | 388 | Stewart, Becky/Goldthwaite Consolidated ISD | 4 | 291 |
| **Starkweather, Brett/**Grandfalls-Royalty Ind SD | 1,11,73 | 388 | Stewart, Becky/Goldthwaite Consolidated ISD | 4 | 291 |
| Starnes, Curtis/Granbury Ind School Dist | 295 | 233 | Stewart, Becky/Stockdale Ind School Dist | 2 | 404 |
| Starnes, Keith/Stephenville Ind School Dist | 3,91 | 148 | Stewart, Bonnie/Harper Ind School Dist | 8,11,69,74,294,296 | 168 |
| Starnes, Rachel/Belton Ind School Dist | 76 | 29 | **Stewart, Bonnie/**Harper Ind School Dist | 1 | 168 |
| Starr, Michelle/Spring Ind School Dist | 15 | 207 | Stewart, Brad/Jacksonville Ind School Dist | 68 | 76 |
| Starr, Pamela/Richland Springs Ind Sch Dist | 73 | 335 | Stewart, Brad/Lufkin Ind School Dist | 73,295,297 | 21 |
| Starr, Shelly/Hemphill Ind School Dist | 16 | 331 | Stewart, Brinson/Timpson Ind School Dist | 67 | 338 |
| Starrett, Christy/Crandall Ind School Dist | 15,68 | 254 | Stewart, Carol/White Oak Ind School Dist | 16 | 176 |
| Starrett, Stacy/Malta Ind School Dist | 1,11 | 52 | Stewart, Deborah, Dr/Cypress-Fairbanks Ind Sch Dist | 15,68 | 189 |
| Startz, Patricia/Falls City Ind School Dist | 295,298 | 253 | Stewart, Denisa/Anna Ind School Dist | 68 | 81 |
| Stary, Alicia/El Campo Ind School Dist | 11,294,296 | 392 | Stewart, Desmontes, Dr/Gainesville Ind School Dist | 1 | 95 |
| Statler, Shelly/Glen Rose Ind School Dist | 16 | 342 | Stewart, Doug/Hughes Springs Ind Sch Dist | 73,76,286 | 74 |
| Staugh, Frederek/Monahans-Wickett-Pyote ISD | 6 | 388 | Stewart, Elizabeth/Argyle Ind School Dist | 2,19 | 124 |
| Staump, Dana/Medina Ind School Dist | 36 | 26 | Stewart, Jennifer/Denton Ind School Dist | 2 | 124 |
| Stauty, Gary/Pleasant Grove Ind School Dist | 4 | 52 | Stewart, Jennifer/Splendora Ind School Dist | 58 | 297 |
| Stearns, Adam/Magnolia Ind School Dist | 2 | 295 | Stewart, Katherine/Grandview Ind School Dist | 16 | 251 |
| Steckly, Suzie/Merkel Ind School Dist | 73 | 363 | Stewart, Kelli/North Lamar Ind School Dist | 1 | 406 |
| Sted, Caleb/Hutto Ind School Dist | 2 | 399 | Stewart, Kim/Northside Ind School Dist | 81 | 39 |
| Steeber, Deana/Argyle Ind School Dist | 8,11,18,280,285,288,296,298 | 124 | Stewart, Lara/Mesquite Ind School Dist | 4 | 115 |
| Steel, Ryan, Dr/Cisco Independent Sch Dist | 1,11 | 133 | Stewart, Laura/Mt Pleasant Ind School Dist | 4 | 366 |
| Steele, April/Ingram Ind School Dist | 4 | 259 | Stewart, Leigh/Broaddus Ind School Dist | 76 | 332 |
| Steele, Charles/Covington ISD School Dist | 6 | 230 | Stewart, Rob/Magnolia Ind School Dist | 79,91 | 295 |
| Steele, Craig/May Ind School Dist | 6 | 62 | Stewart, Robert, Dr/Denton Ind School Dist | 15,68 | 125 |
| Steele, John/Ennis Ind School Dist | 295 | 144 | Stewart, Scott/Crandall Ind School Dist | 5 | 254 |
| Steele, Natalie/May Ind School Dist | 11,58,296,298,752 | 62 | Stewart, Scott/Temple Ind School Dist | 6 | 32 |
| Steelman, Clyde, Dr/Region 11 Ed Service Center | 1,11 | 362 | Stewart, Sheryl/Allen Ind School Dist | 69,294 | 80 |
| Steelman, Trisha/Friona Ind School Dist | 73,76,286,295 | 318 | Stewart, Stacy/Lamesa Ind School Dist | 34,58,77 | 121 |
| Steets, Layne/Dawson Ind School Dist | 1,11,73 | 121 | Stewart, Thomas/Canton Ind School Dist | 3 | 382 |
| Stefka, Charte/Grand Prairie Ind School Dist | 3 | 111 | Stickels, David/Saltillo Ind School Dist | 1,11 | 234 |
| Steger, Marilyn/Bells Ind School Dist | 2,19 | 170 | Stidevent, Wade/Boling Ind School Dist | 1,83 | 392 |
| Steger, Melissa/Grand Prairie Ind School Dist | 69,76 | 111 | Stidham, Heather/McDade Ind School Dist | 8,69,79,88,294 | 27 |
| Steger, Will/Bells Ind School Dist | 3,5 | 170 | Stidham, Mandy/O'Donnell Ind School Dist | 67 | 276 |
| Stehling, Charli/Kerrville Ind School Dist | 68 | 259 | Stieney, Melissaa/Blue Ridge Ind School Dist | 57,73,286 | 81 |
| Steinbecker, Catrina/Milano Ind School Dist | 36,69,79,83,85,88 | 290 | Stille, Lacrsasha/Gainesville Ind School Dist | 15 | 95 |
| Steinberger, Chad/Windthorst Ind School Dist | 67 | 23 | Stilwell, Travis/Tolar Ind School Dist | 1 | 233 |
| Steinbruck, Christopher/Flour Bluff Ind School Dist | 6 | 307 | Stinson, Gayle, Dr/Lake Dallas Ind School Dist | 1 | 126 |
| Steinert, Michael/Ft Worth Ind School Dist | 15,79,83 | 352 | Stobaugh, Nancy/Lexington Ind School Dist | 58 | 266 |
| Steinkamp, Ricky/Crawford Ind School Dist | 67 | 282 | Stobnicki, Sabrina/Harts Bluff Ind School Dist | 79,90 | 366 |
| Stelter, Cody/Brenham Ind School Dist | 27,28 | 388 | Stock, Robert/Pasadena Ind School Dist | 5 | 203 |
| Stephen, Cathy/Archdiocese Galveston-Houston | 15 | 209 | Stockhorst, Rosanne/New Braunfels Ind School Dist | 2 | 92 |
| Stephens, Beverly/Belton Ind School Dist | 36 | 29 | Stockman, Linda/Whiteface Con Ind School Dist | 4 | 78 |
| Stephens, Erin/Hull Daisetta Ind School Dist | 2 | 268 | Stockstill, Greg/Region 16 Ed Service Center | 73 | 324 |
| Stephens, James/Patton Springs Ind School Dist | 73 | 131 | Stockton, Dana/Keene Ind School Dist | 12,31,36,69,83,270 | 251 |
| Stephens, Julie/Carroll Independent Sch Dist | 16,43,46 | 349 | Stockton, Nick/Needville Ind School Dist | 295 | 159 |
| Stephens, Kay/Linden Kildare Cons Ind SD | 67 | 74 | Stockton, Rick/Klein Ind School Dist | 83,88 | 202 |
| Stephens, Kurt/Lufkin Ind School Dist | 88,294 | 21 | Stoddard, Eric/San Vicente Ind School Dist | 11 | 60 |
| Stephens, Lacey/Mount Vernon Ind School Dist | 36,83,85,88,285 | 160 | Stoddard, Jeani/San Vicente Ind School Dist | 285 | 60 |

| NAME/District | JOB FUNCTIONS | PAGE |
|---|---|---|
| Summers, Mellissa/Dublin Ind School Dist | 8,11,31,57,273,286,288,296 | 147 |
| Summers, Priscilla/Denver City Ind School Dist | 16,82 | 409 |
| Summers, Regan/Pleasant Grove Ind School Dist | 37 | 52 |
| Summers, Sue/Dimmitt Ind School Dist | 69 | 74 |
| Sumner, Drew/Jarrell Ind School Dist | 6 | 399 |
| Sumner, Rodney/Tuloso-Midway Ind School Dist | 1 | 308 |
| Sumrak, Ben/Rockwall Ind School Dist | 20,23 | 328 |
| Sumrall, Tennie/Coolidge Ind School Dist | 73,95 | 269 |
| Sumrow, Jennifer/Mount Vernon Ind School Dist | 69,79 | 160 |
| Sung, Elliott/Bloomington Ind School Dist | 73,98,286,295 | 384 |
| Sunga-Collier, Jennifer/South San Antonio Ind Sch Dist | 71 | 45 |
| Sunosky, Laura/New Caney Ind School Dist | 79 | 296 |
| Surdovel, David/Tomball Ind School Dist | 8,45 | 208 |
| Surface, Ally/Eagle Mtn-Saginaw Ind Sch Dist | 298 | 351 |
| Surley, Brandi/Jonesboro Ind School Dist | 59 | 97 |
| Surratt, Scott/Carthage Ind School Dist | 6,35 | 314 |
| Surratt, Stan/Lindale Ind School Dist | 1 | 339 |
| Sustaire, Mark/Saltillo Ind School Dist | 67 | 234 |
| Sustaita, Calixta/Lockney Independent Sch Dist | 4 | 153 |
| Sustaita, Marlena/Granger Ind School Dist | 4 | 399 |
| Sutherland, Gary/Lorena Ind School Dist | 3 | 283 |
| Sutherland, Russ/East Chambers Ind School Dist | 6 | 76 |
| Sutherland, Shannon/Richland Springs Ind Sch Dist | 4 | 335 |
| Sutlive, Dawn/New Summerfield Ind Sch Dist | 4 | 76 |
| Suttle, Bonnie/Allen Ind School Dist | 76 | 80 |
| Suttle, Greg/McKinney Ind School Dist | 3 | 84 |
| Sutton, Deidra/Chapel Hill Ind School Dist | 11 | 339 |
| Sutton, Patricia/Ft Worth Ind School Dist | 275 | 352 |
| Sutton, Tom/Groesbeck Ind School Dist | 67 | 269 |
| Suzi, Martizes/Poth Ind School Dist | 57 | 404 |
| Svoboda, Lisa/Sealy Ind School Dist | 2,11,19 | 25 |
| Swaim, Elizabeth/Aubrey Ind School Dist | 7 | 124 |
| Swain, Casey/Martin's Mill Ind Sch Dist | 77 | 383 |
| Swain, Casey/Martin's Mill Ind Sch Dist | 58 | 383 |
| Swain, Michelle/Round Rock Ind School Dist | 81,92 | 401 |
| Swan, Jennifer/Charlotte Ind School Dist | 73,76,84 | 23 |
| Swan, Sally/Spearman Ind School Dist | 7,35,83,85 | 182 |
| Swaner, Ann/Mumford Ind School Dist | 16 | 59 |
| Swank, Jennifer/Waskom Ind School Dist | 7,85 | 214 |
| Swanks, Pam/Dripping Springs Ind Sch Dist | 5 | 215 |
| Swanlund, Gail/Iola Ind School Dist | 57 | 177 |
| Swann, Stan/Crowley Ind School Dist | 79 | 350 |
| Swanner, Darla/Wylie Ind School Dist | 36,85,88,271 | 364 |
| Swanner, Tammy/Harmony Ind School Dist | 68 | 379 |
| Swanson, Jaime/Beckville Ind School Dist | 4 | 314 |
| Swanson, William/Clint Ind School Dist | 44 | 136 |
| Swanzy, Kayla/Trent Isn School Dist | 2 | 363 |
| Swarb, Wendy/Sudan Ind School Dist | 7,85 | 264 |
| Swart, Marja/Jim Ned Cons Ind School Dist | 16,82 | 363 |
| Swartz, David/Dickinson Ind School Dist | 67 | 164 |
| Swearengen, Thomas/Shelbyville Ind School Dist | 5,8,83,85,88 | 337 |
| Sweeeney, Richard/Brady Ind School Dist | 11,296 | 280 |
| Sweeny, Christy/Campbell Ind School Dist | 7,35 | 238 |
| Sweet, Cane/Anna Ind School Dist | 88 | 81 |
| Sweet, Stephanie/Savoy Ind School Dist | 58 | 150 |
| Sweich, Ken/Rockdale Ind School Dist | 73,76,295 | 290 |
| Swenson, Jessica/Galveston Ind School Dist | 58 | 165 |
| Swenson, Robert/Lohn Ind School Dist | 67 | 280 |
| Swick, Bev/Bremond Ind School Dist | 286 | 327 |
| Swick, Susan/Groesbeck Ind School Dist | 38 | 269 |
| Swinford, Alan/Crane Ind School Dist | 67 | 97 |
| Swinford, Jamye/Crane Ind School Dist | 8,11,15,31,69,74,275,294 | 97 |
| Swinton, Mary/Plano Ind School Dist | 42 | 85 |
| Swofford, Malissa/Nocona Ind School Dist | 73,76,84 | 293 |
| Sykora, Carla/West Ind School Dist | 58 | 285 |
| Sykora, Janice/Woodsboro Ind School Dist | 1,11 | 326 |
| Sylvester, Christie/Evadale Ind School Dist | 16 | 243 |
| Sylvester, Lyida/Beaumont Ind School Dist | 36,83 | 244 |
| Sylvester, Tyrone/Goose Creek Cons Ind Sch Dist | 68 | 192 |
| Syverson, Alicia/Ector Co Ind School Dist | 15,79 | 134 |

### T

| NAME/District | JOB FUNCTIONS | PAGE |
|---|---|---|
| Taber, Chris/La Vernia Ind School Dist | 6 | 404 |
| Taboada, Celia/United Ind School Dist | 16,74 | 390 |
| Tabor, Tyler/Blanket Ind School Dist | 6 | 61 |
| Tackett, Chris/Windthorst Ind School Dist | 6 | 23 |

| NAME/District | JOB FUNCTIONS | PAGE |
|---|---|---|
| Tackett, Cindy/Alvord Ind School Dist | 2 | 405 |
| Tackett, Darla/Windthorst Ind School Dist | 69,270,271 | 23 |
| Taff, Terri/Glen Rose Ind School Dist | 69 | 342 |
| Taft, Stephen/Pine Tree Ind School Dist | 286,295 | 175 |
| Tagle, Amy/Spur Ind School Dist | 23 | 131 |
| Talbert, Brad/Holland Ind School Dist | 6 | 30 |
| Talbert, Clarissa/San Marcos Cons Ind Sch Dist | 58 | 217 |
| Talbert, David/Lake Dallas Ind School Dist | 3 | 126 |
| Talbert, Kathy, Dr/Lewisville Ind School Dist | 58 | 126 |
| Talce, Mindy/Westwood Ind School Dist | 76 | 19 |
| Taldo, Amy/Grapevine-Colleyville Ind SD | 7,35 | 355 |
| Taliaferro, Chris/Scurry Rosser Ind School Dist | 67 | 256 |
| Talley, Tom/Bridgeport Ind School Dist | 67 | 406 |
| Taly, Carol/Braination Schools | 68 | 33 |
| Tamez, Manuel/Bishop Cons Ind School Dist | 2 | 305 |
| Tamyo, Emanuel/Southwest Ind School Dist | 5 | 46 |
| Tanem, Ginger/Cleburne Ind School Dist | 45 | 250 |
| Tanguna, Mariselda/Rio Grande City Ind Sch Dist | 79 | 343 |
| Tanner, Allen/Frenship Ind School Dist | 3 | 272 |
| Tanner, Anneliese/Austin Ind School Dist | 4 | 369 |
| Tanner, Patrick/Allen Ind School Dist | 76,295 | 80 |
| Tanner, Stacy/Perryton Ind School Dist | 29 | 310 |
| Tanton, Debbie/Mesquite Ind School Dist | 74,273 | 115 |
| Tapia, Henery/Huntsville Ind School Dist | 4 | 386 |
| Tapia, Oscar/Harlingen Cons Ind School Dist | 3,4,5,15 | 68 |
| Tarleton, Willie/Midland Ind School Dist | 5 | 288 |
| Tarlton, Elyse/Liberty Hill Ind School Dist | 58,69 | 401 |
| Tarpley, Clay/Hamilton Ind School Dist | 1 | 181 |
| Tarr, Michael/Brady Ind School Dist | 98 | 280 |
| Tarr, Nic/Higgins Ind School Dist | 6,80 | 270 |
| Tarrant, John/Weatherford Ind School Dist | 16,82 | 316 |
| Tarver, Carolyn/Little Elm Ind School Dist | 4 | 128 |
| Tarver, David/Mineral Wells Ind School Dist | 15,68 | 313 |
| Tarver, Jodi/Guthrie Common School Dist | 7 | 260 |
| Tarver, Yolanda/Aubrey Ind School Dist | 5 | 124 |
| Taska, Debra/Tidehaven Ind School Dist | 5,9,11,69,285,296,298 | 279 |
| Tatar, Richard/Port Arthur Ind School Dist | 295 | 246 |
| Tate, Alyese/Victoria Ind School Dist | 81 | 384 |
| Tate, Devin/Beckville Ind School Dist | 1 | 314 |
| Tate, Donna/Pearland Ind School Dist | 298 | 56 |
| Tate, Karla/Lockhart Ind School Dist | 274 | 64 |
| Tate, Lisa/Fairfield Ind School Dist | 68 | 160 |
| Tate, Michelle/Lindale Ind School Dist | 2 | 339 |
| Tatum, Chris/Amarillo Ind School Dist | 68 | 320 |
| Tatum, Cindy/Decatur Ind School Dist | 2,15 | 406 |
| Taubert, Lela/Miles Ind School Dist | 10,36,88 | 329 |
| Taulton, Bryan/Goodrich Ind School Dist | 1,11,83 | 319 |
| Tavenner, Jayne/Region 6 Ed Service Center | 69 | 386 |
| Tawater, Chris/Manor Ind School Dist | 76 | 373 |
| Taylor, Amy/Claude Ind School Dist | 752 | 23 |
| Taylor, Annette/Liberty Ind School Dist | 2 | 269 |
| Taylor, Betsy Adams/Lubbock-Cooper Ind Sch Dist | 13,296 | 274 |
| Taylor, Brady/Woden Ind School Dist | 1 | 301 |
| Taylor, Brenda/Kerrville Ind School Dist | 2 | 259 |
| Taylor, Britney/Leon Ind School Dist | 3,5 | 267 |
| Taylor, Chad/Liberty Ind School Dist | 6 | 269 |
| Taylor, Clay/Tahoka Ind School Dist | 67 | 276 |
| Taylor, David/Graford Ind School Dist | 3 | 313 |
| Taylor, Della/Harlandale Ind School Dist | 58 | 35 |
| Taylor, Dori/Jacksboro Ind Sch Dist | 36,69,83,85 | 242 |
| Taylor, Doug/Belton Ind School Dist | 91 | 29 |
| Taylor, Douglas/Jim Ned Cons Ind School Dist | 4 | 363 |
| Taylor, Gordon/Region 10 Ed Service Center | 1,11 | 120 |
| Taylor, Howard/Clarksville Ind School Dist | 73 | 325 |
| Taylor, Jarryd/Crockett Co Cons Common SD | 6 | 98 |
| Taylor, Jeane/Shelbyville Ind School Dist | 7 | 337 |
| Taylor, Jeanne/Vidor Ind School Dist | 5 | 312 |
| Taylor, Joe/Hearne Ind School Dist | 3 | 327 |
| Taylor, John/Bluff Dale Ind Sch Dist | 1,11,288 | 147 |
| Taylor, Jon/Pharr-San Juan-Alamo Ind SD | 20 | 226 |
| Taylor, Keith/Jonesboro Ind School Dist | 67 | 97 |
| Taylor, Kelly/Calhoun Co Ind School Dist | 13,57,69,74,83,271 | 65 |
| Taylor, Kerry/Eanes Ind School Dist | 20,23 | 372 |
| Taylor, Lahoma/Chilton Ind School Dist | 2 | 148 |
| **Taylor, Larry**/Rocksprings Ind School Dist | 1 | 135 |
| Taylor, Laurie/Plano Ind School Dist | 9 | 85 |

| NAME/District | JOB FUNCTIONS | PAGE |
|---|---|---|
| Taylor, Linda/Boling Ind School Dist | 57 | 392 |
| Taylor, Linda/Royse City Ind School Dist | 38 | 328 |
| Taylor, Logan/Latexo Ind School Dist | 3,5 | 236 |
| Taylor, Lynnette/Gause Ind School Dist | 16,73,295 | 290 |
| Taylor, Maggie/Boys Ranch Ind School Dist | 11,15,57,83,298 | 310 |
| Taylor, Micah/Terrell Ind School Dist | 70 | 256 |
| Taylor, Mike/De Leon Ind School Dist | 295 | 93 |
| Taylor, Mike/Plains Ind School Dist | 5 | 409 |
| Taylor, Netobia/Galveston Ind School Dist | 76 | 165 |
| Taylor, Pam/Cross Roads Ind School Dist | 36 | 219 |
| Taylor, Randy/Denison Ind School Dist | 5 | 171 |
| Taylor, Regina/Allen Ind School Dist | 298 | 80 |
| Taylor, Sage/Corrigan-Camden Ind Sch Dist | 38 | 319 |
| Taylor, Sarah/Cleburne Ind School Dist | 19 | 250 |
| Taylor, Shannon/McMullen Co Ind Sch Dist | 6 | 286 |
| Taylor, Sharon/San Augustine Ind School Dist | 4 | 332 |
| Taylor, Sheri/Tyler Ind School Dist | 68 | 340 |
| Taylor, Sherry/Aledo Ind School Dist | 68 | 315 |
| Taylor, Staci/Houston ISD-North Area | 15 | 195 |
| Taylor, Stephanie/Gholson Ind School Dist | 8,285,286,288,752 | 282 |
| Taylor, Stephanie/Sonora Ind School Dist | 8,11,27,58,88 | 345 |
| Taylor, Steve/Denver City Ind School Dist | 6 | 409 |
| Taylor, Susan/Lipan Ind School Dist | 73 | 233 |
| Taylor, Tamika, Dr/Conroe Ind School Dist | 69,294 | 294 |
| Taylor, Tina/Nueces Canyon Cons Ind SD | 286 | 135 |
| Taylor, Turkessa/Spring Ind School Dist | 69,294 | 207 |
| Teaff, Ginger/Plano Ind School Dist | 45 | 85 |
| Teague, Chad/McKinney Ind School Dist | 68 | 84 |
| Teague, Christopher, Dr/Hillsboro Ind School Dist | 67 | 230 |
| Teal, Glen, Dr/Jim Ned Cons Ind School Dist | 1 | 363 |
| Teal, Suzanne/Carroll Independent Sch Dist | 3 | 349 |
| Tedder, Joel/Normangee Ind School Dist | 3,91 | 267 |
| Tedder, Richard/Cross Roads Ind School Dist | 1,11 | 218 |
| Teems, Kelley/Gunter Ind School Dist | 3,296 | 171 |
| Teer, Janet/Miller Grove Ind School Dist | 2 | 234 |
| Teer, Janice/Saltillo Ind School Dist | 2 | 234 |
| Tefertiller, Leif/Monahans-Wickett-Pyote ISD | 5 | 388 |
| Teichman, Cindy/Iowa Park Consolidated Ind SD | 79 | 395 |
| Tekell, Angela/Waco Ind School Dist | 67 | 284 |
| Tekell, Teressa/Reagan Co Ind School Dist | 69 | 324 |
| Telesca, Julie/Grapevine-Colleyville Ind SD | 4 | 355 |
| Telles, Reyne/Austin Ind School Dist | 71 | 369 |
| Tellez, Myriam/La Joya Ind School Dist | 36 | 222 |
| Tellez, Rita/Ysleta Ind School Dist | 45 | 141 |
| Tellis, Don/Pearland Ind School Dist | 3,91 | 56 |
| Templeton, Carrie/Rankin Ind School Dist | 60 | 380 |
| Templeton, Craig/Harrold Ind School Dist | 8,57,69,83,88,273 | 396 |
| Templeton, Nathan/Laneville Ind School Dist | 8,34,74,83,88,271,273 | 330 |
| Templeton, Robert, Dr/Ingram Ind School Dist | 1 | 259 |
| Templin, Steve/Mabank Ind School Dist | 3,91 | 256 |
| Tencate, Jeannie/Moran Ind School Dist | 271 | 336 |
| Tennery, Jody/Avalon Ind School Dist | 9,34 | 144 |
| Tennison, Clarence/Cross Plains Ind Sch Dist | 3,5 | 66 |
| Tennison, Louis/Karnack Ind School Dist | 6 | 214 |
| Tennison, Travis/Olfen Ind School Dist | 6 | 329 |
| Teran, Rick/Childress Ind School Dist | 1,83 | 77 |
| Terrazas, Daniel/Marion Ind School Dist | 11,57,58 | 177 |
| Terrazas, Velia/Southwest Ind School Dist | 9 | 46 |
| Terrell, Jennifer/Decatur Ind School Dist | 69 | 406 |
| Terrell, Leah/Booker Ind School Dist | 73 | 270 |
| Terrell, Stain/Paint Creek Ind School Dist | 3 | 215 |
| Terrier, Byron, Dr/Region 5 Ed Service Center | 15,16,73 | 247 |
| Terrill, Josh/Christoval Ind School Dist | 295 | 366 |
| Terry, Becky/Hamlin Collegiate Ind Sch Dist | 2,11 | 252 |
| Terry, Chris/Ft Stockton Ind School Dist | 295 | 318 |
| Terry, Debbie/Pine Tree Ind School Dist | 69,288,294 | 175 |
| Terry, Glenda/Midway Ind School Dist | 16 | 78 |

| NAME/District | JOB FUNCTIONS | PAGE |
|---|---|---|
| Terry, Justin, Dr/Forney Ind School Dist | 1 | 254 |
| Terry, Kelley/Madisonville Cons ISD | 4 | 276 |
| Terry, Kevin/Milano Ind School Dist | 73,295 | 290 |
| Terry, Kim/River Road Ind School Dist | 4 | 322 |
| Terry, Rebecca/Pasadena Ind School Dist | 34 | 203 |
| Terry, Rockney/Marlin Ind School Dist | 73 | 149 |
| Terry, Rueben/Caddo Mills Ind Sch Dist | 67 | 238 |
| Tesch, Kim/Normangee Ind School Dist | 36,69,88 | 267 |
| Tesch, William/Blanco Ind School Dist | 6 | 49 |
| Texidor, Manuel/Conroe Ind School Dist | 36,83 | 294 |
| Thacker, Michelle/Hondo Ind School Dist | 4 | 287 |
| Thacker, Robin/Nacogdoches Ind School Dist | 4 | 301 |
| Thane, Michelle/Haskell Cons Ind School Dist | 8,11,57,88,273,296,298 | 215 |
| Thannum, Julie/Carroll Independent Sch Dist | 15,71,297 | 349 |
| Tharpe, Kelly/McGregor Ind School Dist | 10 | 283 |
| Thayer, Tracy/Bandera Ind School Dist | 11,31,91,296,298 | 26 |
| Thedford, Barbara/Industrial Ind School Dist | 4 | 243 |
| Thein, David/Schertz-Cibolo-Univ City ISD | 7 | 178 |
| Therwanger, Danielle/Klondike Ind School Dist | 8,83,288 | 121 |
| Therwhanger, Cindy/Seminole Ind School Dist | 4 | 162 |
| Therwhanger, Kerry/Timpson Ind School Dist | 6 | 338 |
| Thias, Irma/Groom Ind School Dist | 4 | 72 |
| Thibodeaux, Adam/Beaumont Ind School Dist | 297 | 244 |
| Thibodeaux, Jason/Sabine Pass Ind School Dist | 6 | 247 |
| Thibodeaux, Jennifer/Nursery ISD School Dist | 6 | 384 |
| Thibodeaux, Lisa, Dr/Denton Ind School Dist | 10 | 124 |
| Thibodeaux, Michael/Hays Cons Ind School Dist | 4 | 216 |
| Thibodeaux, Stormy/Barbers Hill Ind School Dist | 45 | 75 |
| Thiel, David/La Vega Ind School Dist | 4 | 282 |
| Thieme, Michael/Gregory-Portland Ind Sch Dist | 91 | 333 |
| Thies, Heather/Academy Ind School Dist | 4 | 29 |
| Thiessen, Brad/Amarillo Ind School Dist | 6 | 320 |
| Thill, Arland/Fairfield Ind School Dist | 73,295 | 160 |
| Thill, Crystal/Fairfield Ind School Dist | 4 | 160 |
| Thiry, Eric/Yoakum Ind School Dist | 3 | 122 |
| Thomas-Jimenez, Cinde/Seguin Ind School Dist | 67 | 178 |
| Thomas, Ana/Huntsville Ind School Dist | 7,8,16,57,68,81,273 | 386 |
| Thomas, Angie/Tarkington Ind School Dist | 34 | 269 |
| Thomas, Ashley/Wichita Falls Ind School Dist | 71 | 395 |
| Thomas, Audrey/Waxahachie Ind School Dist | 58 | 146 |
| **Thomas, Autumn/**Texarkana Ind School Dist | 1 | 53 |
| Thomas, Carlene/Texas Dept of Education | 57 | 1 |
| Thomas, Cecil/Wheeler Ind School Dist | 16,73 | 394 |
| Thomas, Celina, Dr/Hutto Ind School Dist | 1 | 399 |
| Thomas, Christy/Jacksboro Ind Sch Dist | 2,84 | 242 |
| Thomas, Danny/Lorenzo Ind School Dist | 73 | 98 |
| Thomas, Darlene/Motley Co Ind School Dist | 2 | 299 |
| Thomas, Donna/Duncanville Ind School Dist | 4 | 108 |
| Thomas, Edward/Killeen Ind School Dist | 5 | 30 |
| Thomas, George/Socorro Ind School Dist | 27,31 | 140 |
| Thomas, Guy/Waller Ind School Dist | 3 | 387 |
| Thomas, James/Lancaster Ind School Dist | 3 | 114 |
| Thomas, Janie/Gary Ind School Dist | 7 | 314 |
| Thomas, Jean/Carthage Ind School Dist | 71 | 314 |
| Thomas, Jimmie/New Boston Ind School Dist | 5 | 52 |
| Thomas, Kathryn/Brookeland Ind School Dist | 4 | 243 |
| Thomas, Kaylia/Boys Ranch Ind Sch Dist | 8,16 | 310 |
| Thomas, Kevin/Jacksboro Ind Sch Dist | 27 | 242 |
| Thomas, Kimberley/Monahans-Wickett-Pyote ISD | 30,38 | 388 |
| Thomas, Mark/Birdville Ind School Dist | 71 | 348 |
| Thomas, Mary, Dr/Austin Ind School Dist | 11,296,298,752 | 369 |
| Thomas, Mike/Spring Branch Ind School Dist | 70 | 206 |
| Thomas, Robert/Woodsboro Ind School Dist | 67 | 326 |
| Thomas, Ross/Abilene Ind School Dist | 39 | 362 |
| Thomas, Sam/Chireno ISD School Dist | 27 | 300 |
| Thomas, Scott/Manor Ind School Dist | 71 | 373 |
| Thomas, Scott/Van Ind School Dist | 67 | 383 |

| NAME/District | JOB FUNCTIONS | PAGE |
|---|---|---|
| Thomas, Shuntae/Crosbyton Cons Ind Sch Dist | 7,83 | 98 |
| Thomas, Vicky/Diboll Ind School Dist | 1 | 20 |
| Thomas, Wanda/Houston Ind School Dist | 11 | 193 |
| Thomas, Wesley/Springtown Ind School Dist | 69 | 316 |
| Thomas, Willie/Robinson Ind School Dist | 16 | 284 |
| Thomas, Zack/Ore City Ind School Dist | 73 | 379 |
| Thomason, Jeff/Boles Ind School Dist | 6 | 238 |
| Thomasson, Michael/Harts Bluff Ind School Dist | 8 | 366 |
| Thompson, Becky/Paint Creek Ind School Dist | 2 | 215 |
| Thompson, Bobby/Mount Vernon Ind School Dist | 5 | 160 |
| Thompson, Brandon/Little Elm Ind School Dist | 76 | 128 |
| Thompson, Brian/Brazos Ind School Dist | 1 | 25 |
| Thompson, Chris/Graford Ind School Dist | 73,84,295 | 313 |
| Thompson, Chuck/City View Ind School Dist | 16 | 394 |
| Thompson, Cornel/West Orange-Cove Cons ISD | 6 | 312 |
| Thompson, Corrine/Mildred Ind School Dist | 81 | 303 |
| Thompson, Daphne/Canton Ind School Dist | 58 | 382 |
| Thompson, Diane/Danbury Ind School Dist | 38 | 56 |
| Thompson, Dwayne/Dallas Ind School Dist | 19 | 102 |
| Thompson, Elisha/La Porte Ind School Dist | 6 | 203 |
| Thompson, Heather/Graford Ind School Dist | 57 | 313 |
| Thompson, Helen/Blue Ridge Ind School Dist | 7 | 81 |
| Thompson, Jeanne/Whitney Ind School Dist | 7 | 231 |
| Thompson, Jennifer/Oglesby Ind School Dist | 67 | 97 |
| Thompson, Jeremy/Era Ind School Dist | 1 | 94 |
| Thompson, Jimmy/Crockett Ind School Dist | 6 | 235 |
| Thompson, Joy/Coleman Ind School Dist | 8,12,34,57,296 | 79 |
| Thompson, Karrie/Hawley Ind School Dist | 16,82 | 253 |
| Thompson, Kathy/Detroit Ind School Dist | 1 | 325 |
| Thompson, Kenneth, Dr/San Antonio Ind School Dist | 73,76,97,98 | 42 |
| Thompson, Kerry/Banquete Ind School Dist | 8 | 305 |
| Thompson, Macie/Lindale Ind School Dist | 8 | 339 |
| Thompson, Marjorie/Breckenridge Ind School Dist | 57 | 344 |
| Thompson, Marty/Chester Ind School Dist | 3 | 377 |
| Thompson, Max, Dr/Banquete Ind School Dist | 1,11,84 | 305 |
| Thompson, Michele/Klein Ind School Dist | 42 | 202 |
| Thompson, Mike/Ranger Ind School Dist | 1,73 | 133 |
| Thompson, Paul/West Rusk Co Cons Ind Sch Dist | 91 | 331 |
| Thompson, Raemi/Big Spring Ind School Dist | 8,12,15,52 | 236 |
| Thompson, Richard/Sharyland Ind School Dist | 6 | 227 |
| Thompson, Robbie/Central Ind School Dist | 73 | 20 |
| Thompson, Ronda/Matagorda Ind School Dist | 59 | 278 |
| Thompson, Ronnie/Liberty-Eylau Ind School Dist | 1 | 51 |
| Thompson, Sandra/Garland Ind School Dist | 29 | 109 |
| Thompson, Stacie/Mt Pleasant Ind School Dist | 2,19 | 366 |
| Thompson, Stephanie/Cross Plains Ind Sch Dist | 4 | 66 |
| Thompson, T/Montague Ind School Dist | 2 | 293 |
| Thompson, Toni/San Antonio Ind School Dist | 15,68,79 | 42 |
| Thompson, Weldon/Coleman Ind School Dist | 3 | 79 |
| Thoms, Kris/Sundown Ind School Dist | 2,11,298 | 232 |
| Thoreson, Scott/Ysleta Ind School Dist | 20,23 | 141 |
| Thorman, Mike/Cumby Ind School Dist | 3,5 | 234 |
| Thornell, Carey/Georgetown Ind School Dist | 274 | 398 |
| Thornell, Robert, Dr/Lewisville Ind School Dist | 8 | 126 |
| Thornhill, Cooper/Blum Ind School Dist | 6 | 230 |
| Thornhill, Sherrie/Silsbee Ind School Dist | 8,15,68,288,296 | 183 |
| Thornton, Billie/Rio Vista Ind School Dist | 2 | 251 |
| Thornton, Jerry/Overton Ind School Dist | 3,5 | 331 |
| Thornton, Louise/Granger Ind School Dist | 2,19 | 399 |
| Thornton, Robyn/Onalaska Ind School Dist | 8,11,16,57,58,69,88 | 320 |
| Thornton, Rodney/Hico Ind School Dist | 6 | 181 |
| Thornton, Shelley/Westphalia Ind School Dist | 2 | 149 |
| Thornton, Shirley/Flour Bluff Ind School Dist | 67 | 307 |
| Thornton, Vicki/Sabine Ind School Dist | 58,77 | 175 |
| Thornton, Will/Edgewood Ind School Dist | 5 | 34 |
| Thornton, William/Edgewood Ind School Dist | 3,5 | 382 |
| Thorp, Kathy/Throckmorton Ind School Dist | 67 | 365 |
| Thorsen, Amber/Granger Ind School Dist | 11,36,69,752 | 399 |
| Thorson, Aaron/Int'l Leadership of Texas Dist | 751 | 112 |
| Thorton, Vicki/White Oak Ind School Dist | 34,58 | 176 |
| Threadgill, Jeff/Callisburg Ind School Dist | 76,295 | 94 |
| Threlkelb, Discha/Fannindel Ind School Dist | 2 | 124 |
| Throgmorton, Rodney/Perryton Ind School Dist | 73,295 | 310 |
| Thuman, Bob/Hamshire Fannett Ind Sch Dist | 67 | 245 |
| Thurman, Denise/St Jo Ind School Dist | 83 | 293 |
| Thurmon, Kyle/Matagorda Ind School Dist | 6 | 278 |

| NAME/District | JOB FUNCTIONS | PAGE |
|---|---|---|
| Thurmond, Cynthia/Laneville Ind School Dist | 16 | 330 |
| Thurston, Lori/Arlington Ind School Dist | 58 | 346 |
| Thweatt, David/Harrold Ind School Dist | 1,11,73 | 396 |
| Tibbels, Charlie/Decatur Ind School Dist | 67 | 406 |
| Tibo, Roxanna/De Leon Ind School Dist | 54 | 93 |
| Tidwell, Christy/Texarkana Ind School Dist | 8,74 | 53 |
| Tidwell, Coty/Post Ind School Dist | 73 | 167 |
| Tidwell, Dianna/Terrell Ind School Dist | 4 | 256 |
| Tidwell, Dianne/Tomball Ind School Dist | 286 | 208 |
| Tidwell, Leanne/Munday Consolidated Ind SD | 271 | 262 |
| Tidwell, Rachel/Rice Ind School Dist | 7 | 303 |
| Tidwell, Rick/Bland Ind School Dist | 1,83 | 238 |
| Tieterse, Kelley/Huntsville Ind School Dist | 58 | 386 |
| Tietjan, Kelly/Rivercrest Ind School Dist | 16,82 | 325 |
| Tieu, Quyen/Sheldon Ind School Dist | 58 | 205 |
| Tijerina, Candy/Liberty Hill Ind School Dist | 57,271 | 401 |
| Tijerina, Diamond/Mission Cons Ind School Dist | 50 | 225 |
| Tilley, Danette/La Porte Ind School Dist | 10 | 203 |
| Tilley, Deb/Ore City Ind School Dist | 33 | 379 |
| Tillman, Brian/Irion Co Ind School Dist | 5 | 241 |
| Timberlake, Terry/Academy Ind School Dist | 295 | 29 |
| Timmons, David/Penelope ISD School Dist | 1 | 231 |
| Timmons, Mary/Lorena Ind School Dist | 67 | 283 |
| Timms, Joe/McMullen Co Ind Sch Dist | 8,31,57,85,273 | 286 |
| Timms, Stephanie/Kenedy Ind School Dist | 2 | 254 |
| Timms, Stephanie/Three Rivers Ind School Dist | 2 | 271 |
| Tindel, Caleb/Paris Ind School Dist | 10,27 | 262 |
| Tindel, Zeb/Honey Grove Ind School Dist | 31 | 150 |
| Tindol, Charles/Italy Ind School Dist | 6 | 145 |
| Tineda, J'Rae/Shallowater Ind School Dist | 16 | 274 |
| Tingle, Eric/Lake Worth Ind School Dist | 8,294 | 358 |
| Tinker, Chrystal/Leggett Ind School Dist | 83 | 319 |
| Tinney, Alton/San Saba Ind School Dist | 5 | 335 |
| Tinnin, Tierney/Cedar Hill Ind School Dist | 97 | 101 |
| Tinsley, Kristen/Kenedy Co Schools | 1 | 257 |
| **Tinsley, Kristen/**Kenedy Co Wide Common Sch Dist | 1,11,57 | 258 |
| Tinsley, Randy/Bushland Ind School Dist | 91 | 321 |
| Tippett, Joyce/Spurger Ind School Dist | 16 | 377 |
| Tippin, Toi/Bloomington Ind School Dist | 83,285 | 384 |
| Tipps, Rod/Sivells Bend Ind School Dist | 6,16,59,73 | 95 |
| Tipton, Beau/Menard Ind School Dist | 3,5 | 288 |
| Tipton, Josh/Midland Ind School Dist | 297 | 288 |
| Tipton, Scott/Bandera Ind School Dist | 2 | 26 |
| Tipton, Scott/Pecos-Barstow-Toyah Ind SD | 2,19 | 326 |
| Tipton, Tony, Dr/Little Elm Ind School Dist | 27,31 | 128 |
| **Tipton, Tony, Dr/**Lumberton Ind School Dist | 1 | 183 |
| Tisdale, Jamie/Humble Ind School Dist | 68 | 200 |
| Tisdale, Rick/Llano Ind School Dist | 67 | 271 |
| Todd, Clay/North Zulch Ind School Dist | 6,60 | 276 |
| Todd, Courtney/Milano Ind School Dist | 12,57,296 | 290 |
| Todd, Heidi/Cleburne Ind School Dist | 2 | 250 |
| Todd, Leslie/Anahuac Ind School Dist | 38 | 75 |
| Todd, Lisa/Thorndale Ind School Dist | 68 | 291 |
| Todd, Matthew/Blue Ridge Ind School Dist | 8,11,69,74,88,294,298 | 81 |
| Toelr, Bridgette/Warren Ind School Dist | 58,69 | 378 |
| Tolbert, Kathy/Frisco Ind School Dist | 7 | 82 |
| Toliver, Caroline/Ballinger Ind School Dist | 8,11,286,288,296,298 | 329 |
| Tollett, Richard/Lytle Ind School Dist | 16,73,76,82,84 | 24 |
| Tollier, Lori/Edgewood Ind School Dist | 73 | 382 |
| Tolman, Mary/Brownsville Ind School Dist | 11 | 66 |
| Tomalin, Jamie/Rockwall Ind School Dist | 2 | 328 |
| Tomas, Michael/Silsbee Ind School Dist | 3,5 | 183 |
| Tomas, Monica/Lamar Cons Ind School Dist | 4 | 157 |
| Tomas, Monica/Sheldon Ind School Dist | 4 | 205 |
| Tomlinson, Katrina/Santa Anna Ind School Dist | 2,11 | 79 |
| Tomson, Tina/Lovejoy Ind School Dist | 2 | 84 |
| Toney, Nancy/Red Oak Ind School Dist | 11,296,298 | 146 |
| Tonne, Allison/Paint Rock Ind School Dist | 16 | 94 |
| Tooley, Lavern/Hico Ind School Dist | 7,85 | 181 |
| Toon, Rodney/Alvarado Ind School Dist | 2,19 | 249 |
| Toran, Ornian/Brenham Ind School Dist | 5 | 388 |
| Torez, Juan/Westwood Ind School Dist | 4,19 | 19 |
| Torres, Ana/El Paso Ind School Dist | 15 | 137 |
| Torres, Armando/San Perlita Ind School Dist | 73,295 | 397 |
| Torres, Cynthia/La Feria Ind School Dist | 15 | 69 |
| Torres, D T/Lometa Ind School Dist | 6 | 264 |

| 1 | Superintendent | 16 | Instructional Media Svcs | 30 | Adult Education | 44 | Science Sec | 58 | Special Education K-12 | 72 | Summer School | 88 | Alternative/At Risk | 277 | Remedial Math K-12 |
|---|---|---|---|---|---|---|---|---|---|---|---|---|---|---|---|
| 2 | Bus/Finance/Purchasing | 17 | Chief Operations Officer | 31 | Career/Sch-to-Work K-12 | 45 | Math K-12 | 59 | Special Education Elem | 73 | Instructional Tech | 89 | Multi-Cultural Curriculum | 280 | Literacy Coach |
| 3 | Buildings And Grounds | 18 | Chief Academic Officer | 32 | Career/Sch-to-Work Elem | 46 | Math Elem | 60 | Special Education Sec | 74 | Inservice Training | 90 | Social Work | 285 | STEM |
| 4 | Food Service | 19 | Chief Financial Officer | 33 | Career/Sch-to-Work Sec | 47 | Math Sec | 61 | Foreign/World Lang K-12 | 75 | Marketing/Distributive | 91 | Safety/Security | 286 | Digital Learning |
| 5 | Transportation | 20 | Art K-12 | 34 | Early Childhood Ed | 48 | English/Lang Arts K-12 | 62 | Foreign/World Lang Elem | 76 | Info Systems | 92 | Magnet School | 288 | Common Core Standards |
| 6 | Athletic | 21 | Art Elem | 35 | Health/Phys Education | 49 | English/Lang Arts Elem | 63 | Foreign/World Lang Sec | 77 | Psychological Assess | 93 | Parental Involvement | 294 | Accountability |
| 7 | Health Services | 22 | Art Sec | 36 | Guidance Services K-12 | 50 | English/Lang Arts Sec | 64 | Religious Education K-12 | 78 | Affirmative Action | 95 | Tech Prep Program | 295 | Network System |
| 8 | Curric/Instruct K-12 | 23 | Music K-12 | 37 | Guidance Services Elem | 51 | Reading K-12 | 65 | Religious Education Elem | 79 | Student Personnel | 97 | Chief Information Officer | 296 | Title II Programs |
| 9 | Curric/Instruct Elem | 24 | Music Elem | 38 | Guidance Services Sec | 52 | Reading Elem | 66 | Religious Education Sec | 80 | Driver Ed/Safety | 98 | Chief Technology Officer | 297 | Webmaster |
| 10 | Curric/Instruct Sec | 25 | Music Sec | 39 | Social Studies K-12 | 53 | Reading Sec | 67 | Teacher Personnel | 81 | School Board President | 270 | Character Education | 298 | Grant Writer/Ptnrships |
| 11 | Federal Program | 26 | Business Education | 40 | Social Studies Elem | 54 | Remedial Reading K-12 | 68 | Teacher Personnel | 82 | Gifted/Talented | 271 | Migrant Education | 750 | Chief Innovation Officer |
| 12 | Title I | 27 | Career & Tech Ed | 41 | Social Studies Sec | 55 | Remedial Reading Elem | 69 | Academic Assessment | 83 | Video Services | 273 | Teacher Mentor | 751 | Chief of Staff |
| 13 | Title V | 28 | Technology Education | 42 | Science K-12 | 56 | Remedial Reading Sec | 70 | Research/Development | 84 | Erate | 274 | Before/After Sch | 752 | Social Emotional Learning |
| 15 | Asst Superintendent | 29 | Family/Consumer Science | 43 | Science Elem | 57 | Bilingual/ELL | 71 | Public Information | 85 | AIDS Education | 275 | Response To Intervention | | |

| NAME/District | JOB FUNCTIONS | PAGE |
|---|---|---|
| Tucker, Jimmy/Woodville Ind School Dist | 67 | 378 |
| Tucker, Jodie/Whitesboro Ind School Dist | 8 | 173 |
| Tucker, Maranda/Whiteface Con Ind School Dist | 9,93,274 | 78 |
| Tucker, Mark/Knox City-O'Brien Cons Ind SD | 10,83,88,275 | 261 |
| Tucker, Misti/Schulenburg Ind School Dist | 31,36 | 152 |
| Tucker, Patti/Spurger Ind School Dist | 58 | 378 |
| Tucker, Sky/Levelland Ind School Dist | 34 | 232 |
| Tucker, Stephanie/Hillsboro Ind School Dist | 11,31,57,58,271 | 230 |
| Tucker, Tammy/Rogers Ind School Dist | 11,296,298 | 32 |
| Tucker, Toby/Canyon Ind School Dist | 6 | 323 |
| Tudon, Sara/Los Fresnos Cons Ind Sch Dist | 8 | 69 |
| Tudyk, Frank/Pleasanton Ind School Dist | 67 | 24 |
| Tuggle, Margaret/Crockett Ind School Dist | 36 | 235 |
| Tugwell, Donna/Rusk Ind School Dist | 58,77 | 77 |
| Tullos, Wendy/Lovelady Ind School Dist | 1 | 236 |
| Tunink, Jennifer/Channelview Ind School Dist | 20,23 | 188 |
| Tunnel, Lynn/Friendswood Ind Sch Dist | 68 | 164 |
| Tunnell, Kim, Dr/Mineola Ind School Dist | 83 | 408 |
| Tunnell, Olin/Brainnation Schools | 67 | 33 |
| Turlington, Amanda/Weimar Ind School Dist | 58 | 91 |
| Turner Jackson, Alice/Ft Worth Ind School Dist | 7 | 352 |
| Turner, Angela/La Vernia Ind School Dist | 73,98,295,297 | 404 |
| Turner, Blake/Ector Ind School Dist | 6 | 150 |
| Turner, Brenda/Haskell Cons Ind School Dist | 2 | 215 |
| Turner, Chad/New Caney Ind School Dist | 67 | 296 |
| Turner, Dan/Alief Ind School Dist | 91 | 186 |
| Turner, Daniel/Haskell Cons Ind School Dist | 5 | 215 |
| Turner, David/Eula Ind School Dist | 16,73,82,83,286 | 66 |
| Turner, Jack/Ganado Ind School Dist | 5 | 242 |
| Turner, Jeff/Allen Ind School Dist | 20,23 | 80 |
| Turner, Jessica/Leon Ind School Dist | 6 | 267 |
| Turner, Josh/Maud Ind School Dist | 6 | 52 |
| Turner, Karen/Lampasas Ind School Dist | 58 | 264 |
| Turner, Kirk/Chireno ISD School Dist | 3 | 300 |
| Turner, Louann/Crockett Ind School Dist | 4 | 235 |
| Turner, Lucas/Hardin Jefferson Ind Sch Dist | 73,295,297 | 182 |
| Turner, Matt/Gilmer Ind School Dist | 6 | 378 |
| Turner, Melinda/Duncanville Ind School Dist | 76 | 108 |
| Turner, Nicole/Karnack Ind School Dist | 69 | 214 |
| Turner, Paula/New Boston Ind School Dist | 67 | 52 |
| Turner, Renee/Apple Springs Ind School Dist | 4 | 376 |
| Turner, Renee/Apple Springs Ind School Dist | 4 | 376 |
| Turner, Rhonda/Quinlan Ind School Dist | 1 | 408 |
| Turner, Roy/Roosevelt Ind School Dist | 3 | 274 |
| Turner, Ryan/Llano Ind School Dist | 2,19,270 | 271 |
| Turner, Scott/Quitman Ind School Dist | 73,295 | 408 |
| Turner, Tracy/Angleton Ind School Dist | 4 | 55 |
| Turney, Mark/Jacksonville Ind School Dist | 5 | 76 |
| Tusa, Johnny/Waco Ind School Dist | 6 | 284 |
| Tutle, Amy/Sunnyvale Ind School Dist | 294 | 117 |
| Tutt, Kim/Slocum ISD School Dist | 38,83,85,88,270,275 | 19 |
| Tuttle, Cicely/Hurst-Euless-Bedford ISD | 15,68 | 356 |
| Tye, Kevin/Connally Ind School Dist | 73 | 282 |
| Tyerman, Nicholas/Onalaska Ind School Dist | 6 | 320 |
| Tyler, Katelyn/Burleson Ind School Dist | 71 | 249 |
| Tyler, Lauren/Central Heights Ind Sch Dist | 38,69,83,85,88,285 | 300 |
| Tyndell, Nikki/Edgewood Ind School Dist | 57 | 382 |
| Tyner, Scott/China Spring Ind School Dist | 295 | 281 |
| Tyner, Scott/Tenaha Ind School Dist | 1 | 338 |
| Tyson, Lela/Calhoun Co Ind School Dist | 69 | 65 |
| Tyus, Darcy/Mexia Ind School Dist | 58 | 270 |

### U

| NAME/District | JOB FUNCTIONS | PAGE |
|---|---|---|
| Ude, Audra/Ft Bend Ind School Dist | 294 | 154 |
| Uecker, David/Hutto Ind School Dist | 5 | 399 |
| Ugarte, Debbie/Rice Cons Ind School Dist | 7 | 90 |
| Ugarte, Diana/Kenedy Ind School Dist | 1,11 | 254 |
| Ukpaka, Cherron/Ft Worth Ind School Dist | 52,280 | 352 |
| **Ulcak, Chris/Moulton Ind School Dist** | 1 | 265 |
| Uloth, Sandra/Walnut Springs Ind Sch Dist | 16 | 51 |
| Ulrich, Debbie/Royal Ind School Dist | 68 | 387 |
| Umhoefer, Darrell/Midway Ind School Dist | 20,23 | 283 |
| Ummel, David, Dr/White Oak Ind School Dist | 67 | 176 |
| Underwood, Dian/San Angelo Ind School Dist | 58 | 367 |
| Underwood, Jay/Anna Ind School Dist | 15,68,79 | 81 |
| Underwood, Matt/Stephenville Ind School Dist | 1 | 148 |

| NAME/District | JOB FUNCTIONS | PAGE |
|---|---|---|
| Underwood, Mickey/Wink Loving Ind School Dist | 4 | 405 |
| Underwood, Rala/Highland Park Ind School Dist | 38 | 322 |
| Underwood, Tommy/Quinlan Ind School Dist | 3,5,7,91 | 240 |
| Underwood, Wesley/San Angelo Ind School Dist | 8,18 | 367 |
| Ungerwood, Sandra/Aubrey Ind School Dist | 83,85 | 124 |
| Unterbrink, Karen/Riviera Ind School Dist | 1 | 261 |
| Upchurch, Carole/Maypearl Ind School Dist | 73,295 | 145 |
| Upchurch, Eric/Arlington Ind School Dist | 15,73 | 346 |
| Upchurch, Pam/Queen City Ind School Dist | 3,5 | 74 |
| Upchurch, Sally/Clint Ind School Dist | 91 | 136 |
| Upchurch, Tiffony/Quinlan Ind School Dist | 71 | 240 |
| Upshaw, Sandra/Laneville Ind School Dist | 2 | 330 |
| Uptmore, Patrick/Waco Ind School Dist | 74,273 | 284 |
| Urban, Paul/Liberty Hill Ind School Dist | 76 | 401 |
| Urbanczyk, James/Floresville Ind School Dist | 73,295,297 | 403 |
| Urbanek, Kevin/Boling Ind School Dist | 6 | 392 |
| Urbano, John/Victoria Ind School Dist | 3,91 | 384 |
| Urbina, Shannon/Int'l Leadership of Texas Dist | 58 | 112 |
| Urias, Amanda/Kermit Ind School Dist | 31,36,270 | 405 |
| Uribe-Center, Laura/Lytle Ind School Dist | 11,68,296,298 | 24 |
| Uribe-Pizana, Mary/Spring Branch Ind School Dist | 273 | 206 |
| Uribe, Eugenia/Garrison Ind School Dist | 36,57,85 | 301 |
| Uriegas, Michael/Carrizo Spgs Cons Ind SD | 33,68,78,79,91 | 131 |
| Uriegas, Sandra/Carrizo Spgs Cons Ind SD | 11,57 | 131 |
| Urquidi, Art/Lake Worth Ind School Dist | 79 | 358 |
| Urquizo, Nora/Crowell Ind School Dist | 4 | 153 |
| Urrabazo, Salvadore/Stockdale Ind School Dist | 67 | 404 |
| Urrabazo, Theresa/San Antonio Ind School Dist | 69,70,294 | 42 |
| Uselman, Amy/Round Rock Ind School Dist | 16 | 401 |
| Uselman, Jeffrey/Round Rock Ind School Dist | 73,286 | 401 |
| Usery, Jacob/Venus Ind School Dist | 295 | 252 |
| Utech, Travis/Willis Ind School Dist | 27,31 | 297 |
| Utley, Meridith/City View Ind School Dist | 10,31,83 | 394 |
| Uttley, Paul, Dr/Paradise Ind School Dist | 1 | 407 |

### V

| NAME/District | JOB FUNCTIONS | PAGE |
|---|---|---|
| Vacha, Emily/Snook Ind School Dist | 7,35 | 63 |
| Vaden, Barbara/Lingleville Ind School Dist | 16,82 | 148 |
| Vaden, Kallen/Temple Ind School Dist | 2,19 | 32 |
| Vahalik, Johnny/San Antonio Ind School Dist | 27,31 | 42 |
| Valderrama, Monica/San Antonio Ind School Dist | 57 | 42 |
| Valdespino-Gay, Juony/Dallas Ind School Dist | 752 | 102 |
| Valdespino, Luis/Arlington Ind School Dist | 752 | 346 |
| Valdez, Gina/Flour Bluff Ind School Dist | 4 | 307 |
| Valdez, Jane/Eagle Mtn-Saginaw Ind Sch Dist | 2 | 351 |
| Valdez, Jennifer/Alvin Ind School Dist | 8,15,37,270 | 54 |
| Valdez, Marcel/La Pryor Ind School Dist | 67 | 411 |
| Valdez, Rick/Somerset Ind School Dist | 91 | 45 |
| Valdez, Sasil/Keene Ind School Dist | 16,82 | 251 |
| Valdez, Victor/Pflugerville Ind School Dist | 16,73,76,295 | 374 |
| Valdonado, Mary/Brownfield Ind Sch Dist | 271 | 364 |
| Valencia, Albert/Ector Co Ind School Dist | 2 | 134 |
| **Valencia, Michael/McCamey Ind School Dist** | 1 | 380 |
| Valenta, Richard, Dr/Denton Ind School Dist | 15,751 | 124 |
| Valentine, Jason/Wimberley Ind School Dist | 285 | 217 |
| Valenzuela, Beatriz/Sabinal Ind School Dist | 38 | 380 |
| Valenzuela, Thomas/Crane Ind School Dist | 73,295 | 97 |
| Valeriano, Laura/Sonora Ind School Dist | 54 | 345 |
| Valerio, Valerie/Marfa Ind School Dist | 76 | 322 |
| Vallejo, Adan/Mercedes Ind School Dist | 5 | 225 |
| Vallejo, Pete/Edcouch Elsa Ind School Dist | 16 | 220 |
| Valles, Ruben/Seagraves Ind School Dist | 3,5 | 162 |
| Valverde, Yirah/Canutillo Ind School Dist | 45 | 136 |
| Van Deaver, Tommy/Maud Ind School Dist | 2 | 52 |
| Van Dyke, Pamela/Eanes Ind School Dist | 297 | 372 |
| Van Fussen, Darren/Devine Ind School Dist | 3 | 286 |
| Van Geem, Edgar/Flour Bluff Ind School Dist | 58,77 | 307 |
| Van Hoose, Dick/Tahoka Ind School Dist | 1 | 276 |
| Van Meter, Trent/Guthrie Common School Dist | 73,295 | 260 |
| Van Ness, Albert/Refugio Ind School Dist | 3 | 326 |
| Van Pelt, Deena/Hardin Jefferson Ind Sch Dist | 58 | 182 |
| Van Ravensway, Pam/Brownsville Ind School Dist | 69,70 | 66 |
| Van Winkle, Chad/Cleburne Ind School Dist | 5 | 250 |
| VanAuken, Jeff/Nixon-Smiley Cons Ind Sch Dist | 2,3,5 | 169 |
| Vance, Cynthia/Union Grove Ind School Dist | 4 | 379 |
| VanCleave, Mason/Hamlin Collegiate Ind Sch Dist | 67 | 252 |

| NAME/District | JOB FUNCTIONS | PAGE |
|---|---|---|
| VanCleave, Tim/Robinson Ind School Dist | 11,15 | 284 |
| Vandagriff, Mindi/Anna Ind School Dist | 73,286 | 81 |
| Vandaveer, Sandra/Sweeny Ind School Dist | 58 | 57 |
| Vandeaver, Pamela/Clarksville Ind School Dist | 2,3 | 325 |
| Vanderbrook, Catherine/New Braunfels Ind School Dist | 4 | 92 |
| Vanderpool, Stephen/Groom Ind School Dist | 8,57,69,275 | 72 |
| Vandersthaas, Stacy/Quitman Ind School Dist | 7 | 408 |
| Vanderveer, Sean/Sherman Ind School Dist | 297 | 172 |
| Vandervoort, Jessica/Clear Creek Ind School Dist | 297 | 163 |
| Vandeventer, Melissa/Dayton Ind School Dist | 2 | 268 |
| Vandever, John/Texas City Ind School Dist | 4 | 166 |
| Vanhook, Kevin/Victoria Ind School Dist | 67 | 384 |
| Vanicer, Wes/Georgetown Ind School Dist | 294 | 398 |
| Vanley, Nancy/Ector Co Ind School Dist | 36 | 134 |
| Vanmatre, Stephen/Premont Ind School Dist | 1,11 | 249 |
| VanMeter, Kalli/Pine Tree Ind School Dist | 58 | 175 |
| Vannatta, Kelley/Whitehouse Ind School Dist | 68 | 341 |
| Vanover, Finis/Livingston Ind School Dist | 6 | 319 |
| Vanpelt, Beena/Orangefield Ind School Dist | 8 | 312 |
| Vanya, Gary/Hemphill Ind School Dist | 6,35 | 331 |
| Vanzant, Michelle/Krum Ind School Dist | 38 | 126 |
| Vardeman, Rachel/Agua Dulce Ind School Dist | 8,11,57,58,69,270 | 305 |
| Vardeman, Weldonna/Hubbard Ind School Dist | 8 | 230 |
| Vargas-Lew, Linda/Edgewood Ind School Dist | 36,78,90 | 34 |
| Vargas, Carlos/London Ind School Dist | 3,5 | 308 |
| Vargas, Christina/Lasara Ind School Dist | 58 | 397 |
| Vargas, Irene/Ft Stockton Ind School Dist | 271 | 318 |
| Varnum, Pam/Pilot Point Ind School Dist | 5 | 129 |
| Vasquez, Amador/Lubbock Ind School Dist | 45 | 272 |
| Vasquez, Annette/Driscoll Ind School Dist | 2,11 | 307 |
| Vasquez, Bruno/Canutillo Ind School Dist | 3,5 | 136 |
| Vasquez, Charity/Region 15 Ed Service Center | 2 | 368 |
| Vasquez, Connie/Ysleta Ind School Dist | 11 | 141 |
| Vasquez, Danny/Driscoll Ind School Dist | 6 | 307 |
| Vasquez, Erika/Alice Ind School Dist | 42 | 248 |
| Vasquez, James/Ysleta Ind School Dist | 79 | 141 |
| Vasquez, Jill/Wylie Ind School Dist | 11,57,271 | 88 |
| Vasquez, Joe/Los Fresnos Cons Ind Sch Dist | 91 | 69 |
| Vasquez, Laura/Somerset Ind School Dist | 5 | 45 |
| Vasquez, Martha/San Antonio Ind School Dist | 61 | 42 |
| Vasquez, Maury/Somerset Ind School Dist | 71 | 45 |
| Vasquez, Ray/Presidio Ind School Dist | 1 | 323 |
| Vasquez, Rosa/Grandfalls-Royalty Ind SD | 4 | 388 |
| Vasquez, Teresa/Kennedale Ind School Dist | 7 | 358 |
| Vaughan, Kevin/Andrews Ind School Dist | 8,30,58,88,273 | 19 |
| Vaughan, Lisa/Goose Creek Cons Ind Sch Dist | 90 | 192 |
| Vaughn, Blake/Frisco Ind School Dist | 3 | 82 |
| Vaughn, Denice/Cooper Ind School Dist | 5 | 123 |
| Vaughn, Jan/North Hopkins Ind School Dist | 2 | 234 |
| Vaughn, Juhree/Windthorst Ind School Dist | 2 | 23 |
| Vaughn, Patricia/Grand Saline Ind School Dist | 4 | 383 |
| Vaughn, Shauni/Wylie Ind School Dist | 58,271 | 364 |
| Vazques, Christina/Lockhart Ind School Dist | 57,271 | 64 |
| Vazquez-Cruz, Juan/Edgewood Ind School Dist | 73 | 34 |
| Vazquez, Gilbert/San Felipe-Del Rio Cons Ind SD | 295 | 382 |
| Vazquez, Lawanda/Apple Springs Ind School Dist | 73,76,98 | 376 |
| Veal-Gooch, Tina/Texarkana Ind School Dist | 71 | 53 |
| Veal, Heidi/Lewisville Ind School Dist | 34 | 126 |
| Vega-Barrio, Rosy/Tornillo Ind School Dist | 1 | 141 |
| Vega, Albert/Canutillo Ind School Dist | 286 | 136 |
| Vega, Jennyann/McAllen Ind School Dist | 16,73,82 | 224 |
| Vega, Judy/McKinney Ind School Dist | 49 | 84 |
| Vega, Nelly/Madisonville Cons ISD | 4 | 276 |
| Vega, Roy/Lasara Ind School Dist | 6 | 397 |
| Vegara, Kathy/Klein Ind School Dist | 57,89 | 202 |
| Vela, Alfredo/Cotulla Ind School Dist | 2,5 | 262 |
| Vela, Dolores/Austwell Tivoli Ind SD | 1 | 326 |

| NAME/District | JOB FUNCTIONS | PAGE |
|---|---|---|
| Vela, Jimmy/Point Isabel Ind Sch Dist | 67 | 70 |
| Vela, Librada/San Diego Ind School Dist | 67 | 132 |
| Vela, Monica/Edcouch Elsa Ind School Dist | 93,271 | 221 |
| Vela, Queta/Comstock Ind School Dist | 4 | 381 |
| Velasquez, Eleazar/Rio Grande City Ind Sch Dist | 67 | 343 |
| Velazquez, Rolando/Lasara Ind School Dist | 67 | 397 |
| Velazquez, Samaris/Stockdale Ind School Dist | 4 | 404 |
| Velenta, Venus, Dr/Pleasanton Ind School Dist | 286,752 | 24 |
| Velez, Luis/Eagle Pass Ind School Dist | 2 | 279 |
| Veliz, Ramiro/United Ind School Dist | 67 | 390 |
| Vella, Nilda/Seguin Ind School Dist | 42 | 178 |
| Velleas, Eugene/Agua Dulce Ind School Dist | 83,88 | 305 |
| Veloz-Powell, Elizabeth, Dr/Alief Ind School Dist | 15,68 | 186 |
| Venghaus, Zachary/Columbus Ind School Dist | 73 | 90 |
| Veno, Tiffany/Garland Ind School Dist | 71 | 109 |
| Vera, Daniel/Manor Ind School Dist | 68 | 373 |
| Vera, Manuel/West Orange-Cove Cons ISD | 5 | 312 |
| Verava, Mariano/Harlandale Ind School Dist | 97 | 35 |
| Verdell, Alex/North East Ind School Dist | 69,70,294 | 37 |
| Verduzco, Manuel/Clint Ind School Dist | 73,98 | 136 |
| Vereecke, Matthew, Dr/Diocese of Dallas Ed Office | 1 | 118 |
| Vergo, Donna/Joaquin Ind School Dist | 68 | 337 |
| Verley, Craig/Mission Cons Ind School Dist | 71 | 225 |
| Vernon, Kelly/Perryton Ind School Dist | 11 | 310 |
| Verrett, Lachlin, Dr/Houston Ind School Dist | 15,58 | 193 |
| Verstuyft, Lloyd, Dr/Southwest Ind School Dist | 1 | 46 |
| Verver, Mary/Tulia Ind School Dist | 271 | 345 |
| Vesely, Todd/Ft Worth Ind School Dist | 6 | 352 |
| Vessels, Ruth/Hereford Ind School Dist | 57 | 123 |
| Vessling, David/Pflugerville Ind School Dist | 3 | 374 |
| Vestal, Ajck/Lovejoy Ind School Dist | 98 | 84 |
| Vestal, Ian/Temple Ind School Dist | 4 | 32 |
| Vezurk, Blake/Anderson-Shiro Cons Ind SD | 2 | 176 |
| Viches, Gina/Ricardo Ind School Dist | 288 | 261 |
| Vick, Christen/Palmer Ind School Dist | 67 | 146 |
| Vickers, Melissa/Woodson Ind School Dist | 2,298 | 365 |
| Vickery, Traci/Garland Ind School Dist | 46 | 109 |
| Vickman, Ann/South Texas Ind School Dist | 16 | 71 |
| Victory, Travis/Clarendon Cons Ind Sch Dist | 8 | 131 |
| Vidal, Monica/West Oso Ind School Dist | 93 | 309 |
| Vidaurri, Maria, Dr/Sharyland Ind School Dist | 1 | 227 |
| Vieregge, Rick/Malakoff Ind School Dist | 67 | 219 |
| Vierra, Annette/Round Rock Ind School Dist | 68 | 401 |
| Viertel, Jay/Beeville Ind School Dist | 27,36 | 28 |
| Vies, Marcella, Dr/San Marcos Cons Ind Sch Dist | 15,68 | 217 |
| Viggerstaff, Josh/Harts Bluff Ind School Dist | 275 | 366 |
| Vigil, Kelly/Pampa Ind School Dist | 16 | 170 |
| Vigtema, Jackie/Whitehouse Ind School Dist | 11,58,271 | 341 |
| Vijil, Veronica, Dr/Fabens Ind School Dist | 1 | 139 |
| Vilema, Francis/Eagle Pass Ind School Dist | 39,42 | 279 |
| Villa, Diana/Andrews Ind School Dist | 68 | 19 |
| Villafranca, Robert/Somerset Ind School Dist | 3,15,79 | 45 |
| Villalba, Joseph/Goose Creek Cons Ind Sch Dist | 2 | 192 |
| Villalobos, Claudia/Rio Hondo Ind School Dist | 67 | 70 |
| Villaneda, Selena/Ingleside Ind School Dist | 16 | 334 |
| Villanueva, Cheryl/Godley Ind School Dist | 31,57,69 | 250 |
| Villanueva, Connie/Monte Alto Ind School Dist | 67 | 226 |
| Villanueva, Diane/Donna Ind School Dist | 58,77,275 | 220 |
| Villanueva, Gustavo/Abilene Ind School Dist | 10,15,27,31 | 362 |
| Villanueva, Joe/Olton Ind School Dist | 3 | 263 |
| Villareal-Morr, Elsa/Rio Grande City Ind Sch Dist | 69,294 | 343 |
| Villareal, Anna/Los Fresnos Cons Ind Sch Dist | 57 | 69 |
| Villareal, Irma/Edinburg Cons Ind School Dist | 12 | 221 |
| Villareal, Joseph/Harlingen Cons Ind School Dist | 10 | 68 |
| Villareal, Laura/Brownsville Ind School Dist | 4 | 66 |
| Villareal, Ricardo/La Joya Ind School Dist | 15,79 | 222 |
| Villarreal, Adelina/Rio Grande City Ind Sch Dist | 27 | 342 |

| | | | | | | | | | |
|---|---|---|---|---|---|---|---|---|---|
| 1 | Superintendent | 16 | Instructional Media Svcs | 30 | Adult Education | 44 | Science Sec | 58 | Special Education K-12 |
| 2 | Bus/Finance/Purchasing | 17 | Chief Operations Officer | 31 | Career/Sch-to-Work K-12 | 45 | Math K-12 | 59 | Special Education Elem |
| 3 | Buildings And Grounds | 18 | Chief Academic Officer | 32 | Career/Sch-to-Work Elem | 46 | Math Elem | 60 | Special Education Sec |
| 4 | Food Service | 19 | Chief Financial Officer | 33 | Career/Sch-to-Work Sec | 47 | Math Sec | 61 | Foreign/World Lang K-12 |
| 5 | Transportation | 20 | Art K-12 | 34 | Early Childhood Ed | 48 | English/Lang Arts K-12 | 62 | Foreign/World Lang Elem |
| 6 | Athletic | 21 | Art Elem | 35 | Health/Phys Education | 49 | English/Lang Arts Elem | 63 | Foreign/World Lang Sec |
| 7 | Health Services | 22 | Art Sec | 36 | Guidance Services K-12 | 50 | English/Lang Arts Sec | 64 | Religious Education K-12 |
| 8 | Curric/Instruct K-12 | 23 | Music K-12 | 37 | Guidance Services Elem | 51 | Reading K-12 | 65 | Religious Education Elem |
| 9 | Curric/Instruct Elem | 24 | Music Elem | 38 | Guidance Services Sec | 52 | Reading Elem | 66 | Religious Education Sec |
| 10 | Curric/Instruct Sec | 25 | Music Sec | 39 | Social Studies K-12 | 53 | Reading Sec | 67 | School Board President |
| 11 | Federal Program | 26 | Business Education | 40 | Social Studies Elem | 54 | Remedial Reading K-12 | 68 | Teacher Personnel |
| 12 | Title I | 27 | Career & Tech Ed | 41 | Social Studies Sec | 55 | Remedial Reading Elem | 69 | Academic Assessment |
| 13 | Title V | 28 | Technology Education | 42 | Science K-12 | 56 | Remedial Reading Sec | 70 | Research/Development |
| 15 | Asst Superintendent | 29 | Family/Consumer Science | 43 | Science Elem | 57 | Bilingual/ELL | 71 | Public Information |

| | | | |
|---|---|---|---|
| 72 | Summer School | 88 | Alternative/At Risk |
| 73 | Instructional Tech | 89 | Multi-Cultural Curriculum |
| 74 | Inservice Training | 90 | Social Work |
| 75 | Marketing/Distributive | 91 | Safety/Security |
| 76 | Info Systems | 92 | Magnet School |
| 77 | Psychological Assess | 93 | Parental Involvement |
| 78 | Affirmative Action | 95 | Tech Prep Program |
| 79 | Student Personnel | 97 | Chief Information Officer |
| 80 | Driver Ed/Safety | 98 | Chief Technology Officer |
| 81 | Gifted/Talented | 270 | Character Education |
| 82 | Video Services | 271 | Migrant Education |
| 83 | Substance Abuse Prev | 273 | Teacher Mentor |
| 84 | Erate | 274 | Before/After Sch |
| 85 | AIDS Education | 275 | Response To Intervention |

| | |
|---|---|
| 277 | Remedial Math K-12 |
| 280 | Literacy Coach |
| 285 | STEM |
| 286 | Digital Learning |
| 288 | Common Core Standards |
| 294 | Accountability |
| 295 | Network System |
| 296 | Title II Programs |
| 297 | Webmaster |
| 298 | Grant Writer/Ptnrships |
| 750 | Chief Innovation Officer |
| 751 | Chief of Staff |
| 752 | Social Emotional Learning |

| NAME/District | JOB FUNCTIONS | PAGE | NAME/District | JOB FUNCTIONS | PAGE |
|---|---|---|---|---|---|
| Villarreal, Alicia, Dr/Somerset Ind School Dist | 48,51 | 45 | Wagner, Jeremy/Lubbock-Cooper Ind Sch Dist | 285 | 274 |
| Villarreal, Dan/North East Ind School Dist | 2,7,15,19,91 | 37 | Wagner, Mark/Hamshire Fannett Ind Sch Dist | 6,35 | 245 |
| Villarreal, Ernie/Valentine Ind School Dist | 2 | 244 | Wagner, Pam/Louise Ind School Dist | 2 | 392 |
| Villarreal, George/Bovina Ind School Dist | 67 | 317 | Wagner, Peter/Southwest Ind School Dist | 6 | 46 |
| Villarreal, Heriberto/Santa Rosa Ind School Dist | 11,73 | 71 | Wagner, Rena/Winnsboro Ind School Dist | 57 | 408 |
| Villarreal, Jennifer/Hidalgo Ind School Dist | 16 | 222 | Wagner, Shane/Sweet Home Ind School Dist | 1,11,73,83,84 | 265 |
| Villarreal, John, Dr/Rockwall Ind School Dist | 1 | 328 | Waide, Paige/Perryton Ind School Dist | 38 | 310 |
| Villarreal, Juan/South Texas Ind School Dist | 3,5,91 | 71 | Wainscott, Sharon/Knox City-O'Brien Cons Ind SD | 68 | 261 |
| Villarreal, Martina/Beeville Ind School Dist | 70,294 | 28 | Waites, Kanesha, Dr/Lancaster Ind School Dist | 93 | 114 |
| Villarreal, Melissa/Sinton Ind School Dist | 2,15 | 334 | Wakefield, Bill/Bonham Ind School Dist | 3,17,91 | 149 |
| Villarreal, Nelinda/Edinburg Cons Ind School Dist | 20,23 | 221 | Wakefield, Carol/Early Ind School Dist | 4 | 62 |
| Villarreal, Rebecca/New Braunfels Ind School Dist | 71 | 92 | Wakeland, Sherri/Frisco Ind School Dist | 74 | 82 |
| Villarreal, Richard/Bovina Ind School Dist | 3,5 | 317 | Walden, Daniel/Donna Ind School Dist | 91 | 220 |
| Villarreal, Viki/Clifton Ind School Dist | 57 | 49 | Walden, Lydia/Highland Park Ind Sch Dist | 36,77,83,88 | 112 |
| Villarrell, Sandy/Runge Ind School Dist | 67 | 254 | Walden, Steve/Quinlan Ind School Dist | 91 | 240 |
| Villegas, Mary/Hidalgo Ind School Dist | 76 | 222 | Waldie, Michael/Gonzales Ind School Dist | 6,35 | 169 |
| Villegas, Omar/Lorenzo Ind School Dist | 3 | 98 | Waldo, Glen/Nazareth Ind School Dist | 1,11,288 | 75 |
| Villerot, Annette/Del Valle Ind School Dist | 1 | 372 | Waldo, Toni/Vernon Ind School Dist | 58,275,286 | 396 |
| Villiarreal, Sandra Ann/La Joya Ind School Dist | 81 | 222 | Waldrep, Jackie/Westbrook Ind School Dist | 4 | 292 |
| Villines, Jennifer/Coppell Ind School Dist | 752 | 102 | Waldrep, Terry/Pittsburg Ind School Dist | 1 | 72 |
| Vincek, Jamie/Lamar Cons Ind School Dist | 74 | 157 | Waldrip, Aaron/Abernathy Ind School Dist | 1 | 179 |
| Vincelette, Melanie/Lewisville Ind School Dist | 7 | 126 | Waldrip, Mike, Dr/Frisco Ind School Dist | 1 | 82 |
| Vincent, David/Princeton Ind School Dist | 73 | 87 | Waldron, Joseph/Abilene Ind School Dist | 15,68 | 362 |
| Vincent, Debra/Northside Ind School Dist | 4 | 396 | Waldrop, Colby/Farwell Ind School Dist | 1 | 317 |
| Vincent, Scott/Hartley Ind School Dist | 1 | 215 | Waldrop, Lori/New Caney Ind School Dist | 58 | 296 |
| Vincet, Monty/Hawley Ind School Dist | 67 | 253 | Waligura, Leann/Leakey Ind School Dist | 4 | 324 |
| Vincik, Sherri/Shiner Ind School Dist | 2,11 | 265 | Walinder, Kari/Andrews Ind School Dist | 67 | 19 |
| Vine, Kim, Dr/Port Arthur Ind School Dist | 8 | 246 | Walker, Adrienne/Birdville Ind School Dist | 11,296,298 | 348 |
| Vines, Thresa/Adrian Ind School Dist | 58 | 310 | Walker, Amy/Springtown Ind School Dist | 67 | 316 |
| Vineyard, Shelley/Humble Ind School Dist | 2 | 200 | Walker, Andre/Houston Ind School Dist | 6 | 193 |
| Vinson, Allison/Birdville Ind School Dist | 27,30,31,73 | 348 | Walker, Angela/Liberty Ind School Dist | 79 | 269 |
| Vinson, David, Dr/Wylie Ind School Dist | 1 | 88 | Walker, Becky/Comal Ind School Dist | 27,31,95 | 91 |
| Vinson, Logan/Anson Ind School Dist | 3,5 | 252 | Walker, Belinda/West Rusk Co Cons Ind Sch Dist | 2 | 331 |
| Vinton, Kim/Region 20 Ed Service Center | 30 | 48 | Walker, Christie/Bowie Ind School Dist | 8,11,57,58,77,88,288,294 | 292 |
| Virdell, Keith/Goldthwaite Consolidated ISD | 6 | 291 | Walker, Clay/Little Elm Ind School Dist | 295 | 128 |
| Vivreet, Mary Ellen/Vidor Ind School Dist | 4 | 312 | Walker, Cody/West Rusk Co Cons Ind Sch Dist | 73,295 | 331 |
| Voelcker, Wanda/Mineral Wells Ind School Dist | 7,35,85 | 313 | Walker, Darlene/Canadian Ind School Dist | 38 | 218 |
| Voelkel, Carla/Dickinson Ind School Dist | 1 | 164 | Walker, David/Gholson Ind School Dist | 67 | 282 |
| Vogelpohl, Margo/Round Rock Ind School Dist | 12,34 | 401 | Walker, David, Dr/Christoval Ind School Dist | 1 | 366 |
| Voight, Alan/Lamar Cons Ind School Dist | 73 | 157 | Walker, Debbie/Willis Ind School Dist | 58 | 297 |
| Voights-Pettit, Tiffany/Baird Ind School Dist | 4 | 65 | Walker, Doretta/North East Ind School Dist | 295 | 37 |
| Voigt, Bunny/D'Hanis Ind School Dist | 76 | 286 | Walker, Fred/Clear Creek Ind School Dist | 4 | 162 |
| Volger, Doyle/Lubbock Ind School Dist | 9,15 | 272 | Walker, Frederick, Dr/Spring Ind School Dist | 3 | 207 |
| Volkmer, Lisa/Bay City Ind School Dist | 11,57,271,273,296 | 278 | Walker, Gina/Hunt Ind School Dist | 2,4 | 258 |
| Vollweiler, Kevin/Celina Ind School Dist | 5 | 81 | Walker, Gwen/Hallsville Ind School Dist | 71,93 | 213 |
| Volmer, Christie/Hereford Ind School Dist | 68 | 123 | Walker, Jeff/Liberty Hill Ind School Dist | 6,35,85 | 401 |
| Volz, Darlene/San Antonio Ind School Dist | 30 | 42 | Walker, Jenny/Olney Ind School Dist | 68 | 410 |
| Voradakis, Susan/Ft Bend Ind School Dist | 10,69 | 153 | Walker, Jimmie, Dr/Alamo Heights Ind School Dist | 8,11,81,296 | 33 |
| Vorajakkmol, Maria/Ganado Ind School Dist | 57 | 242 | Walker, Joe/Godley Ind School Dist | 20,23 | 250 |
| Voss, Serena/Post Ind School Dist | 38,83,88 | 167 | Walker, John/Commerce Independent Sch Dist | 2 | 239 |
| Voth, Michael/Lovejoy Ind School Dist | 73 | 84 | Walker, Karrie/Hays Cons Ind School Dist | 7 | 216 |
| Vrooman, Sabrina/Diocese of Beaumont Sch Office | 2,19 | 247 | Walker, Kerri/Bastrop Ind School Dist | 39 | 26 |
| Vroonland, David, Dr/Mesquite Ind School Dist | 1 | 115 | Walker, Laurie/Ennis Ind School Dist | 2,11 | 144 |
| Vu, Arthur/Harris Co Dept of Ed | 73 | 184 | Walker, Lee/Muleshoe Ind School Dist | 6 | 25 |
| Vu, Julie, Dr/Kennedale Ind School Dist | 15 | 358 | Walker, Marcie/Joshua Ind School Dist | 7 | 251 |
| Vurner, Brett/Nueces Canyon Cons Ind SD | 16,73,298 | 135 | Walker, Marybel/Hunt Ind School Dist | 3 | 258 |
| | | | Walker, Michele/Pine Tree Ind School Dist | 11,57 | 175 |
| **W** | | | Walker, Rhonda/Lindale Ind School Dist | 16 | 339 |
| Wacker, Susie/Randolph Field Ind School Dist | 7 | 42 | Walker, Sam/Lampasas Ind School Dist | 67 | 264 |
| Waclawczyk, Janlen/Judson Ind School Dist | 76 | 36 | Walker, Shelli/Perryton Ind School Dist | 4 | 310 |
| Waddell, Gregg/Aquilla Ind School Dist | 5 | 230 | Walker, Terri/Katy Ind School Dist | 275 | 156 |
| Waddle, Dawn/Palmer Ind School Dist | 6 | 146 | Walker, Tiffany/Georgetown Ind School Dist | 8,11,57,58 | 398 |
| **Wade, Chris**/Smyer Ind School Dist | 1,83 | 232 | Walker, Valerie/School of Excellence In Ed | 285 | 45 |
| Wade, Cindi/Dripping Springs Ind Sch Dist | 84 | 215 | Walker, Whitney/Lampasas Ind School Dist | 79 | 264 |
| Wade, Cynthia/May Ind School Dist | 16 | 62 | Wall, Delinda/Gilmer Ind School Dist | 8,57,83,271 | 378 |
| Wade, Melissa/Frenship Ind School Dist | 11,85 | 272 | Wall, Leigh, Dr/Santa Fe Ind School Dist | 1 | 165 |
| Wade, Rhonda, Dr/Floresville Ind School Dist | 9,36,83 | 403 | Wall, Mike/Willis Ind School Dist | 6 | 297 |
| Wade, Tommy/Jacksonville Ind School Dist | 3,91 | 76 | Wall, Missy/Rockwall Ind School Dist | 90 | 328 |
| Wadleigh, Linda, Dr/La Porte Ind School Dist | 8,15 | 203 | Wall, Murray/Broaddus Ind School Dist | 5 | 332 |
| Wadsworth, Josh/Palmer Ind School Dist | 294 | 404 | Wall, Valerie/Pilot Point Ind School Dist | 73,295 | 129 |
| Wager, Sharon/New Diana Ind School Dist | 73,295 | 379 | Walla, Melisa/Anderson-Shiro Cons Ind SD | 83 | 176 |
| Waggoner, Jacob/Gunter Ind School Dist | 38,83 | 171 | Wallace, Aaron/Tomball Ind School Dist | 3 | 208 |
| Wagner, Bill/La Grange Ind School Dist | 1 | 151 | Wallace, Amanda/Henderson Ind School Dist | 68,79 | 330 |
| Wagner, Dennis/Anahuac Ind School Dist | 1 | 75 | Wallace, Andrew/Edna Ind School Dist | 16 | 242 |
| Wagner, Donald/Diocese of Fort Worth Ed Off | 19 | 360 | Wallace, Connie/Arlington Ind School Dist | 8 | 346 |
| Wagner, Helen/Humble Ind School Dist | 35 | 200 | Wallace, Denise/Region 5 Ed Service Center | 2 | 247 |

| | | | | |
|---|---|---|---|---|
| 1 Superintendent | 16 Instructional Media Svcs | 30 Adult Education | 44 Science Sec | 58 Special Education K-12 |
| 2 Bus/Finance/Purchasing | 17 Chief Operations Officer | 31 Career/Sch-to-Work K-12 | 45 Math K-12 | 59 Special Education Elem |
| 3 Buildings And Grounds | 18 Chief Academic Officer | 32 Career/Sch-to-Work Elem | 46 Math Elem | 60 Special Education Sec |
| 4 Food Service | 19 Chief Financial Officer | 33 Career/Sch-to-Work Sec | 47 Math Sec | 61 Foreign/World Lang K-12 |
| 5 Transportation | 20 Art K-12 | 34 Early Childhood Ed | 48 English/Lang Arts K-12 | 62 Foreign/World Lang Elem |
| 6 Athletic | 21 Art Elem | 35 Health/Phys Education | 49 English/Lang Arts Elem | 63 Foreign/World Lang Sec |
| 7 Health Services | 22 Art Sec | 36 Guidance Services K-12 | 50 English/Lang Arts Sec | 64 Religious Education K-12 |
| 8 Curric/Instruct K-12 | 23 Music K-12 | 37 Guidance Services Elem | 51 Reading K-12 | 65 Religious Education Elem |
| 9 Curric/Instruct Elem | 24 Music Elem | 38 Guidance Services Sec | 52 Reading Elem | 66 Religious Education Sec |
| 10 Curric/Instruct Sec | 25 Music Sec | 39 Social Studies K-12 | 53 Reading Sec | 67 School Board President |
| 11 Federal Program | 26 Business Education | 40 Social Studies Elem | 54 Remedial Reading K-12 | 68 Teacher Personnel |
| 12 Title I | 27 Career & Tech Ed | 41 Social Studies Sec | 55 Remedial Reading Elem | 69 Academic Assessment |
| 13 Title V | 28 Technology Education | 42 Science K-12 | 56 Remedial Reading Sec | 70 Research/Development |
| 15 Asst Superintendent | 29 Family/Consumer Science | 43 Science Elem | 57 Bilingual/ELL | 71 Public Information |

| | | |
|---|---|---|
| 72 Summer School | 88 Alternative/At Risk | 277 Remedial Math K-12 |
| 73 Instructional Tech | 89 Multi-Cultural Curriculum | 280 Literacy Coach |
| 74 Inservice Training | 90 Social Work | 285 STEM |
| 75 Marketing/Distributive | 91 Safety/Security | 286 Digital Learning |
| 76 Info Systems | 92 Magnet School | 288 Common Core Standards |
| 77 Psychological Assess | 93 Parental Involvement | 294 Accountability |
| 78 Affirmative Action | 95 Tech Prep Program | 295 Network System |
| 79 Student Personnel | 97 Chief Information Officer | 296 Title II Programs |
| 80 Driver Ed/Safety | 98 Chief Technology Officer | 297 Webmaster |
| 81 Gifted/Talented | 270 Character Education | 298 Grant Writer/Ptnrships |
| 82 Video Services | 271 Migrant Education | 750 Chief Innovation Officer |
| 83 Substance Abuse Prev | 273 Teacher Mentor | 751 Chief of Staff |
| 84 Erate | 274 Before/After Sch | 752 Social Emotional Learning |
| 85 AIDS Education | 275 Response To Intervention | |

| NAME/District | JOB FUNCTIONS | PAGE | NAME/District | JOB FUNCTIONS | PAGE |
|---|---|---|---|---|---|
| Watson, Nyla, Dr/Pearland Ind School Dist | 8,15,77,273 | 56 | Welch, Chance/Borger Ind School Dist | 1 | 240 |
| Watson, Rodney, Dr/Spring Ind School Dist | 1,288 | 207 | Welch, Christie/Detroit Ind School Dist | 36 | 325 |
| Watson, Teela/Region 11 Ed Service Center | 70 | 362 | Welch, Cindy/Brackett Ind School Dist | 31 | 260 |
| Watson, Willie/Pflugerville Ind School Dist | 68 | 374 | Welch, Clete/Eagle Mtn-Saginaw Ind Sch Dist | 3,5,17 | 351 |
| Watts, Eva/Donna Ind School Dist | 67 | 220 | Welch, Debbie/Burkburnett Ind Sch Dist | 4 | 394 |
| Watts, Mike/Leggett Ind School Dist | 3,5 | 319 | Welch, Greg/Clyde Consolidated Ind SD | 67 | 66 |
| Wayman, Ric/Princeton Ind School Dist | 5 | 87 | Welch, Janae/Deweyville Ind School Dist | 2 | 311 |
| Wayt, Chris/Union Grove Ind School Dist | 3,5 | 379 | Welch, Janet/Somerset Ind School Dist | 4 | 45 |
| Weatherall, Marcene/Keller Ind School Dist | 83 | 357 | Welch, Kim/Bluff Dale Ind Sch Dist | 2 | 147 |
| Weatherbee, Johnna/Lubbock Ind School Dist | 12,93 | 272 | Welch, Mary/Richardson Ind School Dist | 68 | 116 |
| Weatherby, Kim/Brenham Ind School Dist | 2 | 388 | Welch, Philip/Kountze Ind School Dist | 2,19 | 183 |
| Weatherford, Brandon/Broaddus Ind School Dist | 3 | 332 | Welch, Randy/Mabank Ind School Dist | 5 | 256 |
| Weatherford, Gary/Ector Co Ind School Dist | 3 | 134 | Welch, Robin/Wildorado Ind Sch Dist | 57 | 311 |
| Weatherford, Heather/Spring Creek Ind School Dist | 57,58 | 241 | Welch, Ron/Plains Ind School Dist | 6 | 409 |
| Weatherford, Ronda/Prairiland Ind School Dist | 2,296,298 | 263 | Welch, Tracy/Lake Worth Ind School Dist | 6 | 358 |
| Weatherly, Colin/Splendora Ind School Dist | 83,91 | 297 | Welker, Sandra/Centerville Ind School Dist | 58 | 267 |
| Weatherly, Mark, Dr/New Caney Ind School Dist | 10 | 296 | Wellborn, Harold/Kopperl Ind School Dist | 67 | 50 |
| Weaver, Brian/UT Tyler University Acad Dist | 69 | 341 | Wells, Caprica, Dr/North East Ind School Dist | 30 | 37 |
| Weaver, Candice/Lazbuddie Ind School Dist | 67 | 318 | Wells, Danyell/Cedar Hill Ind School Dist | 93 | 101 |
| Weaver, Dandre/DeSoto Ind School Dist | 1 | 108 | Wells, Gina/Big Spring Ind School Dist | 68 | 236 |
| Weaver, David/Marshall Ind School Dist | 71 | 214 | Wells, Griselda, Dr/Los Fresnos Cons Ind Sch Dist | 58 | 69 |
| Weaver, Dawn/Collinsville Ind School Dist | 7,85 | 171 | Wells, Jovan, Dr/Garland Ind School Dist | 18 | 109 |
| Weaver, Dwight/Duncanville Ind School Dist | 6,35 | 108 | Wells, Pam, Dr/Region 4 Ed Service Center | 1 | 213 |
| Weaver, Jeff/Dublin Ind School Dist | 67 | 147 | Wells, Randi/Carrollton-Farmers Branch ISD | 58,90 | 100 |
| Weaver, Lesley/Northwest Ind School Dist | 71 | 129 | Welps, Bryan/River Road Ind School Dist | 6 | 322 |
| Weaver, Mark/Aspermont Ind School Dist | 6 | 344 | Welsh, Marsha/Rockwall Ind School Dist | 280 | 328 |
| Weaver, Michelle/Westphalia Ind School Dist | 67 | 149 | Wendel, Daryl/Devine Ind School Dist | 8,15,68 | 286 |
| Weaver, Neal/Forney Ind School Dist | 6 | 254 | Wendel, Michelle/Sinton Ind School Dist | 16 | 334 |
| Weaver, Teresa/Martinsville Ind School Dist | 67 | 301 | Wendland, Shelli/Bland Ind School Dist | 8,58 | 238 |
| Webb, Alexis/Prosper Ind School Dist | 288 | 88 | Wenmohs, Shelly/Johnson City Ind School Dist | 67 | 49 |
| Webb, Beverly/Brownfield Ind Sch Dist | 4 | 364 | Wentz, Deanna/Alief Ind School Dist | 2,15 | 186 |
| Webb, Daniel/Andrews Ind School Dist | 3,15,91 | 19 | Wenzel, Jana/Bryan Ind School Dist | 73 | 58 |
| Webb, Darren/Lago Vista Ind School Dist | 1 | 373 | Werkheiser, Chrystal/Port Neches-Groves Ind SD | 98 | 246 |
| Webb, Donny/Hudson Ind School Dist | 1,11,57,83 | 20 | Wermuth, Sharon/San Angelo Ind School Dist | 76 | 367 |
| Webb, Jeff/Royse City Ind School Dist | 15,68,273 | 328 | Werner, Alyssa/Bellville Ind School Dist | 4 | 24 |
| Webb, Kenny/Comfort Ind School Dist | 5 | 257 | Wernli, Tracy/Northside Ind School Dist | 79 | 39 |
| Webb, Kim/Garland Ind School Dist | 47 | 109 | Wesley, Cheryl/Cedar Hill Ind School Dist | 67 | 101 |
| Webb, Lauri/Luling Ind School Dist | 83,85,271 | 65 | **Wesley, Wade/Bellevue Ind School Dist** | 1,11 | 77 |
| Webb, Laurinda/Luling Ind School Dist | 57,58 | 65 | Wesley, Wade/Jacksboro Ind Sch Dist | 8,11,57,271,275,288,296,298 | 242 |
| Webb, Mary/Frisco Ind School Dist | 9 | 82 | Wesp, Pete/Randolph Field Ind School Dist | 6 | 42 |
| Webb, Matthew/Humble Ind School Dist | 39 | 200 | Wesson, Jay/San Marcos Cons Ind Sch Dist | 3 | 216 |
| Webb, Michael, Dr/Tomball Ind School Dist | 15,79 | 208 | West, Anthony/Burkburnett Ind Sch Dist | 5 | 394 |
| Webb, Nancy/Anton Ind School Dist | 2 | 232 | West, Brenda/Highland Park Ind Sch Dist | 68 | 112 |
| Webb, Patty/Joshua Ind School Dist | 73 | 251 | West, Brent/Cisco Independent Sch Dist | 6 | 133 |
| Webb, Randy/Malakoff Ind School Dist | 73,95,295 | 219 | West, Dale/Bells Ind School Dist | 6 | 170 |
| Webb, Rick, Dr/Cayuga Ind School Dist | 1,11,288 | 18 | West, Dalton/Florence Ind School Dist | 3 | 398 |
| Webb, Robyn/Coppell Ind School Dist | 11,298 | 102 | West, Dana, Dr/Carrollton-Farmers Branch ISD | 8,15,74,286 | 100 |
| Webb, Shane/Gatesville Ind School Dist | 10 | 96 | West, Dana, Dr/Region 10 Ed Service Center | 8 | 120 |
| Webb, Susan/Crockett Co Cons Common SD | 4 | 98 | West, Daniel/Dumas Ind School Dist | 2,19 | 298 |
| Webb, Tracy/Union Grove Ind School Dist | 58 | 379 | West, Dava/Clear Creek Ind School Dist | 36 | 162 |
| Webber, Judy/Forney Ind School Dist | 8,18,27,30,34,69 | 254 | West, Filke/Sinton Ind School Dist | 4 | 334 |
| Webber, Natalie/Elgin Ind School Dist | 11 | 27 | West, Jaclyn/Lake Worth Ind School Dist | 2 | 358 |
| Webber, Shelly/Lockhart Ind School Dist | 7 | 64 | West, Jim/Ore City Ind School Dist | 3,5 | 379 |
| Webster, Courtney/Manor Ind School Dist | 39 | 373 | West, Josh/Pawnee Ind School Dist | 3 | 28 |
| Webster, James/Sheldon Ind School Dist | 79,83 | 205 | West, Keith, Dr/Madisonville Cons ISD | 15 | 276 |
| Webster, Kari/Canton Ind School Dist | 76,79 | 382 | West, Kelly/Alto Ind School Dist | 1 | 76 |
| Webster, Ron/Klein Ind School Dist | 91 | 202 | West, Lila/Florence Ind School Dist | 8 | 398 |
| Weddell, Alan/Brazosport Ind School Dist | 6,35 | 55 | West, Marti/Archdiocese San Antonio Ed Off | 1 | 47 |
| Weddle, Steven/Prairiland Ind School Dist | 6 | 263 | West, Matthew/Elgin Ind School Dist | 7,91 | 27 |
| Weeks, William/Garrison Ind School Dist | 16,73,84 | 301 | West, Nicholas/Dime Box Ind School Dist | 1,11,84 | 266 |
| Weems, Adriana/Winnsboro Ind School Dist | 76 | 408 | West, Ray, Dr/Shelbyville Ind School Dist | 1 | 337 |
| Weerasinghe, Dash, Dr/Plano Ind School Dist | 69,70,294 | 85 | West, Sally/Hunt Ind School Dist | 16 | 258 |
| Weger, Josh/Bells Ind School Dist | 12,15 | 170 | West, Ted/Electra Ind School Dist | 1 | 394 |
| Wehrmann, Christy/Murchison Ind Sch Dist | 73,295 | 219 | West, Tempie/Roby Cons Ind School Dist | 16 | 152 |
| Weichel, Kristen/Royse City Ind School Dist | 49 | 328 | West, Tim/Cayuga Ind School Dist | 67 | 18 |
| Weidler, Lance/Rockdale Ind School Dist | 3 | 290 | West, Tim/Prairie Valley Ind School Dist | 1,84 | 293 |
| Weimer, Nanette/Pearland Ind School Dist | 15 | 56 | Westbrook, Gary/Anson Ind School Dist | 73,76,98,295 | 252 |
| Weinkaus, Gean/Brownsboro Ind School Dist | 4 | 218 | Westbrook, Jaime/Azle Ind School Dist | 90 | 348 |
| Weir, Amy/Round Rock Ind School Dist | 67 | 401 | Westbrook, Jennifer/Centerville Ind School Dist | 73 | 376 |
| Weir, Laura/Region 11 Ed Service Center | 2 | 362 | Westbrook, Kalinda/Oglesby Ind School Dist | 2 | 97 |
| Weirich, Dwayne/Round Rock Ind School Dist | 6 | 401 | Westbrook, Randi/Frankston Ind School Dist | 2,19 | 18 |
| Weiser, Charlotte/Cisco Independent Sch Dist | 16,73 | 133 | Westbrook, Robert/Milano Ind School Dist | 1 | 290 |
| Weiser, Charlotte/Cisco Independent Sch Dist | 84 | 133 | Westbrooks, Ann/Spring Ind School Dist | 2,19 | 207 |
| Weishuhn, Charlotte/Wall Ind School Dist | 2 | 368 | Westerberg, Tom/Barbers Hill Ind School Dist | 6,35 | 75 |
| Weiss, Gregg, Dr/Silsbee Ind School Dist | 1 | 183 | Westerman, Mona/Godley Ind School Dist | 3 | 250 |
| Welch, Bruce/Cotton Center Ind School Dist | 3 | 179 | Westfall, Rick, Dr/Keller Ind School Dist | 1 | 357 |

| NAME/District | JOB FUNCTIONS | PAGE | NAME/District | JOB FUNCTIONS | PAGE |
|---|---|---|---|---|---|
| Wiburn-Hill, Chiquita/Fannindel Ind School Dist | 8,88,288,752 | 124 | Williams, Cynthia/Spring Ind School Dist | 27,31 | 207 |
| Wickett, Paul/Pottsboro Ind School Dist | 3 | 172 | Williams, Darla/Howe Ind School Dist | 8,11,15,58,69 | 171 |
| Widdecombe, Stacey/Lago Vista Ind School Dist | 4 | 373 | Williams, Datren/Conroe Ind School Dist | 67 | 294 |
| Widder, Catherine/Alamo Heights Ind School Dist | 7 | 33 | Williams, David/Detroit Ind School Dist | 73 | 325 |
| Wideman, Justine/North Lamar Ind School Dist | 7,35,85 | 406 | Williams, David/Godley Ind School Dist | 68,79,91 | 250 |
| Wiebersch, Julie/Caddo Mills Ind Sch Dist | 8 | 238 | Williams, David/Seminole Ind School Dist | 6 | 162 |
| Wiechmann, Joann, Dr/Grapevine-Colleyville Ind SD | 58 | 355 | Williams, David/Waco Ind School Dist | 91 | 284 |
| Wied, Kim/Van Vleck Ind School Dist | 7 | 279 | Williams, Deborah/Bells Ind School Dist | 7,35,85 | 170 |
| Wiedemann, Cindy/Scurry Rosser Ind School Dist | 2 | 256 | Williams, Deborah/Ector Ind School Dist | 2 | 150 |
| Wiederstein, Jody/Higgins Ind School Dist | 58 | 270 | Williams, Dennis/Blooming Grove Ind School Dist | 73,76,295 | 302 |
| Wieding, Alicia/Karnes City Ind School Dist | 298 | 253 | Williams, Dennis/Longview Ind School Dist | 7,15,79,83,88,91,275 | 174 |
| Wieding, Ronnie/Poth Ind School Dist | 27 | 404 | Williams, Diana/Brownsboro Ind School Dist | 7 | 218 |
| Wieghat, Rodney/Needville Ind School Dist | 3,5 | 159 | Williams, Dionne/Hawkins Ind School Dist | 8,11,83,88,296,298 | 407 |
| Wieland, Shuck/Terrell Ind School Dist | 79 | 256 | Williams, Dobie/Granbury Ind School Dist | 2 | 233 |
| Wiese, Kenney/Cranfills Gap ISD School Dist | 67 | 50 | Williams, Donald/Mansfield Ind School Dist | 15,71 | 358 |
| Wiesman, Nicolette/Rogers Ind School Dist | 36,85,88,275,288 | 32 | Williams, Donelle/Houston Ind School Dist | 43 | 193 |
| Wiggins, Betti/Houston Ind School Dist | 4 | 193 | Williams, Doug/Sunnyvale Ind School Dist | 1 | 117 |
| Wiggins, Bill/Plemons-Stinnett-Phillips CISD | 1 | 240 | Williams, Eva/Paris Ind School Dist | 34 | 262 |
| Wiggins, Kendra, Dr/Conroe Ind School Dist | 58 | 294 | Williams, Garry/Lancaster Ind School Dist | 20 | 114 |
| Wiggins, Kevin/Whitewright Ind School Dist | 6 | 173 | Williams, Horace/Longview Ind School Dist | 9,15,36,69,77,286,294 | 174 |
| Wiggins, Ted/Onalaska Ind School Dist | 67 | 320 | Williams, James/Int'l Leadership of Texas Dist | 67 | 112 |
| Wigington, Chris/Bushland Ind School Dist | 1 | 321 | Williams, Jeremy/Eastland Ind School Dist | 15 | 133 |
| Wigington, Jennifer/Alba-Golden Ind School Dist | 11 | 407 | Williams, Jeremy/Wall Ind School Dist | 5,6,8,85,92 | 368 |
| Wilbanks, Edward/Athens Ind School Dist | 27 | 218 | Williams, Joann/Alief Ind School Dist | 50 | 186 |
| Wilbanks, Lori/Taylor Ind School Dist | 3 | 402 | Williams, Josh/Lufkin Ind School Dist | 295 | 21 |
| Wilbur, Andrea/Alvarado Ind School Dist | 88 | 249 | Williams, Josh/Sulphur Springs Ind Sch Dist | 11,15,36,79,88,296 | 235 |
| Wilbur, Christi/North East Ind School Dist | 76 | 37 | Williams, Joy/Lamar Cons Ind School Dist | 67 | 157 |
| Wilburn, Justin/Joaquin Ind School Dist | 16,73,76,295 | 337 | Williams, Justen/Columbia Brazoria ISD | 3 | 56 |
| Wilcots, John/Houston Ind School Dist | 5 | 193 | Williams, Karl/Sunnyvale Ind School Dist | 5 | 117 |
| Wilcox, Craig, Dr/New Summerfield Ind Sch Dist | 8,11,57 | 76 | Williams, Keri/Tomball Ind School Dist | 58 | 208 |
| Wilcox, Dave/Atlanta Ind School Dist | 3,4,5,10,11,15 | 73 | Williams, Kim/Chisum Ind School Dist | 2,11 | 262 |
| Wilcox, Fred/Timpson Ind School Dist | 5 | 338 | Williams, Kristin/Keller Ind School Dist | 2 | 357 |
| Wilcox, James, Dr/Longview Ind School Dist | 1 | 174 | Williams, Larry/Milford Ind School Dist | 58 | 146 |
| Wilcoxson, George/Wills Point Ind School Dist | 67 | 384 | Williams, Laurah/Eastland Ind School Dist | 27 | 133 |
| Wild, Juliana/Dodd City Ind School Dist | 57 | 150 | Williams, Leonard/Mart Ind School Dist | 1 | 283 |
| Wilde, Chris/Wall Ind School Dist | 67 | 368 | Williams, Lisa/Bullard Ind School Dist | 58 | 339 |
| Wilde, John/McAllen Ind School Dist | 79 | 224 | Williams, Llyod/Carthage Ind School Dist | 4 | 314 |
| Wilds, John/Alvin Ind School Dist | 84,295 | 54 | Williams, Lori/Plemons-Stinnett-Phillips CISD | 7,35,83,85 | 241 |
| Wiley, Karen/Forestburg Ind School Dist | 51,54,270 | 293 | Williams, Lynn/Chisum Ind School Dist | 3,5 | 262 |
| Wiley, Nan/Merkel Ind School Dist | 57,271 | 363 | Williams, Madi/Karnack Ind School Dist | 73 | 214 |
| Wiley, Nan/Merkel Ind School Dist | 57,271 | 363 | Williams, Mark/Chillicothe ISD School Dist | 67 | 182 |
| Wilhelm, Jason/Miles Ind School Dist | 6 | 329 | Williams, Mark/Evadale Ind School Dist | 6 | 243 |
| Wilhelm, Jennifer/Allen Ind School Dist | 8,15,294 | 80 | Williams, Marty/Gatesville Ind School Dist | 5 | 96 |
| Wilkes, Tealer/Miami Ind School Dist | 58 | 327 | Williams, Melissa/Clint Ind School Dist | 11 | 136 |
| Wilkins, Christine/Crawford Ind School Dist | 16 | 282 | Williams, Michelle/Fredericksburg Ind School Dist | 73 | 167 |
| Wilkins, David/Hico Ind School Dist | 5 | 181 | Williams, Mike/Ysleta Ind School Dist | 6 | 141 |
| **Wilkins, DeWayne, Dr/Early Ind School Dist** | 1,11,57,83 | 62 | Williams, Paige/Crowley Ind School Dist | 7 | 350 |
| Wilkins, Donna/Atlanta Ind School Dist | 4 | 73 | Williams, Pam/Tarkington Ind School Dist | 73 | 269 |
| Wilkins, Jessica/Wichita Falls Ind School Dist | 297 | 395 | Williams, Patsy/Trent Isn School Dist | 4 | 363 |
| Wilkins, Marcus/Elkhart Ind School Dist | 4 | 18 | Williams, Phillip/Blum Ind School Dist | 73 | 230 |
| Wilkins, Sarah/Boling Ind School Dist | 36 | 392 | Williams, Ray/West Oso Ind School Dist | 4 | 309 |
| Wilkinson, Dawn/Northside Ind School Dist | 58,88 | 396 | Williams, Rhonda/Mt Calm Ind School Dist | 4 | 231 |
| Wilkinson, Debbie/Newcastle Ind School Dist | 8,88,285,288 | 409 | Williams, Robert/Huntington Ind School Dist | 27 | 20 |
| Wilkinson, Shelly/Chester Ind School Dist | 58 | 377 | Williams, Robin/Kerens Ind School Dist | 38,69 | 303 |
| Wilkinson, Shelly/Chester Ind School Dist | 58 | 377 | Williams, Sara/Van Alstyne Ind School Dist | 37 | 173 |
| Wilks, Kellie, Dr/Ector Co Ind School Dist | 16,73,82,98,295 | 134 | Williams, Sharon/Granbury Ind School Dist | 8,11,36,57,273,296,298 | 233 |
| Wilks, Ray/Grand Prairie Ind School Dist | 2 | 111 | Williams, Sheila/Broaddus Ind School Dist | 4 | 332 |
| Willam, Sherylene/Kelton Ind School Dist | 2 | 393 | Williams, Sheila/Evant Ind School Dist | 67 | 96 |
| Wille, Scott/Del Valle Ind School Dist | 34 | 372 | Williams, Shemeka/Lancaster Ind School Dist | 8,15 | 114 |
| Willery, Akilah/Aldine Ind School Dist | 74 | 184 | Williams, Stephanie/Chester Ind School Dist | 2 | 377 |
| Willett Weekly, Julia/Ector Co Ind School Dist | 11 | 134 | Williams, Steve/Allen Ind School Dist | 6 | 80 |
| Willett, Donna/Bryan Ind School Dist | 36,77 | 58 | Williams, Susan/Big Sandy Ind School Dist | 7 | 378 |
| Willey, Christi/Hedley Ind School Dist | 58 | 132 | Williams, Taylor/Slidell Ind School Dist | 1 | 407 |
| Willey, George, Dr/Taylor Ind School Dist | 8,18,275 | 402 | Williams, Theresa, Dr/Plano Ind School Dist | 3,17 | 85 |
| Willhite, Patty/Aledo Ind School Dist | 4 | 315 | Williams, Tiffany/Spring Ind School Dist | 81 | 207 |
| Williams-Scott, Melissa/Dickinson Ind School Dist | 76 | 164 | Williams, Tim/Frenship Ind School Dist | 2,15 | 272 |
| Williams, Ann/Alief Ind School Dist | 67 | 186 | Williams, Tim/Lometa Ind School Dist | 3 | 264 |
| Williams, Beverly/Blackwell Cons Ind Sch Dist | 4 | 304 | Williams, Tim/New Boston Ind School Dist | 84 | 52 |
| Williams, Brian, Dr/Palacios Ind School Dist | 68,69,83,294,296,298 | 278 | Williams, Toby/Gatesville Ind School Dist | 3 | 96 |
| Williams, Bryan/Spring Branch Ind School Dist | 15 | 205 | Williams, Tracy/Kennedale Ind School Dist | 71 | 358 |
| Williams, Carla/West Sabine Ind Sch Dist | 67 | 332 | Williams, Tricia/New Deal Ind School Dist | 38,83,88,270 | 274 |
| Williams, Carlton/Nordheim Ind School Dist | 6 | 122 | Williams, Wes/Roscoe Collegiate Ind Sch Dist | 67 | 304 |
| Williams, Cassandra/Prosper Ind School Dist | 4 | 88 | Williams, Willie/La Vega Ind School Dist | 6,35 | 282 |
| Williams, Charlotte/Queen City Ind School Dist | 1 | 74 | Williams, Yolanda/Waco Ind School DISTRICT | 15 | 284 |
| Williams, Cliff/Willis Ind School Dist | 67 | 297 | Williamson, Christine/San Antonio Ind School Dist | 81 | 42 |
| Williams, Courtney/Hempstead Ind School Dist | 58 | 387 | Williamson, Emily/Livingston Ind School Dist | 73 | 319 |

| | | | | | | | |
|---|---|---|---|---|---|---|---|
| 1 Superintendent | 16 Instructional Media Svcs | 30 Adult Education | 44 Science Sec | 58 Special Education K-12 | 72 Summer School | 88 Alternative/At Risk | 277 Remedial Math K-12 |
| 2 Bus/Finance/Purchasing | 17 Chief Operations Officer | 31 Career/Sch-to-Work K-12 | 45 Math K-12 | 59 Special Education Elem | 73 Instructional Tech | 89 Multi-Cultural Curriculum | 280 Literacy Coach |
| 3 Buildings And Grounds | 18 Chief Academic Officer | 32 Career/Sch-to-Work Elem | 46 Math Elem | 60 Special Education Sec | 74 Inservice Training | 90 Social Work | 285 STEM |
| 4 Food Service | 19 Chief Financial Officer | 33 Career/Sch-to-Work Sec | 47 Math Sec | 61 Foreign/World Lang K-12 | 75 Marketing/Distributive | 91 Safety/Security | 286 Digital Learning |
| 5 Transportation | 20 Art K-12 | 34 Early Childhood Ed | 48 English/Lang Arts K-12 | 62 Foreign/World Lang Elem | 76 Info Systems | 92 Magnet School | 288 Common Core Standards |
| 6 Athletic | 21 Art Elem | 35 Health/Phys Education | 49 English/Lang Arts Elem | 63 Foreign/World Lang Sec | 77 Psychological Assess | 93 Parental Involvement | 294 Accountability |
| 7 Health Services | 22 Art Sec | 36 Guidance Services K-12 | 50 English/Lang Arts Sec | 64 Religious Education K-12 | 78 Affirmative Action | 95 Tech Prep Program | 295 Network System |
| 8 Curric/Instruct K-12 | 23 Music K-12 | 37 Guidance Services Elem | 51 Reading K-12 | 65 Religious Education Elem | 79 Student Personnel | 97 Chief Information Officer | 296 Title II Programs |
| 9 Curric/Instruct Elem | 24 Music Elem | 38 Guidance Services Sec | 52 Reading Elem | 66 Religious Education Sec | 80 Driver Ed/Safety | 98 Chief Technology Officer | 297 Webmaster |
| 10 Curric/Instruct Sec | 25 Music Sec | 39 Social Studies K-12 | 53 Reading Sec | 67 School Board President | 81 Gifted/Talented | 270 Character Education | 298 Grant Writer/Ptnrships |
| 11 Federal Program | 26 Business Education | 40 Social Studies Elem | 54 Remedial Reading K-12 | 68 Teacher Personnel | 82 Video Services | 271 Migrant Education | 750 Chief Innovation Officer |
| 12 Title I | 27 Career & Tech Ed | 41 Social Studies Sec | 55 Remedial Reading Elem | 69 Academic Assessment | 83 Substance Abuse Prev | 273 Teacher Mentor | 751 Chief of Staff |
| 13 Title V | 28 Technology Education | 42 Science K-12 | 56 Remedial Reading Sec | 70 Research/Development | 84 Erate | 274 Before/After Sch | 752 Social Emotional Learning |
| 15 Asst Superintendent | 29 Family/Consumer Science | 43 Science Elem | 57 Bilingual/ELL | 71 Public Information | 85 AIDS Education | 275 Response To Intervention | |

| NAME/District | JOB FUNCTIONS | PAGE |
|---|---|---|
| Wood, Jayma/Karnes City Ind School Dist | 58,77,752 | 253 |
| Wood, Jim/Karnes City Ind School Dist | 3,91 | 253 |
| Wood, John/Kopperl Ind School Dist | 6 | 50 |
| Wood, Kim/Arp Ind School Dist | 4 | 339 |
| Wood, Maryann/Alvarado Ind School Dist | 68,78 | 249 |
| Wood, Michelle/Wichita Falls Ind School Dist | 27,31 | 395 |
| Wood, Mike/Jefferson Ind School Dist | 2 | 277 |
| Wood, Mike/Kilgore Ind School Dist | 6 | 174 |
| Wood, Robin/River Road Ind School Dist | 34,57,58,69,271 | 322 |
| Wood, Steve/Aledo Ind School Dist | 6 | 315 |
| Wood, Wes/Snyder Ind School Dist | 6 | 336 |
| Wood, Yuvonne/Kopperl Ind School Dist | 2 | 50 |
| Woodall, Chuck/Ponder Ind School Dist | 295 | 130 |
| Woodall, Precia/Frost Ind School Dist | 16,73,76,295 | 302 |
| Woodall, Trecia/Beckville Ind School Dist | 73 | 314 |
| Woodard, Alicia/Wichita Falls Ind School Dist | 2 | 395 |
| Woodard, David/West Ind School Dist | 6 | 285 |
| Woodard, Joe/Bruceville-Eddy Ind Sch Dist | 8,288 | 281 |
| Woodard, Johnny/Lefors Ind School Dist | 5 | 170 |
| Woodard, La'Evening/Richardson Ind School Dist | 91 | 116 |
| Woodard, Mary/Mesquite Ind School Dist | 16 | 115 |
| Woodard, Mary Claire/Howe Ind School Dist | 31 | 171 |
| Woodard, Michael/Latexo Ind School Dist | 1 | 236 |
| Woodard, Suzanne/McKinney Ind School Dist | 9,15 | 84 |
| Woodcock, Jodee/Woden Ind School Dist | 8,11,294,296,298 | 301 |
| Woodfin, Jason/Gary Ind School Dist | 2,3,5,11,88 | 314 |
| Woodfin, Terri/Union Grove Ind School Dist | 68 | 379 |
| Woodley, Katie/Elysian Fields Ind School Dist | 36,83 | 213 |
| Woodring, Sarah/Ganado Ind School Dist | 8,288 | 242 |
| Woodruff, Richard/Conroe Ind School Dist | 39 | 294 |
| Woodrum, Maria/Mission Cons Ind School Dist | 4 | 225 |
| Woods Gage, Tonya/Royal Ind School Dist | 58 | 387 |
| Woods-Meals, Jan/Tom Bean Ind School Dist | 73 | 173 |
| Woods, Amy/Higgins Ind School Dist | 2 | 270 |
| Woods, Brian, Dr/Northside Ind School Dist | 1 | 39 |
| Woods, Brittney/Throckmorton Ind School Dist | 2 | 365 |
| Woods, Charity/Kennedale Ind School Dist | 8,58 | 358 |
| Woods, Charles/Alief Ind School Dist | 2,15 | 186 |
| Woods, David/Stephenville Ind School Dist | 5 | 148 |
| Woods, Krysta/Prairie Valley Ind School Dist | 29 | 293 |
| Woods, Lori/Northside Ind School Dist | 57 | 396 |
| Woods, Patty/Dumas Ind School Dist | 4 | 298 |
| Woodson, Patrice/Cedar Hill Ind School Dist | 49 | 101 |
| Woodward, Courtney/Seymour Ind School Dist | 73,76,84 | 28 |
| Woody, Courtney/Wink Loving Ind School Dist | 7,85 | 405 |
| Woody, John/Italy Ind School Dist | 31 | 145 |
| Woody, Whitney/Burleson Ind School Dist | 42 | 249 |
| Woolems, Stacey/Jasper Ind School Dist | 10,11,69,296 | 243 |
| Woolen, Sharona/Marshall Ind School Dist | 58 | 214 |
| Wooley, Lisa/Clear Creek Ind School Dist | 44 | 162 |
| Woolsey, Denise/Cherokee Ind School Dist | 2 | 335 |
| Woosley, Brad/Denver City Ind School Dist | 67 | 409 |
| Wooten, Cheryl/Aledo Ind School Dist | 58 | 315 |
| Wooten, Heather/Evant Ind School Dist | 58,77 | 96 |
| Wooten, Troy/New Caney Ind School Dist | 91 | 296 |
| Wooten, William/DeSoto Ind School Dist | 2 | 108 |
| Wooten, William/Ferris Ind School Dist | 2,19 | 144 |
| Worcester, Terry/Round Rock Ind School Dist | 3,17 | 401 |
| Word, Janet/Childress Ind School Dist | 9 | 77 |
| Word, Mike/Clarendon Cons Ind Sch Dist | 11,93 | 131 |
| **Worrell, Daron/**Comanche Ind School Dist | 1 | 93 |
| Worrell, Daron/Rocksprings Ind School Dist | 11 | 135 |
| Worrell, Pat/Burleson Ind School Dist | 67 | 249 |
| Worsham, Linda/Freer Ind School Dist | 5 | 132 |
| Wortham, Wanda/Pleasant Grove Ind School Dist | 294 | 52 |
| Worthington, Marsha/Gatesville Ind School Dist | 11,31,36,69,273,275,288 | 96 |
| Worthy, Bobby/Whitewright Ind School Dist | 5,8,11,57,74,273,288,294 | 173 |
| Worthy, Kevin/Royse City Ind School Dist | 1 | 328 |
| Woytek, Cheryl/Columbus Ind School Dist | 4 | 90 |
| Wozniak, Doug/San Marcos Cons Ind Sch Dist | 5 | 216 |
| Wrehe, Scott/Carroll Independent Sch Dist | 2,15 | 349 |
| Wreke, Scott/Keller Ind School Dist | 19 | 357 |
| Wren, Joel/Klein Ind School Dist | 20,23 | 202 |
| Wriggle, Megan/West Rusk Co Cons Ind Sch Dist | 7 | 331 |
| Wright, Allison/Three Way Ind School Dist | 59 | 148 |
| Wright, Anita/Sidney Ind School Dist | 2 | 94 |

| NAME/District | JOB FUNCTIONS | PAGE |
|---|---|---|
| Wright, Bryndan/Int'l Leadership of Texas Dist | 17 | 112 |
| Wright, Cheryl/Goldthwaite Consolidated ISD | 36,69,88,270,271 | 291 |
| Wright, Cody/North Hopkins Ind School Dist | 275 | 234 |
| Wright, David/Mansfield Ind School Dist | 79 | 358 |
| Wright, Deborah/Millsap Ind School Dist | 3 | 315 |
| Wright, Dianna/Friona Ind School Dist | 2 | 318 |
| Wright, Eric/Eanes Ind School Dist | 76 | 372 |
| Wright, Eric, Dr/Hays Cons Ind School Dist | 1 | 216 |
| Wright, Erica/McKinney Ind School Dist | 3 | 84 |
| Wright, James/Mt Calm Ind School Dist | 1,11 | 231 |
| Wright, Jeff/Liberty-Eylau Ind School Dist | 3,15 | 51 |
| Wright, Kerry/Region 17 Ed Service Center | 2 | 275 |
| Wright, Lesa/Ore City Ind School Dist | 285 | 379 |
| Wright, Melanie/Austwell Tivoli Ind SD | 16 | 326 |
| Wright, Morgan/Spurger Ind School Dist | 1 | 377 |
| **Wright, Richard/**Agua Dulce Ind School Dist | 1 | 305 |
| Wright, Robert, Dr/Keller Ind School Dist | 27,31,286 | 357 |
| Wright, Ronda/White Settlement Ind Sch Dist | 11 | 360 |
| Wright, Ronny/Goldthwaite Consolidated ISD | 1,11,83 | 291 |
| Wright, Susan/Glen Rose Ind School Dist | 8,11,18,57,58,88,296,298 | 342 |
| Wright, Telena, Dr/Argyle Ind School Dist | 1 | 124 |
| Wright, Tracilynn/Austin Ind School Dist | 36,88 | 369 |
| Wright, Tracy/Banquete Ind School Dist | 67 | 305 |
| Wrighthood, Debbie/Bosqueville Ind School Dist | 67 | 281 |
| Wrinkle, Tammi/Vernon Ind School Dist | 2 | 396 |
| Write, Theresa/Red Lick Ind School Dist | 83,85 | 52 |
| Wrobleski, Kevin/Goose Creek Cons Ind Sch Dist | 42 | 192 |
| Wuest, Kendra/Pawnee Ind School Dist | 8,12,83,88,294 | 28 |
| Wunderlich, Jonathan/Weimar Ind School Dist | 1 | 91 |
| Wurtz, Steven, Dr/Arlington Ind School Dist | 8,18 | 346 |
| Wyatt, Dawn/Rankin Ind School Dist | 2 | 380 |
| Wyatt, Jay/Diboll Ind School Dist | 67 | 20 |
| Wyatt, Rhonda/Richland Springs Ind Sch Dist | 8 | 335 |
| Wyatt, Rhonda/Richland Springs Ind Sch Dist | 8 | 335 |
| Wyatt, Ron/Goose Creek Cons Ind Sch Dist | 68 | 192 |
| Wyatt, Samuel/Rankin Ind School Dist | 1 | 380 |
| Wyatt, Staci/Happy Ind School Dist | 36,752 | 345 |
| Wylie, Aaron/Eagle Mtn-Saginaw Ind Sch Dist | 4 | 351 |
| Wylie, Bridget/Archer City Ind School Dist | 2 | 22 |
| Wyman, Kathryn/La Grange Ind School Dist | 58 | 151 |
| Wynkoop, Gloria/Somerset Ind School Dist | 68 | 45 |
| Wynn, Susie/Booker Ind School Dist | 10,16,69 | 270 |
| Wynn, Susy/Booker Ind School Dist | 69 | 270 |
| Wynne, Latoya/Aldine ISD-Elem Sch Team 3 | 15 | 185 |

**Y**

| NAME/District | JOB FUNCTIONS | PAGE |
|---|---|---|
| Y'Herrera, Ymelda/Braination Schools | 2,19 | 33 |
| Yager, Candy/Coldspring-Oakhurst Cons ISD | 68 | 332 |
| Yakesch, John/Milano Ind School Dist | 67 | 290 |
| Yaklin, Terry/Judson Ind School Dist | 3 | 36 |
| Yaklin, Toby/Riviera Ind School Dist | 3 | 261 |
| Yale, Tiffany/Tom Bean Ind School Dist | 7 | 173 |
| Yamaguchi, Consuelo/Hempstead Ind School Dist | 57 | 387 |
| Yanashita, Denise/Charlotte Ind School Dist | 288 | 23 |
| Yancey, Ronnie/Tarkington Ind School Dist | 3 | 269 |
| Yandell, Kevin/Sabine Ind School Dist | 2 | 175 |
| Yanez, Joseph/Cotulla Ind School Dist | 73 | 262 |
| Yanke, Mike/Gruver Ind School Dist | 67 | 181 |
| Yannotta, David/Goose Creek Cons Ind Sch Dist | 69,294 | 192 |
| Yanowski, Randy/Bremond Ind School Dist | 67 | 327 |
| Yarborough, Margaret/George West Ind School Dist | 5 | 271 |
| Yarbrough, Ann Marie/Richardson Ind School Dist | 39 | 116 |
| Yarbrough, Jeff/Round Rock Ind School Dist | 91 | 401 |
| Yargo, Julie/Anderson-Shiro Cons Ind SD | 4 | 176 |
| Yates, Dana, Dr/Mercedes Ind School Dist | 15 | 225 |
| Yates, Heath/Fruitvale Ind School Dist | 67 | 383 |
| Yates, Joseph/Devine Ind School Dist | 4 | 286 |
| Yates, Kayla/Texhoma Ind School Dist | 11,73,83,275,286,288,296 | 338 |
| **Yates, Kayla/**Texhoma Ind School Dist | 1,11,73,83,288 | 338 |
| Yates, Michelle/Victoria Ind School Dist | 11 | 384 |
| Yates, Shelley/Sabine Ind School Dist | 8,11,83,285,286,288,294,298 | 175 |
| Ybarra, Barbara/Bryan Ind School Dist | 8,15,294 | 58 |
| Ybarra, Pete/Runge Ind School Dist | 3 | 254 |
| Ybarra, Victoria/Red Oak Ind School Dist | 4 | 146 |
| Yeager, Bruce/Ponder Ind School Dist | 1 | 130 |
| Yeager, Elizabeth/Wichita Falls Ind School Dist | 67 | 395 |

| NAME/District | JOB FUNCTIONS | PAGE |
|---|---|---|
| Yeager, Matthew/Garland Ind School Dist | 98 | 109 |
| Yearwood, Brian, Dr/Manor Ind School Dist | 8,11,15,69,81,294,298 | 373 |
| Yentzen, Michelle/Hardin Jefferson Ind Sch Dist | 67 | 182 |
| Yepez, Frances/Ysleta Ind School Dist | 3 | 141 |
| Yeschke, Chris/Leakey Ind School Dist | 1 | 324 |
| Ying, Shun/McKinney Ind School Dist | 295 | 84 |
| Yoakem, Timbra/Mabank Ind School Dist | 58 | 256 |
| Yoakum, Dennis/Commerce Independent Sch Dist | 3,5 | 239 |
| Yocham, Pam/Andrews Ind School Dist | 4 | 19 |
| Yohn, Todd/Pine Tree Ind School Dist | 73 | 175 |
| Yonker, John/Round Rock Ind School Dist | 15 | 401 |
| York, Brandy/Wall Ind School Dist | 58 | 368 |
| York, Dwain/Wimberley Ind School Dist | 1 | 217 |
| York, John/Paducah Ind School Dist | 6 | 97 |
| Yose, Richard/Brazosport Ind School Dist | 15,45,751 | 55 |
| Yost, Donna/Deer Park Ind School Dist | 11 | 191 |
| Yougblood, Clay/Garner Ind School Dist | 67 | 315 |
| Young, Audrey, Dr/Nacogdoches Ind School Dist | 58,752 | 301 |
| Young, Bill/Grand Prairie Ind School Dist | 76 | 111 |
| Young, Bridgette/Franklin Ind School Dist | 4 | 327 |
| Young, Darby/Klein Ind School Dist | 6,35 | 201 |
| Young, David/Los Fresnos Cons Ind Sch Dist | 2 | 69 |
| Young, David, Dr/Abilene Ind School Dist | 1 | 362 |
| Young, Gray/Henderson Ind School Dist | 295 | 330 |
| Young, James, Dr/La Poynor Ind School Dist | 1 | 219 |
| Young, Joe/Brownwood Ind School Dist | 1 | 62 |
| Young, John/Terrell Ind School Dist | 20,23 | 256 |
| Young, Kendall/Kerrville Ind School Dist | 36 | 259 |
| Young, Lissa/Gorman Ind School Dist | 4 | 133 |
| Young, Mark/Livingston Ind School Dist | 4 | 319 |
| Young, Mia/Channelview Ind School Dist | 27,31 | 188 |
| Young, Michelle/Galena Park Ind School Dist | 73,286 | 191 |
| Young, Misty/McKinney Ind School Dist | 46 | 84 |
| Young, Patrick/Ector Co Ind School Dist | 17 | 134 |
| Young, Renee/Lometa Ind School Dist | 58 | 264 |
| Young, Rhea/Splendora Ind School Dist | 16 | 297 |
| Young, Stacie/Rusk Ind School Dist | 2,15,294 | 77 |
| Young, Tamika/Fabens Ind School Dist | 31 | 139 |
| Young, Todd/McKinney Ind School Dist | 31 | 84 |
| Young, Tracey/Skidmore Tynan Ind SD | 36,88 | 29 |
| Young, Travis/Dayton Ind School Dist | 71,83 | 268 |
| Youngblood, Emily/Flour Bluff Ind School Dist | 2 | 307 |
| Youngblood, Jamie/Silsbee Ind School Dist | 73,81 | 183 |
| Youngblood, Kyle/Union Hill Ind School Dist | 2 | 380 |
| Youngblood, Loydette/Splendora Ind School Dist | 36 | 297 |
| Youngs, Mark/Lewisville Ind School Dist | 19 | 126 |
| Younguin, Jack/Garland Ind School Dist | 5 | 109 |
| Yourman, Thomas/Midway Ind School Dist | 3 | 283 |
| Yznaga, Jerri/Eanes Ind School Dist | 3 | 372 |

**Z**

| NAME/District | JOB FUNCTIONS | PAGE |
|---|---|---|
| Zachary, Louis/Austin Ind School Dist | 3 | 369 |
| Zachary, Nancy/Leonard Ind School Dist | 7 | 150 |
| Zahn, Tony/Grapevine-Colleyville Ind SD | 285 | 355 |
| Zalefnik, Becky/Sheldon Ind School Dist | 73,76,285,286 | 205 |
| Zambiasi, Doug/Frisco Ind School Dist | 3,17 | 82 |
| Zambrano, Rosario/Beeville Ind School Dist | 57,58 | 28 |
| Zambrano, Ruth/Harlandale Ind School Dist | 93 | 35 |
| Zamora-Guerra, Norma/McAllen Ind School Dist | 71 | 224 |
| Zamora, Gabe/Olfen Ind School Dist | 1,11,57 | 329 |
| Zamora, Robert/South San Antonio Ind Sch Dist | 6 | 45 |
| Zamora, Ronnie/Los Fresnos Cons Ind Sch Dist | 71 | 69 |
| Zander, Clint/Bosqueville Ind School Dist | 6 | 281 |
| Zapalac, Charlie/Bryan Ind School Dist | 295 | 58 |
| Zapaliac, Mike/Sealy Ind School Dist | 3 | 25 |
| Zapata-Farmer, Alisa/Socorro Ind School Dist | 9,15 | 140 |
| Zapata, Margarito/Prairie Lea Ind School Dist | 67 | 65 |

| NAME/District | JOB FUNCTIONS | PAGE |
|---|---|---|
| Zapata, Minerva/Driscoll Ind School Dist | 4 | 307 |
| Zapata, Rebecca/Hartley Ind School Dist | 4 | 215 |
| Zapata, Sammy/Aransas Co Ind School Dist | 91 | 22 |
| Zapata, Sylvia/La Joya Ind School Dist | 2 | 222 |
| Zaragoza, David/Southside Ind School Dist | 91 | 46 |
| Zastoupil, Kristin/Forney Ind School Dist | 71 | 255 |
| Zavala, Alberto/Diocese of Brownsville Ed Off | 73 | 229 |
| Zavala, Carmen/Zapata Co Ind School Dist | 58 | 410 |
| Zavala, Santiago/Pharr-San Juan-Alamo Ind SD | 297 | 226 |
| Zawhr, Julie/Denton Ind School Dist | 71,97 | 125 |
| Zeal, Bart/Liberty-Eylau Ind School Dist | 91 | 51 |
| Zeigler, Leah/Kress Ind School Dist | 1,11,73,84 | 345 |
| Zeller, Daryl/Abilene Ind School Dist | 67 | 362 |
| Zeller, Jay/Robinson Ind School Dist | 6 | 284 |
| Zemlicka, Brian, Dr/Region 6 Ed Service Center | 15,71 | 386 |
| Zemlicka, Leslee/Willis Ind School Dist | 91 | 297 |
| Zemo, Matthew/Eanes Ind School Dist | 88 | 372 |
| Zepeda, Ana/Monte Alto Ind School Dist | 8 | 226 |
| Zepeda, Marisela/Pharr-San Juan-Alamo Ind SD | 285 | 226 |
| Zepeda, Raymond/Cypress-Fairbanks Ind Sch Dist | 6,35 | 188 |
| Zepeda, Rocky/Del Valle Ind School Dist | 88 | 372 |
| Zernial, Abby/Lumberton Ind School Dist | 2 | 183 |
| Zertuche, David/Pleasanton Ind School Dist | 5 | 24 |
| Zeske, Karen, Dr/Arlington Ind School Dist | 81 | 346 |
| Zettle, Terry/Irving Ind School Dist | 91 | 113 |
| Zgabay, Zach/Dime Box Ind School Dist | 35 | 266 |
| Zlener, Brian, Dr/Mexia Ind School Dist | 2,12 | 270 |
| Zienko, Crystal/Chireno ISD School Dist | 58 | 300 |
| Zigmond, Meghan/Port Aransas Ind School Dist | 16 | 308 |
| Zigtema, Jaculyn/Whitehouse Ind School Dist | 58 | 341 |
| Zimmer, Cherilyn/Mexia Ind School Dist | 73 | 270 |
| Zimmer, Lana/Clear Creek Ind School Dist | 47 | 162 |
| Zimmerer, Diane/Lindsay Ind School Dist | 2 | 95 |
| Zimmerman, Galen/Dripping Springs Ind Sch Dist | 6 | 215 |
| Zimmerman, Lindsey/Point Isabel Ind Sch Dist | 38 | 70 |
| Zimmerman, Marlena/Canutillo Ind School Dist | 42 | 136 |
| Zimmermann, Denise/Spring Ind School Dist | 36 | 207 |
| Zimora, Maria/Duncanville Ind School Dist | 11 | 108 |
| Zinda, Mary/Pleasanton Ind School Dist | 81 | 24 |
| Zingelmann, Robert/Region 4 Ed Service Center | 2,3,19 | 213 |
| Zink, Karen/Redwater Ind School Dist | 73 | 53 |
| Zinke, Courtney/Yoakum Ind School Dist | 38 | 122 |
| Zinn, Troy/Rockdale Ind School Dist | 67 | 290 |
| Zoch, Lus/San Antonio Ind School Dist | 74 | 42 |
| Zoda, Pamela, Dr/Conroe Ind School Dist | 11,298 | 294 |
| Zoeller, Maroba, Dr/Allen Ind School Dist | 11 | 80 |
| Zolman, Johnny/Lovelady Ind School Dist | 4 | 236 |
| Zolman, Phil/Kress Ind School Dist | 11,73,286,294,295,298 | 345 |
| Zschiesche, Jennifer/Hamilton Ind School Dist | 8,15,73 | 181 |
| Zuberbueier, Bill/Comstock Ind School Dist | 67 | 381 |
| Zubia, Marcos/Benavides Ind School Dist | 6 | 132 |
| Zuniga, Ana/Mission Cons Ind School Dist | 2 | 225 |
| Zuniga, Eduardo/United Ind School Dist | 2,3,5,15,73,79 | 390 |
| Zuniga, Irma/La Joya Ind School Dist | 57 | 222 |
| Zuniga, Santos/Raymondville Ind Sch Dist | 5 | 397 |
| Zuniga, Tony/Memphis Ind School Dist | 5 | 181 |
| Zunker, Laura/San Marcos Cons Ind Sch Dist | 58 | 217 |
| Zunker, Tammy/Conroe Ind School Dist | 34,46 | 294 |
| Zwahr, Charlene/West Hardin Co Cons Sch Dist | 16,82 | 183 |
| Zwicke, Philip/Poth Ind School Dist | 5,79,91 | 404 |
| Zyla, Sonia/Region 2 Ed Service Center | 58 | 309 |

| NAME/School | PAGE | NAME/School | PAGE |
|---|---|---|---|
| Camarena, Emily/Dunaway Elem Sch | 146 | Cardenas, Trina/Jubilee Highland Hills [306] | 8 |
| **Camargo, Nora**/Josephine Castaneda Elem Sch | 67 | Cardenas, Yvette/Pillow Elem Sch | 370 |
| Camarillo, Gregorio/Elma Barrera Elem Sch | 71 | Cardin, Richard/Kenedy Middle Sch | 254 |
| Camarrillo, Michael/Incarnate Word Academy | 71 | Cardona, Melissa/MaGee Elem Sch | 306 |
| Camp, Alison/Austin Elem Sch | 362 | Cardoza, Michelle/Berta Palacios Elem Sch | 226 |
| Camp, Harry/Memorial Private High Sch | 211 | **Carew, Stacia**/Rowe Middle Sch | 190 |
| Camp, Tracie/Crenshaw Elem & Mid Sch | 165 | Carielo, Cynthia/Edison High Sch | 43 |
| Campa, Rogelio/Santa Maria Middle Sch | 71 | Carle, Aoi/Village Sch | 212 |
| Campbell, Alexis/Ray Elem Sch | 399 | Carlisle, Gordon/Marshall Leadership Academy | 112 |
| Campbell, Chelsey/Heritage Middle Sch | 272 | Carlisle, Kelly/Abernathy Middle Sch | 179 |
| Campbell, Holly/Gordon Sch | 313 | Carlisle, Whitney/Dickinson Elem Sch | 111 |
| Campbell, Jasen/Wilmer-Hutchins High Sch | 108 | Carlovsky, Ben/Abiding Word Lutheran Sch | 210 |
| Campbell, Jason/Great Lakes Academy | 89 | Carlton, Yvette/Colmesneil Elem Sch | 377 |
| Campbell, Jonathan, Dr/Forney High Sch | 255 | Carmona, Kathleen/Strickland Middle Sch | 125 |
| Campbell, Joshua/Mance Park Middle Sch | 386 | Carmona, Miguel/Achieve Early College High Sch | 224 |
| Campbell, Lindsey/Idea Clg Prep-San Juan [301] | 8 | Carnes, Christopher/Herrera Elem Sch | 196 |
| Campbell, Lisa/Northampton Elem Sch | 202 | Carnett, Stephanie/Carver Center | 288 |
| Campbell, Lori/Silvercrest Elem Sch | 57 | Carnley, Jan/DayStar Academy | 287 |
| Campbell, Robyn/Bernice Chatman Freeman ES | 100 | Caropepe, Jennifer/Llano Junior High Sch | 271 |
| Campbell, Shalon/Uplift Meridian Preparatory [331] | 16 | Caros, Jason/Founders Classical Acad Lwsvll [318] | 3 |
| Campbell, Shana/Cranfills Gap Sch | 50 | Carpenter, Angelia/Ecia-Royse City 3 | 3 |
| Campbell, Tania/Missouri City Middle Sch | 155 | Carpenter, Antoinette/Whitaker Elem Sch | 138 |
| Campbell, Tracie/Cayuga Sch | 18 | Carpenter, Barbra/Memorial Christian Academy | 33 |
| **Campos, Lisa**/Oak Meadow Elem Sch | 38 | Carpenter, Katie/KIPP Austin College Prep [307] | 9 |
| Campos, Rosalva/Freer Junior High Sch | 132 | Carpenter, Sharon/Salyers Elem Sch | 208 |
| Canales, Albert/McAllen High Sch | 224 | Carr, Edris/Grace Fellowship Christian Sch | 119 |
| Canales, Amanda/Idea Clg Prep-Donna [301] | 7 | Carr, Kelley/Lakeside Middle Sch | 128 |
| Canales, Anna/Hebbronville Jr High Sch | 247 | Carr, Lindsay/Belaire Elem Sch | 367 |
| **Canales, Anna**/Navarro Elem Sch | 64 | Carranco, John/Andrews High Sch | 19 |
| Canales, Judith/Garza-Pena Elem Sch | 226 | Carranco, Lawrence/William Hobby Middle Sch | 42 |
| Canales, Lydia/Eisenhauer Rd Baptist DC PS | 48 | Carranza, Amy/Roberts Road Elem Sch | 387 |
| Canales, Norma/Simon Rivera Early Clg HS | 68 | Carranza, Ericka/B L Gray Junior High Sch | 227 |
| Canales, Renee/Best Elem Sch | 187 | Carranza, Jennifer/Clifton Park Elem Sch | 30 |
| Canales, Wendy/Regis Sch of the Sacred Heart | 209 | Carrasco, Berta/Bradford Elem Sch | 367 |
| Canchola, Denise/Patti Welder Middle Sch | 385 | Carrasquillo, Deborah/M G Ellis Primary Sch | 353 |
| Candelaria, Ana/Vista Del Futuro Charter Sch | 17 | Carreathers, Darnisha/Grand Prairie Collegiate Inst | 111 |
| Canino, Nadia/Holy Family Catholic Sch | 166 | Carrejo, Tanya/Waller Junior High Sch | 387 |
| Cannon, Mandi/Great Hearts Monte Vista-South [297] | 4 | Carreon, Elizabeth/St Patrick Cathedral Sch | 143 |
| Cano, Antonio/La Joya Senior High Sch | 223 | Carrero-Diaz, Magda/J W Long Elem Sch | 256 |
| **Cano, Ernestina**/M D Betts Elem Sch | 222 | Carrero, Rebeca/Risd Academy | 117 |
| Cano, Ernestina/Vision Academy | 222 | Carriaga, Benito, Dr/Sgt Leonel Trevino Elem Sch | 227 |
| Cano, Homero/Austin Elem Sch | 221 | **Carrier, Isaac, Dr**/G W Carver Middle Sch | 285 |
| Cano, Lianna/Madison Elem Sch | 44 | Carrillo, Alfredo/Liberty Middle Sch | 227 |
| Cano, Mauricio/Robbin E L Washington Elem Sch | 142 | Carrillo, Jose/Trinity Basin Prep-Ewing [327] | 15 |
| Cano, Michael/Borger Middle Sch | 240 | Carrillo, Pamela/Incarnate Word Elem Sch | 309 |
| Cano, Rodrigo/Whitley Road Elem Sch | 358 | Carrington, DeWayne/Timpson Elem Sch | 338 |
| Canonico, Marcus/Crossroads High Sch | 249 | Carroll, Cherryl/Seashore Learning Center | 14 |
| Cantrell, Paige/Medlin Middle Sch | 129 | Carroll, Chris/Western Academy | 213 |
| Cantu, Adriana/Desert Hills Elem Sch | 136 | Carroll, Ron/Texas Leadership CS-Arlington | 15 |
| Cantu, Ana/Burnet Elem Sch | 194 | Carroll, Ryan/Foster Middle Sch | 175 |
| Cantu, Bertha/Carmen Anaya Elem Sch | 226 | Carroll, Steven/Dudley Magnet Sch | 385 |
| Cantu, Beth/Timothy Baranoff Elem Sch | 370 | Carruth, Kathy/Holy Family Catholic Academy | 118 |
| Cantu, Enrique/Veterans Middle Sch | 343 | Carter, Andrea/La Vernia Junior High Sch | 404 |
| Cantu, Eric/Connally Elem Sch | 282 | Carter, Bobbie/Cooper Elem Sch | 109 |
| Cantu, Jermaine/Wellington High Sch | 90 | Carter, Charlotte/Bebensee Elem Sch | 346 |
| Cantu, Laurie/St Matthew's Episcopal Sch | 229 | Carter, Christopher/Life School Cedar Hill [311] | 10 |
| Cantu, Maryjane/Washington Heights Elem Sch | 355 | Carter, Daniel/Founders Classical Acad Mesq [318] | 3 |
| Cantu, Michelle/Alicia Ruiz Elem Sch | 390 | Carter, Dianne/West Ridge Middle Sch | 372 |
| Cantu, Olga/United South High 9th Grade HS | 391 | Carter, Elisa/Hillcrest Elem Sch | 248 |
| Cantu, Oscar/Russell Elem Sch | 68 | Carter, Erika/Key Middle Sch | 196 |
| Cantu, Yolanda/Jubilee Leadership Academy [306] | 9 | Carter, Hanna/Forsan Jr Sr High Sch | 237 |
| Cantu, Yvette/Noemi Dominguez Elem Sch | 69 | Carter, Ida/J Ruth Smith Academy | 184 |
| Capehart, Chelsea/Central Elem Sch | 256 | Carter, Innetta/Cypresswood Elem Sch | 185 |
| Caperton, Desiree, Dr/Fannin Elem Sch | 58 | Carter, Jana/Royal Ridge Elem Sch | 38 |
| Caperton, Elizabeth/Wylie Preparatory Academy | 90 | Carter, Janee/Lone Oak High Sch | 239 |
| Capetillo, Blanca/Highlands Elem Sch | 193 | Carter, Jason/Roby High Sch | 152 |
| Caplinger, Jennifer/Barksdale Elem Sch | 86 | **Carter, Jordan**/O'Brien Middle Sch | 261 |
| **Carattini, Carla**/Lee Elem Sch | 111 | Carter, Kathryn/L O Donald Elem Sch | 105 |
| Carballo, Janie/John F Peeler Elem Sch | 105 | Carter, Kimberly/H O Whitehurst Elem Sch | 269 |
| Carcano, Benigna/Idea Academy-Tres Lagos [301] | 7 | Carter, Kimberly/Port Neches Elem Sch | 246 |
| Cardenas, Gerardo/Centro Chrn Alpha Omega Acad | 210 | **Carter, Nicki**/Paradise Junior High Sch | 407 |
| **Cardenas, Nick**/Pleasant Valley Elem Sch | 321 | Carter, Norman/Carlisle Sch | 330 |
| Cardenas, Sonya/Carvajal Early Chldhd Center | 43 | Carter, Tangela/Zan Wesley Holmes Jr Mid Sch | 108 |

| NAME/School | PAGE | NAME/School | PAGE |
|---|---|---|---|
| Coleman, Nanette/Int'l Ldrshp TX-Saginaw | 113 | Conyers, Kimberly/Gruver High Sch | 181 |
| Coleman, Phyliss, Dr/St Helen Sch | 57 | Coody, Nina/Robert E Lee Intermediate Sch | 95 |
| Coleman, Rhoda/Palm Elem Sch | 370 | Cook-Costley, Kelly/Nelda Sullivan Middle Sch | 204 |
| Coleman, Tonya/Meadowcreek Elem Sch | 350 | Cook, Cameron/Idea Clg Prep-Hlth Professions [302] | 7 |
| Collet, Becky/Bryan Adult Learning Center | 58 | Cook, Connor/River Oaks Baptist Sch | 212 |
| Colley, Kent/Haskell Junior High Sch | 215 | Cook, Eric/Covenant Classical Sch | 361 |
| Collida, Joanna/Dodd City Sch | 150 | Cook, Jamie/Mt Pleasant Child Dev Center | 366 |
| Collier, Jennifer/Spring Woods High Sch | 206 | Cook, Monica/Montessori School at Starcreek | 89 |
| Collier, Paige/Reed Elem Sch | 400 | Cook, Susan/Covenant Christian Academy | 361 |
| Collins, Audrey/Pietzsch-MacArthur Elem Sch | 245 | Cook, Trent/Neches High Sch | 18 |
| Collins, Clarinda/Baker Koonce Intermediate Sch | 314 | Cook, Trent/Triumph Public HS-Lubbock [329] | 16 |
| Collins, Cory, Dr/Macario Garcia Middle Sch | 155 | Cook, Tricia/Canyon Intermediate Sch | 323 |
| Collins, Debbra/Tsu Charter Lab Sch | 198 | Cook, William/Valentine Sch | 244 |
| Collins, Juanita/Neal Elem Sch | 58 | Cooke, Cynite/KIPP Destiny Middle Sch [308] | 9 |
| Collins, Katrina/Skyview Elem Sch | 117 | Cooksey, Marion/Highpoint School East | 184 |
| Collins, Keith/Kissam Elem Sch | 339 | Cooksey, Stephen/Troup Middle Sch | 340 |
| Collins, Leslie/Covenant Academy | 210 | Cooley, Teresa/Early Primary Sch | 62 |
| Collins, Marques/Kashmere Gardens Elem Sch | 196 | Cooley, Thomas/Kountze Elem Sch | 183 |
| Collins, Pamela/Step by Step Christian Sch | 212 | Cooper, Andrea/Taylor Christian Sch | 229 |
| Collins, Quanda/TCC South-Fwisd Collegiate HS | 354 | Cooper, Ashley/Richardson Classical Academy [318] | 13 |
| Collins, Stephen/High Point Prep Academy | 361 | Cooper, Brady/Uplift Hampton Prep Chtr Sch [331] | 16 |
| Collins, Tremeka/King Early Childhood Center | 198 | Cooper, Brent/Brownsboro High Sch | 218 |
| Collinsworth, Barbara/East Elem Sch | 344 | Cooper, Bridget/Alton O Bowen Elem Sch | 58 |
| Collison, Heather/Liberty Hill Elem Sch | 401 | Cooper, Bryan/Alpha Academy | 295 |
| **Collon-Hernand, Gina**/Herod Elem Sch | 199 | Cooper, Debbie/Red Lick Sch | 53 |
| Colombero, Kayleigh/Etoile Acad Charter Sch | 3 | Cooper, Gionet/Brownfield High Sch | 365 |
| Colvin, Allan/Pride Academy | 388 | Cooper, Jennifer/Nimitz Middle Sch | 38 |
| **Colvin, Charles**/Marshall Middle Sch | 245 | Cooper, Judy/Paul Belton Early Chldhd Ctr | 240 |
| Colvin, Charles/Pathways Alt Learning Center | 245 | Cooper, Kerry/Fine Arts Academy | 360 |
| Colvin, Courtney/Overton Elem Sch | 370 | Cooper, Kerry/Walsh Elem Sch | 315 |
| Colvin, Michael/Comfort Middle Sch | 257 | Cooper, Rebecca/New Deal Elem Sch | 274 |
| Comalander, Gary/Johnson High Sch | 38 | Cooper, Riza/Elgin Middle Sch | 27 |
| Combs, Margaret/Lycee International De Houston | 211 | Cooper, Stephanie/Westbrook Intermediate Sch | 164 |
| Combs, Terry/Joseph Hopkins Elem Sch | 36 | Cope, Steven/Lindsay High Sch | 95 |
| Comer, Stacia/Idea Clg Prep-Round Rock Tech [302] | 8 | Copeland, Ana/St Anthony's Elem Sch | 123 |
| Compton, Angela/Geneva Bailey Intermediate Sch | 406 | Copeland, Brandy/Goddard Junior High Sch | 289 |
| Compton, Betsy/Texas School of the Arts [326] | 15 | Copeland, Danielle/Leo Orr Sr Education Center | 219 |
| Compton, Beverly/Advantage Acad-Grand Prairie W | 100 | Copeland, Danny/Brookesmith High Sch | 62 |
| **Conatser, Kyle**/Wellman-Union Sch | 365 | Copeland, Jamie/Mary Carroll High Sch | 307 |
| **Condarco, Cesar**/Porter High Sch | 297 | Copes, Amy/Longs Creek Elem Sch | 38 |
| Condit, Kendall/Westpark Elem Sch | 355 | **Copley, Kent**/Edward B Cannan Elem Sch | 297 |
| Condren, Christine/Behavior Support Services | 37 | Coppedge, Christine/Williams Elem Sch | 205 |
| Condren, Christine/NE Transition Sch | 38 | Corbett, Sharon/Annunciation Orthodox Sch | 210 |
| Conely, Teri/Larson Elem Sch | 347 | **Cordova, Yesenia**/Brackenridge High Sch | 43 |
| Conklin, Sandy/Samuel Beck Elem Sch | 129 | Core, Tina/Grand Saline Intermediate Sch | 383 |
| **Conklin, Shane**/Major Cheney ES-S Birdville | 349 | Cork, Jenni/T H Johnson Elem Sch | 403 |
| Conkwright, Robin/Dupre Elem Sch | 273 | Cormack, Melanie/Strawn Sch | 314 |
| Conley, Alvin/Nell Burks Elem Sch | 85 | Cormier, Eric/Brazos High Sch | 25 |
| Conley, Derrick/Birch Elem Sch | 175 | Cormier, Phyllis, Dr/Victory Early College HS | 185 |
| Conley, Shannon/Sue Park Broadway Elem Sch | 295 | Cornejo, Nicki/Trinity Charter Sch-Big Sandy [328] | 15 |
| **Conn, Colleen**/West Sabine Jr Sr High Sch | 332 | Cornejo, Nicki/Trinity Charter Sch-Ft Worth [328] | 15 |
| Conn, Teresa/Silverline Montessori Sch | 58 | Cornejo, Nicki/Trinity Charter Sch-Willow Bnd [328] | 15 |
| Connelly, Kimberly/Union Hill Elem Sch | 402 | Cornelius, Bridgette/Cedar Creek High Sch | 26 |
| Connelly, Tom/San Jacinto Elem Sch | 269 | **Cornish, Nicole**/Athens High Sch | 218 |
| Conner, Jennifer/Charter Oak Elem Sch | 30 | Corns, Megan/Red Oak Elem Sch | 146 |
| Conner, Jennifer/Miller Heights Elem Sch | 30 | Cornutt, Dawn/East Ridge Elem Sch | 305 |
| Conness, Monica/Martin Middle Sch | 371 | Corona, Julie/Caldwood Elem Sch | 245 |
| Conover, Wendy/Lytle Elem Sch | 24 | **Corona, Julie**/M L King Middle Sch | 245 |
| Conrad, Barbie/Mabank Junior High Sch | 256 | Coronado, Paul/Bright Beginnings Academic Ctr | 365 |
| Conrad, Matt/Murphy Middle Sch | 86 | **Coronado, Stephanie**/Valley Ranch Elem Sch | 297 |
| Conrardy, Martin/Colorado River Collegiate Acad | 26 | **Corral, Michelle**/Clardy Elem Sch | 137 |
| Conrardy, Martin/Geneisis High Sch | 27 | Correa, Carol/Peebles Elem Sch | 31 |
| Conroy, Holly/French Elem Sch | 202 | Correa, Maria/Ruben Chavira Elem Sch | 382 |
| Constantine, Charmaine/Ser-Ninos Charter Middle Sch | 14 | Correa, Yvonne/Pat Neff Middle Sch | 41 |
| Constantine, Charmaine/Ser-Ninos Elementary | 14 | Correll, Melissa/Career & Technology Institute | 384 |
| Constantinescu, Rachel/Naomi Press Elem Sch | 85 | Corrington, Molly/Sam Houston Elem Sch | 302 |
| Contreras, Abraham/Dalton Early Childhood Center | 381 | Corry, Steve/Deer Park High Sch-S Campus | 191 |
| **Contreras, Abraham**/Robb Elem Sch | 381 | Cortes-Rangel, Amelia/Alice Contreras Elem Sch | 352 |
| Contreras, Carlos/Dell City Sch | 237 | Cortes, Ami/Lucy Read Pre-K Sch | 370 |
| Contreras, Cindy/Rivera Elem Sch | 138 | Cortez, Angela/Camey Elem Sch | 126 |
| **Contreras, Edgar**/Fondren Elem Sch | 194 | Cortez, Christina/George West Primary Sch | 271 |
| Contreras, Elba/Honore Ligarde Elem Sch | 389 | Cortez, Eric/Austwell Tivoli Elem Sch | 326 |
| Contreras, Linda/Crane Elem Sch | 97 | Cortez, Guadalupe/Oakhurst Elem Sch | 354 |
| Contreras, Marena/Tabasco Elem Sch | 223 | Cortez, Guillermo/Anson Jones Elem Sch | 103 |
| Conway, Lillan/Young Learners Elem Sch [293] | 200 | | |

| NAME/School | PAGE |
|---|---|
| Culberson, Lela/Donna Wernecke Elem Sch | 227 |
| Culbertson, Lisa/Hockaday Sch | 119 |
| Culley, Kimberly/Springwoods Village Mid Sch | 208 |
| Cullum, Norma/Dorothy Adkins Middle Sch | 306 |
| Culpepper, Kristi/Bushland High Sch | 321 |
| **Culton, Crystal**/Meadowbrook Middle Sch | 354 |
| Culwell, Nathan/James W Fannin Middle Sch | 321 |
| Cumby, Ebony/Jewel Askew Elem Sch | 199 |
| Cumings, Rosemarie/Bay City Junior High Sch | 278 |
| Cumming, Sarah/Promise Academy | 342 |
| Cummings, Courtney/Wichita Christian Sch | 396 |
| Cummings, Michelle, Dr/Sherrod Elem Sch | 347 |
| Cummings, Renee/Taylor Creek Elem Sch | 264 |
| **Cummings, Robert**/Lueders-Avoca Elem Jr High Sch | 253 |
| Cummings, Robert/Lueders-Avoca High Sch | 253 |
| Cummings, Tommy/Vernon High Sch | 397 |
| Cummins, Betsy/John S Armstrong Elem Sch | 112 |
| Cummins, Lynn, Dr/Livingston High Sch Academy | 320 |
| Cummins, Sara/Covenant Christian Sch | 298 |
| Cunningham, Bethany/Huggins Elem Sch | 158 |
| Cunningham, C/Georgetown Behavioral Hlth CS | 3 |
| Cunningham, Cristy/UT Univ CS-Annunciation | 16 |
| Cunningham, Karma/Davis Elem Sch | 86 |
| Cunningham, Keith/Crockett Elem Sch | 217 |
| Cunningham, Liza/Lorena Elem Sch | 283 |
| **Cunningham, Melissa**/Palmer Elem Sch | 146 |
| Cunningham, Shannon/Kirby Middle Sch | 395 |
| Cunningtubby, Alma/Guadalupe Elem Sch | 273 |
| Cunningtubby, Alma/Jackson Elem Sch | 273 |
| Cuny, Erin/Leafspring School-Sonterra | 48 |
| Cupit, Larry/Corrigan-Camden Elem Sch | 319 |
| Curl, Michael/Kingwood Middle Sch | 201 |
| Curran, Chaney/Remington Point Elem Sch | 351 |
| **Currie, Joshua**/Austin Elem Sch | 340 |
| Curry, Danielle/Pottsboro Elem Sch | 172 |
| **Curry, Danielle**/Pottsboro High Sch | 172 |
| Curry, Mitchell/Scott Johnson Middle Sch | 85 |
| Curry, Rebecca/Cornerstone Christian Academy | 60 |
| Curtis, Charmaine/Thurgood Marshall Elem Sch | 117 |
| Curtis, Josh/Liberty Hill Intermediate Sch | 401 |
| Curtis, Larryl/G L Wiley Opportunity Center | 285 |
| **Curtis, Melissa**/Saginaw Elem Sch | 351 |
| Curtis, Tina/Barbara C Jordan Interm Sch | 178 |
| Curtis, Tonya, Dr/David Crockett Middle Sch | 154 |
| Cynthia, Chairez/La Feria High Sch | 69 |
| Cypert, Karla/Pettus Elem Sch | 28 |
| Cypert, Lauren/Boon Elem Sch | 80 |

**D**

| NAME/School | PAGE |
|---|---|
| D'Argo, Carrie/Hughston Elem Sch | 86 |
| D'Lorm, Raul, Dr/Johnny Economedes High Sch | 222 |
| Dabney, Nicole/Ptaa Mesquite Elem Sch | 13 |
| Daggs, Tammy/River Trails Elem Sch | 356 |
| Dahlquist, Michele/Walnut Bend Elem Sch | 200 |
| Daily, Ricky/Chandler Elem Sch | 218 |
| Daily, William/St Mary Magdalen Sch | 47 |
| Dale, Becky/East Chambers Elem Sch | 76 |
| Dalton, Amanda/Comstock Elem Sch | 82 |
| Dalton, Kelly/Danish Elem Sch | 189 |
| Dameron, Kim/Walker Elem Sch | 191 |
| Damron, Josh/Idalou Middle Sch | 272 |
| Damron, Wayland/Eula High Sch | 66 |
| Damron, Wayland/Eula Middle Sch | 66 |
| Dang, Maeli/Dallas Christian Academy | 119 |
| Daniel, Cindy/Woodland Springs Elem Sch | 358 |
| **Daniel, Drew**/Canadian Middle Sch | 218 |
| Daniel, Krista/Baker Elem Sch | 218 |
| Daniel, Traci/L H Rather Junior High Sch | 149 |
| Danielle, Taylor/County Line Elem Sch | 92 |
| Daniels, Bill/Atascocita High Sch | 200 |
| Daniels, Carra/Rodger & Ellen Beck Jr HS | 157 |
| Daniels, Christopher, Dr/Agua Dulce Secondary Sch | 305 |
| Daniels, Jennifer/Davis Elem Sch | 369 |
| Daniels, Leo-Francis/Oratory Academy & Athenaeum | 229 |

| NAME/School | PAGE |
|---|---|
| Danna, Cathy/L F Smith Elem Sch | 204 |
| Danner, Dave/Fannin Elem Sch | 367 |
| Darden, Dana/Benbrook Elem Sch | 196 |
| Darden, Kimberly/Pace Center | 57 |
| Darden, Leon/Chilton Sch | 149 |
| Darden, Leon/Meadows Elem Sch | 108 |
| Darden, Tyrone/George Gervin Academy | 3 |
| **Darjean, Toshila**/Navarro Middle Sch | 158 |
| Darmstadter, Sally/Stubblefield Learning Center | 20 |
| Darnell, Kandi/Devine Middle Sch | 286 |
| Darrough, Cimberli/Nci CS Without Walls | 11 |
| Dart, Laura/Clarke Elem Sch | 30 |
| Darver, Sherri/St Mark's School of Texas | 120 |
| Daugherty, Melinda/Smith Elem Sch | 197 |
| Daughtrey, Laurie/Jourdanton Elem Sch | 23 |
| Daughtry, Keana/Wilson Elem Sch | 170 |
| Dauphin, Joy/Millsap Elem Sch | 190 |
| Dauphinais, Sarah/Laura Ingalls Wilder Inter Sch | 178 |
| Davalos, Maria/Spring Oaks Middle Sch | 206 |
| Davenport, Jeff/Nichols Elem Sch | 41 |
| **Davenport, Leslie**/Briarhill Middle Sch | 126 |
| Davenport, Natalie, Dr/Bridgeway Preparatory Academy | 2 |
| Davenport, Robin/Cornerstone Christian Sch | 48 |
| **Davenport, Sherri**/Mahaffey Elem Sch | 202 |
| Davenport, Sherri/Schultz Elem Sch | 203 |
| David, Andrea/Jarrell Elem Sch | 399 |
| **David, Bill**/Boyer Elem Sch | 88 |
| Davidheizar, Paul/Alpha Omega Academy | 386 |
| Davidson, L/Henry Metzger Middle Sch | 36 |
| Davidson, Shelby/Van Middle Sch | 383 |
| Davies, MacAire/Deerwood Elem Sch | 201 |
| Davila, Catherine/Rosehill Christian Sch | 212 |
| Davila, Gisela/George Buddy West Elem Sch | 134 |
| Davila, Jason/Patrick Henry Middle Sch | 194 |
| Davila, Noemi/Mission Academy | 44 |
| Davila, Sulema/Pittman Elem Sch | 397 |
| Davila, Tricia/William Paschall Elem Sch | 37 |
| Davis-Martin, Kendria/Byrd Middle Sch | 108 |
| Davis-Troutman, Kristina/Mistral Early Childhood Center | 199 |
| Davis, Adreana/Frank Guzick Elem Sch | 104 |
| Davis, Andrea/Kujawa EC-PK-K Sch | 186 |
| Davis, Blayne/Mumford Sch | 59 |
| Davis, Brittney/Gary Sch | 314 |
| Davis, Christine/Shelton Sch | 120 |
| Davis, Cindy/Vivian Fowler Elem Sch | 366 |
| Davis, Colvin/American Preparatory Institute | 33 |
| Davis, Cynthia/Converse Elem Sch | 36 |
| Davis, Dana/Junction High Sch | 260 |
| Davis, Derek/James Bowie 6th Grade Campus | 321 |
| Davis, Eric/Heritage Academy San Antonio [300] | 5 |
| Davis, Eric/Heritage Academy Windcrest | 5 |
| Davis, Irma/Dishman Elem Sch | 68 |
| **Davis, Jason**/Bailey Junior High Sch | 346 |
| Davis, Jennifer/E Merle Smith Middle Sch | 334 |
| Davis, Jodi/Ruth Borchardt Elem Sch | 83 |
| Davis, John/North Ridge Middle Sch | 349 |
| Davis, Joseph/First Baptist Academy | 119 |
| Davis, Kathryn/E Kolitz Hebrew Language Acad | 3 |
| Davis, Kaylene/Bovina Elem Sch | 317 |
| Davis, Keith/Charles M Blalack Middle Sch | 100 |
| Davis, Kriste/Crosby Kindergarten Center | 188 |
| Davis, Lisa/Golden Acres Elem Sch | 204 |
| **Davis, Mandele**/Dwight D Eisenhower High Sch | 185 |
| Davis, Mandy/J P Dabbs Elem Sch | 191 |
| Davis, Marcella/Kennedy Elem Sch | 309 |
| Davis, Margaret/Alcuin Montessori Sch | 118 |
| Davis, Marian/Holy Trinity Catholic Sch | 118 |
| Davis, Melissa/Comanche Springs Elem Sch | 351 |
| Davis, Melissa/Pearson Elem Sch | 225 |
| Davis, Nika/W E Boswell High Sch | 351 |
| Davis, Paul/Park Meadows Academy | 303 |
| Davis, Renee/Center for Hearing & Speech | 210 |
| Davis, Samora/Tomball Intermediate Sch | 208 |
| Davis, Seth/Seminole Success Center | 162 |

| NAME/School | PAGE |
|---|---|
| Kitto, Sharyn/Wertheimer Middle Sch | 158 |
| Kiture, Andrea/Katy Adventist Christian Sch | 211 |
| Klaerner, Jennifer, Dr/North Oaks Middle Sch | 349 |
| Klander, Charles/West High Sch | 285 |
| Klander, Charles/West Middle Sch | 285 |
| Klapesky, Paula/Mitchell Intermediate Sch | 295 |
| Klas, Shea/Hyde Park Elem Sch | 171 |
| Kleckner, Andrea/Park Crest Elem Sch | 110 |
| Klein, Darynda/Hairgrove Elem Sch | 189 |
| Klein, Laura/Hill Country Elem Sch | 26 |
| Kleinhans, Angela/Montague Elem Sch | 293 |
| Kleypas, Zachary/Park Crest Middle Sch | 374 |
| Klingenberg, Sherry/Calvin Bledsoe Elem Sch | 82 |
| Kluttz, Stacey/Crockett Elem Sch | 239 |
| Knapp, Angela/Harmony Sci Acad-Grand Prairie [299] | 5 |
| Knapp, Misty/W Z Burke Elem Sch | 42 |
| Knapp, Tom/Westwood Terrace Elem Sch | 42 |
| Knickerbocker, Ryan/Ballinger High Sch | 329 |
| Knight, Kelly/McKamy Middle Sch | 127 |
| Knight, Melissa/Harmony Sch Achievement-Houstn [299] | 4 |
| Knight, Robert/Hondo High Sch | 287 |
| Knight, Yolanda/W W Bushman Elem Sch | 107 |
| Knighton, Tracy/Christoval Elem Sch | 366 |
| Knittle, David/Burbank Middle Sch | 195 |
| Knosel, Maria/Raul Yzaguirre Sch for Success | 13 |
| Knowlton, Virgil/Sheridan Elem Sch | 91 |
| Knox, Dee/Dulles Middle Sch | 154 |
| Knox, Lois/Jhw Inspire Acad-Williams Hse | 34 |
| Knutz, Bobbe/Collegiate Acad Tarrant Clg | 355 |
| Kocurek, Christopher/Rancho Isabella Elem Sch | 55 |
| Koder, Chris/George Anderson Elem Sch | 80 |
| Koehl, Michael/Columbus Alternative Sch | 90 |
| Koehler, Cassie/Robert F Koennecke Elem Sch | 179 |
| Koehler, Karl/Atascocita Middle Sch | 200 |
| Koehler, Laura/Grapevine Middle Sch | 356 |
| Koehler, Lisa/Liberty Elem Sch | 348 |
| Koehne, Shauna/Haggard Middle Sch | 86 |
| Koen, Monica/Carrollton Elem Sch | 100 |
| Koenig, Heath/Collegiate Academy Middle Sch | 101 |
| Koenig, Neil/New Boston High Sch | 52 |
| Koenig, Sandra/Perfecto Mancha Elem Sch | 280 |
| Koepke, Kurtis/Hartley Sch | 215 |
| Koepp, Julie/Cross Roads Junior High Sch | 219 |
| Koerth, Michelle/Campbell Elem Sch | 158 |
| Kohli, Jasmeen/Harmony Sch Ingenuity-Houston [299] | 4 |
| Kohli, Pinky/Pebblecreek Montessori Sch | 90 |
| Kolenda, Joe/Guthrie Center | 206 |
| Koller, Mark/Danielson Middle Sch | 400 |
| Komassa, Lori/Oak Hill Elem Sch | 370 |
| Kompelien, Leslie/Krahn Elem Sch | 202 |
| Konesheck, Sara/Sandra Mossman Elem Sch | 163 |
| Koonce, Claire/White Oak Primary Sch | 176 |
| Koonce, Keith/Panola Charter HS [314] | 11 |
| Koontz, Cody/Coppell HS 9th Grade | 102 |
| Koontz, Renee/Rodriguez Middle Sch | 125 |
| Koop, Melissa/Edna Junior High Sch | 242 |
| Koop, Rebecca/Smith Middle Sch | 190 |
| Kopeck, Karen/Tradition Elem Sch | 34 |
| Korenek, Evelyn, Sr/Nazareth Academy | 385 |
| Korobovskaya, Olga, Dr/Downtown Montessori Sch | 103 |
| Korrodi, Diana/Matias De Llano Jr Elem Sch | 391 |
| Kosednar, Mary/Selwyn College Prep Sch | 130 |
| Kosowsky, Avraham/Mesorah High School for Girls | 120 |
| Kosub, Anthony/La Vernia High Sch | 404 |
| Kotara, Daniel/Merkel Elem Sch | 363 |
| Kottwitz, Sherri/Brewer Middle Sch | 360 |
| Kowrach, Justin/Lantern Lane Elem Sch | 154 |
| Koyle, Suzanne/Shawnee Trail Elem Sch | 83 |
| Kozlowski, Shanita/Naumann Elem Sch | 400 |
| Kraft, Karen/Lone Star High Sch | 83 |
| Kramer, Linda/Hockaday Sch | 119 |
| Kramer, Monica/Faith Family Acad-Waxahachie [295] | 3 |
| Krametbauer, Jan/St Jerome Sch | 209 |
| Kratky, Dana/Crosby Elem Sch | 188 |
| Krause, Bradley/Lutheran High Sch | 119 |

| NAME/School | PAGE |
|---|---|
| Krcmar, Laura/Presidential Meadows Elem Sch | 374 |
| Krieger, Amy/Sleepy Hollow Elem Sch | 321 |
| Krieger, Jeff/Arlington Collegiate High Sch | 346 |
| Kristy, Janecka/Weimar Elem Sch | 91 |
| Krol, Tina, Dr/Michael G Killian Middle Sch | 127 |
| Kroll, Laura/Poth Junior High Sch | 404 |
| Kroll, Ronda/Clifton Elem School PK-5 | 49 |
| Kruebbe, Brandon/Beckville Jr Sr High Sch | 314 |
| Kruebbe, Brandon/Beckville Sunset Elem Sch | 314 |
| Krueger, Kandis/O'Bryant Primary Sch | 25 |
| Kubala, Marissa, Dr/Alice High Sch | 248 |
| Kucera, Inez/Newgulf Elem Sch | 392 |
| Kucera, Katie/Edna Elem Sch | 242 |
| Kucukbasol, Celil/Harmony Sch Tech-Houston [299] | 5 |
| Kuecker, Rachelle/Round Top Carmine High Sch | 152 |
| Kuehler, Kellye/Morton Elem Sch | 78 |
| Kuempel, Christopher/Peet Junior High Sch | 295 |
| Kuenning, Tod/Bennie Cole Elem Sch | 39 |
| Kuhlman, Robby/Great Hearts Western Hills [297] | 4 |
| Kuhlmann, Doug/Bronte High Sch | 79 |
| Kunschik, Veronica/Travis World Language Academy | 112 |
| Kuntz, Linda/Our Lady of Victory Sch | 360 |
| Kupcho, Angela/Holy Cross Catholic Sch | 279 |
| Kupper, Kacy/Whitesboro Intermediate Sch | 173 |
| Kusler, Michael/Clifton Middle Sch | 49 |
| Kuster, Karie/Brent Elem Sch | 128 |
| Kutac, Adam/KIPP Connect Houston Primary [309] | 9 |
| Kutac, Donna/Louise High Sch | 392 |
| Kutac, Laura/Flatonia Elem Sch | 151 |
| Kuyatt, Andrea, Dr/Bishop High Sch | 305 |
| Kwan, Victoria/Pomona Elem Sch | 54 |

**L**

| NAME/School | PAGE |
|---|---|
| La Rue, Michelle/Rolling Meadows Elem Sch | 37 |
| Labbe-Maginel, Lara/Knowles Elem Sch | 400 |
| LaBerge, Sarah/William B Travis High Sch | 155 |
| Labrado, Claudia/Wee Wisdom Kindergarten | 144 |
| Lacamu, Jill/Richard Moore Elem Sch | 204 |
| Lackey, Jon/Jayton-Girard Sch | 258 |
| Lackey, Kimberly/Pinnacle Intermediate Sch | 323 |
| Lackey, Lisa/Shadow Forest Elem Sch | 201 |
| Lacoke, Jeff/Ault Elem Sch | 189 |
| Ladd, Bryan/Lexington Elem Sch | 266 |
| Ladd, Steven/Griffin Elem Sch | 340 |
| Lafara, Tracey/Colleyville Elem Sch | 355 |
| LaFleur, Cheryl/O V Calvert Elem Sch | 185 |
| Lahrman, Stephanie/North Star Elem Sch | 142 |
| Lain, Rosie/Goliad Elem Sch | 236 |
| Laird, Emily/Barrett-Lee Early Chldhd Ctr | 188 |
| Laird, Robert/Channelview High Sch | 188 |
| Laisy, Stephanie/Sam Rayburn Sch | 150 |
| Lake, Misty/Chapel Hill Elem Sch | 366 |
| Lakey, Jamie/Robert Cobb Middle Sch | 83 |
| Lalime, Ann, Dr/Stockdick Jr High Sch | 157 |
| Lalmansingh, Shannon/Summerwood Elem Sch | 201 |
| Lam, Edith/Blossom Valley Academy | 130 |
| Lam, Mimi/Whidby Elem Sch | 198 |
| Lamar, Kelly/Canton Elem Sch | 382 |
| Lamb, Jim/Kemp High Sch | 255 |
| Lamb, Randy, Dr/Ecia-Sunnyvale 1 | 3 |
| Lamb, Shawna/West Texas Elem Sch | 241 |
| Lambarri, Blanca/Homer Hanna Early Clg HS | 67 |
| Lambert, Elsa/Dr Raul Garza Jr Elem Sch | 70 |
| Lambert, Jarod, Dr/Bush Elem Sch | 294 |
| Lambert, Kellie/Emma Roberson Elem Sch | 233 |
| Lambert, Rachel/La Pryor High Sch | 411 |
| Lambert, Tanya/Bill Burden Elem Sch | 401 |
| Lambert, Tim/Texas Middle Sch | 53 |
| Lambeth, Erin/McLeod Sch | 74 |
| Lambropulos, Lori/Energy Institute High Sch | 197 |
| Lamers, Patrick/Davis 9th Grade Center | 352 |
| Lanas, Patricia/Bonnie Garcia Elem Sch | 390 |
| Lancaster, Brittany/Miss May Vernon Elem Sch | 329 |
| Lancaster, Jeanette/Woodland Heights Elem Sch | 62 |

| NAME/School | PAGE | NAME/School | PAGE |
|---|---|---|---|
| Leonard, Rebecca/Clear Fork Elem Sch | 64 | Lockyer, Travis/Annapolis Christian Academy | 309 |
| Lepley, Kathy/New Waverly Intermediate Sch | 386 | Loftin, Stacy/Coggin Intermediate Sch | 62 |
| Lerma, George/Tom Browne Middle Sch | 307 | Lofton, Darcele/Bellfort Acad Early Chldhd Ctr | 197 |
| Leslie, Robyn/Pilot Point Middle Sch | 129 | Lofton, Kelle/Ed Franz Elem Sch | 36 |
| Lesniewski, Lindsey/Gardens Elem Sch | 204 | Lofton, Seretha/Forest Oak Middle Sch | 353 |
| Letterer, Mark/Wilson Middle Sch | 87 | Logan, Robert/Grace Christian Sch | 229 |
| Levertov, Rochel/Hebrew Prep School of Austin | 375 | Logan, Stephanie/Beverly Cheatham Elem Sch | 80 |
| Levings, Marci/Incarnate Word Middle Sch | 309 | Lohmiller, Denise, Dr/Plano Head Start Center | 87 |
| Levy, Catherine/Dallas International Sch | 119 | Lohse, Matthew/Taft High Sch | 335 |
| Lewallen, Allison/Morris Middle Sch | 204 | Lojo, Ken/Strake Jesuit College Prep Sch | 210 |
| Lewis, Alicia/Blackshear Elem Sch | 193 | Lomas, Jennifer/Serna Elem Sch | 39 |
| Lewis, Brandi/Elsie Shands Elem Sch | 115 | Lomeli, Arturo/Glenn High Sch | 400 |
| Lewis, Brandy/Bella Cameron Elem Sch | 43 | Loney, Lavonda/Bellaire Elem Sch | 30 |
| Lewis, David/Northwood Hills Elem Sch | 117 | Long, Angela/J O Davis Elem Sch | 113 |
| Lewis, Johnny/Excelsior Elem Sch | 337 | **Long, Chad**/Whitewright High Sch | 173 |
| Lewis, Ku-Masi/Texans Can Acad Fw Westcreek [325] | 14 | Long, Corina/Ehrhart Sch | 3 |
| Lewis, Lesia/West Elem Sch | 299 | Long, Karla/All Saints Episcopal Sch | 342 |
| **Lewis, Lindy**/Amy Parks-Heath Elem Sch | 328 | **Long, Kelly**/Dr Ralph H Poteet High Sch | 115 |
| Lewis, Melanie/Hardin Intermediate Sch | 109 | Long, Larry/Faith Academy | 385 |
| Lewis, Monica/Northland Christian Sch | 211 | Long, Lisa/Hendrick Middle Sch | 86 |
| Lewis, Monique/Central Media Arts Academy | 165 | Long, Rachel/Coronado Middle Sch | 180 |
| Lewis, Nicole/Legacy Middle Sch | 34 | Long, Rebecca, Dr/Spring Virtual Sch | 208 |
| Lewis, Reginald/Wings | 108 | Long, Ronnie/Regents School of Austin | 376 |
| Lewis, Steven/Comanche High Sch | 93 | Long, Stephen/Travis High School of Choice | 263 |
| Lewis, Vinson/Kerr High Sch | 187 | Long, Tamara/Martin Elem Sch | 245 |
| Lewis, Wendy/Mission Bend Christian Academy | 211 | Long, Tim/Awty International Sch | 210 |
| Leyva, Alicia/Horn Elem Sch | 187 | Longcrier, Roy/Windthorst High Sch | 23 |
| Liano, Luis/Triumph Public HS-El Paso East [329] | 15 | Longcrier, Roy/Windthorst Junior High Sch | 23 |
| Liddell, Tamara/Janet Brockett Elem Sch | 359 | Longley, Cathy/Santo Elem Sch | 313 |
| Liendo, Jaime/John B Connally Middle Sch | 40 | Longloy, Mary, Dr/St Jose Sanchez Del Rio Sch | 47 |
| Liesberger, Lauren/Kreinhop Elem Sch | 202 | Longonia, Kasie/Hill Elem Sch | 347 |
| Lightfoot, Traci/Foster Elem Sch | 197 | Longoria, Alfonso/James Tippit Middle Sch | 398 |
| Lightsey, Jeffrey/New Braunfels HS 9th GR Ctr | 92 | Longoria, Alisia/Northeast Early Clg High Sch | 371 |
| Lilie, Ron, Dr/Waelder Sch | 169 | Longoria, Herlinda/E H Gilbert Elem Sch | 35 |
| Lillard, Amanda/Westside Elem Sch | 400 | **Longoria, Liz**/Narciso Cavazos Elem Sch | 223 |
| Lilly, Erica/South Shaver Elem Sch | 205 | Longoria, Lizette/Audie Murphy Middle Sch | 226 |
| Lim, Nirmol/Jones Futures Academy | 198 | Longoria, Sharon/Mt Sacred Heart Sch | 47 |
| Limas, Aminta/Lyndon Baines Johnson Elem Sch | 221 | **Looney, Angela**/Mountain Valley Middle Sch | 92 |
| Limon, Angela/W T Francisco Elem Sch | 349 | Lopez-Brouse, Melissa/Michael Elem Sch | 41 |
| Limon, Anthony/Harry Shimotsu Elem Sch | 227 | Lopez, Adrian/Cater Elem Sch | 32 |
| Limon, Marissa/Dan D Rogers Elem Sch | 103 | Lopez, Aine/Seminole Elem Sch | 162 |
| Linares, Diego, Dr/Martha Raines High Sch | 156 | Lopez, Alejandro/Clemente Martinez Elem Sch | 196 |
| Linares, Diego, Dr/Opportunity Awareness Center | 157 | Lopez, Andrea/Idea Clg Prep-Walzem [305] | 8 |
| Lindgren, Ronald/Timpson High Sch | 338 | Lopez, Angelita/Lotspeich Elem Sch | 308 |
| Lindley, Cynthia/Chandler Elem Sch | 174 | Lopez, Annette/Dr Martha Mead Elem Sch | 40 |
| Lindsey, Angelette, Dr/Newman Int'l Acad-Pioneer | 11 | Lopez, Blanca/Escobar-Rios Elem Sch | 225 |
| Lindsey, Brita/Texas Connections Academy [190] | 194 | Lopez, Bobby/Bob Hope Middle High Sch | 2 |
| Lindsey, Sabrina, Dr/Academy at Carrie F Thomas | 348 | Lopez, Brynn/Fayetteville Sch | 151 |
| Liner, Lariza/Mitchell Elem Sch | 86 | **Lopez, Carlos**/Berry Elem Sch | 346 |
| Ling, Stephanie/Fehl-Price Elem Sch | 245 | Lopez, Cristina/Memorial Intermediate Sch | 248 |
| Linson, Eartha/Wakefield Elem Sch | 172 | Lopez, Eduardo/M B Lamar Middle Sch | 390 |
| Linton, Lisa/Premier HS-Waco [318] | 12 | Lopez, Elena/Webb Elem Sch | 347 |
| **Linwood, Jessica**/Acton Elem Sch | 108 | Lopez, Eli/Saegert Elem Sch | 31 |
| Lipschitz, Christine/Uplift White Rock Hills Prep [331] | 16 | Lopez, Erica/Muriel Vance Forbes Academy | 44 |
| Lira, Brandi/Eastwood Academy | 194 | Lopez, Gabriel/West Briar Middle Sch | 200 |
| Little, Carolyn/Bingham Head Start Ctr | 245 | Lopez, Hector, Dr/Crossroads Academy High Sch | 381 |
| Little, Charles/Vandegrift High Sch | 400 | Lopez, Helena/Math Science & Tech Magnet Sch | 117 |
| Little, Clayton/De Kalb High Sch | 51 | Lopez, Jennifer/Our Lady of Fatima Sch | 166 |
| **Little, James**/Somerville Elem Sch | 63 | Lopez, Johanna/St James Catholic Sch | 179 |
| **Little, Kimberly**/Souder Elem Sch | 352 | Lopez, Jose/B H Hamblen Elem Sch | 188 |
| Little, Vickey/Teague Intermediate Sch | 161 | Lopez, Julianna/Premier HS-Career Tech Ed Ctr [318] | 12 |
| Littlefield, Michael/STEM Early College High Sch | 36 | Lopez, Karina/Edison Middle Sch | 195 |
| Litton, Debbie, Dr/Wood River Elem Sch | 306 | Lopez, Linda/Elodia R Chapa Elem Sch | 223 |
| Livecchi, Anthony/Oak Ridge High Sch | 295 | Lopez, Manuela/Ed Downs Elem Sch | 70 |
| Lizardo, Reny/James Bowie High Sch | 347 | **Lopez, Manuela**/Riverside Middle Sch | 70 |
| Llanos, Armando/Travis Elem Sch | 138 | Lopez, Marco/Idea Clg Prep-Brownsville [301] | 7 |
| Lloyd, Brittany/Highland Sch | 304 | Lopez, Marcos/Edward K Downing Elem Sch | 134 |
| Lloyd, Jonathan/Detroit High Sch | 325 | Lopez, Marina/La Fe Preparatory Sch | 10 |
| Loafman, Casey/Frenship Middle Sch | 272 | Lopez, Marisela/Klein Road Elem Sch | 92 |
| Loan, Lisa/David Crockett Middle Sch | 320 | Lopez, Myrna/Tornillo Elem Sch | 141 |
| Locheed, Kathryn/Aristoi Classical Academy | 1 | Lopez, Nora/Agua Dulce Elem Sch | 305 |
| Locke, Connie/Willow Springs Elem Sch | 31 | Lopez, Richard/Fabens Elem Sch | 139 |
| **Locke, Diana**/Corrigan-Camden High Sch | 319 | Lopez, Rita/Parkland Pre-K Center | 142 |
| Locke, Kelly/I N Range Elem Sch | 115 | Lopez, Roberto/Fannin Middle Sch | 111 |
| Lockwood, Jonica/D A Hulcy Steam Middle Sch | 103 | | |

| NAME/School | PAGE | NAME/School | PAGE |
|---|---|---|---|
| Majewski, James/Clear Creek High Sch | 163 | Marroquin, Ricardo/Harlandale Middle Sch | 36 |
| Majors, Angela/Montessori Academy-North Texas | 174 | Marsh, Kara/Heritage Christian Academy | 58 |
| Makel, Erin/St Edward Catholic Sch | 209 | Marsh, Kimberly/Sewell Elem Sch | 110 |
| Makuta, Marti/Cavazos Middle Sch | 273 | Marsh, Robert/Chapin High Sch | 138 |
| Malcolm, Mitzi/Carver Early Childhood Academy | 320 | Marsh, Sheila/Houston Gateway Acad-Evergreen | 5 |
| Maldonado, April/Eagle Springs Elem Sch | 201 | **Marshall, Andrenetta, Dr**/Keeble EC-PK-K Sch | 186 |
| Maldonado, Francisca/Smith Elem Sch | 372 | **Marshall, Andrenetta, Dr**/Voyde Caraway Elem Sch | 184 |
| **Maldonado, Graciela**/Edgemere Elem Sch | 142 | Marshall, Cathy/Newton Middle Sch | 304 |
| Maldonado, Ismael/H M K Care Academy | 260 | Marshall, Courtney/Collins Elem Sch | 187 |
| Maldonado, Sandra/Aikman Elem Sch | 123 | Marshall, Julie/Hays Magnet Academy | 134 |
| **Maldonado, Virna**/Psja T Jefferson Echs | 227 | Marshall, Leanne/Floresville South Elem Sch | 404 |
| Mallory, Shane/Highland Sch | 304 | **Marshall, Renesiaha**/James R Reynolds Elem Sch | 198 |
| Malo, Mark/Magrill EC-PK-K Sch | 186 | Marshall, Shannon/Dalhart Elem Sch | 99 |
| Malone, Amy/Rahe Bulverde Elem Sch | 92 | Marshall, Todd/Pleasant Grove High Sch | 52 |
| Malone, Dwight/Tisd Child & Adolescent Ctr | 256 | Marshall, Toni/St Peter the Apostle Elem Sch | 209 |
| **Malone, Jennifer**/Tatum Elem Sch | 331 | Martell, Miguel/Julius L Matthey Middle Sch | 46 |
| Malone, Jermon/Aristoi Classical Academy | 1 | Marti, Lauren/Hildebrandt Intermediate Sch | 202 |
| Malone, Lori/W L Higgins Elem Sch | 407 | Martin, Alexandra/Fowler Elem Sch | 395 |
| Malone, Mandy/Barbers Hill Primary Sch | 75 | Martin, Allie/Klenk Elem Sch | 202 |
| Malone, Mark/Randolph High Sch | 42 | Martin, Amanda, Dr/J C Rugel Elem Sch | 115 |
| Malone, Sheterric/Dallas Co Jj CS-Main Camp | 100 | Martin, Ana/Cy-Fair High Sch | 189 |
| **Malone, Tanisha**/Oliver E Clift Elem Sch | 147 | Martin, Blain/Devine Intermediate Sch | 286 |
| Malott, Margaret/O Henry Middle Sch | 371 | Martin, Casey/Good Shepherd Episcopal Sch | 119 |
| Mamaux, Maria/Jan Aragon Middle Sch | 190 | Martin, Christine/Victoria Juv Justice Center | 385 |
| Mamedov, Ahmed/Sch of Sci & Tech Main [320] | 13 | Martin, Curt/Downing Middle Sch | 127 |
| Manago, Joseph/Andress High Sch | 138 | Martin, Destini/William F Barnett Elem Sch | 165 |
| Manchee, Mike/Lorenzo De Zavala Middle Sch | 321 | Martin, Donna/Cunningham Elem Sch | 395 |
| Mancilla, Grace/Southside Elem Sch | 19 | Martin, Gordon/Sudan High Sch | 264 |
| Mancillas, Yvette/Arnoldo Cantu Elem Sch | 226 | Martin, Jennifer/David E Smith Elem Sch | 348 |
| Mancines, Jesenia/Bush Elem Sch | 187 | Martin, Jennifer/Town Center Elem Sch | 102 |
| Mancini, Angela/George W Carver Elem Sch | 193 | Martin, Kimberly/Galena Park High Sch | 192 |
| Maness, Michael/Cypress Ranch High Sch | 189 | Martin, Leslie/Blossom Elem Sch | 263 |
| Mangels, Stephanie/Carroll Middle Sch | 349 | Martin, Ludi/Ludi Pena Martin Accel Ed Ctr | 310 |
| Mank-Allen, Christina/Design & Technology Academy | 38 | Martin, Maya/Idea Academy-Rundberg [302] | 7 |
| Manley, Julee/Sparta Elem Sch | 30 | Martin, Melissa/Francone Elem Sch | 189 |
| Manley, William/Santo J Forte Jr High Sch | 348 | Martin, Melissa/Providence Classical Sch | 212 |
| Mann, Casey/The Jane Justin Sch | 362 | Martin, Patti/La Marque Primary Sch | 166 |
| Mann, Karla/McWhorter Elem Sch | 273 | Martin, Shekita/Linden Kildare High Sch | 74 |
| Mann, Valerie/P M Akin Elem Sch | 89 | Martin, Starla/Celina Elem Sch | 81 |
| **Manning, Emily**/Ponder Elem Sch | 130 | Martin, Stephanie/Barbers Hill Elem Sch North | 75 |
| Mans, Melanie/Mockingbird Elem Sch | 106 | Martinak, Michael/Bedford Junior High Sch | 356 |
| Mansfield, Jason/Faulk Early Childhood Center | 333 | Martinez-Munoz, Dyanne/Health Science Academy | 45 |
| Mansfield, Jason/Kieberger Elem Sch | 333 | **Martinez, Adam**/Dilley Elem Sch | 161 |
| Mantle, Kelly/Forester Elem Sch | 40 | Martinez, Amparo/Hubbard Heights Elem Sch | 353 |
| Mantz, Gary/Freedom Elem Sch | 357 | Martinez, Angelica/Vanguard Academy-Beethoven | 17 |
| Manuel, Monica/Career & Tech Education Center | 82 | Martinez, Anna/Dr Malakoff Elem Sch | 390 |
| Manuel, Richard/Cal & Walt Wester Middle Sch | 82 | Martinez, Antonio/North Side High Sch | 354 |
| Manzano, Vivianne/Idea Clg Prep-Toros [301] | 8 | **Martinez, Beatrice**/Anthon Elem Sch | 381 |
| Mapes, Lauri/Glen Rose Intermediate Sch | 342 | Martinez, Beatris/Classical Center at Vial Sch | 109 |
| Maphies, Alicia/Centennial High Sch | 82 | Martinez, Belen/Memorial Middle Sch | 223 |
| Maples, Matt/Stonegate Christian Academy | 120 | Martinez, Bertha/About Face Alternative ES | 137 |
| Maples, Melody/Stiles Middle Sch | 400 | Martinez, Bertha/Lamar Elem Sch | 138 |
| Marais, Ryno/St Thomas' Episcopal Sch | 212 | Martinez, Candee/Trinity Basin Prep-10th Street [327] | 15 |
| **Marbibi, Tamara**/Jack Frost Elem Sch | 398 | **Martinez, Carlos**/Elias Herrera Middle Sch | 390 |
| Marchante, Meredith/Harmony Sci Acad-Katy [299] | 5 | Martinez, Carolyn/Southwest Prep New Directions [323] | 14 |
| Marchiony, Mary/Bishop Dunne Catholic Sch | 118 | Martinez, Celia/Juan W Caceres Elem Sch | 220 |
| Marcos, Edison/Bexar County Academy [196] | 1 | Martinez, Criselda/John F Kennedy Elem Sch | 221 |
| Mariani, Tammy/Honey Grove High Sch | 150 | Martinez, Daniel/George Gervin Academy | 3 |
| Marioni, April/Ann M Garcia-Enriquez Mid Sch | 140 | Martinez, Daniel/St Gregory the Great Cath Sch | 47 |
| Markle, Bobby/Caldwell Arts Academy | 340 | Martinez, Dawn/St Anne Sch | 209 |
| Maroney, Dawn/Stroman Middle Sch | 385 | Martinez, Diana/H B Zachry Elem Sch | 389 |
| Marquez-Neth, Yvonne/Calallen High Sch | 306 | Martinez, Diane/Our Lady of Perpetual Help Sch | 309 |
| Marquez, Ashley/Nolan Ryan Junior High Sch | 54 | Martinez, Dora/Resurrection Catholic Sch | 209 |
| Marquez, Crystal/Sam Houston Elem Sch | 135 | Martinez, Doreen, Dr/Memorial Parkway Elem Sch | 156 |
| Marquez, Jennifer/Robert R Rojas Elem Sch | 141 | Martinez, Edmond/Clint Early College Academy | 136 |
| Marquez, Marizza/Sunset Valley Elem Sch | 370 | Martinez, Eduardo/Stillman Middle Sch | 68 |
| Marquez, Mauricio/Odessa High Sch | 135 | Martinez, Elisa/Carrizo Springs Elem Sch | 131 |
| Marquez, Michael, Dr/Margaret S McWhirter Elem Sch | 163 | Martinez, Elizabeth/Hutchins Elem Sch | 45 |
| Marquez, Monica/Louise Wolff Kahn Elem Sch | 105 | Martinez, Esmeralda/Odem Elem Sch | 334 |
| Marquez, Ranulfo/Psja Southwest EC High Sch | 227 | Martinez, Gilbert/Eastlake High Sch | 140 |
| Marr, Brian/Klein Alternative Ed Center | 202 | Martinez, Gloria/Sarah King Elem Sch | 44 |
| Marr, Mallory/Bridgeport Intermediate Sch | 406 | Martinez, Gracie/La Encantada Elem Sch | 70 |
| Marrerro, Alba/Texans Can Acad Carrltn-Farmrs [325] | 14 | Martinez, Graciela/John F Kennedy High Sch | 35 |
| Marron, Rebecca/West Memorial Elem Sch | 157 | Martinez, Greg/Five Palms Elem Sch | 45 |
| Marroquin, Christine/Blanche Moore Elem Sch | 306 | | |

| NAME/School | PAGE | NAME/School | PAGE |
|---|---|---|---|
| Miller, Ashley/Miller Elem Sch | 83 | Mireles, Sherry/Ed Rawlinson Middle Sch | 40 |
| Miller, Ashley/Rspa-Channelview | 13 | Mireles, Tina/Morrill Elem Sch | 36 |
| Miller, Barry/Parmer Lane Elem Sch | 374 | Mishler, Julia/Wellborn Middle Sch | 59 |
| Miller, Byron/Hamshire Fannett Elem Sch | 245 | Missildine, Justin/Career & Tech Education Center | 37 |
| Miller, Chad/Ore City Elem Sch | 379 | Mitchell, Allison/Panhandle Elem Sch | 73 |
| Miller, Chris/Blue Ridge High Sch | 81 | Mitchell, Bridget/Jay Thompson Elem Sch | 115 |
| Miller, Cindy/Three Rivers Elem Sch | 271 | Mitchell, Cathryn/Gorzycki Middle Sch | 371 |
| Miller, Clint/Chisum High Sch | 262 | Mitchell, Chavis/Parker Elem Sch | 199 |
| **Miller, Cody**/Larkspur Elem Sch | 38 | Mitchell, Glenn, Dr/Memorial High Sch | 246 |
| **Miller, Connie**/Reagan Elem Sch | 182 | Mitchell, Judy/Phoenix Learning Center | 217 |
| Miller, Donisha/Poteet Elem Sch | 24 | Mitchell, Kalley/Dublin Elem Sch | 147 |
| Miller, Elizabeth/Cesar Chavez Elem Sch | 128 | Mitchell, Leah/Stanton Elem Sch | 277 |
| Miller, Elizabeth/Colin Powell 6th Grade Center | 128 | Mitchell, Leslye/Highland Village Elem Sch | 127 |
| Miller, Elizabeth, Dr/Swenke Elem Sch | 190 | Mitchell, Rachel/Faith Christian Academy | 210 |
| Miller, Grant/Scurry Rosser Middle Sch | 256 | Mitchell, Reginal/Thornton Middle Sch | 190 |
| Miller, James/Encino Park Elem Sch | 38 | Mitchell, Richard/Family Christian Academy | 119 |
| **Miller, Jared**/Crandall High Sch | 254 | **Mitchell, Tricia**/Fred W Edwards Academy | 32 |
| Miller, Jason/Cedar Hill 9th Grade Center | 101 | Mitzner, Kris, Dr/Tays Junior High Sch | 157 |
| Miller, Jason/Cedar Hill High Sch | 101 | Mixer, Blanca/Community of Faith Chrn Sch | 143 |
| Miller, Jessie/Keiko Davidson Elem Sch | 156 | Mixon, Carol/Canyon Creek Elem Sch | 116 |
| Miller, John/Cross Roads High Sch | 219 | Mize, Carol Jo/McLennan Co State Juvenile Sch | 11 |
| Miller, Julie/Patterson Elem Sch | 295 | Mize, Michael/Alba-Golden Jr Sr High Sch | 407 |
| Miller, Kardel/Windsong Ranch Elem Sch | 88 | Mizell, Matthew/Trinidad Sch | 220 |
| Miller, Karl/Odessa Career Tch Early Clg HS | 134 | Moad, Angie/Gonzales Elem Sch | 134 |
| **Miller, Kathleen**/Pearland Jr High School West | 57 | Moczygemba, Brooke/Legacy Christian Academy | 247 |
| Miller, Kendall/E M Daggett Elem Sch | 353 | Moeller, Arron/Martha Hunt Elem Sch | 86 |
| Miller, Lance/Calvary Christian Academy | 361 | Moes, Mathew/Iant Quranic Academy | 119 |
| Miller, Laura/Kermit Junior High Sch | 405 | Moffatt, Alison/Live Oak Classical Sch | 285 |
| Miller, Lindsey/Frank Stone Middle Sch | 406 | Moffett, Daryle/Crowley High Sch | 350 |
| Miller, Lynette/Hastings High Sch | 187 | Moffett, John/Claude Sch | 23 |
| Miller, Mike/Arp Junior High Sch | 339 | **Moffett, Ronda**/City View Elem Sch | 394 |
| Miller, Mindy/Parkview Elem Sch | 351 | Moffitt, Kristin/Westwood-Bales Elem Sch | 164 |
| Miller, Natalie/Edris Childres Elliot Elem Sch | 82 | Mohler, Elizabeth/Rutledge Elem Sch | 400 |
| Miller, Nikki/H G Temple Elem Sch | 20 | Mohler, Holly/School for the Highly Gifted | 112 |
| Miller, Nikki/H G Temple Intermediate Sch | 20 | Molina, Amanda/Anderson Mill Elem Sch | 401 |
| Miller, Queinnise, Dr/Marshall | 197 | Molina, Armando/Francisco S Lara Academy | 389 |
| Miller, Rheatha/Foundation School for Autism [318] | 3 | Molina, Dora/Blanton Elem Sch | 369 |
| Miller, Shawn/Raymond Cooper Junior High Sch | 89 | Molina, Jose/Spur Sch | 131 |
| Miller, Shenequa/Commerce Middle Sch | 239 | **Molina, Lupe**/Allison Elem Sch | 369 |
| Miller, Stephanie/Laura Bush Elem Sch | 204 | Molina, Theresa/Karnes City Junior High Sch | 253 |
| Miller, Susan/Murchison Elem Sch | 219 | Molina, Tiffany/Harmony Sch Innov-Austin [299] | 4 |
| Miller, Susanne/Olson Elem Sch | 80 | Molina, Yesena/Edinburg High Sch | 221 |
| Miller, Tom/Brooks-Quinn Jones Elem Sch | 301 | Molina, Yulia/Dorothy Thompson Middle Sch | 227 |
| Miller, Tonya/Challenge Early Clg High Sch | 196 | Molinar, Lorena/Ft Hancock High Sch | 237 |
| Miller, Virginia, Dr/Guadalupe Regional Middle Sch | 71 | Molinares, Mary/Arlington Park ECC | 103 |
| Miller, Wendy/Harry C Withers Elem Sch | 104 | Mondik, Mayra/Lamar Middle Sch | 371 |
| Milliner, Rodney/Texans Can Academy-Grant East [325] | 14 | Mondragon, Mario/Esperanza Medrano Elementary | 104 |
| Mills, Brent/Woodson Sch | 365 | Monrreal, Raymundo/Jaime Escalante Middle Schl | 226 |
| Mills, Carlette/West Rusk Elem Sch | 331 | Montalbano, Ginger/Duchesne Acad of Sacred Heart | 209 |
| Mills, Donald, Dr/Lighthouse Charter Sch | 10 | Montalvo, Michelle/Caldwell Heights Elem Sch | 401 |
| Mills, Keith/Center Point High Sch | 258 | Montana, Erika/Friona High Sch | 318 |
| Mills, Keith/Center Point Middle Sch | 258 | Montana, Thomasina/Freedom Elem Sch | 46 |
| Mills, Marsha/La Poynor Sch | 219 | Montanio, Tracie/Larkspur Elem Sch | 400 |
| Mills, Monica/Rodriguez Elem Sch | 370 | Montano, James/Jubilee Highland Park [306] | 8 |
| Mills, Scott/McCord Elem Sch | 397 | Montelongo, Alvaro/Looscan Elem Sch | 194 |
| Mills, Tracy/Jackson Elem Sch | 158 | Montelongo, Amanda/Lauro Cavazos Elem Sch | 134 |
| Mills, Wendy/Norman-Sims Elem Sch | 370 | Montelongo, John/Hightower High Sch | 154 |
| Mims, Aleia/Uplift Summit Int'l Prep CS [331] | 16 | Montemayor, Adrian/San Perlita Sch | 397 |
| Mims, Charles/Rio Vista High Sch | 251 | Montemayor, Evelia/Roy P Benavidez Elem Sch | 46 |
| Mims, Deedee/New Hope Christian Academy | 89 | **Montemayor, Karla, Dr**/Drs Reed & Mock Elem Sch | 226 |
| Miner, Pam/Tulia Elem Sch | 345 | Montemayor, Sara/Katherine Tarver Elem Sch | 389 |
| Minix, Melissa/Smithfield Elem Sch | 349 | Montes, Alexandra/Western Hills Elem Sch | 355 |
| Minn, Jeff/Victory Place at Coppell | 102 | Montes, Juan/Francisca Alvarez Elem Sch | 224 |
| Minter, Leslie, Dr/Heritage Christian Academy | 329 | Montes, Terry/Sunrise Mountain Elem Sch | 138 |
| Minton, Ashley/Canyon Ranch Elem Sch | 102 | Montez, Jeremiah/Hfa-Alameda Sch-Art & Design | 5 |
| Minyard, Kimberly/Jubilee Sendero [306] | 9 | **Montgomery, Crystal**/Crockett Elem Sch | 235 |
| Minyard, Rusty/Evadale High Sch | 243 | Montgomery, Phoebe/Reinhardt Elem Sch | 106 |
| **Minyard, Rusty**/Woodville High Sch | 378 | Montgomery, Rebecca/Kilgore Primary Sch | 174 |
| Minyen, Valerie/Compass Academy Charter Sch | 2 | Montoya, Linda/Jones Elem Sch | 58 |
| Mira, Jose/Isabel Pierce Sem Elem Sch | 82 | Moody, Bethany/Birdwell Elem Sch | 340 |
| Miranda, Aaliyah/East Grand Preparatory Academy | 3 | Moody, Charles/The Excel Center Austin [169] | 15 |
| Miranda, Alicia/Myrtle Cooper Elem Sch | 141 | Moody, Denise/Mae Smythe Elem Sch | 204 |
| Miranda, Fernando/H D Hilley Elem Sch | 140 | Moody, John/Southmore Intermediate Sch | 205 |
| Miranda, Francisco/Nimitz High Sch | 114 | Moody, Scott/Columbia High Sch | 56 |
| Miranda, Vanessa/Escuela Montessori-Del Valle | 143 | | |

| NAME/School | PAGE | NAME/School | PAGE |
|---|---|---|---|
| Register, Bridget/Gatesville Intermediate Sch | 97 | Richard, Lisa/Gregory Luna Middle Sch | 40 |
| Rehan, Susan/Vera Escamilla Elem Sch | 185 | Richards, James/Motley Co Sch | 299 |
| **Reichel, Bridgit**/Nadine Johnson Elem Sch | 399 | Richards, Jan/Littlefield Primary Sch | 263 |
| Reidling, Rebecca/Grace Hartman Elem Sch | 328 | Richards, Joey, Dr/Southwest Christian Sch-Prep | 362 |
| Reile, Hilary/Sacred Heart Catholic Sch | 404 | Richards, Megan/Valley Creek Elem Sch | 85 |
| Reilly, Patricia, Dr/Farney Elem Sch | 189 | Richardson, Dara/Blue Hole Primary Sch | 217 |
| Reinhart, Tracey/Montessori Episcopal Sch | 130 | Richardson, Darren/Weldon Elem Sch | 174 |
| Reininger, Charles/David Tex Hill Middle Sch | 37 | Richardson, David/Story Intermediate Sch | 19 |
| Reisner, Mark/Greenville Christian Sch | 240 | Richardson, Jeremy/Pasadena Memorial High Sch | 204 |
| Reiter, Elizabeth/KIPP Austin Connections ES [307] | 9 | **Richardson, Karen**/Reed Elem Sch | 190 |
| Relf, Amanda/Ben Tisinger Elem Sch | 115 | Richardson, Kimberly/Thomas L Marsalis Elem Sch | 107 |
| Remmers, Galen/Misd Developmental Center | 270 | Richardson, Marsha/Community Christian Sch | 170 |
| Rendon, Armando/Int'l Ldrshp TX-Keller | 113 | Richardson, Melinda/Navarro Co Alt Educ Ctr | 303 |
| Rendon, Netassha/Brandenburg Elem Sch | 113 | Richardson, Paula/Tekoa Academy-Port Arthur [324] | 14 |
| Rendon, Silvia/Ysleta High Sch | 143 | Richardson, Stephen/Hackberry Elem Sch | 128 |
| Renfro, Anna/Shady Grove Elem Sch | 358 | Richburg, Leslie/Edgemere Elem Sch | 180 |
| Renner, Ben/Cleburne High Sch | 250 | Richie, Clarisa/Fain Elem Sch | 395 |
| Reno, Debra/C D Landolt Elem Sch | 163 | Richmond, Michael/Sch of Environmental Education | 177 |
| Renteria, Christine/Milton L Kirkpatrick Elem Sch | 354 | Richmond, Sarah/Pittsburg Intermediate Sch | 72 |
| Renteria, Noe/Sundown Lane Elem Sch | 324 | Richter, Gena/Kor Education Sch | 60 |
| Resendez, Alberto/J A Kawas Elem Sch | 389 | Richter, Laura/South Knoll Elem Sch | 59 |
| Resendiz, Pablo/Holland Middle Sch | 194 | Rickman, Jessica/Dr Lee Buice Elem Sch | 134 |
| Resilla, Clare, Dr/Pearl M Hirsch Elem Sch | 208 | Ricks, Kelly/Ray & Jamie Wolman Elem Sch | 157 |
| Resio, Stella/Skidmore Tynan Jr High Sch | 29 | Rico, Angel/Lee Elem Sch | 114 |
| Revels, Deborah/Crockett High Sch | 235 | Rico, Oscar, Dr/Jose Alderete Middle Sch | 136 |
| **Reyes, Amanda**/Michael M Boone Elem Sch | 112 | Ricowatson, Geneva, Dr/Southwest Prep Sch SE [323] | 14 |
| Reyes, Elizabeth/Valley View South Elem Sch | 228 | **Riddick, Danielle**/Vernal Lister Elem Sch | 111 |
| Reyes, Estela/Bay City High Sch | 278 | Rider, Aris/Dallas Environmental Sci Acad | 103 |
| Reyes, Fernando/Harlingen High School South | 68 | Rider, Nathan/P E Wallace Middle Sch | 366 |
| Reyes, Justin/Texans Can Acad Houston SW [325] | 14 | **Ridley, Catherine**/Castleberry High Sch | 350 |
| Reyes, Laura/Impact Early College High Sch | 193 | **Ridley, Cathy**/Leonard Middle Sch | 353 |
| Reyes, Maria/John Q Adams Elem Sch | 105 | Ridout, Michael/Little Cypress Interm Sch | 311 |
| Reyes, Martha/Frank Tejeda Middle Sch | 38 | Riebkes, Brenda/Bear Creek Intermediate Sch | 357 |
| Reyes, Mike/Gutierriez Middle Sch | 68 | Riek, Rene/Transition Center | 356 |
| Reyes, Paula/Govalle Elem Sch | 369 | Rietfors, Gina/Cross Timbers Intermediate Sch | 359 |
| Reyes, Rick/Elgin High Sch | 27 | Riewe, Philip/Irons Middle Sch | 273 |
| Reyes, Sandra/Hector P Garcia Elem Sch | 32 | Riggs, Jill/Herty Primary Sch | 21 |
| Reyes, Vanessa/Sam Rayburn High Sch | 205 | Riha, Ruth/Barrington Place Elem Sch | 154 |
| Reyez, Leida/Veterans Memorial Elem Sch | 343 | Rike, Jim/St Joseph Catholic Sch | 59 |
| Reyna-Garza, Jessica/Carl Waitz Elem Sch | 225 | Riker, Brad/James D Gossett Elem Sch | 380 |
| Reyna, Angela/Parkland Middle Sch | 142 | Riley, Chad/Bishop Lynch High Sch | 118 |
| Reyna, Eliseo/Graduation Prep Academy-Travis | 371 | Riley, Frank/Bracken Christian Sch | 93 |
| Reyna, Eva/Brentwood Middle Sch | 34 | Riley, Phillip/St Monica Catholic Sch | 118 |
| Reyna, Orlando/Sugar Grove Academy | 194 | Riley, Rhonda/Throckmorton Sch | 365 |
| Reyna, Selina/DeLeon Elem Sch | 384 | Rimer, Terri/Long Elem Sch | 289 |
| Reynolds, Alonzo/Andy Dekaney High Sch | 207 | Rincon, Lilly/Jefferson Elem Sch | 197 |
| Reynolds, Donna/Hood-Case Elem Sch | 54 | **Rincon, Melissa**/William James Middle Sch | 355 |
| Reynolds, Ernie/Canyon Middle Sch | 91 | Rinearson, Robyn/Glenn Harmon Elem Sch | 359 |
| Reynolds, Fredia/Wheatley Sch Early Childhood | 246 | Rinehart, Nancy/Atlanta High Sch | 73 |
| Reynolds, Keely/Trinity Charter School-Pegasus [328] | 15 | Rink, Dawn/McCoy Elem Sch | 101 |
| Reynolds, Kent/Hallsburg Elem Sch | 282 | Riojas, Amalia/Sam Houston Elem Sch | 280 |
| Reynolds, Kimberly/Valley Oaks Elem Sch | 206 | Riojas, Jesse, Dr/Mathis High Sch | 334 |
| Reynolds, Shanna/S & S Elem Sch | 172 | Rios-Garcia, Linda/Huppertz Elem Sch | 43 |
| Rhea, Iva Nell/Cypress Cmty Christian Sch | 210 | Rios, Denise/St Augustine Catholic Sch | 209 |
| Rhine, Daresa/Hook Elem Sch | 148 | Rios, Manuel/William D Slider Middle Sch | 141 |
| Rhines, Mico/Thelma Jones Elem Sch | 360 | Rios, Rolando/Cesar Chavez Middle Sch | 223 |
| Rhines, Reggie/Kennedale Junior High Sch | 358 | Rios, Rosanna/Kirchner Elem Sch | 280 |
| Rhines, Valencia/Leadership Acad Como ES | 353 | Ripley, William/Whitehouse Junior High Sch | 341 |
| Rhodes, Canita/Snyder Primary Sch | 336 | Ripple, Dawn/Ward Elem Sch | 363 |
| Rhodes, Craig/Dr Ronald E McNair Junior HS | 54 | Rische, David/Early Learning Ctr North | 357 |
| Rhodes, Gloria/Bonham Elem Sch | 58 | Risinger, Jennifer/Athens Middle Sch | 218 |
| Rhodes, Katina/Bellaire Elem Sch | 356 | Risley, Reagan/Canadian Elem Sch | 218 |
| Rhodes, Lesley/Adams Elem Sch | 346 | Rispoli, Joe/Faith Academy of Marble Falls | 64 |
| Rhodes, Philip/Dumas Intermediate Sch | 298 | Rister, Bobby/T M Clark Elem Sch | 333 |
| Rhodes, William, Dr/Robert & Felice Bryant ES | 157 | Ritchey, David/Lamesa Success Academy | 121 |
| Rhodus, Randal/Hockaday Sch | 119 | **Ritchey, David**/South Elem Sch | 121 |
| Rhymes, Jacqueline/Golden Meadows Elem Sch | 110 | Ritchey, Garrett/Clint High Sch | 136 |
| **Rice, Calvin, Dr**/Paul A Brown Learning Center | 245 | Ritchey, Michael/Big Spring High Sch | 236 |
| Rice, Crystal/Torres Elem Sch | 385 | Ritchie, Walter/Spring Creek Academy | 90 |
| Rice, Darrell, Dr/Northside Alternative High Sch | 41 | Rivas, Marta/Ridgegate Elem Sch | 155 |
| Rice, Donna/Atlanta Primary Sch | 73 | Rivas, Monico/Liberty High Sch | 194 |
| Rice, Michelle/Hoover Elem Sch | 190 | Rivas, Priscilla/Crockett Charter Elem Sch | 196 |
| Rich, Whitney/Deer Park Elem Sch | 191 | Rivera, Conrad/Pyburn Elem Sch | 192 |

# PRINCIPAL INDEX

Market Data Retrieval

| NAME/School | PAGE | NAME/School | PAGE |
|---|---|---|---|
| Smith, Loyd/Phoenix Alt Campus 817 | 250 | Soto, Linda/Lyndon B Johnson Middle Sch | 227 |
| Smith, Lucinda/Rogers Middle Sch | 32 | Soto, Lisa/Leon Daiches Elem Sch | 389 |
| Smith, Lynn/City Lab High Sch | 103 | Soto, Samuel/Bluebonnet Elem Sch | 401 |
| Smith, Lynn/Multiple Careers Magnet Center | 106 | **Soto, Trish**/Reagan Co Elem Sch | 324 |
| Smith, Malcolm/Calvary Episcopal Sch | 159 | Soukup, Theresa/Brookhaven Sch | 285 |
| Smith, Mark/Art & Pat Goforth Elem Sch | 163 | Soulas, Alexis/Harold C Kaffie Middle Sch | 306 |
| Smith, Mary/Dezavala Environ Science Acad | 111 | **Southard, Michelle**/Lockney High Sch | 153 |
| **Smith, Megan**/Sherry & Paul Hamm Elem Sch | 328 | Southard, Michelle/Shallowater Intermediate Sch | 275 |
| Smith, Melissa/Antonio M Ochoa Elem Sch | 220 | Southard, Todd/Pilot Point High Sch | 129 |
| Smith, Melissa/Ed Vanston Middle Sch | 115 | Southworth, Chaisleigh/Raul B Fernandez Elem Sch | 41 |
| **Smith, Melissia, Dr**/Alternative Learning Center | 158 | Sowers, Lori/Indian Creek Elem Sch | 127 |
| Smith, Michael/Bridgeland High Sch | 189 | Sparacello, Leslie/Midland Senior High Sch | 289 |
| Smith, Michael/Hurst Junior High Sch | 356 | **Sparkman, Keith**/Winona High Sch | 341 |
| Smith, Michael/Savoy High Sch | 151 | **Sparks, Brian**/Artemisia Bowden Academy | 43 |
| Smith, Michael/West Hardin High Sch | 184 | Sparks, Brian/Lamar Elem Sch | 44 |
| **Smith, Monica**/A B Duncan Elem Sch | 153 | Sparks, Kathy/Victory Christian Academy | 310 |
| **Smith, Nickolas**/Meadows Elem Sch | 31 | Sparks, Kayla/Three Way Elem Sch | 148 |
| Smith, Patricia/Jhw Inspire Acad-Legacy Ranch | 34 | Sparksgoecke, Kathy/Grandview Hills Elem Sch | 400 |
| Smith, Paul/Smithville High Sch | 27 | Spaugh, Donna/Bayshore Elem Sch | 203 |
| Smith, Rahsan/Polly Ann McRoberts Elem Sch | 157 | Speaks, Monica/Clear View High Sch | 163 |
| Smith, Randi/Bryant Elem Sch | 346 | Spear, Stephanie/Reese Education Center | 272 |
| Smith, Rebecca/Eastside Elem Sch | 268 | Spearman, Cassandra/Hay Branch Elem Sch | 31 |
| Smith, Rhonda/Liberty Middle Sch | 269 | Spears, Christina/Rockport-Fulton Middle Sch | 22 |
| Smith, Rotasha/Conroe High Sch | 294 | Spears, Jennifer/Popham Elem Sch | 372 |
| Smith, Shanica/Young Elem Sch | 198 | Spears, Shelly/Judy Rucker Elem Sch | 88 |
| **Smith, Shannon**/Fred and Patti Shafer ES | 156 | Specia, Christopher/Roan Forest Elem Sch | 38 |
| **Smith, Sharon**/Birch Elem Sch | 175 | Specter, Tristan/Burleson Elem Sch | 134 |
| Smith, Shelby/Madeley Ranch Elem Sch | 296 | Spedding, Bill/Keystone Sch | 48 |
| Smith, Susan/Valley View Sch | 95 | Speed, Maggie/Texas Leadership CS-Midland | 15 |
| Smith, Ted/Aep Center | 30 | Speer, Sandra/Brill Elem Sch | 202 |
| Smith, Theresa/Berne Acad Private Sch | 118 | Speights, Christie/Horace Mann Junior High Sch | 193 |
| Smith, Tim/Wylie High Sch | 364 | Spellmann, Gerrie/Woodridge Elem Sch | 33 |
| Smith, Traci, Dr/Stonewall Flanders Elem Sch | 36 | Spelman, Barbara/New Hope High Sch | 400 |
| Smitherman, Christie/Roland Reynolds Elem Sch | 327 | Spence, Connie, Dr/Kooken Educational Center | 347 |
| Smock, Farrah/Parkhill Junior High Sch | 117 | Spencer, Antoine/Otto Middle Sch | 87 |
| Smolka, David/Bessie Gunstream Elem Sch | 82 | Spencer, Dusty/Canton High Sch | 382 |
| Smothers, David/Sweeny Junior High Sch | 57 | Spencer, Gloria/Plato Academy | 142 |
| Smyder, Christa/A B Harrison Intermediate Sch | 88 | Spencer, Stefanie/Spring Branch Middle Sch | 206 |
| Snavely, William/Memorial Middle Sch | 68 | **Sperry, Jennifer**/Happy Middle High Sch | 345 |
| Sneed, Cynthia/Jubilee-Wells Academies | 9 | Spicer, Brent/Saint Mary's Hall | 48 |
| Sneed, Romikianta/Martin Luther King Jr Lrng Ctr | 105 | **Spillers, Shanna**/Mineral Wells Jr High Sch | 313 |
| Snider, Kimberlyn/Neches Elem Jr High Sch | 18 | Spillman, Freda/Memorial Chrn Academy | 211 |
| Sniffin, Jeanna/Ronald Thornton Middle Sch | 155 | Spitzer, Jennifer/Owen Elem Sch | 128 |
| **Sniffin, Jeanna**/Williams Elem Sch | 399 | Spivey, Frances/Crockett Classical Academy [318] | 2 |
| Snokhous, Vicki/Cypress Creek High Sch | 189 | Spivey, Sandra/Polk Elem Sch | 138 |
| Snow, Ronny/Rusk High Sch | 77 | Sponsel, Sara/Harmony Sch Innov-Carrolltn [299] | 4 |
| Snowden, Ryan/Wall High Sch | 368 | Spoon, Deborah/Tom Cox Intermediate Sch | 295 |
| Snyder, Janie/Southside Elem Sch | 268 | Spraberry, Cody/Forest Trail Elem Sch | 372 |
| Snyder, Jeffrey/Trinity Valley Sch | 362 | Sprang, Gina/Elsik 9th Grade Center | 187 |
| Snyder, Robalyn/Hunters Creek Elem Sch | 206 | Sprayberry, Felicia/Gonzalez Sch for Young Chldrn | 125 |
| Snyder, Scott, Dr/San Saba High Sch | 335 | Sprayberry, Kim/Lynn Lucas Middle Sch | 297 |
| Snyder, Stacia/Marion High Sch | 177 | Springer, Gerald/Pottsboro Middle Sch | 172 |
| **Snyder, Vanessa**/Salazar Elem Sch | 248 | Springer, Laura/Coppell High Sch | 102 |
| Sobelman, Patty/Pines Montessori Sch | 211 | Springs, Marilyn, Sr/Holy Family Catholic Sch | 309 |
| Solano, Beatriz/Kelly Elem Sch | 222 | Sprott, Mariea/Hightower Elem Sch | 86 |
| Solano, Gregorio/Hidalgo Park Elem Sch | 222 | Sproul, Ross/Boerne High Sch | 257 |
| Soldevila, Jorge/Harker Heights High Sch | 31 | Spruell, Carl/Priddy Sch | 292 |
| **Soleyjacks, R**/Bivins Elem Sch | 320 | Spurgers, Kimberly/San Jacinto Elem Sch | 367 |
| **Solis, Darlene**/Ramona Elem Sch | 142 | Spurlock, Oscar/Jerry Junkins Elem Sch | 105 |
| Solis, Lesli/Medina Valley Middle Sch | 287 | **Squalls, Lorie**/Coppell Middle School North | 102 |
| Solis, Maria/Farias Early Childhood Center | 196 | Square, Stephanie/East Early College High Sch | 194 |
| Solis, Maria/Gladys Porter Early Clg HS | 67 | Squires, Jared/Kingdom Preparatory Academy | 275 |
| Solis, Roger/Dilley High Sch | 161 | Squyres, Carrie/Hoffmann Elem Sch | 40 |
| Soliz, Becky/Texas Christian Sch | 212 | Sralla, Scott/Student Reassignment Ctr | 114 |
| Soliz, Maytte/North Heights Elem Sch | 382 | St Ama, Michael/Dr Wright Lassiter Erly Clg HS | 103 |
| Soliz, Yvette/Camino Real Elem Sch | 216 | St John, Keri/Bynum Sch | 289 |
| Solomon, Dana/Phillips Elem Sch | 83 | St Julian, Delilah/Weaver Odom Elem Sch | 185 |
| Somerhalder, Michelle/Timber Creek High Sch | 358 | Stabile, Amy/KIPP Explore Academy [309] | 9 |
| Soriano, Rafael/Padron Elem Sch | 370 | Stackhouse, Stephen/Ft Worth Country Day Sch | 361 |
| Sosa, Andi/Carnahan Elem Sch | 39 | Stadler, Meredith/McQueeney Elem Sch | 179 |
| Sosebee, Kristina/Effie Morris Elem Sch | 358 | Stafford, Amanda/Archer City High Sch | 22 |
| Sotelo, Joseph/Hillcrest High Sch | 104 | Stafford, Jill/Lowery Freshman Center | 80 |
| Soto-Dimas, Luz/Central Elem Sch | 100 | Stafford, Nadia/Gus A Oleson Elem Sch | 185 |
| Soto, Ana/Helen Ball Elem Sch | 140 | Staggs, Becky/Sojourn Academy | 298 |
| **Soto, Benigno**/Long Academy | 199 | | |

| NAME/School | PAGE | NAME/School | PAGE |
|---|---|---|---|
| Telles, Laura/Glass Elem Sch | 280 | Thornhill, Anthony/Lancaster STEM Early Clg HS | 114 |
| Teltschik, Sophie/Hallettsville Jr High Sch | 265 | Thornhill, Tammy/West Ward Elem Sch | 31 |
| Templeton, Craig/Harrold Sch | 396 | Thornton, Ann/Space Center Intermediate Sch | 163 |
| Tennery, Jody/Avalon Sch | 144 | Thornton, Jeff/Larry Brown Sch | 23 |
| Tennison, Alicia/West Side Elem Sch | 76 | Thornton, Ritchie/Estacado Middle Sch | 180 |
| **Tennyson, Analese**/Perez Elem Sch | 260 | Thornton, Robyn/Onalaska Jr Sr High Sch | 320 |
| Teran, Tricia/Bonham Elem Sch | 288 | Thornton, Sarah/Coppell Middle School West | 102 |
| Terrazas, Leticia/Desert Wind Elem Sch | 140 | Thornton, Yvonne/Rosa Parks-Millbrook Sch | 114 |
| Terrell, Reginald/Handley Middle Sch | 353 | Thrash, Michelle/A Plus Academy Elementary [287] | 1 |
| Tessar, Adrienne/William B Travis Elem Sch | 193 | Thurman, Denise/St Jo Elem Sch | 293 |
| Tewell, Leslie/Keller-Harvel Elem Sch | 357 | Thurmon, Kyle/Matagorda Sch | 278 |
| **Thacker, Patricia**/Creighton Elem Sch | 294 | Thurmond, Paula/Southwest Christian Academy | 212 |
| Tharpe, Kelly/H G Isbill Junior High Sch | 283 | Thurston, Alicia/Lucille Nash Elem Sch | 255 |
| Thatcher, Laura/Premier HS-Mission [318] | 12 | Thurston, Duane/Mary Orr Intermediate Sch | 359 |
| Thayer, David/Alice Ponder Elem Sch | 359 | **Tibayan, Edgar, Dr**/Presidio Elem Sch | 323 |
| Theesfield, Debra/Richard Milburn Acad-Midland [319] | 13 | Tidwell, Aaron/Mildred Sch | 303 |
| Theodore, Kecia/Student Opportunity Center | 83 | Tidwell, Amanda/Detroit Middle Sch | 325 |
| Therwhanger, Danielle/Klondike Sch | 121 | **Tidwell, Jerrod**/Tolar Junior High Sch | 234 |
| Thibodeaux, Traci/Reve Preparatory Charter Sch | 13 | Tiemann, Randy/Mathis Middle Sch | 334 |
| Thomas-Boone, Sheila/Ennis Junior High Sch | 144 | Tiemann, Wendy/Timberwilde Elem Sch | 42 |
| Thomas, Ajunta/Rogers Middle Sch | 57 | Tiet, Cindy/Ray Daily Elem Sch | 199 |
| **Thomas, Alena**/Oveta Culp Hobby Elem Sch | 31 | **Tietze, Adam**/Lemm Elem Sch | 202 |
| Thomas, Carla/Culver Elem Sch | 158 | Tijerina, Janie/Edcouch Elsa High Sch | 221 |
| Thomas, Charlotte/Annie Rainwater Elem Sch | 100 | Tillery, Shelby/Big Sandy Sch | 319 |
| Thomas, Chrystal/Scott Elem Sch | 32 | Timberlake, Dianne/China Elem Sch | 183 |
| **Thomas, Derek**/Adelle Turner Elem Sch | 102 | Times, Tricia/Point Alternative Center | 193 |
| Thomas, Derrick, Dr/St Philip's Early Clg HS | 44 | Timm, Ryan/Baxter Elem Sch | 145 |
| Thomas, Ed/San Jacinto Christian Academy | 322 | Timmons, Erika/L A Nelson Elem Sch | 125 |
| Thomas, Ellen/Burton Adventist Academy | 361 | Timms, Joe/McMullen Co Sch | 286 |
| Thomas, James/Bayside Intermediate Sch | 163 | Tims, Angela/Don R Daniel 9th Grade Campus | 315 |
| Thomas, James/Memorial Pathway Academy | 110 | Tindall, Jaime/Woodson Center for Excellence | 363 |
| Thomas, Jamila/Uplift Peak Prep Sch [331] | 16 | Tiner, Brandi/Alto Middle Sch | 76 |
| Thomas, Jenny/Armand Bayou Elem Sch | 163 | Tinklenberg, Jay/Newman Int'l Academy-Arlington | 11 |
| Thomas, Jesse/Crockett Elem Sch | 395 | Tinnon, Samuel/Casis Elem Sch | 369 |
| Thomas, Jorly/Fred Roberts Middle Sch | 204 | Tinoco, Rafael/Hidalgo Elem Sch | 222 |
| Thomas, Keith/Ruth Jones McClendon Mid Sch | 13 | Tinsley, Kristen/Sarita Elem Sch | 258 |
| **Thomas, Kim**/Sudderth Elem Sch | 388 | Tipton, Christina/Fusion Academy-Dallas | 119 |
| Thomas, Lakisha/T W Browne Middle Sch | 107 | Tipton, Krista/Midlothian Heritage High Sch | 145 |
| Thomas, Leslie/Cactus Trails Elem Sch | 140 | Tipton, Verna/Leon Sablatura Middle Sch | 57 |
| Thomas, Michael/Hamilton Park Pacesetter Mag | 116 | Tisdom, Christy/Charles R Drew Elem Sch | 188 |
| **Thomas, Nimmi**/Park Place Elem Sch | 195 | Tite, Erin/Florence Campbell Sch | 163 |
| Thomas, Nirmala/Our Lady Queen of Peace Sch | 57 | Tobey, Loryn/Norris Elem Sch | 83 |
| Thomas, Pam/Bowie Elem Sch | 217 | Todd, Courtney/Milano Elem Sch | 290 |
| Thomas, Pamela/Duncanville HS Collegiate Acad | 109 | Todd, Michele/Wilson Elem Sch | 69 |
| Thomas, Pamela/Marlin High Sch | 149 | Todd, Orfelinda/Vardeman EC-PK-K Sch | 186 |
| Thomas, Sheila/Calk-Wilson Elem Sch | 306 | Tolbert, Marilyn/Starpoint Sch | 362 |
| Thomas, Stephanie/B F Adam Elem Sch | 189 | Tolin, K Renee/St Catherine of Siena Sch | 247 |
| **Thomas, Sueanna**/Jacobs Well Elem Sch | 217 | Toliver, Jana/Lawndale Elem Sch | 321 |
| Thomas, Susan/Denton Classical Academy [318] | 2 | Tomhave, Kindy/Sorters Mill Elem Sch | 297 |
| Thomas, Suzanne/Premier HS-Dayton [318] | 12 | Toney, Kimberly/Holmquist Elem Sch | 187 |
| Thomas, Tom/Bean Elem Sch | 273 | Toney, Steven/E C Brice Elem Sch | 366 |
| **Thomas, Tremayna**/Jean McClung Middle Sch | 353 | Tonne, Allison/Paint Rock Sch | 94 |
| Thomas, Twyla/Refugio Elem Sch | 326 | **Toole, Mrs**/E D Walker Middle Sch | 103 |
| Thomason, Jill/Boles High Sch | 238 | Toperzer, Grayson/Emma Ousley Jr HS | 346 |
| Thome, Kristen/St Thomas More Sch | 210 | Topp, David/Pilgrim Lutheran Sch | 211 |
| Thomman, Amy/Johnson Elem Sch | 58 | Torbert, Kent/West Texas High Sch | 241 |
| Thompson-Conwr, Carolyn/Matthews Alt HS/New Directions | 273 | Torgerson, Betty/Idea Academy-Round Rock Tech [302] | 7 |
| Thompson, Bob/Tomball Connections Acadamy | 208 | **Torres-Rangel, Linda**/J O Schulze Elem Sch | 113 |
| Thompson, Dawn/Lovett Elem Sch | 199 | Torres-Solis, Valerie/Dessau Middle Sch | 374 |
| Thompson, Donna/Coldspring-Oakhurst High Sch | 332 | Torres, Edgar/Lockhart Junior High Sch | 64 |
| Thompson, Fran/St Joseph Catholic Sch | 118 | Torres, Jennifer/Mary Harper Middle Sch | 161 |
| Thompson, Jacqueline/Cullen Middle Sch | 193 | Torres, Jose/Incarnate Word Academy | 309 |
| Thompson, Jay/Terrell High Sch | 256 | Torres, Lou/Bloomington Middle Sch | 384 |
| Thompson, Joy/Coleman Elem Sch | 79 | Torres, Lou/Placedo Elem Sch | 384 |
| Thompson, Kimberly/Garden Villas Elem Sch | 197 | Torres, Naida/Freddy Gonzalez Elem Sch | 221 |
| Thompson, Lauren/Timber Creek Elem Sch | 208 | Torres, Nancy/Fabens Middle Sch | 139 |
| Thompson, Luther/Port Arthur Alternative Center | 246 | Torres, Petra/Del Castillo Elem Sch | 67 |
| Thompson, Roque/Gonzales Junior High Sch | 169 | Torres, Ricardo/Champion Elem Sch | 67 |
| Thompson, Shannon/Mountain Peak Elem Sch | 145 | Torres, Ruby/Positive Solutions Charter Sch | 12 |
| Thompson, Tamra/Brandenburg Intermediate Sch | 108 | Torres, Ruth/Escandon Elem Sch | 221 |
| Thompson, Tasia/Ethridge Elem Sch | 127 | Torres, Sarah/W B Green Junior High Sch | 69 |
| Thorman, Jeff/Zion Lutheran Sch | 120 | Torres, Shannon/Midland Freshman High Sch | 289 |
| Thornburg, Keri/Taylor Elem Sch | 363 | Torrez, Alex/Ojeda Middle Sch | 372 |

| NAME/School | PAGE | NAME/School | PAGE |
|---|---|---|---|
| Watkins, Lisa/Barbers Hill Kindergarten Ctr | 75 | Wells, Mandy/Sam Houston Elem Sch | 58 |
| Watkins, Quintin/Malakoff Middle Sch | 219 | Wells, Micah/Robert M Shoemaker High Sch | 31 |
| Watkins, Ronnie/Lester Davis Sch | 125 | Wells, Sallie/Clariden Sch | 361 |
| Watkins, Sarah/Plano Senior High Sch | 87 | Wells, Scott/Lingleville Sch | 148 |
| Watley, Christy/Hewitt Elem Sch | 283 | Wells, Tina/South Palm Gardens High Sch | 229 |
| Watson, Angelia, Dr/Boerne Middle School South | 257 | **Wendel, Marissa**/Roberts Elem Sch | 278 |
| Watson, Anthony/Stony Point High Sch | 402 | Wendl, Bill/Prestonwood Christian Academy | 90 |
| Watson, Chandra/East Texas Christian Sch | 176 | Wenke, Andrea/South Houston High Sch | 205 |
| Watson, Crystal, Dr/Chester W Nimitz High Sch | 185 | Wentrcek, Jenna/Starkey Elem Sch | 259 |
| Watson, Dixie/Hico Secondary Sch | 181 | Werbiski, Melissa/Paredes Elem Sch | 67 |
| Watson, Dixie/Sanford Fritch Jr High Sch | 241 | Werneke, Amanda/Hebron 9th Grade Campus | 127 |
| Watson, Kassie/Waskom High Sch | 214 | Wernli, Eric/Jose M Lopez Middle Sch | 38 |
| **Watson, Kimberly**/Latexo High Sch | 236 | Wernli, Tracy/Hector Garcia Middle Sch | 40 |
| Watson, Michael, Dr/Dahlstrom Middle Sch | 216 | Werth, Kori/Oak Point Elem Sch | 128 |
| **Watson, Michael, Dr**/Red Simon Middle Sch | 216 | Werts, Bronwyn/Callisburg Middle High Sch | 94 |
| Watson, Sara/Reeces Creek Elem Sch | 31 | **Wesco, Tambia**/G W Kennemer Middle Sch | 109 |
| Watson, Wade/Carthage Junior High Sch | 314 | Wesley, Melissa/Bea Salazar Sch | 100 |
| Watt, Blanda/Texas Online Preparatory Sch | 386 | Wesley, Melissa/Mary Grimes Education Center | 101 |
| Watts, Jennifer/St Thomas Aquinas Sch | 118 | Wessel, Kahrin, Dr/Eagle Christian Academy | 285 |
| Watts, Michael/Disciplinary Alt Ed Program | 58 | **Wesson, Rickyl**/GW Carver 6th GR STEM Lrng Ctr | 114 |
| Watts, Roy/Advantage Acad-Grand Prairie E | 100 | West-Dukes, Edwina/Heritage Elem Sch | 357 |
| Watts, Tammy/North Joshua Elem Sch | 251 | West, Angela/Seagoville High Sch | 106 |
| Waugh-Freeze, Heather/Leon Taylor Junior High Sch | 334 | West, Beth/Rustic Oak Elem Sch | 57 |
| Waugh, Kristina/Richards Young Women Leaders | 371 | West, Darren/New Braunfels Chrn Acad-Lower | 93 |
| Waugh, Sam/Awty International | 210 | West, Shannon/LaRue Miller Elem Sch | 145 |
| Weaver, Amanda/Rhoads Elem Sch | 157 | West, Treasure/Ross Elem Sch | 196 |
| Weaver, Jim/Nixon-Smiley High Sch | 169 | Westbrook, Cynthia/Mathis Intermediate Sch | 334 |
| Weaver, Johnna/Lincoln Humanities/Comm HS | 105 | Westerfield, Angela/Comfort Elem Sch | 257 |
| Weaver, Luci/Virtual Sch | 205 | Westfall, Darrell/Henderson Middle Sch | 183 |
| **Webb, Brady**/New Home Sch | 276 | Westhoff, Beth/Enge-Washington Interm Sch | 269 |
| Webb, Eleanor/Lancaster High Sch | 114 | Weston, Craig/Carson Elem Sch | 406 |
| Webb, Homer/DeSoto Alt Sch | 108 | Weston, Tiffany/Mildred Jenkins Elem Sch | 207 |
| Webb, Jennifer/Dallas Christian Sch | 119 | Weyman, Robert/Early Middle Sch | 62 |
| Webb, Keegan/Gatesville Elem Sch | 97 | Wharton, Kevin, Dr/Legacy Christian Academy | 247 |
| Webb, Linda, Dr/Garza Independence High Sch | 371 | Wheat, Dave/Lanier Middle Sch | 199 |
| Webb, Margaret/Holy Spirit Catholic Sch | 47 | Wheat, Michella/Anson Jones Middle Sch | 39 |
| **Webb, Misty**/Thomas O Hicks Elem Sch | 128 | **Wheat, Michella**/Jones Magnet Middle Sch | 40 |
| **Webb, Robert**/Itasca High Sch | 231 | Wheeler, Brian/St Theresa's Catholic Sch | 375 |
| Webb, Steffanie/Creek Valley Middle Sch | 127 | Wheeler, DeLynn/Roosevelt Elem Sch | 274 |
| Webber, Cynthia, Dr/Leo Adams Middle Sch | 129 | Wheeler, Diane/Melillo Middle Sch | 204 |
| Webber, Melissa/Haslet Elem Sch | 129 | **Wheeler, Sandi**/Spearman High Sch | 182 |
| Webster, Beckie/Monta Jane Akin Elem Sch | 400 | Whetstone, N/Munday Charter Sch | 11 |
| **Webster, Victoria**/Jerry Knight STEM Academy | 359 | Whetstone, Nicole, Dr/University of Texas Elem CS | 16 |
| Wedgeworth, Carolyn/Oak Forest Elem Sch | 312 | Whiffen, Steve/Forney Academic Center | 255 |
| Wedgeworth, Tiffany/New Waverly Elem Sch | 386 | Whileyman, Bud/Austin Elem Sch | 158 |
| Weeden, Diane/Jennie Reid Elem Sch | 203 | Whisenant, Danny/Lufkin Middle Sch | 21 |
| Weedman, Leigh/Green Oaks Sch | 361 | **Whisonant, Donna**/Anne Sullivan Elem Sch | 154 |
| Weeks, Cerise/Corpus Christi Montessori Sch | 2 | Whistler, Tom/Littlefield Elem Sch | 263 |
| Weeks, John/West Ave Elem Sch | 285 | Whitaker, Jeffrey/McGowen Elem Sch | 196 |
| Weeks, Sarah/Arlington Heights High Sch | 352 | Whitaker, Lindsey/Jefferson Elem Sch | 277 |
| Wegener, Chris/Yoakum High Sch | 122 | Whitaker, Lindsey/Jefferson Primary Sch | 277 |
| Wegman, John/J P Bonnette Jr High Sch | 191 | **Whitaker, Lynn**/Harmony Irons-Smith Interm Sch | 379 |
| Wehmeyer, Kelly/Port O'Connor Elem Sch | 65 | Whitaker, Lynn/Union Grove Elem Sch | 379 |
| Weikert, Hank/Luling Primary Sch | 65 | Whitaker, Patsy/Jacksonville Middle Sch | 76 |
| Weiland, Christine/Dorie Miller Elem Sch | 43 | White, Amber/Smith Middle Sch | 250 |
| Weir, Lisa/Memorial High Sch | 206 | White, Amy/Marfa Elem Sch | 322 |
| Weirich, Reese/Murchison Elem Sch | 374 | White, Bobby/Stephen F Austin Elem Sch | 144 |
| **Weis, Amy**/H A Wooden Elem Sch | 146 | White, Cathy/Leo Center | 400 |
| Weiss, Julie/Meridiana Elem Sch | 54 | White, Christopher/Crowley HS 9th Grade Campus | 350 |
| Weiss, Shanna/Trinity Episcopal Sch | 376 | White, Cody/O'Donnell Jr Sr High Sch | 276 |
| Weiss, Tiffany/Travis Science Academy | 32 | **White, Constance**/Hill Elem Sch | 185 |
| Welborn, Becky/Dripping Springs Christ Acad | 217 | White, Constance/Hitchcock Primary Sch | 165 |
| **Welch, David**/Birdie Alexander Elem Sch | 103 | White, Deana/Purple Heart Elem Sch | 141 |
| Welch, Deborah/Rusk Elem Sch | 77 | White, Donita/Advantage Acad-N Duncanville | 100 |
| Welch, Jennifer/Kemp Primary Sch | 255 | White, Ginger/Wolfe City Elem Sch | 240 |
| Welch, Joseph/Del Valle High Sch | 372 | **White, Ian**/Brazosport High Sch | 55 |
| Welch, Mandy/Sweetwater Intermediate Sch | 305 | **White, Jana**/Cherry Elem Sch | 278 |
| Wellman, Randell/Rains High Sch | 323 | White, Jodi/Arnold Middle Sch | 189 |
| Wells, David/Travis Elem Sch | 313 | White, John/Lumberton High Sch | 183 |
| Wells, Demetric/El Campo High Sch | 392 | **White, Katrina**/Michael R Null Middle Sch | 205 |
| Wells, Fidel/Juan Seguin Elem Sch | 154 | White, Kendall/Emery Weiner Sch | 210 |
| Wells, Jason/Birdville High Sch | 348 | White, Kevin/Brady High Sch | 280 |
| Wells, Julia/Raguet Elem Sch | 301 | White, Kristy/Farwell Junior High Sch | 317 |

| School/City/County DISTRICT/CITY/COUNTY | PID | TELEPHONE NUMBER | PAGE |
|---|---|---|---|
| 3D Academy/Donna/Hidalgo | 11454070 | 956/464-1254 | 220 |
| 1621 Place Sch/Rosenberg/Fort Bend | 04282755 | 832/223-0950 | 158 |

### A

| School/City/County DISTRICT/CITY/COUNTY | PID | TELEPHONE NUMBER | PAGE |
|---|---|---|---|
| A & M Consolidated High Sch/College Sta/ Brazos | 01001966 | 979/764-5500 | 59 |
| A & M Consolidated Middle Sch/College Sta/ Brazos | 04918978 | 979/764-5575 | 59 |
| A A Milne Elem Sch/Houston/Harris | 03336688 | 713/778-3420 | 198 |
| A B Anderson Academy/Houston/Harris | 01022702 | 281/878-0370 | 184 |
| A B Duncan Elem Sch/Floydada/Floyd | 01017989 | 806/983-5332 | 153 |
| A B Harrison Intermediate Sch/Wylie/Collin | 04451750 | 972/429-3300 | 88 |
| A B McBay Elem Sch/Mexia/Limestone | 01824330 | 254/562-4030 | 270 |
| A C Blunt Middle Sch/Aransas Pass/ San Patricio | 03050470 | 361/758-2711 | 333 |
| A C Jones High Sch/Beeville/Bee | 00996071 | 361/362-6000 | 28 |
| A C New Middle Sch/Mesquite/Dallas | 03011797 | 972/882-5600 | 115 |
| A C Williams Elem Sch/Commerce/Hunt | 02127434 | 903/886-3758 | 239 |
| A G Elder Elem Sch/Joshua/Johnson | 04755178 | 817/202-2500 | 251 |
| A G Hilliard Elem Sch/Houston/Harris | 01026473 | 713/635-3085 | 193 |
| A Habitat for Learning Daycare/Abilene/ Taylor | 11011032 | 325/692-2481 | 364 |
| A J Briesemeister Mid Sch/Seguin/Guadalupe | 01021643 | 830/401-8711 | 179 |
| A J Martin Elem Sch/Houston/Harris | 01022984 | 281/983-8363 | 187 |
| A L Benavides Elem Sch/San Ygnacio/Zapata | 01062257 | 956/765-5611 | 410 |
| A L Steele Enhanced Lrng Ctr/Schertz/ Guadalupe | 04448870 | 210/945-6401 | 178 |
| A M Aikin Elem Sch/Paris/Lamar | 02110481 | 903/737-7443 | 262 |
| A M Pate Elem Sch/Fort Worth/Tarrant | 01053220 | 817/815-3800 | 352 |
| A N McCallum High Sch/Austin/Travis | 01056404 | 512/414-2519 | 371 |
| A N Rico Elem Sch/Weslaco/Hidalgo | 04288448 | 956/969-6815 | 228 |
| A P Beutel Elem Sch/Lake Jackson/Brazoria | 01001552 | 979/730-7165 | 55 |
| A P Solis Middle Sch/Donna/Hidalgo | 01029607 | 956/464-1650 | 220 |
| A Plus Academy Elem/Dallas/Dallas | 04932168 | 972/557-5578 | 1 |
| A Plus Academy Secondary/Dallas/Dallas | 12238831 | 469/677-1000 | 1 |
| A Plus Unlimited Potential Sch/Houston/ Harris | 12043143 | 713/658-1881 | 210 |
| A Plus Up-Museum Campus/Houston/Harris | 12261436 | 713/955-7543 | 1 |
| A Plus Up-University Campus/Houston/Harris | 12261448 | 713/955-7583 | 1 |
| A R Turner Elem Sch/Willis/Montgomery | 01042776 | 936/856-1289 | 297 |
| A Robison Elem Sch/Cypress/Harris | 05272105 | 281/213-1700 | 189 |
| A V Cato Elem Sch/Fort Worth/Tarrant | 01052305 | 817/252-2400 | 350 |
| A Villarreal Elem Sch/Edinburg/Hidalgo | 04873287 | 956/289-2377 | 221 |
| A W Brown Leadership Academy/Dallas/Dallas | 04881557 | 972/709-4700 | 1 |
| Aaron Parker Elem Sch/Powderly/Wise | 01036674 | 903/732-3066 | 406 |
| Abbett Elem Sch/Garland/Dallas | 03266320 | 972/675-3000 | 109 |
| **ABBOTT IND SCH DIST/ABBOTT/HILL** | 01030709 | 254/582-3011 | 229 |
| Abbott Sch/Abbott/Hill | 01030711 | 254/582-3011 | 230 |
| Abell Junior High Sch/Midland/Midland | 04036996 | 432/689-6200 | 288 |
| Abernathy Elem Sch/Abernathy/Hale | 01021758 | 806/298-4930 | 179 |
| Abernathy High Sch/Abernathy/Hale | 01021760 | 806/298-2563 | 179 |
| **ABERNATHY IND SCH DIST/ABERNATHY/ HALE** | 01021746 | 806/298-2563 | 179 |
| Abernathy Middle Sch/Abernathy/Hale | 01021772 | 806/298-4921 | 179 |
| Abiding Word Lutheran Sch/Houston/Harris | 04993368 | 281/895-7048 | 210 |
| Abilene Christian Sch/Abilene/Taylor | 01481158 | 325/672-6200 | 364 |
| Abilene High Sch/Abilene/Taylor | 01172632 | 325/677-1731 | 362 |
| **ABILENE IND SCH DIST/ABILENE/ TAYLOR** | 01054523 | 325/677-1444 | 362 |
| About Face Alternative ES/El Paso/El Paso | 11982285 | 915/236-3150 | 137 |
| Abraham Lincoln Middle Sch/Port Arthur/ Jefferson | 01033787 | 409/984-8700 | 246 |
| Abundant Life Christian Sch/La Marque/ Galveston | 11715276 | 409/935-8773 | 1 |
| Aca Primary Campus/Arlington/Tarrant | 04890871 | 817/274-2008 | 1 |
| Acad of Academic Exc Youth Vlg/Dallas/ Dallas | 11571185 | 214/698-2200 | 100 |
| Acad of Leadershp & Tech-Mound/Burleson/ Johnson | 01034858 | 817/245-3100 | 249 |
| Academic Behavior Center-East/Houston/ Harris | 04144256 | 713/242-8036 | 184 |
| Academic Behavior Sch-West/Houston/Harris | 11134464 | 713/339-9411 | 184 |
| Academic Career Center/Corp Christi/Nueces | 03396432 | 361/903-6450 | 308 |
| Academy/Mabank/Kaufman | 11457060 | 903/880-1600 | 256 |
| Academy Academic Enhancemnt-ES/Rio Grande Cy/ Starr | 12038564 | 956/716-6941 | 343 |
| Academy Academic Enhancemnt-MS/Rio Grande Cy/ Starr | 12038576 | 956/352-6324 | 343 |
| Academy at Carrie F Thomas/N Richlnd Hls/ Tarrant | 01881144 | 817/547-3000 | 348 |
| Academy at Nola Dunn/Burleson/Johnson | 04919726 | 817/245-3300 | 249 |

| School/City/County DISTRICT/CITY/COUNTY | PID | TELEPHONE NUMBER | PAGE |
|---|---|---|---|
| Academy at World Champions Ctr/Spring/ Montgomery | 12322690 | 281/292-6284 | 298 |
| Academy Careers Engr Science/Conroe/ Montgomery | 12311079 | 832/482-6700 | 294 |
| Academy Elem Sch/LTL RVR Acad/Bell | 00996277 | 254/982-4621 | 29 |
| Academy Health Sci Prof & STEM/La Joya/ Hidalgo | 12233544 | 956/323-2250 | 222 |
| Academy High Sch/Kingsville/Kleberg | 04362991 | 361/384-5041 | 261 |
| Academy High Sch/LTL RVR Acad/Bell | 03397632 | 254/982-4201 | 29 |
| Academy High Sch/Plano/Collin | 11925378 | 972/905-8100 | 85 |
| **ACADEMY IND SCH DIST/LTL RVR ACAD/ BELL** | 00996253 | 254/982-4304 | 29 |
| Academy Intermediate Sch/LTL RVR Acad/Bell | 12104450 | 254/982-0150 | 29 |
| Academy Middle Sch/LTL RVR Acad/Bell | 03397620 | 254/982-4620 | 29 |
| Academy of Accelerated Lrng/Houston/Harris | 05242760 | 713/773-4766 | 1 |
| Academy of Arts at Branson/Burleson/ Johnson | 05091169 | 817/245-3600 | 249 |
| Academy of Choice/Houston/Harris | 01027312 | 713/251-1500 | 206 |
| Academy of Creative Education/San Antonio/ Bexar | 03471953 | 210/407-0740 | 37 |
| Academy of Dallas-Oak Park/Dallas/Dallas | 04881583 | 214/371-9600 | 1 |
| Academy of Science & Tech/The Woodlands/ Montgomery | 05358436 | 936/709-3250 | 294 |
| Academy of Thought & Industry/Austin/ Travis | 12362420 | 512/910-8980 | 375 |
| Academy-Science & Health Prof/Conroe/ Montgomery | 05358448 | 936/709-5731 | 294 |
| Accel Inter Academy-Lancaster/Lancaster/ Dallas | 11824968 | 972/227-2105 | 1 |
| Accelerated Center for Ed/Houston/Harris | 04284399 | 832/386-3672 | 192 |
| Accelerated Intermediate Acad/Houston/ Harris | 05010919 | 713/728-9330 | 1 |
| Ace Alternative Sch/Lufkin/Angelina | 02126674 | 936/630-4152 | 21 |
| ACES Alternative/Brownsboro/Henderson | 11450361 | 903/852-8021 | 218 |
| Achieve Academy/Wylie/Collin | 10968951 | 972/429-2390 | 88 |
| Achieve Early College High Sch/McAllen/ Hidalgo | 11557402 | 956/872-1653 | 224 |
| Achziger Elem Sch/Mesquite/Dallas | 11447132 | 972/290-4180 | 115 |
| Acton Academy/Austin/Travis | 11914692 | 512/320-0596 | 375 |
| Acton Elem Sch/Dallas/Dallas | 01539169 | 972/708-2400 | 108 |
| Acton Elem Sch/Granbury/Hood | 01826326 | 817/408-4200 | 233 |
| Acton Middle Sch/Granbury/Hood | 04033918 | 817/408-4800 | 233 |
| Adams Elem Sch/Arlington/Tarrant | 11919549 | 682/867-2130 | 346 |
| Adams Elem Sch/Cleburne/Johnson | 01034884 | 817/202-2000 | 250 |
| Adams Hill Elem Sch/San Antonio/Bexar | 00998029 | 210/397-1400 | 39 |
| Adaptive Behavior Center/Houston/Harris | 02045367 | 281/897-4174 | 189 |
| Adelfa Botello Callejo ES/Dallas/Dallas | 11827960 | 972/892-5700 | 102 |
| Adella Young Elem Sch/Pasadena/Harris | 01881900 | 713/740-0784 | 203 |
| Adelle R Clark Middle Sch/Frisco/Collin | 04916877 | 469/633-4600 | 82 |
| Adelle Turner Elem Sch/Dallas/Dallas | 01008378 | 972/794-6300 | 102 |
| Adkins Elem Sch/Lantana/Denton | 12033344 | 940/369-1300 | 125 |
| Adolphus Elem Sch/Richmond/Fort Bend | 11923631 | 832/223-4700 | 158 |
| **ADRIAN IND SCH DIST/ADRIAN/ OLDHAM** | 01045522 | 806/538-6203 | 310 |
| Adrian Sch/Adrian/Oldham | 01045534 | 806/538-6203 | 310 |
| Adult Education/Abilene/Taylor | 01538244 | 325/671-4419 | 362 |
| Adult Education Center/Fort Worth/Tarrant | 01538232 | 817/492-7960 | 352 |
| Advanced Lrng Acad-Euclid/San Antonio/ Bexar | 12169955 | 210/738-9760 | 42 |
| Advanced Lrng Acad-Fox Tech/San Antonio/ Bexar | 12177469 | 210/738-9763 | 42 |
| Advantage Acad-Grand Prairie E/Grand Prairie/ Dallas | 12234859 | 214/276-5800 | 100 |
| Advantage Acad-Grand Prairie W/Grand Prairie/ Dallas | 11134414 | 214/276-5800 | 100 |
| Advantage Acad-N Duncanville/Dallas/Dallas | 04819774 | 214/276-5800 | 100 |
| **ADVANTAGE ACADEMY ADMIN OFFICE/ DUNCANVILLE/DALLAS** | 11824891 | 214/276-5800 | 100 |
| Advantage Academy-Waxahachie/Waxahachie/ Dallas | 02743064 | 972/937-9851 | 100 |
| Advent Ridge Academy/San Marcos/Hays | 02233851 | 512/392-9475 | 217 |
| Aep Center/Belton/Bell | 03394563 | 254/215-2571 | 30 |
| Aesa Preparatory Academy/Austin/Hays | 11825601 | 512/560-5584 | 217 |
| Agape Christian Academy/Corsicana/Navarro | 12042266 | 903/641-0900 | 303 |
| Agape Christian Academy/Newton/Newton | 11727700 | 409/379-4611 | 304 |
| Agape Christian Sch/Mission/Hidalgo | 02123581 | 956/585-9773 | 229 |
| Aggieland Country Mont Sch/College Sta/ Brazos | 02853449 | 979/696-1674 | 59 |
| Agnes Cotton Academy/San Antonio/Bexar | 00998380 | 210/738-9780 | 42 |
| Agriculture Science Center/Arlington/ Tarrant | 12231132 | 682/867-9500 | 346 |
| Agua Dulce Elem Sch/Agua Dulce/Nueces | 01043990 | 361/998 2335 | 305 |

| School/City/County DISTRICT/CITY/COUNTY | PID | TELEPHONE NUMBER | PAGE |
|---|---|---|---|
| **AGUA DULCE IND SCH DIST/** | | | |
| **AGUA DULCE/NUECES** | 01043988 | 361/998-2542 | 305 |
| Agua Dulce Secondary Sch/Agua Dulce/Nueces | 03394173 | 361/998-2214 | 305 |
| Ahb Community Sch/Austin/Travis | 12374734 | 512/299-5487 | 375 |
| Aida Escobar Elem Sch/Pharr/Hidalgo | 01030498 | 956/354-2920 | 226 |
| Aikin Elem Sch/Dallas/Dallas | 01881869 | 469/593-1820 | 116 |
| Aikman Elem Sch/Hereford/Deaf Smith | 01012991 | 806/363-7640 | 123 |
| Aim Center/Whitehouse/Smith | 04748022 | 903/839-5556 | 341 |
| Aim Center High Sch/Vidor/Orange | 04288125 | 409/951-8780 | 312 |
| Aim College & Career Prep Acad/Galveston/ | | | |
| Galveston | 11557127 | 409/761-6302 | 165 |
| Airport Drive Elem Sch/Weslaco/Hidalgo | 03251959 | 956/969-6770 | 228 |
| Akiba Academy of Dallas/Dallas/Dallas | 01012135 | 214/295-3400 | 118 |
| Akin Elem Sch/Hale Center/Hale | 01021825 | 806/839-2121 | 180 |
| Akins Early College High Sch/Austin/Travis | 04917687 | 512/841-9900 | 371 |
| Al-Hadi Sch of Accel Lrng/Houston/Harris | 11233888 | 832/617-8363 | 210 |
| Alamo Education Center/Ennis/Ellis | 12037302 | 972/872-7333 | 144 |
| Alamo Elem Sch/Baytown/Harris | 01023574 | 281/420-4595 | 192 |
| Alamo Elem Sch/Fort Stockton/Pecos | 01046849 | 432/336-4016 | 318 |
| Alamo Heights High Sch/San Antonio/Bexar | 00996930 | 210/820-8850 | 33 |
| **ALAMO HEIGHTS IND SCH DIST/** | | | |
| **SAN ANTONIO/BEXAR** | 00996928 | 210/824-2483 | 33 |
| Alamo Heights Jr High Sch/San Antonio/ | | | |
| Bexar | 00996942 | 210/824-3231 | 33 |
| Alamo Junior High Sch/Midland/Midland | 01041435 | 432/689-1700 | 288 |
| Alamo Middle Sch/Alamo/Hidalgo | 03055494 | 956/354-2550 | 226 |
| Alan B Shepard Middle Sch/San Antonio/ | | | |
| Bexar | 00999396 | 210/623-1875 | 45 |
| Alarcon Elem Sch/San Elizario/El Paso | 01016181 | 915/872-3930 | 139 |
| Alba-Golden Elem Sch/Alba/Wood | 01061796 | 903/768-2472 | 407 |
| **ALBA-GOLDEN IND SCH DIST/** | | | |
| **ALBA/WOOD** | 01061784 | 903/768-2472 | 407 |
| Alba-Golden Jr Sr High Sch/Alba/Wood | 01061801 | 903/768-2472 | 407 |
| **ALBANY IND SCH DIST/ALBANY/** | | | |
| **SHACKELFORD** | 01050216 | 325/762-2823 | 336 |
| Albany Jr Sr High Sch/Albany/Shackelford | 01050228 | 325/762-3974 | 336 |
| Albert & Iola Davis Malvern ES/McKinney/ | | | |
| Collin | 04948507 | 469/302-5300 | 84 |
| Alberto & Celia Barrera ES/Rio Grande Cy/ | | | |
| Starr | 01051155 | 956/716-6618 | 343 |
| Albright Middle Sch/Houston/Harris | 02201468 | 281/983-8411 | 187 |
| Alcott Elem Sch/Houston/Harris | 01025091 | 713/732-3540 | 197 |
| Alcuin Montessori Sch/Dallas/Dallas | 01754266 | 972/239-1745 | 118 |
| Alderson Elem Sch/Lubbock/Lubbock | 01038555 | 806/219-8000 | 272 |
| Aldine 9th Grade Sch/Houston/Harris | 04805022 | 281/878-6800 | 185 |
| Aldine Education Center/Houston/Harris | 04949824 | 281/985-6685 | 186 |
| **ALDINE IND SCH DIST/HOUSTON/** | | | |
| **HARRIS** | 01022697 | 281/449-1011 | 184 |
| **ALDINE ISD-ELEM SCH TEAM 1/** | | | |
| **HOUSTON/HARRIS** | 12107347 | 281/985-6467 | 184 |
| **ALDINE ISD-ELEM SCH TEAM 2/** | | | |
| **HOUSTON/HARRIS** | 12107359 | 281/985-6159 | 184 |
| **ALDINE ISD-ELEM SCH TEAM 3/** | | | |
| **HOUSTON/HARRIS** | 12107361 | 281/985-6956 | 185 |
| **ALDINE ISD-HIGH SCH TEAM/** | | | |
| **HOUSTON/HARRIS** | 12107397 | 281/985-6427 | 185 |
| **ALDINE ISD-MIDDLE SCH TEAM/** | | | |
| **HOUSTON/HARRIS** | 12107385 | 281/985-6689 | 186 |
| **ALDINE ISD-PRIMARY TEAM/** | | | |
| **HOUSTON/HARRIS** | 12368280 | 281/449-1011 | 186 |
| Aldine Middle Sch/Houston/Harris | 01022714 | 281/985-6580 | 186 |
| Aldine Senior HS/Houston/Harris | 01022726 | 281/448-5231 | 185 |
| Aldridge Elem Sch/Richardson/Collin | 01006473 | 469/752-0000 | 85 |
| Aledo Christian Sch/Aledo/Parker | 04924630 | 817/441-7357 | 317 |
| Aledo High Sch/Aledo/Parker | 01046320 | 817/441-8711 | 315 |
| **ALEDO IND SCH DIST/ALEDO/PARKER** | 01046306 | 817/441-8327 | 315 |
| Aledo Learning Center/Aledo/Parker | 04920646 | 817/441-5176 | 315 |
| Aledo Middle Sch/Aledo/Parker | 01046332 | 817/441-5198 | 315 |
| Alex Sanger Elem Sch/Dallas/Dallas | 01008392 | 972/749-7600 | 102 |
| Alex W Spence Middle Sch & Tag/Dallas/ | | | |
| Dallas | 01008407 | 972/925-2300 | 102 |
| Alexander Elem Sch/Duncanville/Dallas | 01010307 | 972/708-2500 | 108 |
| Alexander Elem Sch/Houston/Harris | 02227240 | 281/983-8300 | 187 |
| Alexander Middle Sch/Pearland/Brazoria | 10909242 | 832/736-6700 | 56 |
| Alexander Smith Academy/Houston/Harris | 02083917 | 713/266-0920 | 210 |
| Alfonso R Ramirez Elem Sch/Edinburg/ | | | |
| Hidalgo | 11558236 | 956/289-2425 | 221 |
| Alfred Sorensen Elem Sch/San Juan/Hidalgo | 01030486 | 956/354-2910 | 226 |
| Alice Carlson Applied Lrng Ctr/Fort Worth/ | | | |
| Tarrant | 04024462 | 817/815-5700 | 352 |
| Alice Christian Sch/Alice/Jim Wells | 04993837 | 361/668-6636 | 249 |
| Alice Contreras Elem Sch/Fort Worth/ | | | |
| Tarrant | 04924757 | 817/814-7800 | 352 |
| Alice High Sch/Alice/Jim Wells | 01034535 | 361/664-0126 | 248 |
| **ALICE IND SCH DIST/ALICE/** | | | |
| **JIM WELLS** | 01034511 | 361/664-0981 | 248 |
| Alice Johnson Jr High Sch/Channelview/ | | | |
| Harris | 01023093 | 281/452-8030 | 188 |
| Alice Landergin Elem Sch/Amarillo/Potter | 01047130 | 806/326-4650 | 320 |
| Alice Moore Alexander Elem Sch/Denton/ | | | |
| Denton | 01013294 | 940/369-3500 | 125 |
| Alice Ponder Elem Sch/Mansfield/Tarrant | 01054121 | 817/299-7700 | 359 |
| Alice W Douse Elem Sch/Killeen/Bell | 12231338 | 254/336-7480 | 30 |
| Alicia R Chacon Int'l Lang Sch/El Paso/ | | | |
| El Paso | 04364793 | 915/434-9200 | 141 |
| Alicia Ruiz Elem Sch/Laredo/Webb | 04013243 | 956/473-3300 | 390 |
| Alief Ctr for Advanced Careers/Houston/ | | | |
| Harris | 12379772 | 281/988-3550 | 187 |
| Alief Early College High Sch/Houston/ | | | |
| Harris | 11557074 | 281/988-3010 | 187 |
| **ALIEF IND SCH DIST/HOUSTON/** | | | |
| **HARRIS** | 01022972 | 281/498-8110 | 186 |
| Alief Learning Center/Houston/Harris | 03052155 | 281/983-8000 | 187 |
| Alief Middle Sch/Houston/Harris | 01023017 | 281/983-8422 | 187 |
| Alief Montessori Cmty Sch/Houston/Harris | 04813902 | 281/530-9406 | 1 |
| Alief Taylor High Sch/Houston/Harris | 04943179 | 281/988-3500 | 187 |
| Alkek Elem Sch/Bandera/Bandera | 00995780 | 830/460-3900 | 26 |
| All Saints Catholic Sch/Dallas/Collin | 04841923 | 214/217-3300 | 89 |
| All Saints Catholic Sch/Fort Worth/Tarrant | 01054341 | 817/624-2670 | 360 |
| All Saints Episcopal Sch/Beaumont/ | | | |
| Jefferson | 01034303 | 409/892-1755 | 247 |
| All Saints Episcopal Sch/Fort Worth/ | | | |
| Tarrant | 01054248 | 817/560-5700 | 361 |
| All Saints Episcopal Sch/Lubbock/Lubbock | 01039262 | 806/745-7701 | 275 |
| All Saints Episcopal Sch/Tyler/Smith | 02084052 | 903/579-6000 | 342 |
| Allen & William Arnold ES/Pharr/Hidalgo | 01030383 | 956/354-2710 | 226 |
| Allen 6th Grade Campus/Amarillo/Potter | 10008355 | 806/326-3770 | 320 |
| Allen Academy/Bryan/Brazos | 01002180 | 979/776-0731 | 60 |
| Allen Elem Sch/San Antonio/Bexar | 00998172 | 210/397-0800 | 39 |
| Allen High Sch/Allen/Collin | 01006007 | 972/727-0400 | 80 |
| **ALLEN IND SCH DIST/ALLEN/COLLIN** | 01005986 | 972/727-0511 | 80 |
| Alliene Mullendore Elem Sch/N Richlnd Hls/ | | | |
| Tarrant | 01052111 | 817/547-1900 | 348 |
| Allison Elem Sch/Austin/Travis | 01056026 | 512/414-2004 | 369 |
| Alma A Pierce Elem Sch/Laredo/Webb | 01059195 | 956/273-4300 | 389 |
| Alma Brewer Strawn Elem Sch/Dale/Caldwell | 12168858 | 512/398-0630 | 64 |
| Almeda Elem Sch/Houston/Harris | 01025106 | 713/434-5620 | 197 |
| Aloe Elem Sch/Victoria/Victoria | 01058452 | 361/788-9509 | 384 |
| Alonso S Perales Elem Sch/San Antonio/ | | | |
| Bexar | 00997166 | 210/444-8350 | 34 |
| Alonzo De Leon Middle Sch/McAllen/Hidalgo | 03392606 | 956/632-8800 | 224 |
| Alpha Academy/Magnolia/Montgomery | 05264976 | 281/252-2265 | 295 |
| Alpha Omega Academy/Huntsville/Walker | 04993435 | 936/438-8833 | 386 |
| Alpine Christian Sch/Alpine/Brewster | 11076226 | 432/837-5757 | 60 |
| Alpine Elem Sch/Alpine/Brewster | 01002207 | 432/837-7730 | 60 |
| Alpine High Sch/Alpine/Brewster | 01002219 | 432/837-7710 | 60 |
| **ALPINE IND SCH DIST/ALPINE/** | | | |
| **BREWSTER** | 01002192 | 432/837-7700 | 60 |
| Alpine Middle Sch/Alpine/Brewster | 01002221 | 432/837-7720 | 60 |
| Alt Edu Program Phoenix Campus/Azle/ | | | |
| Tarrant | 04452168 | 817/444-4564 | 348 |
| Alta Loma Elem Sch/San Angelo/Tom Green | 01055541 | 325/947-3914 | 367 |
| Alta Vista Elem Sch/Waco/McLennan | 01040144 | 254/662-3050 | 284 |
| Alternative Education Center/Port Neches/ | | | |
| Jefferson | 04747717 | 409/722-5924 | 246 |
| Alternative Education Ctr/Magnolia/ | | | |
| Montgomery | 11924855 | 281/252-2275 | 295 |
| Alternative Education Program/Euless/ | | | |
| Tarrant | 04748230 | 817/354-3398 | 356 |
| Alternative Learning Center/Austin/Travis | 03008673 | 512/414-2554 | 371 |
| Alternative Learning Center/Bridgeport/ | | | |
| Wise | 05270080 | 940/683-1830 | 406 |
| Alternative Learning Center/Rosenberg/ | | | |
| Fort Bend | 03250826 | 832/223-0900 | 158 |
| Alternative Lrng Ctr-East/Houston/Harris | 04036661 | 281/897-4171 | 189 |
| Alternative Lrng Ctr-West/Katy/Harris | 11457503 | 281/855-4310 | 189 |
| Alto Bonito Elem Sch/Rio Grande Cy/Starr | 04867965 | 956/487-6295 | 343 |
| Alto Elem Sch/Alto/Cherokee | 01005211 | 936/587-7174 | 76 |
| Alto High Sch/Alto/Cherokee | 01005223 | 936/858-7110 | 76 |
| **ALTO IND SCH DIST/ALTO/CHEROKEE** | 01005209 | 936/858-7101 | 76 |
| Alto Middle Sch/Alto/Cherokee | 04745056 | 936/858-7140 | 76 |
| Alton Boyd Elem Sch/Allen/Collin | 01824093 | 972/727-0560 | 80 |
| Alton Elem Sch/Alton/Hidalgo | 01388128 | 956/323-7600 | 225 |

| School/City/County DISTRICT/CITY/COUNTY | PID | TELEPHONE NUMBER | PAGE |
|---|---|---|---|
| Alton Elem Sch/Brenham/Washington | 01059054 | 979/277-3870 | 388 |
| Alton Memorial Junior High Sch/Alton/Hidalgo | 05275418 | 956/323-5000 | 225 |
| Alton O Bowen Elem Sch/Bryan/Brazos | 04278455 | 979/209-1300 | 58 |
| Alvarado Elem North Sch/Alvarado/Johnson | 02896960 | 817/783-6863 | 249 |
| Alvarado Elem South Sch/Alvarado/Johnson | 01034808 | 817/783-6880 | 249 |
| Alvarado High Sch/Alvarado/Johnson | 01034779 | 817/783-6940 | 249 |
| **ALVARADO IND SCH DIST/ALVARADO/JOHNSON** | 01034767 | 817/783-6800 | 249 |
| Alvarado Intermediate Sch/Alvarado/Johnson | 04453849 | 817/783-6825 | 249 |
| Alvarado Junior High Sch/Alvarado/Johnson | 01034793 | 817/783-6840 | 249 |
| Alvin Elem Sch/Alvin/Brazoria | 01001394 | 281/585-2511 | 54 |
| Alvin High Sch/Alvin/Brazoria | 01001409 | 281/245-3000 | 54 |
| **ALVIN IND SCH DIST/ALVIN/BRAZORIA** | 01001382 | 281/388-1130 | 54 |
| Alvin ISD Career & Tech Ed Ctr/Manvel/Brazoria | 12177550 | 281/245-2160 | 54 |
| Alvin Junior High Sch/Alvin/Brazoria | 01001411 | 281/245-2770 | 54 |
| Alvis C Story Elem Sch/Allen/Collin | 03004055 | 972/727-0570 | 80 |
| Alvord Elem Sch/Alvord/Wise | 01061538 | 940/427-2881 | 405 |
| Alvord High Sch/Alvord/Wise | 01061540 | 940/427-9643 | 405 |
| **ALVORD IND SCH DIST/ALVORD/WISE** | 01061526 | 940/427-5975 | 405 |
| Alvord Middle Sch/Alvord/Wise | 03008219 | 940/427-5511 | 405 |
| Amanda Rochell Elem Sch/Rockwall/Rockwall | 02104092 | 972/771-2112 | 328 |
| Amarillo Area Ctr Advance Lrng/Amarillo/Potter | 04922773 | 806/326-2800 | 320 |
| Amarillo Collegiate Academy/Amarillo/Randall | 12260626 | 806/352-0171 | 1 |
| Amarillo Collegiate Academy/Amarillo/Randall | 11014577 | 806/352-0171 | 1 |
| Amarillo High Sch/Amarillo/Potter | 01047142 | 806/326-2000 | 320 |
| **AMARILLO IND SCH DIST/AMARILLO/POTTER** | 01047128 | 806/326-1000 | 320 |
| Ambassadors Preparatory Acad/Galveston/Galveston | 11013858 | 409/762-1115 | 1 |
| Amber Terrace Discovery ECC/Desoto/Dallas | 01525948 | 972/223-8757 | 108 |
| Ambleside School of Fredericks/Fredericksbrg/Gillespie | 11223522 | 830/990-9059 | 168 |
| Amelia Elem Sch/Beaumont/Jefferson | 01034107 | 409/617-6000 | 244 |
| American Preparatory Institute/Killeen/Bell | 11239375 | 254/526-1321 | 33 |
| American Youthworks/Austin/Travis | 04459453 | 512/744-1954 | 1 |
| Americas High Sch/El Paso/El Paso | 04455952 | 915/937-2800 | 140 |
| **AMHERST IND SCH DIST/AMHERST/LAMB** | 01036882 | 806/246-7729 | 263 |
| Amherst Sch/Amherst/Lamb | 01036894 | 806/246-3221 | 263 |
| AMI Kids Rio Grande Valley/Los Fresnos/Cameron | 04809858 | 956/233-5795 | 69 |
| Amigos Por Vida Charter Sch/Houston/Harris | 04881600 | 713/349-9945 | 1 |
| Amon Carter-Riverside High Sch/Fort Worth/Tarrant | 01052537 | 817/814-9000 | 352 |
| Amos Elem Sch/Arlington/Tarrant | 01051636 | 682/867-4700 | 346 |
| Amparo Gutierrez Elem Sch/Laredo/Webb | 04013231 | 956/473-4400 | 390 |
| Amy Campbell Elem Sch/Fulshear/Harris | 12308307 | 281/234-4500 | 156 |
| Amy Parks-Heath Elem Sch/Heath/Rockwall | 04364078 | 972/772-4300 | 328 |
| Anahuac Elem Sch/Anahuac/Chambers | 01059069 | 409/267-3600 | 75 |
| Anahuac High Sch/Anahuac/Chambers | 01005091 | 409/267-2013 | 75 |
| **ANAHUAC IND SCH DIST/ANAHUAC/CHAMBERS** | 01005077 | 409/267-3600 | 75 |
| Anahuac Middle Sch/Anahuac/Chambers | 01005106 | 409/267-2042 | 75 |
| Anderson Accelerated High Sch/Big Spring/Howard | 05092357 | 432/264-4115 | 236 |
| Anderson Elem Sch/Arlington/Tarrant | 05347853 | 682/867-7750 | 346 |
| Anderson Elem Sch/Conroe/Montgomery | 01042477 | 936/709-5300 | 294 |
| Anderson Elem Sch/Houston/Harris | 01024700 | 713/726-3600 | 198 |
| Anderson Elem Sch/Lufkin/Angelina | 02201793 | 936/632-5527 | 21 |
| Anderson Elem Sch/Plano/Collin | 04868555 | 469/633-2300 | 82 |
| Anderson Elem Sch/Spring/Harris | 02110613 | 281/891-8360 | 207 |
| Anderson High Sch/Austin/Travis | 01056442 | 512/414-2538 | 371 |
| Anderson Mill Elem Sch/Austin/Williamson | 01541411 | 512/428-3700 | 401 |
| **ANDERSON-SHIRO CONS IND SD/ANDERSON/GRIMES** | 01021344 | 936/873-4500 | 176 |
| Anderson-Shiro Elem Sch/Anderson/Grimes | 01021356 | 936/873-4525 | 176 |
| Anderson-Shiro Jr Sr High Sch/Anderson/Grimes | 03049299 | 936/873-4550 | 176 |
| Andre Elem Sch/Cypress/Harris | 10030322 | 281/463-5500 | 189 |
| Andress High Sch/El Paso/El Paso | 01015735 | 915/236-4000 | 138 |
| Andrew Jackson Elem Sch/McAllen/Hidalgo | 01030008 | 956/971-4277 | 224 |
| Andrews Alternative Sch/Andrews/Andrews | 04801909 | 432/524-1946 | 19 |
| Andrews Elem Sch/Austin/Travis | 01056038 | 512/414-1770 | 369 |
| Andrews High Sch/Andrews/Andrews | 00994724 | 432/524-1910 | 19 |
| **ANDREWS IND SCH DIST/ANDREWS/ANDREWS** | 00994700 | 432/523-3640 | 19 |
| Andrews Middle Sch/Andrews/Andrews | 00994712 | 432/524-1940 | 19 |
| Andy Dekaney High Sch/Houston/Harris | 10910007 | 281/891-7260 | 207 |
| Angela Leal Elem Sch/San Benito/Cameron | 11713436 | 956/276-5055 | 70 |
| Angelo Catholic Sch/San Angelo/Tom Green | 01055931 | 325/949-1747 | 368 |
| Angleton Christian Sch/Angleton/Brazoria | 10016039 | 979/864-3842 | 57 |
| Angleton High Sch/Angleton/Brazoria | 01001497 | 979/864-8001 | 55 |
| **ANGLETON IND SCH DIST/ANGLETON/BRAZORIA** | 01001473 | 979/864-8000 | 55 |
| Angleton Junior High Sch/Angleton/Brazoria | 01001485 | 979/864-8002 | 55 |
| Anita Scott Elem Sch/Royse City/Rockwall | 05096779 | 972/636-3300 | 328 |
| Anita T Dovalina Elem Sch/Laredo/Webb | 02201200 | 956/273-3320 | 389 |
| Ann M Garcia-Enriquez Mid Sch/San Elizario/El Paso | 03004184 | 915/872-3960 | 140 |
| Ann Richards Middle Sch/Mission/Hidalgo | 04868610 | 956/323-2860 | 222 |
| Ann Richards Steam Academy/Dallas/Dallas | 11919903 | 972/892-5400 | 102 |
| Ann Whitney Elem Sch/Hamilton/Hamilton | 01022178 | 254/386-8166 | 181 |
| Anna Education Center/Anna/Collin | 12363278 | 972/924-1340 | 81 |
| Anna High Sch/Anna/Collin | 03051010 | 972/924-1100 | 81 |
| **ANNA IND SCH DIST/ANNA/COLLIN** | 01006021 | 972/924-1000 | 81 |
| Anna May Daulton Elem Sch/Grand Prairie/Tarrant | 10028226 | 817/299-6640 | 359 |
| Anna Middle Sch/Anna/Collin | 01006045 | 972/924-1200 | 81 |
| Annapolis Christian Academy/Corp Christi/Nueces | 04144218 | 361/991-6004 | 309 |
| Anne Frank Elem Sch/Dallas/Dallas | 04757035 | 972/502-5900 | 102 |
| Anne Frank Inspire Academy/San Antonio/Bexar | 12035108 | 210/638-5900 | 34 |
| Anne L MaGee Elem Sch/Edinburg/Hidalgo | 05275183 | 956/289-2306 | 221 |
| Anne Sullivan Elem Sch/Sugar Land/Fort Bend | 12169553 | 281/327-2860 | 154 |
| Annette Perry Elem Sch/Mansfield/Tarrant | 11464960 | 817/804-2800 | 359 |
| Annie Purl Elem Sch/Georgetown/Williamson | 01060895 | 512/943-5080 | 398 |
| Annie Rainwater Elem Sch/Carrollton/Dallas | 04282860 | 972/968-2800 | 100 |
| Annie Sims Elem Sch/Mt Pleasant/Titus | 01055371 | 903/575-2062 | 366 |
| Annie Webb Blanton Elem Sch/Dallas/Dallas | 01008433 | 972/794-1700 | 103 |
| Annunciation Orthodox Sch/Houston/Harris | 01601815 | 713/470-5630 | 210 |
| Anson Elem Sch/Anson/Jones | 01035204 | 325/823-3361 | 252 |
| Anson High Sch/Anson/Jones | 01035216 | 325/823-2404 | 252 |
| **ANSON IND SCH DIST/ANSON/JONES** | 01035199 | 325/823-3671 | 252 |
| Anson Jones Elem Sch/Dallas/Dallas | 01009217 | 972/794-4700 | 103 |
| Anson Jones Middle Sch/San Antonio/Bexar | 00998031 | 210/397-2100 | 39 |
| Anson Middle Sch/Anson/Jones | 01834153 | 325/823-2771 | 252 |
| Anthon Elem Sch/Uvalde/Uvalde | 01057800 | 830/591-2988 | 381 |
| Anthony Aguirre Junior HS/Houston/Harris | 11927730 | 281/860-3300 | 188 |
| Anthony Elem Sch/Anthony/El Paso | 00705561 | 915/886-6510 | 136 |
| Anthony High Sch/Anthony/El Paso | 01015371 | 915/886-6550 | 136 |
| **ANTHONY IND SCH DIST/ANTHONY/EL PASO** | 01015357 | 915/886-6500 | 136 |
| Anthony Middle Sch/Anthony/El Paso | 04935392 | 915/886-6530 | 136 |
| **ANTON IND SCH DIST/ANTON/HOCKLEY** | 01031090 | 806/997-2301 | 232 |
| Anton Sch/Anton/Hockley | 01031117 | 806/997-5211 | 232 |
| Antonian College Prep High Sch/San Antonio/Bexar | 00999736 | 210/344-9265 | 47 |
| Antonio Bruni Elem Sch/Laredo/Webb | 01059200 | 956/273-3000 | 389 |
| Antonio Gonzalez Middle Sch/Laredo/Webb | 05027326 | 956/473-7000 | 390 |
| Antonio M Ochoa Elem Sch/Donna/Hidalgo | 01029566 | 956/464-1900 | 220 |
| Antonio Margil Academy/San Antonio/Bexar | 00998512 | 210/738-9805 | 42 |
| Aoy Elem Sch/El Paso/El Paso | 01015929 | 915/236-0175 | 137 |
| Apache Elem Sch/Fort Stockton/Pecos | 01046851 | 432/336-4161 | 318 |
| Apollo Junior High Sch/Richardson/Dallas | 01826168 | 469/593-7900 | 116 |
| Apple Springs Elem Sch/Apple Springs/Trinity | 01057056 | 936/831-2241 | 376 |
| Apple Springs High Sch/Apple Springs/Trinity | 04033475 | 936/831-2241 | 376 |
| **APPLE SPRINGS IND SCH DIST/APPLE SPRINGS/TRINITY** | 01057044 | 936/831-3344 | 3/6 |
| Applegate Adventist Jr Academy/Round Rock/Williamson | 11816870 | 512/388-7870 | 403 |
| Applied Learning Academy/Fort Worth/Tarrant | 04035837 | 817/815-5500 | 352 |
| **AQUILLA IND SCH DIST/AQUILLA/HILL** | 01030735 | 254/694-3770 | 230 |
| Aquilla Sch/Aquilla/Hill | 01030747 | 254/694-3770 | 230 |
| Arabic Immersion Magnet Sch/Houston/Harris | 12105026 | 713/556-8940 | 196 |
| **ARANSAS CO IND SCH DIST/ROCKPORT/ARANSAS** | 00995120 | 361/790-2212 | 22 |
| Aransas Pass High Sch/Aransas Pass/San Patricio | 01049504 | 361/758-3248 | 333 |
| **ARANSAS PASS IND SCH DIST/ARANSAS PASS/SAN PATRICIO** | 01049487 | 361/758-3466 | 333 |

| School/City/County DISTRICT/CITY/COUNTY | PID | TELEPHONE NUMBER | PAGE |
|---|---|---|---|
| Arapaho Classical Magnet Sch/Richardson/ Dallas | 01011636 | 469/593-6400 | 116 |
| Arbor Creek Middle Sch/Carrollton/Denton | 04288747 | 469/713-5971 | 126 |
| Arcadia Park Elem Sch/Dallas/Dallas | 01008445 | 972/502-5300 | 103 |
| Arch H McCulloch Interm Sch/Dallas/Dallas | 01011040 | 214/780-3500 | 112 |
| **ARCHDIOCESE GALVESTON-HOUSTON/** HOUSTON/HARRIS | 01027855 | 713/741-8704 | 209 |
| **ARCHDIOCESE SAN ANTONIO ED OFF/** SAN ANTONIO/BEXAR | 00999724 | 210/734-2620 | 47 |
| Archer City Elem Sch/Archer City/Archer | 00995209 | 940/574-4506 | 22 |
| Archer City High Sch/Archer City/Archer | 04915782 | 940/574-4713 | 22 |
| **ARCHER CITY IND SCH DIST/** ARCHER CITY/ARCHER | 00995182 | 940/574-4536 | 22 |
| Archway Academy/Houston/Harris | 10019031 | 713/328-0780 | 210 |
| Arden Road Elem Sch/Amarillo/Randall | 03008075 | 806/677-2360 | 323 |
| Argyle High Sch/Argyle/Denton | 04879102 | 940/262-7777 | 124 |
| **ARGYLE IND SCH DIST/ARGYLE/** DENTON | 01013177 | 940/464-7241 | 124 |
| Argyle Intermediate Sch/Argyle/Denton | 11746196 | 940/464-5100 | 124 |
| Argyle Middle Sch/Argyle/Denton | 05026736 | 940/246-2126 | 124 |
| Argyle West Elem Sch/Argyle/Denton | 12364557 | 940/464-7241 | 124 |
| Aristoi Classical Academy/Katy/Harris | 04459489 | 281/391-5003 | 1 |
| Arizona Fleming Elem Sch/Houston/Fort Bend | 04287937 | 281/634-4600 | 154 |
| Arlington Classics Acad-Bowen/Arlington/ Tarrant | 11737145 | 817/303-1553 | 1 |
| Arlington College & Career HS/Arlington/ Tarrant | 12365630 | 682/867-9600 | 346 |
| Arlington Collegiate High Sch/Arlington/ Tarrant | 12034893 | 817/515-3550 | 346 |
| Arlington Heights Chrn Sch/Corp Christi/ Nueces | 02770378 | 361/241-0090 | 309 |
| Arlington Heights High Sch/Fort Worth/ Tarrant | 01052551 | 817/815-1000 | 352 |
| Arlington High Sch/Arlington/Tarrant | 01051648 | 682/867-8100 | 346 |
| **ARLINGTON IND SCH DIST/ARLINGTON/** TARRANT | 01051624 | 682/867-4611 | 346 |
| Arlington Park ECC/Dallas/Dallas | 12318596 | 972/749-5500 | 103 |
| Arlon Seay Elem Sch/Spring Branch/Comal | 04478863 | 830/885-8700 | 91 |
| Armand Bayou Elem Sch/Houston/Galveston | 01523689 | 281/284-5100 | 163 |
| Armando Cerna Elem Sch/Eagle Pass/Maverick | 01041148 | 830/758-7004 | 279 |
| Armando Leal Jr Middle Sch/San Antonio/ Bexar | 00997532 | 210/989-2400 | 35 |
| Armendariz Middle Sch/El Paso/El Paso | 04806650 | 915/236-4800 | 139 |
| Armstrong Elem Sch/Conroe/Montgomery | 01042491 | 936/709-3400 | 294 |
| Armstrong Elem Sch/Missouri City/Fort Bend | 11079591 | 281/634-9410 | 154 |
| Armstrong Middle Sch/Plano/Collin | 01525900 | 469/752-4600 | 86 |
| Arnold Elem Sch/San Antonio/Bexar | 00998419 | 210/438-6530 | 43 |
| Arnold Middle Sch/Cypress/Harris | 01023201 | 281/897-4700 | 189 |
| Arnoldo Cantu Elem Sch/San Juan/Hidalgo | 04032794 | 956/354-2850 | 226 |
| Arp Elem Sch/Arp/Smith | 01050553 | 903/859-4650 | 339 |
| Arp High Sch/Arp/Smith | 01050565 | 903/859-4917 | 339 |
| **ARP IND SCH DIST/ARP/SMITH** | 01050541 | 903/859-8482 | 339 |
| Arp Junior High Sch/Arp/Smith | 03047370 | 903/859-4936 | 339 |
| Arredondo Elem Sch/Richmond/Fort Bend | 12107816 | 832/223-4800 | 158 |
| Arrow-Champions Academy/Houston/Harris | 12039099 | 832/446-6762 | 1 |
| Arrow-Harvest Preparatory Acad/Houston/ Harris | 11729459 | 281/872-5201 | 1 |
| Arrow-Las Americas Lrng Ctr/Houston/Harris | 11848615 | 832/582-7327 | 1 |
| Arrow-Liberation Academy/Meadows Place/ Fort Bend | 11729485 | 281/969-7766 | 1 |
| Arrow-Save Our Streets Ctr/Bryan/Brazos | 12113956 | 979/703-1810 | 1 |
| Art & Pat Goforth Elem Sch/League City/ Galveston | 05009570 | 281/284-6000 | 163 |
| Artemisia Bowden Academy/San Antonio/Bexar | 00998744 | 210/738-9770 | 43 |
| Arthur Kramer Elem Sch/Dallas/Dallas | 03247764 | 972/794-8300 | 103 |
| Arthur L Davila Middle Sch/Bryan/Brazos | 11079292 | 979/209-7150 | 58 |
| Arthur McNeil Elem Sch/McKinney/Collin | 04948492 | 469/302-5200 | 84 |
| Arturo Salazar Elem Sch/Dallas/Dallas | 10023109 | 972/502-1800 | 103 |
| Asa Low Jr Intermediate Sch/Mansfield/ Tarrant | 11452187 | 817/299-3640 | 359 |
| Ascarate Elem Sch/El Paso/El Paso | 01016301 | 915/434-7400 | 141 |
| Ascension Academy/Amarillo/Randall | 11236749 | 806/342-0515 | 324 |
| Ascension Episcopal Sch/Houston/Harris | 01410850 | 713/783-0260 | 210 |
| Ascher Silberstein Elem Sch/Dallas/Dallas | 01008471 | 972/794-1900 | 103 |
| Ash High Sch/Plainview/Hale | 04019467 | 806/293-6010 | 180 |
| Ashbel Smith Elem Sch/Baytown/Harris | 01023586 | 281/420-4615 | 192 |
| Ashford Elem Sch/Houston/Harris | 01418424 | 281/368-2120 | 198 |
| Ashleys Private Sch/Cedar Hill/Dallas | 12105052 | 972/291-1313 | 118 |
| Ashworth Elem Sch/Arlington/Tarrant | 04456774 | 682/867-4800 | 346 |
| Aspermont Elem Sch/Aspermont/Stonewall | 01051428 | 940/989-3323 | 344 |
| Aspermont High Sch/Aspermont/Stonewall | 01051430 | 940/989-2707 | 344 |

| School/City/County DISTRICT/CITY/COUNTY | PID | TELEPHONE NUMBER | PAGE |
|---|---|---|---|
| **ASPERMONT IND SCH DIST/ASPERMONT/** STONEWALL | 01051416 | 940/989-3355 | 344 |
| Assets Academy/Alvin/Brazoria | 04282494 | 281/331-1690 | 54 |
| Assumption Catholic Sch/Houston/Harris | 01028017 | 281/447-2132 | 209 |
| Atascocita High Sch/Humble/Harris | 10028628 | 281/641-7500 | 200 |
| Atascocita Middle Sch/Humble/Harris | 02202371 | 281/641-4600 | 200 |
| Atascocita Springs Elem Sch/Humble/Harris | 11552672 | 281/641-3600 | 200 |
| Atems High Sch/Abilene/Taylor | 11452955 | 325/794-4140 | 362 |
| Athens Christian Academy/Athens/Henderson | 11231763 | 903/675-5135 | 220 |
| Athens High Sch/Athens/Henderson | 01029255 | 903/677-6920 | 218 |
| **ATHENS IND SCH DIST/ATHENS/** HENDERSON | 01029231 | 903/677-6900 | 218 |
| Athens Middle Sch/Athens/Henderson | 01029243 | 903/677-3030 | 218 |
| Atherton Elem Sch/Arlington/Tarrant | 01548471 | 682/867-4900 | 346 |
| Atherton Elem Sch/Houston/Harris | 01025405 | 713/671-4100 | 195 |
| Atkins Middle Sch/Lubbock/Lubbock | 01038529 | 806/219-3000 | 273 |
| Atkinson Elem Sch/Houston/Harris | 01026643 | 713/740-0520 | 203 |
| Atlanta Elem Sch/Atlanta/Cass | 01004683 | 903/796-7164 | 73 |
| Atlanta High Sch/Atlanta/Cass | 01004695 | 903/796-4411 | 73 |
| **ATLANTA IND SCH DIST/ATLANTA/** CASS | 01004671 | 903/796-4194 | 73 |
| Atlanta Middle Sch/Atlanta/Cass | 01004700 | 903/796-7928 | 73 |
| Atlanta Primary Sch/Atlanta/Cass | 01004712 | 903/796-8115 | 73 |
| Atonement Academy/San Antonio/Bexar | 04308543 | 210/695-2240 | 47 |
| Attucks Middle Sch/Houston/Harris | 01025156 | 713/732-3670 | 193 |
| Atwood McDonald Elem Sch/Fort Worth/ Tarrant | 01053086 | 817/815-4800 | 352 |
| Aubrey High Sch/Aubrey/Denton | 01013218 | 940/668-3900 | 124 |
| **AUBREY IND SCH DIST/AUBREY/** DENTON | 01013191 | 940/668-0060 | 124 |
| Aubrey Middle Sch/Aubrey/Denton | 04747389 | 940/668-0200 | 124 |
| Audelia Creek Elem Sch/Dallas/Dallas | 05272650 | 469/593-2900 | 116 |
| Audie Murphy Middle Sch/Alamo/Hidalgo | 11552854 | 956/354-2530 | 226 |
| Audie Murphy Middle Sch/Fort Hood/Bell | 05347827 | 254/336-6530 | 30 |
| Aue Elem Sch/San Antonio/Bexar | 10913217 | 210/397-6750 | 39 |
| Augusto Guerra Elem Sch/Alamo/Hidalgo | 05098789 | 956/354-2810 | 226 |
| Ault Elem Sch/Cypress/Harris | 04285331 | 281/373-2800 | 189 |
| Austin Academic Center/Sulphur Spgs/ Hopkins | 10020937 | 903/885-4942 | 235 |
| Austin Academy for Excellence/Garland/ Dallas | 01010735 | 972/926-2620 | 109 |
| Austin Achieve PS High Sch/Austin/Travis | 12378455 | 512/522-4190 | 1 |
| Austin Achieve PS Manor/Austin/Travis | 11816935 | 512/522-4190 | 1 |
| Austin Achieve PS NE Campus/Austin/Travis | 12378443 | 512/522-4190 | 1 |
| Austin Classical Academy/Austin/Travis | 11925146 | 512/371-8933 | 1 |
| Austin Discovery Academy/Austin/Travis | 11009297 | 512/674-0700 | 1 |
| Austin Eco Bilingual Sch-South/Austin/ Travis | 12107232 | 512/299-5731 | 375 |
| Austin Elem Sch/Abilene/Taylor | 01172840 | 325/690-3920 | 362 |
| Austin Elem Sch/Conroe/Montgomery | 01042532 | 936/709-8400 | 294 |
| Austin Elem Sch/Edinburg/Hidalgo | 01029786 | 956/289-2331 | 221 |
| Austin Elem Sch/Harlingen/Cameron | 01003768 | 956/427-3060 | 68 |
| Austin Elem Sch/Memphis/Hall | 01022099 | 806/259-5930 | 181 |
| Austin Elem Sch/Pampa/Gray | 01020144 | 806/669-4760 | 170 |
| Austin Elem Sch/Pecos/Reeves | 01048407 | 432/447-7541 | 326 |
| Austin Elem Sch/Richmond/Fort Bend | 03323552 | 832/223-1000 | 158 |
| Austin Elem Sch/San Angelo/Tom Green | 01055797 | 325/659-3636 | 367 |
| Austin Elem Sch/Tyler/Smith | 01050967 | 903/262-1765 | 340 |
| Austin Elem Sch/Weatherford/Parker | 03051917 | 817/598-2848 | 317 |
| Austin Environ Sci Acad/Grand Prairie/ Dallas | 01011002 | 972/343-4600 | 111 |
| Austin High Sch/Austin/Travis | 01056650 | 512/414-2505 | 371 |
| Austin High Sch/El Paso/El Paso | 01015515 | 915/236-4200 | 138 |
| Austin High Sch/Houston/Harris | 01024712 | 713/924-1600 | 194 |
| **AUSTIN IND SCH DIST/AUSTIN/** TRAVIS | 01055993 | 512/414-1700 | 369 |
| Austin International Sch/Austin/Travis | 04944094 | 512/331-7806 | 375 |
| **AUSTIN ISD ELEM SCH AREA/** AUSTIN/TRAVIS | 04032304 | 512/414-0038 | 369 |
| **AUSTIN ISD HIGH SCH AREA/** AUSTIN/TRAVIS | 04032328 | 512/414-1942 | 371 |
| **AUSTIN ISD MIDDLE SCH AREA/** AUSTIN/TRAVIS | 12033332 | 512/414-4481 | 371 |
| Austin Jewish Academy/Austin/Travis | 04879580 | 512/735-8350 | 375 |
| Austin Middle Sch/Galveston/Galveston | 01019236 | 409/761-3500 | 165 |
| Austin Middle Sch/Irving/Dallas | 01532006 | 972/600-3100 | 113 |
| Austin Middle Sch/San Juan/Hidalgo | 01030345 | 956/354-2570 | 226 |
| Austin Montessori Elem Sch/Odessa/Ector | 01014561 | 432/456-1029 | 134 |
| Austin Montessori Sch/Austin/Travis | 02861812 | 512/892-0253 | 375 |
| Austin Parkway Elem Sch/Sugar Land/ Fort Bend | 03247049 | 281/634-4001 | 154 |
| Austin Peace Academy/Austin/Travis | 04994001 | 512/926-1737 | 375 |

| School/City/County DISTRICT/CITY/COUNTY | PID | TELEPHONE NUMBER | PAGE |
|---|---|---|---|
| Austin Sch Perform Visual Arts/Austin/Travis | 12370544 | 512/522-7782 | 375 |
| Austin Waldorf Sch/Austin/Hays | 02779594 | 512/288-5942 | 217 |
| Austwell Tivoli Elem Sch/Tivoli/Refugio | 01048445 | 361/286-3222 | 326 |
| **AUSTWELL TIVOLI IND SD/TIVOLI/REFUGIO** | 01048419 | 361/286-3212 | 326 |
| Austwell Tivoli Jr Sr High Sch/Tivoli/Refugio | 01048433 | 361/286-3212 | 326 |
| Autism Treatment Center/Dallas/Dallas | 11221304 | 972/644-2076 | 118 |
| **AVALON IND SCH DIST/AVALON/ELLIS** | 01014937 | 972/627-3251 | 144 |
| Avalon Sch/Avalon/Ellis | 01014949 | 972/627-3251 | 144 |
| Avery Elem Sch/Avery/Red River | 01048093 | 903/684-3116 | 325 |
| **AVERY IND SCH DIST/AVERY/RED RIVER** | 01048081 | 903/684-3460 | 325 |
| Avery Secondary Sch/Avery/Red River | 01048108 | 903/684-3431 | 325 |
| **AVINGER IND SCH DIST/AVINGER/CASS** | 01004724 | 903/562-1355 | 73 |
| Avinger Sch/Avinger/Cass | 01004736 | 903/562-1355 | 73 |
| Avondale Elem Sch/Amarillo/Potter | 01047166 | 806/326-4000 | 320 |
| Avondale House Sch/Houston/Harris | 11228156 | 713/993-9544 | 210 |
| Aw Brown-Fla Early Childhood/Dallas/Dallas | 12161721 | 214/330-8686 | 1 |
| Awty International Sch/Houston/Harris | 01875391 | 713/686-4850 | 210 |
| Axtell Elem Sch/Axtell/McLennan | 03321425 | 254/863-5419 | 281 |
| Axtell High Sch/Axtell/McLennan | 01039547 | 254/863-5301 | 281 |
| **AXTELL IND SCH DIST/AXTELL/MCLENNAN** | 01039535 | 254/863-5301 | 281 |
| Azle Christian Sch/Azle/Tarrant | 12168444 | 817/444-9964 | 361 |
| Azle Elem Sch/Azle/Tarrant | 01051985 | 817/444-1312 | 348 |
| Azle High Sch/Azle/Tarrant | 01051997 | 817/444-5555 | 348 |
| Azle Hornet Academy/Azle/Tarrant | 11848782 | 817/444-4564 | 348 |
| **AZLE IND SCH DIST/AZLE/TARRANT** | 01051973 | 817/444-3235 | 348 |
| Azle Junior High Sch/Azle/Tarrant | 01052006 | 817/444-2564 | 348 |

**B**

| School/City/County DISTRICT/CITY/COUNTY | PID | TELEPHONE NUMBER | PAGE |
|---|---|---|---|
| B F Adam Elem Sch/Houston/Harris | 01023196 | 281/897-4485 | 189 |
| B F Clark Primary Sch/Houston/Harris | 03393806 | 281/891-8600 | 207 |
| B Garza Middle Sch/Weslaco/Hidalgo | 04748890 | 956/969-6774 | 228 |
| B H Hamblen Elem Sch/Channelview/Harris | 04457027 | 281/457-8720 | 188 |
| B H Macon Elem Sch/Dallas/Dallas | 01008500 | 972/794-1500 | 103 |
| B J Smith Elem Sch/Mesquite/Dallas | 04807226 | 972/882-7080 | 115 |
| B L Garza Middle Sch/Edinburg/Hidalgo | 04873249 | 956/289-2480 | 221 |
| B L Gray Junior High Sch/Mission/Hidalgo | 01030541 | 956/580-5333 | 227 |
| B McDaniel Intemediate Sch/Denison/Grayson | 01020352 | 903/462-7200 | 171 |
| B T Washington High Sch/Houston/Harris | 01023885 | 713/696-6600 | 193 |
| B T Washington Perform Arts HS/Dallas/Dallas | 01010163 | 972/925-1200 | 103 |
| B T Wilson 6th Grade Sch/Kerrville/Kerr | 03050509 | 830/257-2207 | 259 |
| Back Elem Sch/Rowlett/Dallas | 02226547 | 972/475-1884 | 109 |
| Bagdad Elem Sch/Leander/Williamson | 04866777 | 512/570-5900 | 400 |
| Bailey Elem Sch/Pasadena/Harris | 01026655 | 713/740-0528 | 203 |
| Bailey Inglish Erly Chldhd Ctr/Bonham/Fannin | 01017410 | 903/583-8141 | 149 |
| Bailey Junior High Sch/Arlington/Tarrant | 01051650 | 682/867-0700 | 346 |
| Bailey Middle Sch/Austin/Travis | 04034259 | 512/414-4990 | 371 |
| Bailey Sch for Performing Arts/Spring/Harris | 10022480 | 281/891-8000 | 207 |
| Baird Elem Sch/Baird/Callahan | 01003299 | 325/854-1400 | 66 |
| Baird High Sch/Baird/Callahan | 01003304 | 325/854-1400 | 66 |
| **BAIRD IND SCH DIST/BAIRD/CALLAHAN** | 01003287 | 325/854-1400 | 65 |
| Baird Middle Sch/Baird/Callahan | 10016704 | 325/854-1400 | 66 |
| Baker 6th Grade Campus/La Porte/Harris | 01026394 | 281/604-6800 | 203 |
| Baker Elem Sch/Canadian/Hemphill | 01029217 | 806/323-5386 | 218 |
| Baker Koonce Intermediate Sch/Carthage/Panola | 01046227 | 903/693-8611 | 314 |
| Baker-Ripley Promise Cmty CS/Houston/Harris | 11457515 | 713/273-3731 | 1 |
| Bakers Preparatory Sch/Stafford/Fort Bend | 11236050 | 281/403-2100 | 159 |
| Balch Springs Chrn Academy/Balch Springs/Dallas | 02152295 | 972/286-8511 | 118 |
| Ball Early Childhood Center/Seguin/Guadalupe | 01021693 | 830/401-1281 | 179 |
| Ball High Sch/Galveston/Galveston | 01019092 | 409/766-5700 | 165 |
| Ballinger Elem Sch/Ballinger/Runnels | 01048811 | 325/365-3527 | 329 |
| Ballinger High Sch/Ballinger/Runnels | 01048835 | 325/365-3547 | 329 |
| **BALLINGER IND SCH DIST/BALLINGER/RUNNELS** | 01048809 | 325/365-3588 | 329 |
| Ballinger Junior High Sch/Ballinger/Runnels | 01048823 | 325/365-3537 | 329 |
| **BALMORHEA IND SCH DIST/BALMORHEA/REEVES** | 01048251 | 432/375-2223 | 325 |
| Balmorhea Sch/Balmorhea/Reeves | 01048263 | 432/375-2224 | 326 |

| School/City/County DISTRICT/CITY/COUNTY | PID | TELEPHONE NUMBER | PAGE |
|---|---|---|---|
| Bammel Elem Sch/Houston/Harris | 01027477 | 281/891-8150 | 207 |
| Bammel Middle Sch/Houston/Harris | 01027489 | 281/891-7900 | 207 |
| Bandera High Sch/Bandera/Bandera | 01558103 | 830/460-3898 | 26 |
| **BANDERA IND SCH DIST/BANDERA/BANDERA** | 00995778 | 830/796-3313 | 26 |
| Bandera Middle Sch/Bandera/Bandera | 00995792 | 830/460-3899 | 26 |
| Bane Elem Sch/Houston/Harris | 01023213 | 713/460-6140 | 189 |
| Banff Sch/Houston/Harris | 03414436 | 281/444-9326 | 210 |
| Bangs High Sch/Bangs/Brown | 01002415 | 325/752-6822 | 61 |
| **BANGS IND SCH DIST/BANGS/BROWN** | 01002398 | 325/752-6612 | 61 |
| Bangs Middle Sch/Bangs/Brown | 02056160 | 325/752-6088 | 61 |
| Banquete Elem Sch/Banquete/Nueces | 01044023 | 361/387-4329 | 305 |
| Banquete High Sch/Banquete/Nueces | 01044035 | 361/387-8588 | 305 |
| **BANQUETE IND SCH DIST/BANQUETE/NUECES** | 01044011 | 361/387-2551 | 305 |
| Banquete Junior High Sch/Banquete/Nueces | 01044047 | 361/387-2551 | 305 |
| Rarack Obama Male Ldrshp Acad/Dallas/Dallas | 11732755 | 972/749-2100 | 103 |
| Barbara Bush Elem Sch/Houston/Harris | 04016063 | 281/368-2150 | 198 |
| Barbara Bush Middle Sch/Irving/Dallas | 04756299 | 972/968-3700 | 100 |
| Barbara Bush Primary Sch/Sulphur Spgs/Hopkins | 04746000 | 903/439-6170 | 235 |
| Barbara C Jordan Interm Sch/Cibolo/Guadalupe | 04808804 | 210/619-4250 | 178 |
| Barbara Cardwell Career Prep/Irving/Dallas | 03053252 | 972/600-6140 | 113 |
| Barbara Cockrell Elem Sch/Pearland/Brazoria | 10909266 | 832/736-6600 | 56 |
| Barbara Fasken Elem Sch/Laredo/Webb | 10007399 | 956/473-4700 | 390 |
| Barbara Gordon Montessori Sch/Colleyville/Tarrant | 01754321 | 817/354-6670 | 361 |
| Barbara Jordan Career Center/Houston/Harris | 01023809 | 713/636-6900 | 196 |
| Barbara Jordan Elem Sch/Dallas/Dallas | 01009126 | 972/925-8100 | 103 |
| Barbara Jordan Elem Sch/Odessa/Ector | 03248744 | 432/456-1299 | 134 |
| Barbara Jordan Elem Sch/Richmond/Fort Bend | 05098430 | 281/634-2800 | 154 |
| Barbara M Manns Daep Sch/Dallas/Dallas | 04020753 | 972/925-7000 | 103 |
| Barbara S Austin Elem Sch/Coppell/Dallas | 03005956 | 214/496-7300 | 102 |
| Barbara Walker Elem Sch/Heartland/Kaufman | 11540514 | 972/427-6030 | 254 |
| Barber Middle Sch/Dickinson/Galveston | 05345958 | 281/229-6900 | 164 |
| Barbers Hill Elem Sch North/Mont Belvieu/Chambers | 12109204 | 281/567-2221 | 75 |
| Barbers Hill Elem Sch South/Mont Belvieu/Chambers | 04939647 | 281/576-3421 | 75 |
| Barbers Hill High Sch/Mont Belvieu/Chambers | 01005132 | 281/576-3400 | 75 |
| **BARBERS HILL IND SCH DIST/MONT BELVIEU/CHAMBERS** | 01005118 | 281/576-2221 | 75 |
| Barbers Hill Kindergarten Ctr/Mont Belvieu/Chambers | 11080485 | 281/576-3407 | 75 |
| Barbers Hill Middle Sch North/Mont Belvieu/Chambers | 02055726 | 281/576-2221 | 75 |
| Barbers Hill Middle Sch South/Mont Belvieu/Chambers | 01005144 | 281/576-2221 | 75 |
| Barbers Hill Primary Sch/Mont Belvieu/Chambers | 01005120 | 281/576-2221 | 75 |
| Barkley-Ruiz Academy/San Antonio/Bexar | 00999308 | 210/978-7940 | 43 |
| Barksdale Elem Sch/Plano/Collin | 04454893 | 469/752-0100 | 86 |
| Barnett Junior High Sch/Arlington/Tarrant | 04035772 | 682/867-5000 | 346 |
| Barrera Veterans Elem Sch/Von Ormy/Bexar | 05027259 | 210/750-8963 | 45 |
| Barrett Elem Sch/Crosby/Harris | 03321683 | 281/328-9320 | 188 |
| Barrett-Lee Early Chldhd Ctr/Channelview/Harris | 11563047 | 281/860-3827 | 188 |
| Barrick Elem Sch/Houston/Harris | 01025778 | 281/405-2500 | 195 |
| Barrington Elem Sch/Austin/Travis | 01056052 | 512/414-2008 | 369 |
| Barrington Place Elem Sch/Sugar Land/Fort Bend | 03328590 | 281/634-4040 | 154 |
| Barron Elem Sch/El Paso/El Paso | 05101831 | 915/236-5075 | 137 |
| Barron Elem Sch/Pflugerville/Travis | 11818531 | 512/594-4300 | 374 |
| Barron Elem Sch/Plano/Collin | 01006370 | 469/752-0200 | 86 |
| Barrow Elem Sch/Brazoria/Brazoria | 01001722 | 979/991-1740 | 56 |
| Bartlett Elem Sch/Bartlett/Bell | 00996291 | 254/527-3353 | 29 |
| Bartlett High Sch/Bartlett/Bell | 00996306 | 254/527-3351 | 29 |
| **BARTLETT IND SCH DIST/BARTLETT/BELL** | 00996289 | 254/527-4247 | 29 |
| Bartlett Middle Sch/Bartlett/Bell | 12037297 | 254/527-4247 | 29 |
| Barton Creek Elem Sch/Austin/Travis | 03397096 | 512/732-9180 | 372 |
| Barton Elem Sch/Irving/Dallas | 01011222 | 972/600-4100 | 113 |
| Barton Hills Elem Sch/Austin/Travis | 01056064 | 512/414-2013 | 369 |
| Barton Middle Sch/Buda/Hays | 04037524 | 512/268-1472 | 216 |
| Barwise Middle Sch/Wichita Falls/Wichita | 01172955 | 940/235-1108 | 395 |
| Basis San Antonio Prim-Med Ctr/San Antonio/Bexar | 11931717 | 210/319-5525 | 1 |

| School/City/County<br>DISTRICT/CITY/COUNTY | PID | TELEPHONE<br>NUMBER | PAGE |
|---|---|---|---|
| Basis San Antonio Primary N/San Antonio/<br>Bexar | 12101123 | 210/775-4125 | 1 |
| Basis San Antonio Shavano/San Antonio/<br>Bexar | 12239756 | 210/874-9250 | 1 |
| Baskin Elem Sch/San Antonio/Bexar | 00998562 | 210/438-6535 | 43 |
| Bassett Middle Sch/El Paso/El Paso | 01015527 | 915/236-6350 | 139 |
| Bassetti Elem Sch/Abilene/Taylor | 04015318 | 325/690-3720 | 362 |
| Basswood Elem Sch/Fort Worth/Tarrant | 11448540 | 817/744-6500 | 357 |
| Bastian Elem Sch/Houston/Harris | 01024724 | 713/732-5830 | 197 |
| Bastrop High Sch/Bastrop/Bastrop | 00995857 | 512/772-7200 | 26 |
| **BASTROP IND SCH DIST/BASTROP/**<br>**BASTROP** | 00995833 | 512/321-2292 | 26 |
| Bastrop Intermediate Sch/Bastrop/Bastrop | 04278651 | 512/772-7450 | 26 |
| Bastrop Middle Sch/Bastrop/Bastrop | 02855681 | 512/772-7400 | 26 |
| Batesville Elem Sch/Batesville/Uvalde | 01057812 | 830/376-4221 | 381 |
| Baty Elem Sch/Austin/Travis | 02848834 | 512/386-3450 | 372 |
| Baxter Elem Sch/Midlothian/Ellis | 03050896 | 469/856-6100 | 145 |
| Baxter Junior High Sch/Fort Worth/Tarrant | 01052484 | 817/568-3530 | 351 |
| Bay Area Christian Sch/League City/<br>Galveston | 01410719 | 281/332-4814 | 166 |
| Bay Area Montessori House/Houston/Harris | 04993291 | 281/480-7022 | 210 |
| Bay City High Sch/Bay City/Matagorda | 01040821 | 979/401-1100 | 278 |
| **BAY CITY IND SCH DIST/BAY CITY/**<br>**MATAGORDA** | 01040819 | 979/401-1000 | 278 |
| Bay City Junior High Sch/Bay City/<br>Matagorda | 01040833 | 979/401-1600 | 278 |
| Bay Colony Elem Sch/Dickinson/Galveston | 01018995 | 281/229-6200 | 164 |
| Bayles Elem Sch/Dallas/Dallas | 01008512 | 972/749-8900 | 103 |
| Bayless Elem Sch/Lubbock/Lubbock | 01038543 | 806/219-5000 | 273 |
| Baylor Clg of Medicine Acad/Houston/Harris | 11920330 | 713/942-1932 | 197 |
| Bayshore Elem Sch/La Porte/Harris | 01026409 | 281/604-4600 | 203 |
| Bayside Intermediate Sch/League City/<br>Galveston | 11554826 | 281/284-3000 | 163 |
| Baytown Christian Academy/Baytown/Harris | 02123749 | 281/421-4150 | 210 |
| Baytown Junior High Sch/Baytown/Harris | 01023598 | 281/420-4560 | 192 |
| Bea Salazar Sch/Carrollton/Dallas | 04449147 | 972/968-5900 | 100 |
| Beacon Hill Academy/San Antonio/Bexar | 00998392 | 210/738-9765 | 43 |
| Bean Elem Sch/Lubbock/Lubbock | 01038660 | 806/219-5100 | 273 |
| Bear Boulevard Pre-School/Houston/Harris | 04949874 | 713/251-7900 | 206 |
| Bear Branch Elem Sch/Kingwood/Harris | 01809354 | 281/641-1600 | 200 |
| Bear Branch Elem Sch/Magnolia/Montgomery | 02202450 | 281/356-4771 | 296 |
| Bear Branch Intermediate Sch/Magnolia/<br>Montgomery | 05097656 | 281/252-2031 | 296 |
| Bear Branch Junior High Sch/Magnolia/<br>Montgomery | 04450524 | 281/356-6088 | 296 |
| Bear Creek Elem Sch/Austin/Travis | 12468232 | 512/414-0040 | 369 |
| Bear Creek Elem Sch/Euless/Tarrant | 03047411 | 817/305-4860 | 355 |
| Bear Creek Elem Sch/Houston/Harris | 01832090 | 281/237-5600 | 156 |
| Bear Creek Intermediate Sch/Keller/Tarrant | 01054028 | 817/744-3650 | 357 |
| Beasley Elem Sch/Beasley/Fort Bend | 01018256 | 832/223-1100 | 158 |
| Beatrice Mayes Institute CS/Houston/Harris | 05010880 | 713/747-5629 | 1 |
| Beaty Early Childhood Sch/Plano/Collin | 05096834 | 469/752-4200 | 86 |
| Beaumont Classical Academy/Beaumont/<br>Jefferson | 11713113 | 409/434-4549 | 1 |
| Beaumont Early Clg High Sch/Beaumont/<br>Jefferson | 12305551 | 409/617-6600 | 245 |
| **BEAUMONT IND SCH DIST/BEAUMONT/**<br>**JEFFERSON** | 01034092 | 409/617-5000 | 244 |
| Beaumont United High Sch/Beaumont/<br>Jefferson | 01033402 | 409/617-5400 | 245 |
| Beaver Tech Ctr-Math & Science/Garland/<br>Dallas | 01010515 | 972/494-8301 | 109 |
| Bebensee Elem Sch/Arlington/Tarrant | 03051266 | 682/867-5100 | 346 |
| Beckendorff Junior High Sch/Katy/Harris | 05337042 | 281/237-8800 | 156 |
| Becker Elem Sch/Austin/Travis | 01056076 | 512/414-2019 | 369 |
| Beckham Elem Sch/Arlington/Tarrant | 04949317 | 682/867-6600 | 346 |
| **BECKVILLE IND SCH DIST/BECKVILLE/**<br>**PANOLA** | 01046186 | 903/678-3311 | 314 |
| Beckville Jr Sr High Sch/Beckville/Panola | 01046203 | 903/678-3851 | 314 |
| Beckville Sunset Elem Sch/Beckville/Panola | 01046198 | 903/678-3601 | 314 |
| Bedford Heights Elem Sch/Bedford/Tarrant | 01391644 | 817/788-3150 | 356 |
| Bedford Junior High Sch/Bedford/Tarrant | 01053749 | 817/788-3101 | 356 |
| Bedichek Middle Sch/Austin/Travis | 01056088 | 512/414-3265 | 371 |
| Bee Cave Elem Sch/Austin/Travis | 04868414 | 512/533-6250 | 373 |
| Bee Cave Middle Sch/Austin/Travis | 12366490 | 737/931-2400 | 373 |
| **BEEVILLE IND SCH DIST/BEEVILLE/**<br>**BEE** | 00996069 | 361/358-7111 | 28 |
| Behavior Support Services/San Antonio/<br>Bexar | 00997697 | 210/356-7520 | 37 |
| Behavior Transition Center/Granbury/Hood | 04749399 | 817/408-4400 | 233 |
| Bel Air Elem Sch/Athens/Henderson | 01029267 | 903/677-6980 | 218 |
| Bel Air High Sch/El Paso/El Paso | 01016313 | 915/434-2000 | 142 |

| School/City/County<br>DISTRICT/CITY/COUNTY | PID | TELEPHONE<br>NUMBER | PAGE |
|---|---|---|---|
| Bel Air Middle Sch/El Paso/El Paso | 01016442 | 915/434-2200 | 142 |
| Bel Nafegar Sanchez Elem Sch/Rosharon/<br>Brazoria | 12380458 | 713/814-7000 | 54 |
| Belaire Elem Sch/San Angelo/Tom Green | 01055553 | 325/659-3639 | 367 |
| Bell County Alternative Sch/LTL RVR Acad/<br>Bell | 04800462 | 254/982-3505 | 29 |
| Bell Elem Sch/Houston/Harris | 01826285 | 281/983-2800 | 198 |
| Bell Elem Sch/Tyler/Smith | 01050761 | 903/262-1820 | 340 |
| Bell Manor Elem Sch/Bedford/Tarrant | 01053763 | 817/354-3370 | 356 |
| Bell's Hill Elem Sch/Waco/McLennan | 01040106 | 254/754-4171 | 285 |
| Bella Cameron Elem Sch/San Antonio/Bexar | 00998732 | 210/978-7960 | 43 |
| Bellaire Elem Sch/Hurst/Tarrant | 01053751 | 817/285-3230 | 356 |
| Bellaire Elem Sch/Killeen/Bell | 00996447 | 254/336-1410 | 30 |
| Bellaire Elem Sch/San Antonio/Bexar | 01545209 | 210/989-2850 | 35 |
| Bellaire High Sch/Bellaire/Harris | 01024736 | 713/295-3704 | 198 |
| **BELLEVUE IND SCH DIST/BELLEVUE/**<br>**CLAY** | 01005481 | 940/928-2104 | 77 |
| Bellevue Sch/Bellevue/Clay | 01005493 | 940/928-2104 | 78 |
| Bellfort Acad Early Chldhd Ctr/Houston/<br>Harris | 11456195 | 713/640-0950 | 197 |
| Bells Elem Sch/Bells/Grayson | 01020247 | 903/965-3601 | 170 |
| Bells High Sch/Bells/Grayson | 03006780 | 903/965-3603 | 170 |
| **BELLS IND SCH DIST/BELLS/GRAYSON** | 01020235 | 903/965-7721 | 170 |
| Bellville High Sch/Bellville/Austin | 00995546 | 979/865-3681 | 25 |
| **BELLVILLE IND SCH DIST/BELLVILLE/**<br>**AUSTIN** | 00995534 | 979/865-3133 | 24 |
| Bellville Junior High Sch/Bellville/Austin | 02224317 | 979/865-5966 | 25 |
| Belmar Elem Sch/Amarillo/Potter | 01047178 | 806/326-4050 | 320 |
| Beltline Elem Sch/Lancaster/Dallas | 02225373 | 972/218-1608 | 114 |
| Belton Early Childhood Sch/Belton/Bell | 12032429 | 254/215-3700 | 30 |
| Belton High Sch/Belton/Bell | 00996320 | 254/215-2200 | 30 |
| **BELTON IND SCH DIST/BELTON/BELL** | 00996318 | 254/215-2000 | 29 |
| Ben Barber Innovation Academy/Mansfield/<br>Tarrant | 05347413 | 682/314-1600 | 359 |
| Ben Bolt-Palito Blanco ES/Ben Bolt/<br>Jim Wells | 02110869 | 361/664-9568 | 248 |
| Ben Bolt-Palito Blanco HS/Ben Bolt/<br>Jim Wells | 01034640 | 361/664-9822 | 248 |
| **BEN BOLT-PALITO BLANCO ISD/**<br>**BEN BOLT/JIM WELLS** | 01034638 | 361/664-9904 | 248 |
| Ben L Brite Elem Sch/Brownsville/Cameron | 10754889 | 956/698-3000 | 67 |
| Ben Milam Elem Sch/Cameron/Milam | 01041772 | 254/697-3641 | 290 |
| Ben Milam Elem Sch/Dallas/Dallas | 02109810 | 972/749-5600 | 103 |
| Ben Milam Elem Sch/Harlingen/Cameron | 01003770 | 956/427-3150 | 68 |
| Ben Milam Elem Sch/McAllen/Hidalgo | 01029920 | 956/971-4333 | 224 |
| Ben Tisinger Elem Sch/Mesquite/Dallas | 01011416 | 972/882-5120 | 115 |
| Benavides Elem Sch/Benavides/Duval | 01014195 | 361/256-3030 | 132 |
| Benavides Elem Sch/Brownsville/Cameron | 04873445 | 956/350-3250 | 67 |
| Benavides Heights Elem Sch/Eagle Pass/<br>Maverick | 01041069 | 830/758-7006 | 279 |
| **BENAVIDES IND SCH DIST/BENAVIDES/**<br>**DUVAL** | 01014171 | 361/256-3000 | 132 |
| Benavides Secondary Sch/Benavides/Duval | 01014183 | 361/256-3040 | 132 |
| Benavidez Elem Sch/Houston/Harris | 04016099 | 713/778-3350 | 198 |
| Benbrook Elem Sch/Fort Worth/Tarrant | 01052587 | 817/815-6400 | 352 |
| Benbrook Elem Sch/Houston/Harris | 01023897 | 713/613-2502 | 196 |
| Benbrook Middle High Sch/Fort Worth/<br>Tarrant | 11711878 | 817/815-7100 | 352 |
| Bending Oaks High Sch/Dallas/Dallas | 03122580 | 972/669-0000 | 118 |
| Bendwood Sch/Houston/Harris | 01027099 | 713/251-5200 | 206 |
| Beneke Elem Sch/Houston/Harris | 02892158 | 281/891-8450 | 207 |
| Benfer Elem Sch/Klein/Harris | 01539171 | 832/484-6000 | 202 |
| Benignus Elem Sch/Klein/Harris | 10028094 | 832/484-7750 | 202 |
| Benito Juarez Middle Sch/Crystal City/<br>Zavala | 01062324 | 830/374-8105 | 410 |
| Benito Martinez Elem Sch/El Paso/El Paso | 03399343 | 915/937-8000 | 140 |
| Benito Martinez Elem Sch/Fort Hancock/<br>Hudspeth | 01032185 | 915/769-1602 | 237 |
| Benjamin Doc Kerley Elem Sch/Hutto/<br>Williamson | 12376201 | 512/759-5410 | 399 |
| **BENJAMIN IND SCH DIST/BENJAMIN/**<br>**KNOX** | 01036442 | 940/459-2231 | 261 |
| Benjamin Sch/Benjamin/Knox | 01036454 | 940/459-2231 | 261 |
| Bennett & Alma Griffin Mid Sch/Frisco/<br>Collin | 05343431 | 469/633-4900 | 82 |
| Bennett Elem Sch/McKinney/Collin | 05243324 | 469/302-5400 | 84 |
| Bennett Elem Sch/Wolfforth/Lubbock | 01038438 | 806/866-4443 | 272 |
| Bennie Cole Elem Sch/San Antonio/Bexar | 12170124 | 210/398-2100 | 39 |
| Bens Branch Elem Sch/Porter/Montgomery | 05356127 | 281/577-8700 | 296 |
| Bentley Elem Sch/Richmond/Fort Bend | 12169474 | 832/223-4900 | 158 |
| Benton A Staley Middle Sch/Frisco/Collin | 01006215 | 469/633-4500 | 82 |
| Berean Christian Academy/Irving/Dallas | 01479868 | 972/438-1440 | 118 |

| School/City/County DISTRICT/CITY/COUNTY | PID | TELEPHONE NUMBER | PAGE |
|---|---|---|---|
| Berkner High Sch/Richardson/Dallas | 01011648 | 469/593-7000 | 116 |
| Berkner STEM Academy/Richardson/Dallas | 12033746 | 469/593-7000 | 116 |
| Berlanga Elem Sch/Corp Christi/Nueces | 11717365 | 361/878-2160 | 306 |
| Bernarda Jaime Jr High Sch/San Diego/Duval | 01014303 | 361/279-3382 | 132 |
| Berne Acad Private Sch/Lancaster/Dallas | 02734958 | 972/218-7373 | 118 |
| Bernice Chatman Freeman ES/Irving/Dallas | 05350018 | 972/968-1700 | 100 |
| Bernshausen Elem Sch/Tomball/Harris | 11926994 | 832/375-8000 | 202 |
| Berry Elem Sch/Arlington/Tarrant | 01051662 | 682/867-0850 | 346 |
| Berry Elem Sch/Houston/Harris | 01025780 | 713/696-2700 | 195 |
| Berry Miller Junior High Sch/Pearland/ Brazoria | 11079553 | 281/997-3900 | 56 |
| Berta Cabaza Middle Sch/San Benito/Cameron | 01004279 | 956/361-6600 | 70 |
| Berta Palacios Elem Sch/Pharr/Hidalgo | 01030369 | 956/354-2930 | 226 |
| Bertram Elem Sch/Bertram/Burnet | 01002764 | 512/355-2111 | 63 |
| Bess Brannen Elem Sch/Lake Jackson/ Brazoria | 01001564 | 979/730-7170 | 55 |
| Bess Race Elem Sch/Crowley/Tarrant | 01052367 | 817/297-5080 | 350 |
| Besse Coleman Middle Sch/Cedar Hill/Dallas | 10006369 | 972/293-4505 | 101 |
| Bessie Gunstream Elem Sch/Frisco/Collin | 05092618 | 469/633-3100 | 82 |
| Bessie Haynes Elem Sch/Pecos/Reeves | 01048328 | 432/447-7497 | 326 |
| Best Elem Sch/Houston/Harris | 03397797 | 713/988-6445 | 187 |
| Besteiro Middle Sch/Brownsville/Cameron | 04034302 | 956/544-3900 | 67 |
| Beta Academy/Houston/Harris | 12105038 | 832/331-2460 | 1 |
| Beth Yeshurun Sch/Houston/Harris | 01480324 | 713/666-1884 | 210 |
| Bethany Christian Sch/Plano/Collin | 02733710 | 972/596-5811 | 89 |
| Bethany Elem Sch/Plano/Collin | 04032988 | 469/752-0300 | 86 |
| Bethel SDA Sch/Texarkana/Bowie | 02850409 | 903/838-4215 | 54 |
| Bethesda Christian Sch/Fort Worth/Tarrant | 03141861 | 817/281-6446 | 361 |
| Bette Perot Elem Sch/Keller/Tarrant | 05350757 | 817/744-4600 | 357 |
| Betty Harwell Middle Sch/Edinburg/Hidalgo | 01029712 | 956/289-2440 | 221 |
| Bettye Haun Elem Sch/Plano/Collin | 04751122 | 469/752-1600 | 86 |
| Bettye Myers Middle Sch/Shady Shores/ Denton | 11919472 | 940/369-1500 | 125 |
| Beulah E Johnson Elem Sch/Humble/Harris | 01022867 | 281/985-6510 | 184 |
| Beverly Cheatham Elem Sch/Allen/Collin | 11552270 | 972/396-3016 | 80 |
| Beverly Hills Intermediate Sch/Houston/ Harris | 01026667 | 713/740-0420 | 203 |
| Bexar Co Learning Center/San Antonio/Bexar | 04915627 | 210/335-1745 | 34 |
| Bexar County Academy/San Antonio/Bexar | 04890857 | 210/432-8600 | 1 |
| Bible Baptist Christian Sch/Wichita Falls/ Wichita | 02153964 | 940/723-2446 | 396 |
| Bible Way Christian Academy/Del Rio/ Val Verde | 04994087 | 830/775-9921 | 382 |
| Big Bend High Sch/Terlingua/Brewster | 10915655 | 432/371-2281 | 60 |
| Big Country Elem Sch/San Antonio/Bexar | 03011632 | 210/645-7560 | 46 |
| Big Sandy Elem Sch/Big Sandy/Upshur | 01057381 | 903/636-5287 | 378 |
| Big Sandy High Sch/Big Sandy/Upshur | 04033487 | 903/636-5287 | 378 |
| BIG SANDY IND SCH DIST/BIG SANDY/ UPSHUR | 01057379 | 903/636-5287 | 378 |
| BIG SANDY IND SCH DIST/LIVINGSTON/ POLK | 01046954 | 936/563-1000 | 319 |
| Big Sandy Junior High Sch/Big Sandy/Upshur | 04801272 | 903/636-5287 | 378 |
| Big Sandy Sch/Dallardsville/Polk | 01046966 | 936/563-1000 | 319 |
| Big Spring High Sch/Big Spring/Howard | 01031909 | 432/264-3641 | 236 |
| BIG SPRING IND SCH DIST/ BIG SPRING/HOWARD | 01031870 | 432/264-3600 | 236 |
| Big Spring Interm Sch/Big Spring/Howard | 12102658 | 432/264-4121 | 236 |
| Big Spring Junior High Sch/Big Spring/ Howard | 01032032 | 432/264-4135 | 236 |
| Big Springs Elem Sch/Garland/Dallas | 01826170 | 469/593-8100 | 116 |
| Big Springs-Brune Charter Sch/Leakey/Real | 05011016 | 830/232-7101 | 1 |
| Big Springs-Cailloux CS/Ingram/Kerr | 11014149 | 830/367-6100 | 2 |
| Bill Brown Elem Sch/Spring Branch/Comal | 03391121 | 830/885-1400 | 91 |
| Bill Burden Elem Sch/Liberty Hill/ Williamson | 10905179 | 512/260-4400 | 401 |
| Bill Childress Elem Sch/Vinton/El Paso | 04451918 | 915/877-7701 | 136 |
| Bill F Davis Intermediate Sch/Wylie/Collin | 05350185 | 972/429 3325 | 88 |
| Bill Hasse Elem Sch/Alvin/Brazoria | 01001435 | 281/585-3397 | 54 |
| Bill J Elliott Elem Sch/Fort Worth/Tarrant | 03053020 | 817/815-4600 | 352 |
| Bill R Johnson Cte Center/Crowley/Tarrant | 11561996 | 817/297-3018 | 350 |
| Bill Sybert Sch/El Paso/El Paso | 05153420 | 915/937-4400 | 140 |
| Bill W Wright Elem Sch/Weatherford/Parker | 01878434 | 817/598-2828 | 317 |
| Bill Worsham Elem Sch/Houston/Harris | 01022910 | 281/985-6520 | 186 |
| Billie Stevenson Elem Sch/Rockwall/ Rockwall | 11918492 | 469/698-7474 | 328 |
| Billy Baines Middle Sch/Missouri City/ Fort Bend | 10027894 | 281/634-6870 | 154 |
| Billy Earl Dade Middle Sch/Dallas/Dallas | 01009152 | 972/749-3800 | 103 |
| Billy Reagan K-8 Educ Ctr/Houston/Harris | 11820558 | 713/556-9575 | 197 |
| Billy Ryan High Sch/Denton/Denton | 01013256 | 940/369-3000 | 125 |
| Billy Vandeventer Middle Sch/Frisco/Collin | 11820065 | 469/633-4350 | 82 |
| Bingham Head Start Ctr/Beaumont/Jefferson | 01034262 | 409/617-6200 | 245 |
| Biotech Academy-Rusk/Houston/Harris | 01024580 | 713/226-4543 | 197 |
| Birch Elem Sch/Longview/Gregg | 01021150 | 903/295-5120 | 175 |
| Birdie Alexander Elem Sch/Dallas/Dallas | 01008419 | 972/749-3100 | 103 |
| Birdville Elem Sch of Fine Art/Haltom City/ Tarrant | 01052044 | 817/547-1500 | 348 |
| Birdville High Sch/N Richlnd Hls/Tarrant | 04872245 | 817/547-8000 | 348 |
| BIRDVILLE IND SCH DIST/HALTOM CITY/ TARRANT | 01052032 | 817/547-5700 | 348 |
| Birdwell Elem Sch/Tyler/Smith | 01050773 | 903/262-1870 | 340 |
| Birkes Elem Sch/Houston/Harris | 05272090 | 281/345-3300 | 189 |
| Birnham Woods Elem Sch/Spring/Montgomery | 11449726 | 832/663-4200 | 294 |
| Bisd Ctr Tech & Advanced Lrng/N Richlnd Hls/ Tarrant | 11559175 | 817/547-3800 | 348 |
| BISHOP CONS IND SCH DIST/ BISHOP/NUECES | 01044059 | 361/584-3591 | 305 |
| Bishop Dunne Catholic Sch/Dallas/Dallas | 01012379 | 214/339-6561 | 118 |
| Bishop Elem Sch/Bishop/Nueces | 01044085 | 361/584-3571 | 305 |
| Bishop Garriga Middle Sch/Corp Christi/ Nueces | 03015975 | 361/851-0853 | 309 |
| Bishop High Sch/Bishop/Nueces | 01044061 | 361/584-2547 | 305 |
| Bishop Lynch High Sch/Dallas/Dallas | 01012381 | 214/324-3607 | 118 |
| Bishop Primary Sch/Bishop/Nueces | 04446987 | 361/584-2434 | 305 |
| Bishop T K Gorman Cath Sch/Tyler/Smith | 01012745 | 903/561-2424 | 342 |
| Bivins Elem Sch/Amarillo/Potter | 01047348 | 806/326-4100 | 320 |
| Black Elem Sch/Cypress/Harris | 10025987 | 281/320-7145 | 189 |
| Black Middle Sch/Houston/Harris | 01023990 | 713/613-2505 | 196 |
| Blackburn Elem Sch/Forney/Kaufman | 05341433 | 469/762-4300 | 255 |
| Blackland Prairie Elem Sch/Round Rock/ Williamson | 04945880 | 512/424-8600 | 401 |
| Blackshear Elem Sch/Austin/Travis | 01056090 | 512/414-2021 | 369 |
| Blackshear Elem Sch/Houston/Harris | 01024334 | 713/942-1481 | 193 |
| Blackshear Elem Sch/Tomball/Harris | 11713931 | 832/375-7600 | 202 |
| Blackshear Magnet Elem Sch/Odessa/Ector | 01014573 | 432/456-1279 | 134 |
| BLACKWELL CONS IND SCH DIST/ BLACKWELL/NOLAN | 01043794 | 325/282-2311 | 304 |
| Blackwell Elem Sch/Blackwell/Nolan | 01809691 | 325/282-2311 | 304 |
| Blake Manor Elem Sch/Manor/Travis | 10915033 | 512/278-4200 | 373 |
| Blakemore Middle Sch/Boys Ranch/Oldham | 04145377 | 806/534-2361 | 310 |
| Blanca E Sanchez Elem Sch/McAllen/Hidalgo | 10910887 | 956/971-1100 | 224 |
| Blanche Dodd Elem Sch/Krum/Denton | 03252692 | 940/482-2603 | 126 |
| Blanche K Bruce Elem Sch/Houston/Harris | 01024360 | 713/226-4560 | 193 |
| Blanche Moore Elem Sch/Corp Christi/Nueces | 01044580 | 361/878-2660 | 306 |
| Blanchette Elem Sch/Beaumont/Jefferson | 01034121 | 409/617-6300 | 245 |
| Blanco Elem Sch/Blanco/Blanco | 01000493 | 830/833-4338 | 49 |
| Blanco High Sch/Blanco/Blanco | 01000508 | 830/833-4337 | 49 |
| BLANCO IND SCH DIST/BLANCO/ BLANCO | 01000481 | 830/833-4414 | 49 |
| Blanco Middle Sch/Blanco/Blanco | 04012342 | 830/833-5570 | 49 |
| Blanco Vista Elem Sch/San Marcos/Hays | 11079424 | 512/268-8506 | 216 |
| Bland Elem Sch/Celeste/Hunt | 01032240 | 903/527-5480 | 238 |
| Bland High Sch/Farmersville/Hunt | 01032252 | 903/776-2161 | 238 |
| BLAND IND SCH DIST/MERIT/HUNT | 01032238 | 903/776-2239 | 238 |
| Bland Middle Sch/Celeste/Hunt | 04746189 | 903/527-5490 | 238 |
| BLANKET IND SCH DIST/BLANKET/ BROWN | 01002427 | 325/748-5311 | 61 |
| Blanket Sch/Blanket/Brown | 01002441 | 325/748-3341 | 61 |
| Blanson Cte High Sch/Houston/Harris | 12309648 | 281/591-4950 | 185 |
| Blanton Elem Sch/Argyle/Denton | 11128570 | 940/369-0700 | 125 |
| Blanton Elem Sch/Arlington/Tarrant | 01051674 | 682/867-1000 | 346 |
| Blanton Elem Sch/Austin/Travis | 01056105 | 512/414-2026 | 369 |
| Blanton Elem Sch/Odessa/Ector | 02126416 | 432/456-1259 | 134 |
| Blaschke-Sheldon Elem Sch/Ingleside/ San Patricio | 01172606 | 361/776-3050 | 334 |
| Blazier Elem Sch/Austin/Travis | 10907256 | 512/841-8800 | 369 |
| Blessed Sacrament Catholic Sch/San Antonio/ Bexar | 00999762 | 210/824-3381 | 47 |
| Blessed Sacrament Sch/Laredo/Webb | 01045182 | 956/722-1222 | 391 |
| Blessing Elem Sch/Blessing/Matagorda | 01040974 | 979/843-4330 | 279 |
| Bleyl Middle Sch/Houston/Harris | 01023237 | 281/897-4340 | 189 |
| Bliss Elem Sch/El Paso/El Paso | 01015747 | 915/236-5150 | 137 |
| Block House Creek Elem Sch/Leander/ Williamson | 03003130 | 512/570-7600 | 400 |
| Blocker Middle Sch/Texas City/Galveston | 01019482 | 409/916-0700 | 166 |
| Bloom Academy Charter Sch/Houston/Harris | 12371316 | 346/333-1320 | 2 |
| BLOOMBURG IND SCH DIST/BLOOMBURG/ CASS | 01004750 | 903/728-5216 | 73 |
| Bloomburg Sch/Bloomburg/Cass | 01004762 | 903/728-5216 | 73 |
| Blooming Grove Elem Sch/Blooming GRV/ Navarro | 03393179 | 903/695-2541 | 302 |
| Blooming Grove High Sch/Blooming GRV/ Navarro | 01043407 | 903/695-2541 | 302 |

| School/City/County DISTRICT/CITY/COUNTY | PID | TELEPHONE NUMBER | PAGE |
|---|---|---|---|
| **BLOOMING GROVE IND SCH DIST/** | | | |
| **BLOOMING GRV/NAVARRO** | 01043392 | 903/695-2541 | 302 |
| Blooming Grove Junior High Sch/Blooming GRV/ Navarro | 04364690 | 903/695-2541 | 302 |
| Bloomington Elem Sch/Bloomington/Victoria | 01058323 | 361/333-8003 | 384 |
| **BLOOMINGTON IND SCH DIST/** | | | |
| **PLACEDO/VICTORIA** | 01058311 | 361/333-8016 | 384 |
| Bloomington Middle Sch/Bloomington/ Victoria | 04745159 | 361/333-8008 | 384 |
| Bloomington Senior High Sch/Bloomington/ Victoria | 01058347 | 361/333-8011 | 384 |
| Blossom Elem Sch/Blossom/Lamar | 01487293 | 903/982-5230 | 263 |
| Blossom Valley Academy/Lewisville/Denton | 04023133 | 972/436-3613 | 130 |
| Blue Haze Elem Sch/Fort Worth/Tarrant | 03049067 | 817/367-2583 | 360 |
| Blue Hole Primary Sch/Wimberley/Hays | 01029102 | 512/847-3407 | 217 |
| Blue Ridge Elem Sch/Blue Ridge/Collin | 01006069 | 972/752-5554 | 81 |
| Blue Ridge Elem Sch/Houston/Fort Bend | 01018127 | 281/634-4520 | 154 |
| Blue Ridge High Sch/Blue Ridge/Collin | 01006071 | 972/752-5554 | 81 |
| **BLUE RIDGE IND SCH DIST/** | | | |
| **BLUE RIDGE/COLLIN** | 01006057 | 972/752-5554 | 81 |
| Blue Ridge Middle Sch/Blue Ridge/Collin | 04009553 | 972/752-4243 | 81 |
| Bluebonnet Elem Sch/Bastrop/Bastrop | 05350159 | 512/772-7680 | 26 |
| Bluebonnet Elem Sch/Flower Mound/Denton | 04920464 | 469/713-5195 | 126 |
| Bluebonnet Elem Sch/Fort Worth/Tarrant | 05090799 | 817/744-4500 | 357 |
| Bluebonnet Elem Sch/Hereford/Deaf Smith | 01013000 | 806/363-7650 | 123 |
| Bluebonnet Elem Sch/Lockhart/Caldwell | 10002662 | 512/398-0900 | 64 |
| Bluebonnet Elem Sch/Round Rock/Williamson | 02893982 | 512/428-7700 | 401 |
| Bluebonnet Trail Elem Sch/Austin/Travis | 01056909 | 512/278-4125 | 373 |
| Bluff Dale Elem Sch/Bluff Dale/Erath | 01017006 | 254/728-3277 | 147 |
| **BLUFF DALE IND SCH DIST/** | | | |
| **BLUFF DALE/ERATH** | 01016997 | 254/728-3277 | 147 |
| **BLUM IND SCH DIST/BLUM/HILL** | 01030761 | 254/874-5231 | 230 |
| Blum Sch/Blum/Hill | 01030773 | 254/874-5231 | 230 |
| Bob & Lola Sandford Elem Sch/Van Alstyne/ Grayson | 12306804 | 903/712-1900 | 173 |
| Bob and Betty Nelson Elem Sch/Alvin/ Brazoria | 12380446 | 713/814-7300 | 54 |
| Bob Beard Elem Sch/Helotes/Bexar | 05274000 | 210/397-6600 | 39 |
| Bob Hope Elem Sch/Port Arthur/Jefferson | 12260638 | 409/983-3244 | 2 |
| Bob Hope Elem Sch/San Antonio/Bexar | 00999580 | 210/927-8180 | 46 |
| Bob Hope Middle High Sch/Port Arthur/ Jefferson | 11663609 | 409/983-3244 | 2 |
| Bob L Kirksey Elem Sch/Booker/Lipscomb | 01038141 | 806/658-4559 | 270 |
| Bob Lewis Elem Sch/San Antonio/Bexar | 04942022 | 210/397-2650 | 39 |
| Bobby Shaw Middle Sch/Pasadena/Harris | 11129433 | 713/740-5268 | 203 |
| Bobbye Behlau Elem Sch/San Antonio/Bexar | 11552048 | 210/398-1000 | 39 |
| Boerne Academy/Boerne/Kendall | 04432106 | 830/572-2600 | 257 |
| Boerne High Sch/Boerne/Kendall | 01035826 | 830/357-2200 | 257 |
| **BOERNE IND SCH DIST/BOERNE/** | | | |
| **KENDALL** | 01035814 | 830/357-2000 | 257 |
| Boerne Middle School North/Boerne/Kendall | 01035840 | 830/357-3100 | 257 |
| Boerne Middle School South/Boerne/Kendall | 04916815 | 830/357-3300 | 257 |
| Boles Elem Sch/Quinlan/Hunt | 01032276 | 903/883-2161 | 238 |
| Boles High Sch/Quinlan/Hunt | 04800632 | 903/883-2918 | 238 |
| **BOLES IND SCH DIST/QUINLAN/HUNT** | 01032264 | 903/883-4464 | 238 |
| Boles Junior High Sch/Arlington/Tarrant | 03011694 | 682/867-8000 | 346 |
| Boles Middle Sch/Quinlan/Hunt | 05101192 | 903/883-4464 | 238 |
| Boling High Sch/Boling/Wharton | 01059547 | 979/657-2816 | 392 |
| **BOLING IND SCH DIST/BOLING/** | | | |
| **WHARTON** | 01059535 | 979/657-2770 | 392 |
| Bonham Academy/San Antonio/Bexar | 00999059 | 210/228-3300 | 43 |
| Bonham Early Ed Sch/Grand Prairie/Dallas | 01010917 | 972/262-4255 | 111 |
| Bonham Elem Sch/Abilene/Taylor | 01172747 | 325/690-3745 | 362 |
| Bonham Elem Sch/Bryan/Brazos | 01002025 | 979/209-1200 | 58 |
| Bonham Elem Sch/El Paso/El Paso | 01015541 | 915/236-8150 | 137 |
| Bonham Elem Sch/Harlingen/Cameron | 01003782 | 956/427-3070 | 68 |
| Bonham Elem Sch/Midland/Midland | 01041538 | 432/240-6000 | 288 |
| Bonham Elem Sch/San Angelo/Tom Green | 02896843 | 325/947-3917 | 367 |
| Bonham High Sch/Bonham/Fannin | 01017381 | 903/583-5567 | 149 |
| **BONHAM IND SCH DIST/BONHAM/** | | | |
| **FANNIN** | 01017367 | 903/583-5526 | 149 |
| Bonham Middle Sch/Odessa/Ector | 01014585 | 432/456-0429 | 134 |
| Bonham Middle Sch/Temple/Bell | 00996722 | 254/215-6600 | 32 |
| Bonham Pre-Kindergarten Sch/San Marcos/ Hays | 12109436 | 512/393-6031 | 217 |
| Bonner Elem Sch/Houston/Harris | 01025417 | 713/943-5740 | 194 |
| Bonner Elem Sch/Tyler/Smith | 01050785 | 903/262-1920 | 340 |
| Bonnie Brae Elem Sch/Fort Worth/Tarrant | 05275872 | 817/814-3700 | 352 |
| Bonnie Ellison Elem Sch/San Antonio/Bexar | 12033631 | 210/398-1850 | 39 |
| Bonnie Garcia Elem Sch/Laredo/Webb | 05350707 | 956/473-8900 | 390 |
| Bonnie Gentry Elem Sch/Mesquite/Dallas | 05273680 | 972/290-4140 | 115 |
| Bonnie Holland Elem Sch/Katy/Harris | 11128609 | 281/234-0500 | 156 |

| School/City/County DISTRICT/CITY/COUNTY | PID | TELEPHONE NUMBER | PAGE |
|---|---|---|---|
| Bonnie P Hopper Primary Sch/Highlands/ Harris | 02110651 | 281/420-4685 | 192 |
| Booker High Sch/Booker/Lipscomb | 01038153 | 806/658-4521 | 270 |
| **BOOKER IND SCH DIST/BOOKER/** | | | |
| **LIPSCOMB** | 01038139 | 806/658-4501 | 270 |
| Booker T Washington Elem Sch/Elgin/Bastrop | 00995895 | 512/281-3411 | 27 |
| Booker T Washington ES/Wichita Falls/ Wichita | 01173222 | 940/235-1196 | 395 |
| Boon Elem Sch/Allen/Collin | 10006242 | 972/747-3331 | 80 |
| Boone Elem Sch/Austin/Travis | 02890540 | 512/414-2537 | 369 |
| Boone Elem Sch/Houston/Harris | 01023067 | 281/983-8308 | 187 |
| **BORDEN CO IND SCH DIST/GAIL/** | | | |
| **BORDEN** | 01000546 | 806/756-4313 | 49 |
| Borden County Sch/Gail/Borden | 01000558 | 806/756-4313 | 49 |
| Borger High Sch/Borger/Hutchinson | 01032654 | 806/273-1029 | 240 |
| **BORGER IND SCH DIST/BORGER/** | | | |
| **HUTCHINSON** | 01032642 | 806/273-6481 | 240 |
| Borger Intermediate Sch/Borger/Hutchinson | 10026955 | 806/273-4342 | 240 |
| Borger Middle Sch/Borger/Hutchinson | 01032680 | 806/273-1037 | 240 |
| Borman Elem Sch/Denton/Denton | 01013232 | 940/369-2500 | 125 |
| Borrego Elem Sch/San Elizario/El Paso | 04939403 | 915/872-3910 | 140 |
| Bose Ikard Elem Sch/Weatherford/Parker | 01046605 | 817/598-2818 | 317 |
| Bosque Co Educational Center/Meridian/ Bosque | 04826533 | 254/435-6098 | 50 |
| Bosqueville Elem Sch/Waco/McLennan | 01039573 | 254/752-6006 | 281 |
| **BOSQUEVILLE IND SCH DIST/** | | | |
| **WACO/MCLENNAN** | 01039561 | 254/757-3113 | 281 |
| Bosqueville Middle Sch/Waco/McLennan | 12036188 | 254/759-7077 | 281 |
| Bosqueville Secondary Sch/Waco/McLennan | 11456781 | 254/752-8513 | 281 |
| Boude Storey Middle Sch/Dallas/Dallas | 01008548 | 972/925-8700 | 103 |
| Boulevard Baptist Chrstn Sch/Burleson/ Johnson | 11663582 | 817/295-4342 | 252 |
| Boulevard Heights Sch/Fort Worth/Tarrant | 01052599 | 817/814-6400 | 352 |
| Boulter Middle Sch/Tyler/Smith | 01050797 | 903/262-1390 | 340 |
| Bovina Elem Sch/Bovina/Parmer | 01046667 | 806/251-1336 | 317 |
| Bovina High Sch/Bovina/Parmer | 11565124 | 806/251-1336 | 317 |
| **BOVINA IND SCH DIST/BOVINA/** | | | |
| **PARMER** | 01046655 | 806/251-1336 | 317 |
| Bovina Middle Sch/Bovina/Parmer | 11565112 | 806/251-1336 | 317 |
| Bowie Elem Sch/Abilene/Taylor | 01172759 | 325/671-4770 | 362 |
| Bowie Elem Sch/Bowie/Montague | 01042221 | 940/689-2950 | 293 |
| Bowie Elem Sch/Corsicana/Navarro | 01043433 | 903/872-6541 | 302 |
| Bowie Elem Sch/Dallas/Dallas | 01011741 | 469/593-6000 | 116 |
| Bowie Elem Sch/Greenville/Hunt | 01032460 | 903/457-2676 | 239 |
| Bowie Elem Sch/Harlingen/Cameron | 01003794 | 956/427-3080 | 68 |
| Bowie Elem Sch/Rosenberg/Fort Bend | 01018268 | 832/223-1200 | 158 |
| Bowie Elem Sch/San Angelo/Tom Green | 01055670 | 325/947-3921 | 367 |
| Bowie Elem Sch/San Marcos/Hays | 01029152 | 512/393-6200 | 217 |
| Bowie Fine Arts Academy/Grand Prairie/ Dallas | 01010929 | 972/262-7348 | 111 |
| Bowie Fine Arts Academy/Midland/Midland | 01041540 | 432/240-6100 | 288 |
| Bowie High Sch/Bowie/Montague | 01042207 | 940/689-2840 | 293 |
| Bowie High Sch/El Paso/El Paso | 01015931 | 915/236-7000 | 138 |
| **BOWIE IND SCH DIST/BOWIE/** | | | |
| **MONTAGUE** | 01042180 | 940/872-1151 | 292 |
| Bowie Intermediate Sch/Bowie/Montague | 01042192 | 940/689-2895 | 293 |
| Bowie Junior High Sch/Bowie/Montague | 01042219 | 940/689-2975 | 293 |
| Bowie Middle Sch/Irving/Dallas | 01011131 | 972/600-3000 | 113 |
| Bowie Middle Sch/Odessa/Ector | 01014597 | 432/456-0439 | 134 |
| Bowie Primary Sch/Sulphur Spgs/Hopkins | 01031648 | 903/885-3772 | 235 |
| Bowman Middle Sch/Plano/Collin | 01006423 | 469/752-4800 | 86 |
| Boyd Elem Sch/Boyd/Wise | 01061564 | 940/433-9520 | 405 |
| Boyd High Sch/Boyd/Wise | 01061576 | 940/433-9580 | 405 |
| **BOYD IND SCH DIST/BOYD/WISE** | 01061552 | 940/433-2327 | 405 |
| Boyd Intermediate Sch/Boyd/Wise | 03046924 | 940/433-9540 | 405 |
| Boyd Middle Sch/Boyd/Wise | 02056196 | 940/433-9560 | 405 |
| Boyer Elem Sch/Prosper/Collin | 12307042 | 469/219-2240 | 88 |
| Boys Ranch High Sch/Boys Ranch/Oldham | 01484485 | 806/534-0032 | 310 |
| **BOYS RANCH IND SCH DIST/** | | | |
| **BOYS RANCH/OLDHAM** | 01484461 | 806/534-2221 | 310 |
| Bozman Intermediate Sch/Conroe/Montgomery | 11449738 | 936/709-1800 | 294 |
| Bracken Christian Sch/Bulverde/Comal | 02192427 | 830/438-3211 | 93 |
| Brackenridge High Sch/San Antonio/Bexar | 00999140 | 210/228-1200 | 43 |
| Brackett High Sch/Brackettville/Kinney | 01036234 | 830/563-2480 | 260 |
| **BRACKETT IND SCH DIST/BRACKETTVILLE/** | | | |
| **KINNEY** | 01036222 | 830/563-2491 | 260 |
| Brackett Junior High Sch/Brackettville/ Kinney | 03410650 | 830/563-2480 | 260 |
| Bradfield Elem Sch/Garland/Dallas | 01010773 | 972/494-8303 | 109 |
| Bradford Elem Sch/Iowa Park/Wichita | 01060077 | 940/592-5841 | 395 |
| Bradford Elem Sch/San Angelo/Tom Green | 01055577 | 325/659-3645 | 367 |
| Bradley Elem Sch/Spring/Montgomery | 12231883 | 832/482-6800 | 294 |

| School/City/County<br>DISTRICT/CITY/COUNTY | PID | TELEPHONE<br>NUMBER | PAGE |
|---|---|---|---|
| Bradley Middle Sch/San Antonio/Bexar | 02178328 | 210/356-2600 | 37 |
| Brady Alternative Sch/Brady/McCulloch | 04447383 | 325/597-2170 | 280 |
| Brady Elem Sch/Brady/McCulloch | 01039456 | 325/597-2590 | 280 |
| Brady High Sch/Brady/McCulloch | 01039432 | 325/597-2491 | 280 |
| **BRADY IND SCH DIST/BRADY/**<br>**MCCULLOCH** | 01039420 | 325/597-2301 | 280 |
| Brady Middle Sch/Brady/McCulloch | 01039444 | 325/597-8110 | 280 |
| Braeburn Elem Sch/Houston/Harris | 01024748 | 713/295-5210 | 198 |
| **BRAINATION SCHOOLS/SAN ANTONIO/**<br>**BEXAR** | 11701354 | 210/638-5000 | 33 |
| Bramlette Elem Sch/Longview/Gregg | 01021007 | 903/803-5600 | 174 |
| Branch Sch/Houston/Harris | 02757144 | 713/465-0288 | 210 |
| Brandeis High Sch/San Antonio/Bexar | 11104146 | 210/397-8200 | 39 |
| Brandenburg Elem Sch/Irving/Dallas | 01011208 | 972/600-7100 | 113 |
| Brandenburg Intermediate Sch/Duncanville/<br>Dallas | 04011788 | 972/708-3100 | 108 |
| Brandon Elem Sch/Lufkin/Angelina | 02201808 | 936/632-5513 | 21 |
| Bransford Elem Sch/Colleyville/Tarrant | 04030497 | 817/305-4920 | 355 |
| Braswell High Sch/Aubrey/Denton | 12165375 | 972/347-7700 | 125 |
| Braun Station Elem Sch/San Antonio/Bexar | 02178330 | 210/397-1550 | 39 |
| Brawner Intermediate Sch/Granbury/Hood | 04947747 | 817/408-4950 | 233 |
| Bray Elem Sch/Cedar Hill/Dallas | 01008287 | 972/291-4231 | 101 |
| Brazos Bend Elem Sch/Sugar Land/Fort Bend | 04749777 | 281/634-5180 | 154 |
| Brazos Christian Sch/Bryan/Brazos | 02164690 | 979/823-1000 | 60 |
| Brazos Credit Recovery HS/Waco/McLennan | 05275884 | 254/754-9422 | 285 |
| Brazos Elem Sch/Orchard/Austin | 00995649 | 979/478-6610 | 25 |
| Brazos High Sch/Wallis/Austin | 00995637 | 979/478-6832 | 25 |
| **BRAZOS IND SCH DIST/WALLIS/**<br>**AUSTIN** | 00995625 | 979/478-6551 | 25 |
| Brazos Middle Sch/Wallis/Austin | 00995663 | 979/478-6814 | 25 |
| Brazos River Charter Sch/Nemo/Somervell | 05011030 | 254/898-9226 | 2 |
| Brazos Sch Inquiry-Bryan/Bryan/Brazos | 04890900 | 979/774-5032 | 2 |
| Brazos Sch Inquiry-Tidwell/Houston/Harris | 11136503 | 713/681-1960 | 2 |
| Brazos Success Academy/Lake Jackson/<br>Brazoria | 12377217 | 979/730-7090 | 55 |
| Brazosport Christian Sch/Lake Jackson/<br>Brazoria | 02164951 | 979/297-0722 | 57 |
| Brazosport High Sch/Freeport/Brazoria | 01001576 | 979/730-7260 | 55 |
| **BRAZOSPORT IND SCH DIST/**<br>**CLUTE/BRAZORIA** | 01001540 | 979/730-7000 | 55 |
| Brazoswood High Sch/Clute/Brazoria | 01001588 | 979/730-7300 | 55 |
| Breckenridge High Sch/Breckenridge/<br>Stephens | 01051349 | 254/559-2231 | 344 |
| **BRECKENRIDGE IND SCH DIST/**<br>**BRECKENRIDGE/STEPHENS** | 01051325 | 254/559-2278 | 344 |
| Breckenridge Jr High Sch/Breckenridge/<br>Stephens | 01051337 | 254/559-6581 | 344 |
| Breeden Elem Sch/Brownsville/Cameron | 11819107 | 956/554-4730 | 67 |
| Bremond Elem Sch/Bremond/Robertson | 04033669 | 254/746-7145 | 327 |
| Bremond High Sch/Bremond/Robertson | 01048562 | 254/746-7061 | 327 |
| **BREMOND IND SCH DIST/BREMOND/**<br>**ROBERTSON** | 01048550 | 254/746-7145 | 327 |
| Bremond Middle Sch/Bremond/Robertson | 04033449 | 254/746-5022 | 327 |
| Brenham Elem Sch/Brenham/Washington | 01059066 | 979/277-3880 | 388 |
| Brenham High Sch/Brenham/Washington | 01059078 | 979/277-3800 | 388 |
| **BRENHAM IND SCH DIST/BRENHAM/**<br>**WASHINGTON** | 01059042 | 979/277-3700 | 388 |
| Brenham Junior High Sch/Brenham/Washington | 04755087 | 979/277-3830 | 388 |
| Brenham Middle Sch/Brenham/Washington | 01059080 | 979/277-3845 | 388 |
| Brent Elem Sch/Little Elm/Denton | 04920127 | 972/947-9451 | 128 |
| Brentfield Elem Sch/Dallas/Dallas | 01399658 | 469/593-5740 | 116 |
| Brentwood Christian Sch/Austin/Travis | 01481201 | 512/835-5983 | 375 |
| Brentwood Elem Sch/Austin/Travis | 01056117 | 512/414-2039 | 369 |
| Brentwood Middle Sch/San Antonio/Bexar | 00997099 | 210/444-7675 | 34 |
| Brewer Academy/San Antonio/Bexar | 04874944 | 210/438-6825 | 43 |
| Brewer High Sch/Fort Worth/Tarrant | 01054212 | 817/367-1200 | 360 |
| Brewer Middle Sch/Fort Worth/Tarrant | 01054195 | 817/367-1267 | 360 |
| Brewster Sch/Edinburg/Hidalgo | 01029683 | 956/289-2334 | 221 |
| Briargate Elem Sch/Missouri City/Fort Bend | 01541320 | 281/634-4560 | 154 |
| Briargrove Elem Sch/Houston/Harris | 01024358 | 713/917-3600 | 198 |
| Briarhill Middle Sch/Lewisville/Denton | 04364652 | 469/713-5975 | 126 |
| Briarmeadow Charter Sch/Houston/Harris | 04755544 | 713/458-5500 | 198 |
| Briarwood Sch/Houston/Harris | 01480518 | 281/493-1070 | 210 |
| Bridge Academy/Weatherford/Parker | 11551903 | 817/598-2847 | 317 |
| Bridge City Elem Sch/Bridge City/Orange | 01045649 | 409/735-0900 | 311 |
| Bridge City High Sch/Bridge City/Orange | 01045613 | 409/735-1600 | 311 |
| **BRIDGE CITY IND SCH DIST/**<br>**BRIDGE CITY/ORANGE** | 01045601 | 409/735-1501 | 311 |
| Bridge City Intermediate Sch/Bridge City/<br>Orange | 04450079 | 409/792-8800 | 311 |
| Bridge City Middle Sch/Bridge City/Orange | 01045625 | 409/735-1700 | 311 |
| Bridge Point Elem Sch/Austin/Travis | 04748010 | 512/732-9200 | 372 |

| School/City/County<br>DISTRICT/CITY/COUNTY | PID | TELEPHONE<br>NUMBER | PAGE |
|---|---|---|---|
| Bridgeland High Sch/Cypress/Harris | 12233166 | 832/349-7600 | 189 |
| Bridgemark Center for Learning/Tyler/Smith | 12469781 | 903/939-3511 | 342 |
| Bridgeport Elem Sch/Bridgeport/Wise | 01061590 | 940/683-5955 | 406 |
| Bridgeport High Sch/Bridgeport/Wise | 01061605 | 940/683-4064 | 406 |
| **BRIDGEPORT IND SCH DIST/**<br>**BRIDGEPORT/WISE** | 01061588 | 940/683-5124 | 406 |
| Bridgeport Intermediate Sch/Bridgeport/<br>Wise | 04028169 | 940/683-5784 | 406 |
| Bridgeport Middle Sch/Bridgeport/Wise | 01061617 | 940/683-2273 | 406 |
| Bridges Accel Lrng Ctr/Colleyville/Tarrant | 04750520 | 817/251-5474 | 355 |
| Bridges Sch/El Paso/El Paso | 02233320 | 915/532-6647 | 143 |
| Bridgeway Preparatory Academy/Carrollton/<br>Dallas | 12370283 | 214/257-8883 | 2 |
| Bright Beginnings Academic Ctr/Brownfield/<br>Terry | 11710135 | 806/637-0757 | 365 |
| Brighter Horizons Academy/Garland/Dallas | 03556591 | 972/675-2062 | 119 |
| Brill Elem Sch/Klein/Harris | 01832131 | 832/484-6150 | 202 |
| Brinker Elem Sch/Plano/Collin | 03047423 | 469/752-0500 | 86 |
| Briscoe Academy/San Antonio/Bexar | 00999085 | 210/228-3305 | 43 |
| Briscoe Elem Sch/Houston/Harris | 01025429 | 713/924-1740 | 194 |
| Briscoe Junior High Sch/Richmond/Fort Bend | 04946016 | 832/223-4000 | 158 |
| Britain Elem Sch/Irving/Dallas | 01011246 | 972/600-3800 | 113 |
| British Int'l Sch of Houston/Katy/Harris | 05135806 | 713/290-9025 | 210 |
| Broaddus Elem Sch/Broaddus/San Augustine | 03473638 | 936/872-3315 | 332 |
| Broaddus High Sch/Broaddus/San Augustine | 01049358 | 936/872-3610 | 332 |
| **BROADDUS IND SCH DIST/BROADDUS/**<br>**SAN AUGUSTINE** | 01049334 | 936/872-3041 | 332 |
| Brock Elem Sch/Brock/Parker | 01046356 | 817/592-6555 | 315 |
| Brock Elem Sch/Burleson/Johnson | 11396997 | 817/245-3800 | 249 |
| Brock High Sch/Weatherford/Parker | 04034443 | 817/596-7425 | 315 |
| **BROCK IND SCH DIST/BROCK/PARKER** | 01046344 | 817/594-7642 | 315 |
| Brock Intermediate Sch/Brock/Parker | 12306957 | 817/594-8017 | 315 |
| Brock Junior High Sch/Brock/Parker | 05342164 | 817/594-3195 | 315 |
| Brockett Elem Sch/Aubrey/Denton | 01013206 | 940/668-0036 | 124 |
| Bronte Elem Sch/Bronte/Coke | 01005766 | 325/473-2251 | 79 |
| Bronte High Sch/Bronte/Coke | 03397163 | 325/473-2521 | 79 |
| **BRONTE IND SCH DIST/BRONTE/COKE** | 01005754 | 325/473-2511 | 79 |
| Brook Ave Elem Sch/Waco/McLennan | 04869949 | 254/750-3562 | 285 |
| Brook Hill Sch/Bullard/Smith | 04881765 | 903/894-5000 | 342 |
| Brook Hills Lower Sch/Bullard/Smith | 11226263 | 903/894-4164 | 342 |
| Brook Village Eec/Wichita Falls/Wichita | 04875261 | 940/235-1132 | 395 |
| **BROOKELAND IND SCH DIST/**<br>**BROOKELAND/JASPER** | 01033141 | 409/698-2677 | 243 |
| Brookeland Sch/Brookeland/Jasper | 01033153 | 409/698-2677 | 243 |
| Brookesmith Elem Sch/Brookesmith/Brown | 04247755 | 325/643-3023 | 62 |
| Brookesmith High Sch/Brookesmith/Brown | 01002477 | 325/643-3023 | 62 |
| **BROOKESMITH IND SCH DIST/**<br>**BROOKESMITH/BROWN** | 01002453 | 325/643-3023 | 61 |
| Brookhaven Elem Sch/Killeen/Bell | 04027646 | 254/336-1440 | 30 |
| Brookhaven Sch/West/McLennan | 12109369 | 254/981-2240 | 285 |
| Brookhollow Christian Academy/Houston/<br>Harris | 11976793 | 281/649-6813 | 210 |
| Brookhollow Elem Sch/Lufkin/Angelina | 00994944 | 936/639-3100 | 21 |
| Brookhollow Elem Sch/Pflugerville/Travis | 04363555 | 512/594-5200 | 374 |
| Brookline Elem Sch/Houston/Harris | 01025431 | 713/845-7400 | 197 |
| Brooks Acad-Science Engineerng/San Antonio/<br>Bexar | 11014113 | 210/633-9006 | 2 |
| **BROOKS CO IND SCH DIST/FALFURRIAS/**<br>**BROOKS** | 01002336 | 361/325-5681 | 61 |
| Brooks Collegiate Academy/San Antonio/<br>Bexar | 12235841 | | 2 |
| Brooks Estrella Academy/San Antonio/Bexar | 12162165 | 210/257-5175 | 2 |
| Brooks Int'l Studies Academy/San Antonio/<br>Bexar | 12161953 | 210/998-4452 | 2 |
| Brooks Lonestar Academy/San Antonio/Bexar | 12260640 | 210/998-4452 | 2 |
| Brooks Oaks Academy/San Antonio/Bexar | 12260652 | 210/627-6013 | 2 |
| Brooks Wester Middle Sch/Mansfield/Tarrant | 05091638 | 682/314-1800 | 359 |
| Brooks-Quinn Jones Elem Sch/Nacogdoches/<br>Nacogdoches | 01420532 | 936/569-5040 | 301 |
| Brookside Intermediate Sch/Friendswood/<br>Galveston | 04365321 | 281/284-3600 | 163 |
| Brookwood Elem Sch/Houston/Galveston | 02043278 | 281/284-5600 | 163 |
| Brookwood Forest Elem Sch/Porter/<br>Montgomery | 12313974 | 281/577-8820 | 296 |
| Brown Elem Sch/Austin/Travis | 01056686 | 512/414-2047 | 369 |
| Brown Elem Sch/Lubbock/Lubbock | 01038567 | 806/219-5300 | 273 |
| Brown Middle Sch/El Paso/El Paso | 10907127 | 915/774-4080 | 139 |
| Brown Middle Sch/Forney/Kaufman | 01035589 | 469/762-4260 | 255 |
| Brown Primary Sch/Smithville/Bastrop | 00995986 | 512/237-2519 | 27 |
| Brownfield High Sch/Brownfield/Terry | 01055096 | 806/637-4523 | 365 |
| **BROWNFIELD IND SCH DIST/**<br>**BROWNFIELD/TERRY** | 01055084 | 806/637-2591 | 364 |

| School/City/County<br>DISTRICT/CITY/COUNTY | PID | TELEPHONE<br>NUMBER | PAGE |
|---|---|---|---|
| Brownfield Middle Sch/Brownfield/Terry | 01055113 | 806/637-7521 | 365 |
| Browning Elem Sch/Houston/Harris | 01023914 | 713/867-5140 | 196 |
| Browning Learning Center/Royse City/<br>Rockwall | 04940036 | 972/635-5077 | 329 |
| Brownsboro Elem Sch/Brownsboro/Henderson | 01029334 | 903/852-6461 | 218 |
| Brownsboro High Sch/Brownsboro/Henderson | 01029346 | 903/852-2321 | 218 |
| **BROWNSBORO IND SCH DIST/**<br>**BROWNSBORO/HENDERSON** | 01029322 | 903/852-3701 | 218 |
| Brownsboro Intermediate Sch/Brownsboro/<br>Henderson | 02131710 | 903/852-7325 | 218 |
| Brownsboro Junior High Sch/Brownsboro/<br>Henderson | 03050080 | 903/852-6931 | 218 |
| Brownsville Academic Center/Brownsville/<br>Cameron | 04015758 | 956/504-6305 | 67 |
| Brownsville Early Clg HS/Brownsville/<br>Cameron | 11103831 | 956/698-1476 | 67 |
| **BROWNSVILLE IND SCH DIST/**<br>**BROWNSVILLE/CAMERON** | 01003445 | 956/548-8000 | 66 |
| Brownsville Lrng Acad High Sch/Brownsville/<br>Cameron | 12315154 | 956/548-8630 | 67 |
| Brownwood Accelerated High Sch/Brownwood/<br>Brown | 04011283 | 325/646-1652 | 62 |
| Brownwood High Sch/Brownwood/Brown | 01002491 | 325/646-9549 | 62 |
| **BROWNWOOD IND SCH DIST/BROWNWOOD/**<br>**BROWN** | 01002489 | 325/643-5644 | 62 |
| Brownwood Middle Sch/Brownwood/Brown | 01002506 | 325/646-9545 | 62 |
| Bruce Aiken Elem Sch/Brownsville/Cameron | 04456748 | 956/986-5200 | 67 |
| Bruce Junior High Sch/Gilmer/Upshur | 01057446 | 903/841-7600 | 379 |
| Bruce Shulkey Elem Sch/Fort Worth/Tarrant | 01052628 | 817/814-8400 | 352 |
| Bruceville-Eddy Elem Sch/Eddy/McLennan | 01039597 | 254/859-5525 | 281 |
| Bruceville-Eddy High Sch/Eddy/McLennan | 01039602 | 254/859-5525 | 281 |
| **BRUCEVILLE-EDDY IND SCH DIST/**<br>**EDDY/MCLENNAN** | 01039585 | 254/859-5525 | 281 |
| Bruceville-Eddy Interm Sch/Eddy/McLennan | 04946872 | 254/859-5525 | 281 |
| Bruceville-Eddy Jr High Sch/Eddy/McLennan | 04448428 | 254/859-5525 | 281 |
| Brule Elem Sch/Navasota/Grimes | 04145418 | 936/825-4275 | 177 |
| Brundreet Middle Sch/Port Aransas/Nueces | 02224575 | 361/749-1209 | 308 |
| Bruni High Sch/Bruni/Webb | 01059169 | 361/747-5415 | 391 |
| Bruni Middle Sch/Bruni/Webb | 01059157 | 361/747-5415 | 391 |
| Brushy Creek Elem Sch/Round Rock/<br>Williamson | 02126894 | 512/428-3000 | 401 |
| Bryan Adams High Sch/Dallas/Dallas | 01008550 | 972/502-4900 | 103 |
| Bryan Adult Learning Center/Bryan/Brazos | 04810962 | 979/703-7740 | 58 |
| Bryan Collegiate High Sch/Bryan/Brazos | 10911154 | 979/209-2790 | 58 |
| Bryan Elem Sch/Mission/Hidalgo | 01030230 | 956/323-4800 | 225 |
| **BRYAN IND SCH DIST/BRYAN/BRAZOS** | 01002013 | 979/209-1000 | 58 |
| Bryant Elem Sch/Arlington/Tarrant | 04035760 | 682/867-5200 | 346 |
| Bryker Woods Elem Sch/Austin/Travis | 01056131 | 512/414-2054 | 369 |
| Bryson Elem Sch/Fort Worth/Tarrant | 02846472 | 817/237-8306 | 351 |
| **BRYSON IND SCH DIST/BRYSON/JACK** | 01032898 | 940/392-3281 | 241 |
| Bryson Sch/Bryson/Jack | 01032903 | 940/392-2601 | 241 |
| Buckalew Elem Sch/The Woodlands/Montgomery | 04806765 | 281/465-3400 | 294 |
| **BUCKHOLTS IND SCH DIST/BUCKHOLTS/**<br>**MILAM** | 01041722 | 254/593-3011 | 290 |
| Buckholts Sch/Buckholts/Milam | 01041734 | 254/593-2744 | 290 |
| Buckner Fanning Christian Sch/San Antonio/<br>Bexar | 04844212 | 210/402-6905 | 47 |
| Buckner Preparatory Sch/Dallas/Dallas | 12378479 | 214/545-6552 | 2 |
| Buda Elem Sch/Buda/Hays | 02855813 | 512/268-8439 | 216 |
| Budewig Intermediate Sch/Houston/Harris | 05272193 | 281/988-3200 | 187 |
| Buell Central High Sch/Pharr/Hidalgo | 04365955 | 956/354-2500 | 226 |
| Buena Vista Elem Sch/Del Rio/Val Verde | 02128294 | 830/778-4600 | 382 |
| **BUENA VISTA IND SCH DIST/**<br>**IMPERIAL/PECOS** | 01046801 | 432/536-2225 | 318 |
| Buena Vista Sch/Imperial/Pecos | 01046813 | 432/536-2336 | 318 |
| Buffalo Creek Elem Sch/Houston/Harris | 04751029 | 713/251-5300 | 206 |
| Buffalo Elem Sch/Buffalo/Leon | 01037563 | 903/322-2473 | 266 |
| Buffalo Gap Elem Sch/Buffalo Gap/Taylor | 02112300 | 325/572-3533 | 363 |
| Buffalo High Sch/Buffalo/Leon | 01037575 | 903/322-2473 | 266 |
| **BUFFALO IND SCH DIST/BUFFALO/**<br>**LEON** | 01037551 | 903/322-3765 | 266 |
| Buffalo Lower Junior High Sch/Buffalo/Leon | 04281804 | 903/322-2473 | 266 |
| Buffalo Upper Junior High Sch/Buffalo/Leon | 12311445 | 903/322-2473 | 267 |
| Bullard Early Childhood Center/Bullard/<br>Smith | 12225224 | 903/894-6389 | 339 |
| Bullard Elem Sch/Bullard/Smith | 01050589 | 903/894-2930 | 339 |
| Bullard High Sch/Bullard/Smith | 01050591 | 903/894-3272 | 339 |
| **BULLARD IND SCH DIST/BULLARD/**<br>**SMITH** | 01050577 | 903/894-6639 | 339 |
| Bullard Intermediate Sch/Bullard/Smith | 04939415 | 903/894-6793 | 339 |
| Bullard Middle Sch/Bullard/Smith | 02178782 | 903/894-6533 | 339 |
| Bullard Primary Sch/Bullard/Smith | 11131371 | 903/894-2890 | 339 |

| School/City/County<br>DISTRICT/CITY/COUNTY | PID | TELEPHONE<br>NUMBER | PAGE |
|---|---|---|---|
| Bullock Elem Sch/Garland/Dallas | 01010553 | 972/494-8308 | 109 |
| Bulverde Creek Elem Sch/San Antonio/Bexar | 10003343 | 210/407-1000 | 37 |
| Buna Elem Sch/Buna/Jasper | 01033189 | 409/994-4840 | 243 |
| Buna High Sch/Buna/Jasper | 01033191 | 409/994-4811 | 243 |
| **BUNA IND SCH DIST/BUNA/JASPER** | 01033177 | 409/994-5101 | 243 |
| Buna Junior High Sch/Buna/Jasper | 01033206 | 409/994-4860 | 243 |
| Bunche Elem Sch/Midland/Midland | 12104371 | 432/240-8600 | 288 |
| Bunker Hill Elem Sch/Houston/Harris | 01027104 | 713/251-5400 | 206 |
| Burbank Elem Sch/Houston/Harris | 01025819 | 713/696-2690 | 195 |
| Burbank High Sch/San Antonio/Bexar | 00999231 | 210/228-1210 | 43 |
| Burbank Middle Sch/Houston/Harris | 01025821 | 713/696-2720 | 195 |
| Burges High Sch/El Paso/El Paso | 01015553 | 915/236-7200 | 138 |
| Burgess Elem Sch/Wichita Falls/Wichita | 01172993 | 940/235-1136 | 395 |
| Burgin Elem Sch/Arlington/Tarrant | 04918930 | 682/867-1300 | 346 |
| Burkburnett High Sch/Burkburnett/Wichita | 01059937 | 940/569-1411 | 394 |
| **BURKBURNETT IND SCH DIST/**<br>**BURKBURNETT/WICHITA** | 01059925 | 940/569-3326 | 394 |
| Burkburnett Middle Sch/Burkburnett/Wichita | 01059949 | 940/569-3381 | 394 |
| Burkeville Elem Sch/Burkeville/Newton | 01043689 | 409/565-4284 | 304 |
| **BURKEVILLE IND SCH DIST/**<br>**BURKEVILLE/NEWTON** | 01043677 | 409/565-2201 | 303 |
| Burkeville Jr Sr High Sch/Burkeville/<br>Newton | 01043691 | 409/565-4284 | 304 |
| Burleson Adventist Sch/Burleson/Johnson | 12469420 | 817/295-6812 | 252 |
| Burleson Co Alt Sch/Caldwell/Burleson | 04802135 | 979/567-2670 | 63 |
| Burleson Collegiate High Sch/Burleson/<br>Johnson | 12168107 | 817/245-1600 | 249 |
| Burleson Early Chldhd Center/San Antonio/<br>Bexar | 11713515 | 210/444-7725 | 34 |
| Burleson Elem Sch/Odessa/Ector | 01014602 | 432/456-1039 | 134 |
| Burleson High Sch/Burleson/Johnson | 01034834 | 817/245-0000 | 249 |
| **BURLESON IND SCH DIST/BURLESON/**<br>**JOHNSON** | 01034810 | 817/245-1000 | 249 |
| **BURLESON MILAM SPEC SERV CO-OP/**<br>**MILANO/MILAM** | 11551771 | 512/455-7801 | 291 |
| Burley Primary Sch/Lufkin/Angelina | 11446023 | 936/639-3100 | 21 |
| **BURNET CONS IND SCH DIST/**<br>**BURNET/BURNET** | 01002752 | 512/756-2124 | 63 |
| Burnet Early Childhood Univ ES/Galveston/<br>Galveston | 11563372 | 409/761-6470 | 165 |
| Burnet Elem Sch/Houston/Harris | 01025443 | 713/924-1780 | 194 |
| Burnet Elem Sch/Midland/Midland | 01041461 | 432/240-6200 | 288 |
| Burnet Elem Sch/Odessa/Ector | 01014614 | 432/456-1049 | 134 |
| Burnet High Sch/Burnet/Burnet | 01002788 | 512/756-6193 | 63 |
| Burnet Middle Sch/Austin/Travis | 01056179 | 512/414-3225 | 371 |
| Burnet Middle Sch/Burnet/Burnet | 01002790 | 512/756-6182 | 63 |
| Burnett Elem Sch/Houston/Harris | 01548433 | 713/740-0536 | 203 |
| Burns Elem Sch/Brownsville/Cameron | 02202682 | 956/548-8490 | 67 |
| Burrus Elem Sch/Houston/Harris | 01023926 | 713/867-5180 | 195 |
| Burton Adventist Academy/Arlington/Tarrant | 02233708 | 817/572-0081 | 361 |
| Burton Elem Sch/Burton/Washington | 01059119 | 979/289-2175 | 389 |
| Burton High Sch/Burton/Washington | 01059121 | 979/289-3830 | 389 |
| Burton Hill Elem Sch/Fort Worth/Tarrant | 01052630 | 817/815-1400 | 352 |
| **BURTON IND SCH DIST/BURTON/**<br>**WASHINGTON** | 01059107 | 979/289-3131 | 388 |
| Bush Elem Sch/Houston/Harris | 04750128 | 713/272-3220 | 187 |
| Bush Elem Sch/Midland/Midland | 03250242 | 432/240-6300 | 288 |
| Bush Elem Sch/The Woodlands/Montgomery | 04454881 | 936/709-1600 | 294 |
| Bush Global Ldrshp Acad/Grand Prairie/<br>Dallas | 04751524 | 972/237-1628 | 111 |
| Bush Middle Sch/San Antonio/Bexar | 04807886 | 210/356-2900 | 37 |
| Bushland Elem Sch/Amarillo/Potter | 01047569 | 806/359-5410 | 321 |
| Bushland High Sch/Amarillo/Potter | 10008070 | 806/359-6683 | 321 |
| **BUSHLAND IND SCH DIST/AMARILLO/**<br>**POTTER** | 01047568 | 806/359-6683 | 321 |
| Bushland Middle Sch/Bushland/Potter | 05345960 | 806/359-5418 | 322 |
| Bussey Middle Sch/Garland/Dallas | 01010436 | 972/494-8391 | 109 |
| Butler Elem Sch/Arlington/Tarrant | 01399775 | 682/867-1010 | 346 |
| Butler Intermediate Sch/Quinlan/Hunt | 01032587 | 903/356-1400 | 240 |
| Butterfield Elem Sch/Sanger/Denton | 11148269 | 940/458-4377 | 130 |
| **BYNUM IND SCH DIST/BYNUM/HILL** | 01030797 | 254/531-2341 | 230 |
| Bynum Sch/Bynum/Hill | 01030802 | 254/623-4251 | 230 |
| Bynum Sch/Midland/Midland | 04268682 | 432/520-0075 | 289 |
| Byrd Middle Sch/Duncanville/Dallas | 01010319 | 972/708-3400 | 108 |
| Byron Craig Middle Sch/Abilene/Taylor | 10913243 | 325/794-4100 | 363 |
| Byron Martin Advanced Tech Ctr/Lubbock/<br>Lubbock | 12037857 | 806/219-2800 | 273 |
| Byron Nelson High Sch/Trophy Club/Denton | 11452321 | 817/698-5600 | 129 |
| Byron P Steele II High Sch/Cibolo/<br>Guadalupe | 10004347 | 210/619-4000 | 178 |

| School/City/County<br>DISTRICT/CITY/COUNTY | PID | TELEPHONE<br>NUMBER | PAGE |
|---|---|---|---|
| **C** | | | |
| C A Tatum Elem Sch/Dallas/Dallas | 10023185 | 972/502-2000 | 103 |
| C B Thompson Middle Sch/Quinlan/Hunt | 01032604 | 903/356-1500 | 240 |
| C C Hardy Elem Sch/Willis/Montgomery | 01042788 | 936/856-1241 | 297 |
| C C Winn High Sch/Eagle Pass/Maverick | 04806894 | 830/757-0828 | 279 |
| C D Fulkes Middle Sch/Round Rock/<br>Williamson | 01061136 | 512/428-3100 | 401 |
| C D Landolt Elem Sch/Friendswood/Galveston | 02043254 | 281/284-5200 | 163 |
| C E King High Sch/Houston/Harris | 01027025 | 346/378-7000 | 205 |
| C E King Middle Sch/Houston/Harris | 01027037 | 281/727-4300 | 205 |
| C E Vail Elem Sch/La Feria/Cameron | 04871069 | 956/797-8460 | 69 |
| C F Carr Elem Sch/Dallas/Dallas | 01008586 | 972/794-4300 | 103 |
| C G Sivells Elem Sch/Wharton/Wharton | 01059717 | 979/532-6866 | 393 |
| C H Yoe High Sch/Cameron/Milam | 01041796 | 254/697-3902 | 290 |
| C J & Anne Hyman Elem Sch/Dallas/Dallas | 05275107 | 972/708-6700 | 108 |
| C J Harris Elem Sch/Pearland/Brazoria | 01001863 | 281/485-4024 | 56 |
| C L Milton Elem Sch/Laredo/Webb | 01059224 | 956/273-4200 | 389 |
| C M MacDonell Elem Sch/Laredo/Webb | 01059377 | 956/273-4000 | 389 |
| C M Rice Middle Sch/Plano/Collin | 04867288 | 469/752-6000 | 86 |
| C O Wilson Middle Sch/Nederland/Jefferson | 01033672 | 409/727-6224 | 245 |
| C P Yeager Elem Sch/Corp Christi/Nueces | 01044774 | 361/878-2920 | 306 |
| C Stainke Elem Sch/Donna/Hidalgo | 01809366 | 956/464-1940 | 220 |
| C T Eddins Elem Sch/McKinney/Collin | 04808426 | 469/302-6600 | 84 |
| C W Beasley Elem Sch/Mesquite/Dallas | 02128555 | 972/882-5160 | 115 |
| C W Cline Elem Sch/Friendswood/Galveston | 01019054 | 281/482-1201 | 164 |
| Cable Elem Sch/San Antonio/Bexar | 00998043 | 210/397-2850 | 39 |
| Cactus Elem Sch/Cactus/Moore | 01042829 | 806/966-5102 | 298 |
| Cactus Ranch Elem Sch/Round Rock/<br>Williamson | 04945892 | 512/424-8000 | 401 |
| Cactus Trails Elem Sch/El Paso/El Paso | 12364416 | 915/938-2600 | 140 |
| Caddo Grove Elem Sch/Joshua/Johnson | 10002650 | 817/202-2500 | 251 |
| Caddo Mills Aep/Caddo Mills/Hunt | 04503884 | 903/527-2075 | 238 |
| Caddo Mills High Sch/Caddo Mills/Hunt | 01032317 | 903/527-3164 | 238 |
| **CADDO MILLS IND SCH DIST/**<br>**CADDO MILLS/HUNT** | 01032290 | 903/527-6056 | 238 |
| Caddo Mills Middle Sch/Caddo Mills/Hunt | 02180046 | 903/527-3161 | 238 |
| Cage Charter Elem Sch/Houston/Harris | 01024750 | 713/924-1700 | 194 |
| Cal & Walt Wester Middle Sch/Frisco/Collin | 05092644 | 469/633-4800 | 82 |
| Calallen High Sch/Corp Christi/Nueces | 01044140 | 361/242-5626 | 306 |
| **CALALLEN IND SCH DIST/CORP CHRISTI/**<br>**NUECES** | 01044114 | 361/242-5600 | 305 |
| Calallen Middle Sch/Corp Christi/Nueces | 01044152 | 361/242-5672 | 306 |
| Calder Road Elem Sch/Dickinson/Galveston | 11553951 | 281/229-7500 | 164 |
| Caldwell Arts Academy/Tyler/Smith | 01050840 | 903/262-2250 | 340 |
| Caldwell Elem Sch/Caldwell/Burleson | 01002659 | 979/567-2404 | 63 |
| Caldwell Elem Sch/Garland/Dallas | 01010450 | 972/926-2500 | 109 |
| Caldwell Elem Sch/Round Rock/Travis | 05098466 | 512/594-6400 | 374 |
| Caldwell Heights Elem Sch/Round Rock/<br>Williamson | 04867329 | 512/428-7300 | 401 |
| Caldwell High Sch/Caldwell/Burleson | 01002661 | 979/567-2401 | 63 |
| **CALDWELL IND SCH DIST/CALDWELL/**<br>**BURLESON** | 01002647 | 979/567-2400 | 63 |
| Caldwell Intermediate Sch/Caldwell/<br>Burleson | 02178457 | 979/567-2403 | 63 |
| Caldwell Middle Sch/Caldwell/Burleson | 01002673 | 979/567-2402 | 63 |
| Caldwood Elem Sch/Beaumont/Jefferson | 01034133 | 409/617-6025 | 245 |
| **CALHOUN CO IND SCH DIST/**<br>**PORT LAVACA/CALHOUN** | 01003158 | 361/552-9728 | 65 |
| Calhoun High Sch/Port Lavaca/Calhoun | 01003160 | 361/552-3775 | 65 |
| Calhoun Middle Sch/Denton/Denton | 01013244 | 940/369-2400 | 125 |
| Calk-Wilson Elem Sch/Corp Christi/Nueces | 01044255 | 361/878-2860 | 306 |
| Callisburg Elem Sch/Gainesville/Cooke | 01007300 | 940/612-4196 | 94 |
| **CALLISBURG IND SCH DIST/**<br>**GAINESVILLE/COOKE** | 01007271 | 940/665-0540 | 94 |
| Callisburg Middle High Sch/Gainesville/<br>Cooke | 04801959 | 940/665-0961 | 94 |
| Calvary Baptist Sch/Conroe/Montgomery | 02193031 | 936/756-0743 | 298 |
| Calvary Chapel Christian Acad/Universal Cty/<br>Bexar | 11231684 | 210/658-8337 | 47 |
| Calvary Christian Academy/Fort Worth/<br>Tarrant | 02192520 | 817/332-3351 | 361 |
| Calvary Christian Sch/Harlingen/Cameron | 02233265 | 956/425-1882 | 72 |
| Calvary Episcopal Sch/Richmond/Fort Bend | 01410707 | 281/342-3161 | 159 |
| Calvary Lutheran Sch/Dallas/Dallas | 01410575 | 214/343-7457 | 119 |
| Calvary Temple Christian Acad/Mesquite/<br>Dallas | 04992807 | 972/286-4935 | 119 |
| **CALVERT IND SCH DIST/CALVERT/**<br>**ROBERTSON** | 01048586 | 979/364-2824 | 327 |
| Calvert Sch/Calvert/Robertson | 01048603 | 979/364-2845 | 327 |
| Calvin Bledsoe Elem Sch/Frisco/Collin | 10016699 | 469/633-3600 | 82 |
| Calvin Nelms Charter Sch/Katy/Harris | 04890950 | 281/398-8031 | 2 |
| Calvin Vincent ECC/Texas City/Galveston | 12035653 | 409/916-0512 | 166 |

| School/City/County<br>DISTRICT/CITY/COUNTY | PID | TELEPHONE<br>NUMBER | PAGE |
|---|---|---|---|
| Camacho Elem Sch/Leander/Williamson | 12106082 | 512/570-7800 | 400 |
| Cambridge Elem Sch/San Antonio/Bexar | 00996954 | 210/822-3611 | 33 |
| Cambridge Sch/Humble/Harris | 12109101 | 281/641-7445 | 200 |
| Cambridge School of Dallas/Dallas/Dallas | 10000195 | 214/357-2995 | 119 |
| Camelot Elem Sch/San Antonio/Bexar | 00997673 | 210/407-1400 | 37 |
| Cameron Dual Lang Magnet Sch/Odessa/Ector | 01014626 | 432/456-1059 | 134 |
| Cameron Elem Sch/Cameron/Milam | 01041760 | 254/697-2381 | 290 |
| **CAMERON IND SCH DIST/CAMERON/**<br>**MILAM** | 01041758 | 254/697-3512 | 290 |
| Cameron Junior High Sch/Cameron/Milam | 01041784 | 254/697-2131 | 290 |
| Camey Elem Sch/The Colony/Denton | 01541306 | 469/713-5951 | 126 |
| Camino Real Elem Sch/Niederwald/Hays | 11079412 | 512/268-8505 | 216 |
| Campbell Elem Sch/Austin/Travis | 01056313 | 512/414-2056 | 369 |
| Campbell Elem Sch/Sugar Land/Fort Bend | 04923313 | 832/223-1300 | 158 |
| **CAMPBELL IND SCH DIST/CAMPBELL/**<br>**HUNT** | 01032329 | 903/862-3259 | 238 |
| Campbell Middle Sch/Houston/Harris | 01829433 | 281/897-4300 | 189 |
| Campbell Sch/Campbell/Hunt | 01032331 | 903/862-3253 | 238 |
| Campestre Elem Sch/El Paso/El Paso | 02177037 | 915/937-7300 | 140 |
| Canadian Elem Sch/Canadian/Hemphill | 02224903 | 806/323-9331 | 218 |
| Canadian High Sch/Canadian/Hemphill | 01029229 | 806/323-5373 | 218 |
| **CANADIAN IND SCH DIST/CANADIAN/**<br>**HEMPHILL** | 01029205 | 806/323-5393 | 218 |
| Canadian Middle Sch/Canadian/Hemphill | 01532068 | 806/323-5351 | 218 |
| Canales Elem Sch/Brownsville/Cameron | 01003603 | 956/548-8900 | 67 |
| Candlewood Elem Sch/San Antonio/Bexar | 03236181 | 210/662-1060 | 36 |
| Caney Creek High Sch/Conroe/Montgomery | 04486688 | 936/709-2000 | 294 |
| Cannon Elem Sch/Grapevine/Tarrant | 01053684 | 817/251-5680 | 355 |
| Cano Gonzalez Elem Sch/Edinburg/Hidalgo | 04452792 | 956/289-2380 | 221 |
| Canterbury Collegiate Academy/Desoto/<br>Dallas | 04903882 | 214/672-9263 | 119 |
| Canterbury Elem Sch/Edinburg/Hidalgo | 03010626 | 956/289-2374 | 221 |
| Canton Elem Sch/Canton/Van Zandt | 01526162 | 903/567-6521 | 382 |
| Canton High Sch/Canton/Van Zandt | 01058103 | 903/567-6561 | 382 |
| **CANTON IND SCH DIST/CANTON/**<br>**VAN ZANDT** | 01058086 | 903/567-4179 | 382 |
| Canton Intermediate Sch/Canton/Van Zandt | 03318399 | 903/567-6418 | 382 |
| Canton Junior High Sch/Canton/Van Zandt | 01058098 | 903/567-4329 | 382 |
| Cantu Elem Sch/Alton/Hidalgo | 02201391 | 956/323-7400 | 225 |
| Canup Early Childhood Center/Princeton/<br>Collin | 12469444 | 469/952-5416 | 87 |
| Canutillo Elem Sch/Canutillo/El Paso | 01015395 | 915/877-7600 | 136 |
| Canutillo High Sch/El Paso/El Paso | 01015412 | 915/877-7800 | 136 |
| **CANUTILLO IND SCH DIST/EL PASO/**<br>**EL PASO** | 01015383 | 915/877-7400 | 136 |
| Canutillo Middle Sch/Canutillo/El Paso | 01548392 | 915/877-7900 | 136 |
| Canyon Creek Elem Sch/Austin/Williamson | 04806478 | 512/428-2800 | 401 |
| Canyon Creek Elem Sch/Richardson/Dallas | 01011650 | 469/593-6500 | 116 |
| Canyon High Sch/Canyon/Randall | 01047946 | 806/677-2740 | 323 |
| Canyon High Sch/New Braunfels/Comal | 01006916 | 830/221-2400 | 91 |
| Canyon Hills Middle Sch/El Paso/El Paso | 01015761 | 915/236-6450 | 139 |
| **CANYON IND SCH DIST/CANYON/**<br>**RANDALL** | 01047934 | 806/677-2600 | 323 |
| Canyon Intermediate Sch/Canyon/Randall | 05341445 | 806/677-2800 | 323 |
| Canyon Junior High Sch/Canyon/Randall | 01047958 | 806/677-2700 | 323 |
| Canyon Lake High Sch/Fischer/Comal | 10913281 | 830/885-1700 | 91 |
| Canyon Middle Sch/New Braunfels/Comal | 01006928 | 830/221-2300 | 91 |
| Canyon Point Elem Sch/Tomball/Harris | 11127784 | 281/357-3122 | 208 |
| Canyon Ranch Elem Sch/Irving/Dallas | 12366074 | 214/496-7200 | 102 |
| Canyon Ridge Elem Sch/San Antonio/Bexar | 10003331 | 210/407-1600 | 37 |
| Canyon Ridge Middle Sch/Austin/Williamson | 05345582 | 512/570-3500 | 400 |
| Canyon Vista Middle Sch/Austin/Williamson | 02223935 | 512/464-8100 | 401 |
| Capistrano Elem Sch/El Paso/El Paso | 01545247 | 915/434-8600 | 142 |
| Capitol Elem Sch/Levelland/Hockley | 01031131 | 806/894-4715 | 232 |
| Capitol School-Austin/Austin/Travis | 11237262 | 512/467-7006 | 375 |
| CapRock Elem Sch/Keller/Tarrant | 11436262 | 817/744-6400 | 357 |
| CapRock High Sch/Amarillo/Potter | 01047207 | 806/326-2200 | 320 |
| Capt D Salinas II Elem Sch/Alamo/Hidalgo | 04363012 | 956/783-1332 | 220 |
| Capt Walter E Clarke Mid Sch/El Paso/<br>El Paso | 04035265 | 915/937-5600 | 140 |
| Cardenas Center/San Antonio/Bexar | 11447247 | 210/444-7900 | 34 |
| Cardiff Junior High Sch/Katy/Harris | 11128594 | 281/234-0600 | 156 |
| Career & Tech Education Center/Frisco/<br>Collin | 11103855 | 469/633-6780 | 82 |
| Career & Tech Education Center/San Antonio/<br>Bexar | 12315130 | 210/407-0743 | 37 |
| Career & Technical Ed Center/Humble/Harris | 05093143 | 281/641-7950 | 200 |
| Career & Technology Institute/Victoria/<br>Victoria | 01540120 | 361/788-9288 | 384 |
| Career Education Center/Wichita Falls/<br>Wichita | 12230891 | 940/235-4316 | 395 |
| Carl E Schluter Elem Sch/Haslet/Denton | 11710238 | 817/698-3900 | 129 |

| School/City/County<br>DISTRICT/CITY/COUNTY | PID | TELEPHONE NUMBER | PAGE |
|---|---|---|---|
| Carl O Hamlin Middle Sch/Corp Christi/Nueces | 01044449 | 361/878-4210 | 306 |
| Carl Schurz Elem Sch/New Braunfels/Comal | 01006978 | 830/627-6680 | 92 |
| Carl Waitz Elem Sch/Alton/Hidalgo | 04012550 | 956/323-6600 | 225 |
| Carl Wanke Elem Sch/San Antonio/Bexar | 10020690 | 210/397-6700 | 39 |
| Carl Wunsche Sr High Sch/Spring/Harris | 01027544 | 281/891-7650 | 207 |
| Carlisle Elem Sch/Plano/Collin | 02225610 | 469/752-0600 | 86 |
| **CARLISLE IND SCH DIST/HENDERSON/RUSK** | 01048940 | 903/861-3801 | 330 |
| Carlisle Sch/Henderson/Rusk | 01048952 | 903/861-3801 | 330 |
| Carlos Coon Elem Sch/San Antonio/Bexar | 01824079 | 210/397-7250 | 39 |
| Carlos Truan Jr High Sch/Edcouch/Hidalgo | 01029633 | 956/262-5820 | 221 |
| Carmen Anaya Elem Sch/Pharr/Hidalgo | 10914285 | 956/784-8500 | 226 |
| Carmen Avila Elem Sch/Edinburg/Hidalgo | 05275171 | 956/289-2307 | 221 |
| Carnahan Elem Sch/San Antonio/Bexar | 11104093 | 210/397-5850 | 39 |
| Carnegie Vanguard High Sch/Houston/Harris | 05099290 | 713/732-3690 | 196 |
| Carol Holt Elem Sch/Arlington/Tarrant | 10908834 | 817/299-6460 | 359 |
| Carolee Booker Elem Sch/Houston/Harris | 11077232 | 281/891-8750 | 207 |
| Carolyn G Bukhair Elem Sch/Dallas/Dallas | 05350769 | 469/593-4900 | 116 |
| Carpenter Elem Sch/Nacogdoches/Nacogdoches | 01043299 | 936/569-5070 | 301 |
| Carpenter Hill Elem Sch/Buda/Hays | 11555545 | 512/268-8509 | 216 |
| Carpenter Middle Sch/Plano/Collin | 01824108 | 469/752-5000 | 86 |
| Carr Middle Sch/Hale Center/Hale | 03391470 | 806/839-2141 | 180 |
| Carrillo Elem Sch/Houston/Harris | 04021721 | 713/924-1870 | 194 |
| **CARRIZO SPGS CONS IND SD/CARRIZO SPGS/DIMMIT** | 01014030 | 830/876-3503 | 131 |
| Carrizo Springs Elem Sch/Carrizo Spgs/Dimmit | 01014066 | 830/876-3513 | 131 |
| Carrizo Springs High Sch/Carrizo Spgs/Dimmit | 01014054 | 830/876-9393 | 131 |
| Carrizo Springs Interm Sch/Carrizo Spgs/Dimmit | 01014080 | 830/876-3561 | 131 |
| Carrizo Springs Jr High Sch/Carrizo Spgs/Dimmit | 01014078 | 830/876-2496 | 131 |
| Carroll Bell Elem Sch/San Antonio/Bexar | 00997398 | 210/989-2900 | 35 |
| Carroll Early Chldhd Center/San Antonio/Bexar | 11539981 | 210/978-7965 | 43 |
| Carroll Elem Sch/Corsicana/Navarro | 01043495 | 903/872-3074 | 302 |
| Carroll Elem Sch/Houston/Harris | 11080382 | 281/727-4100 | 205 |
| Carroll Elem Sch/Southlake/Tarrant | 03006766 | 817/949-4300 | 349 |
| Carroll High Sch/Southlake/Tarrant | 01052288 | 817/949-5600 | 349 |
| **CARROLL INDEPENDENT SCH DIST/SOUTHLAKE/TARRANT** | 01052252 | 817/949-8222 | 349 |
| Carroll Middle Sch/Southlake/Tarrant | 04918552 | 817/949-5400 | 349 |
| Carroll Peak Elem Sch/Fort Worth/Tarrant | 01053244 | 817/814-0700 | 352 |
| Carroll Senior High Sch/Southlake/Tarrant | 01052276 | 817/949-5800 | 349 |
| Carroll T Welch Elem Sch/El Paso/El Paso | 04452003 | 915/926-4400 | 136 |
| Carrollton Classical Academy/Carrollton/Dallas | 11014589 | 972/245-2900 | 2 |
| Carrollton Elem Sch/Carrollton/Dallas | 01008158 | 972/968-1200 | 100 |
| **CARROLLTON-FARMERS BRANCH ISD/CARROLLTON/DALLAS** | 01008134 | 972/968-6100 | 100 |
| Carson Elem Sch/Decatur/Wise | 04914233 | 940/393-7500 | 406 |
| Carter Junior High Sch/Arlington/Tarrant | 01051698 | 682/867-1700 | 346 |
| Carter Park Elem Sch/Fort Worth/Tarrant | 01052654 | 817/815-8600 | 352 |
| Carthage High Sch/Carthage/Panola | 01046239 | 903/693-2552 | 314 |
| **CARTHAGE IND SCH DIST/CARTHAGE/PANOLA** | 01046215 | 903/693-3806 | 314 |
| Carthage Junior High Sch/Carthage/Panola | 01046265 | 903/693-2751 | 314 |
| Carthage Primary Sch/Carthage/Panola | 02104468 | 903/693-2254 | 314 |
| Carvajal Early Chldhd Center/San Antonio/Bexar | 00999097 | 210/978-7970 | 43 |
| Carver Academy Elem Sch/Amarillo/Potter | 03248031 | 806/326-4150 | 320 |
| Carver Center/Midland/Midland | 10005236 | 432/240-6400 | 288 |
| Carver Early Childhood Academy/Amarillo/Potter | 04866167 | 806/326-4200 | 320 |
| Carver Early Education Center/Odessa/Ector | 02856257 | 432/456-1069 | 134 |
| Carver Elem Sch/Georgetown/Williamson | 01060900 | 512/943-5070 | 398 |
| Carver Elem Sch/Greenville/Hunt | 01032472 | 903/457-0777 | 239 |
| Carver High Sch/Houston/Harris | 01022805 | 281/878-0310 | 185 |
| Carver Learning Center/San Angelo/Tom Green | 01055589 | 325/659-3648 | 367 |
| Carylene McClendon Elem Sch/Nevada/Collin | 03046895 | 972/843-6800 | 81 |
| Casa View Elem Sch/Dallas/Dallas | 01008598 | 972/749-7700 | 103 |
| Casey Elem Sch/Austin/Travis | 04869846 | 512/841-6900 | 369 |
| Casis Elem Sch/Austin/Travis | 01056143 | 512/414-2062 | 369 |
| Cassata High Sch/Fort Worth/Tarrant | 02115106 | 817/926-1745 | 360 |
| Cast Med/San Antonio/Bexar | 12309911 | 210/228-3380 | 43 |
| Cast STEM High Sch/Von Ormy/Bexar | 12364519 | 210/622-4810 | 46 |
| Cast Tech High Sch/San Antonio/Bexar | 12238972 | 210/554-2700 | 43 |
| Castle Hills Elem Sch/Lewisville/Denton | 05091729 | 469/713-5952 | 126 |
| Castle Hills Elem Sch/San Antonio/Bexar | 00997685 | 210/407-1800 | 37 |

| School/City/County<br>DISTRICT/CITY/COUNTY | PID | TELEPHONE NUMBER | PAGE |
|---|---|---|---|
| Castleberry Elem Sch/Fort Worth/Tarrant | 01052317 | 817/252-2300 | 350 |
| Castleberry High Sch/Fort Worth/Tarrant | 01052329 | 817/252-2100 | 350 |
| **CASTLEBERRY IND SCH DIST/FORT WORTH/TARRANT** | 01052290 | 817/252-2000 | 349 |
| Castleman Creek Elem Sch/Hewitt/McLennan | 11449568 | 254/761-5755 | 283 |
| Castro Elem Sch/Mission/Hidalgo | 01030242 | 956/323-6800 | 225 |
| Castroville Elem Sch/Castroville/Medina | 01041318 | 830/931-2243 | 287 |
| Cater Elem Sch/Temple/Bell | 00996734 | 254/215-7444 | 32 |
| Cathedral High Sch/El Paso/El Paso | 01016727 | 915/532-3238 | 143 |
| Cathedral of Life Chrn Sch/Balch Springs/Dallas | 05078296 | 972/286-4845 | 119 |
| Cathedral School of St Mary/Austin/Travis | 01003005 | 512/476-1480 | 375 |
| Cathelene Thomas Elem Sch/Slaton/Lubbock | 01039236 | 806/828-5805 | 275 |
| Catherine Bell Elem Sch/Little Elm/Denton | 12168676 | 972/347-7200 | 125 |
| Catherine Bethke Elem Sch/Katy/Harris | 12169943 | 281/234-4200 | 156 |
| Cats Academy-Student Alt Ctr/Angleton/Brazoria | 04013578 | 979/864-8003 | 55 |
| Cavazos Elem Sch/McAllen/Hidalgo | 01029736 | 956/289-2535 | 221 |
| Cavazos Middle Sch/Lubbock/Lubbock | 04032639 | 806/219-3200 | 273 |
| **CAYUGA IND SCH DIST/TENN COLONY/ANDERSON** | 00994401 | 903/928-2102 | 18 |
| Cayuga Sch/Tenn Colony/Anderson | 00994425 | 903/928-2102 | 18 |
| Cecil Everett Elem Sch/Paris/Wise | 01418503 | 903/737-2061 | 406 |
| Cedar Bayou Junior High Sch/Baytown/Harris | 01023603 | 281/420-4570 | 192 |
| Cedar Brook Elem Sch/Houston/Harris | 04032225 | 713/251-5500 | 206 |
| Cedar Creek Elem Sch/Austin/Travis | 01829548 | 512/732-9120 | 372 |
| Cedar Creek Elem Sch/Cedar Creek/Bastrop | 04030734 | 512/772-7600 | 26 |
| Cedar Creek High Sch/Cedar Creek/Bastrop | 11555739 | 512/772-7300 | 26 |
| Cedar Creek Intermediate Sch/Cedar Creek/Bastrop | 05350161 | 512/772-7475 | 26 |
| Cedar Creek Middle Sch/Cedar Creek/Bastrop | 04917883 | 512/772-7425 | 26 |
| Cedar Creek Sch/San Antonio/Bexar | 12231510 | 210/822-3792 | 48 |
| Cedar Crest Elem Sch/Dallas/Dallas | 01008380 | 972/925-7400 | 103 |
| Cedar Grove Elem Sch/El Paso/El Paso | 01016349 | 915/434-7600 | 142 |
| Cedar Grove Elem Sch/Livingston/Polk | 12034984 | 936/328-2240 | 319 |
| Cedar Hill 9th Grade Center/Cedar Hill/Dallas | 10006371 | 469/272-2050 | 101 |
| Cedar Hill Collegiate High Sch/Cedar Hill/Dallas | 11718747 | 469/272-2021 | 101 |
| Cedar Hill High Sch/Cedar Hill/Dallas | 01008299 | 469/272-2000 | 101 |
| **CEDAR HILL IND SCH DIST/CEDAR HILL/DALLAS** | 01008275 | 972/291-1581 | 101 |
| Cedar Park Charter Academy/Cedar Park/Williamson | 12113891 | 512/331-2980 | 2 |
| Cedar Park High Sch/Cedar Park/Williamson | 04808490 | 512/570-1200 | 400 |
| Cedar Park Middle Sch/Cedar Park/Williamson | 01061045 | 512/570-3100 | 400 |
| Cedar Ridge Elem Sch/Waco/McLennan | 01040182 | 254/756-1241 | 285 |
| Cedar Ridge High Sch/Round Rock/Williamson | 11557414 | 512/704-0100 | 401 |
| Cedar Valley Elem Sch/Killeen/Bell | 04027634 | 254/336-1480 | 30 |
| Cedar Valley Middle Sch/Austin/Williamson | 04030306 | 512/428-2300 | 401 |
| Cedars International Academy/Austin/Travis | 05011066 | 512/419-1551 | 2 |
| Cedars Intl Next Generation HS/Austin/Travis | 12260664 | 512/956-4406 | 2 |
| Cedric C Smith Elem Sch/Magnolia/Montgomery | 04922890 | 281/252-2300 | 296 |
| Cele Middle Sch/Pflugerville/Travis | 11923447 | 512/594-3000 | 374 |
| Celeste Elem Sch/Celeste/Hunt | 01032367 | 903/568-4721 | 239 |
| Celeste High Sch/Celeste/Hunt | 04034417 | 903/568-4721 | 239 |
| **CELESTE IND SCH DIST/CELESTE/HUNT** | 01032355 | 903/568-4825 | 238 |
| Celeste Junior High Sch/Celeste/Hunt | 04034405 | 903/568-4721 | 239 |
| Celestino Mauricio Soto ES/Dallas/Dallas | 10023111 | 972/502-5100 | 103 |
| Celia Hays Elem Sch/Rockwall/Rockwall | 10911013 | 469/698-2800 | 328 |
| Celina 6th Grade Center/Celina/Collin | 12035641 | 469/742-9105 | 81 |
| Celina Elem Sch/Celina/Collin | 03046596 | 469/742-9103 | 81 |
| Celina High Sch/Celina/Collin | 01006100 | 469/742-9102 | 81 |
| **CELINA IND SCH DIST/CELINA/COLLIN** | 01006083 | 469/742-9100 | 81 |
| Celina Junior High Sch/Celina/Collin | 01006095 | 469/742-9101 | 81 |
| Celina Primary Sch/Celina/Collin | 12230877 | 469/742-9104 | 81 |
| Centennial Elem Sch/Houston/Harris | 12472178 | 281/641-8800 | 200 |
| Centennial Elem Sch/Lubbock/Lubbock | 10911037 | 806/219-7800 | 273 |
| Centennial Elem Sch/Plano/Collin | 04867276 | 469/752-0700 | 86 |
| Centennial High Sch/Burleson/Johnson | 11547794 | 817/245-0250 | 249 |
| Centennial High Sch/Frisco/Collin | 05272595 | 469/633-5600 | 82 |
| Center Elem Sch/Center/Shelby | 01050280 | 936/598-3625 | 337 |
| Center for Career & Tech Ed/El Paso/El Paso | 01015462 | 915/236-7900 | 138 |
| Center for Hearing & Speech/Houston/Harris | 01875353 | 713/523-3633 | 210 |
| Center for Success/Houston/Harris | 04922888 | 832/386-3637 | 192 |
| Center High Sch/Center/Shelby | 01050292 | 936/598-6173 | 337 |

| School/City/County DISTRICT/CITY/COUNTY | PID | TELEPHONE NUMBER | PAGE |
|---|---|---|---|
| **CENTER IND SCH DIST**/CENTER/ | | | |
| **SHELBY** | 01050278 | 936/598-5642 | 337 |
| Center Intermediate Sch/Center/Shelby | 01050307 | 936/598-6148 | 337 |
| Center Middle Sch/Center/Shelby | 01050319 | 936/598-5619 | 337 |
| Center Point Elem Sch/Center Point/Kerr | 01035981 | 830/634-2257 | 258 |
| Center Point High Sch/Center Point/Kerr | 01035993 | 830/353-8100 | 258 |
| **CENTER POINT IND SCH DIST/** | | | |
| **CENTER POINT/KERR** | 01035979 | 830/634-2171 | 258 |
| Center Point Middle Sch/Center Point/Kerr | 04452883 | 830/634-2244 | 258 |
| Center Roughrider Academy/Center/Shelby | 12305721 | 936/598-1540 | 337 |
| Centerville Elem Sch/Centerville/Leon | 01037599 | 903/536-2235 | 267 |
| Centerville Elem Sch/Garland/Dallas | 01010462 | 972/926-2510 | 109 |
| Centerville Elem Sch/Groveton/Trinity | 01057082 | 936/642-1597 | 376 |
| Centerville High Sch/Groveton/Trinity | 04033451 | 936/642-1597 | 376 |
| **CENTERVILLE IND SCH DIST/** | | | |
| **CENTERVILLE/LEON** | 01037587 | 903/536-7812 | 267 |
| **CENTERVILLE IND SCH DIST/** | | | |
| **GROVETON/TRINITY** | 01057070 | 936/642-1597 | 376 |
| Centerville Jr Sr High Sch/Centerville/ | | | |
| Leon | 01037604 | 903/536-2625 | 267 |
| Central Athens Elem Sch/Athens/Henderson | 01029279 | 903/677-6960 | 218 |
| Central Baptist Academy/Magnolia/ | | | |
| Montgomery | 02153782 | 281/356-2861 | 298 |
| Central Baptist Christian Sch/Center/ | | | |
| Shelby | 02153550 | 936/598-3642 | 338 |
| Central Catholic High Sch/San Antonio/ | | | |
| Bexar | 00999774 | 210/225-6794 | 47 |
| Central Christian Academy/Houston/Harris | 04836708 | 713/468-3248 | 210 |
| Central Elem Sch/Angleton/Brazoria | 02895174 | 979/864-8004 | 55 |
| Central Elem Sch/Carrollton/Dallas | 04364494 | 972/968-1300 | 100 |
| Central Elem Sch/Duncanville/Dallas | 01010321 | 972/708-2600 | 108 |
| Central Elem Sch/Lewisville/Denton | 01013414 | 469/713-5976 | 126 |
| Central Elem Sch/Lubbock/Lubbock | 11715329 | 806/776-2150 | 274 |
| Central Elem Sch/Mabank/Kaufman | 01035694 | 903/880-1380 | 256 |
| Central Elem Sch/Palacios/Matagorda | 01040924 | 361/972-2911 | 278 |
| Central Elem Sch/Pollok/Angelina | 04028286 | 936/853-9390 | 20 |
| Central Elem Sch/Seagoville/Dallas | 01008603 | 972/749-6800 | 103 |
| Central Elem Sch/Stephenville/Erath | 01017147 | 254/965-3716 | 148 |
| Central Elem Sch/Vernon/Wilbarger | 01060572 | 940/553-1859 | 396 |
| Central Freshman Campus/San Angelo/ | | | |
| Tom Green | 01055620 | 325/659-3576 | 367 |
| Central Heights Elem Sch/Nacogdoches/ | | | |
| Nacogdoches | 01043081 | 936/552-3424 | 300 |
| Central Heights High Sch/Nacogdoches/ | | | |
| Nacogdoches | 04364963 | 936/552-3408 | 300 |
| **CENTRAL HEIGHTS IND SCH DIST/** | | | |
| **NACOGDOCHES/NACOGDOCHES** | 01043079 | 936/564-2681 | 300 |
| Central Heights Middle Sch/Nacogdoches/ | | | |
| Nacogdoches | 11710032 | 936/552-3441 | 300 |
| Central High Sch/Fort Worth/Tarrant | 05273460 | 817/744-2000 | 357 |
| Central High Sch/Pollok/Angelina | 00994798 | 936/853-2167 | 20 |
| Central High Sch/San Angelo/Tom Green | 01055591 | 325/659-3434 | 367 |
| **CENTRAL IND SCH DIST/POLLOK/** | | | |
| **ANGELINA** | 00994774 | 936/853-2216 | 20 |
| Central Junior High Sch/Euless/Tarrant | 01053775 | 817/354-3350 | 356 |
| Central Junior High Sch/Pollok/Angelina | 00994803 | 936/853-2115 | 20 |
| Central Media Arts Academy/Galveston/ | | | |
| Galveston | 01019119 | 409/761-6200 | 165 |
| Central Middle Sch/Nederland/Jefferson | 01033684 | 409/727-5765 | 246 |
| Central Middle Sch/Weslaco/Hidalgo | 04014209 | 956/969-6710 | 228 |
| Central Texas Christian Sch/Temple/Bell | 04993112 | 254/939-5700 | 33 |
| Centro Chrn Alpha Omega Acad/Houston/ | | | |
| Harris | 11229136 | 713/697-6726 | 210 |
| Cesar Chavez Academy/El Paso/El Paso | 04035631 | 915/434-9600 | 142 |
| Cesar Chavez Elem Sch/Fort Worth/Tarrant | 05096509 | 817/815-0300 | 352 |
| Cesar Chavez Elem Sch/Little Elm/Denton | 05070490 | 972/947-9452 | 128 |
| Cesar Chavez Elem Sch/Pharr/Hidalgo | 04870326 | 956/354-2720 | 226 |
| Cesar Chavez Learning Center/Dallas/Dallas | 04757176 | 972/925-1000 | 103 |
| Cesar Chavez Middle Sch/Mission/Hidalgo | 03266356 | 956/323-2800 | 223 |
| Cesar Chavez Middle Sch/Waco/McLennan | 05221194 | 254/750-3736 | 285 |
| Cesar E Chavez Academy/Corp Christi/Nueces | 11015557 | 361/561-5651 | 2 |
| Challenge Early Clg High Sch/Houston/ | | | |
| Harris | 05280396 | 713/664-9712 | 196 |
| Challenger Elem Sch/Pearland/Brazoria | 04033906 | 281/485-7912 | 57 |
| Challenger School-Avery Rnch/Austin/ | | | |
| Williamson | 11702592 | 512/341-8000 | 403 |
| Chamberlin Elem Sch/Stephenville/Erath | 01017159 | 254/968-2311 | 148 |
| Chambers Elem Sch/Houston/Harris | 01023029 | 281/983-8313 | 187 |
| Champion Elem Sch/Brownsville/Cameron | 04945103 | 956/832-6200 | 67 |
| Champion High School/Boerne/Kendall | 11080502 | 830/357-2600 | 257 |
| Chancellor Elem Sch/Houston/Harris | 01541344 | 281/983-8318 | 187 |
| Chandler Elem Sch/Allen/Collin | 10028472 | 469/467-1400 | 80 |

| School/City/County DISTRICT/CITY/COUNTY | PID | TELEPHONE NUMBER | PAGE |
|---|---|---|---|
| Chandler Elem Sch/Chandler/Henderson | 01029358 | 903/849-3400 | 218 |
| Chandler Elem Sch/Kilgore/Gregg | 01020912 | 903/988-3904 | 174 |
| Chandler Elem Sch/Victoria/Victoria | 01058593 | 361/788-9587 | 384 |
| Chandler Intermediate Sch/Chandler/ | | | |
| Henderson | 05097709 | 903/849-6436 | 218 |
| Chandler Oaks Elem Sch/Round Rock/ | | | |
| Williamson | 11553315 | 512/704-0400 | 401 |
| Channelview High Sch/Channelview/Harris | 01023081 | 281/452-1450 | 188 |
| **CHANNELVIEW IND SCH DIST/** | | | |
| **CHANNELVIEW/HARRIS** | 01023079 | 281/452-8002 | 188 |
| **CHANNING IND SCH DIST/CHANNING/** | | | |
| **HARTLEY** | 01028794 | 806/235-3432 | 214 |
| Channing Public Sch/Channing/Hartley | 01028809 | 806/235-3719 | 214 |
| Chapa Middle Sch/Kyle/Hays | 10022753 | 512/268-8500 | 216 |
| Chaparral Star Academy/Austin/Travis | 04846595 | 512/989-2672 | 2 |
| Chapel Hill Academy CS/Fort Worth/Tarrant | 11453296 | 817/289-0242 | 2 |
| Chapel Hill Elem Sch/Mt Pleasant/Titus | 05099953 | 903/572-4586 | 366 |
| Chapel Hill High Sch/Mt Pleasant/Titus | 11078028 | 903/572-3925 | 366 |
| Chapel Hill High Sch/Tyler/Smith | 01050620 | 903/566-2311 | 339 |
| **CHAPEL HILL IND SCH DIST/** | | | |
| **MT PLEASANT/TITUS** | 01055307 | 903/572-8096 | 365 |
| **CHAPEL HILL IND SCH DIST/** | | | |
| **TYLER/SMITH** | 01050606 | 903/566-2441 | 339 |
| Chapel Hill Junior High Sch/Mt Pleasant/ | | | |
| Titus | 01055319 | 903/572-3925 | 366 |
| Chapel Hill Middle Sch/Tyler/Smith | 02856659 | 903/566-1491 | 339 |
| Chapel Hill Preparatory Sch/Dallas/Dallas | 01010187 | 972/794-2400 | 103 |
| Chapin High Sch/El Paso/El Paso | 04918655 | 915/236-4400 | 138 |
| Charles A Gill Elem Sch/Dallas/Dallas | 01008615 | 972/749-8400 | 103 |
| Charles Borchers Elem Sch/Laredo/Webb | 05102940 | 956/473-7200 | 390 |
| Charles Clyde Ball Academy/San Antonio/ | | | |
| Bexar | 00998756 | 210/438-6845 | 43 |
| Charles E Nash Elem Sch/Fort Worth/Tarrant | 01053153 | 817/814-9400 | 352 |
| Charles Forbes Middle Sch/Georgetown/ | | | |
| Williamson | 04946640 | 512/943-5150 | 398 |
| Charles H Milby High Sch/Houston/Harris | 01025455 | 713/928-7401 | 194 |
| Charles M Blalack Middle Sch/Carrollton/ | | | |
| Dallas | 02894132 | 972/968-3500 | 100 |
| Charles R Drew Academy/Houston/Harris | 01022740 | 281/878-0360 | 186 |
| Charles R Drew Elem Sch/Crosby/Harris | 01418383 | 281/328-9306 | 188 |
| Charles Rice Learning Center/Dallas/Dallas | 01008627 | 972/749-1100 | 103 |
| Charles Tosch Elem Sch/Mesquite/Dallas | 01011428 | 972/882-5000 | 115 |
| Charlie C McKamy Elem Sch/Dallas/Dallas | 04020545 | 972/968-2400 | 100 |
| Charlie Marshall Elem Sch/Aransas Pass/ | | | |
| San Patricio | 01049499 | 361/758-3455 | 333 |
| Charlotte Anderson Elem Sch/Arlington/ | | | |
| Tarrant | 02897471 | 817/299-7760 | 359 |
| Charlotte Elem Sch/Charlotte/Atascosa | 00995340 | 830/277-1710 | 23 |
| Charlotte High Sch/Charlotte/Atascosa | 00995352 | 830/277-1432 | 23 |
| **CHARLOTTE IND SCH DIST/CHARLOTTE/** | | | |
| **ATASCOSA** | 00995338 | 830/277-1431 | 23 |
| Charlotte Middle Sch/Charlotte/Atascosa | 00995364 | 830/277-1646 | 23 |
| Charlton-Pollard Elem Sch/Beaumont/ | | | |
| Jefferson | 01033476 | 409/617-6075 | 245 |
| Charter Oak Elem Sch/Temple/Bell | 12367638 | 254/215-4000 | 30 |
| Chavez High Sch/Houston/Harris | 04922101 | 713/495-6950 | 194 |
| Cheatham Elem Sch/Clarksville/Red River | 01048134 | 903/427-3891 | 325 |
| Cheri L Cox Elem Sch/Sachse/Collin | 05356206 | 972/429-2500 | 88 |
| **CHEROKEE IND SCH DIST/CHEROKEE/** | | | |
| **SAN SABA** | 01049889 | 325/622-4298 | 335 |
| Cherokee Sch/Cherokee/San Saba | 01049891 | 325/622-4298 | 335 |
| Cherry Elem Sch/Bay City/Matagorda | 01040857 | 979/401-1300 | 278 |
| Chester Elem Sch/Chester/Tyler | 01057202 | 936/969-2211 | 377 |
| Chester High Sch/Chester/Tyler | 04362666 | 936/969-2211 | 377 |
| **CHESTER IND SCH DIST/CHESTER/** | | | |
| **TYLER** | 01057197 | 936/969-2211 | 377 |
| Chester Jordan Elem Sch/El Paso/El Paso | 10911673 | 915/937-8801 | 140 |
| Chester W Nimitz High Sch/Houston/Harris | 01824213 | 281/443-7480 | 185 |
| Chet Burchett Elem Sch/Spring/Harris | 10006943 | 281/891-8630 | 207 |
| Chico Elem Sch/Chico/Wise | 01061631 | 940/644-2220 | 406 |
| Chico High Sch/Chico/Wise | 03317773 | 940/644-5783 | 406 |
| **CHICO IND SCH DIST/CHICO/WISE** | 01061629 | 940/644-2228 | 406 |
| Chico Middle Sch/Chico/Wise | 03317778 | 940/644-5550 | 406 |
| Child Montessori Sch/San Antonio/Bexar | 04993801 | 210/493-6550 | 48 |
| Childress Elem Sch/Childress/Childress | 01005467 | 940/937-6313 | 77 |
| Childress High Sch/Childress/Childress | 01005443 | 940/937-6131 | 77 |
| **CHILDRESS IND SCH DIST/CHILDRESS/** | | | |
| **CHILDRESS** | 01005431 | 940/937-2501 | 77 |
| Childress Junior High Sch/Childress/ | | | |
| Childress | 01005455 | 940/937-3641 | 77 |
| Chillicothe Elem Sch/Chillicothe/Hardeman | 01022362 | 940/852-5521 | 182 |
| Chillicothe High Sch/Chillicothe/Hardeman | 01022374 | 940/852-5391 | 182 |

| School/City/County DISTRICT/CITY/COUNTY | PID | TELEPHONE NUMBER | PAGE |
|---|---|---|---|
| **CHILLICOTHE ISD SCH DIST/** | | | |
| CHILLICOTHE/HARDEMAN | 01022350 | 940/852-5391 | 182 |
| **CHILTON IND SCH DIST/**CHILTON/ | | | |
| FALLS | 01017202 | 254/546-1200 | 148 |
| Chilton Sch/Chilton/Falls | 01017214 | 254/546-1200 | 149 |
| China Elem Sch/China/Hardin | 01022441 | 409/981-6410 | 183 |
| China Spring Elem Sch/China Spring/ | | | |
| McLennan | 01039626 | 254/836-4635 | 281 |
| China Spring High Sch/China Spring/ | | | |
| McLennan | 01039638 | 254/836-1771 | 282 |
| **CHINA SPRING IND SCH DIST/** | | | |
| CHINA SPRING/MCLENNAN | 01039614 | 254/836-1115 | 281 |
| China Spring Intermediate Sch/Waco/ | | | |
| McLennan | 04914805 | 254/759-1200 | 282 |
| China Spring Middle Sch/China Spring/ | | | |
| McLennan | 03413054 | 254/836-4611 | 282 |
| Chinquapin Prep Sch/Highlands/Harris | 01802722 | 281/426-5551 | 210 |
| Chip Richarte High Sch/Georgetown/ | | | |
| Williamson | 03400801 | 512/943-5120 | 398 |
| **CHIRENO ISD SCH DIST/**CHIRENO/ | | | |
| NACOGDOCHES | 01043108 | 936/362-2132 | 300 |
| Chireno Sch/Chireno/Nacogdoches | 01043110 | 936/362-2132 | 300 |
| Chisholm Ridge Elem Sch/Fort Worth/Tarrant | 10003692 | 817/232-0715 | 351 |
| Chisholm Trail Academy/Keene/Johnson | 01480697 | 817/641-6626 | 252 |
| Chisholm Trail Elem Sch/Belton/Bell | 10003721 | 254/316-5100 | 30 |
| Chisholm Trail Elem Sch/Sanger/Denton | 03011228 | 940/458-5297 | 130 |
| Chisholm Trail High Sch/Fort Worth/Tarrant | 11818062 | 817/232-7112 | 351 |
| Chisholm Trail Interm Sch/Fort Worth/ | | | |
| Tarrant | 04288113 | 817/744-3800 | 357 |
| Chisholm Trail Middle Sch/Rhome/Denton | 04804626 | 817/215-0600 | 129 |
| Chisholm Trail Middle Sch/Round Rock/ | | | |
| Williamson | 01824419 | 512/428-2500 | 401 |
| Chisum Elem Sch/Paris/Lamar | 01036612 | 903/737-2820 | 262 |
| Chisum High Sch/Paris/Lamar | 12315049 | 903/737-2800 | 262 |
| **CHISUM IND SCH DIST/**PARIS/LAMAR | 01036600 | 903/737-2830 | 262 |
| Chisum Middle Sch/Paris/Lamar | 12315037 | 903/737-2806 | 262 |
| Choices Leadership Academy/Dallas/Collin | 11227530 | 972/662-0665 | 89 |
| Christ Academy/Wichita Falls/Wichita | 01060481 | 940/692-2853 | 396 |
| Christ Community Sch/Shenandoah/Montgomery | 04993485 | 936/321-6300 | 298 |
| Christ Episcopal Sch/Nacogdoches/ | | | |
| Nacogdoches | 01043380 | 936/564-0621 | 301 |
| Christ the King Cathedral Sch/Lubbock/ | | | |
| Lubbock | 01047673 | 806/795-8283 | 275 |
| Christ the King Sch/Dallas/Dallas | 01012393 | 214/365-1234 | 118 |
| Christ the Redeemer Cath Sch/Houston/ | | | |
| Harris | 12164979 | 281/469-8440 | 209 |
| Christ the Redeemer Sch/Rusk/Cherokee | 11222566 | 903/683-1404 | 77 |
| Christa McAuliffe Elem Sch/McAllen/Hidalgo | 02897237 | 956/971-4400 | 224 |
| Christa McAuliffe Learning Ctr/Richardson/ | | | |
| Dallas | 04030667 | 469/593-5800 | 116 |
| Christa McAuliffe Middle Sch/San Antonio/ | | | |
| Bexar | 03323394 | 210/623-6260 | 46 |
| Christene Moss Elem Sch/Fort Worth/Tarrant | 01052862 | 817/815-3600 | 352 |
| Christian Academy of America/Double Oak/ | | | |
| Denton | 12313780 | 972/539-1458 | 130 |
| Christian Evers Elem Sch/San Antonio/Bexar | 04015461 | 210/397-2550 | 39 |
| Christian Heritage Academy/Palestine/ | | | |
| Anderson | 11465134 | 903/723-4685 | 19 |
| Christian Heritage Sch/Longview/Gregg | 04927864 | 903/663-4151 | 176 |
| Christian Heritage Sch/Tyler/Smith | 02165060 | 903/593-2702 | 342 |
| Christian Life Center Academy/Kingwood/ | | | |
| Harris | 11237834 | 281/319-4673 | 210 |
| Christian Life Preparatory Sch/Fort Worth/ | | | |
| Tarrant | 11549015 | 817/293-1500 | 361 |
| Christian School-Castle Hills/San Antonio/ | | | |
| Bexar | 02165046 | 210/878-1000 | 48 |
| Christie Elem Sch/Plano/Collin | 01006382 | 469/752-0800 | 86 |
| Christoval Elem Sch/Christoval/Tom Green | 01055498 | 325/896-2446 | 366 |
| **CHRISTOVAL IND SCH DIST/** | | | |
| CHRISTOVAL/TOM GREEN | 01055486 | 325/896-2520 | 366 |
| Christoval Jr Sr High Sch/Christoval/ | | | |
| Tom Green | 03055937 | 325/896-2355 | 366 |
| Church Hill Middle Sch/New Braunfels/Comal | 04479764 | 830/221-2800 | 91 |
| Cibolo Creek Elem Sch/Boerne/Kendall | 10031039 | 830/357-4400 | 257 |
| Cibolo Green Elem Sch/San Antonio/Bexar | 11558705 | 210/407-1200 | 37 |
| Cibolo Valley Elem Sch/Cibolo/Guadalupe | 12108638 | 210/619-4700 | 178 |
| Cielo Vista Elem Sch/El Paso/El Paso | 01015577 | 915/236-8375 | 137 |
| Cimarron Elem Sch/Houston/Harris | 01023421 | 832/386-3240 | 192 |
| Cimarron Elem Sch/Katy/Harris | 02110273 | 281/237-6900 | 156 |
| Cinco Ranch High Sch/Katy/Harris | 04866040 | 281/237-7000 | 156 |
| Cinco Ranch Junior High Sch/Katy/Harris | 04939350 | 281/237-7300 | 156 |
| Cisco Elem Sch/Cisco/Eastland | 01014377 | 254/442-1219 | 133 |

| School/City/County DISTRICT/CITY/COUNTY | PID | TELEPHONE NUMBER | PAGE |
|---|---|---|---|
| Cisco High Sch/Cisco/Eastland | 01014365 | 254/442-3051 | 133 |
| **CISCO INDEPENDENT SCH DIST/** | | | |
| CISCO/EASTLAND | 01014353 | 254/442-3056 | 133 |
| Cisco Junior High Sch/Cisco/Eastland | 03246459 | 254/442-3004 | 133 |
| Cisco Learning Center/Cisco/Eastland | 04448040 | 254/442-4852 | 133 |
| Cisneros Pre-K Sch/Garland/Dallas | 10008123 | 972/271-7160 | 109 |
| Cistercian Preparatory Sch/Irving/Dallas | 01012408 | 469/499-5400 | 118 |
| Citadel Christian Sch/Brenham/Washington | 04937077 | 979/830-8480 | 389 |
| City Lab High Sch/Dallas/Dallas | 12305604 | 972/749-2700 | 103 |
| City View Elem Sch/Amarillo/Randall | 11450397 | 806/677-2500 | 323 |
| City View Elem Sch/Wichita Falls/Wichita | 01060003 | 940/855-2351 | 394 |
| **CITY VIEW IND SCH DIST/**WICHITA FALLS/ | | | |
| WICHITA | 01059999 | 940/855-4042 | 394 |
| City View Jr Sr High Sch/Wichita Falls/ | | | |
| Wichita | 04868385 | 940/855-7511 | 394 |
| Clack Middle Sch/Abilene/Taylor | 04015306 | 325/692-1961 | 363 |
| Clara Love Elem Sch/Justin/Denton | 11452333 | 817/698-6600 | 129 |
| Clara Oliver Elem Sch/Dallas/Dallas | 01008641 | 972/749-3400 | 103 |
| Clardy Elem Sch/El Paso/El Paso | 01015589 | 915/236-8450 | 137 |
| Clarence Galm Elem Sch/San Antonio/Bexar | 03010690 | 210/397-1150 | 39 |
| **CLARENDON CONS IND SCH DIST/** | | | |
| CLARENDON/DONLEY | 01014119 | 806/874-2062 | 131 |
| Clarendon Elem Sch/Clarendon/Donley | 01014121 | 806/874-3855 | 131 |
| Clarendon High Sch/Clarendon/Donley | 01014133 | 806/874-2181 | 131 |
| Clarendon Junior High Sch/Clarendon/Donley | 04278467 | 806/874-3232 | 131 |
| Clariden Sch/Southlake/Tarrant | 03268031 | 682/237-0400 | 361 |
| Clark Elem Sch/Laredo/Webb | 01059482 | 956/473-4600 | 390 |
| Clark High Sch/Plano/Collin | 01877387 | 469/752-7200 | 86 |
| Clark Intermediate Sch/Houston/Harris | 05273264 | 281/891-8540 | 207 |
| Clark Intermediate Sch/Spring/Montgomery | 12311067 | 281/939-0600 | 294 |
| Clark Middle Sch/Laredo/Webb | 01826352 | 956/473-7500 | 390 |
| Clark Middle Sch/Princeton/Collin | 01006538 | 469/952-5404 | 87 |
| Clarke Elem Sch/Fort Hood/Bell | 01525869 | 254/336-1510 | 30 |
| Clarkston Elem Sch/Tyler/Smith | 01050802 | 903/262-1980 | 340 |
| **CLARKSVILLE IND SCH DIST/** | | | |
| CLARKSVILLE/RED RIVER | 01048110 | 903/427-3891 | 325 |
| Clarksville Middle High Sch/Clarksville/ | | | |
| Red River | 01048158 | 903/427-3891 | 325 |
| Classical Center at Vial Sch/Garland/ | | | |
| Dallas | 01010589 | 972/240-3710 | 109 |
| Classical Center-Brandenburg/Garland/ | | | |
| Dallas | 01010424 | 972/926-2630 | 109 |
| Classical School of Dallas/Dallas/Dallas | 12468426 | 214/810-0341 | 119 |
| Claude Berkman Elem Sch/Round Rock/ | | | |
| Williamson | 01061095 | 512/464-8250 | 401 |
| Claude Cunningham Middle Sch/Corp Christi/ | | | |
| Nueces | 01044346 | 361/878-4720 | 306 |
| Claude Curtsinger Elem Sch/Frisco/Collin | 04360292 | 469/633-2100 | 82 |
| **CLAUDE IND SCH DIST/**CLAUDE/ | | | |
| ARMSTRONG | 00995302 | 806/226-7331 | 23 |
| Claude Sch/Claude/Armstrong | 00995314 | 806/226-7331 | 23 |
| Clay Classical Academy/Dallas/Dallas | 11663049 | 214/467-4143 | 2 |
| Claybon Elem Sch/Forney/Kaufman | 04947113 | 469/762-4305 | 255 |
| Clayton Elem Sch/Austin/Travis | 10023678 | 512/841-9200 | 369 |
| Clear Brook High Sch/Friendswood/Galveston | 03052416 | 281/284-2100 | 163 |
| Clear Connections Online Acad/League City/ | | | |
| Galveston | 12471526 | 281/284-0000 | 163 |
| Clear Creek Elem Sch/Fort Hood/Bell | 03334551 | 254/336-1550 | 30 |
| Clear Creek High Sch/League City/Galveston | 01018828 | 281/284-1700 | 163 |
| **CLEAR CREEK IND SCH DIST/** | | | |
| LEAGUE CITY/GALVESTON | 01018816 | 281/284-0000 | 162 |
| Clear Creek Intermediate Sch/League City/ | | | |
| Galveston | 11449116 | 281/284-2300 | 163 |
| Clear Creek Intermediate Sch/Sanger/Denton | 01013658 | 940/458-7476 | 130 |
| Clear Falls High Sch/League City/Galveston | 11554838 | 281/284-1100 | 163 |
| Clear Fork Elem Sch/Lockhart/Caldwell | 01003055 | 512/398-0450 | 64 |
| Clear Horizons Early Clg HS/Houston/ | | | |
| Galveston | 10908872 | 281/929-4657 | 163 |
| Clear Lake City Elem Sch/Houston/Galveston | 01018830 | 281/284-4200 | 163 |
| Clear Lake High Sch/Houston/Galveston | 01018854 | 281/284-1900 | 163 |
| Clear Lake Intermediate Sch/Houston/ | | | |
| Galveston | 01018842 | 281/284-3200 | 163 |
| Clear Path Alt High Sch/Webster/Galveston | 05096901 | 281/284-1600 | 163 |
| Clear Spring Elem Sch/New Braunfels/Comal | 11559840 | 830/837-7300 | 91 |
| Clear Spring Elem Sch/San Antonio/Bexar | 00997702 | 210/407-2000 | 37 |
| Clear Springs High Sch/League City/ | | | |
| Galveston | 10908884 | 281/284-1300 | 163 |
| Clear View High Sch/Webster/Galveston | 03052404 | 281/284-1500 | 163 |
| Clearfork Elem Sch/Andrews/Andrews | 02202723 | 432/524-1930 | 19 |
| Cleburn Eubanks Interm Sch/Southlake/ | | | |
| Tarrant | 04946157 | 817/949-5200 | 349 |

| School/City/County DISTRICT/CITY/COUNTY | PID | TELEPHONE NUMBER | PAGE |
|---|---|---|---|
| Cleburne Christian Academy/Cleburne/ Johnson | 04993007 | 817/641-2857 | 252 |
| Cleburne High Sch/Cleburne/Johnson | 01526095 | 817/202-1200 | 250 |
| **CLEBURNE IND SCH DIST/CLEBURNE/ JOHNSON** | 01034872 | 817/202-1100 | 250 |
| Cleckler-Heald Elem Sch/Weslaco/Hidalgo | 04288450 | 956/969-6888 | 228 |
| Clemente Martinez Elem Sch/Houston/Harris | 04289935 | 713/224-1424 | 196 |
| Clements High Sch/Sugar Land/Fort Bend | 02201444 | 281/634-2150 | 154 |
| Clements-Parsons Elem Sch/Copperas Cove/ Coryell | 01007568 | 254/547-2235 | 96 |
| Clendenin Elem Sch/El Paso/El Paso | 02205402 | 915/236-5300 | 137 |
| Cleveland High Sch/Cleveland/Liberty | 01037721 | 281/592-8752 | 267 |
| **CLEVELAND IND SCH DIST/CLEVELAND/ LIBERTY** | 01037719 | 281/592-8717 | 267 |
| Cleveland Middle Sch/Cleveland/Liberty | 01037733 | 281/593-1148 | 267 |
| Clifford Davis Elem Sch/Fort Worth/Tarrant | 05096511 | 817/815-8700 | 352 |
| Clifford Dunn Elem Sch/Houston/Harris | 02894376 | 281/233-4320 | 185 |
| Clifton Career Dev Sch/Austin/Travis | 02127836 | 512/414-3614 | 371 |
| Clifton Early Childhood Sch/Irving/Dallas | 04872960 | 972/600-4200 | 113 |
| Clifton Elem School PK-5/Clifton/Bosque | 01808910 | 254/675-1875 | 49 |
| Clifton High Sch/Clifton/Bosque | 01808908 | 254/675-1845 | 49 |
| **CLIFTON IND SCH DIST/CLIFTON/ BOSQUE** | 01808893 | 254/675-2827 | 49 |
| Clifton Middle Sch/Clifton/Bosque | 03248665 | 254/675-1855 | 49 |
| Clifton Park Elem Sch/Killeen/Bell | 00996459 | 254/336-1580 | 30 |
| Clint Early College Academy/Clint/El Paso | 12031607 | 915/926-8100 | 136 |
| Clint High Sch/Clint/El Paso | 01015448 | 915/926-8300 | 136 |
| **CLINT IND SCH DIST/EL PASO/ EL PASO** | 01015424 | 915/926-4000 | 136 |
| Clint Junior High Sch/Clint/El Paso | 01826209 | 915/926-8000 | 136 |
| Clinton P Russell Elem Sch/Dallas/Dallas | 01009748 | 972/925-8300 | 103 |
| Cloverleaf Elem Sch/Houston/Harris | 01023433 | 832/386-3200 | 192 |
| Club Estates Elem Sch/Corp Christi/Nueces | 02109066 | 361/878-3780 | 306 |
| Club Hill Elem Sch/Garland/Dallas | 01010486 | 972/926-2520 | 109 |
| Clute Intermediate Sch/Clute/Brazoria | 01001605 | 979/730-7230 | 55 |
| **CLYDE CONSOLIDATED IND SD/ CLYDE/CALLAHAN** | 01003316 | 325/893-4222 | 66 |
| Clyde Elem Sch/Clyde/Callahan | 01003328 | 325/893-4788 | 66 |
| Clyde High Sch/Clyde/Callahan | 01003330 | 325/893-2161 | 66 |
| Clyde Intermediate Sch/Clyde/Callahan | 04245305 | 325/893-2815 | 66 |
| Clyde Junior High Sch/Clyde/Callahan | 01003342 | 325/893-5788 | 66 |
| Coahoma Elem Sch/Coahoma/Howard | 01032068 | 432/394-5000 | 237 |
| Coahoma High Sch/Coahoma/Howard | 01032070 | 432/394-5000 | 237 |
| **COAHOMA IND SCH DIST/COAHOMA/ HOWARD** | 01032056 | 432/394-5000 | 237 |
| Coahoma Junior High Sch/Coahoma/Howard | 01032082 | 432/394-5000 | 237 |
| Coakley Middle Sch/Harlingen/Cameron | 01003809 | 956/427-3000 | 68 |
| Coastal Horizons Academy/Taft/San Patricio | 04447278 | 361/528-3959 | 2 |
| Coastal Oaks Christian Sch/Rockport/ Aransas | 04993851 | 361/790-9597 | 22 |
| Cobb Sixth Grade Campus/Houston/Harris | 04884092 | 832/386-2100 | 192 |
| Cockrell Elem Sch/Prosper/Collin | 11831868 | 469/219-2130 | 88 |
| Cockrell Hill Elem Sch/Desoto/Dallas | 03005994 | 972/230-1692 | 108 |
| Coder Elem Sch/Aledo/Parker | 01046318 | 817/441-6095 | 315 |
| Codwell Elem Sch/Houston/Harris | 01826297 | 713/732-3580 | 195 |
| Coggin Intermediate Sch/Brownwood/Brown | 02199918 | 325/646-0462 | 62 |
| Cogin Memorial Elem Sch/Corp Christi/ Nueces | 03017507 | 361/991-6968 | 309 |
| Coker Elem Sch/San Antonio/Bexar | 00997714 | 210/407-2200 | 37 |
| Col John O Ensor Middle Sch/El Paso/ El Paso | 04916102 | 915/937-6000 | 140 |
| Col Menchaca ECC/San Antonio/Bexar | 12307951 | 210/822-1610 | 46 |
| Col Santos Benavides Elem Sch/Laredo/Webb | 01059509 | 956/473-4900 | 390 |
| Colbert Elem Sch/Dayton/Liberty | 05342516 | 936/258-2727 | 268 |
| Colby Glass Elem Sch/San Antonio/Bexar | 00998316 | 210/397-1950 | 39 |
| Coldspring Intermediate Sch/Coldspring/ San Jacinto | 02896465 | 936/653-1152 | 332 |
| **COLDSPRING-OAKHURST CONS ISD/ COLDSPRING/SAN JACINTO** | 01049401 | 936/653-1115 | 332 |
| Coldspring-Oakhurst High Sch/Coldspring/ San Jacinto | 01049413 | 936/653-1140 | 332 |
| Coldwell Elem Sch/El Paso/El Paso | 01015591 | 915/236-8525 | 137 |
| Coleman Elem Sch/Cleburne/Johnson | 01034901 | 817/202-2030 | 250 |
| Coleman Elem Sch/Coleman/Coleman | 03047942 | 325/625-3546 | 79 |
| Coleman High Sch/Coleman/Coleman | 01005833 | 325/625-2156 | 79 |
| **COLEMAN IND SCH DIST/COLEMAN/ COLEMAN** | 01005819 | 325/625-3575 | 79 |
| Coleman Junior High Sch/Coleman/Coleman | 03391339 | 325/625-3593 | 79 |
| Coleman Junior High Sch/Waxahachie/Ellis | 12311366 | 972/923-4790 | 146 |
| Coles High Sch & Ed Center/Corp Christi/ Nueces | 03051008 | 361/878-7380 | 306 |

| School/City/County DISTRICT/CITY/COUNTY | PID | TELEPHONE NUMBER | PAGE |
|---|---|---|---|
| Colin Powell 6th Grade Center/Little Elm/ Denton | 12168274 | 972/947-9446 | 128 |
| Colin Powell Elem Sch/Grand Prairie/Dallas | 04751536 | 972/642-3961 | 111 |
| Colin Powell Elem Sch/The Woodlands/ Montgomery | 04284545 | 936/709-1700 | 294 |
| College & Career Center/La Joya/Hidalgo | 11449477 | 956/323-2230 | 223 |
| College Career & Tech Acad/Los Fresnos/ Cameron | 12368357 | 956/254-5296 | 69 |
| College Career & Tech Academy/Pharr/ Hidalgo | 11128532 | 956/784-8515 | 226 |
| College Career Technology Acad/El Paso/ El Paso | 04288278 | 915/236-7700 | 138 |
| College Hill Elem Sch/Plainview/Hale | 01021930 | 806/293-6035 | 180 |
| College Hills Elem Sch/College Sta/Brazos | 01001978 | 979/764-5565 | 59 |
| College Park Elem Sch/Deer Park/Harris | 01026411 | 281/604-4400 | 203 |
| College Station High Sch/College Sta/ Brazos | 11823641 | 979/694-5800 | 59 |
| **COLLEGE STATION IND SCH DIST/ COLLEGE STA/BRAZOS** | 01001954 | 979/764-5400 | 59 |
| College Station Middle Sch/College Sta/ Brazos | 01001980 | 979/764-5545 | 59 |
| College Street Elem Sch/Lindale/Smith | 01050694 | 903/881-4350 | 339 |
| College View High Sch/College Sta/Brazos | 04451205 | 979/764-5540 | 59 |
| Collegiate Acad Tarrant Clg/Hurst/Tarrant | 12035897 | 817/515-6775 | 355 |
| Collegiate Academy/The Colony/Denton | 12472489 | 469/948-2507 | 126 |
| Collegiate Academy at Weis/Galveston/ Galveston | 11557103 | 409/761-6100 | 165 |
| Collegiate Academy Middle Sch/Cedar Hill/ Dallas | 03237795 | 469/272-2021 | 101 |
| Collegiate High Sch/Corp Christi/Nueces | 10912586 | 361/698-2425 | 306 |
| Collegiate Prep Academy/Cedar Hill/Dallas | 12108626 | 972/293-4502 | 101 |
| Colleyville Elem Sch/Colleyville/Tarrant | 01053696 | 817/305-4940 | 355 |
| Colleyville Heritage High Sch/Colleyville/ Tarrant | 04447890 | 817/305-4700 | 355 |
| Colleyville Middle Sch/Colleyville/Tarrant | 01539262 | 817/305-4900 | 355 |
| Collier Elem Sch/San Antonio/Bexar | 00997403 | 210/989-2950 | 35 |
| Collins Elem Sch/El Paso/El Paso | 02043216 | 915/236-5375 | 137 |
| Collins Elem Sch/Houston/Harris | 04868127 | 713/272-3250 | 187 |
| Collins Garden Elem Sch/San Antonio/Bexar | 00999102 | 210/228-3310 | 43 |
| Collins Intermediate Sch/Corsicana/Navarro | 01043469 | 903/872-3979 | 302 |
| Collins Intermediate Sch/The Woodlands/ Montgomery | 03325342 | 281/298-3800 | 294 |
| Collins-Parr Elem Sch/San Diego/Duval | 01014286 | 361/279-3382 | 132 |
| Collinsville Elem Sch/Collinsville/Grayson | 10902036 | 903/429-3077 | 171 |
| Collinsville High Sch/Collinsville/Grayson | 01020285 | 903/429-6164 | 171 |
| **COLLINSVILLE IND SCH DIST/ COLLINSVILLE/GRAYSON** | 01020261 | 903/429-6272 | 171 |
| Colmesneil Elem Sch/Colmesneil/Tyler | 01057238 | 409/837-5757 | 377 |
| Colmesneil High Sch/Colmesneil/Tyler | 01057240 | 409/837-2225 | 377 |
| **COLMESNEIL IND SCH DIST/ COLMESNEIL/TYLER** | 01057226 | 409/837-5757 | 377 |
| Colonial Hills Elem Sch/San Antonio/Bexar | 00997726 | 210/407-2400 | 37 |
| Colonies North Elem Sch/San Antonio/Bexar | 00998067 | 210/397-1700 | 39 |
| Colony Bend Elem Sch/Sugar Land/Fort Bend | 02126387 | 281/634-4080 | 154 |
| Colony Meadows Elem Sch/Sugar Land/ Fort Bend | 03393181 | 281/634-4120 | 154 |
| Colorado Elem Sch/Colorado City/Mitchell | 01042104 | 325/728-3471 | 292 |
| Colorado High Sch/Colorado City/Mitchell | 01042075 | 325/728-3424 | 292 |
| **COLORADO IND SCH DIST/COLORADO CITY/ MITCHELL** | 01042063 | 325/728-5312 | 292 |
| Colorado Middle Sch/Colorado City/Mitchell | 01042087 | 325/728-2673 | 292 |
| Colorado River Collegiate Acad/Bastrop/ Bastrop | 12037144 | 512/772-7230 | 26 |
| Colt Elem Sch/Marble Falls/Burnet | 02845612 | 830/693-3474 | 64 |
| **COLUMBIA BRAZORIA ISD/WEST COLUMBIA/ BRAZORIA** | 01001710 | 979/345-5147 | 56 |
| Columbia Heights Elem Sch/San Antonio/ Bexar | 00997415 | 210/989-3000 | 35 |
| Columbia High Sch/West Columbia/Brazoria | 01001746 | 979/799-1720 | 56 |
| Columbus Alternative Sch/Columbus/Colorado | 12313194 | 979/732-2963 | 90 |
| Columbus Elem Sch/Columbus/Colorado | 01006758 | 979/732-2078 | 90 |
| Columbus High Sch/Columbus/Colorado | 01006760 | 979/732-5746 | 90 |
| **COLUMBUS IND SCH DIST/COLUMBUS/ COLORADO** | 01006746 | 979/732-5704 | 90 |
| Columbus Junior High Sch/Columbus/Colorado | 01006772 | 979/732-2891 | 90 |
| Comal Academy/New Braunfels/Comal | 12178267 | 830/221-2951 | 91 |
| Comal Discipline Center/New Braunfels/ Comal | 11450921 | 830/221-2950 | 91 |
| **COMAL IND SCH DIST/NEW BRAUNFELS/ COMAL** | 01006887 | 830/221-2000 | 91 |
| Comanche Early Childhood Ctr/Comanche/ Comanche | 12173669 | 325/356-2440 | 93 |

| School/City/County DISTRICT/CITY/COUNTY | PID | TELEPHONE NUMBER | PAGE |
|---|---|---|---|
| Comanche Elem Sch/Comanche/Comanche | 03004677 | 325/356-2727 | 93 |
| Comanche High Sch/Comanche/Comanche | 01531985 | 325/356-2581 | 93 |
| **COMANCHE IND SCH DIST/COMANCHE/ COMANCHE** | 01007051 | 325/356-2727 | 93 |
| Comanche Springs Elem Sch/Fort Worth/ Tarrant | 10902995 | 817/847-8700 | 351 |
| Comfort Elem Sch/Comfort/Kendall | 01035876 | 830/995-6410 | 257 |
| Comfort High Sch/Comfort/Kendall | 01035888 | 830/995-6430 | 257 |
| **COMFORT IND SCH DIST/COMFORT/ KENDALL** | 01035864 | 830/995-6400 | 257 |
| Comfort Middle Sch/Comfort/Kendall | 04035174 | 830/995-6420 | 257 |
| Commerce Elem Sch/Commerce/Hunt | 01032393 | 903/886-3757 | 239 |
| Commerce High Sch/Commerce/Hunt | 01032408 | 903/886-3756 | 239 |
| **COMMERCE INDEPENDENT SCH DIST/ COMMERCE/HUNT** | 01032381 | 903/886-3755 | 239 |
| Commerce Middle Sch/Commerce/Hunt | 01032410 | 903/886-3795 | 239 |
| Commonwealth Elem Sch/Sugar Land/Fort Bend | 04749789 | 281/634-5120 | 154 |
| Communications Arts High Sch/San Antonio/ Bexar | 04368713 | 210/397-6043 | 40 |
| Community Christian Sch/Mineral Wells/ Palo Pinto | 02208222 | 940/328-1333 | 314 |
| Community Christian Sch/Orange/Orange | 02208234 | 409/883-4531 | 312 |
| Community Christian Sch/Pampa/Gray | 04835687 | 806/665-3393 | 170 |
| Community High Sch/Nevada/Collin | 03003128 | 972/843-6500 | 81 |
| **COMMUNITY IND SCH DIST/NEVADA/ COLLIN** | 01006124 | 972/843-8400 | 81 |
| Community Learning Center/Humble/Harris | 04370259 | 281/641-7400 | 200 |
| Community Montessori Sch/Georgetown/ Williamson | 02785098 | 512/863-7920 | 403 |
| Community of Faith Chrn Sch/El Paso/ El Paso | 02744094 | 915/584-2561 | 143 |
| Community Sch/Pasadena/Harris | 12037077 | 713/740-0298 | 204 |
| Community Services Sch/Houston/Harris | 11717509 | 713/967-5285 | 196 |
| Como Montessori Sch/Fort Worth/Tarrant | 01052707 | 817/815-7200 | 352 |
| **COMO PICKTON CONS IND SD/ COMO/HOPKINS** | 01031466 | 903/488-3671 | 234 |
| Como Pickton Sch/Como/Hopkins | 01031478 | 903/488-3671 | 234 |
| Compass Academy Charter Sch/Odessa/Ector | 11733955 | 432/272-1836 | 2 |
| Compass Center/Jacksonville/Cherokee | 04448997 | 903/589-3926 | 76 |
| Compass Rose Academy/San Antonio/Bexar | 12260676 | 210/540-9265 | 2 |
| Comquest Academy/Tomball/Harris | 04881662 | 281/516-0611 | 2 |
| Comstock Elem Sch/McKinney/Collin | 11820091 | 469/633-3900 | 82 |
| **COMSTOCK IND SCH DIST/COMSTOCK/ VAL VERDE** | 01057898 | 432/292-4444 | 381 |
| Comstock Sch/Comstock/Val Verde | 01057903 | 432/292-4444 | 381 |
| Concordia High Sch/Round Rock/Williamson | 10015372 | 512/248-2547 | 403 |
| Concordia Lutheran High Sch/Tomball/Harris | 02233344 | 281/351-2547 | 210 |
| Concordia Lutheran Sch/San Antonio/Bexar | 00999657 | 210/479-1477 | 48 |
| Condit Elem Sch/Bellaire/Harris | 01024762 | 713/295-5255 | 198 |
| Condra Sch for Educ Innovation/Lubbock/ Lubbock | 12378510 | 806/407-0878 | 2 |
| Connally Early Childhood Ctr/Waco/McLennan | 12179895 | 254/750-7160 | 282 |
| Connally Early Clg Career Tech/Waco/ McLennan | 12311201 | 254/296-6700 | 282 |
| Connally Elem Sch/Waco/McLennan | 01039690 | 254/750-7100 | 282 |
| Connally High Sch/Waco/McLennan | 01039652 | 254/296-6700 | 282 |
| **CONNALLY IND SCH DIST/WACO/ MCLENNAN** | 01039640 | 254/296-6460 | 282 |
| Connally Junior High Sch/Elm Mott/McLennan | 01039664 | 254/296-7700 | 282 |
| Connally Primary Sch/Elm Mott/McLennan | 05048758 | 254/296-7600 | 282 |
| Connection School of Houston/Cypress/ Harris | 12177859 | 832/544-6031 | 210 |
| Conroe 9th Grade High Sch/Conroe/ Montgomery | 11920433 | 936/709-4000 | 294 |
| Conroe Adventist Academy/Conroe/Montgomery | 11239258 | 936/756-5078 | 298 |
| Conroe High Sch/Conroe/Montgomery | 01042453 | 936/709-5700 | 294 |
| **CONROE IND SCH DIST/CONROE/ MONTGOMERY** | 01042439 | 936/709-7752 | 294 |
| Constance Hulbert Elem Sch/El Paso/El Paso | 05231151 | 915/434-6900 | 142 |
| Construction Careers Academy/San Antonio/ Bexar | 11448978 | 210/397-4294 | 40 |
| Converse Elem Sch/Converse/Bexar | 00997594 | 210/945-1210 | 36 |
| Cook Elem Sch/Austin/Travis | 01391917 | 512/414-2510 | 369 |
| Cook Jr Elem Sch/Houston/Harris | 01025833 | 713/636-6040 | 195 |
| Cook Middle Sch/Houston/Harris | 02896673 | 281/897-4400 | 189 |
| Cooke Elem Sch/Cleburne/Johnson | 01034949 | 817/202-2060 | 250 |
| Cooley Elem Sch/El Paso/El Paso | 01015606 | 915/236-8600 | 137 |
| Coolidge Elem Sch/Coolidge/Limestone | 01038024 | 254/786-2206 | 269 |
| **COOLIDGE IND SCH DIST/COOLIDGE/ LIMESTONE** | 01038012 | 254/786-2206 | 269 |
| Coolidge Jr Sr High Sch/Coolidge/Limestone | 04914453 | 254/786-4612 | 269 |
| Coop Elem Sch/Houston/Harris | 01025857 | 713/696-2630 | 195 |

| School/City/County DISTRICT/CITY/COUNTY | PID | TELEPHONE NUMBER | PAGE |
|---|---|---|---|
| Cooper Elem Sch/Cooper/Delta | 01013115 | 903/395-2111 | 124 |
| Cooper Elem Sch/Garland/Dallas | 01010747 | 972/675-3010 | 109 |
| Cooper High Sch/Abilene/Taylor | 01172709 | 325/691-1000 | 363 |
| **COOPER IND SCH DIST/COOPER/DELTA** | 01013103 | 903/395-2111 | 123 |
| Cooper Jr Sr High Sch/Cooper/Delta | 01013127 | 903/395-2111 | 124 |
| Copeland Elem Sch/Houston/Harris | 04016635 | 281/856-1400 | 189 |
| Coppell Classical Academy/Coppell/Dallas | 11459680 | 972/393-3077 | 2 |
| Coppell High Sch/Coppell/Dallas | 01008342 | 214/496-6100 | 102 |
| Coppell HS 9th Grade/Coppell/Dallas | 12310867 | 214/496-3800 | 102 |
| **COPPELL IND SCH DIST/COPPELL/ DALLAS** | 01008328 | 214/496-6000 | 102 |
| Coppell Middle School East/Coppell/Dallas | 03247099 | 214/496-6600 | 102 |
| Coppell Middle School North/Coppell/Dallas | 04808799 | 214/496-7100 | 102 |
| Coppell Middle School West/Coppell/Dallas | 02109353 | 214/496-8600 | 102 |
| Copperas Cove High Sch/Copperas Cove/ Coryell | 01007570 | 254/547-2534 | 96 |
| **COPPERAS COVE IND SCH DIST/ COPPERAS COVE/CORYELL** | 01007556 | 254/547-1227 | 96 |
| Copperas Cove Jr High Sch/Copperas Cove/ Coryell | 01007582 | 254/547-6959 | 96 |
| Copperfield Elem Sch/Austin/Travis | 04803050 | 512/594-5800 | 374 |
| Copperfield Elem Sch/Converse/Bexar | 12034178 | 210/619-0460 | 36 |
| Cora Spencer Elem Sch/Grand Prairie/ Tarrant | 10028214 | 817/299-6680 | 359 |
| Coram Deo Academy/Flower Mound/Denton | 10000183 | 682/237-0232 | 130 |
| Coram Deo Academy-Collin Cnty/Plano/Collin | 11825883 | 469/854-1300 | 89 |
| Coram Deo Academy-Dallas/Dallas/Dallas | 11825871 | 972/385-6410 | 119 |
| Corey Acad Fine Arts/Arlington/Tarrant | 02897172 | 682/867-3900 | 346 |
| Corina Pena Elem Sch/Penitas/Hidalgo | 10914405 | 956/323-2750 | 223 |
| Corinth Classical Acad Upper/Corinth/ Denton | 12161733 | 940/497-0059 | 2 |
| Corinth Classical Acad-Grammar/Hickory Creek/ Denton | 12161769 | 940/321-1144 | 2 |
| Corinth Elem Sch/Corinth/Denton | 03391432 | 940/497-4010 | 126 |
| Cornelius Elem Sch/Houston/Harris | 01025144 | 713/845-7405 | 197 |
| Cornerstone Academy/Houston/Harris | 04808921 | 713/251-1600 | 206 |
| Cornerstone Christian Academy/Bryan/Brazos | 11712236 | 979/694-8200 | 60 |
| Cornerstone Christian Academy/Granbury/ Hood | 04937625 | 817/910-8076 | 234 |
| Cornerstone Christian Academy/McKinney/ Collin | 11227968 | 972/562-8200 | 89 |
| Cornerstone Christian Sch/Abilene/Taylor | 03023398 | 325/676-8232 | 364 |
| Cornerstone Christian Sch/San Angelo/ Tom Green | 03025580 | 325/655-3439 | 368 |
| Cornerstone Christian Sch/San Antonio/ Bexar | 04953655 | 210/979-6161 | 48 |
| Cornerstone Elem Sch/Sugar Land/Fort Bend | 10912873 | 281/634-6400 | 154 |
| Coronado Elem Sch/Amarillo/Potter | 01047219 | 806/326-4250 | 320 |
| Coronado High Sch/El Paso/El Paso | 01015943 | 915/236-2000 | 138 |
| Coronado High Sch/Lubbock/Lubbock | 01038581 | 806/219-1100 | 273 |
| Coronado Middle Sch/Plainview/Hale | 01021942 | 806/293-6020 | 180 |
| Coronado Village Elem Sch/Universal Cty/ Bexar | 00997609 | 210/945-5110 | 36 |
| Corpus Christi Catholic Sch/Houston/Harris | 01027908 | 713/664-3351 | 209 |
| Corpus Christi College Prep HS/Corp Christi/ Nueces | 11016109 | 361/225-4240 | 2 |
| **CORPUS CHRISTI IND SCH DIST/ CORP CHRISTI/NUECES** | 01044176 | 361/695-7200 | 306 |
| Corpus Christi Montessori Sch/Corp Christi/ Nueces | 10016766 | 361/852-0707 | 2 |
| Corrigan-Camden Elem Sch/Corrigan/Polk | 01047013 | 936/398-2501 | 319 |
| Corrigan-Camden High Sch/Corrigan/Polk | 01047001 | 936/398-2543 | 319 |
| **CORRIGAN-CAMDEN IND SCH DIST/ CORRIGAN/POLK** | 01046980 | 936/398-2341 | 319 |
| Corrigan-Camden Jr High Sch/Corrigan/Polk | 03004316 | 936/398-2962 | 319 |
| Corsicana High Sch/Corsicana/Navarro | 01043457 | 903/874-8211 | 302 |
| **CORSICANA IND SCH DIST/CORSICANA/ NAVARRO** | 01043421 | 903/874-7441 | 302 |
| Corsicana Middle Sch/Corsicana/Navarro | 01043445 | 430/775-6200 | 302 |
| Coston Elem Sch/Lufkin/Angelina | 00994956 | 936/639-3118 | 21 |
| **COTTON CENTER IND SCH DIST/ COTTON CENTER/HALE** | 01021784 | 806/879-2160 | 179 |
| Cotton Center Sch/Cotton Center/Hale | 01021796 | 806/879-2176 | 180 |
| Cotton Vly Early College HS/Fabens/El Paso | 11716505 | 915/765-2609 | 139 |
| Cottonwood Creek Elem Sch/Coppell/Dallas | 04454166 | 214/496-8300 | 102 |
| Cottonwood Creek Elem Sch/Hutto/Williamson | 10020808 | 512/759-5430 | 399 |
| Cottonwood Elem Sch/Cleveland/Liberty | 12469456 | 281/761-7540 | 268 |
| Cotulla High Sch/Cotulla/La Salle | 01037214 | 830/879-2374 | 262 |
| **COTULLA IND SCH DIST/COTULLA/ LA SALLE** | 01037197 | 830/879-3073 | 262 |
| Coulson Tough Elem Sch/Spring/Montgomery | 05093014 | 281/465-5900 | 294 |

| School/City/County DISTRICT/CITY/COUNTY | PID | TELEPHONE NUMBER | PAGE |
|---|---|---|---|
| Country Day Sch of Arlington/Arlington/Tarrant | 03016864 | 817/275-0851 | 361 |
| Country Place Elem Sch/Carrollton/Dallas | 01418242 | 972/968-1400 | 100 |
| County Line Elem Sch/New Braunfels/Comal | 02896908 | 830/627-6610 | 92 |
| Coupland Elem Sch/Coupland/Williamson | 01060821 | 512/856-2422 | 398 |
| **COUPLAND IND SCH DIST/COUPLAND/ WILLIAMSON** | 01060819 | 512/856-2422 | 398 |
| Cove Charter Academy/Copperas Cove/Coryell | 11932060 | 254/238-8231 | 2 |
| Covenant Academy/Cypress/Harris | 05347190 | 281/373-2233 | 210 |
| Covenant Christian Academy/Colleyville/Tarrant | 02164705 | 817/281-4333 | 361 |
| Covenant Christian Academy/McAllen/Hidalgo | 04993916 | 956/686-7886 | 229 |
| Covenant Christian Sch/Conroe/Montgomery | 02192439 | 936/890-8080 | 298 |
| Covenant Classical Sch/Fort Worth/Tarrant | 11234985 | 817/820-0884 | 361 |
| Covenant Preparatory Sch/Humble/Harris | 04247016 | 281/359-1090 | 210 |
| Covenant Sch/Dallas/Dallas | 10000573 | 214/358-5818 | 119 |
| **COVINGTON ISD SCH DIST/COVINGTON/ HILL** | 01030826 | 254/854-2215 | 230 |
| Covington Middle Sch/Austin/Travis | 02891130 | 512/414-3276 | 371 |
| Covington Sch/Covington/Hill | 01030838 | 254/854-2215 | 230 |
| Cowan Elem Sch/Austin/Travis | 04917699 | 512/841-2700 | 369 |
| Cox Elem Sch/Cedar Park/Williamson | 04939960 | 512/570-6000 | 400 |
| Coyle Middle Sch/Rowlett/Dallas | 01010498 | 972/475-3711 | 109 |
| Coyote Ridge Elem Sch/Carrollton/Denton | 10014574 | 469/713-5994 | 127 |
| Crain Elem Sch/Victoria/Victoria | 01058531 | 361/573-7453 | 384 |
| Crandall Compass Academy/Crandall/Kaufman | 04744650 | 972/427-6100 | 254 |
| Crandall High Sch/Crandall/Kaufman | 01035553 | 972/427-6150 | 254 |
| **CRANDALL IND SCH DIST/CRANDALL/ KAUFMAN** | 01035539 | 972/427-6000 | 254 |
| Crandall Middle Sch/Crandall/Kaufman | 01553165 | 972/427-6080 | 254 |
| Crane Elem Sch/Crane/Crane | 01007829 | 432/558-1050 | 97 |
| Crane High Sch/Crane/Crane | 01007843 | 432/558-1030 | 97 |
| **CRANE IND SCH DIST/CRANE/CRANE** | 01007817 | 432/558-1022 | 97 |
| Crane Middle Sch/Crane/Crane | 01007831 | 432/558-1040 | 97 |
| **CRANFILLS GAP ISD SCH DIST/ CRANFILLS GAP/BOSQUE** | 01000601 | 254/597-2505 | 50 |
| Cranfills Gap Sch/Cranfills Gap/Bosque | 01000625 | 254/597-2505 | 50 |
| Cravens Early Childhood Acad/Houston/Harris | 05090593 | 281/727-2100 | 205 |
| Crawford Elem Sch/Crawford/McLennan | 01039717 | 254/486-9083 | 282 |
| Crawford Elem Sch/Edinburg/Hidalgo | 11558250 | 956/289-2410 | 221 |
| Crawford High Sch/Crawford/McLennan | 01039729 | 254/486-2381 | 282 |
| **CRAWFORD IND SCH DIST/CRAWFORD/ MCLENNAN** | 01039705 | 254/486-2381 | 282 |
| Creedmoor Elem Sch/Creedmoor/Travis | 10020949 | 512/386-3950 | 372 |
| Creek Valley Middle Sch/Carrollton/Denton | 05010464 | 469/713-5184 | 127 |
| Creek View Elem Sch/College Sta/Brazos | 11446047 | 979/694-5890 | 59 |
| Creekside Elem Sch/Lewisville/Denton | 03325550 | 469/713-5953 | 127 |
| Creekside Elem Sch/Livingston/Polk | 04286103 | 936/328-2150 | 319 |
| Creekside Forest Elem Sch/Spring/Harris | 11449556 | 281/357-4526 | 208 |
| Creekside Intermediate Sch/League City/Galveston | 04015253 | 281/284-3500 | 163 |
| Creekside Park Jr High Sch/The Woodlands/Harris | 12169333 | 281/357-3282 | 208 |
| Creekview Elem Sch/The Woodlands/Harris | 12107854 | 281/357-3070 | 208 |
| Creekview High Sch/Carrollton/Dallas | 04810182 | 972/968-4800 | 100 |
| Creekview Middle Sch/Fort Worth/Tarrant | 05341897 | 817/237-4261 | 351 |
| Creekwood Middle Sch/Kingwood/Harris | 02125503 | 281/641-4400 | 200 |
| Creighton Elem Sch/Conroe/Montgomery | 04948399 | 936/709-2900 | 294 |
| Crenshaw Elem & Mid Sch/Crystal Beach/Galveston | 11563396 | 409/761-6350 | 165 |
| Crenshaw Elem Sch/Channelview/Harris | 02846408 | 281/457-3080 | 188 |
| Crespo Elem Sch/Houston/Harris | 04016104 | 713/845-7492 | 194 |
| Crestmont Christian Prep Sch/Boerne/Kendall | 12363072 | 210/254-4534 | 257 |
| Crestmont Prep Sch/Boerne/Kendall | 12313948 | 210/254-4534 | 257 |
| Crestview Elem Sch/Canyon/Randall | 04365503 | 806/677-2780 | 323 |
| Crestview Elem Sch/Graham/Young | 01062116 | 940/549-6023 | 409 |
| Crestview Elem Sch/Live Oak/Bexar | 01379490 | 210/945-5111 | 36 |
| Crestview Elem Sch/Lubbock/Lubbock | 03240675 | 806/794-3661 | 272 |
| Crestview Elem Sch/New Boston/Bowie | 01001071 | 903/628-6521 | 52 |
| Crestview Elem Sch/Waco/McLennan | 01040194 | 254/776-1704 | 285 |
| Crisman Sch/Longview/Gregg | 02233332 | 903/758-9741 | 176 |
| Cristo Rey Dallas College Prep/Dallas/Dallas | 12238881 | 469/844-7956 | 119 |
| Cristo Rey Jesuit Clg Prep HS/Houston/Harris | 11450464 | 281/501-1298 | 210 |
| Criswell Elem Sch/Forney/Kaufman | 02894259 | 469/762-4310 | 255 |
| Crockett Aec-Pineywoods/Crockett/Houston | 04800993 | 936/546-5972 | 235 |
| Crockett Charter Elem Sch/Houston/Harris | 01023902 | 713/802-4780 | 196 |
| Crockett Classical Academy/Crockett/Houston | 11848914 | 936/546-0487 | 2 |
| **CROCKETT CO CONS COMMON SD/ OZONA/CROCKETT** | 01007855 | 325/392-5501 | 98 |
| Crockett Early Education Sch/Grand Prairie/Dallas | 12225169 | 972/262-5353 | 111 |
| Crockett Elem Sch/Borger/Hutchinson | 01032666 | 806/273-1054 | 240 |
| Crockett Elem Sch/Bryan/Brazos | 01002051 | 979/209-2960 | 58 |
| Crockett Elem Sch/Crockett/Houston | 01031741 | 936/544-3758 | 235 |
| Crockett Elem Sch/El Paso/El Paso | 01015618 | 915/236-8675 | 137 |
| Crockett Elem Sch/Greenville/Hunt | 01032484 | 903/457-2684 | 239 |
| Crockett Elem Sch/Harlingen/Cameron | 01003811 | 956/427-3090 | 68 |
| Crockett Elem Sch/San Angelo/Tom Green | 01055606 | 325/947-3925 | 367 |
| Crockett Elem Sch/San Marcos/Hays | 01029138 | 512/393-6400 | 217 |
| Crockett Elem Sch/Weatherford/Parker | 01046576 | 817/598-2811 | 317 |
| Crockett Elem Sch/Wichita Falls/Wichita | 01173002 | 940/235-1140 | 395 |
| Crockett High Sch/Austin/Travis | 01056167 | 512/414-2532 | 371 |
| Crockett High Sch/Crockett/Houston | 01553139 | 936/544-2193 | 235 |
| **CROCKETT IND SCH DIST/CROCKETT/ HOUSTON** | 01031715 | 936/544-2125 | 235 |
| Crockett Intermediate Sch/Paris/Lamar | 01036703 | 903/737-7450 | 262 |
| Crockett Junior High Sch/Crockett/Houston | 01031727 | 936/544-2125 | 235 |
| Crockett Middle Sch/Irving/Dallas | 01011143 | 972/600-4700 | 113 |
| Crockett Middle Sch/Odessa/Ector | 01014640 | 432/456-0449 | 134 |
| Crockett Middle Sch/Pecos/Reeves | 01048392 | 432/447-7461 | 326 |
| Cromack Elem Sch/Brownsville/Cameron | 01003512 | 956/548-8820 | 67 |
| Crosby Elem Sch/Crosby/Harris | 11697698 | 281/328-9360 | 188 |
| Crosby Elem Sch/El Paso/El Paso | 01015773 | 915/236-5450 | 137 |
| Crosby Elem Sch/Forney/Kaufman | 10002648 | 469/762-4315 | 255 |
| Crosby High Sch/Crosby/Harris | 01023158 | 281/328-9237 | 188 |
| **CROSBY IND SCH DIST/CROSBY/ HARRIS** | 01023134 | 281/328-9200 | 188 |
| Crosby Kindergarten Center/Crosby/Harris | 03321695 | 281/328-9370 | 188 |
| Crosby Middle Sch/Crosby/Harris | 01023160 | 281/328-9264 | 188 |
| Crosby Middle Sch/Hitchcock/Galveston | 01019286 | 409/316-6542 | 165 |
| **CROSBYTON CONS IND SCH DIST/ CROSBYTON/CROSBY** | 01007908 | 806/675-7331 | 98 |
| Crosbyton Elem Sch/Crosbyton/Crosby | 01007946 | 806/675-7331 | 98 |
| Crosbyton High Sch/Crosbyton/Crosby | 01007922 | 806/675-7331 | 98 |
| Cross Lutheran Sch/New Braunfels/Comal | 02733863 | 830/625-3969 | 93 |
| Cross Oaks Elem Sch/Crossroads/Denton | 11559151 | 972/347-7100 | 125 |
| Cross of Christ Lutheran Sch/Desoto/Dallas | 03142815 | 972/223-9586 | 119 |
| Cross Plains Elem Sch/Cross Plains/Callahan | 01003366 | 254/725-6123 | 66 |
| Cross Plains High Sch/Cross Plains/Callahan | 01003378 | 254/725-6121 | 66 |
| **CROSS PLAINS IND SCH DIST/ CROSS PLAINS/CALLAHAN** | 01003354 | 254/725-6121 | 66 |
| Cross Roads Elem Sch/Malakoff/Henderson | 03390397 | 903/489-1774 | 219 |
| Cross Roads High Sch/Malakoff/Henderson | 01029372 | 903/489-1275 | 219 |
| **CROSS ROADS IND SCH DIST/ MALAKOFF/HENDERSON** | 01029360 | 903/489-2001 | 218 |
| Cross Roads Junior High Sch/Malakoff/Henderson | 03390385 | 903/489-2667 | 219 |
| Cross Timbers Elem Sch/Azle/Tarrant | 04813158 | 817/444-3802 | 348 |
| Cross Timbers Intermediate Sch/Arlington/Tarrant | 04149268 | 817/299-3560 | 359 |
| Cross Timbers Middle Sch/Grapevine/Tarrant | 04447905 | 817/251-5320 | 355 |
| Crossroads Academy/Cedar Hill/Dallas | 11231800 | 972/293-9093 | 119 |
| Crossroads Academy High Sch/Uvalde/Uvalde | 12370245 | 830/333-7002 | 381 |
| Crossroads Alt Tech Sch/Houston/Harris | 10028252 | 281/988-3266 | 187 |
| Crossroads Alternative Center/San Antonio/Bexar | 12169618 | 210/622-4670 | 46 |
| Crossroads Christian Academy/Fort Worth/Tarrant | 11226768 | 817/378-0100 | 361 |
| Crossroads Connect Academy/Bloomington/Victoria | 12468763 | 361/237-3061 | 384 |
| Crossroads High Sch/Burleson/Johnson | 04808177 | 817/245-0500 | 249 |
| Crossroads High Sch/Copperas Cove/Coryell | 04452053 | 254/547-9164 | 96 |
| Crossroads Sch/Houston/Harris | 04023353 | 713/977-1221 | 210 |
| Crosstimbers Academy/Weatherford/Parker | 10795027 | 817/594-6220 | 2 |
| Crosswinds Accelerated HS/Grand Prairie/Dallas | 03393387 | 972/522-2950 | 111 |
| Crouch Elem Sch/Grand Prairie/Tarrant | 04456786 | 682/867-0200 | 346 |
| Crow Leadership Academy/Arlington/Tarrant | 01051703 | 682/867-1850 | 346 |
| Crowell Elem Sch/Crowell/Foard | 01018098 | 940/684-1878 | 153 |
| Crowell High Sch/Crowell/Foard | 01018103 | 940/684-1331 | 153 |
| **CROWELL IND SCH DIST/CROWELL/ FOARD** | 01018086 | 940/684-1403 | 153 |
| Crowley High Sch/Crowley/Tarrant | 01052379 | 817/297-5810 | 350 |
| Crowley HS 9th Grade Campus/Crowley/Tarrant | 04364315 | 817/297-5845 | 350 |
| **CROWLEY IND SCH DIST/CROWLEY/ TARRANT** | 01052355 | 817/297-5800 | 350 |

| School/City/County<br>DISTRICT/CITY/COUNTY | PID | TELEPHONE<br>NUMBER | PAGE |
|---|---|---|---|
| Crowley Learning Center/Crowley/Tarrant | 04755128 | 817/297-6992 | 350 |
| Crowley Middle Sch/Fort Worth/Tarrant | 04035459 | 817/370-5650 | 350 |
| Crown of Life Lutheran Sch/Colleyville/<br>Tarrant | 04836916 | 817/251-1881 | 361 |
| Crutchfield Elem Sch/Sherman/Grayson | 01020649 | 903/891-6565 | 172 |
| Cryar Intermediate Sch/Conroe/Montgomery | 05344667 | 936/709-7300 | 294 |
| Crystal City High Sch/Crystal City/Zavala | 01062336 | 830/374-2341 | 410 |
| **CRYSTAL CITY IND SCH DIST/**<br>**CRYSTAL CITY/ZAVALA** | 01062295 | 830/374-2367 | 410 |
| Cte Early College High Sch/Weslaco/Hidalgo | 12032649 | 956/969-6742 | 228 |
| Cuero High Sch/Cuero/De Witt | 01013696 | 361/275-1900 | 122 |
| **CUERO IND SCH DIST/CUERO/DE WITT** | 01013684 | 361/275-1900 | 121 |
| Cuero Junior High Sch/Cuero/De Witt | 01013701 | 361/275-1900 | 122 |
| **CULBERSON CO ALLAMOORE IND SD/**<br>**VAN HORN/CULBERSON** | 01008029 | 432/283-2245 | 99 |
| Cullen Middle Sch/Houston/Harris | 01024798 | 713/746-8180 | 193 |
| Cullender Kindergarten/Monahans/Ward | 01832234 | 432/943-5252 | 388 |
| Culver Elem Sch/Rosenberg/Fort Bend | 12364131 | 832/223-5600 | 158 |
| Cumberland Academy/Tyler/Smith | 04813445 | 903/581-2890 | 2 |
| Cumby Elem Sch/Cumby/Hopkins | 01857301 | 903/994-2260 | 234 |
| Cumby High Sch/Cumby/Hopkins | 05342736 | 903/994-2260 | 234 |
| **CUMBY IND SCH DIST/CUMBY/HOPKINS** | 01031492 | 903/994-2260 | 234 |
| Cummings Elem Sch/Houston/Harris | 02201470 | 281/983-8328 | 187 |
| Cunae International Sch/Spring/Harris | 11720076 | 281/516-3770 | 210 |
| Cunningham Elem Sch/Austin/Travis | 01056155 | 512/414-2067 | 369 |
| Cunningham Elem Sch/Houston/Harris | 01024774 | 713/295-5223 | 198 |
| Cunningham Elem Sch/Wichita Falls/Wichita | 01173014 | 940/235-1144 | 395 |
| Curington Elem Sch/Boerne/Kendall | 01035852 | 830/357-4000 | 257 |
| Curtis Elem Sch/Beaumont/Jefferson | 01034248 | 409/617-6050 | 245 |
| Curtis Elem Sch/Weatherford/Parker | 03006065 | 817/598-2838 | 317 |
| Cushing Elem Sch/Cushing/Nacogdoches | 01043146 | 936/326-4234 | 300 |
| **CUSHING IND SCH DIST/CUSHING/**<br>**NACOGDOCHES** | 01043134 | 936/326-4890 | 300 |
| Cushing Jr Sr High Sch/Cushing/Nacogdoches | 01043158 | 936/326-4890 | 300 |
| Cy-Fair High Sch/Cypress/Harris | 01023249 | 281/897-4600 | 189 |
| Cypress Bendadventist ES/Jefferson/Marion | 02234386 | 903/665-7402 | 277 |
| Cypress Cmty Christian Sch/Houston/Harris | 02164731 | 281/469-8829 | 210 |
| Cypress Creek High Sch/Houston/Harris | 01548407 | 281/897-4200 | 189 |
| Cypress Elem Sch/Cedar Park/Williamson | 03049378 | 512/570-5400 | 400 |
| Cypress Falls High Sch/Houston/Harris | 04016582 | 281/856-1000 | 189 |
| Cypress Grove Intermediate Sch/College Sta/<br>Brazos | 04282470 | 979/694-5600 | 59 |
| Cypress Lakes High Sch/Katy/Harris | 11077385 | 281/856-3800 | 189 |
| Cypress Park High Sch/Cypress/Harris | 11077373 | 281/373-2300 | 189 |
| Cypress Ranch High Sch/Cypress/Harris | 11077373 | 281/373-2300 | 189 |
| Cypress Ridge High Sch/Houston/Harris | 05026322 | 281/807-8045 | 189 |
| Cypress Springs High Sch/Cypress/Harris | 04751598 | 281/345-3000 | 189 |
| Cypress Woods High Sch/Cypress/Harris | 10025999 | 281/213-1800 | 189 |
| **CYPRESS-FAIRBANKS IND SCH DIST/**<br>**HOUSTON/HARRIS** | 01023184 | 281/897-4000 | 188 |
| Cypresswood Elem Sch/Humble/Harris | 12104395 | 281/227-3370 | 185 |

**D**

| | | | |
|---|---|---|---|
| D A Hulcy Steam Middle Sch/Dallas/Dallas | 12109462 | 214/932-7400 | 103 |
| D C Cannon Elem Sch/Quinlan/Hunt | 02199607 | 903/356-1300 | 240 |
| D D Hachar Elem Sch/Laredo/Webb | 01059248 | 956/273-3500 | 389 |
| D L Rountree Elem Sch/Allen/Collin | 01005998 | 972/727-0550 | 80 |
| D McRae Elem Sch/Fort Worth/Tarrant | 01052733 | 817/814-0500 | 352 |
| D P Morris Elem Sch/Arlington/Tarrant | 04804377 | 817/299-7860 | 359 |
| **D'HANIS IND SCH DIST/D HANIS/**<br>**MEDINA** | 01041162 | 830/363-7216 | 286 |
| D'Hanis Sch/D Hanis/Medina | 01041174 | 830/363-7216 | 286 |
| Da Vinci School Science & Arts/El Paso/<br>El Paso | 11014125 | 915/584-4024 | 2 |
| Daep/China Spring/McLennan | 12035158 | 254/836-0676 | 282 |
| Daep/Schertz/Guadalupe | 05342920 | 210/945-6413 | 178 |
| Daep/WHT Settlemt/Tarrant | 11935426 | 817/367-1364 | 360 |
| Daep Center/Atlanta/Cass | 04447060 | 903/799-1044 | 73 |
| Daep Sch/La Porte/Harris | 12469298 | 281/604-7350 | 203 |
| Daep/Seas Center/Garciasville/Starr | 03390531 | 956/488-0014 | 343 |
| Daffron Elem Sch/Plano/Collin | 03333791 | 469/752-0900 | 86 |
| Daggett Montessori Elem Sch/Fort Worth/<br>Tarrant | 04946054 | 817/814-6300 | 353 |
| Dahlstrom Middle Sch/Buda/Hays | 02855796 | 512/268-8441 | 216 |
| Dailey Middle Sch/Austin/Travis | 11556226 | 512/386-3600 | 372 |
| Daingerfield High Sch/Daingerfield/Morris | 01042958 | 903/645-3968 | 299 |
| Daingerfield Jr High Sch/Daingerfield/<br>Morris | 01042960 | 903/645-2261 | 299 |
| **DAINGERFIELD-LONE STAR IND SD/**<br>**DAINGERFIELD/MORRIS** | 01042946 | 903/645-2239 | 299 |
| Dale B Davis Elem Sch/Carrollton/Dallas | 01418254 | 972/968-1500 | 100 |

| School/City/County<br>DISTRICT/CITY/COUNTY | PID | TELEPHONE<br>NUMBER | PAGE |
|---|---|---|---|
| Dalhart Christian Academy/Dalhart/Dallam | 04994099 | 806/244-6482 | 99 |
| Dalhart Elem Sch/Dalhart/Dallam | 01008081 | 806/244-7350 | 99 |
| Dalhart High Sch/Dalhart/Dallam | 01008093 | 806/244-7300 | 99 |
| **DALHART IND SCH DIST/DALHART/**<br>**DALLAM** | 01008067 | 806/244-7810 | 99 |
| Dalhart Intermediate Sch/Dalhart/Dallam | 02882402 | 806/244-7380 | 99 |
| Dalhart Junior High Sch/Dalhart/Dallam | 01008079 | 806/244-7825 | 99 |
| Dallas Academy/Dallas/Dallas | 01012771 | 214/324-1481 | 119 |
| Dallas Christian Academy/Dallas/Dallas | 03017399 | 214/528-6327 | 119 |
| Dallas Christian Sch/Mesquite/Dallas | 01479820 | 972/270-5495 | 119 |
| Dallas Co Jj Aae-Letot Ctr/Dallas/Dallas | 11571214 | 214/956-2036 | 100 |
| Dallas Co Jj Aae-Medlock/Dallas/Dallas | 11571173 | 972/225-9735 | 100 |
| Dallas Co Jj Aae-SAU/Dallas/Dallas | 11571202 | 214/860-4370 | 100 |
| Dallas Co Jj CS-Drc Campus/Dallas/Dallas | 11571197 | 214/637-6136 | 100 |
| Dallas Co Jj CS-Main Camp/Dallas/Dallas | 04893603 | 214/637-6136 | 100 |
| **DALLAS CO SCHOOLS/DALLAS/DALLAS** | 02090673 | 214/598-2200 | 99 |
| Dallas Environmental Sci Acad/Dallas/<br>Dallas | 01009853 | 972/794-3950 | 103 |
| **DALLAS IND SCH DIST/DALLAS/**<br>**DALLAS** | 01008354 | 972/925-3700 | 102 |
| Dallas International Sch/Dallas/Collin | 11748015 | 469/250-0001 | 89 |
| Dallas International Sch/Dallas/Dallas | 05162275 | 972/991-6379 | 119 |
| Dallas Park Elem Sch/Fort Worth/Tarrant | 05092565 | 817/370-5620 | 350 |
| Dalton Early Childhood Center/Uvalde/<br>Uvalde | 01057836 | 830/591-4933 | 381 |
| **DAMON IND SCH DIST/DAMON/**<br>**BRAZORIA** | 01001796 | 979/742-3457 | 56 |
| Damon Sch/Damon/Brazoria | 01001801 | 979/742-3457 | 56 |
| Dan D Rogers Elem Sch/Dallas/Dallas | 01008718 | 972/794-8800 | 103 |
| Dan Dipert Career & Tech Ctr/Arlington/<br>Tarrant | 12231144 | 682/867-9500 | 346 |
| Dan F Long Middle Sch/Dallas/Dallas | 02128713 | 972/968-4100 | 100 |
| Dan J Kubacak Elem Sch/Santa Fe/Galveston | 04920414 | 409/925-9600 | 165 |
| Dan Powell Intermediate Sch/Fort Worth/<br>Tarrant | 10012411 | 817/568-3523 | 352 |
| Danbury Elem Sch/Danbury/Brazoria | 01001825 | 979/922-8787 | 56 |
| Danbury High Sch/Danbury/Brazoria | 01001837 | 979/922-1226 | 56 |
| **DANBURY IND SCH DIST/DANBURY/**<br>**BRAZORIA** | 01001813 | 979/922-1218 | 56 |
| Danbury Middle Sch/Danbury/Brazoria | 05027015 | 979/922-1226 | 56 |
| Danforth Junior High Sch/Wimberley/Hays | 04744832 | 512/847-2181 | 217 |
| Daniel Intermediate Sch/Duncanville/Dallas | 03048166 | 972/708-3200 | 108 |
| Daniel Ramirez Elem Sch/Pharr/Hidalgo | 02178378 | 956/354-2880 | 226 |
| Daniel Singleterry Sr Elem Sch/Donna/<br>Hidalgo | 05330317 | 956/464-1845 | 220 |
| Daniel Webster Elem Sch/Dallas/Dallas | 01008720 | 972/794-6100 | 103 |
| Daniels Acad of Sci & Math/Grand Prairie/<br>Dallas | 01010840 | 972/264-7803 | 111 |
| Daniels Elem Sch/Kerrville/Kerr | 01036131 | 830/257-2208 | 259 |
| Danielson Middle Sch/Leander/Williamson | 12473184 | 512/570-3900 | 400 |
| Danish Elem Sch/Houston/Harris | 10002143 | 281/955-4981 | 189 |
| Danny Jones Middle Sch/Mansfield/Tarrant | 05347425 | 682/314-4600 | 359 |
| Danville Middle Sch/New Braunfels/Comal | 12307298 | 830/837-7400 | 91 |
| **DARROUZETT IND SCH DIST/**<br>**DARROUZETT/LIPSCOMB** | 01038165 | 806/624-2221 | 270 |
| Darrouzett Sch/Darrouzett/Lipscomb | 01038177 | 806/624-3001 | 270 |
| Dartmouth Elem Sch/Richardson/Dallas | 01011662 | 469/593-8400 | 116 |
| Darul Arqam Sch/Houston/Harris | 04993239 | 713/948-0094 | 210 |
| Darul Arqam School-North/Houston/Harris | 11551185 | 281/583-1984 | 210 |
| Darwin L Gilmore Elem Sch/League City/<br>Galveston | 10004191 | 281/284-6400 | 163 |
| Daugherty Elem Sch/Garland/Dallas | 01010759 | 972/926-2530 | 109 |
| Dave Blair Elem Sch/Farmers BRNCH/Dallas | 05098363 | 972/968-1000 | 100 |
| Davenport High Sch/San Antonio/Comal | 12468139 | 830/837-7500 | 91 |
| David Anthony Middle Sch/Cypress/Harris | 12032314 | 281/373-5660 | 189 |
| David Crockett Academy/San Antonio/Bexar | 00998421 | 210/738-9785 | 43 |
| David Crockett Elem Sch/Baytown/Harris | 02128567 | 281/420-4645 | 192 |
| David Crockett Elem Sch/Corp Christi/<br>Nueces | 01044310 | 361/878-2220 | 306 |
| David Crockett Elem Sch/Marshall/Harrison | 01028639 | 903/927-8880 | 214 |
| David Crockett Middle Sch/Amarillo/Potter | 01047221 | 806/326-3300 | 320 |
| David Crockett Middle Sch/Richmond/<br>Fort Bend | 10912859 | 281/634-6380 | 154 |
| David E Smith Elem Sch/Haltom City/Tarrant | 01052056 | 817/547-1600 | 348 |
| David Elem Sch/The Woodlands/Montgomery | 03325354 | 281/298-4700 | 294 |
| David G Burnet Elem Sch/Dallas/Dallas | 01008744 | 972/794-3000 | 103 |
| David K Sellars Elem Sch/Fort Worth/<br>Tarrant | 01052757 | 817/815-9200 | 353 |
| David L Walker Interm Sch/Fort Worth/<br>Tarrant | 11562005 | 817/568-2745 | 350 |
| David McCall Elem Sch/Plano/Collin | 10008331 | 469/752-4500 | 86 |
| David S Crockett ECC/Ennis/Ellis | 05035012 | 972/872-7131 | 144 |

| School/City/County DISTRICT/CITY/COUNTY | PID | TELEPHONE NUMBER | PAGE |
|---|---|---|---|
| David Sanchez Elem Sch/La Feria/Cameron | 10915265 | 956/797-8550 | 69 |
| David Tex Hill Middle Sch/San Antonio/ Bexar | 12033540 | 210/356-8000 | 37 |
| David W Carter High Sch/Dallas/Dallas | 01008691 | 214/932-5700 | 103 |
| Davila Elem Sch/Houston/Harris | 03336690 | 713/924-1851 | 194 |
| Davis 9th Grade Center/Everman/Tarrant | 11006336 | 817/568-5280 | 352 |
| Davis 9th Grade Sch/Houston/Harris | 11919707 | 281/873-1800 | 185 |
| Davis Elem Sch/Austin/Travis | 04015150 | 512/414-2580 | 369 |
| Davis Elem Sch/Garland/Dallas | 01010503 | 972/494-8205 | 109 |
| Davis Elem Sch/Plano/Collin | 01006394 | 469/752-1000 | 86 |
| Davis Elem Sch/Royse City/Rockwall | 03004586 | 972/636-9549 | 329 |
| Davis Middle Sch/San Antonio/Bexar | 00998768 | 210/978-7920 | 43 |
| Davis Senior High Sch/Houston/Harris | 11821277 | 281/539-4070 | 185 |
| Dawson Elem Sch/Austin/Travis | 01056430 | 512/414-2070 | 369 |
| Dawson Elem Sch/Corp Christi/Nueces | 04754916 | 361/878-0140 | 306 |
| **DAWSON IND SCH DIST/DAWSON/ NAVARRO** | 01043524 | 254/578-1031 | 302 |
| **DAWSON IND SCH DIST/WELCH/DAWSON** | 01012795 | 806/489-7461 | 121 |
| Dawson Sch/Dawson/Navarro | 01043536 | 254/578-1031 | 302 |
| Dawson Sch/Welch/Dawson | 01012812 | 806/489-7461 | 121 |
| Dawson-Hillmon Alt Ed Center/Queen City/ Cass | 04744234 | 903/796-0774 | 74 |
| DayStar Academy/Castroville/Medina | 11815400 | 830/931-0808 | 287 |
| Dayton High Sch/Dayton/Liberty | 01037795 | 936/258-2510 | 268 |
| **DAYTON IND SCH DIST/DAYTON/ LIBERTY** | 01037771 | 936/258-2667 | 268 |
| De Chaumes Elem Sch/Houston/Harris | 01025869 | 713/696-2676 | 195 |
| De Kalb Elem Sch/De Kalb/Bowie | 01000821 | 903/667-2328 | 51 |
| De Kalb High Sch/De Kalb/Bowie | 01000833 | 903/667-2422 | 51 |
| **DE KALB IND SCH DIST/DE KALB/ BOWIE** | 01000819 | 903/667-2566 | 51 |
| De Kalb Middle Sch/De Kalb/Bowie | 01000845 | 903/667-2834 | 51 |
| De La Vina Elem Sch/Edinburg/Hidalgo | 02856025 | 956/289-2366 | 221 |
| De Leon Elem Sch/De Leon/Comanche | 01007104 | 254/893-8220 | 93 |
| De Leon High Sch/De Leon/Comanche | 01007116 | 254/893-8240 | 93 |
| **DE LEON IND SCH DIST/DE LEON/ COMANCHE** | 01007099 | 254/893-8210 | 93 |
| De Santiago EC-PK-K Sch/Houston/Harris | 04805010 | 281/985-7500 | 186 |
| De Zavala Elem Sch/Channelview/Harris | 01023108 | 281/452-6008 | 188 |
| De Zavala Elem Sch/Fort Worth/Tarrant | 01052771 | 817/814-5600 | 353 |
| De Zavala Elem Sch/Houston/Harris | 01025479 | 713/924-1888 | 194 |
| De Zavala Elem Sch/San Antonio/Bexar | 00999138 | 210/978-7975 | 43 |
| De Zavala Elem Sch/San Marcos/Hays | 02896087 | 512/393-6250 | 217 |
| Deady Middle Sch/Houston/Harris | 01025560 | 713/845-7411 | 193 |
| Dean H Krueger Elem Sch/San Antonio/Bexar | 10009488 | 210/397-3850 | 40 |
| Dean Highland Elem Sch/Waco/McLennan | 01040209 | 254/752-3751 | 285 |
| Dean Leaman Junior High Sch/Fulshear/ Fort Bend | 12165301 | 832/223-5200 | 158 |
| Dean Middle Sch/Houston/Harris | 01023225 | 713/460-6153 | 189 |
| Deanna Davenport Elem Sch/Canutillo/ El Paso | 03325469 | 915/886-6400 | 136 |
| Dearing Elem Sch/Round Rock/Travis | 12033045 | 512/594-4500 | 374 |
| Debakey High Sch-Health Prof/Houston/ Harris | 01385437 | 713/741-2410 | 196 |
| Decatur High Sch/Decatur/Wise | 01061679 | 940/393-7200 | 406 |
| **DECATUR IND SCH DIST/DECATUR/ WISE** | 01061655 | 940/393-7100 | 406 |
| Decker Elem Sch/Austin/Travis | 04866090 | 512/278-4150 | 373 |
| Decker Middle Sch/Austin/Travis | 11397056 | 512/278-4630 | 373 |
| Decker Prairie Elem Sch/Magnolia/Harris | 02202606 | 281/357-3134 | 208 |
| Deep Wood Elem Sch/Round Rock/Williamson | 01541423 | 512/464-4400 | 401 |
| Deepwater Elem Sch/Pasadena/Harris | 01023330 | 832/668-8300 | 191 |
| Deepwater Junior High Sch/Pasadena/Harris | 01023342 | 832/668-7600 | 191 |
| Deer Creek Elem Sch/Cedar Park/Williamson | 05345570 | 512/570-6300 | 400 |
| Deer Creek Elem Sch/Crowley/Tarrant | 01401433 | 817/297-5880 | 350 |
| Deer Park Elem Sch/Deer Park/Harris | 01023354 | 832/668-8000 | 191 |
| Deer Park High Sch-N Campus/Deer Park/ Harris | 01023366 | 832/668-7300 | 191 |
| Deer Park High Sch-S Campus/Deer Park/ Harris | 02203014 | 832/668-7200 | 191 |
| **DEER PARK IND SCH DIST/DEER PARK/ HARRIS** | 01023316 | 832/668-7000 | 191 |
| Deer Park Junior High Sch/Deer Park/Harris | 01023378 | 832/668-7500 | 191 |
| Deerpark HS Wolters Campus/Deer Park/ Harris | 03391224 | 832/668-7400 | 191 |
| Deerpark Middle Sch/Austin/Williamson | 03067784 | 512/464-6600 | 401 |
| Deerwood Elem Sch/Kingwood/Harris | 02848688 | 281/641-2200 | 201 |
| Degan Elem Sch/Lewisville/Denton | 01013438 | 469/713-5967 | 127 |
| Del Castillo Elem Sch/Brownsville/Cameron | 01003536 | 956/982-2600 | 67 |
| Del Norte Heights Elem Sch/El Paso/El Paso | 01016351 | 915/434-2400 | 142 |
| Del Rio Freshman Sch/Del Rio/Val Verde | 02202333 | 830/778-4400 | 382 |
| Del Rio High Sch/Del Rio/Val Verde | 01057965 | 830/778-4300 | 382 |

| School/City/County DISTRICT/CITY/COUNTY | PID | TELEPHONE NUMBER | PAGE |
|---|---|---|---|
| Del Rio Middle Sch/Del Rio/Val Verde | 01057977 | 830/778-4500 | 382 |
| Del Valle Dist Alt Ed Program/Austin/ Travis | 12035067 | 512/386-3180 | 372 |
| Del Valle Elem Sch/Del Valle/Travis | 05102914 | 512/386-3350 | 372 |
| Del Valle Elem Sch/El Paso/El Paso | 11713022 | 915/434-9300 | 142 |
| Del Valle High Sch/Del Valle/Travis | 01056791 | 512/386-3200 | 372 |
| Del Valle High Sch/El Paso/El Paso | 03010975 | 915/434-3000 | 142 |
| **DEL VALLE IND SCH DIST/DEL VALLE/ TRAVIS** | 01056789 | 512/386-3010 | 372 |
| Del Valle Middle Sch/Del Valle/Travis | 01056806 | 512/386-3400 | 372 |
| Del Valle Middle Sch/El Paso/El Paso | 01545259 | 915/434-3300 | 142 |
| Del Valle Opportunity Center/Del Valle/ Travis | 03473547 | 512/386-3300 | 372 |
| Delay Middle Sch/Lewisville/Denton | 01013440 | 469/713-5191 | 127 |
| Delco Primary Sch/Austin/Travis | 05098454 | 512/594-6200 | 374 |
| DeLeon Elem Sch/Victoria/Victoria | 02112257 | 361/788-9553 | 384 |
| Delia Gonzalez Garcia ES/Rio Grande Cy/ Starr | 04452352 | 956/849-8450 | 343 |
| **DELL CITY IND SCH DIST/DELL CITY/ HUDSPETH** | 01032147 | 915/964-2663 | 237 |
| Dell City Sch/Dell City/Hudspeth | 01032159 | 915/964-2663 | 237 |
| Della Icenhower Interm Sch/Arlington/ Tarrant | 05350068 | 817/299-2700 | 359 |
| Dellview Elem Sch/San Antonio/Bexar | 00997738 | 210/407-2600 | 37 |
| Deloras E Thompson Elem Sch/Houston/Harris | 04452871 | 281/891-8480 | 207 |
| Delta Academy/El Paso/El Paso | 04828543 | 915/774-0447 | 137 |
| Democracy Prep Stewart/San Antonio/Bexar | 00998988 | 210/438-6875 | 43 |
| Denison High Sch/Denison/Grayson | 01020326 | 903/462-7125 | 171 |
| **DENISON IND SCH DIST/DENISON/ GRAYSON** | 01020297 | 903/462-7000 | 171 |
| Dennis Miller Elem Sch/Richardson/Collin | 04366791 | 469/752-2700 | 86 |
| Denton Calvary Academy/Denton/Denton | 05302023 | 940/320-1944 | 130 |
| Denton Classical Academy/Denton/Denton | 12162957 | 940/565-8333 | 2 |
| Denton Creek Elem Sch/Coppell/Dallas | 04808787 | 214/496-8100 | 102 |
| Denton Creek Sch/Roanoke/Denton | 04917845 | 817/215-0920 | 129 |
| Denton High Sch/Denton/Denton | 04011817 | 940/369-2000 | 125 |
| **DENTON IND SCH DIST/DENTON/ DENTON** | 01013220 | 940/369-0000 | 124 |
| Denver Alternative Center/Wichita Falls/ Wichita | 04286921 | 940/235-1101 | 395 |
| Denver City High Sch/Denver City/Yoakum | 01062037 | 806/592-5950 | 409 |
| **DENVER CITY IND SCH DIST/ DENVER CITY/YOAKUM** | 01062013 | 806/592-5900 | 409 |
| Depelchin-Richmond Charter Sch/Richmond/ Fort Bend | 12100428 | 713/558-3980 | 2 |
| Deport Elem Sch/Deport/Lamar | 01036806 | 903/652-3325 | 263 |
| Dequeen Elem Sch/Port Arthur/Jefferson | 01033763 | 409/984-8900 | 246 |
| Deretchin Elem Sch/The Woodlands/ Montgomery | 10007569 | 832/592-8700 | 294 |
| Derry Elem Sch/Port Isabel/Cameron | 01004073 | 956/943-0070 | 70 |
| Desert Hills Elem Sch/El Paso/El Paso | 03051345 | 915/926-4500 | 136 |
| Desert View Middle Sch/El Paso/El Paso | 02131071 | 915/434-5300 | 142 |
| Desert Wind Elem Sch/El Paso/El Paso | 05272313 | 915/937-7800 | 140 |
| Desertaire Elem Sch/El Paso/El Paso | 03325495 | 915/434-6400 | 142 |
| Design & Technology Academy/San Antonio/ Bexar | 11452230 | 210/356-2237 | 38 |
| DeSoto Alt Sch/Desoto/Dallas | 04749296 | 972/223-2242 | 108 |
| DeSoto High Sch/Desoto/Dallas | 01010266 | 972/230-0726 | 108 |
| **DESOTO IND SCH DIST/DESOTO/ DALLAS** | 01010242 | 972/223-6666 | 108 |
| DeSoto Pvt Sch & Day Care Ctr/Desoto/ Dallas | 02734829 | 972/223-6450 | 119 |
| Dessau Elem Sch/Austin/Travis | 03011656 | 512/594-4600 | 374 |
| Dessau Middle Sch/Austin/Travis | 04920206 | 512/594-2600 | 374 |
| Detroit Elem Sch/Detroit/Red River | 01048184 | 903/674-3137 | 325 |
| Detroit High Sch/Detroit/Red River | 05256864 | 903/674-2646 | 325 |
| **DETROIT IND SCH DIST/DETROIT/ RED RIVER** | 01048172 | 903/674-6131 | 325 |
| Detroit Middle Sch/Detroit/Red River | 01048196 | 903/674-2646 | 325 |
| Devers Elem Sch/Devers/Liberty | 01037836 | 936/549-7591 | 268 |
| **DEVERS IND SCH DIST/DEVERS/ LIBERTY** | 01037824 | 936/549-7591 | 268 |
| Devine High Sch/Devine/Medina | 01041215 | 830/851-0895 | 286 |
| **DEVINE IND SCH DIST/DEVINE/ MEDINA** | 01041198 | 830/851-0795 | 286 |
| Devine Intermediate Sch/Devine/Medina | 03318844 | 830/851-0495 | 286 |
| Devine Middle Sch/Devine/Medina | 01041227 | 830/851-0695 | 286 |
| Devonian Elem Sch/Andrews/Andrews | 00994736 | 432/524-1950 | 19 |
| Dew Elem Sch/Teague/Freestone | 01018440 | 903/389-2828 | 160 |
| **DEW IND SCH DIST/TEAGUE/ FREESTONE** | 01018438 | 903/389-2828 | 160 |
| Deweyville Elem Sch/Orange/Newton | 01043720 | 409/746-2731 | 311 |

| School/City/County DISTRICT/CITY/COUNTY | PID | TELEPHONE NUMBER | PAGE |
|---|---|---|---|
| **DEWEYVILLE IND SCH DIST/** ORANGE/NEWTON | 01043718 | 409/746-2731 | 311 |
| Deweyville Jr Sr High Sch/Orange/Newton | 01043732 | 409/746-2685 | 311 |
| DeWitt Perry Middle Sch/Carrollton/Dallas | 01008225 | 972/968-4400 | 100 |
| Dezavala Elem Sch/Midland/Midland | 01041485 | 432/240-6600 | 288 |
| Dezavala Environ Science Acad/Grand Prairie/ Dallas | 01540015 | 972/642-0448 | 111 |
| Diamond Hill Elem Sch/Fort Worth/Tarrant | 01052783 | 817/815-0400 | 353 |
| Diamond Hill-Jarvis High Sch/Fort Worth/ Tarrant | 01052795 | 817/815-0000 | 353 |
| Diane Patrick Elem Sch/Grand Prairie/ Tarrant | 12105985 | 682/867-0600 | 346 |
| Diane Winborn Elem Sch/Katy/Harris | 02131679 | 281/237-6650 | 156 |
| Diaz Junior High Sch/Hidalgo/Hidalgo | 02202436 | 956/843-4350 | 222 |
| Diaz-Villarreal Elem Sch/Mission/Hidalgo | 04457833 | 956/323-2470 | 223 |
| Diboll High Sch/Diboll/Angelina | 00994839 | 936/829-5626 | 20 |
| **DIBOLL IND SCH DIST/DIBOLL/** ANGELINA | 00994815 | 936/829-4718 | 20 |
| Diboll Junior High Sch/Diboll/Angelina | 00994841 | 936/829-5225 | 20 |
| Diboll Primary Sch/Diboll/Angelina | 03240314 | 936/829-4671 | 20 |
| Dickinson Alt Lrng Center/Dickinson/ Galveston | 04747810 | 281/229-6300 | 164 |
| Dickinson Elem Sch/Grand Prairie/Dallas | 02126727 | 972/641-1664 | 111 |
| Dickinson High Sch/Dickinson/Galveston | 01018983 | 281/229-6400 | 164 |
| **DICKINSON IND SCH DIST/DICKINSON/** GALVESTON | 01018969 | 281/229-6000 | 164 |
| Digital Arts Tech Acad-Adams/Grand Prairie/ Dallas | 01010943 | 972/262-1934 | 111 |
| Dillard Spec Achievement Ctr/Allen/Collin | 04913148 | 972/727-7163 | 80 |
| Dilley Early Clg High Sch/Dilley/Frio | 12171752 | 830/965-1814 | 161 |
| Dilley Elem Sch/Dilley/Frio | 01018581 | 830/965-1313 | 161 |
| Dilley High Sch/Dilley/Frio | 01018593 | 830/965-1814 | 161 |
| **DILLEY IND SCH DIST/DILLEY/FRIO** | 01018579 | 830/965-1912 | 161 |
| Dillingham Intermediate Sch/Sherman/ Grayson | 01020601 | 903/891-6495 | 172 |
| **DIME BOX IND SCH DIST/DIME BOX/** LEE | 01037422 | 979/884-2324 | 266 |
| Dime Box Sch/Dime Box/Lee | 01037446 | 979/884-3366 | 266 |
| Dimmitt Alternative Center/Dimmitt/Castro | 04448636 | 806/647-5186 | 74 |
| Dimmitt High Sch/Dimmitt/Castro | 01004970 | 806/647-3105 | 74 |
| **DIMMITT IND SCH DIST/DIMMITT/** CASTRO | 01004968 | 806/647-3101 | 74 |
| Dimmitt Middle Sch/Dimmitt/Castro | 01004994 | 806/647-3108 | 74 |
| **DIOCESE CORPUS CHRISTI ED OFF/** CORP CHRISTI/NUECES | 01045170 | 361/882-6191 | 309 |
| **DIOCESE OF AMARILLO ED OFFICE/** AMARILLO/POTTER | 01047659 | 806/383-2243 | 322 |
| **DIOCESE OF AUSTIN ED OFFICE/** AUSTIN/TRAVIS | 01420568 | 512/949-2497 | 375 |
| **DIOCESE OF BEAUMONT SCH OFFICE/** BEAUMONT/JEFFERSON | 01034339 | 409/924-4300 | 247 |
| **DIOCESE OF BROWNSVILLE ED OFF/** SAN JUAN/HIDALGO | 01004372 | 956/781-5323 | 229 |
| **DIOCESE OF DALLAS ED OFFICE/** DALLAS/DALLAS | 01012367 | 214/528-2240 | 118 |
| **DIOCESE OF EL PASO ED OFFICE/** EL PASO/EL PASO | 01016703 | 915/872-8426 | 143 |
| **DIOCESE OF FORT WORTH ED OFF/** FORT WORTH/TARRANT | 01054339 | 817/560-3300 | 360 |
| **DIOCESE OF LAREDO ED OFFICE/** LAREDO/WEBB | 04938095 | 956/753-5208 | 391 |
| **DIOCESE OF LUBBOCK ED OFFICE/** LUBBOCK/LUBBOCK | 02204290 | 806/795-8283 | 275 |
| **DIOCESE OF SAN ANGELO ED OFF/** SAN ANGELO/TOM GREEN | 01055929 | 325/651-7500 | 368 |
| **DIOCESE OF TYLER ED OFFICE/** TYLER/SMITH | 03014660 | 903/534-1077 | 342 |
| **DIOCESE OF VICTORIA ED OFFICE/** VICTORIA/VICTORIA | 02181727 | 361/573-0828 | 385 |
| Dirks-Anderson Sch/Fort Davis/Jeff Davis | 01033335 | 432/426-4454 | 244 |
| Disciplinary Alt Ed Program/Bryan/Brazos | 04034211 | 979/209-2752 | 58 |
| Disciplinary Alt Ed Program/Deer Park/ Harris | 10011792 | 832/668-7407 | 191 |
| Disciplinary Alt Ed Program/Donna/Hidalgo | 04750051 | 956/464-1954 | 220 |
| Disciplinary Alt Ed Program/Weslaco/ Hidalgo | 05273472 | 956/969-6916 | 228 |
| Discipline Alt Education Pgrm/Cedar Hill/ Dallas | 04918289 | 972/293-4504 | 101 |
| Discipline Ed Alternative Sch/Quinlan/Hunt | 04871203 | 903/356-1575 | 240 |
| Dishman Elem Sch/Beaumont/Jefferson | 04806923 | 409/617-6250 | 245 |
| Dishman Elem Sch/Combes/Cameron | 01003823 | 956/427-3100 | 68 |
| Ditto Elem Sch/Arlington/Tarrant | 01548483 | 682/867-3100 | 346 |

| School/City/County DISTRICT/CITY/COUNTY | PID | TELEPHONE NUMBER | PAGE |
|---|---|---|---|
| Divide Elem Sch/Mountain Home/Kerr | 01036026 | 830/640-3322 | 258 |
| **DIVIDE ISD SCH DIST/MOUNTAIN HOME/** KERR | 01036014 | 830/640-3322 | 258 |
| Dixie Elem Sch/Tyler/Smith | 01050814 | 903/262-2040 | 340 |
| Dobie Middle Sch/Austin/Travis | 01056181 | 512/414-3270 | 371 |
| Dobie Primary Sch/Dallas/Dallas | 01011727 | 469/593-4100 | 116 |
| **DODD CITY IND SCH DIST/DODD CITY/** FANNIN | 01017422 | 903/583-7585 | 150 |
| Dodd City Sch/Dodd City/Fannin | 01017434 | 903/583-7585 | 150 |
| Dodd Elem Sch/Wylie/Collin | 04876899 | 972/429-3440 | 88 |
| Dodson Primary Sch/Denver City/Yoakum | 12036009 | 806/592-5931 | 409 |
| Doerre Intermediate Sch/Klein/Harris | 02227187 | 832/249-5700 | 202 |
| Dogan Elem Sch/Houston/Harris | 01025481 | 713/671-4110 | 193 |
| Dogwood Elem Sch/New Caney/Montgomery | 12305707 | 281/577-2960 | 296 |
| Dolly F Vogel Intermediate Sch/Spring/ Montgomery | 04948387 | 832/663-4300 | 294 |
| Dolores Huerta Elem Sch/Fort Worth/Tarrant | 05344526 | 817/814-4400 | 353 |
| Dolores Linton Elem Sch/San Antonio/Bexar | 02110120 | 210/397-0750 | 40 |
| Dolores W McClatchey Elem Sch/Midlothian/ Ellis | 12172665 | 469/856-6600 | 145 |
| Dolph Briscoe Middle Sch/San Antonio/Bexar | 11552153 | 210/398-1100 | 40 |
| Dolphin Terrace Elem Sch/El Paso/El Paso | 01016363 | 915/434-6500 | 142 |
| Domingo Trevino Middle Sch/Alton/Hidalgo | 11557050 | 956/323-2810 | 223 |
| Don Carter Elem Sch/Richmond/Fort Bend | 12308371 | 832/223-5500 | 158 |
| Don Durham Intermediate Sch/Southlake/ Tarrant | 04449458 | 817/949 5300 | 349 |
| Don Jeter Elem Sch/Manvel/Brazoria | 05011729 | 281/245-3055 | 54 |
| Don Jose Gallego Elem Sch/Laredo/Webb | 01059212 | 956/273-3100 | 389 |
| Don R Daniel 9th Grade Campus/Aledo/Parker | 11712042 | 817/441-4504 | 315 |
| Don Whitt Elem Sch/Sachse/Collin | 11434795 | 972/429-2560 | 88 |
| Donald Leonetti Elem Sch/Missouri City/ Fort Bend | 12232124 | 281/327-3190 | 154 |
| Donald T Shields Elem Sch/Glenn Heights/ Ellis | 02132049 | 972/617-4799 | 146 |
| Donna High Sch/Donna/Hidalgo | 01029578 | 956/464-1700 | 220 |
| **DONNA IND SCH DIST/DONNA/HIDALGO** | 01029554 | 956/464-1600 | 220 |
| Donna Lewis Elem Sch/Houston/Harris | 10022478 | 281/891-8720 | 207 |
| Donna North High Sch/Donna/Hidalgo | 11920093 | 956/464-4190 | 220 |
| Donna Park Elem Sch/Hurst/Tarrant | 01053799 | 817/285-3285 | 356 |
| Donna Shepard Intermediate Sch/Mansfield/ Tarrant | 04949135 | 817/299-5940 | 359 |
| Donna Wernecke Elem Sch/McAllen/Hidalgo | 10915344 | 956/928-1063 | 227 |
| Dooley Elem Sch/Plano/Collin | 02130895 | 469/752-1100 | 86 |
| Dora M Sauceda Middle Sch/Donna/Hidalgo | 05343522 | 956/464-1360 | 220 |
| Dora Romero Elem Sch/Brownsville/Cameron | 11711581 | 956/254-5210 | 69 |
| Dorie Miller Elem Sch/San Antonio/Bexar | 00998926 | 210/978-7995 | 43 |
| Dorie Miller Interm Sch/Ennis/Ellis | 05035000 | 972/872-3775 | 144 |
| Doris Cullins-Lake Pointe ES/Rowlett/ Rockwall | 03049304 | 972/412-3070 | 328 |
| Doris Miller Middle Sch/San Marcos/Hays | 04365060 | 512/393-6660 | 217 |
| Dorothea Brown Middle Sch/McAllen/Hidalgo | 01523706 | 956/632-8700 | 224 |
| Dorothy Adkins Middle Sch/Corp Christi/ Nueces | 12106551 | 361/878-3800 | 306 |
| Dorothy Carlton Center/Cypress/Harris | 02045379 | 281/213-1950 | 189 |
| Dorothy Smith Pullen Elem Sch/Rockwall/ Rockwall | 04846739 | 972/772-1177 | 328 |
| Dorothy Thompson Middle Sch/Progreso/ Hidalgo | 02178213 | 956/565-1275 | 227 |
| Dorris Jones Elem Sch/Rockwall/Rockwall | 05100186 | 972/772-1070 | 328 |
| **DOSS CONSOLIDATED COMMON SD/** DOSS/GILLESPIE | 01019664 | 830/669-2411 | 167 |
| Doss Elem Sch/Austin/Travis | 01056193 | 512/414-2365 | 369 |
| Doss Elem Sch/Doss/Gillespie | 01019676 | 830/669-2411 | 167 |
| Double File Trail Elem Sch/Round Rock/ Williamson | 02893994 | 512/428-7400 | 401 |
| Douglas B Bussey Elem Sch/Houston/Harris | 05274115 | 281/878-1501 | 185 |
| Douglas Benold Middle Sch/Georgetown/ Williamson | 04455421 | 512/943-5090 | 398 |
| Douglas Elem Sch/Tyler/Smith | 01050838 | 903/262-2100 | 340 |
| Douglas MacArthur High Sch/Houston/Harris | 01022764 | 281/985-6330 | 185 |
| Douglass ECLC/Sulphur Spgs/Hopkins | 01031650 | 903/885-4516 | 235 |
| Douglass Elem Sch/El Paso/El Paso | 01015955 | 915/236-8750 | 137 |
| **DOUGLASS IND SCH DIST/DOUGLASS/** NACOGDOCHES | 01043160 | 936/569-9804 | 300 |
| Douglass Sch/Douglass/Nacogdoches | 01043172 | 936/569-9804 | 300 |
| Dove Elem Sch/Grapevine/Tarrant | 01053701 | 817/251-5700 | 355 |
| Dover Elem Sch/Richardson/Dallas | 01011674 | 469/593-4200 | 116 |
| Dowell Elem Sch/El Paso/El Paso | 01015785 | 915/236-5525 | 137 |
| Dowling Elem Sch/Odessa/Ector | 01014652 | 432/456-1079 | 134 |
| Dowling Elem Sch/Port Arthur/Jefferson | 01033775 | 409/984-4960 | 246 |
| Downing Middle Sch/Flower Mound/Denton | 05091705 | 469/713-5962 | 127 |
| Downtown Montessori Sch/Dallas/Dallas | 12471148 | 972/749-2500 | 103 |

| School/City/County DISTRICT/CITY/COUNTY | PID | TELEPHONE NUMBER | PAGE |
|---|---|---|---|
| Dozier Elem Sch/Fort Worth/Tarrant | 12166367 | 817/847-6340 | 351 |
| Dr Abraham P Cano Fresh Acad/Harlingen/ Cameron | 11920172 | 956/430-4900 | 68 |
| Dr AL Draper Intermediate Sch/Wylie/Collin | 10915708 | 972/429-3350 | 88 |
| Dr Alejo Salinas Sch/Hidalgo/Hidalgo | 04867757 | 956/843-4250 | 222 |
| Dr Allan & Carolyn Bird Ed Ctr/Plano/ Collin | 11717987 | 469/752-2200 | 86 |
| Dr Americo Paredes Elem Sch/Mission/ Hidalgo | 10028202 | 956/323-2730 | 223 |
| Dr Antonio Banuelos Elem Sch/Baytown/ Harris | 12035809 | 281/420-1230 | 192 |
| Dr Armando Cuellar Middle Sch/Weslaco/ Hidalgo | 01030632 | 956/969-6720 | 228 |
| Dr Bernard Harris Middle Sch/San Antonio/ Bexar | 10023393 | 210/356-4100 | 38 |
| Dr Bruce Wood Elem Sch/Terrell/Kaufman | 04149177 | 972/563-3750 | 256 |
| Dr Bryan C Jack Elem Sch/Tyler/Smith | 10911520 | 903/262-3260 | 340 |
| Dr C M Cash Elem Sch/San Benito/Cameron | 01004188 | 956/361-6700 | 70 |
| Dr Carlos Castaneda Elem Sch/McAllen/ Hidalgo | 04948064 | 956/632-8882 | 224 |
| Dr David C Walker Elem Sch/San Antonio/ Bexar | 11015480 | 210/654-4411 | 45 |
| Dr Dennis Cantu Health Sci Sch/Laredo/Webb | 11924685 | 956/795-3874 | 389 |
| Dr E R Richter Elem Sch/Dayton/Liberty | 02129937 | 936/258-7126 | 268 |
| Dr Edward Roberson Middle Sch/Houston/ Harris | 11452010 | 281/891-7700 | 207 |
| Dr Erwin & Elizabeth Pink ES/Frisco/Collin | 10004672 | 469/633-3500 | 82 |
| Dr Fermin Calderon Elem Sch/Del Rio/ Val Verde | 04145389 | 830/778-4620 | 382 |
| Dr Gene Burton C & C Academy/Rockwall/ Rockwall | 12468658 | 469/698-0660 | 328 |
| Dr Harmon W Kelley Elem Sch/San Antonio/ Bexar | 04813457 | 210/431-9881 | 45 |
| Dr Henry Cuellar Elem Sch/Laredo/Webb | 04875211 | 956/473-2700 | 390 |
| Dr Hornedo Middle Sch/El Paso/El Paso | 04288280 | 915/236-3300 | 139 |
| Dr J C Cannaday Elem Sch/Mesquite/Dallas | 03050963 | 972/882-5060 | 115 |
| Dr James D Foster Elem Sch/Riesel/McLennan | 04914647 | 254/896-2297 | 284 |
| Dr James P Terry Middle Sch/Mesquite/ Dallas | 10027337 | 972/882-5650 | 115 |
| Dr James Red Duke Elem Sch/Manvel/Brazoria | 12035926 | 281/245-3400 | 54 |
| Dr Jandrucko Early Learners/Arlington/ Tarrant | 12380460 | 817/299-7650 | 359 |
| Dr Javier Saenz Middle Sch/Penitas/Hidalgo | 05346794 | 956/323-2830 | 223 |
| Dr JM Ogle Elem Sch/McKinney/Collin | 10022387 | 469/633-3525 | 82 |
| Dr Joaquin Cigarroa Middle Sch/Laredo/Webb | 02201183 | 956/273-6100 | 389 |
| Dr Joe Bernal Middle Sch/San Antonio/Bexar | 12033629 | 210/398-1900 | 40 |
| Dr Joe Ward Elem Sch/San Antonio/Bexar | 05273434 | 210/397-6800 | 40 |
| Dr Joey Pirrung Elem Sch/Mesquite/Dallas | 03011929 | 972/882-7170 | 115 |
| Dr John D Horn High Sch/Mesquite/Dallas | 04914817 | 972/882-5200 | 115 |
| Dr Johnny T Clark Jr Elem Sch/Baytown/ Harris | 12035794 | 281/420-7450 | 193 |
| Dr Joseph E Torres/El Paso/El Paso | 01015797 | 915/236-5225 | 137 |
| Dr Kirk Lewis Career & Tech HS/Houston/ Harris | 11927247 | 713/740-5320 | 204 |
| Dr Lee Buice Elem Sch/Odessa/Ector | 12105741 | 432/456-1339 | 134 |
| Dr Leo Cigarroa High Sch/Laredo/Webb | 02201195 | 956/273-6800 | 389 |
| Dr Linda Henrie Elem Sch/Dallas/Dallas | 12108872 | 972/290-4200 | 115 |
| Dr Lonnie Green Elem Sch/Del Rio/Val Verde | 04878263 | 830/778-4750 | 382 |
| Dr M L Garza-Gonzalez Chtr Sch/Corp Christi/ Nueces | 04467515 | 361/881-9988 | 2 |
| Dr Mae Jones-Clark Elem Sch/Beaumont/ Jefferson | 01033517 | 409/617-6350 | 245 |
| Dr Malakoff Elem Sch/Laredo/Webb | 10007387 | 956/473-4800 | 390 |
| Dr Mario Ramirez Elem Sch/Rio Grande Cy/ Starr | 10005925 | 956/487-4457 | 343 |
| Dr Martha Mead Elem Sch/San Antonio/Bexar | 10020676 | 210/397-1750 | 40 |
| Dr Nixon Elem Sch/El Paso/El Paso | 03399862 | 915/236-5900 | 137 |
| Dr Pablo Perez Elem Sch/McAllen/Hidalgo | 10910899 | 956/971-1125 | 224 |
| Dr Palmira Mendiola Elem Sch/Mission/ Hidalgo | 11719258 | 956/323-2420 | 223 |
| Dr Pat Henderson Elem Sch/San Antonio/ Bexar | 11552139 | 210/398-1050 | 40 |
| Dr Paul Saenz Junior High Sch/San Antonio/ Bexar | 11015507 | 210/431-9881 | 45 |
| Dr R D Cathey Middle Sch/McAllen/Hidalgo | 01030010 | 956/971-4300 | 224 |
| Dr R E Margo Elem Sch/Weslaco/Hidalgo | 01030656 | 956/969-6800 | 228 |
| Dr Ralph H Poteet High Sch/Mesquite/Dallas | 02894388 | 972/882-5300 | 115 |
| Dr Raul Garza Jr Elem Sch/San Benito/ Cameron | 04768448 | 956/361-6900 | 70 |
| Dr Ronald E McNair Junior HS/Pearland/ Brazoria | 12374746 | 713/814-7200 | 54 |
| Dr S Perez Elem Sch/Laredo/Webb | 02895083 | 956/473-3600 | 390 |

| School/City/County DISTRICT/CITY/COUNTY | PID | TELEPHONE NUMBER | PAGE |
|---|---|---|---|
| Dr Shirley J Williamson ES/Houston/Harris | 10003367 | 832/386-4000 | 192 |
| Dr Sue Shook Elem Sch/El Paso/El Paso | 10911697 | 915/937-7100 | 140 |
| Dr Tomas Rivera Elem Sch/Crystal City/ Zavala | 12363785 | 830/374-8078 | 410 |
| Dr William Long Elem Sch/Pharr/Hidalgo | 01030371 | 956/354-2750 | 226 |
| Dr Winn Murnin Elem Sch/San Antonio/Bexar | 10020688 | 210/397-4550 | 40 |
| Dr Wright Lassiter Erly Clg HS/Dallas/ Dallas | 04019821 | 214/860-2356 | 103 |
| Dragonfly International Sch/Dripping Spgs/ Hays | 11221940 | 512/858-9780 | 217 |
| Drane Learning Center/Corsicana/Navarro | 12306165 | 903/874-8281 | 302 |
| Draw Acad Early Learning Ctr/Houston/ Harris | 12163913 | 713/706-3729 | 2 |
| Draw Academy/Houston/Harris | 05099252 | 713/706-3729 | 2 |
| Dripping Springs Christ Acad/Dripping Spgs/ Hays | 11829671 | 512/858-9738 | 217 |
| Dripping Springs Elem Sch/Dripping Spgs/ Hays | 02845545 | 512/858-3700 | 215 |
| Dripping Springs High Sch/Dripping Spgs/ Hays | 01029035 | 512/858-3100 | 215 |
| **DRIPPING SPRINGS IND SCH DIST/ DRIPPING SPGS/HAYS** | 01029011 | 512/858-3000 | 215 |
| Dripping Springs Middle Sch/Dripping Spgs/ Hays | 02845557 | 512/858-3400 | 216 |
| **DRISCOLL IND SCH DIST/DRISCOLL/ NUECES** | 01044798 | 361/387-7349 | 307 |
| Driscoll Middle Sch/Corp Christi/Nueces | 01044358 | 361/878-4660 | 306 |
| Driscoll Middle Sch/San Antonio/Bexar | 04017768 | 210/356-3200 | 38 |
| Driscoll Sch/Driscoll/Nueces | 01044803 | 361/387-7349 | 307 |
| Drs Reed & Mock Elem Sch/San Juan/Hidalgo | 04840278 | 956/354-2890 | 226 |
| Dubiski Career High Sch/Grand Prairie/ Dallas | 11452668 | 972/343-7800 | 111 |
| Dublin Elem Sch/Dublin/Erath | 01017020 | 254/445-2577 | 147 |
| Dublin High Sch/Dublin/Erath | 01017032 | 254/445-0362 | 147 |
| **DUBLIN IND SCH DIST/DUBLIN/ERATH** | 01017018 | 254/445-3341 | 147 |
| Dublin Intermediate Sch/Dublin/Erath | 04865527 | 254/445-2618 | 147 |
| Dubose Intermediate Sch/Alice/Jim Wells | 01034547 | 361/664-7512 | 248 |
| Duchesne Acad of Sacred Heart/Houston/ Harris | 01027910 | 713/468-8211 | 209 |
| Dudley Magnet Sch/Victoria/Victoria | 01058476 | 361/788-9517 | 385 |
| Dueitt Middle Sch/Spring/Harris | 02110625 | 281/891-7800 | 207 |
| Duff Elem Sch/Arlington/Tarrant | 01051727 | 682/867-2000 | 346 |
| Dulles Elem Sch/Sugar Land/Fort Bend | 01525998 | 281/634-5830 | 154 |
| Dulles High Sch/Sugar Land/Fort Bend | 01018153 | 281/634-5600 | 154 |
| Dulles Middle Sch/Sugar Land/Fort Bend | 02201456 | 281/634-5750 | 154 |
| **DUMAS IND SCH DIST/DUMAS/MOORE** | 01042817 | 806/935-6461 | 298 |
| Dumas Intermediate Sch/Dumas/Moore | 11562988 | 806/935-6474 | 298 |
| Dumas Junior High Sch/Dumas/Moore | 01042831 | 806/935-4155 | 298 |
| Dumas Senior High Sch/Dumas/Moore | 01042843 | 806/935-4151 | 298 |
| Dunaway Elem Sch/Waxahachie/Ellis | 03008788 | 972/923-4646 | 146 |
| Dunbar College Prep Academy/Lubbock/ Lubbock | 01038593 | 806/219-3400 | 273 |
| Dunbar Early Education Center/Texarkana/ Bowie | 01001241 | 903/794-8112 | 53 |
| Dunbar Middle Sch/Dickinson/Galveston | 01019004 | 281/229-6600 | 164 |
| Dunbar Primary Sch/Lufkin/Angelina | 00995027 | 936/630-4500 | 21 |
| Duncanville High Sch/Duncanville/Dallas | 01010333 | 972/708-3700 | 109 |
| Duncanville HS Collegiate Acad/Duncanville/ Dallas | 12368888 | 972/708-3885 | 109 |
| **DUNCANVILLE IND SCH DIST/ DUNCANVILLE/DALLAS** | 01010292 | 972/708-2000 | 108 |
| Dunn Elem Sch/Arlington/Tarrant | 01051739 | 682/867-3200 | 346 |
| Dupre Elem Sch/Lubbock/Lubbock | 01038608 | 806/219-5400 | 273 |
| Durham Elem Sch/Houston/Harris | 01023976 | 713/613-2527 | 196 |
| Durham Middle Sch/Lewisville/Denton | 05091717 | 469/713-5963 | 127 |
| Durkee Elem Sch/Houston/Harris | 01025871 | 713/696-2835 | 195 |
| Duryea Elem Sch/Katy/Harris | 05346627 | 281/856-5174 | 189 |
| Dwight D Eisenhower High Sch/Houston/ Harris | 01022776 | 281/878-0900 | 185 |
| Dwight Middle Sch/San Antonio/Bexar | 00999425 | 210/977-7300 | 45 |
| Dyess Elem Sch/Abilene/Taylor | 01172905 | 325/690-3795 | 363 |
| **E** | | | |
| E A Jones Elem Sch/Missouri City/Fort Bend | 01018141 | 281/634-4960 | 154 |
| E A Lawhon Elem Sch/Pearland/Brazoria | 01001851 | 281/412-1445 | 57 |
| E B Comstock Middle Sch/Dallas/Dallas | 01008689 | 972/794-1300 | 103 |
| E B Guerra Elem Sch/Edinburg/Hidalgo | 04873263 | 956/289-2530 | 221 |
| E B Reyna Elem Sch/Palmview/Hidalgo | 03323423 | 956/323-2390 | 223 |
| E C Brice Elem Sch/Mt Pleasant/Titus | 01055383 | 903/575-2057 | 366 |
| E C Mason Elem Sch/Manvel/Brazoria | 01001447 | 281/245-2832 | 54 |
| E D Walker Middle Sch/Dallas/Dallas | 10023159 | 972/502-6100 | 103 |

| School/City/County<br>DISTRICT/CITY/COUNTY | PID | TELEPHONE<br>NUMBER | PAGE |
|---|---|---|---|
| E E & Jovita Mireles Elem Sch/Corp Christi/ | | | |
| Nueces | 04913980 | 361/878-0120 | 306 |
| E H Gilbert Elem Sch/San Antonio/Bexar | 00997489 | 210/989-3050 | 35 |
| E J Moss Intermediate Sch/Lindale/Smith | 01050670 | 903/881-4200 | 340 |
| E Kolitz Hebrew Language Acad/San Antonio/ | | | |
| Bexar | 11931767 | 210/302-6900 | 3 |
| E L Kent Elem Sch/Carrollton/Dallas | 03248988 | 972/968-2000 | 100 |
| E M Daggett Elem Sch/Fort Worth/Tarrant | 01052745 | 817/814-5500 | 353 |
| E M Daggett Middle Sch/Fort Worth/Tarrant | 01052848 | 817/814-5200 | 353 |
| E M Pease Middle Sch/San Antonio/Bexar | 00998081 | 210/397-2950 | 40 |
| E Merle Smith Middle Sch/Sinton/ | | | |
| San Patricio | 01049786 | 361/364-6840 | 334 |
| E Ray Elem Sch/Fort Worth/Tarrant | 01052472 | 817/568-3545 | 352 |
| E Rudd Intermediate Sch/Van Vleck/ | | | |
| Matagorda | 02889773 | 979/245-6561 | 279 |
| E S McKenzie Elem Sch/Mesquite/Dallas | 02110065 | 972/882-5140 | 115 |
| E T Wrenn Middle Sch/San Antonio/Bexar | 00997154 | 210/444-8475 | 34 |
| E White Elem Sch/Houston/Harris | 01024657 | 713/778-3490 | 198 |
| Eagle Christian Academy/Waco/McLennan | 02951194 | 254/772-2122 | 285 |
| Eagle Heights Christian Acad/Pearland/ | | | |
| Brazoria | 02730237 | 281/485-6330 | 57 |
| Eagle Heights Elem Sch/Fort Worth/Tarrant | 01052018 | 817/237-4161 | 348 |
| Eagle Lake Intermediate Sch/Eagle Lake/ | | | |
| Colorado | 01006796 | 979/234-3531 | 90 |
| Eagle Lake Primary Sch/Eagle Lake/Colorado | 01006801 | 979/234-3531 | 90 |
| Eagle Mountain Elem Sch/Fort Worth/Tarrant | 01052410 | 817/236-7191 | 351 |
| **EAGLE MTN-SAGINAW IND SCH DIST/** | | | |
| **SAGINAW/TARRANT** | 01052408 | 817/232-0880 | 351 |
| Eagle Pass High Sch/Eagle Pass/Maverick | 01041083 | 830/773-2381 | 279 |
| **EAGLE PASS IND SCH DIST/** | | | |
| **EAGLE PASS/MAVERICK** | 01041057 | 830/773-5181 | 279 |
| Eagle Pass Junior High Sch/Eagle Pass/ | | | |
| Maverick | 01041095 | 830/758-7037 | 279 |
| Eagle Ridge Elem Sch/Keller/Tarrant | 10970942 | 817/744-6300 | 357 |
| Eagle Springs Elem Sch/Humble/Harris | 10028604 | 281/641-3100 | 201 |
| Eanes Elem Sch/Austin/Travis | 01056856 | 512/732-9100 | 372 |
| **EANES IND SCH DIST/AUSTIN/TRAVIS** | 01056844 | 512/732-9000 | 372 |
| Earl & Hazel Harris Academy/Houston/Harris | 04867202 | 281/878-7900 | 184 |
| Earl & Lottie Wolford Elem Sch/McKinney/ | | | |
| Collin | 04920713 | 469/302-4700 | 84 |
| Earl Rudder Middle Sch/San Antonio/Bexar | 02178366 | 210/397-5000 | 40 |
| Earl Slaughter Elem Sch/McKinney/Collin | 04358122 | 469/302-6100 | 84 |
| Early Childhood Campus/Kerrville/Kerr | 04866569 | 830/257-1335 | 259 |
| Early Childhood Center/Corp Christi/Nueces | 04450469 | 361/694-9036 | 307 |
| Early Childhood Center/Crockett/Houston | 02762010 | 936/544-2125 | 235 |
| Early Childhood Center/Eagle Pass/Maverick | 01877416 | 830/758-7027 | 279 |
| Early Childhood Center/Lindale/Smith | 04945634 | 903/881-4400 | 340 |
| Early Childhood Center/Natalia/Medina | 04273405 | 830/663-9739 | 287 |
| Early Childhood Center/Pasadena/Harris | 11133147 | 832/668-8390 | 191 |
| Early Childhood Dev Center/Corp Christi/ | | | |
| Nueces | 04498186 | 361/825-3366 | 306 |
| Early Childhood Sch/Lumberton/Hardin | 04288888 | 409/923-7695 | 183 |
| Early Clg High Sch/Round Rock/Williamson | 12230839 | 512/704-1650 | 401 |
| Early College High Sch/Dallas/Dallas | 10030815 | 972/968-6200 | 100 |
| Early College High Sch/Edcouch/Hidalgo | 12035550 | 956/262-4731 | 221 |
| Early College High Sch/Fort Hood/Bell | 12107050 | 254/336-0260 | 30 |
| Early College High Sch/Harlingen/Cameron | 10910928 | 956/430-9690 | 68 |
| Early College High Sch-Midland/Midland/ | | | |
| Midland | 11565681 | 432/685-4641 | 288 |
| Early College HS at Timberview/Arlington/ | | | |
| Tarrant | 12305599 | 682/314-1391 | 359 |
| Early Elem Sch/Early/Brown | 01002568 | 325/646-5511 | 62 |
| Early High Sch/Early/Brown | 01002570 | 325/643-4593 | 62 |
| **EARLY IND SCH DIST/EARLY/BROWN** | 01002556 | 325/646-7934 | 62 |
| Early Learning Ctr North/Fort Worth/ | | | |
| Tarrant | 11558743 | 817/744-6700 | 357 |
| Early Learning Ctr South/Fort Worth/ | | | |
| Tarrant | 12232813 | 817/743-8300 | 357 |
| Early Middle Sch/Early/Brown | 02131916 | 325/643-5665 | 62 |
| Early Primary Sch/Early/Brown | 04036659 | 325/643-9622 | 62 |
| Earnest O Woods Interm Sch/Wills Point/ | | | |
| Van Zandt | 03049873 | 903/873-5100 | 384 |
| East Avenue Primary Sch/Gonzales/Gonzales | 01019872 | 830/672-2826 | 169 |
| East Bernard Elem Sch/East Bernard/Wharton | 01059585 | 979/335-7519 | 392 |
| East Bernard High Sch/East Bernard/Wharton | 01059597 | 979/335-7519 | 392 |
| **EAST BERNARD IND SCH DIST/** | | | |
| **EAST BERNARD/WHARTON** | 01059573 | 979/335-7519 | 392 |
| East Bernard Jr High Sch/East Bernard/ | | | |
| Wharton | 02056184 | 979/335-7519 | 392 |
| East Central Development Ctr/San Antonio/ | | | |
| Bexar | 02896910 | 210/633-3020 | 34 |
| East Central High Sch/San Antonio/Bexar | 00997001 | 210/634-7100 | 34 |

| School/City/County<br>DISTRICT/CITY/COUNTY | PID | TELEPHONE<br>NUMBER | PAGE |
|---|---|---|---|
| **EAST CENTRAL IND SCH DIST/** | | | |
| **SAN ANTONIO/BEXAR** | 00996992 | 210/648-7861 | 34 |
| East Chambers Elem Sch/Winnie/Chambers | 04943117 | 409/296-6100 | 76 |
| East Chambers High Sch/Winnie/Chambers | 01005182 | 409/296-4184 | 76 |
| **EAST CHAMBERS IND SCH DIST/** | | | |
| **WINNIE/CHAMBERS** | 01005156 | 409/296-6100 | 76 |
| East Chambers Jr High Sch/Winnie/Chambers | 01005168 | 409/296-4183 | 76 |
| East Chambers Primary Sch/Winnie/Chambers | 01005170 | 409/296-2980 | 76 |
| East Cliff Elem Sch/Portland/San Patricio | 01049554 | 361/777-4255 | 333 |
| East Early College High Sch/Houston/Harris | 10021618 | 713/847-4809 | 194 |
| East Elem Sch/Breckenridge/Stephens | 01051351 | 254/559-6531 | 344 |
| East Elem Sch/Brownwood/Brown | 02199932 | 325/646-2937 | 62 |
| East Elem Sch/Corp Christi/Nueces | 01044138 | 361/242-5938 | 306 |
| East Elem Sch/Hallsville/Harrison | 03322209 | 903/668-5984 | 213 |
| East Elem Sch/Lubbock/Lubbock | 12309208 | 806/776-2109 | 274 |
| East Ft Worth Montessori Acad/Fort Worth/ | | | |
| Tarrant | 02774764 | 817/496-3003 | 3 |
| East Grand Preparatory Academy/Dallas/ | | | |
| Dallas | 11014876 | 214/824-4747 | 3 |
| East Handley Elem Sch/Fort Worth/Tarrant | 01052836 | 817/815-4400 | 353 |
| East Middle Sch/Desoto/Dallas | 01010254 | 972/223-0690 | 108 |
| East Montana Middle Sch/El Paso/El Paso | 04032110 | 915/926-5200 | 136 |
| East Point Elem Sch/El Paso/El Paso | 01016375 | 915/434-4500 | 142 |
| East Ridge Elem Sch/Sweetwater/Nolan | 01043926 | 325/235-5282 | 305 |
| East Side Elem Sch/Jacksonville/Cherokee | 01005259 | 903/586-5146 | 76 |
| East Side Intermediate Sch/Palacios/ | | | |
| Matagorda | 01040936 | 361/972-2544 | 278 |
| East Terrell Hills Elem Sch/San Antonio/ | | | |
| Bexar | 00997764 | 210/407-2800 | 38 |
| East Texas Christian Academy/Tyler/Smith | 02233435 | 903/561-8642 | 342 |
| East Texas Christian Sch/Longview/Gregg | 04931657 | 903/757-7891 | 176 |
| East Texas Mont Prep Academy/Longview/ | | | |
| Gregg | 12226450 | 903/803-5000 | 174 |
| East TX Charter Sch-Chadwick/Longview/ | | | |
| Gregg | 04891576 | 903/753-9400 | 3 |
| Eastern Hills Elem Sch/Fort Worth/Tarrant | 01052898 | 817/815-4500 | 353 |
| Eastern Hills High Sch/Fort Worth/Tarrant | 01052903 | 817/815-4000 | 353 |
| Eastern Hills Middle Sch/Harker HTS/Bell | 03007320 | 254/336-1100 | 31 |
| Eastlake High Sch/El Paso/El Paso | 11552945 | 915/937-3600 | 140 |
| Eastland High Sch/Eastland/Eastland | 01014420 | 254/631-5000 | 133 |
| **EASTLAND IND SCH DIST/EASTLAND/** | | | |
| **EASTLAND** | 01014406 | 254/631-5120 | 133 |
| Eastland Middle Sch/Eastland/Eastland | 01014432 | 254/631-5040 | 133 |
| Eastridge Elem Sch/Amarillo/Potter | 01047233 | 806/326-4300 | 320 |
| Eastridge Elem Sch/Red Oak/Ellis | 04030760 | 972/617-2266 | 146 |
| Eastside Elem Sch/Cleveland/Liberty | 04756005 | 281/592-0125 | 268 |
| Eastside Memorial High Sch/Austin/Travis | 01056002 | 512/414-5810 | 371 |
| Eastview High Sch/Georgetown/Williamson | 04807903 | 512/943-1800 | 398 |
| Eastwood Academy/Houston/Harris | 04943430 | 713/924-1697 | 194 |
| Eastwood Heights Elem Sch/El Paso/El Paso | 01016387 | 915/434-4600 | 142 |
| Eastwood High Sch/El Paso/El Paso | 01016399 | 915/434-4000 | 142 |
| Eastwood Knolls Elem Sch/El Paso/El Paso | 01016416 | 915/434-4400 | 142 |
| Eastwood Middle Sch/El Paso/El Paso | 01016404 | 915/434-4300 | 142 |
| Ebby Halliday Elem Sch/Dallas/Dallas | 11732743 | 972/925-1800 | 103 |
| Ecia-Rowlett 2/Rowlett/Dallas | 11014424 | 972/412-8080 | 3 |
| Ecia-Royse City 3/Royse City/Rockwall | 12260688 | 972/636-2600 | 3 |
| Ecia-Sunnyvale 1/Sunnyvale/Dallas | 11014412 | 214/628-9152 | 3 |
| Ector Clg Prep Success Acad/Odessa/Ector | 01014664 | 432/456-0479 | 134 |
| **ECTOR CO IND SCH DIST/ODESSA/** | | | |
| **ECTOR** | 01014547 | 432/456-0000 | 134 |
| Ector Co Youth Alt Center/Odessa/Ector | 01826194 | 432/456-0049 | 134 |
| **ECTOR IND SCH DIST/ECTOR/FANNIN** | 01017458 | 903/961-2355 | 150 |
| Ector Sch/Ector/Fannin | 01857193 | 903/961-2355 | 150 |
| Ed Downs Elem Sch/San Benito/Cameron | 01004190 | 956/361-6720 | 70 |
| Ed Franz Elem Sch/Live Oak/Bexar | 00997647 | 210/945-5640 | 36 |
| Ed Rawlinson Middle Sch/San Antonio/Bexar | 05273410 | 210/397-4900 | 40 |
| Ed Vanston Middle Sch/Mesquite/Dallas | 01011442 | 972/882-5801 | 115 |
| Ed White E-STEM Magnet Sch/El Lago/ | | | |
| Galveston | 01018866 | 281/284-4300 | 163 |
| Ed Willkie Middle Sch/Fort Worth/Tarrant | 11449415 | 817/237-9631 | 351 |
| Edcouch Elsa High Sch/Edcouch/Hidalgo | 01029657 | 956/262-6944 | 221 |
| **EDCOUCH ELSA IND SCH DIST/** | | | |
| **EDCOUCH/HIDALGO** | 01029621 | 956/262-6000 | 220 |
| Eddie Finley Jr High Sch/Waxahachie/Ellis | 01015333 | 972/923-4680 | 146 |
| Eddy & Debbie Peach Elem Sch/Arlington/ | | | |
| Tarrant | 12170095 | 682/867-6100 | 346 |
| **EDEN CONS IND SCH DIST/EDEN/** | | | |
| **CONCHO** | 01007180 | 325/869-4121 | 94 |
| Eden Elem Sch/Eden/Concho | 01007192 | 325/869-4121 | 94 |
| Eden High Sch/Eden/Concho | 01007207 | 325/869-4121 | 94 |
| Edgar Glover Elem Sch/Missouri City/ | | | |
| Fort Bend | 04287949 | 281/634-4920 | 154 |

| School/City/County DISTRICT/CITY/COUNTY | PID | TELEPHONE NUMBER | PAGE |
|---|---|---|---|
| Edge Middle Sch/Nevada/Collin | 01006136 | 972/843-6670 | 81 |
| Edgemere Elem Sch/El Paso/El Paso | 01016428 | 915/434-4700 | 142 |
| Edgemere Elem Sch/Plainview/Hale | 01021954 | 806/293-6040 | 180 |
| Edgewood Elem Sch/Edgewood/Van Zandt | 01058127 | 903/896-4773 | 382 |
| Edgewood Elem Sch/Houston/Harris | 01027116 | 713/251-5600 | 206 |
| Edgewood Fine Arts Academy/San Antonio/Bexar | 04954465 | 210/444-7925 | 34 |
| Edgewood High Sch/Edgewood/Van Zandt | 01058139 | 903/896-4856 | 382 |
| **EDGEWOOD IND SCH DIST/EDGEWOOD/VAN ZANDT** | 01058115 | 903/896-4332 | 382 |
| **EDGEWOOD IND SCH DIST/SAN ANTONIO/BEXAR** | 00997075 | 210/444-4500 | 34 |
| Edgewood Intermediate Sch/Edgewood/Van Zandt | 04913368 | 903/896-2143 | 383 |
| Edgewood Middle Sch/Edgewood/Van Zandt | 02948599 | 903/896-1530 | 383 |
| Edinburg Alternative Academy/Edinburg/Hidalgo | 04429068 | 956/289-2598 | 221 |
| Edinburg Classical Academy/Edinburg/Hidalgo | 11848938 | 956/720-4361 | 3 |
| **EDINBURG CONS IND SCH DIST/EDINBURG/HIDALGO** | 01029671 | 956/289-2300 | 221 |
| Edinburg High Sch/Edinburg/Hidalgo | 01029695 | 956/289-2400 | 221 |
| Edinburg North High Sch/Edinburg/Hidalgo | 03392644 | 956/289-2500 | 221 |
| Edinburg South Middle Sch/Edinburg/Hidalgo | 02110285 | 956/289-2415 | 221 |
| Edison High Sch/San Antonio/Bexar | 00998627 | 210/738-9720 | 43 |
| Edison Middle Sch/Houston/Harris | 01025493 | 713/924-1800 | 195 |
| Edith & Ethel Carman Elem Sch/San Juan/Hidalgo | 03055482 | 956/354-2700 | 226 |
| Edmund Cody Elem Sch/San Antonio/Bexar | 02178342 | 210/397-1650 | 40 |
| Edna Alternative Sch/Edna/Jackson | 12032613 | 361/782-9051 | 242 |
| Edna Bigham Mays Elem Sch/Troy/Bell | 04939037 | 254/938-0304 | 33 |
| Edna Elem Sch/Edna/Jackson | 01033000 | 361/782-2953 | 242 |
| Edna High Sch/Edna/Jackson | 01033024 | 361/782-5255 | 242 |
| **EDNA IND SCH DIST/EDNA/JACKSON** | 01032991 | 361/782-3573 | 242 |
| Edna Junior High Sch/Edna/Jackson | 01033036 | 361/782-2351 | 242 |
| Edna Mae Fielder Elem Sch/Katy/Harris | 04032823 | 281/237-6450 | 156 |
| Edna Rowe Elem Sch/Dallas/Dallas | 01009724 | 972/749-8800 | 103 |
| Edris Childres Elliot Elem Sch/McKinney/Collin | 11103881 | 469/633-3750 | 82 |
| Eduardo Mata Mont Sch/Dallas/Dallas | 04755439 | 972/749-7500 | 103 |
| Education Connection/Killeen/Bell | 11229124 | 254/526-9299 | 33 |
| Edward B Cannan Elem Sch/Willis/Montgomery | 04872180 | 936/890-8660 | 297 |
| Edward H Cary Middle Sch/Dallas/Dallas | 01008756 | 972/502-7600 | 104 |
| Edward H White Middle Sch/San Antonio/Bexar | 00997972 | 210/356-5900 | 38 |
| Edward J Briscoe Elem Sch/Fort Worth/Tarrant | 03253385 | 817/814-0300 | 353 |
| Edward K Downing Elem Sch/Odessa/Ector | 12105727 | 432/456-1319 | 134 |
| Edward Titche Elem Sch/Dallas/Dallas | 01008770 | 972/794-2100 | 104 |
| Edwards-Johnson Memorial MS/Silsbee/Hardin | 01022647 | 409/980-7870 | 183 |
| Edwin F Williams Interm Sch/Perryton/Ochiltree | 01045467 | 806/435-3436 | 310 |
| Edwin J Kiest Elem Sch/Dallas/Dallas | 01008782 | 972/502-5600 | 104 |
| Edwin M Wells Middle Sch/Houston/Harris | 01541368 | 281/891-7750 | 207 |
| Effie Morris Elem Sch/Lake Worth/Tarrant | 01054080 | 817/306-4260 | 358 |
| Egly Elem Sch/Brownsville/Cameron | 11539987 | 956/548-8850 | 67 |
| Ehrhardt Elem Sch/Klein/Harris | 02057554 | 832/484-6200 | 202 |
| Ehrhart Sch/Beaumont/Jefferson | 05010983 | 409/839-8200 | 3 |
| Eiland Elem Sch/Houston/Harris | 04033047 | 832/484-6900 | 202 |
| Einstein School Plano/Plano/Collin | 12362107 | 972/564-8040 | 89 |
| Eisenhauer Rd Baptist DC PS/San Antonio/Bexar | 02869096 | 210/655-6831 | 48 |
| Eisenhower Elem Sch/Edinburg/Hidalgo | 01029815 | 956/289-2540 | 221 |
| Eisenhower Elem Sch/Grand Prairie/Dallas | 01010864 | 972/262-3717 | 111 |
| Eisenhower Middle Sch/San Antonio/Bexar | 00997752 | 210/356-3500 | 38 |
| Eisenhower Ninth Grade Sch/Houston/Harris | 04805034 | 281/878-7700 | 185 |
| Ekklesia Christian Sch/Fort Worth/Tarrant | 04993045 | 817/332-1202 | 361 |
| El Campo High Sch/El Campo/Wharton | 01059614 | 979/543-6341 | 392 |
| **EL CAMPO IND SCH DIST/EL CAMPO/WHARTON** | 01059602 | 979/543-6771 | 392 |
| El Campo Middle Sch/El Campo/Wharton | 01059626 | 979/543-6362 | 392 |
| El Dorado Elem Sch/San Antonio/Bexar | 00997776 | 210/407-3000 | 38 |
| El Dorado High Sch/El Paso/El Paso | 05272296 | 915/937-3200 | 140 |
| El Jardin Elem Sch/Brownsville/Cameron | 01003550 | 956/831-6000 | 67 |
| El Paso Academy East/El Paso/El Paso | 10015164 | 915/590-8589 | 3 |
| El Paso Academy West/El Paso/El Paso | 04932209 | 915/845-7997 | 3 |
| El Paso Adventist Jr Academy/El Paso/El Paso | 01480104 | 915/855-7312 | 143 |
| El Paso Country Day Sch/El Paso/El Paso | 02950310 | 915/533-4492 | 143 |
| El Paso High Sch/El Paso/El Paso | 01015967 | 915/236-2500 | 139 |
| **EL PASO IND SCH DIST/EL PASO/EL PASO** | 01015450 | 915/230-2000 | 137 |
| **EL PASO ISD-ELEMENTARY/EL PASO/EL PASO** | 11982247 | 915/230-2485 | 137 |
| **EL PASO ISD-HIGH SCHOOLS/EL PASO/EL PASO** | 11982259 | 915/236-2500 | 138 |
| **EL PASO ISD-MIDDLE SCHOOLS/EL PASO/EL PASO** | 11982261 | 915/230-2213 | 139 |
| El Paso Jewish Academy/El Paso/El Paso | 01875303 | 915/833-0808 | 143 |
| El Paso Leadership Academy/El Paso/El Paso | 12113970 | 915/298-3900 | 3 |
| El Paso NE Children's Ed Ctr/El Paso/El Paso | 02869371 | 915/751-9487 | 143 |
| Eladio Martinez Learning Ctr/Dallas/Dallas | 03336925 | 972/794-6900 | 104 |
| Elaine S Schlather Interm Sch/Cibolo/Guadalupe | 11457333 | 210/619-4300 | 178 |
| Eldorado Elem Sch/Eldorado/Schleicher | 01050008 | 325/853-2514 | 335 |
| Eldorado High Sch/Eldorado/Schleicher | 01049094 | 325/853-2514 | 335 |
| Eldorado Middle Sch/Eldorado/Schleicher | 03005889 | 325/853-2514 | 335 |
| Eleanor Tinsley Elem Sch/Houston/Harris | 04951645 | 713/778-8400 | 198 |
| Electra Elem Sch/Electra/Wichita | 01060027 | 940/432-3815 | 394 |
| **ELECTRA IND SCH DIST/ELECTRA/WICHITA** | 01060015 | 940/495-3683 | 394 |
| Electra Jr Senior High Sch/Electra/Wichita | 01060039 | 940/432-3812 | 394 |
| Elfida P Chavez Elem Sch/El Paso/El Paso | 04757310 | 915/937-8300 | 140 |
| Elgin Elem Sch/Elgin/Bastrop | 11559034 | 512/281-3457 | 27 |
| Elgin High Sch/Elgin/Bastrop | 00995900 | 512/281-3438 | 27 |
| **ELGIN IND SCH DIST/ELGIN/BASTROP** | 00995883 | 512/281-3434 | 27 |
| Elgin Intermediate Sch/Elgin/Bastrop | 12469212 | 512/281-9701 | 27 |
| Elgin Middle Sch/Elgin/Bastrop | 00995912 | 512/281-3382 | 27 |
| Elias Herrera Middle Sch/Laredo/Webb | 12472269 | 956/473-6900 | 390 |
| Eligio Kika De La Garza Sch/Mission/Hidalgo | 02949050 | 956/323-2380 | 223 |
| Eliot Elem Sch/Houston/Harris | 01025895 | 713/671-3670 | 195 |
| Elisabeth Ney Elem Sch/Lake Jackson/Brazoria | 01001617 | 979/730-7190 | 55 |
| Elisha M Pease Elem Sch/Dallas/Dallas | 01008794 | 214/932-3800 | 104 |
| Elite College Prep Acad-Bowie/Houston/Harris | 12114003 | 832/649-2700 | 3 |
| Elizabeth Smith Elem Sch/Mansfield/Tarrant | 05347384 | 817/299-6980 | 359 |
| Elkhart Elem Sch/Elkhart/Anderson | 00994449 | 903/764-2979 | 18 |
| Elkhart High Sch/Elkhart/Anderson | 00994451 | 903/764-5161 | 18 |
| **ELKHART IND SCH DIST/ELKHART/ANDERSON** | 00994437 | 903/764-2952 | 18 |
| Elkhart Intermediate Sch/Elkhart/Anderson | 11711842 | 903/764-8535 | 18 |
| Elkhart Middle Sch/Elkhart/Anderson | 04446688 | 903/764-2459 | 18 |
| Elkins Elem Sch/Fort Worth/Tarrant | 03049055 | 817/237-0805 | 351 |
| Elkins High Sch/Missouri City/Fort Bend | 04016350 | 281/634-2600 | 154 |
| Ella Barnes Elem Sch/Corp Christi/Nueces | 04019443 | 361/878-7330 | 306 |
| Ella Schorlemmer Elem Sch/Victoria/Victoria | 11450115 | 361/788-2860 | 385 |
| Ellen B Lane Sch/Houston/Harris | 01022788 | 281/985-6350 | 185 |
| Elliot Grant Middle Sch/Corp Christi/Nueces | 04286488 | 361/878-3740 | 306 |
| Elliott Elem Sch/Irving/Dallas | 01011155 | 972/600-4300 | 113 |
| Ellis Elem Sch/Arlington/Tarrant | 03250709 | 682/867-7900 | 346 |
| Ellison High Sch/Killeen/Bell | 01829366 | 254/336-0600 | 31 |
| Elm Creek Elem Sch/Atascosa/Bexar | 04750738 | 210/622-4430 | 46 |
| Elm Grove Elem Sch/Buda/Hays | 04920244 | 512/268-8440 | 216 |
| Elm Grove Elem Sch/Kingwood/Harris | 01829457 | 281/641-1700 | 201 |
| Elma Barrera Elem Sch/Santa Rosa/Cameron | 03345823 | 956/636-9870 | 71 |
| Elmer Bondy Intermediate Sch/Pasadena/Harris | 04036972 | 713/740-0430 | 204 |
| Elmer C Watson High Sch/Fort Worth/Tarrant | 04747999 | 817/238-7925 | 351 |
| Elmore Elem Sch/Houston/Harris | 11932539 | 713/672-7466 | 195 |
| Elodia R Chapa Elem Sch/Mission/Hidalgo | 04031714 | 956/323-2400 | 223 |
| Eloise Japhet Academy/San Antonio/Bexar | 00998782 | 210/228-3345 | 43 |
| Elolf Elem Sch/Converse/Bexar | 04288101 | 210/661-1130 | 36 |
| Eloy Salazar Elem Sch/Donna/Hidalgo | 05343534 | 956/464-1977 | 220 |
| Elrod Elem Sch/Houston/Harris | 01024786 | 713/778-3330 | 198 |
| Elsie Robertson Middle Sch/Lancaster/Dallas | 01011363 | 972/218-1660 | 114 |
| Elsie Shands Elem Sch/Mesquite/Dallas | 01011454 | 972/290-4020 | 115 |
| Elsik 9th Grade Center/Houston/Harris | 04809107 | 281/988-3239 | 187 |
| Elsik High Sch/Houston/Harris | 01418369 | 281/988-3150 | 187 |
| Elva C Lobit Middle Sch/Dickinson/Galveston | 12167347 | 281/229-7700 | 164 |
| Elysian Fields Elem Sch/Elysian Flds/Harrison | 01028445 | 903/633-2465 | 213 |
| Elysian Fields High Sch/Elysian Flds/Harrison | 01028469 | 903/633-2455 | 213 |
| **ELYSIAN FIELDS IND SCH DIST/ELYSIAN FLDS/HARRISON** | 01028433 | 903/633-2420 | 213 |
| Elysian Fields Middle Sch/Elysian Flds/Harrison | 04363359 | 903/633-2306 | 213 |

| School/City/County<br>DISTRICT/CITY/COUNTY | PID | TELEPHONE<br>NUMBER | PAGE | School/City/County<br>DISTRICT/CITY/COUNTY | PID | TELEPHONE<br>NUMBER | PAGE |
|---|---|---|---|---|---|---|---|
| Emerson Elem Sch/Amarillo/Potter | 01047245 | 806/326-4350 | 320 | **EULA IND SCH DIST/CLYDE/CALLAHAN** | 01003380 | 325/529-3186 | 66 |
| Emerson Elem Sch/Houston/Harris | 01024425 | 713/917-3630 | 198 | Eula Middle Sch/Clyde/Callahan | 04914673 | 325/529-3605 | 66 |
| Emerson Elem Sch/Midland/Midland | 01041502 | 432/240-6700 | 288 | Euless Junior High Sch/Euless/Tarrant | 01053804 | 817/354-3340 | 356 |
| Emery Elem Sch/Katy/Harris | 11560497 | 281/855-9080 | 189 | Eustace High Sch/Eustace/Henderson | 01029401 | 903/425-5161 | 219 |
| Emery Weiner Sch/Houston/Harris | 02848262 | 832/204-5900 | 210 | **EUSTACE IND SCH DIST/EUSTACE/** | | | |
| Emile Elem Sch/Bastrop/Bastrop | 00995845 | 512/772-7620 | 26 | **HENDERSON** | 01029384 | 903/425-5151 | 219 |
| Emiliano Zapata Elem Sch/Mission/Hidalgo | 05278977 | 956/323-2700 | 223 | Eustace Intermediate Sch/Eustace/Henderson | 04447266 | 903/425-5181 | 219 |
| Emma Frey Discip Alt Ed Pgrm/San Antonio/ | | | | Eustace Middle Sch/Eustace/Henderson | 01029396 | 903/425-5171 | 219 |
| Bexar | 04788826 | 210/444-8230 | 35 | Eustace Primary Sch/Eustace/Henderson | 03008685 | 903/425-5191 | 219 |
| Emma Ousley Jr HS/Arlington/Tarrant | 04757023 | 682/867-5700 | 346 | Evadale Elem Jr High Sch/Evadale/Jasper | 01033220 | 409/276-1337 | 243 |
| Emma Roberson Elem Sch/Granbury/Hood | 02848482 | 817/408-4500 | 233 | Evadale High Sch/Evadale/Jasper | 04032653 | 409/276-1337 | 243 |
| Emma Vera Elem Sch/Roma/Starr | 04282200 | 956/849-4552 | 343 | **EVADALE IND SCH DIST/EVADALE/** | | | |
| Emmanuel Christian Sch/Gonzales/Gonzales | 02191631 | 830/519-4086 | 169 | **JASPER** | 01033218 | 409/276-1337 | 243 |
| Emmett J Conrad High Sch/Dallas/Dallas | 10023147 | 972/502-2300 | 104 | Evangelina Garza Elem Sch/Mission/Hidalgo | 11449489 | 956/323-2350 | 223 |
| Emmott Elem Sch/Houston/Harris | 02848709 | 281/897-4500 | 189 | Evans Elem Sch/Corp Christi/Nueces | 01044360 | 361/878-2240 | 306 |
| Encinal Elem Sch/Encinal/La Salle | 01037240 | 956/948-5324 | 262 | Evans Middle Sch/Lubbock/Lubbock | 01038634 | 806/219-3600 | 273 |
| Encino Park Elem Sch/San Antonio/Bexar | 03250319 | 210/407-3200 | 38 | Evans Middle Sch/McKinney/Collin | 05343168 | 469/302-7100 | 84 |
| Endeavor HS-J F Campbell Ctr/Channelview/ | | | | **EVANT IND SCH DIST/EVANT/CORYELL** | 01007635 | 254/471-3160 | 96 |
| Harris | 04034015 | 281/860-3800 | 188 | Evant Sch/Evant/Coryell | 01007647 | 254/471-5536 | 96 |
| Energized for Excellence ECC/Houston/ | | | | Evelyn S Thompson Elem Sch/Houston/Harris | 01022790 | 281/878-0333 | 185 |
| Harris | 11077000 | 281/779-4411 | 198 | Evelyn Turlington Elem Sch/Hockley/Waller | 11456975 | 936/372-0100 | 387 |
| Energized for Excellence ES/Houston/Harris | 04815091 | 713/773-3600 | 198 | Everest Academy/Stafford/Fort Bend | 12374758 | 281/261-3030 | 159 |
| Energized for Excellence MS/Houston/Harris | 11076991 | 713/773-3600 | 199 | Everette Lee Degolyer Elem Sch/Dallas/ | | | |
| Energized for STEM Acad Ctrl/Houston/ | | | | Dallas | 04282781 | 972/794-2800 | 104 |
| Harris | 12469937 | 713/641-1630 | 199 | Everhart Mgnt Acad/Cltrl Study/Longview/ | | | |
| Energized for STEM Academy HS/Houston/ | | | | Gregg | 01857234 | 903/803-5400 | 174 |
| Harris | 11555428 | 713/641-1630 | 199 | Everman Academy High Sch/Everman/Tarrant | 11929623 | 817/568-3520 | 352 |
| Energized for STEM Academy MS/Houston/ | | | | **EVERMAN IND SCH DIST/FORT WORTH/** | | | |
| Harris | 11555416 | 713/773-3600 | 199 | **TARRANT** | 01052460 | 817/568-3500 | 351 |
| Energy Institute High Sch/Houston/Harris | 11920328 | 713/802-4620 | 197 | Everman Joe C Bean High Sch/Everman/ | | | |
| Enge-Washington Interm Sch/Groesbeck/ | | | | Tarrant | 01052496 | 817/568-5200 | 352 |
| Limestone | 03318155 | 254/729-4103 | 269 | Evers Park Elem Sch/Denton/Denton | 02845923 | 940/369-2600 | 125 |
| England Elem Sch/Austin/Williamson | 11821320 | 512/704-1200 | 402 | Evins Regional Juvenile Ctr/Edinburg/ | | | |
| Enhanced Horizons/Ingram/Kerr | 12163066 | 830/367-4330 | 3 | Hidalgo | 04220525 | 956/289-5500 | 3 |
| Ennis High Sch/Ennis/Ellis | 01014975 | 972/872-3500 | 144 | Evolution Academy-Beaumont/Beaumont/ | | | |
| **ENNIS IND SCH DIST/ENNIS/ELLIS** | 01014963 | 972/872-7000 | 144 | Jefferson | 11931779 | 409/239-5553 | 3 |
| Ennis Junior High Sch/Ennis/Ellis | 02131538 | 972/872-3850 | 144 | Evolution Academy-Houston/Spring/Harris | 11932503 | 281/907-6440 | 3 |
| Enrique Camarena Elem Sch/Mission/Hidalgo | 10028197 | 956/323-2720 | 223 | Evolution Academy-Richardson/Richardson/ | | | |
| Epic Daep Alt Sch/Mont Belvieu/Chambers | 10915277 | 281/576-2221 | 75 | Dallas | 05220982 | 972/907-3755 | 3 |
| Epiphany Lutheran Sch/Houston/Harris | 03018630 | 713/896-1316 | 210 | Excalibur Sch/Denver City/Yoakum | 04746232 | 806/592-5950 | 409 |
| Epiphany Montessori Sch/Kingsville/Kleberg | 01036428 | 361/592-2871 | 261 | Excel Academy Charter Sch/Houston/Harris | 12161977 | 713/222-4577 | 3 |
| Epiphany of the Lord Cath Sch/Katy/Harris | 12468323 | 832/391-6500 | 209 | Excel Adventist Academy/Missouri City/ | | | |
| Episcopal Day Sch/Brownsville/Cameron | 01004360 | 956/542-5231 | 72 | Fort Bend | 11222932 | 281/835-0770 | 159 |
| Episcopal High Sch/Bellaire/Harris | 02950346 | 713/512-3400 | 210 | Excel Center-Fort Worth/Fort Worth/Tarrant | 11704447 | 817/335-6429 | 3 |
| Episcopal Sch Dallas-Mid Upper/Dallas/ | | | | Excel High Sch/Longview/Gregg | 11718759 | 903/295-6753 | 175 |
| Dallas | 01875195 | 214/358-4368 | 119 | Excellence In Leadership Acad/Mission/ | | | |
| Episcopal Sch of Dallas-Lower/Dallas/ | | | | Hidalgo | 11816387 | 956/424-9504 | 3 |
| Dallas | 10015803 | 214/353-5818 | 119 | Excelsior Elem Sch/Center/Shelby | 01050333 | 936/598-5866 | 337 |
| Epps Island Elem Sch/Houston/Harris | 01026291 | 832/484-5800 | 202 | **EXCELSIOR IND SCH DIST/CENTER/** | | | |
| **ERA IND SCH DIST/ERA/COOKE** | 01007312 | 940/665-5961 | 94 | **SHELBY** | 01050321 | 936/598-5866 | 337 |
| Era Sch/Era/Cooke | 01007324 | 940/665-5961 | 94 | Explorations Preparatory Sch/Flower Mound/ | | | |
| Ereckson Middle Sch/Allen/Collin | 05343144 | 972/747-3308 | 80 | Denton | 12314069 | 972/539-0601 | 130 |
| Erma Nash Elem Sch/Mansfield/Tarrant | 01054133 | 817/299-6900 | 359 | Ezzell Elem Sch/Hallettsville/Lavaca | 01037276 | 361/798-4448 | 265 |
| Ernesto Serna Elem Sch/El Paso/El Paso | 04916114 | 915/937-4800 | 140 | **EZZELL IND SCH DIST/HALLETTSVILLE/** | | | |
| Escandon Elem Sch/Edinburg/Hidalgo | 01029798 | 956/289-2545 | 221 | **LAVACA** | 01037264 | 361/798-4448 | 264 |
| Eschool Prep Virtual Sch/Texarkana/Bowie | 12362470 | 903/794-3651 | 53 | | | | |
| Escobar-Rios Elem Sch/Mission/Hidalgo | 11079333 | 956/323-8400 | 225 | **F** | | | |
| Escondido Elem Sch/Converse/Bexar | 12308010 | 210/662-2250 | 36 | | | | |
| Escontrias Early Childhood Ctr/El Paso/ | | | | F C Weinert Elem Sch/Seguin/Guadalupe | 01021667 | 830/401-1241 | 179 |
| El Paso | 04487761 | 915/937-4200 | 140 | F L Moffett Primary Sch/Center/Shelby | 03161380 | 936/598-6266 | 337 |
| Escontrias Elem Sch/El Paso/El Paso | 01016222 | 915/937-4100 | 140 | F P Caillet Elem Sch/Dallas/Dallas | 01008847 | 972/794-3200 | 104 |
| Escuela Montessori-Del Valle/El Paso/ | | | | F R Scobee Elem Sch/San Antonio/Bexar | 03010705 | 210/397-0700 | 40 |
| El Paso | 02869424 | 915/584-9215 | 143 | Fabens Elem Sch/Fabens/El Paso | 01016155 | 915/765-2650 | 139 |
| Esparza Elem Sch/Edinburg/Hidalgo | 05275195 | 956/289-2308 | 221 | Fabens High Sch/Fabens/El Paso | 01016131 | 915/765-2620 | 139 |
| Esperanza Medrano Elementary/Dallas/Dallas | 01010058 | 972/794-3300 | 104 | **FABENS IND SCH DIST/FABENS/** | | | |
| Esprit International Sch/The Woodlands/ | | | | **EL PASO** | 01016129 | 915/765-2600 | 139 |
| Montgomery | 11903772 | 281/298-9200 | 298 | Fabens Middle Sch/Fabens/El Paso | 01016143 | 915/765-2630 | 139 |
| Estacado High Sch/Lubbock/Lubbock | 01038622 | 806/766-1400 | 273 | Fabra Elem Sch/Boerne/Kendall | 03005841 | 830/357-4200 | 257 |
| Estacado Middle Sch/Plainview/Hale | 01021966 | 806/293-6015 | 180 | Fadden-McKeown-Chambliss ES/Beeville/Bee | 00996083 | 361/362-6050 | 28 |
| Estella Stewart Elem Sch/Huntsville/Walker | 01058725 | 936/435-6700 | 386 | Fain Elem Sch/Wichita Falls/Wichita | 01173026 | 940/235-1148 | 395 |
| Estrada Achievement Center/San Antonio/ | | | | Fair Oaks Ranch Elem Sch/Fair Oaks/Kendall | 04369729 | 830/357-4800 | 257 |
| Bexar | 03056175 | 210/438-6820 | 43 | Fairfield Elem Sch/Fairfield/Freestone | 01018464 | 903/389-2148 | 160 |
| Eternity Christian Sch/Houston/Harris | 04993241 | 281/999-5107 | 210 | Fairfield High Sch/Fairfield/Freestone | 01018476 | 903/389-4177 | 160 |
| Ethridge Elem Sch/Garland/Dallas | 01010785 | 972/675-3020 | 109 | **FAIRFIELD IND SCH DIST/FAIRFIELD/** | | | |
| Ethridge Elem Sch/The Colony/Denton | 03325548 | 469/713-5954 | 127 | **FREESTONE** | 01018452 | 903/389-2532 | 160 |
| Etoile Acad Charter Sch/Houston/Harris | 12310673 | 713/201-5714 | 3 | Fairfield Intermediate Sch/Fairfield/ | | | |
| Etoile Elem Sch/Etoile/Nacogdoches | 01043201 | 936/465-9404 | 300 | Freestone | 11719284 | 903/389-7095 | 160 |
| **ETOILE IND SCH DIST/ETOILE/** | | | | Fairfield Junior High Sch/Fairfield/ | | | |
| **NACOGDOCHES** | 01043196 | 936/465-9404 | 300 | Freestone | 01018490 | 903/389-4210 | 160 |
| Eugenia P Rayzor Elem Sch/Argyle/Denton | 05096444 | 940/369-4100 | 125 | Fairhill Sch/Dallas/Dallas | 02083761 | 972/233-1026 | 119 |
| Eula Elem Sch/Clyde/Callahan | 01003392 | 325/529-3212 | 66 | Fairmeadows Elem Sch/Duncanville/Dallas | 01010345 | 972/708-2700 | 109 |
| Eula High Sch/Clyde/Callahan | 04914685 | 325/529-3605 | 66 | Fairmont Elem Sch/Pasadena/Harris | 03323318 | 832/668-8500 | 191 |

| School/City/County DISTRICT/CITY/COUNTY | PID | TELEPHONE NUMBER | PAGE |
|---|---|---|---|
| Fairmont Junior High Sch/Pasadena/Harris | 04281567 | 832/668-7800 | 191 |
| Fairview Accelerated Sch/San Angelo/ | | | |
| Tom Green | 04247444 | 325/651-7656 | 368 |
| Fairview Elem Sch/Sherman/Grayson | 01020613 | 903/891-6580 | 172 |
| Fairview Junior High Sch/Alvin/Brazoria | 11070973 | 281/245-3100 | 54 |
| Fairview-Miss Jewel Elem Sch/Copperas Cove/ | | | |
| Coryell | 01007594 | 254/547-4212 | 96 |
| Faith Academy/Bellville/Austin | 04935146 | 979/865-1811 | 25 |
| Faith Academy/Victoria/Victoria | 02156693 | 361/573-2484 | 385 |
| Faith Academy of Marble Falls/Marble Falls/ | | | |
| Burnet | 04933318 | 830/798-1333 | 64 |
| Faith Christian Academy/Brownsville/ | | | |
| Cameron | 11222944 | 956/546-7726 | 72 |
| Faith Christian Academy/Dilley/Frio | 04993655 | 830/965-1324 | 162 |
| Faith Christian Academy/El Paso/El Paso | 04994180 | 915/594-3305 | 143 |
| Faith Christian Academy/Palmhurst/Hidalgo | 11934989 | 956/581-1465 | 229 |
| Faith Christian Academy/Pasadena/Harris | 04856679 | 713/943-9978 | 210 |
| Faith Christian Academy/Wharton/Wharton | 10985662 | 979/531-1000 | 393 |
| Faith Christian Sch/Grapevine/Tarrant | 04872403 | 817/442-9144 | 361 |
| Faith Family Acad-Waxahachie/Waxahachie/ | | | |
| Ellis | 02161739 | 972/937-3704 | 3 |
| Faith Family Academy-Oak Cliff/Dallas/ | | | |
| Dallas | 04850326 | 214/375-7682 | 3 |
| Faith Lutheran Sch/Plano/Collin | 02083735 | 972/423-7448 | 89 |
| Faith West Academy/Katy/Harris | 03417373 | 281/391-5683 | 210 |
| Falcon Pass Elem Sch/Houston/Galveston | 05096884 | 281/284-6200 | 163 |
| Falcon Ridge Elem Sch/Huffman/Harris | 12310594 | 281/324-7100 | 200 |
| Falfurrias Elem Sch/Falfurrias/Brooks | 01002350 | 361/325-8040 | 61 |
| Falfurrias High Sch/Falfurrias/Brooks | 01002362 | 361/325-8091 | 61 |
| Falfurrias Junior High Sch/Falfurrias/ | | | |
| Brooks | 01002374 | 361/325-8071 | 61 |
| Fall Creek Elem Sch/Humble/Harris | 11079618 | 281/641-3400 | 201 |
| Fallbrook Academy/Houston/Harris | 12315362 | 281/880-1360 | 3 |
| Falls Career High Sch/Marble Falls/Burnet | 10020822 | 830/798-3621 | 64 |
| Falls City Elem Sch/Falls City/Karnes | 01035371 | 830/254-3551 | 253 |
| Falls City High Sch/Falls City/Karnes | 01035383 | 830/254-3551 | 253 |
| **FALLS CITY IND SCH DIST/** | | | |
| **FALLS CITY/KARNES** | 01035369 | 830/254-3551 | 253 |
| Family Christian Academy/Dallas/Dallas | 11231799 | 214/324-4399 | 119 |
| Family Christian Academy/Houston/Harris | 05422582 | 713/455-4483 | 211 |
| Fannin Elem Sch/Bryan/Brazos | 01002063 | 979/209-3800 | 58 |
| Fannin Elem Sch/Corsicana/Navarro | 01043471 | 903/874-3728 | 302 |
| Fannin Elem Sch/Midland/Midland | 01041552 | 432/240-6800 | 289 |
| Fannin Elem Sch/San Angelo/Tom Green | 01055682 | 325/947-3930 | 367 |
| Fannin Middle Sch/Grand Prairie/Dallas | 01010931 | 972/262-8668 | 111 |
| Fannindel Elem Sch/Pecan Gap/Delta | 01013153 | 903/359-6314 | 124 |
| Fannindel High Sch/Ladonia/Delta | 01013165 | 903/367-7251 | 124 |
| **FANNINDEL IND SCH DIST/LADONIA/** | | | |
| **DELTA** | 01013141 | 903/367-7251 | 124 |
| Fanny Finch Elem Sch/McKinney/Collin | 01006253 | 469/302-5600 | 84 |
| Farias Early Childhood Center/Houston/ | | | |
| Harris | 10003898 | 713/691-8730 | 196 |
| Farias Elem Sch/Alamo/Hidalgo | 01030448 | 956/354-2760 | 226 |
| Farine Elem Sch/Irving/Dallas | 01011129 | 972/600-7900 | 113 |
| Farley Middle Sch/Hutto/Williamson | 11080526 | 512/759-2050 | 399 |
| Farmers Branch Elem Sch/Farmers BRNCH/ | | | |
| Dallas | 01008172 | 972/968-1600 | 101 |
| Farmersville High Sch/Farmersville/Collin | 01006150 | 972/782-7757 | 82 |
| **FARMERSVILLE IND SCH DIST/** | | | |
| **FARMERSVILLE/COLLIN** | 01006148 | 972/782-6601 | 82 |
| Farmersville Intermediate Sch/Farmersville/ | | | |
| Collin | 04918851 | 972/782-8108 | 82 |
| Farmersville Jr High Sch/Farmersville/ | | | |
| Collin | 01006162 | 972/782-6202 | 82 |
| Farney Elem Sch/Cypress/Harris | 04916334 | 281/373-2850 | 189 |
| Farrell Elem Sch/Grand Prairie/Tarrant | 03250711 | 682/867-0300 | 347 |
| Farris Early Childhood Center/Wichita Falls/ | | | |
| Wichita | 11444661 | 940/235-4302 | 395 |
| Farwell Elem Sch/Farwell/Parmer | 01046708 | 806/481-9131 | 317 |
| Farwell High Sch/Farwell/Parmer | 01046710 | 806/481-3351 | 317 |
| **FARWELL IND SCH DIST/FARWELL/** | | | |
| **PARMER** | 01046693 | 806/481-3371 | 317 |
| Farwell Junior High Sch/Farwell/Parmer | 01046722 | 806/481-9260 | 317 |
| Fasken Elem Sch/Midland/Midland | 12104369 | 432/240-8400 | 289 |
| Father Yermo Elem Sch/El Paso/El Paso | 01016739 | 915/532-6875 | 143 |
| Father Yermo High Sch/El Paso/El Paso | 01016741 | 915/533-3185 | 143 |
| Faubion Elem Sch/Cedar Park/Williamson | 01061019 | 512/570-7500 | 400 |
| Faulk Early Childhood Center/Aransas Pass/ | | | |
| San Patricio | 01049516 | 361/758-3141 | 333 |
| Faulk Middle Sch/Brownsville/Cameron | 01003562 | 956/548-8500 | 67 |
| Faustina Academy/Irving/Dallas | 05331220 | 972/254-6726 | 119 |
| Faye Webb Elem Sch/Corp Christi/Nueces | 10025846 | 361/878-2740 | 306 |

| School/City/County DISTRICT/CITY/COUNTY | PID | TELEPHONE NUMBER | PAGE |
|---|---|---|---|
| **FAYETTEVILLE IND SCH DIST/** | | | |
| **FAYETTEVILLE/FAYETTE** | 01017666 | 979/378-4242 | 151 |
| Fayetteville Sch/Fayetteville/Fayette | 01017678 | 979/378-4242 | 151 |
| Fehl-Price Elem Sch/Beaumont/Jefferson | 01034195 | 409/617-6400 | 245 |
| Felix Botello Elem Sch/Dallas/Dallas | 10023094 | 972/502-4600 | 104 |
| Felix Morales Elem Sch/Pasadena/Harris | 04015629 | 713/740-0664 | 204 |
| Fellowship Academy/Kennedale/Tarrant | 11231907 | 817/483-2400 | 361 |
| Fellowship Collegiate Academy/Dallas/ | | | |
| Dallas | 11824994 | 214/672-9200 | 119 |
| Fenley PK Center/San Antonio/Bexar | 12173774 | 210/921-7000 | 35 |
| Ferdinand Herff Academy/San Antonio/Bexar | 00998823 | 210/228-3330 | 43 |
| Fern Bluff Elem Sch/Round Rock/Williamson | 04017794 | 512/428-2100 | 402 |
| Ferndell Henry Center for Lrng/Rosharon/ | | | |
| Fort Bend | 11561910 | 281/327-6000 | 154 |
| Ferris High Sch/Ferris/Ellis | 01015060 | 972/544-3737 | 145 |
| **FERRIS IND SCH DIST/FERRIS/ELLIS** | 01015034 | 972/544-3858 | 144 |
| Ferris Intermediate Sch/Ferris/Ellis | 03241681 | 972/544-8662 | 145 |
| Ferris Junior High Sch/Ferris/Ellis | 01015058 | 972/544-2279 | 145 |
| Field Elem Sch/Houston/Harris | 01024009 | 713/867-5190 | 196 |
| Fields Elem Sch/San Antonio/Bexar | 12170112 | 210/398-2150 | 40 |
| Fields Store Elem Sch/Waller/Waller | 05035062 | 936/931-4050 | 387 |
| Fiest Elem Sch/Houston/Harris | 03251961 | 281/463-5838 | 189 |
| Filemon B Vela Middle Sch/Brownsville/ | | | |
| Cameron | 03325586 | 956/548-7770 | 67 |
| Fine Arts Academy/Fort Worth/Tarrant | 10904852 | 817/367-5396 | 360 |
| Finley Elem Sch/Laredo/Webb | 03007514 | 956/473-4500 | 390 |
| Finley-Oates Elem Sch/Bonham/Fannin | 01017379 | 903/640-4090 | 149 |
| Firewheel Christian Academy/Garland/Dallas | 02207228 | 972/495-0851 | 119 |
| First Baptist Acad-Univ City/Universal Cty/ | | | |
| Bexar | 02165084 | 210/658-5331 | 48 |
| First Baptist Academy/Dallas/Dallas | 01480972 | 972/453-1321 | 119 |
| First Baptist Academy/Houston/Harris | 04798924 | 713/290-2500 | 211 |
| First Baptist Christian Acad/Pasadena/ | | | |
| Harris | 03371705 | 281/991-9191 | 211 |
| First Baptist Christian Sch/Marble Falls/ | | | |
| Burnet | 02731140 | 830/693-3930 | 64 |
| First Baptist Church Sch/Beeville/Bee | 04993693 | 361/358-4161 | 29 |
| First Baptist Church Sch/Brenham/ | | | |
| Washington | 02783583 | 979/836-6411 | 389 |
| First Baptist Sch/Brownsville/Cameron | 01479686 | 956/542-4854 | 72 |
| First Christian Academy/Pearland/Brazoria | 11236048 | 281/760-4201 | 58 |
| First Christian Day Sch/Waxahachie/Ellis | 02743088 | 972/937-1952 | 147 |
| First Colony Middle Sch/Sugar Land/ | | | |
| Fort Bend | 02857380 | 281/634-3240 | 154 |
| Fisher Elem Sch/Pasadena/Harris | 01026679 | 713/740-0552 | 204 |
| Fitzgerald Elem Sch/Arlington/Tarrant | 02226418 | 682/867-5300 | 347 |
| Five Palms Elem Sch/San Antonio/Bexar | 00999437 | 210/645-3850 | 45 |
| Flatonia Elem Sch/Flatonia/Fayette | 01017707 | 361/865-2941 | 151 |
| Flatonia High Sch/Flatonia/Fayette | 01017719 | 361/865-2941 | 151 |
| **FLATONIA IND SCH DIST/FLATONIA/** | | | |
| **FAYETTE** | 01017692 | 361/865-2941 | 151 |
| Fleming Middle Sch/Houston/Harris | 01025584 | 713/671-4170 | 196 |
| Fletcher Elem Sch/Beaumont/Jefferson | 01033505 | 409/617-6100 | 245 |
| Flint Academy/Arlington/Tarrant | 11225843 | 817/277-0620 | 361 |
| Florence Black Elem Sch/Mesquite/Dallas | 01011478 | 972/882-7240 | 115 |
| Florence Campbell Sch/League City/ | | | |
| Galveston | 12365642 | 281/284-6600 | 163 |
| Florence Elem Sch/Florence/Williamson | 01060845 | 254/793-2497 | 398 |
| Florence Elem Sch/Southlake/Tarrant | 01538684 | 817/744-4700 | 357 |
| Florence High Sch/Florence/Williamson | 01060857 | 254/793-2495 | 398 |
| Florence Hill Elem Sch/Grand Prairie/ | | | |
| Dallas | 01010876 | 972/264-0802 | 111 |
| **FLORENCE IND SCH DIST/FLORENCE/** | | | |
| **WILLIAMSON** | 01060833 | 254/793-2850 | 398 |
| Florence J Scott Elem Sch/Roma/Starr | 01051246 | 956/849-1175 | 343 |
| Florence Middle Sch/Florence/Williamson | 03472414 | 254/793-2504 | 398 |
| Flores Elem Sch/Uvalde/Uvalde | 01057824 | 830/591-2976 | 381 |
| Flores-Zapata Elem Sch/Edinburg/Hidalgo | 11558248 | 956/289-2445 | 221 |
| Floresville Alternative Ctr/Floresville/ | | | |
| Wilson | 04363244 | 830/393-5368 | 404 |
| Floresville High Sch/Floresville/Wilson | 01061277 | 830/393-5370 | 404 |
| **FLORESVILLE IND SCH DIST/** | | | |
| **FLORESVILLE/WILSON** | 01061265 | 830/393-5300 | 403 |
| Floresville Middle Sch/Floresville/Wilson | 01061291 | 830/393-5350 | 404 |
| Floresville North Elem Sch/Floresville/ | | | |
| Wilson | 01061306 | 830/393-5310 | 404 |
| Floresville South Elem Sch/Floresville/ | | | |
| Wilson | 03050705 | 830/393-5325 | 404 |
| Flossie Floyd Green Elem Sch/Allen/Collin | 04356411 | 972/727-0370 | 80 |
| Flour Bluff Elem Sch/Corp Christi/Nueces | 01044827 | 361/694-9500 | 308 |
| Flour Bluff High Sch/Corp Christi/Nueces | 01044839 | 361/694-9100 | 308 |

| School/City/County DISTRICT/CITY/COUNTY | PID | TELEPHONE NUMBER | PAGE |
|---|---|---|---|
| **FLOUR BLUFF IND SCH DIST/** | | | |
| **CORP CHRISTI/NUECES** | 01044815 | 361/694-9000 | 307 |
| Flour Bluff Interm Sch/Corp Christi/Nueces | 01044841 | 361/694-9400 | 308 |
| Flour Bluff Junior High Sch/Corp Christi/ Nueces | 01044853 | 361/694-9300 | 308 |
| Flour Bluff Primary Sch/Corp Christi/ Nueces | 01420544 | 361/694-9400 | 308 |
| Flower Mound 9th Grade Center/Flower Mound/ Denton | 12033942 | 469/713-5999 | 127 |
| Flower Mound Elem Sch/Flower Mound/Denton | 02857433 | 469/713-5955 | 127 |
| Flower Mound High Sch/Flower Mound/Denton | 04850936 | 469/713-5192 | 127 |
| Floyd Hoffman Middle Sch/Houston/Harris | 01399749 | 713/613-7670 | 186 |
| Floydada High Sch/Floydada/Floyd | 01017991 | 806/983-2340 | 153 |
| **FLOYDADA IND SCH DIST/FLOYDADA/** | | | |
| **FLOYD** | 01017977 | 806/983-3498 | 153 |
| Focus Academy/Sugar Land/Fort Bend | 12230671 | 281/240-0663 | 159 |
| Foerster Elem Sch/Houston/Harris | 01024803 | 713/726-3604 | 194 |
| Folks Middle Sch/San Antonio/Bexar | 11918193 | 210/398-1600 | 40 |
| **FOLLETT IND SCH DIST/FOLLETT/** | | | |
| **LIPSCOMB** | 01038191 | 806/653-2301 | 270 |
| Follett Sch/Follett/Lipscomb | 01038206 | 806/653-2301 | 270 |
| Folsom Elem Sch/Prosper/Collin | 01006564 | 469/219-2110 | 88 |
| Fondren Elem Sch/Houston/Harris | 01025194 | 713/726-3611 | 194 |
| Fondren Middle Sch/Houston/Harris | 01024815 | 713/778-3360 | 199 |
| Fonville Middle Sch/Houston/Harris | 01025912 | 713/696-2825 | 196 |
| Fonwood Early Childhood Center/Houston/ Harris | 11931066 | 713/633-0781 | 196 |
| Ford Elem Sch/Spring/Montgomery | 01829495 | 832/592-5700 | 294 |
| Ford High Sch/Quinlan/Hunt | 01032599 | 903/356-1600 | 240 |
| Forest Brook Middle Sch/Houston/Harris | 11563140 | 713/631-7720 | 194 |
| Forest Creek Elem Sch/Round Rock/ Williamson | 04452338 | 512/464-5350 | 402 |
| Forest Hill Elem Sch/Amarillo/Potter | 01047269 | 806/326-4400 | 320 |
| Forest Ln Acad of Arts & Comm/Dallas/ Dallas | 04850900 | 469/593-1850 | 116 |
| Forest Meadow Jr High Sch/Dallas/Dallas | 01011686 | 469/593-1500 | 116 |
| Forest North Elem Sch/Austin/Williamson | 01541435 | 512/464-6750 | 402 |
| Forest Oak Middle Sch/Fort Worth/Tarrant | 01052927 | 817/815-8200 | 353 |
| Forest Park Middle Sch/Longview/Gregg | 01021019 | 903/446-2510 | 175 |
| Forest Ridge Elem Sch/College Sta/Brazos | 10012318 | 979/694-5801 | 59 |
| Forest Trail Elem Sch/Austin/Travis | 02222400 | 512/732-9160 | 372 |
| Forest Vista Elem Sch/Flower Mound/Denton | 04757229 | 469/713-5194 | 127 |
| **FORESTBURG IND SCH DIST/** | | | |
| **FORESTBURG/MONTAGUE** | 01042257 | 940/964-2323 | 293 |
| Forestburg Sch/Forestburg/Montague | 01042269 | 940/964-2323 | 293 |
| Forester Elem Sch/San Antonio/Bexar | 11104108 | 210/397-0200 | 40 |
| Forestridge Elem Sch/Dallas/Dallas | 01011698 | 469/593-8500 | 116 |
| Forestwood Middle Sch/Flower Mound/Denton | 04036063 | 469/713-5972 | 127 |
| Forman Elem Sch/Plano/Collin | 01006411 | 469/752-1200 | 86 |
| Forney Academic Center/Forney/Kaufman | 04750063 | 469/762-4350 | 255 |
| Forney High Sch/Forney/Kaufman | 01035591 | 469/762-4200 | 255 |
| **FORNEY IND SCH DIST/FORNEY/** | | | |
| **KAUFMAN** | 01035565 | 972/564-4055 | 254 |
| Forsan Elem Sch/Forsan/Howard | 01032109 | 432/457-0091 | 237 |
| **FORSAN IND SCH DIST/FORSAN/** | | | |
| **HOWARD** | 01032094 | 432/457-2223 | 237 |
| Forsan Jr Sr High Sch/Forsan/Howard | 01032111 | 432/457-2223 | 237 |
| Fort Bend Alternative Sch/Rosenberg/ Fort Bend | 04478306 | 281/239-3431 | 158 |
| Fort Bend Baptist Academy ES/Sugar Land/ Fort Bend | 04993538 | 281/263-9100 | 159 |
| Fort Bend Christian Academy MS/Sugar Land/ Fort Bend | 05291955 | 281/263-9191 | 159 |
| Fort Bend Christian Academy-HS/Sugar Land/ Fort Bend | 05291967 | 281/263-9175 | 159 |
| **FORT DAVIS IND SCH DIST/** | | | |
| **FORT DAVIS/JEFF DAVIS** | 01033323 | 432/426-4440 | 244 |
| Fort Davis Jr Sr High Sch/Fort Davis/ Jeff Davis | 01033347 | 432/426-4444 | 244 |
| Fort Settlement Middle Sch/Sugar Land/ Fort Bend | 04947149 | 281/634-6440 | 154 |
| Fort Worth Academy/Fort Worth/Tarrant | 02233459 | 817/370-1191 | 361 |
| Fort Worth Christian Sch/N Richlnd Hls/ Tarrant | 01481005 | 817/281-6504 | 361 |
| Fossil Hill Middle Sch/Fort Worth/Tarrant | 03047071 | 817/744-3050 | 357 |
| Fossil Ridge High Sch/Fort Worth/Tarrant | 04366662 | 817/744-1700 | 357 |
| Foster Elem Sch/Arlington/Tarrant | 01051753 | 682/867-5350 | 347 |
| Foster Elem Sch/Houston/Harris | 01024827 | 713/746-8260 | 197 |
| Foster Elem Sch/Kingwood/Harris | 01026162 | 281/641-1400 | 201 |
| Foster Middle Sch/Longview/Gregg | 01021033 | 903/446-2710 | 175 |
| Foster Village Elem Sch/N Richlnd Hls/ Tarrant | 02110900 | 817/547-3100 | 348 |

| School/City/County DISTRICT/CITY/COUNTY | PID | TELEPHONE NUMBER | PAGE |
|---|---|---|---|
| Foundation School for Autism/San Antonio/ Bexar | 11832563 | 210/402-0253 | 3 |
| Founders Christian Sch/Spring/Harris | 12368228 | 281/602-8006 | 211 |
| Founders Classical Acad Flower/Flower Mound/ Denton | 12161745 | 972/899-2521 | 3 |
| Founders Classical Acad Frisco/Frisco/ Denton | 12363735 | 972/532-0952 | 3 |
| Founders Classical Acad Leandr/Leander/ Williamson | 12042216 | 512/259-0103 | 3 |
| Founders Classical Acad Lwsvll/Lewisville/ Denton | 11662980 | 469/464-3415 | 3 |
| Founders Classical Acad Mesq/Mesquite/ Dallas | 12161757 | 469/453-0977 | 3 |
| Founders Classical Acad Schrtz/Schertz/ Guadalupe | 12173554 | 210/510-2618 | 3 |
| Four Points Middle Sch/Austin/Williamson | 11557036 | 512/570-3700 | 400 |
| Fowler Elem Sch/Killeen/Bell | 00996485 | 254/336-1760 | 31 |
| Fowler Elem Sch/Wichita Falls/Wichita | 01173040 | 940/235-1152 | 395 |
| Fox Run Elem Sch/San Antonio/Bexar | 03329025 | 210/407-3400 | 38 |
| Fox Technical High Sch/San Antonio/Bexar | 00998483 | 210/738-9730 | 43 |
| Foy H Moody High Sch/Corp Christi/Nueces | 01044396 | 361/878-7340 | 306 |
| Frances Corprew Elem Sch/Mt Pleasant/Titus | 01055395 | 903/575-2050 | 366 |
| Frances M Rhodes Elem Sch/San Antonio/ Bexar | 05097747 | 210/397-4000 | 40 |
| Frances Norton Elem Sch/Allen/Collin | 04749014 | 972/396-6918 | 80 |
| Francis R Scobee Middle Sch/San Antonio/ Bexar | 04868218 | 210/645-7500 | 46 |
| Francisca Alvarez Elem Sch/McAllen/Hidalgo | 01029994 | 956/971-4471 | 224 |
| Francisco Barrientes Mid Sch/Edinburg/ Hidalgo | 10909981 | 956/289-2430 | 221 |
| Francisco Farias Elem Sch/Laredo/Webb | 01059262 | 956/273-3400 | 389 |
| Francisco Medrano Middle Sch/Dallas/Dallas | 11130315 | 972/925-1300 | 104 |
| Francisco S Lara Academy/Laredo/Webb | 04752619 | 956/273-7900 | 389 |
| Francone Elem Sch/Houston/Harris | 02045393 | 281/897-4512 | 189 |
| Frank & Sue McBee Elem Sch/Austin/Travis | 04917675 | 512/841-2500 | 369 |
| Frank B Agnew Middle Sch/Mesquite/Dallas | 01011492 | 972/882-5750 | 115 |
| Frank D Moates Elem Sch/Glenn Heights/ Dallas | 03047100 | 972/230-2881 | 108 |
| Frank Elem Sch/Klein/Harris | 10910198 | 832/375-7000 | 202 |
| Frank Guzick Elem Sch/Dallas/Dallas | 10023173 | 972/502-3900 | 104 |
| Frank L Madla Accel Coll Acad/San Antonio/ Bexar | 04802630 | 210/533-3655 | 3 |
| Frank L Madla Early College HS/San Antonio/ Bexar | 12163016 | 210/486-3686 | 3 |
| Frank M Tejeda Academy/San Antonio/Bexar | 04035112 | 210/989-4900 | 35 |
| Frank Macias Elem Sch/Horizon City/El Paso | 04931906 | 915/926-4600 | 137 |
| Frank Madla Elem Sch/San Antonio/Bexar | 00999499 | 210/645-3800 | 45 |
| Frank Newman Middle Sch/Cotulla/La Salle | 01037226 | 830/879-4376 | 262 |
| Frank Roberts Elem Sch/San Benito/Cameron | 01004205 | 956/361-6740 | 70 |
| Frank Seale Middle Sch/Midlothian/Ellis | 02896398 | 972/775-6145 | 145 |
| Frank Stone Middle Sch/Paris/Wise | 01036650 | 903/737-2041 | 406 |
| Frank Tejeda Middle Sch/San Antonio/Bexar | 04946341 | 210/356-5600 | 38 |
| Frankford Middle Sch/Dallas/Collin | 04811497 | 469/752-5200 | 86 |
| Franklin D Roosevelt High Sch/Dallas/ Dallas | 01008861 | 972/925-6800 | 104 |
| Franklin Elem Sch/Hillsboro/Hill | 01172474 | 254/582-4130 | 230 |
| Franklin Elem Sch/Houston/Harris | 01025508 | 713/924-1820 | 195 |
| Franklin Elem Sch/San Antonio/Bexar | 00998407 | 210/738-9790 | 43 |
| Franklin Elem Sch/Wichita Falls/Wichita | 01172967 | 940/235-1156 | 395 |
| Franklin High Sch/El Paso/El Paso | 04035681 | 915/236-2200 | 139 |
| Franklin High Sch/Franklin/Robertson | 01048627 | 979/828-7100 | 327 |
| Franklin HS 9th Grade Center/El Paso/ El Paso | 11982273 | 915/236-2400 | 139 |
| **FRANKLIN IND SCH DIST/FRANKLIN/** | | | |
| **ROBERTSON** | 01048615 | 979/828-7000 | 327 |
| Franklin Int'l Exploratory MS/Dallas/ Dallas | 02896324 | 972/502-7100 | 104 |
| Franklin Middle Sch/Franklin/Robertson | 03391262 | 979/828-7200 | 327 |
| Franklin Monroe Gilbert ES/Irving/Dallas | 04451176 | 972/600-0400 | 113 |
| Frankston Elem Sch/Frankston/Anderson | 04272528 | 903/876-2214 | 18 |
| Frankston High Sch/Frankston/Anderson | 00994487 | 903/876-3219 | 18 |
| **FRANKSTON IND SCH DIST/FRANKSTON/** | | | |
| **ANDERSON** | 00994463 | 903/876-2556 | 18 |
| Frankston Middle Sch/Frankston/Anderson | 04272530 | 903/876-2215 | 18 |
| Franz Elem Sch/Katy/Harris | 05344318 | 281/237-8600 | 156 |
| Frassati Catholic High Sch/Spring/Harris | 12115693 | 832/616-3217 | 209 |
| Frazier Elem Sch/Burleson/Johnson | 01034822 | 817/245-3000 | 250 |
| Frazier Elem Sch/Houston/Harris | 01387318 | 713/740-0560 | 204 |
| Frazier Elem Sch/Houston/Harris | 02177946 | 713/896-3475 | 189 |
| Fred and Patti Shafer ES/Katy/Harris | 11822049 | 281/234-1900 | 156 |
| Fred Booth Elem Sch/San Benito/Cameron | 01004217 | 956/361-6860 | 70 |

| School/City/County DISTRICT/CITY/COUNTY | PID | TELEPHONE NUMBER | PAGE |
|---|---|---|---|
| Fred Douglass Early Chldhd Ctr/Sherman/Grayson | 01418345 | 903/891-6545 | 172 |
| Fred Douglass Elem Sch/Jacksonville/Cherokee | 02226860 | 903/586-6519 | 76 |
| Fred Elem Sch/Fred/Tyler | 01057290 | 409/429-3240 | 378 |
| Fred H Tally Elem Sch/Kerrville/Kerr | 05100368 | 830/257-2222 | 259 |
| Fred McWhorter Elem Sch/Mesquite/Dallas | 01011466 | 972/882-7020 | 115 |
| Fred Moore High Sch/Denton/Denton | 03473535 | 940/369-4000 | 125 |
| Fred R Sanders Elem Sch/Corp Christi/Nueces | 01044645 | 361/878-2820 | 306 |
| Fred Roberts Middle Sch/Houston/Harris | 12160739 | 713/740-5390 | 204 |
| Fred W Edwards Academy/Temple/Bell | 12035770 | 254/215-6944 | 32 |
| Fredda Nottingham Alt Educ Ctr/Dayton/Liberty | 12168509 | 936/257-4100 | 268 |
| Freddy Gonzalez Elem Sch/Edinburg/Hidalgo | 01418498 | 956/289-2520 | 221 |
| Frederick A Douglass Lrng Acad/Cleveland/Liberty | 11078602 | 281/592-7595 | 268 |
| Frederick Douglass Academy/San Antonio/Bexar | 00998770 | 210/228-3315 | 43 |
| Frederick Douglass Elem Sch/Dallas/Dallas | 03247805 | 972/794-1400 | 104 |
| Fredericksburg Elem Sch/Fredericksbrg/Gillespie | 01019717 | 830/997-9595 | 167 |
| Fredericksburg High Sch/Fredericksbrg/Gillespie | 01019705 | 830/997-7551 | 167 |
| **FREDERICKSBURG IND SCH DIST/FREDERICKSBRG/GILLESPIE** | 01019688 | 830/997-9551 | 167 |
| Fredericksburg Middle Sch/Fredericksbrg/Gillespie | 01857222 | 830/997-7657 | 167 |
| Fredericksburg Primary Sch/Fredericksbrg/Gillespie | 01401419 | 830/997-7421 | 167 |
| Fredonia Elem Sch/Nacogdoches/Nacogdoches | 01043304 | 936/569-5080 | 301 |
| Fredonia Hill Baptist Academy/Nacogdoches/Nacogdoches | 01875511 | 936/564-4472 | 302 |
| Freedom Elem Sch/Keller/Tarrant | 05090804 | 817/744-4800 | 357 |
| Freedom Elem Sch/Laredo/Webb | 12231455 | 956/473-1600 | 390 |
| Freedom Elem Sch/San Antonio/Bexar | 10012095 | 210/882-1603 | 46 |
| Freeman Elem Sch/Garland/Dallas | 01010400 | 972/494-8371 | 109 |
| Freeman Elem Sch/Houston/Harris | 01026681 | 713/740-0568 | 204 |
| Freeport Elem Sch/Freeport/Brazoria | 01001655 | 979/730-7175 | 55 |
| Freeport Intermediate Sch/Freeport/Brazoria | 01001629 | 979/730-7240 | 55 |
| Freer High Sch/Freer/Duval | 01809201 | 361/394-6717 | 132 |
| **FREER IND SCH DIST/FREER/DUVAL** | 01809196 | 361/394-6025 | 132 |
| Freer Junior High Sch/Freer/Duval | 01809213 | 361/394-7102 | 132 |
| Freiheit Elem Sch/New Braunfels/Comal | 01006954 | 830/221-2700 | 92 |
| French Elem Sch/Klein/Harris | 12110681 | 832/375-8100 | 202 |
| Frenship High Sch/Wolfforth/Lubbock | 01038426 | 806/866-4440 | 272 |
| **FRENSHIP IND SCH DIST/WOLFFORTH/LUBBOCK** | 01038402 | 806/866-9541 | 272 |
| Frenship Middle Sch/Wolfforth/Lubbock | 02177075 | 806/866-4464 | 272 |
| Friendship Elem Sch/Keller/Tarrant | 10028551 | 817/744-6200 | 357 |
| Friendship Pre-Sch & Chrn Acad/Beaumont/Jefferson | 11243613 | 409/898-0489 | 247 |
| Friendswood High Sch/Friendswood/Galveston | 01019030 | 281/482-3413 | 164 |
| **FRIENDSWOOD IND SCH DIST/FRIENDSWOOD/GALVESTON** | 01019028 | 281/482-1267 | 164 |
| Friendswood Junior High Sch/Friendswood/Galveston | 01019042 | 281/996-6200 | 164 |
| Friona Elem Sch/Friona/Parmer | 01046746 | 806/250-2240 | 318 |
| Friona High Sch/Friona/Parmer | 01046758 | 806/250-3951 | 318 |
| **FRIONA IND SCH DIST/FRIONA/PARMER** | 01046734 | 806/250-2747 | 318 |
| Friona Junior High Sch/Friona/Parmer | 01046760 | 806/250-2788 | 318 |
| Friona Primary Sch/Friona/Parmer | 03241514 | 806/250-3935 | 318 |
| Frisco High Sch/Frisco/Collin | 01006203 | 469/633-5500 | 82 |
| **FRISCO IND SCH DIST/FRISCO/COLLIN** | 01006186 | 469/633-6000 | 82 |
| Frisco ISD Early Childhood Sch/Frisco/Collin | 11448485 | 469/633-3825 | 82 |
| Frisco Montessori Academy/Frisco/Denton | 04929537 | 972/712-7400 | 130 |
| Frontier Elem Sch/Angleton/Brazoria | 03393026 | 979/864-8005 | 55 |
| Frontier High Sch/Mansfield/Tarrant | 11715393 | 682/314-1600 | 359 |
| Frost Elem Sch/Frost/Navarro | 11833866 | 903/682-2541 | 302 |
| Frost Elem Sch/Houston/Harris | 01025209 | 713/732-3490 | 197 |
| Frost Elem Sch/Richmond/Fort Bend | 04923325 | 832/223-1500 | 158 |
| Frost High Sch/Frost/Navarro | 01043562 | 903/682-2541 | 303 |
| **FROST IND SCH DIST/FROST/NAVARRO** | 01043550 | 903/682-2711 | 302 |
| Frostwood Elem Sch/Houston/Harris | 01027128 | 713/251-5700 | 206 |
| **FRUITVALE IND SCH DIST/FRUITVALE/VAN ZANDT** | 01058141 | 903/896-1191 | 383 |
| Fruitvale Junior High Sch/Fruitvale/Van Zandt | 03397101 | 903/896-4363 | 383 |
| Fruitvale Senior High Sch/Fruitvale/Van Zandt | 04810936 | 903/896-4363 | 383 |
| **FT BEND IND SCH DIST/SUGAR LAND/FORT BEND** | 01018115 | 281/634-1000 | 153 |
| Ft Concho Elem Sch/San Angelo/Tom Green | 01055632 | 325/659-3654 | 367 |
| **FT ELLIOTT CONS IND SCH DIST/BRISCOE/WHEELER** | 01059779 | 806/375-2454 | 393 |
| Ft Elliott Sch/Briscoe/Wheeler | 01059781 | 806/375-2454 | 393 |
| Ft Hancock High Sch/Fort Hancock/Hudspeth | 01032197 | 915/769-1604 | 237 |
| **FT HANCOCK IND SCH DIST/FORT HANCOCK/HUDSPETH** | 01032173 | 915/769-3811 | 237 |
| Ft Hancock Middle Sch/Fort Hancock/Hudspeth | 05099111 | 915/769-1603 | 237 |
| Ft Sam Houston Elem Sch/San Antonio/Bexar | 01534951 | 210/368-8800 | 35 |
| **FT SAM HOUSTON IND SCH DIST/SAN ANTONIO/BEXAR** | 01534949 | 210/368-8701 | 35 |
| Ft Stockton High Sch/Fort Stockton/Pecos | 01046887 | 432/336-4101 | 318 |
| **FT STOCKTON IND SCH DIST/FORT STOCKTON/PECOS** | 01046837 | 432/336-4000 | 318 |
| Ft Stockton Intermediate Sch/Fort Stockton/Pecos | 01539224 | 432/336-4141 | 318 |
| Ft Stockton Middle Sch/Fort Stockton/Pecos | 01046899 | 432/336-4131 | 318 |
| Ft Worth Academy of Fine Arts/Fort Worth/Tarrant | 04146113 | 817/924-1482 | 3 |
| Ft Worth Adventist Jr Academy/Fort Worth/Tarrant | 04993069 | 817/370-7177 | 361 |
| Ft Worth Country Day Sch/Fort Worth/Tarrant | 01054250 | 817/732-7718 | 361 |
| **FT WORTH IND SCH DIST/FORT WORTH/TARRANT** | 01052525 | 817/871-2000 | 352 |
| Full Armor Christian Academy/Henderson/Rusk | 04467046 | 903/655-8489 | 331 |
| Fulshear High Sch/Fulshear/Fort Bend | 12165313 | 832/223-5000 | 158 |
| Fulton 4-5 Learning Center/Fulton/Aransas | 00995132 | 361/790-2240 | 22 |
| Furneaux Elem Sch/Carrollton/Dallas | 02178081 | 972/968-1800 | 101 |
| Furr Elem Sch/McKinney/Collin | 12363826 | 469/219-2280 | 88 |
| Furr High Sch/Houston/Harris | 01025510 | 713/675-1118 | 195 |
| Fusion Acad-Houston Galleria/Houston/Harris | 12312217 | 713/963-9096 | 211 |
| Fusion Academy-Austin/Austin/Travis | 12312190 | 512/330-0188 | 375 |
| Fusion Academy-Dallas/Dallas/Dallas | 12312205 | 214/363-4615 | 119 |
| Fusion Academy-Plano/Plano/Collin | 12312229 | 972/403-9018 | 89 |
| Fusion Academy-Southlake/Southlake/Tarrant | 12312231 | 817/416-0306 | 361 |
| Fusion Academy-Sugarland/Sugar Land/Fort Bend | 12312243 | 281/207-9506 | 159 |
| Fusion Academy-the Woodlands/The Woodlands/Montgomery | 12312255 | 281/419-1436 | 298 |

## G

| | | | |
|---|---|---|---|
| G H Whitcomb Elem Sch/Houston/Galveston | 01018878 | 281/284-4900 | 163 |
| G L Wiley Opportunity Center/Waco/McLennan | 04036714 | 254/757-3829 | 285 |
| G R Porter Elem Sch/Mesquite/Dallas | 02043204 | 972/290-4000 | 115 |
| G W Carver Early Childhood Ctr/Ennis/Ellis | 11456743 | 972/872-3730 | 144 |
| G W Carver Middle Sch/Waco/McLennan | 01040273 | 254/757-0787 | 285 |
| G W Harby Junior High Sch/Alvin/Brazoria | 02109420 | 281/585-6626 | 54 |
| G W Kennemer Middle Sch/Dallas/Dallas | 03244592 | 972/708-3600 | 109 |
| G W Robinson Elem Sch/Seabrook/Galveston | 10025949 | 281/284-6500 | 163 |
| Gabe P Allen Charter Sch/Dallas/Dallas | 01008885 | 972/794-5100 | 104 |
| Gainesville High Sch/Gainesville/Cooke | 01007362 | 940/665-5528 | 95 |
| **GAINESVILLE IND SCH DIST/GAINESVILLE/COOKE** | 01007348 | 940/665-4362 | 95 |
| Gainesville Jr High Sch/Gainesville/Cooke | 01007374 | 940/665-4062 | 95 |
| Gainesville State Sch/Gainesville/Cooke | 04459697 | 940/665-0701 | 3 |
| Galatas Elem Sch/The Woodlands/Montgomery | 04014625 | 936/709-5000 | 294 |
| Gale Pond Alamo Steam Academy/Odessa/Ector | 01014559 | 432/456-1019 | 134 |
| Galena Park Cte Early Clg HS/Houston/Harris | 12235047 | 281/459-7198 | 192 |
| Galena Park Elem Sch/Galena Park/Harris | 01023457 | 832/386-1670 | 192 |
| Galena Park High Sch/Galena Park/Harris | 01023471 | 832/386-2800 | 192 |
| **GALENA PARK IND SCH DIST/HOUSTON/HARRIS** | 01023419 | 832/386-1000 | 191 |
| Galena Park Middle Sch/Galena Park/Harris | 01023469 | 832/386-1700 | 192 |
| Galindo Elem Sch/Austin/Travis | 03249279 | 512/414-1756 | 369 |
| Gallegos Elem Sch/Brownsville/Cameron | 04945127 | 956/547-4230 | 67 |
| Gallegos Elem Sch/Houston/Harris | 04016116 | 713/924-1830 | 195 |
| Galloway Elem Sch/Mesquite/Dallas | 01011404 | 972/882-5101 | 115 |
| Galloway Sch/Friendswood/Galveston | 04934738 | 281/338-9510 | 166 |
| **GALVESTON IND SCH DIST/GALVESTON/GALVESTON** | 01019078 | 409/766-5100 | 164 |
| Ganado Elem Sch/Ganado/Jackson | 01033062 | 361/771-4250 | 242 |
| Ganado High Sch/Ganado/Jackson | 01033074 | 361/771-4300 | 242 |

| School/City/County DISTRICT/CITY/COUNTY | PID | TELEPHONE NUMBER | PAGE |
|---|---|---|---|
| **GANADO IND SCH DIST**/GANADO/ JACKSON | 01033050 | 361/771-4200 | 242 |
| Ganado Junior High Sch/Ganado/Jackson | 11690729 | 361/771-4300 | 243 |
| Garcia Elem Sch/Grand Prairie/Dallas | 01010967 | 972/237-0001 | 111 |
| Garcia Elem Sch/Houston/Harris | 04016130 | 713/696-2900 | 196 |
| Garcia Middle Sch/Houston/Harris | 12309674 | 281/878-3730 | 186 |
| Garcia Young Men's Leadership/Austin/ Travis | 10907220 | 512/841-9400 | 371 |
| Garcia-Leza EC-PK-K Sch/Houston/Harris | 11448875 | 281/985-6037 | 186 |
| Garden Oaks Montessori/Houston/Harris | 01024023 | 713/696-2930 | 197 |
| Garden Park Elem Sch/Brownsville/Cameron | 01003574 | 956/982-2630 | 67 |
| Garden Ridge Elem Sch/Flower Mound/Denton | 04016025 | 469/713-5956 | 127 |
| Garden Ridge Elem Sch/Garden Ridge/Comal | 01006930 | 830/837-7000 | 92 |
| Garden Villas Elem Sch/Houston/Harris | 01025211 | 713/845-7484 | 197 |
| Gardendale Elem Sch/San Antonio/Bexar | 00997221 | 210/444-8150 | 35 |
| Gardens Elem Sch/Pasadena/Harris | 01026693 | 713/740-0576 | 204 |
| Gardner Preparatory Sch/Lancaster/Dallas | 12033320 | 972/275-1539 | 119 |
| Garfield Elem Sch/Del Rio/Val Verde | 01057991 | 830/778-4700 | 382 |
| Garfield Elem Sch/Houston/Harris | 01026708 | 713/740-0584 | 204 |
| Garland Christian Academy/Garland/Dallas | 01012226 | 972/487-0043 | 119 |
| Garland Classical Academy/Garland/Dallas | 11459678 | 972/840-1100 | 3 |
| Garland High Sch/Garland/Dallas | 01010539 | 972/494-8492 | 109 |
| **GARLAND IND SCH DIST**/GARLAND/ DALLAS | 01010395 | 972/494-8201 | 109 |
| Garland McMeans Junior HS/Katy/Harris | 04908454 | 281/237-8000 | 156 |
| Garner Elem Sch/Weatherford/Parker | 01046382 | 940/682-4251 | 315 |
| Garner Fine Arts Academy/Grand Prairie/ Dallas | 03007265 | 972/262-5000 | 111 |
| **GARNER IND SCH DIST**/WEATHERFORD/ PARKER | 01046370 | 940/682-4251 | 315 |
| Garner Middle Sch/San Antonio/Bexar | 00997788 | 210/356-3800 | 38 |
| Garrett Elem Sch/Houston/Harris | 11717432 | 281/727-4200 | 205 |
| Garrett Primary Sch/Lufkin/Angelina | 00994968 | 936/634-8418 | 21 |
| Garriga Elem Sch/Port Isabel/Cameron | 01004085 | 956/943-0080 | 70 |
| Garrison Elem Sch/Garrison/Nacogdoches | 01043225 | 936/347-7010 | 301 |
| **GARRISON IND SCH DIST**/GARRISON/ NACOGDOCHES | 01043213 | 936/347-7000 | 301 |
| Garrison Middle Sch/Garrison/Nacogdoches | 04762779 | 936/347-7020 | 301 |
| Garrison Senior High Sch/Garrison/ Nacogdoches | 01043237 | 936/347-7030 | 301 |
| Garwood Elem Sch/Garwood/Colorado | 01006813 | 979/758-3531 | 91 |
| **GARY IND SCH DIST**/GARY/PANOLA | 01046277 | 903/685-2291 | 314 |
| Gary Sch/Gary/Panola | 01046289 | 903/685-2291 | 314 |
| Gary W Campbell High Sch/Kaufman/Kaufman | 04451940 | 972/932-8789 | 255 |
| Garza Elem Sch/Brownsville/Cameron | 01539975 | 956/982-2660 | 67 |
| Garza Independence High Sch/Austin/Travis | 04806686 | 512/414-8600 | 371 |
| Garza-Pena Elem Sch/San Juan/Hidalgo | 03009263 | 956/354-2800 | 226 |
| Gates Elem Sch/San Antonio/Bexar | 00998964 | 210/978-7980 | 43 |
| Gatesville Elem Sch/Gatesville/Coryell | 01007673 | 254/865-7262 | 97 |
| Gatesville High Sch/Gatesville/Coryell | 01007685 | 254/865-8281 | 97 |
| **GATESVILLE IND SCH DIST**/ GATESVILLE/CORYELL | 01007661 | 254/865-7251 | 96 |
| Gatesville Intermediate Sch/Gatesville/ Coryell | 04447292 | 254/865-2526 | 97 |
| Gatesville Junior High Sch/Gatesville/ Coryell | 01007697 | 254/865-8271 | 97 |
| Gatesville Primary Sch/Gatesville/Coryell | 01007702 | 254/865-7264 | 97 |
| Gateway Academy/Childress/Childress | 04446420 | 940/937-3099 | 77 |
| Gateway Academy/Houston/Harris | 11225398 | 713/659-7900 | 211 |
| Gateway Alternative Ed Center/Burkburnett/ Wichita | 04745991 | 940/569-0850 | 394 |
| Gateway Charter Academy/Dallas/Dallas | 11848823 | 214/375-1921 | 3 |
| Gateway Charter Elem Academy/Dallas/Dallas | 05010775 | 214/375-2039 | 3 |
| Gateway Christian Sch/San Antonio/Bexar | 01410525 | 210/674-5703 | 48 |
| Gateway College Prep Sch/Georgetown/ Williamson | 11704485 | 512/868-4947 | 3 |
| Gateway Daep Sch/Bastrop/Bastrop | 03399240 | 512/772-7820 | 26 |
| Gateway Elem Sch/Borger/Hutchinson | 02126753 | 806/273-1044 | 240 |
| Gateway High Sch/Killeen/Bell | 03107724 | 254/336-1700 | 31 |
| Gateway Middle Sch/Killeen/Bell | 04368763 | 254/336-1690 | 31 |
| Gateway Tech High Sch/Georgetown/ Williamson | 11539840 | 512/868-5299 | 3 |
| Gateway to Graduation Academy/San Benito/ Cameron | 11558755 | 956/361-6446 | 70 |
| Gattis Elem Sch/Round Rock/Williamson | 04017809 | 512/428-2000 | 402 |
| Gause Elem Sch/Gause/Milam | 01041813 | 979/279-5891 | 290 |
| **GAUSE IND SCH DIST**/GAUSE/MILAM | 01041801 | 979/279-5891 | 290 |
| Gen Tommy Franks Elem Sch/Midland/Midland | 01041473 | 432/240-6500 | 289 |
| Gene A Buinger Cte Academy/Bedford/Tarrant | 01053957 | 817/354-3542 | 356 |
| Gene Howe Elem Sch/Amarillo/Randall | 01047960 | 806/677-2380 | 323 |
| Gene M Reed Elem Sch/Allen/Collin | 02200385 | 972/727-0580 | 80 |
| Gene Pike Middle Sch/Justin/Denton | 01013555 | 817/215-0400 | 129 |

| School/City/County DISTRICT/CITY/COUNTY | PID | TELEPHONE NUMBER | PAGE |
|---|---|---|---|
| Geneisis High Sch/Bastrop/Bastrop | 11450452 | 512/772-7230 | 27 |
| General Colin Powell Elem Sch/El Paso/ El Paso | 11449207 | 915/774-7775 | 137 |
| General Ricardo Sanchez ES/Rio Grande Cy/ Starr | 04949173 | 956/487-7043 | 343 |
| Generation One Academy/Houston/Harris | 11817305 | 713/654-8008 | 211 |
| Genesis Academy/Brookesmith/Brown | 12366804 | 713/955-4414 | 62 |
| Geneva Bailey Intermediate Sch/Paris/Wise | 04749583 | 903/737-7971 | 406 |
| Geneva Heights Elem Sch/Dallas/Dallas | 01009645 | 972/749-7400 | 104 |
| Geneva School of Boerne/Boerne/Kendall | 10013659 | 830/755-6101 | 257 |
| Genoa Elem Sch/Houston/Harris | 01026710 | 713/740-0592 | 204 |
| George & Deborah Purefoy ES/Frisco/Collin | 11558365 | 469/633-3875 | 82 |
| George A Thompson Interm Sch/Houston/ Harris | 01026980 | 713/740-0510 | 204 |
| George Anderson Elem Sch/Allen/Collin | 04749002 | 972/396-6924 | 80 |
| George B Dealey Mont Intl Acad/Dallas/ Dallas | 04282779 | 972/794-8400 | 104 |
| George Buddy West Elem Sch/Odessa/Ector | 12105739 | 432/456-1329 | 134 |
| George Bush High Sch/Richmond/Fort Bend | 04947125 | 281/634-6060 | 154 |
| George Clarke Elem Sch/Fort Worth/Tarrant | 01052939 | 817/814-6100 | 353 |
| George Dawson Middle Sch/Southlake/Tarrant | 05070660 | 817/949-5500 | 349 |
| George E Kelly Elem Sch/San Antonio/Bexar | 00999152 | 210/228-3350 | 43 |
| George Gervin Academy/San Antonio/Bexar | 04467125 | 210/568-8800 | 3 |
| George H Gentry Jr High Sch/Baytown/Harris | 02179712 | 281/420-4590 | 193 |
| George H W Bush Elem Sch/Addison/Dallas | 11713307 | 972/925-1700 | 104 |
| George I Sanchez Charter HS/Houston/Harris | 02083905 | 713/926-1112 | 3 |
| George Junior High Sch/Rosenberg/Fort Bend | 02110091 | 832/223-3600 | 158 |
| George Peabody Elem Sch/Dallas/Dallas | 01008902 | 972/794-5200 | 104 |
| George Ranch High Sch/Richmond/Fort Bend | 11553494 | 832/223-4200 | 158 |
| George Vogel Elem Sch/Seguin/Guadalupe | 03391119 | 830/401-8745 | 179 |
| George W Bush Elem Sch/Wylie/Collin | 12109785 | 972/429-2600 | 88 |
| George W Bush New Tech Odessa/Odessa/Ector | 04420854 | 432/456-6989 | 134 |
| George W Carver Early Ed Ctr/Lockhart/ Caldwell | 01003043 | 512/398-0060 | 64 |
| George W Carver Elem Sch/Baytown/Harris | 01023627 | 281/420-4600 | 193 |
| George W Truett Elem Sch/Dallas/Dallas | 01008926 | 972/749-8000 | 104 |
| George Wagner Middle Sch/Georgetown/ Williamson | 12232306 | 512/943-1830 | 398 |
| George Washington Carver ES/Garland/Dallas | 10907385 | 972/487-4415 | 110 |
| George Washington Carver ES/Karnack/ Harrison | 01028586 | 903/679-3111 | 214 |
| George Washington Middle Sch/Laredo/Webb | 04364030 | 956/473-7600 | 390 |
| George West Elem Sch/George West/Live Oak | 01038268 | 361/449-1914 | 271 |
| George West High Sch/George West/Live Oak | 01038270 | 361/449-1914 | 271 |
| **GEORGE WEST IND SCH DIST**/ GEORGE WEST/LIVE OAK | 01038256 | 361/449-1914 | 271 |
| George West Junior High Sch/George West/ Live Oak | 01038282 | 361/449-1914 | 271 |
| George West Primary Sch/George West/ Live Oak | 01038294 | 361/449-1914 | 271 |
| Georgetown Alt Program/Georgetown/ Williamson | 04946652 | 512/943-5196 | 398 |
| Georgetown Behavioral Hlth CS/Georgetown/ Williamson | 12362690 | 254/644-9111 | 3 |
| Georgetown Charter Academy/Georgetown/ Williamson | 12100375 | 512/863-9236 | 4 |
| Georgetown High Sch/Georgetown/Williamson | 01060871 | 512/943-5100 | 398 |
| **GEORGETOWN IND SCH DIST**/ GEORGETOWN/WILLIAMSON | 01060869 | 512/943-5000 | 398 |
| Georgia Kimball Elem Sch/Mesquite/Dallas | 02856051 | 972/290-4120 | 115 |
| Gerald Sonntag Elem Sch/McKinney/Collin | 11558353 | 469/633-3850 | 82 |
| Geraldine Palmer Elem Sch/Pharr/Hidalgo | 01030412 | 956/354-2860 | 226 |
| Gerard Elem Sch/Cleburne/Johnson | 02855825 | 817/202-2130 | 250 |
| **GHOLSON IND SCH DIST**/WACO/ MCLENNAN | 01039731 | 254/829-1528 | 282 |
| Gholson Sch/Waco/McLennan | 01039743 | 254/829-1528 | 282 |
| Gibson Caldwell Elem Sch/McKinney/Collin | 01006291 | 469/302-5500 | 84 |
| Giddens Elem Sch/Cedar Park/Williamson | 04455809 | 512/570-5600 | 400 |
| Giddens Steadham Elem Sch/Rowlett/Dallas | 04866650 | 972/463-5887 | 110 |
| Giddings Elem Sch/Giddings/Lee | 01037460 | 979/542-2886 | 266 |
| Giddings High Sch/Giddings/Lee | 01037472 | 979/542-3351 | 266 |
| **GIDDINGS IND SCH DIST**/GIDDINGS/ LEE | 01037458 | 979/542-2854 | 266 |
| Giddings Intermediate Sch/Giddings/Lee | 04745458 | 979/542-4403 | 266 |
| Giddings Middle Sch/Giddings/Lee | 01037484 | 979/542-2057 | 266 |
| Giddings State Sch/Giddings/Lee | 01809562 | 979/542-4500 | 4 |
| Giesinger Elem Sch/Conroe/Montgomery | 03325366 | 936/709-2600 | 294 |
| Gilbert Cuellar Jr Elem Sch/Dallas/Dallas | 04457724 | 972/749-6400 | 104 |
| Gilbert Gerdes Jr High Sch/Luling/Caldwell | 01003110 | 830/875-2121 | 65 |
| Gilbert Intermediate Sch/Stephenville/ Erath | 02222149 | 254/968-4664 | 148 |

| School/City/County DISTRICT/CITY/COUNTY | PID | TELEPHONE NUMBER | PAGE |
|---|---|---|---|
| Gilbert Mircovich Elem Sch/Ingleside/ San Patricio | 04800888 | 361/776-1683 | 334 |
| Gilbert Willie Sr Elem Sch/Terrell/Kaufman | 01035761 | 972/563-1443 | 256 |
| Gilbreath-Reed Career Tech Ctr/Garland/ Dallas | 12231340 | 972/487-4588 | 110 |
| Gillespie County High Sch/Fredericksbrg/ Gillespie | 05351634 | 830/990-4598 | 167 |
| Gillett Intermediate Sch/Kingsville/ Kleberg | 01036313 | 361/595-8200 | 260 |
| Gillette Elem Sch/San Antonio/Bexar | 00997441 | 210/989-3100 | 35 |
| Gilmer Elem Sch/Gilmer/Upshur | 01057410 | 903/841-7700 | 379 |
| Gilmer High Sch/Gilmer/Upshur | 01057422 | 903/841-7500 | 379 |
| **GILMER IND SCH DIST/GILMER/ UPSHUR** | 01057408 | 903/841-7400 | 378 |
| Gilmer Intermediate Sch/Gilmer/Upshur | 01057434 | 903/841-7800 | 379 |
| Ginger McNabb Elm Sch/Spring/Harris | 10022466 | 281/891-8690 | 207 |
| Ginnings Elem Sch/Denton/Denton | 01013268 | 940/369-2700 | 125 |
| Girls' School of Austin/Austin/Travis | 10914936 | 512/478-7827 | 375 |
| Gisd Alternative Ed Center/Garland/Dallas | 04806387 | 972/926-2691 | 110 |
| Givens Early Childhood Center/Paris/Lamar | 01036741 | 903/737-7466 | 263 |
| Gladewater High Sch/Gladewater/Gregg | 01020883 | 903/845-5591 | 174 |
| **GLADEWATER IND SCH DIST/ GLADEWATER/GREGG** | 01020857 | 903/845-6991 | 174 |
| Gladewater Middle Sch/Gladewater/Gregg | 01020895 | 903/845-2243 | 174 |
| Gladewater Primary Sch/Gladewater/Gregg | 01020871 | 903/845-2254 | 174 |
| Gladys Polk Elem Sch/Richwood/Brazoria | 01001590 | 979/730-7200 | 55 |
| Gladys Porter Early Clg HS/Brownsville/ Cameron | 01003653 | 956/548-7800 | 67 |
| Glass Elem Sch/Eagle Pass/Maverick | 01041100 | 830/758-7042 | 280 |
| **GLASSCOCK CO IND SCH DIST/ GARDEN CITY/GLASSCOCK** | 01019781 | 432/354-2230 | 168 |
| Glasscock Co Sch/Garden City/Glasscock | 01019808 | 432/354-2244 | 168 |
| Gleason Elem Sch/Houston/Harris | 04916358 | 281/517-6800 | 189 |
| Glen Couch Elem Sch/Garland/Dallas | 10008111 | 972/240-1801 | 110 |
| Glen Cove Elem Sch/El Paso/El Paso | 01824196 | 915/434-5500 | 142 |
| Glen Loch Elem Sch/The Woodlands/ Montgomery | 02110388 | 281/298-4900 | 294 |
| Glen Oaks Elem Sch/McKinney/Collin | 01006265 | 469/302-6400 | 84 |
| Glen Oaks Sch/Dallas/Dallas | 02740000 | 972/231-3135 | 119 |
| Glen Park Elem Sch/Fort Worth/Tarrant | 01052941 | 817/815-8800 | 353 |
| Glen Rose Elem Sch/Glen Rose/Somervell | 01051090 | 254/898-3503 | 342 |
| Glen Rose High Sch/Glen Rose/Somervell | 01051105 | 254/898-3800 | 342 |
| **GLEN ROSE IND SCH DIST/GLEN ROSE/ SOMERVELL** | 01051088 | 254/898-3900 | 342 |
| Glen Rose Intermediate Sch/Glen Rose/ Somervell | 04010760 | 254/898-3600 | 342 |
| Glen Rose Junior High Sch/Glen Rose/ Somervell | 02056172 | 254/898-3700 | 342 |
| Glencrest 6th Grade Middle Sch/Fort Worth/ Tarrant | 01809885 | 817/815-8400 | 353 |
| Glenda Dawson High Sch/Pearland/Brazoria | 05231486 | 281/412-8800 | 57 |
| Glenhope Elem Sch/Colleyville/Tarrant | 04363660 | 817/251-5720 | 355 |
| Glenmore Elem Sch/San Angelo/Tom Green | 01055644 | 325/659-3657 | 367 |
| Glenn Harmon Elem Sch/Arlington/Tarrant | 03047083 | 817/299-7780 | 359 |
| Glenn High Sch/Leander/Williamson | 12165387 | 512/570-1400 | 400 |
| Glenn Middle Sch/San Angelo/Tom Green | 01055694 | 325/947-3841 | 367 |
| Glenn York Elem Sch/Pearland/Brazoria | 11711139 | 281/245-2100 | 54 |
| Glenoaks Elem Sch/San Antonio/Bexar | 00998110 | 210/397-2300 | 40 |
| Glenwood Elem Sch/Amarillo/Potter | 01047271 | 806/326-4450 | 320 |
| Glenwood Private Sch/Conroe/Montgomery | 02768844 | 936/756-1223 | 298 |
| Global Innovation Sch/Sugar Land/Fort Bend | 04265159 | 281/980-5800 | 159 |
| Global Leadership Academy/Terrell/Kaufman | 12375879 | 972/551-5796 | 256 |
| Global Prep Academy/Crowley/Tarrant | 11926968 | 817/297-3018 | 350 |
| Gloria B Sammons Elem Sch/Houston/Harris | 01022946 | 281/878-0955 | 184 |
| Gloria Deo Academy/Bulverde/Comal | 11818725 | 830/708-5463 | 93 |
| Gloria Marshall Elem Sch/Spring/Harris | 11719038 | 281/491-4900 | 207 |
| Goals Learning Center/Round Rock/ Williamson | 12167488 | 512/464-5153 | 402 |
| Goddard Junior High Sch/Midland/Midland | 01041514 | 432/689-1300 | 289 |
| Godley Elem Sch/Godley/Johnson | 01034975 | 817/592-4410 | 250 |
| Godley High Sch/Godley/Johnson | 03392539 | 817/592-4320 | 250 |
| **GODLEY IND SCH DIST/GODLEY/ JOHNSON** | 01034963 | 817/389-2536 | 250 |
| Godley Intermediate Sch/Godley/Johnson | 04914752 | 817/592-4380 | 250 |
| Godley Middle Sch/Godley/Johnson | 03392527 | 817/592-4340 | 250 |
| Godwin Elem Sch/Princeton/Collin | 04868000 | 469/952-5402 | 87 |
| **GOLD-BURG IND SCH DIST/BOWIE/ MONTAGUE** | 01042283 | 940/872-3562 | 293 |
| Gold-Burg Sch/Bowie/Montague | 01042295 | 940/872-3562 | 293 |
| Golden Acres Elem Sch/Pasadena/Harris | 01026722 | 713/740-0600 | 204 |
| Golden Meadows Elem Sch/Garland/Dallas | 01010541 | 972/494-8373 | 110 |
| Golden Rule CS-DeSoto/Desoto/Dallas | 11663673 | 469/248-4463 | 4 |

| School/City/County DISTRICT/CITY/COUNTY | PID | TELEPHONE NUMBER | PAGE |
|---|---|---|---|
| Golden Rule CS-Grand Prairie/Grand Prairie/ Dallas | 11832202 | 214/988-3257 | 4 |
| Golden Rule CS-Illinois/Dallas/Dallas | 05220994 | 214/333-9330 | 4 |
| Golden Rule CS-Pleasant Grove/Dallas/ Dallas | 11663661 | 469/341-5780 | 4 |
| Golden Rule CS-Sunnyside/Dallas/Dallas | 11663659 | 214/393-6911 | 4 |
| Golden Rule CS-Wilmer/Wilmer/Dallas | 12260729 | 972/525-6204 | 4 |
| **GOLDTHWAITE CONSOLIDATED ISD/ GOLDTHWAITE/MILLS** | 01041942 | 325/648-3531 | 291 |
| Goldthwaite Elem Sch/Goldthwaite/Mills | 01041954 | 325/648-3055 | 291 |
| Goldthwaite High Sch/Goldthwaite/Mills | 01041966 | 325/648-3081 | 291 |
| Goldthwaite Middle Sch/Goldthwaite/Mills | 04871851 | 325/648-3630 | 291 |
| Golfcrest Elem Sch/Houston/Harris | 01025522 | 713/845-7425 | 197 |
| Goliad Elem Sch/Big Spring/Howard | 01031959 | 432/264-4111 | 236 |
| Goliad Elem Sch/Goliad/Goliad | 01019846 | 361/645-3206 | 168 |
| Goliad Elem Sch/Odessa/Ector | 01014690 | 432/456-1109 | 134 |
| Goliad Elem Sch/San Angelo/Tom Green | 01055656 | 325/659-3660 | 367 |
| Goliad High Sch/Goliad/Goliad | 01019834 | 361/645-3257 | 168 |
| **GOLIAD IND SCH DIST/GOLIAD/ GOLIAD** | 01019810 | 361/645-3259 | 168 |
| Goliad Middle Sch/Goliad/Goliad | 01019822 | 361/645-3146 | 168 |
| Gonzales Early Childhood Ctr/San Antonio/ Bexar | 12376926 | 210/438-6830 | 43 |
| Gonzales Elem Sch/Gonzales/Gonzales | 04885747 | 830/672-1467 | 169 |
| Gonzales Elem Sch/Odessa/Ector | 01014705 | 432/456-1119 | 134 |
| Gonzales High Sch/Gonzales/Gonzales | 01019896 | 830/672-7535 | 169 |
| **GONZALES IND SCH DIST/GONZALES/ GONZALES** | 01019860 | 830/672-9551 | 169 |
| Gonzales Junior High Sch/Gonzales/Gonzales | 01019901 | 830/672-8641 | 169 |
| Gonzales Primary Academy/Gonzales/Gonzales | 12103303 | 830/519-4110 | 169 |
| Gonzalez Elem Sch/Brownsville/Cameron | 02892134 | 956/831-6030 | 67 |
| Gonzalez Sch for Young Chldrn/Denton/ Denton | 11559163 | 940/369-4360 | 125 |
| Gonzalo & Sofia Garcia ES/El Paso/El Paso | 10915318 | 915/877-1200 | 136 |
| Good Shepherd Catholic Sch/Garland/Dallas | 01012410 | 972/272-6533 | 118 |
| Good Shepherd Episcopal Sch/Dallas/Dallas | 01012329 | 214/357-1610 | 119 |
| Good Shepherd Sch/Tyler/Smith | 11236452 | 903/592-4045 | 342 |
| Good Tree Academy/Plano/Collin | 11975268 | 972/836-6322 | 89 |
| Goodman Elem Sch/Arlington/Tarrant | 01051777 | 682/867-2200 | 347 |
| Goodrich Elem Sch/Goodrich/Polk | 01047037 | 936/365-1100 | 319 |
| **GOODRICH IND SCH DIST/GOODRICH/ POLK** | 01047025 | 936/365-1100 | 319 |
| Goodrich Middle High Sch/Goodrich/Polk | 05341885 | 936/365-1100 | 319 |
| Goodson Middle Sch/Cypress/Harris | 04943765 | 281/373-2350 | 189 |
| Goodwater Mont Charter Sch/Georgetown/ Williamson | 12260731 | 512/966-5484 | 4 |
| Goodwin Frazier Elem Sch/New Braunfels/ Comal | 01006942 | 830/221-2200 | 92 |
| **GOOSE CREEK CONS IND SCH DIST/ BAYTOWN/HARRIS** | 01023562 | 281/420-4800 | 192 |
| Goose Creek Memorial High Sch/Baytown/ Harris | 11079620 | 281/421-4400 | 193 |
| **GORDON IND SCH DIST/GORDON/ PALO PINTO** | 01045950 | 254/693-5582 | 313 |
| Gordon Sch/Gordon/Palo Pinto | 01045962 | 254/693-5342 | 313 |
| Gorman High Sch/Gorman/Eastland | 01014468 | 254/734-3171 | 133 |
| **GORMAN IND SCH DIST/GORMAN/ EASTLAND** | 01014444 | 254/734-3171 | 133 |
| Gorman Middle Sch/Gorman/Eastland | 11718917 | 254/734-3171 | 133 |
| Gorzycki Middle Sch/Austin/Travis | 11540667 | 512/841-8600 | 371 |
| Goshen Creek Elem Sch/Springtown/Parker | 01046540 | 817/220-0272 | 316 |
| Govalle Elem Sch/Austin/Travis | 01056222 | 512/414-2078 | 369 |
| Grace Academy/Georgetown/Williamson | 05270004 | 512/864-9500 | 403 |
| Grace Academy of Dallas/Dallas/Dallas | 02858293 | 214/696-5648 | 119 |
| Grace Christian Academy/Houston/Harris | 11234624 | 281/488-4883 | 211 |
| Grace Christian Academy-Brock/Brock/Parker | 12365147 | 682/262-9288 | 317 |
| Grace Christian Academy-Main/Perrin/Jack | 12365135 | 682/262-9288 | 242 |
| Grace Christian Sch/Pharr/Hidalgo | 04953485 | 956/787-0701 | 229 |
| Grace Classical Christian Acad/Granbury/ Hood | 12379540 | 817/771-4951 | 234 |
| Grace Community Jr Sr High Sch/Tyler/Smith | 04304028 | 903/566-5661 | 342 |
| Grace Community Sch/Tyler/Smith | 02123593 | 903/593-1977 | 342 |
| Grace Covenant Academy/Frisco/Denton | 12107787 | 972/836-9422 | 130 |
| Grace E Hardeman Elem Sch/Watauga/Tarrant | 01052070 | 817/547-2800 | 348 |
| Grace England ECC/Houston/Harris | 11822714 | 832/375-7900 | 202 |
| Grace Fellowship Christian Sch/Sunnyvale/ Dallas | 05287071 | 972/226-4499 | 119 |
| Grace Hartman Elem Sch/Rockwall/Rockwall | 05100198 | 972/772-2080 | 328 |
| Grace Lutheran Sch/Brenham/Washington | 01059133 | 979/836-2030 | 389 |
| Grace Prep Academy/Arlington/Tarrant | 04867563 | 817/557-3399 | 361 |
| Grace Raymond Academy/Houston/Harris | 01022817 | 281/985-6550 | 185 |
| Grace Sch/Houston/Harris | 02992461 | 713/782-4421 | 211 |

| School/City/County DISTRICT/CITY/COUNTY | PID | TELEPHONE NUMBER | PAGE |
|---|---|---|---|
| Graciela Garcia Elem Sch/Pharr/Hidalgo | 05098791 | 956/354-2790 | 226 |
| Graduation Prep Acad-Navarro/Austin/Travis | 12179613 | 512/414-2896 | 371 |
| Graduation Prep Academy-Travis/Austin/ Travis | 12179601 | 512/414-6635 | 371 |
| Grady B Rasco Middle Sch/Lake Jackson/ Brazoria | 04363749 | 979/730-7225 | 55 |
| Grady Burnett Jr Senior HS/Wylie/Collin | 05350197 | 972/429-3200 | 88 |
| **GRADY IND SCH DIST/LENORAH/ MARTIN** | 01040730 | 432/459-2444 | 277 |
| Grady Sch/Lenorah/Martin | 01040742 | 432/459-2445 | 277 |
| Graebner Elem Sch/San Antonio/Bexar | 00999164 | 210/228-3320 | 43 |
| Graford Elem Sch/Graford/Palo Pinto | 01045998 | 940/664-3101 | 313 |
| **GRAFORD IND SCH DIST/GRAFORD/ PALO PINTO** | 01045986 | 940/664-3101 | 313 |
| Graford Jr Sr High Sch/Graford/Palo Pinto | 04750087 | 940/664-3101 | 313 |
| Graham Elem Sch/Austin/Travis | 01056234 | 512/414-2395 | 369 |
| Graham High Sch/Graham/Young | 01062130 | 940/549-1504 | 409 |
| **GRAHAM IND SCH DIST/GRAHAM/YOUNG** | 01062104 | 940/549-0595 | 409 |
| Graham Junior High Sch/Graham/Young | 01062128 | 940/549-2002 | 409 |
| Granbury High Sch/Granbury/Hood | 01031399 | 817/408-4600 | 233 |
| **GRANBURY IND SCH DIST/GRANBURY/ HOOD** | 01031375 | 817/408-4000 | 233 |
| Granbury Middle Sch/Granbury/Hood | 01031404 | 817/408-4850 | 233 |
| Grand Oaks High Sch/Spring/Montgomery | 12312360 | 281/939-0000 | 294 |
| Grand Prairie Collegiate Inst/Grand Prairie/ Dallas | 11925689 | 972/343-3120 | 111 |
| Grand Prairie Early Clg HS/Grand Prairie/ Dallas | 12168614 | 972/809-5711 | 111 |
| Grand Prairie Fine Arts Acad/Grand Prairie/ Dallas | 11925677 | 972/237-5603 | 111 |
| Grand Prairie High Sch/Grand Prairie/ Dallas | 01010888 | 972/809-5711 | 111 |
| **GRAND PRAIRIE IND SCH DIST/ GRAND PRAIRIE/DALLAS** | 01010814 | 972/237-4000 | 111 |
| Grand Saline Elem Sch/Grand Saline/ Van Zandt | 01058177 | 903/962-7526 | 383 |
| Grand Saline High Sch/Grand Saline/ Van Zandt | 01058189 | 903/962-7533 | 383 |
| **GRAND SALINE IND SCH DIST/ GRAND SALINE/VAN ZANDT** | 01058165 | 903/962-7546 | 383 |
| Grand Saline Intermediate Sch/Grand Saline/ Van Zandt | 04447216 | 903/962-5515 | 383 |
| Grand Saline Middle Sch/Grand Saline/ Van Zandt | 02108646 | 903/962-7537 | 383 |
| Grandfalls Royalty Sch/Grandfalls/Ward | 01058945 | 432/547-2266 | 388 |
| **GRANDFALLS-ROYALTY IND SD/ GRANDFALLS/WARD** | 01058919 | 432/547-2266 | 388 |
| Grandview Elem Sch/Grandview/Johnson | 01035008 | 817/866-4600 | 251 |
| Grandview High Sch/Grandview/Johnson | 01035010 | 817/866-4520 | 251 |
| Grandview Hills Elem Sch/Austin/Williamson | 10914340 | 512/570-6800 | 400 |
| **GRANDVIEW IND SCH DIST/GRANDVIEW/ JOHNSON** | 01034999 | 817/866-4500 | 251 |
| Grandview Junior High Sch/Grandview/ Johnson | 02200555 | 817/866-4660 | 251 |
| Grandview-Hopkins Elem Sch/Groom/Gray | 01020065 | 806/669-3831 | 169 |
| **GRANDVIEW-HOPKINS IND SCH DIST/ GROOM/GRAY** | 01020053 | 806/669-3831 | 169 |
| **GRANGER IND SCH DIST/GRANGER/ WILLIAMSON** | 01060912 | 512/859-2613 | 399 |
| Granger Sch/Granger/Williamson | 01060924 | 512/859-2173 | 399 |
| Grangerland Interm Sch/Conroe/Montgomery | 02126856 | 936/709-3500 | 294 |
| Grape Creek Elem Sch/San Angelo/Tom Green | 01055527 | 325/655-1735 | 367 |
| Grape Creek High Sch/San Angelo/Tom Green | 04447151 | 325/653-1852 | 367 |
| **GRAPE CREEK IND SCH DIST/ SAN ANGELO/TOM GREEN** | 01055515 | 325/658-7823 | 367 |
| Grape Creek Middle Sch/San Angelo/ Tom Green | 04748060 | 325/655-1735 | 367 |
| Grapeland Elem Sch/Grapeland/Houston | 01031765 | 936/687-2317 | 236 |
| Grapeland High Sch/Grapeland/Houston | 01031777 | 936/687-4661 | 236 |
| **GRAPELAND IND SCH DIST/GRAPELAND/ HOUSTON** | 01031753 | 936/687-4619 | 235 |
| Grapeland Junior High Sch/Grapeland/ Houston | 05342152 | 936/687-2351 | 236 |
| Grapevine Elem Sch/Grapevine/Tarrant | 04281232 | 817/251-5735 | 355 |
| Grapevine High Sch/Grapevine/Tarrant | 01053713 | 817/251-5210 | 355 |
| Grapevine Middle Sch/Grapevine/Tarrant | 01053725 | 817/251-5660 | 356 |
| **GRAPEVINE-COLLEYVILLE IND SD/ GRAPEVINE/TARRANT** | 01053672 | 817/251-5200 | 355 |
| Graves Elem Sch/Eagle Pass/Maverick | 01041071 | 830/758-7043 | 280 |
| Grayson Christian Sch/Sherman/Grayson | 02153897 | 903/892-3304 | 174 |
| Great Hearts Forest Heights/San Antonio/ Bexar | 12362731 | 210/892-3665 | 4 |
| Great Hearts Irving/Irving/Dallas | 12163004 | 469/759-3030 | 4 |
| Great Hearts Monte Vista-North/San Antonio/ Bexar | 12177225 | 210/888-9485 | 4 |
| Great Hearts Monte Vista-South/San Antonio/ Bexar | 12160961 | 210/888-9485 | 4 |
| Great Hearts Northern Oaks/San Antonio/ Bexar | 12160662 | 210/888-9483 | 4 |
| Great Hearts Western Hills/San Antonio/ Bexar | 12362729 | 210/888-9488 | 4 |
| Great Lakes Academy/Plano/Collin | 10000391 | 972/517-7498 | 89 |
| Great Oaks Elem Sch/Round Rock/Williamson | 04754447 | 512/464-6850 | 402 |
| Greathouse Elem Sch/Midland/Midland | 04037005 | 432/240-6900 | 289 |
| Green Acres Elem Sch/Dumas/Moore | 01042855 | 806/935-4157 | 298 |
| Green B Trimble Tech High Sch/Fort Worth/ Tarrant | 01052953 | 817/815-2500 | 353 |
| Green Elem Sch/El Paso/El Paso | 04035667 | 915/236-3000 | 137 |
| Green Oaks Sch/Arlington/Tarrant | 11231359 | 817/496-5100 | 361 |
| Green Valley Elem Sch/Houston/Harris | 01023483 | 832/386-4390 | 192 |
| Green Valley Elem Sch/N Richlnd Hls/ Tarrant | 04015605 | 817/547-3400 | 348 |
| Green Valley Elem Sch/Schertz/Guadalupe | 05275793 | 210/619-4450 | 178 |
| Greenbriar Elem Sch/Fort Worth/Tarrant | 01052965 | 817/814-7400 | 353 |
| Greenfield Elem Sch/Fort Worth/Tarrant | 10022868 | 817/237-0357 | 351 |
| Greenhill Sch/Addison/Dallas | 01012783 | 972/628-5400 | 119 |
| Greenleaf Elem Sch/Splendora/Montgomery | 05352262 | 281/689-8020 | 297 |
| Greens Prairie Elem Sch/College Sta/Brazos | 11709435 | 979/694-5870 | 59 |
| Greenspoint Elem Sch/Houston/Harris | 12165765 | 281/985-7800 | 185 |
| Greentree Elem Sch/Kingwood/Harris | 02125527 | 281/641-1900 | 201 |
| Greenville Alt Center/Greenville/Hunt | 04750817 | 903/457-2688 | 239 |
| Greenville Christian Sch/Greenville/Hunt | 02164884 | 903/454-1111 | 240 |
| Greenville High Sch/Greenville/Hunt | 02177063 | 903/457-2550 | 239 |
| **GREENVILLE IND SCH DIST/ GREENVILLE/HUNT** | 01032446 | 903/457-2500 | 239 |
| Greenville Middle Sch/Greenville/Hunt | 01032501 | 903/457-2620 | 239 |
| Greenville Sixth Grade Center/Greenville/ Hunt | 01032496 | 903/457-2660 | 239 |
| Greenways Intermediate Sch/Amarillo/ Randall | 05264885 | 806/677-2460 | 323 |
| Greenwood Elem Sch/Midland/Midland | 01041409 | 432/685-7821 | 288 |
| Greenwood Forest Elem Sch/Houston/Harris | 01026306 | 832/484-5700 | 202 |
| Greenwood High Sch/Midland/Midland | 01041411 | 432/685-7806 | 288 |
| Greenwood Hills Elem Sch/Richardson/Dallas | 01011703 | 469/593-6100 | 116 |
| **GREENWOOD IND SCH DIST/MIDLAND/ MIDLAND** | 01041394 | 432/683-6461 | 288 |
| Greenwood Interm Sch/Midland/Midland | 12365070 | 432/685-7819 | 288 |
| Gregg Elem Sch/Houston/Harris | 01025223 | 713/845-7432 | 197 |
| Gregorio Esparza Elem Sch/San Antonio/ Bexar | 00998093 | 210/397-1850 | 40 |
| Gregory Luna Middle Sch/San Antonio/Bexar | 05347580 | 210/397-5300 | 40 |
| Gregory-Lincoln Education Ctr/Houston/ Harris | 01024035 | 713/942-1400 | 194 |
| Gregory-Portland High Sch/Portland/ San Patricio | 01049566 | 361/777-4251 | 333 |
| **GREGORY-PORTLAND IND SCH DIST/ PORTLAND/SAN PATRICIO** | 01049530 | 361/777-1091 | 333 |
| Gregory-Portland Mid Sch/Portland/ San Patricio | 01049578 | 361/777-4042 | 333 |
| Greta Oppe Elem Sch/Galveston/Galveston | 03012210 | 409/761-6500 | 165 |
| Griffin Elem Sch/Tyler/Smith | 01050888 | 903/262-2310 | 340 |
| Griffin Middle Sch/The Colony/Denton | 02179554 | 469/713-5973 | 127 |
| Griffin Sch/Austin/Travis | 11233606 | 512/454-5797 | 375 |
| Griggs EC-PK-K Sch/Houston/Harris | 12309698 | 281/985-3760 | 186 |
| Grissom Elem Sch/Houston/Harris | 01025247 | 713/434-5660 | 197 |
| Groesbeck High Sch/Groesbeck/Limestone | 01038062 | 254/729-4101 | 269 |
| **GROESBECK IND SCH DIST/GROESBECK/ LIMESTONE** | 01038048 | 254/729-4100 | 269 |
| Groesbeck Middle Sch/Groesbeck/Limestone | 01038074 | 254/729-4102 | 269 |
| **GROOM IND SCH DIST/GROOM/CARSON** | 01004554 | 806/248-7474 | 72 |
| Groom Sch/Groom/Carson | 01004566 | 806/248-7474 | 72 |
| Gross Elem Sch/Houston/Harris | 04951633 | 713/778-8450 | 199 |
| Groves Elem Sch/Groves/Jefferson | 01033969 | 409/962-1531 | 246 |
| Groves Elem Sch/Humble/Harris | 12235944 | 281/641-5000 | 201 |
| Groves Middle Sch/Groves/Jefferson | 01034054 | 409/962-0225 | 246 |
| Groveton Elem Sch/Groveton/Trinity | 01057111 | 936/642-1182 | 377 |
| **GROVETON IND SCH DIST/GROVETON/ TRINITY** | 01057109 | 936/642-1473 | 377 |
| Groveton Jr Sr High Sch/Groveton/Trinity | 01057123 | 936/642-1128 | 377 |
| Grulla Elem Sch/Rio Grande Cy/Starr | 01051131 | 956/487-3306 | 343 |
| Grulla High Sch/Rio Grande Cy/Starr | 11559515 | 956/487-7278 | 343 |
| Grulla Middle Sch/Grulla/Starr | 01051129 | 956/487-5558 | 343 |
| Gruver Elem Sch/Gruver/Hansford | 01022269 | 806/733-2031 | 181 |
| Gruver High Sch/Gruver/Hansford | 01022271 | 806/733-2477 | 181 |

| School/City/County DISTRICT/CITY/COUNTY | PID | TELEPHONE NUMBER | PAGE |
|---|---|---|---|
| **GRUVER IND SCH DIST**/GRUVER/ HANSFORD | 01022257 | 806/733-2001 | 181 |
| Gruver Junior High Sch/Gruver/Hansford | 01022283 | 806/733-2081 | 181 |
| Guadalupe Elem Sch/Lubbock/Lubbock | 01038672 | 806/219-5500 | 273 |
| Guadalupe Regional Middle Sch/Brownsville/ Cameron | 05153559 | 956/504-5568 | 71 |
| Guajardo Elem Sch/Texas City/Galveston | 01019547 | 409/916-0300 | 166 |
| Guerrero Thompson Elem Sch/Austin/Travis | 11923215 | 512/414-8400 | 369 |
| Guess Elem Sch/Beaumont/Jefferson | 01033531 | 409/617-6125 | 245 |
| Guidance Center/Pasadena/Harris | 04896318 | 713/740-0792 | 204 |
| Guidepost Montessori-Brush Crk/Cedar Park/ Williamson | 11902194 | 512/259-3333 | 403 |
| Guidepost Montessori-Stonebria/Frisco/ Collin | 05423146 | 214/387-8202 | 89 |
| Guillen Middle Sch/El Paso/El Paso | 01015979 | 915/236-4900 | 139 |
| Guillermo Flores Elem Sch/Mission/Hidalgo | 02104535 | 956/323-2760 | 223 |
| Gulledge Elem Sch/Plano/Collin | 04366777 | 469/752-1300 | 86 |
| Gullett Elem Sch/Austin/Travis | 01056246 | 512/414-2082 | 369 |
| Gunn Junior High Sch/Arlington/Tarrant | 01051789 | 682/867-5400 | 347 |
| Gunter Elem Sch/Gunter/Grayson | 01020455 | 903/433-5315 | 171 |
| Gunter High Sch/Gunter/Grayson | 03055925 | 903/433-1542 | 171 |
| **GUNTER IND SCH DIST**/GUNTER/ GRAYSON | 01020443 | 903/433-4750 | 171 |
| Gunter Middle Sch/Gunter/Grayson | 04447981 | 903/433-1545 | 171 |
| Gus A Oleson Elem Sch/Houston/Harris | 01022922 | 281/985-6530 | 185 |
| Gus Birdwell Elem Sch/Spearman/Hansford | 01022324 | 806/659-2565 | 182 |
| Gus Garcia Middle Sch/San Antonio/Bexar | 00997245 | 210/444-8075 | 35 |
| Gus Winston Cain Elem Sch/Whitehouse/Smith | 01051002 | 903/839-5600 | 341 |
| **GUSTINE IND SCH DIST**/GUSTINE/ COMANCHE | 01007128 | 325/667-7981 | 93 |
| Gustine Sch/Gustine/Comanche | 01007130 | 325/667-7303 | 93 |
| Guthrie Center/Houston/Harris | 01545273 | 713/251-1300 | 206 |
| **GUTHRIE COMMON SCH DIST**/ GUTHRIE/KING | 01036193 | 806/596-4466 | 260 |
| Guthrie Sch/Guthrie/King | 01036210 | 806/596-4466 | 260 |
| Gutierriez Middle Sch/Harlingen/Cameron | 04748711 | 956/430-4400 | 68 |
| Guzman Elem Sch/Donna/Hidalgo | 03321475 | 956/464-1920 | 220 |
| GW Carver 6th GR STEM Lrng Ctr/Lancaster/ Dallas | 11711995 | 972/218-1577 | 114 |
| **H** | | | |
| H A Wooden Elem Sch/Red Oak/Ellis | 01015254 | 972/617-2977 | 146 |
| H B Gonzalez Elem Sch/San Antonio/Bexar | 00997233 | 210/444-7800 | 35 |
| H B Zachry Elem Sch/Laredo/Webb | 01540132 | 956/273-4900 | 389 |
| H C Carleston Elem Sch/Pearland/Brazoria | 02112245 | 281/412-1412 | 57 |
| H C Schochler Elem Sch/Channelview/Harris | 01023110 | 281/452-2880 | 188 |
| H D Hilley Elem Sch/El Paso/El Paso | 02109509 | 915/937-8400 | 140 |
| H D Staples Elem Sch/Joshua/Johnson | 01035034 | 817/202-2500 | 251 |
| H E Charles Middle Sch/El Paso/El Paso | 01418280 | 915/236-6550 | 139 |
| H F Stevens Middle Sch/Crowley/Tarrant | 01052381 | 817/297-5840 | 350 |
| H G Isbill Junior High Sch/Mc Gregor/ McLennan | 01039901 | 254/840-3251 | 283 |
| H G Temple Elem Sch/Diboll/Angelina | 00994827 | 936/829-6950 | 20 |
| H G Temple Intermediate Sch/Diboll/ Angelina | 11917058 | 936/829-6900 | 20 |
| H Grady Spruce High Sch/Dallas/Dallas | 01008940 | 972/892-5500 | 104 |
| H I Holland ES-Lisbon/Dallas/Dallas | 01009384 | 972/749-1900 | 104 |
| H M K Care Academy/Kingsville/Kleberg | 11934599 | 361/595-8600 | 260 |
| H M King High Sch/Kingsville/Kleberg | 01036296 | 361/595-8600 | 260 |
| H O Whitehurst Elem Sch/Groesbeck/ Limestone | 02845595 | 254/729-4104 | 269 |
| H R Jefferies Junior High Sch/Comanche/ Comanche | 01007087 | 325/356-5220 | 93 |
| H V Helbing Elem Sch/Fort Worth/Tarrant | 01052991 | 817/815-0500 | 353 |
| H W Schulze Elem Sch/San Antonio/Bexar | 00997518 | 210/989-3250 | 35 |
| Hacienda Heights Elem Sch/El Paso/El Paso | 01016430 | 915/434-2500 | 142 |
| Hackberry Elem Sch/Frisco/Denton | 05277088 | 972/947-9453 | 128 |
| Hackney Primary Sch/Lufkin/Angelina | 00994970 | 936/634-3324 | 21 |
| Hafley Development Center/Fort Worth/ Tarrant | 10003719 | 817/232-2071 | 351 |
| Haggard Middle Sch/Plano/Collin | 01006435 | 469/752-5400 | 86 |
| Hailey Elem Sch/The Woodlands/Montgomery | 01829483 | 832/663-4100 | 294 |
| Hairgrove Elem Sch/Houston/Harris | 03398246 | 713/896-5015 | 189 |
| Hale Center High Sch/Hale Center/Hale | 01021837 | 806/839-2452 | 180 |
| **HALE CENTER IND SCH DIST**/ HALE CENTER/HALE | 01021813 | 806/839-2451 | 180 |
| Hale Elem Sch/Arlington/Tarrant | 04808701 | 682/867-1530 | 347 |
| Hallettsville Elem Sch/Hallettsville/ Lavaca | 01037290 | 361/798-2242 | 265 |
| Hallettsville High Sch/Hallettsville/ Lavaca | 01037305 | 361/798-2242 | 265 |
| **HALLETTSVILLE IND SCH DIST**/ HALLETTSVILLE/LAVACA | 01037288 | 361/798-2242 | 265 |
| Hallettsville Jr High Sch/Hallettsville/ Lavaca | 01037317 | 361/798-2242 | 265 |
| Hallie Randall Elem Sch/Fruitvale/ Van Zandt | 01058153 | 903/896-4466 | 383 |
| Hallsburg Elem Sch/Waco/McLennan | 01039767 | 254/875-2331 | 282 |
| **HALLSBURG IND SCH DIST**/WACO/ MCLENNAN | 01039755 | 254/875-2331 | 282 |
| Hallsville High Sch/Hallsville/Harrison | 01028500 | 903/668-5990 | 213 |
| **HALLSVILLE IND SCH DIST**/ HALLSVILLE/HARRISON | 01028483 | 903/668-5990 | 213 |
| Hallsville Intermediate Sch/Hallsville/ Harrison | 01558139 | 903/668-5989 | 213 |
| Hallsville Junior High Sch/Hallsville/ Harrison | 01028524 | 903/668-5986 | 213 |
| Halpin Early Chldhd Lrng Ctr/Houston/ Harris | 04454946 | 713/778-6720 | 199 |
| Haltom High Sch/Haltom City/Tarrant | 01052082 | 817/547-6000 | 348 |
| Haltom Middle Sch/Haltom City/Tarrant | 01052094 | 817/547-4000 | 348 |
| Hamilton Elem Sch/Cypress/Harris | 03327182 | 281/370-0990 | 190 |
| Hamilton High Sch/Hamilton/Hamilton | 01022180 | 254/386-8167 | 181 |
| **HAMILTON IND SCH DIST**/HAMILTON/ HAMILTON | 01022166 | 254/386-3149 | 181 |
| Hamilton Junior High Sch/Hamilton/Hamilton | 02200804 | 254/386-8168 | 181 |
| Hamilton Middle Sch/Cypress/Harris | 04016594 | 281/320-7000 | 190 |
| Hamilton Middle Sch/Houston/Harris | 01024047 | 713/802-4725 | 197 |
| Hamilton Park Pacesetter Mag/Dallas/Dallas | 01011715 | 469/593-3900 | 116 |
| Hamlet Elem Sch/Amarillo/Potter | 01047283 | 806/326-4500 | 320 |
| **HAMLIN COLLEGIATE IND SCH DIST**/ HAMLIN/JONES | 01035228 | 325/576-2722 | 252 |
| Hamlin Elem Sch/Hamlin/Jones | 01035230 | 325/576-3191 | 252 |
| Hamlin High Sch/Hamlin/Jones | 01035242 | 325/576-3624 | 252 |
| Hampton-Moreno-Dugat ECC/Beeville/Bee | 00996095 | 361/362-6040 | 28 |
| Hamshire Fannett Elem Sch/Beaumont/ Jefferson | 01033622 | 409/794-1412 | 245 |
| Hamshire Fannett High Sch/Hamshire/ Jefferson | 01033634 | 409/243-2131 | 245 |
| **HAMSHIRE FANNETT IND SCH DIST**/ HAMSHIRE/JEFFERSON | 01033610 | 409/243-2133 | 245 |
| Hamshire Fannett Interm Sch/Beaumont/ Jefferson | 03394238 | 409/794-1558 | 245 |
| Hamshire Fannett Middle Sch/Beaumont/ Jefferson | 01033646 | 409/794-1502 | 245 |
| Handley Elem Sch/Garland/Dallas | 01010606 | 972/926-2540 | 110 |
| Handley Middle Sch/Fort Worth/Tarrant | 01052989 | 817/815-4200 | 353 |
| Hanes Elem Sch/Irving/Dallas | 01011167 | 972/600-3600 | 113 |
| Hanna Springs Elem Sch/Lampasas/Lampasas | 01037123 | 512/556-2152 | 264 |
| Happy Elem Sch/Happy/Swisher | 01051521 | 806/558-2561 | 345 |
| **HAPPY IND SCH DIST**/HAPPY/SWISHER | 01051519 | 806/558-5331 | 345 |
| Happy Middle High Sch/Happy/Swisher | 01051533 | 806/558-5311 | 345 |
| Harbach-Ripley Charter Sch/Houston/Harris | 11834456 | 713/669-5202 | 4 |
| Hardin Elem Sch/Hardin/Liberty | 01037850 | 936/298-2114 | 268 |
| Hardin High Sch/Liberty/Liberty | 01037862 | 936/298-2118 | 268 |
| **HARDIN IND SCH DIST**/HARDIN/ LIBERTY | 01037848 | 936/298-2112 | 268 |
| Hardin Intermediate Sch/Duncanville/Dallas | 03048178 | 972/708-3300 | 109 |
| **HARDIN JEFFERSON IND SCH DIST**/ SOUR LAKE/HARDIN | 01022439 | 409/981-6400 | 182 |
| Hardin Junior High Sch/Hardin/Liberty | 11014838 | 936/298-2054 | 268 |
| Hardin-Jefferson High Sch/Sour Lake/Hardin | 01022453 | 409/981-6430 | 183 |
| Hardwick Elem Sch/Lubbock/Lubbock | 01038684 | 806/219-5600 | 273 |
| Hardy Oak Elem Sch/San Antonio/Bexar | 04924549 | 210/407-3600 | 38 |
| Hargill Elem Sch/Hargill/Hidalgo | 01029724 | 956/289-2338 | 221 |
| Harker Heights Elem Sch/Harker HTS/Bell | 00996497 | 254/336-2050 | 31 |
| Harker Heights High Sch/Harker HTS/Bell | 04368787 | 254/336-0800 | 31 |
| Harlan High Sch/San Antonio/Bexar | 12230310 | 210/398-2200 | 40 |
| Harlandale Alternative Center/San Antonio/ Bexar | 00997544 | 210/989-5200 | 35 |
| Harlandale High Sch/San Antonio/Bexar | 00997465 | 210/989-1000 | 35 |
| **HARLANDALE IND SCH DIST**/ SAN ANTONIO/BEXAR | 00997350 | 210/989-4300 | 35 |
| Harlandale Middle Sch/San Antonio/Bexar | 00997453 | 210/989-2000 | 36 |
| Harlean Beal Elem Sch/Fort Worth/Tarrant | 01052915 | 817/815-8500 | 353 |
| Harlem Elem Sch/Baytown/Harris | 01023639 | 281/420-4910 | 193 |
| Harleton Elem Sch/Harleton/Harrison | 01028548 | 903/777-4092 | 213 |
| Harleton High Sch/Harleton/Harrison | 01028550 | 903/777-2711 | 213 |
| **HARLETON IND SCH DIST**/HARLETON/ HARRISON | 01028536 | 903/777-2372 | 213 |
| Harleton Junior High Sch/Harleton/Harrison | 01028562 | 903/777-3010 | 214 |
| **HARLINGEN CONS IND SCH DIST**/ HARLINGEN/CAMERON | 01003756 | 956/430-9500 | 68 |

| School/City/County DISTRICT/CITY/COUNTY | PID | TELEPHONE NUMBER | PAGE |
|---|---|---|---|
| Harlingen High Sch/Harlingen/Cameron | 01003847 | 956/427-3600 | 68 |
| Harlingen High School South/Harlingen/Cameron | 02893932 | 956/427-3800 | 68 |
| Harlingen Sch of Health Prof/Harlingen/Cameron | 12032285 | 956/430-4078 | 68 |
| Harlow Elem Sch/Anna/Collin | 12226230 | 972/924-1320 | 81 |
| Harmony Elem Sch/San Antonio/Bexar | 00997013 | 210/633-0231 | 34 |
| Harmony High Sch/Big Sandy/Upshur | 01057472 | 903/725-5495 | 379 |
| Harmony Hills Elem Sch/San Antonio/Bexar | 00997790 | 210/407-3800 | 38 |
| **HARMONY IND SCH DIST/BIG SANDY/ UPSHUR** | 01057458 | 903/725-5492 | 379 |
| Harmony Irons-Smith Interm Sch/Big Sandy/Upshur | 04946303 | 903/725-7077 | 379 |
| Harmony Junior High Sch/Big Sandy/Upshur | 02845870 | 903/725-5485 | 379 |
| Harmony Sch Achievement-Houstn/Houston/Harris | 12260743 | 281/855-2500 | 4 |
| Harmony Sch Adv-Houston/Houston/Harris | 11734947 | 281/741-8899 | 4 |
| Harmony Sch DSC-Houston/Houston/Harris | 11557062 | 281/861-5105 | 4 |
| Harmony Sch Endeavor-Austin/Austin/Williamson | 11734923 | 512/284-9880 | 4 |
| Harmony Sch Endeavor-Houston/Houston/Harris | 11548449 | 281/999-8400 | 4 |
| Harmony Sch Enrichment-Houston/Houston/Harris | 12260755 | 281/999-0606 | 4 |
| Harmony Sch Exc-Austin/Austin/Travis | 11512608 | 512/693-0000 | 4 |
| Harmony Sch Exc-El Paso/El Paso/El Paso | 12179235 | 915/307-4772 | 4 |
| Harmony Sch Exc-Houston/Houston/Harris | 11013652 | 713/983-8668 | 4 |
| Harmony Sch Exc-Laredo/Laredo/Webb | 12260767 | 956/791-0007 | 4 |
| Harmony Sch Exc-San Antonio/San Antonio/Bexar | 12162658 | 210/645-7166 | 4 |
| Harmony Sch Exc-Sugar Land/Sugar Land/Fort Bend | 12309363 | 832/532-0728 | 4 |
| Harmony Sch Excellence-Dallas/Dallas/Dallas | 11559084 | 972/296-1000 | 4 |
| Harmony Sch Exploration-Houstn/Houston/Harris | 11932541 | 832/831-7406 | 4 |
| Harmony Sch Fine Arts & Tech/Houston/Harris | 11559046 | 832/433-7001 | 4 |
| Harmony Sch Ingenuity-Houston/Houston/Harris | 11448306 | 713/664-1020 | 4 |
| Harmony Sch Innov-Austin/Austin/Travis | 12163705 | 512/300-0895 | 4 |
| Harmony Sch Innov-Brownsville/Brownsville/Cameron | 12260779 | 956/544-1348 | 4 |
| Harmony Sch Innov-Carrolltn/Carrollton/Denton | 11548451 | 469/892-5556 | 4 |
| Harmony Sch Innov-Dallas/Dallas/Collin | 11818189 | 214/321-0100 | 4 |
| Harmony Sch Innov-El Paso/El Paso/El Paso | 11446918 | 915/757-2929 | 4 |
| Harmony Sch Innov-Euless/Euless/Tarrant | 12039051 | 817/554-2800 | 4 |
| Harmony Sch Innov-Ft Worth/Fort Worth/Tarrant | 11818359 | 817/386-5505 | 4 |
| Harmony Sch Innov-Garland/Garland/Dallas | 12179223 | 469/814-0059 | 4 |
| Harmony Sch Innov-Gran Prairie/Grand Prairie/Dallas | 12378522 | 972/269-6182 | 4 |
| Harmony Sch Innov-Houston/Houston/Harris | 11013664 | 713/541-3030 | 4 |
| Harmony Sch Innov-Laredo/Laredo/Webb | 12163042 | 956/568-9495 | 4 |
| Harmony Sch Innov-San Antonio/San Antonio/Bexar | 11559096 | 210/265-1715 | 4 |
| Harmony Sch Innov-Sugar Land/Sugar Land/Fort Bend | 11719789 | 281/302-6445 | 5 |
| Harmony Sch Innov-Waco/Waco/McLennan | 12260781 | 254/235-0321 | 5 |
| Harmony Sch Sci-Austin/Austin/Travis | 11013688 | 512/821-1700 | 5 |
| Harmony Sch Sci-Houston/Houston/Harris | 05010878 | 713/729-4400 | 5 |
| Harmony Sch Tech-Houston/Houston/Harris | 11734935 | 281/444-1555 | 5 |
| Harmony Sci Acad-Austin/Austin/Travis | 05301706 | 512/835-7900 | 5 |
| Harmony Sci Acad-Beaumont/Beaumont/Jefferson | 11013690 | 409/838-4000 | 5 |
| Harmony Sci Acad-Brownsville/Brownsville/Cameron | 11132143 | 956/574-9555 | 5 |
| Harmony Sci Acad-Bryan/Bryan/Brazos | 11013705 | 979/779-2100 | 5 |
| Harmony Sci Acad-Carrollton/Carrollton/Denton | 12163729 | 972/394-9560 | 5 |
| Harmony Sci Acad-Cedar Park/Austin/Travis | 12235231 | 512/494-5151 | 5 |
| Harmony Sci Acad-Cypress/Cypress/Harris | 12362717 | 281/444-1555 | 5 |
| Harmony Sci Acad-El Paso/El Paso/El Paso | 10915825 | 915/859-4620 | 5 |
| Harmony Sci Acad-Euless/Euless/Tarrant | 11548463 | 817/354-3000 | 5 |
| Harmony Sci Acad-Ft Worth/Fort Worth/Tarrant | 11013640 | 817/263-0700 | 5 |
| Harmony Sci Acad-Garland/Garland/Dallas | 11559060 | 972/212-4777 | 5 |
| Harmony Sci Acad-Grand Prairie/Grand Prairie/Dallas | 11132131 | 972/642-9911 | 5 |
| Harmony Sci Acad-Houston/Houston/Harris | 11565021 | 713/492-0214 | 5 |
| Harmony Sci Acad-Katy/Katy/Fort Bend | 11735630 | 832/437-3926 | 5 |

| School/City/County DISTRICT/CITY/COUNTY | PID | TELEPHONE NUMBER | PAGE |
|---|---|---|---|
| Harmony Sci Acad-Laredo/Laredo/Webb | 11132076 | 956/712-1177 | 5 |
| Harmony Sci Acad-Lubbock/Lubbock/Lubbock | 11013717 | 806/747-1000 | 5 |
| Harmony Sci Acad-Odessa/Odessa/Ector | 11559058 | 432/363-6000 | 5 |
| Harmony Sci Acad-Pflugerville/Pflugerville/Travis | 11132090 | 512/251-5000 | 5 |
| Harmony Sci Acad-Plano/Plano/Collin | 12260793 | 972/596-0041 | 5 |
| Harmony Sci Acad-San Antonio/San Antonio/Bexar | 11013729 | 210/674-7788 | 5 |
| Harmony Sci Acad-Sugar Land/Sugar Land/Fort Bend | 11132088 | 281/265-2525 | 5 |
| Harmony Sci Acad-Waco/Waco/McLennan | 11013731 | 254/751-7878 | 5 |
| Harmony Science Acad-Dallas/Dallas/Dallas | 05368041 | 469/730-2477 | 5 |
| Harold Branch Acad Career/Tech/Corp Christi/Nueces | 11925017 | 361/878-4780 | 306 |
| Harold C Kaffie Middle Sch/Corp Christi/Nueces | 03050999 | 361/878-3700 | 306 |
| Harold Cade Middle Sch/Victoria/Victoria | 11557115 | 361/788-2840 | 385 |
| Harold Lang Middle Sch/Dallas/Dallas | 10908353 | 972/925-2400 | 104 |
| Harper Daep Sch/Houston/Harris | 02129858 | 713/802-4760 | 196 |
| Harper Elem Sch/Harper/Gillespie | 01019743 | 830/864-4044 | 168 |
| Harper Elem Sch/Princeton/Collin | 11076666 | 469/952-5409 | 87 |
| Harper High Sch/Harper/Gillespie | 10005119 | 830/864-4044 | 168 |
| **HARPER IND SCH DIST/HARPER/ GILLESPIE** | 01019731 | 830/864-4044 | 168 |
| Harper Middle Sch/Harper/Gillespie | 11445768 | 830/864-4044 | 168 |
| Harpool Middle Sch/Argyle/Denton | 11128556 | 940/369-1700 | 125 |
| Harrell Budd Elem Sch/Dallas/Dallas | 01008964 | 972/502-8400 | 104 |
| Harrington Elem Sch/Plano/Collin | 01824134 | 469/752-1500 | 86 |
| Harris Academy/San Antonio/Bexar | 00999190 | 210/228-1220 | 43 |
| **HARRIS CO DEPT OF ED/HOUSTON/ HARRIS** | 02091055 | 713/694-6300 | 184 |
| Harris Co Detention Center/Houston/Harris | 03475428 | 713/222-4100 | 184 |
| Harris Co Juvenile Justice CS/Houston/Harris | 04813536 | 713/222-4100 | 5 |
| Harris Co Youth Village/Seabrook/Harris | 01809328 | 281/326-2521 | 184 |
| Harris Cty Leadership Academy/Katy/Harris | 05010830 | 713/222-4629 | 5 |
| Harris Elem Sch/Austin/Travis | 01056258 | 512/414-2085 | 369 |
| Harrison Lane Elem Sch/Hurst/Tarrant | 01053816 | 817/285-3270 | 356 |
| Harrison-Jefferson-Madison ES/Port Lavaca/Calhoun | 01003196 | 361/552-5253 | 65 |
| **HARROLD IND SCH DIST/HARROLD/ WILBARGER** | 01060508 | 940/886-2213 | 396 |
| Harrold Sch/Harrold/Wilbarger | 01060510 | 940/886-2213 | 396 |
| Harry C Withers Elem Sch/Dallas/Dallas | 03336937 | 972/794-5000 | 104 |
| Harry H Herndon Interm Sch/Fate/Rockwall | 11462431 | 469/721-8101 | 329 |
| Harry McKillop Elem Sch/Melissa/Collin | 01006332 | 972/837-2632 | 85 |
| Harry S Truman Middle Sch/Grand Prairie/Dallas | 02110340 | 972/641-7676 | 111 |
| Harry Shimotsu Elem Sch/Mission/Hidalgo | 10915332 | 956/583-5643 | 227 |
| Harry Stone Montessori Academy/Dallas/Dallas | 04020765 | 972/794-3400 | 104 |
| Hart Elem Sch/Austin/Travis | 04806703 | 512/841-2100 | 370 |
| Hart Elem Sch/El Paso/El Paso | 01015981 | 915/412-5499 | 138 |
| Hart Elem Sch/Hart/Castro | 01005027 | 806/938-2142 | 75 |
| Hart Elem Sch/Lucas/Collin | 04914568 | 469/742-8200 | 84 |
| **HART IND SCH DIST/HART/CASTRO** | 01005015 | 806/938-2143 | 75 |
| Hart Junior Senior High Sch/Hart/Castro | 01005039 | 806/938-2141 | 75 |
| **HARTLEY IND SCH DIST/HARTLEY/ HARTLEY** | 01028823 | 806/365-4458 | 215 |
| Hartley Sch/Hartley/Hartley | 01028835 | 806/365-4458 | 215 |
| Hartman Elem Sch/Wylie/Collin | 01006617 | 972/429-3480 | 89 |
| Hartman Middle Sch/Houston/Harris | 01025118 | 713/845-7435 | 198 |
| Harts Bluff Elem Sch/Mt Pleasant/Titus | 01055357 | 903/577-1146 | 366 |
| **HARTS BLUFF IND SCH DIST/ MT PLEASANT/TITUS** | 01055345 | 903/577-1146 | 366 |
| Hartsfield Elem Sch/Houston/Harris | 01024841 | 713/746-8280 | 198 |
| Harvard Elem Sch/Houston/Harris | 01024061 | 713/867-5210 | 197 |
| Harvest Christian Academy/Edinburg/Hidalgo | 11135951 | 956/383-8967 | 229 |
| Harvest Christian Academy/Watauga/Tarrant | 04888139 | 817/485-1660 | 361 |
| Harvey Elem Sch/Kingsville/Kleberg | 01036260 | 361/592-4327 | 260 |
| Harvey S Brown Elem Sch/Houston/Harris | 10012394 | 281/860-1400 | 188 |
| Harvey Turner Elem Sch/Pasadena/Harris | 04015631 | 713/740-0768 | 204 |
| Harwell Elem Sch/Lubbock/Lubbock | 01038579 | 806/219-5700 | 273 |
| Harwood Junior High Sch/Bedford/Tarrant | 01053828 | 817/354-3360 | 356 |
| **HASKELL CONS IND SCH DIST/ HASKELL/HASKELL** | 01028873 | 940/864-2602 | 215 |
| Haskell Elem Sch/Haskell/Haskell | 01028885 | 940/864-2654 | 215 |
| Haskell High Sch/Haskell/Haskell | 01172448 | 940/864-8535 | 215 |
| Haskell Junior High Sch/Rochester/Haskell | 01028940 | 940/864-5981 | 215 |
| Haslet Elem Sch/Haslet/Denton | 01013529 | 817/215-0850 | 129 |
| Hassler Elem Sch/Klein/Harris | 04853586 | 832/484-7100 | 202 |
| Hastings 9th Grade Center/Houston/Harris | 04809119 | 281/988-3139 | 187 |

| School/City/County<br>DISTRICT/CITY/COUNTY | PID | TELEPHONE<br>NUMBER | PAGE |
|---|---|---|---|
| Hastings Elem Sch/Duncanville/Dallas | 01010357 | 972/708-2800 | 109 |
| Hastings High Sch/Houston/Harris | 01023005 | 281/988-3110 | 187 |
| Hattie Dyer Elem Sch/Krum/Denton | 01013359 | 940/482-2604 | 126 |
| Haude Elem Sch/Spring/Harris | 01026318 | 832/484-5600 | 202 |
| Hauke Academic Alt High Sch/Conroe/<br>Montgomery | 01541409 | 936/709-3420 | 294 |
| Hawkins Elem Sch/El Paso/El Paso | 01015620 | 915/236-8900 | 138 |
| Hawkins Elem Sch/Hawkins/Wood | 01061825 | 903/769-0536 | 407 |
| Hawkins High Sch/Hawkins/Wood | 01061837 | 903/769-0571 | 407 |
| **HAWKINS IND SCH DIST/HAWKINS/<br>WOOD** | 01061813 | 903/769-2181 | 407 |
| Hawkins Middle Sch/Hawkins/Wood | 01553270 | 903/769-0552 | 408 |
| Hawley Elem Sch/Hawley/Jones | 01035278 | 325/537-2721 | 253 |
| Hawley High Sch/Hawley/Jones | 04801674 | 325/537-2722 | 253 |
| **HAWLEY IND SCH DIST/HAWLEY/JONES** | 01035266 | 325/537-2214 | 253 |
| Hawley Middle Sch/Hawley/Jones | 01035280 | 325/537-2070 | 253 |
| Hawthorne Academy/San Antonio/Bexar | 00998457 | 210/738-9795 | 43 |
| Hay Branch Elem Sch/Killeen/Bell | 02897213 | 254/336-2080 | 31 |
| Haynes Elem Sch/Killeen/Bell | 11718474 | 254/336-6750 | 31 |
| Haynes Northwest Academy/Wichita Falls/<br>Wichita | 01173064 | 940/235-1160 | 395 |
| **HAYS CONS IND SCH DIST/KYLE/HAYS** | 01029059 | 512/268-2141 | 216 |
| Hays Magnet Academy/Odessa/Ector | 01014717 | 432/456-1129 | 134 |
| Hays Middle Sch/Frisco/Collin | 12363838 | 469/219-2260 | 88 |
| Hazel Harvey Peace Elem Sch/Fort Worth/<br>Tarrant | 11554553 | 817/814-8800 | 353 |
| Hazel Ingram Elem Sch/Ferris/Ellis | 01015046 | 972/544-3212 | 145 |
| Hazel S Pattison Elem Sch/Katy/Harris | 03249126 | 281/237-5450 | 156 |
| Hcal/Hereford/Deaf Smith | 12172081 | 806/363-7720 | 123 |
| HCC Life Skills/Houston/Harris | 11555492 | 713/718-6882 | 199 |
| Headwaters Sch/Austin/Travis | 11228364 | 512/443-8843 | 375 |
| Headwaters Sch/Austin/Travis | 11551197 | 512/480-8142 | 375 |
| Health Careers High Sch/San Antonio/Bexar | 02226559 | 210/397-5400 | 40 |
| Health Science Academy/San Antonio/Bexar | 11712602 | 210/977-7278 | 45 |
| Healy-Murphy Center/San Antonio/Bexar | 01479533 | 210/223-2944 | 48 |
| Hearne Elem Sch/Hearne/Robertson | 01048653 | 979/279-3341 | 327 |
| Hearne Elem Sch/Houston/Harris | 03007837 | 281/983-8333 | 187 |
| Hearne High Sch/Hearne/Robertson | 01048665 | 979/279-2332 | 327 |
| **HEARNE IND SCH DIST/HEARNE/<br>ROBERTSON** | 01048641 | 979/279-3200 | 327 |
| Hearne Junior High Sch/Hearne/Robertson | 01048689 | 979/279-2449 | 327 |
| Heartlight Boarding Sch/Hallsville/<br>Harrison | 12313986 | 903/668-2173 | 214 |
| Heather Glen Elem Sch/Garland/Dallas | 01010577 | 972/270-2881 | 110 |
| Hebbronville Elem Sch/Hebbronville/<br>Jim Hogg | 01034482 | 361/527-3203 | 247 |
| Hebbronville High Sch/Hebbronville/<br>Jim Hogg | 01034494 | 361/527-3203 | 247 |
| Hebbronville Jr High Sch/Hebbronville/<br>Jim Hogg | 01034509 | 361/527-3203 | 247 |
| Hebrew Prep School of Austin/Austin/Travis | 04994025 | 512/977-0770 | 375 |
| Hebron 9th Grade Campus/Carrollton/Denton | 11553717 | 469/713-5996 | 127 |
| Hebron High Sch/Carrollton/Denton | 04850948 | 469/713-5183 | 127 |
| Hebron Valley Elem Sch/Carrollton/Denton | 03249607 | 469/713-5182 | 127 |
| Hector Garcia Early Clg HS/Laredo/Webb | 11073676 | 956/273-7700 | 389 |
| Hector Garcia Middle Sch/San Antonio/Bexar | 11448966 | 210/397-8400 | 40 |
| Hector P Garcia Elem Sch/Temple/Bell | 00996746 | 254/215-6100 | 32 |
| Hector P Garcia Middle Sch/Dallas/Dallas | 10908339 | 972/502-5500 | 104 |
| Hedgcoxe Elem Sch/Plano/Collin | 03333806 | 469/752-1700 | 86 |
| **HEDLEY IND SCH DIST/HEDLEY/<br>DONLEY** | 01014145 | 806/856-5323 | 132 |
| Hedley Sch/Hedley/Donley | 01014157 | 806/856-5323 | 132 |
| Hedrick Middle Sch/Lewisville/Denton | 01013464 | 469/713-5188 | 127 |
| Heflin Elem Sch/Houston/Harris | 02177972 | 281/531-1144 | 187 |
| Heights Elem Sch/Laredo/Webb | 01059274 | 956/273-3600 | 389 |
| Heights Elem Sch/Texas City/Galveston | 01019511 | 409/916-0500 | 166 |
| Heights High Sch/Houston/Harris | 01024229 | 713/865-4400 | 197 |
| Helen Ball Elem Sch/El Paso/El Paso | 04365979 | 915/937-8202 | 140 |
| Helen Edwards Early Chldhd Ctr/Kaufman/<br>Kaufman | 05278238 | 972/932-0800 | 255 |
| Helen Major Elm Sch/Houston/Harris | 11452008 | 281/891-8870 | 207 |
| Helena Park Elem Sch/Nederland/Jefferson | 01033696 | 409/722-0462 | 246 |
| Helms Elem Sch/Houston/Harris | 01024073 | 713/867-5130 | 197 |
| Helotes Elem Sch/Helotes/Bexar | 00998122 | 210/397-3800 | 40 |
| Helping Hand Charter Sch/Austin/Travis | 12362705 | 512/751-4534 | 5 |
| Hemmenway Elem Sch/Katy/Harris | 11077361 | 281/856-9870 | 190 |
| Hemphill Elem Sch/Hemphill/Sabine | 01049279 | 409/787-3371 | 332 |
| Hemphill Elem Sch/Kyle/Hays | 04920256 | 512/268-4688 | 216 |
| **HEMPHILL IND SCH DIST/HEMPHILL/<br>SABINE** | 01049267 | 409/787-3371 | 331 |
| Hemphill Middle Sch/Hemphill/Sabine | 04448301 | 409/787-3371 | 332 |
| Hemphill Senior High Sch/Hemphill/Sabine | 01049281 | 409/787-3371 | 332 |
| Hempstead Elem Sch/Hempstead/Waller | 01058787 | 979/826-2452 | 387 |
| Hempstead High Sch/Hempstead/Waller | 01058799 | 979/826-3331 | 387 |
| **HEMPSTEAD IND SCH DIST/HEMPSTEAD/<br>WALLER** | 01058775 | 979/826-3304 | 387 |
| Hempstead Middle Sch/Hempstead/Waller | 01058804 | 979/826-2530 | 387 |
| Henderson Elem Sch/Bryan/Brazos | 01002087 | 979/209-1560 | 58 |
| Henderson Elem Sch/Forney/Kaufman | 05277064 | 469/762-4320 | 255 |
| Henderson Elem Sch/Midland/Midland | 01041526 | 432/240-7000 | 289 |
| Henderson High Sch/Henderson/Rusk | 01049009 | 903/655-5000 | 330 |
| **HENDERSON IND SCH DIST/HENDERSON/<br>RUSK** | 01048976 | 903/655-5000 | 330 |
| Henderson Junior High Sch/Stephenville/<br>Erath | 01017173 | 254/968-6967 | 148 |
| Henderson Middle Sch/El Paso/El Paso | 01015632 | 915/236-0700 | 139 |
| Henderson Middle Sch/Henderson/Rusk | 01878458 | 903/655-5400 | 330 |
| Henderson Middle Sch/Sour Lake/Hardin | 01022465 | 409/981-6420 | 183 |
| Hendrick Middle Sch/Plano/Collin | 03008221 | 469/752-5600 | 86 |
| Hendrickson High Sch/Pflugerville/Travis | 05276010 | 512/594-1100 | 374 |
| Henrietta Elem Sch/Henrietta/Clay | 01005558 | 940/720-7910 | 78 |
| Henrietta High Sch/Henrietta/Clay | 01005560 | 940/720-7930 | 78 |
| **HENRIETTA IND SCH DIST/HENRIETTA/<br>CLAY** | 01005546 | 940/720-7900 | 78 |
| Henrietta Junior High Sch/Henrietta/Clay | 01005572 | 940/720-7920 | 78 |
| Henry B Gonzales Pla/Dallas/Dallas | 10023161 | 972/502-3300 | 104 |
| Henry B Gonzalez Elem Sch/Eagle Pass/<br>Maverick | 04871071 | 830/758-7099 | 280 |
| Henry B Gonzalez Elem Sch/Mission/Hidalgo | 04868622 | 956/323-2460 | 223 |
| Henry Bauerschlag Elem Sch/League City/<br>Galveston | 05009582 | 281/284-6100 | 163 |
| Henry Brauchle Elem Sch/San Antonio/Bexar | 03324958 | 210/397-1500 | 40 |
| Henry Dye Boggess Elem Sch/Murphy/Collin | 05096858 | 469/752-4000 | 86 |
| Henry Ford Elem Sch/Pharr/Hidalgo | 01030424 | 956/354-2770 | 226 |
| Henry Metzger Middle Sch/San Antonio/Bexar | 05347712 | 210/662-2210 | 36 |
| Henry Middle Sch/Cedar Park/Williamson | 05093052 | 512/570-3400 | 400 |
| Henry Scott Middle Sch/Denison/Grayson | 12037869 | 903/462-7180 | 171 |
| Henry Steubing Elem Sch/San Antonio/Bexar | 04754760 | 210/397-4350 | 40 |
| Henry W Longfellow Academy/Dallas/Dallas | 01008988 | 972/749-5400 | 104 |
| Herbert Boldt Elem Sch/San Antonio/Bexar | 12106989 | 210/398-2000 | 40 |
| Herbert Marcus Elem Sch/Dallas/Dallas | 01008990 | 972/794-2900 | 104 |
| Hereford High Sch/Hereford/Deaf Smith | 01013024 | 806/363-7620 | 123 |
| **HEREFORD IND SCH DIST/HEREFORD/<br>DEAF SMITH** | 01012989 | 806/363-7600 | 123 |
| Hereford Junior High Sch/Hereford/<br>Deaf Smith | 01013036 | 806/363-7630 | 123 |
| Hereford Preparatory Academy/Hereford/<br>Deaf Smith | 11823639 | 806/363-7740 | 123 |
| Herfurth Elem Sch/Rowlett/Dallas | 03055511 | 972/475-7994 | 110 |
| Heritage Academy/Windcrest/Bexar | 12378558 | 210/354-7753 | 5 |
| Heritage Academy Del Rio/Del Rio/Val Verde | 12260808 | 830/774-6230 | 5 |
| Heritage Academy San Antonio/Windcrest/<br>Bexar | 12178566 | 210/354-7753 | 5 |
| Heritage Academy Windcrest/Windcrest/Bexar | 12378546 | 210/354-7753 | 5 |
| Heritage Christian Academy/Pearland/<br>Brazoria | 11230240 | 713/436-8422 | 58 |
| Heritage Christian Academy/Rockwall/<br>Rockwall | 04763230 | 972/772-3003 | 329 |
| Heritage Elem Sch/Deer Park/Harris | 10901434 | 281/604-2600 | 203 |
| Heritage Elem Sch/Grapevine/Tarrant | 03389659 | 817/305-4820 | 356 |
| Heritage Elem Sch/Houston/Harris | 04912754 | 281/891-8510 | 207 |
| Heritage Elem Sch/Keller/Tarrant | 03009859 | 817/744-4900 | 357 |
| Heritage Elem Sch/Lewisville/Denton | 04036518 | 469/713-5985 | 127 |
| Heritage Elem Sch/San Antonio/Bexar | 04876435 | 210/882-1607 | 46 |
| Heritage High Sch/Frisco/Collin | 11448473 | 469/633-5900 | 82 |
| Heritage Middle Sch/Colleyville/Tarrant | 04012598 | 817/305-4790 | 356 |
| Heritage Middle Sch/Lubbock/Lubbock | 11717781 | 806/794-9400 | 272 |
| Heritage Middle Sch/San Antonio/Bexar | 04748632 | 210/648-6500 | 34 |
| Heritage Rose Elem Sch/Rosharon/Fort Bend | 11551599 | 281/327-5400 | 154 |
| Heritage Sch/Fredericksbrg/Gillespie | 04761359 | 830/997-6597 | 168 |
| Herman E Utley Middle Sch/Rockwall/<br>Rockwall | 11453741 | 972/771-5281 | 328 |
| Herman Furlough Jr Middle Sch/Terrell/<br>Kaufman | 01035797 | 972/563-7501 | 256 |
| Herman Jones Elem Sch/Prairie View/Waller | 04012354 | 936/372-4200 | 387 |
| Herman Lawson Early Chldhd Ctr/McKinney/<br>Collin | 11447144 | 469/302-2400 | 84 |
| **HERMLEIGH IND SCH DIST/HERMLEIGH/<br>SCURRY** | 01050046 | 325/863-2451 | 336 |
| Hermleigh Sch/Hermleigh/Scurry | 01050058 | 325/863-2451 | 336 |
| Hernandez Elem Sch/San Marcos/Hays | 01029164 | 512/393-6100 | 217 |
| Herod Elem Sch/Houston/Harris | 01024853 | 713/778-3315 | 199 |
| Herrera Elem Sch/El Paso/El Paso | 11449192 | 915/230-5000 | 138 |
| Herrera Elem Sch/Houston/Harris | 04016697 | 713/696-2800 | 196 |

| School/City/County DISTRICT/CITY/COUNTY | PID | TELEPHONE NUMBER | PAGE |
|---|---|---|---|
| Herty Primary Sch/Lufkin/Angelina | 00994982 | 936/639-2241 | 21 |
| Hettie Halstead Elem Sch/Copperas Cove/ Coryell | 01007609 | 254/547-3440 | 96 |
| Hewitt Elem Sch/Hewitt/McLennan | 02045422 | 254/761-5750 | 283 |
| Hfa-Alameda Sch-Art & Design/San Antonio/ Bexar | 11832379 | 210/226-4031 | 5 |
| Hickman Elem Sch/Garland/Dallas | 01382825 | 972/675-3150 | 110 |
| Hicks Elem Sch/Corp Christi/Nueces | 01044504 | 361/878-2200 | 306 |
| Hicks Elem Sch/Houston/Harris | 04453239 | 281/983-8040 | 187 |
| Hico Elem Sch/Hico/Hamilton | 01022207 | 254/796-2183 | 181 |
| **HICO IND SCH DIST/HICO/HAMILTON** | 01022192 | 254/796-2182 | 181 |
| Hico Secondary Sch/Hico/Hamilton | 04867874 | 254/796-2184 | 181 |
| Hidalgo Academy/Hidalgo/Hidalgo | 04921432 | 956/843-4390 | 222 |
| Hidalgo Early College High Sch/Hidalgo/ Hidalgo | 01553127 | 956/843-4300 | 222 |
| Hidalgo Elem Sch/Hidalgo/Hidalgo | 01029839 | 956/843-4225 | 222 |
| **HIDALGO IND SCH DIST/HIDALGO/ HIDALGO** | 01029827 | 956/843-4404 | 222 |
| Hidalgo Park Elem Sch/Pharr/Hidalgo | 05341421 | 956/843-4275 | 222 |
| Hidden Cove Elem Sch/San Antonio/Bexar | 02894326 | 210/623-6220 | 46 |
| Hidden Forest Elem Sch/San Antonio/Bexar | 01824031 | 210/407-4000 | 38 |
| Hidden Hollow Elem Sch/Kingwood/Harris | 03333521 | 281/641-2400 | 201 |
| Hidden Lakes Elem Sch/Keller/Tarrant | 04921614 | 817/744-5000 | 357 |
| Higgins Elem Sch/Whitehouse/Smith | 03049902 | 903/839-5580 | 341 |
| **HIGGINS IND SCH DIST/HIGGINS/ LIPSCOMB** | 01038220 | 806/852-2171 | 270 |
| Higgins Sch/Higgins/Lipscomb | 01038232 | 806/852-2631 | 270 |
| High Country Elem Sch/Fort Worth/Tarrant | 04946597 | 817/306-8007 | 351 |
| **HIGH ISLAND IND SCH DIST/ HIGH ISLAND/GALVESTON** | 01019250 | 409/286-5317 | 165 |
| High Island Sch/High Island/Galveston | 01019262 | 409/286-5313 | 165 |
| High Point Academy/Fort Worth/Tarrant | 12163353 | 817/600-6401 | 5 |
| High Point Elem Sch/Navasota/Grimes | 10025822 | 936/825-1130 | 177 |
| High Point Elem Sch/Temple/Bell | 11926047 | 254/316-5000 | 30 |
| High Point Prep Academy/Arlington/Tarrant | 11231749 | 817/394-3100 | 361 |
| High Pointe Elem Sch/Cedar Hill/Dallas | 02893114 | 972/291-7874 | 101 |
| High School Ahead Acad MS/Houston/Harris | 11555507 | 713/696-2643 | 194 |
| High School for Law & Justice/Houston/ Harris | 02227527 | 713/867-5100 | 195 |
| Highland Elem Sch/Plainview/Hale | 01021978 | 806/293-6045 | 180 |
| Highland Forest Elem Sch/San Antonio/Bexar | 05070141 | 210/333-7385 | 34 |
| Highland Heights Elem Sch/Houston/Harris | 01024085 | 713/696-2920 | 194 |
| Highland Hills Elem Sch/San Antonio/Bexar | 00998835 | 210/438-6860 | 43 |
| **HIGHLAND IND SCH DIST/ROSCOE/ NOLAN** | 01043859 | 325/766-3652 | 304 |
| Highland Lakes Elem Sch/Granite SHLS/ Burnet | 04801777 | 830/798-3650 | 64 |
| Highland Meadows Elem Sch/Dallas/Dallas | 05345764 | 972/502-5200 | 104 |
| Highland Middle Sch/Fort Worth/Tarrant | 04808828 | 817/847-5143 | 351 |
| Highland Park Elem Sch/Amarillo/Potter | 03315878 | 806/335-1334 | 322 |
| Highland Park Elem Sch/Austin/Travis | 01056260 | 512/414-2090 | 370 |
| Highland Park Elem Sch/Nederland/Jefferson | 01033701 | 409/722-0236 | 246 |
| Highland Park Elem Sch/Pflugerville/Travis | 10022416 | 512/594-6800 | 374 |
| Highland Park Elem Sch/San Antonio/Bexar | 00998847 | 210/228-3335 | 43 |
| Highland Park Elem Sch/Texarkana/Bowie | 01001253 | 903/794-8001 | 53 |
| Highland Park High Sch/Amarillo/Potter | 04914441 | 806/335-2821 | 322 |
| Highland Park High Sch/Dallas/Dallas | 01011052 | 214/780-3700 | 112 |
| **HIGHLAND PARK IND SCH DIST/ DALLAS/DALLAS** | 01011038 | 214/780-3000 | 112 |
| **HIGHLAND PARK IND SCH DIST/ AMARILLO/POTTER** | 01047582 | 806/335-2823 | 322 |
| Highland Park Middle Sch/Amarillo/Potter | 01047594 | 806/335-2821 | 322 |
| Highland Park Middle Sch/Dallas/Dallas | 04360125 | 214/780-3600 | 112 |
| Highland PK Presbyterian Sch/Dallas/Dallas | 01479741 | 214/525-6500 | 119 |
| Highland Sch/Roscoe/Nolan | 01043861 | 325/766-3651 | 304 |
| Highland Village Elem Sch/Lewisville/ Denton | 02131019 | 469/713-5957 | 127 |
| Highlander Sch/Dallas/Dallas | 01479935 | 214/348-3220 | 119 |
| Highlands Elem Sch/Cedar Hill/Dallas | 03006493 | 972/291-0496 | 101 |
| Highlands Elem Sch/Highlands/Harris | 01023641 | 281/420-4900 | 193 |
| Highlands Elem Sch/Sugar Land/Fort Bend | 02892926 | 281/634-4160 | 154 |
| Highlands High Sch/San Antonio/Bexar | 00998859 | 210/438-6800 | 43 |
| Highlands Junior High Sch/Highlands/Harris | 01023653 | 281/420-4695 | 193 |
| Highlands Sch/Irving/Dallas | 04146195 | 972/554-1980 | 118 |
| Highpoint School East/Houston/Harris | 04747133 | 713/696-2160 | 184 |
| Highpoint School North/Houston/Harris | 04942228 | 713/696-2195 | 184 |
| Hightower Elem Sch/Plano/Collin | 04811473 | 469/752-1800 | 86 |
| Hightower High Sch/Missouri City/Fort Bend | 04808610 | 281/634-5240 | 154 |
| Hildebrandt Intermediate Sch/Klein/Harris | 01026320 | 832/249-5100 | 202 |
| Hill Country Adventist Sch/Kerrville/Kerr | 03017349 | 830/257-3903 | 259 |
| Hill Country Christian Sch/Austin/Travis | 04880797 | 512/331-7036 | 375 |
| Hill Country Christian Sch/San Marcos/Hays | 04993980 | 512/353-8976 | 217 |

| School/City/County DISTRICT/CITY/COUNTY | PID | TELEPHONE NUMBER | PAGE |
|---|---|---|---|
| Hill Country Clg Prep High Sch/Spring Branch/ Comal | 12469793 | 830/885-9000 | 92 |
| Hill Country Elem Sch/Pipe Creek/Bandera | 04362599 | 830/460-3901 | 26 |
| Hill Country High Sch/Kerrville/Kerr | 03473511 | 830/257-2232 | 259 |
| Hill Country Middle Sch/Austin/Travis | 01401445 | 512/732-9220 | 372 |
| Hill Country Montessori Sch/Boerne/Kendall | 11849683 | 830/229-5377 | 257 |
| Hill Country Yth Rch-Najim Sch/Ingram/Kerr | 12100387 | 830/367-6100 | 5 |
| Hill Elem Sch/Arlington/Tarrant | 01051791 | 682/867-2300 | 347 |
| Hill Elem Sch/Austin/Travis | 01056272 | 512/414-2369 | 370 |
| Hill Elem Sch/Houston/Harris | 05097228 | 281/878-7775 | 185 |
| Hill School of Fort Worth/Fort Worth/ Tarrant | 01875597 | 817/923-9482 | 361 |
| Hillander Sch/Midland/Midland | 01480829 | 432/684-8681 | 289 |
| Hillcrest Elem Sch/Alice/Jim Wells | 01034561 | 361/660-2095 | 248 |
| Hillcrest Elem Sch/Austin/Travis | 02130429 | 512/386-3550 | 372 |
| Hillcrest Elem Sch/Dumas/Moore | 01042867 | 806/935-5629 | 298 |
| Hillcrest Elem Sch/Nederland/Jefferson | 01033713 | 409/722-3484 | 246 |
| Hillcrest Elem Sch/Plainview/Hale | 01021980 | 806/293-6050 | 180 |
| Hillcrest Elem Sch/San Antonio/Bexar | 00999176 | 210/228-3340 | 43 |
| Hillcrest High Sch/Dallas/Dallas | 01009009 | 972/502-6800 | 104 |
| Hillcrest Prof Dev Sch/Waco/McLennan | 04288668 | 254/772-4286 | 285 |
| Hillcrest Sch/Midland/Midland | 04994154 | 432/570-7444 | 289 |
| Hillsboro Elem Sch/Hillsboro/Hill | 03008269 | 254/582-4140 | 230 |
| Hillsboro High Sch/Hillsboro/Hill | 01172498 | 254/582-4100 | 230 |
| **HILLSBORO IND SCH DIST/HILLSBORO/ HILL** | 01030852 | 254/582-8585 | 230 |
| Hillsboro Intermediate Sch/Hillsboro/Hill | 05026750 | 254/582-4170 | 230 |
| Hillsboro Junior High Sch/Hillsboro/Hill | 01172503 | 254/582-4120 | 230 |
| Hillside Acad for Excellence/Garland/ Dallas | 01010591 | 972/926-2550 | 110 |
| Hillside Elem Sch/Amarillo/Randall | 11450402 | 806/677-2520 | 323 |
| Hillside Elem Sch/El Paso/El Paso | 01015644 | 915/236-0100 | 138 |
| Hilltop Elem Sch/Argyle/Denton | 01013189 | 940/464-0564 | 124 |
| Hillwood Middle Sch/Fort Worth/Tarrant | 04921638 | 817/744-3350 | 357 |
| Hinojosa EC-PK-K Sch/Houston/Harris | 04754485 | 281/985-4750 | 186 |
| Hinojosa Elem Sch/Mission/Hidalgo | 05278381 | 956/584-4990 | 227 |
| Hirsch Elem Sch/San Antonio/Bexar | 00998809 | 210/978-7985 | 43 |
| Hirschi High Sch/Wichita Falls/Wichita | 01173076 | 940/235-1070 | 395 |
| Hitchcock High Sch/Hitchcock/Galveston | 01019298 | 409/316-6544 | 165 |
| **HITCHCOCK IND SCH DIST/HITCHCOCK/ GALVESTON** | 01019274 | 409/316-6545 | 165 |
| Hitchcock Primary Sch/Hitchcock/Galveston | 11719272 | 409/316-6467 | 165 |
| Hobbs Williams Elem Sch/Grand Prairie/ Dallas | 11157155 | 972/522-2700 | 111 |
| Hockaday Sch/Dallas/Dallas | 01012123 | 214/363-6311 | 119 |
| Hodge Elem Sch/Denton/Denton | 03009732 | 940/369-2800 | 125 |
| Hodges Bend Middle Sch/Houston/Fort Bend | 03011395 | 281/634-3000 | 154 |
| Hodges Elem Sch/Balch Springs/Dallas | 01011430 | 972/290-4040 | 115 |
| Hodges Elem Sch/Lubbock/Lubbock | 01038701 | 806/219-5800 | 273 |
| Hoffmann Elem Sch/San Antonio/Bexar | 11448954 | 210/397-8350 | 40 |
| Hoffmann Lane Elem Sch/New Braunfels/Comal | 05090684 | 830/221-2500 | 92 |
| Hofius Intermediate Sch/Klein/Harris | 12315764 | 832/375-8800 | 202 |
| Hogg Middle Sch/Houston/Harris | 01024097 | 713/802-4700 | 197 |
| Holbrook Elem Sch/Houston/Harris | 01857260 | 713/460-6165 | 190 |
| Holiday Heights Elem Sch/N Richlnd Hls/ Tarrant | 01052109 | 817/547-2600 | 348 |
| Holiman Elem Sch/San Angelo/Tom Green | 01055668 | 325/659-3663 | 367 |
| Holland Elem Sch/Holland/Bell | 00996409 | 254/657-2525 | 30 |
| Holland High Sch/Holland/Bell | 00996411 | 254/657-2523 | 30 |
| **HOLLAND IND SCH DIST/HOLLAND/ BELL** | 00996395 | 254/657-0175 | 30 |
| Holland Medical High Sch/Abilene/Taylor | 11452943 | 325/794-4120 | 363 |
| Holland Middle Sch/Holland/Bell | 04245161 | 254/657-2224 | 30 |
| Holland Middle Sch/Houston/Harris | 02043319 | 713/671-3860 | 194 |
| Hollaway Sixth Grade Sch/Whitehouse/Smith | 01051026 | 903/839-5656 | 341 |
| Hollenstein Career & Tech Ctr/Fort Worth/ Tarrant | 11713527 | 817/306-1925 | 351 |
| Hollibrook Elem Sch/Houston/Harris | 01023263 | 713/251-5800 | 206 |
| Holliday Elem Sch/Holliday/Archer | 00995223 | 940/586-1986 | 22 |
| Holliday High Sch/Holliday/Archer | 00995235 | 940/586-1624 | 22 |
| **HOLLIDAY IND SCH DIST/HOLLIDAY/ ARCHER** | 00995211 | 940/586-1281 | 22 |
| Holliday Middle Sch/Holliday/Archer | 02844802 | 940/586-1314 | 22 |
| Hollis T Dietz Elem Sch/Heartland/Kaufman | 12231118 | 972/427-6050 | 254 |
| Holmquist Elem Sch/Houston/Harris | 10910174 | 281/988-3024 | 187 |
| Holmsley Elem Sch/Houston/Harris | 02848731 | 281/463-5885 | 190 |
| Holub Middle Sch/Houston/Harris | 02126428 | 281/983-8433 | 187 |
| Holy Cross Catholic Academy/Amarillo/ Randall | 01047661 | 806/355-9637 | 324 |
| Holy Cross Catholic HS/Odessa/Ector | 12368852 | 432/713-0143 | 135 |
| Holy Cross Catholic Sch/Bay City/Matagorda | 01027922 | 979/245-5632 | 279 |

| School/City/County DISTRICT/CITY/COUNTY | PID | TELEPHONE NUMBER | PAGE |
|---|---|---|---|
| Holy Cross Christian Academy/Burleson/Johnson | 11228405 | 817/295-7232 | 252 |
| Holy Cross of San Antonio Sch/San Antonio/Bexar | 00999803 | 210/433-9395 | 47 |
| Holy Family Catholic Academy/Irving/Dallas | 01012422 | 972/255-0205 | 118 |
| Holy Family Catholic Sch/Austin/Williamson | 04911827 | 512/246-4455 | 403 |
| Holy Family Catholic Sch/Corp Christi/Nueces | 01045211 | 361/884-9142 | 309 |
| Holy Family Catholic Sch/Fort Worth/Tarrant | 01054353 | 817/737-4201 | 360 |
| Holy Family Catholic Sch/Galveston/Galveston | 01028029 | 409/765-6607 | 166 |
| Holy Ghost Catholic Sch/Houston/Harris | 01027934 | 713/668-5327 | 209 |
| Holy Name Catholic Sch/San Antonio/Bexar | 00999815 | 210/333-7356 | 47 |
| Holy Rosary Sch/Rosenberg/Fort Bend | 01857272 | 281/342-5813 | 159 |
| Holy Spirit Catholic Sch/San Antonio/Bexar | 00999839 | 210/349-1169 | 47 |
| Holy Spirit Episcopal Sch/Houston/Harris | 01875389 | 713/468-5138 | 211 |
| Holy Trinity Catholic High Sch/Temple/Bell | 04885072 | 254/771-0787 | 33 |
| Holy Trinity Catholic Sch/Dallas/Dallas | 01012434 | 214/526-5113 | 118 |
| Holy Trinity Catholic Sch/Grapevine/Tarrant | 04307159 | 817/421-8000 | 360 |
| Holy Trinity Episcopal Sch/Houston/Harris | 05256826 | 281/459-4323 | 211 |
| Homer Drive Elem Sch/Beaumont/Jefferson | 03326839 | 409/617-6225 | 245 |
| Homer Hanna Early Clg HS/Brownsville/Cameron | 01003586 | 956/548-7600 | 67 |
| Homer J Morris Middle Sch/McAllen/Hidalgo | 02856726 | 956/618-7300 | 224 |
| Homestead Elem Sch/Carrollton/Denton | 04850950 | 469/713-5181 | 127 |
| Hommel Elem Sch/Everman/Tarrant | 01526148 | 817/568-3540 | 352 |
| Hondo High Sch/Hondo/Medina | 01041241 | 830/426-3341 | 287 |
| HONDO IND SCH DIST/HONDO/MEDINA | 01041239 | 830/426-3027 | 287 |
| Honey Elem Sch/Lubbock/Lubbock | 02202101 | 806/219-5900 | 273 |
| Honey Grove Elem Sch/Honey Grove/Fannin | 01017484 | 903/378-2264 | 150 |
| Honey Grove High Sch/Honey Grove/Fannin | 01017496 | 903/378-2264 | 150 |
| HONEY GROVE IND SCH DIST/HONEY GROVE/FANNIN | 01017472 | 903/378-2264 | 150 |
| Honey Grove Middle Sch/Honey Grove/Fannin | 03240302 | 903/378-2264 | 150 |
| Honor Roll Sch/Sugar Land/Fort Bend | 04028066 | 281/265-7888 | 160 |
| Honore Ligarde Elem Sch/Laredo/Webb | 03052959 | 956/273-3900 | 389 |
| Hood-Case Elem Sch/Alvin/Brazoria | 04750829 | 281/585-5786 | 54 |
| Hook Elem Sch/Stephenville/Erath | 04945567 | 254/968-3213 | 148 |
| Hooks Elem Sch/Hooks/Bowie | 01000869 | 903/547-2291 | 51 |
| Hooks High Sch/Hooks/Bowie | 01000871 | 903/547-2215 | 51 |
| HOOKS IND SCH DIST/HOOKS/BOWIE | 01000857 | 903/547-6077 | 51 |
| Hooks Junior High Sch/Hooks/Bowie | 01000883 | 903/547-2568 | 51 |
| Hoover Elem Sch/Azle/Tarrant | 04035916 | 817/444-7766 | 348 |
| Hoover Elem Sch/Katy/Harris | 12233154 | 832/667-7301 | 190 |
| Hope Academy/La Joya/Hidalgo | 10912469 | 956/323-2900 | 223 |
| Hope High Sch/Port Lavaca/Calhoun | 03397084 | 361/552-7084 | 65 |
| Hopewell Middle Sch/Round Rock/Williamson | 04452340 | 512/464-5200 | 402 |
| Hopkins Elem Sch/Victoria/Victoria | 01058517 | 361/788-9527 | 385 |
| Hopper Middle Sch/Cypress/Harris | 10966680 | 281/463-5353 | 190 |
| Horace Mann Junior High Sch/Baytown/Harris | 01023665 | 281/420-4585 | 193 |
| Horace Mann Middle Sch/Amarillo/Potter | 01047295 | 806/326-3700 | 320 |
| Horizon Heights Sch/El Paso/El Paso | 02199516 | 915/937-7400 | 140 |
| Horizon High Sch/El Paso/El Paso | 05100344 | 915/926-4200 | 137 |
| Horizon Middle Sch/El Paso/El Paso | 10004359 | 915/926-4700 | 137 |
| Horizon Montessori I McAllen/McAllen/Hidalgo | 11014905 | 956/631-0234 | 5 |
| Horizon Montessori II Weslaco/Weslaco/Hidalgo | 11014917 | 956/969-0044 | 5 |
| Horizon Montessori III Hrlgtn/Harlingen/Cameron | 11564699 | 956/423-8200 | 5 |
| Horizon Montessori Pearland/Pearland/Brazoria | 12378560 | 281/485-2500 | 5 |
| Horn Elem Sch/Bellaire/Harris | 01024865 | 713/295-5264 | 199 |
| Horn Elem Sch/Houston/Harris | 10002894 | 281/988-3223 | 187 |
| Horne Elem Sch/Houston/Harris | 02045381 | 281/463-5954 | 190 |
| Hornsby-Dunlap Elem Sch/Austin/Travis | 02907117 | 512/386-3650 | 372 |
| House Creek Elementray Sch/Copperas Cove/Coryell | 11715173 | 254/518-3000 | 96 |
| Houser Elem Sch/Conroe/Montgomery | 02126868 | 832/663-4000 | 295 |
| Housman Elem Sch/Houston/Harris | 01027154 | 713/251-5900 | 206 |
| Houston Academy Int'l Studies/Houston/Harris | 10021620 | 713/942-1430 | 197 |
| Houston Adventist Academy/Cypress/Harris | 11229629 | 713/896-0071 | 211 |
| Houston Christian High Sch/Houston/Harris | 01480441 | 713/580-6000 | 211 |
| Houston Elem Sch/Austin/Travis | 01532094 | 512/414-2517 | 370 |
| Houston Elem Sch/Conroe/Montgomery | 01042544 | 936/709-5100 | 295 |
| Houston Elem Sch/Denison/Grayson | 01020340 | 903/462-7300 | 171 |
| Houston Elem Sch/Harlingen/Cameron | 01003859 | 956/427-3110 | 68 |
| Houston Elem Sch/Lancaster/Dallas | 01011349 | 972/218-1513 | 114 |
| Houston Elem Sch/Mineral Wells/Palo Pinto | 01046083 | 940/325 3427 | 313 |
| Houston Gateway Acad-Evergreen/Houston/Harris | 04926781 | 713/649-2706 | 5 |
| Houston Gateway Academy-Coral/Houston/Harris | 05221314 | 713/923-5060 | 5 |
| Houston Gateway Elite Clg Prep/Houston/Harris | 12260822 | 832/649-2700 | 6 |
| Houston Heights High Sch/Houston/Harris | 04891825 | 713/868-9797 | 6 |
| HOUSTON IND SCH DIST/HOUSTON/HARRIS | 01023770 | 713/556-6000 | 193 |
| HOUSTON ISD-ACHIEVE 180/HOUSTON/HARRIS | 12310958 | 713/556-7102 | 193 |
| HOUSTON ISD-EAST AREA/HOUSTON/HARRIS | 12170253 | 713/556-8998 | 194 |
| HOUSTON ISD-NORTH AREA/HOUSTON/HARRIS | 12170239 | 713/556-8998 | 195 |
| HOUSTON ISD-NORTHWEST AREA/HOUSTON/HARRIS | 12179974 | 713/556-8999 | 196 |
| HOUSTON ISD-SOUTH AREA/HOUSTON/HARRIS | 12170241 | 713/556-4447 | 197 |
| HOUSTON ISD-WEST AREA/HOUSTON/HARRIS | 12170265 | 713/556-9123 | 198 |
| Houston Learning Academy/Houston/Harris | 11238412 | 281/449-1532 | 211 |
| Houston Middle Sch/Irving/Dallas | 01532018 | 972/600-7500 | 113 |
| Howard Burnham Elem Sch/El Paso/El Paso | 04813952 | 915/584-9499 | 6 |
| Howard Dobbs Elem Sch/Rockwall/Rockwall | 01048720 | 972/771-5232 | 328 |
| Howard Early Childhood Center/San Antonio/Bexar | 00996966 | 210/832-5900 | 33 |
| Howard Norman Elem Sch/Hutto/Williamson | 12167701 | 512/759-5480 | 399 |
| Howe High Sch/Howe/Grayson | 01020493 | 903/745-4400 | 171 |
| HOWE IND SCH DIST/HOWE/GRAYSON | 01020479 | 903/532-3228 | 171 |
| Howe Intermediate Sch/Howe/Grayson | 01020481 | 903/745-4200 | 171 |
| Howe Middle Sch/Howe/Grayson | 01020508 | 903/745-4300 | 171 |
| Howell Middle Sch/Victoria/Victoria | 01058529 | 361/578-1561 | 385 |
| Hoyland Elem Sch/Houston/Harris | 11451987 | 281/891-8810 | 207 |
| Hubbard Elem Sch/De Kalb/Bowie | 01000912 | 903/667-2645 | 51 |
| Hubbard Elem Sch/Hubbard/Hill | 01030929 | 254/576-2359 | 231 |
| Hubbard Heights Elem Sch/Fort Worth/Tarrant | 01053000 | 817/814-7500 | 353 |
| Hubbard High Sch/Hubbard/Hill | 01030931 | 254/576-2549 | 231 |
| HUBBARD IND SCH DIST/DE KALB/BOWIE | 01000900 | 903/667-2645 | 51 |
| HUBBARD IND SCH DIST/HUBBARD/HILL | 01030917 | 254/576-2564 | 230 |
| Hubbard Middle Sch/Tyler/Smith | 01050864 | 903/262-1560 | 340 |
| HUCKABAY IND SCH DIST/STEPHENVILLE/ERATH | 01017056 | 254/968-5274 | 147 |
| Huckabay Sch/Stephenville/Erath | 01017068 | 254/968-8476 | 148 |
| Hudson Bend Middle Sch/Austin/Travis | 04920189 | 512/533-6400 | 373 |
| Hudson Elem Sch/Brownsville/Cameron | 04808517 | 956/574-6400 | 67 |
| Hudson High Sch/Lufkin/Angelina | 00994877 | 936/875-9232 | 20 |
| HUDSON IND SCH DIST/LUFKIN/ANGELINA | 00994853 | 936/875-3351 | 20 |
| Hudson Middle Sch/Lufkin/Angelina | 00994889 | 936/875-9295 | 20 |
| Hudson Middle Sch/Sachse/Dallas | 04035473 | 972/675-3070 | 110 |
| Hudson Pep Elem Sch/Longview/Gregg | 01021045 | 903/803-5100 | 175 |
| Huebner Elem Sch/San Antonio/Bexar | 04755867 | 210/407-4200 | 38 |
| Hueco Elem Sch/El Paso/El Paso | 02199528 | 915/937-7600 | 140 |
| Huffines Middle Sch/Lewisville/Denton | 01541318 | 469/713-5990 | 127 |
| Huffman Elem Sch/Huffman/Harris | 03004768 | 281/324-1399 | 200 |
| Huffman Elem Sch/Plano/Collin | 02225593 | 469/752-1900 | 86 |
| HUFFMAN IND SCH DIST/HUFFMAN/HARRIS | 01026112 | 281/324-1871 | 200 |
| Huffman Middle Sch/Huffman/Harris | 01026136 | 281/324-2598 | 200 |
| Huggins Elem Sch/Fulshear/Fort Bend | 02045355 | 832/223-1600 | 158 |
| Hughes Elem Sch/McKinney/Collin | 12172897 | 469/219-2230 | 88 |
| Hughes Middle Sch/Burleson/Johnson | 01034846 | 817/245-0600 | 250 |
| Hughes Road Elem Sch/Dickinson/Galveston | 02846496 | 281/229-6700 | 164 |
| Hughes Springs Elem Sch/Hughes Spgs/Cass | 01004798 | 903/639-3881 | 74 |
| Hughes Springs High Sch/Hughes Spgs/Cass | 01004803 | 903/639-3841 | 74 |
| HUGHES SPRINGS IND SCH DIST/HUGHES SPGS/CASS | 01004786 | 903/639-3800 | 73 |
| Hughes Springs Jr High Sch/Hughes Spgs/Cass | 01004815 | 903/639-3812 | 74 |
| Hughey Elem Sch/El Paso/El Paso | 01015656 | 915/236-0250 | 138 |
| Hughston Elem Sch/Plano/Collin | 01401366 | 469/752-2000 | 86 |
| Hull Daisetta Elem Sch/Hull/Liberty | 01037898 | 936/536-6321 | 268 |
| Hull Daisetta High Sch/Daisetta/Liberty | 01037903 | 936/536-6321 | 269 |
| HULL DAISETTA IND SCH DIST/DAISETTA/LIBERTY | 01037886 | 936/536-6321 | 268 |
| Hull Daisetta Junior High Sch/Daisetta/Liberty | 01037915 | 936/536-6321 | 269 |
| Humble Christian Sch/Humble/Harris | 11225128 | 281/441-1313 | 211 |

| School/City/County<br>DISTRICT/CITY/COUNTY | PID | TELEPHONE<br>NUMBER | PAGE |
|---|---|---|---|
| Humble Classical Academy/Humble/Harris | 11925184 | 281/913-5107 | 6 |
| Humble Elem Sch/Humble/Harris | 01026174 | 281/641-1100 | 201 |
| Humble High Sch/Humble/Harris | 01026186 | 281/641-6300 | 201 |
| **HUMBLE IND SCH DIST**/HUMBLE/<br>**HARRIS** | 01026150 | 281/641-1000 | 200 |
| Humble Middle Sch/Humble/Harris | 01026198 | 281/641-4170 | 201 |
| Humphrey's Highland Elem Sch/Amarillo/<br>Potter | 01047312 | 806/326-4550 | 320 |
| Hunstville Classical Academy/Huntsville/<br>Walker | 11014591 | 936/291-0203 | 6 |
| Hunt Elem Sch/Cuero/De Witt | 01013713 | 361/275-1900 | 122 |
| **HUNT IND SCH DIST**/HUNT/KERR | 01036038 | 830/238-4893 | 258 |
| Hunt Sch/Hunt/Kerr | 01036040 | 830/238-4893 | 259 |
| Hunters Creek Elem Sch/Houston/Harris | 01027166 | 713/251-6000 | 206 |
| Hunters Glen Elem Sch/Missouri City/<br>Fort Bend | 02857366 | 281/634-4640 | 154 |
| Huntington Elem Sch/Huntington/Angelina | 00994906 | 936/876-5194 | 20 |
| Huntington High Sch/Huntington/Angelina | 00994918 | 936/876-4150 | 21 |
| **HUNTINGTON IND SCH DIST**/<br>**HUNTINGTON/ANGELINA** | 00994891 | 936/876-4287 | 20 |
| Huntington Intermediate Sch/Huntington/<br>Angelina | 03319513 | 936/876-3432 | 21 |
| Huntington Middle Sch/Huntington/Angelina | 00994920 | 936/876-4722 | 21 |
| Huntington-Surrey Sch/Austin/Travis | 03141897 | 512/502-5400 | 375 |
| Huntsville Elem Sch/Huntsville/Walker | 03318985 | 936/435-6850 | 386 |
| Huntsville High Sch/Huntsville/Walker | 01058696 | 936/435-6100 | 386 |
| **HUNTSVILLE IND SCH DIST**/<br>**HUNTSVILLE/WALKER** | 01058672 | 936/435-6300 | 386 |
| Huntsville Intermediate Sch/Huntsville/<br>Walker | 01058701 | 936/435-6500 | 386 |
| Huppertz Elem Sch/San Antonio/Bexar | 00998548 | 210/438-6580 | 43 |
| Hurla M Midkiff Elem Sch/Palmhurst/Hidalgo | 05274969 | 956/323-7000 | 225 |
| Hurshel Antwine Elem Sch/El Paso/El Paso | 10005559 | 915/937-6400 | 140 |
| Hurst Hills Elem Sch/Hurst/Tarrant | 01053830 | 817/285-3295 | 356 |
| Hurst Junior High Sch/Hurst/Tarrant | 01053842 | 817/285-3220 | 356 |
| **HURST-EULESS-BEDFORD ISD**/<br>**BEDFORD/TARRANT** | 01053737 | 817/283-4461 | 356 |
| Huston Academy/Stephenville/Erath | 04891605 | 254/965-8883 | 6 |
| Hutchins Elem Sch/El Campo/Wharton | 01059638 | 979/543-5481 | 392 |
| Hutchins Elem Sch/San Antonio/Bexar | 00999449 | 210/977-7200 | 45 |
| Hutchinson Elem Sch/Richmond/Fort Bend | 10004086 | 832/223-1700 | 158 |
| Hutchinson Middle Sch/Lubbock/Lubbock | 01038713 | 806/219-3800 | 273 |
| Hutto Elem Sch/Hutto/Williamson | 01060962 | 512/759-2094 | 399 |
| Hutto High Sch/Hutto/Williamson | 01060950 | 512/759-4700 | 399 |
| **HUTTO IND SCH DIST**/HUTTO/<br>**WILLIAMSON** | 01060948 | 512/759-3771 | 399 |
| Hutto Middle Sch/Hutto/Williamson | 04866430 | 512/759-4541 | 399 |
| Hyde Park Elem Middle Sch/Austin/Travis | 02084131 | 512/465-8338 | 376 |
| Hyde Park Elem Sch/Denison/Grayson | 01020364 | 903/462-7350 | 171 |
| Hyde Park High Sch/Austin/Travis | 12361218 | 512/465-8333 | 376 |

I

| | | | |
|---|---|---|---|
| I C Evans Elem Sch/Burkburnett/Wichita | 01059987 | 940/569-3311 | 394 |
| I H Kempner High Sch/Sugar Land/Fort Bend | 03048946 | 281/634-2300 | 154 |
| I M Terrell Elem Sch/Fort Worth/Tarrant | 04812398 | 817/815-1900 | 353 |
| I N Range Elem Sch/Mesquite/Dallas | 01011507 | 972/882-5180 | 115 |
| I S Rogers Elem Sch/Frisco/Collin | 03003116 | 469/633-2000 | 82 |
| I W & Eleanor Hyde Elem Sch/League City/<br>Galveston | 04365307 | 281/284-5800 | 163 |
| I W Evans Intermediate Sch/Bonham/Fannin | 01017393 | 903/583-2914 | 149 |
| Iago Junior High Sch/Boling/Wharton | 01059559 | 979/657-2826 | 392 |
| Iant Quranic Academy/Richardson/Dallas | 11234856 | 972/231-5698 | 119 |
| Iboc Christian Academy/Dallas/Dallas | 05013026 | 972/572-4262 | 119 |
| Ida Lee Bright Elem Sch/Frisco/Collin | 04942357 | 469/633-2700 | 82 |
| Idalou Elem Sch/Idalou/Lubbock | 01038464 | 806/892-2524 | 272 |
| Idalou High Sch/Idalou/Lubbock | 01038476 | 806/892-2123 | 272 |
| **IDALOU IND SCH DIST**/IDALOU/<br>**LUBBOCK** | 01038452 | 806/892-1900 | 272 |
| Idalou Middle Sch/Idalou/Lubbock | 01038488 | 806/892-2133 | 272 |
| Idea Academy-Achieve/Haltom City/Tarrant | 12368254 | 817/885-4700 | 6 |
| Idea Academy-Alamo/Alamo/Hidalgo | 11557098 | 956/588-4005 | 6 |
| Idea Academy-Bluff Springs/Austin/Travis | 12173877 | 512/822-4200 | 6 |
| Idea Academy-Brackenridge/San Antonio/<br>Bexar | 12232033 | 210/239-4300 | 6 |
| Idea Academy-Brownsville/Brownsville/<br>Cameron | 11824061 | 956/832-5150 | 6 |
| Idea Academy-Burke/San Antonio/Bexar | 12370738 | 210/239-4650 | 6 |
| Idea Academy-Carver/San Antonio/Bexar | 11824073 | 210/223-8885 | 6 |
| Idea Academy-Converse/Converse/Bexar | 12472843 | 210/529-3800 | 6 |
| Idea Academy-Donna/Donna/Hidalgo | 04931827 | 956/464-0203 | 6 |
| Idea Academy-Eastside/San Antonio/Bexar | 12106836 | 210/239-4800 | 6 |

| School/City/County<br>DISTRICT/CITY/COUNTY | PID | TELEPHONE<br>NUMBER | PAGE |
|---|---|---|---|
| Idea Academy-Edgecliff/Fort Worth/Tarrant | 12472908 | 817/885-4800 | 6 |
| Idea Academy-Edgemere/El Paso/El Paso | 12311639 | 915/444-0200 | 6 |
| Idea Academy-Edinburg/Edinburg/Hidalgo | 11728807 | 956/287-6100 | 6 |
| Idea Academy-Elsa/Elsa/Hidalgo | 12311653 | 956/567-4700 | 6 |
| Idea Academy-Ewing Halsell/San Antonio/<br>Bexar | 12232045 | 210/239-4850 | 6 |
| Idea Academy-Frontier/Brownsville/Cameron | 10751801 | 956/541-2002 | 6 |
| Idea Academy-Hardy/Houston/Harris | 12472805 | 832/844-4100 | 6 |
| Idea Academy-Harlingen/Harlingen/Cameron | 12472922 | 956/564-7200 | 6 |
| Idea Academy-Harvey Najim/San Antonio/<br>Bexar | 12232069 | 210/239-4900 | 6 |
| Idea Academy-Hidden Meadow/San Antonio/<br>Bexar | 12472867 | 210/529-3900 | 6 |
| Idea Academy-Hlth Professions/Austin/<br>Travis | 12370697 | 512/822-4350 | 6 |
| Idea Academy-Horizon Vista/El Paso/El Paso | 12472829 | | 6 |
| Idea Academy-Ingram Hills/San Antonio/<br>Bexar | 12311732 | 210/529-3700 | 6 |
| Idea Academy-Judson/San Antonio/Bexar | 12173827 | 210/529-3600 | 6 |
| Idea Academy-Kyle/Kyle/Hays | 12309789 | 512/822-4300 | 6 |
| Idea Academy-Los Encinos/McAllen/Hidalgo | 12370752 | 956/429-4150 | 6 |
| Idea Academy-Mays/San Antonio/Bexar | 12173841 | 210/529-3200 | 6 |
| Idea Academy-McAllen/McAllen/Hidalgo | 11824085 | 956/429-4100 | 6 |
| Idea Academy-Mesa Hills/El Paso/El Paso | 12370659 | 915/888-4050 | 6 |
| Idea Academy-Mission/Mission/Hidalgo | 10751837 | 956/583-8315 | 6 |
| Idea Academy-Monterrey Park/San Antonio/<br>Bexar | 12106874 | 210/239-4200 | 6 |
| Idea Academy-Montopolis/Austin/Travis | 11819121 | 512/646-2800 | 6 |
| Idea Academy-North Mission/Mission/Hidalgo | 12106769 | 956/424-4300 | 6 |
| Idea Academy-Owassa/Pharr/Hidalgo | 12311677 | 956/588-4300 | 6 |
| Idea Academy-Palmview/Mission/Hidalgo | 12472984 | 956/272-5394 | 6 |
| Idea Academy-Parmer Park/Austin/Travis | 12370714 | 512/822-4850 | 6 |
| Idea Academy-Pflugerville/Pflugerville/<br>Travis | 12311689 | 512/822-4700 | 6 |
| Idea Academy-Pharr/Pharr/Hidalgo | 11557086 | 956/283-1515 | 6 |
| Idea Academy-Quest/Edinburg/Hidalgo | 10751825 | 956/287-1003 | 7 |
| Idea Academy-Rio Grande City/Rio Grande Cy/<br>Starr | 12230047 | 956/263-4900 | 7 |
| Idea Academy-Rio Vista/Socorro/El Paso | 12311706 | 915/444-0188 | 7 |
| Idea Academy-Rise/Fort Worth/Tarrant | 12370673 | 817/885-4150 | 7 |
| Idea Academy-Riverview/Brownsville/Cameron | 12106783 | 956/832-5900 | 7 |
| Idea Academy-Robindale/Brownsville/Cameron | 12370776 | 956/832-5300 | 7 |
| Idea Academy-Round Rock Tech/Round Rock/<br>Williamson | 12472881 | 512/822-4750 | 7 |
| Idea Academy-Rundberg/Austin/Travis | 12106800 | 512/822-4800 | 7 |
| Idea Academy-San Benito/San Benito/Cameron | 10751813 | 956/399-5252 | 7 |
| Idea Academy-San Juan/San Juan/Hidalgo | 11455098 | 956/702-5150 | 7 |
| Idea Academy-South Flores/San Antonio/<br>Bexar | 11926786 | 210/239-4150 | 7 |
| Idea Academy-Spears/Houston/Harris | 12472788 | 832/844-4200 | 7 |
| Idea Academy-Sports Park/Olmito/Cameron | 12473005 | 956/377-8000 | 7 |
| Idea Academy-Tres Lagos/McAllen/Hidalgo | 12232007 | 956/375-8550 | 7 |
| Idea Academy-Walzem/San Antonio/Bexar | 12106898 | 210/239-4600 | 7 |
| Idea Academy-Weslaco/Weslaco/Hidalgo | 11728819 | 956/351-4100 | 7 |
| Idea Academy-Weslaco Pike/Weslaco/Hidalgo | 12042163 | 956/351-4850 | 7 |
| Idea Clg Prep-Achieve/Haltom City/Tarrant | 12368266 | 817/885-4700 | 7 |
| Idea Clg Prep-Alamo/Alamo/Hidalgo | 11751933 | 956/588-4005 | 7 |
| Idea Clg Prep-Bluff Sprgs/Austin/Travis | 12173865 | 512/822-4200 | 7 |
| Idea Clg Prep-Brackenridge/San Antonio/<br>Bexar | 12232021 | 210/239-4300 | 7 |
| Idea Clg Prep-Brownsville/Brownsville/<br>Cameron | 11926798 | 956/832-5150 | 7 |
| Idea Clg Prep-Burke/San Antonio/Bexar | 12370740 | 210/239-4650 | 7 |
| Idea Clg Prep-Carver/San Antonio/Bexar | 12106824 | 210/223-8885 | 7 |
| Idea Clg Prep-Converse/Converse/Bexar | 12472855 | 210/529-3800 | 7 |
| Idea Clg Prep-Donna/Donna/Hidalgo | 11751945 | 956/464-0203 | 7 |
| Idea Clg Prep-Eastside/San Antonio/Bexar | 12106848 | 210/239-4800 | 7 |
| Idea Clg Prep-Edgecliff/Fort Worth/Tarrant | 12472910 | 817/885-4800 | 7 |
| Idea Clg Prep-Edgemere/El Paso/El Paso | 12311627 | 915/444-0200 | 7 |
| Idea Clg Prep-Edinburg/Edinburg/Hidalgo | 11751907 | 956/287-6100 | 7 |
| Idea Clg Prep-Elsa/Elsa/Hidalgo | 12311641 | 956/567-4700 | 7 |
| Idea Clg Prep-Ewing Halsell/San Antonio/<br>Bexar | 12232423 | 210/239-4850 | 7 |
| Idea Clg Prep-Frontier/Brownsville/Cameron | 11751969 | 956/541-2002 | 7 |
| Idea Clg Prep-Hardy/Houston/Harris | 12472817 | 832/844-4100 | 7 |
| Idea Clg Prep-Harlingen/Harlingen/Cameron | 12472958 | 956/564-7200 | 7 |
| Idea Clg Prep-Harvey Najim/San Antonio/<br>Bexar | 12232057 | 210/239-4900 | 7 |
| Idea Clg Prep-Hidden Meadow/San Antonio/<br>Bexar | 12472879 | 210/529-3900 | 7 |
| Idea Clg Prep-Hlth Professions/Austin/<br>Travis | 12370702 | 512/822-4350 | 7 |

| School/City/County DISTRICT/CITY/COUNTY | PID | TELEPHONE NUMBER | PAGE |
|---|---|---|---|
| Idea Clg Prep-Horizon Vista/El Paso/ El Paso | 12472831 | | 7 |
| Idea Clg Prep-Ingram Hills/San Antonio/ Bexar | 12311720 | 210/529-3700 | 7 |
| Idea Clg Prep-Judson/San Antonio/Bexar | 12173839 | 210/529-3600 | 7 |
| Idea Clg Prep-Kyle/Kyle/Hays | 12309791 | 512/822-4300 | 7 |
| Idea Clg Prep-Los Encinos/McAllen/Hidalgo | 12370764 | 956/429-4150 | 7 |
| Idea Clg Prep-Mays/San Antonio/Bexar | 12173853 | 210/529-3200 | 7 |
| Idea Clg Prep-McAllen/McAllen/Hidalgo | 11926815 | 956/429-4100 | 8 |
| Idea Clg Prep-Mesa Hills/El Paso/El Paso | 12370661 | 915/888-4050 | 8 |
| Idea Clg Prep-Monterrey Park/San Antonio/ Bexar | 12106886 | 210/239-4200 | 8 |
| Idea Clg Prep-Montopolis/Austin/Travis | 11926827 | 512/646-2800 | 8 |
| Idea Clg Prep-N Mission/McAllen/Hidalgo | 12106771 | 956/424-4300 | 8 |
| Idea Clg Prep-Owassa/Pharr/Hidalgo | 12311665 | 956/588-4300 | 8 |
| Idea Clg Prep-Palmview/Mission/Hidalgo | 12472996 | 956/272-5394 | 8 |
| Idea Clg Prep-Parmer Park/Austin/Travis | 12370726 | 512/822-4850 | 8 |
| Idea Clg Prep-Pflugerville/Pflugerville/ Travis | 12311691 | 512/822-4700 | 8 |
| Idea Clg Prep-Pharr/Pharr/Hidalgo | 11751957 | 956/283-1515 | 8 |
| Idea Clg Prep-Quest/Edinburg/Hidalgo | 11751971 | 956/287-1003 | 8 |
| Idea Clg Prep-Rio Grande City/Rio Grande Cy/ Starr | 12380563 | 956/263-4900 | 8 |
| Idea Clg Prep-Rio Vista/Socorro/El Paso | 12311718 | 915/444-0188 | 8 |
| Idea Clg Prep-Rise/Fort Worth/Tarrant | 12370685 | 817/885-4150 | 8 |
| Idea Clg Prep-Riverview/Brownsville/ Cameron | 12106795 | 956/832-5900 | 8 |
| Idea Clg Prep-Robindale/Brownsville/ Cameron | 12370788 | 956/832-5300 | 8 |
| Idea Clg Prep-Round Rock Tech/Round Rock/ Williamson | 12472893 | 512/822-4750 | 8 |
| Idea Clg Prep-Rundberg/Austin/Travis | 12106812 | 512/822-4800 | 8 |
| Idea Clg Prep-San Juan/San Juan/Hidalgo | 11748039 | 956/588-4021 | 8 |
| Idea Clg Prep-South Flores/San Antonio/ Bexar | 12106862 | 210/239-4150 | 8 |
| Idea Clg Prep-Spears/Houston/Harris | 12472790 | 832/844-4200 | 8 |
| Idea Clg Prep-Sports Park/Olmito/Cameron | 12473017 | 956/377-8000 | 8 |
| Idea Clg Prep-Toros/Edinburg/Hidalgo | 12173889 | 956/287-6350 | 8 |
| Idea Clg Prep-Tres Lagos/McAllen/Hidalgo | 12232019 | 956/252-9227 | 8 |
| Idea Clg Prep-Walzem/San Antonio/Bexar | 12106903 | 210/239-4600 | 8 |
| Idea Clg Prep-Weslaco/Weslaco/Hidalgo | 11751921 | 956/351-4100 | 8 |
| Idea Clg Prep-Weslaco Pike/Weslaco/Hidalgo | 12042199 | 956/351-4850 | 8 |
| Idea Mission/Mission/Hidalgo | 11751919 | 956/583-8315 | 8 |
| Idea San Benito/San Benito/Cameron | 11732690 | 956/583-8315 | 8 |
| Iduma Elem Sch/Killeen/Bell | 05271864 | 254/336-2590 | 31 |
| Ignacio Zaragoza Elem Sch/Dallas/Dallas | 01008732 | 972/749-8600 | 104 |
| Ignite Middle Sch/Dallas/Dallas | 12318601 | 972/794-7770 | 104 |
| Igo Elem Sch/Jarrell/Williamson | 12363412 | 512/746-4805 | 399 |
| Ilm Academy/Houston/Harris | 10986874 | 713/464-4720 | 211 |
| Imagene Glenn Elem Sch/Yantis/Wood | 05342645 | 903/383-2462 | 408 |
| Imagine Intl Academy-N Texas/McKinney/ Collin | 11827738 | 214/491-1500 | 8 |
| Iman Academy Southeast/Webster/Harris | 04927670 | 281/204-8710 | 211 |
| Iman Academy-Southwest/Houston/Harris | 04927668 | 281/498-1345 | 211 |
| Immaculate Conception Catholic/Denton/ Denton | 04420696 | 940/381-1155 | 130 |
| Immaculate Conception Sch/Grand Prairie/ Dallas | 01012446 | 972/264-8777 | 118 |
| Immaculate Conception Sch/Rio Grande Cy/ Starr | 01004384 | 956/487-2558 | 344 |
| Immanuel Christian Sch/El Paso/El Paso | 11231593 | 915/778-6160 | 143 |
| Immanuel Lutheran Sch/Giddings/Lee | 01037525 | 979/542-3319 | 266 |
| Immanuel Lutheran Sch/Mercedes/Hidalgo | 05324930 | 956/565-3208 | 229 |
| Imogene Gideon Elem Sch/Arlington/Tarrant | 04949123 | 817/299-7800 | 359 |
| Impact Center/Buda/Hays | 04359932 | 512/268-8473 | 216 |
| Impact Early College High Sch/Baytown/ Harris | 11552593 | 281/420-4802 | 193 |
| Incarnate Word Academy/Brownsville/Cameron | 01004401 | 956/546-4486 | 71 |
| Incarnate Word Academy/Corp Christi/Nueces | 01045209 | 361/883-0857 | 309 |
| Incarnate Word Academy/Houston/Harris | 01027984 | 713/227-3637 | 209 |
| Incarnate Word Elem Sch/Corp Christi/ Nueces | 01045235 | 361/883-0857 | 309 |
| Incarnate Word High Sch/San Antonio/Bexar | 00999841 | 210/829-3100 | 47 |
| Incarnate Word Middle Sch/Corp Christi/ Nueces | 01045247 | 361/883-0857 | 309 |
| Independence Elem Sch/Fort Worth/Tarrant | 10028549 | 817/744-6100 | 357 |
| Independence Elem Sch/Lewisville/Denton | 11079577 | 469/713-5212 | 127 |
| Independence High Sch/Frisco/Collin | 12032895 | 469/633-5400 | 82 |
| Indian Creek Elem Sch/Carrollton/Denton | 02857445 | 469/713-5180 | 127 |
| Indian Creek Elem Sch/San Antonio/Bexar | 00999621 | 210/623-6520 | 46 |
| Indian Ridge Middle Sch/El Paso/El Paso | 03250864 | 915/434-5400 | 142 |
| Indian Spring Middle Sch/Waco/McLennan | 11819339 | 254/757-6200 | 285 |
| Indian Springs Elem Sch/San Antonio/Comal | 11825106 | 830/885-9300 | 92 |
| Indian Springs Middle Sch/Keller/Tarrant | 04945945 | 817/744-3200 | 357 |
| Industrial Elem Sch East/Vanderbilt/ Jackson | 01033139 | 361/284-3317 | 243 |
| Industrial Elem Sch West/Inez/Jackson | 01033115 | 361/782-3325 | 243 |
| Industrial High Sch/Vanderbilt/Jackson | 01033098 | 361/284-3216 | 243 |
| **INDUSTRIAL IND SCH DIST/ VANDERBILT/JACKSON** | 01033086 | 361/284-3226 | 243 |
| Industrial Junior High Sch/Vanderbilt/ Jackson | 01033103 | 361/284-3226 | 243 |
| Industrial Trades Center/Texas City/ Galveston | 12232409 | 409/916-0710 | 166 |
| Inez Carroll Academy/Houston/Harris | 01022843 | 281/878-0340 | 185 |
| Inez Foster Academy/San Antonio/Bexar | 00998873 | 210/438-6855 | 43 |
| Infinity Early College HS/Porter/ Montgomery | 11927900 | 281/577-2890 | 296 |
| Ingleside High Sch/Ingleside/San Patricio | 01172589 | 361/776-2712 | 334 |
| **INGLESIDE IND SCH DIST/INGLESIDE/ SAN PATRICIO** | 01049592 | 361/776-7631 | 333 |
| Ingleside Primary Sch/Ingleside/ San Patricio | 01172577 | 361/776-3060 | 334 |
| Ingram Elem Sch/Ingram/Kerr | 01036064 | 830/367-5751 | 259 |
| **INGRAM IND SCH DIST/INGRAM/KERR** | 01036052 | 830/367-5517 | 259 |
| Ingram Middle Sch/Ingram/Kerr | 12160313 | 830/367-4012 | 259 |
| Ingram Tom Moore High Sch/Ingram/Kerr | 02110857 | 830/367-4111 | 259 |
| Innovation Design Entrep Acad/Dallas/ Dallas | 12109474 | 972/794-6800 | 104 |
| Inspire Academy/Colleyville/Tarrant | 12322884 | 817/966-4821 | 361 |
| Inspired for Excellence Acad W/Houston/ Harris | 11555404 | 832/834-5295 | 199 |
| Inspired Vision Elem Sch/Dallas/Dallas | 04931762 | 214/391-7964 | 8 |
| Inspired Vision Secondary Sch/Dallas/ Dallas | 05000304 | 972/285-5758 | 8 |
| Instruction & Guidance Center/McAllen/ Hidalgo | 04014699 | 956/971-4393 | 224 |
| Int'l Ldrship TX-Lancaster/Lancaster/ Dallas | 12233726 | 469/862-4237 | 112 |
| Int'l Ldrshp TX-Arlington ES/Arlington/ Dallas | 11917955 | 817/496-0400 | 112 |
| Int'l Ldrshp TX-Arlngtn GR PR/Grand Prairie/ Dallas | 12163779 | 682/808-5960 | 112 |
| Int'l Ldrshp TX-College Sta/College Sta/ Dallas | 12313637 | 979/704-6027 | 112 |
| Int'l Ldrshp TX-East Ft Worth/Fort Worth/ Dallas | 12233752 | 817/395-1766 | 112 |
| Int'l Ldrshp TX-Garland/Garland/Dallas | 11928502 | 972/414-8000 | 112 |
| Int'l Ldrshp TX-Garland HS/Garland/Dallas | 11931937 | 972/414-3414 | 112 |
| Int'l Ldrshp TX-Grand Prairie/Grand Prairie/ Dallas | 12233738 | 469/348-7960 | 113 |
| Int'l Ldrshp TX-Katy/Katy/Dallas | 12233788 | 281/394-9417 | 113 |
| Int'l Ldrshp TX-Katy Westpark/Richmond/ Dallas | 12233805 | 832/222-9470 | 113 |
| Int'l Ldrshp TX-Keller/Fort Worth/Dallas | 12043155 | 817/665-0646 | 113 |
| Int'l Ldrshp TX-Keller Saginaw/Fort Worth/ Dallas | 12233776 | 682/250-3701 | 113 |
| Int'l Ldrshp TX-Lanc-DeSoto HS/Desoto/ Dallas | 12313601 | 469/786-2850 | 113 |
| Int'l Ldrshp TX-N Richlnd Hill/N Richlnd Hls/ Dallas | 12233764 | 817/576-9031 | 113 |
| Int'l Ldrshp TX-Orem/Houston/Dallas | 12313625 | 713/987-9435 | 113 |
| Int'l Ldrshp TX-Saginaw/Fort Worth/Dallas | 12233697 | 682/250-3600 | 113 |
| Int'l Ldrshp TX-Westpark/Houston/Dallas | 12233790 | 346/203-4126 | 113 |
| Int'l Ldrshp TX-Windmill Lakes/Houston/ Dallas | 12233817 | 832/667-0453 | 113 |
| Int'l Ldrshp TX-Wml-Orem HS/Houston/Dallas | 12313613 | 832/649-6817 | 113 |
| **INT'L LEADERSHIP OF TEXAS DIST/ RICHARDSON/DALLAS** | 12261400 | 972/479-9078 | 112 |
| International High Sch/Austin/Travis | 10007258 | 512/414-6817 | 371 |
| International Newcomer Academy/Fort Worth/ Tarrant | 04143214 | 817/815-5600 | 353 |
| International Sch of Americas/San Antonio/ Bexar | 04284260 | 210/356-0900 | 38 |
| Iola Elem Sch/Iola/Grimes | 03410624 | 936/394-2361 | 177 |
| **IOLA IND SCH DIST/IOLA/GRIMES** | 01021370 | 936/394-2361 | 177 |
| Iola Junior Senior High Sch/Iola/Grimes | 01021382 | 936/394-2361 | 177 |
| **IOWA PARK CONSOLIDATED IND SD/ IOWA PARK/WICHITA** | 01060065 | 940/592-4193 | 395 |
| Iowa Park High Sch/Iowa Park/Wichita | 01060091 | 940/592-2144 | 395 |
| Ira C Ogden Academy/San Antonio/Bexar | 00998586 | 210/738-9815 | 43 |
| Ira Cross Jr Elem Sch/Killeen/Bell | 05271876 | 254/336-2550 | 31 |
| **IRA IND SCH DIST/IRA/SCURRY** | 01050072 | 325/573-2628 | 336 |
| Ira Sch/Ira/Scurry | 01050096 | 325/573-2628 | 336 |

| School/City/County DISTRICT/CITY/COUNTY | PID | TELEPHONE NUMBER | PAGE |
|---|---|---|---|
| James A Arthur Interm Sch/Kennedale/Tarrant | 01054042 | 817/563-8300 | 358 |
| James B Havard Elem Sch/Houston/Harris | 04808866 | 832/386-3710 | 192 |
| James Bilhartz Jr Elem Sch/Dallas/Dallas | 05275092 | 972/708-6600 | 109 |
| James Bonham Elem Sch/McAllen/Hidalgo | 01029932 | 956/971-4440 | 224 |
| James Bonham Middle Sch/Amarillo/Potter | 01047180 | 806/326-3100 | 320 |
| James Bowie 6th Grade Campus/Amarillo/Potter | 12033722 | 806/326-3270 | 321 |
| James Bowie Elem Sch/Baytown/Harris | 01023677 | 281/420-4605 | 193 |
| James Bowie Elem Sch/Dallas/Dallas | 01009085 | 972/925-6600 | 104 |
| James Bowie Elem Sch/Ennis/Ellis | 03007942 | 972/872-7234 | 144 |
| James Bowie Elem Sch/Simms/Bowie | 01001198 | 903/543-2245 | 53 |
| James Bowie High Sch/Arlington/Tarrant | 03397876 | 682/867-4400 | 347 |
| James Bowie High Sch/Austin/Travis | 03249267 | 512/414-5247 | 371 |
| James Bowie High Sch/Simms/Bowie | 01001203 | 903/543-2275 | 53 |
| James Bowie Middle Sch/Amarillo/Potter | 01047192 | 806/326-3200 | 321 |
| James Bowie Middle Sch/Richmond/Fort Bend | 11715410 | 281/327-6200 | 154 |
| James Bowie Middle Sch/Simms/Bowie | 11128908 | 903/543-2275 | 53 |
| James Butler Bonham Elem Sch/Houston/Harris | 01024346 | 713/778-3480 | 194 |
| James Carson Elem Sch/San Antonio/Bexar | 04809042 | 210/397-1100 | 40 |
| James D Gossett Elem Sch/Rankin/Upton | 01057666 | 432/693-2455 | 380 |
| James D Kerr Elem Sch/Allen/Collin | 04913136 | 214/495-6765 | 80 |
| James Deanda Elem Sch/Houston/Harris | 11735135 | 713/556-9550 | 198 |
| James E Poole Elem Sch/Big Sandy/Upshur | 01057460 | 903/725-5496 | 379 |
| James E Randolph Elem Sch/Fulshear/Harris | 12033801 | 281/234-3800 | 156 |
| James E Rudder High Sch/Bryan/Brazos | 11079280 | 979/209-7900 | 58 |
| James E Taylor High Sch/Katy/Harris | 02045408 | 281/237-3100 | 156 |
| James F Bay Elem Sch/Seabrook/Galveston | 01018880 | 281/284-4600 | 163 |
| James F Cooper Acad at Navarro/San Antonio/Bexar | 04455500 | 210/438-6810 | 44 |
| James F DeLaney Elem Sch/Kennedale/Tarrant | 03004354 | 817/563-8400 | 358 |
| James Garland Walsh Middle Sch/Round Rock/Williamson | 11130834 | 512/704-0800 | 402 |
| James H Ross Elem Sch/League City/Galveston | 01018921 | 281/284-4500 | 163 |
| James L Coble Middle Sch/Arlington/Tarrant | 10028240 | 682/314-4900 | 359 |
| James L Collins Catholic Sch/Corsicana/Navarro | 01012458 | 903/872-1751 | 303 |
| James L Wright Elem Sch/Perryton/Ochiltree | 01045493 | 806/435-2371 | 310 |
| James Madison High Sch/Dallas/Dallas | 01009114 | 972/925-2800 | 104 |
| James Martin High Sch/Arlington/Tarrant | 02177415 | 682/867-8600 | 347 |
| James Masters Elem Sch/Converse/Bexar | 11452280 | 210/945-1150 | 36 |
| James Mitchell Elem Sch/Georgetown/Williamson | 11079644 | 512/943-1820 | 398 |
| James Neill Elem Sch/Richmond/Fort Bend | 12232136 | 281/327-3760 | 154 |
| James Nikki Rowe High Sch/McAllen/Hidalgo | 03323564 | 956/632-5100 | 224 |
| James P Butler Elem Sch/El Paso/El Paso | 11920536 | 915/937-8900 | 140 |
| James Pace Early Clg HS/Brownsville/Cameron | 01418228 | 956/548-7700 | 67 |
| James Patterson Elem Sch/Richmond/Fort Bend | 12232112 | 281/327-4260 | 154 |
| James R Brooks Middle Sch/Midland/Midland | 04477651 | 432/685-7837 | 288 |
| James R Newman Elem Sch/Frisco/Collin | 12032883 | 469/633-3975 | 83 |
| James R Reynolds Elem Sch/Houston/Harris | 01025352 | 713/731-5590 | 198 |
| James Reese Career Tech Center/Sugar Land/Fort Bend | 12370178 | 281/327-7300 | 154 |
| James Russell Lowell Mid Sch/San Antonio/Bexar | 00999205 | 210/228-1225 | 44 |
| James S Hogg Elem Sch/Dallas/Dallas | 01009097 | 972/502-8600 | 104 |
| James S Hogg Middle Sch/Tyler/Smith | 01050852 | 903/262-1500 | 340 |
| James Steele Accelerated HS/Roanoke/Denton | 11554462 | 817/698-5800 | 129 |
| James Street Elem Sch/Coldspring/San Jacinto | 01049437 | 936/653-1187 | 332 |
| James Tippit Middle Sch/Georgetown/Williamson | 01060883 | 512/943-5040 | 398 |
| James W Fannin Elem Sch/Corp Christi/Nueces | 01044372 | 361/878-2260 | 306 |
| James W Fannin Middle Sch/Amarillo/Potter | 01047257 | 806/326-3500 | 321 |
| James Williams Elem Sch/Katy/Harris | 04917493 | 281/237-7200 | 156 |
| Jan Aragon Middle Sch/Houston/Harris | 04943753 | 281/856-5100 | 190 |
| Jane A Hambric Sch/El Paso/El Paso | 04916126 | 915/937-4600 | 140 |
| Jane Long Elem Sch/Harlingen/Cameron | 02856037 | 956/427-3140 | 68 |
| Jane Long Elem Sch/Richmond/Fort Bend | 01018282 | 832/223-1900 | 158 |
| Jane Wessendorff Middle Sch/Rosenberg/Fort Bend | 01018270 | 832/223-3300 | 158 |
| Janet Brockett Elem Sch/Arlington/Tarrant | 10006888 | 817/299-6620 | 359 |
| Janice Stanly Scott Elem Sch/McKinney/Collin | 12027993 | 469/633-4000 | 83 |
| Janie Stark Elem School/Farmers BRNCH/Dallas | 01008201 | 972/968-3300 | 101 |
| Janowski Elem Sch/Houston/Harris | 01025962 | 713/696-2844 | 196 |
| Jarrell Elom Sch/Jarrell/Williamson | 12036944 | 512/746-2170 | 399 |
| Jarrell High Sch/Jarrell/Williamson | 12036920 | 512/746-2188 | 399 |
| **JARRELL IND SCH DIST/JARRELL/ WILLIAMSON** | 01060974 | 512/746-2124 | 399 |
| Jarrell Intermediate Sch/Jarrell/Williamson | 12036956 | 512/746-4805 | 399 |
| Jarrell Middle Sch/Jarrell/Williamson | 12036932 | 512/746-4180 | 399 |
| Jasper Classical Academy/Jasper/Jasper | 11456212 | 409/489-9222 | 8 |
| Jasper High Sch/Jasper/Jasper | 01523720 | 409/384-3242 | 244 |
| Jasper High Sch/Plano/Collin | 04453887 | 469/752-7400 | 86 |
| **JASPER IND SCH DIST/JASPER/ JASPER** | 01033244 | 409/384-2401 | 243 |
| Jasper Junior High Sch/Jasper/Jasper | 01033268 | 409/384-3585 | 244 |
| Jay Thompson Elem Sch/Mesquite/Dallas | 04364810 | 972/882-7190 | 115 |
| Jayne Ann Miller Elem Sch/Lubbock/Lubbock | 01038696 | 806/219-8100 | 273 |
| **JAYTON-GIRARD IND SCH DIST/ JAYTON/KENT** | 01035931 | 806/237-2991 | 258 |
| Jayton-Girard Sch/Jayton/Kent | 01035943 | 806/237-2991 | 258 |
| Jean & Betty Schmalz Elem Sch/Houston/Harris | 04948741 | 281/237-4500 | 156 |
| Jean C Few Primary Sch/Jasper/Jasper | 04867989 | 409/489-9808 | 244 |
| Jean E Stewart Elem Sch/Montgomery/Montgomery | 12028600 | 936/709-4200 | 295 |
| Jean Hines-Caldwell Elem Sch/Houston/Harris | 10003903 | 713/726-3700 | 198 |
| Jean Massieu Acad for the Deaf/Arlington/Tarrant | 04892441 | 817/460-0396 | 8 |
| Jean McClung Middle Sch/Fort Worth/Tarrant | 11711919 | 817/815-5300 | 353 |
| Jeanette Hayes Elem Sch/Katy/Harris | 04452247 | 281/237-3200 | 156 |
| Jefferson Achievement Ctr/Abilene/Taylor | 01172735 | 325/794-4150 | 363 |
| Jefferson Avenue Elem Sch/Seguin/Guadalupe | 01021679 | 830/401-8727 | 179 |
| Jefferson Christian Academy/Jefferson/Marion | 01480805 | 903/665-3973 | 277 |
| Jefferson Co Youth Academy/Beaumont/Jefferson | 04913382 | 409/720-4078 | 244 |
| Jefferson Elem Sch/Edinburg/Hidalgo | 01029803 | 956/289-2385 | 222 |
| Jefferson Elem Sch/Harlingen/Cameron | 01003861 | 956/427-3120 | 68 |
| Jefferson Elem Sch/Houston/Harris | 01025986 | 713/696-2778 | 197 |
| Jefferson Elem Sch/Jefferson/Marion | 01040699 | 903/665-2461 | 277 |
| Jefferson Elem Sch/Sherman/Grayson | 01020625 | 903/891-6610 | 172 |
| Jefferson Elem Sch/Temple/Bell | 00996772 | 254/215-5500 | 32 |
| Jefferson Elem Sch/Wichita Falls/Wichita | 01173117 | 940/235-1168 | 395 |
| Jefferson High Sch/El Paso/El Paso | 01015694 | 915/236-7400 | 139 |
| Jefferson High Sch/Jefferson/Marion | 01040704 | 903/665-2461 | 277 |
| **JEFFERSON IND SCH DIST/JEFFERSON/ MARION** | 01040687 | 903/665-2461 | 277 |
| Jefferson Junior High Sch/Jefferson/Marion | 01040728 | 903/665-2461 | 277 |
| Jefferson Primary Sch/Jefferson/Marion | 10015023 | 903/665-2461 | 277 |
| Jennie Reid Elem Sch/La Porte/Harris | 01026382 | 281/604-4500 | 203 |
| Jensen Elem Sch/Pasadena/Harris | 01026758 | 713/740-0608 | 204 |
| Jerry Junkins Elem Sch/Carrollton/Dallas | 10019885 | 972/502-2400 | 105 |
| Jerry Knight STEM Academy/Mansfield/Tarrant | 12469779 | 817/299-5090 | 359 |
| Jersey Village High Sch/Jersey Vlg/Harris | 01023275 | 713/896-3400 | 190 |
| Jess Harben Elem Sch/Richardson/Dallas | 01399660 | 469/593-8800 | 116 |
| Jesse McGowen Elem Sch/McKinney/Collin | 10909187 | 469/302-7500 | 85 |
| Jessie Jensen Elem Sch/Mission/Hidalgo | 01030539 | 956/580-5252 | 227 |
| Jessup Elem Sch/Houston/Harris | 01026760 | 713/740-0616 | 204 |
| Jesuit College Prep Sch/Dallas/Dallas | 01012460 | 972/387-8700 | 118 |
| Jesus Chapel Sch/El Paso/El Paso | 04020985 | 915/593-1153 | 143 |
| Jewel Askew Elem Sch/Houston/Harris | 01826273 | 281/368-2100 | 199 |
| Jewel C Wietzel Center/San Antonio/Bexar | 01541289 | 210/989-3280 | 36 |
| Jewel S Houston Academy/Houston/Harris | 05274127 | 281/878-7745 | 186 |
| Jhw Inspire Acad-Afton Oaks/San Antonio/Bexar | 04814011 | 210/638-5500 | 34 |
| Jhw Inspire Acad-Legacy Ranch/Gonzales/Bexar | 12174120 | 210/638-5300 | 34 |
| Jhw Inspirc Acad-Meridell/Liberty Hill/Bexar | 12035110 | 512/528-2100 | 34 |
| Jhw Inspire Acad-Rockdale/Rockdale/Bexar | 11701378 | 210/638-5700 | 34 |
| Jhw Inspire Acad-Williams Hse/Lometa/Bexar | 11832331 | 210/638-5800 | 34 |
| Jhw Inspire Academy-Bell Co/Killeen/Bexar | 12233219 | 254/618-4280 | 34 |
| Jhw Inspire Academy-Hays Co/San Marcos/Bexar | 05243312 | 210/638-5400 | 34 |
| Jill Stone-Vickery Meadow ES/Dallas/Dallas | 04810405 | 972/502-7900 | 105 |
| Jim Barnes Middle Sch/Seguin/Guadalupe | 05342023 | 830/401-8756 | 179 |
| Jim G Martin Elem Sch/San Antonio/Bexar | 11552141 | 210/398-1400 | 40 |
| **JIM HOGG CO IND SCH DIST/ HEBBRONVILLE/JIM HOGG** | 01034470 | 361/527-3203 | 247 |
| **JIM NED CONS IND SCH DIST/ TUSCOLA/TAYLOR** | 01054896 | 325/554-7500 | 363 |
| Jim Ned High Sch/Tuscola/Taylor | 01054913 | 325/554-7755 | 363 |
| Jim Ned Middle Sch/Tuscola/Taylor | 04745032 | 325/554-7870 | 363 |

| School/City/County<br>DISTRICT/CITY/COUNTY | PID | TELEPHONE<br>NUMBER | PAGE |
|---|---|---|---|
| Jimmie Tyler Brashear Elem Sch/Dallas/<br>Dallas | 10023123 | 972/502-2600 | 105 |
| Jimmy Carter Early Clg HS/La Joya/Hidalgo | 11719260 | 956/323-2200 | 223 |
| Jimmy Elrod Elem Sch/San Antonio/Bexar | 03050511 | 210/397-1800 | 40 |
| Jjaep Sch/Houston/Harris | 11555480 | 713/394-4000 | 199 |
| Jo Ann Ford Elem Sch/Georgetown/Williamson | 05343742 | 512/943-5180 | 398 |
| Jo Ella Exley Elem Sch/Katy/Harris | 05344306 | 281/237-8400 | 156 |
| Jo Kelly Sch/Fort Worth/Tarrant | 01809897 | 817/815-5900 | 353 |
| Jo Nelson Middle Sch/Santa Rosa/Cameron | 03345835 | 956/636-9850 | 71 |
| Joan Link Elm Sch/Houston/Harris | 02178299 | 281/891-8390 | 207 |
| Joan Postma Elem Sch/Cypress/Harris | 10747989 | 281/345-3660 | 190 |
| Joan Y Ervin Elem Sch/Lubbock/Lubbock | 01038725 | 806/219-8200 | 273 |
| Joaquin Elem Sch/Joaquin/Shelby | 01050369 | 936/269-3128 | 337 |
| Joaquin High Sch/Joaquin/Shelby | 01050383 | 936/269-3128 | 337 |
| **JOAQUIN IND SCH DIST/JOAQUIN/**<br>**SHELBY** | 01050357 | 936/269-3128 | 337 |
| Joaquin Junior High Sch/Joaquin/Shelby | 05035086 | 936/269-3128 | 337 |
| Joe Barnhart Magnet Academy/Beeville/Bee | 12225626 | 361/358-6262 | 28 |
| Joe Dale Sparks Campus/Denton/Denton | 11452929 | 940/349-2468 | 125 |
| Joe E Moreno Elem Sch/Houston/Harris | 10003886 | 281/405-2150 | 196 |
| Joe Hubenak Elem Sch/Richmond/Fort Bend | 11447223 | 832/223-2900 | 158 |
| Joe K Bryant Elem Sch/Anna/Collin | 01006033 | 972/924-1300 | 81 |
| Joe Lawrence Elem Sch/Mesquite/Dallas | 01011533 | 972/882-7000 | 115 |
| Joe Lee Johnson Elem Sch/Austin/Williamson | 12167476 | 512/704-1400 | 402 |
| Joe M Adams Junior High Sch/Fulshear/<br>Harris | 12367406 | 281/234-3400 | 156 |
| Joe M Pirtle Flem Sch/Temple/Bell | 01876931 | 254/215-3400 | 30 |
| Joe Tison Middle Sch/Weatherford/Parker | 04748761 | 817/598-2960 | 317 |
| Joe Wright Elem Sch/Jacksonville/Cherokee | 01005297 | 903/586-5286 | 76 |
| John & Nelda Partin Elem Sch/Van Alstyne/<br>Grayson | 01020754 | 903/482-8805 | 173 |
| John & Olive Hinojosa Elem Sch/Rio Grande Cy/<br>Starr | 03323320 | 956/487-3710 | 343 |
| John A Baker Elem Sch/McKinney/Collin | 10915198 | 469/219-2120 | 88 |
| John A Sippel Elem Sch/Schertz/Guadalupe | 11130511 | 210/619-4600 | 178 |
| John B Connally High Sch/Austin/Travis | 04454221 | 512/594-0800 | 374 |
| John B Connally Middle Sch/San Antonio/<br>Bexar | 04809054 | 210/397-1000 | 40 |
| John C French Elem Sch/Cuero/De Witt | 01013725 | 361/275-1900 | 122 |
| John C Holmgreen Center/San Antonio/Bexar | 01539963 | 210/397-6100 | 40 |
| John C Webb Elem Sch/Navasota/Grimes | 02227852 | 936/825-1120 | 177 |
| John Cooper Sch/The Woodlands/Montgomery | 03161354 | 281/367-0900 | 298 |
| John D Spicer Elem Sch/Haltom City/Tarrant | 03393014 | 817/547-3300 | 349 |
| John Doedyns Elem Sch/San Juan/Hidalgo | 01030400 | 956/354-2740 | 226 |
| John Drugan Elem Sch/El Paso/El Paso | 10005547 | 915/937-6800 | 140 |
| John F Kennedy Elem Sch/Edinburg/Hidalgo | 04452807 | 956/289-2390 | 222 |
| John F Kennedy Elem Sch/Elsa/Hidalgo | 01029669 | 956/262-6027 | 221 |
| John F Kennedy High Sch/San Antonio/Bexar | 00997269 | 210/444-8040 | 35 |
| John F Kennedy Sch/Mercedes/Hidalgo | 01030163 | 956/514-2300 | 225 |
| John F Peeler Elem Sch/Dallas/Dallas | 01009140 | 972/502-8300 | 105 |
| John F Ward Elem Sch/Houston/Galveston | 03325524 | 281/284-5400 | 163 |
| John Glenn Elem Sch/San Antonio/Bexar | 00998146 | 210/397-2250 | 40 |
| John H Guyer High Sch/Denton/Denton | 10001826 | 940/369-1000 | 125 |
| John H Reagan Elem Sch/Dallas/Dallas | 01009190 | 972/502-8200 | 105 |
| John H Shary Elem Sch/Mission/Hidalgo | 04359918 | 956/580-5282 | 227 |
| John Haley Elem Sch/Irving/Dallas | 01011193 | 972/600-6600 | 113 |
| John Hanby Elem Sch/Mesquite/Dallas | 01011545 | 972/882-5040 | 115 |
| John Ireland Elem Sch/Dallas/Dallas | 01009164 | 972/749-4900 | 105 |
| John J Ciavarra Elem Sch/Devine/Medina | 01041203 | 830/851-0395 | 286 |
| John J Pershing Elem Sch/Dallas/Dallas | 01009176 | 972/794-8600 | 105 |
| John Jay High Sch/San Antonio/Bexar | 00998158 | 210/397-2700 | 40 |
| John Jay Sci & Engineer Acad/San Antonio/<br>Bexar | 04809016 | 210/397-2773 | 40 |
| John L Patton Academic Center/Dallas/<br>Dallas | 11551393 | 214/932-5160 | 105 |
| John M Stuart Career Tech HS/Baytown/<br>Harris | 01023691 | 281/420-4550 | 193 |
| John M Tidwell Middle Sch/Roanoke/Denton | 11554474 | 817/698-5900 | 129 |
| John Marshall High Sch/San Antonio/Bexar | 00998160 | 210/397-7100 | 40 |
| John McKeever Elem Sch/Alamo/Hidalgo | 01030357 | 956/354-2860 | 226 |
| John Neely Bryan Elem Sch/Dallas/Dallas | 01008562 | 972/502-8500 | 105 |
| John Paul II High Sch/Plano/Collin | 10015360 | 972/867-0005 | 89 |
| John Paul Stevens High Sch/San Antonio/<br>Bexar | 10009490 | 210/397-6450 | 40 |
| John Q Adams Elem Sch/Dallas/Dallas | 01008366 | 972/794-1200 | 105 |
| John R Good Elem Sch/Irving/Dallas | 01011210 | 972/600-3300 | 114 |
| John S Armstrong Elem Sch/Dallas/Dallas | 01011064 | 214/780-3100 | 112 |
| John S Bradfield Elem Sch/Dallas/Dallas | 01011076 | 214/780-3200 | 112 |
| John T White Elem Sch/Fort Worth/Tarrant | 11711907 | 817/814-7900 | 353 |
| John Tower Elem Sch/Wichita Falls/Wichita | 01059975 | 940/855-3221 | 394 |
| John W Armstrong Elem Sch/Sachse/Dallas | 05096808 | 972/414-7480 | 110 |
| John W Carpenter Elem Sch/Dallas/Dallas | 01009205 | 972/794-6000 | 105 |

| School/City/County<br>DISTRICT/CITY/COUNTY | PID | TELEPHONE<br>NUMBER | PAGE |
|---|---|---|---|
| John W Runyon Elem Sch/Dallas/Dallas | 01009736 | 972/749-6100 | 105 |
| John Winship Elem Sch/Spring/Harris | 01027491 | 281/891-8210 | 207 |
| Johnny Economedes High Sch/Edinburg/<br>Hidalgo | 04922905 | 956/289-2450 | 222 |
| Johns Elem Sch/Arlington/Tarrant | 01051765 | 682/867-2500 | 347 |
| **JOHNSON CITY IND SCH DIST/**<br>**JOHNSON CITY/BLANCO** | 01000510 | 830/868-7410 | 49 |
| Johnson Daep/Grand Prairie/Dallas | 03007253 | 972/262-7244 | 111 |
| Johnson Elem Sch/Bryan/Brazos | 01002099 | 979/209-1460 | 58 |
| Johnson Elem Sch/El Paso/El Paso | 01016002 | 915/236-3925 | 138 |
| Johnson Elem Sch/Forney/Kaufman | 01035577 | 469/762-4325 | 255 |
| Johnson Elem Sch/Prosper/Collin | 12469717 | 469/219-2340 | 88 |
| Johnson Ferguson Academy/Brenham/<br>Washington | 10016027 | 979/836-4156 | 389 |
| Johnson High Sch/Buda/Hays | 12362133 | 512/268-8512 | 216 |
| Johnson High Sch/San Antonio/Bexar | 11128518 | 210/356-0400 | 38 |
| Johnson Ranch Elem Sch/Bulverde/Comal | 11450945 | 830/885-8600 | 92 |
| Johnston Elem Sch/Abilene/Taylor | 01172797 | 325/671-4845 | 363 |
| Johnston Elem Sch/Irving/Dallas | 01011117 | 972/600-7700 | 114 |
| Johnston-McQueen Elem Sch/Longview/Gregg | 01021095 | 903/803-5300 | 175 |
| Jollyville Elem Sch/Austin/Williamson | 04017811 | 512/428-2200 | 402 |
| Jones Aca of Fine Arts & Dual/Arlington/<br>Tarrant | 01051894 | 682/867-3580 | 347 |
| Jones Early Literacy Center/Texarkana/<br>Bowie | 01001239 | 903/793-4871 | 53 |
| Jones EC-PK-K Sch/Humble/Harris | 11074694 | 281/446-1576 | 186 |
| Jones Elem Sch/Brackettville/Kinney | 01036246 | 830/563-2492 | 260 |
| Jones Elem Sch/Bryan/Brazos | 03400605 | 979/209-3900 | 58 |
| Jones Elem Sch/Humble/Harris | 11074682 | 281/446-6168 | 185 |
| Jones Elem Sch/Midland/Midland | 01041576 | 432/240-7200 | 289 |
| Jones Elem Sch/Tyler/Smith | 01050890 | 903/262-2360 | 340 |
| Jones Futures Academy/Houston/Harris | 12037089 | 713/733-1111 | 198 |
| Jones Magnet Middle Sch/San Antonio/Bexar | 12471370 | 210/397-2230 | 40 |
| Jones Middle Sch/Humble/Harris | 12309662 | 281/985-3720 | 186 |
| **JONESBORO IND SCH DIST/JONESBORO/**<br>**CORYELL** | 01007714 | 254/463-2111 | 97 |
| Jonesboro Sch/Jonesboro/Coryell | 01007726 | 254/463-2111 | 97 |
| Jordan Elem Sch/Austin/Travis | 04014936 | 512/414-2578 | 370 |
| Jordan High Sch/Fulshear/Harris | 12468220 | 281/234-9000 | 156 |
| Jorge R Gutierrez ECC/Edcouch/Hidalgo | 04931956 | 956/262-0040 | 221 |
| Jose A Valdez High Sch/Laredo/Webb | 11713072 | 956/273-8000 | 389 |
| Jose Alderete Middle Sch/Canutillo/El Paso | 10022258 | 915/877-6600 | 136 |
| Jose Antonio Navarro Elem Sch/Corsicana/<br>Navarro | 01043483 | 903/874-1011 | 302 |
| Jose Borrego Middle Sch/Monte Alto/Hidalgo | 10901379 | 956/262-1374 | 226 |
| Jose Damian Elem Sch/El Paso/El Paso | 04011128 | 915/877-6800 | 136 |
| Jose De Escandon Elem Sch/McAllen/Hidalgo | 02043333 | 956/971-4511 | 224 |
| Jose De Escandon Elem Sch/Mission/Hidalgo | 04039156 | 956/323-2410 | 223 |
| Jose M Lopez Middle Sch/San Antonio/Bexar | 10911051 | 210/356-5000 | 38 |
| Jose May Elem Sch/Dallas/Dallas | 12169125 | 972/749-4800 | 105 |
| Josefa L Sambrano Elem Sch/San Elizario/<br>El Paso | 04278584 | 915/872-3950 | 140 |
| Joseph C Martin Elem Sch/Laredo/Webb | 01059236 | 956/273-4100 | 389 |
| Joseph Gilbert Elem Sch/Austin/Travis | 11732729 | 512/386-3800 | 372 |
| Joseph Hopkins Elem Sch/San Antonio/Bexar | 00997623 | 210/661-1120 | 36 |
| Joseph J Rhoads Learning Ctr/Dallas/Dallas | 01009231 | 972/749-1000 | 105 |
| Josephine Castaneda Elem Sch/Brownsville/<br>Cameron | 01003483 | 956/548-8800 | 67 |
| Joshua 9th Grade Campus/Joshua/Johnson | 11718565 | 817/202-2500 | 251 |
| Joshua Christian Academy/Joshua/Johnson | 11225984 | 817/295-7377 | 252 |
| Joshua High Sch/Joshua/Johnson | 01035046 | 817/202-2500 | 251 |
| **JOSHUA IND SCH DIST/JOSHUA/**<br>**JOHNSON** | 01035022 | 817/426-7500 | 251 |
| Joshua SDA Multi Grade Sch/Joshua/Johnson | 03405758 | 817/556-2109 | 252 |
| Joslin Elem Sch/Austin/Travis | 01056301 | 512/414-2094 | 370 |
| Jourdanton Elem Sch/Jourdanton/Atascosa | 00995388 | 830/769-2121 | 23 |
| Jourdanton High Sch/Jourdanton/Atascosa | 00995390 | 830/769-2350 | 23 |
| **JOURDANTON IND SCH DIST/**<br>**JOURDANTON/ATASCOSA** | 00995376 | 830/769-3548 | 23 |
| Jourdanton Junior High Sch/Jourdanton/<br>Atascosa | 02111899 | 830/769-2234 | 23 |
| Jowell Elem Sch/Katy/Harris | 02896661 | 281/463-5966 | 190 |
| Joy James Elem Sch/Fort Worth/Tarrant | 01052343 | 817/252-2500 | 350 |
| Joy Sch/Houston/Harris | 05026578 | 713/523-0660 | 211 |
| Jstem Academy/Converse/Bexar | 12177574 | 210/945-1159 | 36 |
| Juan D Salinas Middle Sch/Mission/Hidalgo | 11449465 | 956/323-2850 | 223 |
| Juan Diego Academy/Mission/Hidalgo | 11715240 | 956/583-2752 | 229 |
| Juan N Seguin Elem Sch/Houston/Harris | 05099305 | 713/845-5600 | 198 |
| Juan N Seguin Elem Sch/Mission/Hidalgo | 05346809 | 956/323-2710 | 223 |
| Juan Seguin Elem Sch/Grand Prairie/Dallas | 05342619 | 972/522-7100 | 111 |
| Juan Seguin Elem Sch/McAllen/Hidalgo | 01172462 | 956/971-4565 | 224 |
| Juan Seguin Elem Sch/Richmond/Fort Bend | 11448409 | 281/634-9850 | 154 |

| School/City/County DISTRICT/CITY/COUNTY | PID | TELEPHONE NUMBER | PAGE |
|---|---|---|---|
| Juan Seguin Elem Sch/Weatherford/Parker | 01046588 | 817/598-2814 | 317 |
| Juan Seguin High Sch/Arlington/Tarrant | 05096561 | 682/867-6700 | 347 |
| Juan W Caceres Elem Sch/Donna/Hidalgo | 03410222 | 956/464-1995 | 220 |
| Juarez-Lincoln Elem Sch/Laredo/Webb | 04038449 | 956/473-3000 | 390 |
| Juarez-Lincoln High Sch/Mission/Hidalgo | 04031726 | 956/323-2890 | 223 |
| Jubilee Academic Center/San Antonio/Bexar | 05010672 | 210/333-6227 | 8 |
| Jubilee Brownsville/Brownsville/Cameron | 12044616 | 956/509-2690 | 8 |
| Jubilee Harlingen/Harlingen/Cameron | 12044630 | 956/708-2030 | 8 |
| Jubilee Highland Hills/San Antonio/Bexar | 12044599 | 210/634-7590 | 8 |
| Jubilee Highland Park/San Antonio/Bexar | 11834523 | 210/801-8030 | 8 |
| Jubilee Kingsville/Kingsville/Kleberg | 11929221 | 361/516-0840 | 9 |
| Jubilee Lake View Univ Prep/San Antonio/ Bexar | 12238532 | 210/963-3900 | 9 |
| Jubilee Leadership Academy/Brownsville/ Cameron | 12260834 | 956/641-4250 | 9 |
| Jubilee Livingway/Brownsville/Cameron | 12044642 | 956/708-2020 | 9 |
| Jubilee San Antonio/San Antonio/Bexar | 12044604 | 210/278-3880 | 9 |
| Jubilee Sendero/San Antonio/Bexar | 12375403 | 210/380-9538 | 9 |
| Jubilee Wells Branch/Austin/Travis | 11932046 | 512/872-8440 | 9 |
| Jubilee Westwood/San Antonio/Bexar | 12375398 | 210/963-3930 | 9 |
| Jubilee-Wells Academies/Austin/Travis | 12108834 | 512/872-8440 | 9 |
| Judge Andy Mireles Elem Sch/San Antonio/ Bexar | 11713905 | 210/398-1500 | 41 |
| Judge Barefoot Sanders Law Mag/Dallas/ Dallas | 01553048 | 972/925-5950 | 105 |
| Judge Frank Berry Middle Sch/Mesquite/ Dallas | 04750116 | 972/882-5850 | 115 |
| Judge Oscar De La Fuente ES/San Benito/ Cameron | 10026656 | 956/361-6820 | 70 |
| Judson Early College Academy/Universal Cty/ Bexar | 11452278 | 210/619-0200 | 36 |
| Judson High Sch/Converse/Bexar | 04813213 | 210/945-1100 | 36 |
| **JUDSON IND SCH DIST/LIVE OAK/ BEXAR** | 00997582 | 210/945-5100 | 36 |
| Judson Learning Academy/San Antonio/Bexar | 04362381 | 210/651-4080 | 36 |
| Judson Middle Sch/Converse/Bexar | 11561802 | 210/357-0801 | 36 |
| Judson Robinson Elem Sch/Houston/Harris | 05099288 | 713/450-7108 | 195 |
| Judson Secondary Alt Sch/Converse/Bexar | 04448648 | 210/619-0330 | 36 |
| Judson Steam Academy/Longview/Gregg | 01021071 | 903/446-2610 | 175 |
| Judy Hajek Elem Sch/Burleson/Johnson | 11220609 | 817/245-3700 | 250 |
| Judy K Miller Elem Sch/Mansfield/Tarrant | 12104993 | 817/299-7550 | 359 |
| Judy Rucker Elem Sch/Prosper/Collin | 10011510 | 469/219-2100 | 88 |
| Julia Garcia Middle Sch/Brownsville/ Cameron | 05095737 | 956/832-6300 | 67 |
| Julian T Saldivar Elem Sch/Dallas/Dallas | 04456499 | 972/794-2000 | 105 |
| Julien C Gallardo Elem Sch/San Antonio/ Bexar | 10012071 | 210/882-1609 | 46 |
| Julius Dorsey Elem Sch/Dallas/Dallas | 01009255 | 972/749-6300 | 105 |
| Julius L Matthey Middle Sch/San Antonio/ Bexar | 00999542 | 210/882-1601 | 46 |
| Junction Elem Sch/Junction/Kimble | 01036167 | 325/446-2055 | 260 |
| Junction High Sch/Junction/Kimble | 01036179 | 325/446-3326 | 260 |
| **JUNCTION IND SCH DIST/JUNCTION/ KIMBLE** | 01036155 | 325/446-3510 | 259 |
| Junction Middle Sch/Junction/Kimble | 01036181 | 325/446-2464 | 260 |
| June R Thompson Elem Sch/Carrollton/Dallas | 01008263 | 972/968-3400 | 101 |
| June W Davis Elem Sch/Fort Worth/Tarrant | 12367121 | 817/885-5700 | 350 |
| Justice Raul A Gonzalez ES/Weslaco/Hidalgo | 01030606 | 956/969-6760 | 228 |
| Justin Elem Sch/Justin/Denton | 01013531 | 817/215-0800 | 129 |
| Justin F Kimball High Sch/Dallas/Dallas | 01009035 | 972/502-2100 | 105 |
| Justin Wakeland High Sch/Frisco/Collin | 10031936 | 469/633-5700 | 83 |
| JW & Ruth Christie Elem Sch/Frisco/Collin | 04868543 | 469/633-2400 | 83 |

## K

| School/City/County DISTRICT/CITY/COUNTY | PID | TELEPHONE NUMBER | PAGE |
|---|---|---|---|
| K B Polk Elem Sch/Dallas/Dallas | 01009267 | 972/794-8900 | 105 |
| Kahla Middle Sch/Houston/Harris | 10000559 | 281/345-3260 | 190 |
| Kaiser Elem Sch/Houston/Harris | 01832129 | 832/484-6100 | 202 |
| Kallison Elem Sch/San Antonio/Bexar | 12230712 | 210/398-2350 | 41 |
| Kardia Christian Academy/Houston/Harris | 11224605 | 281/378-4040 | 211 |
| Karen Wagner High Sch/San Antonio/Bexar | 10003446 | 210/662-5000 | 36 |
| **KARNACK IND SCH DIST/KARNACK/ HARRISON** | 01028574 | 903/679-3117 | 214 |
| Karnes City Early Clg HS/Karnes City/ Karnes | 12169905 | 830/780-2321 | 253 |
| Karnes City High Sch/Karnes City/Karnes | 01035436 | 830/780-2321 | 253 |
| **KARNES CITY IND SCH DIST/ KARNES CITY/KARNES** | 01035395 | 830/780-2321 | 253 |
| Karnes City Junior High Sch/Karnes City/ Karnes | 01809495 | 830/780-2321 | 253 |
| Karnes City Primary Sch/Karnes City/Karnes | 12169917 | 830/780-2321 | 254 |
| Kashmere Gardens Elem Sch/Houston/Harris | 01025998 | 713/671-4160 | 196 |
| Kashmere High Sch/Houston/Harris | 01026007 | 713/636-6400 | 194 |
| Katherine Anne Porter Sch/Wimberley/Hays | 04892453 | 512/847-6867 | 9 |
| Katherine G Johnson STEM Acad/Greenville/ Hunt | 12305680 | 903/454-5050 | 239 |
| Katherine Johnson Tech Mag Sch/Desoto/ Dallas | 12309442 | 972/274-8026 | 108 |
| Katherine Tarver Elem Sch/Laredo/Webb | 01059315 | 956/273-4800 | 389 |
| Kathlyn Joy Gilliam Academy/Dallas/Dallas | 11552842 | 972/925-1400 | 105 |
| Kathryn Griffis Elem Sch/Caddo Mills/Hunt | 11075648 | 903/527-3525 | 238 |
| Kathryn S McWhorter Elem Sch/Dallas/Dallas | 04945086 | 972/968-2600 | 101 |
| Kathy Caraway Elem Sch/Austin/Williamson | 01824421 | 512/464-5500 | 402 |
| Katy Adventist Christian Sch/Katy/Harris | 12314007 | 281/392-5603 | 211 |
| Katy Elem Sch/Katy/Harris | 01026241 | 281/237-6550 | 156 |
| Katy High Sch/Katy/Harris | 01026253 | 281/237-6700 | 156 |
| **KATY IND SCH DIST/KATY/HARRIS** | 01026227 | 281/396-6000 | 155 |
| Katy Junior High Sch/Katy/Harris | 01026265 | 281/237-6800 | 156 |
| Kaufer High Sch/Riviera/Kleberg | 01036416 | 361/296-3607 | 261 |
| Kauffman Leadership Academy/Cleburne/ Johnson | 12260846 | 682/459-2800 | 9 |
| Kaufman Christian Sch/Kaufman/Kaufman | 04762822 | 972/932-4672 | 256 |
| Kaufman Elem Sch/Spring/Montgomery | 10027832 | 832/592-5600 | 295 |
| Kaufman High Sch/Kaufman/Kaufman | 01035632 | 972/932-2811 | 255 |
| **KAUFMAN IND SCH DIST/KAUFMAN/ KAUFMAN** | 01035606 | 972/932-2622 | 255 |
| Kay Franklin Elem Sch/San Antonio/Bexar | 11918181 | 210/398-1700 | 41 |
| Kay Granger Elem Sch/Keller/Denton | 10913114 | 817/698-1100 | 129 |
| Kazen Elem Sch/Laredo/Webb | 04038425 | 956/473-4200 | 390 |
| Kealing Middle Sch/Austin/Travis | 02891142 | 512/414-3214 | 371 |
| Keeble EC-PK-K Sch/Houston/Harris | 04805008 | 281/878-6860 | 186 |
| Keefer Crossing Middle Sch/New Caney/ Montgomery | 02179009 | 281/577-8840 | 296 |
| Keeley Elem Sch/Rowlett/Dallas | 03397462 | 972/412-2140 | 110 |
| Keenan Elem Sch/Montgomery/Montgomery | 01042659 | 936/276-5500 | 296 |
| Keene Adventist Elem Sch/Keene/Johnson | 01480685 | 817/645-9125 | 252 |
| Keene Alternative Learning Ctr/Keene/ Johnson | 04247482 | 817/774-5370 | 251 |
| Keene Elem Sch/Keene/Johnson | 01035072 | 817/774-5323 | 251 |
| **KEENE IND SCH DIST/KEENE/JOHNSON** | 01035060 | 817/774-5200 | 251 |
| Keene Junior High Sch/Keene/Johnson | 04354578 | 817/774-5311 | 251 |
| Keene Wanda R Smith High Sch/Keene/Johnson | 04354580 | 817/774-5225 | 251 |
| Keiko Davidson Elem Sch/Katy/Harris | 12033813 | 281/234-2500 | 156 |
| Keith Elem Sch/Cypress/Harris | 05346615 | 281/213-1744 | 190 |
| Keller Ctr Advanced Learning/Keller/ Tarrant | 12170186 | 817/743-8000 | 357 |
| Keller Elem Sch/Brownsville/Cameron | 11449269 | 956/547-4400 | 67 |
| Keller High Sch/Keller/Tarrant | 02222424 | 817/744-1400 | 357 |
| **KELLER IND SCH DIST/KELLER/ TARRANT** | 01053983 | 817/744-1000 | 357 |
| Keller Learning Center/Keller/Tarrant | 03392735 | 817/744-4465 | 357 |
| Keller Middle Sch/Keller/Tarrant | 01054004 | 817/744-2900 | 357 |
| Keller Middle Sch/Pasadena/Harris | 11129419 | 713/740-5284 | 204 |
| Keller-Harvel Elem Sch/Keller/Tarrant | 01053995 | 817/744-5100 | 357 |
| Kelley Elem Sch/Denver City/Yoakum | 01062025 | 806/592-5920 | 409 |
| Kelly Elem Sch/Pharr/Hidalgo | 02202424 | 956/843-4200 | 222 |
| Kelly Lane Middle Sch/Pflugerville/Travis | 10022428 | 512/594-2800 | 374 |
| Kelly-Pharr Elem Sch/Pharr/Hidalgo | 03055470 | 956/354-2870 | 227 |
| Kelso Elem Sch/Houston/Harris | 01024889 | 713/845-7451 | 198 |
| **KELTON IND SCH DIST/WHEELER/ WHEELER** | 01059808 | 806/826-5795 | 393 |
| Kelton Sch/Wheeler/Wheeler | 01059810 | 806/826-5795 | 393 |
| Kemp High Sch/Kemp/Kaufman | 01035670 | 903/498-1401 | 255 |
| **KEMP IND SCH DIST/KEMP/KAUFMAN** | 01035656 | 903/498-1314 | 255 |
| Kemp Intermediate Sch/Kemp/Kaufman | 03018719 | 903/498-1403 | 255 |
| Kemp Junior High Sch/Kemp/Kaufman | 02055350 | 903/498-1402 | 255 |
| Kemp Primary Sch/Kemp/Kaufman | 01035668 | 903/498-1404 | 255 |
| Kemp-Carver Elem Sch/Bryan/Brazos | 01002075 | 979/209-3700 | 58 |
| Kendall Elem Sch/Boerne/Kendall | 04916803 | 830/357-4600 | 257 |
| Kendrick Elem Sch/Waco/McLennan | 01040261 | 254/752-3316 | 285 |
| **KENEDY CO SCHOOLS/SARITA/KENEDY** | 02091342 | 361/294-5381 | 257 |
| **KENEDY CO WIDE COMMON SCH DIST/ SARITA/KENEDY** | 01035905 | 361/294-5381 | 258 |
| Kenedy Elem Sch/Kenedy/Karnes | 01035474 | 830/583-4100 | 254 |
| Kenedy High Sch/Kenedy/Karnes | 01035462 | 830/583-4100 | 254 |
| **KENEDY IND SCH DIST/KENEDY/ KARNES** | 01035450 | 830/583-4100 | 254 |
| Kenedy Middle Sch/Kenedy/Karnes | 01035486 | 830/583-4100 | 254 |
| Kenley Sch/Abilene/Taylor | 11231658 | 325/698-3220 | 364 |
| Kenmont Montessori Sch/Brownsville/Cameron | 02825997 | 956/542-0500 | 72 |
| **KENNARD IND SCH DIST/KENNARD/ HOUSTON** | 01031791 | 936/655-2161 | 236 |
| Kennard Sch/Kennard/Houston | 01031806 | 936/655-2161 | 236 |
| Kennedale Alternative Ed Prog/Kennedale/ Tarrant | 04918253 | 817/563-8060 | 358 |

| School/City/County<br>DISTRICT/CITY/COUNTY | PID | TELEPHONE NUMBER | PAGE |
|---|---|---|---|
| Kennedale High Sch/Kennedale/Tarrant | 01054066 | 817/563-8100 | 358 |
| **KENNEDALE IND SCH DIST**/KENNEDALE/<br>**TARRANT** | 01054030 | 817/563-8000 | 358 |
| Kennedale Junior High Sch/Kennedale/<br>Tarrant | 01054054 | 817/563-8200 | 358 |
| Kennedy Elem Sch/Corp Christi/Nueces | 01045089 | 361/806-5920 | 309 |
| Kennedy Elem Sch/Eagle Pass/Maverick | 05000940 | 830/758-7189 | 280 |
| Kennedy Elem Sch/Houston/Harris | 01024126 | 713/696-2686 | 196 |
| Kennedy Elem Sch/Houston/Harris | 01418371 | 281/983-8338 | 187 |
| Kennedy Middle Sch/Pharr/Hidalgo | 11552878 | 956/354-2650 | 227 |
| Kennedy-Curry Middle Sch/Dallas/Dallas | 01009401 | 972/925-1600 | 105 |
| Kennedy-Powell Elem Sch/Temple/Bell | 00996760 | 254/215-6000 | 32 |
| Kennedy-Zapata Elem Sch/El Cenizo/Webb | 04364042 | 956/473-4100 | 390 |
| Kenneth D Black Elem Sch/Houston/Harris | 03246772 | 281/878-0350 | 185 |
| Kenneth Davis Elem Sch/Arlington/Tarrant | 04949111 | 817/299-7840 | 359 |
| Kenneth E Little Elem Sch/Bacliff/<br>Galveston | 01018971 | 281/229-7000 | 164 |
| Kenneth White Jr High Sch/Mission/Hidalgo | 03052090 | 956/323-3600 | 225 |
| Kentwood Early Childhood Ctr/Big Spring/<br>Howard | 11816399 | 432/264-4130 | 236 |
| Kerens Elem Sch/Kerens/Navarro | 01043598 | 903/396-7941 | 303 |
| Kerens High Sch/Kerens/Navarro | 01043603 | 903/396-2931 | 303 |
| **KERENS IND SCH DIST**/KERENS/<br>**NAVARRO** | 01043586 | 903/396-2924 | 303 |
| Kerens Middle Sch/Kerens/Navarro | 02846642 | 903/396-2570 | 303 |
| Kermit Elem Sch/Kermit/Winkler | 01061473 | 432/586-1020 | 405 |
| Kermit High Sch/Kermit/Winkler | 01061447 | 432/586-1050 | 405 |
| **KERMIT IND SCH DIST**/KERMIT/<br>**WINKLER** | 01061423 | 432/586-1000 | 405 |
| Kermit Junior High Sch/Kermit/Winkler | 01061461 | 432/586-1040 | 405 |
| Kerr High Sch/Houston/Harris | 04285094 | 281/983-8484 | 187 |
| Kerr Middle Sch/Burleson/Johnson | 04748955 | 817/245-0750 | 250 |
| Kerrville Discipline Alt Sch/Kerrville/<br>Kerr | 04037536 | 830/257-1332 | 259 |
| **KERRVILLE IND SCH DIST**/KERRVILLE/<br>**KERR** | 01036076 | 830/257-2200 | 259 |
| Kessler Sch/Dallas/Dallas | 03371468 | 214/942-2220 | 119 |
| Ketelsen Elem Sch/Houston/Harris | 01024138 | 713/220-5050 | 197 |
| Key Elem Sch/Arlington/Tarrant | 01399787 | 682/867-5500 | 347 |
| Key Middle Sch/Houston/Harris | 01025900 | 713/636-6000 | 196 |
| Key Sch/Fort Worth/Tarrant | 03141835 | 817/446-3738 | 361 |
| Keys Academy/El Paso/El Paso | 04284337 | 915/937-4000 | 140 |
| Keys Academy/Harlingen/Cameron | 03401518 | 956/427-3220 | 68 |
| Keys Elem Academy/El Paso/El Paso | 12032132 | 915/937-4104 | 140 |
| Keys High Sch/Euless/Tarrant | 03052260 | 817/354-3580 | 356 |
| Keystone Sch/San Antonio/Bexar | 01000467 | 210/735-4022 | 48 |
| Ki Charter Academy/San Marcos/Hays | 12108066 | 512/618-0787 | 9 |
| Kidwell Elem Sch/Iowa Park/Wichita | 01060089 | 940/592-4322 | 395 |
| Kieberger Elem Sch/Aransas Pass/<br>San Patricio | 01049528 | 361/758-3113 | 333 |
| Kiest Park Christian Academy/Dallas/Dallas | 02207101 | 214/331-1536 | 119 |
| Kiker Elem Sch/Austin/Travis | 04014948 | 512/414-2584 | 370 |
| Kilgore High Sch/Kilgore/Gregg | 01020974 | 903/988-3901 | 174 |
| **KILGORE IND SCH DIST**/KILGORE/<br>**GREGG** | 01020900 | 903/988-3900 | 174 |
| Kilgore Intermediate Sch/Kilgore/Gregg | 01020936 | 903/988-3903 | 174 |
| Kilgore Middle Sch/Kilgore/Gregg | 01020962 | 903/988-3902 | 174 |
| Kilgore Primary Sch/Kilgore/Gregg | 01020950 | 903/988-3905 | 174 |
| Killam Elem Sch/Laredo/Webb | 11077452 | 956/473-2600 | 390 |
| Killeen Adventist Jr Academy/Killeen/Bell | 02233760 | 254/699-9466 | 33 |
| Killeen High Sch/Killeen/Bell | 00996514 | 254/336-7208 | 31 |
| **KILLEEN IND SCH DIST**/KILLEEN/<br>**BELL** | 00996423 | 254/336-0000 | 30 |
| Killeen ISD Career Center/Killeen/Bell | 01601774 | 254/336-3800 | 31 |
| Killough Middle Sch/Houston/Harris | 01526021 | 281/983-8444 | 187 |
| Kimberlin Acad for Excellence/Garland/<br>Dallas | 01010565 | 972/926-2560 | 110 |
| Kimmie M Brown Elem Sch/Dayton/Liberty | 01037783 | 936/257-2796 | 268 |
| Kinder HS Perform & Visual Art/Houston/<br>Harris | 01023811 | 713/942-1960 | 197 |
| Kinder Ranch Elem Sch/San Antonio/Comal | 11719428 | 830/885-8900 | 92 |
| Kindred Elem Sch/San Antonio/Bexar | 00999451 | 210/977-7575 | 45 |
| King Early Childhood Center/Houston/Harris | 05349928 | 713/797-7900 | 198 |
| Kingdom Academy/Houston/Harris | 11230329 | 713/450-0021 | 211 |
| Kingdom Life Academy/Tyler/Smith | 12169527 | 903/283-3444 | 342 |
| Kingdom Preparatory Academy/Lubbock/<br>Lubbock | 11227059 | 806/767-9334 | 275 |
| Kings Academy Chrn Sch/Tyler/Smith | 11222425 | 903/534-9992 | 342 |
| Kings Manor Elem Sch/Kingwood/Montgomery | 04946030 | 281/577-2940 | 297 |
| Kingsborough Middle Sch/San Antonio/Bexar | 00997477 | 210/989-2200 | 36 |
| Kingsland Sch/Kingsland/Llano | 12260858 | 325/388-0020 | 9 |

| School/City/County<br>DISTRICT/CITY/COUNTY | PID | TELEPHONE NUMBER | PAGE |
|---|---|---|---|
| **KINGSVILLE IND SCH DIST**/<br>**KINGSVILLE/KLEBERG** | 01036258 | 361/592-3387 | 260 |
| Kingwood High Sch/Kingwood/Harris | 02067860 | 281/641-6900 | 201 |
| Kingwood Middle Sch/Kingwood/Harris | 01540039 | 281/641-4200 | 201 |
| Kingwood Park High Sch/Kingwood/Harris | 04286189 | 281/641-6600 | 201 |
| Kinkeade Early Childhood Sch/Irving/Dallas | 04872984 | 972/600-6500 | 114 |
| KIPP 3D Academy/Houston/Harris | 11704356 | 832/230-0566 | 9 |
| KIPP Acad West MS/Houston/Harris | 12163810 | 832/230-0573 | 9 |
| KIPP Academy MS/Houston/Harris | 04454489 | 832/328-1051 | 9 |
| KIPP Aspire Academy/San Antonio/Bexar | 05282588 | 210/735-7300 | 9 |
| KIPP Austin Acad Arts Letters/Austin/<br>Travis | 11702499 | 512/501-3640 | 9 |
| KIPP Austin Beacon Prep/Austin/Travis | 11823457 | 512/651-1918 | 9 |
| KIPP Austin Brave HS/Austin/Travis | 12260860 | 512/651-2225 | 9 |
| KIPP Austin College Prep/Austin/Travis | 05243348 | 512/501-4969 | 9 |
| KIPP Austin Collegiate/Austin/Travis | 11702487 | 512/501-3586 | 9 |
| KIPP Austin Comunidad/Austin/Travis | 11702504 | 512/501-3911 | 9 |
| KIPP Austin Connections ES/Austin/Travis | 11834389 | 512/651-5537 | 9 |
| KIPP Austin Leadership ES/Austin/Travis | 11932498 | 512/651-2168 | 9 |
| KIPP Austin Obras/Austin/Travis | 11932486 | 512/651-2069 | 9 |
| KIPP Austin Vista Middle Sch/Austin/Travis | 11823469 | 512/651-1921 | 9 |
| KIPP Camino Academy/San Antonio/Bexar | 11702516 | 210/829-4200 | 9 |
| KIPP Climb Academy/Houston/Harris | 12260872 | 832/230-0578 | 9 |
| KIPP Connect Houston High Sch/Houston/<br>Harris | 12320252 | 281/879-3023 | 9 |
| KIPP Connect Houston MS/Houston/Harris | 12163860 | 281/879-3023 | 9 |
| KIPP Connect Houston Primary/Houston/<br>Harris | 12260884 | 281/879-3023 | 9 |
| KIPP Courage College Prep/Houston/Harris | 11823483 | 713/251-3800 | 9 |
| KIPP Destiny Elem Sch/Dallas/Dallas | 11931949 | 972/323-4220 | 9 |
| KIPP Destiny Middle Sch/Dallas/Dallas | 12161135 | 972/323-4225 | 9 |
| KIPP Dream Prep/Houston/Harris | 10805268 | 832/230-0566 | 9 |
| KIPP Esperanza Dual Lang Acad/San Antonio/<br>Bexar | 12032326 | 210/888-6601 | 9 |
| KIPP Explore Academy/Houston/Harris | 11704409 | 832/230-0547 | 9 |
| KIPP Generations Collegiate HS/Houston/<br>Harris | 11834432 | 832/230-0566 | 9 |
| KIPP Houston High Sch/Houston/Harris | 11704332 | 832/328-1082 | 9 |
| KIPP Intrepid Prep Sch/Houston/Harris | 11396117 | 281/879-3100 | 9 |
| KIPP Legacy Prep Sch/Houston/Harris | 11704423 | 832/230-0567 | 9 |
| KIPP Liberation College Prep/Houston/<br>Harris | 11014620 | 832/230-0564 | 9 |
| KIPP Nexus MS/Houston/Harris | 12305654 | 832/230-0553 | 9 |
| KIPP Nexus Primary-Houston/Houston/Harris | 12260896 | 832/230-0553 | 10 |
| KIPP Northeast College Prep/Houston/Harris | 11931951 | 832/230-0567 | 10 |
| KIPP Oak Cliff Academy/Dallas/Dallas | 12369442 | 972/323-4240 | 10 |
| KIPP Peace Elem Sch/Houston/Harris | 11818658 | 832/230-0564 | 10 |
| KIPP Pleasant Grove Mid Sch/Dallas/Dallas | 12260913 | 972/323-4235 | 10 |
| KIPP Pleasant Grove Primary/Dallas/Dallas | 12260901 | 972/323-4230 | 10 |
| KIPP Poder Academy/San Antonio/Bexar | 12112586 | 210/888-6513 | 10 |
| KIPP Polaris Academy for Boys/Houston/<br>Harris | 11014618 | 832/230-0567 | 10 |
| KIPP Prime College Prep/Houston/Harris | 12174285 | 832/230-0578 | 10 |
| KIPP Sharp Prep/Houston/Harris | 11409714 | 281/879-3000 | 10 |
| KIPP Sharpstown College Prep/Houston/<br>Harris | 11449817 | 281/879-3005 | 10 |
| KIPP Shine Prep/Houston/Harris | 11220245 | 832/328-1051 | 10 |
| KIPP Somos Collegiate High Sch/San Antonio/<br>Bexar | 12367937 | | 10 |
| KIPP Spirit College Prep/Houston/Harris | 10817168 | 832/230-0562 | 10 |
| KIPP Sunnyside High Sch/Houston/Harris | 11704320 | 832/230-0562 | 10 |
| KIPP Truth Academy/Dallas/Dallas | 10031895 | 972/323-4215 | 10 |
| KIPP Truth Elem Sch/Dallas/Dallas | 12161123 | 972/323-4240 | 10 |
| KIPP UN Mundo Dual Lang Acad/San Antonio/<br>Bexar | 11823495 | 210/824-1905 | 10 |
| KIPP Unity Primary/Houston/Harris | 12112598 | 832/230-0572 | 10 |
| KIPP University Prep High Sch/San Antonio/<br>Bexar | 11445407 | 210/290-8720 | 10 |
| KIPP Voyage Academy for Girls/Houston/<br>Harris | 11704368 | 832/230-0567 | 10 |
| KIPP Zenith Academy/Houston/Harris | 11916121 | 832/230-0562 | 10 |
| Kirby Hall Sch/Austin/Travis | 02084143 | 512/474-1770 | 376 |
| Kirby Middle Sch/San Antonio/Bexar | 00997635 | 210/661-1140 | 36 |
| Kirby Middle Sch/Wichita Falls/Wichita | 01173155 | 940/235-1113 | 395 |
| **KIRBYVILLE CONS IND SCH DIST**/<br>**KIRBYVILLE/JASPER** | 01033282 | 409/423-2284 | 244 |
| Kirbyville Elem Sch/Kirbyville/Jasper | 01033309 | 409/423-8526 | 244 |
| Kirbyville High Sch/Kirbyville/Jasper | 01033311 | 409/423-7500 | 244 |
| Kirbyville Junior High Sch/Kirbyville/<br>Jasper | 01033294 | 409/420-0692 | 244 |
| Kirchner Elem Sch/Quemado/Maverick | 01041112 | 830/758-7045 | 280 |
| Kirk Elem Sch/Houston/Harris | 04916346 | 713/849-8250 | 190 |

| School/City/County DISTRICT/CITY/COUNTY | PID | TELEPHONE NUMBER | PAGE |
|---|---|---|---|
| Kirkpatrick Middle Sch/Fort Worth/Tarrant | 01053115 | 817/814-4200 | 353 |
| Kissam Elem Sch/Tyler/Smith | 04278649 | 903/566-8334 | 339 |
| Kitty Hawk Middle Sch/Universal Cty/Bexar | 01523665 | 210/945-1220 | 36 |
| Kleb Intermediate Sch/Klein/Harris | 02178275 | 832/249-5500 | 202 |
| Kleberg Elem Sch/Dallas/Dallas | 01009279 | 972/749-6500 | 105 |
| Kleberg Elem Sch/Kingsville/Kleberg | 01036272 | 361/592-2615 | 260 |
| Klein Alternative Ed Center/Klein/Harris | 05273769 | 832/249-4801 | 202 |
| Klein Cain High Sch/Houston/Harris | 12231247 | 832/375-8400 | 202 |
| Klein Collins High Sch/Spring/Harris | 04941626 | 832/484-5500 | 202 |
| Klein Forest High Sch/Houston/Harris | 02043321 | 832/484-4500 | 202 |
| Klein High Sch/Klein/Harris | 01026332 | 832/484-4000 | 202 |
| **KLEIN IND SCH DIST/KLEIN/HARRIS** | 01026289 | 832/249-4000 | 201 |
| Klein Intermediate Sch/Houston/Harris | 02227204 | 832/249-4900 | 202 |
| Klein Oak High Sch/Spring/Harris | 02178263 | 832/484-5000 | 202 |
| Klein Road Elem Sch/New Braunfels/Comal | 11436248 | 830/221-1700 | 92 |
| Klenk Elem Sch/Houston/Harris | 04017938 | 832/484-6800 | 202 |
| Klentzman Intermediate Sch/Houston/Harris | 04364444 | 281/983-8477 | 187 |
| Kline Whitis Elem Sch/Lampasas/Lampasas | 01037159 | 512/556-8291 | 264 |
| **KLONDIKE IND SCH DIST/LAMESA/ DAWSON** | 01012824 | 806/462-7334 | 121 |
| Klondike Sch/Lamesa/Dawson | 01012850 | 806/462-7332 | 121 |
| **KNIPPA IND SCH DIST/KNIPPA/ UVALDE** | 01057692 | 830/934-2176 | 380 |
| Knippa Sch/Knippa/Uvalde | 01057721 | 830/934-2176 | 380 |
| Knowledge Seeker Christian Sch/Lewisville/ Denton | 04992728 | 972/353-3981 | 130 |
| Knowles Elem Sch/Cedar Park/Williamson | 05272442 | 512/570-6200 | 400 |
| Knox City Elem Sch/Knox City/Knox | 01036519 | 940/657-3147 | 261 |
| Knox City High Sch/Knox City/Knox | 01036521 | 940/657-3565 | 261 |
| **KNOX CITY-O'BRIEN CONS IND SD/ KNOX CITY/KNOX** | 01036507 | 940/657-3521 | 261 |
| Knox Early Chldhd Center/San Antonio/Bexar | 00999334 | 210/228-3365 | 44 |
| Knox Junior High Sch/The Woodlands/ Montgomery | 01829471 | 832/592-8400 | 295 |
| Kocurek Elem Sch/Austin/Travis | 02890538 | 512/414-2547 | 370 |
| Kohfeldt Elem Sch/Texas City/Galveston | 01019523 | 409/916-0400 | 166 |
| Kohrville Elem Sch/Tomball/Harris | 05096092 | 832/484-7200 | 202 |
| Kolda Elem Sch/Corp Christi/Nueces | 11821100 | 361/878-2980 | 306 |
| Kolter Elem Sch/Houston/Harris | 01024891 | 713/726-3630 | 199 |
| Kooken Educational Center/Arlington/ Tarrant | 03250694 | 682/867-7152 | 347 |
| **KOPPERL IND SCH DIST/KOPPERL/ BOSQUE** | 01000663 | 254/889-3502 | 50 |
| Kopperl Sch/Kopperl/Bosque | 01000675 | 254/889-3502 | 50 |
| Kor Education Sch/College Sta/Brazos | 12173906 | 979/777-1213 | 60 |
| Kostoryz Elem Sch/Corp Christi/Nueces | 01044487 | 361/878-2540 | 306 |
| Kountze Elem Sch/Kountze/Hardin | 01022532 | 409/246-3877 | 183 |
| Kountze High Sch/Kountze/Hardin | 01022518 | 409/246-3474 | 183 |
| **KOUNTZE IND SCH DIST/KOUNTZE/ HARDIN** | 01022491 | 409/246-3352 | 183 |
| Kountze Intermediate Sch/Kountze/Hardin | 11073028 | 409/246-8230 | 183 |
| Kountze Middle Sch/Kountze/Hardin | 01022520 | 409/246-3551 | 183 |
| Krahn Elem Sch/Klein/Harris | 02178287 | 832/484-6500 | 202 |
| Kranz Junior High Sch/Dickinson/Galveston | 12307107 | 281/309-3600 | 164 |
| Krause Elem Sch/Brenham/Washington | 01059092 | 979/277-3860 | 388 |
| Kreinhop Elem Sch/Spring/Harris | 05347592 | 832/484-7400 | 202 |
| Kress Elem Sch/Kress/Swisher | 01051557 | 806/684-2326 | 345 |
| **KRESS IND SCH DIST/KRESS/SWISHER** | 01051545 | 806/684-2652 | 345 |
| Kress Jr Sr High Sch/Kress/Swisher | 01051569 | 806/684-2651 | 345 |
| Kriewald Road Elem Sch/San Antonio/Bexar | 04808983 | 210/645-7550 | 46 |
| Krimmel Intermediate Sch/Klein/Harris | 10804836 | 832/375-7200 | 202 |
| Krueger Middle Sch/San Antonio/Bexar | 00997829 | 210/356-4700 | 38 |
| Krum Early Education Center/Krum/Denton | 11126912 | 940/482-2605 | 126 |
| Krum High Sch/Krum/Denton | 01013361 | 940/482-2601 | 126 |
| **KRUM IND SCH DIST/KRUM/DENTON** | 01013347 | 940/482-2600 | 126 |
| Krum Middle Sch/Krum/Denton | 02131112 | 940/482-2602 | 126 |
| Kruse Elem Sch/Pasadena/Harris | 01026772 | 713/740-0624 | 204 |
| Kuehnle Elem Sch/Klein/Harris | 03245510 | 832/484-6650 | 202 |
| Kuentz Elem Sch/Helotes/Bexar | 11448992 | 210/397-8050 | 41 |
| Kujawa EC-PK-K/Houston/Harris | 11074709 | 281/878-1514 | 186 |
| Kujawa Elem Sch/Houston/Harris | 05274103 | 281/878-1530 | 184 |
| Kurth Primary Sch/Lufkin/Angelina | 00994994 | 936/639-3279 | 21 |
| Kyle Elem Sch/Kyle/Hays | 01029097 | 512/268-3311 | 216 |

## L

| School/City/County DISTRICT/CITY/COUNTY | PID | TELEPHONE NUMBER | PAGE |
|---|---|---|---|
| L A Gililland Elem Sch/Fort Worth/Tarrant | 01052422 | 817/232-0331 | 351 |
| L A Morgan Elem Sch/Galveston/Galveston | 01019169 | 409/761-6700 | 165 |
| L A Nelson Elem Sch/Denton/Denton | 10909125 | 940/369-1400 | 125 |
| L B Johnson Elem Sch/San Antonio/Bexar | 00997300 | 210/444-8175 | 35 |
| L C Smith Elem Sch/Raymondville/Willacy | 01060730 | 956/689-8172 | 397 |
| L E Monahan Elem Sch/Houston/Harris | 02176095 | 281/454-2900 | 205 |
| L F Blanton Elem Sch/Carrollton/Dallas | 01008146 | 972/968-1100 | 101 |
| L F Smith Elem Sch/Pasadena/Harris | 01026942 | 713/740-0720 | 204 |
| L G Pinkston High Sch/Dallas/Dallas | 01009281 | 972/502-2700 | 105 |
| L H Rather Junior High Sch/Bonham/Fannin | 01017408 | 903/583-7474 | 149 |
| L J Christen Middle Sch/Laredo/Webb | 01059327 | 956/273-6400 | 389 |
| L L Hotchkiss Elem Sch/Dallas/Dallas | 01009293 | 972/749-7000 | 105 |
| L L Pugh Elem Sch/Houston/Harris | 01025716 | 713/671-3820 | 194 |
| L O Donald Elem Sch/Dallas/Dallas | 01009308 | 972/794-5300 | 105 |
| L P Waters Early Childhood Ctr/Greenville/ Hunt | 04948583 | 903/457-2680 | 239 |
| L V Stockard Middle Sch/Dallas/Dallas | 01009310 | 972/794-5700 | 105 |
| L W Kolarik 9th Grade Center/Channelview/ Harris | 11158020 | 713/378-3400 | 188 |
| La Academia De Estrellas CS/Dallas/Dallas | 11014632 | 214/946-8908 | 10 |
| La Encantada Elem Sch/San Benito/Cameron | 01004229 | 956/361-6760 | 70 |
| La Fe Preparatory Sch/El Paso/El Paso | 11015478 | 915/533-4690 | 10 |
| La Feria Academy/La Feria/Cameron | 11540019 | 956/797-8360 | 69 |
| La Feria High Sch/La Feria/Cameron | 01003952 | 956/797-8370 | 69 |
| **LA FERIA IND SCH DIST/LA FERIA/ CAMERON** | 01003940 | 956/797-8300 | 69 |
| La Gloria Elem Sch/Falfurrias/Jim Wells | 02129353 | 361/325-2330 | 248 |
| **LA GLORIA IND SCH DIST/FALFURRIAS/ JIM WELLS** | 01034664 | 361/325-2330 | 248 |
| La Grange Elem Sch/La Grange/Fayette | 04235996 | 979/968-4700 | 151 |
| La Grange High Sch/La Grange/Fayette | 01017757 | 979/968-4800 | 151 |
| **LA GRANGE IND SCH DIST/LA GRANGE/ FAYETTE** | 01017721 | 979/968-7000 | 151 |
| La Grange Middle Sch/La Grange/Fayette | 01017769 | 979/968-4747 | 151 |
| La Joya Early College HS/La Joya/Hidalgo | 11930593 | 956/323-2930 | 223 |
| **LA JOYA IND SCH DIST/LA JOYA/ HIDALGO** | 01029841 | 956/323-2000 | 222 |
| La Joya Senior High Sch/La Joya/Hidalgo | 01029865 | 956/323-2870 | 223 |
| La Joya West Academy/La Joya/Hidalgo | 04287901 | 956/323-2260 | 223 |
| La Marque Elem Sch/La Marque/Galveston | 01019339 | 409/908-5056 | 166 |
| La Marque High Sch/La Marque/Galveston | 01019353 | 409/938-4261 | 166 |
| La Marque Middle Sch/La Marque/Galveston | 01019377 | 409/938-4286 | 166 |
| La Marque Primary Sch/La Marque/Galveston | 04808268 | 409/935-3020 | 166 |
| La Mesa Elem Sch/Plainview/Hale | 03236428 | 806/293-6055 | 180 |
| La Paloma Elem Sch/San Benito/Cameron | 02845935 | 956/361-6780 | 70 |
| La Paz Language Academy/El Paso/El Paso | 11224320 | 915/584-5100 | 143 |
| La Porte Elem Sch/La Porte/Harris | 01026435 | 281/604-4700 | 203 |
| La Porte High Sch/La Porte/Harris | 01026447 | 281/604-7500 | 203 |
| **LA PORTE IND SCH DIST/LA PORTE/ HARRIS** | 01026370 | 281/604-7000 | 203 |
| La Porte Junior High Sch/La Porte/Harris | 01026459 | 281/604-6600 | 203 |
| **LA POYNOR IND SCH DIST/LARUE/ HENDERSON** | 01029413 | 903/876-4057 | 219 |
| La Poynor Sch/Larue/Henderson | 01029425 | 903/876-4057 | 219 |
| La Pryor Elem Sch/La Pryor/Zavala | 04033437 | 830/365-4009 | 411 |
| La Pryor High Sch/La Pryor/Zavala | 01062386 | 830/365-4007 | 411 |
| **LA PRYOR IND SCH DIST/LA PRYOR/ ZAVALA** | 01062374 | 830/365-4000 | 411 |
| La Union Elem Sch/Rio Grande Cy/Starr | 01051143 | 956/487-3404 | 343 |
| La Vega Elem Sch/Waco/McLennan | 01039793 | 254/299-6755 | 283 |
| La Vega High Sch/Waco/McLennan | 01039810 | 254/299-6820 | 283 |
| **LA VEGA IND SCH DIST/WACO/ MCLENNAN** | 01039779 | 254/299-6700 | 282 |
| La Vega IS-H P Miles Campus/Bellmead/ McLennan | 01039781 | 254/299-6770 | 283 |
| La Vega Junior High Sch/Waco/McLennan | 01039808 | 254/299-6790 | 283 |
| La Vega Primary Center/Waco/McLennan | 02223557 | 254/299-6730 | 283 |
| La Vernia Christian Agape Acad/La Vernia/ Wilson | 12165545 | 830/779-6361 | 404 |
| La Vernia High Sch/La Vernia/Wilson | 01061332 | 830/779-6630 | 404 |
| **LA VERNIA IND SCH DIST/LA VERNIA/ WILSON** | 01061318 | 830/779-6600 | 404 |
| La Vernia Intermediate Sch/La Vernia/ Wilson | 01061320 | 830/779-6640 | 404 |
| La Vernia Junior High Sch/La Vernia/Wilson | 03004445 | 830/779-6650 | 404 |
| La Vernia Primary Sch/La Vernia/Wilson | 04931891 | 830/779-6660 | 404 |
| La Villa Early Clg High Sch/La Villa/ Hidalgo | 03245560 | 956/262-4715 | 224 |
| **LA VILLA IND SCH DIST/LA VILLA/ HIDALGO** | 01029891 | 956/262-4755 | 223 |
| La Villa Middle Sch/La Villa/Hidalgo | 04247511 | 956/262-4760 | 224 |
| La Villita Elem Sch/Irving/Dallas | 11157442 | 972/968-6900 | 101 |
| Labay Middle Sch/Houston/Harris | 02226121 | 281/463-5800 | 190 |
| Lackland Elem Sch/San Antonio/Bexar | 01808843 | 210/357-5053 | 37 |
| **LACKLAND IND SCH DIST/SAN ANTONIO/ BEXAR** | 01808829 | 210/357-5000 | 37 |
| Lacy Elem Sch/Princeton/Collin | 01006514 | 469/952-5401 | 87 |
| Lady Bird Johnson Middle Sch/Irving/Dallas | 11717092 | 972/600-0500 | 114 |
| Lago Vista Elem Sch/Lago Vista/Travis | 01056882 | 512/267-8340 | 373 |

| School/City/County<br>DISTRICT/CITY/COUNTY | PID | TELEPHONE NUMBER | PAGE |
|---|---|---|---|
| Lago Vista High Sch/Lago Vista/Travis | 01526150 | 512/267-8300 | 373 |
| **LAGO VISTA IND SCH DIST/** | | | |
| **LAGO VISTA/TRAVIS** | 01056870 | 512/267-8300 | 373 |
| Lago Vista Intermediate Sch/Lago Vista/Travis | 12169606 | 512/267-8300 | 373 |
| Lago Vista Middle Sch/Lago Vista/Travis | 04745044 | 512/267-8300 | 373 |
| Lagos Elem Sch/Manor/Travis | 12230267 | 512/278-4360 | 374 |
| LaGrone Advanced Tech Complex/Denton/Denton | 10021852 | 940/369-4850 | 125 |
| Laguna Madre Christian Academy/Laguna Vista/Cameron | 11230123 | 956/943-4446 | 72 |
| Lake Air Mont Magnet Sch/Waco/McLennan | 01040297 | 254/772-1910 | 285 |
| Lake Belton Middle Sch/Temple/Bell | 04916310 | 254/215-2900 | 30 |
| Lake Cities Montessori Sch/Garland/Dallas | 11902182 | 214/440-4930 | 119 |
| Lake Country Christian Sch/Fort Worth/Tarrant | 02164834 | 817/236-8703 | 361 |
| Lake Creek High Sch/Montgomery/Montgomery | 12363058 | 936/276-4000 | 296 |
| Lake Dallas Elem Sch/Lake Dallas/Denton | 02130728 | 940/497-2222 | 126 |
| Lake Dallas High Sch/Corinth/Denton | 01013397 | 940/497-4031 | 126 |
| **LAKE DALLAS IND SCH DIST/** | | | |
| **LAKE DALLAS/DENTON** | 01013373 | 940/497-4039 | 126 |
| Lake Dallas Middle Sch/Lake Dallas/Denton | 01809172 | 940/497-4037 | 126 |
| Lake Highlands Elem Sch/Dallas/Dallas | 01011753 | 469/593-2100 | 116 |
| Lake Highlands High Sch/Dallas/Dallas | 01011765 | 469/593-1000 | 117 |
| Lake Highlands Jr High Sch/Dallas/Dallas | 01011777 | 469/593-1600 | 117 |
| Lake Jackson Intermediate Sch/Lake Jackson/Brazoria | 01001643 | 979/730-7250 | 55 |
| Lake Olympia Middle Sch/Missouri City/Fort Bend | 04016348 | 281/634-3520 | 154 |
| Lake Pointe Elem Sch/Austin/Travis | 05070218 | 512/533-6500 | 373 |
| Lake Pointe Elem Sch/Fort Worth/Tarrant | 11072787 | 817/236-8801 | 351 |
| Lake Ridge Elem Sch/Cedar Hill/Dallas | 05097826 | 972/293-4501 | 101 |
| Lake Ridge High Sch/Mansfield/Tarrant | 11818622 | 682/314-0400 | 359 |
| Lake Travis Elem Sch/Austin/Travis | 10011871 | 512/533-6300 | 373 |
| Lake Travis High Sch/Austin/Travis | 02223571 | 512/533-6100 | 373 |
| **LAKE TRAVIS IND SCH DIST/** | | | |
| **AUSTIN/TRAVIS** | 02178653 | 512/533-6000 | 373 |
| Lake Travis Middle Sch/Spicewood/Travis | 02223595 | 512/533-6200 | 373 |
| Lake View High Sch/San Angelo/Tom Green | 01055711 | 325/659-3500 | 367 |
| Lake Worth High Sch/Lake Worth/Tarrant | 01054092 | 817/306-4230 | 358 |
| **LAKE WORTH IND SCH DIST/** | | | |
| **LAKE WORTH/TARRANT** | 01054078 | 817/306-4200 | 358 |
| Lakehill Preparatory Sch/Dallas/Dallas | 01479923 | 214/826-2931 | 119 |
| Lakeland Christian Academy/Lewisville/Denton | 11230800 | 972/219-3939 | 130 |
| Lakeland Elem Sch/Humble/Harris | 01026203 | 281/641-1200 | 201 |
| Lakeland Elem Sch/Lewisville/Denton | 01013476 | 469/713-5992 | 127 |
| Lakeshore Elem Sch/Houston/Harris | 11450347 | 281/641-3500 | 201 |
| Lakeside Elem Sch/Coppell/Dallas | 04030277 | 214/496-7600 | 102 |
| Lakeside Middle Sch/Little Elm/Denton | 03007693 | 972/947-9445 | 128 |
| Lakeview Centennial High Sch/Garland/Dallas | 01525950 | 972/240-3740 | 110 |
| Lakeview Elem Sch/Amarillo/Randall | 03007825 | 806/677-2830 | 323 |
| Lakeview Elem Sch/Little Elm/Denton | 10012605 | 972/947-9454 | 128 |
| Lakeview Elem Sch/Mabank/Kaufman | 04454087 | 903/880-1361 | 256 |
| Lakeview Elem Sch/Sugar Land/Fort Bend | 01018165 | 281/634-4200 | 154 |
| Lakeview Elem Sch/Trophy Club/Denton | 02200775 | 817/215-0750 | 129 |
| Lakeview Middle Sch/The Colony/Denton | 03249360 | 469/713-5974 | 127 |
| Lakeway Elem Sch/Austin/Travis | 01029047 | 512/533-6350 | 373 |
| Lakewood Elem Sch/Belton/Bell | 02895071 | 254/215-3100 | 30 |
| Lakewood Elem Sch/Dallas/Dallas | 01009322 | 972/749-7300 | 105 |
| Lakewood Elem Sch/Euless/Tarrant | 01053854 | 817/354-3375 | 356 |
| Lakewood Elem Sch/Tomball/Harris | 02202618 | 281/357-3260 | 208 |
| Lamar & Norma Hunt Middle Sch/Frisco/Collin | 11558341 | 469/633-5200 | 83 |
| Lamar Academy/McAllen/Hidalgo | 03052612 | 956/632-3222 | 224 |
| Lamar Bruni Vergara Middle Sch/Laredo/Webb | 10021577 | 956/473-6600 | 390 |
| Lamar Co Head Start Center/Paris/Lamar | 12170863 | 903/737-7469 | 263 |
| **LAMAR CONS IND SCH DIST/** | | | |
| **ROSENBERG/FORT BEND** | 01018232 | 832/223-0000 | 157 |
| Lamar Consolidated High Sch/Rosenberg/Fort Bend | 01018294 | 832/223-3000 | 158 |
| Lamar Early Education Center/Odessa/Ector | 01014743 | 432/456-1159 | 134 |
| Lamar Elem Sch/Amarillo/Potter | 01047324 | 806/326-4600 | 321 |
| Lamar Elem Sch/Del Rio/Val Verde | 01058000 | 830/778-4730 | 382 |
| Lamar Elem Sch/Denison/Grayson | 01020376 | 903/462-7400 | 171 |
| Lamar Elem Sch/El Paso/El Paso | 01016014 | 915/236-3150 | 138 |
| Lamar Elem Sch/Greenville/Hunt | 01032525 | 903/457-0765 | 239 |
| Lamar Elem Sch/Harlingen/Cameron | 01003873 | 956/427-3130 | 68 |
| Lamar Elem Sch/Midland/Midland | 01041588 | 432/240-7300 | 289 |
| Lamar Elem Sch/Mineral Wells/Palo Pinto | 01046045 | 940/325-5303 | 313 |
| Lamar Elem Sch/New Braunfels/Comal | 01857143 | 830/627-6890 | 92 |
| Lamar Elem Sch/Pampa/Gray | 01020170 | 806/669-4880 | 170 |
| Lamar Elem Sch/San Angelo/Tom Green | 01055565 | 325/947-3900 | 367 |
| Lamar Elem Sch/San Antonio/Bexar | 00998574 | 210/738-9800 | 44 |
| Lamar Elem Sch/The Woodlands/Montgomery | 01042489 | 832/592-5800 | 295 |
| Lamar Elem Sch/Wichita Falls/Wichita | 01173129 | 940/235-1172 | 395 |
| Lamar High Sch/Houston/Harris | 01024487 | 713/522-5960 | 199 |
| Lamar Junior High Sch/Rosenberg/Fort Bend | 01018309 | 832/223-3200 | 158 |
| Lamar Middle Sch/Austin/Travis | 01056325 | 512/414-3217 | 371 |
| Lamar Middle Sch/Flower Mound/Denton | 03010456 | 469/713-5966 | 127 |
| Lamar Middle Sch/Irving/Dallas | 01011234 | 972/600-4400 | 114 |
| Lamar Middle Sch/Temple/Bell | 00996784 | 254/215-6444 | 32 |
| Lamar Primary Sch/Sulphur Spgs/Hopkins | 01031674 | 903/885-4550 | 235 |
| Lamar-Delta Alternative Ctr/Paris/Wise | 04750178 | 903/737-7963 | 407 |
| Lamesa High Sch/Lamesa/Dawson | 01012898 | 806/872-8385 | 121 |
| **LAMESA IND SCH DIST/LAMESA/** | | | |
| **DAWSON** | 01012862 | 806/872-5461 | 121 |
| Lamesa Middle Sch/Lamesa/Dawson | 01012903 | 806/872-8301 | 121 |
| Lamesa Success Academy/Lamesa/Dawson | 11917199 | 806/872-5410 | 121 |
| Lamkin Elem Sch/Cypress/Harris | 01023287 | 281/897-4775 | 190 |
| Lampasas High Sch/Lampasas/Lampasas | 01037135 | 512/564-2310 | 264 |
| **LAMPASAS IND SCH DIST/LAMPASAS/** | | | |
| **LAMPASAS** | 01037111 | 512/556-6224 | 264 |
| Lampasas Middle Sch/Lampasas/Lampasas | 01037147 | 512/556-3101 | 264 |
| Lancaster Elem Sch/El Paso/El Paso | 02200074 | 915/434-3400 | 142 |
| Lancaster High Sch/Lancaster/Dallas | 01011351 | 972/218-1800 | 114 |
| **LANCASTER IND SCH DIST/LANCASTER/** | | | |
| **DALLAS** | 01011337 | 972/218-1400 | 114 |
| Lancaster STEM Early Clg HS/Lancaster/Dallas | 12308450 | 972/218-1861 | 114 |
| Lance Thompson Elem Sch/Argyle/Denton | 12363151 | 817/698-1800 | 129 |
| Landis Elem Sch/Houston/Harris | 03252862 | 281/983-8343 | 187 |
| Landrum Middle Sch/Houston/Harris | 01027130 | 713/251-3700 | 206 |
| **LANEVILLE IND SCH DIST/LANEVILLE/** | | | |
| **RUSK** | 01049061 | 903/863-5353 | 330 |
| Laneville Sch/Laneville/Rusk | 01049085 | 903/863-5353 | 330 |
| Langford Elem Sch/Austin/Travis | 02110118 | 512/414-1765 | 370 |
| Langham Creek High Sch/Houston/Harris | 02848717 | 281/463-5400 | 190 |
| Langham Elem Sch/Nederland/Jefferson | 01033725 | 409/722-4324 | 246 |
| Language Development Center/Eagle Pass/Maverick | 04021707 | 830/758-7047 | 280 |
| Lanier Middle Sch/Houston/Harris | 01024504 | 713/942-1900 | 199 |
| Lanny Frasier Middle Sch/Mesquite/Dallas | 12375219 | 972/290-4300 | 115 |
| Lansberry Elem Sch/Trinity/Trinity | 01057159 | 936/594-3567 | 377 |
| Lantern Lane Elem Sch/Missouri City/Fort Bend | 01826235 | 281/634-4680 | 154 |
| Lantrip Elem Sch/Houston/Harris | 01025596 | 713/924-1670 | 195 |
| **LAREDO IND SCH DIST/LAREDO/WEBB** | 01059183 | 956/273-1000 | 389 |
| Larkspur Elem Sch/Leander/Williamson | 12365513 | 512/570-8100 | 400 |
| Larkspur Elem Sch/San Antonio/Bexar | 00997831 | 210/407-4600 | 38 |
| Larry Brown Sch/Jourdanton/Atascosa | 04450251 | 830/769-2925 | 23 |
| Larry D Guinn Spec Pgrms Ctr/Plano/Collin | 11718943 | 469/752-6900 | 86 |
| Larry G Smith Elem Sch/Mesquite/Dallas | 10908327 | 972/502-4800 | 105 |
| Larson Elem Sch/Grand Prairie/Tarrant | 04754461 | 682/867-0000 | 347 |
| LaRue Miller Elem Sch/Midlothian/Ellis | 11122306 | 469/856-6500 | 145 |
| Las Americas Newcomer Mid Sch/Houston/Harris | 05099329 | 713/773-5300 | 199 |
| Las Colinas Elem Sch/Irving/Dallas | 02894120 | 972/968-2200 | 101 |
| Las Lomas Elem Sch/San Antonio/Bexar | 11820455 | 210/356-7000 | 38 |
| Las Palmas Elem Sch/San Antonio/Bexar | 10007179 | 210/444-8050 | 35 |
| Las Yescas Elem Sch/San Benito/Cameron | 01004011 | 956/233-6955 | 69 |
| Lasara Elem Sch/Lasara/Willacy | 01060649 | 956/642-3271 | 397 |
| Lasara High Sch/Lasara/Willacy | 11564974 | 956/642-3271 | 397 |
| **LASARA IND SCH DIST/LASARA/** | | | |
| **WILLACY** | 01060637 | 956/642-3271 | 397 |
| Lasater Elem Sch/Falfurrias/Brooks | 01002386 | 361/325-8060 | 61 |
| Latexo Elem Sch/Latexo/Houston | 01031832 | 936/546-5630 | 236 |
| Latexo High Sch/Latexo/Houston | 04748876 | 936/544-5638 | 236 |
| **LATEXO IND SCH DIST/LATEXO/** | | | |
| **HOUSTON** | 01031820 | 936/544-5664 | 236 |
| Laura Bush Elem Sch/Houston/Harris | 10029000 | 713/740-0928 | 204 |
| Laura Bush Middle Sch/Lubbock/Lubbock | 11716490 | 806/776-0750 | 274 |
| Laura Ingalls Wilder Elem Sch/Pearland/Brazoria | 10908169 | 281/245-3090 | 54 |
| Laura Ingalls Wilder Inter Sch/Schertz/Guadalupe | 04746270 | 210/619-4200 | 178 |
| Laura Reeves Primary Sch/Silsbee/Hardin | 01022594 | 409/980-7850 | 183 |
| Laura Steele Montessori Acad/San Antonio/Bexar | 12305537 | 210/438-6870 | 44 |
| Laura Welch Bush Elem Sch/Austin/Williamson | 05102952 | 512/570-6100 | 400 |
| Laurel Mountain Elem Sch/Austin/Williamson | 02893970 | 512/464-4300 | 402 |
| Laureles Elem Sch/Los Fresnos/Cameron | 04918758 | 956/254-5141 | 69 |

| School/City/County DISTRICT/CITY/COUNTY | PID | TELEPHONE NUMBER | PAGE |
|---|---|---|---|
| Laurenzo ECC/Houston/Harris | 05349916 | 713/924-0350 | 195 |
| Lauro Cavazos Elem Sch/Odessa/Ector | 03248732 | 432/456-1309 | 134 |
| Lavace Stewart Elem Sch/Kemah/Galveston | 01019315 | 281/284-4700 | 163 |
| Law Elem Sch/Houston/Harris | 01025285 | 713/732-3630 | 198 |
| Lawler Middle Sch/Frisco/Collin | 12308345 | 469/633-4150 | 83 |
| Lawn Elem Sch/Lawn/Taylor | 01054901 | 325/583-2256 | 363 |
| Lawndale Elem Sch/Amarillo/Potter | 01047336 | 806/326-4700 | 321 |
| Lawrence A Eckert Elem Sch/Houston/Harris | 04032586 | 281/985-6380 | 185 |
| Lawrence D Bell High Sch/Hurst/Tarrant | 01053787 | 817/282-2551 | 356 |
| Lawson Academy/Houston/Harris | 12160595 | 713/225-1551 | 10 |
| Lawson Middle Sch/Houston/Harris | 01025168 | 713/434-5600 | 194 |
| **LAZBUDDIE IND SCH DIST**/LAZBUDDIE/ PARMER | 01046772 | 806/965-2156 | 318 |
| Lazbuddie Sch/Lazbuddie/Parmer | 01046796 | 806/965-2153 | 318 |
| Le Noir Elem Sch/Donna/Hidalgo | 03252991 | 956/464-1685 | 220 |
| Leadership Acad Como ES/Fort Worth/Tarrant | 01052692 | 817/815-6500 | 353 |
| Leadership Acad Mitchell Blvd/Fort Worth/ Tarrant | 01053127 | 817/815-9000 | 353 |
| Leadership Academy/Tyler/Smith | 12261199 | 903/561-1002 | 10 |
| Leadership Prep Sch Secondary/Frisco/ Collin | 12378613 | 972/370-3650 | 10 |
| Leadership Prep School Elem/Frisco/Collin | 11712808 | 972/294-6921 | 10 |
| Leafspring School-Sonterra/San Antonio/ Bexar | 05312896 | 210/495-5222 | 48 |
| League City Elem Sch/League City/Galveston | 01018907 | 281/284-4400 | 163 |
| League City Intermediate Sch/League City/ Galveston | 02178029 | 281/284-3400 | 163 |
| **LEAKEY IND SCH DIST**/LEAKEY/REAL | 01048055 | 830/232-5595 | 324 |
| Leakey Sch/Leakey/Real | 01048067 | 830/232-5595 | 324 |
| Leal Elem Sch/Mission/Hidalgo | 02227943 | 956/323-4600 | 225 |
| Leander High Sch/Leander/Williamson | 01061021 | 512/570-1000 | 400 |
| **LEANDER IND SCH DIST**/LEANDER/ WILLIAMSON | 01061007 | 512/570-0000 | 399 |
| Leander Middle Sch/Leander/Williamson | 04455811 | 512/570-3200 | 400 |
| Leary Elem Sch/Texarkana/Bowie | 01000936 | 903/838-8960 | 51 |
| **LEARY IND SCH DIST**/TEXARKANA/ BOWIE | 01000924 | 903/838-8960 | 51 |
| Lebanon Trail High Sch/Frisco/Collin | 12165399 | 469/633-6600 | 83 |
| Lee A McShan Jr Elem Sch/Dallas/Dallas | 10006802 | 972/502-3800 | 105 |
| Lee Elem Sch/Abilene/Taylor | 01172838 | 325/671-4895 | 363 |
| Lee Elem Sch/Caddo Mills/Hunt | 01032305 | 903/527-3162 | 238 |
| Lee Elem Sch/Grand Prairie/Dallas | 01010979 | 972/262-6785 | 111 |
| Lee Elem Sch/Houston/Harris | 10002155 | 713/849-8281 | 190 |
| Lee Elem Sch/Irving/Dallas | 01011301 | 972/600-7800 | 114 |
| Lee Elem Sch/Port Arthur/Jefferson | 01033866 | 409/984-8300 | 246 |
| Lee H Means Elem Sch/Harlingen/Cameron | 11434783 | 956/427-3377 | 68 |
| Lee Middle Sch/San Angelo/Tom Green | 01055759 | 325/947-3871 | 367 |
| **LEFORS IND SCH DIST**/LEFORS/GRAY | 01020077 | 806/835-2533 | 170 |
| Lefors Sch/Lefors/Gray | 01020089 | 806/835-2533 | 170 |
| Legacy Christian Academy/Beaumont/ Jefferson | 10915423 | 409/924-0500 | 247 |
| Legacy Christian Academy/Frisco/Collin | 05256802 | 469/633-1330 | 89 |
| Legacy Christian Academy/San Antonio/Bexar | 02192647 | 210/674-0490 | 48 |
| Legacy Classical Chrn Academy/Haslet/ Tarrant | 12313998 | 817/382-2322 | 361 |
| Legacy Early College High Sch/Taylor/ Williamson | 12036839 | 512/352-9596 | 402 |
| Legacy Elem Sch/Lubbock/Lubbock | 12035172 | 806/792-3800 | 272 |
| Legacy High Sch/Mansfield/Tarrant | 10908822 | 682/314-0600 | 359 |
| Legacy High Sch/Tyler/Smith | 01050943 | 903/262-2625 | 340 |
| Legacy Middle Sch/San Antonio/Bexar | 10029787 | 210/648-3118 | 34 |
| Legacy of Educl Excellence HS/San Antonio/ Bexar | 00997910 | 210/356-0800 | 38 |
| Legacy Prep Charter Acad-Plano/Plano/ Collin | 11916884 | 469/998-0213 | 10 |
| Legacy Prep Chtr Acad-Mesquite/Mesquite/ Dallas | 11917503 | 469/287-8610 | 10 |
| Legacy Preparatory Chrn Acad/Magnolia/ Montgomery | 11224514 | 936/337-2000 | 298 |
| Legacy Sch of Sport Sciences/Spring/Harris | 12362664 | 713/396-0837 | 10 |
| **LEGGETT IND SCH DIST**/LEGGETT/ POLK | 01047051 | 936/398-2804 | 319 |
| Leggett Sch/Leggett/Polk | 01047063 | 936/398-2412 | 319 |
| Lehman High Sch/Kyle/Hays | 05352365 | 512/268-8454 | 216 |
| Leila P Cowart Elem Sch/Dallas/Dallas | 01009334 | 972/794-5500 | 105 |
| Lemm Elem Sch/Spring/Harris | 02110675 | 832/484-6300 | 202 |
| Lenore Kirk Hall Elem Sch/Dallas/Dallas | 01009346 | 972/794-5400 | 105 |
| Leo A Rizzuto Elem Sch/La Porte/Harris | 02223856 | 281/604-6500 | 203 |
| Leo Adams Middle Sch/Haslet/Denton | 12375221 | 817/541-8000 | 129 |
| Leo Center/Leander/Williamson | 03390816 | 512/570-2230 | 400 |
| Leo J Leo Elem Sch/Mission/Hidalgo | 02848456 | 956/323-2370 | 223 |

| School/City/County DISTRICT/CITY/COUNTY | PID | TELEPHONE NUMBER | PAGE |
|---|---|---|---|
| Leo Orr Sr Education Center/Malakoff/ Henderson | 04866349 | 903/489-4132 | 219 |
| Leon Daiches Elem Sch/Laredo/Webb | 01059339 | 956/273-3200 | 389 |
| Leon Elem Sch/Jewett/Leon | 01037630 | 903/626-1425 | 267 |
| Leon Heights Elem Sch/Belton/Bell | 00996356 | 254/215-3200 | 30 |
| Leon High Sch/Jewett/Leon | 01037642 | 903/626-1476 | 267 |
| **LEON IND SCH DIST**/JEWETT/LEON | 01037628 | 903/626-1400 | 267 |
| Leon Sablatura Middle Sch/Pearland/ Brazoria | 04752451 | 281/412-1500 | 57 |
| Leon Springs Elem Sch/San Antonio/Bexar | 03397656 | 210/397-4400 | 41 |
| Leon Taylor Junior High Sch/Ingleside/ San Patricio | 01172591 | 361/776-2232 | 334 |
| Leon Valley Christian Academy/San Antonio/ Bexar | 11225192 | 210/684-5662 | 48 |
| Leon Valley Elem Sch/San Antonio/Bexar | 00998184 | 210/397-4650 | 41 |
| Leonard Brautigam Center/Houston/Harris | 04455419 | 281/807-8684 | 190 |
| Leonard Elem Sch/Leonard/Fannin | 01017513 | 903/587-2316 | 150 |
| Leonard High Sch/Leonard/Fannin | 01017525 | 903/587-3556 | 150 |
| **LEONARD IND SCH DIST**/LEONARD/ FANNIN | 01017501 | 903/587-2318 | 150 |
| Leonard Intermediate Sch/Leonard/Fannin | 04920622 | 903/587-8303 | 150 |
| Leonard Junior High Sch/Leonard/Fannin | 03242219 | 903/587-2315 | 150 |
| Leonard Middle Sch/Fort Worth/Tarrant | 01053048 | 817/815-6200 | 353 |
| Leonard Shanklin Elem Sch/Luling/Caldwell | 01003108 | 830/875-2515 | 65 |
| Leonelo H Gonzalez Elem Sch/McAllen/ Hidalgo | 03392618 | 956/971-4577 | 224 |
| Leonides G Cigarroa Elem Sch/Dallas/Dallas | 10023202 | 972/502-2900 | 105 |
| Leslie A Stemmons Elem Sch/Dallas/Dallas | 01009358 | 972/794-4900 | 105 |
| Lester Davis Sch/Denton/Denton | 04748242 | 940/369-4050 | 125 |
| Levelland ABC/Levelland/Hockley | 01857296 | 806/894-6959 | 232 |
| Levelland Christian Sch/Levelland/Hockley | 04994116 | 806/894-6019 | 233 |
| Levelland High Sch/Levelland/Hockley | 01031167 | 806/894-8515 | 232 |
| **LEVELLAND IND SCH DIST**/LEVELLAND/ HOCKLEY | 01031129 | 806/894-9628 | 232 |
| Levelland Intermediate Sch/Levelland/ Hockley | 01031143 | 806/894-3060 | 232 |
| Levelland Middle Sch/Levelland/Hockley | 01031179 | 806/894-6355 | 232 |
| **LEVERETTS CHAPEL IND SCH DIST**/ OVERTON/RUSK | 01049097 | 903/834-6675 | 330 |
| Leveretts Chapel Sch/Overton/Rusk | 01049102 | 903/834-3181 | 330 |
| Levi Fry Intermediate Sch/Texas City/ Galveston | 01019535 | 409/916-0600 | 166 |
| Levine Academy/Dallas/Collin | 02848286 | 972/248-3032 | 89 |
| Lewis Elem Sch/Forney/Kaufman | 10027973 | 469/762-4330 | 255 |
| Lewis Elem Sch/Houston/Harris | 01025601 | 713/845-7453 | 195 |
| Lewisville Elem Sch/Lewisville/Denton | 11553729 | 469/713-5995 | 127 |
| Lewisville High Sch/Lewisville/Denton | 01013488 | 469/713-5190 | 127 |
| Lewisville HS-B Harmon Campus/Lewisville/ Denton | 11718369 | 469/713-5201 | 127 |
| Lewisville HS-Killough/Lewisville/Denton | 04754710 | 469/713-5987 | 127 |
| **LEWISVILLE IND SCH DIST**/ LEWISVILLE/DENTON | 01013402 | 469/713-5200 | 126 |
| Lewisville Learning Center/Lewisville/ Denton | 03249621 | 469/713-5185 | 127 |
| Lexington Creek Elem Sch/Missouri City/ Fort Bend | 04287951 | 281/634-5000 | 154 |
| Lexington Elem Sch/Lexington/Lee | 04354140 | 979/773-2525 | 266 |
| Lexington High Sch/Lexington/Lee | 02112312 | 979/773-2255 | 266 |
| **LEXINGTON IND SCH DIST**/LEXINGTON/ LEE | 01037496 | 979/773-2254 | 266 |
| Lexington Middle Sch/Lexington/Lee | 01037513 | 979/773-2254 | 266 |
| Libby Cash Maus Middle Sch/Frisco/Collin | 11558327 | 469/633-5250 | 83 |
| Libby Elem Sch/Carthage/Panola | 01046253 | 903/693-8862 | 314 |
| Liberal Arts & Science Academy/Austin/ Travis | 10907244 | 512/414-5272 | 371 |
| Liberty Baptist Sch/Lewisville/Denton | 11231646 | 972/436-3493 | 130 |
| Liberty Campus/Victoria/Victoria | 03250747 | 361/788-9650 | 385 |
| Liberty Christian Academy/Sherman/Grayson | 12042369 | 903/328-6037 | 174 |
| Liberty Christian Sch/Argyle/Denton | 02207175 | 940/294-2000 | 130 |
| Liberty Elem Sch/Azle/Tarrant | 02043371 | 817/444-1317 | 348 |
| Liberty Elem Sch/Colleyville/Tarrant | 10003276 | 817/744-6000 | 357 |
| Liberty Elem Sch/Eagle Pass/Maverick | 05095816 | 830/758-7156 | 280 |
| Liberty Elem Sch/Flower Mound/Denton | 05091690 | 469/713-5958 | 127 |
| Liberty Elem Sch/Fort Worth/Tarrant | 01054200 | 817/367-1312 | 360 |
| Liberty Elem Sch/Liberty/Liberty | 01037953 | 936/336-3603 | 269 |
| Liberty Grove Elem Sch/Rowlett/Dallas | 10907397 | 972/487-4416 | 110 |
| Liberty High Sch/Frisco/Collin | 10750675 | 469/633-5800 | 83 |
| Liberty High Sch/Houston/Harris | 10003939 | 713/458-5555 | 194 |
| Liberty High Sch/Liberty/Liberty | 01037939 | 936/336-6483 | 269 |
| Liberty Hill Elem Sch/Liberty Hill/ Williamson | 01061071 | 512/379-3260 | 401 |

| School/City/County DISTRICT/CITY/COUNTY | PID | TELEPHONE NUMBER | PAGE |
|---|---|---|---|
| Liberty Hill High Sch/Liberty Hill/ Williamson | 01418620 | 512/260-5500 | 401 |
| **LIBERTY HILL IND SCH DIST/ LIBERTY HILL/WILLIAMSON** | 01061069 | 512/260-5580 | 401 |
| Liberty Hill Intermediate Sch/Liberty Hill/ Williamson | 04918112 | 512/379-3200 | 401 |
| Liberty Hill Middle Sch/Killeen/Bell | 04811409 | 254/336-1370 | 31 |
| Liberty Hill Middle Sch/Liberty Hill/ Williamson | 02109432 | 512/379-3300 | 401 |
| **LIBERTY IND SCH DIST/LIBERTY/ LIBERTY** | 01037927 | 936/336-7213 | 269 |
| Liberty Junior High Sch/Dallas/Dallas | 01399672 | 469/593-7888 | 117 |
| Liberty Middle Sch/Liberty/Liberty | 01037941 | 936/336-3582 | 269 |
| Liberty Middle Sch/Pharr/Hidalgo | 01030450 | 956/354-2610 | 227 |
| Liberty High Sch/San Benito/Cameron | 05356139 | 956/233-3900 | 69 |
| Liberty-Eylau Early Chldhd Ctr/Texarkana/ Bowie | 01000962 | 903/831-5352 | 52 |
| Liberty-Eylau Elem Sch/Texarkana/Bowie | 01000986 | 903/831-5390 | 52 |
| Liberty-Eylau High Sch/Texarkana/Bowie | 01000974 | 903/832-1530 | 52 |
| **LIBERTY-EYLAU IND SCH DIST/ TEXARKANA/BOWIE** | 01000948 | 903/832-1535 | 51 |
| Liberty-Eylau Middle Sch/Texarkana/Bowie | 01000998 | 903/838-5555 | 52 |
| Lida Hooe Elem Sch/Dallas/Dallas | 01009360 | 972/794-6700 | 105 |
| Lieck Elem Sch/San Antonio/Bexar | 11713917 | 210/398-1450 | 41 |
| Lieder Elem Sch/Houston/Harris | 01829445 | 281/463-5928 | 190 |
| Liestman Elem Sch/Houston/Harris | 01826261 | 281/983-8348 | 187 |
| Life High School-Waxahachie/Waxahachie/ Ellis | 12103913 | 469/708-4444 | 10 |
| Life Middle School Waxahachie/Waxahachie/ Ellis | 11595442 | 972/937-0715 | 10 |
| Life School Carrollton/Carrollton/Dallas | 12375257 | 469/701-1355 | 10 |
| Life School Cedar Hill/Cedar Hill/Dallas | 11595428 | 972/293-2825 | 10 |
| Life School Lancaster/Lancaster/Dallas | 11014515 | 972/274-7950 | 10 |
| Life School Mountain Creek/Dallas/Dallas | 11935359 | 214/623-0012 | 10 |
| Life School Oak Cliff/Dallas/Dallas | 04814401 | 214/376-8200 | 10 |
| Life School Red Oak/Red Oak/Ellis | 11014503 | 469/552-9200 | 10 |
| Lifegate Christian Sch/Seguin/Guadalupe | 04924381 | 830/372-0850 | 179 |
| Lifestyle Christian Sch/Conroe/Montgomery | 04937479 | 936/756-9383 | 298 |
| Light Farms Elem Sch/Celina/Collin | 12109010 | 469/219-2140 | 88 |
| Lighthouse Charter Sch/San Antonio/Bexar | 05282667 | 210/674-4100 | 10 |
| Lighthouse Chtr Sch-B Campus/San Antonio/ Bexar | 12163171 | 210/257-6746 | 10 |
| Lighthouse Learning Center/Clute/Brazoria | 04033700 | 979/730-7340 | 55 |
| Lillian Elem Sch/Alvarado/Johnson | 01035125 | 817/783-6815 | 249 |
| Lillion E Luehrs Jr High Sch/Bishop/Nueces | 01044073 | 361/584-3576 | 305 |
| Lily B Clayton Elem Sch/Fort Worth/Tarrant | 01053050 | 817/814-5400 | 353 |
| Lincoln Elem Sch/Edinburg/Hidalgo | 04806507 | 956/289-2525 | 222 |
| Lincoln Elem Sch/Montgomery/Montgomery | 12363060 | 936/276-4700 | 296 |
| Lincoln Humanities/Comm HS/Dallas/Dallas | 01009372 | 972/925-7600 | 105 |
| Lincoln Junior High Sch/Coldspring/ San Jacinto | 01049425 | 936/653-1166 | 333 |
| Lincoln Middle Sch/El Paso/El Paso | 01016026 | 915/236-3400 | 139 |
| Lincoln Middle Sch/San Angelo/Tom Green | 01055723 | 325/659-3550 | 367 |
| Lincoln Park Sch/Brownsville/Cameron | 02127733 | 956/548-7880 | 67 |
| Linda Herrington Elem Sch/Round Rock/ Williamson | 11714416 | 512/704-1900 | 402 |
| Linda Jobe Middle Sch/Mansfield/Tarrant | 11452199 | 682/314-4400 | 359 |
| Linda Lyon Elem Sch/Heath/Rockwall | 12232370 | 214/771-4910 | 328 |
| Linda Tutt High Sch/Sanger/Denton | 04865618 | 940/458-5701 | 130 |
| Lindale High Sch/Lindale/Smith | 01050668 | 903/881-4050 | 340 |
| **LINDALE IND SCH DIST/LINDALE/ SMITH** | 01050656 | 903/881-4000 | 339 |
| Lindale Junior High Sch/Lindale/Smith | 01050682 | 903/881-4150 | 340 |
| Linden Elem Sch/Linden/Cass | 01826144 | 903/756-5471 | 74 |
| **LINDEN KILDARE CONS IND SD/ LINDEN/CASS** | 01004827 | 903/756-7071 | 74 |
| Linden Kildare High Sch/Linden/Cass | 01004865 | 903/756-5314 | 74 |
| Linder Elem Sch/Austin/Travis | 01056349 | 512/414-2398 | 370 |
| Lindsay Elem Sch/Lindsay/Cooke | 01007439 | 940/668-8923 | 95 |
| Lindsay High Sch/Lindsay/Cooke | 05341419 | 940/668-8474 | 95 |
| **LINDSAY IND SCH DIST/LINDSAY/ COOKE** | 01007427 | 940/668-8923 | 95 |
| Lindsey Elem Sch/Katy/Fort Bend | 12230815 | 832/223-5400 | 158 |
| **LINGLEVILLE IND SCH DIST/ LINGLEVILLE/ERATH** | 01017082 | 254/968-2596 | 148 |
| Lingleville Sch/Lingleville/Erath | 01017094 | 254/968-2596 | 148 |
| Links Academy/Godley/Johnson | 12368931 | 817/592-4410 | 250 |
| Lion Lane Sch/Houston/Harris | 04949862 | 713/251-6100 | 206 |
| **LIPAN IND SCH DIST/LIPAN/HOOD** | 01031416 | 254/646-2266 | 233 |
| Lipan Sch/Lipan/Hood | 01031428 | 254/646-2266 | 233 |
| Liscano Elem Sch/Frisco/Collin | 12308357 | 469/633-2275 | 83 |
| Lisd STEM Acad-Bridlewood/Flower Mound/ Denton | 04812635 | 469/713-5193 | 127 |
| Lisd STEM Acad-Donald/Flower Mound/Denton | 03249372 | 469/713-5198 | 127 |
| Lisd STEM Acad-Polser/Carrollton/Denton | 04364664 | 469/713-5978 | 127 |
| Little Cypress Elem Sch/Orange/Orange | 01045663 | 409/886-2838 | 311 |
| Little Cypress Interm Sch/Orange/Orange | 01529994 | 409/886-4245 | 311 |
| Little Cypress Jr High Sch/Orange/Orange | 01045687 | 409/883-2317 | 311 |
| **LITTLE CYPRESS MAURICEVILLE SD/ ORANGE/ORANGE** | 01045651 | 409/883-2232 | 311 |
| Little Cypress-Mauriceville HS/Orange/ Orange | 01045675 | 409/886-5821 | 311 |
| Little Elem Sch/Arlington/Tarrant | 01051844 | 682/867-3300 | 347 |
| Little Elm High Sch/Little Elm/Denton | 01401392 | 972/947-9443 | 128 |
| **LITTLE ELM IND SCH DIST/ LITTLE ELM/DENTON** | 01013490 | 972/947-9340 | 128 |
| Little Flower Sch/San Antonio/Bexar | 00999865 | 210/732-9207 | 47 |
| Littlefield Elem Sch/Littlefield/Lamb | 01036923 | 806/385-6217 | 263 |
| Littlefield High Sch/Littlefield/Lamb | 01036947 | 806/385-5683 | 263 |
| **LITTLEFIELD IND SCH DIST/ LITTLEFIELD/LAMB** | 01036911 | 806/385-3844 | 263 |
| Littlefield Junior High Sch/Littlefield/ Lamb | 01036959 | 806/385-3922 | 263 |
| Littlefield Primary Sch/Littlefield/Lamb | 01036961 | 806/385-3922 | 263 |
| Live Oak Academy/Buda/Hays | 04923882 | 512/268-8462 | 216 |
| Live Oak Classical Sch/Waco/McLennan | 10900870 | 254/714-1007 | 285 |
| Live Oak Elem Sch/Austin/Williamson | 03007356 | 512/428-3800 | 402 |
| Live Oak Learning Center/Rockport/Aransas | 00995144 | 361/790-2260 | 22 |
| Live Oak Ridge Middle Sch/Killeen/Bell | 05097058 | 254/336-2490 | 31 |
| Lively Elem Sch/Irving/Dallas | 01011258 | 972/600-6700 | 114 |
| Lively Middle Sch/Austin/Travis | 01056210 | 512/414-3207 | 371 |
| Living Rock Academy/Bulverde/Comal | 12314198 | 830/387-2929 | 93 |
| Living Stones Christian Sch/Alvin/Brazoria | 02192398 | 281/331-0086 | 58 |
| Living Water Christian Sch/Rosenberg/ Fort Bend | 04856667 | 281/342-6336 | 160 |
| Living Word Christian Academy/Houston/ Harris | 02153641 | 713/686-5538 | 211 |
| Livingston High Sch/Livingston/Polk | 01047099 | 936/328-8600 | 320 |
| Livingston High Sch Academy/Livingston/ Polk | 12305719 | 936/328-8600 | 320 |
| **LIVINGSTON IND SCH DIST/ LIVINGSTON/POLK** | 01047075 | 936/328-2100 | 319 |
| Livingston Junior High Sch/Livingston/Polk | 01047104 | 936/328-2120 | 320 |
| Lizzie Burgess Alt Sch/Seguin/Guadalupe | 03049706 | 830/379-1108 | 179 |
| Lizzie Curtis Elem Sch/Fort Worth/Denton | 12363333 | 817/541-8901 | 129 |
| Lizzie Nell C McClure Elem Sch/McKinney/ Collin | 11555600 | 469/302-9400 | 85 |
| Llano Christian Academy/Llano/Llano | 12314186 | 325/247-4942 | 271 |
| Llano Elem Sch/Llano/Llano | 01038359 | 325/247-5718 | 271 |
| Llano High Sch/Llano/Llano | 01038361 | 325/248-2200 | 271 |
| **LLANO IND SCH DIST/LLANO/LLANO** | 01038347 | 325/247-4747 | 271 |
| Llano Junior High Sch/Llano/Llano | 01038373 | 325/247-4659 | 271 |
| Lloyd & Dolly Bentsen Elem Sch/McAllen/ Hidalgo | 10011417 | 956/686-0426 | 227 |
| Lloyd M Bentsen Elem Sch/Mission/Hidalgo | 04946822 | 956/323-2480 | 223 |
| Lloyd M Knowlton Elem Sch/San Antonio/ Bexar | 02848509 | 210/397-2600 | 41 |
| Lloyd R Ferguson Elem Sch/League City/ Galveston | 03325536 | 281/284-5500 | 163 |
| Locke Hill Elem Sch/San Antonio/Bexar | 00998196 | 210/397-1600 | 41 |
| Lockhart Elem Sch/Houston/Harris | 01024906 | 713/942-1950 | 198 |
| Lockhart High Sch/Lockhart/Caldwell | 01003067 | 512/398-0300 | 64 |
| **LOCKHART IND SCH DIST/LOCKHART/ CALDWELL** | 01003031 | 512/398-0000 | 64 |
| Lockhart Junior High Sch/Lockhart/Caldwell | 01003079 | 512/398-0770 | 64 |
| Lockhart Pride High Sch/Lockhart/Caldwell | 03399549 | 512/398-0130 | 64 |
| Lockney Elem Sch/Lockney/Floyd | 01018036 | 806/652-3321 | 153 |
| Lockney High Sch/Lockney/Floyd | 01018048 | 806/652-3325 | 153 |
| **LOCKNEY INDEPENDENT SCH DIST/ LOCKNEY/FLOYD** | 01018024 | 806/652-2104 | 153 |
| Lockney Junior High Sch/Lockney/Floyd | 01018050 | 806/652-2236 | 153 |
| Logan Elem Sch/El Paso/El Paso | 01015814 | 915/236-5750 | 138 |
| Logos Preparatory Academy/Sugar Land/ Fort Bend | 11223950 | 281/565-6467 | 160 |
| **LOHN IND SCH DIST/LOHN/McCULLOCH** | 01039482 | 325/344-5749 | 280 |
| Lohn Sch/Lohn/McCulloch | 01039494 | 325/344-5749 | 280 |
| Lois Lindsey Elem Sch/McKinney/Collin | 11916925 | 972/908-4000 | 80 |
| Lola Mae Carter Academy/Houston/Harris | 04805046 | 281/878-7760 | 184 |
| Loma Alta Middle Sch/San Antonio/Medina | 12369533 | 830/931-2243 | 287 |
| Loma Park Elem Sch/San Antonio/Bexar | 00997295 | 210/444-8250 | 35 |
| Loma Terrace Elem Sch/El Paso/El Paso | 01016454 | 915/434-2600 | 142 |
| Loma Verde Elem Sch/El Paso/El Paso | 05153418 | 915/937-8600 | 140 |
| Lomax Elem Sch/La Porte/Harris | 01824251 | 281/604-4300 | 203 |

| School/City/County DISTRICT/CITY/COUNTY | PID | TELEPHONE NUMBER | PAGE |
|---|---|---|---|
| Lomax Junior High Sch/La Porte/Harris | 02894168 | 281/604-6700 | 203 |
| Lomax Middle Sch/Pasadena/Harris | 10913279 | 713/740-5230 | 204 |
| **LOMETA IND SCH DIST/LOMETA/ LAMPASAS** | 01037161 | 512/752-3384 | 264 |
| Lometa Sch/Lometa/Lampasas | 01037173 | 512/752-3384 | 264 |
| **LONDON IND SCH DIST/CORP CHRISTI/ NUECES** | 01044865 | 361/855-0183 | 308 |
| London Sch/Corp Christi/Nueces | 01044877 | 361/855-0092 | 308 |
| Lone Oak College St Campus/Lone Oak/Hunt | 12233934 | 903/634-2071 | 239 |
| Lone Oak Elem Sch/Lone Oak/Hunt | 01032551 | 903/662-5151 | 239 |
| Lone Oak High Sch/Lone Oak/Hunt | 01032563 | 903/662-0980 | 239 |
| **LONE OAK IND SCH DIST/LONE OAK/ HUNT** | 01032549 | 903/634-5247 | 239 |
| Lone Oak Middle Sch/Lone Oak/Hunt | 03020255 | 903/662-5121 | 239 |
| Lone Star Early Childhood Ctr/New Braunfels/ Comal | 12312578 | 830/627-6820 | 92 |
| Lone Star Elem Sch/Fort Worth/Tarrant | 04921626 | 817/744-5200 | 357 |
| Lone Star Elem Sch/Montgomery/Montgomery | 10031443 | 936/276-4500 | 296 |
| Lone Star High Sch/Frisco/Collin | 11558315 | 469/633-5300 | 83 |
| Lone Star Language Academy/Plano/Collin | 12260925 | 972/244-7220 | 10 |
| Long Academy/Houston/Harris | 01024449 | 713/778-3380 | 199 |
| Long Early Childhood Center/Abilene/Taylor | 01172802 | 325/671-4594 | 363 |
| Long Elem Sch/Midland/Midland | 01041564 | 432/240-7400 | 289 |
| Long Intermediate Sch/Bryan/Brazos | 03244683 | 979/209-6500 | 58 |
| Longbranch Elem Sch/Midlothian/Ellis | 01015151 | 469/856-6200 | 145 |
| Longfellow Elem Sch/Houston/Harris | 01025297 | 713/295-5268 | 199 |
| Longfellow Middle Sch/San Antonio/Bexar | 00998495 | 210/438-6520 | 44 |
| Longoria Middle Sch/Edinburg/Hidalgo | 11719416 | 956/289-2486 | 222 |
| Longs Creek Elem Sch/San Antonio/Bexar | 04757061 | 210/407-4800 | 38 |
| Longview Christian Academy/Longview/Gregg | 02153665 | 903/759-0626 | 176 |
| Longview Christian Sch/Longview/Gregg | 02207292 | 903/297-3501 | 176 |
| Longview Early Graduation HS/Longview/ Gregg | 01809304 | 903/381-3921 | 175 |
| Longview High Sch/Longview/Gregg | 01021083 | 903/663-1301 | 175 |
| **LONGVIEW IND SCH DIST/LONGVIEW/ GREGG** | 01020986 | 903/381-2200 | 174 |
| **LOOP IND SCH DIST/LOOP/GAINES** | 01018684 | 806/487-6412 | 162 |
| Loop Sch/Loop/Gaines | 01018696 | 806/487-6412 | 162 |
| Looscan Elem Sch/Houston/Harris | 01026021 | 713/696-2760 | 194 |
| Lopez Early College High Sch/Brownsville/ Cameron | 04034314 | 956/982-7400 | 67 |
| Lopez-Riggins Elem Sch/Los Fresnos/Cameron | 02894314 | 956/233-6916 | 69 |
| **LORAINE IND SCH DIST/LORAINE/ MITCHELL** | 01042128 | 325/737-2225 | 292 |
| Loraine Sch/Loraine/Mitchell | 01042130 | 325/737-2225 | 292 |
| Loraine T Golbow Elem Sch/Katy/Harris | 03249114 | 281/237-5350 | 156 |
| Lord of Life Lutheran Sch/Friendswood/ Galveston | 04993564 | 281/482-0481 | 166 |
| Lorena Elem Sch/Lorena/McLennan | 01039834 | 254/857-4613 | 283 |
| Lorena High Sch/Lorena/McLennan | 01039846 | 254/857-4604 | 283 |
| **LORENA IND SCH DIST/LORENA/ MCLENNAN** | 01039822 | 254/857-3616 | 283 |
| Lorena Middle Sch/Lorena/McLennan | 02890033 | 254/857-4621 | 283 |
| Lorena Primary Sch/Lorena/McLennan | 05352054 | 254/857-8909 | 283 |
| Lorene S Kirkpatrick Elem Sch/Maypearl/ Ellis | 01015113 | 972/435-1010 | 145 |
| Lorenzo De Zavala Elem Sch/Baytown/Harris | 04019479 | 281/420-4920 | 193 |
| Lorenzo De Zavala Elem Sch/Crystal City/ Zavala | 01062300 | 830/374-8080 | 410 |
| Lorenzo De Zavala Elem Sch/Dallas/Dallas | 02109822 | 972/892-6400 | 105 |
| Lorenzo De Zavala Elem Sch/Edinburg/ Hidalgo | 03267063 | 956/289-2350 | 222 |
| Lorenzo De Zavala Middle Sch/Amarillo/ Potter | 10008367 | 806/326-3400 | 321 |
| Lorenzo De Zavala Middle Sch/Irving/Dallas | 05090555 | 972/600-6000 | 114 |
| Lorenzo De Zavala Middle Sch/La Joya/ Hidalgo | 01029889 | 956/323-2770 | 223 |
| Lorenzo De Zavala Spec Emp Sch/Corp Christi/ Nueces | 01044786 | 361/878-2720 | 306 |
| Lorenzo Dezavala Middle Sch/Pasadena/ Harris | 05102885 | 713/740-0544 | 204 |
| Lorenzo Elem Sch/Lorenzo/Crosby | 01007960 | 806/634-5593 | 98 |
| Lorenzo G Loya Primary Sch/San Elizario/ El Paso | 03394161 | 915/872-3940 | 140 |
| **LORENZO IND SCH DIST/LORENZO/ CROSBY** | 01007958 | 806/634-5591 | 98 |
| Lorenzo Jr Sr High Sch/Lorenzo/Crosby | 01007972 | 806/634-5592 | 98 |
| Loreta Hickey Elem Sch/Plano/Collin | 05096860 | 469/752-4100 | 86 |
| Loretto Acad Elem Sch/El Paso/El Paso | 01016806 | 915/566-8400 | 143 |
| Loretto Acad-Middle High Sch/El Paso/ El Paso | 01016791 | 915/566-8400 | 143 |
| Los Cuates Middle Sch/Los Fresnos/Cameron | 01004047 | 956/254-5182 | 69 |
| Los Encinos Ses Elem Sch/Corp Christi/ Nueces | 01044516 | 361/878-2600 | 307 |
| **LOS FRESNOS CONS IND SCH DIST/ LOS FRESNOS/CAMERON** | 01004009 | 956/254-5000 | 69 |
| Los Fresnos Elem Sch/Los Fresnos/Cameron | 01004023 | 956/233-6900 | 69 |
| Los Fresnos High Sch/Los Fresnos/Cameron | 01004035 | 956/254-5300 | 69 |
| Los Fresnos United Sch/San Benito/Cameron | 11456901 | 956/254-5250 | 69 |
| Los Obispos Middle Sch/Laredo/Webb | 04455926 | 956/473-7800 | 391 |
| Los Reyes Elem Sch/Helotes/Bexar | 11822843 | 210/398-1200 | 41 |
| Losoya Intermediate Sch/San Antonio/Bexar | 03008245 | 210/882-1602 | 46 |
| Lost Pines Elem Sch/Bastrop/Bastrop | 05350173 | 512/772-7700 | 27 |
| Lotspeich Elem Sch/Robstown/Nueces | 01044920 | 361/767-6655 | 308 |
| Louie Welch Middle Sch/Houston/Harris | 02043307 | 713/778-3300 | 199 |
| Louis G Lobit Elem Sch/Dickinson/Galveston | 12167335 | 281/229-7600 | 164 |
| Louis Reicher Catholic Sch/Waco/McLennan | 01002960 | 254/754-2041 | 285 |
| Louise Cabaniss Elem Sch/Grand Prairie/ Tarrant | 11073690 | 817/299-6480 | 359 |
| Louise Elem Sch/Louise/Wharton | 01059676 | 979/648-2262 | 392 |
| Louise High Sch/Louise/Wharton | 01059688 | 979/648-2202 | 392 |
| **LOUISE IND SCH DIST/LOUISE/ WHARTON** | 01059664 | 979/648-2982 | 392 |
| Louise Junior High Sch/Louise/Wharton | 11071812 | 979/648-2262 | 392 |
| Louise Wolff Kahn Elem Sch/Dallas/Dallas | 04757102 | 972/502-1400 | 105 |
| Love Elem Sch/Houston/Harris | 01024140 | 713/867-0840 | 197 |
| Lovejoy Elem Sch/Allen/Collin | 01006239 | 469/742-8100 | 84 |
| Lovejoy High Sch/Lucas/Collin | 10025858 | 469/742-8700 | 84 |
| **LOVEJOY IND SCH DIST/ALLEN/ COLLIN** | 01006227 | 469/742-8000 | 84 |
| Lovelady Elem Middle Sch/Lovelady/Houston | 01031856 | 936/636-7636 | 236 |
| **LOVELADY IND SCH DIST/LOVELADY/ HOUSTON** | 01031844 | 936/636-7616 | 236 |
| Lovelady Jr Sr High Sch/Lovelady/Houston | 01031868 | 936/636-7636 | 236 |
| Lovett Elem Sch/Houston/Harris | 01024918 | 713/295-5258 | 199 |
| Lowe Elem Sch/Princeton/Collin | 12363606 | 469/952-5419 | 87 |
| Lowery Elem Sch/Houston/Harris | 02126430 | 281/463-5900 | 190 |
| Lowery Freshman Center/Allen/Collin | 04866741 | 972/396-6975 | 80 |
| Lowery Road Elem Sch/Fort Worth/Tarrant | 04919439 | 817/815-4700 | 353 |
| Lubbock Adult Learning Center/Lubbock/ Lubbock | 04018516 | 806/281-5750 | 10 |
| Lubbock Christian Sch/Lubbock/Lubbock | 01480714 | 806/796-8700 | 275 |
| **LUBBOCK IND SCH DIST/LUBBOCK/ LUBBOCK** | 01038490 | 806/766-1000 | 272 |
| Lubbock Junior Academy/Lubbock/Lubbock | 11816545 | 806/793-8614 | 275 |
| Lubbock Senior High Sch/Lubbock/Lubbock | 01038751 | 806/219-1600 | 273 |
| Lubbock-Cooper High Sch/Lubbock/Lubbock | 01039042 | 806/863-7105 | 274 |
| **LUBBOCK-COOPER IND SCH DIST/ LUBBOCK/LUBBOCK** | 01039030 | 806/863-7100 | 274 |
| Lubbock-Cooper Middle Sch/Lubbock/Lubbock | 01039066 | 806/863-7104 | 274 |
| Lucas Christian Academy/Lucas/Collin | 04954415 | 972/429-4362 | 89 |
| Lucas Pre-K Center/Beaumont/Jefferson | 01033567 | 409/617-6450 | 245 |
| Lucian Adams Elem Sch/Port Arthur/ Jefferson | 11826356 | 409/984-4100 | 246 |
| Lucile M Hendricks Elem Sch/McAllen/ Hidalgo | 11104017 | 956/971-1145 | 224 |
| Lucile Rogers Ashley Elem Sch/Frisco/ Collin | 10016687 | 469/633-3700 | 83 |
| Lucille Nash Elem Sch/Kaufman/Kaufman | 01035644 | 972/932-6415 | 255 |
| Lucio Middle Sch/Brownsville/Cameron | 04751184 | 956/831-4550 | 67 |
| Luckey Ranch Elem Sch/San Antonio/Medina | 12369545 | 830/931-2243 | 287 |
| Lucy Mae McDonald Elem Sch/Ferris/Ellis | 05230717 | 972/544-3405 | 145 |
| Lucy Read Pre-K Sch/Austin/Travis | 10025468 | 512/419-9400 | 370 |
| Lucy Rede Franco Middle Sch/Presidio/ Presidio | 01047881 | 432/229-3113 | 323 |
| Lucyle Collins Middle Sch/Fort Worth/ Tarrant | 10030970 | 817/306-4250 | 358 |
| Ludi Pena Martin Accel Ed Ctr/Perryton/ Ochiltree | 04913576 | 806/434-0389 | 310 |
| Lueders-Avoca Elem Jr High Sch/Lueders/ Jones | 01035307 | 325/228-4211 | 253 |
| Lueders-Avoca High Sch/Avoca/Jones | 01035319 | 325/773-2785 | 253 |
| **LUEDERS-AVOCA IND SCH DIST/ LUEDERS/JONES** | 01035292 | 325/228-4211 | 253 |
| Luella Merrett Elem Sch/Fort Worth/Tarrant | 01053309 | 817/815-6600 | 353 |
| Lufkin High Sch/Lufkin/Angelina | 00995015 | 936/632-7721 | 21 |
| **LUFKIN IND SCH DIST/LUFKIN/ ANGELINA** | 00994932 | 936/634-6696 | 21 |
| Lufkin Middle Sch/Lufkin/Angelina | 00995003 | 936/630-4444 | 21 |
| Lujan-Chavez Elem Sch/El Paso/El Paso | 04941793 | 915/937-8700 | 140 |
| Lula Belle Goodman Elem Sch/Fresno/ Fort Bend | 04921547 | 281/634-5985 | 155 |
| Luling High Sch/Luling/Caldwell | 02884137 | 830/875-2458 | 65 |

| School/City/County DISTRICT/CITY/COUNTY | PID | TELEPHONE NUMBER | PAGE |
|---|---|---|---|
| **LULING IND SCH DIST**/LULING/ | | | |
| CALDWELL | 01003093 | 830/875-3191 | 64 |
| Luling Primary Sch/Luling/Caldwell | 02200969 | 830/875-2223 | 65 |
| Lumberton High Sch/Lumberton/Hardin | 01022568 | 409/923-7890 | 183 |
| **LUMBERTON IND SCH DIST**/LUMBERTON/ | | | |
| HARDIN | 01022544 | 409/923-7580 | 183 |
| Lumberton Intermediate Sch/Lumberton/ | | | |
| Hardin | 02046505 | 409/923-7790 | 183 |
| Lumberton Middle Sch/Lumberton/Hardin | 01022556 | 409/923-7581 | 183 |
| Lumberton Primary Sch/Lumberton/Hardin | 01022570 | 409/923-7490 | 183 |
| Lumin E Dallas Community Sch/Dallas/Dallas | 04814358 | 214/824-8950 | 10 |
| Lumin Lindsley Park Cmty Sch/Dallas/Dallas | 05013143 | 214/321-9155 | 11 |
| Luna Elem Sch/Garland/Dallas | 02226107 | 972/675-3040 | 110 |
| Lundy Elem Sch/El Paso/El Paso | 11449180 | 915/230-5075 | 138 |
| Luther & Anna Bolin Elem Sch/Parker/Collin | 04913124 | 214/495-6750 | 80 |
| Luther Jones Elem Sch/Corp Christi/Nueces | 03333090 | 361/878-0100 | 307 |
| Lutheran High Sch/Dallas/Dallas | 02152257 | 214/349-8912 | 119 |
| Lutheran High Sch/San Antonio/Bexar | 04951152 | 210/694-4962 | 48 |
| Lutheran High School North/Houston/Harris | 02157324 | 713/880-3131 | 211 |
| Lutheran South Academy/Houston/Harris | 01410771 | 281/464-8299 | 211 |
| Lycee International De Houston/Houston/ | | | |
| Harris | 12468529 | 832/474-1013 | 211 |
| Lydia Patterson Institute/El Paso/El Paso | 01480075 | 915/533-8286 | 143 |
| **LYFORD CONS IND SCH DIST**/ | | | |
| LYFORD/WILLACY | 01060651 | 956/347-3900 | 397 |
| Lyford Elem Sch/Lyford/Willacy | 03050743 | 956/347-3911 | 397 |
| Lyford High Sch/Lyford/Willacy | 01060675 | 956/347-3909 | 397 |
| Lyford Middle Sch/Lyford/Willacy | 01060687 | 956/347-3910 | 397 |
| Lyles Middle Sch/Garland/Dallas | 03009378 | 972/240-3720 | 110 |
| Lyndon B Johnson Elem Sch/Edinburg/Hidalgo | 01878410 | 956/289-2358 | 222 |
| Lyndon B Johnson Elem Sch/Johnson City/ | | | |
| Blanco | 01000522 | 830/868-4028 | 49 |
| Lyndon B Johnson Elem Sch/Odessa/Ector | 03248756 | 432/456-1289 | 134 |
| Lyndon B Johnson High Sch/Austin/Travis | 01056454 | 512/414-2543 | 371 |
| Lyndon B Johnson High Sch/Johnson City/ | | | |
| Blanco | 01000534 | 830/868-4025 | 49 |
| Lyndon B Johnson High Sch/Laredo/Webb | 04946377 | 956/473-5100 | 391 |
| Lyndon B Johnson Middle Sch/Johnson City/ | | | |
| Blanco | 04245240 | 830/868-9025 | 49 |
| Lyndon B Johnson Middle Sch/Pharr/Hidalgo | 01826314 | 956/354-2590 | 227 |
| Lyndon Baines Johnson Elem Sch/Elsa/ | | | |
| Hidalgo | 03237393 | 956/262-2161 | 221 |
| Lynn Lucas Middle Sch/Willis/Montgomery | 02177996 | 936/856-1274 | 297 |
| Lyons Elem Sch/Houston/Harris | 04036312 | 713/696-2870 | 196 |
| Lytle Elem Sch/Lytle/Atascosa | 00995417 | 830/709-5130 | 24 |
| Lytle High Sch/Lytle/Atascosa | 00995429 | 830/709-5105 | 24 |
| **LYTLE IND SCH DIST**/LYTLE/ | | | |
| ATASCOSA | 00995405 | 830/709-5100 | 24 |
| Lytle Junior High Sch/Lytle/Atascosa | 04940361 | 830/709-5115 | 24 |
| Lytle Primary Sch/Lytle/Atascosa | 04972534 | 830/709-5140 | 24 |

### M

| School/City/County DISTRICT/CITY/COUNTY | PID | TELEPHONE NUMBER | PAGE |
|---|---|---|---|
| M B Lamar High Sch/Arlington/Tarrant | 01051832 | 682/867-8300 | 347 |
| M B Lamar Middle Sch/Laredo/Webb | 01059353 | 956/273-6200 | 390 |
| M C Williams Middle Sch/Houston/Harris | 01024152 | 713/696-2600 | 194 |
| M D Betts Elem Sch/Edinburg/Hidalgo | 04873251 | 956/289-2560 | 222 |
| M G Ellis Primary Sch/Fort Worth/Tarrant | 05096523 | 817/814-3800 | 353 |
| M H Moore Elem Sch/Fort Worth/Tarrant | 01053062 | 817/815-0600 | 353 |
| M H Specht Elem Sch/San Antonio/Comal | 05090701 | 830/885-1500 | 92 |
| M L King Middle Sch/Beaumont/Jefferson | 01033452 | 409/617-5850 | 245 |
| M Robinson Elem Sch/Katy/Harris | 11077359 | 281/855-1240 | 190 |
| M S Ryan Elem Sch/Laredo/Webb | 01059365 | 956/273-4400 | 390 |
| Mabank Daep/Mabank/Kaufman | 05090983 | 903/880-1320 | 256 |
| Mabank High Sch/Mabank/Kaufman | 01035709 | 903/880-1600 | 256 |
| **MABANK IND SCH DIST**/MABANK/ | | | |
| KAUFMAN | 01035682 | 903/880-1300 | 255 |
| Mabank Intermediate Sch/Mabank/Kaufman | 01035711 | 903/880-1640 | 256 |
| Mabank Junior High Sch/Mabank/Kaufman | 11157167 | 903/880-1670 | 256 |
| Mabel B Wesley Elem Sch/Houston/Harris | 01024164 | 713/696-2860 | 194 |
| MacAria Gorena Elem Sch/Edinburg/Hidalgo | 11719404 | 956/289-2460 | 222 |
| Macario Garcia Middle Sch/Sugar Land/ | | | |
| Fort Bend | 04365876 | 281/634-3160 | 155 |
| MacArthur 9th Grade Sch/Houston/Harris | 04867214 | 281/985-7400 | 185 |
| MacArthur Elem Sch/Galena Park/Harris | 01023445 | 832/386-4630 | 192 |
| MacArthur Elem-Interm Sch/El Paso/El Paso | 01015668 | 915/236-0625 | 138 |
| MacArthur High Sch/Irving/Dallas | 01011260 | 972/600-7200 | 114 |
| MacArthur High Sch/San Antonio/Bexar | 00997740 | 210/356-7600 | 38 |
| MacGregor Elem Sch/Houston/Harris | 01024932 | 713/942-1990 | 199 |
| MacKenzie Middle Sch/Lubbock/Lubbock | 01038763 | 806/219-4200 | 273 |
| Madden Elem Sch/Richmond/Fort Bend | 12105313 | 281/327-2740 | 155 |
| Madeley Ranch Elem Sch/Montgomery/ | | | |
| Montgomery | 11456987 | 936/276-4600 | 296 |
| Madge Griffith Elem Sch/Clute/Brazoria | 03316729 | 979/730-7180 | 55 |
| Mading Elem Sch/Houston/Harris | 01025302 | 713/732-3560 | 194 |
| Madison Elem Sch/San Antonio/Bexar | 00998471 | 210/438-6545 | 44 |
| Madison High Sch/Houston/Harris | 01025273 | 713/433-9801 | 194 |
| Madison High Sch/San Antonio/Bexar | 01523677 | 210/356-1400 | 38 |
| Madison Middle Sch/Abilene/Taylor | 01172814 | 325/692-5661 | 363 |
| **MADISONVILLE CONS ISD**/MADISONVILLE/ | | | |
| MADISON | 01040596 | 936/348-2797 | 276 |
| Madisonville Elem Sch/Madisonville/Madison | 01040601 | 936/348-2261 | 276 |
| Madisonville High Sch/Madisonville/Madison | 01040613 | 936/348-2721 | 276 |
| Madisonville Intermediate Sch/Madisonville/ | | | |
| Madison | 02131772 | 936/348-2921 | 276 |
| Madisonville Jr High Sch/Madisonville/ | | | |
| Madison | 01040625 | 936/348-3587 | 276 |
| Mae Luster Stephens Jr HS/Linden/Cass | 01004841 | 903/756-5381 | 74 |
| Mae Smythe Elem Sch/Pasadena/Harris | 01026954 | 713/740-0728 | 204 |
| Mae Stevens Early Learng Acad/Copperas Cove/ | | | |
| Coryell | 01007623 | 254/547-8289 | 96 |
| Maedgen Elem Sch/Lubbock/Lubbock | 01038775 | 806/219-6200 | 273 |
| MaGee Elem Sch/Corp Christi/Nueces | 01044164 | 361/242-5900 | 306 |
| Magellan Int'l Sch-Anderson Ln/Austin/ | | | |
| Travis | 11927118 | 512/782-2327 | 376 |
| Maggie B Selman Elem Sch/Sealy/Austin | 00995596 | 979/885-6659 | 25 |
| Magin Rivas Elem Sch/Donna/Hidalgo | 02895124 | 956/464 1990 | 220 |
| Magnolia Elem Sch/Magnolia/Montgomery | 01042594 | 281/356-6434 | 296 |
| Magnolia Elem Sch/Pearland/Brazoria | 10909254 | 281/727-1750 | 57 |
| Magnolia High Sch/Magnolia/Montgomery | 01042609 | 281/356-3572 | 296 |
| **MAGNOLIA IND SCH DIST**/MAGNOLIA/ | | | |
| MONTGOMERY | 01042582 | 281/356-3571 | 295 |
| Magnolia Intermediate Sch/Magnolia/ | | | |
| Montgomery | 05097644 | 281/252-2033 | 296 |
| Magnolia Junior High Sch/Magnolia/ | | | |
| Montgomery | 01042611 | 281/356-1327 | 296 |
| Magnolia Montessori for All/Austin/Travis | 12114041 | 512/522-2429 | 11 |
| Magnolia Parkway Elem Sch/Magnolia/ | | | |
| Montgomery | 11127095 | 281/252-7440 | 296 |
| Magnolia West High Sch/Magnolia/Montgomery | 10028642 | 281/252-2550 | 296 |
| Magoffin Middle Sch/El Paso/El Paso | 01015826 | 915/774-4040 | 139 |
| Magrill EC-PK-K Sch/Humble/Harris | 01399751 | 281/233-4300 | 186 |
| Mahaffey Elem Sch/Tomball/Harris | 12166783 | 832/375-8300 | 202 |
| Mahanay Elem Sch/Houston/Harris | 01023043 | 281/983-8355 | 187 |
| Main Street Imtermediate Sch/Taylor/ | | | |
| Williamson | 02199750 | 512/365-1999 | 403 |
| Mainland Prep Classical Acad/La Marque/ | | | |
| Galveston | 04814425 | 409/934-9100 | 11 |
| Major Cheney ES-S Birdville/Haltom City/ | | | |
| Tarrant | 01052185 | 817/547-2300 | 349 |
| Malakoff Elem Sch/Malakoff/Henderson | 01029451 | 903/489-0313 | 219 |
| Malakoff High Sch/Malakoff/Henderson | 01029463 | 903/489-1527 | 219 |
| **MALAKOFF IND SCH DIST**/MALAKOFF/ | | | |
| HENDERSON | 01029449 | 903/489-1152 | 219 |
| Malakoff Middle Sch/Malakoff/Henderson | 01029475 | 903/489-0264 | 219 |
| Malala Yousafzai Elem Sch/Richmond/ | | | |
| Fort Bend | 12380484 | 281/327-5700 | 155 |
| Malcolm Rector Technical HS/Nacogdoches/ | | | |
| Nacogdoches | 04363402 | 936/205-1000 | 301 |
| Malone Elem Sch/Malone/Hill | 01030993 | 254/533-2321 | 231 |
| **MALONE INDEPENDENT SCH DIST**/ | | | |
| MALONE/HILL | 01030981 | 254/533-2321 | 231 |
| Malta Elem Sch/New Boston/Bowie | 01001021 | 903/667-2950 | 52 |
| **MALTA IND SCH DIST**/NEW BOSTON/ | | | |
| BOWIE | 01001019 | 903/667-2950 | 52 |
| Manara Acad Leadership Acad/Irving/Dallas | 12260949 | 972/304-1155 | 11 |
| Manara Acad-Arlington STEM/Arlington/ | | | |
| Tarrant | 12260937 | 972/304-1155 | 11 |
| Manara Acad-Irving Elem Sch/Irving/Dallas | 11453595 | 972/304-1155 | 11 |
| Mance Park Middle Sch/Huntsville/Walker | 01881986 | 936/435-6400 | 386 |
| Mandarin Immersion Magnet Sch/Houston/ | | | |
| Harris | 11820546 | 713/295-5276 | 199 |
| Mann Middle Sch/Abilene/Taylor | 01172826 | 325/672-8493 | 363 |
| Manns High Middle School Daep/Dallas/ | | | |
| Dallas | 04282767 | 972/925-7000 | 105 |
| Manor Elem Early Learning Ctr/Manor/Travis | 04174081 | 512/278-4100 | 374 |
| Manor Excel Academy/Manor/Travis | 04447747 | 512/278-4851 | 374 |
| Manor High Sch/Manor/Travis | 12363163 | 512/278-4800 | 374 |
| **MANOR IND SCH DIST**/MANOR/TRAVIS | 01056894 | 512/278-4000 | 373 |
| Manor Middle Sch/Killeen/Bell | 00996526 | 254/336-1310 | 31 |
| Manor Middle Sch/Manor/Travis | 01056923 | 512/278-4600 | 374 |
| Manor New Tech High Sch/Manor/Travis | 10915057 | 512/278-4875 | 374 |
| Manor New Tech Middle Sch/Manor/Travis | 12230255 | 512/278-4300 | 374 |

| School/City/County DISTRICT/CITY/COUNTY | PID | TELEPHONE NUMBER | PAGE |
|---|---|---|---|
| Manor Senior High Sch/Manor/Travis | 01056911 | 512/278-4665 | 374 |
| Mansfield High Sch/Mansfield/Tarrant | 01054145 | 682/314-0100 | 359 |
| **MANSFIELD IND SCH DIST/MANSFIELD/ TARRANT** | 01054119 | 817/299-6300 | 358 |
| Manuel Jara Elem Sch/Fort Worth/Tarrant | 01052680 | 817/814-4500 | 353 |
| Manvel High Sch/Manvel/Brazoria | 10021199 | 281/245-2232 | 54 |
| Manvel Junior High Sch/Manvel/Brazoria | 12104541 | 281/245-3700 | 54 |
| Manzano Middle Sch/Brownsville/Cameron | 11554890 | 956/548-9800 | 67 |
| Maple Lawn Elem Sch/Dallas/Dallas | 01009413 | 972/925-2500 | 105 |
| Maplebrook Elem Sch/Humble/Harris | 04948753 | 281/641-2900 | 201 |
| Maplewood Elem Sch/Austin/Travis | 01056375 | 512/414-4402 | 370 |
| Maran-Ata Christian Academy/El Paso/ El Paso | 11234832 | 915/592-1909 | 143 |
| **MARATHON IND SCH DIST/MARATHON/ BREWSTER** | 01002233 | 432/386-4431 | 60 |
| Marathon Sch/Marathon/Brewster | 01002245 | 432/386-4431 | 60 |
| Marble Falls Elem Sch/Marble Falls/Burnet | 01002831 | 830/693-2385 | 64 |
| Marble Falls High Sch/Marble Falls/Burnet | 01002843 | 830/693-4375 | 64 |
| **MARBLE FALLS IND SCH DIST/ MARBLE FALLS/BURNET** | 01002817 | 830/693-4357 | 64 |
| Marble Falls Middle Sch/Marble Falls/ Burnet | 01002855 | 830/693-4439 | 64 |
| Marcell Elem Sch/Mission/Hidalgo | 01030254 | 956/323-6400 | 225 |
| Marcella Elem Sch/Houston/Harris | 10907103 | 281/878-0860 | 185 |
| Marcia R Garza Elem Sch/Alamo/Hidalgo | 01030436 | 956/354-2780 | 227 |
| Marcus 9th Grade Center/Flower Mound/ Denton | 12033930 | 469/713-5998 | 127 |
| Marcus High Sch/Flower Mound/Denton | 02132104 | 469/713-5196 | 127 |
| Marcy Elem Sch/Big Spring/Howard | 01031997 | 432/264-4144 | 236 |
| Marfa Elem Sch/Marfa/Presidio | 01047831 | 432/729-4252 | 322 |
| **MARFA IND SCH DIST/MARFA/ PRESIDIO** | 01047829 | 432/729-4252 | 322 |
| Marfa Jr Sr High Sch/Marfa/Presidio | 01047843 | 432/729-4252 | 322 |
| Margaret B Henderson Elem Sch/Dallas/ Dallas | 01009396 | 972/749-2900 | 105 |
| Margaret Galubenski Achiev Ctr/Gainesville/ Cooke | 04801868 | 940/665-0277 | 95 |
| Margaret L Felty Elem Sch/Waxahachie/Ellis | 11131981 | 972/923-4616 | 146 |
| Margaret Long Wisdom High Sch/Houston/ Harris | 01024566 | 713/787-1700 | 199 |
| Margaret S McWhirter Elem Sch/Webster/ Galveston | 01018919 | 281/284-4800 | 163 |
| Margaret Wills Elem Sch/Amarillo/Potter | 01047350 | 806/326-5650 | 321 |
| Maria Alicia P Munoz Sch/Donna/Hidalgo | 04750049 | 956/464-1310 | 220 |
| Maria Moreno Elem Sch/Dallas/Dallas | 04456475 | 972/502-3100 | 105 |
| Marilyn J Miller Elem Sch/Fort Worth/ Tarrant | 10030968 | 817/306-4280 | 358 |
| Marin B Fenwick Academy/San Antonio/Bexar | 00998524 | 210/438-6540 | 44 |
| Marine Creek Collegiate HS/Fort Worth/ Tarrant | 12101135 | 817/515-7784 | 353 |
| Marine Creek Leadership Acad/Lake Worth/ Tarrant | 03241277 | 817/306-4270 | 358 |
| Marine Creek Middle Sch/Fort Worth/Tarrant | 12365771 | 817/847-2945 | 351 |
| Marine Military Academy/Harlingen/Cameron | 01004499 | 956/423-6006 | 72 |
| Marion High Sch/Marion/Guadalupe | 01021502 | 830/914-1075 | 177 |
| **MARION IND SCH DIST/MARION/ GUADALUPE** | 01021485 | 830/914-2803 | 177 |
| Marion Middle Sch/Marion/Guadalupe | 01021514 | 830/914-1070 | 177 |
| Mark T Voss Middle Sch/Boerne/Kendall | 12375233 | 830/357-3500 | 257 |
| Mark Twain Dual Language Acad/San Antonio/ Bexar | 00998536 | 210/738-9745 | 44 |
| Mark Twain Elem Sch/Alvin/Brazoria | 01001461 | 281/585-5318 | 54 |
| Mark Twain Elem Sch/Dallas/Dallas | 01009425 | 972/749-3000 | 105 |
| Mark Twain Elem Sch/Houston/Harris | 01025039 | 713/295-5230 | 199 |
| Mark Twain Elem Sch/Richardson/Dallas | 01011789 | 469/593-4800 | 117 |
| Mark White Elem Sch/Houston/Harris | 12170291 | 713/556-6571 | 199 |
| Markham Elem Sch/Markham/Matagorda | 01040986 | 979/843-4340 | 279 |
| Marlin Elem Sch/Marlin/Falls | 01017240 | 254/883-3232 | 149 |
| Marlin High Sch/Marlin/Falls | 01017252 | 254/883-2394 | 149 |
| **MARLIN IND SCH DIST/MARLIN/FALLS** | 01017238 | 254/883-3585 | 149 |
| Marlin Middle Sch/Marlin/Falls | 02128282 | 254/883-9241 | 149 |
| Marshall/Houston/Harris | 01025950 | 713/226-2600 | 197 |
| Marshall Elem Sch/Houston/Harris | 01026564 | 281/636-4606 | 196 |
| Marshall High Sch/Marshall/Harrison | 01028677 | 903/927-8800 | 214 |
| **MARSHALL IND SCH DIST/MARSHALL/ HARRISON** | 01028603 | 903/927-8700 | 214 |
| Marshall Junior High Sch/Marshall/Harrison | 01028665 | 903/927-8784 | 214 |
| Marshall Kendricks Middle Sch/Pasadena/ Harris | 12160727 | 713/740-5380 | 204 |
| Marshall Law & Med Svc Mag HS/San Antonio/ Bexar | 12365678 | 210/397-7100 | 41 |

| School/City/County DISTRICT/CITY/COUNTY | PID | TELEPHONE NUMBER | PAGE |
|---|---|---|---|
| Marshall Leadership Academy/Grand Prairie/ Dallas | 05342621 | 972/522-7200 | 112 |
| Marshall Middle Sch/Beaumont/Jefferson | 01034157 | 409/617-5900 | 245 |
| Mart Elem Sch/Mart/McLennan | 01039860 | 254/876-2762 | 283 |
| Mart High Sch/Mart/McLennan | 01039884 | 254/876-2574 | 283 |
| **MART IND SCH DIST/MART/MCLENNAN** | 01039858 | 254/876-2523 | 283 |
| Martha Hunt Elem Sch/Murphy/Collin | 10008343 | 469/752-4400 | 86 |
| Martha Raines High Sch/Katy/Harris | 11565095 | 281/237-1500 | 156 |
| Martha Reid Elem Sch/Arlington/Tarrant | 05347396 | 817/299-6960 | 359 |
| Martha Turner Reilly Elem Sch/Dallas/ Dallas | 01009683 | 972/749-7800 | 105 |
| Marti Elem Sch/Cleburne/Johnson | 01034913 | 817/202-1650 | 250 |
| Martin Elem Sch/Beaumont/Jefferson | 01033579 | 409/617-6425 | 245 |
| Martin Luther King Academy/San Antonio/ Bexar | 00998885 | 210/978-7935 | 44 |
| Martin Luther King Jr Lrng Ctr/Dallas/ Dallas | 01008677 | 972/502-8100 | 105 |
| Martin Middle Sch/Austin/Travis | 01056387 | 512/414-3243 | 371 |
| Martin Middle Sch/Corp Christi/Nueces | 01044530 | 361/878-4690 | 307 |
| Martin Walker Elem Sch/Copperas Cove/ Coryell | 01545211 | 254/547-2283 | 96 |
| Martin Weiss Elem Sch/Dallas/Dallas | 01009437 | 972/749-4000 | 106 |
| **MARTIN'S MILL IND SCH DIST/ BEN WHEELER/VAN ZANDT** | 01058191 | 903/479-3872 | 383 |
| Martin's Mill Sch/Ben Wheeler/Van Zandt | 01058206 | 903/479-3234 | 383 |
| Martinez Elem Sch/Abilene/Taylor | 01172694 | 325/794-4160 | 363 |
| **MARTINSVILLE IND SCH DIST/ NACOGDOCHES/NACOGDOCHES** | 01043249 | 936/564-3455 | 301 |
| Martinsville Sch/Nacogdoches/Nacogdoches | 01043251 | 936/564-3455 | 301 |
| Marvin Elem Sch/Waxahachie/Ellis | 01015307 | 972/923-4670 | 147 |
| Marvin P Baker Middle Sch/Corp Christi/ Nueces | 01044217 | 361/878-4600 | 307 |
| Mary & Frank Yturria Elem Sch/Brownsville/ Cameron | 04015746 | 956/350-3200 | 67 |
| Mary Allen Elem Sch/Stratford/Sherman | 01050498 | 806/366-3340 | 338 |
| Mary Austin Holley Elem Sch/Houston/ Fort Bend | 10912861 | 281/634-3850 | 155 |
| Mary Branch Elem Sch/Bryan/Brazos | 03325598 | 979/209-2900 | 58 |
| Mary Burks Marek Elem Sch/Pearland/ Brazoria | 05346304 | 281/245-3232 | 54 |
| Mary Carroll High Sch/Corp Christi/Nueces | 01044542 | 361/878-5140 | 307 |
| Mary Catherine Harris Sch/Bryan/Brazos | 11452319 | 979/209-2812 | 58 |
| Mary DeShazo Elem Sch/Muleshoe/Bailey | 00995704 | 806/272-7364 | 25 |
| Mary E Smithey Pace High Sch/Duncanville/ Dallas | 04037689 | 972/708-2470 | 109 |
| Mary Evans Elem Sch/Allen/Collin | 11079840 | 972/747-3373 | 80 |
| Mary Grett Sch/Corp Christi/Nueces | 01532070 | 361/878-1738 | 307 |
| Mary Grimes Education Center/Carrollton/ Dallas | 01525936 | 972/968-5600 | 101 |
| Mary Harper Middle Sch/Dilley/Frio | 01018608 | 830/965-2195 | 161 |
| Mary Harris Intermediate Sch/Fort Worth/ Tarrant | 11562017 | 817/370-7571 | 350 |
| Mary Hartman Elem Sch/San Antonio/Bexar | 05272234 | 210/564-1520 | 36 |
| Mary Help of Christians Sch/Laredo/Webb | 01045259 | 956/722-3966 | 391 |
| Mary Hoge Middle Sch/Weslaco/Hidalgo | 04034871 | 956/969-6730 | 228 |
| Mary Hull Elem Sch/San Antonio/Bexar | 00998213 | 210/397-0950 | 41 |
| Mary Immaculate Sch/Farmers BRNCH/Dallas | 01012484 | 972/243-7105 | 118 |
| Mary Jo Sheppard Elem Sch/Mansfield/ Tarrant | 10006876 | 817/299-6600 | 359 |
| Mary Lillard Intermediate Sch/Mansfield/ Tarrant | 10028238 | 817/276-6260 | 359 |
| Mary Lou Fisher Elem Sch/San Antonio/Bexar | 10020705 | 210/397-4450 | 41 |
| Mary Louise Phillips Elem Sch/Fort Worth/ Tarrant | 01053256 | 817/815-1600 | 353 |
| Mary M Boals Elem Sch/Frisco/Collin | 05272600 | 469/633-3300 | 83 |
| Mary Martin Elem Sch/Weatherford/Parker | 04452675 | 817/598-2910 | 317 |
| Mary McAshan Gibbs PK Center/Huntsville/ Walker | 01058684 | 936/435-6550 | 386 |
| Mary McLeod Bethune Elem Sch/Dallas/Dallas | 04456516 | 972/502-1300 | 106 |
| Mary Moore Elem Sch/Arlington/Tarrant | 03325457 | 682/867-8900 | 347 |
| Mary Moss Elem Sch/Mesquite/Dallas | 04033023 | 972/882-7130 | 115 |
| Mary Orr Intermediate Sch/Mansfield/ Tarrant | 01172618 | 817/299-2600 | 359 |
| Mary Walke Stephens Elem Sch/Houston/ Harris | 01022893 | 281/985-6560 | 185 |
| Mason Elem Sch/Cedar Park/Williamson | 04282365 | 512/570-5500 | 400 |
| Mason Elem Sch/Mason/Mason | 01040792 | 325/347-1122 | 278 |
| Mason High Sch/Mason/Mason | 01040807 | 325/347-1122 | 278 |
| **MASON IND SCH DIST/MASON/MASON** | 01040780 | 325/347-1144 | 278 |
| Mason Junior High Sch/Mason/Mason | 11447003 | 325/347-1122 | 278 |
| Massey Ranch Elem Sch/Pearland/Brazoria | 10028082 | 281/727-1700 | 57 |
| Masters Sch/San Marcos/Hays | 04824925 | 512/392-4322 | 217 |

| School/City/County<br>DISTRICT/CITY/COUNTY | PID | TELEPHONE NUMBER | PAGE |
|---|---|---|---|
| Mata Intermediate Sch/Houston/Harris | 04868696 | 281/983-7800 | 187 |
| **MATAGORDA IND SCH DIST/MATAGORDA/** | | | |
| **MATAGORDA** | 01040895 | 979/863-7693 | 278 |
| Matagorda Sch/Matagorda/Matagorda | 01040900 | 979/863-7693 | 278 |
| Math Science & Tech Magnet Sch/Richardson/ | | | |
| Dallas | 04366818 | 469/593-7300 | 117 |
| Mathews Elem Sch/Austin/Travis | 01056399 | 512/414-4406 | 370 |
| Mathews Elem Sch/Plano/Collin | 03014672 | 469/752-2300 | 86 |
| Mathis Elem Sch/Mathis/San Patricio | 01049657 | 361/547-4106 | 334 |
| Mathis High Sch/Mathis/San Patricio | 01049669 | 361/547-4131 | 334 |
| **MATHIS IND SCH DIST/MATHIS/** | | | |
| **SAN PATRICIO** | 01049645 | 361/547-3378 | 334 |
| Mathis Intermediate Sch/Mathis/ | | | |
| San Patricio | 01049671 | 361/547-2472 | 334 |
| Mathis Middle Sch/Mathis/San Patricio | 01049663 | 361/547-2381 | 334 |
| Matias De Llano Jr Elem Sch/Laredo/Webb | 04038437 | 956/473-4000 | 391 |
| Matthews Alt HS/New Directions/Lubbock/ | | | |
| Lubbock | 04285006 | 806/219-2600 | 273 |
| Mattie A Teague Middle Sch/Humble/Harris | 01022881 | 281/233-4310 | 186 |
| Mattie B Hambrick Middle Sch/Houston/ | | | |
| Harris | 01022829 | 281/985-6570 | 186 |
| Matzke Elem Sch/Houston/Harris | 01023299 | 281/897-4450 | 190 |
| **MAUD IND SCH DIST/MAUD/BOWIE** | 01001033 | 903/585-2219 | 52 |
| Maud Sch/Maud/Bowie | 01001045 | 903/585-2219 | 52 |
| Maude I Logan Elem Sch/Fort Worth/Tarrant | 01052812 | 817/815-3700 | 353 |
| Maude Moore Wood Elem Sch/Killeen/Bell | 00996461 | 254/336-1650 | 31 |
| Maudrie M Walton Elem Sch/Fort Worth/ | | | |
| Tarrant | 01053335 | 817/815-3300 | 354 |
| Maurice Wolfe Elem Sch/Houston/Harris | 01026239 | 281/237-2250 | 156 |
| Mauriceville Elem Sch/Orange/Orange | 02179023 | 409/745-1615 | 311 |
| Mauriceville Middle Sch/Orange/Orange | 01045699 | 409/745-3970 | 311 |
| Maurine Cain Middle Sch/Rockwall/Rockwall | 04846727 | 972/772-1170 | 328 |
| Maverick Elem Sch/San Antonio/Bexar | 00998603 | 210/438-6550 | 44 |
| Max Vaughan Elem Sch/Allen/Collin | 03235333 | 972/727-0470 | 80 |
| Maxdale Elem Sch/Killeen/Bell | 04941896 | 254/336-2460 | 31 |
| Maxfield Elem Sch/Gorman/Eastland | 01014456 | 254/734-3171 | 133 |
| Maxine & Lutrell Watts ES/Cibolo/Guadalupe | 04871980 | 210/619-4400 | 178 |
| May Elem Sch/May/Brown | 01002594 | 254/259-3711 | 62 |
| May High Sch/May/Brown | 01002609 | 254/259-2131 | 62 |
| **MAY IND SCH DIST/MAY/BROWN** | 01002582 | 254/259-2091 | 62 |
| Maya Angelou High Sch/Dallas/Dallas | 01809134 | 972/925-7000 | 106 |
| Mayde Creek Elem Sch/Houston/Harris | 02201626 | 281/237-3950 | 156 |
| Mayde Creek High Sch/Houston/Harris | 02227266 | 281/237-3000 | 156 |
| Mayde Creek Junior High Sch/Houston/Harris | 02110261 | 281/237-3900 | 156 |
| Maydell Jenks Elem Sch/Katy/Harris | 12169931 | 281/234-4100 | 156 |
| Mayes Elem Sch/Denison/Grayson | 01020390 | 903/462-7500 | 171 |
| Maypearl High Sch/Maypearl/Ellis | 03007033 | 972/435-1020 | 145 |
| **MAYPEARL IND SCH DIST/MAYPEARL/** | | | |
| **ELLIS** | 01015101 | 972/435-2116 | 145 |
| Maypearl Intermediate Sch/Maypearl/Ellis | 12102581 | 972/435-1099 | 145 |
| Maypearl Middle Sch/Maypearl/Ellis | 05092187 | 972/435-1015 | 145 |
| McAllen High Sch/McAllen/Hidalgo | 01030034 | 956/632-3100 | 224 |
| **MCALLEN IND SCH DIST/MCALLEN/** | | | |
| **HIDALGO** | 01029918 | 956/618-6000 | 224 |
| McAnally Intermediate Sch/Aledo/Parker | 05276395 | 817/441-8347 | 315 |
| McAndrew Elem Sch/Boerne/Bexar | 11918179 | 210/398-1750 | 41 |
| McAuliffe Elem Sch/Lewisville/Denton | 03010470 | 469/713-5959 | 127 |
| McAuliffe Middle Sch/Houston/Fort Bend | 02892914 | 281/634-3360 | 155 |
| McCall Elem Sch/Willow Park/Parker | 11102356 | 817/441-4500 | 315 |
| McCamey High Sch/Mc Camey/Upton | 01057642 | 432/652-3666 | 380 |
| **MCCAMEY IND SCH DIST/MC CAMEY/** | | | |
| **UPTON** | 01057616 | 432/652-3666 | 380 |
| McCamey Middle Sch/Mc Camey/Upton | 01057628 | 432/652-3666 | 380 |
| McCamey Primary Sch/Mc Camey/Upton | 01057630 | 432/652-3666 | 380 |
| McCarroll Middle Sch/Decatur/Wise | 01061681 | 940/393-7300 | 406 |
| McCasland Christian Academy/Georgetown/ | | | |
| Williamson | 12266888 | 512/863-9903 | 403 |
| McCollum High Sch/San Antonio/Bexar | 00997427 | 210/989-1500 | 36 |
| McCord Elem Sch/Vernon/Wilbarger | 02178469 | 940/553-4381 | 397 |
| McCormick Middle Sch/Buda/Hays | 12170722 | 512/268-8508 | 216 |
| McCowan Middle Sch/Glenn Heights/Dallas | 10904773 | 972/274-8090 | 108 |
| McCoy Elem Sch/Carrollton/Dallas | 01826156 | 972/968-2300 | 101 |
| McCullough Junior High Sch/Spring/ | | | |
| Montgomery | 01526136 | 832/592-5100 | 295 |
| **MCDADE IND SCH DIST/MC DADE/** | | | |
| **BASTROP** | 00995936 | 512/273-2522 | 27 |
| McDade Sch/Mc Dade/Bastrop | 00995948 | 512/273-2522 | 27 |
| McDermott Elem Sch/San Antonio/Bexar | 04015473 | 210/397-5100 | 41 |
| McDougle Elem Sch/Houston/Harris | 05347607 | 832/484-7550 | 202 |
| McDowell Middle Sch/Hondo/Medina | 01041253 | 830/426-2261 | 287 |
| McFee Elem Sch/Katy/Harris | 10966678 | 281/463-5380 | 190 |
| McGill Elem Sch/San Angelo/Tom Green | 01055735 | 325/947-3934 | 367 |

| School/City/County<br>DISTRICT/CITY/COUNTY | PID | TELEPHONE NUMBER | PAGE |
|---|---|---|---|
| McGowen Elem Sch/Houston/Harris | 01025924 | 713/636-6979 | 196 |
| McGregor Elem Sch/Mc Gregor/McLennan | 01039925 | 254/840-3204 | 283 |
| McGregor High Sch/Mc Gregor/McLennan | 01039913 | 254/840-2853 | 283 |
| **MCGREGOR IND SCH DIST/MC GREGOR/** | | | |
| **MCLENNAN** | 01039896 | 254/840-2828 | 283 |
| McGregor Primary Sch/Mc Gregor/McLennan | 12035146 | 254/840-2973 | 283 |
| McKamy Middle Sch/Flower Mound/Denton | 04754722 | 469/713-5991 | 127 |
| McKinney Boyd High Sch/McKinney/Collin | 10028496 | 469/302-3400 | 85 |
| McKinney Christian Academy/McKinney/Collin | 04931152 | 214/544-2658 | 89 |
| McKinney Daep Learning Center/McKinney/ | | | |
| Collin | 03396808 | 469/302-7800 | 85 |
| McKinney High Sch/McKinney/Collin | 01006289 | 469/302-5700 | 85 |
| **MCKINNEY IND SCH DIST/MCKINNEY/** | | | |
| **COLLIN** | 01006241 | 469/302-4000 | 84 |
| McKinney North High Sch/McKinney/Collin | 04920684 | 469/302-4300 | 85 |
| McLaughlin Strickland ES/Farmers BRNCH/ | | | |
| Dallas | 01008213 | 972/968-5700 | 101 |
| **MCLEAN IND SCH DIST/MCLEAN/GRAY** | 01020106 | 806/779-2301 | 170 |
| McLean Sch/McLean/Gray | 01020118 | 806/779-2301 | 170 |
| McLean Sixth Grade Sch/Fort Worth/Tarrant | 04919441 | 817/814-5700 | 354 |
| McLennan Co Challenge Academy/Waco/ | | | |
| McLennan | 04873471 | 254/754-0803 | 285 |
| McLennan Co State Juvenile Sch/Mart/ | | | |
| McLennan | 04885175 | 254/297-8200 | 11 |
| **MCLEOD IND SCH DIST/MC LEOD/CASS** | 01004891 | 903/796-7181 | 74 |
| McLeod Sch/Bivins/Cass | 01004906 | 903/796-7181 | 74 |
| McMasters Elem Sch/Pasadena/Harris | 01026784 | 713/740-0640 | 204 |
| McMath Middle Sch/Denton/Denton | 04810895 | 940/369-3300 | 125 |
| McMichael Middle Sch/Nacogdoches/ | | | |
| Nacogdoches | 01043342 | 936/552-0519 | 301 |
| McMillan Junior High Sch/Wylie/Collin | 01172436 | 972/492-3225 | 89 |
| McMillen High Sch/Plano/Collin | 11717999 | 469/752-8600 | 86 |
| McMullan Elem Sch/Channelview/Harris | 01878408 | 281/452-1154 | 188 |
| **MCMULLEN CO IND SCH DIST/** | | | |
| **TILDEN/MCMULLEN** | 01040560 | 361/274-2000 | 286 |
| McMullen Co Sch/Tilden/McMullen | 01040572 | 361/274-2000 | 286 |
| McNair Elem Sch/Denton/Denton | 03009744 | 940/369-3600 | 125 |
| McNamara Elem Sch/Houston/Harris | 01024982 | 713/778-3460 | 199 |
| McNeil High Sch/Austin/Williamson | 03007306 | 512/464-6300 | 402 |
| McNeill Elem Sch/Richmond/Fort Bend | 11397070 | 832/223-2800 | 158 |
| McNiel Middle Sch/Wichita Falls/Wichita | 01173143 | 940/235-1118 | 395 |
| McQueeney Elem Sch/Mc Queeney/Guadalupe | 01021722 | 830/401-8738 | 179 |
| McReynolds Middle Sch/Houston/Harris | 01025613 | 713/671-3650 | 196 |
| McSpedden Elem Sch/Frisco/Collin | 12032871 | 469/633-4025 | 83 |
| McWhorter Elem Sch/Lubbock/Lubbock | 01038799 | 806/219-6100 | 273 |
| Mead Middle Sch/Houston/Harris | 12309650 | 281/985-3700 | 186 |
| Meador Elem Sch/Houston/Harris | 01026796 | 713/740-0648 | 204 |
| Meador Elem Sch/Willis/Montgomery | 11130523 | 936/890-7550 | 297 |
| Meadow Creek Elem Sch/Bedford/Tarrant | 03249009 | 817/354-3500 | 356 |
| **MEADOW IND SCH DIST/MEADOW/TERRY** | 01055149 | 806/539-2246 | 365 |
| Meadow Oaks Academy/Mesquite/Dallas | 03143091 | 972/285-6895 | 120 |
| Meadow Sch/Meadow/Terry | 01055163 | 806/539-2246 | 365 |
| Meadow Village Elem Sch/San Antonio/Bexar | 00998225 | 210/397-0650 | 41 |
| Meadow Wood Elem Sch/Houston/Harris | 01027178 | 713/251-6200 | 206 |
| Meadowbrook Elem Sch/Corp Christi/Nueces | 01044554 | 361/878-2620 | 307 |
| Meadowbrook Elem Sch/Fort Worth/Tarrant | 01053098 | 817/815-4900 | 354 |
| Meadowbrook Middle Sch/Fort Worth/Tarrant | 01053103 | 817/815-4300 | 354 |
| Meadowcreek Elem Sch/Fort Worth/Tarrant | 02897196 | 817/370-5690 | 350 |
| Meadowland CS Stepping Stones/San Antonio/ | | | |
| Bexar | 12362779 | 830/331-4094 | 11 |
| Meadowland CS-Oaks Acad/Boerne/Kendall | 11704435 | 830/331-4094 | 11 |
| Meadows Elem Sch/Desoto/Dallas | 02895253 | 972/224-0960 | 108 |
| Meadows Elem Sch/Fort Hood/Bell | 00996540 | 254/336-1870 | 31 |
| Meadows Elem Sch/Meadows Place/Fort Bend | 01018189 | 281/634-4720 | 155 |
| Meadows Elem Sch/Plano/Collin | 01006356 | 469/752-2400 | 86 |
| Means Young Womens Ldrshp Acad/Austin/ | | | |
| Travis | 01056284 | 512/414-3234 | 371 |
| Medina Elem Sch/Medina/Bandera | 01172412 | 830/589-2731 | 26 |
| **MEDINA IND SCH DIST/MEDINA/** | | | |
| **BANDERA** | 00995807 | 830/589-2855 | 26 |
| Medina Secondary Sch/Medina/Bandera | 04450172 | 830/589-2851 | 26 |
| Medina Valley High Sch/Castroville/Medina | 01041289 | 830/931-2243 | 287 |
| **MEDINA VALLEY IND SCH DIST/** | | | |
| **CASTROVILLE/MEDINA** | 01041277 | 830/931-2243 | 287 |
| Medina Valley Lacoste ES/La Coste/Medina | 01041291 | 830/931-2243 | 287 |
| Medina Valley Middle Sch/Castroville/ | | | |
| Medina | 01041306 | 830/931-2243 | 287 |
| Medio Creek Elem Sch/San Antonio/Bexar | 11711232 | 210/622-4950 | 46 |
| Medlin Middle Sch/Trophy Club/Denton | 04804614 | 817/215-0500 | 129 |
| Mel Parmley Elem Sch/Willis/Montgomery | 03053044 | 936/856-1231 | 297 |
| Melba Passmore Elem Sch/Alvin/Brazoria | 04033346 | 281/585-6696 | 54 |
| Melillo Middle Sch/Houston/Harris | 11129421 | 713/740-5260 | 204 |

| School/City/County DISTRICT/CITY/COUNTY | PID | TELEPHONE NUMBER | PAGE |
|---|---|---|---|
| Melissa High Sch/Melissa/Collin | 02848901 | 972/837-4216 | 85 |
| **MELISSA IND SCH DIST/MELISSA/** | | | |
| **COLLIN** | 01006320 | 972/837-2411 | 85 |
| Melissa Middle Sch/Melissa/Collin | 11445811 | 972/837-4355 | 85 |
| Memorial 9th Grade Academy/Port Arthur/ | | | |
| Jefferson | 01033880 | 409/984-4900 | 246 |
| Memorial Christian Academy/Killeen/Bell | 02725103 | 254/526-5403 | 33 |
| Memorial Chrn Academy/Houston/Harris | 11231490 | 281/493-3700 | 211 |
| Memorial Drive Elem Sch/Houston/Harris | 01027180 | 713/251-6300 | 206 |
| Memorial Early College HS/New Braunfels/ | | | |
| Comal | 04429056 | 830/221-2900 | 92 |
| Memorial Elem Sch/Houston/Harris | 01024176 | 713/867-5150 | 199 |
| Memorial Elem Sch/New Braunfels/Comal | 04808971 | 830/627-6470 | 92 |
| Memorial Elem Sch/Plano/Collin | 01006447 | 469/752-2500 | 86 |
| Memorial Elem Sch/Weslaco/Hidalgo | 03251973 | 956/969-6780 | 228 |
| Memorial Hall High Sch/Houston/Harris | 01480269 | 713/688-5566 | 211 |
| Memorial High Sch/Frisco/Collin | 12308333 | 469/633-7300 | 83 |
| Memorial High Sch/Houston/Harris | 01027207 | 713/251-2500 | 206 |
| Memorial High Sch/McAllen/Hidalgo | 02110364 | 956/632-5201 | 224 |
| Memorial High Sch/Port Arthur/Jefferson | 01033919 | 409/984-4000 | 246 |
| Memorial High Sch/San Antonio/Bexar | 00997312 | 210/444-8300 | 35 |
| Memorial High School-Cate/Port Arthur/ | | | |
| Jefferson | 01033892 | 409/984-4750 | 246 |
| Memorial Intermediate Sch/Alice/Jim Wells | 01034597 | 361/660-2080 | 248 |
| Memorial Junior High Sch/Eagle Pass/ | | | |
| Maverick | 02896128 | 830/758-7053 | 280 |
| Memorial Lutheran Sch/Houston/Harris | 02235706 | 713/782-4022 | 211 |
| Memorial Middle Sch/Edinburg/Hidalgo | 01029700 | 956/289-2470 | 222 |
| Memorial Middle Sch/Harlingen/Cameron | 01003835 | 956/427-3020 | 68 |
| Memorial Middle Sch/Houston/Harris | 01027192 | 713/251-3900 | 206 |
| Memorial Middle Sch/Kingsville/Kleberg | 01036337 | 361/595-8675 | 260 |
| Memorial Middle Sch/Laredo/Webb | 01059303 | 956/273-6600 | 390 |
| Memorial Middle Sch/Mission/Hidalgo | 04287896 | 956/323-2820 | 223 |
| Memorial Middle Sch/Winnsboro/Wood | 01061954 | 903/342-5711 | 408 |
| Memorial Park Academy/Richardson/Dallas | 12309040 | 469/593-0450 | 117 |
| Memorial Parkway Elem Sch/Katy/Harris | 01832117 | 281/237-5850 | 156 |
| Memorial Parkway Jr High Sch/Katy/Harris | 02177049 | 281/237-5800 | 156 |
| Memorial Pathway Academy/Garland/Dallas | 01010618 | 972/926-2650 | 110 |
| Memorial Private High Sch/Houston/Harris | 10989888 | 281/759-2288 | 211 |
| Memphis High Sch/Memphis/Hall | 01022104 | 806/259-5910 | 181 |
| **MEMPHIS IND SCH DIST/MEMPHIS/** | | | |
| **HALL** | 01022087 | 806/259-5900 | 180 |
| Memphis Middle Sch/Memphis/Hall | 01022116 | 806/259-5920 | 181 |
| Menard Elem Middle Sch/Menard/Menard | 01041370 | 325/396-2348 | 288 |
| Menard High Sch/Menard/Menard | 01041382 | 325/396-2513 | 288 |
| **MENARD IND SCH DIST/MENARD/** | | | |
| **MENARD** | 01041368 | 325/396-2404 | 288 |
| Menchaca Elem Sch/Manchaca/Travis | 01056363 | 512/414-2333 | 370 |
| Mendenhall Elem Sch/Plano/Collin | 01006368 | 469/752-2600 | 86 |
| Mendez Elem Sch/San Marcos/Hays | 11540461 | 512/393-6060 | 217 |
| Mendez Middle Sch/Austin/Travis | 03011682 | 512/414-3284 | 371 |
| Mercedes Academic Academy/Mercedes/Hidalgo | 12032962 | 956/825-5076 | 225 |
| Mercedes Early College HS/Mercedes/Hidalgo | 11074515 | 956/825-5180 | 225 |
| Mercedes High Sch/Mercedes/Hidalgo | 01030175 | 956/514-2100 | 225 |
| **MERCEDES IND SCH DIST/MERCEDES/** | | | |
| **HIDALGO** | 01030149 | 956/514-2000 | 225 |
| Mercer-Blumberg Learning Ctr/Seguin/ | | | |
| Guadalupe | 04453980 | 830/401-8690 | 179 |
| Meridian Alternative Sch/Meridian/Bosque | 04804391 | 254/435-6047 | 50 |
| Meridian Elem Sch/Meridian/Bosque | 01000704 | 254/435-2731 | 50 |
| **MERIDIAN IND SCH DIST/MERIDIAN/** | | | |
| **BOSQUE** | 01000699 | 254/435-2081 | 50 |
| Meridian Middle High Sch/Meridian/Bosque | 04357740 | 254/435-2723 | 50 |
| Meridian World Charter Sch/Round Rock/ | | | |
| Williamson | 11729502 | 512/660-5230 | 11 |
| Meridiana Elem Sch/Iowa Colony/Brazoria | 12169113 | 281/245-3636 | 54 |
| Meridith-Dunbar EC Academy/Temple/Bell | 00996710 | 254/215-6700 | 32 |
| Merit Academy/Dallas/Dallas | 11929128 | 214/736-8375 | 120 |
| Merkel Elem Sch/Merkel/Taylor | 01054951 | 325/928-4795 | 363 |
| Merkel High Sch/Merkel/Taylor | 01054949 | 325/928-4667 | 363 |
| **MERKEL IND SCH DIST/MERKEL/** | | | |
| **TAYLOR** | 01054925 | 325/928-5813 | 363 |
| Merkel Middle Sch/Merkel/Taylor | 01054937 | 325/928-5511 | 363 |
| Merrifield Elem Sch/Duncanville/Dallas | 01010369 | 972/708-2900 | 109 |
| Merriman Park Elem Sch/Dallas/Dallas | 01881132 | 469/593-2800 | 117 |
| Merryhill Sch/Arlington/Tarrant | 11551733 | 817/472-9494 | 361 |
| Merrywood Sch/Duncanville/Dallas | 02734910 | 972/298-0110 | 120 |
| Mesa Verde Elem Sch/Amarillo/Potter | 01047362 | 806/326-4800 | 321 |
| Mesa Vista Elem Sch/El Paso/El Paso | 01016478 | 915/434-2700 | 142 |
| Mesita Elem Sch/El Paso/El Paso | 01016038 | 915/236-6850 | 138 |
| Mesorah High School for Girls/Dallas/ | | | |
| Dallas | 05343041 | 214/420-1990 | 120 |

| School/City/County DISTRICT/CITY/COUNTY | PID | TELEPHONE NUMBER | PAGE |
|---|---|---|---|
| Mesquite Academy Aec of Choice/Mesquite/ | | | |
| Dallas | 04366404 | 972/882-7570 | 115 |
| Mesquite High Sch/Mesquite/Dallas | 01011569 | 972/882-7800 | 115 |
| **MESQUITE IND SCH DIST/MESQUITE/** | | | |
| **DALLAS** | 01011399 | 972/288-6411 | 115 |
| Messiah Luth Classical Academy/Keller/ | | | |
| Tarrant | 11235070 | 817/431-5486 | 361 |
| Metcalf Elem Sch/Houston/Harris | 03398234 | 281/856-1152 | 190 |
| Metro Elem School of Design/Corp Christi/ | | | |
| Nueces | 01044671 | 361/878-2780 | 307 |
| Metro Opportunity Sch/Fort Worth/Tarrant | 01881948 | 817/814-6700 | 354 |
| Metroplex Chapel Academy/Euless/Tarrant | 04423686 | 817/267-1000 | 361 |
| Metzler Elem Sch/Klein/Harris | 10001943 | 832/484-7900 | 202 |
| Mexia High Sch/Mexia/Limestone | 01038103 | 254/562-4010 | 270 |
| **MEXIA IND SCH DIST/MEXIA/** | | | |
| **LIMESTONE** | 01038086 | 254/562-4000 | 270 |
| Mexia Junior High Sch/Mexia/Limestone | 01038115 | 254/562-4020 | 270 |
| Meyer Elem Sch/Hondo/Medina | 01041265 | 830/426-3161 | 287 |
| Meyer Elem Sch/Houston/Harris | 01526033 | 281/891-8270 | 207 |
| Meyer Elem Sch/Richmond/Fort Bend | 02856972 | 832/223-2000 | 158 |
| Meyer High Sch/Waco/McLennan | 11478832 | 254/754-2288 | 11 |
| Meyerland Perf-Visual Arts MS/Houston/ | | | |
| Harris | 01024695 | 713/726-3616 | 199 |
| Meyerpark Charter Sch/Houston/Harris | 11014797 | 713/729-9712 | 11 |
| Meyersville Elem Sch/Meyersville/De Witt | 01013749 | 361/275-3639 | 122 |
| **MEYERSVILLE IND SCH DIST/** | | | |
| **MEYERSVILLE/DE WITT** | 01013737 | 361/277-5817 | 122 |
| **MIAMI IND SCH DIST/MIAMI/ROBERTS** | 01048536 | 806/868-3971 | 327 |
| Miami Sch/Miami/Roberts | 01048548 | 806/868-3971 | 327 |
| Michael E Fossum Middle Sch/McAllen/ | | | |
| Hidalgo | 11104029 | 956/971-1105 | 224 |
| Michael Elem Sch/San Antonio/Bexar | 04865943 | 210/397-3900 | 41 |
| Michael G Killian Middle Sch/Lewisville/ | | | |
| Denton | 10910617 | 469/713-5977 | 127 |
| Michael L Griffin Elem Sch/Katy/Harris | 10027870 | 281/237-8700 | 156 |
| Michael M Boone Elem Sch/Dallas/Dallas | 12469004 | 214/780-4100 | 112 |
| Michael R Null Middle Sch/Houston/Harris | 01027075 | 281/436-2800 | 205 |
| Mickey Leland Clg Prep for Men/Houston/ | | | |
| Harris | 11717523 | 713/226-2668 | 196 |
| Mid-Valley Christian Sch/Weslaco/Hidalgo | 02153952 | 956/968-6232 | 229 |
| Middle College at HCC Fraga/Houston/Harris | 12107725 | 713/228-3408 | 195 |
| Middle College at HCC Gulfton/Houston/ | | | |
| Harris | 12107737 | 713/662-2551 | 195 |
| Middle Level Learning Center/Fort Worth/ | | | |
| Tarrant | 02110314 | 817/814-6800 | 354 |
| Midland Academy Charter Sch/Midland/ | | | |
| Midland | 04903076 | 432/686-0003 | 11 |
| Midland Alternative Program/Midland/ | | | |
| Midland | 11924829 | 432/240-4700 | 289 |
| Midland Christian Sch/Midland/Midland | 01480843 | 432/694-1661 | 289 |
| Midland Classical Academy/Midland/Midland | 12169747 | 432/694-0995 | 289 |
| Midland Freshman High Sch/Midland/Midland | 01041497 | 432/689-1200 | 289 |
| **MIDLAND IND SCH DIST/MIDLAND/** | | | |
| **MIDLAND** | 01041423 | 432/689-1000 | 288 |
| Midland Senior High Sch/Midland/Midland | 01041590 | 432/689-1100 | 289 |
| Midlothian Heritage High Sch/Midlothian/ | | | |
| Ellis | 12109058 | 469/856-5400 | 145 |
| Midlothian High Sch/Midlothian/Ellis | 01015163 | 469/856-5100 | 145 |
| **MIDLOTHIAN IND SCH DIST/** | | | |
| **MIDLOTHIAN/ELLIS** | 01015137 | 469/856-5000 | 145 |
| Midway Alternative High Sch/Canyon/Randall | 11450385 | 806/677-2455 | 323 |
| Midway High Sch/Waco/McLennan | 01039951 | 254/761-5650 | 284 |
| **MIDWAY IND SCH DIST/HENRIETTA/** | | | |
| **CLAY** | 01005584 | 940/476-2215 | 78 |
| **MIDWAY IND SCH DIST/WOODWAY/** | | | |
| **MCLENNAN** | 01039937 | 254/761-5600 | 283 |
| Midway Middle Sch/Hewitt/McLennan | 01557642 | 254/761-5680 | 284 |
| Midway Park Elem Sch/Euless/Tarrant | 01053866 | 817/354-3380 | 356 |
| Midway Sch/Henrietta/Clay | 01005596 | 940/476-2215 | 78 |
| Miguel Carrillo Jr Elem Sch/San Antonio/ | | | |
| Bexar | 04364107 | 210/977-7550 | 45 |
| Mike Moseley Elem Sch/Grand Prairie/Dallas | 10910631 | 972/522-2800 | 112 |
| Mike Moses Middle Sch/Nacogdoches/ | | | |
| Nacogdoches | 03317591 | 936/569-5001 | 301 |
| Milam Elem Sch/Conroe/Montgomery | 01042441 | 936/709-5200 | 295 |
| Milam Elem Sch/El Paso/El Paso | 01015838 | 915/236-0325 | 138 |
| Milam Elem Sch/Midland/Midland | 01041459 | 432/240-7500 | 289 |
| Milam Elem Sch/Wichita Falls/Wichita | 01172979 | 940/235-1176 | 395 |
| Milam Magnet Elem Sch/Odessa/Ector | 01014755 | 432/456-1169 | 134 |
| Milano Elem Sch/Milano/Milam | 02110106 | 512/455-2062 | 290 |
| Milano High Sch/Milano/Milam | 05242631 | 512/455-9333 | 290 |
| **MILANO IND SCH DIST/MILANO/MILAM** | 01041825 | 512/455-2533 | 290 |

| School/City/County DISTRICT/CITY/COUNTY | PID | TELEPHONE NUMBER | PAGE |
|---|---|---|---|
| Milano Junior High Sch/Milano/Milam | 01041849 | 512/455-6701 | 290 |
| **MILDRED IND SCH DIST/CORSICANA/** | | | |
| **NAVARRO** | 01043615 | 903/872-6505 | 303 |
| Mildred Jenkins Elem Sch/Spring/Harris | 01526045 | 281/891-8300 | 207 |
| Mildred M Hawk Elem Sch/Corinth/Denton | 10001838 | 940/369-1800 | 125 |
| Mildred Sch/Corsicana/Navarro | 01043627 | 903/872-6505 | 303 |
| **MILES IND SCH DIST/MILES/RUNNELS** | 01048847 | 325/468-2861 | 329 |
| Miles Sch/Miles/Runnels | 01048859 | 325/468-2861 | 329 |
| **MILFORD IND SCH DIST/MILFORD/** | | | |
| **ELLIS** | 01015187 | 972/493-2911 | 146 |
| Milford Sch/Milford/Ellis | 01015199 | 972/493-2921 | 146 |
| Mill St Elem Sch/Lewisville/Denton | 01013426 | 469/713-5965 | 127 |
| Miller Career & Tech Center/Katy/Harris | 03053264 | 281/237-6300 | 156 |
| Miller Elem Sch/Arlington/Tarrant | 02132180 | 682/867-8400 | 347 |
| Miller Elem Sch/Little Elm/Collin | 12167282 | 469/633-2075 | 83 |
| **MILLER GROVE IND SCH DIST/** | | | |
| **CUMBY/HOPKINS** | 01031521 | 903/459-3288 | 234 |
| Miller Grove Sch/Cumby/Hopkins | 01031533 | 903/459-3288 | 234 |
| Miller Heights Elem Sch/Belton/Bell | 00996368 | 254/215-3300 | 30 |
| Miller HS-Metro Sch of Design/Corp Christi/ | | | |
| Nueces | 01044621 | 361/878-5100 | 307 |
| Miller Intermediate Sch/Houston/Harris | 04914594 | 281/531-3430 | 187 |
| Miller Jordan Middle Sch/San Benito/ | | | |
| Cameron | 02112520 | 956/361-6650 | 70 |
| Miller's Point Elem Sch/Converse/Bexar | 03007875 | 210/945-5114 | 36 |
| Mills Elem Sch/Austin/Travis | 04806698 | 512/841-2400 | 370 |
| Millsap Elem Sch/Cypress/Harris | 01548419 | 281/897-4470 | 190 |
| Millsap Elem Sch/Millsap/Parker | 03321516 | 940/682-3121 | 315 |
| Millsap High Sch/Millsap/Parker | 01046409 | 940/682-3182 | 316 |
| **MILLSAP IND SCH DIST/MILLSAP/** | | | |
| **PARKER** | 01046394 | 940/682-4994 | 315 |
| Millsap Middle Sch/Millsap/Parker | 04941389 | 940/682-4489 | 316 |
| Milstead Middle Sch/Houston/Harris | 10913267 | 713/740-5238 | 204 |
| Milton B Lee Acad of Sci & Eng/San Antonio/ | | | |
| Bexar | 11589998 | 210/431-9881 | 45 |
| Milton Cooper Elem Sch/Houston/Harris | 10006931 | 281/891-8660 | 207 |
| Milton L Kirkpatrick Elem Sch/Fort Worth/ | | | |
| Tarrant | 01053036 | 817/814-4600 | 354 |
| Mimi Farley Elem Sch/Boys Ranch/Oldham | 01484473 | 806/534-2248 | 310 |
| Mims Elem Sch/Mission/Hidalgo | 02856714 | 956/323-4400 | 225 |
| Mina Elem Sch/Bastrop/Bastrop | 00995869 | 512/772-7640 | 27 |
| Mineola Elem Sch/Mineola/Wood | 01061875 | 903/569-2466 | 408 |
| Mineola High Sch/Mineola/Wood | 01061887 | 903/569-3000 | 408 |
| **MINEOLA IND SCH DIST/MINEOLA/** | | | |
| **WOOD** | 01061851 | 903/569-2448 | 408 |
| Mineola Middle Sch/Mineola/Wood | 01061899 | 903/569-5338 | 408 |
| Mineola Primary Sch/Mineola/Wood | 01061863 | 903/569-5488 | 408 |
| Mineral Wells Academy/Mineral Wells/ | | | |
| Palo Pinto | 04921341 | 940/325-3033 | 313 |
| Mineral Wells High Sch/Mineral Wells/ | | | |
| Palo Pinto | 01046069 | 940/325-4408 | 313 |
| **MINERAL WELLS IND SCH DIST/** | | | |
| **MINERAL WELLS/PALO PINTO** | 01046019 | 940/325-6404 | 313 |
| Mineral Wells Jr High Sch/Mineral Wells/ | | | |
| Palo Pinto | 01046071 | 940/325-0711 | 313 |
| Minshew Elem Sch/McKinney/Collin | 05343156 | 469/302-7300 | 85 |
| Miraibeau B Lamar Elem Sch/Baytown/Harris | 01023706 | 281/420-4625 | 193 |
| Mirus Academy/Katy/Harris | 11662942 | 281/392-4477 | 211 |
| Misd Developmental Center/Mexia/Limestone | 11444879 | 254/562-4023 | 270 |
| Miss May Vernon Elem Sch/Fate/Rockwall | 10907086 | 972/635-5006 | 329 |
| Mission Academy/San Antonio/Bexar | 11128049 | 210/438-6880 | 44 |
| Mission Bend Christian Academy/Houston/ | | | |
| Harris | 11235288 | 281/497-4057 | 211 |
| Mission Bend Elem Sch/Houston/Fort Bend | 02126375 | 281/634-4240 | 155 |
| Mission Collegiate High Sch/Alton/Hidalgo | 11848811 | 956/323-6120 | 225 |
| **MISSION CONS IND SCH DIST/** | | | |
| **MISSION/HIDALGO** | 01030228 | 956/323-5500 | 225 |
| Mission Early College High Sch/El Paso/ | | | |
| El Paso | 10751124 | 915/937-1200 | 141 |
| Mission Glen Elem Sch/Houston/Fort Bend | 02892938 | 281/634-4280 | 155 |
| Mission High Sch/Mission/Hidalgo | 01030266 | 956/323-5700 | 225 |
| Mission Junior High Sch/Mission/Hidalgo | 01030278 | 956/323-3300 | 225 |
| Mission Options Academy/Mission/Hidalgo | 11818103 | 956/323-3960 | 225 |
| Mission Ridge Elem Sch/El Paso/El Paso | 12030782 | 915/938-2000 | 141 |
| Mission Valley Elem Sch/El Paso/El Paso | 03250888 | 915/434-3700 | 142 |
| Mission Valley Elem Sch/Victoria/Victoria | 01540118 | 361/788-9514 | 385 |
| Mission West Elem Sch/Houston/Fort Bend | 03393193 | 281/634-4320 | 155 |
| Missouri City Middle Sch/Missouri City/ | | | |
| Fort Bend | 01526007 | 281/634-3440 | 155 |
| Mistral Early Childhood Center/Houston/ | | | |
| Harris | 10003927 | 713/773-6253 | 199 |
| Mitchell Elem Sch/Bryan/Brazos | 04884949 | 979/209-1400 | 58 |

| School/City/County DISTRICT/CITY/COUNTY | PID | TELEPHONE NUMBER | PAGE |
|---|---|---|---|
| Mitchell Elem Sch/Dallas/Collin | 04016324 | 469/752-2800 | 86 |
| Mitchell Elem Sch/Houston/Harris | 01025625 | 713/991-8190 | 198 |
| Mitchell Intermediate Sch/The Woodlands/ | | | |
| Montgomery | 04454037 | 832/592-8500 | 295 |
| Mittelstadt Elem Sch/Klein/Harris | 03397216 | 832/484-6700 | 202 |
| Mitzi Bond Elem Sch/El Paso/El Paso | 02129884 | 915/236-2925 | 138 |
| Mockingbird Elem Sch/Coppell/Dallas | 03393466 | 214/496-8200 | 102 |
| Mockingbird Elem Sch/Dallas/Dallas | 01009891 | 972/749-7200 | 106 |
| Mohawk Elem Sch/Richardson/Dallas | 01011791 | 469/593-6600 | 117 |
| Moises E Molina High Sch/Dallas/Dallas | 04755477 | 972/502-1000 | 106 |
| Moises Vela Middle Sch/Harlingen/Cameron | 10007698 | 956/427-3479 | 68 |
| Momentous Sch/Dallas/Dallas | 03414371 | 214/915-1890 | 120 |
| Mona Montessori McKinney/McKinney/Collin | 03137975 | 972/542-5825 | 89 |
| Monaco Elem Sch/Aubrey/Denton | 05342918 | 940/668-0000 | 124 |
| Monahans Education Center HS/Monahans/Ward | 05277052 | 432/943-2019 | 388 |
| Monahans High Sch/Monahans/Ward | 01058995 | 432/943-2519 | 388 |
| **MONAHANS-WICKETT-PYOTE ISD/** | | | |
| **MONAHANS/WARD** | 01058957 | 432/943-6711 | 388 |
| Monarch Sch/Houston/Harris | 04937950 | 713/479-0800 | 211 |
| Monroe S May Jr Elem Sch/San Antonio/Bexar | 04754758 | 210/397-2000 | 41 |
| Monta Jane Akin Elem Sch/Leander/ | | | |
| Williamson | 12230803 | 512/570-8000 | 400 |
| Montague Elem Sch/Montague/Montague | 01042324 | 940/894-2811 | 293 |
| **MONTAGUE IND SCH DIST/MONTAGUE/** | | | |
| **MONTAGUE** | 01042312 | 940/894-2811 | 293 |
| Montague Village Elem Sch/Fort Hood/Bell | 04806569 | 254/336-2230 | 31 |
| Montana Vista Elem Sch/El Paso/El Paso | 02845636 | 915/926-5307 | 137 |
| Montclair Elem Sch/Corp Christi/Nueces | 01044578 | 361/878-0160 | 307 |
| Montclair Elem Sch/Garland/Dallas | 01010620 | 972/279-4041 | 110 |
| Monte Alto Ealry Clg High Sch/Edcouch/ | | | |
| Hidalgo | 11540485 | 956/262-6152 | 226 |
| Monte Alto Elem Sch/Monte Alto/Hidalgo | 01030321 | 956/262-6101 | 226 |
| **MONTE ALTO IND SCH DIST/** | | | |
| **MONTE ALTO/HIDALGO** | 01030319 | 956/567-3100 | 226 |
| Monte Cristo Elem Sch/Edinburg/Hidalgo | 03344415 | 956/289-2362 | 222 |
| Monterey Senior High Sch/Lubbock/Lubbock | 01038804 | 806/219-1900 | 273 |
| Montessori Acad Hernandez ES/Dallas/Dallas | 04456463 | 972/925-2700 | 106 |
| Montessori Academy-Arlington/Arlington/ | | | |
| Tarrant | 03016931 | 817/274-1548 | 361 |
| Montessori Academy-North Texas/Sherman/ | | | |
| Grayson | 11973222 | 903/893-3500 | 174 |
| Montessori Children's House/Fort Worth/ | | | |
| Tarrant | 01481055 | 817/732-0252 | 361 |
| Montessori Episcopal Sch/Lewisville/Denton | 01410680 | 972/221-3533 | 130 |
| Montessori Mastery Sch-Odessa/Odessa/Ector | 12375908 | 432/631-2405 | 135 |
| Montessori Sch International/San Antonio/ | | | |
| Bexar | 02982832 | 210/614-1665 | 48 |
| Montessori Sch of North Dallas/Dallas/ | | | |
| Collin | 03404493 | 972/985-8844 | 89 |
| Montessori Sch of San Antonio/San Antonio/ | | | |
| Bexar | 01754242 | 210/492-3553 | 48 |
| Montessori School at Starcreek/Allen/ | | | |
| Collin | 11589651 | 972/727-2800 | 89 |
| Montessori School Downtown/Houston/Harris | 04885591 | 713/520-6801 | 211 |
| Montgomery Achievement Center/Henderson/ | | | |
| Rusk | 12312956 | 903/655-5552 | 330 |
| Montgomery Christian Academy/Montgomery/ | | | |
| Montgomery | 12361311 | 936/622-4598 | 298 |
| Montgomery Elem Sch/Houston/Harris | 01025314 | 713/434-5640 | 194 |
| Montgomery Elem Sch/Montgomery/Montgomery | 01042635 | 936/276-3600 | 296 |
| Montgomery Elem Sch/San Antonio/Bexar | 00997843 | 210/407-5000 | 38 |
| Montgomery High Sch/Montgomery/Montgomery | 02177984 | 936/276-3000 | 296 |
| **MONTGOMERY IND SCH DIST/** | | | |
| **MONTGOMERY/MONTGOMERY** | 01042623 | 936/276-2000 | 296 |
| Montgomery Junior High Sch/Montgomery/ | | | |
| Montgomery | 01042647 | 936/276-3300 | 296 |
| Montwood High Sch/El Paso/El Paso | 03323473 | 915/937-2400 | 141 |
| Montwood Middle Sch/El Paso/El Paso | 04753182 | 915/937-5800 | 141 |
| Moody Elem Sch/Moody/McLennan | 01039987 | 254/853-2155 | 284 |
| Moody High Sch/Moody/McLennan | 01039999 | 254/853-3622 | 284 |
| **MOODY IND SCH DIST/MOODY/** | | | |
| **MCLENNAN** | 01039975 | 254/853-2172 | 284 |
| Moody Middle Sch/Moody/McLennan | 03392876 | 254/853-2181 | 284 |
| Mooneyham Elem Sch/McKinney/Collin | 10912720 | 469/633-3650 | 93 |
| Moore Elem Sch/Houston/Harris | 02110352 | 281/370-4040 | 190 |
| Moore Mst Magnet Sch/Tyler/Smith | 01050905 | 903/262-1640 | 340 |
| Moorhead Junior High Sch/Conroe/Montgomery | 01042568 | 936/709-2400 | 295 |
| Mora Elem Sch/San Antonio/Bexar | 12309064 | 210/398-2400 | 41 |
| Morales Junior High Sch/Uvalde/Uvalde | 02222448 | 830/591-2980 | 381 |
| **MORAN IND SCH DIST/MORAN/** | | | |
| **SHACKELFORD** | 01050242 | 325/945-3101 | 336 |
| Moran Sch/Moran/Shackelford | 01050254 | 325/945-3101 | 336 |

| School/City/County DISTRICT/CITY/COUNTY | PID | TELEPHONE NUMBER | PAGE |
|---|---|---|---|
| Morehead Middle Sch/El Paso/El Paso | 01016040 | 915/236-3500 | 139 |
| Moreno Junior High Sch/Beeville/Bee | 00996124 | 361/358-6262 | 28 |
| **MORGAN IND SCH DIST/MORGAN/** | | | |
| **BOSQUE** | 01000728 | 254/635-2311 | 50 |
| Morgan Mill Elem Sch/Morgan Mill/Erath | 01017123 | 254/968-4921 | 148 |
| **MORGAN MILL IND SCH DIST/** | | | |
| **MORGAN MILL/ERATH** | 01017111 | 254/968-4921 | 148 |
| Morgan Sch/Morgan/Bosque | 02112192 | 254/635-2311 | 50 |
| Morningside Elem Sch/Brownsville/Cameron | 02892122 | 956/982-2760 | 67 |
| Morningside Elem Sch/Dumas/Moore | 01042879 | 806/935-4153 | 298 |
| Morningside Elem Sch/Fort Worth/Tarrant | 01053139 | 817/814-0600 | 354 |
| Morningside Elem Sch/New Braunfels/Comal | 11079436 | 830/837-7100 | 92 |
| Morningside Elem Sch/The Colony/Denton | 04036075 | 469/713-5970 | 128 |
| Morningside Middle Sch/Fort Worth/Tarrant | 01053141 | 817/815-8300 | 354 |
| Morrill Elem Sch/San Antonio/Bexar | 00997491 | 210/989-3150 | 36 |
| Morris Middle Sch/Houston/Harris | 05347877 | 713/740-0672 | 204 |
| Morris Upchurch Middle Sch/Queen City/Cass | 01809017 | 903/796-6412 | 74 |
| Morriss Elem Sch/Texarkana/Bowie | 10907438 | 903/791-2262 | 53 |
| Morton Elem Sch/Arlington/Tarrant | 01558880 | 682/867-5600 | 347 |
| Morton Elem Sch/Morton/Cochran | 01005687 | 806/266-5505 | 78 |
| Morton High Sch/Morton/Cochran | 01005699 | 806/266-5505 | 78 |
| **MORTON IND SCH DIST/MORTON/** | | | |
| **COCHRAN** | 01005675 | 806/266-5505 | 78 |
| Morton Junior High Sch/Morton/Cochran | 01005704 | 806/266-5505 | 78 |
| Morton Ranch Elem Sch/Katy/Harris | 11128611 | 281/234-0300 | 156 |
| Morton Ranch High Sch/Katy/Harris | 05344320 | 281/237-7800 | 157 |
| Morton Ranch Jr High Sch/Katy/Harris | 05264718 | 281/237-7400 | 157 |
| Mosaic Academy/Amarillo/Potter | 11223649 | 817/204-0300 | 322 |
| Moses Menger Elem Sch/Corp Christi/Nueces | 01044566 | 361/878-2640 | 307 |
| Moss Elem Sch/Big Spring/Howard | 01032006 | 432/264-4148 | 236 |
| Moss Haven Elem Sch/Dallas/Dallas | 01525974 | 469/593-2200 | 117 |
| Most Holy Trinity Sch/El Paso/El Paso | 01483948 | 915/751-2566 | 143 |
| Most Precious Catholic Sch/Corp Christi/ Nueces | 01600471 | 361/852-4800 | 309 |
| **MOTLEY CO IND SCH DIST/MATADOR/** | | | |
| **MOTLEY** | 01043043 | 806/347-2676 | 299 |
| Motley Co Sch/Matador/Motley | 01043055 | 806/347-2676 | 299 |
| Moulton Elem Sch/Moulton/Lavaca | 01037331 | 361/596-4605 | 265 |
| Moulton High Sch/Moulton/Lavaca | 01037343 | 361/596-4691 | 265 |
| **MOULTON IND SCH DIST/MOULTON/** | | | |
| **LAVACA** | 01037329 | 361/596-4609 | 265 |
| Mount Carmel Academy/Houston/Harris | 05099238 | 713/643-2008 | 195 |
| Mount Pleasant High Sch/Mt Pleasant/Titus | 01055400 | 903/575-2020 | 366 |
| Mount Vernon Elem Sch/Mount Vernon/ Franklin | 01018397 | 903/537-2266 | 160 |
| Mount Vernon High Sch/Mount Vernon/ Franklin | 01018402 | 903/537-3700 | 160 |
| **MOUNT VERNON IND SCH DIST/** | | | |
| **MOUNT VERNON/FRANKLIN** | 01018385 | 903/537-2546 | 160 |
| Mount Vernon Middle Sch/Mount Vernon/ Franklin | 01018414 | 903/537-2267 | 160 |
| Mountain Peak Elem Sch/Midlothian/Ellis | 04745800 | 469/856-6300 | 145 |
| Mountain Valley Elem Sch/Canyon Lake/Comal | 11926877 | 830/885-9500 | 92 |
| Mountain Valley Middle Sch/Canyon Lake/ Comal | 11079450 | 830/885-1300 | 92 |
| Mountain View Elem Sch/Harker HTS/Bell | 03051503 | 254/336-1900 | 31 |
| Mountain View High Sch/El Paso/El Paso | 03237408 | 915/926-5000 | 137 |
| Mountaintop Learning Center/Houston/Harris | 04993332 | 713/808-9284 | 211 |
| Mountainview Elem Sch/Waco/McLennan | 01040314 | 254/772-2520 | 285 |
| Moye Elem Sch/El Paso/El Paso | 01015890 | 915/230-5100 | 138 |
| Mozelle Brown Elem Sch/Whitehouse/Smith | 01539250 | 903/839-5610 | 341 |
| Msgr Kelly Catholic HS/Beaumont/Jefferson | 01034365 | 409/866-2351 | 247 |
| Mt Auburn Steam Academy/Dallas/Dallas | 01009487 | 972/749-8500 | 106 |
| Mt Calm Elem Sch/Mount Calm/Hill | 01031014 | 254/993-2611 | 231 |
| Mt Calm High Sch/Mount Calm/Hill | 11710484 | 254/993-2611 | 231 |
| **MT CALM IND SCH DIST/MOUNT CALM/** | | | |
| **HILL** | 01031002 | 254/993-2611 | 231 |
| **MT ENTERPRISE IND SCH DIST/** | | | |
| **MT ENTERPRISE/RUSK** | 01049126 | 903/822-3575 | 330 |
| Mt Enterprise Sch/Mt Enterprise/Rusk | 01049140 | 903/822-3545 | 331 |
| Mt Pleasant Child Dev Center/Mt Pleasant/ Titus | 04870091 | 903/575-2092 | 366 |
| Mt Pleasant Christian Sch/Mt Pleasant/ Titus | 04992883 | 903/577-1550 | 366 |
| **MT PLEASANT IND SCH DIST/** | | | |
| **MT PLEASANT/TITUS** | 01055369 | 903/575-2000 | 366 |
| Mt Pleasant Junior High Sch/Mt Pleasant/ Titus | 04747494 | 903/575-2110 | 366 |
| Mt Sacred Heart Sch/San Antonio/Bexar | 00999877 | 210/342-6711 | 47 |
| Mt Saint Michael Catholic Sch/Dallas/ Dallas | 04430299 | 214/337-0244 | 118 |
| Mueller Elem Sch/Klein/Harris | 11452113 | 832/375-7300 | 202 |
| Muenster Elem Sch/Muenster/Cooke | 04281610 | 940/759-2282 | 95 |
| Muenster High Sch/Muenster/Cooke | 01007477 | 940/759-2281 | 95 |
| **MUENSTER IND SCH DIST/MUENSTER/** | | | |
| **COOKE** | 01007453 | 940/759-2281 | 95 |
| Muleshoe High Sch/Muleshoe/Bailey | 00995728 | 806/272-7302 | 25 |
| **MULESHOE IND SCH DIST/MULESHOE/** | | | |
| **BAILEY** | 00995699 | 806/272-7400 | 25 |
| Mullin Elem Sch/Mullin/Mills | 12166240 | 325/985-3374 | 291 |
| **MULLIN IND SCH DIST/MULLIN/MILLS** | 01041978 | 855/467-0030 | 291 |
| Mullin Middle High Sch/Mullin/Mills | 01041980 | 855/467-0030 | 291 |
| Mullin Oaks Sch/Brownwood/Mills | 12166214 | 325/203-5315 | 291 |
| Multiple Careers Magnet Center/Dallas/ Dallas | 01010046 | 972/925-2200 | 106 |
| **MUMFORD IND SCH DIST/MUMFORD/** | | | |
| **BRAZOS** | 01048691 | 979/279-3678 | 59 |
| Mumford Sch/Mumford/Brazos | 01048706 | 979/279-3678 | 59 |
| Munday Charter Sch/Austin/Travis | 12362676 | 512/791-2270 | 11 |
| **MUNDAY CONSOLIDATED IND SD/** | | | |
| **MUNDAY/KNOX** | 01036533 | 940/422-4241 | 262 |
| Munday Elem Sch/Munday/Knox | 01036545 | 940/422-4321 | 262 |
| Munday High Sch/Munday/Knox | 01036557 | 940/422-4321 | 262 |
| Murchison Elem Sch/Murchison/Henderson | 01029499 | 903/469-3636 | 219 |
| Murchison Elem Sch/Pflugerville/Travis | 04920191 | 512/594-6000 | 374 |
| **MURCHISON IND SCH DIST/MURCHISON/** | | | |
| **HENDERSON** | 01029487 | 903/469-3636 | 219 |
| Murchison Middle Sch/Austin/Travis | 01392129 | 512/414-3254 | 371 |
| Muriel Vance Forbes Academy/San Antonio/ Bexar | 00998938 | 210/438-6850 | 44 |
| Murphy Middle Sch/Murphy/Collin | 05274397 | 469/752-7000 | 86 |
| Murray E Boone Elem Sch/San Antonio/Bexar | 00998237 | 210/397-1450 | 41 |
| Murry Fly Elem Sch/Odessa/Ector | 02178251 | 432/456-1269 | 134 |
| Myatt Elem Sch/El Campo/Wharton | 03007019 | 979/543-7514 | 392 |
| Myra Green Middle Sch/Raymondville/Willacy | 01060742 | 956/689-8171 | 397 |
| Myrtle Cooper Elem Sch/El Paso/El Paso | 03009847 | 915/937-7700 | 141 |

**N**

| School/City/County DISTRICT/CITY/COUNTY | PID | TELEPHONE NUMBER | PAGE |
|---|---|---|---|
| N A Howry Intermediate Sch/Lake Worth/ Tarrant | 01054107 | 817/306-4240 | 358 |
| N L Trevino Elem Sch/Edinburg/Hidalgo | 04873275 | 956/289-2550 | 222 |
| N M Harrel Elem Sch/Kingsville/Kleberg | 01036351 | 361/592-9305 | 260 |
| N Q Henderson Elem Sch/Houston/Harris | 01025637 | 713/671-4195 | 196 |
| N W Harllee Early Chldhd Ctr/Dallas/Dallas | 12169711 | 972/925-6500 | 106 |
| Naaman Forest High Sch/Garland/Dallas | 03055523 | 972/675-3091 | 110 |
| Nacogdoches Christian Academy/Nacogdoches/ Nacogdoches | 11829657 | 936/462-1021 | 302 |
| Nacogdoches High Sch/Nacogdoches/ Nacogdoches | 01043316 | 936/564-2466 | 301 |
| **NACOGDOCHES IND SCH DIST/** | | | |
| **NACOGDOCHES/NACOGDOCHES** | 01043275 | 936/569-5000 | 301 |
| Nadine Johnson Elem Sch/Hutto/Williamson | 05221338 | 512/759-5400 | 399 |
| Nancy J Cochran Elem Sch/Dallas/Dallas | 01008665 | 972/794-4600 | 106 |
| Nancy Moseley Elem Sch/Dallas/Dallas | 01009516 | 972/749-6700 | 106 |
| Nancy Neal Elem Sch/Mansfield/Tarrant | 11715408 | 817/299-1270 | 359 |
| Nancy Smith Elem Sch/Albany/Shackelford | 01050230 | 325/762-3384 | 336 |
| Nanny Elem Sch/Riviera/Kleberg | 01036404 | 361/296-2446 | 261 |
| Naomi Pasemann Elem Sch/Taylor/Williamson | 04803438 | 512/352-1016 | 403 |
| Naomi Press Elem Sch/McKinney/Collin | 10909175 | 469/302-7600 | 85 |
| Narciso Cavazos Elem Sch/Mission/Hidalgo | 04805979 | 956/323-2430 | 223 |
| Nash Elem Sch/Nash/Bowie | 01001289 | 903/838-4321 | 53 |
| Natalia Elem Sch/Natalia/Medina | 01041332 | 830/663-2837 | 287 |
| Natalia High Sch/Natalia/Medina | 01041344 | 830/663-4417 | 287 |
| **NATALIA IND SCH DIST/NATALIA/** | | | |
| **MEDINA** | 01041320 | 830/663-4416 | 287 |
| Natalia Junior High Sch/Natalia/Medina | 01041356 | 830/663-4027 | 287 |
| Nathan Adams Elem Sch/Dallas/Dallas | 01009530 | 972/794-2600 | 106 |
| Nathan Howell Elem Sch/Haltom City/Tarrant | 01053191 | 817/814-9300 | 354 |
| Nathaniel Hawthorne Elem Sch/Dallas/Dallas | 01009504 | 972/749-4700 | 106 |
| Naumann Elem Sch/Cedar Park/Williamson | 04808488 | 512/570-5800 | 400 |
| Navarro Co Alt Educ Ctr/Corsicana/Navarro | 12307640 | 903/872-4502 | 303 |
| Navarro Early College High Sch/Austin/ Travis | 01056337 | 512/414-2514 | 371 |
| Navarro Elem Sch/Bryan/Brazos | 03047837 | 979/209-1260 | 58 |
| Navarro Elem Sch/Lockhart/Caldwell | 01003081 | 512/398-0690 | 64 |
| Navarro Elem Sch/Seguin/Guadalupe | 01021538 | 830/372-1933 | 178 |
| Navarro High Sch/Seguin/Guadalupe | 01021540 | 830/372-1931 | 178 |
| **NAVARRO IND SCH DIST/SEGUIN/** | | | |
| **GUADALUPE** | 01021526 | 830/372-1930 | 178 |
| Navarro Intermediate Sch/Seguin/Guadalupe | 04745018 | 830/372-1943 | 178 |
| Navarro Junior High Sch/Seguin/Guadalupe | 10774188 | 830/401-5550 | 178 |
| Navarro Mid Sch/Houston/Harris | 01025003 | 713/924-1760 | 195 |
| Navarro Middle Sch/Rosenberg/Fort Bend | 03009861 | 832/223-3700 | 158 |
| Navasota High Sch/Navasota/Grimes | 01021423 | 936/825-4250 | 177 |

| School/City/County DISTRICT/CITY/COUNTY | PID | TELEPHONE NUMBER | PAGE |
|---|---|---|---|
| **NAVASOTA IND SCH DIST**/NAVASOTA/ GRIMES | 01021409 | 936/825-4200 | 177 |
| Navasota Junior High Sch/Navasota/Grimes | 01021435 | 936/825-4225 | 177 |
| Navo Middle Sch/Aubrey/Denton | 10021876 | 972/347-7500 | 125 |
| Nazarene Christian Academy/Crowley/Tarrant | 10754384 | 817/297-7003 | 361 |
| Nazarene Christian Academy/Hereford/ Deaf Smith | 11230525 | 806/364-1697 | 123 |
| Nazareth Academy/Victoria/Victoria | 00999906 | 361/573-6651 | 385 |
| **NAZARETH IND SCH DIST**/NAZARETH/ CASTRO | 01005041 | 806/945-2231 | 75 |
| Nazareth Sch/Nazareth/Castro | 01005053 | 806/945-2231 | 75 |
| Nci CS Without Walls/Houston/Harris | 11016111 | 713/779-4856 | 11 |
| NE Transition Sch/San Antonio/Bexar | 11452216 | 210/356-7520 | 38 |
| Neal Dillman Elem Sch/Muleshoe/Bailey | 00995730 | 806/272-7383 | 25 |
| Neal Elem Sch/Bryan/Brazos | 04753481 | 979/209-3860 | 58 |
| Neal Elem Sch/San Antonio/Bexar | 00998445 | 210/738-9810 | 44 |
| Nebbie Williams Elem Sch/Rockwall/Rockwall | 04454130 | 972/772-0502 | 328 |
| Neches Elem Jr High Sch/Neches/Anderson | 00994504 | 903/584-3401 | 18 |
| Neches High Sch/Neches/Anderson | 00994516 | 903/584-3311 | 18 |
| **NECHES IND SCH DIST**/NECHES/ ANDERSON | 00994499 | 903/584-3311 | 18 |
| Ned E Williams Elem Sch/Longview/Gregg | 11818074 | 903/803-5500 | 175 |
| Nederland High Sch/Nederland/Jefferson | 01033737 | 409/727-2741 | 246 |
| **NEDERLAND IND SCH DIST**/NEDERLAND/ JEFFERSON | 01033660 | 409/724-2391 | 245 |
| Needville Elem Sch/Needville/Fort Bend | 01018361 | 979/793-4241 | 159 |
| Needville High Sch/Needville/Fort Bend | 01018373 | 979/793-4158 | 159 |
| **NEEDVILLE IND SCH DIST**/NEEDVILLE/ FORT BEND | 01018347 | 979/793-4158 | 159 |
| Needville Junior High Sch/Needville/ Fort Bend | 04912857 | 979/793-4250 | 159 |
| Needville Middle Sch/Needville/Fort Bend | 02128749 | 979/793-3027 | 159 |
| Neff Early Learning Center/Houston/Harris | 12170289 | 713/778-3470 | 199 |
| Neff Elem Sch/Houston/Harris | 01024528 | 713/556-9566 | 199 |
| Negley Elem Sch/Kyle/Hays | 10022739 | 512/268-8501 | 216 |
| Neidig Elem Sch/Elgin/Bastrop | 10001163 | 512/281-9702 | 27 |
| Neil Armstrong Elem Sch/San Antonio/Bexar | 00999463 | 210/623-8787 | 45 |
| Nelda Sullivan Middle Sch/Pasadena/Harris | 12170162 | 713/740-5420 | 204 |
| Nell Burks Elem Sch/McKinney/Collin | 01006306 | 469/302-6200 | 85 |
| Nellie M Reddix Center/San Antonio/Bexar | 00998201 | 210/397-2401 | 41 |
| Nelson Early Chldhd Ed Ctr/San Antonio/ Bexar | 12305630 | 210/438-6555 | 44 |
| Nelson Middle Sch/Frisco/Collin | 12167268 | 469/633-4100 | 83 |
| Nesmith Elem Sch/Lavon/Collin | 11148374 | 972/843-6100 | 81 |
| Netherland Alt Ed Sch/Nederland/Jefferson | 04748993 | 409/727-5241 | 246 |
| Nettie Baccus Elem Sch/Granbury/Hood | 03007681 | 817/408-4300 | 233 |
| Nettie Marshall Elem Sch/Nacogdoches/ Nacogdoches | 01043328 | 936/569-5062 | 301 |
| New Boston High Sch/New Boston/Bowie | 01001083 | 903/628-6551 | 52 |
| **NEW BOSTON IND SCH DIST**/ NEW BOSTON/BOWIE | 01001069 | 903/628-2521 | 52 |
| New Boston Middle Sch/New Boston/Bowie | 01001095 | 903/628-6588 | 52 |
| New Braunfels Chrn Acad-Lower/New Braunfels/ Comal | 02733954 | 830/629-6222 | 93 |
| New Braunfels High Sch/New Braunfels/Comal | 01007001 | 830/627-6000 | 92 |
| New Braunfels HS 9th GR Ctr/New Braunfels/ Comal | 11822324 | 830/629-8600 | 92 |
| **NEW BRAUNFELS IND SCH DIST**/ NEW BRAUNFELS/COMAL | 01006966 | 830/643-5700 | 92 |
| New Braunfels Middle Sch/New Braunfels/ Comal | 01007013 | 830/627-6270 | 92 |
| New Caney Elem Sch/New Caney/Montgomery | 01042673 | 281/577-8720 | 297 |
| New Caney High Sch/New Caney/Montgomery | 01042685 | 281/577-2800 | 297 |
| **NEW CANEY IND SCH DIST**/NEW CANEY/ MONTGOMERY | 01042661 | 281/577-8600 | 296 |
| New Caney Middle Sch/Porter/Montgomery | 10915576 | 281/577-8860 | 297 |
| New Deal Elem Sch/New Deal/Lubbock | 01039092 | 806/746-5849 | 274 |
| New Deal High Sch/New Deal/Lubbock | 01039107 | 806/746-5933 | 274 |
| **NEW DEAL IND SCH DIST**/NEW DEAL/ LUBBOCK | 01039080 | 806/746-5833 | 274 |
| New Deal Middle Sch/New Deal/Lubbock | 03047265 | 806/746-6633 | 274 |
| New Diana High Sch/Diana/Upshur | 01057513 | 903/663-8001 | 379 |
| **NEW DIANA IND SCH DIST**/DIANA/ UPSHUR | 01057484 | 903/663-8000 | 379 |
| New Diana Middle Sch/Diana/Upshur | 04034388 | 903/663-8002 | 379 |
| New Frontiers Christian Acad/Wills Point/ Van Zandt | 11224148 | 903/873-2440 | 384 |
| New Heights Christian Academy/Houston/ Harris | 04993198 | 713/861-9101 | 211 |
| **NEW HOME IND SCH DIST**/NEW HOME/ LYNN | 01039274 | 806/924-7543 | 275 |
| New Home Sch/New Home/Lynn | 01039286 | 806/924-7543 | 276 |

| School/City/County DISTRICT/CITY/COUNTY | PID | TELEPHONE NUMBER | PAGE |
|---|---|---|---|
| New Hope Academy/Lubbock/Lubbock | 12230229 | 806/863-7109 | 274 |
| New Hope Christian Academy/Plano/Collin | 12239861 | 972/656-9951 | 89 |
| New Hope High Sch/Leander/Williamson | 05102976 | 512/570-2200 | 400 |
| New Horizons High Sch/Joshua/Johnson | 04278675 | 817/202-2500 | 251 |
| New Horizons Learning Center/Greenville/ Hunt | 03396200 | 903/457-2688 | 239 |
| New Horizons Ranch Sch/Goldthwaite/Mills | 02897586 | 325/938-5518 | 11 |
| New Life Academy/Euless/Tarrant | 12306397 | 817/267-1000 | 361 |
| New Life Academy/Lubbock/Lubbock | 02191667 | 806/763-0117 | 275 |
| New Life Christian Academy/Dallas/Dallas | 12166771 | 214/327-6522 | 120 |
| New Life Christian Academy/San Antonio/ Bexar | 04993758 | 210/679-6001 | 48 |
| New Pathways Center/Harlingen/Cameron | 05096705 | 956/427-3250 | 68 |
| New Star Sch/Plano/Collin | 11222607 | 972/897-9217 | 89 |
| **NEW SUMMERFIELD IND SCH DIST**/ NEW SUMMERFLD/CHEROKEE | 01005340 | 903/726-3306 | 76 |
| New Summerfield Sch/New Summerfld/Cherokee | 01005352 | 903/726-3306 | 76 |
| New Tech High Sch at Waskow/Belton/Bell | 04871461 | 254/215-2500 | 30 |
| New Tech High Sch-Coppell/Coppell/Dallas | 11132636 | 214/496-5900 | 102 |
| New Tech HS at BF Darrell/Dallas/Dallas | 02109834 | 214/932-7600 | 106 |
| New Waverly Elem Sch/New Waverly/Walker | 01058751 | 936/344-2900 | 386 |
| New Waverly High Sch/New Waverly/Walker | 01058749 | 936/344-6451 | 386 |
| **NEW WAVERLY IND SCH DIST**/ NEW WAVERLY/WALKER | 01058737 | 936/344-6751 | 386 |
| New Waverly Intermediate Sch/New Waverly/ Walker | 05342176 | 936/344-6601 | 386 |
| New Waverly Junior High Sch/New Waverly/ Walker | 03047174 | 936/344-2246 | 386 |
| New World Montessori Sch/El Paso/El Paso | 05342542 | 915/593-8091 | 143 |
| **NEWCASTLE IND SCH DIST**/NEWCASTLE/ YOUNG | 01062166 | 940/846-3531 | 409 |
| Newcastle Sch/Newcastle/Young | 01062178 | 940/846-3531 | 410 |
| Newcomer Center/Arlington/Tarrant | 04808713 | 682/867-7100 | 347 |
| Newell E Woolls Interm Sch/Hondo/Medina | 04911932 | 830/426-7666 | 287 |
| Newgulf Elem Sch/Boling/Wharton | 01059561 | 979/657-2837 | 392 |
| Newman Elem Sch/El Paso/El Paso | 01015840 | 915/236-5825 | 138 |
| Newman Elem Sch/Laredo/Webb | 02109975 | 956/473-3800 | 391 |
| Newman Int'l Acad-Cedar Hill/Cedar Hill/ Dallas | 12161991 | 972/293-5460 | 11 |
| Newman Int'l Acad-Ft Worth/Fort Worth/ Tarrant | 12260987 | 817/655-2255 | 11 |
| Newman Int'l Acad-Grace/Arlington/Tarrant | 12260975 | 682/220-9210 | 11 |
| Newman Int'l Acad-Mansfield/Mansfield/ Tarrant | 12260963 | 682/400-4010 | 11 |
| Newman Int'l Acad-Pioneer/Arlington/ Tarrant | 12378625 | 682/331-7095 | 11 |
| Newman Int'l Academy-Arlington/Arlington/ Tarrant | 11704473 | 682/207-5175 | 11 |
| Newman Smith High Sch/Carrollton/Dallas | 01418266 | 972/968-5200 | 101 |
| Newport Elem Sch/Crosby/Harris | 02181595 | 281/328-9330 | 188 |
| Newton Collins Elem Sch/Austin/Travis | 12307925 | 512/386-3900 | 372 |
| Newton Elem Sch/Newton/Newton | 01043768 | 409/420-6600 | 304 |
| Newton High Sch/Newton/Newton | 01043782 | 409/420-6600 | 304 |
| **NEWTON IND SCH DIST**/NEWTON/ NEWTON | 01043744 | 409/420-6600 | 304 |
| Newton Middle Sch/Newton/Newton | 01043770 | 409/420-6600 | 304 |
| Newton Rayzor Elem Sch/Denton/Denton | 01013282 | 940/369-3700 | 125 |
| Neysa Callison Elem Sch/Round Rock/ Williamson | 11130860 | 512/704-0700 | 402 |
| Nichols Elem Sch/Frisco/Collin | 11820089 | 469/633-3950 | 83 |
| Nichols Elem Sch/San Antonio/Bexar | 05097759 | 210/397-4050 | 41 |
| Nichols Intermediate Sch/Jacksonville/ Cherokee | 04932429 | 903/541-0213 | 76 |
| Nichols Junior High Sch/Arlington/Tarrant | 01051856 | 682/867-2600 | 347 |
| Nichols-Saw Mill Elem Sch/Magnolia/ Montgomery | 05097632 | 281/252-2133 | 296 |
| Nimitz 9th Grade Sch/Houston/Harris | 04867226 | 281/209-8200 | 185 |
| Nimitz Elem Sch/Kerrville/Kerr | 01036117 | 830/257-2209 | 259 |
| Nimitz High Sch/Irving/Dallas | 01011272 | 972/600-5700 | 114 |
| Nimitz Middle Sch/Odessa/Ector | 01014767 | 432/456-0469 | 134 |
| Nimitz Middle Sch/San Antonio/Bexar | 00997855 | 210/356-5300 | 38 |
| Nita Pearson Elem Sch/Rowlett/Dallas | 05345439 | 972/463-7568 | 110 |
| Nitsch Elem Sch/Houston/Harris | 02110687 | 832/484-6400 | 202 |
| **NIXON-SMILEY CONS IND SCH DIST**/ NIXON/GONZALES | 01019937 | 830/582-1536 | 169 |
| Nixon-Smiley Elem Sch/Smiley/Gonzales | 01019949 | 830/582-1536 | 169 |
| Nixon-Smiley High Sch/Nixon/Gonzales | 01019951 | 830/582-1536 | 169 |
| Nixon-Smiley Middle Sch/Nixon/Gonzales | 01019963 | 830/582-1536 | 169 |
| Noble-Reed Elem Sch/Crandall/Kaufman | 12380496 | 972/427-6060 | 254 |
| Nocona Elem Sch/Nocona/Montague | 01042362 | 940/825-3151 | 293 |
| Nocona High Sch/Nocona/Montague | 01042348 | 940/825-3264 | 293 |

| School/City/County DISTRICT/CITY/COUNTY | PID | TELEPHONE NUMBER | PAGE |
|---|---|---|---|
| **NOCONA IND SCH DIST/NOCONA/** | | | |
| **MONTAGUE** | 01042336 | 940/825-3267 | 293 |
| Nocona Middle Sch/Nocona/Montague | 01042350 | 940/825-3121 | 293 |
| Noel A Smith Elem Sch/Frisco/Collin | 04744612 | 469/633-2200 | 83 |
| Noel Elem Sch/Odessa/Ector | 02126404 | 432/456-1249 | 134 |
| Noel Grisham Middle Sch/Austin/Williamson | 01530034 | 512/428-2650 | 402 |
| Noemi Dominguez Elem Sch/La Feria/Cameron | 01003988 | 956/797-8430 | 69 |
| Nola Kathryn Wilson Elem Sch/Crandall/ | | | |
| Kaufman | 04454312 | 972/427-6040 | 254 |
| Nolan Catholic High Sch/Fort Worth/Tarrant | 01054377 | 817/457-2920 | 360 |
| Nolan Creek Sch/Belton/Bell | 12260999 | 254/939-4491 | 11 |
| Nolan Middle Sch/Harker HTS/Bell | 00996552 | 254/336-1150 | 31 |
| Nolan Richardson Middle Sch/El Paso/ | | | |
| El Paso | 04806648 | 915/236-6650 | 139 |
| Nolan Ryan Junior High Sch/Pearland/ | | | |
| Brazoria | 11070985 | 281/245-3210 | 54 |
| Nolanville Elem Sch/Nolanville/Bell | 00996564 | 254/336-2180 | 31 |
| Noonan Elem Sch/Alice/Jim Wells | 01034602 | 361/664-7591 | 248 |
| **NORDHEIM IND SCH DIST/NORDHEIM/** | | | |
| **DE WITT** | 01013751 | 361/938-5211 | 122 |
| Nordheim Sch/Nordheim/De Witt | 01013763 | 361/938-5211 | 122 |
| Norma Dorsey Elem Sch/Rowlett/Dallas | 04450976 | 972/463-5595 | 110 |
| Norma J Paschal Elem Sch/Schertz/Guadalupe | 05275781 | 210/619-4500 | 178 |
| Norma Krueger Elem Sch/Marion/Guadalupe | 01021497 | 830/914-1060 | 178 |
| Norma Krueger Elem Sch-Karrer/Marion/ | | | |
| Guadalupe | 05343326 | 830/914-1065 | 178 |
| Norman Thomas Elem Sch/Freer/Duval | 01809225 | 361/394-6800 | 132 |
| Norman-Sims Elem Sch/Austin/Travis | 01056466 | 512/414-2347 | 370 |
| Normandy Crossing Elem Sch/Houston/Harris | 05274440 | 832/386-1600 | 192 |
| Normangee Elem Sch/Normangee/Leon | 01037666 | 936/396-9999 | 267 |
| **NORMANGEE IND SCH DIST/NORMANGEE/** | | | |
| **LEON** | 01037654 | 936/396-3111 | 267 |
| Normangee Middle Sch/Normangee/Leon | 11459642 | 936/396-3111 | 267 |
| Normangee Senior High Sch/Normangee/Leon | 11459654 | 936/396-6111 | 267 |
| Norris Elem Sch/Frisco/Collin | 12107000 | 469/633-4075 | 83 |
| North Avenue Interm Sch/Gonzales/Gonzales | 01019913 | 830/672-9557 | 169 |
| North Belt Elem Sch/Humble/Harris | 01026215 | 281/641-1300 | 201 |
| North Belton Middle Sch/Temple/Bell | 04035887 | 254/316-5200 | 30 |
| North Bridge Elem Sch/Weslaco/Hidalgo | 03393076 | 956/969-6810 | 228 |
| North Central Texas Academy/Granbury/Hood | 02153562 | 254/897-4822 | 234 |
| North Creek Elem Sch/Melissa/Collin | 10901135 | 972/837-4530 | 85 |
| North Crowley 9th Grade Campus/Fort Worth/ | | | |
| Tarrant | 05271553 | 817/297-5896 | 350 |
| North Crowley High Sch/Fort Worth/Tarrant | 04807680 | 817/263-1250 | 350 |
| North Dallas Adventist Academy/Richardson/ | | | |
| Dallas | 02850552 | 972/234-6322 | 120 |
| North Dallas High Sch/Dallas/Dallas | 01009499 | 972/925-1500 | 106 |
| North Early Learning Center/Orange/Orange | 01045845 | 409/882-5434 | 312 |
| North East Alternative Center/San Antonio/ | | | |
| Bexar | 04017782 | 210/356-7400 | 38 |
| **NORTH EAST IND SCH DIST/** | | | |
| **SAN ANTONIO/BEXAR** | 00997661 | 210/407-0000 | 37 |
| North Elem Sch/Breckenridge/Stephens | 01051363 | 254/559-6511 | 344 |
| North Elem Sch/Fort Worth/Tarrant | 01054224 | 817/367-1323 | 360 |
| North Elem Sch/Hallsville/Harrison | 01028495 | 903/668-5981 | 213 |
| North Elem Sch/Lamesa/Dawson | 01012915 | 806/872-5428 | 121 |
| North Elem Sch/Lubbock/Lubbock | 05027065 | 806/776-2700 | 274 |
| North Euless Elem Sch/Euless/Tarrant | 01053878 | 817/354-3505 | 356 |
| North Forest High Sch/Houston/Harris | 01026526 | 713/636-4300 | 194 |
| North Forney High Sch/Forney/Kaufman | 11465029 | 469/762-4210 | 255 |
| North Garland High Sch/Garland/Dallas | 01010632 | 972/675-3110 | 120 |
| North Heights Alt Sch/Amarillo/Potter | 01047489 | 806/326-2850 | 321 |
| North Heights Elem Sch/Del Rio/Val Verde | 01058024 | 830/778-4777 | 382 |
| North Hi Mount Elem Sch/Fort Worth/Tarrant | 01053165 | 817/815-1500 | 354 |
| **NORTH HOPKINS IND SCH DIST/** | | | |
| **SULPHUR SPGS/HOPKINS** | 01031545 | 903/945-2192 | 234 |
| North Hopkins Sch/Sulphur Spgs/Hopkins | 01031557 | 903/945-2192 | 234 |
| North Houston Early College HS/Houston/ | | | |
| Harris | 11152284 | 713/696-6168 | 197 |
| North Joshua Elem Sch/Burleson/Johnson | 04452364 | 817/426-7500 | 251 |
| North Lake Early Clg High Sch/Irving/ | | | |
| Dallas | 12377774 | 972/502-7803 | 106 |
| North Lamar High Sch/Paris/Wise | 01036662 | 903/737-2011 | 407 |
| **NORTH LAMAR IND SCH DIST/** | | | |
| **PARADISE/WISE** | 01036636 | 903/737-2000 | 406 |
| North Loop Christian Academy/El Paso/ | | | |
| El Paso | 04994192 | 915/859-8090 | 144 |
| North Loop Elem Sch/El Paso/El Paso | 01016480 | 915/434-2800 | 142 |
| North Mesquite High Sch/Mesquite/Dallas | 01011571 | 972/882-7900 | 115 |
| North Oaks Middle Sch/Haltom City/Tarrant | 01052135 | 817/547-4600 | 349 |
| North Park Christian Academy/N RichInd HIs/ | | | |
| Tarrant | 03380196 | 817/498-8456 | 361 |
| North Plains Opportunity Ctr/Dumas/Moore | 12033978 | 806/935-8774 | 298 |
| North Pointe Elem Sch/Houston/Galveston | 04365319 | 281/284-5900 | 163 |
| North Richland Middle Sch/N RichInd HIs/ | | | |
| Tarrant | 01052123 | 817/547-4200 | 349 |
| North Ridge Elem Sch/Lubbock/Lubbock | 02895198 | 806/793-6686 | 272 |
| North Ridge Elem Sch/N RichInd HIs/Tarrant | 03052492 | 817/547-3200 | 349 |
| North Ridge Middle Sch/N RichInd HIs/ | | | |
| Tarrant | 03251894 | 817/547-5200 | 349 |
| North Riverside Elem Sch/Fort Worth/ | | | |
| Tarrant | 04806789 | 817/744-5300 | 357 |
| North Shore 10th Grade Ctr/Houston/Harris | 12307099 | 832/386-4880 | 192 |
| North Shore Elem Sch/Houston/Harris | 01023500 | 832/386-4660 | 192 |
| North Shore Middle Sch/Houston/Harris | 01023524 | 832/386-2600 | 192 |
| North Shore Ninth Grade Center/Houston/ | | | |
| Harris | 01023512 | 832/386-3400 | 192 |
| North Shore Senior High Sch/Houston/Harris | 04837788 | 832/386-4100 | 192 |
| North Side High Sch/Fort Worth/Tarrant | 01053177 | 817/814-4000 | 354 |
| North Star Elem Sch/El Paso/El Paso | 05097620 | 915/434-6700 | 142 |
| North Texas Collegiate Acad-E/Little Elm/ | | | |
| Denton | 05010787 | 972/292-3562 | 11 |
| North Texas Collegiate Acad-N/Denton/ | | | |
| Denton | 11014400 | 940/383-1972 | 11 |
| North Texas Collegiate Acad-S/Lewisville/ | | | |
| Denton | 11014395 | 972/221-3564 | 11 |
| North Texas Leadership Academy/Keller/ | | | |
| Tarrant | 12105480 | 817/562-2931 | 361 |
| North West Head Start Center/Wichita Falls/ | | | |
| Wichita | 11551915 | 940/235-4307 | 395 |
| **NORTH ZULCH IND SCH DIST/** | | | |
| **NORTH ZULCH/MADISON** | 01040637 | 936/241-7100 | 276 |
| North Zulch Sch/North Zulch/Madison | 01040649 | 936/241-7100 | 277 |
| Northampton Elem Sch/Klein/Harris | 01026356 | 832/484-5550 | 202 |
| Northbrook Elem Sch/Fort Worth/Tarrant | 11072775 | 817/232-0086 | 351 |
| Northbrook High Sch/Houston/Harris | 01027221 | 713/251-2800 | 206 |
| Northbrook Middle Sch/Houston/Harris | 03397905 | 713/251-4100 | 206 |
| Northeast Christian Academy/El Paso/ | | | |
| El Paso | 02152348 | 915/755-1155 | 144 |
| Northeast Early Clg High Sch/Austin/Travis | 01056296 | 512/414-2523 | 371 |
| Northern Hills Elem Sch/San Antonio/Bexar | 02126167 | 210/407-5200 | 38 |
| Northgate Crossing Elem Sch/Spring/Harris | 11077244 | 281/891-8780 | 207 |
| Northlake Elem Sch/Dallas/Dallas | 01011806 | 469/593-2300 | 117 |
| Northlake Elem Sch/Garland/Dallas | 01382928 | 972/494-8359 | 110 |
| Northland Christian Sch/Houston/Harris | 02153445 | 281/440-1060 | 211 |
| Northline Elem Sch/Houston/Harris | 01026045 | 713/696-2890 | 196 |
| Northpointe Intermediate Sch/Tomball/ | | | |
| Harris | 05279385 | 281/357-3020 | 208 |
| Northrich Elem Sch/Richardson/Dallas | 01011818 | 469/593-6200 | 117 |
| Northside Alt Middle Sch/San Antonio/Bexar | 04503949 | 210/397-2070 | 41 |
| Northside Alt Middle Sch-North/San Antonio/ | | | |
| Bexar | 04774710 | 210/397-2070 | 41 |
| Northside Alternative High Sch/San Antonio/ | | | |
| Bexar | 02226432 | 210/397-7080 | 41 |
| Northside Baptist Sch/Victoria/Victoria | 01481287 | 361/578-1568 | 385 |
| Northside Christian Academy/Carthage/ | | | |
| Panola | 04992924 | 903/693-7700 | 314 |
| Northside Elem Sch/Angleton/Brazoria | 01001514 | 979/864-8006 | 55 |
| Northside Elem Sch/Cleveland/Liberty | 01037757 | 281/592-4628 | 268 |
| Northside Elem Sch/Desoto/Dallas | 01010278 | 972/224-6709 | 108 |
| Northside Elem Sch/El Campo/Wharton | 01059640 | 979/543-5812 | 392 |
| Northside Elem Sch/Waxahachie/Ellis | 01015319 | 972/923-4610 | 147 |
| Northside Elem Sch/Houston/Harris | 01025974 | 713/226-4900 | 197 |
| **NORTHSIDE IND SCH DIST/SAN ANTONIO/** | | | |
| **BEXAR** | 00998017 | 210/397-8500 | 39 |
| **NORTHSIDE IND SCH DIST/VERNON/** | | | |
| **WILBARGER** | 01060534 | 940/552-2551 | 396 |
| Northside Interm Sch/Henderson/Rusk | 01878446 | 903/655-5300 | 330 |
| Northside Primary Sch/Palestine/Anderson | 00994542 | 903/731-8020 | 19 |
| Northside Sch/Vernon/Wilbarger | 01060546 | 940/552-2551 | 396 |
| Northside Sch Innovation Tech/San Antonio/ | | | |
| Bexar | 03403530 | 210/397-7070 | 41 |
| Northstar Sch/Arlington/Tarrant | 11157002 | 817/478-5852 | 361 |
| Northwest Crossing Elem Sch/San Antonio/ | | | |
| Bexar | 02178354 | 210/397-0600 | 41 |
| Northwest Early College HS/El Paso/El Paso | 11080497 | 915/877-1700 | 136 |
| Northwest Elem Sch/Austin/Travis | 02896075 | 512/594-4400 | 374 |
| Northwest Elem Sch/Brownwood/Brown | 01002520 | 325/646-0707 | 62 |
| Northwest Elem Sch/Hereford/Deaf Smith | 01013048 | 806/363-7660 | 123 |
| Northwest High Sch/Justin/Denton | 01013543 | 817/215-0200 | 129 |
| **NORTHWEST IND SCH DIST/JUSTIN/** | | | |
| **DENTON** | 01013517 | 817/215-0000 | 128 |
| Northwest Special Program Ctr/Justin/ | | | |
| Denton | 03473145 | 817/215-0900 | 129 |

| School/City/County DISTRICT/CITY/COUNTY | PID | TELEPHONE NUMBER | PAGE |
|---|---|---|---|
| Northwood Elem Sch/San Antonio/Bexar | 00997867 | 210/407-5400 | 38 |
| Northwood Hills Elem Sch/Dallas/Dallas | 01011820 | 469/593-4300 | 117 |
| Northwood Montessori Sch/Houston/Harris | 01601827 | 281/444-9433 | 211 |
| Norwood Elem Sch/Burleson/Johnson | 01522623 | 817/245-3400 | 250 |
| Notre Dame Catholic Sch/Wichita Falls/ Wichita | 01054389 | 940/692-6041 | 396 |
| Notre Dame Sch/Dallas/Dallas | 01012496 | 214/720-3911 | 118 |
| Notre Dame Sch/Kerrville/Kerr | 00999918 | 830/257-6707 | 259 |
| Nottingham Country Elem Sch/Katy/Harris | 02130223 | 281/237-5500 | 157 |
| Nottingham Elem Sch/Houston/Harris | 01027233 | 713/251-6400 | 206 |
| Nova Academy Cedar Hill/Cedar Hill/Dallas | 12261008 | 972/291-1900 | 11 |
| Nova Academy Prichard/Dallas/Dallas | 11935361 | 972/808-7470 | 11 |
| Nova Academy Scyene/Dallas/Dallas | 05368065 | 214/381-3088 | 11 |
| Nova Academy-Prichard/Dallas/Dallas | 04931786 | 972/808-7470 | 11 |
| Novus Academy/Grapevine/Tarrant | 11224473 | 817/488-4555 | 361 |
| **NUECES CANYON CONS IND SD/ BARKSDALE/EDWARDS** | 01014872 | 830/234-3514 | 135 |
| Nueces Canyon Elem Sch/Camp Wood/Edwards | 01014884 | 830/597-3218 | 135 |
| Nueces Canyon Jr Sr High Sch/Barksdale/ Edwards | 01014896 | 830/234-3524 | 135 |
| Nursery Elem Sch/Victoria/Victoria | 01058426 | 361/575-6882 | 384 |
| **NURSERY ISD SCH DIST/VICTORIA/ VICTORIA** | 01058414 | 361/575-6882 | 384 |
| Nye Elem Sch/Laredo/Webb | 01059494 | 956/473-3700 | 391 |
| Nyos Charter Sch-Lamar Campus/Austin/ Travis | 05286508 | 512/583-6967 | 11 |
| Nyos Charter School-M M Campus/Austin/ Travis | 04814451 | 512/275-1593 | 11 |

## O

| School/City/County DISTRICT/CITY/COUNTY | PID | TELEPHONE NUMBER | PAGE |
|---|---|---|---|
| O A Peterson Elem Sch/Fort Worth/Denton | 11104081 | 817/698-5000 | 129 |
| O C Taylor Elem Sch/Colleyville/Tarrant | 02895095 | 817/305-4870 | 356 |
| O D Wyatt High Sch/Fort Worth/Tarrant | 01053189 | 817/815-8000 | 354 |
| O G Wiederstein Elem Sch/Cibolo/Guadalupe | 01021629 | 210/619-4550 | 178 |
| O H Herman Middle Sch/Van Vleck/Matagorda | 01041045 | 979/245-6401 | 279 |
| O H Stowe Elem Sch/Haltom City/Tarrant | 01052147 | 817/547-2400 | 349 |
| O Henry Elem Sch/Garland/Dallas | 01011844 | 469/593-8200 | 117 |
| O Henry Middle Sch/Austin/Travis | 01056478 | 512/414-3229 | 371 |
| O L Slaton Middle Sch/Lubbock/Lubbock | 01038907 | 806/219-4400 | 273 |
| O M Roberts Elem Sch/Lake Jackson/Brazoria | 01001667 | 979/730-7205 | 56 |
| O P Norman Junior High Sch/Kaufman/Kaufman | 01035620 | 972/932-2410 | 255 |
| O V Calvert Elem Sch/Houston/Harris | 03399812 | 281/985-6360 | 185 |
| O'Banion Middle Sch/Garland/Dallas | 01010644 | 972/279-6103 | 110 |
| O'Brien Middle Sch/O Brien/Knox | 01534016 | 940/657-3731 | 261 |
| O'Bryant Intermediate Sch/Bellville/Austin | 04354243 | 979/865-3671 | 25 |
| O'Bryant Primary Sch/Bellville/Austin | 00995560 | 979/865-5907 | 25 |
| O'Connell High Sch/Galveston/Galveston | 01028031 | 409/765-5534 | 166 |
| O'Connor Elem Sch/Victoria/Victoria | 01058555 | 361/788-9572 | 385 |
| O'Dell Elem Sch/Celina/Collin | 12230865 | 469/742-9106 | 81 |
| O'Donnell Elem Sch/Odonnell/Lynn | 01039327 | 806/428-3244 | 276 |
| **O'DONNELL IND SCH DIST/ODONNELL/ LYNN** | 01039315 | 806/428-3241 | 276 |
| O'Donnell Intermediate Sch/Fabens/El Paso | 01016167 | 915/765-2640 | 139 |
| O'Donnell Jr Sr High Sch/Odonnell/Lynn | 01039339 | 806/428-3247 | 276 |
| O'Donnell Middle Sch/Houston/Harris | 04015459 | 281/495-6000 | 187 |
| O'Shea Keleher Elem Sch/El Paso/El Paso | 03009823 | 915/937-7200 | 141 |
| Oak Creek Elem Sch/New Braunfels/Comal | 11450933 | 830/837-7200 | 92 |
| Oak Crest Elem Sch/San Antonio/Bexar | 00997037 | 210/648-9484 | 34 |
| Oak Crest Private Sch/Carrollton/Dallas | 10968597 | 214/483-5400 | 120 |
| Oak Dale Elem Sch/Amarillo/Potter | 01047374 | 806/326-4850 | 321 |
| Oak Forest Elem Sch/Houston/Harris | 01024205 | 713/613-2536 | 197 |
| Oak Forest Elem Sch/Humble/Harris | 04367599 | 281/641-2800 | 201 |
| Oak Forest Elem Sch/Vidor/Orange | 01045766 | 409/951-8860 | 312 |
| Oak Grove Elem Sch/Brownfield/Terry | 01055137 | 806/637-6455 | 365 |
| Oak Grove Elem Sch/San Antonio/Bexar | 00997879 | 210/407-5600 | 38 |
| Oak Hill Academy/Dallas/Dallas | 04992819 | 214/353-8804 | 120 |
| Oak Hill Elem Sch/Austin/Travis | 01056480 | 512/414-2336 | 370 |
| Oak Hills Junior High Sch/Montgomery/ Montgomery | 04801935 | 936/276-4300 | 296 |
| Oak Hills Terrace Elem Sch/San Antonio/ Bexar | 00998251 | 210/397-0550 | 41 |
| Oak Meadow Elem Sch/San Antonio/Bexar | 03396315 | 210/407-5800 | 38 |
| Oak Meadows Elem Sch/Austin/Travis | 11434769 | 512/278-4175 | 374 |
| Oak Park Special Emphasis Sch/Corp Christi/ Nueces | 01044592 | 361/878-2120 | 307 |
| Oak Point Elem Sch/Oak Point/Denton | 11074503 | 972/947-9455 | 128 |
| Oak Ridge Elem Sch/Conroe/Montgomery | 01042518 | 832/592-5900 | 295 |
| Oak Ridge Elem Sch/Lubbock/Lubbock | 11445847 | 806/794-5200 | 272 |
| Oak Ridge High Sch/Conroe/Montgomery | 02126870 | 832/592-5300 | 295 |
| Oak Ridge HS 9th Grade Campus/Conroe/ Montgomery | 11552464 | 281/465-5000 | 295 |

| School/City/County DISTRICT/CITY/COUNTY | PID | TELEPHONE NUMBER | PAGE |
|---|---|---|---|
| Oak Run Middle Sch/New Braunfels/Comal | 03391092 | 830/627-6400 | 92 |
| Oak Springs Elem Sch/Austin/Travis | 01056492 | 512/414-4413 | 370 |
| Oak Woods Sch/Granbury/Hood | 03325691 | 817/408-4750 | 233 |
| Oakcrest Intermediate Sch/Cypress/Harris | 12107830 | 281/357-3033 | 208 |
| Oakhurst Elem Sch/Fort Worth/Tarrant | 01053206 | 817/814-9500 | 354 |
| Oakland Elem Sch/Richmond/Fort Bend | 10027909 | 281/634-3730 | 155 |
| Oaklawn Elem Sch/Fort Worth/Tarrant | 01053218 | 817/815-9100 | 354 |
| Oakley Elem Sch/New Caney/Montgomery | 11719246 | 281/577-5970 | 297 |
| Oakmont Elem Sch/Fort Worth/Tarrant | 04454207 | 817/370-5610 | 350 |
| Oaks Elem Sch/Humble/Harris | 02108634 | 281/641-1890 | 201 |
| Oakview Primary Sch/New Boston/Bowie | 11527574 | 903/628-8900 | 52 |
| Oakwood Elem Sch/Oakwood/Leon | 01037692 | 903/545-2106 | 267 |
| **OAKWOOD IND SCH DIST/OAKWOOD/ LEON** | 01037680 | 903/545-2666 | 267 |
| Oakwood Intermediate Sch/College Sta/ Brazos | 02111241 | 979/764-5530 | 59 |
| Oakwood Jr Sr High Sch/Oakwood/Leon | 01037707 | 903/545-2140 | 267 |
| Oakwood Terrace Elem Sch/Euless/Tarrant | 01053880 | 817/354-3386 | 356 |
| Oates Elem Sch/Houston/Harris | 01025649 | 713/671-3800 | 195 |
| Obadiah Knight Elem Sch/Dallas/Dallas | 01009542 | 972/749-5300 | 106 |
| Obra D Tompkins High Sch/Katy/Harris | 11925897 | 281/234-1000 | 157 |
| Ochoa STEM Academy/Milam/Grand Prairie/ Dallas | 01010838 | 972/262-7131 | 112 |
| Odem Elem Sch/Odem/San Patricio | 01049712 | 361/368-3881 | 334 |
| Odem High Sch/Odem/San Patricio | 01049724 | 361/368-8121 | 334 |
| Odem Intermediate Sch/Odem/San Patricio | 12310491 | 361/368-8121 | 334 |
| Odem Junior High Sch/Odem/San Patricio | 01049736 | 361/368-8121 | 334 |
| **ODEM-EDROY IND SCH DIST/ ODEM/SAN PATRICIO** | 01049700 | 361/368-8121 | 334 |
| Odessa Career Tch Early Clg HS/Odessa/ Ector | 12105753 | 432/456-6409 | 134 |
| Odessa Christian Sch/Odessa/Ector | 01480063 | 432/362-6311 | 135 |
| Odessa Collegiate Academy/Odessa/Ector | 12105765 | 432/456-6429 | 134 |
| Odessa High Sch/Odessa/Ector | 01014779 | 432/456-0029 | 135 |
| Odessa Kilpatrick Elem Sch/Katy/Harris | 05273628 | 281/237-7600 | 157 |
| Odom Academy/Beaumont/Jefferson | 01034183 | 409/617-5925 | 245 |
| Odom Elem Sch/Austin/Travis | 01056507 | 512/414-2388 | 370 |
| Odyssey Academy Bay Area ES/El Lago/Harris | 12375843 | 281/326-4555 | 11 |
| Odyssey Academy Galveston/Galveston/ Galveston | 04892740 | 409/750-9289 | 11 |
| Odyssey Sch/Austin/Travis | 04891289 | 512/472-2262 | 376 |
| **OGLESBY IND SCH DIST/OGLESBY/ CORYELL** | 01007740 | 254/456-2271 | 97 |
| Oglesby Sch/Oglesby/Coryell | 01007752 | 254/456-2271 | 97 |
| Oilton Elem Sch/Bruni/Webb | 01059171 | 361/586-5415 | 391 |
| Ojeda Middle Sch/Austin/Travis | 05301744 | 512/386-3500 | 372 |
| Old Settlers Elem Sch/Flower Mound/Denton | 04288759 | 469/713-5993 | 128 |
| Old Town Elem Sch/Round Rock/Williamson | 03052337 | 512/428-7600 | 402 |
| Old Union Elem Sch/Southlake/Tarrant | 04946145 | 817/949-4600 | 349 |
| **OLFEN IND SCH DIST/ROWENA/ RUNNELS** | 01048873 | 325/442-4301 | 329 |
| Olfen Sch/Rowena/Runnels | 01048885 | 325/442-4301 | 329 |
| Olga Kohlberg Elem Sch/El Paso/El Paso | 04757401 | 915/236-2850 | 138 |
| Olga Leonard Elem Sch/Katy/Harris | 12367418 | 281/234-4600 | 157 |
| Olive Tree Montessori Academy/Fort Worth/ Tarrant | 12043533 | 817/460-5000 | 11 |
| Oliveira Middle Sch/Brownsville/Cameron | 01877351 | 956/548-8530 | 67 |
| Oliver E Clift Elem Sch/Waxahachie/Ellis | 11718709 | 972/923-4720 | 147 |
| Oliver Elem Sch/Stamford/Jones | 01035333 | 325/773-5713 | 253 |
| Oliver W Holmes Academy/Dallas/Dallas | 01009566 | 972/925-8500 | 106 |
| Oliver Wendell Holmes High Sch/San Antonio/ Bexar | 00998263 | 210/397-7000 | 41 |
| Olivero Garza Elem Sch/Mission/Hidalgo | 02884125 | 956/580-5353 | 227 |
| Olle Middle Sch/Houston/Harris | 01023055 | 281/983-8455 | 187 |
| Ollie Ogrady Elem Sch/Mission/Hidalgo | 03009926 | 956/323-4200 | 225 |
| Ollie Perry Storm Elem Sch/San Antonio/ Bexar | 00999255 | 210/978-8005 | 44 |
| Olmito Elem Sch/Brownsville/Cameron | 05356141 | 956/233-3950 | 69 |
| Olmos Elem Sch/San Antonio/Bexar | 00997881 | 210/407-6000 | 38 |
| Olney Elem Sch/Olney/Young | 01062207 | 940/564-5608 | 410 |
| Olney High Sch/Olney/Young | 01062219 | 940/564-5637 | 410 |
| **OLNEY IND SCH DIST/OLNEY/YOUNG** | 01062192 | 940/564-3519 | 410 |
| Olney Junior High Sch/Olney/Young | 01062221 | 940/564-3517 | 410 |
| Olsen Elem Sch/Port Aransas/Nueces | 01809756 | 361/749-1212 | 308 |
| Olsen Park Elem Sch/Amarillo/Potter | 01047386 | 806/326-4900 | 321 |
| Olson Elem Sch/Allen/Collin | 11451963 | 972/562-1800 | 80 |
| Olton High Sch/Olton/Lamb | 01036997 | 806/285-2691 | 263 |
| **OLTON IND SCH DIST/OLTON/LAMB** | 01036973 | 806/285-2641 | 263 |
| Olton Junior High Sch/Olton/Lamb | 01037006 | 806/285-2681 | 263 |
| Olympia Elem Sch/Universal Cty/Bexar | 02109949 | 210/945-5113 | 36 |
| Onalaska Elem Sch/Onalaska/Polk | 01809811 | 936/646-1010 | 320 |

| School/City/County<br>DISTRICT/CITY/COUNTY | PID | TELEPHONE<br>NUMBER | PAGE |
|---|---|---|---|
| **ONALASKA IND SCH DIST**/ONALASKA/<br>POLK | 01809809 | 936/646-1000 | 320 |
| Onalaska Jr Sr High Sch/Onalaska/Polk | 03391406 | 936/646-1020 | 320 |
| Open Door Christian Sch/Graham/Young | 12472300 | 940/549-2339 | 410 |
| Open Doors Christian Academy/Gun Barrel Cy/<br>Henderson | 04025129 | 903/887-3621 | 220 |
| Opportunity Awareness Center/Katy/Harris | 02045410 | 281/237-6350 | 157 |
| Options Academic High Sch/Texarkana/Bowie | 04920490 | 903/793-5632 | 53 |
| Options High Sch/El Paso/El Paso | 10911685 | 915/937-1300 | 141 |
| Oralia R Rodriguez Elem Sch/Seguin/<br>Guadalupe | 11589807 | 830/401-8774 | 179 |
| Oran M Roberts Elem Sch/Dallas/Dallas | 01009554 | 972/749-8700 | 106 |
| Orange Grove Elem & Inter Sch/Orange Grove/<br>Jim Wells | 03008776 | 361/384-9358 | 248 |
| Orange Grove Elem Sch/Houston/Harris | 01022934 | 281/985-6540 | 185 |
| Orange Grove High Sch/Orange Grove/<br>Jim Wells | 01034705 | 361/384-2330 | 248 |
| **ORANGE GROVE IND SCH DIST/**<br>ORANGE GROVE/JIM WELLS | 01034688 | 361/384-2495 | 248 |
| Orange Grove Jr High Sch/Orange Grove/<br>Jim Wells | 01523732 | 361/384-2323 | 248 |
| Orange Grove Primary Sch/Orange Grove/<br>Jim Wells | 01034690 | 361/384-2316 | 248 |
| Orangefield Elem Sch/Orange/Orange | 01045728 | 409/735-5346 | 312 |
| Orangefield High Sch/Orange/Orange | 01045742 | 409/735-3851 | 312 |
| **ORANGEFIELD IND SCH DIST/**<br>ORANGE/ORANGE | 01045704 | 409/735-5337 | 312 |
| Orangefield Junior High Sch/Orange/Orange | 01045730 | 409/735-6737 | 312 |
| Oratory Academy & Athenaeum/Pharr/Hidalgo | 02760646 | 956/781-3056 | 229 |
| Ore City Elem Sch/Ore City/Upshur | 01057537 | 903/968-3300 | 379 |
| Ore City High Sch/Ore City/Upshur | 01057549 | 903/968-3300 | 379 |
| **ORE CITY IND SCH DIST**/ORE CITY/<br>UPSHUR | 01057525 | 903/968-3300 | 379 |
| Ore City Middle Sch/Ore City/Upshur | 03047289 | 903/968-3300 | 379 |
| Orr Elem Sch/Tyler/Smith | 01050917 | 903/262-2400 | 340 |
| Ortega Elem Sch/Austin/Travis | 01056519 | 512/414-4417 | 370 |
| Ortiz Elem Sch/Abilene/Taylor | 04015320 | 325/671-4945 | 363 |
| Ortiz Elem Sch/Brownsville/Cameron | 01003500 | 956/698-1100 | 67 |
| Ortiz Middle Sch/Houston/Harris | 05099317 | 713/845-5650 | 195 |
| Osborne Elem Sch/Houston/Harris | 01024217 | 281/405-2525 | 196 |
| Oticel Parker Elem Sch/Houston/Harris | 04367563 | 281/233-8930 | 185 |
| Otis Brown Elem Sch/Irving/Dallas | 01011284 | 972/600-4000 | 114 |
| Otis Spears Elem Sch/Frisco/Collin | 05092632 | 469/633-2900 | 83 |
| Otto Middle Sch/Plano/Collin | 11554802 | 469/752-8500 | 87 |
| Ouida Springer Elem Sch/Rockwall/Rockwall | 05351622 | 972/772-7160 | 328 |
| Our Lady of Fatima Sch/Galena Park/Harris | 01028043 | 713/674-5832 | 209 |
| Our Lady of Fatima Sch/Texas City/<br>Galveston | 01028055 | 409/945-3326 | 166 |
| Our Lady of Grace Academy/Pleasanton/<br>Atascosa | 11818787 | 830/569-8073 | 24 |
| Our Lady of Guadalupe Sch/Houston/Harris | 01028067 | 713/224-6904 | 209 |
| Our Lady of Lourdes Cath Sch/Hitchcock/<br>Galveston | 01028081 | 409/925-3224 | 166 |
| Our Lady of Perpetual Help Sch/Corp Christi/<br>Nueces | 01045273 | 361/991-3305 | 309 |
| Our Lady of Perpetual Help Sch/Dallas/<br>Dallas | 01012513 | 214/351-3396 | 118 |
| Our Lady of Refuge Sch/Eagle Pass/Maverick | 00999944 | 830/773-3531 | 280 |
| Our Lady of Sorrows Sch/McAllen/Hidalgo | 01004425 | 956/686-3651 | 229 |
| Our Lady of the Gulf Cath Sch/Port Lavaca/<br>Calhoun | 04467826 | 361/552-6140 | 65 |
| Our Lady of the Hills Cath HS/Kerrville/<br>Kerr | 05286390 | 830/895-0501 | 259 |
| Our Lady of the Rosary Sch/Corp Christi/<br>Nueces | 11532658 | 361/939-9847 | 309 |
| Our Lady of Victory Sch/Fort Worth/Tarrant | 01054391 | 817/924-5123 | 360 |
| Our Lady of Victory Sch/Victoria/Victoria | 00999968 | 361/575-5391 | 385 |
| Our Lady Queen of Peace Sch/Richwood/<br>Brazoria | 02903551 | 979/265-3909 | 57 |
| Our Lady-Perpetual Help Sch/Selma/<br>Guadalupe | 00999932 | 210/651-6811 | 179 |
| Our Redeemer Lutheran Sch/Dallas/Dallas | 01012288 | 214/368-1371 | 120 |
| Our Savior Lutheran Sch/Houston/Harris | 01027702 | 713/290-8277 | 211 |
| Outley Elem Sch/Houston/Harris | 04033009 | 281/584-0655 | 187 |
| Overton Elem Sch/Austin/Travis | 10901745 | 512/841-9300 | 370 |
| Overton Elem Sch/Lubbock/Lubbock | 01038830 | 806/219-6300 | 273 |
| Overton Elem Sch/Overton/Rusk | 01049164 | 903/834-6144 | 331 |
| **OVERTON IND SCH DIST**/OVERTON/<br>RUSK | 01049152 | 903/834-6145 | 331 |
| Overton Ray Elem Sch/Burkburnett/Wichita | 01055951 | 940/569-5253 | 394 |
| Overton Secondary Sch/Overton/Rusk | 01049176 | 903/834-6143 | 331 |
| Oveta Culp Hobby Elem Sch/Fort Hood/Bell | 05347815 | 254/336-6500 | 31 |

| School/City/County<br>DISTRICT/CITY/COUNTY | PID | TELEPHONE<br>NUMBER | PAGE |
|---|---|---|---|
| Ovilla Christian Sch/Red Oak/Ellis | 04881844 | 972/617-1177 | 147 |
| Owen Elem Sch/The Colony/Denton | 03010482 | 469/713-5950 | 128 |
| Owen Goodnight Middle Sch/San Marcos/Hays | 01029140 | 512/393-6550 | 217 |
| Owens Elem Sch/Houston/Harris | 02201547 | 281/463-5915 | 190 |
| Owens Elem Sch/Tyler/Smith | 02846264 | 903/262-2175 | 340 |
| Owens Intermediate Sch/Houston/Harris | 04285109 | 281/983-8466 | 187 |
| Oyster Creek Elem Sch/Sugar Land/Fort Bend | 04851033 | 281/634-5910 | 155 |
| Ozona Elem Sch/Ozona/Crockett | 01007879 | 325/392-5501 | 98 |
| Ozona High Sch/Ozona/Crockett | 01007867 | 325/392-5501 | 98 |
| Ozona Middle Sch/Ozona/Crockett | 01007881 | 325/392-5501 | 98 |

## P

| School/City/County<br>DISTRICT/CITY/COUNTY | PID | TELEPHONE<br>NUMBER | PAGE |
|---|---|---|---|
| P E Wallace Middle Sch/Mt Pleasant/Titus | 01055424 | 903/575-2040 | 366 |
| P H Greene Elem Sch/Webster/Galveston | 01523691 | 281/284-5000 | 163 |
| P M Akin Elem Sch/Wylie/Collin | 03052911 | 972/429-3400 | 89 |
| Pace Academy/Carthage/Panola | 12312774 | 903/694-7554 | 314 |
| Pace Alternative Campus/Longview/Gregg | 11718761 | 903/295-5130 | 175 |
| Pace Center/Pearland/Brazoria | 05070268 | 281/412-1599 | 57 |
| Pace Sch/Pflugerville/Travis | 11544405 | 512/594-1900 | 374 |
| Paciano Prada Elem Sch/Laredo/Webb | 04287822 | 956/473-3500 | 391 |
| Packsaddle Elem Sch/Kingsland/Llano | 04913423 | 325/388-8129 | 271 |
| Padron Elem Sch/Austin/Travis | 12035213 | 512/841-9600 | 370 |
| **PADUCAH IND SCH DIST**/PADUCAH/<br>COTTLE | 01007776 | 806/492-3524 | 97 |
| Paducah Sch/Paducah/Cottle | 01007805 | 806/492-2009 | 97 |
| Page Middle Sch/San Antonio/Bexar | 00999267 | 210/228-1230 | 44 |
| Paige Elem Sch/Houston/Harris | 01025807 | 713/696-2855 | 196 |
| **PAINT CREEK IND SCH DIST/**<br>HASKELL/HASKELL | 01028914 | 940/864-2471 | 215 |
| Paint Creek Sch/Haskell/Haskell | 01028926 | 940/864-2471 | 215 |
| **PAINT ROCK IND SCH DIST/**<br>PAINT ROCK/CONCHO | 01007245 | 325/732-4314 | 94 |
| Paint Rock Sch/Paint Rock/Concho | 01007252 | 325/732-4314 | 94 |
| Palacios High Sch/Palacios/Matagorda | 01040948 | 361/972-2571 | 278 |
| **PALACIOS IND SCH DIST**/PALACIOS/<br>MATAGORDA | 01040912 | 361/972-5491 | 278 |
| Palacios Junior High Sch/Palacios/<br>Matagorda | 01040950 | 361/972-2417 | 278 |
| Palestine High Sch/Palestine/Anderson | 00994578 | 903/731-8005 | 19 |
| **PALESTINE IND SCH DIST**/PALESTINE/<br>ANDERSON | 00994528 | 210/731-8000 | 18 |
| Palestine Jr High Sch/Palestine/Anderson | 02200373 | 903/731-8008 | 19 |
| Palm Elem Sch/Austin/Travis | 03008659 | 512/414-2545 | 370 |
| Palm Grove Elem Sch/Brownsville/Cameron | 01418230 | 956/982-3850 | 67 |
| Palm Heights Baptist Sch/San Antonio/Bexar | 02727814 | 210/923-8600 | 48 |
| Palm Tree Academy/El Paso/El Paso | 12314162 | 915/229-2190 | 144 |
| Palmer Elem Sch/Missouri City/Fort Bend | 02857378 | 281/634-4760 | 155 |
| Palmer Elem Sch/Palmer/Ellis | 01015228 | 972/449-3132 | 146 |
| Palmer High Sch/Palmer/Ellis | 01015230 | 972/449-3487 | 146 |
| **PALMER IND SCH DIST**/PALMER/ELLIS | 01015216 | 972/449-3389 | 146 |
| Palmer Middle Sch/Palmer/Ellis | 03047241 | 972/449-3319 | 146 |
| Palmer-Laakso Elem Sch/San Benito/Cameron | 04452663 | 956/254-5121 | 69 |
| Palmview High Sch/Mission/Hidalgo | 05100954 | 956/323-2880 | 223 |
| Palo Alto Elem Sch/San Antonio/Bexar | 00999475 | 210/977-7125 | 45 |
| Palo Alto Middle Sch/Killeen/Bell | 04368775 | 254/336-1200 | 31 |
| Palo Duro High Sch/Amarillo/Potter | 01047398 | 806/326-2400 | 321 |
| Palo Pinto Elem Sch/Palo Pinto/Palo Pinto | 01046112 | 940/659-2745 | 313 |
| **PALO PINTO IND SCH DIST 906/**<br>PALO PINTO/PALO PINTO | 01046100 | 940/659-2745 | 313 |
| Paloma Creek Elem Sch/Aubrey/Denton | 10909137 | 972/347-7300 | 125 |
| Pampa High Sch/Pampa/Gray | 01020194 | 806/669-4800 | 170 |
| **PAMPA IND SCH DIST**/PAMPA/GRAY | 01020132 | 806/669-4700 | 170 |
| Pampa Junior High Sch/Pampa/Gray | 01020182 | 806/669-4900 | 170 |
| Pampa Learning Center/Pampa/Gray | 03394056 | 806/669-4750 | 170 |
| Panda Path Sch/Houston/Harris | 04949850 | 713/251-8000 | 206 |
| Panhandle Elem Sch/Panhandle/Carson | 01004607 | 806/537-3579 | 73 |
| Panhandle High Sch/Panhandle/Carson | 01004619 | 806/537-3851 | 73 |
| **PANHANDLE IND SCH DIST**/PANHANDLE/<br>CARSON | 01004592 | 806/537-3568 | 72 |
| Panhandle Junior High Sch/Panhandle/Carson | 01004621 | 806/537-3541 | 73 |
| Panola Charter HS/Carthage/Panola | 04930366 | 903/693-6355 | 11 |
| Panola Early College High Sch/Carthage/<br>Panola | 11834391 | 903/693-6355 | 11 |
| Pantego Christian Academy/Arlington/<br>Tarrant | 02123531 | 817/460-3315 | 362 |
| Pantego Christian Academy/Mansfield/<br>Tarrant | 11224667 | 817/522-5900 | 361 |
| **PANTHER CREEK CONS IND SD/**<br>VOSS/COLEMAN | 01005950 | 325/357-4449 | 79 |
| Panther Creek Sch/Voss/Coleman | 01005962 | 325/357-4449 | 79 |
| Paradise Elem Sch/Paradise/Wise | 01061734 | 940/969-5046 | 407 |
| Paradise High Sch/Paradise/Wise | 04020791 | 940/969-5010 | 407 |

| School/City/County DISTRICT/CITY/COUNTY | PID | TELEPHONE NUMBER | PAGE |
|---|---|---|---|
| **PARADISE IND SCH DIST**/PARADISE/ WISE | 01061722 | 940/969-2501 | 407 |
| Paradise Intermediate Sch/Paradise/Wise | 04866428 | 940/969-5032 | 407 |
| Paradise Junior High Sch/Paradise/Wise | 04431073 | 940/969-5034 | 407 |
| Paragon Prep Middle Sch/Austin/Travis | 04846624 | 512/459-5040 | 376 |
| Paramount Terrace Elem Sch/Amarillo/Potter | 01047403 | 806/326-4950 | 321 |
| Paratus Classical Academy/Houston/Harris | 12379564 | 281/547-0060 | 211 |
| Paredes Elem Sch/Brownsville/Cameron | 04945115 | 956/574-5582 | 67 |
| Paredes Middle Sch/Austin/Travis | 04904264 | 512/841-6800 | 372 |
| Paris High Sch/Paris/Lamar | 01036753 | 903/737-7400 | 263 |
| **PARIS IND SCH DIST**/PARIS/LAMAR | 01036698 | 903/737-7473 | 262 |
| Paris Junior High Sch/Paris/Lamar | 01036777 | 903/737-7434 | 263 |
| Parish Episcopal Sch/Dallas/Dallas | 01012290 | 972/239-8011 | 120 |
| Parish Sch/Houston/Harris | 02757156 | 713/467-4696 | 211 |
| Park Crest Elem Sch/Garland/Dallas | 01010656 | 972/926-2571 | 110 |
| Park Crest Middle Sch/Pflugerville/Travis | 04363543 | 512/594-2400 | 374 |
| Park Elem Sch/El Paso/El Paso | 03399874 | 915/236-5975 | 138 |
| Park Glen Elem Sch/Fort Worth/Tarrant | 03319006 | 817/744-5400 | 357 |
| Park Hills Elem Sch/Amarillo/Potter | 01047439 | 806/326-4750 | 321 |
| Park Lakes Elem Sch/Humble/Harris | 10028616 | 281/641-3200 | 201 |
| Park Meadows Academy/Corsicana/Navarro | 12174144 | 903/872-2391 | 303 |
| Park Place Elem Sch/Houston/Harris | 01025663 | 713/845-7458 | 195 |
| Park Row Chrn Academy/Arlington/Tarrant | 02775316 | 817/277-1021 | 362 |
| Park View Intermediate Sch/Pasadena/Harris | 01026801 | 713/740-0460 | 204 |
| Park Village Elem Sch/San Antonio/Bexar | 00997659 | 210/637-4890 | 36 |
| Parkdale Elem Sch/Waco/McLennan | 01040352 | 254/772-2170 | 285 |
| Parker Elem Sch/Galveston/Galveston | 01019183 | 409/761-6600 | 165 |
| Parker Elem Sch/Houston/Harris | 01024956 | 713/726-3634 | 199 |
| Parker Elem Sch/Midland/Midland | 02199968 | 432/240-7600 | 289 |
| Parkhill Junior High Sch/Dallas/Dallas | 01881857 | 469/593-5600 | 117 |
| Parkland Elem Sch/El Paso/El Paso | 01016492 | 915/434-6600 | 142 |
| Parkland High Sch/El Paso/El Paso | 01016519 | 915/434-6000 | 142 |
| Parkland Middle Sch/El Paso/El Paso | 01016507 | 915/434-6300 | 142 |
| Parkland Pre-K Center/El Paso/El Paso | 11919381 | 915/435-7800 | 142 |
| Parks Elem Sch/Pasadena/Harris | 01026813 | 713/740-0680 | 204 |
| Parkside Baptist Academy/Mesquite/Dallas | 11235367 | 972/613-7833 | 120 |
| Parkside Elem Sch/Georgetown/Williamson | 11130779 | 512/570-7100 | 400 |
| Parkview Christian Academy/Waco/McLennan | 02153938 | 254/753-0159 | 286 |
| Parkview Elem Sch/Fort Worth/Tarrant | 02105412 | 817/744-5500 | 357 |
| Parkview Elem Sch/Fort Worth/Tarrant | 11072763 | 817/237-5121 | 351 |
| Parkview School-Levelland/Levelland/Mills | 12166238 | 806/568-1420 | 291 |
| Parkview School-Lubbock/Lubbock/Mills | 12166226 | 806/568-1420 | 292 |
| Parkway Elem Sch/Fort Worth/Tarrant | 04282341 | 817/568-5710 | 350 |
| Parkway Elem Sch/Lewisville/Denton | 04364420 | 469/713-5979 | 128 |
| Parkway Elem Sch/Longview/Gregg | 01021174 | 903/295-5151 | 175 |
| Parkwood Elem Sch/Pasadena/Harris | 01023392 | 832/668-8200 | 191 |
| Parkwood Hill Intermediate Sch/Fort Worth/ Tarrant | 04921602 | 817/744-4000 | 358 |
| Parmer Lane Elem Sch/Austin/Travis | 02178304 | 512/594-4000 | 374 |
| Parnell Elem Sch/Jasper/Jasper | 01033256 | 409/384-2212 | 244 |
| Parsons Elem Sch/Lubbock/Lubbock | 01038610 | 806/219-6400 | 273 |
| Parsons Pre-K Sch/Garland/Dallas | 10008109 | 972/675-8065 | 110 |
| Pasadena Classical Academy/Pasadena/Harris | 11925196 | 281/372-8999 | 11 |
| Pasadena High Sch/Pasadena/Harris | 01026825 | 713/740-0310 | 204 |
| **PASADENA IND SCH DIST**/PASADENA/ HARRIS | 01026631 | 713/740-0000 | 203 |
| Pasadena Memorial High Sch/Pasadena/Harris | 05273408 | 713/740-0390 | 204 |
| Paso Del Norte Sch/El Paso/El Paso | 05272301 | 915/937-6200 | 141 |
| Pasodale Elem Sch/El Paso/El Paso | 01016521 | 915/434-8500 | 142 |
| Pat & Katherine Fowler Mid Sch/Plano/ Collin | 10912691 | 469/633-5050 | 83 |
| Pat Cooper Elem Sch/Georgetown/Williamson | 02223026 | 512/943-5060 | 398 |
| Pat Neff Middle Sch/San Antonio/Bexar | 00998275 | 210/397-4100 | 41 |
| Pat Reynolds Elem Sch/Houston/Harris | 01027506 | 281/891-8240 | 207 |
| Pathfinder Achievement Center/Garland/ Dallas | 01545223 | 972/494-8520 | 110 |
| Pathways 3H Campus/Mountain Home/Kerr | 12362640 | 512/560-8132 | 11 |
| Pathways Academic Campus/Killeen/Bell | 03474618 | 254/336-7250 | 31 |
| Pathways Alt Learning Center/Beaumont/ Jefferson | 03394525 | 409/617-5206 | 245 |
| Pathways High Sch/Denison/Grayson | 04453186 | 903/462-7150 | 171 |
| Patricia J Blattman Elem Sch/San Antonio/ Bexar | 05273422 | 210/397-4600 | 41 |
| Patricia Paetow High Sch/Katy/Harris | 12231259 | 281/234-4900 | 157 |
| Patricia S Garza Elem Sch/Donna/Hidalgo | 04868012 | 956/464-1886 | 220 |
| Patricio Perez Elem Sch/Mission/Hidalgo | 04868634 | 956/323-2450 | 223 |
| Patrick Henry Middle Sch/Houston/Harris | 01026057 | 713/696-2650 | 194 |
| Patsy Sommer Elem Sch/Austin/Williamson | 11130858 | 512/704-0600 | 402 |
| Patterson Elem Sch/Conroe/Montgomery | 12033033 | 936/709-4300 | 295 |
| Patterson Elem Sch/Houston/Harris | 01025675 | 713/943-5750 | 195 |
| Patterson Middle Sch/Killeen/Bell | 00996473 | 254/336-7100 | 31 |
| Patti Welder Middle Sch/Victoria/Victoria | 01058634 | 361/575-4553 | 385 |

| School/City/County DISTRICT/CITY/COUNTY | PID | TELEPHONE NUMBER | PAGE |
|---|---|---|---|
| Patton Elem Sch/Austin/Travis | 02857328 | 512/414-1780 | 370 |
| **PATTON SPRINGS IND SCH DIST**/ AFTON/DICKENS | 01013933 | 806/689-2220 | 131 |
| Patton Springs Sch/Afton/Dickens | 01013945 | 806/689-2220 | 131 |
| Paul A Brown Learning Center/Beaumont/ Jefferson | 04948466 | 409/617-5720 | 245 |
| Paul Belton Early Chldhd Ctr/Borger/ Hutchinson | 01032678 | 806/273-1059 | 240 |
| Paul Keyes Elem Sch/Irving/Dallas | 01011296 | 972/600-3400 | 114 |
| Paul L Dunbar Learning Center/Dallas/ Dallas | 01009578 | 972/794-6600 | 106 |
| Paul Laurence Dunbar High Sch/Fort Worth/ Tarrant | 01053232 | 817/815-3000 | 354 |
| Paul Moreno Elem Sch/El Paso/El Paso | 04918667 | 915/236-0400 | 138 |
| Paul R Haas Middle Sch/Corp Christi/Nueces | 01044451 | 361/878-4240 | 307 |
| Paul Revere Middle Sch/Houston/Harris | 02111942 | 713/917-3500 | 199 |
| Paul W Ott Elem Sch/San Antonio/Bexar | 05347578 | 210/397-5550 | 41 |
| **PAWNEE IND SCH DIST**/PAWNEE/BEE | 00996148 | 361/456-7256 | 28 |
| Pawnee Sch/Pawnee/Bee | 00996162 | 361/456-7256 | 28 |
| Pays Sch/San Angelo/Tom Green | 11925122 | 325/947-3912 | 367 |
| PCA Dr Sarah Strinden Elem Sch/Lufkin/ Angelina | 12263111 | 936/634-5515 | 11 |
| PCA Dr Terry Robbins Mid Sch/Lufkin/ Angelina | 12263123 | 936/634-5515 | 11 |
| Peach Creek Elem Sch/Splendora/Montgomery | 01042738 | 281/689-3114 | 297 |
| Pearce High Sch/Richardson/Dallas | 01011739 | 460/503 5000 | 117 |
| Pearcy STEM Academy/Arlington/Tarrant | 04918928 | 682/867-5555 | 347 |
| Pearl Hall Elem Sch/South Houston/Harris | 01026837 | 713/740-0688 | 204 |
| Pearl M Hirsch Elem Sch/Spring/Harris | 01824263 | 281/891-8330 | 208 |
| Pearland High Sch/Pearland/Brazoria | 01001887 | 281/997-7445 | 57 |
| **PEARLAND IND SCH DIST**/PEARLAND/ BRAZORIA | 01001849 | 281/485-3203 | 56 |
| Pearland Jr High School East/Pearland/ Brazoria | 01001875 | 281/485-2481 | 57 |
| Pearland Jr High School South/Pearland/ Brazoria | 05070256 | 281/727-1500 | 57 |
| Pearland Jr High School West/Pearland/ Brazoria | 04033889 | 281/412-1222 | 57 |
| Pearsall High Sch/Pearsall/Frio | 01018646 | 830/334-8011 | 161 |
| **PEARSALL IND SCH DIST**/PEARSALL/ FRIO | 01018610 | 830/334-8001 | 161 |
| Pearsall Intermediate Sch/Pearsall/Frio | 01018658 | 830/334-3316 | 161 |
| Pearsall Junior High Sch/Pearsall/Frio | 01018660 | 830/334-8021 | 161 |
| Pearson Early Childhood Sch/Plano/Collin | 05096872 | 469/752-4300 | 87 |
| Pearson Elem Sch/Mission/Hidalgo | 01030280 | 956/323-4000 | 225 |
| Pearson Middle Sch/Frisco/Collin | 12110057 | 469/633-4450 | 83 |
| Pearson Ranch Middle Sch/Austin/Williamson | 12226541 | 512/704-1500 | 402 |
| Pease Communication/Tech Acad/Midland/ Midland | 01041605 | 432/240-7700 | 289 |
| Pease Elem Sch/Odessa/Ector | 01014781 | 432/456-1179 | 135 |
| Peaster Elem Sch/Weatherford/Parker | 01046435 | 817/341-5000 | 316 |
| Peaster High Sch/Weatherford/Parker | 04750544 | 817/341-5000 | 316 |
| **PEASTER IND SCH DIST**/WEATHERFORD/ PARKER | 01046423 | 817/341-5000 | 316 |
| Peaster Middle Sch/Weatherford/Parker | 04750532 | 817/341-5000 | 316 |
| Pebble Creek Elem Sch/College Sta/Brazos | 04451190 | 979/764-5595 | 59 |
| Pebble Hill High Sch/El Paso/El Paso | 11552903 | 915/937-9400 | 141 |
| Pebble Hills Elem Sch/El Paso/El Paso | 02110596 | 915/434-5600 | 142 |
| Pebblecreek Montessori Sch/Plano/Collin | 05312535 | 972/908-3797 | 90 |
| Pecan Creek Elem Sch/Denton/Denton | 05273692 | 940/369-4400 | 125 |
| Pecan Grove Elem Sch/Richmond/Fort Bend | 03048934 | 281/634-4800 | 155 |
| Pecan Ridge High Sch/San Saba/Mills | 12166252 | 325/372-4092 | 292 |
| Pecan Springs Elem Sch/Austin/Travis | 01056545 | 512/414-4445 | 370 |
| Pecan Trail Interm Sch/College Sta/Brazos | 12233178 | 979/694-5874 | 59 |
| Pecan Valley Elem Sch/San Antonio/Bexar | 00997063 | 210/333-1230 | 34 |
| Peck Elem Sch/Houston/Harris | 01024920 | 713/845-7463 | 198 |
| Pecos High Sch/Pecos/Reeves | 01048380 | 432/447-7400 | 326 |
| Pecos Kindergarten/Pecos/Reeves | 01857387 | 432/447-7596 | 326 |
| **PECOS-BARSTOW-TOYAH IND SD**/ PECOS/REEVES | 01048304 | 432/447-7201 | 326 |
| Peebles Elem Sch/Killeen/Bell | 00996576 | 254/336-2120 | 31 |
| Peet Junior High Sch/Conroe/Montgomery | 01042570 | 936/709-3700 | 295 |
| Peete Elem Sch/Tyler/Smith | 01050979 | 903/262-2460 | 340 |
| Pegasus Sch Liberal Arts & Sci/Dallas/ Dallas | 04757970 | 214/740-9991 | 11 |
| Pena Elem Sch/Brownsville/Cameron | 11449257 | 956/547-7100 | 67 |
| **PENELOPE ISD SCH DIST**/PENELOPE/ HILL | 01031026 | 254/533-2215 | 231 |
| Penelope Sch/Penelope/Hill | 01031038 | 254/533-2215 | 231 |
| Percy Neblitt Elem Sch/Sherman/Grayson | 10900820 | 903/891-6670 | 172 |
| Perez Elem Sch/Austin/Travis | 10030463 | 512/841-9100 | 370 |
| Perez Elem Sch/Brownsville/Cameron | 01003641 | 956/982-2800 | 67 |

| School/City/County DISTRICT/CITY/COUNTY | PID | TELEPHONE NUMBER | PAGE |
|---|---|---|---|
| Perez Elem Sch/Kingsville/Kleberg | 01036301 | 361/592-8511 | 260 |
| Perfecto Mancha Elem Sch/Eagle Pass/Maverick | 11559802 | 830/758-7216 | 280 |
| Perkins Middle Sch/Brownsville/Cameron | 03011230 | 956/831-8770 | 67 |
| Perkins Middle Sch/De Leon/Comanche | 03047277 | 254/893-8230 | 93 |
| Permian Basin Classical Acad/Midland/Midland | 12363723 | 432/217-6122 | 11 |
| Permian High Sch/Odessa/Ector | 01014793 | 432/456-0039 | 135 |
| Perrin Alt Learning Center/Denison/Grayson | 11075600 | 903/891-6680 | 172 |
| **PERRIN-WHITT CONS IND SCH DIST/ PERRIN/JACK** | 01032965 | 940/798-3718 | 242 |
| Perrin-Whitt Elem Sch/Perrin/Jack | 01032989 | 940/798-2395 | 242 |
| Perrin-Whitt High Sch/Perrin/Jack | 04032665 | 940/798-3718 | 242 |
| Perryton High Sch/Perryton/Ochiltree | 01045479 | 806/435-3633 | 310 |
| **PERRYTON IND SCH DIST/PERRYTON/ OCHILTREE** | 01045455 | 806/435-5478 | 310 |
| Perryton Junior High Sch/Perryton/Ochiltree | 01553191 | 806/435-3601 | 310 |
| Perryton Kindergarten/Perryton/Ochiltree | 04865008 | 806/435-2463 | 310 |
| Pershing Elem Sch/San Antonio/Bexar | 00998897 | 210/738-9820 | 44 |
| Pershing Middle Sch/Houston/Harris | 01024877 | 713/295-5240 | 199 |
| Pershing Park Elem Sch/Killeen/Bell | 00996588 | 254/336-1790 | 31 |
| Personalized Lrng Prep Houston/Dallas/Dallas | 01009803 | 972/749-5800 | 106 |
| Pete & Gracie Hosp Elem Sch/Frisco/Collin | 12032869 | 469/633-4050 | 83 |
| Pete Ford Middle Sch/Allen/Collin | 01006019 | 972/727-0590 | 80 |
| Pete Gallego Elem Sch/Eagle Pass/Maverick | 04871083 | 830/758-7130 | 280 |
| Peter E Hyland Center/Baytown/Harris | 01023615 | 281/420-4555 | 193 |
| Peters Colony Elem Sch/The Colony/Denton | 02112142 | 469/713-5179 | 128 |
| **PETERSBURG IND SCH DIST/ PETERSBURG/HALE** | 01021863 | 806/667-3585 | 180 |
| Petersburg Sch/Petersburg/Hale | 01021875 | 806/667-3585 | 180 |
| Petersen Elem Sch/Houston/Harris | 01025326 | 713/434-5630 | 198 |
| Peterson Middle Sch/Kerrville/Kerr | 01036090 | 830/257-2204 | 259 |
| **PETROLIA CONS IND SCH DIST/ PETROLIA/CLAY** | 01005601 | 940/524-3555 | 78 |
| Petrolia Elem Sch/Petrolia/Clay | 11071707 | 940/524-3433 | 78 |
| Petrolia Jr Sr High Sch/Petrolia/Clay | 01005625 | 940/524-3264 | 78 |
| Petronila Elem Sch/Robstown/Nueces | 01044097 | 361/387-2834 | 305 |
| Petrosky Elem Sch/Houston/Harris | 02043280 | 281/983-8366 | 187 |
| Pettus Elem Sch/Pettus/Bee | 00996186 | 361/375-2296 | 28 |
| **PETTUS IND SCH DIST/PETTUS/BEE** | 00996174 | 361/375-2296 | 28 |
| Pettus Secondary Sch/Pettus/Bee | 00996198 | 361/375-2296 | 28 |
| **PEWITT CONS IND SCH DIST/ OMAHA/MORRIS** | 01043005 | 903/884-2136 | 299 |
| Pewitt Elem Sch/Omaha/Morris | 01043017 | 903/884-2404 | 299 |
| Pewitt High Sch/Omaha/Morris | 01043029 | 903/884-2293 | 299 |
| Pewitt Junior High Sch/Omaha/Morris | 01043031 | 903/884-2505 | 299 |
| Pfc Mario Ybarra Elem Sch/Weslaco/Hidalgo | 01030644 | 956/969-6587 | 228 |
| Pfc Robert Hernandez Mid Sch/Round Rock/Williamson | 11557438 | 512/424-8800 | 402 |
| Pflugerville Elem Sch/Pflugerville/Travis | 01056947 | 512/594-3800 | 374 |
| Pflugerville High Sch/Pflugerville/Travis | 01056959 | 512/594-0500 | 374 |
| **PFLUGERVILLE IND SCH DIST/ PFLUGERVILLE/TRAVIS** | 01056935 | 512/594-0000 | 374 |
| Pflugerville Middle Sch/Pflugerville/Travis | 01056961 | 512/594-2000 | 374 |
| Pharr San Juan Alamo High Sch/San Juan/Hidalgo | 01030474 | 956/354-2300 | 227 |
| Pharr San Juan Alamo North HS/Pharr/Hidalgo | 03325732 | 956/354-2360 | 227 |
| **PHARR-SAN JUAN-ALAMO IND SD/ PHARR/HIDALGO** | 01030333 | 956/354-2000 | 226 |
| Phillips Elem Sch/Frisco/Collin | 11820077 | 469/633-3925 | 83 |
| Phillips Elem Sch/Kaufman/Kaufman | 02178770 | 972/932-4500 | 255 |
| Phoenix Alt Campus 817/Cleburne/Johnson | 04807719 | 817/202-2160 | 250 |
| Phoenix Center/Terrell/Kaufman | 04450122 | 972/563-6319 | 256 |
| Phoenix High Sch/Elgin/Bastrop | 04028327 | 512/281-9774 | 27 |
| Phoenix Learning Center/San Marcos/Hays | 03381061 | 512/393-6864 | 217 |
| Pickle Elem Sch/Austin/Travis | 04943820 | 512/841-8400 | 370 |
| Piedmont Global Academy/Dallas/Dallas | 01009138 | 972/749-4100 | 106 |
| Pieper Ranch Middle Sch/San Antonio/Comal | 12307286 | 830/885-9600 | 92 |
| Pierce Early Childhood Sch/Irving/Dallas | 04872972 | 972/600-3700 | 114 |
| Pietzsch-MacArthur Elem Sch/Beaumont/Jefferson | 01034212 | 409/617-6475 | 245 |
| Pilgrim Academy/Houston/Harris | 01024530 | 713/458-4672 | 199 |
| Pilgrim Lutheran Sch/Houston/Harris | 01027714 | 713/432-7082 | 211 |
| Pillow Elem Sch/Austin/Travis | 01056557 | 512/414-2350 | 370 |
| Pilot Point Elem Sch/Pilot Point/Denton | 02844814 | 940/686-8710 | 129 |
| Pilot Point High Sch/Pilot Point/Denton | 01013593 | 940/686-8740 | 129 |
| **PILOT POINT IND SCH DIST/ PILOT POINT/DENTON** | 01013581 | 940/686-8700 | 129 |

| School/City/County DISTRICT/CITY/COUNTY | PID | TELEPHONE NUMBER | PAGE |
|---|---|---|---|
| Pilot Point Intermediate Sch/Pilot Point/Denton | 04865058 | 940/686-8720 | 129 |
| Pilot Point Middle Sch/Pilot Point/Denton | 02055336 | 940/686-8730 | 129 |
| Pin Oak Middle Sch/Bellaire/Harris | 05099331 | 713/295-6500 | 199 |
| Pine Drive Christian Sch/Hitchcock/Galveston | 02828262 | 281/534-4881 | 166 |
| Pine Forest Elem Sch/Humble/Harris | 02848690 | 281/641-2100 | 201 |
| Pine Forest Elem Sch/Vidor/Orange | 01045778 | 409/951-8800 | 312 |
| Pine Ridge Elem Sch/Livingston/Polk | 01047087 | 936/328-2160 | 320 |
| Pine Shadows Elem Sch/Houston/Harris | 01027245 | 713/251-6500 | 206 |
| **PINE TREE IND SCH DIST/LONGVIEW/ GREGG** | 01021148 | 903/295-5000 | 175 |
| Pine Tree Junior High Sch/Longview/Gregg | 02222797 | 903/295-5081 | 175 |
| Pine Tree Middle Sch/Longview/Gregg | 01021198 | 903/295-5160 | 175 |
| Pine Tree Primary Sch/Longview/Gregg | 01021203 | 903/295-5095 | 175 |
| Pine Tree Senior High Sch/Longview/Gregg | 01021162 | 903/295-5031 | 175 |
| Piner Middle Sch/Sherman/Grayson | 01020651 | 903/891-6470 | 172 |
| Pines Montessori Sch/Kingwood/Harris | 02233368 | 281/358-8933 | 211 |
| Piney Point Elem Sch/Houston/Harris | 01024542 | 713/917-3610 | 199 |
| Piney Woods Elem Sch/Splendora/Montgomery | 11465524 | 281/689-3073 | 297 |
| Pineywoods Community Academy/Lufkin/Angelina | 04892752 | 936/634-5515 | 11 |
| Pinnacle Intermediate Sch/Amarillo/Randall | 12306969 | 806/677-2570 | 323 |
| Pioneer Crossing Elem Sch/Austin/Travis | 11456535 | 512/278-4250 | 374 |
| Pioneer Elem Sch/Graham/Young | 01062142 | 940/549-2442 | 409 |
| Pioneer Heritage Middle Sch/Frisco/Collin | 05092656 | 469/633-4700 | 83 |
| Pittman Elem Sch/Raymondville/Willacy | 01060766 | 956/689-8173 | 397 |
| Pittsburg Elem Sch/Pittsburg/Camp | 01004528 | 903/856-6472 | 72 |
| Pittsburg High Sch/Pittsburg/Camp | 01004542 | 903/856-3646 | 72 |
| **PITTSBURG IND SCH DIST/PITTSBURG/ CAMP** | 01004504 | 903/856-3628 | 72 |
| Pittsburg Intermediate Sch/Pittsburg/Camp | 05026748 | 903/855-3395 | 72 |
| Pittsburg Junior High Sch/Pittsburg/Camp | 01004530 | 903/856-6432 | 72 |
| Pittsburg Primary Sch/Pittsburg/Camp | 01004516 | 903/856-6482 | 72 |
| PK Academy at West Avenue/San Antonio/Bexar | 00997960 | 210/407-8600 | 38 |
| Placedo Elem Sch/Placedo/Victoria | 01058359 | 361/333-8000 | 384 |
| Plain Elem Sch/Leander/Williamson | 10023288 | 512/570-6600 | 400 |
| Plains Elem Sch/Plains/Yoakum | 01062099 | 806/456-7401 | 409 |
| Plains High Sch/Plains/Yoakum | 01062075 | 806/456-7401 | 409 |
| **PLAINS IND SCH DIST/PLAINS/ YOAKUM** | 01062063 | 806/456-7401 | 409 |
| Plains Middle Sch/Plains/Yoakum | 01062087 | 806/456-7401 | 409 |
| Plainview Christian Academy/Plainview/Hale | 04950861 | 806/296-6034 | 180 |
| Plainview High Sch/Plainview/Hale | 01022001 | 806/293-6005 | 180 |
| **PLAINVIEW IND SCH DIST/PLAINVIEW/ HALE** | 01021904 | 806/296-6392 | 180 |
| Plano East Senior High Sch/Plano/Collin | 02130900 | 469/752-9000 | 87 |
| Plano Head Start Center/Plano/Collin | 11423992 | 469/752-7160 | 87 |
| **PLANO IND SCH DIST/PLANO/COLLIN** | 01006344 | 469/752-8100 | 85 |
| Plano Senior High Sch/Plano/Collin | 01401380 | 469/752-9300 | 87 |
| Plano West Senior High Sch/Plano/Collin | 04867290 | 469/752-9600 | 87 |
| Plato Academy/El Paso/El Paso | 04918277 | 915/434-9000 | 142 |
| Pleasant Grove Elem Sch/Dallas/Dallas | 04456504 | 972/892-5000 | 106 |
| Pleasant Grove Elem Sch/Texarkana/Bowie | 01001124 | 903/838-0528 | 52 |
| Pleasant Grove High Sch/Texarkana/Bowie | 02893059 | 903/832-8005 | 52 |
| **PLEASANT GROVE IND SCH DIST/ TEXARKANA/BOWIE** | 01001112 | 903/831-4086 | 52 |
| Pleasant Grove Interm Sch/Texarkana/Bowie | 11555076 | 903/832-0001 | 52 |
| Pleasant Grove Middle Sch/Texarkana/Bowie | 01558115 | 903/831-4295 | 52 |
| Pleasant Hill Elem Sch/Austin/Travis | 01056569 | 512/414-4453 | 370 |
| Pleasant Hill Elem Sch/Leander/Williamson | 05345568 | 512/570-6400 | 400 |
| Pleasant Run Elem Sch/Lancaster/Dallas | 01011375 | 972/218-1538 | 114 |
| Pleasant Valley Elem Sch/Amarillo/Potter | 01047415 | 806/326-5000 | 321 |
| Pleasanton Elem Sch/Pleasanton/Atascosa | 00995467 | 830/569-1340 | 24 |
| Pleasanton High Sch/Pleasanton/Atascosa | 00995479 | 830/569-1250 | 24 |
| **PLEASANTON IND SCH DIST/ PLEASANTON/ATASCOSA** | 00995431 | 830/569-1200 | 24 |
| Pleasanton Junior High Sch/Pleasanton/Atascosa | 00995481 | 830/569-1280 | 24 |
| Pleasanton Primary Sch/Pleasanton/Atascosa | 04750958 | 830/569-1325 | 24 |
| Pleasantville Elem Sch/Houston/Harris | 01025699 | 713/671-3840 | 195 |
| **PLEMONS-STINNETT-PHILLIPS CISD/ STINNETT/HUTCHINSON** | 01032836 | 806/878-2858 | 240 |
| Plum Creek Elem Sch/Joshua/Johnson | 02893085 | 817/202-2500 | 251 |
| Plum Creek Elem Sch/Lockhart/Caldwell | 02896116 | 512/398-0570 | 64 |
| Plummer Elem Sch/Cedar Hill/Dallas | 01008316 | 972/291-4058 | 101 |
| Plummer Middle Sch/Houston/Harris | 10000456 | 281/539-4000 | 186 |
| Poe Elem Sch/Houston/Harris | 01024970 | 713/535-3780 | 199 |
| Poe Middle Sch/San Antonio/Bexar | 00998794 | 210/228-1235 | 44 |
| Poetry Community Christian Sch/Terrell/Kaufman | 11227152 | 972/563-7227 | 256 |

| School/City/County DISTRICT/CITY/COUNTY | PID | TELEPHONE NUMBER | PAGE |
|---|---|---|---|
| Point Alternative Center/Highlands/Harris | 11721641 | 281/420-4630 | 193 |
| **POINT ISABEL IND SCH DIST/** | | | |
| **PORT ISABEL/CAMERON** | 01004061 | 956/943-0000 | 70 |
| Polk Elem Sch/El Paso/El Paso | 02129872 | 915/236-2775 | 138 |
| Polly Ann McRoberts Elem Sch/Katy/Harris | 04757073 | 281/237-2000 | 157 |
| Polly Ryon Middle Sch/Richmond/Fort Bend | 11923643 | 832/223-4500 | 158 |
| Polly Tadlock Elem Sch/Frisco/Collin | 11103879 | 469/633-3775 | 83 |
| Polytechnic High Sch/Fort Worth/Tarrant | 01053270 | 817/814-0000 | 354 |
| Pomeroy Elem Sch/Pasadena/Harris | 01026849 | 713/740-0696 | 204 |
| Pomona Elem Sch/Manvel/Brazoria | 12231015 | 281/245-3670 | 54 |
| Pond Springs Elem Sch/Austin/Williamson | 01061112 | 512/464-4200 | 402 |
| Ponder Elem Sch/Ponder/Denton | 04272542 | 940/479-8230 | 130 |
| Ponder High Sch/Ponder/Denton | 01013622 | 940/479-8210 | 130 |
| **PONDER IND SCH DIST/PONDER/** | | | |
| **DENTON** | 01013610 | 940/479-8200 | 130 |
| Ponder Junior High Sch/Ponder/Denton | 10012667 | 940/479-8220 | 130 |
| Ponderosa Elem Sch/Houston/Harris | 01027518 | 281/891-8180 | 208 |
| Poolville Elem Sch/Poolville/Parker | 01046461 | 817/599-3308 | 316 |
| Poolville High Sch/Poolville/Parker | 05101037 | 817/599-5134 | 316 |
| **POOLVILLE IND SCH DIST/POOLVILLE/** | | | |
| **PARKER** | 01046459 | 817/594-4452 | 316 |
| Poolville Junior High Sch/Poolville/Parker | 05101025 | 817/594-4539 | 316 |
| Pope Elem Sch/Arlington/Tarrant | 01051868 | 682/867-2750 | 347 |
| Pope Elem Sch/Cypress/Harris | 11919379 | 281/373-2340 | 190 |
| Popham Elem Sch/Del Valle/Travis | 01056820 | 512/386-3750 | 372 |
| Por Vida Academy Charter HS/San Antonio/ Bexar | 00999750 | 210/775-1132 | 12 |
| Port Aransas High Sch/Port Aransas/Nueces | 01044891 | 361/749-1206 | 308 |
| **PORT ARANSAS IND SCH DIST/** | | | |
| **PORT ARANSAS/NUECES** | 01044889 | 361/749-1200 | 308 |
| Port Arthur Alternative Center/Port Arthur/ Jefferson | 01526083 | 409/984-8650 | 246 |
| **PORT ARTHUR IND SCH DIST/** | | | |
| **PORT ARTHUR/JEFFERSON** | 01033749 | 409/989-6222 | 246 |
| Port Houston Elem Sch/Houston/Harris | 01025704 | 713/671-3890 | 195 |
| Port Isabel High Sch/Port Isabel/Cameron | 01004097 | 956/943-0030 | 70 |
| Port Isabel Junior High Sch/Port Isabel/ Cameron | 01808958 | 956/943-0060 | 70 |
| Port Neches Elem Sch/Port Neches/Jefferson | 01033983 | 409/722-2262 | 246 |
| Port Neches Middle Sch/Port Neches/ Jefferson | 01033995 | 409/722-8115 | 246 |
| Port Neches-Groves High Sch/Port Neches/ Jefferson | 01034004 | 409/729-7644 | 246 |
| **PORT NECHES-GROVES IND SD/** | | | |
| **PORT NECHES/JEFFERSON** | 01033957 | 409/722-4244 | 246 |
| Port O'Connor Elem Sch/Port O Connor/ Calhoun | 01003249 | 361/983-2341 | 65 |
| Porter Elem Sch/Porter/Montgomery | 01042714 | 281/577-2920 | 297 |
| Porter High Sch/Porter/Montgomery | 11713462 | 281/577-5900 | 297 |
| Portia Ross Taylor Elem Sch/Plano/Collin | 10023941 | 469/633-3625 | 83 |
| Positive Redirection Center/San Benito/ Cameron | 03390543 | 956/361-6275 | 70 |
| Positive Solutions Charter Sch/San Antonio/ Bexar | 04848074 | 210/299-1025 | 12 |
| Post Elem Sch/Houston/Harris | 01023304 | 713/896-3488 | 190 |
| Post Elem Sch/Post/Garza | 01019602 | 806/495-3414 | 167 |
| Post High Sch/Post/Garza | 01019614 | 806/495-2770 | 167 |
| **POST IND SCH DIST/POST/GARZA** | 01019597 | 806/495-3343 | 167 |
| Post Middle Sch/Post/Garza | 01019626 | 806/495-2874 | 167 |
| Post Oak Montessori Sch/Bellaire/Harris | 01875406 | 713/661-6688 | 212 |
| Poteet Elem Sch/Poteet/Atascosa | 00995508 | 830/742-3503 | 24 |
| Poteet High Sch/Poteet/Atascosa | 00995510 | 830/742-3521 | 24 |
| **POTEET IND SCH DIST/POTEET/** | | | |
| **ATASCOSA** | 00995493 | 830/742-3567 | 24 |
| Poteet Intermediate Campus/Poteet/Atascosa | 05278812 | 830/742-3697 | 24 |
| Poteet Junior High Sch/Poteet/Atascosa | 00995522 | 830/742-3571 | 24 |
| Poth Elem Sch/Poth/Wilson | 01061356 | 830/484-3321 | 404 |
| Poth High Sch/Poth/Wilson | 01061368 | 830/484-3322 | 404 |
| **POTH IND SCH DIST/POTH/WILSON** | 01061344 | 830/484-3330 | 404 |
| Poth Junior High Sch/Poth/Wilson | 01061370 | 830/484-3323 | 404 |
| Potranco Elem Sch/San Antonio/Medina | 10012552 | 830/931-2243 | 287 |
| Pottsboro Elem Sch/Pottsboro/Grayson | 01020534 | 903/771-2981 | 172 |
| Pottsboro High Sch/Pottsboro/Grayson | 01020546 | 903/771-0085 | 172 |
| **POTTSBORO IND SCH DIST/POTTSBORO/** | | | |
| **GRAYSON** | 01020510 | 903/771-0083 | 172 |
| Pottsboro Middle Sch/Pottsboro/Grayson | 01418333 | 903/771-2982 | 172 |
| Powell Elem Sch/San Antonio/Bexar | 00998328 | 210/397-0450 | 41 |
| Prairie Creek Elem Sch/Richardson/Dallas | 01011856 | 469/593-6300 | 117 |
| Prairie Harbor Alternative Sch/Wallis/ Austin | 11931834 | 979/478-6024 | 25 |
| **PRAIRIE LEA IND SCH DIST/** | | | |
| **PRAIRIE LEA/CALDWELL** | 01003122 | 512/488-2328 | 65 |
| Prairie Lea Sch/Prairie Lea/Caldwell | 01003134 | 512/488-2328 | 65 |
| Prairie Trail Elem Sch/Flower Mound/Denton | 04364432 | 469/713-5980 | 128 |
| **PRAIRIE VALLEY IND SCH DIST/** | | | |
| **NOCONA/MONTAGUE** | 01042374 | 940/825-4425 | 293 |
| Prairie Valley Sch/Nocona/Montague | 01042386 | 940/825-4425 | 293 |
| Prairie View Elem Sch/Rhome/Denton | 04804597 | 817/215-0550 | 129 |
| Prairie Vista Middle Sch/Fort Worth/ Tarrant | 10902983 | 817/847-9210 | 351 |
| Prairiland High Sch/Pattonville/Lamar | 01036818 | 903/652-5681 | 263 |
| **PRAIRILAND IND SCH DIST/** | | | |
| **PATTONVILLE/LAMAR** | 01036789 | 903/652-6476 | 263 |
| Prairiland Junior High Sch/Pattonville/ Lamar | 10001412 | 903/652-5681 | 263 |
| Pre-K Academy at Midland Clg/Midland/ Midland | 12378663 | 432/685-4500 | 289 |
| Premier Academy/Keller/Tarrant | 11228144 | 817/745-0034 | 362 |
| Premier HS-Abilene/Abilene/Taylor | 04932182 | 325/698-8111 | 12 |
| Premier HS-Amarillo/Amarillo/Randall | 12100416 | 806/367-5447 | 12 |
| Premier HS-Arlington/Arlington/Tarrant | 12261058 | 682/350-8865 | 12 |
| Premier HS-Brenham Miracle Frm/Brenham/ Washington | 11925237 | 979/836-0901 | 12 |
| Premier HS-Brownsville/Brownsville/Cameron | 04881674 | 956/550-0084 | 12 |
| Premier HS-Brownwood Early/Early/Brown | 11925249 | 325/643-3735 | 12 |
| Premier HS-Career Tech Ed Ctr/Edinburg/ Hidalgo | 12160856 | 956/386-1793 | 12 |
| Premier HS-Comanche/Comanche/Comanche | 11815474 | 325/356-9673 | 12 |
| Premier HS-Dayton/Dayton/Liberty | 11848835 | 936/257-8017 | 12 |
| Premier HS-Del Rio/Del Rio/Val Verde | 04881703 | 830/703-1631 | 12 |
| Premier HS-El Paso East/El Paso/El Paso | 12161939 | 915/633-1598 | 12 |
| Premier HS-El Paso West/El Paso/El Paso | 11565617 | 915/581-4300 | 12 |
| Premier HS-Fort Worth/Fort Worth/Tarrant | 04881715 | 817/731-2028 | 12 |
| Premier HS-Granbury/Granbury/Hood | 11565629 | 817/573-0435 | 12 |
| Premier HS-Huntsville/Huntsville/Walker | 11565631 | 936/439-5204 | 12 |
| Premier HS-Irving South/Irving/Dallas | 11848847 | 972/254-1016 | 12 |
| Premier HS-Laredo/Laredo/Webb | 04881727 | 956/723-7788 | 12 |
| Premier HS-Lewisville/Lewisville/Denton | 11925275 | 972/521-1592 | 12 |
| Premier HS-Lubbock/Lubbock/Lubbock | 04881739 | 806/763-1518 | 12 |
| Premier HS-Midland/Midland/Midland | 04891588 | 432/682-0384 | 12 |
| Premier HS-Mission/Mission/Hidalgo | 11014486 | 956/424-9290 | 12 |
| Premier HS-N Austin/Austin/Travis | 11565655 | 512/614-4537 | 12 |
| Premier HS-New Braunfels/New Braunfels/ Comal | 11565643 | 830/609-6606 | 12 |
| Premier HS-North Houston/Houston/Harris | 12173542 | 281/537-7272 | 12 |
| Premier HS-Palmview/Palmview/Hidalgo | 11014498 | 956/584-8458 | 12 |
| Premier HS-Pflugerville/Pflugerville/ Travis | 12160844 | 512/969-5100 | 12 |
| Premier HS-Pharr/Pharr/Hidalgo | 04891590 | 956/781-8800 | 12 |
| Premier HS-S Austin/Austin/Travis | 05010713 | 512/444-8442 | 12 |
| Premier HS-San Angelo/San Angelo/Tom Green | 12363747 | 325/823-7758 | 12 |
| Premier HS-San Antonio East/San Antonio/ Bexar | 12261046 | 210/650-0944 | 12 |
| Premier HS-San Antonio West/San Antonio/ Bexar | 12261034 | 830/587-4730 | 12 |
| Premier HS-San Juan/San Juan/Hidalgo | 11565679 | 956/961-4721 | 12 |
| Premier HS-Texarkana/Texarkana/Bowie | 12173578 | 430/200-4385 | 12 |
| Premier HS-Tyler/Tyler/Smith | 04881741 | 903/592-5222 | 12 |
| Premier HS-Waco/Waco/McLennan | 04881753 | 254/752-0441 | 12 |
| Premont Collegiate High Sch/Premont/ Jim Wells | 01034755 | 361/348-3915 | 249 |
| Premont Early College Academy/Premont/ Jim Wells | 01034729 | 361/348-3915 | 249 |
| **PREMONT IND SCH DIST/PREMONT/** | | | |
| **JIM WELLS** | 01034717 | 361/348-3915 | 248 |
| Prep for Early College HS/Rio Grande Cy/ Starr | 12235401 | 956/352-6349 | 343 |
| Presa Elem Sch/El Paso/El Paso | 01016533 | 915/434-8700 | 142 |
| Presbyterian Pan American Sch/Kingsville/ Kleberg | 01036430 | 361/592-4307 | 261 |
| Presbyterian Sch/Houston/Harris | 03560229 | 713/520-0284 | 212 |
| Presidential Meadows Elem Sch/Manor/Travis | 10915045 | 512/278-4225 | 374 |
| Presidio Elem Sch/Presidio/Presidio | 01047879 | 432/229-3200 | 323 |
| Presidio High Sch/Presidio/Presidio | 02887866 | 432/229-3365 | 323 |
| **PRESIDIO IND SCH DIST/PRESIDIO/** | | | |
| **PRESIDIO** | 01047867 | 432/229-3275 | 323 |
| Preston Elem Sch/Allen/Collin | 12230487 | 972/908-8780 | 80 |
| Preston Hollow Elem Sch/Dallas/Dallas | 01009619 | 972/794-8500 | 106 |
| Preston Hollow Presby Sch/Dallas/Dallas | 01479791 | 214/368-3886 | 120 |
| Prestonwood Christian Academy/Plano/Collin | 04924628 | 972/820-5300 | 90 |
| Prestonwood Elem Sch/Dallas/Dallas | 01011868 | 469/593-6700 | 117 |
| Prestwick STEM Academy/The Colony/Denton | 12036918 | 972/947-9450 | 128 |
| Price Elem Sch/San Antonio/Bexar | 00999487 | 210/977-7225 | 45 |
| Price T Young Elem Sch/Marshall/Harrison | 01028689 | 903/927-8850 | 214 |

| School/City/County DISTRICT/CITY/COUNTY | PID | TELEPHONE NUMBER | PAGE |
|---|---|---|---|
| **PRIDDY IND SCH DIST**/PRIDDY/MILLS | 01042001 | 325/966-3323 | 292 |
| Priddy Sch/Priddy/Mills | 01042013 | 325/966-3323 | 292 |
| Pride Academy/Brenham/Washington | 04449886 | 979/277-3890 | 388 |
| Pride Sch/Huntington/Angelina | 04282949 | 936/876-4287 | 21 |
| Prince of Peace Catholic Sch/Plano/Collin | 03410363 | 972/380-5505 | 89 |
| Prince of Peace Christian Sch/Carrollton/Denton | 02858281 | 972/447-0532 | 130 |
| Princeton High Sch/Princeton/Collin | 01006526 | 469/952-5405 | 87 |
| **PRINCETON IND SCH DIST**/PRINCETON/COLLIN | 01006502 | 469/952-5400 | 87 |
| **PRINGLE-MORSE CONS ISD**/MORSE/HANSFORD | 01022295 | 806/733-2507 | 182 |
| Pringle-Morse Sch/Morse/Hansford | 01022300 | 806/733-2507 | 182 |
| Priority Intervention Academy/Lubbock/Lubbock | 02110302 | 806/219-2400 | 273 |
| Pritchard Junior High Sch/Bells/Grayson | 01020259 | 903/965-3602 | 170 |
| Pro-Vision Academy/Houston/Harris | 04922034 | 713/748-0030 | 12 |
| Progreso Early Childhood Sch/Progreso/Hidalgo | 05349801 | 956/565-6473 | 227 |
| Progreso Early Clg Academy/Progreso/Hidalgo | 11928019 | 956/565-4142 | 227 |
| Progreso Elem Sch/Progreso/Hidalgo | 11540473 | 956/565-1335 | 227 |
| Progreso High Sch/Progreso/Hidalgo | 02203923 | 956/565-4142 | 227 |
| **PROGRESO IND SCH DIST**/PROGRESO/HIDALGO | 01030503 | 956/565-3002 | 227 |
| Progressive High Sch/Missouri City/Fort Bend | 04365890 | 281/634-2900 | 155 |
| Project Chrysalis Middle Sch/Houston/Harris | 04454453 | 713/924-1700 | 195 |
| Promesa Clg Prep-Brownsville/Brownsville/Cameron | 12378675 | 956/295-7778 | 12 |
| Promesa Clg Prep-E Austin Key/Austin/Travis | 11540643 | 512/287-5000 | 12 |
| Promesa Clg Prep-E Austin MLK/Austin/Travis | 11849023 | 512/287-5050 | 12 |
| Promesa Clg Prep-W Corp Cristi/Corp Christi/Nueces | 12378687 | 361/400-8293 | 12 |
| Promise Academy/Tyler/Smith | 12166757 | 903/630-7369 | 342 |
| Promise Cmty Sch-New Nghbr/Houston/Harris | 12162012 | 713/273-3731 | 12 |
| Promise Community Sch Ripley/Houston/Harris | 05195052 | 713/315-6429 | 12 |
| Prosper High Sch/Prosper/Collin | 04169012 | 469/219-2180 | 88 |
| **PROSPER IND SCH DIST**/PROSPER/COLLIN | 01006552 | 469/219-2000 | 88 |
| Provan Opportunity Center/Pflugerville/Travis | 04299198 | 512/594-3600 | 374 |
| Providence Catholic Sch/San Antonio/Bexar | 00999970 | 210/224-6651 | 47 |
| Providence Christian Sch/Dallas/Dallas | 04992845 | 214/302-2800 | 120 |
| Providence Classical Sch/Spring/Harris | 11824877 | 281/320-0500 | 212 |
| Providence Elem Sch/Aubrey/Denton | 05343455 | 940/369-1900 | 125 |
| Provident Heights Elem Sch/Waco/McLennan | 01040364 | 254/750-3930 | 285 |
| Psja Elvis J Ballew Echs/Pharr/Hidalgo | 11454408 | 956/354-2520 | 227 |
| Psja Memorial HS/Alamo/Hidalgo | 04754033 | 956/354-2420 | 227 |
| Psja Sonia Sotomayer HS/Pharr/Hidalgo | 03346566 | 956/354-2510 | 227 |
| Psja Southwest EC High Sch/Pharr/Hidalgo | 11552880 | 956/354-2480 | 227 |
| Psja T Jefferson Echs/Pharr/Hidalgo | 11128520 | 956/784-8525 | 227 |
| Ptaa Greenville Elem Sch/Greenville/Hunt | 12378637 | 903/257-3920 | 13 |
| Ptaa Mesquite Elem Sch/Mesquite/Dallas | 12378651 | 972/285-6895 | 13 |
| Ptaa Royse City Elem Sch/Royse City/Rockwall | 12378649 | 469/707-3505 | 13 |
| Ptaa-Greenville Mid High Sch/Greenville/Hunt | 12261010 | 903/454-7153 | 13 |
| Ptaa-Mesquite Mid High Sch/Mesquite/Dallas | 12261022 | 972/375-9672 | 13 |
| Puckett Elem Sch/Amarillo/Potter | 01548469 | 806/326-5050 | 321 |
| Pullam Elem Sch/Brownsville/Cameron | 11449245 | 956/547-3700 | 67 |
| Purnell Support Center/Lewisville/Denton | 12170136 | 469/713-5199 | 128 |
| Purple Heart Elem Sch/El Paso/El Paso | 12105064 | 915/938-2200 | 141 |
| Purple Sage Elem Sch/Austin/Williamson | 02126909 | 512/428-3500 | 402 |
| Purple Sage Elem Sch/Houston/Harris | 03397981 | 832/386-3100 | 192 |
| Puster Elem Sch/Fairview/Collin | 11127760 | 469/742-8300 | 84 |
| Putegnat Elem Sch/Brownsville/Cameron | 01003457 | 956/548-8930 | 67 |
| Putnam Elem Sch/El Paso/El Paso | 01016052 | 915/236-3225 | 138 |
| Pyburn Elem Sch/Houston/Harris | 01023536 | 832/386-3150 | 192 |

**Q**

| School/City/County DISTRICT/CITY/COUNTY | PID | TELEPHONE NUMBER | PAGE |
|---|---|---|---|
| Qalam Collegiate Academy/Richardson/Dallas | 12043234 | 972/437-2526 | 120 |
| Quail Valley Elem Sch/Missouri City/Fort Bend | 01418319 | 281/634-5040 | 155 |
| Quail Valley Middle Sch/Missouri City/Fort Bend | 01541332 | 281/634-3600 | 155 |
| Quanah High Sch/Quanah/Hardeman | 01022403 | 940/663-2791 | 182 |

| School/City/County DISTRICT/CITY/COUNTY | PID | TELEPHONE NUMBER | PAGE |
|---|---|---|---|
| **QUANAH IND SCH DIST**/QUANAH/HARDEMAN | 01022398 | 940/663-2281 | 182 |
| Queen City High Sch/Queen City/Cass | 01004932 | 903/796-8259 | 74 |
| **QUEEN CITY IND SCH DIST**/QUEEN CITY/CASS | 01004920 | 903/796-8256 | 74 |
| Queens Intermediate Sch/Houston/Harris | 01026851 | 713/740-0470 | 204 |
| Quest Academy/Stafford/Fort Bend | 12367779 | 281/261-9200 | 159 |
| Quest Early College High Sch/Humble/Harris | 04303971 | 281/641-7300 | 201 |
| Quest High Sch/Burnet/Burnet | 04238546 | 512/756-6747 | 63 |
| **QUINLAN IND SCH DIST**/QUINLAN/HUNT | 01032575 | 903/356-1200 | 240 |
| Quinn Middle Sch/Waco/McLennan | 11478820 | 254/754-8000 | 13 |
| Quitman Elem Sch/Quitman/Wood | 01061916 | 903/763-5000 | 408 |
| Quitman High Sch/Quitman/Wood | 01061928 | 903/763-5000 | 408 |
| **QUITMAN IND SCH DIST**/QUITMAN/WOOD | 01061904 | 903/763-5000 | 408 |
| Quitman Junior High Sch/Quitman/Wood | 01061930 | 903/763-5000 | 408 |

**R**

| School/City/County DISTRICT/CITY/COUNTY | PID | TELEPHONE NUMBER | PAGE |
|---|---|---|---|
| R A Hall Elem Sch/Beeville/Bee | 00996112 | 361/362-6060 | 28 |
| R C Conley Elem Sch/Houston/Harris | 02201389 | 281/537-5418 | 185 |
| R C Loflin Middle Sch/Joshua/Johnson | 01035058 | 817/202-2500 | 251 |
| R D McAdams Junior High Sch/Dickinson/Galveston | 01019016 | 281/229-7100 | 164 |
| R E Good Elem Sch/Carrollton/Dallas | 01008196 | 972/968-1900 | 101 |
| R F Patterson Elem Sch/Arlington/Tarrant | 04456736 | 817/563-8600 | 358 |
| R J Richey Elem Sch/Burnet/Burnet | 10758794 | 512/756-2609 | 63 |
| R K Driggers Elem Sch/San Antonio/Bexar | 10913205 | 210/397-5900 | 41 |
| R L Isaacs Elem Sch/Houston/Harris | 01025558 | 713/671-4120 | 196 |
| R L Martin Elem Sch/Brownsville/Cameron | 01003548 | 956/982-2730 | 67 |
| R L Paschal High Sch/Fort Worth/Tarrant | 01053282 | 817/814-5000 | 354 |
| R L Turner High Sch/Carrollton/Dallas | 01008237 | 972/968-5400 | 101 |
| R M Sorrells Sch-Ed & Soc Srvs/Dallas/Dallas | 01553036 | 972/925-5940 | 106 |
| R O'Hara Lanier Middle Sch/Freeport/Brazoria | 04363737 | 979/730-7220 | 56 |
| R P Harris Elem Sch/Houston/Harris | 01025728 | 713/450-7100 | 195 |
| R Q Sims Intermediate Sch/Mexia/Limestone | 02890966 | 254/562-4025 | 270 |
| R S Kimbrough Middle Sch/Mesquite/Dallas | 04033035 | 972/882-5900 | 116 |
| R V Groves Elem Sch/Wylie/Collin | 05035294 | 972/429-3460 | 89 |
| Raba Elem Sch/San Antonio/Bexar | 04921406 | 210/397-1350 | 41 |
| Radford Sch/El Paso/El Paso | 01016686 | 915/565-2700 | 144 |
| Radiant STEM Academy/Irving/Dallas | 12225690 | 214/245-5125 | 120 |
| Rafael Cantu Jr High Sch/Palmhurst/Hidalgo | 11079321 | 956/323-7800 | 225 |
| Rafael Galvan Elem Sch/Corp Christi/Nueces | 03333105 | 361/878-2800 | 307 |
| Rafaela T Barrera Elem Sch/Roma/Starr | 04282212 | 956/486-2475 | 343 |
| Raguet Elem Sch/Nacogdoches/Nacogdoches | 01043330 | 936/569-5052 | 301 |
| Rahe Bulverde Elem Sch/Bulverde/Comal | 01006899 | 830/885-1600 | 92 |
| Rainard School for the Gifted/Houston/Harris | 02998518 | 713/647-7246 | 212 |
| Rains Elem Sch/Mumford/Rains | 01047908 | 903/473-2222 | 323 |
| Rains High Sch/Emory/Rains | 01047910 | 903/473-2222 | 323 |
| **RAINS IND SCH DIST**/EMORY/RAINS | 01047893 | 903/473-2222 | 323 |
| Rains Intermediate Sch/Emory/Rains | 05276888 | 903/473-2222 | 323 |
| Rains Junior High Sch/Emory/Rains | 01047922 | 903/473-2222 | 323 |
| Ralls Elem Sch/Ralls/Crosby | 01007996 | 806/253-2546 | 98 |
| Ralls High Sch/Ralls/Crosby | 01008005 | 806/253-2571 | 98 |
| **RALLS IND SCH DIST**/RALLS/CROSBY | 01007984 | 806/253-2509 | 98 |
| Ralls Middle Sch/Ralls/Crosby | 04245410 | 806/253-2549 | 98 |
| Ralph Eickenroht Elem Sch/Houston/Harris | 11451999 | 281/891-8840 | 208 |
| Ralph G Goodman Elem Sch/Houston/Harris | 01022831 | 281/878-0355 | 186 |
| Ralph Langley Elem Sch/San Antonio/Bexar | 11448980 | 210/397-0150 | 41 |
| Ralph Parr Elem Sch/League City/Galveston | 11449099 | 281/284-4100 | 163 |
| Ralph Pfluger Elem Sch/Buda/Hays | 11555533 | 512/268-8510 | 216 |
| Ramey Elem Sch/Tyler/Smith | 01050929 | 903/262-2505 | 340 |
| Ramirez Charter Sch/Lubbock/Lubbock | 02907064 | 806/219-6500 | 273 |
| **RAMIREZ COMMON SCH DIST**/REALITOS/DUVAL | 01014250 | 361/539-4343 | 132 |
| Ramirez Elem Sch/Realitos/Duval | 01014262 | 361/539-4343 | 132 |
| Ramirez-Burks Elem Sch/Cotulla/La Salle | 01037202 | 830/879-2511 | 262 |
| Ramiro Barrera Middle Sch/Roma/Starr | 11072202 | 956/486-2670 | 343 |
| Ramona Bang Elem Sch/Houston/Harris | 03327209 | 281/897-4760 | 190 |
| Ramona Elem Sch/El Paso/El Paso | 01016545 | 915/434-7700 | 142 |
| Ranch Academy/Canton/Van Zandt | 04892776 | 903/479-3601 | 13 |
| Ranch Academy-Tyler/Canton/Van Zandt | 11704722 | 903/479-3601 | 13 |
| Rancho Isabella Elem Sch/Angleton/Brazoria | 02845947 | 979/864-8007 | 55 |
| Rancho Sienna Elem Sch/Georgetown/Williamson | 12305733 | 512/260-4450 | 401 |
| Rancho Verde Elem Sch/Brownsville/Cameron | 11129861 | 956/254-5230 | 70 |
| Ranchview High Sch/Irving/Dallas | 05098375 | 972/968-5000 | 101 |
| Rancier Middle Sch/Killeen/Bell | 00996590 | 254/336-1250 | 31 |
| Randall High Sch/Amarillo/Randall | 03048922 | 806/677-2333 | 324 |

| School/City/County DISTRICT/CITY/COUNTY | PID | TELEPHONE NUMBER | PAGE |
|---|---|---|---|
| Randolph Elem Sch/Universal Cty/Bexar | 01601798 | 210/357-2345 | 42 |
| **RANDOLPH FIELD IND SCH DIST/ UNIVERSAL CTY/BEXAR** | 01601786 | 210/357-2300 | 42 |
| Randolph Foster High Sch/Richmond/ Fort Bend | 04946028 | 832/223-3800 | 158 |
| Randolph High Sch/Universal Cty/Bexar | 01601803 | 210/357-2400 | 42 |
| Randolph Middle Sch/Universal Cty/Bexar | 03237745 | 210/357-2430 | 42 |
| Rangel Women's Leadership Sch/Dallas/ Dallas | 05345752 | 972/749-5200 | 106 |
| **RANGER IND SCH DIST/RANGER/ EASTLAND** | 01014470 | 254/647-1187 | 133 |
| Ranger Sch/Ranger/Eastland | 02046048 | 254/647-3216 | 133 |
| Rangerville Elem Sch/San Benito/Cameron | 01004255 | 956/361-6840 | 70 |
| Rankin Elem Sch/Arlington/Tarrant | 01051870 | 682/867-2800 | 347 |
| Rankin High Sch/Rankin/Upton | 01057678 | 432/693-2451 | 380 |
| **RANKIN IND SCH DIST/RANKIN/UPTON** | 01057654 | 432/693-2461 | 380 |
| Rann Elem Sch/Decatur/Wise | 01061667 | 940/393-7600 | 406 |
| Rapoport Acad-E Campus ES/Waco/McLennan | 04814009 | 254/799-4191 | 13 |
| Rapoport Acad-N Campus ES/Waco/McLennan | 11848897 | 254/313-1313 | 13 |
| Raquel Cavazos Elem Sch/Mission/Hidalgo | 05275420 | 956/323-7200 | 225 |
| Rasor Elem Sch/Plano/Collin | 03456666 | 469/752-2900 | 87 |
| Raul B Fernandez Elem Sch/San Antonio/ Bexar | 03324960 | 210/397-1900 | 41 |
| Raul C Martinez Elem Sch/Houston/Harris | 04016128 | 713/671-3680 | 196 |
| Raul Longoria Elem Sch/Pharr/Hidalgo | 01540077 | 956/354-2820 | 227 |
| Raul Perales Middle Sch/Laredo/Webb | 12308230 | 956/473-6800 | 391 |
| Raul Quintanilla Middle Sch/Dallas/Dallas | 04755465 | 972/502-3200 | 106 |
| Raul Yzaguirre Middle Sch/San Juan/Hidalgo | 04919568 | 956/354-2630 | 227 |
| Raul Yzaguirre Sch for Success/Brownsville/ Cameron | 12168901 | 956/574-7100 | 13 |
| Raul Yzaguirre Sch for Success/Houston/ Harris | 04467565 | 713/640-3700 | 13 |
| Rawson Saunders Sch/Austin/Travis | 11231672 | 512/476-8382 | 376 |
| Ray & Jamie Wolman Elem Sch/Katy/Harris | 11822025 | 281/234-1700 | 157 |
| Ray D Corbett Junior High Sch/Schertz/ Guadalupe | 01021588 | 210/619-4150 | 178 |
| Ray Daily Elem Sch/Houston/Harris | 10910514 | 281/368-2111 | 199 |
| Ray Darr Elem Sch/Eagle Pass/Maverick | 02855904 | 830/758-7060 | 280 |
| Ray Elem Sch/Hutto/Williamson | 10904797 | 512/759-5450 | 399 |
| Ray Johnson 6th Grade Ctr/Fort Worth/ Tarrant | 12115617 | 817/615-3670 | 352 |
| Ray L Shotwell Middle Sch/Houston/Harris | 01857246 | 281/878-0960 | 186 |
| Rayburn Elem Sch/San Antonio/Bexar | 00997506 | 210/989-3200 | 36 |
| Rayburn Intermediate Sch/Bryan/Brazos | 03244695 | 979/209-6600 | 58 |
| Raye McCoy Elem Sch/Georgetown/Williamson | 01420570 | 512/943-5030 | 398 |
| Raye-Allen Elem Sch/Temple/Bell | 00996796 | 254/215-5800 | 32 |
| Raymond & Tirza Martin HS/Laredo/Webb | 01059391 | 956/273-7100 | 390 |
| Raymond Cooper Junior High Sch/Wylie/ Collin | 10748361 | 972/429-3250 | 89 |
| Raymond Mays Middle Sch/Troy/Bell | 02887828 | 254/938-2543 | 33 |
| Raymond Telles/Lafarelle MS/El Paso/ El Paso | 04288292 | 915/236-7800 | 137 |
| Raymondville High Sch/Raymondville/Willacy | 01060778 | 956/689-8170 | 397 |
| **RAYMONDVILLE IND SCH DIST/ RAYMONDVILLE/WILLACY** | 01060716 | 956/689-2471 | 397 |
| Raymondville Options Academy/Raymondville/ Willacy | 12312401 | 956/689-8185 | 397 |
| Reach High Sch/Fort Worth/Tarrant | 04359994 | 817/252-2390 | 350 |
| Reading Junior High Sch/Richmond/Fort Bend | 11553482 | 832/223-4400 | 158 |
| Reagan Co Elem Sch/Big Lake/Reagan | 01048029 | 325/884-3741 | 324 |
| Reagan Co High Sch/Big Lake/Reagan | 01048031 | 325/884-3714 | 324 |
| **REAGAN CO IND SCH DIST/BIG LAKE/ REAGAN** | 01048017 | 325/884-3705 | 324 |
| Reagan Co Middle Sch/Big Lake/Reagan | 01048043 | 325/884-3728 | 324 |
| Reagan Elem Sch/Abilene/Taylor | 01172785 | 325/690-3627 | 363 |
| Reagan Elem Sch/Quanah/Hardeman | 01022415 | 940/663-2171 | 182 |
| Reagan Elem Sch/San Angelo/Tom Green | 01055709 | 325/659-3666 | 367 |
| Reagan Magnet Elem Sch/Odessa/Ector | 01014808 | 432/456-1189 | 135 |
| Realm Secondary Sch/Burleson/Johnson | 12369959 | 817/245-1700 | 250 |
| Reaves Elem Sch/Conroe/Montgomery | 01042506 | 936/709-5400 | 295 |
| Reba Cobb Carroll Elem Sch/Frisco/Collin | 10912718 | 469/633-3725 | 83 |
| Rebecca Creek Elem Sch/Spring Branch/Comal | 05090696 | 830/885-1800 | 92 |
| Recovery Education Campus/Ralls/Crosby | 12103195 | 806/253-2549 | 98 |
| Red Bluff Elem Sch/Pasadena/Harris | 01026863 | 713/740-0704 | 204 |
| **RED LICK IND SCH DIST/TEXARKANA/ BOWIE** | 01001136 | 903/838-8230 | 52 |
| Red Lick Sch/Texarkana/Bowie | 01001148 | 903/838-8230 | 53 |
| Red Oak Elem Sch/Red Oak/Ellis | 01015266 | 972/617-3523 | 146 |
| Red Oak High Sch/Red Oak/Ellis | 01015280 | 972/617-3535 | 146 |
| **RED OAK IND SCH DIST/RED OAK/ ELLIS** | 01015242 | 972/617-2941 | 146 |
| Red Oak Middle Sch/Red Oak/Ellis | 01015278 | 972/617-0066 | 146 |
| Red Rock Elem Sch/Red Rock/Bastrop | 04453253 | 512/772-7660 | 27 |
| Red Sands Elem Sch/El Paso/El Paso | 04880400 | 915/926-5400 | 137 |
| Red Simon Middle Sch/Kyle/Hays | 11454393 | 512/268-8507 | 216 |
| Redeemer Episcopal Sch/Eagle Pass/Maverick | 01410939 | 830/773-5122 | 280 |
| Redeemer Lutheran Sch/Austin/Travis | 01056997 | 512/451-6478 | 376 |
| Redeemer Lutheran Sch/Fort Worth/Tarrant | 01411012 | 817/560-0032 | 362 |
| Redeemer Montessori Sch/Irving/Dallas | 02851063 | 972/257-3517 | 120 |
| Redland Oaks Elem Sch/San Antonio/Bexar | 03250321 | 210/407-6200 | 38 |
| Redwater Elem Sch/Redwater/Bowie | 01001162 | 903/671-3425 | 53 |
| Redwater High Sch/Redwater/Bowie | 01001174 | 903/671-3421 | 53 |
| **REDWATER IND SCH DIST/REDWATER/ BOWIE** | 01001150 | 903/671-3481 | 53 |
| Redwater Junior High Sch/Redwater/Bowie | 04840228 | 903/671-3227 | 53 |
| Redwater Middle Sch/Redwater/Bowie | 02130182 | 903/671-3412 | 53 |
| Reece EC-PK-K Sch/Houston/Harris | 04453875 | 281/878-0800 | 186 |
| Reeces Creek Elem Sch/Killeen/Bell | 03244700 | 254/336-2150 | 31 |
| Reed Academy/Houston/Harris | 04285276 | 281/985-6670 | 185 |
| Reed Elem Sch/Cedar Park/Williamson | 12035720 | 512/570-7700 | 400 |
| Reed Elem Sch/Houston/Harris | 03397931 | 713/896-5035 | 190 |
| Reed Middle Sch/Duncanville/Dallas | 01010371 | 972/708-3500 | 109 |
| Rees Elem Sch/Houston/Harris | 02227307 | 281/531-1444 | 187 |
| Reese Education Center/Lubbock/Lubbock | 04748981 | 806/885-4910 | 272 |
| Reeves Hinger Elem Sch/Canyon/Randall | 01047972 | 806/677-2870 | 324 |
| Refugio Elem Sch/Refugio/Refugio | 01048483 | 361/526-4844 | 326 |
| Refugio High Sch/Refugio/Refugio | 01048469 | 361/526-2344 | 326 |
| **REFUGIO IND SCH DIST/REFUGIO/ REFUGIO** | 01048457 | 361/526-2325 | 326 |
| Refugio Junior High Sch/Refugio/Refugio | 11848902 | 361/526-2434 | 326 |
| Regency Place Elem Sch/San Antonio/Bexar | 00997893 | 210/407-6400 | 38 |
| Regents Academy/Nacogdoches/Nacogdoches | 11225788 | 936/559-7343 | 302 |
| Regents School of Austin/Austin/Travis | 04295910 | 512/899-8095 | 376 |
| Regina Mater/Austin/Travis | 12361488 | 512/524-1799 | 376 |
| Regina-Howell Elem Sch/Beaumont/Jefferson | 01034236 | 409/617-6190 | 245 |
| **REGION 1 ED SERVICE CENTER/ EDINBURG/HIDALGO** | 01030553 | 956/984-6000 | 229 |
| **REGION 2 ED SERVICE CENTER/ CORP CHRISTI/NUECES** | 01045003 | 361/561-8400 | 309 |
| **REGION 3 ED SERVICE CENTER/ VICTORIA/VICTORIA** | 01058438 | 361/573-0731 | 385 |
| **REGION 4 ED SERVICE CENTER/ HOUSTON/HARRIS** | 01027556 | 713/462-7708 | 213 |
| **REGION 5 ED SERVICE CENTER/ BEAUMONT/JEFFERSON** | 01034298 | 409/951-1700 | 247 |
| **REGION 6 ED SERVICE CENTER/ HUNTSVILLE/WALKER** | 01058763 | 936/435-8400 | 386 |
| **REGION 7 ED SERVICE CENTER/ KILGORE/GREGG** | 01021291 | 903/988-6700 | 176 |
| **REGION 8 ED SERVICE CENTER/ PITTSBURG/TITUS** | 01055450 | 903/575-2600 | 72 |
| **REGION 9 ED SERVICE CENTER/ WICHITA FALLS/WICHITA** | 01060120 | 940/322-6928 | 396 |
| **REGION 10 ED SERVICE CENTER/ RICHARDSON/DALLAS** | 01012032 | 972/348-1700 | 120 |
| **REGION 11 ED SERVICE CENTER/ WHT SETTLEMT/TARRANT** | 01054171 | 817/740-3600 | 362 |
| **REGION 12 ED SERVICE CENTER/ WACO/MCLENNAN** | 01040120 | 254/297-1212 | 286 |
| **REGION 13 ED SERVICE CENTER/ AUSTIN/TRAVIS** | 02101545 | 512/919-5313 | 376 |
| **REGION 14 ED SERVICE CENTER/ ABILENE/TAYLOR** | 01054975 | 325/675-8600 | 364 |
| **REGION 15 ED SERVICE CENTER/ SAN ANGELO/TOM GREEN** | 01055814 | 325/658-6571 | 368 |
| **REGION 16 ED SERVICE CENTER/ AMARILLO/RANDALL** | 01047984 | 806/677-5000 | 324 |
| **REGION 17 ED SERVICE CENTER/ LUBBOCK/LUBBOCK** | 01039248 | 806/792-4000 | 275 |
| **REGION 18 ED SERVICE CENTER/ MIDLAND/MIDLAND** | 01041693 | 432/563-2380 | 290 |
| **REGION 19 ED SERVICE CENTER/ EL PASO/EL PASO** | 01016246 | 915/780-5052 | 144 |
| **REGION 20 ED SERVICE CENTER/ SAN ANTONIO/BEXAR** | 00999645 | 210/370-5200 | 48 |
| Regis Sch of the Sacred Heart/Houston/ Harris | 04022050 | 713/682-8383 | 209 |
| Reicher Catholic High Sch/Waco/McLennan | 01002879 | 254/752-8349 | 285 |
| Reilly Elem Sch/Austin/Travis | 01056583 | 512/414-4464 | 370 |
| Reinhardt Elem Sch/Dallas/Dallas | 01009695 | 972/749-7900 | 106 |
| Remington Point Elem Sch/Fort Worth/ Tarrant | 05276890 | 817/232-1342 | 351 |
| Remynse Elem Sch/Grand Prairie/Tarrant | 04949290 | 682/867-0500 | 347 |
| Rennell Elem Sch/Cypress/Harris | 11560485 | 281/213-1550 | 190 |

| School/City/County DISTRICT/CITY/COUNTY | PID | TELEPHONE NUMBER | PAGE |
|---|---|---|---|
| Renner Middle Sch/Plano/Collin | 03333818 | 469/752-5800 | 87 |
| Reno Elem Sch/Azle/Parker | 04884937 | 817/221-5001 | 316 |
| Resaca Middle Sch/Los Fresnos/Cameron | 04019481 | 956/254-5159 | 70 |
| Resnik Middle Sch/Von Ormy/Bexar | 12165789 | 210/623-6589 | 46 |
| Resurrection Catholic Sch/Houston/Harris | 01028134 | 713/674-5545 | 209 |
| Reuben Johnson Elem Sch/McKinney/Collin | 04750647 | 469/302-6500 | 85 |
| Reve Preparatory Charter Sch/Houston/ Harris | 12362638 | 832/982-2083 | 13 |
| Reynaldo G Garza Elem Sch/McAllen/Hidalgo | 02199475 | 956/971-4554 | 224 |
| Reynolds Middle Sch/Prosper/Collin | 11555026 | 469/219-2165 | 88 |
| Rhea Elem Sch/Forney/Kaufman | 11130652 | 469/762-4360 | 255 |
| Rhoads Elem Sch/Katy/Harris | 05344332 | 281/237-8500 | 157 |
| Rhodes Middle Sch/San Antonio/Bexar | 00999279 | 210/978-7925 | 44 |
| Rhodes School-Lee/Houston/Harris | 11013872 | 281/458-4334 | 13 |
| Ricardo Elem Middle Sch/Kingsville/Kleberg | 01036387 | 361/592-6465 | 261 |
| Ricardo Estrada Middle Sch/El Paso/El Paso | 11561556 | 915/926-4800 | 137 |
| **RICARDO IND SCH DIST/KINGSVILLE/ KLEBERG** | 01036375 | 361/593-0703 | 261 |
| Ricardo Salinas Elem Sch/Universal Cty/ Bexar | 10754970 | 210/659-5045 | 37 |
| Rice Challenge Academy/Eagle Lake/Colorado | 12305642 | 979/234-3531 | 91 |
| **RICE CONS IND SCH DIST/ALTAIR/ COLORADO** | 01006784 | 979/234-3531 | 90 |
| Rice Elem Sch/Conroe/Montgomery | 01829469 | 936/709-2700 | 295 |
| Rice Elem Sch/Rice/Navarro | 01043653 | 903/326-4151 | 303 |
| Rice Elem Sch/Tyler/Smith | 01050931 | 903/262-2555 | 340 |
| Rice High Sch/Altair/Colorado | 01006825 | 979/234-3531 | 91 |
| Rice High Sch/Rice/Navarro | 04867769 | 903/326-4502 | 303 |
| **RICE IND SCH DIST/RICE/NAVARRO** | 01043641 | 903/326-4287 | 303 |
| Rice Intermediate Middle Sch/Rice/Navarro | 11552971 | 903/326-4190 | 303 |
| Rice Junior High Sch/Altair/Colorado | 11540057 | 979/234-3531 | 91 |
| Rice Sch/Houston/Harris | 04289923 | 713/349-1800 | 197 |
| Richard E Cavazos Elem Sch/Nolanville/Bell | 11449336 | 254/336-7000 | 31 |
| Richard J Lee Elem Sch/Irving/Dallas | 12035330 | 214/496-7900 | 102 |
| Richard J Wilson Elem Sch/Fort Worth/ Tarrant | 01053385 | 817/814-7700 | 354 |
| Richard King High Sch/Corp Christi/Nueces | 01044475 | 361/906-3400 | 307 |
| Richard Lagow Elem Sch/Dallas/Dallas | 01009669 | 972/749-6600 | 106 |
| Richard Milburn Acad-Amarillo/Amarillo/ Randall | 05011004 | 806/463-2284 | 13 |
| Richard Milburn Acad-CC/Corp Christi/ Nueces | 04892788 | 361/225-4424 | 13 |
| Richard Milburn Acad-Ft Worth/Fort Worth/ Tarrant | 05286584 | 817/731-7627 | 13 |
| Richard Milburn Acad-Houston/Houston/ Harris | 05286572 | 281/209-3505 | 13 |
| Richard Milburn Acad-Killeen/Killeen/Bell | 04893160 | 254/634-4444 | 13 |
| Richard Milburn Acad-Lubbock/Lubbock/ Lubbock | 04892790 | 806/740-0811 | 13 |
| Richard Milburn Acad-Midland/Midland/ Midland | 04892805 | 432/203-9829 | 13 |
| Richard Milburn Acad-Odessa/Odessa/Ector | 05286596 | 432/614-1859 | 13 |
| Richard Milburn Acad-Pasadena/Pasadena/ Harris | 12261072 | 832/730-4570 | 13 |
| Richard Moore Elem Sch/Houston/Harris | 01881895 | 713/740-0656 | 204 |
| **RICHARDS IND SCH DIST/RICHARDS/ GRIMES** | 01021459 | 936/851-2364 | 177 |
| Richards Independent Sch/Richards/Grimes | 01021461 | 936/851-2364 | 177 |
| Richards Young Women Leaders/Austin/Travis | 10907232 | 512/414-3236 | 371 |
| Richardson Classical Academy/Richardson/ Dallas | 12162969 | 972/479-9584 | 13 |
| Richardson Elem Sch/Dimmitt/Castro | 01005003 | 806/647-4131 | 75 |
| Richardson Heights Elem Sch/Richardson/ Dallas | 01011870 | 469/593-4400 | 117 |
| Richardson High Sch/Richardson/Dallas | 01011882 | 469/593-3000 | 117 |
| **RICHARDSON IND SCH DIST/ RICHARDSON/DALLAS** | 01011624 | 469/593-0000 | 116 |
| Richardson North Jr High Sch/Richardson/ Dallas | 01011909 | 469/593-5300 | 117 |
| Richardson Terrace Elem Sch/Richardson/ Dallas | 01011911 | 469/593-8700 | 117 |
| Richardson West Arts & Tech/Richardson/ Dallas | 01011923 | 469/593-3700 | 117 |
| Richey Elem Sch/Pasadena/Harris | 01026875 | 713/740-0712 | 204 |
| Richland Collegiate High Sch/Dallas/Dallas | 11014864 | 972/761-6888 | 13 |
| Richland Elem Sch/Richardson/Dallas | 01399684 | 469/593-4650 | 117 |
| Richland Elem Sch/Richland Hls/Tarrant | 01052159 | 817/547-2000 | 349 |
| Richland High Sch/N Richlnd Hls/Tarrant | 01052161 | 817/547-7000 | 349 |
| Richland Middle Sch/N Richlnd Hls/Tarrant | 01052163 | 817/547-4400 | 349 |
| **RICHLAND SPRINGS IND SCH DIST/ RICHLAND SPGS/SAN SABA** | 01049918 | 325/452-3524 | 335 |
| Richland Springs Sch/Richland Spgs/ San Saba | 01049920 | 325/452-3427 | 335 |
| Rick Ogden Elem Sch/Humble/Harris | 11555351 | 281/233-8901 | 185 |
| Rick Reedy High Sch/Frisco/Collin | 12106991 | 469/633-6400 | 83 |
| Rick Schneider Middle Sch/Houston/Harris | 10028991 | 713/740-0920 | 204 |
| Riddle Elem Sch/Plano/Collin | 05272612 | 469/633-3200 | 83 |
| Rider High Sch/Wichita Falls/Wichita | 01173179 | 940/235-1077 | 395 |
| Ridge Creek Elem Sch/Humble/Harris | 11925081 | 281/641-3700 | 201 |
| Ridge Point High Sch/Missouri City/ Fort Bend | 11561908 | 281/327-5200 | 155 |
| Ridgecrest Elem Sch/Amarillo/Potter | 01047427 | 806/326-5100 | 321 |
| Ridgecrest Elem Sch/Houston/Harris | 01027257 | 713/251-6600 | 206 |
| Ridgegate Elem Sch/Houston/Fort Bend | 02126399 | 281/634-4840 | 155 |
| Ridgemont Early Literacy Ctr/Houston/ Fort Bend | 12371653 | 281/634-9810 | 155 |
| Ridgemont Elem Sch/Houston/Fort Bend | 01018191 | 281/634-4880 | 155 |
| Ridgetop Elem Sch/Austin/Travis | 01056595 | 512/414-4469 | 370 |
| Ridgeview Elem Sch/Keller/Tarrant | 11710329 | 817/744-6600 | 358 |
| Ridgeview Elem Sch/San Antonio/Bexar | 00997908 | 210/407-6600 | 38 |
| Ridgeview Middle Sch/Round Rock/Williamson | 04938875 | 512/424-8400 | 402 |
| Ridgewood Elem Sch/Port Neches/Jefferson | 01034016 | 409/722-7641 | 247 |
| Ridglea Hills Elem Sch/Fort Worth/Tarrant | 01053294 | 817/815-1700 | 354 |
| Riesel High Sch/Riesel/McLennan | 01040027 | 254/896-3171 | 284 |
| **RIESEL IND SCH DIST/RIESEL/ McLENNAN** | 01040003 | 254/896-6411 | 284 |
| Ringgold Elem Sch/Rio Grande Cy/Starr | 01051181 | 956/716-6929 | 343 |
| Ringgold Middle Sch/Rio Grande Cy/Starr | 01051167 | 956/716-6851 | 343 |
| Rio Bravo Middle Sch/El Paso/El Paso | 04754435 | 915/434-8400 | 142 |
| Rio Grande City High Sch/Rio Grande Cy/ Starr | 01051193 | 956/488-6000 | 343 |
| **RIO GRANDE CITY IND SCH DIST/ RIO GRANDE CY/STARR** | 01051117 | 956/716-6700 | 342 |
| Rio Hondo Elem Sch/Rio Hondo/Cameron | 01004114 | 956/748-1050 | 70 |
| Rio Hondo High Sch/Rio Hondo/Cameron | 01004126 | 956/748-1200 | 70 |
| **RIO HONDO IND SCH DIST/RIO HONDO/ CAMERON** | 01004102 | 956/748-1000 | 70 |
| Rio Hondo Middle Sch/Rio Hondo/Cameron | 01004138 | 956/748-1150 | 70 |
| Rio Vista Elem Sch/Rio Vista/Johnson | 03047198 | 817/373-2151 | 251 |
| Rio Vista High Sch/Rio Vista/Johnson | 01035149 | 817/373-2009 | 251 |
| **RIO VISTA IND SCH DIST/RIO VISTA/ JOHNSON** | 01035137 | 817/373-2241 | 251 |
| Rio Vista Middle Sch/Rio Vista/Johnson | 03246540 | 817/760-0766 | 252 |
| Riojas Elem Sch/Pflugerville/Travis | 11548542 | 512/594-4100 | 374 |
| Ripley House Middle Sch/Houston/Harris | 11827790 | 713/315-6429 | 13 |
| Risd Academy/Dallas/Dallas | 03010755 | 469/593-3300 | 117 |
| Rise Academy/Lubbock/Lubbock | 04892817 | 806/744-0438 | 13 |
| Rise Academy/Tyler/Smith | 04808579 | 903/262-3040 | 340 |
| Rise School of Austin/Austin/Travis | 05313785 | 512/891-1682 | 376 |
| Rise School of Dallas/Dallas/Dallas | 05378163 | 214/373-7473 | 120 |
| Rising Scholars Acad of S TX/San Benito/ Cameron | 12104589 | 956/399-4358 | 71 |
| Rising Star Elem Sch/Rising Star/Eastland | 01014523 | 254/643-2431 | 133 |
| Rising Star High Sch/Rising Star/Eastland | 01014535 | 254/643-3521 | 133 |
| **RISING STAR IND SCH DIST/ RISING STAR/EASTLAND** | 01014511 | 254/643-1981 | 133 |
| Rita Drabek Elem Sch/Sugar Land/Fort Bend | 04947929 | 281/634-6570 | 155 |
| Rita Smith Elem Sch/Wylie/Collin | 10915693 | 972/429-2540 | 89 |
| River Bend Elem Sch/College Sta/Brazos | 12363591 | 979/694-5841 | 59 |
| River City Believers Academy/Selma/ Guadalupe | 12052039 | 210/656-2999 | 179 |
| River City Christian Sch/San Antonio/Bexar | 11225570 | 210/384-0297 | 48 |
| River Oaks Academy/Houston/Harris | 11238424 | 713/783-7200 | 212 |
| River Oaks Baptist Sch/Houston/Harris | 01480350 | 713/623-6938 | 212 |
| River Oaks Elem Sch/Austin/Travis | 04035825 | 512/594-5000 | 374 |
| River Oaks Elem Sch/Houston/Harris | 01418436 | 713/942-1460 | 199 |
| River Pines Elem Sch/Humble/Harris | 10911544 | 281/641-3300 | 201 |
| River Place Elem Sch/Austin/Williamson | 10914338 | 512/570-6900 | 400 |
| River Ridge Elem Sch/Austin/Williamson | 11450995 | 512/570-7300 | 400 |
| River Road High Sch/Amarillo/Potter | 01047611 | 806/383-8867 | 322 |
| **RIVER ROAD IND SCH DIST/ AMARILLO/POTTER** | 01047609 | 806/381-7800 | 322 |
| River Road Middle Sch/Amarillo/Potter | 01047635 | 806/383-8721 | 322 |
| River Trails Elem Sch/Fort Worth/Tarrant | 05097046 | 817/285-3235 | 356 |
| River Valley Intermediate Sch/Mc Gregor/ McLennan | 11567299 | 254/761-5699 | 284 |
| Rivera Elem Sch/El Paso/El Paso | 01418292 | 915/236-3700 | 138 |
| Riverchase Elem Sch/Coppell/Dallas | 04920311 | 972/968-2900 | 101 |
| Rivercrest Elem Sch/Bogata/Red River | 01048225 | 903/632-5214 | 325 |
| Rivercrest High Sch/Bogata/Red River | 01048237 | 903/632-5204 | 325 |
| **RIVERCREST IND SCH DIST/ BOGATA/RED RIVER** | 01048213 | 903/632-5203 | 325 |

| School/City/County DISTRICT/CITY/COUNTY | PID | TELEPHONE NUMBER | PAGE |
|---|---|---|---|
| Rivercrest Junior High Sch/Bogata/ Red River | 01048249 | 903/632-5204 | 325 |
| Riverside Applied Lrng Center/Fort Worth/ Tarrant | 01052604 | 817/815-5800 | 354 |
| Riverside High Sch/El Paso/El Paso | 01016571 | 915/434-7000 | 142 |
| Riverside Middle Sch/El Paso/El Paso | 01016583 | 915/434-7300 | 142 |
| Riverside Middle Sch/Fort Worth/Tarrant | 01053323 | 817/814-9200 | 354 |
| Riverside Middle Sch/San Benito/Cameron | 10031924 | 956/361-6940 | 70 |
| Riverside Park Academy/San Antonio/Bexar | 00999281 | 210/228-3355 | 44 |
| Rivertree Academy/Fort Worth/Tarrant | 12363395 | 817/420-9310 | 362 |
| Riverwood Middle Sch/Kingwood/Harris | 03394719 | 281/641-4800 | 201 |
| **RIVIERA IND SCH DIST/RIVIERA/ KLEBERG** | 01036399 | 361/296-3101 | 261 |
| Roan Forest Elem Sch/San Antonio/Bexar | 05101544 | 210/407-6800 | 38 |
| Roanoke Elem Sch/Roanoke/Denton | 01013579 | 817/215-0650 | 129 |
| Roark Elem Sch/Arlington/Tarrant | 01051882 | 682/867-2900 | 347 |
| Robb Elem Sch/Uvalde/Uvalde | 01057848 | 830/591-4947 | 381 |
| Robbie E Howard Jr High Sch/Waxahachie/ Ellis | 11131979 | 972/923-4771 | 147 |
| Robbin E L Washington Elem Sch/El Paso/ El Paso | 04948313 | 915/434-5900 | 142 |
| Robert & Felice Bryant ES/Katy/Harris | 12231285 | 281/234-4300 | 157 |
| Robert B Green Academy/San Antonio/Bexar | 00999293 | 210/228-3325 | 44 |
| Robert Brabham Middle Sch/Willis/ Montgomery | 05351684 | 936/890-2312 | 297 |
| Robert Cobb Middle Sch/Frisco/Collin | 11558339 | 469/633-4300 | 83 |
| Robert Driscoll Jr Elem Sch/Robstown/ Nueces | 01044932 | 361/767-6641 | 308 |
| Robert E King Elem Sch/Katy/Harris | 04948739 | 281/237-6850 | 157 |
| Robert E Lee Elem Sch/Eagle Pass/Maverick | 01041124 | 830/758-7062 | 280 |
| Robert E Lee Elem Sch/Edinburg/Hidalgo | 01029762 | 956/289-2342 | 222 |
| Robert E Lee Freshman High Sch/Midland/ Midland | 01041447 | 432/689-1250 | 289 |
| Robert E Lee High Sch/Baytown/Harris | 01023718 | 281/420-4535 | 193 |
| Robert E Lee Intermediate Sch/Gainesville/ Cooke | 04752671 | 940/668-6662 | 95 |
| Robert E Lee Sr High Sch/Midland/Midland | 01041617 | 432/689-1600 | 289 |
| Robert F Hunt Elem Sch/Diana/Upshur | 04034376 | 903/663-8004 | 379 |
| Robert F Koennecke Elem Sch/Seguin/ Guadalupe | 03009914 | 830/401-8741 | 179 |
| Robert G Cole Jr/Sr High Sch/San Antonio/ Bexar | 11074890 | 210/368-8730 | 35 |
| Robert L Crippen Elem Sch/Porter/ Montgomery | 04450653 | 281/577-8740 | 297 |
| Robert L Stevenson Primary Sch/Alvin/ Brazoria | 01534121 | 281/585-3349 | 54 |
| Robert L Thornton Elem Sch/Dallas/Dallas | 01009657 | 972/794-8000 | 106 |
| **ROBERT LEE IND SCH DIST/ ROBERT LEE/COKE** | 01005780 | 325/453-4555 | 79 |
| Robert Lee Sch/Robert Lee/Coke | 01005792 | 325/453-4555 | 79 |
| Robert M Beren Academy/Houston/Harris | 01027790 | 713/723-7170 | 212 |
| Robert M Shoemaker High Sch/Killeen/Bell | 04368804 | 254/336-0900 | 31 |
| Robert R Rojas Elem Sch/El Paso/El Paso | 03009835 | 915/937-8500 | 141 |
| Robert R Shaw Ctr for Steam/Katy/Harris | 12239457 | 281/396-7652 | 157 |
| Robert S Hyer Elem Sch/Dallas/Dallas | 01011088 | 214/780-3300 | 112 |
| Robert T Hill Middle Sch/Dallas/Dallas | 01009700 | 972/502-5700 | 106 |
| Robert Vela High Sch/Edinburg/Hidalgo | 11822910 | 956/289-2650 | 222 |
| Roberta Rylander Elem Sch/Katy/Harris | 05344344 | 281/237-8300 | 157 |
| Roberta Tipps Elem Sch/Mansfield/Tarrant | 05273642 | 817/299-6920 | 359 |
| Roberts Elem Sch/Bay City/Matagorda | 01040869 | 979/401-1500 | 278 |
| Roberts Elem Sch/El Paso/El Paso | 01016604 | 915/236-3775 | 138 |
| Roberts Elem Sch/Houston/Harris | 01024944 | 713/295-5272 | 199 |
| Roberts Middle Sch/Fulshear/Fort Bend | 12364129 | 832/223-5300 | 158 |
| Roberts Road Elem Sch/Hockley/Waller | 02896178 | 936/931-0300 | 387 |
| Robertson Elem Sch/Little Elm/Collin | 10912706 | 469/633-3675 | 83 |
| Robindell Private Sch/Houston/Harris | 01480300 | 713/667-9895 | 212 |
| Robinson Elem Sch/Robinson/McLennan | 03319501 | 254/662-5000 | 284 |
| Robinson High Sch/Robinson/McLennan | 01040053 | 254/662-3840 | 284 |
| **ROBINSON IND SCH DIST/ROBINSON/ MCLENNAN** | 01040039 | 254/662-0194 | 284 |
| Robinson Intermediate Sch/Robinson/ McLennan | 04939374 | 254/662-6113 | 284 |
| Robinson Junior High Sch/Robinson/McLennan | 01040065 | 254/662-3843 | 284 |
| Robinson Middle Sch/Plano/Collin | 04145391 | 469/752-6200 | 87 |
| Robinson Primary Sch/Robinson/McLennan | 01040041 | 254/662-0251 | 284 |
| Robstown High Sch/Robstown/Nueces | 01044944 | 361/387-5999 | 308 |
| **ROBSTOWN IND SCH DIST/ROBSTOWN/ NUECES** | 01044906 | 361/767-6600 | 308 |
| **ROBY CONS IND SCH DIST/ROBY/ FISHER** | 01017886 | 325/776-2222 | 152 |
| Roby Elem Sch/Roby/Fisher | 01017903 | 325/776-2222 | 152 |
| Roby High Sch/Roby/Fisher | 04914544 | 325/776-2223 | 152 |

| School/City/County DISTRICT/CITY/COUNTY | PID | TELEPHONE NUMBER | PAGE |
|---|---|---|---|
| **ROCHELLE IND SCH DIST/ROCHELLE/ MCCULLOCH** | 01039509 | 325/243-5224 | 281 |
| Rochelle Sch/Rochelle/McCulloch | 01039511 | 325/243-5224 | 281 |
| Rock Hill High Sch/Frisco/Collin | 12468098 | 469/219-2300 | 88 |
| Rock Prairie Elem Sch/College Sta/Brazos | 03236399 | 979/764-5570 | 59 |
| Rockbrook Elem Sch/Lewisville/Denton | 05271852 | 469/713-5968 | 128 |
| Rockdale Elem Sch/Rockdale/Milam | 01041863 | 512/430-6030 | 291 |
| Rockdale High Sch/Rockdale/Milam | 01041875 | 512/430-6140 | 291 |
| **ROCKDALE IND SCH DIST/ROCKDALE/ MILAM** | 01041851 | 512/430-6000 | 290 |
| Rockdale Intermediate Sch/Rockdale/Milam | 11540631 | 512/430-6200 | 291 |
| Rockdale Junior High Sch/Rockdale/Milam | 01041887 | 512/430-6100 | 291 |
| Rockenbaugh Elem Sch/Southlake/Tarrant | 04747315 | 817/949-4700 | 349 |
| Rockport-Fulton High Sch/Rockport/Aransas | 00995168 | 361/790-2220 | 22 |
| Rockport-Fulton Middle Sch/Rockport/ Aransas | 00995170 | 361/790-2230 | 22 |
| **ROCKSPRINGS IND SCH DIST/ ROCKSPRINGS/EDWARDS** | 01014901 | 830/683-4137 | 135 |
| Rocksprings Sch/Rocksprings/Edwards | 01014913 | 830/683-2140 | 135 |
| Rockwall High Sch/Rockwall/Rockwall | 01048732 | 972/771-7339 | 328 |
| **ROCKWALL IND SCH DIST/ROCKWALL/ ROCKWALL** | 01048718 | 972/771-0605 | 328 |
| Rockwall Quest Academy/Rockwall/Rockwall | 04364080 | 972/772-2077 | 328 |
| Rockwall-Heath High Sch/Heath/Rockwall | 10012693 | 972/772-2474 | 328 |
| Rodeo Palms Junior High Sch/Manvel/ Brazoria | 01001459 | 281/245-2078 | 54 |
| Rodger & Ellen Beck Jr HS/Katy/Harris | 04452259 | 281/237-3300 | 157 |
| Rodolfo Centeno Elem Sch/Laredo/Webb | 05350692 | 956/473-8800 | 391 |
| Rodriguez Elem Sch/Austin/Travis | 04869858 | 512/841-7200 | 370 |
| Rodriguez Elem Sch/Harlingen/Cameron | 05343338 | 956/430-4060 | 68 |
| Rodriguez Elem Sch/San Marcos/Hays | 12380472 | 512/757-8490 | 217 |
| Rodriguez Middle Sch/Aubrey/Denton | 12305616 | 972/347-7050 | 125 |
| Rodriguez Montessori Elem Sch/San Antonio/ Bexar | 12471423 | 210/438-6873 | 44 |
| Roel & Celia Saenz Elem Sch/Roma/Starr | 11072232 | 956/849-7230 | 343 |
| Rogene Worley Middle Sch/Mansfield/Tarrant | 01172620 | 682/314-5100 | 359 |
| Roger E Sides Elem Sch/Karnes City/Karnes | 01035424 | 830/780-2321 | 254 |
| Rogers Elem Sch/Rogers/Bell | 00996655 | 254/642-3250 | 32 |
| Rogers High Sch/Rogers/Bell | 00996667 | 254/642-3224 | 32 |
| **ROGERS IND SCH DIST/ROGERS/BELL** | 00996643 | 254/642-3802 | 32 |
| Rogers Middle Sch/Pearland/Brazoria | 05271723 | 832/736-6400 | 57 |
| Rogers Middle Sch/Prosper/Collin | 04920672 | 469/219-2150 | 88 |
| Rogers Middle Sch/Rogers/Bell | 04365125 | 254/642-3011 | 32 |
| Rogers Middle Sch/San Antonio/Bexar | 00998811 | 210/438-6840 | 44 |
| Roland Reynolds Elem Sch/Franklin/ Robertson | 01048639 | 979/828-7300 | 327 |
| Rolling Hills Elem Sch/Amarillo/Potter | 01047623 | 806/383-8621 | 322 |
| Rolling Hills Elem Sch/Lancaster/Dallas | 03240417 | 972/218-1525 | 114 |
| Rolling Meadows Elem Sch/San Antonio/Bexar | 11561570 | 210/945-5700 | 37 |
| Roma High Sch/Roma/Starr | 01051272 | 956/849-1333 | 343 |
| **ROMA IND SCH DIST/ROMA/STARR** | 01051222 | 956/849-1377 | 343 |
| Roma Instructional Sch/Roma/Starr | 04365333 | 956/849-2803 | 343 |
| Roma Middle Sch/Roma/Starr | 01051284 | 956/849-1434 | 343 |
| Romulo Martinez Elem Sch/Mission/Hidalgo | 04918722 | 956/584-4900 | 228 |
| Ronald E McNair Elem Sch/Dallas/Dallas | 03018692 | 972/794-6200 | 106 |
| Ronald E McNair Middle Sch/Atascosa/Bexar | 00999633 | 210/622-4480 | 46 |
| Ronald Reagan Elem Sch/Cedar Park/ Williamson | 11450971 | 512/570-7200 | 400 |
| Ronald Reagan High Sch/San Antonio/Bexar | 04865876 | 210/356-1800 | 38 |
| Ronald Reagan Middle Sch/Grand Prairie/ Dallas | 05342633 | 972/522-7300 | 112 |
| Ronald Thornton Middle Sch/Missouri City/ Fort Bend | 12312011 | 281/327-3870 | 155 |
| Ronnie Crownover Middle Sch/Corinth/Denton | 05096432 | 940/369-4700 | 125 |
| Roosevelt Alexander Elem Sch/Katy/Harris | 04803646 | 281/237-7100 | 157 |
| Roosevelt Alt Sch/Mission/Hidalgo | 03393521 | 956/323-3900 | 225 |
| Roosevelt Elem Sch/Houston/Harris | 01026069 | 713/696-2820 | 197 |
| Roosevelt Elem Sch/Laredo/Webb | 04455938 | 956/473-3400 | 391 |
| Roosevelt Elem Sch/Lubbock/Lubbock | 01039121 | 806/842-3284 | 274 |
| Roosevelt Elem Sch/San Antonio/Bexar | 10007167 | 210/444-8375 | 35 |
| Roosevelt High Sch/Lubbock/Lubbock | 01039145 | 806/842-3283 | 274 |
| Roosevelt High Sch/Windcrest/Bexar | 00997934 | 210/356-2200 | 38 |
| **ROOSEVELT IND SCH DIST/LUBBOCK/ LUBBOCK** | 01039119 | 806/842-3282 | 274 |
| Roosevelt Junior High Sch/Lubbock/Lubbock | 04917869 | 806/842-3218 | 274 |
| Roosevelt-Wilson Elem Sch/Texas City/ Galveston | 01019559 | 409/916-0200 | 166 |
| Rooster Springs Elem Sch/Austin/Hays | 10904981 | 512/465-6200 | 216 |
| **ROPES IND SCH DIST/ROPESVILLE/ HOCKLEY** | 01031234 | 806/562-4031 | 232 |
| Ropes Sch/Ropesville/Hockley | 01031246 | 806/562-4031 | 232 |

| School/City/County DISTRICT/CITY/COUNTY | PID | TELEPHONE NUMBER | PAGE |
|---|---|---|---|
| Roque Guerra Jr Elem Sch/Rio Grande Cy/ Starr | 01051210 | 956/716-6982 | 343 |
| Rosa Guerrero Elem Sch/El Paso/El Paso | 04035679 | 915/236-3075 | 138 |
| Rosa Parks Elem Sch/Fresno/Fort Bend | 10912885 | 281/634-6390 | 155 |
| Rosa Parks-Millbrook Sch/Lancaster/Dallas | 02896788 | 972/218-1564 | 114 |
| Rosanky Christian Academy/Rosanky/Bastrop | 11229617 | 512/360-3109 | 27 |
| Roscoe Collegiate High Sch/Roscoe/Nolan | 01043902 | 325/766-3327 | 304 |
| **ROSCOE COLLEGIATE IND SCH DIST/ ROSCOE/NOLAN** | 01043885 | 325/766-3629 | 304 |
| Roscoe Collegiate Mont ECC/Roscoe/Nolan | 12232605 | 325/766-3323 | 304 |
| Roscoe Elem Sch/Roscoe/Nolan | 01043897 | 325/766-3323 | 304 |
| Roscoe Wilson Elem Sch/Lubbock/Lubbock | 01038866 | 806/219-7500 | 273 |
| Rose Garden Elem Sch/Schertz/Guadalupe | 01021590 | 210/619-4350 | 178 |
| Rose Haggar Elem Sch/Dallas/Collin | 04366789 | 469/752-1400 | 87 |
| Rose M Avalos P-Tech Sch/Houston/Harris | 12365616 | 281/985-2100 | 185 |
| Rosebud-Lott Elem Sch/Lott/Falls | 01017290 | 254/583-7965 | 149 |
| Rosebud-Lott High Sch/Lott/Falls | 11565461 | 254/583-7967 | 149 |
| **ROSEBUD-LOTT IND SCH DIST/ LOTT/FALLS** | 01017276 | 254/583-4510 | 149 |
| Rosebud-Lott Middle Sch/Lott/Falls | 01017317 | 254/583-7962 | 149 |
| Rosedale Sch/Austin/Travis | 02127848 | 512/414-3617 | 370 |
| Rosehill Christian Sch/Tomball/Harris | 04466535 | 281/351-8114 | 212 |
| Rosehill Elem Sch/Tomball/Harris | 05279373 | 281/357-3075 | 208 |
| Rosemeade Elem Sch/Carrollton/Dallas | 02227905 | 972/968-3000 | 101 |
| Rosemont 6th Grade Center/Fort Worth/ Tarrant | 04866222 | 817/814-7300 | 354 |
| Rosemont Elem & Prep Lang MS/Dallas/Dallas | 01009712 | 972/749-5000 | 106 |
| Rosemont Elem Sch/Fort Worth/Tarrant | 11711880 | 817/815-5200 | 354 |
| Rosemont Middle Sch/Fort Worth/Tarrant | 01053347 | 817/814-7200 | 354 |
| Rosemont Primary Sch/Dallas/Dallas | 10006797 | 972/502-3850 | 106 |
| Rosenberg Elem Sch/Galveston/Galveston | 11451078 | 409/761-6800 | 165 |
| Rosendo Benavides Elem Sch/Sullivan City/ Hidalgo | 02202876 | 956/323-2360 | 223 |
| Rosewood Head Start Center/Wichita Falls/ Wichita | 05364552 | 940/235-4309 | 395 |
| Rosita Valley Elem Sch/Eagle Pass/Maverick | 04021692 | 830/758-7065 | 280 |
| Rosita Valley Literacy Academy/Eagle Pass/ Maverick | 04806911 | 830/758-7067 | 280 |
| Ross Baldwin Elem Sch/Austin/Travis | 11552555 | 512/841-8900 | 370 |
| Ross Elem Sch/Houston/Harris | 01025792 | 713/226-4550 | 196 |
| Ross Elem Sch/Odessa/Ector | 01014810 | 432/456-1199 | 135 |
| Ross Middle Sch/El Paso/El Paso | 01015670 | 915/236-0800 | 139 |
| Ross S Sterling High Sch/Baytown/Harris | 01023720 | 281/420-4500 | 193 |
| Ross Sterling Middle Sch/Humble/Harris | 10911532 | 281/641-6000 | 201 |
| Rotan Elem Sch/Rotan/Fisher | 01017927 | 325/735-3182 | 152 |
| Rotan High Sch/Rotan/Fisher | 01017939 | 325/735-3041 | 152 |
| **ROTAN IND SCH DIST/ROTAN/FISHER** | 01017915 | 325/735-2332 | 152 |
| Roth Elem Sch/Spring/Harris | 02227163 | 832/484-6600 | 202 |
| Round Rock Christian Academy/Round Rock/ Williamson | 02785165 | 512/255-4491 | 403 |
| Round Rock High Sch/Round Rock/Williamson | 01061124 | 512/464-6000 | 402 |
| **ROUND ROCK IND SCH DIST/ ROUND ROCK/WILLIAMSON** | 01061083 | 512/464-5000 | 401 |
| Round Rock Opportunity Center/Round Rock/ Williamson | 02949476 | 512/428-2900 | 402 |
| Round Top Carmine Elem Sch/Round Top/ Fayette | 01017783 | 979/249-3200 | 152 |
| Round Top Carmine High Sch/Carmine/Fayette | 01017795 | 979/278-3252 | 152 |
| **ROUND TOP-CARMINE IND SCH DIST/ CARMINE/FAYETTE** | 01017771 | 979/278-3252 | 151 |
| Rouse High Sch/Leander/Williamson | 11130781 | 512/570-2000 | 400 |
| Routh Roach Elem Sch/Garland/Dallas | 01010668 | 972/926-2580 | 110 |
| Rowe Lane Elem Sch/Pflugerville/Travis | 10006852 | 512/594-6600 | 375 |
| Rowe Middle Sch/Cypress/Harris | 12471502 | 346/227-6220 | 190 |
| Rowland Elem Sch/Victoria/Victoria | 01058567 | 361/788-9549 | 385 |
| Rowlett Elem Sch/Rowlett/Dallas | 01010670 | 972/475-3380 | 110 |
| Rowlett High Sch/Rowlett/Dallas | 04450988 | 972/463-1712 | 110 |
| Roy Cisneros Elem Sch/San Antonio/Bexar | 00997130 | 210/444-7850 | 35 |
| Roy J Smith Middle Sch/Killeen/Bell | 12225949 | 254/336-1050 | 31 |
| Roy J Wollam Elem Sch/Santa Fe/Galveston | 02897134 | 409/925-2770 | 165 |
| Roy Lee Walker Elem Sch/McKinney/Collin | 04920701 | 469/302-4600 | 85 |
| Roy P Benavidez Elem Sch/San Antonio/Bexar | 00999401 | 210/977-7175 | 46 |
| Roy Roberts Elem Sch/Lubbock/Lubbock | 10911025 | 806/219-7900 | 273 |
| Royal Early Childhood Center/Brookshire/ Waller | 03393686 | 281/934-3181 | 387 |
| Royal Elem Sch/Brookshire/Waller | 01058828 | 281/934-3166 | 387 |
| Royal High Sch/Brookshire/Waller | 01058842 | 281/934-2215 | 387 |
| **ROYAL IND SCH DIST/PATTISON/ WALLER** | 01058816 | 281/934-2248 | 387 |
| Royal Junior High Sch/Brookshire/Waller | 01058830 | 281/934-2241 | 387 |
| Royal Point Academy/San Antonio/Bexar | 04993825 | 210/674-5310 | 48 |
| Royal Ridge Elem Sch/San Antonio/Bexar | 05118975 | 210/407-7000 | 38 |
| Royalwood Elem Sch/Houston/Harris | 01027051 | 281/454-2700 | 205 |
| Royse City High Sch/Royse City/Rockwall | 01048794 | 972/636-9991 | 329 |
| **ROYSE CITY IND SCH DIST/ ROYSE CITY/ROCKWALL** | 01048770 | 972/636-2413 | 328 |
| Royse City Middle Sch/Royse City/Rockwall | 01048782 | 972/636-9544 | 329 |
| Rspa Northeast-Humble/Humble/Harris | 12361505 | 281/319-9300 | 13 |
| Rspa Northshore/Houston/Harris | 12361517 | 281/459-9797 | 13 |
| Rspa Northwest-Living Word/Houston/Harris | 12261216 | 832/562-2822 | 13 |
| Rspa-Channelview/Channelview/Harris | 12261228 | 281/864-7015 | 13 |
| Rspa-E Northshore/Houston/Harris | 11933832 | 281/459-9797 | 13 |
| Rspa-NE Humble/Humble/Harris | 12261204 | 281/319-9300 | 13 |
| Ruben Chavira Elem Sch/Del Rio/Val Verde | 03009598 | 830/778-4660 | 382 |
| Ruben Hinojosa Elem Sch/Mercedes/Hidalgo | 01030151 | 956/514-2277 | 225 |
| Ruben Rodriguez Elem Sch/Edcouch/Hidalgo | 02857005 | 956/262-4712 | 221 |
| Rubicon Academy/The Woodlands/Montgomery | 04932431 | 936/273-9111 | 298 |
| Ruby Shaw Elem Sch/Mesquite/Dallas | 02201884 | 972/882-7060 | 116 |
| Ruby Sue Clifton Middle Sch/Houston/Harris | 02043292 | 713/613-2516 | 197 |
| Ruby Thompson Elem Sch/Houston/Harris | 01024994 | 713/746-8250 | 198 |
| Ruby Young Elem Sch/Desoto/Dallas | 01010280 | 972/223-6505 | 108 |
| Rucker Elem Sch/Houston/Harris | 01025687 | 713/845-7467 | 195 |
| Rudy Silva Elem Sch/Weslaco/Hidalgo | 01030618 | 956/969-6790 | 228 |
| Rufino Mendoza Elem Sch/Fort Worth/Tarrant | 01052769 | 817/814-4700 | 354 |
| Rufus C Burleson Elem Sch/Dallas/Dallas | 01008574 | 972/749-4500 | 106 |
| **RULE IND SCH DIST/RULE/HASKELL** | 01028964 | 940/997-2521 | 215 |
| Rule Sch/Rule/Haskell | 01028976 | 940/997-2521 | 215 |
| Rummel Creek Elem Sch/Houston/Harris | 01027269 | 713/251-6700 | 206 |
| **RUNGE IND SCH DIST/RUNGE/KARNES** | 01035503 | 830/239-4315 | 254 |
| Runge Sch/Runge/Karnes | 01035515 | 830/239-4315 | 254 |
| Runn Elem Sch/Donna/Hidalgo | 01029619 | 956/464-1864 | 220 |
| Running Brushy Middle Sch/Cedar Park/ Williamson | 04915809 | 512/570-3300 | 400 |
| Runyan Elem Sch/Conroe/Montgomery | 01042520 | 936/709-2800 | 295 |
| Rush Elem Sch/Lubbock/Lubbock | 01038880 | 806/219-6700 | 273 |
| Rushing Middle Sch/Prosper/Collin | 12469705 | 469/219-2370 | 88 |
| Rusk Elem Sch/El Paso/El Paso | 01015682 | 915/236-0475 | 138 |
| Rusk Elem Sch/Midland/Midland | 01041629 | 432/240-7800 | 289 |
| Rusk Elem Sch/Rusk/Cherokee | 01005376 | 903/683-2595 | 77 |
| Rusk High Sch/Rusk/Cherokee | 01005388 | 903/683-5401 | 77 |
| **RUSK IND SCH DIST/RUSK/CHEROKEE** | 01005364 | 903/683-5592 | 77 |
| Rusk Intermediate Sch/Rusk/Cherokee | 05341859 | 903/683-1726 | 77 |
| Rusk Junior High Sch/Rusk/Cherokee | 01005390 | 903/683-2502 | 77 |
| Rusk Primary Sch/Rusk/Cherokee | 02130194 | 903/683-6106 | 77 |
| Russell Elem Sch/Brownsville/Cameron | 01003689 | 956/548-8960 | 68 |
| Russell Lee Elem Sch/Austin/Travis | 01056600 | 512/414-2098 | 370 |
| Russell Schupmann Elem Sch/Glenn Heights/ Ellis | 02894003 | 972/617-2685 | 146 |
| Rustic Oak Elem Sch/Pearland/Brazoria | 04033891 | 281/482-5400 | 57 |
| Ruth Borchardt Elem Sch/Plano/Collin | 04942826 | 469/633-2800 | 83 |
| Ruth Cherry Interm Sch/Royse City/Rockwall | 11462443 | 972/636-3301 | 329 |
| Ruth Dowell Middle Sch/McKinney/Collin | 01006318 | 469/302-6700 | 85 |
| Ruth Jones McClendon Mid Sch/San Antonio/ Bexar | 12261412 | 210/568-8800 | 13 |
| Rutledge Elem Sch/Austin/Williamson | 10006890 | 512/570-6500 | 400 |

## S

| | | | |
|---|---|---|---|
| S & S Cons High Sch/Sadler/Grayson | 01020584 | 903/564-3768 | 172 |
| **S & S CONS IND SCH DIST/ SADLER/GRAYSON** | 01020560 | 903/564-6051 | 172 |
| S & S Cons Middle Sch/Sadler/Grayson | 02857184 | 903/564-7626 | 172 |
| S & S Elem Sch/Southmayd/Grayson | 01020572 | 903/893-0767 | 172 |
| S C Lee Junior High Sch/Copperas Cove/ Coryell | 04452041 | 254/542-7877 | 96 |
| S C Red Elem Sch/Houston/Harris | 01025340 | 713/726-3638 | 199 |
| S H Crowley Intermediate Sch/Crowley/ Tarrant | 11079711 | 817/297-5960 | 350 |
| S M Seabourn Elem Sch/Mesquite/Dallas | 01011583 | 972/882-7040 | 116 |
| S S Conner Elem Sch/Dallas/Dallas | 01009798 | 972/749-8200 | 106 |
| S S Dillow Elem Sch/Fort Worth/Tarrant | 01052800 | 817/814-0400 | 354 |
| S W Carter Elem Sch/Shelbyville/Shelby | 01050400 | 936/598-7363 | 337 |
| Sabas Perez Eng & Tech Sch/Laredo/Webb | 05347968 | 956/795-3800 | 390 |
| Sabinal Elem Sch/Sabinal/Uvalde | 01057745 | 830/988-2436 | 380 |
| Sabinal High Sch/Sabinal/Uvalde | 01057757 | 830/988-2475 | 380 |
| **SABINAL IND SCH DIST/SABINAL/ UVALDE** | 01057733 | 830/988-2472 | 380 |
| Sabine Elem Sch/Kilgore/Gregg | 01021227 | 903/984-5320 | 175 |
| Sabine High Sch/Gladewater/Gregg | 01021239 | 903/984-8587 | 175 |
| **SABINE IND SCH DIST/GLADEWATER/ GREGG** | 01021215 | 903/984-8564 | 175 |
| Sabine Middle Sch/Gladewater/Gregg | 01021241 | 903/984-4767 | 175 |
| **SABINE PASS IND SCH DIST/ SABINE PASS/JEFFERSON** | 01034066 | 409/971-2321 | 247 |
| Sabine Pass Sch/Sabine Pass/Jefferson | 01034078 | 409/971-2321 | 247 |

| School/City/County DISTRICT/CITY/COUNTY | PID | TELEPHONE NUMBER | PAGE |
|---|---|---|---|
| Sachse High Sch/Sachse/Dallas | 05096793 | 972/414-7450 | 110 |
| Sacred Heart Catholic Sch/Floresville/ Wilson | 01000027 | 830/393-2117 | 404 |
| Sacred Heart Catholic Sch/Hallettsville/ Lavaca | 00999994 | 361/798-5349 | 265 |
| Sacred Heart Catholic Sch/La Grange/ Fayette | 01002893 | 979/968-3223 | 152 |
| Sacred Heart Sch/Conroe/Montgomery | 01028146 | 936/756-3848 | 298 |
| Sacred Heart Sch/Crosby/Harris | 01028158 | 281/328-6561 | 209 |
| Sacred Heart Sch/Del Rio/Val Verde | 00999982 | 830/775-3274 | 382 |
| Sacred Heart Sch/Muenster/Cooke | 01054432 | 940/759-2511 | 96 |
| Sacred Heart Sch/Rockport/Aransas | 02136942 | 361/729-2672 | 22 |
| Sacred Heart Sch/Uvalde/Uvalde | 01000015 | 830/278-2661 | 381 |
| Sadie Woodard Elem Sch/Cypress/Harris | 12105167 | 281/373-2303 | 190 |
| Saegert Elem Sch/Killeen/Bell | 10030724 | 254/336-6660 | 31 |
| Saenz Elem Sch/Alice/Jim Wells | 01034573 | 361/664-4981 | 248 |
| Sagamore Hill Elem Sch/Fort Worth/Tarrant | 01053361 | 817/815-5000 | 354 |
| Sageland Elem Sch/El Paso/El Paso | 01016595 | 915/434-4800 | 142 |
| Saginaw Elem Sch/Fort Worth/Tarrant | 01052434 | 817/232-0631 | 351 |
| Saginaw High Sch/Fort Worth/Tarrant | 10003707 | 817/306-0914 | 351 |
| Saigling Elem Sch/Plano/Collin | 01540003 | 469/752-3000 | 87 |
| Saint Constantine Sch/Houston/Harris | 12320630 | 832/975-7075 | 212 |
| Saint Mary's Hall/San Antonio/Bexar | 00999669 | 210/483-9100 | 48 |
| Saint Peters Classical Sch/Fort Worth/ Tarrant | 11226859 | 817/294-0124 | 362 |
| Salado Elem Sch/San Antonio/Bexar | 00997051 | 210/648-3310 | 34 |
| Salado High Sch/Salado/Bell | 00996681 | 254/947-6985 | 32 |
| **SALADO IND SCH DIST/SALADO/BELL** | 00996679 | 254/947-6900 | 32 |
| Salado Junior High Sch/Salado/Bell | 11075765 | 254/947-6935 | 32 |
| Salazar Crossroads Academy/Robstown/Nueces | 02127343 | 361/767-6600 | 308 |
| Salazar Elem Sch/Alice/Jim Wells | 01034626 | 361/664-6263 | 248 |
| Salem Lutheran Sch/Tomball/Harris | 01027817 | 281/351-8223 | 212 |
| Salem Sayers Baptist Academy/Adkins/Bexar | 02984658 | 210/649-1178 | 48 |
| Salinas Elem Sch/Alton/Hidalgo | 04809755 | 956/323-6200 | 226 |
| Salinas Elem Sch/Laredo/Webb | 01548500 | 956/473-3200 | 391 |
| Salinas STEM Early College Sch/La Joya/ Hidalgo | 11823615 | 956/323-2240 | 223 |
| Sally K Ride Elem Sch/The Woodlands/ Montgomery | 02200012 | 281/465-2800 | 295 |
| Sallye Moore Clg&Career Prep/Grand Prairie/ Dallas | 04945177 | 972/660-2261 | 112 |
| **SALTILLO IND SCH DIST/SALTILLO/ HOPKINS** | 01031571 | 903/537-2386 | 234 |
| Saltillo Sch/Saltillo/Hopkins | 01031583 | 903/537-2386 | 234 |
| Salvador Garcia Middle Sch/Laredo/Webb | 04364054 | 956/473-5000 | 391 |
| Salvador H Sanchez Middle Sch/El Paso/ El Paso | 03323485 | 915/937-5200 | 141 |
| Salyards Middle Sch/Cypress/Harris | 11713137 | 281/373-2400 | 190 |
| Salyers Elem Sch/Spring/Harris | 01027520 | 281/891-8570 | 208 |
| Sam & Ann Roach Middle Sch/Frisco/Collin | 10004684 | 469/633-5000 | 83 |
| Sam Fordyce Elem Sch/Sullivan City/Hidalgo | 05100942 | 956/323-2490 | 223 |
| Sam Houston Elem Sch/Bryan/Brazos | 03007784 | 979/209-1360 | 58 |
| Sam Houston Elem Sch/Corp Christi/Nueces | 01044463 | 361/878-2520 | 307 |
| Sam Houston Elem Sch/Corsicana/Navarro | 10902048 | 903/874-6971 | 302 |
| Sam Houston Elem Sch/Denton/Denton | 02177025 | 940/369-2900 | 125 |
| Sam Houston Elem Sch/Eagle Pass/Maverick | 04806909 | 830/758-7069 | 280 |
| Sam Houston Elem Sch/Ennis/Ellis | 01015008 | 972/872-7285 | 144 |
| Sam Houston Elem Sch/Houston/Harris | 10910655 | 832/386-4430 | 192 |
| Sam Houston Elem Sch/La Feria/Cameron | 01003990 | 956/797-8490 | 69 |
| Sam Houston Elem Sch/Marshall/Harrison | 01028718 | 903/927-8860 | 214 |
| Sam Houston Elem Sch/McAllen/Hidalgo | 01030072 | 956/971-4484 | 224 |
| Sam Houston Elem Sch/Midland/Midland | 01041631 | 432/240-7100 | 289 |
| Sam Houston Elem Sch/Odessa/Ector | 01014834 | 432/456-1139 | 135 |
| Sam Houston Elem Sch/Port Arthur/Jefferson | 01033878 | 409/984-4800 | 246 |
| Sam Houston Elem Sch/Weslaco/Hidalgo | 11713350 | 956/969-6740 | 229 |
| Sam Houston High Sch/Arlington/Tarrant | 01051909 | 682/867-8200 | 347 |
| Sam Houston High Sch/San Antonio/Bexar | 00998861 | 210/978-7900 | 44 |
| Sam Houston Math Sci Tech HS/Houston/ Harris | 01025936 | 713/696-0200 | 197 |
| Sam Houston Middle Sch/Amarillo/Potter | 01047300 | 806/326-3600 | 321 |
| Sam Houston Middle Sch/Garland/Dallas | 01010694 | 972/926-2640 | 110 |
| Sam Jamison Middle Sch/Pearland/Brazoria | 02179841 | 281/412-1440 | 57 |
| Sam Rayburn Elem Sch/McAllen/Hidalgo | 02043357 | 956/971-4363 | 224 |
| Sam Rayburn High Sch/Pasadena/Harris | 01026928 | 713/740-0330 | 205 |
| **SAM RAYBURN IND SCH DIST/ IVANHOE/FANNIN** | 01017549 | 903/664-2255 | 150 |
| Sam Rayburn Middle Sch/San Antonio/Bexar | 00998287 | 210/397-2150 | 41 |
| Sam Rayburn Sch/Ivanhoe/Fannin | 01017563 | 903/664-2165 | 150 |
| Sam Rayburn Steam Acad/Grand Prairie/ Dallas | 01010993 | 972/264-8900 | 112 |
| Sam Rosen Elem Sch/Fort Worth/Tarrant | 01053373 | 817/814-4800 | 354 |
| Sam Rutherford Elem Sch/Mesquite/Dallas | 01011595 | 972/290-4060 | 116 |
| Sam Tasby Middle Sch/Dallas/Dallas | 10023135 | 972/502-1900 | 106 |
| Sampson Elem Sch/Cypress/Harris | 05096743 | 281/213-1600 | 190 |
| Samuel Beck Elem Sch/Trophy Club/Denton | 04804573 | 817/215-0450 | 129 |
| Samuel Clemens High Sch/Schertz/Guadalupe | 01021605 | 210/945-6501 | 178 |
| Samuel Houston Elem Sch/Huntsville/Walker | 01058713 | 936/435-6750 | 386 |
| San Angelo Christian Academy/San Angelo/ Tom Green | 02120993 | 325/651-8363 | 368 |
| **SAN ANGELO IND SCH DIST/ SAN ANGELO/TOM GREEN** | 01055539 | 325/947-3700 | 367 |
| San Antonio Academy-Texas/San Antonio/ Bexar | 01479466 | 210/733-7331 | 48 |
| San Antonio Christian Sch/San Antonio/ Bexar | 01479519 | 210/340-1864 | 48 |
| **SAN ANTONIO IND SCH DIST/ SAN ANTONIO/BEXAR** | 00998366 | 210/554-2200 | 42 |
| San Augustine Elem Sch/San Augustine/ San Augustine | 01049372 | 936/275-3424 | 332 |
| **SAN AUGUSTINE IND SCH DIST/ SAN AUGUSTINE/SAN AUGUSTINE** | 01049360 | 936/275-2306 | 332 |
| San Augustine Mid High Sch/San Augustine/ San Augustine | 01049384 | 936/275-9603 | 332 |
| **SAN BENITO CONS IND SCH DIST/ SAN BENITO/CAMERON** | 01004140 | 956/361-6100 | 70 |
| San Benito High Sch/San Benito/Cameron | 01004267 | 956/361-6500 | 71 |
| San Carlos Elem Sch/Edinburg/Hidalgo | 03012193 | 956/289-2370 | 222 |
| San Diego High Sch/San Diego/Duval | 01014315 | 361/279-3544 | 132 |
| **SAN DIEGO IND SCH DIST/SAN DIEGO/ DUVAL** | 01014274 | 361/279-3382 | 132 |
| San Elizario High Sch/San Elizario/El Paso | 01016193 | 915/872-3970 | 140 |
| **SAN ELIZARIO IND SCH DIST/ SAN ELIZARIO/EL PASO** | 01016179 | 915/872-3900 | 139 |
| San Felipe Memorial Middle Sch/Del Rio/ Val Verde | 01058012 | 830/778-4560 | 382 |
| **SAN FELIPE-DEL RIO CONS IND SD/ DEL RIO/VAL VERDE** | 01057941 | 830/778-4000 | 381 |
| San Isidro Elem Sch/Laredo/Webb | 12308242 | 956/473-6700 | 391 |
| **SAN ISIDRO IND SCH DIST/ SAN ISIDRO/STARR** | 01051296 | 956/481-3100 | 343 |
| San Isidro Sch/San Isidro/Starr | 01051301 | 956/481-3100 | 344 |
| San Jacinto Adult Learning Ctr/El Paso/ El Paso | 04806662 | 915/230-3200 | 137 |
| San Jacinto Christian Academy/Amarillo/ Potter | 02207034 | 806/372-2285 | 322 |
| San Jacinto Elem Sch/Amarillo/Potter | 01047465 | 806/326-5200 | 321 |
| San Jacinto Elem Sch/Baytown/Harris | 01023744 | 281/420-4670 | 193 |
| San Jacinto Elem Sch/Conroe/Montgomery | 02110390 | 281/465-7700 | 295 |
| San Jacinto Elem Sch/Dallas/Dallas | 01009815 | 972/749-4200 | 106 |
| San Jacinto Elem Sch/Deer Park/Harris | 01023407 | 832/668-7900 | 191 |
| San Jacinto Elem Sch/Liberty/Liberty | 01037965 | 936/336-3161 | 269 |
| San Jacinto Elem Sch/Odessa/Ector | 01014846 | 432/456-1219 | 135 |
| San Jacinto Elem Sch/San Angelo/Tom Green | 01055773 | 325/659-3675 | 367 |
| San Jacinto Intermediate Sch/Pasadena/ Harris | 01026930 | 713/740-0480 | 205 |
| San Jacinto Junior High Sch/Midland/ Midland | 01041643 | 432/689-1350 | 289 |
| San Juan Diego Cath High Sch/Austin/Travis | 05153523 | 512/804-1935 | 375 |
| San Leon Elem Sch/Dickinson/Galveston | 10905131 | 281/229-7400 | 164 |
| San Luis Elem Sch/Eagle Pass/Maverick | 01041136 | 830/758-7071 | 280 |
| San Marcos Baptist Academy/San Marcos/Hays | 01029190 | 512/353-2400 | 217 |
| **SAN MARCOS CONS IND SCH DIST/ SAN MARCOS/HAYS** | 01029114 | 512/393-6700 | 216 |
| San Marcos High Sch/San Marcos/Hays | 01029176 | 512/393-6800 | 217 |
| San Martin De Porres Sch/Weslaco/Hidalgo | 04880149 | 956/973-8642 | 229 |
| San Pedro Elem Sch/Robstown/Nueces | 01044918 | 361/767-6648 | 308 |
| **SAN PERLITA IND SCH DIST/ SAN PERLITA/WILLACY** | 01060780 | 956/248-5563 | 397 |
| San Perlita Sch/San Perlita/Willacy | 01857430 | 956/248-5250 | 397 |
| San Saba Elem Sch/San Saba/San Saba | 01049956 | 325/372-3019 | 335 |
| San Saba High Sch/San Saba/San Saba | 01049968 | 325/372-3786 | 335 |
| **SAN SABA IND SCH DIST/SAN SABA/ SAN SABA** | 01049944 | 325/372-3771 | 335 |
| San Saba Middle Sch/San Saba/San Saba | 01418577 | 325/372-3200 | 335 |
| San Vicente Elem Sch/Bg BND NTL Pk/ Brewster | 01002271 | 432/477-2220 | 60 |
| **SAN VICENTE IND SCH DIST/ BG BND NTL PK/BREWSTER** | 01002269 | 432/477-2220 | 60 |
| Sanborn Elem Sch/Amarillo/Potter | 01047477 | 806/326-5250 | 321 |
| Sanchez Elem Sch/Austin/Travis | 01056521 | 512/414-4423 | 370 |
| Sanchez Elem Sch/Houston/Harris | 02857964 | 713/845-7472 | 195 |
| Sanchez-Ochoa Elem Sch/Laredo/Webb | 01059250 | 956/273-4500 | 390 |
| Sanderson Public Sch/Sanderson/Terrell | 01055060 | 432/345-2515 | 364 |
| Sandra Day O'Connor High Sch/Helotes/Bexar | 04809030 | 210/397-4800 | 41 |

| School/City/County<br>DISTRICT/CITY/COUNTY | PID | TELEPHONE NUMBER | PAGE |
|---|---|---|---|
| Sandra Mossman Elem Sch/League City/Galveston | 11449104 | 281/284-4000 | 163 |
| **SANDS CONSOLIDATED ISD/ACKERLY/DAWSON** | 01012941 | 432/353-4888 | 121 |
| Sands Sch/Ackerly/Dawson | 01012953 | 432/353-4744 | 121 |
| Sandy McNutt Elem Sch/Arlington/Tarrant | 12170100 | 682/867-9100 | 347 |
| Sanford Fritch Elem Sch/Fritch/Hutchinson | 01032783 | 806/397-0159 | 241 |
| Sanford Fritch High Sch/Fritch/Hutchinson | 01032800 | 806/359-0159 | 241 |
| Sanford Fritch Jr High Sch/Fritch/Hutchinson | 02178225 | 806/397-0159 | 241 |
| **SANFORD-FRITCH IND SCH DIST/FRITCH/HUTCHINSON** | 01032771 | 806/397-0159 | 241 |
| Sanger 6th Grade Sch/Sanger/Denton | 11148257 | 940/458-3699 | 130 |
| Sanger High Sch/Sanger/Denton | 01528122 | 940/458-7497 | 130 |
| **SANGER IND SCH DIST/SANGER/DENTON** | 01013646 | 940/458-7438 | 130 |
| Sanger Middle Sch/Sanger/Denton | 01013660 | 940/458-7916 | 130 |
| Santa Anna Elem Sch/Santa Anna/Coleman | 01005936 | 325/348-3138 | 80 |
| Santa Anna High Sch/Santa Anna/Coleman | 01005948 | 325/348-3137 | 80 |
| **SANTA ANNA IND SCH DIST/SANTA ANNA/COLEMAN** | 01005924 | 325/348-3136 | 79 |
| Santa Clara Catholic Academy/Dallas/Dallas | 04309341 | 214/333-9423 | 118 |
| Santa Cruz Elem Sch/Buda/Hays | 11396428 | 512/312-2137 | 217 |
| Santa Fe Elem Sch/Cleburne/Johnson | 10905143 | 817/202-2300 | 250 |
| Santa Fe High Sch/Santa Fe/Galveston | 01019444 | 409/927-3100 | 165 |
| **SANTA FE IND SCH DIST/SANTA FE/GALVESTON** | 01019432 | 409/925-3526 | 165 |
| Santa Fe Junior High Sch/Santa Fe/Galveston | 01019456 | 409/925-9300 | 165 |
| Santa Gertrudis Elem MS/Kingsville/Kleberg | 01809548 | 361/384-5046 | 261 |
| **SANTA GERTRUDIS IND SCH DIST/KINGSVILLE/KLEBERG** | 01809536 | 361/384-5087 | 261 |
| Santa Maria Elem Sch/Laredo/Webb | 01059406 | 956/273-4600 | 390 |
| Santa Maria High Sch/Santa Maria/Cameron | 04036453 | 956/565-9144 | 71 |
| **SANTA MARIA IND SCH DIST/SANTA MARIA/CAMERON** | 01004308 | 956/565-6308 | 71 |
| Santa Maria Junior High Sch/Santa Maria/Cameron | 12319966 | 956/565-5348 | 71 |
| Santa Maria Middle Sch/Santa Maria/Cameron | 04036441 | 956/565-6309 | 71 |
| Santa Rita Elem Sch/Midland/Midland | 02199956 | 432/240-7900 | 289 |
| Santa Rita Elem Sch/San Angelo/Tom Green | 01055785 | 325/659-3672 | 367 |
| Santa Rosa High Sch/Santa Rosa/Cameron | 01004334 | 956/636-9830 | 71 |
| **SANTA ROSA IND SCH DIST/SANTA ROSA/CAMERON** | 01004322 | 956/636-9800 | 71 |
| Santiago Garcia Elem Sch/Edcouch/Hidalgo | 01029645 | 956/262-4741 | 221 |
| Santo Elem Sch/Santo/Palo Pinto | 02110417 | 940/769-3215 | 313 |
| **SANTO IND SCH DIST/SANTO/PALO PINTO** | 01046124 | 940/769-2835 | 313 |
| Santo J Forte Jr High Sch/Azle/Tarrant | 04866973 | 817/270-1133 | 348 |
| Santo Jr Sr High Sch/Santo/Palo Pinto | 04749167 | 940/769-3847 | 313 |
| Santo Nino Elem Sch/Laredo/Webb | 01059418 | 956/273-4700 | 390 |
| Santos Livas Elem Sch/Alamo/Hidalgo | 04288527 | 956/354-2840 | 227 |
| Sarah King Elem Sch/San Antonio/Bexar | 00999224 | 210/978-7990 | 44 |
| Sarah Zumwalt Middle Sch/Dallas/Dallas | 01009827 | 972/749-3600 | 106 |
| Sarita Elem Sch/Sarita/Kenedy | 01035929 | 361/294-5381 | 258 |
| Sartartia Middle Sch/Sugar Land/Fort Bend | 04947137 | 281/634-6310 | 155 |
| Satori Elem Sch/Galveston/Galveston | 10009660 | 409/763-7022 | 166 |
| Savannah Elem Sch/Aubrey/Denton | 10021864 | 972/347-7400 | 125 |
| Savannah Heights Interm Sch/Von Ormy/Bexar | 10915253 | 210/750-8964 | 45 |
| Savannah Lakes Elem Sch/Rosharon/Brazoria | 11070961 | 281/245-3214 | 55 |
| Savoy Elem Sch/Savoy/Fannin | 01017587 | 903/965-7738 | 151 |
| Savoy High Sch/Savoy/Fannin | 04942151 | 903/965-4024 | 151 |
| **SAVOY IND SCH DIST/SAVOY/FANNIN** | 01017575 | 903/965-5262 | 150 |
| Scanlan Oaks Elem Sch/Missouri City/Fort Bend | 05345520 | 281/634-3950 | 155 |
| Scarborough Elem Sch/Houston/Harris | 01026100 | 713/696-2710 | 196 |
| Scarborough Elem Sch/San Antonio/Bexar | 11104110 | 210/397-8000 | 41 |
| Scarborough High Sch/Houston/Harris | 01024231 | 713/613-2200 | 197 |
| Scenic Hills Christian Academy/San Antonio/Bexar | 02234441 | 210/523-2312 | 48 |
| Sch Health Prof-Townview Ctr/Dallas/Dallas | 02896295 | 972/925-5930 | 106 |
| Sch of Environmental Education/Plantersville/Grimes | 04775116 | 936/894-2141 | 177 |
| Sch of Sci & Tech Advancement/Houston/Harris | 12261113 | 713/266-2522 | 13 |
| Sch of Sci & Tech Excellence/Houston/Harris | 12261149 | 832/672-6671 | 13 |
| Sch of Sci & Tech Main/San Antonio/Bexar | 10916001 | 210/804-0222 | 13 |
| Sch of Sci & Tech Northwest/San Antonio/Bexar | 12362755 | 210/530-8366 | 13 |
| Sch of Sci & Tech-Alamo/San Antonio/Bexar | 11527615 | 210/657-6400 | 13 |
| Sch of Sci & Tech-Corpus Crsti/Corp Christi/Nueces | 11457876 | 361/851-2450 | 13 |
| Sch of Sci & Tech-Discovery/Leon Valley/Bexar | 11155274 | 210/543-1111 | 13 |
| Sch of Sci & Tech-Hill Country/San Antonio/Bexar | 12375427 | 210/688-9758 | 13 |
| Sch of Sci & Tech-Houston/Houston/Harris | 12261137 | 346/270-2101 | 13 |
| Sch of Sci & Tech-Spring/Spring/Harris | 12375439 | 832/698-2179 | 13 |
| Sch of Sci & Tech-Sugarland/Richmond/Fort Bend | 12362743 | 281/277-7923 | 13 |
| Schallert Elem Sch/Alice/Jim Wells | 01034614 | 361/664-6361 | 248 |
| Schanen Estates Elem Sch/Corp Christi/Nueces | 01044669 | 361/878-2940 | 307 |
| Scharbauer Elem Sch/Midland/Midland | 02848420 | 432/240-8000 | 289 |
| Schell Elem Sch/Richardson/Collin | 10911738 | 469/752-6600 | 87 |
| Schenck Elem Sch/San Antonio/Bexar | 00998902 | 210/438-6865 | 44 |
| Schertz Elem Sch/Schertz/Guadalupe | 01021617 | 210/619-4650 | 178 |
| **SCHERTZ-CIBOLO-UNIV CITY ISD/SCHERTZ/GUADALUPE** | 01021552 | 210/945-6200 | 178 |
| Schiff Elem Sch/Missouri City/Fort Bend | 11079589 | 281/634-9450 | 155 |
| Schimelpfenig Middle Sch/Plano/Collin | 02108000 | 469/752-6400 | 87 |
| Schindewolf Intermediate Sch/Spring/Harris | 05096080 | 832/249-5900 | 203 |
| **SCHLEICHER CO IND SCH DIST/ELDORADO/SCHLEICHER** | 01049982 | 325/853-2514 | 335 |
| School at St George Place/Houston/Harris | 05099343 | 713/625-1499 | 199 |
| School for Talented & Gifted/Dallas/Dallas | 12377762 | 972/794-1800 | 106 |
| School for the Highly Gifted/Grand Prairie/Dallas | 12113968 | 972/343-7864 | 112 |
| School for Young Children/Houston/Harris | 02754207 | 713/520-8310 | 212 |
| School of Choice/New Braunfels/Comal | 04452091 | 830/629-8650 | 92 |
| **SCHOOL OF EXCELLENCE IN ED/SAN ANTONIO/BEXAR** | 11828823 | 210/431-9881 | 45 |
| School of the Woods/Houston/Harris | 01410898 | 713/686-8811 | 212 |
| Schrade Middle Sch/Rowlett/Dallas | 04806375 | 972/463-8790 | 110 |
| Schulenburg Elem Sch/Schulenburg/Fayette | 01553074 | 979/743-4221 | 152 |
| Schulenburg High Sch/Schulenburg/Fayette | 01017824 | 979/743-3605 | 152 |
| **SCHULENBURG IND SCH DIST/SCHULENBURG/FAYETTE** | 01017800 | 979/743-3448 | 152 |
| Schultz Elem Sch/Tomball/Harris | 04286969 | 832/484-7000 | 203 |
| Schultz Junior High Sch/Waller/Waller | 01018177 | 936/931-9103 | 387 |
| Science Acad of South Texas/Mercedes/Cameron | 04017380 | 956/565-4620 | 71 |
| Science Hall Elem Sch/Kyle/Hays | 10022741 | 512/268-8502 | 216 |
| Scofield Christian Sch/Dallas/Dallas | 02123543 | 214/349-6843 | 120 |
| Scoggins Middle Sch/McKinney/Collin | 11103867 | 469/633-5150 | 83 |
| Scotland Park Elem Sch/Wichita Falls/Wichita | 01173038 | 940/235-1180 | 395 |
| Scotsdale Elem Sch/El Paso/El Paso | 01016600 | 915/434-4800 | 142 |
| Scott Elem Sch/Temple/Bell | 00996825 | 254/215-6222 | 32 |
| Scott Johnson Elem Sch/Huntsville/Walker | 01881974 | 936/435-6250 | 386 |
| Scott Johnson Middle Sch/McKinney/Collin | 04922266 | 469/302-4900 | 85 |
| Scroggins Elem Sch/Houston/Harris | 01026095 | 713/671-4130 | 196 |
| Scurry Rosser Elem Sch/Scurry/Kaufman | 01035735 | 972/452-8823 | 256 |
| Scurry Rosser High Sch/Scurry/Kaufman | 01035747 | 972/452-8823 | 256 |
| **SCURRY ROSSER IND SCH DIST/SCURRY/KAUFMAN** | 01035723 | 972/452-8823 | 256 |
| Scurry Rosser Middle Sch/Scurry/Kaufman | 02857249 | 972/452-8823 | 256 |
| Seabrook Intermediate Sch/Seabrook/Galveston | 01018933 | 281/284-3100 | 163 |
| Seadrift Sch/Seadrift/Calhoun | 01003184 | 361/785-3511 | 65 |
| Seagoville Elem Sch/Seagoville/Dallas | 01009839 | 972/892-7900 | 106 |
| Seagoville High Sch/Dallas/Dallas | 01009841 | 972/892-5900 | 106 |
| Seagoville Middle Sch/Dallas/Dallas | 02109846 | 972/892-7100 | 106 |
| Seagoville North Elem Sch/Seagoville/Dallas | 11824530 | 972/892-5300 | 107 |
| Seagraves Elem Sch/Seagraves/Gaines | 01018725 | 806/387-2015 | 162 |
| Seagraves High Sch/Seagraves/Gaines | 01018737 | 806/387-2520 | 162 |
| **SEAGRAVES IND SCH DIST/SEAGRAVES/GAINES** | 01018713 | 806/387-2035 | 162 |
| Seagraves Junior High Sch/Seagraves/Gaines | 01018749 | 806/387-2646 | 162 |
| Seale Junior High Sch/Robstown/Nueces | 01539200 | 361/767-6631 | 308 |
| Sealy Elem Sch/Sealy/Austin | 04238493 | 979/885-3852 | 25 |
| Sealy High Sch/Sealy/Austin | 00995613 | 979/885-3515 | 25 |
| **SEALY IND SCH DIST/SEALY/AUSTIN** | 00995584 | 979/885-3516 | 25 |
| Sealy Junior High Sch/Sealy/Austin | 03245376 | 979/885-3292 | 25 |
| Seashore Learning Center/Corp Christi/Nueces | 04467553 | 361/949-1222 | 14 |
| Seashore Middle Academy/Corp Christi/Nueces | 10971128 | 361/654-1134 | 14 |
| Seco Mines Elem Sch/Eagle Pass/Maverick | 02127018 | 830/758-7073 | 280 |
| Second Baptist Sch/Houston/Harris | 01480348 | 713/365-2310 | 212 |

| School/City/County DISTRICT/CITY/COUNTY | PID | TELEPHONE NUMBER | PAGE |
|---|---|---|---|
| Secondary Alternative Center/Harlingen/Cameron | 04931530 | 956/427-3210 | 68 |
| Seele Elem Sch/New Braunfels/Comal | 01007037 | 830/627-6750 | 92 |
| Seguin Christian Academy/Seguin/Guadalupe | 11238175 | 830/433-4131 | 179 |
| Seguin Early Child Hood Ctr/Richmond/Fort Bend | 04803775 | 832/223-2200 | 158 |
| Seguin High Sch/Seguin/Guadalupe | 01021734 | 830/401-8000 | 179 |
| **SEGUIN IND SCH DIST/SEGUIN/GUADALUPE** | 01021631 | 830/401-8600 | 178 |
| Sellers Middle Sch/Garland/Dallas | 01010709 | 972/494-8337 | 110 |
| Selwyn College Prep Sch/Argyle/Denton | 01013672 | 940/382-6771 | 130 |
| Seminary Hills Park Elem Sch/Fort Worth/Tarrant | 05344538 | 817/814-7600 | 354 |
| Seminole Elem Sch/Seminole/Gaines | 01018775 | 432/758-3615 | 162 |
| Seminole Elem Sch/Seminole/Gaines | 01018787 | 432/758-5873 | 162 |
| **SEMINOLE IND SCH DIST/SEMINOLE/GAINES** | 01018751 | 432/758-3662 | 162 |
| Seminole Junior High Sch/Seminole/Gaines | 01018799 | 432/758-9431 | 162 |
| Seminole Primary Sch/Seminole/Gaines | 01018804 | 432/758-5841 | 162 |
| Seminole Success Center/Seminole/Gaines | 04447242 | 432/758-2772 | 162 |
| Senator Judith Zaffirini ES/Laredo/Webb | 04875223 | 956/473-2900 | 391 |
| Sendera Ranch Elem Sch/Haslet/Denton | 11104079 | 817/698-3500 | 129 |
| Ser-Ninos Charter Middle Sch/Houston/Harris | 12320238 | 713/592-6055 | 14 |
| Ser-Ninos Charter School II/Houston/Harris | 11832317 | 713/432-9400 | 14 |
| Ser-Ninos Elementary/Houston/Harris | 04459465 | 713/667-6145 | 14 |
| Serene Hills Elem Sch/Austin/Travis | 11074254 | 512/533-7400 | 373 |
| Serenity High Sch/McKinney/Collin | 04920696 | 469/302-7830 | 85 |
| Serna Elem Sch/San Antonio/Bexar | 04017770 | 210/407-7200 | 39 |
| Seton Home Charter Education/San Antonio/Bexar | 12362767 | 512/560-8132 | 14 |
| Settlers Way Elem Sch/Sugar Land/Fort Bend | 02226688 | 281/634-4360 | 155 |
| Seven Hills Elem Sch/Newark/Denton | 03055509 | 817/215-0700 | 129 |
| Seven Lakes High Sch/Katy/Harris | 10002870 | 281/237-2800 | 157 |
| Seven Lakes Junior High Sch/Katy/Harris | 11822051 | 281/234-2100 | 157 |
| Sewell Elem Sch/Sachse/Dallas | 04035461 | 972/675-3050 | 110 |
| Seymour Elem Sch/Seymour/Baylor | 00996033 | 940/889-2533 | 28 |
| Seymour High Sch/Seymour/Baylor | 00996045 | 940/889-2947 | 28 |
| **SEYMOUR IND SCH DIST/SEYMOUR/BAYLOR** | 00996021 | 940/889-3525 | 28 |
| Seymour Middle Sch/Seymour/Baylor | 05035153 | 940/889-4548 | 28 |
| Sgt Jose Carrasco Elem Sch/El Paso/El Paso | 12307494 | 915/938-2400 | 141 |
| Sgt Leonel Trevino Elem Sch/San Juan/Hidalgo | 01540065 | 956/354-2900 | 227 |
| Sgt Manuel Chacon Middle Sch/Mercedes/Hidalgo | 01030187 | 956/514-2200 | 225 |
| Sgt Roberto Ituarte Elem Sch/El Paso/El Paso | 10021888 | 915/937-7000 | 141 |
| Sgt William Harrell Middle Sch/Mercedes/Hidalgo | 12225315 | 956/825-5140 | 225 |
| Shackelford Elem Sch/Waxahachie/Ellis | 03049029 | 972/923-4666 | 147 |
| Shackelford Junior High Sch/Arlington/Tarrant | 01399799 | 682/867-3600 | 347 |
| Shadow Creek High Sch/Pearland/Brazoria | 12165442 | 281/245-3800 | 55 |
| Shadow Forest Elem Sch/Kingwood/Harris | 04038176 | 281/641-2600 | 201 |
| Shadow Oaks Elem Sch/Houston/Harris | 01027271 | 713/251-6800 | 206 |
| Shadow Ridge Middle Sch/Flower Mound/Denton | 10004103 | 469/713-5984 | 128 |
| Shadowbriar Elem Sch/Houston/Harris | 04016087 | 281/368-2160 | 200 |
| Shadowglen Elem Sch/Manor/Travis | 12108327 | 512/278-4700 | 374 |
| Shady Brook Elem Sch/Bedford/Tarrant | 01053919 | 817/354-3513 | 356 |
| Shady Grove Elem Sch/Burnet/Burnet | 01002776 | 512/756-2126 | 64 |
| Shady Grove Elem Sch/Keller/Tarrant | 03392747 | 817/744-5600 | 358 |
| Shady Oaks Elem Sch/Hurst/Tarrant | 01053921 | 817/285-3240 | 356 |
| Shady Shores Elem Sch/Shady Shores/Denton | 10753706 | 940/497-4035 | 126 |
| Shadycrest Elem Sch/Pearland/Brazoria | 01001899 | 281/412-1404 | 57 |
| Shadydale Elem Sch/Houston/Harris | 01026605 | 713/633-5150 | 196 |
| Shallowater Elem Sch/Shallowater/Lubbock | 01039169 | 806/832-4531 | 275 |
| Shallowater High Sch/Shallowater/Lubbock | 01039183 | 806/832-4531 | 275 |
| **SHALLOWATER IND SCH DIST/SHALLOWATER/LUBBOCK** | 01039157 | 806/832-4531 | 274 |
| Shallowater Intermediate Sch/Shallowater/Lubbock | 01039171 | 806/832-4531 | 275 |
| Shallowater Middle Sch/Shallowater/Lubbock | 03241667 | 806/832-4531 | 275 |
| Shamrock Elem Sch/Shamrock/Wheeler | 01059860 | 806/256-3227 | 393 |
| Shamrock High Sch/Shamrock/Wheeler | 04801715 | 806/256-2241 | 394 |
| **SHAMROCK IND SCH DIST/SHAMROCK/WHEELER** | 01059858 | 806/256-3492 | 393 |
| Shamrock Junior High Sch/Shamrock/Wheeler | 04801703 | 806/256-3227 | 394 |
| Shannon High Sch/Haltom City/Tarrant | 03329348 | 817/547-5400 | 349 |
| Sharon Shannon Elem Sch/Rockwall/Rockwall | 10911001 | 469/698-2900 | 328 |
| Sharp Elem Sch/Brownsville/Cameron | 01003691 | 956/982-2930 | 68 |

| School/City/County DISTRICT/CITY/COUNTY | PID | TELEPHONE NUMBER | PAGE |
|---|---|---|---|
| Sharpstown High Sch/Houston/Harris | 01024607 | 713/771-7215 | 194 |
| Sharpstown International Acad/Houston/Harris | 01024619 | 713/778-3440 | 200 |
| Sharyland Adv Academic Academy/Mission/Hidalgo | 12035342 | 956/584-6467 | 228 |
| Sharyland Alternative Ed Ctr/Mission/Hidalgo | 12035366 | 956/584-6407 | 228 |
| Sharyland High Sch/Mission/Hidalgo | 01526069 | 956/580-5300 | 228 |
| **SHARYLAND IND SCH DIST/MISSION/HIDALGO** | 01030527 | 956/580-5200 | 227 |
| Sharyland North Jr High Sch/McAllen/Hidalgo | 10011429 | 956/686-1415 | 228 |
| Sharyland Pioneer High Sch/Mission/Hidalgo | 12035354 | 956/271-1600 | 228 |
| Shaw Spec Emphasis Sch/Corp Christi/Nueces | 01044528 | 361/878-2100 | 307 |
| Shawnee Trail Elem Sch/Frisco/Collin | 04917247 | 469/633-2500 | 83 |
| Shearn Elem Sch/Houston/Harris | 01025376 | 713/295-5236 | 196 |
| Sheffield Primary Elem Sch/Dallas/Dallas | 02845715 | 972/968-3100 | 101 |
| Shekinah Radiance Acad-Garland/Dallas/Dallas | 12163365 | 214/320-2500 | 14 |
| Shelbyville High Sch/Shelbyville/Shelby | 01050412 | 936/598-7323 | 337 |
| **SHELBYVILLE IND SCH DIST/SHELBYVILLE/SHELBY** | 01050395 | 936/598-2641 | 337 |
| Shelbyville Middle Sch/Shelbyville/Shelby | 01553244 | 936/598-5146 | 337 |
| Sheldon Early Childhood Acad/Houston/Harris | 11452034 | 281/456-6800 | 205 |
| Sheldon Early Clg High Sch/Houston/Harris | 12033772 | 281/727-3500 | 205 |
| Sheldon Elem Sch/Houston/Harris | 01027063 | 281/456-6700 | 205 |
| **SHELDON IND SCH DIST/HOUSTON/HARRIS** | 01027013 | 281/727-2000 | 205 |
| Sheldon Lake Elem Sch/Houston/Harris | 12377815 | 281/727-1100 | 205 |
| Shelton Sch/Dallas/Dallas | 11829970 | 972/774-1772 | 120 |
| Shepard Elem Sch/Plano/Collin | 01006461 | 469/752-3100 | 87 |
| Shepherd High Sch/Shepherd/San Jacinto | 01049463 | 936/628-3371 | 333 |
| **SHEPHERD IND SCH DIST/SHEPHERD/SAN JACINTO** | 01049449 | 936/628-3396 | 333 |
| Shepherd Intermediate Sch/Shepherd/San Jacinto | 01553232 | 936/628-6764 | 333 |
| Shepherd Middle Sch/Shepherd/San Jacinto | 04801870 | 936/628-3377 | 333 |
| Shepherd of the Hills Luth Sch/San Antonio/Bexar | 02235378 | 210/614-3741 | 48 |
| Shepherd Primary Sch/Shepherd/San Jacinto | 01049451 | 936/628-3302 | 333 |
| Sheppard AFB Elem Sch/Sheppard Afb/Wichita | 01173181 | 940/235-1184 | 395 |
| Shepton High Sch/Plano/Collin | 02225634 | 469/752-7600 | 87 |
| Sheridan Elem Sch/Katy/Harris | 04016609 | 281/856-1420 | 190 |
| Sheridan Elem Sch/Sheridan/Colorado | 01006837 | 979/234-3531 | 91 |
| Sherman Elem Sch/Houston/Harris | 01024372 | 713/226-2627 | 196 |
| Sherman High Sch/Sherman/Grayson | 01020663 | 903/891-6440 | 172 |
| **SHERMAN IND SCH DIST/SHERMAN/GRAYSON** | 01020596 | 903/891-6400 | 172 |
| Sherrod Elem Sch/Arlington/Tarrant | 02109262 | 682/867-3700 | 347 |
| Sherry & Paul Hamm Elem Sch/Rockwall/Rockwall | 12471708 | 469/698-2854 | 328 |
| Sherwood Elem Sch/Houston/Harris | 01027283 | 713/251-6900 | 206 |
| Sherwood Forest Mont Sch/Houston/Harris | 02757120 | 713/464-5791 | 212 |
| Shields Elem Sch/Victoria/Victoria | 01058579 | 361/788-9593 | 385 |
| Shiloh Sch/Manvel/Brazoria | 11230630 | 281/489-1290 | 58 |
| Shiner Catholic School-St Paul/Shiner/Lavaca | 04972522 | 361/594-2313 | 265 |
| Shiner Elem Sch/Shiner/Lavaca | 01037367 | 361/594-3131 | 265 |
| Shiner High Sch/Shiner/Lavaca | 01037379 | 361/594-3251 | 265 |
| **SHINER IND SCH DIST/SHINER/LAVACA** | 01037355 | 361/594-3121 | 265 |
| Shirley Dill Brothers Elem Sch/Pearland/Brazoria | 12231027 | 281/245-3660 | 55 |
| Shirley Hall Middle Sch/Weatherford/Parker | 01046629 | 817/598-2822 | 317 |
| Shirley J Howsman Elem Sch/San Antonio/Bexar | 00998299 | 210/397-2350 | 41 |
| Shive Elem Sch/Vernon/Wilbarger | 01060596 | 940/553-4309 | 397 |
| Shorehaven Elem Sch/Garland/Dallas | 01010711 | 972/494-8346 | 110 |
| Short Elem Sch/Arlington/Tarrant | 01051911 | 682/867-5850 | 347 |
| Shsu CS-Brighton Academy/The Woodlands/Montgomery | 10986484 | 281/465-4111 | 14 |
| Shsu CS-Cypress Trails/Spring/Harris | 12261242 | 936/294-3229 | 14 |
| Shsu CS-Greengate Academy/Spring/Harris | 04792205 | 281/288-0880 | 14 |
| Shsu CS-Little Geniuses Acad/Humble/Harris | 12136491 | 832/995-5916 | 14 |
| Shugart Elem Sch/Garland/Dallas | 03009380 | 972/240-3700 | 110 |
| **SIDNEY IND SCH DIST/SIDNEY/COMANCHE** | 01007154 | 254/842-5500 | 94 |
| Sidney Lanier Expressive Arts/Dallas/Dallas | 01009774 | 972/794-4400 | 107 |
| Sidney Lanier High Sch/San Antonio/Bexar | 00999310 | 210/978-7910 | 44 |
| Sidney Poynter Elem Sch/Fort Worth/Tarrant | 10004622 | 817/568-5730 | 350 |

| School/City/County<br>DISTRICT/CITY/COUNTY | PID | TELEPHONE<br>NUMBER | PAGE |
|---|---|---|---|
| Sidney Sch/Sidney/Comanche | 01007178 | 254/842-5500 | 94 |
| Siebert Elem Sch/Eastland/Eastland | 01014418 | 254/631-5080 | 133 |
| Sienna Crossing Elem Sch/Missouri City/ | | | |
| Fort Bend | 04808608 | 281/634-3680 | 155 |
| **SIERRA BLANCA IND SCH DIST/** | | | |
| **SIERRA BLANCA/HUDSPETH** | 01032202 | 915/369-3741 | 237 |
| Sierra Blanca Sch/Sierra Blanca/Hudspeth | 01032214 | 915/369-2781 | 238 |
| Sierra Vista Elem Sch/El Paso/El Paso | 04035277 | 915/937-8100 | 141 |
| Sigler Elem Sch/Plano/Collin | 01006409 | 469/752-3200 | 87 |
| Silsbee Elem Sch/Silsbee/Hardin | 03047916 | 409/980-7856 | 183 |
| Silsbee High Sch/Silsbee/Hardin | 01022635 | 409/980-7877 | 183 |
| **SILSBEE IND SCH DIST/SILSBEE/** | | | |
| **HARDIN** | 01022582 | 409/980-7800 | 183 |
| Silva Health Magnet High Sch/El Paso/ | | | |
| El Paso | 04035693 | 915/236-7600 | 139 |
| Silver Creek Elem Sch/Azle/Tarrant | 03004067 | 817/444-0257 | 348 |
| Silver Lake Elem Sch/Grapevine/Tarrant | 04363658 | 817/251-5750 | 356 |
| Silvercrest Elem Sch/Pearland/Brazoria | 05070244 | 832/736-6000 | 57 |
| Silverlake Elem Sch/Pearland/Brazoria | 04807678 | 713/436-8000 | 57 |
| Silverline Montessori Sch/Pearland/ | | | |
| Brazoria | 11818804 | 713/436-5070 | 58 |
| **SILVERTON IND SCH DIST/SILVERTON/** | | | |
| **BRISCOE** | 01002300 | 806/823-2476 | 61 |
| Silverton Sch/Silverton/Briscoe | 01002312 | 806/823-2476 | 61 |
| Silvestre & Reyes Elem Sch/El Paso/El Paso | 12167646 | 915/877-1300 | 136 |
| **SIMMS IND SCH DIST/SIMMS/BOWIE** | 01001186 | 903/543-2219 | 53 |
| Simon Rivera Early Clg HS/Brownsville/ | | | |
| Cameron | 03095767 | 956/831-8700 | 68 |
| Simon Youth Academy/Katy/Harris | 12231261 | 281/396-6046 | 157 |
| Simonton Christian Academy/Simonton/ | | | |
| Fort Bend | 04496059 | 281/346-2303 | 160 |
| Sinclair Elem Sch/Houston/Harris | 01024243 | 713/867-5161 | 197 |
| Sinclair Elem Sch/San Antonio/Bexar | 02129743 | 210/648-4620 | 34 |
| Sinton Elem Sch/Sinton/San Patricio | 01049798 | 361/364-6900 | 334 |
| Sinton High Sch/Sinton/San Patricio | 01049803 | 361/364-6650 | 334 |
| **SINTON IND SCH DIST/SINTON/** | | | |
| **SAN PATRICIO** | 01049762 | 361/364-6800 | 334 |
| **SIVELLS BEND IND SCH DIST/** | | | |
| **GAINESVILLE/COOKE** | 01007489 | 940/665-6411 | 95 |
| Sivells Bend Sch/Gainesville/Cooke | 01007491 | 940/665-6411 | 95 |
| Skaggs Elem Sch/Plano/Collin | 04453899 | 469/752-3300 | 87 |
| Skidmore Tynan Elem Sch/Skidmore/Bee | 00996227 | 361/287-3425 | 29 |
| Skidmore Tynan High Sch/Skidmore/Bee | 00996239 | 361/287-3426 | 29 |
| **SKIDMORE TYNAN IND SD/SKIDMORE/** | | | |
| **BEE** | 00996215 | 361/287-3426 | 29 |
| Skidmore Tynan Jr High Sch/Skidmore/Bee | 00996241 | 361/287-3426 | 29 |
| Skinner Elem Sch/Brownsville/Cameron | 01003639 | 956/982-2830 | 68 |
| Skipcha Elem Sch/Harker HTS/Bell | 10030736 | 254/336-6690 | 31 |
| Sky Harbor Elem Sch/San Antonio/Bexar | 02110429 | 210/623-6580 | 47 |
| Skyline High Sch/Dallas/Dallas | 01009865 | 972/502-3400 | 107 |
| Skyview Elem Sch/Dallas/Dallas | 01011935 | 469/593-2400 | 117 |
| Slack Elem Sch/Lufkin/Angelina | 00995065 | 936/639-2279 | 21 |
| Slaton High Sch/Slaton/Lubbock | 01039212 | 806/828-5833 | 275 |
| **SLATON IND SCH DIST/SLATON/** | | | |
| **LUBBOCK** | 01039195 | 806/828-6591 | 275 |
| Slaton Junior High Sch/Slaton/Lubbock | 01039224 | 806/828-6583 | 275 |
| Sleepy Hollow Elem Sch/Amarillo/Potter | 02127757 | 806/326-5300 | 321 |
| Slidell Elem Sch/Decatur/Wise | 01061760 | 940/466-3118 | 407 |
| **SLIDELL IND SCH DIST/SLIDELL/** | | | |
| **WISE** | 01061758 | 940/535-5260 | 407 |
| Slidell Secondary Sch/Slidell/Wise | 04804755 | 940/535-5260 | 407 |
| Sloan Creek Intermediate Sch/Fairview/ | | | |
| Collin | 11127772 | 469/742-8400 | 84 |
| **SLOCUM ISD SCH DIST/ELKHART/** | | | |
| **ANDERSON** | 00994633 | 903/478-3624 | 19 |
| Slocum Sch/Elkhart/Anderson | 00994657 | 903/478-3624 | 19 |
| Small Middle Sch/Austin/Travis | 04869872 | 512/841-6700 | 3/2 |
| Smith Elem Sch/Austin/Travis | 01056832 | 512/386-3850 | 372 |
| Smith Elem Sch/Duncanville/Dallas | 01010383 | 972/708-3000 | 109 |
| Smith Elem Sch/Forney/Kaufman | 11130640 | 469/762-4365 | 255 |
| Smith Elem Sch/Houston/Harris | 01023031 | 281/983-8380 | 187 |
| Smith Elem Sch/Houston/Harris | 01024255 | 713/613-2542 | 197 |
| Smith Elem Sch/Lubbock/Lubbock | 03008714 | 806/219-6800 | 273 |
| Smith Elem Sch/Princeton/Collin | 12105076 | 469/952-5411 | 87 |
| Smith Elem Sch/Richmond/Fort Bend | 01018323 | 832/223-2300 | 158 |
| Smith Elem Sch/San Antonio/Bexar | 00998976 | 210/228-3360 | 44 |
| Smith Elem Sch/Spring/Harris | 02892146 | 281/891-8420 | 208 |
| Smith Elem Sch/Victoria/Victoria | 01058581 | 361/788-9605 | 385 |
| Smith Magnet Middle Sch/Beaumont/Jefferson | 01033426 | 409/617-5825 | 245 |
| Smith Middle Sch/Cleburne/Johnson | 01034896 | 817/202-1500 | 250 |
| Smith Middle Sch/Cypress/Harris | 11451482 | 281/213-1010 | 190 |
| Smithfield Elem Sch/N Richlnd Hls/Tarrant | 01052197 | 817/547-2100 | 349 |

| School/City/County<br>DISTRICT/CITY/COUNTY | PID | TELEPHONE<br>NUMBER | PAGE |
|---|---|---|---|
| Smithfield Middle Sch/N Richlnd Hls/ | | | |
| Tarrant | 01418589 | 817/547-5000 | 349 |
| Smithson Valley High Sch/Spring Branch/ | | | |
| Comal | 01525924 | 830/885-1000 | 92 |
| Smithson Valley Middle Sch/Spring Branch/ | | | |
| Comal | 01006904 | 830/885-1200 | 92 |
| Smithville Elem Sch/Smithville/Bastrop | 00995998 | 512/237-2406 | 27 |
| Smithville High Sch/Smithville/Bastrop | 00996007 | 512/237-2451 | 27 |
| **SMITHVILLE IND SCH DIST/** | | | |
| **SMITHVILLE/BASTROP** | 00995974 | 512/237-2487 | 27 |
| Smithville Junior High Sch/Smithville/ | | | |
| Bastrop | 00996019 | 512/237-2407 | 27 |
| Smyer Elem Sch/Smyer/Hockley | 01031284 | 806/234-2935 | 232 |
| **SMYER IND SCH DIST/SMYER/HOCKLEY** | 01031272 | 806/234-2935 | 232 |
| Smyer Jr Sr High Sch/Smyer/Hockley | 03399070 | 806/234-2935 | 232 |
| Smylie Wilson Middle Sch/Lubbock/Lubbock | 01039004 | 806/219-4600 | 273 |
| Sneed Elem Sch/Houston/Harris | 03328655 | 713/789-6979 | 187 |
| **SNOOK IND SCH DIST/SNOOK/** | | | |
| **BURLESON** | 01002685 | 979/272-8307 | 63 |
| Snook Sch/Snook/Burleson | 01002697 | 979/272-8307 | 63 |
| Snow Heights Elem Sch/N Richlnd Hls/ | | | |
| Tarrant | 01052202 | 817/547-2200 | 349 |
| Snyder Elem Sch/Spring/Montgomery | 11920445 | 832/663-4400 | 295 |
| Snyder High Sch/Snyder/Scurry | 01050163 | 325/574-8800 | 336 |
| **SNYDER IND SCH DIST/SNYDER/** | | | |
| **SCURRY** | 01050101 | 325/574-8900 | 336 |
| Snyder Intermediate Sch/Snyder/Scurry | 12033851 | 325/574-8650 | 336 |
| Snyder Junior High Sch/Snyder/Scurry | 01050137 | 325/574-8700 | 336 |
| Snyder Primary Sch/Snyder/Scurry | 01050125 | 325/574-8600 | 336 |
| Socorro High Sch/El Paso/El Paso | 01016234 | 915/937-2000 | 141 |
| **SOCORRO IND SCH DIST/EL PASO/** | | | |
| **EL PASO** | 01016208 | 915/937-0000 | 140 |
| Socorro Middle Sch/El Paso/El Paso | 03323629 | 915/937-5000 | 141 |
| Sojourn Academy/Conroe/Montgomery | 04993497 | 281/298-5800 | 298 |
| Solar Prep Sch for Girls-Bonhm/Dallas/ | | | |
| Dallas | 12169735 | 972/749-4300 | 107 |
| Solar Preparatory for Boys/Dallas/Dallas | 12318613 | 972/794-7100 | 107 |
| Solomon P Ortiz Interm Sch/Robstown/Nueces | 03051929 | 361/767-6662 | 308 |
| Somerset Early Chldhd Ctr/Somerset/Bexar | 04912027 | 866/852-9865 | 45 |
| Somerset Elem Sch/Somerset/Bexar | 00999358 | 866/852-9864 | 45 |
| Somerset High Sch/Somerset/Bexar | 00999372 | 210/750-8958 | 45 |
| **SOMERSET IND SCH DIST/SOMERSET/** | | | |
| **BEXAR** | 00999346 | 866/852-9858 | 45 |
| Somerset Junior High Sch/Von Ormy/Bexar | 00999360 | 210/750-8967 | 45 |
| Somerville Elem Sch/Somerville/Burleson | 01002726 | 979/596-1502 | 63 |
| Somerville High Sch/Somerville/Burleson | 01002738 | 979/596-1534 | 63 |
| **SOMERVILLE IND SCH DIST/** | | | |
| **SOMERVILLE/BURLESON** | 01002714 | 979/596-2153 | 63 |
| Somerville Intermediate Sch/Somerville/ | | | |
| Burleson | 12363369 | 979/596-1502 | 63 |
| Sonny & Allegra Nance ES/Fort Worth/Denton | 10012320 | 817/698-1950 | 129 |
| Sonora Elemementary Sch/Sonora/Sutton | 01051480 | 325/387-6940 | 345 |
| Sonora High Sch/Sonora/Sutton | 01051492 | 325/387-6940 | 345 |
| **SONORA IND SCH DIST/SONORA/** | | | |
| **SUTTON** | 01051478 | 325/387-6940 | 345 |
| Sonora Middle Sch/Sonora/Sutton | 01051507 | 325/387-6940 | 345 |
| Sorters Mill Elem Sch/Porter/Montgomery | 10903339 | 281/577-8780 | 297 |
| Sory Elem Sch/Sherman/Grayson | 11070650 | 903/891-6650 | 172 |
| Souder Elem Sch/Everman/Tarrant | 01052513 | 817/568-3580 | 352 |
| Sour Lake Elem Sch/Sour Lake/Hardin | 01022489 | 409/981-6440 | 183 |
| South Athens Elem Sch/Athens/Henderson | 01029281 | 903/677-6970 | 218 |
| South Belt Elem Sch/Houston/Harris | 11450000 | 713/740-5276 | 205 |
| South Belton Middle Sch/Belton/Bell | 11712341 | 254/215-3000 | 30 |
| South Bosque Elem Sch/Waco/McLennan | 03322443 | 254/761-5720 | 284 |
| South Davis Elem Sch/Arlington/Tarrant | 01051715 | 682/867-3800 | 347 |
| South Early College High Sch/Houston/ | | | |
| Harris | 10003915 | 713/732-3623 | 198 |
| South Elem Sch/Breckenridge/Stephens | 01051375 | 254/559-6554 | 344 |
| South Elem Sch/Daingerfield/Morris | 01172559 | 903/645-3501 | 299 |
| South Elem Sch/Lamesa/Dawson | 01012927 | 806/872-5401 | 121 |
| South Elem Sch/Levelland/Hockley | 01031181 | 806/894-6255 | 232 |
| South Elem Sch/Lubbock/Lubbock | 01039078 | 806/863-7102 | 274 |
| South Elem Sch/Midland/Midland | 01041655 | 432/240-8100 | 289 |
| South Euless Elem Sch/Euless/Tarrant | 01053892 | 817/354-3521 | 356 |
| South Garland High Sch/Garland/Dallas | 01010682 | 972/926-2700 | 110 |
| South Georgia Elem Sch/Amarillo/Potter | 01047441 | 806/326-5350 | 321 |
| South Grand Prairie 9th GR Ctr/Grand Prairie/ | | | |
| Dallas | 05092034 | 972/264-1769 | 112 |
| South Grand Prairie Echs/Grand Prairie/ | | | |
| Dallas | 12168602 | 972/343-7640 | 112 |
| South Grand Prairie High Sch/Grand Prairie/ | | | |
| Dallas | 01010981 | 972/343-1500 | 112 |

| School/City/County<br>DISTRICT/CITY/COUNTY | PID | TELEPHONE<br>NUMBER | PAGE |
|---|---|---|---|
| South Hi Mount Elem Sch/Fort Worth/Tarrant | 01053397 | 817/815-1800 | 354 |
| South Hills Elem Sch/Fort Worth/Tarrant | 01053402 | 817/814-5800 | 354 |
| South Hills High Sch/Fort Worth/Tarrant | 04815261 | 817/814-7000 | 354 |
| South Houston Elem Sch/South Houston/<br>Harris | 01026887 | 713/740-0736 | 205 |
| South Houston High Sch/South Houston/<br>Harris | 01026899 | 713/740-0350 | 205 |
| South Houston Intermediate Sch/South Houston/<br>Harris | 01026904 | 713/740-0490 | 205 |
| South Knoll Elem Sch/College Sta/Brazos | 01001992 | 979/764-5580 | 59 |
| South Lawn Elem Sch/Amarillo/Potter | 01047453 | 806/326-5400 | 321 |
| South Oak Cliff High Sch/Dallas/Dallas | 01009786 | 214/932-7000 | 107 |
| South Palm Gardens High Sch/Weslaco/<br>Hidalgo | 04034869 | 956/969-6621 | 229 |
| South Park Middle Sch/Corp Christi/Nueces | 01044633 | 361/878-4720 | 307 |
| South San Antonio Career Ctr/San Antonio/<br>Bexar | 01877349 | 210/977-7350 | 46 |
| South San Antonio High Sch/San Antonio/<br>Bexar | 00999504 | 210/977-7400 | 46 |
| **SOUTH SAN ANTONIO IND SCH DIST/**<br>**SAN ANTONIO/BEXAR** | 00999384 | 210/977-7000 | 45 |
| South Shaver Elem Sch/Pasadena/Harris | 01026916 | 713/740-0842 | 205 |
| South Texas Christian Academy/McAllen/<br>Hidalgo | 03017375 | 956/682-1117 | 229 |
| South Texas HS for Health Prof/Mercedes/<br>Cameron | 02231815 | 956/565-2237 | 71 |
| **SOUTH TEXAS IND SCH DIST/**<br>**MERCEDES/CAMERON** | 01808984 | 956/565-2454 | 71 |
| South Texas ISD Med Professns/Olmito/<br>Cameron | 01808996 | 956/214-6100 | 71 |
| South Texas Prep Academy/Edinburg/Cameron | 11123908 | 956/381-5522 | 71 |
| South TX ISD World Scholars/Edinburg/<br>Cameron | 01809005 | 956/383-1684 | 71 |
| South Waco Elem Sch/Waco/McLennan | 01040405 | 254/753-6802 | 285 |
| South Ward Elem Sch/Longview/Gregg | 01021112 | 903/803-5200 | 175 |
| Southard Middle Sch/Princeton/Collin | 05342724 | 469/952-5419 | 87 |
| Southcrest Christian Sch/Lubbock/Lubbock | 04994130 | 806/797-7400 | 275 |
| Southeast Early Childhood Ctr/Sweetwater/<br>Nolan | 12468622 | 325/235-3482 | 305 |
| Southeast Elem Sch/Sweetwater/Nolan | 01172553 | 325/235-9222 | 305 |
| Southern Hills Elem Sch/Wichita Falls/<br>Wichita | 01172981 | 940/235-1188 | 395 |
| Southgate Elem Sch/Garland/Dallas | 01010723 | 972/926-2590 | 110 |
| **SOUTHLAND IND SCH DIST/SOUTHLAND/**<br>**GARZA** | 01019638 | 806/996-5339 | 167 |
| Southland Sch/Southland/Garza | 01019640 | 806/996-5339 | 167 |
| Southmayd Elem Sch/Houston/Harris | 01025742 | 713/924-1720 | 195 |
| Southminster Sch/Missouri City/Fort Bend | 03371547 | 281/261-8872 | 160 |
| Southmore Intermediate Sch/Pasadena/Harris | 01026966 | 713/740-0500 | 205 |
| Southmost Elem Sch/Brownsville/Cameron | 03051620 | 956/548-8870 | 68 |
| Southridge Elem Sch/Lewisville/Denton | 04850912 | 469/713-5187 | 128 |
| Southside Alternative Sch/San Antonio/<br>Bexar | 04745094 | 210/882-1604 | 46 |
| Southside Elem Sch/Angleton/Brazoria | 01001526 | 979/864-8008 | 55 |
| Southside Elem Sch/Cleveland/Liberty | 01037769 | 281/592-0594 | 268 |
| Southside Elem Sch/Mabank/Kaufman | 02199542 | 903/880-1340 | 256 |
| Southside Elem Sch/Palestine/Anderson | 00994592 | 903/731-8023 | 19 |
| Southside High Sch/San Antonio/Bexar | 00999530 | 210/882-1606 | 46 |
| **SOUTHSIDE IND SCH DIST/SAN ANTONIO/**<br>**BEXAR** | 00999516 | 210/882-1600 | 46 |
| Southwest Adventist Jr Academy/Dallas/<br>Dallas | 02233667 | 214/948-1666 | 120 |
| Southwest Christian Academy/Houston/Harris | 02995516 | 281/561-7400 | 212 |
| Southwest Christian Sch/Fort Worth/Tarrant | 02233447 | 817/294-0350 | 362 |
| Southwest Christian Sch-Prep/Fort Worth/<br>Tarrant | 11566087 | 817/294-9596 | 362 |
| Southwest Cmty Christian Acad/Houston/<br>Harris | 04797516 | 281/575-9400 | 212 |
| Southwest Elem Sch/Belton/Bell | 00996370 | 254/215-3500 | 30 |
| Southwest Elem Sch/San Antonio/Bexar | 00999592 | 210/622-4420 | 47 |
| Southwest High Sch/Fort Worth/Tarrant | 01053414 | 817/814-8000 | 354 |
| Southwest High Sch/San Antonio/Bexar | 00999619 | 210/622-4500 | 47 |
| **SOUTHWEST IND SCH DIST/SAN ANTONIO/**<br>**BEXAR** | 00999578 | 210/622-4300 | 46 |
| Southwest Legacy High Sch/Von Ormy/Bexar | 12230906 | 210/623-6539 | 47 |
| Southwest Prep New Directions/San Antonio/<br>Bexar | 12164888 | 210/829-8017 | 14 |
| Southwest Prep Sch NE/San Antonio/Bexar | 04813469 | 210/829-8017 | 14 |
| Southwest Prep Sch NW/San Antonio/Bexar | 10019055 | 210/432-2634 | 14 |
| Southwest Prep Sch SE/San Antonio/Bexar | 10019043 | 210/333-1403 | 14 |
| Southwest Prep-Seguin/Seguin/Guadalupe | 12261151 | 830/549-5930 | 14 |

| School/City/County<br>DISTRICT/CITY/COUNTY | PID | TELEPHONE<br>NUMBER | PAGE |
|---|---|---|---|
| Southwest Preparatory-NW ES/San Antonio/<br>Bexar | 12261163 | 210/819-7860 | 14 |
| Southwest Sch-Bissonnet/Houston/Harris | 12027931 | 713/988-5839 | 14 |
| Southwest Sch-Discovery MS/Houston/Harris | 05010854 | 713/954-9528 | 14 |
| Southwest Sch-Empowerment HS/Houston/<br>Harris | 12260690 | 713/954-9528 | 14 |
| Southwest Sch-Mangum/Houston/Harris | 11704784 | 713/688-0505 | 14 |
| Southwest Schools-Phoenix/Houston/Harris | 12100181 | 346/571-6060 | 14 |
| Southwood Valley Elem Sch/College Sta/<br>Brazos | 02202761 | 979/764-5590 | 59 |
| Space Center Intermediate Sch/Houston/<br>Galveston | 04015265 | 281/284-3300 | 163 |
| Sparks Elem Sch/Pasadena/Harris | 02225115 | 713/740-0744 | 205 |
| Sparta Elem Sch/Belton/Bell | 03049598 | 254/215-3600 | 30 |
| Spc Rafael Hernando Middle Sch/El Paso/<br>El Paso | 11449398 | 915/937-9800 | 141 |
| Spearman High Sch/Spearman/Hansford | 01022336 | 806/659-2584 | 182 |
| **SPEARMAN IND SCH DIST/SPEARMAN/**<br>**HANSFORD** | 01022312 | 806/659-3233 | 182 |
| Spearman Junior High Sch/Spearman/Hansford | 01022348 | 806/659-2563 | 182 |
| Speegleville Elem Sch/Waco/McLennan | 01040118 | 254/761-5730 | 284 |
| Speer Elem Sch/Arlington/Tarrant | 01051923 | 682/867-4000 | 347 |
| Spence Elem Sch/Houston/Harris | 10000468 | 281/539-4050 | 185 |
| Spicer Alternative Ed Center/Bellville/<br>Austin | 04754318 | 979/865-7095 | 25 |
| Spicewood Elem Sch/Austin/Williamson | 01061150 | 512/428-3600 | 402 |
| Spicewood Elem Sch/Spicewood/Burnet | 05341407 | 830/798-3675 | 64 |
| Spicewood Park Elem Sch/San Antonio/Bexar | 11712389 | 210/622-4999 | 47 |
| Spillane Middle Sch/Cypress/Harris | 10000547 | 281/213-1645 | 190 |
| Splendora High Sch/Splendora/Montgomery | 01042740 | 281/689-8008 | 297 |
| **SPLENDORA IND SCH DIST/SPLENDORA/**<br>**MONTGOMERY** | 01042726 | 281/689-3128 | 297 |
| Splendora Junior High Sch/Splendora/<br>Montgomery | 01042752 | 281/689-6343 | 297 |
| Spradley Elem Sch/Frisco/Collin | 12307030 | 469/219-2250 | 88 |
| Spring Baptist Academy/Spring/Harris | 12235633 | 281/353-5448 | 212 |
| Spring Branch Academic Inst/Houston/Harris | 12308826 | 713/251-1901 | 206 |
| Spring Branch Elem Sch/Houston/Harris | 01027295 | 713/251-7000 | 206 |
| **SPRING BRANCH IND SCH DIST/**<br>**HOUSTON/HARRIS** | 01027087 | 713/464-1511 | 205 |
| Spring Branch Middle Sch/Houston/Harris | 01027300 | 713/251-4400 | 206 |
| Spring Branch Middle Sch/Spring Branch/<br>Comal | 04808189 | 830/885-8800 | 92 |
| Spring Creek Academy/Plano/Collin | 12314150 | 972/517-6730 | 90 |
| Spring Creek Elem Sch/College Sta/Brazos | 12104242 | 979/694-5838 | 59 |
| Spring Creek Elem Sch/Dallas/Dallas | 01011947 | 469/593-4500 | 117 |
| Spring Creek Elem Sch/Garland/Dallas | 02127769 | 972/675-3060 | 110 |
| **SPRING CREEK IND SCH DIST/**<br>**SKELLYTOWN/HUTCHINSON** | 01032812 | 806/273-6791 | 241 |
| Spring Creek Sch/Skellytown/Hutchinson | 01032824 | 806/273-6791 | 241 |
| Spring Early College Academy/Houston/<br>Harris | 11719040 | 281/891-6880 | 208 |
| Spring Forest Middle Sch/Houston/Harris | 01027324 | 713/251-4600 | 206 |
| Spring Garden Elem Sch/Bedford/Tarrant | 02201614 | 817/354-3395 | 356 |
| Spring High Sch/Spring/Harris | 01027532 | 281/891-7000 | 208 |
| Spring Hill Elem Sch/Pflugerville/Travis | 04454233 | 512/594-5400 | 375 |
| Spring Hill High Sch/Longview/Gregg | 01021277 | 903/446-3300 | 175 |
| **SPRING HILL IND SCH DIST/**<br>**LONGVIEW/GREGG** | 01021253 | 903/759-4404 | 175 |
| Spring Hill Intermediate Sch/Longview/<br>Gregg | 01021265 | 903/323-7701 | 176 |
| Spring Hill Junior High Sch/Longview/Gregg | 01021289 | 903/323-7718 | 176 |
| Spring Hill Primary Sch/Longview/Gregg | 04906509 | 903/323-7848 | 176 |
| **SPRING IND SCH DIST/HOUSTON/**<br>**HARRIS** | 01027465 | 281/891-6000 | 207 |
| Spring Lake Park Elem Sch/Texarkana/Bowie | 03007045 | 903/794-7525 | 53 |
| Spring Leadership Acad Mid Sch/Houston/<br>Harris | 12365941 | 281/891-8050 | 208 |
| Spring Meadows Elem Sch/San Antonio/Bexar | 02896855 | 210/662-1050 | 37 |
| Spring Oaks Middle Sch/Houston/Harris | 01027336 | 713/251-4800 | 206 |
| Spring Shadows Elem Sch/Houston/Harris | 01027348 | 713/251-7100 | 206 |
| Spring Valley Elem Sch/Dallas/Dallas | 01011961 | 469/593-4600 | 117 |
| Spring Valley Elem Sch/Hewitt/McLennan | 02906967 | 254/761-5710 | 284 |
| Spring Virtual Sch/Houston/Harris | 11927728 | 281/891-6223 | 208 |
| Spring Woods High Sch/Houston/Harris | 01027362 | 713/251-3100 | 206 |
| Spring Woods Middle Sch/Houston/Harris | 01027350 | 713/251-5000 | 206 |
| Springdale Elem Sch/Fort Worth/Tarrant | 01053426 | 817/814-9600 | 354 |
| Springlake-Earth Elem Mid Sch/Earth/Lamb | 01037056 | 806/257-3310 | 264 |
| Springlake-Earth High Sch/Earth/Lamb | 01037068 | 806/257-3819 | 264 |
| **SPRINGLAKE-EARTH IND SCH DIST/**<br>**EARTH/LAMB** | 01037044 | 806/257-3310 | 264 |
| Springridge Elem Sch/Richardson/Dallas | 01011959 | 469/593-8600 | 117 |

| School/City/County DISTRICT/CITY/COUNTY | PID | TELEPHONE NUMBER | PAGE |
|---|---|---|---|
| Springtown Elem Sch/Springtown/Parker | 01046538 | 817/220-2498 | 316 |
| Springtown High Sch/Springtown/Parker | 01046526 | 817/220-3888 | 316 |
| **SPRINGTOWN IND SCH DIST/** **SPRINGTOWN/PARKER** | 01046514 | 817/220-7243 | 316 |
| Springtown Intermediate Sch/Springtown/ Parker | 04918459 | 817/220-1219 | 316 |
| Springtown Middle Sch/Springtown/Parker | 02894962 | 817/220-7455 | 316 |
| Springwoods Village Mid Sch/Spring/Harris | 12365953 | 281/891-8100 | 208 |
| **SPUR IND SCH DIST/SPUR/DICKENS** | 01013969 | 806/271-3272 | 131 |
| Spur Sch/Spur/Dickens | 01013983 | 806/271-3385 | 131 |
| Spurger Elem Sch/Spurger/Tyler | 01057264 | 409/429-3464 | 378 |
| Spurger High Sch/Spurger/Tyler | 01057276 | 409/429-3464 | 378 |
| **SPURGER IND SCH DIST/SPURGER/** **TYLER** | 01057252 | 409/429-3464 | 377 |
| Spurling Christian Academy/Arlington/ Tarrant | 11915191 | 817/465-1122 | 362 |
| SS Cyril & Methodius Sch/Corp Christi/ Nueces | 01045314 | 361/853-9392 | 309 |
| SS Peter & Paul Sch/New Braunfels/Comal | 01000065 | 830/625-4531 | 93 |
| Ssg Manuel R Puentes Mid Sch/El Paso/ El Paso | 11920524 | 915/937-9200 | 141 |
| St Agnes Academy/Houston/Harris | 01028237 | 713/219-5400 | 209 |
| St Alban's Episcopal Day Sch/Harlingen/ Cameron | 01479662 | 956/428-2326 | 72 |
| St Ambrose Sch/Houston/Harris | 01028172 | 713/686-6990 | 209 |
| St Andrew Catholic Sch/Fort Worth/Tarrant | 01054456 | 817/924-8917 | 360 |
| St Andrew's Episcopal Day Sch/Amarillo/ Potter | 01047647 | 806/376-9501 | 322 |
| St Andrew's Episcopal Sch/Austin/Travis | 01057018 | 512/452-5779 | 376 |
| St Ann's Sch/Midland/Midland | 01055967 | 432/684-4563 | 289 |
| St Anne Catholic Elem Sch/Tomball/Harris | 02229707 | 281/351-0093 | 209 |
| St Anne Catholic Sch/Beaumont/Jefferson | 01034391 | 409/832-5939 | 247 |
| St Anne Sch/Houston/Harris | 01028249 | 713/526-3279 | 209 |
| St Anthony Academy/Dallas/Dallas | 01012549 | 214/421-3645 | 14 |
| St Anthony Cathedral Sch/Beaumont/ Jefferson | 01034406 | 409/832-3486 | 247 |
| St Anthony Catholic Elem Sch/San Antonio/ Bexar | 01000106 | 210/732-8801 | 47 |
| St Anthony Catholic High Sch/San Antonio/ Bexar | 01000118 | 210/832-5600 | 47 |
| St Anthony of Padua Sch/The Woodlands/ Montgomery | 04942785 | 281/296-0300 | 298 |
| St Anthony Sch/Columbus/Colorado | 01000091 | 979/732-5505 | 91 |
| St Anthony Sch/Harlingen/Cameron | 01004437 | 956/423-2486 | 71 |
| St Anthony Sch/Robstown/Nueces | 01045326 | 361/387-3814 | 309 |
| St Anthony's Elem Sch/Hereford/Deaf Smith | 01047714 | 806/364-1952 | 123 |
| St Anthony's of Padua Elem/Dalhart/Dallam | 01047702 | 806/244-4811 | 99 |
| St Augustine Catholic Sch/Houston/Harris | 01028213 | 713/946-9050 | 209 |
| St Augustine Elem Middle Sch/Laredo/Webb | 01045443 | 956/724-1176 | 391 |
| St Augustine High Sch/Laredo/Webb | 01045338 | 956/724-8131 | 391 |
| St Austin Catholic Sch/Austin/Travis | 01002922 | 512/477-3751 | 375 |
| St Bernard of Clairvaux Sch/Dallas/Dallas | 01012563 | 214/321-2897 | 118 |
| St Catherine of Siena Sch/Port Arthur/ Jefferson | 01034418 | 409/962-3011 | 247 |
| St Catherine's Montessori Sch/Houston/ Harris | 01600469 | 713/665-2195 | 209 |
| St Cecilia Catholic Sch/Houston/Harris | 01028251 | 713/468-9515 | 209 |
| St Cecilia Sch/Dallas/Dallas | 01012525 | 214/948-8628 | 118 |
| St Christopher Catholic Sch/Houston/Harris | 01028275 | 713/649-0009 | 209 |
| St Clare of Assisi Sch/Houston/Harris | 04423703 | 281/286-3595 | 209 |
| St Clement's Parish Sch/El Paso/El Paso | 01016698 | 915/533-4248 | 144 |
| St Cyprian's Episcopal Sch/Lufkin/Angelina | 00995118 | 936/632-1720 | 21 |
| St Dominic Savio Catholic HS/Austin/ Williamson | 11564704 | 512/388-8846 | 403 |
| St Edward Catholic Sch/Spring/Harris | 01534303 | 281/353-4570 | 209 |
| St Elizabeth Ann Seton Sch/Keller/Tarrant | 04928583 | 817/431-4845 | 360 |
| St Elizabeth of Hungary Sch/Dallas/Dallas | 01012575 | 214/331-5139 | 118 |
| St Elizabeth Sch/Alice/Jim Wells | 01045340 | 361/664-6271 | 249 |
| St Elizabeth Seton Cath Sch/Houston/Harris | 04484109 | 281/461-1444 | 209 |
| St Elmo Elem Sch/Austin/Travis | 01056648 | 512/414-4477 | 370 |
| St Francis DeSales Sch/Houston/Harris | 01028287 | 713/774-4447 | 209 |
| St Francis Episcopal Sch/Houston/Harris | 01027726 | 713/458-6100 | 212 |
| St Francis Sch/Austin/Travis | 12314019 | 512/454-0848 | 376 |
| St Gabriel's Catholic Sch/Austin/Travis | 04879073 | 512/327-7755 | 375 |
| St George Episcopal Sch/San Antonio/Bexar | 01479569 | 210/342-4263 | 48 |
| St George Sch/Fort Worth/Tarrant | 01054468 | 817/222-1221 | 360 |
| St Gerard Catholic High Sch/San Antonio/ Bexar | 01000156 | 210/533-8061 | 47 |
| St Gregory Cathedral Sch/Tyler/Smith | 01012587 | 903/595-4109 | 342 |
| St Gregory the Great Cath Sch/San Antonio/ Bexar | 01000041 | 210/342-0281 | 47 |

| School/City/County DISTRICT/CITY/COUNTY | PID | TELEPHONE NUMBER | PAGE |
|---|---|---|---|
| St Helen Catholic Sch/Georgetown/ Williamson | 05153535 | 512/868-0744 | 403 |
| St Helen Sch/Pearland/Brazoria | 04794227 | 281/485-2845 | 57 |
| St Ignatius College Prep Sch/Fort Worth/ Tarrant | 11571446 | 817/801-4801 | 362 |
| St Ignatius Martyr Cath Sch/Austin/Travis | 01002934 | 512/442-8547 | 375 |
| St James Catholic Sch/Seguin/Guadalupe | 01000168 | 830/379-2878 | 179 |
| St James Day Sch/Texarkana/Bowie | 01479595 | 903/793-5554 | 54 |
| St James Episcopal Sch/Corp Christi/Nueces | 01045132 | 361/883-0835 | 309 |
| St James Episcopal Sch/Del Rio/Val Verde | 01058074 | 830/775-9911 | 382 |
| St James the Apostle Sch/San Antonio/Bexar | 01000170 | 210/924-1201 | 47 |
| St Jerome Sch/Houston/Harris | 01028184 | 713/468-7946 | 209 |
| St Jo Elem Sch/Saint Jo/Montague | 01042415 | 940/995-2541 | 293 |
| St Jo High Sch/Saint Jo/Montague | 01042427 | 940/995-2532 | 293 |
| **ST JO IND SCH DIST/SAINT JO/** **MONTAGUE** | 01042403 | 940/995-2668 | 293 |
| St John Berchman's Sch/San Antonio/Bexar | 02203703 | 210/433-0411 | 47 |
| St John Bosco Sch/San Antonio/Bexar | 01000182 | 210/432-8011 | 47 |
| St John Early Childhood Center/Cypress/ Harris | 12314057 | 281/304-5546 | 212 |
| St John Paul II Catholic Sch/Houston/ Harris | 03077765 | 281/496-1500 | 209 |
| St John Paul II High Sch/Corp Christi/ Nueces | 11401516 | 361/855-5744 | 309 |
| St John Paul II High Sch/New Braunfels/ Comal | 11705142 | 830/643-0802 | 93 |
| St John the Apostle Cath Sch/N Richlnd Hls/ Tarrant | 01054470 | 817/284-2228 | 360 |
| St John XXIII Preparatory HS/Katy/Harris | 10756215 | 281/693-1000 | 209 |
| St John's Episcopal Day Sch/McAllen/ Hidalgo | 01410874 | 956/686-0231 | 229 |
| St John's Episcopal Sch/Abilene/Taylor | 01055034 | 325/695-8870 | 364 |
| St John's Episcopal Sch/Dallas/Dallas | 01012305 | 214/328-9131 | 120 |
| St John's Episcopal Sch/Odessa/Ector | 01410692 | 432/337-6431 | 135 |
| St John's Sch/Houston/Harris | 01028421 | 713/850-0222 | 212 |
| St Jose Sanchez Del Rio Sch/San Antonio/ Bexar | 05286340 | 210/497-0323 | 47 |
| St Joseph Academy/Brownsville/Cameron | 01004449 | 956/542-3581 | 71 |
| St Joseph Catholic Sch/Arlington/Tarrant | 04420701 | 817/419-6800 | 360 |
| St Joseph Catholic Sch/Bryan/Brazos | 01002946 | 979/822-6641 | 59 |
| St Joseph Catholic Sch/Edinburg/Hidalgo | 01004451 | 956/383-3957 | 229 |
| St Joseph Catholic Sch/Killeen/Bell | 01002958 | 254/634-7272 | 33 |
| St Joseph Catholic Sch/Richardson/Dallas | 05153547 | 972/234-4679 | 118 |
| St Joseph Catholic Sch/Waxahachie/Ellis | 04021874 | 972/937-0956 | 147 |
| St Joseph Catholic Sch/Yoakum/Lavaca | 01000223 | 361/293-9000 | 265 |
| St Joseph Elem Sch/Amarillo/Randall | 01047740 | 806/359-1604 | 324 |
| St Joseph High Sch/Victoria/Victoria | 01000209 | 361/573-2446 | 385 |
| St Joseph Sch/Alice/Jim Wells | 01045388 | 361/664-4642 | 249 |
| St Joseph Sch/Baytown/Harris | 01028304 | 281/422-9749 | 209 |
| St Joseph Sch/El Paso/El Paso | 01016882 | 915/566-1661 | 143 |
| St Laurence Catholic Sch/Sugar Land/ Fort Bend | 04022048 | 281/980-0500 | 159 |
| St Louis Catholic Sch/Austin/Travis | 01002972 | 512/614-6622 | 375 |
| St Louis Early Childhood Ctr/Tyler/Smith | 01050955 | 903/262-1180 | 341 |
| St Louis Sch/Castroville/Medina | 03266318 | 830/931-3544 | 287 |
| St Luke Catholic Sch/Brownsville/Cameron | 04307317 | 956/544-7982 | 71 |
| St Luke Catholic Sch/San Antonio/Bexar | 01000053 | 210/434-2011 | 47 |
| St Luke Sch/Denison/Grayson | 02083840 | 903/465-2653 | 174 |
| St Luke's Episcopal Sch/San Antonio/Bexar | 00999695 | 210/826-0664 | 48 |
| St Margaret Mary Sch/San Antonio/Bexar | 01000259 | 210/534-6137 | 47 |
| St Maria Goretti Sch/Arlington/Tarrant | 01054482 | 817/275-5081 | 360 |
| St Mark Catholic Sch/Plano/Collin | 02181155 | 972/578-0610 | 89 |
| St Mark Lutheran Sch/Houston/Harris | 01027740 | 713/468-2623 | 212 |
| St Mark's Episcopal Sch/Houston/Harris | 01027752 | 713/667-7030 | 212 |
| St Mark's Sch/El Paso/El Paso | 02743387 | 915/581-2032 | 144 |
| St Mark's School of Texas/Dallas/Dallas | 01012147 | 214/346-8000 | 120 |
| St Martha Catholic Sch/Kingwood/Harris | 04420543 | 281/358-5523 | 209 |
| St Martin De Porres Cath Sch/Prosper/ Collin | 11815292 | 469/362-2400 | 89 |
| St Mary Catholic Sch/League City/Galveston | 02138017 | 281/332-4014 | 166 |
| St Mary Catholic Sch/Orange/Orange | 01034444 | 409/883-8913 | 312 |
| St Mary Catholic Sch/West/McLennan | 01002996 | 254/826-5991 | 285 |
| St Mary Elem Sch/Fredericksbrg/Gillespie | 01000273 | 830/997-3914 | 168 |
| St Mary Magdalen Sch/San Antonio/Bexar | 01000285 | 210/735-1381 | 47 |
| St Mary Magdalene Sch/Humble/Harris | 04942797 | 281/446-8535 | 209 |
| St Mary of Carmel Sch/Dallas/Dallas | 01012630 | 214/748-2934 | 118 |
| St Mary Purification Mont Sch/Houston/ Harris | 02114011 | 713/522-9276 | 209 |
| St Mary's Academy Charter Sch/Beeville/Bee | 01045390 | 361/358-5601 | 14 |
| St Mary's Catholic Sch/Gainesville/Cooke | 01054494 | 940/665-5395 | 96 |
| St Mary's Catholic Sch/Longview/Gregg | 01012642 | 903/753-1657 | 176 |
| St Mary's Catholic Sch/Temple/Bell | 01003017 | 254/778-8141 | 33 |

| School/City/County DISTRICT/CITY/COUNTY | PID | TELEPHONE NUMBER | PAGE |
|---|---|---|---|
| St Mary's Central Catholic Sch/Odessa/ Ector | 01055981 | 432/337-6052 | 135 |
| St Mary's Sch/Brownsville/Cameron | 01004463 | 956/546-1805 | 71 |
| St Mary's Sch/Taylor/Williamson | 01002908 | 512/352-2313 | 403 |
| St Maryis Cathedral Sch/Amarillo/Potter | 01047776 | 806/376-9112 | 322 |
| St Marys Catholic Sch/Sherman/Grayson | 01012654 | 903/893-2127 | 173 |
| St Matthew Catholic Sch/San Antonio/Bexar | 04145793 | 210/478-5099 | 47 |
| St Matthew's Episcopal Sch/Edinburg/ Hidalgo | 01560651 | 956/383-4202 | 229 |
| St Matthews Catholic Sch/El Paso/El Paso | 11532828 | 915/581-8801 | 143 |
| St Michael Catholic Sch/Houston/Harris | 01028196 | 713/621-6847 | 209 |
| St Michael Sch/Cuero/De Witt | 01000326 | 361/274-3854 | 123 |
| St Michael Sch/Weimar/Colorado | 01000338 | 979/725-8461 | 91 |
| St Michael's Catholic Academy/Austin/ Travis | 02229537 | 512/328-2323 | 375 |
| St Michael's Learning Academy/Houston/ Harris | 12314021 | 713/977-0566 | 212 |
| St Michaels Episcopal Sch/Bryan/Brazos | 01002178 | 979/822-2715 | 60 |
| St Monica Catholic Sch/Dallas/Dallas | 01012537 | 214/351-5688 | 118 |
| St Monica Sch/Converse/Bexar | 01000340 | 210/658-6701 | 47 |
| St Nicholas Sch/Houston/Harris | 04993227 | 713/791-9977 | 212 |
| St Patrick Cathedral Sch/El Paso/El Paso | 01016959 | 915/532-4142 | 143 |
| St Patrick Catholic Sch/Lufkin/Angelina | 01034456 | 936/634-6719 | 21 |
| St Patrick Sch/Corp Christi/Nueces | 01045302 | 361/852-1211 | 309 |
| St Patrick Sch/Dallas/Dallas | 01012678 | 214/348-8070 | 118 |
| St Paul Catholic Sch/San Antonio/Bexar | 01000376 | 210/732-2741 | 47 |
| St Paul Lutheran Sch/Bishop/Nueces | 01045156 | 361/584-2778 | 309 |
| St Paul Lutheran Sch/Fort Worth/Tarrant | 01054298 | 817/332-4563 | 362 |
| St Paul Lutheran Sch/Giddings/Lee | 01037549 | 979/366-2218 | 266 |
| St Paul Lutheran Sch/McAllen/Hidalgo | 01030694 | 956/682-2345 | 229 |
| St Paul Lutheran Sch/Thorndale/Milam | 01041930 | 512/898-2711 | 291 |
| St Paul the Apostle Sch/Richardson/Dallas | 01012680 | 972/235-3263 | 118 |
| St Paul's Episcopal Sch/Waco/McLennan | 01040546 | 254/753-0246 | 286 |
| St Paul's Episcopal Sch/Woodville/Tyler | 03017789 | 409/283-7555 | 378 |
| St Paul's Preparatory Academy/Arlington/ Tarrant | 04886014 | 817/561-3500 | 362 |
| St Peter Prince of Apostles/San Antonio/ Bexar | 01000388 | 210/824-3171 | 47 |
| St Peter the Apostle Elem Sch/Houston/ Harris | 01028330 | 713/747-9484 | 209 |
| St Peter the Apostle Sch/WHT Settlemt/ Tarrant | 01054511 | 817/246-2032 | 360 |
| St Philip & St Augustine Acad/Dallas/ Dallas | 01012707 | 214/381-4973 | 118 |
| St Philip Catholic Sch/El Campo/Wharton | 01000405 | 979/543-2901 | 393 |
| St Philip's Academy-Frisco/Frisco/Collin | 11735226 | 214/929-7787 | 90 |
| St Philip's Early Clg HS/San Antonio/Bexar | 12034403 | 210/486-2406 | 44 |
| St Philip's Episcopal Sch/Beeville/Bee | 01410496 | 361/358-6242 | 29 |
| St Philip's Episcopal Sch/Dallas/Dallas | 02083797 | 214/421-5221 | 120 |
| St Philip's Episcopal Sch/Uvalde/Uvalde | 01057886 | 830/278-1350 | 381 |
| St Pius X Catholic Sch/San Antonio/Bexar | 01000417 | 210/824-6431 | 47 |
| St Pius X High Sch/Houston/Harris | 01028366 | 713/692-3581 | 209 |
| St Pius X Sch/Corp Christi/Nueces | 01045429 | 361/992-1343 | 309 |
| St Pius X Sch/Dallas/Dallas | 01012719 | 972/279-2339 | 118 |
| St Pius X Sch/El Paso/El Paso | 01016961 | 915/262-4846 | 143 |
| St Raphael Catholic Sch/El Paso/El Paso | 01857181 | 915/598-2241 | 143 |
| St Rita Catholic Sch/Dallas/Dallas | 01012721 | 972/239-3203 | 118 |
| St Rita Catholic Sch/Fort Worth/Tarrant | 01054444 | 817/451-9383 | 360 |
| St Rose of Lima Sch/Houston/Harris | 01028378 | 713/691-0104 | 209 |
| St Rose of Lima Sch/Schulenburg/Fayette | 01000429 | 979/743-3080 | 152 |
| St Stephen's Episcopal Sch/Austin/Travis | 01057032 | 512/327-1213 | 376 |
| St Stephen's Episcopal Sch/Houston/Harris | 01410886 | 713/821-9100 | 212 |
| St Stephen's Episcopal Sch/Wimberley/Hays | 04012811 | 512/847-9857 | 217 |
| St Theresa Sch/Houston/Harris | 01028380 | 713/864-4536 | 209 |
| St Theresa Sch/Sugar Land/Fort Bend | 11532830 | 281/494-1156 | 159 |
| St Theresa's Catholic Sch/Austin/Travis | 02903484 | 512/451-7105 | 375 |
| St Thomas Apostle Episc Sch/Houston/Harris | 01410800 | 281/333-1340 | 212 |
| St Thomas Aquinas Sch/Dallas/Dallas | 01012733 | 214/826-0566 | 118 |
| St Thomas Episcopal Sch/San Antonio/Bexar | 01875080 | 210/494-3509 | 48 |
| St Thomas High Sch/Houston/Harris | 01028392 | 713/864-6348 | 210 |
| St Thomas More Catholic Sch/San Antonio/ Bexar | 01000443 | 210/655-2882 | 47 |
| St Thomas More Sch/Houston/Harris | 01028407 | 713/729-3434 | 210 |
| St Thomas' Episcopal Sch/Houston/Harris | 01027788 | 713/666-3111 | 212 |
| St Vincent De Paul Sch/Houston/Harris | 01028201 | 713/666-2345 | 210 |
| Stacey Jr Sr High Sch/San Antonio/Bexar | 01808831 | 210/357-5100 | 37 |
| Stafford Alt Ed Campus/Stafford/Fort Bend | 04503858 | 281/261-9270 | 159 |
| Stafford Early Childhd Ctr/San Antonio/ Bexar | 11713503 | 210/444-7900 | 35 |
| Stafford Elem Sch/Italy/Ellis | 01015084 | 972/483-6342 | 145 |
| Stafford Elem Sch/San Antonio/Bexar | 00997324 | 210/444-8400 | 35 |
| Stafford Elem Sch/Stafford/Fort Bend | 04942008 | 281/261-9229 | 159 |
| Stafford High Sch/Stafford/Fort Bend | 03316793 | 281/261-9239 | 159 |
| Stafford Intermediate Sch/Stafford/ Fort Bend | 04010289 | 281/208-6100 | 159 |
| Stafford Middle Sch/Stafford/Fort Bend | 03316781 | 281/261-9215 | 159 |
| **STAFFORD MUNICIPAL SCH DIST/** STAFFORD/FORT BEND | 02228624 | 281/261-9200 | 159 |
| Stafford Primary Sch/Stafford/Fort Bend | 02228636 | 281/261-9203 | 159 |
| Staggs Acad Intl STEM Studies/Laredo/Webb | 12361206 | 956/326-2861 | 14 |
| Stahl Elem Sch/San Antonio/Bexar | 01881821 | 210/407-7400 | 39 |
| Stamford High Sch/Stamford/Jones | 01035357 | 325/773-2701 | 253 |
| **STAMFORD IND SCH DIST/STAMFORD/** JONES | 01035321 | 325/773-2705 | 253 |
| Stamford Middle Sch/Stamford/Jones | 01035345 | 325/773-2651 | 253 |
| Stan C Stanley Elem Sch/Katy/Harris | 11448564 | 281/234-1400 | 157 |
| Stanton Elem Sch/El Paso/El Paso | 01015876 | 915/236-6125 | 138 |
| Stanton Elem Sch/Stanton/Martin | 01040766 | 432/756-2285 | 277 |
| Stanton High Sch/Stanton/Martin | 01040778 | 432/756-3326 | 277 |
| **STANTON IND SCH DIST/STANTON/** MARTIN | 01040754 | 432/607-3700 | 277 |
| Stanton Middle Sch/Stanton/Martin | 01418539 | 432/756-2544 | 277 |
| Stanton-Smith Elem Sch/Whitehouse/Smith | 11072373 | 903/839-5730 | 341 |
| Starkey Elem Sch/Kerrville/Kerr | 01036105 | 830/257-2210 | 259 |
| Starpoint Sch/Fort Worth/Tarrant | 02238186 | 817/257-7141 | 362 |
| Starrett Elem Sch/Grand Prairie/Tarrant | 03011709 | 682/867-0400 | 347 |
| Stars Accelerated High Sch/Granbury/Hood | 04282236 | 817/408-4450 | 233 |
| Startzville Elem Sch/Canyon Lake/Comal | 01397026 | 830/885-8000 | 92 |
| Stateline Christian Sch/Texline/Dallam | 11231660 | 806/362-4320 | 99 |
| Steam Academy at Stribling/Burleson/ Johnson | 01034860 | 817/245-3500 | 250 |
| Steam Middle Sch/Burleson/Johnson | 12107206 | 817/245-1500 | 250 |
| Stehlik Elem Sch/Houston/Harris | 04032603 | 281/878-0300 | 184 |
| Steiner Ranch Elem Sch/Austin/Williamson | 04455823 | 512/570-5700 | 400 |
| Stell Middle Sch/Brownsville/Cameron | 01003706 | 956/698-0363 | 68 |
| Stelle Claughton Middle Sch/Houston/Harris | 05273252 | 281/891-7950 | 208 |
| STEM Academy-Killeen/Killeen/Bell | 12366244 | 254/336-7836 | 31 |
| STEM Acadeny-Lewisville/Lewisville/Denton | 11663037 | 972/316-6700 | 14 |
| STEM Early College High Sch/San Antonio/ Bexar | 12032986 | 210/989-3500 | 36 |
| STEM2 Preparatory Academy/Harlingen/ Cameron | 12364650 | 956/368-6100 | 68 |
| Step by Step Christian Sch/Tomball/Harris | 02751786 | 281/351-2888 | 212 |
| Step Charter School II/Houston/Harris | 11014890 | 281/988-7797 | 14 |
| Stephen C Foster Elem Sch/Dallas/Dallas | 01009762 | 972/794-8100 | 107 |
| Stephen F Austin Elem Sch/Baytown/Harris | 01023756 | 281/420-4620 | 193 |
| Stephen F Austin Elem Sch/Dayton/Liberty | 01037800 | 936/258-2535 | 268 |
| Stephen F Austin Elem Sch/Ennis/Ellis | 01015010 | 972/872-7190 | 144 |
| Stephen F Austin Elem Sch/Gregory/ San Patricio | 01049542 | 361/777-4252 | 333 |
| Stephen F Austin High Sch/Sugar Land/ Fort Bend | 04365888 | 281/634-2000 | 155 |
| Stephen F Austin Middle Sch/Amarillo/ Potter | 01047154 | 806/326-3000 | 321 |
| Stephen F Austin Middle Sch/Bryan/Brazos | 03400590 | 979/209-6700 | 58 |
| Stephen F Austin Primary/Slaton/Lubbock | 01039200 | 806/828-5813 | 275 |
| Stephen F Austin STEM Academy/Freeport/ Brazoria | 01001679 | 979/730-7160 | 56 |
| Stephen F Austin Univ CS/Nacogdoches/ Nacogdoches | 05097979 | 936/468-5899 | 14 |
| Stephens Elem Sch/Rowlett/Dallas | 04284301 | 972/463-5790 | 111 |
| Stephens Elem Sch/Shady Shores/Denton | 11128568 | 940/369-0800 | 125 |
| Stephenville Christian Sch/Stephenville/ Erath | 11231737 | 254/965-4821 | 148 |
| Stephenville High Sch/Stephenville/Erath | 01017161 | 254/968-4141 | 148 |
| **STEPHENVILLE IND SCH DIST/** STEPHENVILLE/ERATH | 01017135 | 254/968-7990 | 148 |
| Sterling Aviation High Sch/Houston/Harris | 01025338 | 713/991-0510 | 198 |
| **STERLING CITY IND SCH DIST/** STERLING CITY/STERLING | 01051387 | 325/378-4781 | 344 |
| Sterling Elem Sch/Sterling City/Sterling | 01051399 | 325/378-5821 | 344 |
| Sterling H Fly Jr High Sch/Crystal City/ Zavala | 01062350 | 830/374-2371 | 410 |
| Sterling Middle High Sch/Sterling City/ Sterling | 04503834 | 325/378-5821 | 344 |
| Steubing Ranch Elem Sch/San Antonio/Bexar | 10003329 | 210/407-7600 | 39 |
| Stevens Elem Sch/Houston/Harris | 01024267 | 713/613-2546 | 194 |
| Stevens Park Elem Sch/Dallas/Dallas | 01009889 | 972/794-4200 | 107 |
| Stevenson Middle Sch/San Antonio/Bexar | 01379921 | 210/397-7300 | 41 |
| Stewart Creek Elem Sch/Montgomery/ Montgomery | 05231216 | 936/276-3500 | 296 |
| Stewart Elem Sch/Hitchcock/Galveston | 01018892 | 409/316-6543 | 165 |
| Stewart Elem Sch/Lubbock/Lubbock | 01038921 | 806/219-6900 | 273 |
| Stewart's Creek Elem Sch/The Colony/Denton | 02179566 | 469/713-5960 | 128 |

| School/City/County<br>DISTRICT/CITY/COUNTY | PID | TELEPHONE<br>NUMBER | PAGE |
|---|---|---|---|
| Stiles Middle Sch/Leander/Williamson | 11823330 | 512/570-3800 | 400 |
| Stillman Middle Sch/Brownsville/Cameron | 01003495 | 956/698-1000 | 68 |
| Stinson Elem Sch/Richardson/Collin | 04916281 | 469/752-3400 | 87 |
| Stinson Middle Sch/San Antonio/Bexar | 03398131 | 210/397-3600 | 41 |
| Stipes Elem Sch/Irving/Dallas | 10023240 | 972/600-4500 | 114 |
| Stockdale Elem Sch/Stockdale/Wilson | 01061394 | 830/996-1612 | 404 |
| Stockdale Elem Sch/Stockdale/Wilson | 01061409 | 830/996-3103 | 404 |
| **STOCKDALE IND SCH DIST/STOCKDALE/**<br>**WILSON** | 01061382 | 830/996-3551 | 404 |
| Stockdale Junior High Sch/Stockdale/Wilson | 01061411 | 830/996-3153 | 404 |
| Stockdick Jr High Sch/Katy/Harris | 12231273 | 281/234-2700 | 157 |
| Stockton Junior High Sch/Conroe/Montgomery | 12471916 | 936/709-4500 | 295 |
| Stone Oak Elem Sch/San Antonio/Bexar | 04455407 | 210/407-7800 | 39 |
| Stonegate Christian Academy/Irving/Dallas | 02164872 | 972/790-0070 | 120 |
| Stonegate Elem Sch/Bedford/Tarrant | 01053933 | 817/285-3250 | 356 |
| Stonehill Christian Academy/Pflugerville/<br>Travis | 02233734 | 512/763-2776 | 376 |
| Stonewall Elem Sch/Stonewall/Gillespie | 01019729 | 830/990-4599 | 167 |
| Stonewall Flanders Elem Sch/San Antonio/<br>Bexar | 00997439 | 210/989-3300 | 36 |
| Stony Point High Sch/Round Rock/Williamson | 04867317 | 512/428-7000 | 402 |
| Story Intermediate Sch/Palestine/Anderson | 01808788 | 903/731-8015 | 19 |
| Stovall EC-PK-K Sch/Houston/Harris | 03336016 | 281/591-8500 | 186 |
| Strack Intermediate Sch/Klein/Harris | 01539183 | 832/249-5400 | 203 |
| Strake Jesuit College Prep Sch/Houston/<br>Harris | 01028419 | 713/774-7651 | 210 |
| Stratford High Sch/Houston/Harris | 01027374 | 713/251-3400 | 206 |
| Stratford High Sch/Stratford/Sherman | 01050515 | 806/366-3330 | 338 |
| **STRATFORD IND SCH DIST/STRATFORD/**<br>**SHERMAN** | 01050486 | 806/366-3300 | 338 |
| Stratford Junior High Sch/Stratford/<br>Sherman | 01050503 | 806/366-3320 | 338 |
| **STRAWN IND SCH DIST/STRAWN/**<br>**PALO PINTO** | 01046150 | 254/672-5313 | 314 |
| Strawn Sch/Strawn/Palo Pinto | 02111318 | 254/672-5313 | 314 |
| Strickland Middle Sch/Denton/Denton | 01013323 | 940/369-4200 | 125 |
| Stroman Middle Sch/Victoria/Victoria | 01058464 | 361/578-2711 | 385 |
| Stuard Elem Sch/Aledo/Parker | 04920634 | 817/441-5103 | 315 |
| Stuart Place Elem Sch/Harlingen/Cameron | 01003897 | 956/427-3160 | 69 |
| Stubblefield Alternative Acad/Willis/<br>Montgomery | 04282262 | 936/856-1302 | 297 |
| Stubblefield Learning Center/Lufkin/<br>Angelina | 04447034 | 936/634-1100 | 20 |
| Stuber Elem Sch/Prosper/Collin | 12363840 | 469/219-2290 | 88 |
| Stuchbery Elem Sch/Houston/Harris | 01026978 | 713/740-0752 | 205 |
| Student Opportunity Center/Frisco/Collin | 04916889 | 469/633-6700 | 83 |
| Student Reassignment Ctr/Irving/Dallas | 04451059 | 972/600-3900 | 114 |
| Student Support Center/Corp Christi/Nueces | 02203040 | 361/878-2840 | 307 |
| Stults Road Elem Sch/Dallas/Dallas | 01011973 | 469/593-2500 | 117 |
| Success High Sch/Fort Worth/Tarrant | 04420725 | 817/815-2700 | 354 |
| Success High Sch/Round Rock/Williamson | 11561946 | 512/704-1300 | 402 |
| Suchma Elementary/Conroe/Montgomery | 12368785 | 936/709-4400 | 295 |
| Sudan Elem Sch/Sudan/Lamb | 01037094 | 806/227-2431 | 264 |
| Sudan High Sch/Sudan/Lamb | 01037109 | 806/227-2431 | 264 |
| **SUDAN IND SCH DIST/SUDAN/LAMB** | 01037082 | 806/227-2431 | 264 |
| Sudderth Elem Sch/Monahans/Ward | 01059028 | 432/943-5101 | 388 |
| Sudie Williams Tag Acad/Dallas/Dallas | 01010204 | 972/794-8700 | 107 |
| Sue Ann Mackey Elem Sch/Balch Springs/<br>Dallas | 05345623 | 972/290-4160 | 116 |
| Sue Creech Elem Sch/Katy/Harris | 04917481 | 281/237-8850 | 157 |
| Sue Crouch Intermediate Sch/Fort Worth/<br>Tarrant | 10019718 | 817/370-5670 | 350 |
| Sue E Rattan Elem Sch/Anna/Collin | 10901123 | 972/924-1400 | 81 |
| Sue Park Broadway Elem Sch/Spring/<br>Montgomery | 10910992 | 281/465-2900 | 295 |
| Sue Wilson Stafford Middle Sch/Frisco/<br>Collin | 11103843 | 469/633-5100 | 83 |
| Sugar Grove Academy/Houston/Harris | 04454477 | 713/271-0214 | 194 |
| Sugar Land Middle Sch/Sugar Land/Fort Bend | 01418321 | 281/634-3080 | 155 |
| Sugar Loaf Elem Sch/Killeen/Bell | 00996605 | 254/336-1940 | 31 |
| Sugar Mill Elem Sch/Sugar Land/Fort Bend | 02226664 | 281/634-4440 | 155 |
| Sul Ross Elem Sch/Bryan/Brazos | 01002154 | 979/209-1500 | 58 |
| Sul Ross Middle Sch/San Antonio/Bexar | 00998304 | 210/397-6350 | 41 |
| Sullivan Elem Sch/San Benito/Cameron | 01004293 | 956/361-6880 | 71 |
| **SULPHUR BLUFF IND SCH DIST/**<br>**SULPHUR BLUFF/HOPKINS** | 01031595 | 903/945-2460 | 235 |
| Sulphur Bluff Sch/Sulphur Bluff/Hopkins | 01809407 | 903/945-2460 | 235 |
| Sulphur Springs Elem Sch/Sulphur Spgs/<br>Hopkins | 01031636 | 903/855-8466 | 235 |
| Sulphur Springs High Sch/Sulphur Spgs/<br>Hopkins | 01031698 | 903/885-2158 | 235 |

| School/City/County<br>DISTRICT/CITY/COUNTY | PID | TELEPHONE<br>NUMBER | PAGE |
|---|---|---|---|
| **SULPHUR SPRINGS IND SCH DIST/**<br>**SULPHUR SPGS/HOPKINS** | 01031624 | 903/885-2153 | 235 |
| Sulphur Springs Middle Sch/Sulphur Spgs/<br>Hopkins | 01031686 | 903/885-7741 | 235 |
| Summer Creek High Sch/Houston/Harris | 11450335 | 281/641-5400 | 201 |
| Summer Creek Middle Sch/Crowley/Tarrant | 11079723 | 817/297-5090 | 350 |
| Summerwood Elem Sch/Houston/Harris | 05344198 | 281/641-3000 | 201 |
| Summit Christian Academy/Cedar Park/<br>Williamson | 02153598 | 512/250-1369 | 403 |
| Summit Christian Academy/Huntsville/Walker | 04993447 | 936/295-9601 | 386 |
| Summit Education Center/Duncanville/Dallas | 04450419 | 972/708-2570 | 109 |
| Summit High Sch/Arlington/Tarrant | 04363438 | 682/314-0800 | 359 |
| Summit Hill Elem Sch/Howe/Grayson | 12365989 | 903/745-4100 | 171 |
| Summitt Elem Sch/Austin/Travis | 01056662 | 512/414-4484 | 370 |
| Sun Ridge Middle Sch/El Paso/El Paso | 04941808 | 915/937-6600 | 141 |
| Sun Valley Elem Sch/San Antonio/Bexar | 00999607 | 210/645-7570 | 47 |
| Sundown Elem Sch/Katy/Harris | 02177051 | 281/237-5400 | 157 |
| Sundown Elem Sch/Sundown/Hockley | 01031313 | 806/229-5021 | 232 |
| Sundown High Sch/Sundown/Hockley | 01031325 | 806/229-5021 | 232 |
| **SUNDOWN IND SCH DIST/SUNDOWN/**<br>**HOCKLEY** | 01031301 | 806/229-3021 | 232 |
| Sundown Lane Elem Sch/Amarillo/Randall | 01539248 | 806/677-2400 | 324 |
| Sundown Middle Sch/Sundown/Hockley | 01031337 | 806/229-5021 | 233 |
| Sunnybrook Christian Academy/San Antonio/<br>Bexar | 04938239 | 210/674-8000 | 48 |
| Sunnyvale Elem Sch/Sunnyvale/Dallas | 10022090 | 972/226-7601 | 117 |
| Sunnyvale High Sch/Sunnyvale/Dallas | 11076680 | 972/203-4600 | 117 |
| **SUNNYVALE IND SCH DIST/SUNNYVALE/**<br>**DALLAS** | 01012018 | 972/226-5974 | 117 |
| Sunnyvale Middle Sch/Sunnyvale/Dallas | 01012020 | 972/226-2922 | 117 |
| Sunray Elem Sch/Sunray/Moore | 01042922 | 806/948-4222 | 299 |
| Sunray High Sch/Sunray/Moore | 01042934 | 806/948-5515 | 299 |
| **SUNRAY IND SCH DIST/SUNRAY/MOORE** | 01042910 | 806/948-4411 | 299 |
| Sunray Middle Sch/Sunray/Moore | 04929329 | 806/948-4444 | 299 |
| Sunrise Elem Sch/Amarillo/Potter | 01047491 | 806/326-5450 | 321 |
| Sunrise Mountain High Sch/El Paso/El Paso | 01826211 | 915/236-5675 | 138 |
| Sunrise-McMillian Elem Sch/Fort Worth/<br>Tarrant | 01053440 | 817/815-3900 | 354 |
| Sunset Elem Sch/Dumas/Moore | 01042881 | 806/935-2127 | 298 |
| Sunset High Sch/Dallas/Dallas | 01009906 | 972/502-1500 | 107 |
| Sunset Valley Elem Sch/Austin/Travis | 01056674 | 512/414-2392 | 370 |
| Sunset Valley Elem Sch/Fort Worth/Tarrant | 12170198 | 817/743-8200 | 358 |
| Sunshine Cottage Sch-Deaf Chld/San Antonio/<br>Bexar | 01479430 | 210/824-0579 | 48 |
| Susannah Dickinson Elem Sch/Sugar Land/<br>Fort Bend | 04033621 | 832/223-1400 | 158 |
| Susie T Fuentes Elem Sch/Kyle/Hays | 04920268 | 512/268-7827 | 216 |
| Sutton Elem Sch/Houston/Harris | 01024633 | 713/778-3400 | 200 |
| Sweeny Christian Sch/Sweeny/Brazoria | 02729575 | 979/548-6001 | 58 |
| Sweeny Elem Sch/Sweeny/Brazoria | 01001930 | 979/491-8300 | 57 |
| Sweeny High Sch/Sweeny/Brazoria | 01001928 | 979/491-8100 | 57 |
| **SWEENY IND SCH DIST/SWEENY/**<br>**BRAZORIA** | 01001904 | 979/491-8000 | 57 |
| Sweeny Junior High Sch/Sweeny/Brazoria | 01001942 | 979/491-8200 | 57 |
| Sweet Home Elem Sch/Sweet Home/Lavaca | 01037393 | 361/293-3221 | 265 |
| **SWEET HOME IND SCH DIST/**<br>**SWEET HOME/LAVACA** | 01037381 | 361/293-3221 | 265 |
| Sweetwater High Sch/Sweetwater/Nolan | 01043976 | 325/235-4371 | 305 |
| Sweetwater Intermediate Sch/Sweetwater/<br>Nolan | 01043940 | 325/235-3491 | 305 |
| **SWEETWATER ISD SCH DIST/**<br>**SWEETWATER/NOLAN** | 01043914 | 325/235-8601 | 304 |
| Sweetwater Middle Sch/Sweetwater/Nolan | 01043952 | 325/236-6303 | 305 |
| Swenke Elem Sch/Cypress/Harris | 11451494 | 281/213-1200 | 190 |
| Swift Elem Sch/Arlington/Tarrant | 01051935 | 682/867-4100 | 347 |
| Sycamore Academy/Keene/Johnson | 12313833 | 817/645-0895 | 252 |
| Sycamore Elem Sch/Fort Worth/Tarrant | 01052393 | 817/568-5700 | 350 |
| Sycamore Springs Elem Sch/Austin/Hays | 12305666 | 512/858-3900 | 216 |
| Sycamore Springs Middle Sch/Austin/Hays | 12305678 | 512/858-3600 | 216 |
| Sylvan Rodriguez Elem Sch/Houston/Harris | 05009532 | 713/295-3870 | 200 |

**T**

| School/City/County<br>DISTRICT/CITY/COUNTY | PID | TELEPHONE<br>NUMBER | PAGE |
|---|---|---|---|
| T A Howard Middle Sch/Arlington/Tarrant | 04170619 | 682/314-1050 | 359 |
| T A Sims Elem Sch/Fort Worth/Tarrant | 03253361 | 817/814-0800 | 354 |
| T F Birmingham Elem Sch/Wylie/Collin | 02845650 | 972/429-3420 | 89 |
| T G Allen Elem Sch/Corp Christi/Nueces | 01044188 | 361/878-2140 | 307 |
| T G Terry Elem Sch/Dallas/Dallas | 01009944 | 972/749-3200 | 107 |
| T H Johnson Elem Sch/Taylor/Williamson | 11712004 | 512/352-2275 | 403 |
| T H McDonald Junior High Sch/Katy/Harris | 03597618 | 281/237-5300 | 157 |
| T H McDonald Middle Sch/Mesquite/Dallas | 01011557 | 972/882-5700 | 116 |
| T H Rogers Sch/Houston/Harris | 01024578 | 713/917-3565 | 200 |
| T L Pink Elem Sch/Richmond/Fort Bend | 04746309 | 832/223-2100 | 158 |

| School/City/County<br>DISTRICT/CITY/COUNTY | PID | TELEPHONE<br>NUMBER | PAGE |
|---|---|---|---|
| T M Clark Elem Sch/Portland/San Patricio | 01049580 | 361/777-4045 | 333 |
| T S Hancock Elem Sch/Houston/Harris | 01023251 | 281/897-4523 | 190 |
| T W Browne Middle Sch/Dallas/Dallas | 01009970 | 972/502-2500 | 107 |
| T W Ogg Elem Sch/Clute/Brazoria | 01001681 | 979/730-7195 | 56 |
| Tabasco Elem Sch/La Joya/Hidalgo | 04805981 | 956/323-2440 | 223 |
| Tafolla Middle Sch/San Antonio/Bexar | 00999322 | 210/978-7930 | 44 |
| Taft Elem Sch/Port Arthur/Jefferson | 01034028 | 409/962-2262 | 247 |
| Taft High Sch/Taft/San Patricio | 01049865 | 361/528-2636 | 335 |
| **TAFT IND SCH DIST/TAFT/**<br>**SAN PATRICIO** | 01049827 | 361/528-2636 | 334 |
| Taft Junior High Sch/Taft/San Patricio | 01049877 | 361/528-2636 | 335 |
| Tahoka Elem Sch/Tahoka/Lynn | 01039365 | 806/561-4350 | 276 |
| Tahoka High Sch/Tahoka/Lynn | 01039377 | 806/561-4538 | 276 |
| **TAHOKA IND SCH DIST/TAHOKA/LYNN** | 01039341 | 806/561-4105 | 276 |
| Tahoka Middle Sch/Tahoka/Lynn | 04038413 | 806/561-4539 | 276 |
| Talkington Sch Young Women/Lubbock/Lubbock | 11434771 | 806/219-2200 | 273 |
| Talley Elem Sch/Frisco/Collin | 12308151 | 469/633-2175 | 83 |
| Tammaron Elem Sch/Katy/Fort Bend | 12471100 | 832/223-5700 | 158 |
| Tanglewood Elem Sch/Fort Worth/Tarrant | 01053464 | 817/814-5900 | 354 |
| Tanglewood Middle Sch/Houston/Harris | 04016075 | 713/625-1411 | 200 |
| Tannahill Intermediate Sch/Fort Worth/<br>Tarrant | 04803452 | 817/367-1370 | 360 |
| Tarkington High Sch/Cleveland/Liberty | 01038000 | 281/592-7739 | 269 |
| **TARKINGTON IND SCH DIST/**<br>**CLEVELAND/LIBERTY** | 01037977 | 281/592-8781 | 269 |
| Tarkington Intermediate Sch/Cleveland/<br>Liberty | 03319642 | 281/592-6134 | 269 |
| Tarkington Middle Sch/Cleveland/Liberty | 01037991 | 281/592-7737 | 269 |
| Tarkington Primary Sch/Cleveland/Liberty | 01037989 | 281/592-7736 | 269 |
| Tarver Elem Sch/Temple/Bell | 10900868 | 254/215-3800 | 30 |
| Tarver-Rendon Elem Sch/Burleson/Tarrant | 01054169 | 817/299-7880 | 359 |
| Tascosa High Sch/Amarillo/Potter | 01047506 | 806/326-2600 | 321 |
| Tate Springs Christian Sch/Arlington/<br>Tarrant | 11746275 | 817/478-7091 | 362 |
| Tatom Elem Sch/Monahans/Ward | 01059030 | 432/943-2769 | 388 |
| Tatum Elem Sch/Farmersville/Collin | 01006174 | 972/782-7251 | 82 |
| Tatum Elem Sch/Tatum/Rusk | 01049190 | 903/947-0352 | 331 |
| Tatum High Sch/Tatum/Rusk | 01049205 | 903/947-6482 | 331 |
| **TATUM IND SCH DIST/TATUM/RUSK** | 01049188 | 903/947-6482 | 331 |
| Tatum Middle Sch/Tatum/Rusk | 01418565 | 903/947-6482 | 331 |
| Tatum Primary Sch/Tatum/Rusk | 02230108 | 903/947-6485 | 331 |
| Tavola Elem Sch/New Caney/Montgomery | 01878422 | 281/577-2900 | 297 |
| Taylor Career & Tech Ctr/Beaumont/<br>Jefferson | 03054763 | 409/617-5740 | 245 |
| Taylor Christian Sch/McAllen/Hidalgo | 01875456 | 956/686-7574 | 229 |
| Taylor Creek Elem Sch/Copperas Cove/<br>Lampasas | 11445263 | 512/564-2585 | 264 |
| Taylor Elem Sch/Abilene/Taylor | 01172864 | 325/671-4970 | 363 |
| Taylor Elem Sch/Mercedes/Hidalgo | 01030216 | 956/514-2388 | 225 |
| Taylor High Sch/Taylor/Williamson | 01061186 | 512/365-6326 | 403 |
| **TAYLOR IND SCH DIST/TAYLOR/**<br>**WILLIAMSON** | 01061162 | 512/365-1391 | 402 |
| Taylor Middle Sch/Taylor/Williamson | 01061198 | 512/352-2815 | 403 |
| Taylor Opportunity Center/Taylor/<br>Williamson | 12036827 | 512/365-8089 | 403 |
| Taylor Ray Elem Sch/Rosenberg/Fort Bend | 02045343 | 832/223-2400 | 158 |
| Tays Junior High Sch/Katy/Harris | 12168896 | 281/234-2400 | 157 |
| TCC South-Fwisd Collegiate HS/Fort Worth/<br>Tarrant | 12172483 | 817/515-4402 | 354 |
| Teague Elem Sch/Pasadena/Harris | 01548457 | 713/740-0760 | 205 |
| Teague Elem Sch/Teague/Freestone | 01018517 | 254/739-1350 | 161 |
| Teague High Sch/Teague/Freestone | 01018529 | 254/739-1500 | 161 |
| **TEAGUE IND SCH DIST/TEAGUE/**<br>**FREESTONE** | 01018505 | 254/739-1300 | 161 |
| Teague Intermediate Sch/Teague/Freestone | 02055037 | 254/739-3303 | 161 |
| Teague Junior High Sch/Teague/Freestone | 04447993 | 254/739-1350 | 161 |
| Teague Lion Academy/Teague/Freestone | 12166991 | 254/739-1444 | 161 |
| Team Sch/Cleburne/Johnson | 04014560 | 817/202-2160 | 250 |
| Tecc-East/Lewisville/Denton | 11553705 | 469/713-5211 | 128 |
| Technical Education Center/Sugar Land/<br>Fort Bend | 03393789 | 281/634-5671 | 155 |
| Ted Flores Elem Sch/Pearsall/Frio | 01018672 | 830/334-4108 | 161 |
| Ted Polk Middle Sch/Carrollton/Dallas | 04756287 | 972/968-4600 | 101 |
| Tegeler Career Center/Pasadena/Harris | 04036984 | 713/740-0410 | 205 |
| Tejas School of Choice/El Paso/El Paso | 03010987 | 915/434-9900 | 143 |
| Tekoa Academy-Orange/Orange/Orange | 11704796 | 409/886-9864 | 14 |
| Tekoa Academy-Port Arthur/Port Arthur/<br>Jefferson | 04903105 | 409/982-5400 | 14 |
| Temple Charter Academy/Temple/Bell | 04886131 | 254/206-2013 | 14 |
| Temple Christian Academy/Flower Mound/<br>Denton | 10017318 | 972/874-8700 | 130 |
| Temple Christian Sch/Fort Worth/Tarrant | 01410991 | 817/457-0770 | 362 |

| School/City/County<br>DISTRICT/CITY/COUNTY | PID | TELEPHONE<br>NUMBER | PAGE |
|---|---|---|---|
| Temple High Sch/Temple/Bell | 00996837 | 254/215-7000 | 32 |
| **TEMPLE IND SCH DIST/TEMPLE/BELL** | 00996708 | 254/215-8473 | 32 |
| **TENAHA IND SCH DIST/TENAHA/**<br>**SHELBY** | 01050424 | 936/248-5000 | 337 |
| Tenaha Sch/Tenaha/Shelby | 01050448 | 936/248-5000 | 338 |
| Tenie Holmes Elem Sch/Bay City/Matagorda | 01040883 | 979/401-1400 | 278 |
| Tenney Sch/Houston/Harris | 01480415 | 713/783-6990 | 212 |
| Tennyson Middle Sch/Waco/McLennan | 01040429 | 254/772-1440 | 285 |
| Teravista Elem Sch/Round Rock/Williamson | 11130846 | 512/704-0500 | 402 |
| **TERLINGUA COMMON SCH DIST/**<br>**TERLINGUA/BREWSTER** | 01002283 | 432/371-2281 | 60 |
| Terlingua Elem Sch/Terlingua/Brewster | 01002295 | 432/371-2281 | 60 |
| Terra Vista Middle Sch/Lubbock/Lubbock | 10030372 | 806/796-0076 | 272 |
| Terrace Elem Sch/Houston/Harris | 01027386 | 713/251-7200 | 206 |
| Terrace Hills Middle Sch/El Paso/El Paso | 01015888 | 915/236-6750 | 139 |
| Terrell Alternative Ed Center/Terrell/<br>Kaufman | 04875687 | 972/563-6319 | 256 |
| **TERRELL CO IND SCH DIST/**<br>**SANDERSON/TERRELL** | 01055046 | 432/345-2515 | 364 |
| Terrell Elem Sch/Denison/Grayson | 01020314 | 903/462-7550 | 171 |
| Terrell High Sch/Terrell/Kaufman | 01035802 | 972/563-7525 | 256 |
| **TERRELL IND SCH DIST/TERRELL/**<br>**KAUFMAN** | 01035759 | 972/563-7504 | 256 |
| Terrell Wells Middle Sch/San Antonio/Bexar | 00997568 | 210/989-2600 | 36 |
| Terry High Sch/Rosenberg/Fort Bend | 02110089 | 832/223-3400 | 158 |
| Tesc-West/Lewisville/Denton | 03254145 | 469/713-5186 | 128 |
| Texans Can Acad Carrltn-Farmrs/Dallas/<br>Dallas | 11014163 | 972/243-2178 | 14 |
| Texans Can Acad Dallas North/Dallas/Dallas | 04467113 | 214/824-4226 | 14 |
| Texans Can Acad Dallas Pl Grv/Dallas/<br>Dallas | 11014151 | 972/225-1194 | 14 |
| Texans Can Acad Fw Lancaster/Fort Worth/<br>Tarrant | 05011042 | 817/735-1515 | 14 |
| Texans Can Acad Fw Westcreek/Fort Worth/<br>Tarrant | 04925787 | 817/531-3223 | 14 |
| Texans Can Acad Garland/Garland/Dallas | 12260705 | 972/441-7202 | 14 |
| Texans Can Acad Houston Hobby/Houston/<br>Harris | 11567304 | 832/379-4226 | 14 |
| Texans Can Acad Houston North/Houston/<br>Harris | 04813407 | 713/659-4226 | 14 |
| Texans Can Acad Houston SW/Houston/Harris | 12260810 | 281/918-4316 | 14 |
| Texans Can Acad San Antonio/San Antonio/<br>Bexar | 05010634 | 210/923-1226 | 14 |
| Texans Can Acad-Highlands HS/San Antonio/<br>Bexar | 12378699 | 210/354-9340 | 44 |
| Texans Can Acad-Oak Cliff/Dallas/Dallas | 04924769 | 214/943-2244 | 14 |
| Texans Can Academy Austin/Austin/Travis | 05220944 | 512/477-4226 | 14 |
| Texans Can Academy-Grant East/Dallas/<br>Dallas | 12163717 | 972/228-4226 | 14 |
| **TEXARKANA IND SCH DIST/TEXARKANA/**<br>**BOWIE** | 01001215 | 903/794-3651 | 53 |
| Texas Academy Math & Science/Denton/Denton | 04022153 | 940/565-3606 | 15 |
| Texas Academy of Biomed Sci/Fort Worth/<br>Tarrant | 11711892 | 817/515-1660 | 354 |
| Texas Christian Sch/Houston/Harris | 04481066 | 281/550-6060 | 212 |
| Texas City High Sch/Texas City/Galveston | 01019561 | 409/916-0800 | 166 |
| **TEXAS CITY IND SCH DIST/**<br>**TEXAS CITY/GALVESTON** | 01019470 | 409/916-0100 | 166 |
| Texas Connections Academy/Houston/Harris | 11555399 | 281/661-8293 | 194 |
| **TEXAS DEPT OF EDUCATION/**<br>**AUSTIN/TRAVIS** | 00994396 | 512/463-9734 | 1 |
| Texas Early College High Sch/Marshall/<br>Harrison | 11704655 | 903/935-4109 | 15 |
| Texas Empowerment Academy/Austin/Travis | 04813483 | 512/494-1076 | 15 |
| Texas Empowerment Academy/Austin/Travis | 12161824 | 512/928-0118 | 15 |
| Texas High Sch/Texarkana/Bowie | 01001344 | 903/794-3891 | 53 |
| Texas Leadership Charter Acad/San Angelo/<br>Tom Green | 11231713 | 325/653-3200 | 15 |
| Texas Leadership CS-Abilene/Abilene/Taylor | 12115758 | 325/480-3500 | 15 |
| Texas Leadership CS-Arlington/Arlington/<br>Tarrant | 12115710 | 817/385-9338 | 15 |
| Texas Leadership CS-Midland/Midland/<br>Midland | 11930804 | 432/242-7117 | 15 |
| Texas Middle Sch/Texarkana/Bowie | 01001306 | 903/793-5631 | 53 |
| Texas Military Institute/San Antonio/Bexar | 01000479 | 210/698-7171 | 48 |
| Texas Neurorehab Center/Austin/Travis | 02204654 | 512/444-4835 | 376 |
| Texas Online Preparatory Sch/Lewisville/<br>Walker | 11931896 | 888/263-6497 | 386 |
| Texas Prep School-San Marcos/San Marcos/<br>Hays | 04949678 | 512/805-3000 | 15 |
| Texas Preparatory Sch-Austin/Austin/Travis | 11932242 | 512/928-3000 | 15 |

| School/City/County DISTRICT/CITY/COUNTY | PID | TELEPHONE NUMBER | PAGE |
|---|---|---|---|
| Texas Sch Blind & Visually Imp/Austin/ Travis | 01810078 | 512/454-8631 | 15 |
| Texas School for the Deaf/Austin/Travis | 01810107 | 512/462-5353 | 15 |
| Texas School of the Arts/Edgecliff Vlg/ Tarrant | 11013860 | 817/732-8372 | 15 |
| Texas Serenity Academy/Houston/Harris | 04893184 | 281/820-9540 | 15 |
| Texas Serenity Academy-Gano/Houston/Harris | 12261187 | 713/699-3443 | 15 |
| Texas Virtual Acad Hallsville/Lewisville/ Denton | 11014888 | 866/360-0161 | 15 |
| Texhoma Elem Sch/Texhoma/Sherman | 00863137 | 806/827-7400 | 338 |
| **TEXHOMA IND SCH DIST/TEXHOMA/ SHERMAN** | 01050527 | 806/827-7400 | 338 |
| **TEXLINE IND SCH DIST/TEXLINE/ DALLAM** | 01008108 | 806/362-4667 | 99 |
| Texline Sch/Texline/Dallam | 01008110 | 806/362-4284 | 99 |
| Texoma Alternative Center/Iowa Park/ Wichita | 04911451 | 940/592-1410 | 394 |
| Texoma Christian Sch/Sherman/Grayson | 02747773 | 903/893-7076 | 174 |
| The Bridge Sch/Houston/Harris | 12313845 | 713/974-2066 | 212 |
| The Colony High Sch/The Colony/Denton | 02896623 | 469/713-5178 | 128 |
| The Discovery Sch/Edinburg/Hidalgo | 02761183 | 956/381-1117 | 229 |
| The Excel Center Austin/Austin/Travis | 12163030 | 512/531-5500 | 15 |
| The Fay Sch/Houston/Harris | 03560358 | 713/681-8300 | 212 |
| The Fulton Sch/Heath/Rockwall | 10756473 | 972/772-4445 | 329 |
| The Humanist Academy/Irving/Dallas | 12180325 | 972/646-1085 | 120 |
| The Jane Justin Sch/Fort Worth/Tarrant | 12314033 | 817/390-2831 | 362 |
| The King's Academy/Dripping Spgs/Hays | 12032211 | 512/858-4700 | 217 |
| The Kinkaid Sch/Houston/Harris | 01027647 | 713/782-1640 | 212 |
| The Lawson Academy/Houston/Harris | 05273965 | 713/225-1551 | 15 |
| The Learning Center/New Caney/Montgomery | 04754227 | 281/577-2850 | 297 |
| The Oakridge Sch/Arlington/Tarrant | 02205385 | 817/451-4994 | 362 |
| The Phoenix Academy/Mansfield/Tarrant | 04452699 | 682/314-1700 | 360 |
| The Steam Academy at Mambrino/Granbury/ Hood | 04749387 | 817/408-4900 | 233 |
| The Summit Sch/Pasadena/Harris | 05347889 | 713/740-0290 | 205 |
| The Varnett School-SW/Houston/Harris | 02950372 | 713/723-4699 | 15 |
| The Westwood School-Upper/Dallas/Dallas | 12313857 | 972/239-8598 | 120 |
| The Woodlands Classical Acad/The Woodlands/ Montgomery | 11848964 | 936/242-1541 | 15 |
| The Woodlands High Sch/The Woodlands/ Montgomery | 04454025 | 936/709-1200 | 295 |
| The Woodlands HS-9th GR Campus/The Woodlands/ Montgomery | 04923777 | 832/592-8200 | 295 |
| The Woodlands Methodist Sch/Spring/ Montgomery | 12313936 | 281/882-8220 | 298 |
| The Woodlands-College Park HS/The Woodlands/ Montgomery | 10007571 | 936/709-3000 | 295 |
| Theiss Elem Sch/Klein/Harris | 01026368 | 832/484-5900 | 203 |
| Thelma E Page-Richardson ES/Dallas/Dallas | 11925964 | 972/892-8100 | 107 |
| Thelma Jones Elem Sch/Arlington/Tarrant | 05273630 | 817/299-6940 | 360 |
| Theodore Roosevelt Elem Sch/McAllen/ Hidalgo | 01030060 | 956/971-4424 | 224 |
| Thigpen-Zavala Elem Sch/McAllen/Hidalgo | 01030101 | 956/971-4377 | 224 |
| Thomas A Edison Elem Sch/Gainesville/Cooke | 01007415 | 940/665-6091 | 95 |
| Thomas Arnold Elem Sch/Salado/Bell | 00996693 | 254/947-6925 | 32 |
| Thomas B Francis Elem Sch/Humble/Harris | 01022960 | 281/985-6500 | 185 |
| Thomas B Gray Elem Sch/Houston/Harris | 03246760 | 281/878-0660 | 184 |
| Thomas Buzbee Vocational Sch/New Waverly/ Walker | 03395660 | 936/344-7238 | 15 |
| Thomas C Marsh Prep Academy/Dallas/Dallas | 01009994 | 972/502-6600 | 107 |
| Thomas Elem Sch/Abilene/Taylor | 04015344 | 325/671-4995 | 363 |
| Thomas Elem Sch/Plano/Collin | 01824110 | 469/752-3500 | 87 |
| Thomas Elem Sch/Richmond/Fort Bend | 11447211 | 832/223-4600 | 158 |
| Thomas Haley Elem Sch/Irving/Dallas | 01011313 | 972/600-7000 | 114 |
| Thomas Hancock Elem Sch/Houston/Harris | 12169486 | 713/740-5430 | 205 |
| Thomas Hatchett Elem Sch/San Antonio/Bexar | 05347566 | 210/397-6850 | 42 |
| Thomas J Rusk Elem Sch/Nacogdoches/ Nacogdoches | 05343118 | 936/569-3100 | 301 |
| Thomas J Rusk Middle Sch/Dallas/Dallas | 01010008 | 972/925-2000 | 107 |
| Thomas J Stovall Middle Sch/Houston/Harris | 01022958 | 281/878-0670 | 186 |
| Thomas Jefferson High Sch/Dallas/Dallas | 01009956 | 972/502-7300 | 107 |
| Thomas Jefferson High Sch/San Antonio/ Bexar | 00998639 | 210/438-6570 | 44 |
| Thomas Jefferson Middle Sch/Port Arthur/ Jefferson | 01033907 | 409/984-4860 | 246 |
| Thomas Justiss Elem Sch/Paris/Lamar | 01036765 | 903/737-7458 | 263 |
| Thomas L Marsalis Elem Sch/Dallas/Dallas | 01009968 | 972/749-3500 | 107 |
| Thomas Manor Elem Sch/El Paso/El Paso | 01016624 | 915/434-7500 | 143 |
| Thomas Middle Sch/Houston/Harris | 01025089 | 713/732-3500 | 198 |
| Thomas O Hicks Elem Sch/Frisco/Denton | 05347372 | 469/713-5981 | 128 |
| Thomas S Grantham Academy/Houston/Harris | 02225696 | 281/985-6590 | 186 |
| Thomas Tolbert Elem Sch/Dallas/Dallas | 04456487 | 972/794-5900 | 107 |

| School/City/County DISTRICT/CITY/COUNTY | PID | TELEPHONE NUMBER | PAGE |
|---|---|---|---|
| Thomas Wesley Andrews Elem Sch/Plano/ Collin | 05096846 | 469/752-3900 | 87 |
| Thompson Learning Center/Converse/Bexar | 11452266 | 210/945-5053 | 37 |
| Thorndale Elem Sch/Thorndale/Milam | 01041916 | 512/898-2912 | 291 |
| Thorndale High Sch/Thorndale/Milam | 01041928 | 512/898-2321 | 291 |
| **THORNDALE IND SCH DIST/THORNDALE/ MILAM** | 01041904 | 512/898-2538 | 291 |
| Thorndale Middle Sch/Thorndale/Milam | 04800694 | 512/898-2670 | 291 |
| Thornton Elem Sch/Arlington/Tarrant | 01051947 | 682/867-4200 | 347 |
| Thornton Elem Sch/Temple/Bell | 00996849 | 254/215-5700 | 32 |
| Thornton Middle Sch/Katy/Harris | 04036142 | 281/856-1500 | 190 |
| Thornwood Elem Sch/Houston/Harris | 01027398 | 713/251-7300 | 206 |
| Thousand Oaks Elem Sch/San Antonio/Bexar | 01881833 | 210/407-8000 | 39 |
| Thrall Elem Sch/Thrall/Williamson | 01061239 | 512/898-5293 | 403 |
| Thrall High Sch/Thrall/Williamson | 04944331 | 512/898-5193 | 403 |
| **THRALL IND SCH DIST/THRALL/ WILLIAMSON** | 01061227 | 512/898-0062 | 403 |
| Thrall Middle Sch/Thrall/Williamson | 01061241 | 512/898-5328 | 403 |
| Three Lakes Middle Sch/Tyler/Smith | 01050759 | 903/952-4400 | 341 |
| Three Rivers Elem Sch/Three Rivers/ Live Oak | 01038311 | 361/786-3592 | 271 |
| **THREE RIVERS IND SCH DIST/ THREE RIVERS/LIVE OAK** | 01038309 | 361/786-3626 | 271 |
| Three Rivers Jr Sr High Sch/Three Rivers/ Live Oak | 01038323 | 361/786-3531 | 271 |
| Three Way Elem Sch/Stephenville/Erath | 01017197 | 254/965-6496 | 148 |
| **THREE WAY IND SCH DIST/STEPHENVILLE/ ERATH** | 01017185 | 254/965-6496 | 148 |
| Threeway High Sch/Stephenville/Erath | 12309894 | 254/965-9496 | 148 |
| **THROCKMORTON IND SCH DIST/ THROCKMORTON/THROCKMORTON** | 01055228 | 940/849-2411 | 365 |
| Throckmorton Sch/Throckmorton/Throckmorton | 01055230 | 940/849-9981 | 365 |
| Thunderbird Elem Sch/Plainview/Hale | 01022013 | 806/293-6060 | 180 |
| Thurgood Marshall Elem Sch/Dallas/Dallas | 10007430 | 469/593-6800 | 117 |
| Thurgood Marshall High Sch/Missouri City/ Fort Bend | 05098442 | 281/634-6630 | 155 |
| Tibbals Elem Sch/Murphy/Collin | 10011936 | 972/429-2520 | 89 |
| Tice Elem Sch/Houston/Harris | 01881883 | 832/386-4050 | 192 |
| Tidehaven High Sch/Elmaton/Matagorda | 01040998 | 979/843-4310 | 279 |
| **TIDEHAVEN IND SCH DIST/ELMATON/ MATAGORDA** | 01040962 | 979/843-4300 | 279 |
| Tidehaven Intermediate Sch/Elmaton/ Matagorda | 01041007 | 361/843-4320 | 279 |
| Tierra Blanca Early Child Ctr/Hereford/ Deaf Smith | 12364870 | 806/363-7680 | 123 |
| Tierra Del Sol Elem Sch/El Paso/El Paso | 02110601 | 915/434-5800 | 143 |
| Tiger Academy/Smithville/Bastrop | 12173451 | 512/237-5142 | 27 |
| Tiger Trail Sch/Houston/Harris | 04949886 | 713/251-8100 | 206 |
| Tijerina Elem Sch/Houston/Harris | 02111954 | 713/924-1790 | 195 |
| Timber Creek Elem Sch/Flower Mound/Denton | 01824146 | 469/713-5961 | 128 |
| Timber Creek Elem Sch/Livingston/Polk | 02223894 | 936/328-2180 | 320 |
| Timber Creek Elem Sch/The Woodlands/Harris | 11815943 | 281/357-3060 | 208 |
| Timber Creek High Sch/Fort Worth/Tarrant | 11448552 | 817/744-2300 | 358 |
| Timber Lakes Elem Sch/New Caney/Montgomery | 12468579 | 281/689-4375 | 297 |
| Timber Ridge Elem Sch/Killeen/Bell | 10002052 | 254/336-6630 | 31 |
| Timberline Elem Sch/Grapevine/Tarrant | 02043383 | 817/251-5770 | 356 |
| Timbers Elem Sch/Humble/Harris | 02125105 | 281/641-2000 | 201 |
| Timberview High Sch/Arlington/Tarrant | 05347401 | 682/314-1300 | 360 |
| Timberview Middle Sch/Fort Worth/Tarrant | 11551458 | 817/744-2600 | 358 |
| Timberwilde Elem Sch/San Antonio/Bexar | 02110132 | 210/397-0400 | 42 |
| Timberwood Middle Sch/Humble/Harris | 04808672 | 281/641-3800 | 201 |
| Timberwood Park Elem Sch/San Antonio/Comal | 11079448 | 830/885-8500 | 92 |
| Timmerman Elem Sch/Pflugerville/Travis | 02848822 | 512/594-4200 | 375 |
| Timothy Baranoff Elem Sch/Austin/Travis | 04869834 | 512/841-7100 | 370 |
| Timpson Elem Sch/Timpson/Shelby | 04748333 | 936/254-2462 | 338 |
| Timpson High Sch/Timpson/Shelby | 01050462 | 936/254-3125 | 338 |
| **TIMPSON IND SCH DIST/TIMPSON/ SHELBY** | 01050450 | 936/254-2463 | 338 |
| Timpson Middle Sch/Timpson/Shelby | 04801727 | 936/254-2078 | 338 |
| **TIOGA IND SCH DIST/TIOGA/GRAYSON** | 01020699 | 940/437-2366 | 172 |
| Tioga Sch/Tioga/Grayson | 01020704 | 940/437-2366 | 172 |
| Tippin Elem Sch/El Paso/El Paso | 05344409 | 915/230-5150 | 138 |
| Tipps Elem Sch/Houston/Harris | 05272117 | 281/345-3350 | 191 |
| Tisd Child & Adolescent Ctr/Terrell/ Kaufman | 03004639 | 972/551-8960 | 256 |
| Tivy High Sch/Kerrville/Kerr | 01036129 | 830/257-2212 | 259 |
| Tobias Elem Sch/Kyle/Hays | 05273226 | 512/268-8437 | 216 |
| Tolar Elem Sch/Tolar/Hood | 01031442 | 254/835-4028 | 233 |
| Tolar High Sch/Tolar/Hood | 04869999 | 254/835-4316 | 234 |
| **TOLAR IND SCH DIST/TOLAR/HOOD** | 01031430 | 254/835-4718 | 233 |
| Tolar Junior High Sch/Tolar/Hood | 11074632 | 254/835-5207 | 234 |
| Toler Elem Sch/Garland/Dallas | 01545235 | 972/226-3922 | 111 |

| School/City/County DISTRICT/CITY/COUNTY | PID | TELEPHONE NUMBER | PAGE |
|---|---|---|---|
| Toltech T-STEM Academy/San Antonio/Bexar | 11819951 | 210/444-8425 | 35 |
| Tom & Nita Nichols Middle Sch/Burleson/ Johnson | 12305692 | 817/202-2500 | 251 |
| Tom Bean Elem Sch/Tom Bean/Grayson | 01020728 | 903/546-6333 | 173 |
| Tom Bean High Sch/Tom Bean/Grayson | 01020730 | 903/546-6319 | 173 |
| **TOM BEAN IND SCH DIST/TOM BEAN/ GRAYSON** | 01020716 | 903/546-6076 | 173 |
| Tom Bean Middle Sch/Tom Bean/Grayson | 03047746 | 903/546-6161 | 173 |
| Tom Browne Middle Sch/Corp Christi/Nueces | 01044243 | 361/878-4270 | 307 |
| Tom C Clark High Sch/San Antonio/Bexar | 01824067 | 210/397-5150 | 42 |
| Tom C Gooch Elem Sch/Dallas/Dallas | 01009918 | 972/794-2500 | 107 |
| Tom Cox Intermediate Sch/Spring/Montgomery | 11157117 | 281/465-3200 | 295 |
| Tom Green Elem Sch/Buda/Hays | 02896740 | 512/268-8438 | 216 |
| Tom Landry Elem Sch/Irving/Dallas | 04449123 | 972/968-2100 | 101 |
| Tom Lea Elem Sch/El Paso/El Paso | 11449178 | 915/230-5450 | 138 |
| Tom R Ellisor Elem Sch/Magnolia/Montgomery | 10012148 | 281/252-7400 | 296 |
| Tom W Field Elem Sch/Dallas/Dallas | 01010010 | 972/794-2700 | 107 |
| Tom Wilson Elem Sch/Katy/Harris | 11822037 | 281/234-1600 | 157 |
| Tomas Rivera Elem Sch/Denton/Denton | 04281579 | 940/369-3800 | 125 |
| Tomball Connections Acadamy/Tomball/Harris | 03396494 | 281/357-3281 | 208 |
| Tomball Elem Sch/Tomball/Harris | 01027582 | 281/357-3280 | 208 |
| Tomball High Sch/Tomball/Harris | 01027594 | 281/357-3220 | 208 |
| **TOMBALL IND SCH DIST/TOMBALL/ HARRIS** | 01027568 | 281/357-3100 | 208 |
| Tomball Intermediate Sch/Tomball/Harris | 01027611 | 281/357-3150 | 208 |
| Tomball Junior High Sch/Tomball/Harris | 01027609 | 281/357-3000 | 208 |
| Tomball Memorial High Sch/Tomball/Harris | 11709411 | 281/357-3230 | 208 |
| Tomball Star Academy/Tomball/Harris | 12305549 | 281/357-3222 | 208 |
| Tony Gonzalez Elem Sch/Santa Maria/Cameron | 01004310 | 956/565-6309 | 71 |
| Tool Elem Sch/Kemp/Henderson | 10901070 | 903/432-2637 | 219 |
| Torah Day School of Dallas/Dallas/Collin | 11180683 | 972/964-0090 | 90 |
| Torah Day School of Houston/Houston/Harris | 02824565 | 713/777-2000 | 212 |
| Torah Girls Academy/Houston/Harris | 11919018 | 713/936-0644 | 212 |
| Tornillo Elem Sch/Tornillo/El Paso | 03442718 | 915/765-3100 | 141 |
| Tornillo High Sch/Tornillo/El Paso | 01016284 | 915/765-3500 | 141 |
| **TORNILLO IND SCH DIST/TORNILLO/ EL PASO** | 01016260 | 915/765-3000 | 141 |
| Tornillo Intermediate Sch/Tornillo/El Paso | 11078274 | 915/765-3350 | 141 |
| Tornillo Junior High Sch/Tornillo/El Paso | 04745111 | 915/765-3400 | 141 |
| Torres Elem Sch/Victoria/Victoria | 11450103 | 361/788-2850 | 385 |
| Town Center Elem Sch/Coppell/Dallas | 04278687 | 214/496-7800 | 102 |
| Town East Christian Sch/San Antonio/Bexar | 02191679 | 210/648-2601 | 48 |
| Towne Creek Sch/Missouri City/Fort Bend | 02995554 | 281/499-8030 | 160 |
| Townewest Elem Sch/Sugar Land/Fort Bend | 01826247 | 281/634-4480 | 155 |
| Townley Elem Sch/Fort Worth/Tarrant | 11457462 | 817/568-3560 | 352 |
| Townley Elem Sch/Irving/Dallas | 01829407 | 972/600-6800 | 114 |
| Townsell Elem Sch/Irving/Dallas | 05273094 | 972/600-5500 | 114 |
| Townview Mag HS-Bus & Mngmnt/Dallas/Dallas | 01009449 | 972/925-5920 | 107 |
| Townview Mag HS-Sci & Eng/Dallas/Dallas | 02228090 | 972/925-5960 | 107 |
| Townview Mag HS-Talent & Gift/Dallas/ Dallas | 02200490 | 972/925-5970 | 107 |
| Tradewind Elem Sch/Amarillo/Potter | 10912237 | 806/326-5500 | 321 |
| Tradition Elem Sch/Saint Hedwig/Bexar | 00997025 | 210/649-2021 | 34 |
| Trafton Academy/Houston/Harris | 11239234 | 713/723-3732 | 212 |
| Transition Center/Bedford/Tarrant | 01809938 | 817/354-3537 | 356 |
| Transition Center/Fort Worth/Tarrant | 05344514 | 817/814-6418 | 354 |
| Transmountain Early College HS/El Paso/ El Paso | 11076848 | 915/236-5000 | 139 |
| Trautmann Elem Sch/Laredo/Webb | 02176576 | 956/473-3100 | 391 |
| Trautmann Middle Sch/Laredo/Webb | 04455940 | 956/473-7400 | 391 |
| Travis Bryan High Sch/Bryan/Brazos | 01002049 | 979/209-2400 | 59 |
| Travis Early College High Sch/Austin/ Travis | 01056727 | 512/414-2527 | 371 |
| Travis Early College High Sch/San Antonio/ Bexar | 11128063 | 210/738-9830 | 44 |
| Travis Elem Sch/Edinburg/Hidalgo | 04487747 | 956/289-2354 | 222 |
| Travis Elem Sch/El Paso/El Paso | 01015709 | 915/236-6200 | 138 |
| Travis Elem Sch/Greenville/Hunt | 01032537 | 903/457-2660 | 239 |
| Travis Elem Sch/Harlingen/Cameron | 01003902 | 956/427-3170 | 69 |
| Travis Elem Sch/Houston/Harris | 01024281 | 713/802-4790 | 197 |
| Travis Elem Sch/Memphis/Hall | 01022128 | 806/259-5940 | 181 |
| Travis Elem Sch/Mercedes/Hidalgo | 01030199 | 956/514-2366 | 225 |
| Travis Elem Sch/Midland/Midland | 01041667 | 432/240-8200 | 289 |
| Travis Elem Sch/Mineral Wells/Palo Pinto | 01046095 | 940/325-7801 | 313 |
| Travis Elem Sch/Pampa/Gray | 01020211 | 806/669-4950 | 170 |
| Travis Elem Sch/Port Arthur/Jefferson | 01033933 | 409/984-4700 | 246 |
| Travis Elem Sch/Rosenberg/Fort Bend | 01018335 | 832/223-2500 | 158 |
| Travis Elem Sch/San Marcos/Hays | 01029188 | 512/393-6450 | 217 |
| Travis Heights Elem Sch/Austin/Travis | 01056698 | 512/414-4495 | 370 |
| Travis High School of Choice/Paris/Lamar | 04751081 | 903/737-7560 | 263 |
| Travis Intermediate Sch/Conroe/Montgomery | 01042465 | 936/709-7000 | 295 |
| Travis Magnet Elem Sch/Odessa/Ector | 01014858 | 432/456-1229 | 135 |

| School/City/County DISTRICT/CITY/COUNTY | PID | TELEPHONE NUMBER | PAGE |
|---|---|---|---|
| Travis Middle Sch/Irving/Dallas | 01011325 | 972/600-0100 | 114 |
| Travis Middle Sch/Port Lavaca/Calhoun | 01003275 | 361/552-3784 | 65 |
| Travis Middle Sch/Quanah/Hardeman | 01022427 | 940/663-2226 | 182 |
| Travis Primary Sch/Sulphur Spgs/Hopkins | 01031703 | 903/885-5246 | 235 |
| Travis Science Academy/Temple/Bell | 00996851 | 254/215-6300 | 32 |
| Travis World Language Academy/Grand Prairie/ Dallas | 01011014 | 972/262-2990 | 112 |
| Treasure Forest Elem Sch/Houston/Harris | 04477675 | 713/251-7400 | 206 |
| Treasure Hills Elem Sch/Harlingen/Cameron | 02045331 | 956/427-3180 | 69 |
| Treetops International Sch/Euless/Tarrant | 02084090 | 817/283-1771 | 15 |
| **TRENT ISN SCH DIST/TRENT/TAYLOR** | 01054987 | 325/862-6125 | 363 |
| Trent Middle Sch/Frisco/Collin | 12107012 | 469/633-4400 | 83 |
| Trent Sch/Trent/Taylor | 01054999 | 325/862-6125 | 363 |
| Trenton Elem Sch/Trenton/Fannin | 01017616 | 903/989-2244 | 151 |
| Trenton High Sch/Trenton/Fannin | 01017628 | 903/989-2242 | 151 |
| **TRENTON IND SCH DIST/TRENTON/ FANNIN** | 01017604 | 903/989-2245 | 151 |
| Trenton Middle Sch/Trenton/Fannin | 05341861 | 903/989-2243 | 151 |
| Trevino Comm & Fine Art Sch/Laredo/Webb | 04289753 | 956/273-7800 | 390 |
| Triangle Adventist Chrn Sch/Groves/ Jefferson | 03405772 | 409/963-3806 | 247 |
| Trimmier Elem Sch/Killeen/Bell | 04806571 | 254/336-2270 | 31 |
| Trinidad Garza Early College/Dallas/Dallas | 10023965 | 214/860-3680 | 107 |
| **TRINIDAD IND SCH DIST/TRINIDAD/ HENDERSON** | 01029504 | 903/778-2673 | 219 |
| Trinidad Sch/Trinidad/Henderson | 01029516 | 903/778-2415 | 220 |
| Trinity Baptist Temple Academy/Fort Worth/ Tarrant | 04993071 | 817/237-4255 | 362 |
| Trinity Basin Prep-10th Street/Dallas/ Dallas | 11849059 | 214/296-9302 | 15 |
| Trinity Basin Prep-Ewing/Dallas/Dallas | 04890998 | 214/942-8846 | 15 |
| Trinity Basin Prep-Ft Worth/Fort Worth/ Tarrant | 11849073 | 817/840-7501 | 15 |
| Trinity Basin Prep-Jefferson/Dallas/Dallas | 11849061 | 214/941-4881 | 15 |
| Trinity Charter Sch-Amarillo/Amarillo/ Randall | 12322705 | 512/706-7566 | 15 |
| Trinity Charter Sch-Big Sandy/Big Sandy/ Upshur | 11930634 | 903/565-6801 | 15 |
| Trinity Charter Sch-Bokenkamp/Corp Christi/ Nueces | 12100492 | 361/994-1214 | 15 |
| Trinity Charter Sch-Brenham/Brenham/ Washington | 12378508 | 281/392-7505 | 15 |
| Trinity Charter Sch-Ft Worth/Fort Worth/ Tarrant | 12378493 | 903/565-6801 | 15 |
| Trinity Charter Sch-Landing/Corp Christi/ Nueces | 12378754 | 361/217-3185 | 15 |
| Trinity Charter Sch-New Hope/McAllen/ Hidalgo | 12260951 | 361/563-7979 | 15 |
| Trinity Charter Sch-New Life/Canyon Lake/ Comal | 10014706 | 830/964-4390 | 15 |
| Trinity Charter Sch-Parke/Houston/Harris | 12378481 | 361/994-1214 | 15 |
| Trinity Charter Sch-Willow Bnd/Tyler/Smith | 12378467 | 512/459-1000 | 15 |
| Trinity Charter School-Krause/Katy/ Fort Bend | 11014943 | 281/392-7505 | 15 |
| Trinity Charter School-Pegasus/Lockhart/ Caldwell | 11935505 | 512/432-1655 | 15 |
| Trinity Charter School-Spring/Spring/ Harris | 12322717 | 512/706-7566 | 15 |
| Trinity Christian Academy/Addison/Dallas | 01802667 | 972/931-8325 | 120 |
| Trinity Christian Academy/San Antonio/ Bexar | 02192659 | 210/653-2800 | 48 |
| Trinity Christian Academy/Willow Park/ Parker | 04880814 | 817/441-7901 | 317 |
| Trinity Christian Elem Sch/Lubbock/Lubbock | 04145913 | 806/791-6581 | 275 |
| Trinity Christian Jr Sr HS/Lubbock/Lubbock | 02164987 | 806/791-6583 | 275 |
| Trinity Christian Sch/Cedar Hill/Dallas | 02159360 | 972/291-2505 | 120 |
| Trinity Episcopal Sch/Austin/Travis | 04885319 | 512/472-9525 | 376 |
| Trinity Episcopal Sch/Galveston/Galveston | 01019585 | 409/765-9391 | 166 |
| Trinity Episcopal Sch/Marshall/Harrison | 01028782 | 903/938-3513 | 214 |
| Trinity Episcopal Sch/Victoria/Victoria | 01058660 | 361/573-3220 | 385 |
| Trinity High Sch/Euless/Tarrant | 01053945 | 817/571-0271 | 357 |
| Trinity High Sch/Trinity/Trinity | 03006778 | 936/594-3560 | 377 |
| Trinity Hts Gifted & Talented/Dallas/ Dallas | 12378871 | 972/925-7500 | 107 |
| **TRINITY IND SCH DIST/TRINITY/ TRINITY** | 01057147 | 936/594-3569 | 377 |
| Trinity Lutheran Chldrn's Ctr/Houston/ Harris | 01027831 | 713/224-3207 | 212 |
| Trinity Lutheran Sch/Amarillo/Potter | 01048005 | 806/352-5620 | 322 |
| Trinity Lutheran Sch/San Angelo/Tom Green | 01055917 | 325/947-1275 | 368 |
| Trinity Lutheran Sch/Spring/Harris | 01027829 | 281/376-5810 | 212 |
| Trinity Meadows Interm Sch/Keller/Tarrant | 10031613 | 817/744-4300 | 358 |

| School/City/County DISTRICT/CITY/COUNTY | PID | TELEPHONE NUMBER | PAGE |
|---|---|---|---|
| Trinity Middle Sch/Trinity/Trinity | 01057161 | 936/594-2321 | 377 |
| Trinity School of Midland/Midland/Midland | 01041708 | 432/697-3281 | 289 |
| Trinity School of Texas/Longview/Gregg | 01021332 | 903/753-0612 | 176 |
| Trinity Springs Middle Sch/Fort Worth/Tarrant | 10748270 | 817/744-3500 | 358 |
| Trinity Valley Sch/Fort Worth/Tarrant | 01054274 | 817/321-0100 | 362 |
| Triumph Public HS-Brownsville/Brownsville/Cameron | 12320159 | 956/372-1433 | 15 |
| Triumph Public HS-El Paso East/El Paso/El Paso | 11834420 | 915/298-3637 | 15 |
| Triumph Public HS-El Paso West/El Paso/El Paso | 04892738 | 915/532-7216 | 15 |
| Triumph Public HS-Laredo South/Laredo/Webb | 11663647 | 956/723-0345 | 15 |
| Triumph Public HS-Loredo North/Laredo/Webb | 04891631 | 956/722-0747 | 15 |
| Triumph Public HS-Lubbock/Lubbock/Lubbock | 04893598 | 806/744-0330 | 16 |
| Triumph Public HS-McAllen/McAllen/Hidalgo | 04892465 | 956/618-2303 | 16 |
| Triumph Public HS-Mercedes/Mercedes/Hidalgo | 11014802 | 956/565-5417 | 16 |
| Triumph Public HS-San Benito/San Benito/Cameron | 11704461 | 956/276-9930 | 16 |
| Trivium Academy/Carrollton/Denton | 12173425 | 469/855-5531 | 16 |
| Troup Elem Sch/Troup/Smith | 01050711 | 903/842-3071 | 340 |
| Troup High Sch/Troup/Smith | 01050723 | 903/842-3065 | 340 |
| **TROUP IND SCH DIST/TROUP/SMITH** | 01050709 | 903/842-3067 | 340 |
| Troup Middle Sch/Troup/Smith | 01050735 | 903/842-3081 | 340 |
| Trout Primary Sch/Lufkin/Angelina | 00995077 | 936/639-3274 | 21 |
| Troy Elem Sch/Troy/Bell | 00996904 | 254/938-2503 | 33 |
| Troy High Sch/Troy/Bell | 00996916 | 254/938-2561 | 33 |
| **TROY IND SCH DIST/TROY/BELL** | 00996899 | 254/938-2595 | 33 |
| Truce Learning Center/Fort Worth/Tarrant | 04451554 | 817/252-2490 | 350 |
| True Cross Catholic Sch/Dickinson/Galveston | 01028225 | 281/337-5212 | 166 |
| Truett Wilson Middle Sch/Haslet/Denton | 11818543 | 817/698-7900 | 129 |
| Truitt Middle Sch/Houston/Harris | 03327194 | 281/856-1100 | 191 |
| Truman Elem Sch/Edinburg/Hidalgo | 01029748 | 956/289-2555 | 222 |
| Truman Price Elem Sch/Donna/Hidalgo | 01418486 | 956/464-1303 | 220 |
| Tsu Charter Lab Sch/Houston/Harris | 10910502 | 713/313-6754 | 198 |
| Tulia Elem Sch/Tulia/Swisher | 01051583 | 806/995-4141 | 345 |
| Tulia High Sch/Tulia/Swisher | 01051595 | 806/995-2759 | 345 |
| **TULIA IND SCH DIST/TULIA/SWISHER** | 01051571 | 806/995-4591 | 345 |
| Tulia Junior High Sch/Tulia/Swisher | 01051600 | 806/995-4842 | 345 |
| Tuloso-Midway High Sch/Corp Christi/Nueces | 02226315 | 361/903-6700 | 309 |
| **TULOSO-MIDWAY IND SCH DIST/CORP CHRISTI/NUECES** | 01045015 | 361/903-6400 | 308 |
| Tuloso-Midway Intermediate Sch/Corp Christi/Nueces | 01045053 | 361/903-6550 | 309 |
| Tuloso-Midway Middle Sch/Corp Christi/Nueces | 01045041 | 361/903-6600 | 309 |
| Tuloso-Midway Primary Sch/Corp Christi/Nueces | 02129004 | 361/903-6500 | 309 |
| **TURKEY-QUITAQUE CONS IND SD/TURKEY/HALL** | 01022130 | 806/455-1411 | 181 |
| Turner College-Career High Sch/Pearland/Brazoria | 11917266 | 281/727-1600 | 57 |
| Turner Prekindergarten Academy/Waxahachie/Ellis | 12225913 | 972/923-4690 | 147 |
| Turning Point Secondary Sch/Arlington/Tarrant | 04039053 | 682/867-3050 | 347 |
| Tuscany Heights Elem Sch/San Antonio/Bexar | 11558717 | 210/407-8200 | 39 |
| Twin Creeks Middle Sch/Spring/Harris | 02227620 | 281/891-7850 | 208 |
| Two Dimensions Prep Academy/Houston/Harris | 04886143 | 281/227-4700 | 16 |
| Two Dimensions Prep-Vickery/Houston/Harris | 11704813 | 281/227-4700 | 16 |
| Two Dimensions-Corsicana/Corsicana/Navarro | 11704801 | 281/227-4700 | 16 |
| Tyler Adventist Sch/Tyler/Smith | 02234398 | 903/595-6706 | 342 |
| Tyler Career & Technology Ctr/Tyler/Smith | 12311108 | 903/262-1024 | 341 |
| Tyler Classical Academy/Tyler/Smith | 11848976 | 903/504-5690 | 16 |
| Tyler Early College High Sch/Tyler/Smith | 12305563 | 903/262-3040 | 341 |
| Tyler High Sch/Tyler/Smith | 01050876 | 903/262-2850 | 341 |
| **TYLER IND SCH DIST/TYLER/SMITH** | 01050747 | 903/262-1000 | 340 |
| Tyler Street Christian Academy/Dallas/Dallas | 01012343 | 214/941-9717 | 120 |
| Tynan Early Childhood Ctr/San Antonio/Bexar | 00998990 | 210/738-9835 | 44 |
| Tyrrell Elem Sch/Port Arthur/Jefferson | 01033921 | 409/984-4660 | 246 |

### U

| School/City/County DISTRICT/CITY/COUNTY | PID | TELEPHONE NUMBER | PAGE |
|---|---|---|---|
| Uhland Elem Sch/Uhland/Hays | 12308395 | 512/268-8503 | 216 |
| Ulrich Intermediate Sch/Houston/Harris | 11551939 | 832/375-7500 | 203 |
| Ume Prep Acad-Dallas/Dallas/Dallas | 11849102 | 214/445-6243 | 16 |
| Ume Prep Acad-Duncanville/Duncanville/Dallas | 12261254 | 972/296-0084 | 16 |
| Umphrey Lee Elem Sch/Dallas/Dallas | 01009023 | 972/749-3900 | 107 |

| School/City/County DISTRICT/CITY/COUNTY | PID | TELEPHONE NUMBER | PAGE |
|---|---|---|---|
| Underwood Elem Sch/Andrews/Andrews | 00994762 | 432/524-1960 | 19 |
| Union Grove Elem Sch/Gladewater/Upshur | 01057563 | 903/845-3481 | 379 |
| **UNION GROVE IND SCH DIST/GLADEWATER/UPSHUR** | 01057551 | 903/845-5509 | 379 |
| Union Grove Jr Sr High Sch/Gladewater/Upshur | 01057575 | 903/845-5506 | 379 |
| Union Grove Middle Sch/Harker HTS/Bell | 05347839 | 254/336-6580 | 31 |
| Union Hill Elem Sch/Round Rock/Williamson | 05096030 | 512/424-8700 | 402 |
| **UNION HILL IND SCH DIST/GILMER/UPSHUR** | 01057587 | 903/762-2140 | 380 |
| Union Hill Sch/Gilmer/Upshur | 01057599 | 903/762-2138 | 380 |
| Union Park Elem Sch/Aubrey/Denton | 12368759 | 940/369-0900 | 125 |
| United Day Sch/Laredo/Webb | 01481304 | 956/723-7261 | 392 |
| United High 9th Grade HS/Laredo/Webb | 12308228 | 956/473-2400 | 391 |
| United High Sch/Laredo/Webb | 01059511 | 956/473-5600 | 391 |
| **UNITED IND SCH DIST/LAREDO/WEBB** | 01059470 | 956/473-6201 | 390 |
| United Middle Sch/Laredo/Webb | 02949177 | 956/473-7300 | 391 |
| United South High 9th Grade HS/Laredo/Webb | 12308199 | 956/473-1400 | 391 |
| United South High Sch/Laredo/Webb | 03336171 | 956/473-5400 | 391 |
| United South Middle Sch/Laredo/Webb | 03336169 | 956/473-7700 | 391 |
| United Step Academy/Laredo/Webb | 04875182 | 956/473-6500 | 391 |
| Unity Christian Sch/Denison/Grayson | 11816375 | 903/465-1909 | 174 |
| Univ of Houston Charter Sch/Houston/Harris | 04757902 | 713/743-9111 | 16 |
| Univ TX Charter High Sch/Austin/Travis | 12375922 | 512/232-5000 | 16 |
| Universal Academy-Coppell/Coppell/Dallas | 05010696 | 972/393-5834 | 16 |
| Universal Academy-Irving/Irving/Dallas | 04813500 | 972/255-1800 | 16 |
| University High Sch/Austin/Travis | 12161915 | 512/382-0072 | 16 |
| University High Sch/Waco/McLennan | 01040431 | 254/756-1843 | 285 |
| University of Texas Elem CS/Austin/Travis | 05286613 | 512/495-3300 | 16 |
| University Park Elem Sch/Dallas/Dallas | 01011090 | 214/780-3400 | 112 |
| University Preparatory HS/Corp Christi/Nueces | 10022117 | 361/694-9780 | 308 |
| Uphaus Early Childhood Center/Austin/Travis | 11848744 | 512/414-5520 | 370 |
| Upland Heights Elem Sch/Lubbock/Lubbock | 12234768 | 806/698-6611 | 272 |
| Uplift Ascend Preparatory/Fort Worth/Tarrant | 12375283 | 817/768-4300 | 16 |
| Uplift Elevate Preparatory/Fort Worth/Tarrant | 12375271 | 817/764-3600 | 16 |
| Uplift Gradus Preparatory/Desoto/Dallas | 12160870 | 214/451-5551 | 16 |
| Uplift Grand Preparatory/Grand Prairie/Dallas | 12038928 | 972/854-0600 | 16 |
| Uplift Hampton Prep Chtr Sch/Dallas/Dallas | 11150365 | 972/421-1982 | 16 |
| Uplift Heights Prep Prim Sch/Dallas/Dallas | 12240339 | 214/873-9700 | 16 |
| Uplift Heights Prep Sch Sec/Dallas/Dallas | 11589417 | 214/442-7094 | 16 |
| Uplift Infinity Prep Sch/Irving/Dallas | 11728900 | 469/621-9200 | 16 |
| Uplift Lee Prep Sch/Grand Prairie/Dallas | 12106927 | 972/262-6785 | 112 |
| Uplift Luna Prep Primary/Dallas/Dallas | 11574498 | 214/442-7882 | 16 |
| Uplift Luna Prep Secondary/Dallas/Dallas | 11826069 | 214/445-3300 | 16 |
| Uplift Meridian Preparatory/Fort Worth/Tarrant | 11818593 | 817/288-1700 | 16 |
| Uplift Mighty Preparatory Acad/Fort Worth/Tarrant | 11828287 | 817/288-3800 | 16 |
| Uplift North Hills Prep Sch/Irving/Dallas | 04758039 | 972/501-0645 | 16 |
| Uplift Peak Prep Sch/Dallas/Dallas | 10804630 | 214/276-0879 | 16 |
| Uplift Pinnacle Prep Primary/Dallas/Dallas | 11728912 | 214/442-6100 | 16 |
| Uplift Summit Int'l Prep CS/Arlington/Tarrant | 10969852 | 817/287-5121 | 16 |
| Uplift Triumph Preparatory/Dallas/Dallas | 11927912 | 972/590-5100 | 16 |
| Uplift White Rock Hills Prep/Dallas/Dallas | 12238477 | 469/914-7500 | 16 |
| Uplift Williams Prep Chtr Sch/Dallas/Dallas | 11150377 | 214/276-0352 | 16 |
| Uplift Wisdom Prep Primary Sch/Dallas/Dallas | 12240353 | 972/330-7291 | 16 |
| Uplift Wisdom Prep Sec Sch/Dallas/Dallas | 12240341 | 972/330-7291 | 16 |
| Urban Park Elem Sch/Dallas/Dallas | 01010022 | 972/794-1100 | 107 |
| Ursula Stephens Elem Sch/Katy/Harris | 10913293 | 281/234-0200 | 157 |
| Ursuline Academy/Dallas/Dallas | 01012757 | 469/232-1800 | 118 |
| UT Tyler Univ Acad-Longview/Longview/Smith | 12317035 | 903/663-8219 | 341 |
| UT Tyler Univ Acad-Palestine/Palestine/Smith | 12100143 | 903/705-4330 | 341 |
| UT Tyler Univ Acad-Tyler/Tyler/Smith | 11917888 | 903/705-4330 | 341 |
| **UT TYLER UNIVERSITY ACAD DIST/TYLER/SMITH** | 12317047 | 903/730-3988 | 341 |
| UT Univ CS-Annunciation/Georgetown/Williamson | 12369210 | 512/654-7755 | 16 |
| UT Univ CS-Laurel Ridge/San Antonio/Bexar | 12100454 | 210/491-9400 | 16 |
| UT Univ CS-Memorial Hermann/Houston/Harris | 12100430 | 713/939-7272 | 16 |
| UT Univ CS-Methodist Children/Waco/McLennan | 12100442 | 512/471-4864 | 16 |
| UT Univ CS-Settlement Home/Austin/Travis | 12100466 | 512/836-2150 | 16 |

| School/City/County DISTRICT/CITY/COUNTY | PID | TELEPHONE NUMBER | PAGE |
|---|---|---|---|
| **UTOPIA IND SCH DIST**/UTOPIA/ **UVALDE** | 01057769 | 830/966-1928 | 381 |
| Utopia Sch/Utopia/Uvalde | 01057783 | 830/966-3339 | 381 |
| Utpb STEM Academy/Odessa/Ector | 12105492 | 432/552-2580 | 16 |
| **UVALDE CONS IND SCH DIST**/ **UVALDE/UVALDE** | 01057795 | 830/278-6655 | 381 |
| Uvalde High Sch/Uvalde/Uvalde | 01057850 | 830/591-2950 | 381 |
| **V** | | | |
| V R Eaton High Sch/Haslet/Denton | 12106745 | 817/698-7300 | 129 |
| Val Verde Christian Academy/Groves/ Jefferson | 11748821 | 409/962-8822 | 247 |
| Vale Middle Sch/San Antonio/Bexar | 11104122 | 210/397-5700 | 42 |
| **VALENTINE IND SCH DIST**/VALENTINE/ **JEFF DAVIS** | 01033359 | 432/467-2671 | 244 |
| Valentine Sch/Valentine/Jeff Davis | 01033361 | 432/467-2671 | 244 |
| Valle Verde Early College HS/El Paso/ El Paso | 10908638 | 915/434-1500 | 143 |
| Valley Christian Heritage Sch/Alamo/ Hidalgo | 02873645 | 956/787-9743 | 229 |
| Valley Christian High Sch/Brownsville/ Cameron | 01754254 | 956/542-5222 | 72 |
| Valley Creek Elem Sch/McKinney/Collin | 03396793 | 469/302-4800 | 85 |
| Valley Hi Elem Sch/San Antonio/Bexar | 00998330 | 210/397-0350 | 42 |
| Valley Mills Elem Sch/Valley Mills/Bosque | 01000766 | 254/932-5526 | 50 |
| **VALLEY MILLS IND SCH DIST**/ **VALLEY MILLS/BOSQUE** | 01000754 | 254/932-5210 | 50 |
| Valley Millsjr Sr High Sch/Valley Mills/ Bosque | 01000778 | 254/932-5251 | 50 |
| Valley Oaks Elem Sch/Houston/Harris | 01027403 | 713/251-7500 | 206 |
| Valley Ranch Elem Sch/Irving/Dallas | 04454178 | 214/496-8500 | 102 |
| Valley Ranch Elem Sch/Porter/Montgomery | 10760084 | 281/577-8760 | 297 |
| Valley Ridge Elem Sch/Lewisville/Denton | 04452235 | 469/713-5982 | 128 |
| Valley Sch/Turkey/Hall | 01022154 | 806/455-1411 | 181 |
| Valley View 5th Grade Campus/Pharr/Hidalgo | 11136967 | 956/340-1400 | 228 |
| Valley View Early College Sch/Hidalgo/ Hidalgo | 12035055 | 956/340-1200 | 228 |
| Valley View Elem Sch/Austin/Travis | 02127599 | 512/732-9140 | 372 |
| Valley View Elem Sch/Hidalgo/Hidalgo | 01030577 | 956/340-1450 | 228 |
| Valley View High Sch/Pharr/Hidalgo | 03049653 | 956/340-1500 | 228 |
| **VALLEY VIEW IND SCH DIST**/ **PHARR/HIDALGO** | 01030565 | 956/340-1000 | 228 |
| **VALLEY VIEW ISD-COOKE CO**/ **VALLEY VIEW/COOKE** | 01007506 | 940/726-3659 | 95 |
| Valley View Junior High Sch/Pharr/Hidalgo | 03322948 | 956/340-1300 | 228 |
| Valley View North Elem Sch/Pharr/Hidalgo | 04801208 | 956/340-1600 | 228 |
| Valley View Sch/Valley View/Cooke | 01007518 | 940/726-3659 | 95 |
| Valley View South Elem Sch/Hidalgo/Hidalgo | 10915538 | 956/340-1650 | 228 |
| Valley West Elem Sch/Houston/Harris | 04454465 | 713/773-6151 | 200 |
| Valor Preparatory Academy/Waco/McLennan | 12378572 | 254/235-0575 | 286 |
| Valor South Austin/Austin/Travis | 12366787 | 512/646-4170 | 17 |
| Van Alstyne High Sch/Van Alstyne/Grayson | 01020766 | 903/482-8803 | 173 |
| **VAN ALSTYNE IND SCH DIST**/ **VAN ALSTYNE/GRAYSON** | 01020742 | 903/482-8802 | 173 |
| Van Alstyne Middle Sch/Van Alstyne/Grayson | 01020778 | 903/482-8804 | 173 |
| Van Buren Elem Sch/Groves/Jefferson | 01034030 | 409/962-6511 | 247 |
| Van High Sch/Van/Van Zandt | 01058256 | 903/963-8623 | 383 |
| Van Horn Schools/Van Horn/Culberson | 01008043 | 432/283-2245 | 99 |
| **VAN IND SCH DIST**/VAN/VAN ZANDT | 01058232 | 903/963-8713 | 383 |
| Van Intermediate Sch/Van/Van Zandt | 11917723 | 903/963-8331 | 383 |
| Van Junior High Sch/Van/Van Zandt | 01058268 | 903/963-8321 | 383 |
| Van Middle Sch/Van/Van Zandt | 11070076 | 903/963-1461 | 383 |
| Van Raub Elem Sch/Boerne/Kendall | 12313481 | 830/357-4100 | 257 |
| Van Vleck Elem Sch/Van Vleck/Matagorda | 01041021 | 979/245-8681 | 279 |
| Van Vleck High Sch/Van Vleck/Matagorda | 01041033 | 979/245-4664 | 279 |
| **VAN VLECK IND SCH DIST**/VAN VLECK/ **MATAGORDA** | 01041019 | 979/323-5000 | 279 |
| Van Zandt-Guinn Elem Sch/Fort Worth/ Tarrant | 01052977 | 817/815-2000 | 354 |
| Vandagriff Elem Sch/Aledo/Parker | 03250474 | 817/441-8771 | 315 |
| Vandegrift High Sch/Austin/Williamson | 11450983 | 512/570-2300 | 400 |
| Vanguard Academy-Beethoven/Edinburg/ Hidalgo | 12261266 | 956/318-0211 | 17 |
| Vanguard Academy-Mozart/Alamo/Hidalgo | 11932632 | 956/702-2548 | 17 |
| Vanguard Academy-Picasso/Pharr/Hidalgo | 11833995 | 956/702-0134 | 17 |
| Vanguard Academy-Rembrandt/Pharr/Hidalgo | 05010957 | 956/781-1701 | 17 |
| Vanguard College Prepatory Sch/Waco/ McLennan | 01480790 | 254/772-8111 | 286 |
| Vanguard International Academy/Arlington/ Tarrant | 11813816 | 817/274-6444 | 362 |
| Vanguard Preparatory Sch/Dallas/Dallas | 12313819 | 972/404-1616 | 120 |

| School/City/County DISTRICT/CITY/COUNTY | PID | TELEPHONE NUMBER | PAGE |
|---|---|---|---|
| Vardeman EC-PK-K Sch/Houston/Harris | 12309686 | 281/985-3740 | 186 |
| Varnett School Southeast/Houston/Harris | 12261230 | 713/726-7654 | 17 |
| Varnett School-East/Houston/Harris | 11015533 | 713/637-6574 | 17 |
| Varnett School-NE/Houston/Harris | 11015545 | 713/631-4396 | 17 |
| Vaughn Elem Sch/Frisco/Collin | 12167270 | 469/633-2575 | 84 |
| Veda Knox Elem Sch/Arlington/Tarrant | 04994329 | 682/867-2051 | 347 |
| Vega Elem Sch/McKinney/Collin | 05243300 | 469/302-5100 | 85 |
| Vega Elem Sch/Vega/Oldham | 01045560 | 806/267-2126 | 311 |
| **VEGA IND SCH DIST**/VEGA/OLDHAM | 01045558 | 806/267-2123 | 310 |
| Vega Jr Sr High Sch/Vega/Oldham | 01045572 | 806/267-2126 | 311 |
| Velasco Elem Sch/Freeport/Brazoria | 01001708 | 979/730-7210 | 56 |
| Velma Penny Elem Sch/Lindale/Smith | 04366167 | 903/881-4250 | 340 |
| Venable Village Elem Sch/Fort Hood/Bell | 04368799 | 254/336-1980 | 31 |
| Venture High Sch/Arlington/Tarrant | 01051741 | 682/867-6400 | 347 |
| Venus Elem Sch/Venus/Johnson | 04884054 | 972/366-3748 | 252 |
| Venus High Sch/Venus/Johnson | 01035187 | 972/366-8815 | 252 |
| **VENUS IND SCH DIST**/VENUS/JOHNSON | 01035163 | 972/366-3448 | 252 |
| Venus Middle Sch/Venus/Johnson | 04287731 | 972/366-3358 | 252 |
| Venus Primary Sch/Venus/Johnson | 01035175 | 972/366-3268 | 252 |
| Vera Escamilla Elem Sch/Houston/Harris | 04032598 | 281/985-6390 | 185 |
| Veramendi Elem Sch/New Braunfels/Comal | 12235932 | 830/608-5900 | 92 |
| Verda Mae Adams Elem Sch/San Antonio/Bexar | 00997362 | 210/989-2800 | 36 |
| **VERIBEST IND SCH DIST**/VERIBEST/ **TOM GREEN** | 01055826 | 325/655-2851 | 368 |
| Veribest Sch/Veribest/Tom Green | 01055838 | 325/655-2851 | 368 |
| Veritas Academy/Austin/Travis | 11228273 | 512/891-1673 | 376 |
| Veritas Christian Academy/Bellaire/Harris | 11234595 | 713/773-9605 | 212 |
| Vermillion Elem Sch/Brownsville/Cameron | 02110584 | 956/831-6060 | 68 |
| Vernagene Mott Elem Sch/Pflugerville/ Travis | 12235360 | 512/594-4700 | 375 |
| Vernal Lister Elem Sch/Garland/Dallas | 04367678 | 972/675-3030 | 111 |
| Vernon & Kathy Lewis Mid Sch/Houston/ Harris | 11555363 | 281/209-8257 | 186 |
| Vernon High Sch/Vernon/Wilbarger | 01060601 | 940/553-3377 | 397 |
| **VERNON IND SCH DIST**/VERNON/ **WILBARGER** | 01060560 | 940/553-1900 | 396 |
| Vernon Middle Sch/Harlingen/Cameron | 01003914 | 956/427-3040 | 69 |
| Vernon Middle Sch/Vernon/Wilbarger | 01060613 | 940/552-6231 | 397 |
| Vernon Price Elem Sch/Garland/Dallas | 02128543 | 972/290-4100 | 116 |
| Versia L Williams Elem Sch/Fort Worth/ Tarrant | 01053490 | 817/814-9700 | 354 |
| Vestal Elem Sch/San Antonio/Bexar | 00997570 | 210/989-3350 | 36 |
| Veterans Hill Elem Sch/Round Rock/ Williamson | 12033459 | 512/759-3030 | 399 |
| Veterans Memorial Academy/San Benito/ Cameron | 04941884 | 956/276-6000 | 71 |
| Veterans Memorial Early Clg HS/Brownsville/ Cameron | 11554905 | 956/574-5600 | 68 |
| Veterans Memorial Elem Sch/Laredo/Webb | 12105208 | 956/473-1200 | 391 |
| Veterans Memorial Elem Sch/Roma/Starr | 12034776 | 956/849-1717 | 343 |
| Veterans Memorial High Sch/Corp Christi/ Nueces | 12106563 | 361/878-7900 | 307 |
| Veterans Memorial High Sch/Mission/Hidalgo | 04288802 | 956/323-3000 | 226 |
| Veterans Memorial High Sch/San Antonio/ Bexar | 12165428 | 210/619-0220 | 37 |
| Veterans Middle Sch/Donna/Hidalgo | 04892130 | 956/464-1350 | 220 |
| Veterans Middle Sch/Rio Grande Cy/Starr | 10903509 | 956/488-0252 | 343 |
| Vic Robertson Elem Sch/Round Rock/ Williamson | 02043395 | 512/428-3300 | 402 |
| Vickers Elem Sch/Victoria/Victoria | 01058610 | 361/788-9579 | 385 |
| Vickery Elem Sch/Flower Mound/Denton | 05271840 | 469/713-5969 | 128 |
| Victor Fields Elem Sch/McAllen/Hidalgo | 01029982 | 956/971-4344 | 224 |
| Victor H Hexter Elem Sch/Dallas/Dallas | 01010034 | 972/502-5800 | 107 |
| Victoria Christian Sch/Victoria/Victoria | 11238357 | 361/573-5345 | 385 |
| Victoria East High Sch/Victoria/Victoria | 01058622 | 361/788-2820 | 385 |
| **VICTORIA IND SCH DIST**/VICTORIA/ **VICTORIA** | 01058440 | 361/576-3131 | 384 |
| Victoria Juv Justice Center/Victoria/ Victoria | 11819327 | 361/575-0399 | 385 |
| Victoria Walker Elem Sch/Baytown/Harris | 10907505 | 281/421-1800 | 193 |
| Victoria West High Sch/Victoria/Victoria | 01058608 | 361/788-2830 | 385 |
| Victory Baptist Academy/Weatherford/Parker | 12317164 | 817/596-2711 | 317 |
| Victory Christian Academy/Decatur/Wise | 12364818 | 940/626-4730 | 407 |
| Victory Christian Academy/Perryton/ Ochiltree | 04994104 | 806/435-3476 | 310 |
| Victory Early College HS/Houston/Harris | 10907098 | 281/810-5675 | 185 |
| Victory Lakes Intermediate Sch/League City/ Galveston | 05096896 | 281/284-3700 | 164 |
| Victory Life Academy/Brownwood/Brown | 04993150 | 325/641-2223 | 62 |
| Victory Place at Coppell/Coppell/Dallas | 04940323 | 214/496-8032 | 102 |
| Vida N Clover Elem Sch/San Juan/Hidalgo | 01030395 | 956/354-2730 | 227 |
| Vidor Elem Sch/Vidor/Orange | 01045780 | 409/951-8830 | 312 |

| School/City/County DISTRICT/CITY/COUNTY | PID | TELEPHONE NUMBER | PAGE |
|---|---|---|---|
| Vidor High Sch/Vidor/Orange | 01045792 | 409/951-8900 | 312 |
| **VIDOR IND SCH DIST/VIDOR/ORANGE** | 01045754 | 409/951-8700 | 312 |
| Vidor Junior High Sch/Vidor/Orange | 01045807 | 409/951-8970 | 312 |
| Vidor Middle Sch/Vidor/Orange | 02201901 | 409/951-8880 | 312 |
| Villa Nueva Elem Sch/Brownsville/Cameron | 01003720 | 956/542-3957 | 68 |
| Village Elem Sch/Georgetown/Williamson | 04807915 | 512/943-5140 | 398 |
| Village Fair-Elem Daep/Dallas/Dallas | 04503872 | 972/925-7000 | 107 |
| Village Parkway Chrn Sch/San Antonio/Bexar | 03569158 | 210/680-8187 | 48 |
| Village Sch/Houston/Harris | 01875377 | 281/496-7900 | 212 |
| Village Technical Sch/Duncanville/Dallas | 11934264 | 469/454-4441 | 17 |
| Villareal Elem Sch/Olmito/Cameron | 01004059 | 956/233-3975 | 70 |
| Villarreal Elem Sch/San Antonio/Bexar | 00998108 | 210/397-5800 | 42 |
| Villarreal Elem Sch/Zapata/Zapata | 01062283 | 956/765-4321 | 410 |
| Vincent Middle Sch/Beaumont/Jefferson | 01034286 | 409/617-5950 | 245 |
| Vincent Patlan Elem Sch/Seguin/Guadalupe | 03009902 | 830/401-1221 | 179 |
| Vincent W Miller Interm Sch/Pasadena/ Harris | 01026992 | 713/740-0450 | 205 |
| Vine Sch/Victoria/Victoria | 12113059 | 361/212-8463 | 385 |
| Vines EC-PK-K Sch/Houston/Harris | 04867197 | 281/878-7950 | 186 |
| Vines High Sch/Plano/Collin | 01525912 | 469/752-7800 | 87 |
| Vineyard Ranch Elem Sch/San Antonio/Bexar | 11820443 | 210/356-7200 | 39 |
| Viola Cobb Elem Sch/Channelview/Harris | 01023122 | 281/452-7788 | 188 |
| Viola DeWalt High Sch/La Porte/Harris | 02223870 | 281/604-6900 | 203 |
| Viola M Coleman High Sch/Midland/Midland | 03052143 | 432/689-5000 | 289 |
| Virginia Myers Elem Sch/San Antonio/Bexar | 04754772 | 210/397-6650 | 42 |
| Virginia Reinhardt Elem Sch/Rockwall/ Rockwall | 02856908 | 972/771-5247 | 328 |
| Viridian Elem Sch/Arlington/Tarrant | 12033447 | 817/864-0550 | 357 |
| Virtual Learning Academy/Flower Mound/ Denton | 12170148 | 972/350-1870 | 128 |
| Virtual Sch/Pasadena/Harris | 12169371 | 713/740-0124 | 205 |
| Visd Alternative Ed Sch/Vernon/Wilbarger | 04941224 | 940/552-2252 | 397 |
| Vision Academy/Edinburg/Hidalgo | 11558262 | 956/289-2584 | 222 |
| Vista Alt Learning Center/Colleyville/ Tarrant | 04447917 | 817/251-5466 | 356 |
| Vista Del Futuro Charter Sch/El Paso/ El Paso | 11728974 | 915/855-8143 | 17 |
| Vista Del Sol Sch/El Paso/El Paso | 02199530 | 915/937-7500 | 141 |
| Vista Hills Elem Sch/El Paso/El Paso | 01545261 | 915/434-5700 | 143 |
| Vista Ridge High Sch/Cedar Park/Williamson | 05272430 | 512/570-1800 | 400 |
| Vista Ridge Middle Sch/Fort Worth/Tarrant | 12232825 | 817/743-8400 | 358 |
| Vistas High Sch/Houston/Harris | 10797594 | 832/484-7650 | 203 |
| Vivian Field Middle Sch/Farmers BRNCH/ Dallas | 01008184 | 972/968-3900 | 101 |
| Vivian Fowler Elem Sch/Mt Pleasant/Titus | 01055412 | 903/575-2070 | 366 |
| Voss Farms Elem Sch/New Braunfels/Comal | 12235920 | 830/608-5800 | 92 |
| Voyde Caraway Elem Sch/Houston/Harris | 04019039 | 281/878-0320 | 184 |
| Vysehrad Elem Sch/Hallettsville/Lavaca | 01037410 | 361/798-4118 | 265 |
| **VYSEHRAD IND SCH DIST/HALLETTSVILLE/ LAVACA** | 01037408 | 361/798-4118 | 265 |

### W

| School/City/County DISTRICT/CITY/COUNTY | PID | TELEPHONE NUMBER | PAGE |
|---|---|---|---|
| W A Blair Elem Sch/Dallas/Dallas | 01010113 | 972/794-1600 | 107 |
| W A Carpenter Elem Sch/Deer Park/Harris | 01023328 | 832/668-8400 | 191 |
| W A Martin Elem Sch/Crandall/Kaufman | 01035541 | 972/427-6020 | 254 |
| W A Meacham Middle Sch/Fort Worth/Tarrant | 01053517 | 817/815-0200 | 355 |
| W A Porter Elem Sch/Hurst/Tarrant | 01418591 | 817/547-2900 | 349 |
| W A Todd Middle Sch/Donna/Hidalgo | 11920108 | 956/464-1800 | 220 |
| W B Bizzell Academy/Navasota/Grimes | 11927950 | 936/825-4296 | 177 |
| W B Green Junior High Sch/La Feria/Cameron | 01003976 | 956/797-8400 | 69 |
| W B Ray High Sch/Corp Christi/Nueces | 01044736 | 361/878-7300 | 307 |
| W B Travis Vanguard & Academy/Dallas/ Dallas | 04921951 | 972/794-7500 | 107 |
| W C Andrews Elem Sch/Portland/San Patricio | 02046517 | 361/777-4048 | 333 |
| W C Cunningham Middle Sch/Houston/Harris | 02177726 | 832/386-4470 | 192 |
| W C Stripling Middle Sch/Fort Worth/ Tarrant | 01053529 | 817/815-1300 | 355 |
| W E Boswell High Sch/Fort Worth/Tarrant | 01052446 | 817/237-3314 | 351 |
| W E Chalmers Elem Sch/Gainesville/Cooke | 01007386 | 940/665-4147 | 95 |
| W E Greiner Explor Arts Acad/Dallas/Dallas | 01010072 | 972/925-7100 | 107 |
| W F George Middle Sch/Iowa Park/Wichita | 01060106 | 940/592-2196 | 395 |
| W F Peavy Primary Sch/Lufkin/Angelina | 04933980 | 936/875-9344 | 20 |
| W H Adamson High Sch/Dallas/Dallas | 01010084 | 972/749-1400 | 107 |
| W H Bonner Elem Sch/Lufkin/Angelina | 00994865 | 936/875-9212 | 20 |
| W H Burnett Early Chldhd Ctr/Terrell/ Kaufman | 01035773 | 972/563-1452 | 256 |
| W H Gaston Middle Sch/Dallas/Dallas | 01010096 | 972/502-5400 | 107 |
| W H Wilson Elem Sch/Coppell/Dallas | 04010411 | 214/496-7500 | 102 |
| W I Stevenson Middle Sch/Houston/Harris | 04149074 | 713/943-5700 | 195 |
| W J Turner Elem Sch/Fort Worth/Tarrant | 01053488 | 817/814-4900 | 355 |
| W L Higgins Elem Sch/Paris/Wise | 03161392 | 903/737-2081 | 407 |
| W M Green Elem Sch/Fort Worth/Tarrant | 01053543 | 817/815-8900 | 355 |

| School/City/County DISTRICT/CITY/COUNTY | PID | TELEPHONE NUMBER | PAGE |
|---|---|---|---|
| W O Gray Elem Sch/Balch Springs/Dallas | 04850388 | 972/882-7280 | 116 |
| W P Hobby Elem Sch/Houston/Harris | 01025259 | 713/434-5650 | 198 |
| W P McLean Middle Sch/Fort Worth/Tarrant | 01053555 | 817/814-5300 | 355 |
| W R Fort Elem Sch/Royse City/Rockwall | 05356165 | 972/636-3304 | 329 |
| W R Hatfield Elem Sch/Justin/Denton | 04804585 | 817/215-0350 | 129 |
| W S Permenter Middle Sch/Cedar Hill/Dallas | 01008304 | 972/291-5270 | 101 |
| W T Francisco Elem Sch/Haltom City/Tarrant | 01052226 | 817/547-1700 | 349 |
| W T Hall Education Center/Houston/Harris | 04922785 | 281/985-7446 | 185 |
| W T White High Sch/Dallas/Dallas | 01010125 | 972/502-6200 | 107 |
| W W Bushman Elem Sch/Dallas/Dallas | 01010137 | 972/749-1800 | 107 |
| W W Pinkerton Elem Sch/Coppell/Dallas | 01008330 | 214/496-6800 | 102 |
| W W Samuell High Sch/Dallas/Dallas | 01010149 | 972/892-5100 | 107 |
| W Z Burke Elem Sch/San Antonio/Bexar | 04921391 | 210/397-1300 | 42 |
| Waco Center for Youth-Spec Ed/Waco/ McLennan | 03217276 | 254/756-2171 | 17 |
| Waco Charter Sch/Waco/McLennan | 04467527 | 254/754-8169 | 17 |
| Waco High Sch/Waco/McLennan | 01040376 | 254/776-1150 | 285 |
| **WACO IND SCH DIST/WACO/MCLENNAN** | 01040132 | 254/755-9473 | 284 |
| Waco Montessori Sch/Waco/McLennan | 03404182 | 254/754-3966 | 286 |
| **WAELDER IND SCH DIST/WAELDER/ GONZALES** | 01020003 | 830/788-7161 | 169 |
| Waelder Sch/Waelder/Gonzales | 01020015 | 830/788-7221 | 169 |
| Waggoner Creek Elem Sch/Texarkana/Bowie | 12232289 | 903/255-3301 | 53 |
| Wainwright Elem Sch/Houston/Harris | 01024293 | 713/613-2550 | 197 |
| Wake Village Elem Sch/Wake Village/Bowie | 01001356 | 903/838-4261 | 53 |
| Wakefield Elem Sch/Sherman/Grayson | 01020675 | 903/891-6595 | 172 |
| Walcott Elem Sch/Hereford/Deaf Smith | 01013098 | 806/289-5222 | 123 |
| **WALCOTT IND SCH DIST/HEREFORD/ DEAF SMITH** | 01013086 | 806/289-5222 | 123 |
| Walden Sch/Sugar Land/Fort Bend | 01875339 | 281/980-0022 | 160 |
| Walipp Tsu Prep Academy/Houston/Harris | 11733967 | 713/741-3600 | 17 |
| Walker Creek Elem Sch/N RichInd HIs/ Tarrant | 10004701 | 817/547-3500 | 349 |
| Walker Elem Sch/Katy/Harris | 04916322 | 281/345-3200 | 191 |
| Walker Junior High Sch/Monahans/Ward | 01059004 | 432/943-4622 | 388 |
| Walker Station Elem Sch/Sugar Land/ Fort Bend | 04016336 | 281/634-4400 | 155 |
| Wall Elem Sch/Wall/Tom Green | 01055864 | 325/651-7790 | 368 |
| Wall High Sch/Wall/Tom Green | 03238775 | 325/651-7521 | 368 |
| **WALL IND SCH DIST/WALL/TOM GREEN** | 01055840 | 325/651-7790 | 368 |
| Wall Middle Sch/Wall/Tom Green | 01055876 | 325/651-7648 | 368 |
| Wallace Accelerated High Sch/Colorado City/ Mitchell | 10016742 | 325/728-2392 | 292 |
| Wallace Elem Sch/Dallas/Dallas | 01011985 | 469/593-2600 | 117 |
| Wallace Jefferson Middle Sch/San Antonio/ Bexar | 11104134 | 210/397-3700 | 42 |
| Wallace Middle Sch/Kyle/Hays | 01029073 | 512/268-2891 | 216 |
| Waller Christian Academy/Waller/Harris | 11934393 | 936/372-0901 | 212 |
| Waller High Sch/Waller/Waller | 01058892 | 936/372-3654 | 387 |
| **WALLER IND SCH DIST/WALLER/ WALLER** | 01058866 | 936/931-3685 | 387 |
| Waller Junior High Sch/Waller/Waller | 04803268 | 936/931-1353 | 387 |
| Wally Watkins Elem Sch/Wylie/Collin | 11551850 | 972/429-2580 | 89 |
| Walnut Bend Elem Sch/Gainesville/Cooke | 01007544 | 940/665-5990 | 96 |
| Walnut Bend Elem Sch/Houston/Harris | 01024645 | 713/917-3540 | 200 |
| **WALNUT BEND IND SCH DIST/ GAINESVILLE/COOKE** | 01007532 | 940/665-5990 | 96 |
| Walnut Creek Elem Sch/Austin/Travis | 01056703 | 512/414-4499 | 370 |
| Walnut Creek Elem Sch/Azle/Tarrant | 01052020 | 817/444-4045 | 348 |
| Walnut Creek Private Sch/Mansfield/Tarrant | 03565530 | 817/473-4406 | 362 |
| Walnut Glen Academy Excellence/Garland/ Dallas | 01010797 | 972/494-8330 | 111 |
| Walnut Grove Elem Sch/Southlake/Tarrant | 04356710 | 817/949-4400 | 349 |
| Walnut Grove Middle Sch/Midlothian/Ellis | 10016792 | 469/856-5700 | 145 |
| Walnut Hill Elem Sch/Dallas/Dallas | 01010151 | 972/502-7800 | 107 |
| Walnut Springs Elem Sch/Dripping Spgs/Hays | 04447371 | 512/858-3800 | 216 |
| Walnut Springs Elem Sch/New Braunfels/ Comal | 03240699 | 830/627-6540 | 93 |
| **WALNUT SPRINGS IND SCH DIST/ WALNUT SPGS/BOSQUE** | 01000780 | 254/797-2133 | 51 |
| Walnut Springs Sch/Walnut Spgs/Bosque | 01000792 | 254/797-2133 | 51 |
| Walsh Elem Sch/Aledo/Parker | 12226448 | 817/207-3355 | 315 |
| Walt Disney Elem Sch/Alvin/Brazoria | 01881065 | 281/585-6234 | 55 |
| Walter & Lois Curtis Mid Sch/Allen/Collin | 04288072 | 972/727-0340 | 80 |
| Walter E Floyd Elem Sch/Balch Springs/ Dallas | 01011480 | 972/882-7100 | 116 |
| Walter Hall Elem Sch/League City/Galveston | 02043266 | 281/284-5300 | 164 |
| Walter Matthys Elem Sch/South Houston/ Harris | 04015617 | 713/740-0632 | 205 |
| Walter Moses Burton Elem Sch/Fresno/ Fort Bend | 04452273 | 281/634-5080 | 155 |

| School/City/County DISTRICT/CITY/COUNTY | PID | TELEPHONE NUMBER | PAGE |
|---|---|---|---|
| Walter Wilkinson Middle Sch/Mesquite/Dallas | 01011600 | 972/882-5950 | 116 |
| Waltrip High Sch/Houston/Harris | 01024308 | 713/688-1361 | 197 |
| Walzem Elem Sch/San Antonio/Bexar | 00997958 | 210/407-8400 | 39 |
| Ward Elem Sch/Abilene/Taylor | 04015332 | 325/690-3666 | 363 |
| Ware Elem Sch/Longview/Gregg | 01021136 | 903/803-5700 | 175 |
| Warner Elem Sch/Cypress/Harris | 10915473 | 281/213-1650 | 191 |
| Warren Elem Sch/Warren/Tyler | 01057305 | 409/547-2240 | 378 |
| Warren High Sch/San Antonio/Bexar | 05097761 | 210/397-4200 | 42 |
| Warren High Sch/Warren/Tyler | 01057317 | 409/547-2240 | 378 |
| **WARREN IND SCH DIST/WARREN/TYLER** | 01057288 | 409/547-2241 | 378 |
| Warren Junior High Sch/Warren/Tyler | 01057329 | 409/547-2246 | 378 |
| Warren Middle Sch/Forney/Kaufman | 11130638 | 469/762-4250 | 255 |
| Washington Early Childhood Ctr/Marshall/Harrison | 02110637 | 903/927-8790 | 214 |
| Washington Early Childhood Ctr/Palestine/Anderson | 11556367 | 903/731-8030 | 19 |
| Washington Elem Sch/Big Spring/Howard | 01032044 | 432/264-4126 | 237 |
| Washington Elem Sch/Port Arthur/Jefferson | 01033751 | 409/984-8600 | 246 |
| Washington Elem Sch/San Antonio/Bexar | 00999023 | 210/738-9840 | 44 |
| Washington Elem Sch/Sherman/Grayson | 01020687 | 903/891-6700 | 172 |
| Washington Heights Elem Sch/Fort Worth/Tarrant | 01053567 | 817/815-0700 | 355 |
| Washington Junior High Sch/Conroe/Montgomery | 04923399 | 936/709-7400 | 295 |
| Washington STEM Academy/Midland/Midland | 01041679 | 432/240-8300 | 289 |
| Waskom Elem Sch/Waskom/Harrison | 01028756 | 903/687-3361 | 214 |
| Waskom High Sch/Waskom/Harrison | 01028768 | 903/687-3361 | 214 |
| **WASKOM IND SCH DIST/WASKOM/HARRISON** | 01028744 | 903/687-3361 | 214 |
| Waskom Middle Sch/Waskom/Harrison | 01028770 | 903/687-3361 | 214 |
| Watauga Elem Sch/Watauga/Tarrant | 01052238 | 817/547-2700 | 349 |
| Watauga Middle Sch/Watauga/Tarrant | 01052240 | 817/547-4800 | 349 |
| Water Oak Sch/Sulphur Spgs/Hopkins | 11231634 | 903/439-3044 | 235 |
| Water Valley Elem Sch/Water Valley/Tom Green | 01055890 | 325/484-2478 | 368 |
| **WATER VALLEY IND SCH DIST/WATER VALLEY/TOM GREEN** | 01055888 | 325/484-2478 | 368 |
| Water Valley Jr Sr High Sch/Water Valley/Tom Green | 01055905 | 325/484-2478 | 368 |
| Waterloo Oaks Elem Sch/Cedar Hill/Dallas | 03396535 | 972/291-5290 | 101 |
| Waterloo Sch/Austin/Travis | 12363709 | 512/447-7781 | 376 |
| Waters Elem Sch/Lubbock/Lubbock | 02226705 | 806/219-7000 | 273 |
| Watkins Middle Sch/Houston/Harris | 02179803 | 281/463-5850 | 191 |
| Watson Junior High Sch/Muleshoe/Bailey | 00995716 | 806/272-7349 | 26 |
| Watson Tech Center Math & Sci/Garland/Dallas | 01010527 | 972/926-2600 | 111 |
| Waverly Park Elem Sch/Fort Worth/Tarrant | 01053579 | 817/815-6700 | 355 |
| Waxahachie Challenge Academy/Waxahachie/Ellis | 12313089 | 972/923-4695 | 147 |
| Waxahachie Global High Sch/Waxahachie/Ellis | 04282298 | 972/923-4761 | 147 |
| Waxahachie High Sch/Waxahachie/Ellis | 01015321 | 972/923-4600 | 147 |
| Waxahachie HS of Choice/Waxahachie/Ellis | 11134141 | 972/923-4695 | 147 |
| **WAXAHACHIE IND SCH DIST/WAXAHACHIE/ELLIS** | 01015292 | 972/923-4631 | 146 |
| Waxahachie Preparatory Academy/Waxahachie/Ellis | 12165650 | 972/937-0440 | 147 |
| Wayne A Cox Elem Sch/Roanoke/Denton | 11924910 | 817/698-7200 | 129 |
| Wayne D Boshears Center/Tyler/Smith | 11925108 | 903/262-1350 | 341 |
| Wayne Stuart Ryan Elem Sch/Denton/Denton | 04948765 | 940/369-4600 | 125 |
| Wayside Altamira Academy/Austin/Travis | 12161771 | 512/220-9105 | 17 |
| Wayside Eden Park Academy/Austin/Travis | 04813419 | 512/358-1800 | 17 |
| Wayside Middle Sch/Fort Worth/Tarrant | 01052458 | 817/232-0541 | 351 |
| Wayside Real Learning Academy/Austin/Travis | 12107244 | 512/438-7325 | 17 |
| Wayside Sci-Tech Middle & HS/Austin/Travis | 11934082 | 512/220-9120 | 17 |
| Weatherford 9th Grade Center/Weatherford/Parker | 05264938 | 817/598-2847 | 317 |
| Weatherford Christian Sch/Weatherford/Parker | 11133549 | 817/596-7807 | 317 |
| Weatherford Elem Sch/Plano/Collin | 01006485 | 469/752-3600 | 87 |
| Weatherford High Sch/Weatherford/Parker | 01046617 | 817/598-2858 | 317 |
| **WEATHERFORD IND SCH DIST/WEATHERFORD/PARKER** | 01046564 | 817/598-2800 | 316 |
| Weaver Elem Sch/Garland/Dallas | 01010448 | 972/494-8311 | 111 |
| Weaver Odom Elem Sch/Houston/Harris | 01022752 | 281/878-0390 | 185 |
| **WEBB CONS IND SCH DIST/BRUNI/WEBB** | 01059145 | 361/747-5415 | 391 |
| Webb Elem Sch/Arlington/Tarrant | 04035758 | 682/867-4300 | 347 |
| Webb Elem Sch/Olton/Lamb | 01036985 | 806/285-2657 | 263 |
| Webb Middle Sch/Austin/Travis | 04014950 | 512/414-3258 | 372 |
| Webb Middle Sch/Garland/Dallas | 01383049 | 972/675-3080 | 111 |
| Weber Elem Sch/Houston/Galveston | 05243063 | 281/284-6300 | 164 |
| Wedgewood Academy/Fort Worth/Tarrant | 11225685 | 817/924-9095 | 362 |
| Wedgewood Elem Sch/Friendswood/Galveston | 04032017 | 281/284-5700 | 164 |
| Wedgeworth Elem Sch/Waxahachie/Ellis | 02845820 | 972/923-4640 | 147 |
| Wedgwood 6th Grade Middle Sch/Fort Worth/Tarrant | 04143226 | 817/814-8300 | 355 |
| Wedgwood Middle Sch/Fort Worth/Tarrant | 01053581 | 817/814-8200 | 355 |
| Wee Wisdom Kindergarten/El Paso/El Paso | 02869436 | 915/592-6036 | 144 |
| Weimar Elem Sch/Weimar/Colorado | 01006851 | 979/725-6009 | 91 |
| Weimar High Sch/Weimar/Colorado | 01006863 | 979/725-9504 | 91 |
| **WEIMAR IND SCH DIST/WEIMAR/COLORADO** | 01006849 | 979/725-9504 | 91 |
| Weimar Junior High Sch/Weimar/Colorado | 01006875 | 979/725-9515 | 91 |
| Weiss High Sch/Pflugerville/Travis | 12235786 | 512/594-1400 | 375 |
| Welder Elem Sch/Sinton/San Patricio | 01049815 | 361/364-6600 | 334 |
| Weldon Corbell Elem Sch/Frisco/Collin | 10022404 | 469/633-3550 | 84 |
| Weldon Elem Sch/Gladewater/Gregg | 02223492 | 903/845-6921 | 174 |
| Weldon Gibson Elem Sch/Corp Christi/Nueces | 01044437 | 361/878-2500 | 307 |
| Weldon Smith Elem Sch/Corp Christi/Nueces | 01044700 | 361/878-2760 | 307 |
| Wellborn Middle Sch/College Sta/Brazos | 12307511 | 979/694-5880 | 59 |
| Wellington Elem Sch/Flower Mound/Denton | 04812776 | 469/713-5989 | 128 |
| Wellington Elem Sch/Wellington/Collingsworth | 01006710 | 806/447-3112 | 90 |
| Wellington High Sch/Wellington/Collingsworth | 01006722 | 806/447-3172 | 90 |
| **WELLINGTON IND SCH DIST/WELLINGTON/COLLINGSWORTH** | 01006708 | 806/447-3102 | 90 |
| Wellington Junior High Sch/Wellington/Collingsworth | 01006734 | 806/447-3152 | 90 |
| **WELLMAN UNION IND SCH DIST/WELLMAN/TERRY** | 01055199 | 806/637-4910 | 365 |
| Wellman-Union Elem Sch/Wellman/Terry | 01055204 | 806/637-4619 | 365 |
| Wells Branch Elem Sch/Austin/Williamson | 02856740 | 512/428-3400 | 402 |
| Wells Elem Sch/Cypress/Harris | 12233142 | 832/349-7400 | 191 |
| Wells Elem Sch/Plano/Collin | 01824122 | 469/752-3700 | 87 |
| Wells Elem Sch/Wells/Cherokee | 01005417 | 936/867-4400 | 77 |
| Wells High Sch/Wells/Cherokee | 01005429 | 936/867-4400 | 77 |
| **WELLS IND SCH DIST/WELLS/CHEROKEE** | 01005405 | 936/867-4466 | 77 |
| Wellspring Christian Acad/Denton/Denton | 04023145 | 940/591-9900 | 130 |
| Wernli Elem Sch/San Antonio/Bexar | 12471382 | 210/398-2450 | 42 |
| Wertheimer Middle Sch/Rosenberg/Fort Bend | 11151656 | 832/223-4100 | 158 |
| Weslaco East High Sch/Weslaco/Hidalgo | 04920323 | 956/969-6950 | 229 |
| Weslaco High Sch/Weslaco/Hidalgo | 01420491 | 956/969-6700 | 229 |
| **WESLACO IND SCH DIST/WESLACO/HIDALGO** | 01030589 | 956/969-6500 | 228 |
| Wesley Academy/Houston/Harris | 04907230 | 713/266-3341 | 212 |
| Wesley Prep Sch/Dallas/Dallas | 11020813 | 214/706-9568 | 120 |
| West Ave Elem Sch/Waco/McLennan | 04944666 | 254/750-3900 | 285 |
| West Birdville Elementary/Haltom City/Tarrant | 01052214 | 817/547-2500 | 349 |
| West Brazos Junior High Sch/Brazoria/Brazoria | 01001784 | 979/991-1730 | 56 |
| West Briar Middle Sch/Houston/Harris | 05099355 | 281/368-2140 | 200 |
| West Brook High Sch/Beaumont/Jefferson | 01034145 | 409/617-5500 | 245 |
| West Campus High Sch/San Antonio/Bexar | 12364868 | 210/977-7015 | 46 |
| West Central Elem Sch/Hereford/Deaf Smith | 11558016 | 806/363-7690 | 123 |
| West Columbia Elem Sch/West Columbia/Brazoria | 01001760 | 979/799-1760 | 56 |
| West Cypress Hills Elem Sch/Spicewood/Travis | 12036803 | 512/533-7500 | 373 |
| West Dallas Community Sch/Dallas/Dallas | 04929056 | 214/634-1927 | 120 |
| West Elem Sch/Daingerfield/Morris | 01172541 | 903/645-2901 | 299 |
| West Elem Sch/Fort Worth/Tarrant | 01054236 | 817/367-1334 | 360 |
| West Elem Sch/Grand Prairie/Tarrant | 04757047 | 682/867-0100 | 347 |
| West Elem Sch/Lubbock/Lubbock | 11078016 | 806/776-0700 | 274 |
| West Elem Sch/West/McLennan | 01040508 | 254/981-2000 | 285 |
| West End Elem Sch/Industry/Austin | 00995572 | 979/357-2595 | 25 |
| West Foundation Elem Sch/Wichita Falls/Wichita | 04456695 | 940/235-1192 | 396 |
| West Handley Elem Sch/Fort Worth/Tarrant | 04285898 | 817/815-5100 | 355 |
| **WEST HARDIN CO CONS SCH DIST/SARATOGA/HARDIN** | 01022659 | 936/274-5061 | 183 |
| West Hardin Elem Sch/Saratoga/Hardin | 01022661 | 936/274-5061 | 184 |
| West Hardin High Sch/Saratoga/Hardin | 01022673 | 936/274-5061 | 184 |
| West High Sch/West/McLennan | 01040510 | 254/981-2050 | 285 |
| West Hurst Elem Sch/Hurst/Tarrant | 01053969 | 817/285-3290 | 357 |
| **WEST IND SCH DIST/WEST/MCLENNAN** | 01040481 | 254/981-2050 | 285 |
| West Lake Middle Sch/Humble/Harris | 12320161 | 281/641-5800 | 201 |
| West Main Elem Sch/Lancaster/Dallas | 01011387 | 972/218-1551 | 114 |
| West Memorial Elem Sch/Katy/Harris | 01026277 | 281/237-6600 | 157 |

| School/City/County<br>DISTRICT/CITY/COUNTY | PID | TELEPHONE<br>NUMBER | PAGE |
|---|---|---|---|
| West Memorial Jr High Sch/Katy/Harris | 01529982 | 281/237-6400 | 157 |
| West Mesquite High Sch/Mesquite/Dallas | 01525962 | 972/882-7600 | 116 |
| West Middle Sch/Desoto/Dallas | 03005982 | 972/230-1820 | 108 |
| West Middle Sch/West/McLennan | 01040091 | 254/981-2120 | 285 |
| **WEST ORANGE-COVE CONS ISD/** | | | |
| **ORANGE/ORANGE** | 01045819 | 409/882-5437 | 312 |
| West Orange-Stark Elem Sch/Orange/Orange | 01045821 | 409/882-5630 | 312 |
| West Orange-Stark High Sch/Orange/Orange | 01045936 | 409/882-5570 | 312 |
| West Orange-Stark Middle Sch/Orange/Orange | 01045948 | 409/882-5520 | 312 |
| West Oso Elem Sch/Corp Christi/Nueces | 01045106 | 361/806-5930 | 309 |
| West Oso High Sch/Corp Christi/Nueces | 01045118 | 361/806-5960 | 309 |
| **WEST OSO IND SCH DIST/CORP CHRISTI/** | | | |
| **NUECES** | 01045065 | 361/806-5900 | 309 |
| West Oso Junior High Sch/Corp Christi/ | | | |
| Nueces | 01045091 | 361/806-5950 | 309 |
| West Plano Montessori Sch/Plano/Collin | 02733526 | 972/618-8844 | 90 |
| West Ridge Middle Sch/Austin/Travis | 03008738 | 512/732-9240 | 372 |
| **WEST RUSK CO CONS IND SCH DIST/** | | | |
| **NEW LONDON/RUSK** | 01049217 | 903/392-7850 | 331 |
| West Rusk Elem Sch/New London/Rusk | 01049229 | 903/392-7857 | 331 |
| West Rusk High Sch/New London/Rusk | 01049243 | 903/392-7857 | 331 |
| West Rusk Intermediate Sch/New London/Rusk | 11818232 | 903/392-7856 | 331 |
| West Rusk Junior High Sch/New London/Rusk | 01049255 | 903/392-7855 | 331 |
| West Sabine Elem Sch/Pineland/Sabine | 01049308 | 409/584-2205 | 332 |
| **WEST SABINE IND SCH DIST/** | | | |
| **PINELAND/SABINE** | 01049293 | 409/584-2655 | 332 |
| West Sabine Jr Sr High Sch/Pineland/Sabine | 01049310 | 409/584-2525 | 332 |
| West Side Elem Sch/Jacksonville/Cherokee | 01005302 | 903/586-5165 | 76 |
| West Texas Elem Sch/Stinnett/Hutchinson | 03006558 | 806/878-2103 | 241 |
| West Texas High Sch/Stinnett/Hutchinson | 03006534 | 806/878-2456 | 241 |
| West Texas Middle Sch/Stinnett/Hutchinson | 03006546 | 806/878-2247 | 241 |
| West University Elem Sch/Houston/Harris | 01025041 | 713/295-5215 | 200 |
| West Ward Elem Sch/Killeen/Bell | 00996617 | 254/336-1830 | 31 |
| **WESTBROOK IND SCH DIST/WESTBROOK/** | | | |
| **MITCHELL** | 01042154 | 325/644-2311 | 292 |
| Westbrook Intermediate Sch/Friendswood/ | | | |
| Galveston | 10007777 | 281/284-3800 | 164 |
| Westbrook Sch/Westbrook/Mitchell | 01042178 | 325/644-2311 | 292 |
| Westbury Christian Sch/Houston/Harris | 02083890 | 713/551-8100 | 212 |
| Westbury High Sch/Houston/Harris | 01025053 | 713/723-6015 | 198 |
| Westchester Acad Int'l Studies/Houston/ | | | |
| Harris | 04920555 | 713/251-1800 | 207 |
| Westcliff Elem Sch/Fort Worth/Tarrant | 01053593 | 817/814-6000 | 355 |
| Westcreek Elem Sch/Fort Worth/Tarrant | 01053608 | 817/814-8600 | 355 |
| Wester Elem Sch/Lubbock/Lubbock | 01038971 | 806/219-7100 | 273 |
| Western Academy/Houston/Harris | 11744045 | 713/461-7000 | 213 |
| Western Hills Academy/El Paso/El Paso | 02869486 | 915/584-6642 | 144 |
| Western Hills Elem Sch/El Paso/El Paso | 01016117 | 915/774-4060 | 138 |
| Western Hills Elem Sch/Fort Worth/Tarrant | 01053610 | 817/815-6800 | 355 |
| Western Hills Elem Sch/Temple/Bell | 00996887 | 254/215-5600 | 32 |
| Western Hills High Sch/Benbrook/Tarrant | 01053658 | 817/815-6000 | 355 |
| Western Hills Primary Sch/Fort Worth/ | | | |
| Tarrant | 04919453 | 817/815-6900 | 355 |
| Western Plateau Elem Sch/Amarillo/Potter | 01047520 | 806/326-5550 | 321 |
| Westfield High Sch/Houston/Harris | 01526057 | 281/891-7130 | 208 |
| Westhoff Elem Sch/Westhoff/De Witt | 01013799 | 830/236-5519 | 122 |
| **WESTHOFF IND SCH DIST/WESTHOFF/** | | | |
| **DE WITT** | 01013787 | 830/236-5519 | 122 |
| Westlake Academy/Westlake/Denton | 05286601 | 817/490-5757 | 17 |
| Westlake High Sch/Austin/Travis | 01056868 | 512/732-9280 | 372 |
| Westlake Lutheran Academy/Richmond/ | | | |
| Fort Bend | 11455426 | 281/341-9910 | 160 |
| Westlawn Elem Sch/Texarkana/Bowie | 01001265 | 903/223-4252 | 54 |
| Westover Park Jr High Sch/Amarillo/Randall | 04365022 | 806/677-2420 | 324 |
| Westpark Elem Sch/Fort Worth/Tarrant | 03053018 | 817/815-7000 | 355 |
| **WESTPHALIA IND SCH DIST/** | | | |
| **LOTT/FALLS** | 01017329 | 254/584-4988 | 149 |
| Westphalia Sch/Lott/Falls | 01017343 | 254/584-4988 | 149 |
| Westside Elem Sch/Angleton/Brazoria | 01001538 | 979/864-8009 | 55 |
| Westside Elem Sch/Cedar Park/Williamson | 11130767 | 512/570-7000 | 400 |
| Westside High Sch/Houston/Harris | 04815065 | 281/920-8000 | 200 |
| Westview Middle Sch/Austin/Travis | 03049952 | 512/594-2200 | 375 |
| Westview Sch/Houston/Harris | 02749604 | 713/973-1900 | 213 |
| Westwind Elem Sch/Lubbock/Lubbock | 04356617 | 806/799-3731 | 272 |
| Westwood Elem Sch/Houston/Harris | 01027439 | 713/251-2100 | 207 |
| Westwood Elem Sch/Palestine/Anderson | 00994671 | 903/729-1771 | 19 |
| Westwood High Sch/Austin/Williamson | 02126911 | 512/464-4000 | 402 |
| Westwood High Sch/Palestine/Anderson | 00994683 | 903/729-1773 | 19 |
| **WESTWOOD IND SCH DIST/PALESTINE/** | | | |
| **ANDERSON** | 00994669 | 903/729-1776 | 19 |
| Westwood JHS Math Sci Ldrshp/Dallas/Dallas | 01011997 | 469/593-3600 | 117 |

| School/City/County<br>DISTRICT/CITY/COUNTY | PID | TELEPHONE<br>NUMBER | PAGE |
|---|---|---|---|
| Westwood Junior High Sch/Palestine/ | | | |
| Anderson | 00994695 | 903/723-0423 | 19 |
| Westwood Montessori/IB Sch/Dallas/Dallas | 03144174 | 972/239-8598 | 120 |
| Westwood Primary Sch/Palestine/Anderson | 02111760 | 903/729-1774 | 19 |
| Westwood Terrace Elem Sch/San Antonio/ | | | |
| Bexar | 00998342 | 210/397-0300 | 42 |
| Westwood-Bales Elem Sch/Friendswood/ | | | |
| Galveston | 01019066 | 281/482-3341 | 164 |
| Wetmore Elem Sch/San Antonio/Bexar | 04946339 | 210/407-8800 | 39 |
| Wharton Alternative Sch/Wharton/Wharton | 04033645 | 979/532-6262 | 393 |
| Wharton Dual Language Academy/Houston/ | | | |
| Harris | 01024310 | 713/535-3771 | 200 |
| Wharton Elem Sch/Wharton/Wharton | 01059729 | 979/532-6882 | 393 |
| Wharton High Sch/Wharton/Wharton | 01059731 | 979/532-6800 | 393 |
| **WHARTON IND SCH DIST/WHARTON/** | | | |
| **WHARTON** | 01059690 | 979/532-3612 | 393 |
| Wharton Junior High Sch/Wharton/Wharton | 01059743 | 979/532-6840 | 393 |
| Wheat Elem Sch/Woodville/Tyler | 01057367 | 409/283-2452 | 378 |
| Wheat Middle Sch/Cleburne/Johnson | 01034925 | 817/202-1300 | 250 |
| Wheatley Alt Ed Center/Temple/Bell | 04753106 | 254/215-5655 | 32 |
| Wheatley High Sch/Houston/Harris | 01025651 | 713/671-3900 | 194 |
| Wheatley Sch Early Childhood/Port Arthur/ | | | |
| Jefferson | 01033854 | 409/984-8750 | 246 |
| Wheeler Ave Christian Academy/Houston/ | | | |
| Harris | 11458272 | 713/579-2792 | 213 |
| **WHEELER IND SCH DIST/WHEELER/** | | | |
| **WHEELER** | 01059896 | 806/826-5241 | 394 |
| Wheeler Sch/Wheeler/Wheeler | 01059901 | 806/826-5241 | 394 |
| Wheelock Elem Sch/Lubbock/Lubbock | 01038995 | 806/219-7200 | 273 |
| Whidby Elem Sch/Houston/Harris | 01025065 | 713/746-8170 | 198 |
| Whispering Hills Achieve Ctr/Flatonia/ | | | |
| Fayette | 12035093 | 361/865-3083 | 151 |
| Whispering Pines Elem Sch/Humble/Harris | 03394159 | 281/641-2500 | 201 |
| Whitaker Elem Sch/El Paso/El Paso | 03006895 | 915/236-6275 | 138 |
| White Deer Elem Sch/White Deer/Carson | 01004657 | 806/883-2311 | 73 |
| **WHITE DEER IND SCH DIST/** | | | |
| **WHITE DEER/CARSON** | 01004633 | 806/883-2311 | 73 |
| White Deer Jr Sr High Sch/White Deer/ | | | |
| Carson | 01004669 | 806/883-2311 | 73 |
| White Oak High Sch/White Oak/Gregg | 01021320 | 903/291-2004 | 176 |
| **WHITE OAK IND SCH DIST/WHITE OAK/** | | | |
| **GREGG** | 01021306 | 903/291-2200 | 176 |
| White Oak Intermediate Sch/White Oak/Gregg | 03380988 | 903/291-2101 | 176 |
| White Oak Middle Sch/Porter/Montgomery | 01042697 | 281/577-8800 | 297 |
| White Oak Middle Sch/White Oak/Gregg | 01399737 | 903/291-2055 | 176 |
| White Oak Primary Sch/White Oak/Gregg | 01021318 | 903/291-2160 | 176 |
| White Rock Elem Sch/Dallas/Dallas | 01012006 | 469/593-2700 | 117 |
| White Rock Montessori Sch/Dallas/Dallas | 02735706 | 214/324-5580 | 120 |
| White Rock North Sch/Dallas/Dallas | 02180709 | 214/348-7410 | 120 |
| **WHITE SETTLEMENT IND SCH DIST/** | | | |
| **FORT WORTH/TARRANT** | 01054183 | 817/367-1300 | 360 |
| **WHITEFACE CON IND SCH DIST/** | | | |
| **WHITEFACE/COCHRAN** | 01005728 | 806/287-1154 | 78 |
| Whiteface Elem Sch/Whiteface/Cochran | 01005730 | 806/287-1285 | 78 |
| Whiteface High Sch/Whiteface/Cochran | 01005742 | 806/287-1104 | 79 |
| Whitehouse High Sch/Whitehouse/Smith | 01051014 | 903/839-5551 | 341 |
| **WHITEHOUSE IND SCH DIST/** | | | |
| **WHITEHOUSE/SMITH** | 01050993 | 903/839-5500 | 341 |
| Whitehouse Junior High Sch/Whitehouse/ | | | |
| Smith | 04946298 | 903/839-5590 | 341 |
| Whitesboro High Sch/Whitesboro/Grayson | 01020807 | 903/564-4114 | 173 |
| **WHITESBORO IND SCH DIST/** | | | |
| **WHITESBORO/GRAYSON** | 01020780 | 903/564-4200 | 173 |
| Whitesboro Intermediate Sch/Whitesboro/ | | | |
| Grayson | 01020792 | 903/564-4180 | 173 |
| Whitesboro Middle Sch/Whitesboro/Grayson | 01020819 | 903/564-4236 | 173 |
| Whiteside Elem Sch/Lubbock/Lubbock | 02202096 | 806/219-7300 | 273 |
| Whitestone Elem Sch/Leander/Williamson | 01061033 | 512/570-7400 | 400 |
| Whitewright Elem Sch/Whitewright/Grayson | 01020833 | 903/364-2155 | 173 |
| Whitewright High Sch/Whitewright/Grayson | 01020845 | 903/364-2155 | 173 |
| **WHITEWRIGHT IND SCH DIST/** | | | |
| **WHITEWRIGHT/GRAYSON** | 01020821 | 903/364-2155 | 173 |
| Whitewright Middle Sch/Whitewright/Grayson | 01397038 | 903/364-2155 | 173 |
| **WHITHARRAL IND SCH DIST/** | | | |
| **WHITHARRAL/HOCKLEY** | 01031349 | 806/299-1184 | 233 |
| Whitharral Sch/Whitharral/Hockley | 01031351 | 806/299-1135 | 233 |
| Whitley Road Elem Sch/Watauga/Tarrant | 02854388 | 817/744-5800 | 358 |
| Whitney Elem Sch/Whitney/Hill | 01031064 | 254/694-3456 | 231 |
| Whitney High Sch/Whitney/Hill | 01031076 | 254/694-3457 | 231 |
| **WHITNEY IND SCH DIST/WHITNEY/** | | | |
| **HILL** | 01031052 | 254/694-2254 | 231 |
| Whitney Intermediate Sch/Whitney/Hill | 04762949 | 254/694-7303 | 231 |

| School/City/County DISTRICT/CITY/COUNTY | PID | TELEPHONE NUMBER | PAGE |
|---|---|---|---|
| Whitney M Young Jr Elem Sch/Dallas/Dallas | 01010230 | 972/749-2000 | 107 |
| Whitney Middle Sch/Whitney/Hill | 01031088 | 254/946-6568 | 231 |
| Whitt Fine Arts Academy/Grand Prairie/ Dallas | 04945189 | 972/264-5024 | 112 |
| Whittier Elem Sch/Amarillo/Potter | 01047532 | 806/326-5600 | 321 |
| Whittier Elem Sch/Houston/Harris | 01025754 | 713/671-3810 | 195 |
| Whittier Middle Sch/San Antonio/Bexar | 00998653 | 210/738-9755 | 44 |
| Wichita Christian Sch/Wichita Falls/ Wichita | 11829499 | 940/763-1347 | 396 |
| Wichita Falls High Sch/Wichita Falls/ Wichita | 01173234 | 940/235-1084 | 396 |
| **WICHITA FALLS IND SCH DIST/ WICHITA FALLS/WICHITA** | 01060132 | 940/235-1000 | 395 |
| Widen Elem Sch/Austin/Travis | 03008661 | 512/414-2556 | 370 |
| Wieland Elem Sch/Pflugerville/Travis | 10911269 | 512/594-3900 | 375 |
| Wiggs Middle Sch/El Paso/El Paso | 02907038 | 915/236-3600 | 139 |
| Wilbur E Lucas Elem Sch/Hidalgo/Hidalgo | 05090543 | 956/340-1700 | 228 |
| Wilchester Elem Sch/Houston/Harris | 01027441 | 713/251-7700 | 207 |
| Wild Peach Elem Sch/Brazoria/Brazoria | 02109494 | 979/991-1750 | 56 |
| Wildcat Learning Alt Center/Portland/ San Patricio | 12368802 | 361/777-4051 | 333 |
| Wildcat Way Sch/Houston/Harris | 05092864 | 713/251-8200 | 207 |
| Wilderness Oak Elem Sch/San Antonio/Bexar | 10003317 | 210/407-9200 | 39 |
| **WILDORADO IND SCH DIST/WILDORADO/ OLDHAM** | 01045584 | 806/426-3317 | 311 |
| Wildorado Sch/Wildorado/Oldham | 01045596 | 806/426-3317 | 311 |
| Wildwood Elem Sch/Tomball/Harris | 1210/842 | 281/357-3040 | 208 |
| Wilemon Steam Academy/Waxahachie/Ellis | 12313118 | 972/923-4780 | 147 |
| Wiley Middle Sch/Leander/Williamson | 10023290 | 512/570-3600 | 401 |
| Wilkerson Intermediate Sch/The Woodlands/ Montgomery | 01042556 | 832/592-8900 | 295 |
| Wilkinson Elem Sch/Conroe/Montgomery | 11449714 | 936/709-1500 | 295 |
| Will Rogers Academy/San Antonio/Bexar | 00998665 | 210/738-9825 | 44 |
| Will Rogers Elem Sch/Amarillo/Potter | 01047544 | 806/326-5150 | 321 |
| Willbern Elem Sch/Houston/Harris | 04019194 | 281/897-3820 | 191 |
| William & Abbie Allen Elem Sch/Frisco/ Collin | 11448497 | 469/633-3800 | 84 |
| William Adams Middle Sch/Alice/Jim Wells | 01034523 | 361/660-2055 | 248 |
| William Anderson Elem Sch/Dallas/Dallas | 01010199 | 972/749-6200 | 107 |
| William B Miller Elem Sch/Dallas/Dallas | 01010060 | 972/502-8700 | 107 |
| William B Travis 6th GR Campus/Amarillo/ Potter | 12033710 | 806/326-3870 | 321 |
| William B Travis Elem Sch/Baytown/Harris | 01023768 | 281/420-4660 | 193 |
| William B Travis Elem Sch/Corp Christi/ Nueces | 01044724 | 361/878-2700 | 307 |
| William B Travis Elem Sch/Ennis/Ellis | 01015022 | 972/872-7455 | 144 |
| William B Travis Elem Sch/Marshall/ Harrison | 01028732 | 903/927-8780 | 214 |
| William B Travis High Sch/Richmond/ Fort Bend | 10027882 | 281/634-7000 | 155 |
| William B Travis Middle Sch/Amarillo/ Potter | 01047518 | 806/326-3800 | 321 |
| William B Travis Middle Sch/McAllen/ Hidalgo | 01030113 | 956/971-4242 | 224 |
| William Beverly Elem Sch/Allen/Collin | 04810120 | 469/752-0400 | 87 |
| William D Slider Middle Sch/El Paso/ El Paso | 03399355 | 915/937-5400 | 141 |
| William D Surratt Elem Sch/Clint/El Paso | 01015436 | 915/926-8200 | 137 |
| William F Barnett Elem Sch/Santa Fe/ Galveston | 12376677 | 409/925-9700 | 165 |
| William G Gravitt Jr High Sch/Denver City/ Yoakum | 01062051 | 806/592-5940 | 409 |
| William H Atwell Law Academy/Dallas/Dallas | 01010175 | 972/794-6400 | 107 |
| William Hobby Middle Sch/San Antonio/Bexar | 00998354 | 210/397-6300 | 42 |
| William Howard Taft High Sch/San Antonio/ Bexar | 02848511 | 210/397-6000 | 42 |
| William J Brennan High Sch/San Antonio/ Bexar | 11552165 | 210/398-1250 | 42 |
| William J Clinton Elem Sch/Penitas/Hidalgo | 10914417 | 956/323-2740 | 223 |
| William J Thornton Elem Sch/San Antonio/ Bexar | 03252111 | 210/397-3950 | 42 |
| William James Middle Sch/Fort Worth/ Tarrant | 01053622 | 817/814-0200 | 355 |
| William Lipscomb Elem Sch/Dallas/Dallas | 01010101 | 972/794-7300 | 107 |
| William Monnig Middle Sch/Fort Worth/ Tarrant | 01053634 | 817/815-1200 | 355 |
| William Paschall Elem Sch/San Antonio/ Bexar | 04945921 | 210/662-2240 | 37 |
| William Pearce Elem Sch/San Antonio/Bexar | 00999566 | 210/882-1605 | 46 |
| William R Carmichael Elem Sch/Houston/ Harris | 01857258 | 281/878-0345 | 184 |

| School/City/County DISTRICT/CITY/COUNTY | PID | TELEPHONE NUMBER | PAGE |
|---|---|---|---|
| William Velasquez Elem Sch/Richmond/ Fort Bend | 10030748 | 832/223-2600 | 159 |
| William's Community Sch/Austin/Travis | 12240183 | 512/250-5700 | 376 |
| Williams Elem Sch/Arlington/Tarrant | 04019871 | 682/867-5900 | 347 |
| Williams Elem Sch/Austin/Travis | 01532109 | 512/414-2525 | 371 |
| Williams Elem Sch/Garland/Dallas | 01010802 | 972/926-2610 | 111 |
| Williams Elem Sch/Georgetown/Williamson | 12472544 | 512/943-5160 | 399 |
| Williams Elem Sch/Lubbock/Lubbock | 01418515 | 806/219-7400 | 274 |
| Williams Elem Sch/Pasadena/Harris | 01027001 | 713/740-0776 | 205 |
| Williams Elem Sch/Richmond/Fort Bend | 02856984 | 832/223-2700 | 159 |
| Williams High Sch/Plano/Collin | 01006459 | 469/752-8300 | 87 |
| Willie B Ermel Elem Sch/Houston/Harris | 01532020 | 713/466-5220 | 184 |
| Willie E Brown Elem Sch/Mansfield/Tarrant | 04804365 | 817/299-5860 | 360 |
| Willie E Williams Elem Sch/Magnolia/ Montgomery | 04363103 | 281/356-6866 | 296 |
| Willie J Hargrave High Sch/Huffman/Harris | 01026124 | 281/324-1845 | 200 |
| Willis Classical Academy/Willis/Montgomery | 11459692 | 936/890-0100 | 17 |
| Willis High Sch/Willis/Montgomery | 01042805 | 936/856-1250 | 297 |
| **WILLIS IND SCH DIST/WILLIS/ MONTGOMERY** | 01042764 | 936/856-1200 | 297 |
| Willis Lane Elem Sch/Keller/Tarrant | 04749313 | 817/744-5700 | 358 |
| Willow Bend Academy-Plano/Plano/Collin | 11564405 | 972/599-7882 | 90 |
| Willow Bend Elem Sch/Lubbock/Lubbock | 10030360 | 806/796-0090 | 272 |
| Willow Creek Elem Sch/Kingwood/Harris | 03051474 | 281/641-2300 | 201 |
| Willow Creek Elem Sch/Saginaw/Tarrant | 11555557 | 817/232-2845 | 351 |
| Willow Creek Elem Sch/Tomball/Harris | 04806777 | 281/357-3080 | 208 |
| Willow Springs Elem Sch/Killeen/Bell | 02897225 | 254/336-2020 | 31 |
| Willow Springs Middle Sch/Allen/Collin | 11924908 | 469/742-8500 | 84 |
| Willow Vista Intermediate Sch/Amarillo/ Potter | 11445586 | 806/383-8820 | 322 |
| Willow Wood Junior High Sch/Tomball/Harris | 05279397 | 281/357-3030 | 208 |
| Willowridge High Sch/Houston/Fort Bend | 02043230 | 281/634-2450 | 155 |
| Wills Point High Sch/Wills Point/Van Zandt | 01058294 | 903/873-5100 | 384 |
| **WILLS POINT IND SCH DIST/ WILLS POINT/VAN ZANDT** | 01058270 | 903/873-3161 | 383 |
| Wills Point Junior High Sch/Wills Point/ Van Zandt | 04803488 | 903/873-5100 | 384 |
| Wills Point Middle Sch/Wills Point/ Van Zandt | 01058309 | 903/873-5100 | 384 |
| Wills Point Primary Sch/Wills Point/ Van Zandt | 01058282 | 903/873-5100 | 384 |
| Wilma Fisher Elem Sch/Frisco/Collin | 04942369 | 469/633-2600 | 84 |
| Wilmer Early Chldhd Center/Wilmer/Dallas | 12169723 | 469/660-7296 | 107 |
| Wilmer-Hutchins Elem Sch/Dallas/Dallas | 11732779 | 972/925-2600 | 108 |
| Wilmer-Hutchins High Sch/Dallas/Dallas | 11732767 | 972/925-2900 | 108 |
| Wilshire Elem Sch/Euless/Tarrant | 01053971 | 817/354-3529 | 357 |
| Wilshire Elem Sch/San Antonio/Bexar | 00997984 | 210/407-9400 | 39 |
| Wilson & Young Middle Sch/Odessa/Ector | 01014729 | 432/456-0459 | 135 |
| Wilson Early College High Sch/Port Arthur/ Jefferson | 12310233 | 409/984-8960 | 246 |
| Wilson Elem Sch/Harlingen/Cameron | 01381510 | 956/427-3190 | 69 |
| Wilson Elem Sch/Houston/Harris | 02201535 | 281/463-5941 | 191 |
| Wilson Elem Sch/Houston/Harris | 04019041 | 281/878-0990 | 184 |
| Wilson Elem Sch/Pampa/Gray | 01020223 | 806/669-4930 | 170 |
| Wilson Elem Sch/San Antonio/Bexar | 00998718 | 210/738-9845 | 44 |
| **WILSON IND SCH DIST/WILSON/LYNN** | 01039391 | 806/628-6261 | 276 |
| Wilson Middle Sch/Plano/Collin | 01006497 | 469/752-6700 | 87 |
| Wilson Montessori Elem Sch/Houston/Harris | 01024671 | 713/942-1470 | 200 |
| Wilson Sch/Wilson/Lynn | 01039406 | 806/628-6261 | 276 |
| Wimberley High Sch/Wimberley/Hays | 02855801 | 512/847-5729 | 217 |
| **WIMBERLEY IND SCH DIST/WIMBERLEY/ HAYS** | 02903408 | 512/847-2414 | 217 |
| Wimbish World Language Academy/Arlington/ Tarrant | 01051961 | 682/867-6000 | 347 |
| Windcrest Elem Sch/San Antonio/Bexar | 00997996 | 210/407-9600 | 39 |
| Windermere Elem Sch/Pflugerville/Travis | 03318997 | 512/594-4800 | 375 |
| Windermere Primary Sch/Pflugerville/Travis | 04803048 | 512/594-5600 | 375 |
| Windle Sch for Young Children/Denton/ Denton | 01826182 | 940/369-3900 | 125 |
| Windsong Intermediate Sch/Friendswood/ Galveston | 04851071 | 281/482-0111 | 164 |
| Windsong Ranch Elem Sch/Prosper/Collin | 12172885 | 469/219-2220 | 88 |
| Windsor Elem Sch/Amarillo/Potter | 02178031 | 806/326-5700 | 321 |
| Windsor Park Elem Sch/Corp Christi/Nueces | 01044750 | 361/878-3770 | 307 |
| Windsor Village Elem Sch/Houston/Harris | 01025388 | 713/726-3642 | 198 |
| Windthorst Elem Sch/Windthorst/Archer | 00995285 | 940/423-6679 | 23 |
| Windthorst High Sch/Windthorst/Archer | 00995297 | 940/423-6680 | 23 |
| **WINDTHORST IND SCH DIST/ WINDTHORST/ARCHER** | 00995273 | 940/423-6688 | 23 |
| Windthorst Junior High Sch/Windthorst/ Archer | 11450737 | 940/423-6605 | 23 |
| Winfree Academy-Dallas/Dallas/Dallas | 12044264 | 469/930-5199 | 17 |

| School/City/County DISTRICT/CITY/COUNTY | PID | TELEPHONE NUMBER | PAGE |
|---|---|---|---|
| Winfree Academy-Grand Prairie/Grand Prairie/ Dallas | 11013901 | 214/204-2030 | 17 |
| Winfree Academy-Irving/Irving/Dallas | 05010763 | 972/251-2010 | 17 |
| Winfree Academy-Lewisville/Lewisville/ Denton | 05009843 | 214/222-2200 | 17 |
| Winfree Academy-N Rchlnd Hills/Richland Hls/ Tarrant | 11013913 | 817/590-2240 | 17 |
| Winfree Academy-Richardson/Richardson/ Dallas | 05009855 | 972/234-9855 | 17 |
| Wings/Desoto/Dallas | 12108999 | 972/274-8219 | 108 |
| Wink Elem Sch/Wink/Winkler | 01061497 | 432/527-3880 | 405 |
| Wink High Sch/Wink/Winkler | 01061502 | 432/527-3880 | 405 |
| **WINK LOVING IND SCH DIST/ WINK/WINKLER** | 01061485 | 432/527-3880 | 405 |
| Winkley Elem Sch/Leander/Williamson | 10023276 | 512/570-6700 | 401 |
| Winn Elem Sch/Austin/Travis | 01056739 | 512/414-2390 | 371 |
| Winnetka Elem Sch/Dallas/Dallas | 01010216 | 972/749-5100 | 108 |
| Winnsboro Elem Sch/Winnsboro/Wood | 01061966 | 903/342-3548 | 408 |
| Winnsboro High Sch/Winnsboro/Wood | 01061978 | 903/342-3641 | 408 |
| **WINNSBORO IND SCH DIST/WINNSBORO/ WOOD** | 01061942 | 903/342-3737 | 408 |
| Winona Elem Sch/Winona/Smith | 01051040 | 903/939-4800 | 341 |
| Winona High Sch/Winona/Smith | 01051052 | 903/939-4100 | 341 |
| **WINONA IND SCH DIST/WINONA/SMITH** | 01051038 | 903/939-4000 | 341 |
| Winona Intermediate Sch/Winona/Smith | 12034673 | 903/939-4800 | 341 |
| Winona Middle Sch/Winona/Smith | 02129377 | 903/939-4040 | 341 |
| Winston Churchill High Sch/San Antonio/ Bexar | 00998005 | 210/356-0000 | 39 |
| Winston Elem Sch/San Antonio/Bexar | 00997348 | 210/444-8450 | 35 |
| Winston Sch/Dallas/Dallas | 01875286 | 214/691-6950 | 120 |
| Winston School San Antonio/San Antonio/ Bexar | 02083644 | 210/615-6544 | 48 |
| Winters Elem Sch/Winters/Runnels | 01048926 | 325/754-5577 | 329 |
| Winters High Sch/Winters/Runnels | 01048938 | 325/754-5516 | 330 |
| **WINTERS IND SCH DIST/WINTERS/ RUNNELS** | 01048914 | 325/754-5574 | 329 |
| Winters Junior High Sch/Winters/Runnels | 04865369 | 325/754-5518 | 330 |
| Wise Elem Fine Arts Magnet Sch/Tyler/Smith | 01050618 | 903/566-2271 | 339 |
| Woden Elem Sch/Nacogdoches/Nacogdoches | 01043366 | 936/564-2386 | 301 |
| Woden High Sch/Nacogdoches/Nacogdoches | 04921808 | 936/564-7903 | 301 |
| **WODEN IND SCH DIST/NACOGDOCHES/ NACOGDOCHES** | 01043354 | 936/564-2073 | 301 |
| Woden Junior High Sch/Nacogdoches/ Nacogdoches | 04921793 | 936/564-7903 | 301 |
| Wolf Ranch Elem Sch/Georgetown/Williamson | 04034962 | 512/943-5050 | 399 |
| Wolfe City Elem Sch/Wolfe City/Hunt | 01032628 | 903/496-2032 | 240 |
| Wolfe City High Sch/Wolfe City/Hunt | 01032630 | 903/496-2891 | 240 |
| **WOLFE CITY IND SCH DIST/ WOLFE CITY/HUNT** | 01032616 | 903/496-2283 | 240 |
| Wolfe City Middle Sch/Wolfe City/Hunt | 02131320 | 903/496-7333 | 240 |
| Wolffarth Elem Sch/Lubbock/Lubbock | 01039016 | 806/219-7600 | 274 |
| Wolflin Elem Sch/Amarillo/Potter | 01047556 | 806/326-5750 | 321 |
| Wonderland Sch/San Marcos/Hays | 01480609 | 512/392-9404 | 217 |
| Wood Elem Sch/Arlington/Tarrant | 01881936 | 682/867-1100 | 348 |
| Wood Middle Sch/San Antonio/Bexar | 02126143 | 210/356-6200 | 39 |
| Wood River Elem Sch/Corp Christi/Nueces | 02896130 | 361/242-7560 | 306 |
| Woodcreek Elem Sch/Katy/Harris | 10913308 | 281/234-0100 | 157 |
| Woodcreek Junior High Sch/Katy/Harris | 11128582 | 281/234-0800 | 157 |
| Woodcreek Middle Sch/Houston/Harris | 11552684 | 281/641-5200 | 201 |
| Woodcrest Elem Sch/Port Neches/Jefferson | 01034042 | 409/724-2309 | 247 |
| Woodgate Intermediate Sch/Waco/McLennan | 04034912 | 254/761-5690 | 284 |
| Woodlake Elem Sch/San Antonio/Bexar | 01878381 | 210/662-2220 | 37 |
| Woodlake Hills Middle Sch/San Antonio/ Bexar | 04446468 | 210/661-1110 | 37 |
| Woodland Acres Elem Sch/Houston/Harris | 01023548 | 832/386-2220 | 192 |
| Woodland Acres Middle Sch/Houston/Harris | 01023550 | 832/386-4700 | 192 |
| Woodland Elem Sch/Graham/Young | 01062154 | 940/549-4090 | 409 |
| Woodland Heights Elem Sch/Brownwood/Brown | 01002544 | 325/646-8633 | 62 |
| Woodland Hills Elem Sch/Kingwood/Harris | 01401421 | 281/641-1500 | 201 |
| Woodland Springs Elem Sch/Keller/Tarrant | 05350745 | 817/744-5900 | 358 |
| Woodlands Christian Academy/The Woodlands/ Montgomery | 04930603 | 936/273-2555 | 298 |
| Woodlands Elem Sch/Amarillo/Potter | 04866179 | 806/326-5800 | 321 |
| Woodlands Preparatory Sch/Tomball/Harris | 05275511 | 281/561-0600 | 213 |
| Woodlawn Academy/San Antonio/Bexar | 00998691 | 210/438-6560 | 44 |
| Woodlawn Elem Sch/Corp Christi/Nueces | 01044762 | 361/878-2900 | 307 |
| Woodlawn Hills Elem Sch/San Antonio/Bexar | 00998706 | 210/438-6565 | 44 |
| Woodridge Elem Sch/Desoto/Dallas | 01881845 | 972/223-3800 | 108 |
| Woodridge Elem Sch/San Antonio/Bexar | 00996980 | 210/826-8021 | 33 |
| Woodridge Forest Middle Sch/Porter/ Montgomery | 12033875 | 281/577-8880 | 297 |
| Woodroe Petty Elem Sch/Taft/San Patricio | 01049853 | 361/528-2636 | 335 |

| School/City/County DISTRICT/CITY/COUNTY | PID | TELEPHONE NUMBER | PAGE |
|---|---|---|---|
| Woodrow Wilson Daep Sch/Texas City/ Galveston | 05278379 | 409/916-0280 | 166 |
| Woodrow Wilson Elem Sch/Denton/Denton | 01013335 | 940/369-4500 | 126 |
| Woodrow Wilson Elem Sch/McAllen/Hidalgo | 01030125 | 956/971-4525 | 224 |
| Woodrow Wilson High Sch/Dallas/Dallas | 01010228 | 972/502-4400 | 108 |
| Woodrow Wilson Jr High Sch/Dayton/Liberty | 01037812 | 936/258-2309 | 268 |
| Woods Elem Sch/Tyler/Smith | 01050981 | 903/262-1280 | 341 |
| Woodsboro Elem Sch/Woodsboro/Refugio | 01048500 | 361/543-4518 | 326 |
| **WOODSBORO IND SCH DIST/WOODSBORO/ REFUGIO** | 01048495 | 361/543-4518 | 326 |
| Woodsboro Jr Sr High Sch/Woodsboro/Refugio | 01048512 | 361/543-4622 | 326 |
| Woodson Center for Excellence/Abilene/ Taylor | 04304133 | 325/671-4736 | 363 |
| **WOODSON IND SCH DIST/WOODSON/ THROCKMORTON** | 01055254 | 940/345-6521 | 365 |
| Woodson PK-5 Sch/Houston/Harris | 01025120 | 713/732-3600 | 194 |
| Woodson Sch/Woodson/Throckmorton | 01055266 | 940/345-6521 | 365 |
| Woodstone Elem Sch/San Antonio/Bexar | 01824043 | 210/407-9800 | 39 |
| Woodview Elem Sch/Houston/Harris | 01027453 | 713/251-7800 | 207 |
| Woodville High Sch/Woodville/Tyler | 01057343 | 409/283-3714 | 378 |
| **WOODVILLE IND SCH DIST/WOODVILLE/ TYLER** | 01057331 | 409/283-3752 | 378 |
| Woodville Intermediate Sch/Woodville/Tyler | 02224393 | 409/283-2549 | 378 |
| Woodville Middle Sch/Woodville/Tyler | 01057355 | 409/283-7109 | 378 |
| Woodway Elem Sch/Fort Worth/Tarrant | 03340342 | 817/814-8700 | 355 |
| Woodway Elem Sch/Waco/McLennan | 01039949 | 254/761-5740 | 284 |
| Wooldridge Elem Sch/Austin/Travis | 01056741 | 512/414-2353 | 371 |
| Wooten Elem Sch/Austin/Travis | 01056753 | 512/414-2315 | 371 |
| Workman Junior High Sch/Arlington/Tarrant | 01051686 | 682/867-1200 | 348 |
| World Languages Institute/Fort Worth/ Tarrant | 12033796 | 817/815-2200 | 355 |
| Worth Heights Elem Sch/Fort Worth/Tarrant | 01053646 | 817/814-6200 | 355 |
| Wortham Elem Sch/Wortham/Freestone | 01018555 | 254/765-3080 | 161 |
| Wortham High Sch/Wortham/Freestone | 04800292 | 254/765-3094 | 161 |
| **WORTHAM IND SCH DIST/WORTHAM/ FREESTONE** | 01018543 | 254/765-3095 | 161 |
| Wortham Middle Sch/Wortham/Freestone | 04800280 | 254/765-3523 | 161 |
| Wortham Oaks Elem Sch/San Antonio/Bexar | 12308008 | 210/945-5750 | 37 |
| Worthing High Sch/Houston/Harris | 01025170 | 713/733-3433 | 194 |
| Wright Elem Sch/Lubbock/Lubbock | 01039028 | 806/219-7700 | 274 |
| Wright Elem Sch/San Antonio/Bexar | 00997520 | 210/989-3400 | 36 |
| Wunderlich Intermediate Sch/Houston/Harris | 01418450 | 832/249-5200 | 203 |
| Wyatt Elem Sch/Plano/Collin | 04916293 | 469/752-3800 | 87 |
| Wylie East Elem Sch/Abilene/Taylor | 12365305 | 325/437-2330 | 364 |
| Wylie East High Sch/Wylie/Collin | 10915710 | 972/429-3150 | 89 |
| Wylie East Junior High Sch/Abilene/Taylor | 12110124 | 325/437-2360 | 364 |
| Wylie Elem Sch/Henderson/Rusk | 01048988 | 903/655-5200 | 330 |
| Wylie High Sch/Abilene/Taylor | 01055022 | 325/690-1181 | 364 |
| Wylie High Sch/Wylie/Collin | 01172424 | 972/429-3100 | 89 |
| **WYLIE IND SCH DIST/ABILENE/ TAYLOR** | 01055008 | 325/692-4353 | 364 |
| **WYLIE IND SCH DIST/WYLIE/COLLIN** | 01006605 | 972/429-3000 | 88 |
| Wylie Intermediate Sch/Abilene/Taylor | 02180137 | 325/692-7961 | 364 |
| Wylie Preparatory Academy/Wylie/Collin | 10013908 | 972/442-1388 | 90 |
| Wylie Primary Sch/Henderson/Rusk | 01049035 | 903/655-5100 | 330 |
| Wylie West Early Childhood Ctr/Abilene/ Taylor | 01055010 | 325/437-2351 | 364 |
| Wylie West Elem Sch/Abilene/Taylor | 03241710 | 325/692-6554 | 364 |
| Wylie West Junior High Sch/Abilene/Taylor | 04235960 | 325/695-1910 | 364 |
| **X** | | | |
| Xavier Educational Academy/Houston/Harris | 12361232 | 832/303-9638 | 213 |
| Xavier Preparatory Sch/Lancaster/Dallas | 12234615 | 214/741-4485 | 120 |
| Xenia Voigt Elem Sch/Round Rock/Williamson | 01413929 | 512/428-7500 | 402 |
| **Y** | | | |
| Yale Elem Sch/Richardson/Dallas | 01399696 | 469/593-8300 | 117 |
| **YANTIS IND SCH DIST/YANTIS/WOOD** | 01061980 | 903/383-2463 | 408 |
| Yantis Sch/Yantis/Wood | 01061992 | 903/383-2462 | 408 |
| Yarbrough Elem Sch/Midland/Midland | 12104357 | 432/240-8500 | 289 |
| Yates High Sch/Houston/Harris | 01024451 | 713/748-5400 | 194 |
| Yavneh Academy-Dallas/Dallas/Dallas | 04149270 | 214/295-3500 | 120 |
| Yeager Elem Sch/Houston/Harris | 01418395 | 281/440-4914 | 191 |
| Yellowstone Academy/Houston/Harris | 05342750 | 713/741-8000 | 213 |
| Yellowstone Clg Prep CS/Houston/Harris | 12378704 | 713/655-0596 | 17 |
| YES Prep Brays Oaks/Houston/Harris | 11834470 | 713/967-8400 | 17 |
| YES Prep East End/Houston/Harris | 10758861 | 713/967-7800 | 17 |
| YES Prep Fifth Ward/Houston/Harris | 11935373 | 713/924-0600 | 17 |
| YES Prep Gulfton/Houston/Harris | 11014101 | 713/967-9800 | 17 |
| YES Prep Hobby/Houston/Harris | 12378716 | 713/842-5600 | 17 |
| YES Prep Hoffman/Houston/Harris | 12044551 | 713/924-5400 | 17 |
| YES Prep North Centrl/Houston/Harris | 10758847 | 281/227-2044 | 17 |

| School/City/County<br>DISTRICT/CITY/COUNTY | PID | TELEPHONE NUMBER | PAGE |
|---|---|---|---|
| YES Prep North Forest/Houston/Harris | 11563138 | 713/967-8600 | 17 |
| YES Prep Northbrook MS/Houston/Harris | 12044549 | 713/251-4200 | 17 |
| YES Prep Northline/Houston/Harris | 12261278 | 713/842-5400 | 17 |
| YES Prep Northside/Houston/Harris | 11720037 | 713/924-0400 | 17 |
| YES Prep NW/Houston/Harris | 12378728 | 713/842-5510 | 17 |
| YES Prep Southeast/Houston/Harris | 04813275 | 713/910-2510 | 17 |
| YES Prep Southside/Houston/Harris | 12163028 | 713/924-5500 | 17 |
| YES Prep Southwest/Houston/Fort Bend | 10758859 | 713/413-0001 | 17 |
| YES Prep West/Houston/Harris | 11540370 | 713/967-8200 | 17 |
| YES Prep White Oak/Houston/Harris | 11934410 | 713/924-5300 | 17 |
| Yoakum High Sch/Yoakum/De Witt | 01013816 | 361/293-3442 | 122 |
| **YOAKUM IND SCH DIST**/YOAKUM/<br>**DE WITT** | 01013804 | 361/293-3162 | 122 |
| Yoakum Intermediate Sch/Yoakum/De Witt | 01013828 | 361/293-3001 | 122 |
| Yoakum Junior High Sch/Yoakum/De Witt | 01013830 | 361/293-3111 | 122 |
| Yoakum Primary Annex Sch/Yoakum/De Witt | 01013842 | 361/293-2011 | 122 |
| Yoakum Primary Sch/Yoakum/De Witt | 01013854 | 361/293-2011 | 122 |
| York Junior High Sch/Spring/Montgomery | 02856829 | 832/592-8600 | 295 |
| Yorkshire Academy/Houston/Harris | 02753253 | 281/531-6088 | 213 |
| Yorktown Christian Academy/Corp Christi/<br>Nueces | 04993899 | 361/985-9960 | 309 |
| Yorktown Elem Sch/Yorktown/De Witt | 01013880 | 361/564-2252 | 122 |
| Yorktown High Sch/Yorktown/De Witt | 01013878 | 361/564-2252 | 122 |
| **YORKTOWN IND SCH DIST**/YORKTOWN/<br>**DE WITT** | 01013866 | 361/564-2252 | 122 |
| Yorktown Junior High Sch/Yorktown/De Witt | 02177398 | 361/564-2252 | 122 |
| Youens Elem Sch/Houston/Harris | 01022996 | 281/983-8383 | 188 |
| Young Elem Sch/Decatur/Wise | 11562081 | 940/393-7400 | 406 |
| Young Elem Sch/Houston/Harris | 01025015 | 713/732-3590 | 198 |
| Young Elem Sch/Seminole/Gaines | 01018763 | 432/758-3636 | 162 |
| Young Junior High Sch/Arlington/Tarrant | 01881924 | 682/867-3400 | 348 |
| Young Learners Elem Sch/Houston/Harris | 11834509 | 713/772-7100 | 200 |
| Young Men's Leadership Academy/Fort Worth/<br>Tarrant | 11821318 | 817/815-3400 | 355 |
| Young Men's Leadership Academy/San Antonio/<br>Bexar | 12106458 | 210/354-9652 | 44 |
| Young Mens Ldrshp Acad-Flornce/Dallas/<br>Dallas | 01008835 | 972/749-6000 | 108 |
| Young Mens Leadership Academy/Grand Prairie/<br>Dallas | 11823304 | 972/264-8651 | 112 |
| Young Scholars Acad Excellence/Houston/<br>Harris | 04813251 | 713/654-1400 | 194 |
| Young Women Steam Acad-Blch Sp/Dallas/<br>Dallas | 11919886 | 972/892-5800 | 108 |
| Young Women's Leadership Acad/El Paso/<br>El Paso | 12177988 | 915/434-1300 | 143 |
| Young Women's Leadership Acad/Fort Worth/<br>Tarrant | 11554541 | 817/815-2400 | 355 |
| Young Women's Leadership Acad/Midland/<br>Midland | 12364935 | 432/240-8700 | 289 |
| Young Women's Leadership Acad/San Antonio/<br>Bexar | 11128051 | 210/438-6525 | 45 |
| Young Womens College Prep Acad/Houston/<br>Harris | 11717511 | 713/942-1441 | 197 |
| Young Womens Leadership Acad/Grand Prairie/<br>Dallas | 11823299 | 972/343-7400 | 112 |
| Youngblood Intermediate Sch/Houston/Harris | 04453265 | 281/983-8020 | 188 |
| Ysleta Community Learning Ctr/El Paso/<br>El Paso | 04918265 | 915/434-9400 | 143 |
| Ysleta Elem Sch/El Paso/El Paso | 01016648 | 915/434-8900 | 143 |
| Ysleta High Sch/El Paso/El Paso | 01016650 | 915/434-8000 | 143 |
| **YSLETA IND SCH DIST**/EL PASO/<br>**EL PASO** | 01016296 | 915/434-0000 | 141 |
| Ysleta Middle Sch/El Paso/El Paso | 01399713 | 915/434-8200 | 143 |
| Ysleta Pre-K Center/El Paso/El Paso | 02857110 | 915/434-9500 | 143 |
| YW Steam Research & Prep Acad/El Paso/<br>El Paso | 12233427 | 915/236-4830 | 137 |
| Ywla Primary Sch/San Antonio/Bexar | 12365472 | 210/554-2710 | 45 |

**Z**

| | | | |
|---|---|---|---|
| Zach White Elem Sch/El Paso/El Paso | 01016105 | 915/236-2700 | 138 |
| Zacharias Ecla/Somerset/Bexar | 12109503 | 210/750-8959 | 45 |
| Zachry Middle Sch/San Antonio/Bexar | 02848523 | 210/397-7400 | 42 |
| Zack Motley Elem Sch/Mesquite/Dallas | 01011612 | 972/882-5080 | 116 |
| Zamora Middle Sch/San Antonio/Bexar | 10023317 | 210/977-7278 | 46 |
| Zan Wesley Holmes Jr Mid Sch/Dallas/Dallas | 11825364 | 214/932-7800 | 108 |
| **ZAPATA CO IND SCH DIST**/ZAPATA/<br>**ZAPATA** | 01062245 | 956/765-6546 | 410 |
| Zapata High Sch/Zapata/Zapata | 01062271 | 956/765-0280 | 410 |
| Zapata Middle Sch/Zapata/Zapata | 02178471 | 956/765-6542 | 410 |
| Zapata North Elem Sch/Zapata/Zapata | 02199970 | 956/765-6917 | 410 |

| School/City/County<br>DISTRICT/CITY/COUNTY | PID | TELEPHONE NUMBER | PAGE |
|---|---|---|---|
| Zapata South Elem Sch/Zapata/Zapata | 01062269 | 956/765-4332 | 410 |
| Zavala Elem Sch/Austin/Travis | 01056765 | 512/414-2318 | 371 |
| Zavala Elem Sch/El Paso/El Paso | 01015711 | 915/236-0550 | 138 |
| Zavala Elem Sch/Harlingen/Cameron | 01003938 | 956/427-3200 | 69 |
| Zavala Magnet Elem Sch/Odessa/Ector | 01014860 | 432/456-1239 | 135 |
| Zavalla Elem Sch/Zavalla/Angelina | 00995091 | 936/897-2611 | 21 |
| Zavalla High Sch/Zavalla/Angelina | 00995106 | 936/897-2301 | 21 |
| **ZAVALLA IND SCH DIST**/ZAVALLA/<br>**ANGELINA** | 00995089 | 936/897-2271 | 21 |
| Zelma Hutsell Elem Sch/Katy/Harris | 01832105 | 281/237-6500 | 157 |
| **ZEPHYR IND SCH DIST**/ZEPHYR/BROWN | 01002611 | 325/739-5331 | 62 |
| Zephyr Sch/Zephyr/Brown | 01002623 | 325/739-5331 | 62 |
| Zilker Elem Sch/Austin/Travis | 01056777 | 512/414-2327 | 371 |
| Zion Lutheran Sch/Dallas/Dallas | 01012355 | 214/363-1630 | 120 |
| Zion Lutheran Sch/Georgetown/Williamson | 01061253 | 512/863-5345 | 403 |
| Zue S Bales Intermediate Sch/Friendswood/<br>Galveston | 12367808 | 281/482-8255 | 164 |
| Zundy Elem Sch/Wichita Falls/Wichita | 01060405 | 940/235-1123 | 396 |
| Zwink Elem Sch/Klein/Harris | 11822726 | 832/375-7800 | 203 |

| DISTRICT | URL | PAGE |
|---|---|---|
| Abbott Ind School Dist | abbottisd.org/ | 229 |
| Abernathy Ind School Dist | abernathyisd.com/ | 179 |
| Abilene Ind School Dist | abileneisd.org | 362 |
| Academy Ind School Dist | academyisd.net/ | 29 |
| Adrian Ind School Dist | adrianisd.net/ | 310 |
| Advantage Academy Admin Office | advantageisd.com/ | 100 |
| Agua Dulce Ind School Dist | adisd.esc2.net/ | 305 |
| Alamo Heights Ind School Dist | ahisd.net/ | 33 |
| Alba-Golden Ind School Dist | agisd.com/ | 407 |
| Albany Ind School Dist | albanyisd.net/ | 336 |
| Aldine Ind School Dist | aldineisd.org/ | 184 |
| Aledo Ind School Dist | aledoisd.org/ | 315 |
| Alice Ind School Dist | aliceisd.net/ | 248 |
| Alief Ind School Dist | aliefisd.net/ | 186 |
| Allen Ind School Dist | allenisd.org | 80 |
| Alpine Ind School Dist | alpine.esc18.net/ | 60 |
| Alto Ind School Dist | alto.esc7.net/ | 76 |
| Alvarado Ind School Dist | alvaradoisd.net/ | 249 |
| Alvin Ind School Dist | alvinisd.net/ | 54 |
| Alvord Ind School Dist | alvordisd.net/ | 405 |
| Amarillo Ind School Dist | amaisd.org/ | 320 |
| Amherst Ind School Dist | amherstisd.schooldesk.net/ | 263 |
| Anahuac Ind School Dist | sites.google.com/aisdpanthers.com/anahuacisd/home | 75 |
| Anderson-Shiro Cons Ind SD | ascisd.net/ | 176 |
| Andrews Ind School Dist | andrews.esc18.net | 19 |
| Angleton Ind School Dist | angletonisd.net/ | 55 |
| Anna Ind School Dist | annaisd.org/ | 81 |
| Anson Ind School Dist | ansontigers.com/ | 252 |
| Anthony Ind School Dist | anthonyisd.net/ | 136 |
| Anton Ind School Dist | antonisd.org/ | 232 |
| Apple Springs Ind School Dist | asisd.com/ | 376 |
| Aquilla Ind School Dist | aquillaisd.net/ | 230 |
| Aransas Co Ind School Dist | acisd.org/ | 22 |
| Aransas Pass Ind School Dist | apisd.org/ | 333 |
| Archer City Ind School Dist | archercityisd.net/ | 22 |
| Argyle Ind School Dist | argyleisd.com/ | 124 |
| Arlington Ind School Dist | aisd.net/ | 346 |
| Arp Ind School Dist | home.arpisd.org/ | 339 |
| Aspermont Ind School Dist | aspermontisd.com/ | 344 |
| Athens Ind School Dist | athensisd.net/ | 218 |
| Atlanta Ind School Dist | atlisd.net/ | 73 |
| Aubrey Ind School Dist | aubreyisd.net/ | 124 |
| Austin Ind School Dist | austinisd.org/ | 369 |
| Austwell Tivoli Ind SD | atisd.net/ | 326 |
| Avalon Ind School Dist | avalonisd.net/ | 144 |
| Avery Ind School Dist | averyisd.net/ | 325 |
| Avinger Ind School Dist | avingerisd.net/ | 73 |
| Axtell Ind School Dist | axtellisd.net/ | 281 |
| Azle Ind School Dist | azleisd.net/ | 348 |
| Baird Ind School Dist | bairdisd.org/ | 65 |
| Ballinger Ind School Dist | ballingerisd.net/ | 329 |
| Balmorhea Ind School Dist | bisdbears.esc18.net/ | 325 |
| Bandera Ind School Dist | banderaisd.net/ | 26 |
| Bangs Ind School Dist | bangsisd.net | 61 |
| Banquete Ind School Dist | banqueteisd.esc2.net | 305 |
| Barbers Hill Ind School Dist | bhisd.net | 75 |
| Bartlett Ind School Dist | bartlett.txed.net/ | 29 |
| Bastrop Ind School Dist | bisdtx.org/ | 26 |
| Bay City Ind School Dist | bcblackcats.net/ | 278 |
| Beaumont Ind School Dist | bmtisd.com/ | 244 |
| Beckville Ind School Dist | beckvilleisd.net/home | 314 |
| Beeville Ind School Dist | beevilleisd.net/ | 28 |
| Bellevue Ind School Dist | bellevueisd.org/ | 77 |
| Bells Ind School Dist | bellsisd.net/ | 170 |
| Bellville Ind School Dist | bellvilleisd.org/ | 24 |
| Belton Ind School Dist | bisd.net | 29 |
| Ben Bolt-Palito Blanco ISD | bbpbschools.net | 248 |
| Benavides Ind School Dist | benavidesisd.net/ | 132 |
| Benjamin Ind School Dist | benjaminisd.net/ | 261 |
| Big Sandy Ind School Dist | bigsandyisd.net/ | 319 |
| Big Sandy Ind School Dist | bigsandyisd.org/ | 378 |
| Big Spring Ind School Dist | bsisd.esc18.net/ | 236 |
| Birdville Ind School Dist | birdvilleschools.net/ | 348 |

| DISTRICT | URL | PAGE |
|---|---|---|
| Poteet Ind School Dist | poteet.k12.tx.us/ | 24 |
| Poth Ind School Dist | pothisd.us/ | 404 |
| Pottsboro Ind School Dist | pottsboroisd.org/ | 172 |
| Prairie Lea Ind School Dist | prairielea.txed.net/ | 65 |
| Prairie Valley Ind School Dist | prairievalleyisd.net/ | 293 |
| Prairiland Ind School Dist | prairiland.net/ | 263 |
| Premont Ind School Dist | premontisd.net/ | 248 |
| Presidio Ind School Dist | presidio-isd.net/ | 323 |
| Priddy Ind School Dist | priddyisd.net/ | 292 |
| Princeton Ind School Dist | princetonisd.net/ | 87 |
| Pringle-Morse Cons ISD | pringlemorsecisd.net/ | 182 |
| Progreso Ind School Dist | progreso.schooldesk.net/ | 227 |
| Prosper Ind School Dist | prosper-isd.net | 88 |
| Quanah Ind School Dist | qisd.net/ | 182 |
| Queen City Ind School Dist | qcisd.net/ | 74 |
| Quinlan Ind School Dist | quinlanisd.net/ | 240 |
| Quitman Ind School Dist | quitmanisd.net/ | 408 |
| Rains Ind School Dist | rainsisd.org/ | 323 |
| Ralls Ind School Dist | rallsisd.org/ | 98 |
| Ramirez Common School Dist | ramirezcsd.esc2.net/ | 132 |
| Randolph Field Ind School Dist | rfisd.net/ | 42 |
| Ranger Ind School Dist | ranger.esc14.net/ | 133 |
| Rankin Ind School Dist | rankinisd.net | 380 |
| Raymondville Ind Sch Dist | raymondvilleisd.org/ | 397 |
| Reagan Co Ind School Dist | reagancountyisd.net/ | 324 |
| Red Lick Ind School Dist | redlickisd.com/ | 52 |
| Red Oak Ind School Dist | redoakisd.org/ | 146 |
| Redwater Ind School Dist | redwaterisd.org/ | 53 |
| Refugio Ind School Dist | refugioisd.net/ | 326 |
| Ricardo Ind School Dist | ricardoisd.us/ | 261 |
| Rice Cons Ind School Dist | ricecisd.org | 90 |
| Rice Ind School Dist | rice-isd.org/ | 303 |
| Richards Ind School Dist | richardsisd.net/ | 177 |
| Richardson Ind School Dist | risd.org/group/schools/schools_main.html | 116 |
| Richland Springs Ind Sch Dist | rscoyotes.net/ | 335 |
| Riesel Ind School Dist | rieselisd.org/ | 284 |
| Rio Grande City Ind Sch Dist | rgccisd.org/ | 342 |
| Rio Hondo Ind School Dist | riohondoisd.net/ | 70 |
| Rio Vista Ind School Dist | rvisd.net/ | 251 |
| Rising Star Ind Sch Dist | risingstarisd.org/ | 133 |
| River Road Ind School Dist | rrisd.net/ | 322 |
| Rivercrest Ind School Dist | rivercrestisd.net/ | 325 |
| Riviera Ind School Dist | rivieraisd.us/ | 261 |
| Robert Lee Ind School Dist | rlisd.net | 79 |
| Robinson Ind School Dist | risdweb.org/ | 284 |
| Robstown Ind School Dist | robstownisd.org/ | 308 |
| Roby Cons Ind School Dist | robycisd.org/ | 152 |
| Rochelle Ind School Dist | rochelleisd.net/ | 281 |
| Rockdale Ind School Dist | rockdaleisd.net/ | 290 |
| Rocksprings Ind School Dist | rockspringsisd.net/ | 135 |
| Rockwall Ind School Dist | rockwallisd.com | 328 |
| Rogers Ind School Dist | rogersisd.org/ | 32 |
| Roma Ind School Dist | romaisd.com/ | 343 |
| Roosevelt Ind School Dist | roosevelt.k12.tx.us/ | 274 |
| Ropes Ind School Dist | ropesisd.us/ | 232 |
| Roscoe Collegiate Ind Sch Dist | roscoe.esc14.net/default.aspx?name=risd.home | 304 |
| Rosebud-Lott Ind School Dist | rlisd.org | 149 |
| Rotan Ind School Dist | rotan.org/ | 152 |
| Round Rock Ind School Dist | roundrockisd.org/ | 401 |
| Round Top-Carmine Ind Sch Dist | rtcisd.net/ | 151 |
| Royal Ind School Dist | royal-isd.net/ | 387 |
| Royse City Ind School Dist | rcisd.org/ | 328 |
| Rule Ind School Dist | rule.esc14.net/ | 215 |
| Runge Ind School Dist | rungeisd.org/ | 254 |
| Rusk Ind School Dist | ruskisd.net/ | 77 |
| S & S Cons Ind School Dist | sscisd.net/ | 172 |
| Sabinal Ind School Dist | sabinalisd.net/ | 380 |
| Sabine Ind School Dist | sabineisd.org/ | 175 |
| Sabine Pass Ind School Dist | sabinepass.net/ | 247 |
| Salado Ind School Dist | saladoisd.org/ | 32 |
| Saltillo Ind School Dist | saltilloisd.net/ | 234 |
| Sam Rayburn Ind School Dist | srisd.org/ | 150 |
| San Angelo Ind School Dist | saisd.org | 367 |
| San Antonio Ind School Dist | saisd.net/page/dis-homepage/ | 42 |

| DISTRICT | URL | PAGE |
|---|---|---|
| Stamford Ind School Dist | stamford.esc14.net/ | 253 |
| Stanton Ind School Dist | stanton.esc18.net/ | 277 |
| Stephenville Ind School Dist | sville.us/ | 148 |
| Sterling City Ind School Dist | sterlingcityisd.net/ | 344 |
| Stockdale Ind School Dist | stockdaleisd.org/ | 404 |
| Stratford Ind School Dist | stratfordisd.net/ | 338 |
| Strawn Ind School Dist | strawnschool.net/ | 314 |
| Sudan Ind School Dist | sudanisd.net/ | 264 |
| Sulphur Bluff Ind School Dist | sulphurbluffisd.net/ | 235 |
| Sulphur Springs Ind Sch Dist | ssisd.net/ | 235 |
| Sundown Ind School Dist | sundownisd.com/ | 232 |
| Sunnyvale Ind School Dist | sunnyvaleisd.com/ | 117 |
| Sunray Ind School Dist | region16.net/sunrayisd/ | 299 |
| Sweeny Ind School Dist | sweenyisd.org/ | 57 |
| Sweet Home Ind School Dist | sweethomeisd.org/ | 265 |
| Sweetwater ISD School Dist | sweetwaterisd.net | 304 |
| Taft Ind School Dist | taftisd.net/ | 334 |
| Tahoka Ind School Dist | tahokaisd.us/ | 276 |
| Tarkington Ind School Dist | tarkingtonisd.net/ | 269 |
| Tatum Ind School Dist | tatumisd.org/ | 331 |
| Taylor Ind School Dist | taylorisd.org/ | 402 |
| Teague Ind School Dist | teagueisd.org/ | 161 |
| Temple Ind School Dist | tisd.org/ | 32 |
| Tenaha Ind School Dist | tenahaisd.com/ | 337 |
| Terlingua Common School Dist | terlinguacsd.com/ | 60 |
| Terrell Co Ind School Dist | terrell.esc18.net/ | 364 |
| Terrell Ind School Dist | terrellisd.org/ | 256 |
| Texarkana Ind School Dist | txkisd.net/ | 53 |
| Texas City Ind School Dist | tcisd.org/ | 166 |
| Texhoma Ind School Dist | texhomaisd.net/ | 338 |
| Texline Ind School Dist | texlineisd.net/ | 99 |
| Thorndale Ind School Dist | thorndale.txed.net | 291 |
| Thrall Ind School Dist | thrallisd.com/ | 403 |
| Three Rivers Ind School Dist | trisd.org/ | 271 |
| Three Way Ind School Dist | twisd.us/ | 148 |
| Throckmorton Ind School Dist | throck.org/ | 365 |
| Tidehaven Ind School Dist | tidehavenisd.com | 279 |
| Timpson Ind School Dist | timpsonisd.com/ | 338 |
| Tioga Ind School Dist | tiogaisd.net/ | 172 |
| Tolar Ind School Dist | tolarisd.org/tolarisd/site/default.asp | 233 |
| Tom Bean Ind School Dist | tombean-isd.org | 173 |
| Tomball Ind School Dist | tomballisd.net/ | 208 |
| Tornillo Ind School Dist | tisd.us/ | 141 |
| Trent Isn School Dist | trentisd.org/ | 363 |
| Trenton Ind School Dist | trentonisd.com/ | 151 |
| Trinidad Ind School Dist | trinidadisd.com/ | 219 |
| Trinity Ind School Dist | trinityisd.net/ | 377 |
| Troup Ind School Dist | troupisd.org/ | 340 |
| Troy Ind School Dist | troyisd.org/ | 33 |
| Tulia Ind School Dist | tuliaisd.net/ | 345 |
| Tuloso-Midway Ind School Dist | tmisd.us/ | 308 |
| Turkey-Quitaque Cons Ind SD | valleypatriots.com/ | 181 |
| Tyler Ind School Dist | tylerisd.org/ | 340 |
| Union Grove Ind School Dist | ugisd.org/ | 379 |
| Union Hill Ind School Dist | uhisd.com/ | 380 |
| United Ind School Dist | uisd.net/ | 390 |
| UT Tyler University Acad Dist | uttia.org/ | 341 |
| Utopia Ind School Dist | utopiaisd.net/ | 381 |
| Uvalde Cons Ind School Dist | ucisd.net/ | 381 |
| Valentine Ind School Dist | valentineisd.com/ | 244 |
| Valley Mills Ind School Dist | vmisd.net/ | 50 |
| Valley View Ind School Dist | vviewisd.net/ | 228 |
| Valley View ISD-Cooke Co | vvisd.net/ | 95 |
| Van Alstyne Ind School Dist | vanalstyneisd.org/ | 173 |
| Van Ind School Dist | vanschools.org/ | 383 |
| Van Vleck Ind School Dist | vvisd.org/ | 279 |
| Vega Ind School Dist | vegalonghorn.com/ | 310 |
| Venus Ind School Dist | venusisd.net/ | 252 |
| Veribest Ind School Dist | veribestisd.net/ | 368 |
| Vernon Ind School Dist | vernonisd.org/ | 396 |
| Victoria Ind School Dist | visd.com | 384 |
| Vidor Ind School Dist | vidorisd.org/ | 312 |
| Vysehrad Ind School Dist | vysehrad.k12.tx.us/ | 265 |
| Waco Ind School Dist | wacoisd.org | 284 |

| DISTRICT | URL | PAGE |
|---|---|---|
| Waelder Ind School Dist | waelderisd.org/ | 169 |
| Walcott Ind School Dist | walcottisd.com/ | 123 |
| Wall Ind School Dist | wallisd.net/ | 368 |
| Waller Ind School Dist | wallerisd.net/ | 387 |
| Walnut Bend Ind School Dist | walnutbendisd.net/site/default.aspx?PageID=1 | 96 |
| Walnut Springs Ind Sch Dist | walnutspringsisd.net/ | 51 |
| Warren Ind School Dist | warrenisd.net/ | 378 |
| Waskom Ind School Dist | waskomisd.net/ | 214 |
| Water Valley Ind School Dist | wvisd.net/Page/1 | 368 |
| Waxahachie Ind School Dist | wisd.org/ | 146 |
| Weatherford Ind School Dist | weatherfordisd.com/ | 316 |
| Webb Cons Ind School Dist | webbcisd.org/ | 391 |
| Weimar Ind School Dist | weimarisd.org | 91 |
| Wellington Ind School Dist | wellingtonisd.net/ | 90 |
| Wellman Union Ind School Dist | wellman.esc17.net/ | 365 |
| Wells Ind School Dist | wells.esc7.net | 77 |
| Weslaco Ind School Dist | wisd.us/ | 228 |
| West Hardin Co Cons Sch Dist | westhardin.org/ | 183 |
| West Ind School Dist | westisd.net/ | 285 |
| West Orange-Cove Cons ISD | woccisd.net/ | 312 |
| West Oso Ind School Dist | westosoisd.net/ | 309 |
| West Rusk Co Cons Ind Sch Dist | westrusk.esc7.net | 331 |
| West Sabine Ind Sch Dist | westsabineisd.net/ | 332 |
| Westbrook Ind School Dist | westbrookisd.com/ | 292 |
| Westhoff Ind School Dist | westhoffisd.org/ | 122 |
| Westphalia Ind School Dist | westphaliaisd.org/ | 149 |
| Westwood Ind School Dist | westwoodisd.net/ | 19 |
| Wharton Ind School Dist | whartonisd.net/ | 393 |
| Wheeler Ind School Dist | wheelerschools.net/ | 394 |
| White Deer Ind School Dist | whitedeerisd.net/ | 73 |
| White Oak Ind School Dist | woisd.net/isd/ | 176 |
| White Settlement Ind Sch Dist | wsisd.com/ | 360 |
| Whiteface Con Ind School Dist | whitefaceschool.net/ | 78 |
| Whitehouse Ind School Dist | whitehouseisd.org/ | 341 |
| Whitesboro Ind School Dist | whitesboroisd.org/ | 173 |
| Whitewright Ind School Dist | whitewrightisd.com/ | 173 |
| Whitharral Ind School Dist | whitharralisd.org/ | 233 |
| Whitney Ind School Dist | whitney.k12.tx.us/ | 231 |
| Wichita Falls Ind School Dist | wfisd.net/ | 395 |
| Wildorado Ind Sch Dist | wildoradoisd.org/ | 311 |
| Willis Ind School Dist | willisisd.org/ | 297 |
| Wills Point Ind School Dist | wpisd.com/ | 383 |
| Wilson Ind School Dist | wilson.esc17.net/ | 276 |
| Wimberley Ind School Dist | wimberleyisd.net/ | 217 |
| Windthorst Ind School Dist | windthorstisd.net/ | 23 |
| Wink Loving Ind School Dist | wlisd.net/ | 405 |
| Winnsboro Ind School Dist | winnsboroisd.org/ | 408 |
| Winona Ind School Dist | winonaisd.org/home/ | 341 |
| Winters Ind School Dist | wintersisd.org/ | 329 |
| Woden Ind School Dist | wodenisd.org/ | 301 |
| Wolfe City Ind School Dist | wcisd.net/ | 240 |
| Woodsboro Ind School Dist | wisd.net | 326 |
| Woodson Ind School Dist | woodsonisd.net/ | 365 |
| Woodville Ind School Dist | woodvilleeagles.org/ | 378 |
| Wortham Ind School Dist | worthamisd.org/ | 161 |
| Wylie Ind School Dist | wylieisd.net | 88 |
| Wylie Ind School Dist | wyliebulldogs.org/ | 364 |
| Yantis Ind School Dist | yantisisd.net/ | 408 |
| Yoakum Ind School Dist | yoakumisd.net | 122 |
| Yorktown Ind School Dist | yisd.org/ | 122 |
| Ysleta Ind School Dist | yisd.net/ | 141 |
| Zapata Co Ind School Dist | zcisd.org/ | 410 |
| Zavalla Ind School Dist | zavallaisd.org/ | 21 |
| Zephyr Ind School Dist | zephyrisd.net/ | 62 |

| CMO No. | PID | CMO Name | Address | Phone |
|---|---|---|---|---|
| 001 | 11912383 | Estem Public Charter Schools | 200 River Market Ave Ste 225, Little Rock AR 72201 | (501) 324-9200 |
| 002 | 11916092 | KIPP Delta Public Schools | 320 Missouri, Helena AR 72342 | (870) 753-9035 |
| 003 | 12319502 | Lisa Academy Foundation | 10825 Financial Centre Pkwy, Little Rock AR 72211 | (501) 916-9450 |
| 004 | 12376823 | Academies of Math & Science | 2980 N Campbell Ave, Tucson AZ 85719 | (520) 887-5392 |
| 005 | 11912826 | Academy of Tucson Inc | 10720 E 22nd St, Tucson AZ 85748 | (520) 733-0096 |
| 006 | 11914305 | Accelerated Learning Ctr | 4105 E Shea Blvd, Phoenix AZ 85028 | (602) 485-0309 |
| 007 | 11914288 | Allen-Cochran Enterprises | 1700 E Elliot Rd Ste 9, Tempe AZ 85284 | (480) 632-1940 |
| 008 | 11914264 | American Basic Schools LLC | 131 E Southern Ave, Mesa AZ 85210 | (480) 655-7868 |
| 009 | 11928033 | American Leadership Acad Inc | 2250 E Germann Rd Ste 14, Chandler AZ 85286 | (480) 420-2101 |
| 010 | 11912761 | Arizona Agribus&Equine Ctr Org | 315 E Mulberry Dr, Phoenix AZ 85012 | (602) 297-8500 |
| 011 | 11912759 | Arizona Charter Schools | 5704 E Grant Rd, Tucson AZ 85712 | (520) 545-0575 |
| 012 | 12376835 | Asu Preparatory Acad Network | PO Box 876705, Tempe AZ 85287 | (602) 496-3322 |
| 013 | 11912723 | Basis School Inc | 7975 N Hayden Rd Ste B202, Scottsdale AZ 85258 | (480) 289-2088 |
| 014 | 11914525 | Benjamin Franklin Chtr Schools | 690 E Warner Rd Ste 141, Gilbert AZ 85296 | (480) 264-3710 |
| 015 | 11912668 | Blueprint Education | 5651 W Talavi Blvd Ste 170, Glendale AZ 85306 | (602) 674-5555 |
| 016 | 11914226 | Bright Beginnings School Inc | 400 N Andersen Blvd, Chandler AZ 85224 | (480) 821-1404 |
| 017 | 11912620 | CAFA Inc | 4055 E Warner Rd, Gilbert AZ 85296 | (480) 635-1900 |
| 018 | 11913387 | Career Success Schools | 3816 N 27th Ave, Phoenix AZ 85017 | (602) 285-5525 |
| 019 | 11913351 | Center for Academic Success | 1843 Paseo San Luis, Sierra Vista AZ 85635 | (520) 458-9309 |
| 020 | 11914173 | Compass High School Inc | PO Box 17810, Tucson AZ 85731 | (520) 296-4070 |
| 021 | 11914159 | Cornerstone Charter School Inc | 7107 N Black Canyon Hwy, Phoenix AZ 85021 | (602) 595-2198 |
| 022 | 11914147 | Country Gardens Educl Svcs | 6313 W Southern Ave, Laveen AZ 85339 | (602) 237-3741 |
| 023 | 11914111 | Eastpointe High School Inc | 8495 E Broadway Blvd, Tucson AZ 85710 | (520) 731-8180 |
| 024 | 11914068 | Educational Impact Inc | 1950 E Placita Sin Nombre, Tucson AZ 85718 | (520) 296-0656 |
| 025 | 11914044 | Eduprize Schools Inc | 4567 W Roberts Rd, Queen Creek AZ 85142 | (480) 888-1610 |
| 026 | 11912395 | Espiritu Community Development | 222 E Olympic Dr, Phoenix AZ 85042 | (602) 243-7788 |
| 027 | 12378118 | Fit Kids Inc Champion Schools | 6991 E Camelback Rd Ste D300, Scottsdale AZ 85251 | (480) 386-7071 |
| 028 | 11914032 | GAR LLC | 8253 W Thunderbird Rd Ste 105, Peoria AZ 85381 | (602) 334-4104 |
| 029 | 11913234 | Great Hearts Academies | 4801 E Washington St Ste 250, Phoenix AZ 85034 | (602) 438-7045 |
| 030 | 11913985 | Heritage Academy Inc | 32 S Center St, Mesa AZ 85210 | (480) 969-5641 |
| 031 | 11914434 | Humanities & Sciences Acad US | 5201 N 7th St, Phoenix AZ 85014 | (602) 650-1333 |
| 032 | 11911781 | Imagine Southwest Regional | 1843 W 16th Ave, Apache Jct AZ 85120 | (480) 355-0502 |
| 033 | 11913179 | Kingman Academy of Learning | 3410 N Burbank St, Kingman AZ 86409 | (928) 681-2400 |
| 034 | 11913167 | Leading Edge Charter Solutions | 633 E Ray Rd Ste 132, Gilbert AZ 85296 | (480) 633-0414 |
| 035 | 11913143 | Learning Matters Educl Group | 4744 W Grovers Ave, Glendale AZ 85308 | (602) 439-5026 |
| 036 | 11913959 | Legacy Traditional Schools | 3125 S Gilbert Rd, Chandler AZ 85286 | (480) 270-5438 |
| 037 | 11914599 | Leona Group LLC-AZ | 7500 N Dreamy Draw Dr Ste 220, Phoenix AZ 85020 | (602) 953-2933 |
| 038 | 11914381 | Mgrm Pinnacle Education Inc | 2224 W Southern Ave Ste 1, Tempe AZ 85282 | (480) 755-8222 |
| 039 | 11913911 | Montessori Schoolhouse Tucson | 1301 E Fort Lowell Rd, Tucson AZ 85719 | (520) 319-8668 |
| 040 | 11913923 | Montessori Schools Flagstaff | 2212 E Cedar Ave, Flagstaff AZ 86004 | (928) 774-1600 |
| 041 | 12305874 | Pima Prevention Partnership | 1477 W Commerce Ct, Tucson AZ 85746 | (520) 791-2711 |
| 042 | 12306309 | Plc Charter Schools | 2504 S 91st Ave, Tolleson AZ 85353 | (623) 474-2120 |
| 043 | 11912101 | Pointe Educational Services | 10215 N 43rd Ave, Phoenix AZ 85051 | (602) 843-2014 |
| 044 | 11913519 | PPEP and Affiliates | 802 E 46th St, Tucson AZ 85713 | (520) 622-3553 |
| 045 | 11913856 | Rose Management Group | 3686 W Orange Grove Rd Ste 192, Tucson AZ 85741 | (520) 797-4884 |
| 046 | 11913832 | Self Development Chtr Sch Org | 1709 N Greenfield Rd, Mesa AZ 85205 | (480) 641-2640 |
| 047 | 11913337 | Sequoia Schools-Edkey Inc | 1460 S Horne Bldg 6, Mesa AZ 85204 | (480) 461-3200 |
| 048 | 11912979 | Skyline Education | 7450 S 40th St 7500, Phoenix AZ 85042 | (877) 225-2118 |
| 049 | 11913349 | Sonoran Schools Inc | 1489 W Elliot Rd Ste 103, Gilbert AZ 85233 | (480) 940-5440 |
| 050 | 11913806 | Southern Arizona Cmty Acad Inc | 2470 N Tucson Blvd, Tucson AZ 85716 | (520) 319-6113 |
| 051 | 11912929 | The Charter Foundation Inc | 1150 N Country Club Rd Ste 100, Tucson AZ 85716 | (520) 296-1100 |
| 052 | 11911901 | The Edge School Inc | 2555 E 1st St, Tucson AZ 85716 | (520) 881-1389 |
| 053 | 11912890 | Tucson International Academy | 2700 W Broadway Blvd, Tucson AZ 85745 | (520) 792-3255 |
| 054 | 11912802 | Albert Einstein Academies | 3035 Ash St, San Diego CA 92102 | (619) 795-1190 |
| 055 | 11913686 | Alliance College-Ready Pub Sch | 601 S Figueroa St Fl 4, Los Angeles CA 90017 | (213) 943-4930 |
| 056 | 12305812 | Alpha Public Schools | PO Box 21366, San Jose CA 95151 | (408) 455-6355 |
| 057 | 12262961 | Alta Public Schools | 2410 Broadway, Huntington Pk CA 90255 | (323) 923-0383 |
| 058 | 11912785 | American Indian Model Schools | 171 12th St, Oakland CA 94607 | (510) 893-8701 |
| 059 | 12262911 | Amethod Public Schools | 2101 Livingston St, Oakland CA 94606 | (510) 436-0172 |
| 060 | 12379124 | Aspire Bay Area Region | 1001 22nd Ave Ste 200, Oakland CA 94606 | (510) 568-3101 |

| CMO No. | PID | CMO Name | Address | Phone |
|---|---|---|---|---|
| 061 | 12379136 | Aspire Central Vly Area Region | 3311 Morada Ln, Stockton CA 95212 | (209) 647-3047 |
| 062 | 12379148 | Aspire Los Angeles Area Region | 5901 E Slauson Ave, Los Angeles CA 90040 | (323) 837-9920 |
| 063 | 11913648 | Aspire Public Schools | 1001 22nd Ave Ste 100, Oakland CA 94606 | (510) 434-5000 |
| 064 | 11912656 | Bright Star Education Group | 600 S La Fayette Park Pl, Los Angeles CA 90057 | (323) 954-9957 |
| 065 | 11913404 | California Montessori Projects | 5330A Gibbons Dr Ste 700, Carmichael CA 95608 | (916) 971-2432 |
| 066 | 11913399 | Camino Nuevo Charter Academy | 3435 W Temple St, Los Angeles CA 90026 | (213) 417-3400 |
| 067 | 11912709 | Ceiba Public Schools | 260 W Riverside Dr, Watsonville CA 95076 | (831) 740-8800 |
| 068 | 12260028 | Citizens of the World Chtr Sch | 5371 Wilshire Blvd Ste 210, Los Angeles CA 90036 | (323) 634-7109 |
| 069 | 11912565 | Civicorps Schools | 101 Myrtle St, Oakland CA 94607 | (510) 992-7800 |
| 070 | 11912539 | Community Learning Center Schs | 1900 3rd St, Alameda CA 94501 | (510) 263-9266 |
| 071 | 11912527 | Core-Cmty Options Resources Ed | 321 16th St, Marysville CA 95901 | (530) 742-2786 |
| 072 | 12377413 | Da Vinci Schools | 201 N Douglas St, El Segundo CA 90245 | (310) 725-5800 |
| 073 | 12110435 | Downtown College Prep | 1400 Parkmoor Ave Ste 206, San Jose CA 95126 | (408) 271-8120 |
| 074 | 12261486 | Ednovate Inc | 350 S Figueroa St Ste 350, Los Angeles CA 90071 | (213) 454-0599 |
| 075 | 11912436 | Education for Change | 333 Hegenberger Rd Ste 600, Oakland CA 94621 | (510) 568-7936 |
| 076 | 11912412 | Environmental Charter Schools | 2625 Manhattn Bch Blvd Ste 100, Redondo Beach CA 90278 | (310) 214-3408 |
| 077 | 11913301 | Envision Education | 111 Myrtle St Ste 203, Oakland CA 94607 | (510) 451-2415 |
| 078 | 12179015 | Equitas Academy Chtr Sch Inc | 1700 W Pico Blvd, Los Angeles CA 90015 | (213) 201-0440 |
| 079 | 12305824 | Fenton Charter Public Schools | 8928 Sunland Blvd, Sun Valley CA 91352 | (818) 962-3630 |
| 080 | 11912357 | Five Keys Charter Schools Inc | 70 Oak Grove St, San Francisco CA 94107 | (415) 734-3310 |
| 081 | 12262935 | Fortune School of Education | 2890 Gateway Oaks Dr Ste 100, Sacramento CA 95833 | (916) 924-8633 |
| 082 | 11913258 | Gateway Community Charters | 5112 Arnold Ave Ste A, McClellan CA 95652 | (916) 286-5129 |
| 083 | 11912319 | Golden Valley Charter Schools | 3585 Maple St Ste 101, Ventura CA 93003 | (805) 642-3435 |
| 084 | 11913595 | Green Dot Public Schools | 1149 S Hill St Ste 600, Los Angeles CA 90015 | (323) 565-1600 |
| 085 | 12239598 | Grimmway Schools | 5080 California Ave Ste 100, Bakersfield CA 93309 | (661) 432-7880 |
| 086 | 11912280 | High Desert Partnsp Acad Excel | 17500 Mana Rd, Apple Valley CA 92307 | (760) 946-5414 |
| 087 | 11913222 | High Tech High | 2861 Womble Rd, San Diego CA 92106 | (619) 243-5000 |
| 088 | 11913583 | ICEF Public Schools | 3855 W Slauson Ave, Los Angeles CA 90043 | (323) 290-6900 |
| 089 | 11912266 | Innovative Education Managemnt | 4535 Missouri Flat Rd Ste 1A, Placerville CA 95667 | (800) 979-4436 |
| 090 | 11913375 | Isana Academies | 3580 Wilshire Blvd Ste 1130, Los Angeles CA 90010 | (323) 291-1211 |
| 091 | 11913181 | King-Chavez Neighborhood Schs | 2260 Island Ave, San Diego CA 92102 | (619) 525-7320 |
| 092 | 11916054 | KIPP Bay Area Public Schools | 1000 Broadway Ste 460, Oakland CA 94607 | (510) 465-5477 |
| 093 | 11913571 | KIPP Foundation | 135 Main St Ste 1700, San Francisco CA 94105 | (415) 399-1556 |
| 094 | 11916169 | KIPP Socal Public Schools | 3601 E 1st St, Los Angeles CA 90063 | (213) 489-4461 |
| 095 | 11913155 | Leadership Public Schools | 99 Linden St, Oakland CA 94607 | (510) 830-3780 |
| 096 | 12260030 | Los Angeles Education Corps | 3635 Atlantic Ave, Long Beach CA 90807 | (562) 216-1790 |
| 097 | 11913557 | Magnolia Ed & Research Fdn | 250 E 1st St Ste 1500, Los Angeles CA 90012 | (213) 628-3634 |
| 098 | 11912187 | National Univ Academy System | 1980 University Dr Ste 30, Vista CA 92083 | (760) 630-4080 |
| 099 | 12262777 | Navigator Schools | 650 San Benito St Ste 230, Hollister CA 95023 | (831) 217-4880 |
| 100 | 12361373 | Olive Grove Charter Schools | 2353 S Broadway, Santa Maria CA 93454 | (805) 623-1111 |
| 101 | 11935907 | Opportunities for Learning | 320 N Halstead St Ste 220, Pasadena CA 91107 | (888) 207-1119 |
| 102 | 11913052 | Options for Youth Inc | 320 N Halstead St Ste 280, Pasadena CA 91107 | (888) 389-9992 |
| 103 | 12262923 | Pacific Charter Institute | 1401 El Camino Ave Ste 510, Sacramento CA 95815 | (866) 992-9033 |
| 104 | 11912125 | Para Los Ninos PCS | 5000 Hollywood Blvd, Los Angeles CA 90027 | (213) 250-4800 |
| 105 | 11913521 | Partnerships to Uplift Cmty | 1405 N San Fernando Blvd 303, Burbank CA 91504 | (818) 559-7699 |
| 106 | 11912060 | Real Journey Academies | 1425 W Foothill Blvd Ste 100, Upland CA 91786 | (909) 888-8458 |
| 107 | 11912046 | Roads Education Organization | 2999 Cleveland Ave Ste D, Santa Rosa CA 95403 | (707) 843-4676 |
| 108 | 11912034 | Rocketship Education | 350 Twin Dolphin Dr Ste 109, Redwood City CA 94065 | (877) 806-0920 |
| 109 | 11911872 | Rocklin Academy Charter Schs | 2204 Plaza Dr Ste 200, Rocklin CA 95765 | (916) 778-4544 |
| 110 | 11912008 | Semillas Sociedad Civil | 4736 Huntington Dr S, Los Angeles CA 90032 | (323) 352-3148 |
| 111 | 11911987 | St Hope Public Schools | PO Box 5038, Sacramento CA 95817 | (916) 649-7900 |
| 112 | 12101381 | Summit Public Schools | 780 Broadway St, Redwood City CA 94063 | (650) 257-9880 |
| 113 | 11911925 | The Accelerated School | 116 E Mlk Jr Blvd, Los Angeles CA 90011 | (323) 235-6343 |
| 114 | 12378742 | The Classical Academies | 157 E Valley Pkwy, Escondido CA 92025 | (760) 842-8000 |
| 115 | 11911884 | The Learner-Centered School | 3325 Hacienda Way, Antioch CA 94509 | (925) 755-7311 |
| 116 | 11911846 | Tracy Learning Center | 51 E Beverly Pl, Tracy CA 95376 | (209) 290-0511 |
| 117 | 11911822 | Value Schools | 680 Wilshire Pl Ste 315, Los Angeles CA 90005 | (213) 388-8676 |
| 118 | 12306244 | Western Sierra Charter Schools | 41267 Highway 41, Oakhurst CA 93644 | (559) 642-1422 |
| 119 | 12262791 | Ypi Charter Schools | 10660 White Oak Ave B101, Granada Hills CA 91344 | (818) 834-5805 |
| 120 | 12321684 | Colorado Early College Network | 4405 N Chestnut St Ste E, Colorado Spgs CO 80907 | (719) 955-4685 |

| CMO No. | PID | CMO Name | Address | Phone |
|---|---|---|---|---|
| 121 | 12378156 | Dsst Public School Foundation | 3401 Quebec St Ste 2000, Denver CO 80207 | (303) 524-6324 |
| 122 | 12322432 | Global Village Charter Collab | 555 W 112th Ave, Northglenn CO 80234 | (720) 353-4113 |
| 123 | 11916078 | KIPP Colorado | 1390 Lawrence St Ste 200, Denver CO 80204 | (303) 934-3245 |
| 124 | 12305886 | Rocky Mountain Prep Schools | 7808 Cherry Creek Dr S, Denver CO 80231 | (720) 863-8920 |
| 125 | 12110356 | Strive Preparatory Schools | 2480 W 26th Ave Ste 360B, Denver CO 80211 | (720) 772-4300 |
| 126 | 12322626 | Tatonka Education Services | 10375 Park Meadows Dr Ste 230, Lone Tree CO 80124 | (303) 296-6500 |
| 127 | 11913090 | The New America Schools Netwk | 925 S Niagara St Ste 140/400, Denver CO 80224 | (303) 800-0058 |
| 128 | 11913698 | Achievement First Network | 370 James St Ste 404, New Haven CT 06513 | (203) 773-3223 |
| 129 | 11915414 | Jumoke Academy Inc | 999 Asylum Ave Ste 200, Hartford CT 06105 | (860) 216-9636 |
| 130 | 11913650 | Aspira Educl Management Org | 1220 L St NW Ste 701, Washington DC 20005 | (202) 835-3600 |
| 131 | 11913363 | Center City Public Charter Sch | 900 2nd St NE Ste 221, Washington DC 20002 | (202) 589-0202 |
| 132 | 11912591 | Cesar Chavez Public Chtr Schs | 3701 Hayes St NE, Washington DC 20019 | (202) 547-3975 |
| 133 | 11912503 | DC Prep | 707 Edgewood St NE, Washington DC 20017 | (202) 635-4590 |
| 134 | 11913260 | Friendship Public Charter Sch | 111 O St NW, Washington DC 20001 | (202) 281-1700 |
| 135 | 11914836 | KIPP DC | 2600 Virginia Ave NW Ste 900, Washington DC 20037 | (202) 223-4505 |
| 136 | 11912010 | See Forever Foundation | 600 Pennsylvania Ave SE, Washington DC 20003 | (202) 797-8250 |
| 137 | 11911860 | The Seed Foundation | 1730 Rh Isl Ave NW Ste 1102, Washington DC 20036 | (202) 785-4123 |
| 138 | 11914680 | Academica | 6340 Sunset Dr, Miami FL 33143 | (305) 669-2906 |
| 139 | 11914549 | Accelerated Learning Solutions | 5850 T G Lee Blvd Ste 345, Orlando FL 32822 | (888) 437-9353 |
| 140 | 11914496 | Charter School Associates Inc | 5471 N University Dr, Coral Springs FL 33067 | (954) 414-5767 |
| 141 | 11914678 | Charter Schools USA | 800 Corporate Dr Ste 700, Ft Lauderdale FL 33334 | (954) 202-3500 |
| 142 | 11912541 | Cmty & Eco Dev Org Gadsden Co | 20 E Washington St, Quincy FL 32351 | (850) 627-7656 |
| 143 | 11914630 | Edisonlearning Inc | 1 E Broward Blvd Ste 1111, Ft Lauderdale FL 33301 | (877) 890-7088 |
| 144 | 12261709 | Forza Education Management LLC | PO Box 830, Parrish FL 34219 | (727) 642-9319 |
| 145 | 11916420 | Imagine South Florida Regional | 13790 NW 4th St Ste 108, Sunrise FL 33325 | (954) 870-5023 |
| 146 | 11916406 | Imagine Southeast Regional | 775 Town Center Blvd, Palm Coast FL 32164 | (888) 709-8010 |
| 147 | 11916157 | KIPP Jacksonville Schools | 1440 McDuff Ave N, Jacksonville FL 32254 | (904) 683-6643 |
| 148 | 12179651 | Lake Wales Charter Schools | 130 E Central Ave, Lake Wales FL 33853 | (863) 679-6560 |
| 149 | 11913569 | Lighthouse Academies | 29140 Chapel Park Dr Bldg 5A, Wesley Chapel FL 33543 | (800) 901-6943 |
| 150 | 11913947 | LII Licensing Inc | 6710 86th Ave N, Pinellas Park FL 33782 | (727) 768-0989 |
| 151 | 11914379 | Rader Group | 101A Business Centre Dr, Miramar Beach FL 32550 | (850) 650-3984 |
| 152 | 11913789 | Superior Schools | 861 N Hercules Ave, Clearwater FL 33765 | (727) 799-1200 |
| 153 | 11916224 | KIPP Metro Atlanta Schools | 1445 Maynard Rd NW, Atlanta GA 30331 | (404) 924-6310 |
| 154 | 12240195 | Mountain Ed Chtr High School | 1963 Tom Bell Rd, Cleveland GA 30528 | (706) 219-4664 |
| 155 | 12259990 | Gem Innovation Schools | PO Box 86, Deary ID 83823 | (208) 238-1388 |
| 156 | 11913466 | Acero Charter Schools Inc | 209 W Jackson Blvd Ste 500, Chicago IL 60606 | (312) 637-3900 |
| 157 | 11913662 | American Quality Schools Corp | 1315 Butterfield Rd Ste 224, Downers Grove IL 60515 | (312) 226-3355 |
| 158 | 11912670 | Betty Shabazz Intl Chtr Sch | 7822 S Dobson Ave, Chicago IL 60619 | (773) 651-1221 |
| 159 | 11912606 | Catalyst Schools | 6727 S California Ave, Chicago IL 60629 | (773) 295-7001 |
| 160 | 11912553 | Civitas Education Partners | 1006 S Michigan Ave Ste 301, Chicago IL 60605 | (312) 733-6790 |
| 161 | 11913636 | Concept Schools | 1336 Basswood Rd, Schaumburg IL 60173 | (847) 824-3380 |
| 162 | 11912333 | Galapagos Charter | 3051 Rotary Rd, Rockford IL 61109 | (779) 368-0852 |
| 163 | 11914812 | KIPP Chicago | 2007 S Halsted St, Chicago IL 60608 | (312) 733-8108 |
| 164 | 12110447 | Lawndale Educ & Reg Network | 3021 W Carroll Ave, Chicago IL 60612 | (773) 584-4399 |
| 165 | 11913545 | Noble Network of Charter Sch | 1 N State St Ste 700, Chicago IL 60602 | (312) 521-5287 |
| 166 | 11913038 | Perspectives Charter Schools | 1530 S State St Ste 200, Chicago IL 60605 | (312) 604-2200 |
| 167 | 12260016 | Regeneration Schools | 1816 W Garfield Blvd, Chicago IL 60609 | (773) 778-9455 |
| 168 | 11913246 | GEO Foundation | 1630 N Meridian St Ste 350, Indianapolis IN 46202 | (317) 536-1027 |
| 169 | 12315427 | Goodwill Education Initiatives | 1635 W Michigan St, Indianapolis IN 46222 | (317) 524-4265 |
| 170 | 11916145 | KIPP Indy Public Schools | 1740 E 30th St, Indianapolis IN 46218 | (317) 547-5477 |
| 171 | 12179027 | Tindley Accelerated Schools | 3960 Meadows Dr, Indianapolis IN 46205 | (317) 545-1745 |
| 172 | 11913430 | Algiers Charter School Assoc | 2401 Westbend Pkwy Ste 2001, New Orleans LA 70114 | (504) 302-7001 |
| 173 | 12115203 | Collegiate Academies | 2625 Thalia St, New Orleans LA 70113 | (504) 503-0008 |
| 174 | 11930816 | Crescent City Schools | 3811 N Galvez St, New Orleans LA 70117 | (504) 708-4136 |
| 175 | 11912369 | Firstline Schools Inc | 300 N Broad St Ste 207, New Orleans LA 70119 | (504) 267-9038 |
| 176 | 11930725 | Friends of King Schools | 1617 Caffin Ave, New Orleans LA 70117 | (504) 940-2243 |
| 177 | 12372592 | Idea Public Schools S Louisiana | 804 Main St, Baton Rouge LA 70802 | (225) 963-6539 |
| 178 | 12179039 | Inspirenola Charter Schools | 2401 Westbend Pkwy Ste 4040, New Orleans LA 70114 | (504) 227-3057 |
| 179 | 12259213 | Jcfa Charter Schools | 475 Manhattan Blvd, Harvey LA 70058 | (504) 410-3121 |
| 180 | 11916250 | KIPP New Orleans Schools | 1307 Oretha Castle Haley Blvd, New Orleans LA 70113 | (504) 373-6269 |

| CMO No. | PID | CMO Name | Address | Phone |
|---|---|---|---|---|
| 181 | 11912058 | Renew Schools Inc | 1001 Lake Forest Blvd Ste 710, New Orleans LA 70127 | (504) 367-3307 |
| 182 | 11911913 | The Choice Foundation | 3201 Live Oak St, New Orleans LA 70118 | (504) 861-8370 |
| 183 | 12110411 | The Einstein Group Inc | 5316 Michoud Blvd, New Orleans LA 70129 | (504) 324-7450 |
| 184 | 11913296 | Excel Academy | 58 Moore St, East Boston MA 02128 | (617) 874-4080 |
| 185 | 11916171 | KIPP Massachusetts Chtr Schs | 90 High Rock St, Lynn MA 01902 | (781) 598-1609 |
| 186 | 12306086 | The Community Group | 190 Hampshire St Ste 2, Lawrence MA 01840 | (978) 682-6628 |
| 187 | 12260004 | Up Education Network | 90 Canal St Ste 600, Boston MA 02114 | (617) 307-5980 |
| 188 | 11913428 | Baltimore Curriculum Project | 2707 E Fayette St, Baltimore MD 21224 | (410) 675-7000 |
| 189 | 11912577 | City Neighbors Inc | 4301 Raspe Ave, Baltimore MD 21206 | (410) 325-2627 |
| 190 | 11914666 | Connections Academy | 10960 Grantchester Way Fl 3, Columbia MD 21044 | (443) 529-1000 |
| 191 | 11916470 | Imagine Mid-Atlantic Regional | 4415 Nicole Dr Ste C, Lanham MD 20706 | (301) 316-1802 |
| 192 | 11915830 | KIPP Baltimore | 2000 Edgewood St, Baltimore MD 21216 | (410) 291-2583 |
| 193 | 11912228 | Living Classrooms Foundation | 802 S Caroline St, Baltimore MD 21231 | (410) 685-0295 |
| 194 | 11914252 | American Institutional Mgmt | 5728 Schaefer Rd Ste 200, Dearborn MI 48126 | (313) 624-2000 |
| 195 | 11914240 | Bardwell Group | 19800 Beech Daly Rd, Redford MI 48240 | (313) 450-0642 |
| 196 | 11914501 | Charter School Admin Services | 20820 Greenfield Rd, Oak Park MI 48237 | (248) 569-7787 |
| 197 | 11914484 | Choice Schools Associates LLC | 5251 Clyde Park Ave SW, Wyoming MI 49509 | (616) 785-8440 |
| 198 | 11911858 | Cornerstone Education Group | 306 E 4th St, Royal Oak MI 48067 | (248) 439-6228 |
| 199 | 11914642 | CS Partners LLC | 869 S Old US 23 Ste 500, Brighton MI 48114 | (810) 229-5145 |
| 200 | 11914094 | EdTec Central LLC | 10 S Main St Ste 101, Mount Clemens MI 48043 | (248) 582-8100 |
| 201 | 11914343 | Education Enrichmnet Services | 19236 W 11 Mile Rd, Lathrup Vlg MI 48076 | (248) 905-5030 |
| 202 | 11914070 | Education Management&Networks | 27704 Franklin Rd, Southfield MI 48034 | (248) 327-7673 |
| 203 | 11912345 | Foundation for Behavioral Res | 600 S Lincoln St, Augusta MI 49012 | (269) 731-5796 |
| 204 | 11914446 | Global Educational Excellence | 2455 S Industrial Hwy Ste A, Ann Arbor MI 48104 | (734) 369-9500 |
| 205 | 11914018 | Hamadeh Educational Services | PO Box 1440, Dearborn MI 48121 | (313) 565-0507 |
| 206 | 11913973 | Innovative Teaching Solutions | 18470 W 10 Mile Rd Ste 100, Southfield MI 48075 | (248) 799-2780 |
| 207 | 11913961 | Lakeshore Educl Management | 12955 Robins Ridge Rd, Charlevoix MI 49720 | (231) 547-4264 |
| 208 | 11916597 | Leona Group LLC-Midwest | 2125 University Park Dr, Okemos MI 48864 | (517) 333-9030 |
| 209 | 11913935 | MJ Management Services Inc | PO Box 1014, Flat Rock MI 48134 | (734) 675-5505 |
| 210 | 11914575 | National Heritage Academies | 3850 Broadmoor Ave SE Ste 201, Grand Rapids MI 49512 | (877) 223-6402 |
| 211 | 11913868 | PrepNet LLC | 3755 36th St SE Ste 250, Grand Rapids MI 49512 | (616) 726-8900 |
| 212 | 12038734 | Promise Schools | 15000 Trojan St, Detroit MI 48235 | (313) 964-2339 |
| 213 | 11914367 | Romine Group LLC | 7877 Stead St Ste 100, Utica MI 48317 | (586) 731-5300 |
| 214 | 11913818 | Solid Rock Management Company | 3031 W Grand Blvd Ste 524, Detroit MI 48202 | (313) 873-7625 |
| 215 | 11913753 | Technical Academy Group LLC | 4801 Oakman Blvd, Dearborn MI 48126 | (313) 625-4700 |
| 216 | 11911793 | Youth Visions Solutions | 1450 25th St, Detroit MI 48216 | (313) 558-9022 |
| 217 | 12262284 | Harvest Network of Schools | 1300 Olson Memorial Hwy, Minneapolis MN 55411 | (612) 876-4105 |
| 218 | 12262301 | Hiawatha Academies | 1611 E 46th St, Minneapolis MN 55407 | (612) 455-4004 |
| 219 | 12115033 | KIPP Minnesota Public Schools | 5034 Oliver Ave N, Minneapolis MN 55430 | (612) 287-9700 |
| 220 | 12262387 | MN Transitions Charter Schs | 2872 26th Ave S, Minneapolis MN 55406 | (612) 722-9013 |
| 221 | 11914355 | Sabis Educational Systems | 6385 Beach Rd, Eden Prairie MN 55344 | (952) 918-1850 |
| 222 | 12261462 | Confluence Academies | 611 N 10th St Ste 525, Saint Louis MO 63101 | (314) 588-8554 |
| 223 | 12115021 | KIPP Kansas City | 2700 E 18th St Ste 155B, Kansas City MO 64127 | (816) 241-3994 |
| 224 | 11916303 | KIPP St Louis Public Schools | 1310 Papin St Ste 203, Saint Louis MO 63103 | (314) 349-1388 |
| 225 | 12115019 | KIPP Charlotte Public Schools | 931 Wilann Dr, Charlotte NC 28215 | (704) 537-2044 |
| 226 | 11916119 | KIPP Enc College Prep Pub Schs | 320 Pleasant Hill Rd, Gaston NC 27832 | (252) 308-6932 |
| 227 | 12179431 | Teamcfa | 9935D Rea Rd Ste 167, Charlotte NC 28277 | (704) 774-3038 |
| 228 | 12309351 | The Roger Bacon Academy | 3610 Thaddeus Lott Ln NE, Leland NC 28451 | (910) 655-3600 |
| 229 | 12378924 | Camden's Charter Sch Network | 879 Beideman Ave, Camden NJ 08105 | (856) 365-1000 |
| 230 | 12306593 | College Achieve Ctl CS Network | 365 Emerson Ave, Plainfield NJ 07062 | (908) 625-1879 |
| 231 | 12110332 | Ilearn Schools Inc | 33-00 Broadway Ste 301, Fair Lawn NJ 07410 | (201) 773-9140 |
| 232 | 11916327 | KIPP New Jersey | 60 Park Pl Ste 802, Newark NJ 07102 | (973) 622-0905 |
| 233 | 11912694 | Beginning with Children Fndn | 217 Havemeyer St Ste 2, Brooklyn NY 11211 | (212) 750-9320 |
| 234 | 11912644 | Brighter Choice Charter Schs | 250 Central Ave, Albany NY 12206 | (518) 694-4100 |
| 235 | 11912498 | Democracy Prep Public Schools | 1767 Park Ave Fl 4, New York NY 10035 | (212) 281-1248 |
| 236 | 12262894 | Excellence Community Schools | 2090 7th Ave Ste 605, New York NY 10027 | (212) 222-5071 |
| 237 | 11912371 | Explore Schools Inc | 20 Jay St Ste 211, Brooklyn NY 11201 | (718) 989-6730 |
| 238 | 12161604 | Great Oaks Foundation | 200 Broadway 3rd Fl, New York NY 10038 | (917) 239-3641 |
| 239 | 11912292 | Harlem Village Academies | 15 Penn Plz Ste 15, New York NY 10001 | (646) 812-9501 |
| 240 | 12370362 | Hebrew Public Charter Schools | 555 8th Ave Rm 1703, New York NY 10018 | (212) 792-6234 |

| No. | PID | CMO Name | Address | Phone |
|---|---|---|---|---|
| 241 | 12114986 | KIPP Albany Public Schools | 321 Northern Blvd, Albany NY 12210 | (518) 694-9494 |
| 242 | 11914824 | KIPP NYC Public Schools | 1501 Broadway Ste 1000, New York NY 10036 | (212) 991-2610 |
| 243 | 12377906 | New Visions Charter Network | 205 E 42nd St Fl 4, New York NY 10017 | (212) 645-5110 |
| 244 | 11912084 | Public Prep Network Inc | 192 E 151st St Frnt 1, Bronx NY 10451 | (212) 346-6000 |
| 245 | 11912943 | Success Academy Charter Schls | 95 Pine St Fl 6, New York NY 10005 | (646) 597-4641 |
| 246 | 11913478 | Uncommon Schools | 826 Broadway Fl 9, New York NY 10003 | (212) 844-3584 |
| 247 | 11914563 | Victory Education Partners | 135 W 41st St Fl 5, New York NY 10036 | (212) 786-7900 |
| 248 | 12179819 | Accel Schools | 4700 Rockside Rd Ste 345, Independence OH 44131 | (216) 583-5230 |
| 249 | 11913416 | Breakthrough Charter Schools | 3615 Superior Ave E Ste 4403A, Cleveland OH 44114 | (216) 456-2086 |
| 250 | 11912632 | Buckeye on-Line School Success | 119 E 5th St, E Liverpool OH 43920 | (330) 385-1987 |
| 251 | 12106575 | Carpe Diem Learning Systems | 301 N Breiel Blvd Ste B, Middletown OH 45042 | (513) 217-3400 |
| 252 | 11914654 | Constellation Schools | 5730 Broadview Rd, Parma OH 44134 | (216) 712-7600 |
| 253 | 12378120 | Educational Empowerment Group | 1814 S Main St, Akron OH 44301 | (330) 956-7203 |
| 254 | 12319069 | Educational Solutions | 1500 W 3rd Ave Ste 125, Columbus OH 43212 | (614) 299-1007 |
| 255 | 11914460 | Eschool Consultants | 4480 Refugee Rd, Columbus OH 43232 | (614) 322-7996 |
| 256 | 11916509 | Imagine Ohio Regional | 11518 Banning Rd, Mount Vernon OH 43050 | (614) 930-1184 |
| 257 | 11916066 | KIPP Columbus | 2980 Inspire Dr, Columbus OH 43224 | (614) 263-6137 |
| 258 | 11914393 | Performance Academies LLC | 2 Easton Oval Ste 525, Columbus OH 43219 | (614) 512-2151 |
| 259 | 11913480 | Summit Academy Management | 2791 Mogadore Rd, Akron OH 44312 | (330) 670-8470 |
| 260 | 12363034 | United Schools Network | 1469 E Main St, Columbus OH 43205 | (614) 299-5284 |
| 261 | 12377803 | Dove Public Charter Schools | 9212 N Kelley Ave Ste 100, Oklahoma City OK 73131 | (405) 605-0201 |
| 262 | 12305745 | KIPP Okc Public Schools | PO Box 14128, Oklahoma City OK 73113 | (405) 849-9700 |
| 263 | 12115069 | KIPP Tulsa Public Charter Schs | 1661 E Virgin St, Tulsa OK 74106 | (918) 794-8652 |
| 264 | 12361452 | Santa Fe South Public Schools | 4825 S Shields Blvd, Oklahoma City OK 73129 | (405) 601-5440 |
| 265 | 11913117 | Mastery Lrng Inst-Arthur Acad | 13717 SE Division St, Portland OR 97236 | (503) 762-6061 |
| 266 | 12379045 | Belmont Charter Network | 1301 Belmont Ave, Philadelphia PA 19104 | (215) 790-1294 |
| 267 | 11914185 | Charter School Management Inc | 419 Avenue of the States, Chester PA 19013 | (610) 447-0200 |
| 268 | 11912448 | EdSys Inc | 201 Stanwix St Ste 100, Pittsburgh PA 15222 | (412) 690-2489 |
| 269 | 11916274 | KIPP Philadelphia Public Schs | 5070 Parkside Ave Ste 3500D, Philadelphia PA 19131 | (215) 294-8596 |
| 270 | 11913129 | Mastery Charter Schools | 5700 Wayne Ave, Philadelphia PA 19144 | (215) 866-9000 |
| 271 | 11914408 | Omnivest Properties Management | 115 Pheasant Run Ste 210, Newtown PA 18940 | (215) 497-8301 |
| 272 | 11913026 | Propel Schools | 3447 E Carson St Ste 200, Pittsburgh PA 15203 | (412) 325-7305 |
| 273 | 11912888 | Universal Companies Inc | 800 S 15th St, Philadelphia PA 19146 | (215) 732-6518 |
| 274 | 12312499 | Charter Institute at Erskine | 1201 Main St Ste 300, Columbia SC 29201 | (803) 849-2464 |
| 275 | 12161719 | Capstone Education Group | PO Box 22569, Memphis TN 38122 | (901) 416-3640 |
| 276 | 11914628 | Chancelight Behavioral Hlth-Ed | 1321 Murfreesboro Pike Ste 702, Nashville TN 37217 | (615) 361-4000 |
| 277 | 12377918 | Compass Community Schools | 61 N McLean Blvd, Memphis TN 38104 | (901) 618-7422 |
| 278 | 12319629 | Freedom Prep Academy Network | 778 Parkrose Ave, Memphis TN 38109 | (901) 881-1149 |
| 279 | 12038813 | Gestalt Community Schools | 2650 Thsnd Oaks Blvd Ste 1400, Memphis TN 38118 | (901) 213-5161 |
| 280 | 12305850 | Green Dot Pub Schs-Tennessee | 4950 Fairley Rd, Memphis TN 38109 | (901) 730-8160 |
| 281 | 12468725 | Journey Community Schools LLC | 802 Rozelle St, Memphis TN 38104 | (901) 646-6530 |
| 282 | 11916200 | KIPP Memphis Collegiate Schs | 2670 Union Avenue Ext Ste 1100, Memphis TN 38112 | (901) 452-2682 |
| 283 | 11916236 | KIPP Nashville | 123 Douglas Ave, Nashville TN 37207 | (615) 226-4484 |
| 284 | 12038825 | Lead Public Schools | 2835 Brick Church Pike, Nashville TN 37207 | (615) 815-1264 |
| 285 | 12110461 | Republic Schools | 3307 Brick Church Pike, Nashville TN 37207 | (615) 921-6620 |
| 286 | 11911896 | The Influence 1 Foundation | 665 Madison Ave, Memphis TN 38103 | (901) 526-1944 |
| 287 | 11912993 | A Plus Charter Schools | 8225 Bruton Rd, Dallas TX 75217 | (214) 381-3226 |
| 288 | 12315738 | Arrow Academy | PO Box 12207, College Sta TX 77842 | (979) 703-8820 |
| 289 | 11913105 | Baker-Ripley | PO Box 271389, Houston TX 77277 | (713) 667-9400 |
| 290 | 11912618 | Calvin Nelms Charter Schools | 20625 Clay Rd, Katy TX 77449 | (281) 398-8031 |
| 291 | 11912486 | Democratic Schools Research | 410 Bethel Ln, Bryan TX 77802 | (979) 775-2152 |
| 292 | 11912450 | East Waco Innovative Sch Dev | 1020 Elm St Ste 100, Waco TX 76704 | (254) 754-8000 |
| 293 | 11913325 | Educational Leadership Inc | 3333 Bering Dr Ste 200, Houston TX 77057 | (713) 784-6345 |
| 294 | 12361414 | Evolution Academy Charter Schs | 1101 S Sherman St, Richardson TX 75081 | (972) 907-3755 |
| 295 | 11913284 | Faith Family Academy Chtr Schs | 1608 Osprey Dr, Desoto TX 75115 | (972) 224-4110 |
| 296 | 11912321 | Golden Rule Schools Inc | 2602 W Illinois Ave, Dallas TX 75233 | (214) 333-9330 |
| 297 | 12160947 | Great Hearts Texas | 824 Broadway St Ste 101, San Antonio TX 78215 | (210) 888-9475 |
| 298 | 11912307 | Gulf Coast Council of La Raza | 4129 Greenwood Dr, Corp Christi TX 78416 | (361) 881-9988 |
| 299 | 11913624 | Harmony Pub Schs-Cosmos Found | 9321 W Sam Houston Pkwy S, Houston TX 77099 | (713) 343-3333 |
| 300 | 12374772 | Heritage Academy Inc | 12470 Woman Hollering Rd, Schertz TX 78154 | (210) 659-0329 |

| CMO No. | PID | CMO Name | Address | Phone |
|---|---|---|---|---|
| 301 | 12371835 | **Idea Public Schools** | 2115 W Pike Blvd, Weslaco TX 78596 | (956) 377-80□ |
| 302 | 12372554 | **Idea Public Schools Austin** | 2800 S Interstate 35 Ste 265, Austin TX 78704 | (512) 822-4959 |
| 303 | 12372566 | **Idea Public Schools El Paso** | 813 N Kansas St Ste 100, El Paso TX 79902 | (915) 201-1959 |
| 304 | 12372580 | **Idea Public Schools Tarrant** | 600 Bryan Ave Ste 220, Fort Worth TX 76104 | (817) 885-4050 |
| 305 | 12372578 | **Idea Public Schs San Antonio** | 12500 San Pedro Ave Ste 500, San Antonio TX 78216 | (210) 239-4250 |
| 306 | 11913193 | **Jubilee Academic Center Inc** | 4434 Roland Rd, San Antonio TX 78222 | (210) 333-6227 |
| 307 | 11915828 | **KIPP Texas Public Schs Austin** | 8509 FM 969 Ste 513, Austin TX 78724 | (512) 501-3643 |
| 308 | 11916080 | **KIPP Texas Public Schs Dallas** | 1545 S Ewing Ave, Dallas TX 75216 | (972) 323-4200 |
| 309 | 11916133 | **KIPP Texas Public Schs Houston** | 10711 Kipp Way Dr, Houston TX 77099 | (832) 328-1051 |
| 310 | 11916298 | **KIPP Texas Public Schs Sa** | 731 Fredericksburg Rd, San Antonio TX 78201 | (210) 787-3197 |
| 311 | 11913131 | **Life School** | 132 E Ovilla Rd Ste 1A, Red Oak TX 75154 | (469) 850-5433 |
| 312 | 11912163 | **New Frontiers Public Schools** | 138 Fair Ave, San Antonio TX 78223 | (210) 519-3900 |
| 313 | 11913040 | **Orenda Education** | 2951 Williams Dr, Georgetown TX 78628 | (512) 869-3020 |
| 314 | 11912137 | **Panola Charter Schools** | PO Box 610, Carthage TX 75633 | (903) 693-6355 |
| 315 | 11912096 | **Por Vida Inc** | 1135 Mission Rd, San Antonio TX 78210 | (210) 532-8816 |
| 316 | 12113918 | **Priority Charter Schools** | 275 FM 2483, Morgans Point TX 76513 | (254) 206-2013 |
| 317 | 11913014 | **Raul Yzaguirre Sch-Success Org** | 2950 Broadway St, Houston TX 77017 | (713) 640-3700 |
| 318 | 12233855 | **Responsive Education Solutions** | PO Box 292730, Lewisville TX 75029 | (972) 316-3663 |
| 319 | 11913507 | **Richard Milburn Academy Inc** | 13003 Jones Maltsberger Rd, San Antonio TX 78247 | (830) 557-6181 |
| 320 | 11913002 | **Riverwalk Education Foundation** | 5300 Wurzbach Rd Ste 800, San Antonio TX 78238 | (210) 957-1955 |
| 321 | 11912981 | **Salvaging Teens at Risk Inc** | 4601 N Interstate 35, Denton TX 76207 | (940) 383-6655 |
| 322 | 11911999 | **South Texas Educ Technologies** | 2402 E Business 83, Weslaco TX 78596 | (956) 969-3092 |
| 323 | 11912967 | **Southwest Winners Foundation** | 1258 Austin Hwy, San Antonio TX 78209 | (210) 829-8017 |
| 324 | 11912931 | **Tekoa Academy Accel Studies** | 327 Thomas Blvd, Port Arthur TX 77640 | (409) 982-5400 |
| 325 | 11913674 | **Texans Can Academies** | 325 W 12th St, Dallas TX 75208 | (214) 944-1985 |
| 326 | 11911937 | **Texas Center for Arts & Acad** | 3901 S Hulen St, Fort Worth TX 76109 | (817) 766-2390 |
| 327 | 12378857 | **Trinity Basin Preparatory** | 2730 N State Highway 360, Grand Prairie TX 75050 | (214) 946-9100 |
| 328 | 11912905 | **Trinity Charter Schools** | 8305 Cross Park Dr, Austin TX 78754 | (512) 706-7564 |
| 329 | 11912955 | **Triumph Public High Schools** | PO Box 15644, San Antonio TX 78212 | (210) 227-0295 |
| 330 | 11911834 | **Two Dimensions Prep Chtr Acad** | 12121 Veterans Memorial Dr # 7, Houston TX 77067 | (281) 227-4700 |
| 331 | 11913454 | **Uplift Education** | 1825 Market Ctr Blvd Ste 500, Dallas TX 75207 | (469) 621-8500 |
| 332 | 11911810 | **Varnett Public School Inc** | 5025 S Willow Dr, Houston TX 77035 | (713) 667-4051 |
| 333 | 11912876 | **Winfree Academy Charter Schs** | 1555 Valwood Pkwy Ste 160, Carrollton TX 75006 | (972) 869-3250 |
| 334 | 11912864 | **YES Prep Public Schools** | 5515 South Loop E Ste B, Houston TX 77033 | (713) 967-9000 |
| 335 | 11914616 | **Imagine Schools Inc** | 1900 Gallows Rd Ste 250, Vienna VA 22182 | (703) 527-2600 |
| 336 | 11914604 | **K12 Inc** | 2300 Corporate Park Dr, Herndon VA 20171 | (866) 283-0300 |
| 337 | 12305836 | **Green Dot Pub Schs-Washington** | 6020 Rainier Ave S, Seattle WA 98118 | (206) 659-0956 |
| 338 | 12377786 | **Open Sky Education** | 20935 Swenson Dr Ste 101, Waukesha WI 53186 | (262) 542-9546 |
| 339 | 12306000 | **Seeds of Health Inc** | 1445 S 32nd St, Milwaukee WI 53215 | (414) 672-3430 |